CHRISTENSEN'S ULTIMATE MOVIE TV ROCK 'N' ROLL AND SPORTS ADDRESS DIRECTORY

4TH EDITION

CHRISTENSEN'S ULTIMATE MOVIE TV ROCK 'N' ROLL AND SPORTS ADDRESS DIRECTORY

4TH EDITION

Roger Christensen

PUBLISHING COMPANY
Post Office Box 900189
San Diego, CA 92190

Praise To God For

•Eternal Life and Faith

For God so loved the world that He gave His only begotten Son
that whoever believeth in Him should not perish, but have Everlasting Life
John 3:16

And without Faith it is impossible to please God, because anyone
who comes to Him must believe that He exists and that He rewards
those who earnestly seek Him.
Hebrews 11:6

•Treasures In Heaven

Do not store up for yourselves treasures on earth, where moth and rust
destroy, and where the thieves break in and steal. But store up for yourselves,
treasures in Heaven, where moth and rust do not destroy,
and where thieves do not break in and steal. For where your treasure is,
there your heart will be also.
Matthew 6:19-21

•Strength and Endurance

I can do everything through Him who gives me strength.
Philippians 4:13

•My Loving Parents And Family
•My Precious Children
•My True Blue Friends
•My Wonderful Pastor And Church

Rejoice in the Lord always...Let your gentleness be evident to all...
And the peace of God, which transcends all understanding, will guard your
hearts and your minds in Christ Jesus...whatever is true, what ever is noble,
whatever is right, whatever is pure, whatever is lovely, whatever is admirable-if
anything is excellent or praiseworthy-think about such things. Whatever you
have learned or received or heard from me, or seen in me-put it
into practice. And the peace of God will be with you.
Philippians 4:4-9

I Give All Thanks, Praise and Glory to The Lord

Dedication

To My Loving Christian Parents
Jo and Chris Christensen

...and my God will meet all your needs according to his glorious riches in Jesus Christ.
Philippians 4:19

For all your unconditional love, support and prayers, I graciously dedicate this book to you, for without your help, encouragement and sharing dreams together, this publication would have never been possible.

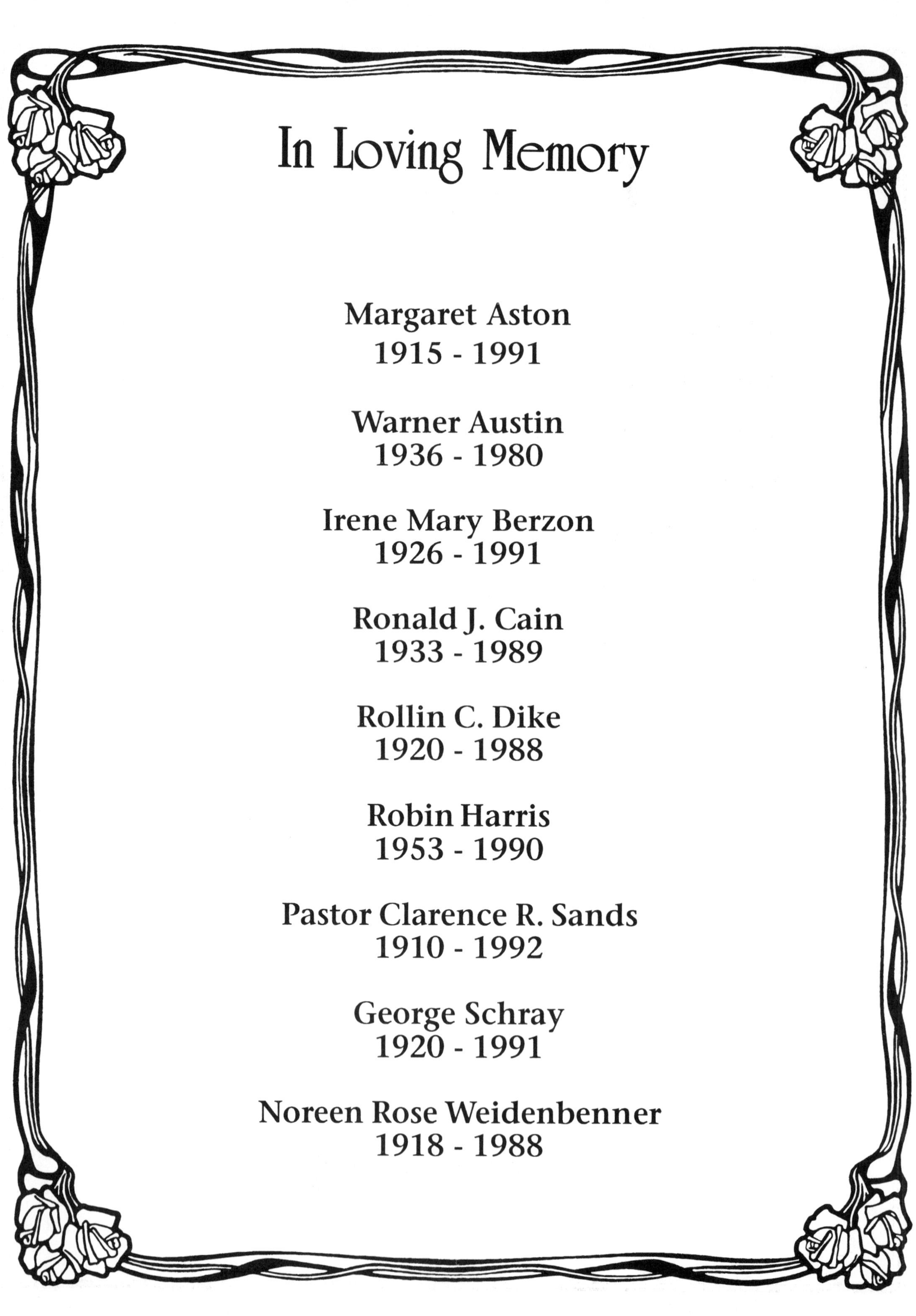

In Loving Memory

Margaret Aston
1915 - 1991

Warner Austin
1936 - 1980

Irene Mary Berzon
1926 - 1991

Ronald J. Cain
1933 - 1989

Rollin C. Dike
1920 - 1988

Robin Harris
1953 - 1990

Pastor Clarence R. Sands
1910 - 1992

George Schray
1920 - 1991

Noreen Rose Weidenbenner
1918 - 1988

Contents

Christensen's Ultimate Movie, TV, Rock 'N' Roll and Sports Address Directory (4th Edition)

Published by Cardiff-By-The-Sea Publishing Company
Post Office Box 900189 • San Diego, CA 92190

Printed in the United States of America

ISBN 0-960-80386-6

Preface

Christensen's Ultimate Movie, TV, Rock & Roll and Sports Address Directory (Fourth Edition) is an encyclopedic listing which contains well over 40,000 entries in the form of celebrity addresses, memorabilia listings, and photographic reproductions. It is the most extensive directory of its kind ever published.

The purpose of this directory is to assist the millions of fans from all walks of life who want to write letters to their favorite celebrities, no matter what field of entertainment they may be in. We feel the cross-section of celebrities represented is quite extensive and covers a wide range of diversified talent. This directory can be most useful in requesting an autographed picture of your favorite movie star, sending a birthday greeting to your favorite sports celebrity, requesting a TV script from the actual writer, asking the advice of a prominent director, composer, cartoonist or sports announcer which technical school they would recommend, or probing the mind of the ever-controversial film critic to get their first-hand opinion what this year's box office sleeper may be.

Looking for a rare baseball card? How about an 8x10 glossy portrait of your favorite star? Where might you find an audio cassette from your favorite old radio serial or a mint copy of the first album the Beatles ever recorded? Do you know who was on the cover of the very first TV Guide? Perhaps you want to sell your baseball card collection, or wish to rekindle your collection from childhood? Would you like to purchase any of this valuable memorabilia for your collection? You'll find all this and much more in this directory.

Throughout the many years of the entertainment industry, various booklets, magazines and maps to the stars' homes have been published. The purpose of the Celebrity Address section of this directory is to provide a thorough source whereby fans can reach their favorite celebrities by one means only - via the U.S. Postal System. We do not, in publishing this directory, nor in our own collecting practices of celebrity autographs advocate or encourage in any way, shape or form fans to visit ANY of the celebrities at either their own homes, or their place of business. Most celebrities are good about responding to fan mail. Please be patient in your desire for a reply and always include a self-addressed stamped envelope of appropriate size and postage to accommodate your request.

We assume no responsibility for addresses in this book which are incorrect due to a celebrity moving from a place of residence and leaving no forwarding address, the changing of agents, managers and/or public relation firms, the refusal to accept or answer mail, non-renewal of a membership in a Guild, Union or Local, death, disease or divorce. Nor do we insinuate that every personality personally answers his or her mail.

Since the inception of this directory in 1977, countless hours of time-consuming painstaking research and labor has been consumed. It will be published annually with address update supplements issued between editions.

This book provides an exciting nostalgic journey into the past as well as giving you a present day front-row seat. This **Movie, TV, Rock 'N' Roll and Sports Address Directory** is obviously the **Ultimate!**

Very Special Thanks To

Lise' and Scott Dike
...the midnight oil crew
at Design Mode Graphic Arts
for your conceptual insight & production of my book

Paul Hunt
...your faith in me over the years.

Tom Jordan
...your endless talent

Sherrie and Sy Sussman
...my dearest friends and second family

Georgia Terry
...for always being there

Bill Dossey and Diane Pella
...Bill for your hard work and Diane for the beautiful cover

Nahid Vassef
...for your professional expertise

and all of you for your
...caring guidance
...endless patience
...specialized talents
...continued encouragement
... for your treasured friendships most of all

My Friends at Kooky's Diner
Dave Young (Best Friend and dining buddy)
Mary Lou and Liz (Waitresses)
...for all your great cheeseburgers, fries, shakes, hot coffee
and incredibly stimulating conversation

My Friends at Round Table Pizza
Brent, Greg, Maryellen, Pat and Matt
...all the great pizzas, sandwiches and loud music

A Note
From the Author

The most satisfying things about compiling this directory are the wonderful letters I receive and the collectors whom I meet. They tell me of all the responses they get from the people they write to and the interesting stories that they share.

While speaking at a book convention several years ago I noticed an elderly gentleman sitting in the very back row of the auditorium-as I was fielding questions from the audience. When my presentation was over I packed up my briefcase and prepared to leave the Glendale Auditorium.

As I turned around I noticed the older gentleman had not gotten out of his chair. He called me over and said, "Roger, could I speak privately with you and have your autograph for my book?" I said, "Sure, I'd be honored to." As I walked closer to where he was seated I noticed a walker laying down next to his chair. As he handed me the book to autograph, I noticed the crippling signs of arthritis in both of his hands.

He then turned and pointed to a name on a page near the middle of the book. As he looked at me I could see the emotion in his eyes and hear a quiver in his voice as he proudly asked, "Do you know who this actor is?" Yes, I do", I replied, "though not personally." "Well", he said, "This is my son who I put up for adoption 32 years ago, I found out his stage name and tracked him down using your book in the Los Angeles Public Library. We are now the best of friends and spend a lot of time together eating'Dodger Dogs' and rooting for the the team from the left field bleachers. In addition, I have a beautiful daughter-in-law and two handsome grandsons in elementary school.

I was choked up with emotion as he shared his story with me . It was an incredible feeling to think that the directory had helped him locate his son and other loved ones he never knew he had.

The most frequently asked question I receive other than how do I gather all these addresses is - where did you come up the idea for this book?

While stationed at Tan Son Nhut Air Base in Saigon, I regularly visited the base hospital to chat with and encourage those wounded in action and those awaiting their return to Stateside.

During that period in our governments history, all Vietnam-based personnel could send postage-free letters anywhere in the world, just by writing "FREE" in the upper right-hand corner of the envelope. One afternoon, while visiting with a 19 year old wounded soldier, the subject of autograph collecting came up as we were both avid collectors. He asked me, "Wouldn't it be a dream come true if someone would put together a sort of 'ultimate address book'? That truly would be the icing on the cake with us being able to send off for autographs at no charge. That way we would only have to worry about staying alive - and getting paper and envelopes to request additions for our hobby."

Well, it's twenty-two years later and you're holding the Fourth Edition in your hands ... Dreams *do* come true.

Roger Christensen

Advertiser's Index

Celebrity

ADDRESSES

A

A D LIFE	JAZZ GROUP	POST OFFICE BOX 8305	HOUSTON, TX	77288
A MILLION RUMORS	ROCK & ROLL GROUP	165 S UNION BLVD #220	LAKEWOOD, CO	80228
A-440	ROCK & ROLL GROUP	151 S EL CAMINO DR	BEVERLY HILLS, CA	90212
A-TRAX	C & W GROUP	1001 24TH ST #313	BILLINGS, MT	59102
AADLAND, BEVERLY	ACTRESS	POST OFFICE BOX 1115	CANYON COUNTRY, CA	91350
AAGAARD, GARY	ARTIST	2314 N 52ND ST	SEATTLE, WA	98103
AAKER, LEE	ACTOR	POST OFFICE BOX 1595	RESEDA, CA	91337
AAL, ANDREA	ACTRESS	L A TALENT, 8335 SUNSET BLVD	LOS ANGELES, CA	90069
AAL, DEBORAH	TV-FILM EXECUTIVE	1800 CENTURY PARK E #200	LOS ANGELES, CA	90067
AALDA, MARIANN	ACTRESS	280 S BEVERLY DR #400	BEVERLY HILLS, CA	90212
AAMES, WILLIE	ACTOR-SINGER	LIGHT, 901 BRINGHAM AVE	LOS ANGELES, CA	90049
AARON, CAROLINE	ACTRESS	9301 WILSHIRE BLVD #312	BEVERLY HILLS, CA	90210
AARON, CHLOE	TV PRODUCER-EXECUTIVE	PBS-TV, 609 5TH AVE	NEW YORK, NY	10017
AARON, HENRY "HANK"	BASEBALL	1611 ADAMS DR, SW	ATLANTA, GA	30311
AARON, PAUL	WRI-DIR-PROD	CAA, 9830 WILSHIRE BLVD	BEVERLY HILLS, CA	90212
AARON, TOMMY	GOLFER	POST OFFICE BOX 12458	PALM BCH GARDENS, FL	33410
ABATEMARCO, FRANK	TV WRITER	UTA, 9560 WILSHIRE BL, 5TH FL	BEVERLY HILLS, CA	90212
ABBADO, CLAUDIO	COMPOSER	220 E MICHIGAN AVE	CHICAGO, IL	60604
ABBASSI, ELIZABETH	ACTRESS	43 E 60TH ST	NEW YORK, NY	10022
ABBATE, DAVID	WRITER	555 W 57TH ST #1230	NEW YORK, NY	10019
ABBENE, BERNARD V	WRITER	8955 BEVERLY BLVD	WEST HOLLYWOOD, CA	90048
ABBOT, RUSS	ACTOR-SINGER	BBC-TV, 56 WOOD LN	LONDON W12 7RJ	ENGLAND
ABBOTT, BRUCE	ACTOR	MTA, 9320 WILSHIRE BL, 3RD FL	BEVERLY HILLS, CA	90212
ABBOTT, DIHANNE	ACTRESS	460 W AVE 46	LOS ANGELES, CA	90065
ABBOTT, GEORGE	WRITER-PRODUCER	1020 5TH AVE #1009	NEW YORK, NY	10028
ABBOTT, GLENN	BASEBALL-COACH	POST OFFICE BOX 11087	TACOMA, WA	98411
ABBOTT, GREGORY	SINGER-SONGWRITER	POST OFFICE BOX 68	BERGENFIELD, NJ	07621
ABBOTT, JIM	BASEBALL	POST OFFICE BOX 2000	ANAHEIM, CA	92803
ABBOTT, JOHN	ACTOR	6424 IVARENE AVE	LOS ANGELES, CA	90068
ABBOTT, KURT	BASEBALL	POST OFFICE BOX 2769	HUNTSVILLE, AL	35804
ABBOTT, KYLE	BASEBALL	POST OFFICE BOX 7575	PHILADELPHIA, PA	19101
ABBOTT, PAUL	BASEBALL	TWINS, 501 CHICAGO AVE S	MINNEAPOLIS, MN	55415
ABBOTT, PHILIP	ACTOR-DIRECTOR	5400 SHIRLEY AVE	TARZANA, CA	91356
ABBOTT, SHEPARD	SCREENWRITER	555 W 57TH ST #1230	NEW YORK, NY	10019
ABBOTT, TERRY	BASEBALL COACH	POST OFFICE BOX 5646	PRINCETON, WV	24740
ABBOTT-FISH, CHRIS	TV WRITER-PRODUCER	MTA, 9320 WILSHIRE BL, 3RD FL	BEVERLY HILLS, CA	90212
ABC BAND	ROCK & ROLL GROUP	17397 SANTA BARBARA	DETROIT, MI	48221
ABDELNABY, ALAA	BASKETBALL	700 NE MULTNOMAH ST #600	PORTLAND, OR	97232
ABDO, JOHN	BODYBUILDER	7325 W IRVING PARK RD	CHICAGO, IL	60634
ABDO, NICHOLAS	DIRECTOR-PRODUCER	3500 W OLIVE AVE #1400	BURBANK, CA	91505
ABDUL, PAULA	SINGER-CHOREOGRAPHER	POST OFFICE BOX 885288	SAN FRANCISCO, CA	91488
ABDUL-JABBAR, KAREEM	ACTOR-BASKETBALL	1170 STONE CANYON RD	LOSN ANGELES, CA	90077
ABEL, RONALD M	CONDUCTOR	334 N HARPER AVE	LOS ANGELES, CA	90048
ABELES, ARTHUR	FILM EXECUTIVE	81 PICCADILLY	LONDON W1	ENGLAND
ABELEW, ALAN	ACTOR	4148 SEA VIEW DR	LOS ANGELES, CA	90065
ABELS, LAUREN	ACTRESS	SCHWARTZ, 935 N CROFT AVE	LOS ANGELES, CA	90069
ABERCROMBIE, IAN	ACTOR	1050 N GARDNER	LOS ANGELES, CA	90046
ABERCROMBIE, JOHN	BASEBALL	POST OFFICE BOX 611	WATERLOO, IA	50704
ABERCROMBIE, MEIL	U S CONGRESSMAN	300 ALA MOANA BLVD #4104	HONOLULU, HI	96850
ABERG, SIV	ACTRESS-MODEL	POST OFFICE BOX 1721	BEVERLY HILLS, CA	90213
ABERNATHY, DONZALEIGH AVIS	ACTRESS	10100 SANTA MONICA BLVD #1600	LOS ANGELES, CA	90067
ABERNATHY, MACK	SINGER	BRUMLEY MGMT, 2 MUSIC SQUARE S	NASHVILLE, TN	37203
ABESON, MARION	WRITER-LYRICIST	46 W 83RD ST	NEW YORK, NY	10024
ABEY, DENNIS	WRITER-PRODUCER	AB & C, 36 PERCY ST	LONDON W1	ENGLAND
ABNER, SHAWN	BASEBALL	333 W 35TH ST	CHICAGO, IL	60616
ABNEY, WILLIAM	ACTOR	PBR, 138 PUTNEY BRIDGE RD	LONDON SW15 2NQ	ENGLAND
ABRAHAM, F MURRAY	ACTOR	STE, 888 7TH AVE, 18TH FLOOR	NEW YORK, NY	10106
ABRAHAM, MARC L	WRITER	UTA, 9560 WILSHIRE BL, 5TH FL	BEVERLY HILLS, CA	90212
ABRAHAM, RALPH	PRODUCER	POST OFFICE BOX 2539	MESA, AZ	85204
ABRAHAM, RALPH E	TV DIRECTOR	2146 N YALE	MESA, AZ	85213
ABRAHAM, SETH	FILM EXECUTIVE	HBO, 1100 6TH AVE	NEW YORK, NY	10036
ABRAHAMS, JIM	FILM WRITER-DIRECTOR	UTA, 9560 WILSHIRE BL, 5TH FL	BEVERLY HILLS, CA	90212
ABRAHAMS, MORT	WRITER-PRODUCER	3936 ETHEL AVE	NORTH HOLLYWOOD, CA	91604
ABRAMHOFF, SHARYN	WRITER	2312 PISANI PL	VENICE, CA	90291
ABRAMOWITZ, DAVID	TV WRITER	9242 BEVERLY DR #200	BEVERLY HILLS, CA	90210
ABRAMOWITZ, JAY B	TV DIRECTOR	346 1/2 N SPALDING AVE	LOS ANGELES, CA	90036
ABRAMOWITZ, TEDDY	TV EXECUTIVE	349 E 52ND ST	NEW YORK, NY	10022
ABRAMS, ELLIOTT	TV EXECUTIVE	ITC ENTERTAINMENT, INC 115 E 57TH ST	NEW YORK, NY	10022
ABRAMS, MUHAL RICHARD	PIANIST	POST OFFICE BOX 612 (TSS)	NEW YORK, NY	10108
ABRAMS, ROBERT	ATTORNEY GENERAL	STATE CAPITOL BUILDING	ALBANY, NY	12224
ABRAMS & ANDERSON	COMEDY DUO	POST OFFICE BOX 4585	PORTSMOUTH, NH	03801
ABRAVANEL, DAVID B	COMPOSER	4303 COLDWATER CANYON AVE	STUDIO CITY, CA	91604
ABREU, BOB	BASEBALL	POST OFFICE BOX 1556	ASHEVILLE, NC	28802
ABREU, FRANKLIN	BASEBALL	POST OFFICE BOX 12557	ST PETERSBURG, FL	33733

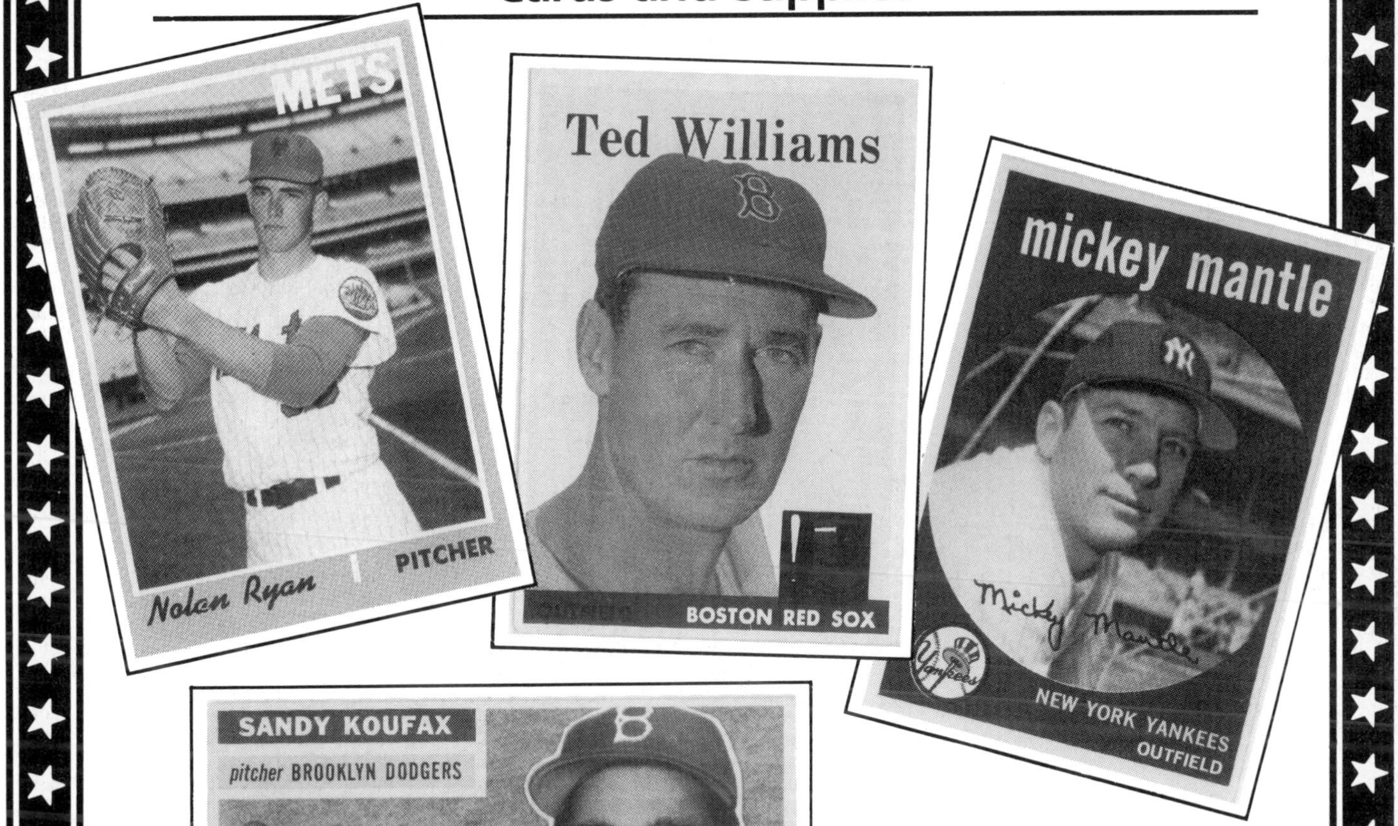

ABROMS, EDWARD	FILM EDITOR	ACE, 1041 N FORMOSA AVE	WEST HOLLYWOOD, CA	90046
ABROMS, EDWARD M	FILM DIRECTOR	10913 FRUITLINE DR #108	STUDIO CITY, CA	91604
ABRUZZO, RAY	ACTOR	20334 PACIFIC COAST HWY	MALIBU, CA	90265
ABSTON, DEAN	ACTOR	11846 VENTURA BLVD #100	STUDIO CITY, CA	91604
ABUDATO, RICHIE	BASKETBALL COACH	REUNION ARENA, 777 SPORTS ST	DALLAS, TX	75207
ABZUG, BELA	POLITICIAN	2 5TH AVE	NEW YORK, NY	10011
ACAMPORA, RALPH	BASEBALL EXECUTIVE	ALBANY YANKEES, HERITAGE PARK	ALBANY, NY	12211
ACCORSI, ERNIE	FOOTBALL EXECUTIVE	BROWNS, 80 1ST ST	BEREA, OH	44017
ACEBO, ALEXANDER V	AUDITOR	PAVILION OFF BLDG, 109 STATE ST	MONTPELIER, VT	05602
ACES & EIGHTS	C & W GROUP	GREG, 1686 CATALPA RD	CLEVELAND, OH	44112
ACETI, JOSEPH	TV DIRECTOR	225 CENTRAL PARK W	NEW YORK, NY	10024
ACEVEDO, HECTOR	BASEBALL SCOUT	POST OFFICE BOX 90111	ARLINGTON, TX	76004
ACKER, JIM	BASEBALL	POST OFFICE BOX 3690, STA "B"	CALGARY, ALB T2B 4M4	CANADA
ACKER, SHARON	ACTRESS	6310 SAN VICENTE BLVD #407	LOS ANGELES, CA	90048
ACKERLEY, BARRY	BASKETBALL EXECUTIVE	POST OFFICE BOX C-900911	SEATTLE, WA	98109
ACKERMAN, ANDY	FILM EDITOR	8383 WILSHIRE BLVD #923	BEVERLY HILLS, CA	90211
ACKERMAN, BETTYE	ACTRESS	302 N ALPINE DR	BEVERLY HILLS, CA	90210
ACKERMAN, FORREST	ACTOR-AUTHOR	2495 GLENDOWER AVE	HOLLYWOOD, CA	90027
ACKERMAN, GARY	U S CONGRESSMAN	118-35 QUEENS BLVD	FOREST HILLS, NY	11375
ACKERMAN, HAROLD	WRITER	214 1/2 S MARTEL AVE	LOS ANGELES, CA	90036
ACKERMAN, LESLIE	ACTRESS	15301 VENTURA BLVD #345	SHERMAN OAKS, CA	91403
ACKERMAN, STEVE	WRITER	4525 LEMP AVE	NORTH HOLLYWOOD, CA	91602
ACKLAND, JOSS	ACTOR	ICM, 388-396 OXFORD ST	LONDON W1	ENGLAND
ACKLES, BOB	FOOTBALL EXECUTIVE	COWBOYS, 1 COWBOYS PARKWAY	IRVING, TX	75063
ACKRILL, KEITH	TV DIRECTOR	29 TANYARD LN, ALVECHURCH	BIRMINGHAM B48 7LL	ENGLAND
ACKROYD, DAVID	ACTOR	12525 OTSEGO ST	NORTH HOLLYWOOD, CA	91607
ACKROYD, TIMOTHY	ACTOR	33 CHEPSTOW RD	LONDON W2 5BP	ENGLAND
ACOSTA, CLEMENTE	BASEBALL	POST OFFICE BOX 12	MIDLAND, TX	79702
ACOSTA, OSCAR	BASEBALL COACH	POST OFFICE BOX 75089	OKLAHOMA CITY, OK	73147
ACOUSTIC ALCHEMY	GUITAR DUO	COXHEAD, ART & MUSIC CORP		
		LIONS CHAMBERS, NORTHGATE		
		CLECKHEATON	WEST YORKS BD19 3H2	ENGLAND
ACOVONE, JAY	ACTOR	151 S EL CAMINO DR	BEVERLY HILLS, CA	90212
ACQUANETTA	ACTRESS	BASCHUCK, 4415 N ARCADIA LN	PHOENIX, AZ	85018
ACRE, MARK	BASEBALL	POST OFFICE BOX 11363	RENO, NV	89510
ACREE, DENNIS	ACTOR	5960 BALCOM AVE	ENCINO, CA	91316
ACRES, MARK	BASKETBALL	POST OFFICE BOX 76	ORLANDO, FL	32802
ACT II	C & W GROUP	ROUTE #4, BOX 290-MG	TEXARKANA, AR	75502
ACTA, MANNY	BASEBALL COACH	POST OFFICE BOX 1556	ASHEVILLE, NC	28802
ACTON, KEITH	HOCKEY	FLYERS, SPECTRUM, PATTISON PL	PHILADELPHIA, PA	19148
ACTON, LOREN	ASTRONAUT	LOCKHEED, 3251 HANOVER ST	PALO ALTO, CA	94304
ACUFF, ROY	SINGER-PRODUCER	POST OFFICE BOX 4623	NASHVILLE, TN	37216
ACUNA, ED	ARTIST	17 ERMINE ST	FAIRFIELD, CT	06430
ACUNTO, RICHARD J	ACTOR	5750 WILSHIRE BLVD #580	LOS ANGELES, CA	90037
ADAIR, ALICE	ACTRESS	WM MORRIS, 1350 AVE OF AMERICAS	NEW YORK, NY	10019
ADAIR, DEBORAH	ACTRESS	10100 SANTA MONICA BLVD #700	LOS ANGELES, CA	90067
ADAIR, DIANE	ACTRESS	8075 W 3RD ST #550	LOS ANGELES, CA	90048
ADAIR, RICK	BASEBALL-COACH	INDIANS, CLEVELAND STADIUM	CLEVELAND, OH	44114
ADAM, DAVID	BASEBALL	POST OFFICE BOX 30160	SAN BERNARDINO, CA	92413
ADAM, HRH PRINCE HANS	PRINCE	SCHLOSS	VAUDUZ	LIECTENSTEIN
ADAM, JOHN	BASEBALL TRAINER	BREWERS, 201 S 46TH ST	MILWAUKEE, WI	53214
ADAM, KEN	ART DIRECTOR	34 MONTPELIER ST	LONDON SW7	ENGLAND
ADAM, PETER	DIRECTOR-PRODUCER	BBC-TV, 56 WOOD LN	LONDON W12 7RJ	ENGLAND
ADAMO, RALPH	ACTOR-TV WRITER	ATKINS, 303 S CRESCENT HEIGHTS	LOS ANGELES, CA	90048
ADAMO, SAM	ACTOR	4810 KLUMP AVE	NORTH HOLLYWOOD, CA	91601
ADAMS, ANITA	ACTRESS	WILSON, 291 S LA CIENEGA BL #306	BEVERLY HILLS, CA	90211
ADAMS, ANTHONY W	COMPOSER-CONDUCTOR	5021 STROHM AVE	NORTH HOLLYWOOD, CA	91601
ADAMS, ARTHUR	ACTOR	1256 LONGWOOD AVE	LOS ANGELES, CA	90019
ADAMS, ASHBY	ACTOR	335 N MAPLE DR #360	BEVERLY HILLS, CA	90210
ADAMS, BEVERLY	ACTRESS-MODEL	SEE - SASSOON, BEVERLY ADAMS		
ADAMS, BOBBY	FOOTBALL	N Y GIANTS, GIANTS STADIUM	EAST RUTHERFORD, NJ	07073
ADAMS, BRIAN	WRESTLER	SEE - DEMOLITION		
ADAMS, BROCK	U S SENATOR	2988 JACKSON FEDERAL BUILDING		
		915 2ND AVE	SEATTLE, WA	98174
ADAMS, BROOKE	ACTRESS	2451 HOLLY DR	LOS ANGELES, CA	90068
ADAMS, BRYAN	SINGER	ALLEN, 406-408 WATER ST	VANCOUVER, BC V6B 1A4	CANADA
ADAMS, BRYAN	WRESTLER	SEE - CRUSH		
ADAMS, CATLIN	ACTRESS-WRITER	1801 AVE OF THE STARS #1250	LOS ANGELES, CA	90067
ADAMS, CATTE	ACTRESS	9229 SUNSET BLVD #520	LOS ANGELES, CA	90069
ADAMS, CECILY	ACTRESS	9300 WILSHIRE BLVD #410	BEVERLY HILLS, CA	90212
ADAMS, CHRISTOPHER R	ACTOR	POST OFFICE BOX 19180-A	LOS ANGELES, CA	90019
ADAMS, CINDY	FILM CRITIC	1050 5TH AVE	NEW YORK, NY	10028
ADAMS, CLAUDIA C	TV WRITER	PLESHETTE, 2700 N BEACHWOOD DR	LOS ANGELES, CA	90068
ADAMS, DAVE	BASEBALL	POST OFFICE BOX 12	MIDLAND, TX	79702
ADAMS, DAVE	WRITER	12132 E 187TH ST	ARTESIA, CA	90701
ADAMS, DAVID	BASEBALL	POST OFFICE BOX 20849	CHARLESTON, SC	29413
ADAMS, DEREK	BASEBALL	POST OFFICE BOX 418	SAINT CHARLES, IL	60174
ADAMS, DON	ACT-WRI-DIR	WITZER, 6310 SAN VICENTE #407	LOS ANGELES, CA	90048
ADAMS, EARLE	ACTOR	546 N CITRUS AVE	LOS ANGELES, CA	90036
ADAMS, EDIE	ACTRESS-SINGER	8040 OKEAN TERR	LOS ANGELES, CA	90046
ADAMS, EDIE	COSTUME DESIGNER	13949 VENTURA BLVD #309	SHERMAN OAKS, CA	91423
ADAMS, EDWARD	PHOTOGRAPHER	435 W 57TH ST	NEW YORK, NY	10017
ADAMS, GENTLEMAN CHRIS	WRESTLER	POST OFFICE BOX 190349	DALLAS, TX	75219
ADAMS, GEORGE	FOOTBALL	PATRIOTS, FOXBORO STADIUM, RT #1	FOXBORO, MA	02035
ADAMS, GLENN	BASEBALL-INSTRUCTOR	TWINS, 501 CHICAGO AVE S	MINNEAPOLIS, MN	55415

Name	Occupation	Address	City	Zip/Country
ADAMS, GREG	HOCKEY	CANUCKS, 100 N RENFREW ST	VANCOUVER, BC V5K 3N7	CANADA
ADAMS, HARRY G	ACTOR	11701 TEXAS AVE #106	LOS ANGELES, CA	90025
ADAMS, JACQUELINE	BROADCAST JOURNALIST	CBS NEWS, 524 W 57TH ST	NEW YORK, NY	10019
ADAMS, JANE	ACTRESS	ICM, 8899 BEVERLY BLVD	LOS ANGELES, CA	90048
ADAMS, JANIS WARD	ACTRESS	5455 WILSHIRE BLVD #1406	LOS ANGELES, CA	90036
ADAMS, JEANNE	ACTRESS	8960 CYNTHIA ST #303	WEST HOLLYWOOD, CA	90069
ADAMS, JEB	ACTOR	5914 MURIETTA AVE #2	VAN NUYS, CA	91401
ADAMS, JENNIFER	ACTRESS	1800 N HIGHLAND AVE #405	LOS ANGELES, CA	90028
ADAMS, JOEY	ACT-WRI-COMED	1050 5TH AVE	NEW YORK, NY	10021
ADAMS, JOHN	GOLFER	POST OFFICE BOX 109601	PALM BCH GARDENS, FL	33418
ADAMS, JULIE	ACTRESS	5915 CORBIN AVE	TARZANA, CA	91356
ADAMS, K S "BUD," JR	FOOTBALL EXECUTIVE	OILERS, 6910 FANNIN ST	HOUSTON, TX	77070
ADAMS, KELLY WOOD	ACTRESS-WRITER	333 E 69TH ST	NEW YORK, NY	10021
ADAMS, LAUREL	ACTRESS	4051 RADFORD AVE #A	STUDIO CITY, CA	91604
ADAMS, LEW V	TV DIRECTOR	DGA, 7920 SUNSET BLVD, 6TH FL	LOS ANGELES, CA	90046
ADAMS, MARGO	PERSONALITY	JENNIFER J KING, ATTORNEY AT LAW		
		18062 IRVINE BLVD	TUSTIN, CA	92680
ADAMS, MARK	COLUMNIST	VARIETY, 34/35 NEWMAN ST	LONDON W1P 3PD	ENGLAND
ADAMS, MARLA	ACTRESS	247 S BEVERLY DR #102	BEVERLY HILLS, CA	90210
ADAMS, MARY KAY	ACTRESS	9000 SUNSET BLVD #1200	LOS ANGELES, CA	90069
ADAMS, MASON	ACTOR	900 5TH AVE	NEW YORK, NY	10021
ADAMS, MAUD	ACTRESS-MODEL	12700 VENTURA BLVD #700	LOS ANGELES, CA	90067
ADAMS, MIA	ACTRESS	8040 OKEAN TERR	LOS ANGELES, CA	90046
ADAMS, MICHAEL	BASKETBALL	POST OFFICE BOX 4658	DENVER, CO	80204
ADAMS, PEPPER	SAXOPHONIST	UPTOWN, 4672 VICTORIA AVE	MONTREAL, QUE H30 2N1	CANADA
ADAMS, RICHARD	AUTHOR	26 CHURCH ST, WHITCHURCH	HANTS	ENGLAND
ADAMS, STEVE	TREASURER	STATE CAPITOL BUILDING	NASHVILLE, TN	37243
ADAMS, STEVEN S	TV WRITER	130 W 42ND ST #1804	NEW YORK, NY	10036
ADAMS, TERRY	BASEBALL	1524 W NEBRASKA AVE	PEORIA, IL	61604
ADAMS, TOMMY	BASEBALL	POST OFFICE BOX 30160	SAN BERNARDINO, CA	92413
ADAMS, TONY	FILM PRODUCER	20521 ROCA CHICA DR	MALIBU, CA	90265
ADAMS-MC QUEEN, NEILE	ACTRESS	2323 BOWMONT DR	BEVERLY HILLS, CA	90210
ADAMSON, AL	FILM DIRECTOR	INDEPENDENT-INTL PICTURES		
		223 STATE HIGHWAY #18	EAST BRUNSWICK, NJ	08816
ADAMSON, JOEL	BASEBALL	POST OFFICE BOX 10336	CLEARWATER, FL	34617
ADATO, PERRY MILLER	TV DIRECTOR-PRODUCER	3 FRASER RD	WESTPORT, CT	06880
ADC BAND	ROCK & ROLL GROUP	17397 SANTA BARBARA DR	DETROIT, MI	48221
ADCOCK BAND, EDDIE	C & W GROUP	ROUTE #5, BOX 19-A	WARRENTOWN, VA	22186
ADDAMS, CHARLES	CARTOONIST	N Y MAGAZINE, 25 W 43RD ST	NEW YORK, NY	10036
ADDEO, RICHARD	BASEBALL EXECUTIVE	800 HOME RUN LN	MEMPHIS, TN	38104
ADDERLEY, JANET	ACTRESS	9229 SUNSET BLVD #311	LOS ANGELES, CA	90069
ADDERLY, HERB	FOOTBALL	98 PELHAM RD	PHILADELPHIA, PA	19119
ADDISON, ANNE	TV EXECUTIVE	1035 5TH AVE	NEW YORK, NY	10028
ADDISON, JOHN M	COMPOSER	1948 PALISADES DR	PACIFIC PALISADES, CA	90272
ADDISON, WALTER	ACTOR	8150 BEVERLY BLVD #201	LOS ANGELES, CA	90048
ADDISON ALTMAN, NANCY	ACTRESS	425 W END AVE	NEW YORK, NY	10024
ADDISON BROTHERS, THE	C & W GROUP	5625 "O" ST BLDG #7	LINCOLN, NE	68510
ADDISON-LICAMELI, AMY	WRITER-STORY EDITOR	171 W 71ST ST #3-A	NEW YORK, NY	10023
ADDUCI, JIM	BASEBALL	5929 S SAWYER	EVERGREEN PARK, IL	60642
ADDY, WESLEY	ACTOR	88 CENTRAL PARK W	NEW YORK, NY	10023
ADELMAN, BARRY	WRITER-PRODUCER	22724 TOWN CRIER RD	WOODLAND HILLS, CA	91364
ADELMAN, RICK	BASKETBALL COACH	700 NE MULTNOMAH ST #600	PORTLAND, OR	97232
ADELSON, GARY	FILM WRITER-PRODUCER	10000 W WASHINGTON BLVD #4900	CULVER CITY, CA	90232
ADELSON, MERV	TV PRODUCER	600 SARBONNE RD	LOS ANGELES, CA	90077
ADES, DAN	ACTOR	652 N LA JOLLA AVE	LOS ANGELES, CA	90048
ADICKES, MARK	FOOTBALL	POST OFFICE BOX 17247 (DULLES)	WASHINGTON, DC	20041
ADJANI, ISABELLE	ACTRESS	ICM, 33 RUE MARBEUF	PARIS 75008	FRANCE
ADKINS, HAZEL	SINGER-SONGWRITER	POST OFFICE BOX 646		
		COOPER STATION	NEW YORK, NY	10276
ADKINS, ROB	BASEBALL	POST OFFICE BOX 1110	MYRTLE BEACH, SC	29578
ADKINS, STEVE	BASEBALL	CUBS, 2ND & RIVERSIDE DR	DES MOINES, IA	50309
ADLER, ABRAHAM	TV DIRECTOR	10 DESSER PL	EDISON, NJ	08817
ADLER, ALAN J	SCREENWRITER	9000 SUNSET BLVD #1200	LOS ANGELES, CA	90069
ADLER, EDWARD	TV WRITER	10000 SANTA MONICA BLVD #305	LOS ANGELES, CA	90067
ADLER, GARY	ACTOR	18 E READING AVE	STATEN ISLAND, NY	10308
ADLER, GERALD L	TV EXECUTIVE	145 N ALMONT DR #1230	LOS ANGELES, CA	90048
ADLER, JERRY	TALENT AGENT	12725 VENTURA BLVD #D	STUDIO CITY, CA	91604
ADLER, LARRY	ACTOR	26 WYNDHAM ST	LONDON W1	ENGLAND
ADLER, LOU	DIRECTOR-PRODUCER	3969 VILLA COSTERA	MALIBU, CA	90265
ADLER, MATT	ACTOR	1924 TALMADGE ST	LOS ANGELES, CA	90027
ADLER, NATHAN	ACTOR	9255 DOHENY RD #2205	WEST HOLLYWOOD, CA	90069
ADLER, PHILIP	FILM DIRECTOR	WM MORRIS, 31-32 SOHO SQ	LONDON W1V 5DG	ENGLAND
ADLER, RICHARD	COMPOSER-LYRICIST	8 E 83RD ST	NEW YORK, NY	10028
ADLER, SAMUEL	CONDUCTOR	54 RAILROAD MILLS RD	PITTSFORD, NY	14534
ADLER, STELLA	ACTOR-DIRECTOR	1016 5TH AVE	NEW YORK, NY	10019
ADLON, PERCY	TV WRITER	R/W/G, 8428 MELROSE PL #C	LOS ANGELES, CA	90069
ADNOPOZ, DAVID	ACTOR-WRITER	1194 N LOS ROBLES AVE	PASADENA, CA	91104
ADOLPH, DAVE	FOOTBALL COACH	RAIDERS, 332 CENTER ST	EL SEGUNDO, CA	90245
ADONIS, FRANK	ACTOR	ATKINS, 303 S CRESCENT HEIGHTS	LOS ANGELES, CA	90048
ADOTTA, KIP	COMEDIAN	WILLARD ALEXANDER, INC		
		660 MADISON AVE	NEW YORK, NY	10021
ADRIAN, IRIS	ACTRESS	3341 FLOYD TERR	LOS ANGELES, CA	90068
ADRIAN, LOUIS	CONDUCTOR	3612-A LAKESHORE BLVD	LAKEPORT, CA	95453
ADU, SADE	SINGER	SEE - SADE		
AEROSMITH	ROCK & ROLL GROUP	COLLINS/BARASSO, 215 1ST ST	CAMBRIDGE, MA	02142

AFENIR, TROY	BASEBALL	POST OFFICE BOX 23290	NASHVILLE, TN	37202
AFFE, PETER	TV EXECUTIVE	BUENA VISTA TELEVISION		
		500 PARK AVE, 10TH FLOOR	NEW YORK, NY	10022
AFFLECK, WILLIAM C	TV DIRECTOR	22198 REINHARDT DR	WOODHAVEN, MI	48183
AFRIAT, ALAN	TV DIRECTOR-PRODUCER	24 COMBEMARTIN RD	LONDON SW18 5PR	ENGLAND
AFRO-CUBAN BAND	ROCK & ROLL GROUP	LOVE ZAGER PRODUCTIONS		
		1697 BROADWAY	NEW YORK, NY	10019
AGAJANIAN, J C	AUTO RACER	900 N HILLCREST RD	BEVERLY HILLS, CA	90210
AGAR, JOHN	ACTOR	639 N HOLLYWOOD WY	BURBANK, CA	91505
AGASSI, ANDRE	TENNIS	7820 DANA POINT CT	LAS VEGAS, NV	89117
AGAZZI, JAMES J	TV WRITER	POST OFFICE BOX 24086	LOS ANGELES, CA	90024
AGEE, MEL	FOOTBALL	POST OFFICE BOX 535000	INDIANPOLIS, IN	46253
AGEE, TOMMIE	FOOTBALL	COWBOYS, 1 COWBOYS PARKWAY	IRVING, TX	75063
AGGANIS, GREG	BASEBALL EXECUTIVE	2501 ALLEN AVE, SE	CANTON, OH	44707
AGGANIS, MIKE	BASEBALL EXECUTIVE	2501 ALLEN AVE, SE	CANTON, OH	44707
AGHAYAN, RAY	COSTUME DESIGNER	9314 LLOYDCREST DR	BEVERLY HILLS, CA	90210
AGNEW, RAY	FOOTBALL	PATRIOTS, FOXBORO STADIUM, RT #1	FOXBORO, MA	02035
AGNEW, SPIRO	VICE-PRESIDENT	78 COLUMBIA DR	RANCHO MIRAGE, CA	92270
AGNOS, ART	MAYOR	42 GRAYSTONE TERR	SAN FRANCISCO, CA	94114
AGOSTO, JUAN	BASEBALL	250 STADIUM PLAZA	ST LOUIS, MO	63102
AGRAN, LINDA	DIRECTOR-PRODUCER	PANAVISION UK, LTD		
		114 THE CHAMBERS		
		CHELSEA HARBOUR	LONDON SW10 OXF	ENGLAND
AGRIESTI, LOU K	COMPOSER-CONDUCTOR	3518 S TOWNER ST	SANTA ANA, CA	92707
AGRONSKY, MARTIN	TV PRODUCER	4001 BRANDYWINE ST	WASHINGTON, DC	20016
AGUAYO, LUIS	BASEBALL	POST OFFICE BOX 2365	PAWTUCKET, RI	02861
AGUILA, JUAN	BASEBALL SCOUT	REDS, 100 RIVERFRONT STADIUM	CINCINNATI, OH	45202
AGUILERA, RICK	BASEBALL	TWINS, 501 CHICAGO AVE S	MINNEAPOLIS, MN	55415
AGUIRRE, CARLOS L	ARTIST	516 CURTIS ST	ALBANY, CA	94706
AGUIRRE, MARK	BASKETBALL	THE PALACE OF AUBURN HILLS		
		2 CHAMPIONSHIP DR	AUBURN HILLS, MI	48326
AGULAR, LOUIE	FOOTBALL	N Y JETS, 1000 FULTON AVE	HEMPSTEAD, NY	11550
AGUTTER, JENNY	ACTRESS	6882 CAMROSE DR	LOS ANGELES, CA	90068
AHERN, BRIAN	BASEBALL	800 HOME RUN LN	MEMPHIS, TN	38104
AHN, RALPH	ACTOR	14709 CLYMER ST	MISSION HILLS, CA	91345
AIDEKMAN, ALAN	TV WRITER	6371 W 5TH ST	LOS ANGELES, CA	90048
AIDEM, BETSY	ACTRESS	5750 WILSHIRE BLVD #512	LOS ANGELES, CA	90036
AIDMAN, BETTY HYATT	ACTRESS	525 N PALM DR	BEVERLY HILLS, CA	90210
AIDMAN, CHARLES	ACT-WRI-DIR	525 N PALM DR	BEVERLY HILLS, CA	90210
AIELLO, DANNY	ACTOR	4 THORNHILL DR	RAMSEY, NJ	07446
AIELLO, RICK	ACTOR	10000 SANTA MONICA BLVD #305	LOS ANGELES, CA	90067
AIKMAN, TROY	FOOTBALL	COWBOYS, 1 COWBOYS PARKWAY	IRVING, TX	75063
AILES, ROGER E	PRODUCER-DIRECTOR	AILES COMM, 456 W 43RD ST	NEW YORK, NY	10036
AILEY, ALVIN	CHOREOGRAPHER	C C DANCE, 229 E 59TH ST	NEW YORK, NY	10022
AIMEE, ANOUK	ACTRESS	4 RUE DE PONTHIEU	F-75008 PARIS	FRANCE
AINGE, DANNY	BASEBALL-BASKETBALL	10 ORDWAY RD	WELLESLEY, MA	02181
AIR SUPPLY	ROCK & ROLL GROUP	1990 S BUNDY DR #590	LOS ANGELES, CA	90025
AITKEN, DOUG	FILM DIRECTOR	TANDRIDGE PRIORY LODGE		
		OLD OXTED	SURREY RH8 9JU	ENGLAND
AITKEN, MARIA	ACTRESS	WHITEHALL, 125 GLOUCESTER RD	LONDON SW7 4TE	ENGLAND
AJAYE, FRANKLYN	COMEDIAN-ACTOR	1312 S ORANGE DR	LOS ANGELES, CA	90019
AJIN	ARTIST	123 W 44TH ST	NEW YORK, NY	10036
AKAKA, DANIEL K	U S SENATOR	POST OFFICE BOX 50144	HONOLULU, HI	96850
AKEEM	WRESTLER	SEE - ONE MAN GANG		
AKERFELDS, DARREL	BASEBALL	17336 E RICE CIR #F	AURORA, CO	80015
AKERMAN, JOSEPH L	WRITER	1858 FOX HILLS DR	LOS ANGELES, CA	90025
AKERS, KAREN	ACTRESS-SINGER	337 W 43RD ST #1-B	NEW YORK, NY	10036
AKERS, TIMOTHY WAYNE	MUSIC ARRANGER	8512 BAY HILL BLVD	ORLANDO, FL	32819
AKIN, SUSAN	BEAUTY CONTESTANT	1325 BROADWALK	ATLANTIC CITY, NJ	08401
AKINS, CLAUDE	ACTOR	1927 MIDLOTHIAN DR	ALTADENA, CA	91001
AKINS, JEWEL	SINGER-SONGWRITER	GOOD, 2500 NW 39TH ST	OKLAHOMA CITY, OK	73112
AKIYOSHI, TOSHIKO	COMPOSER-PIANIST	5820 WILSHIRE BLVD #301	LOS ANGELES, CA	90036
AL-ASSAD, HAFEZX	PRESIDENT	PRESIDENTIAL PALACE	DAMASCUS	SYRIA
ALABAMA	C & W GROUP	POST OFFICE BOX 529	FORT PAYNE, AL	35967
ALAIMO, MARC	ACTOR	9255 SUNSET BLVD #515	LOS ANGELES, CA	90069
ALAMO CHORTETTES, THE	C & W GROUP	BUN JAK, 331 PROPSECT ST	BERLIN, NH	03570
ALAN, BUDDY	SINGER	1225 N CHESTER AVE	BAKERSFIELD, CA	93308
ALAN, CRAIG	ACTOR	2029 CENTURY PARK E #600	LOS ANGELES, CA	90067
ALAN, KENYON	ACTOR	8665 WILSHIRE BLVD #208	BEVERLY HILLS, CA	90211
ALAN, SYLVIA	TV WRITER	CAA, 9830 WILSHIRE BLVD	BEVERLY HILLS, CA	90212
ALARIE, MARK	BASKETBALL	BULLETS, 1 HARRY S TRUMAN DR	LANDOVER, MD	20785
ALARIMO, JOHN	WRITER	POST OFFICE BOX 1446	STUDIO CITY, CA	91604
ALARM, THE	ROCK & ROLL GROUP	47 BERNARD ST, SAINT ALBANS	HERTS	ENGLAND
ALASKEY, JOE	COMEDIAN	1717 N HIGHLAND AVE #414	LOS ANGELES, CA	90028
ALBA, ROSE	ACTRESS	60 CHANDOS PL	LONDON WC 2	ENGLAND
ALBANESE, MICHAEL	TV DIRECTOR	132 HIGH ST	LEONIA, NJ	07605
ALBANS, SAMUEL	WRITER	1417 VETERAN AVE #201	LOS ANGELES, CA	90024
ALBECK, ANDY	FILM EXECUTIVE	727 7TH AVE	NEW YORK, NY	10019
ALBEE, EDWARD	WRITER-PRODUCER	14 HARRISON ST	NEW YORK, NY	10013
ALBEE, LURA	ACTRESS	KROLL, 390 W END AVE	NEW YORK, NY	10024
ALBERG, MILDRED F	WRITER-PRODUCER	555 W 57TH ST #1230	NEW YORK, NY	10019
ALBERGHETTI, ANNA MARIA	ACTRESS-SINGER	293 S REEVES DR	BEVERLY HILLS, CA	90212
ALBERRO, JOSE	BASEBALL	POST OFFICE BOX 309	GASTONA, NC	28053
ALBERS, KRISTI	GOLFER	2750 VOLUSA AVE #B	DAYTON BEACH, FL	32114
ALBERT, ALLAN	WRITER	561 BROADWAY	NEW YORK, NY	10012

ALBERT, CARL	U S CONGRESSMAN	ROUTE #2	MC ALESTER, OK 74501
ALBERT, DONNIE RAY	SINGER	CAMI, 165 W 57TH ST	NEW YORK, NY 10019
ALBERT, EDDIE	ACTOR	719 AMALFI DR	PACIFIC PAL, CA 90272
ALBERT, EDWARD	ACTOR	10100 SANTA MONICA BLVD #1600	LOS ANGELES, CA 90067
ALBERT, FRANKIE	FOOTBALL	1 STANFORD DR	RANCHO MIRAGE, CA 92270
ALBERT, GARY	TV HOST-SPORTSCASTER	SOUNDS GOOD TO ME PRODUCTIONS	
		144-18 NORTHERN BLVD	FLUSHING, NY 11354
ALBERT, MARV	SPORTSCASTER	MSG NETWORK, 2 PENNSYLVANIA AVE	NEW YORK, NY 10001
ALBERT, PRINCE OF MONACO	PRINCE	PALAIS DE MONACO	98015 MONTE CARLO 518 MONACO
ALBERT, TIM	BASEBALL	POST OFFICE BOX 855	BELOIT, WI 53511
ALBERTS, AL & THE ORIGINALS	VOCAL GROUP	CEE, 193 KONHAUS RD	MECHANICSBURG, PA 17055
ALBERTSON, MAURA DHU	ACTRESS	1618 SUNSET PLAZA DR	LOS ANGELES, CA 90069
ALBI, DOMINICK	WRI-DIR-PROD	251 W 92ND ST #3-C	NEW YORK, NY 10023
ALBIDREZ, LUIS	WRITER	13419 HARVEST AVE	NORWALK, CA 90650
ALBIN, DOLORES	ACTRESS	9255 SUNSET BLVD #515	LOS ANGELES, CA 90069
ALBO, JOHN	WRITER	POST OFFICE BOX 3024	SEAL BEACH, CA 90740
ALBORANO, PETE	BASEBALL	POST OFFICE BOX 15050	READING, PA 19612
ALBRECHT, ANDREW	BASEBALL	POST OFFICE BOX 2148	WOODBRIDGE, VA 22193
ALBRECHT, ARDON D	TV WRITER	8955 BEVERLY BLVD	WEST HOLLYWOOD, CA 90048
ALBRECHT, HOWARD	TV WRITER	3632 BEVERLY RIDGE DR	SHERMAN OAKS, CA 91423
ALBRECHT, PATRICIA ALICE	ACTRESS	1803 1/2 N VAN NESS AVE	HOLLYWOOD, CA 90028
ALBRECHT, PEGGY FREES	ACTRESS-WRITER	20701 WELLS DR	WOODLAND HILLS, CA 91364
ALBRECHT, RICHARD	TV WRITER	20701 WELLS DR	WOODLAND HILLS, CA 91364
ALBRECHT, ROBERT	DIRECTOR	3017 N CLIFTON AVE	CHICAGO, IL 60657
ALBRIGHT, DONN	RAY BRADBURY EXPERT	MULVEY, 156 5TH AVE	NEW YORK, NY 10010
ALBRIGHT, DR TENLEY	DOCTOR	2 COMMONWEALTH AVE	BOSTON, MA 02117
ALBRIGHT, ERIC	BASEBALL	POST OFFICE BOX 2785	LAKELAND, FL 33806
ALBRIGHT, GERALD	SAXOPHONIST	888 7TH AVE #1602	NEW YORK, NY 10019
ALBRIGHT, LOLA	ACTRESS	POST OFFICE BOX 6067	GLENDALE, CA 91225
ALBRITTON, VINCE	FOOTBALL	COWBOYS, 1 COWBOYS PARKWAY	IRVING, TX 75063
ALBRO, MICHAEL	TV DIRECTOR	WJLA, 4461 CONNECTICUT AVE, NW	WASHINGTON, DC 20008
ALBUS, JIM	GOLFER	PGA SENIORS, 112 T P C BLVD	PONTE VEDRA BEACH, FL 32082
ALCH, ALAN	WRITER	125 WASHINGTON AVE #F	SANTA MONICA, CA 90403
ALCIVAR, BOB E	COMPOSER	12713 CHANDLER BLVD	NORTH HOLLYWOOD, CA 91607
ALCORN, JOHN	ARTIST	VICKI MORGAN, 194 3RD AVE	NEW YORK, NY 10003
ALCORN, STEPHEN	ARTIST	POST OFFICE BOX 179	LYME, CT 06371
ALCROFT, JAMIE	ACT-WRI-COMED	151 S EL CAMINO DR	BEVERLY HILLS, CA 90212
ALDA, ALAN	ACT-WRI-DIR	641 LEXINGTON AVE #1400	NEW YORK, NY 10022
ALDA, ANTONY	ACTOR	15 SEAVIEW DR N	ROLLING HILLS, CA 90274
ALDA, ELIZABETH	ACTRESS	19432 COLLIER ST	TARZANA, CA 91356
ALDA, RUTANYA	ACTRESS	3500 W OLIVE AVE #1400	BURBANK, CA 91505
ALDEN, GINGER	MODEL	4152 ROYAL CREST PL	MEMPHIS, TN 38138
ALDEN, NORMAN	ACTOR	9300 WILSHIRE BLVD #410	BEVERLY HILLS, CA 90212
ALDER, JIMMY	BASEBALL	POST OFFICE BOX 2785	LAKELAND, FL 33806
ALDERETE, ROSEMARY	WRITER-PRODUCER	816 S MONTEBELLO BLVD	MONTEBELLO, CA 90640
ALDERMAN, BRUCE	COLUMNIST	VARIETY, 33 CHAMPS ELYSEES	PARIS 75008 FRANCE
ALDERMAN, MARY	WRITER-PRODUCER	POST OFFICE BOX 352	NEW CANAAN, CT 06840
ALDERSON, SANDY	BASEBALL EXECUTIVE	ATHLETICS'S, OAKLAND COLISEUM	OAKLAND, CA 94621
ALDERTON, JOHN	FOOTBALL REFEREE	NFL, 410 PARK AVE	NEW YORK, NY 10022
ALDO NOVA	ROCK & ROLL GROUP	PEARLMAN, 888 7TH AVE, 37TH FL	NEW YORK, NY 10019
ALDRED, SCOTT	BASEBALL	8527 TIM TAM TRAIL	FLUSHING, MI 48433
ALDREDGE, THEONI V	COSTUME DESIGNER	425 LAFAYETTE ST	NEW YORK, NY 10003
ALDRETE, MIKE	BASEBALL	231 VIA DEL PINAR	MONTEREY, CA 93940
ALDRETE, RICH	BASEBALL	POST OFFICE BOX 5599	LITTLE ROCK, AR 72215
ALDRICH, ADELL	TV DIRECTOR	556 S NORTON AVE	LOS ANGELES, CA 90020
ALDRICH, WILLIAM M	FILM PRODUCER	210 S WESTGATE AVE	LOS ANGELES, CA 90049
ALDRIDGE, RUSTY	SINGER	GOOD, 2500 NW 39TH ST	OKLAHOMA CITY, OK 73112
ALDRIDGE, VIRGINIA	ACTRESS-WRITER	976 1/2 PALM AVE	LOS ANGELES, CA 90069
ALDRIN, EDWIN "BUZZ"	ASTRONAUT	233 EMERALD BAY	LAGUNA BEACH, CA 92651
ALECK, JIMMY	COMEDIAN	9200 SUNSET BLVD #428	LOS ANGELES, CA 90069
ALEONG, AKI	ACTOR	6220 HILLANDALE DR	LOS ANGELES, CA 90042
ALERT, RED	RAP GROUP-RAPWRITERS	SEE - RED ALERT	
ALESIA, FRANK	WRITER-PRODUCER	805 N ELM DR	BEVERLY HILLS, CA 90210
ALETHIA	ROCK & ROLL GROUP	1254 LAMAR CIR #312	MEMPHIS, TN 38114
ALETTER, FRANK	ACTOR	5430 CORBIN AVE	TARZANA, CA 91356
ALETTER, KYLE	ACTRESS	POST OFFICE BOX 402	ENCINO, CA 91316
ALEXANDER, AXEL	COMPOSER-CONDUCTOR	BERT BRECHT STR #2	BAD VILBEL 6368 GERMANY
ALEXANDER, BARBARA	ACTRESS	145 S FAIRFAX AVE #310	LOS ANGELES, CA 90036
ALEXANDER, BILL	U S CONGRESSMAN	POST OFFICE BOX 3848	BATESVILLE, AR 75201
ALEXANDER, BOBBY	SINGER	POST OFFICE BOX 40764	NASHVILLE, TN 37204
ALEXANDER, BRANDY	ACTRESS	12229 MONTAGUE ST	ARLETA, CA 91331
ALEXANDER, BRUCE	FOOTBALL	LIONS, 1200 FEATHERSTONE RD	PONTIAC, MI 48432
ALEXANDER, DAN	DIRECTOR	DGA, 7950 SUNSET BLVD	LOS ANGELES, CA 90046
ALEXANDER, DANIELE	SINGER	POST OFFICE BOX 158558	NASHVILLE, TN 37215
ALEXANDER, DAVID	FOOTBALL	EAGLES, BROAD ST & PATTISON AVE	PHILADELPHIA, PA 19148
ALEXANDER, DAVID	TV DIRECTOR	3907 GOODLAND AVE	NORTH HOLLYWOOD, CA 91604
ALEXANDER, DENISE	ACTRESS	345 N MAPLE DR #183	BEVERLY HILLS, CA 90210
ALEXANDER, DON	BASEBALL COACH	POST OFFICE BOX 651	AUBURN, NY 13021
ALEXANDER, GARY	BASEBALL (MINORS)	POST OFFICE BOX 3449	SCRANTON, PA 18505
ALEXANDER, GERALD	BASEBALL	POST OFFICE BOX 75089	OKLAHOMA CITY, OK 73147
ALEXANDER, HAL	TV DIRECTOR	24211 PHILIPRIMM ST	WOODLAND HILLS, CA 91364
ALEXANDER, HUBBARD	FOOTBALL COACH	COWBOYS, 1 COWBOYS PARKWAY	IRVING, TX 75063
ALEXANDER, HUGH	BASEBALL-SCOUT	1060 W ADDISON ST	CHICAGO, IL 60613
ALEXANDER, JACE	ACTOR	11726 SAN VICENTE BLVD #300	LOS ANGELES, CA 90049

Name	Occupation	Address	City	Zip/Country
ALEXANDER, JANE	ACTRESS	RURAL ROUTE #2, GORDON RD	CARMEL, NY	10512
ALEXANDER, JASON	ACTOR	329 N WETHERLY DR #101	BEVERLY HILLS, CA	90211
ALEXANDER, JEFF	COMPOSER-CONDUCTOR	921 N SPAULDING AVE #5	LOS ANGELES, CA	90046
ALEXANDER, JESSE	TV EDITOR	17820 HATTON ST	RESEDA, CA	91335
ALEXANDER, KARL	TV WRITER	8955 BEVERLY BLVD	WEST HOLLYWOOD, CA	90048
ALEXANDER, KIRK	DIRECTOR	132 E 61ST ST	NEW YORK, NY	10021
ALEXANDER, LARRY H	TV WRITER	CONWAY, 280 S BEVERLY DR #513	BEVERLY HILLS, CA	90212
ALEXANDER, LAWRENCE E	DIRECTOR	ZOE PRODS, 100 W 57TH ST	NEW YORK, NY	10022
ALEXANDER, LLOYD	WRITER	1005 DREXEL AVE	DREXEL HILL, PA	19026
ALEXANDER, LORI E	COMPOSER	3711 S CANFIELD	LOS ANGELES, CA	90034
ALEXANDER, LOUIS	ACTOR	DON SCHWARTZ, 8749 SUNSET BLVD	LOS ANGELES, CA	90069
ALEXANDER, MANNY	BASEBALL	POST OFFICE BOX 230	HAGERSTOWN, MD	21740
ALEXANDER, NEWELL	ACTOR	10000 RIVERSIDE DR #6	TOLUCA LAKE, CA	91602
ALEXANDER, RICHARD "DICK"	ACTOR	23388 MULHOLLAND DR	WOODLAND HILLS, CA	91364
ALEXANDER, SAMUEL	DIRECTOR	ZEPLIN, 850 7TH AVE	NEW YORK, NY	10019
ALEXANDER, SCOTTY	SINGER	POST OFFICE BOX 1381	TUALATIN, OR	97062
ALEXANDER, TERENCE	ACTOR	169 QUEENSGATE #8-A	LONDON SW7 5EH	ENGLAND
ALEXANDER, TERRY	ACTOR	ABC-TV, "ONE LIFE TO LIVE"		
		56 W 66TH ST	NEW YORK, NY	10023
ALEXANDER, THEA	AUTHORESS	POST OFFICE BOX 26880	TEMPE, AZ	85282
ALEXANDER, THOMAS R	COMPOSER	837 HUNTLEY DR	LOS ANGELES, CA	90069
ALEXANDER, VAN	CONDUCTOR	16373 ROYAL HILLS DR	ENCINO, CA	91436
ALEXANDER-WILLIS, HOPE	ACTRESS	GILLY, 8721 SUNSET BLVD #103	LOS ANGELES, CA	90069
ALEXANDRA, TIANA	ACT-DAN-SING-PROD	815 N CAMDEN DR	BEVERLY HILLS, CA	90210
ALEXIS, KIM	MODEL	ELITE MODELS, 111 E 22ND ST	NEW YORK, NY	10010
ALFIERI, CESARE	CONDUCTOR	253 W 73RD ST #7-M	NEW YORK, NY	10023
ALFIERI, RICHARD	ACTOR-WRITER	636 KELTON AVE	LOS ANGELES, CA	90024
ALFOND, HAROLD	BASEBALL EXECUTIVE	FENWAY PARK, 4 YAWKEY WY	BOSTON, MA	02215
ALFONSO, CARLOS	BASEBALL COACH	S F GIANTS, CANDLESTICK PARK	SAN FRANICSCO, CA	94124
ALFONSO, KRISTIAN	ACTRESS	POST OFFICE BOX 93-1628	LOS ANGELES, CA	90093
ALFONSO, OZZIE	DIRECTOR	46 LEWIS PARKWAY	YONKERS, NY	10705
ALFONZO, EDGAR	BASEBALL	POST OFFICE BOX 1742	PALM SPRINGS, CA	92263
ALFORD, BRENDA	SINGER	EAI, 2211 INDUSTRIAL BLVD	SARASOTA, FL	33580
ALFORD, STEVE	BASKETBALL	REUNION ARENA, 777 SPORTS ST	DALLAS, TX	75207
ALHANTI, IRIS	ACTRESS	1308 N HAVENHURST DR #29	LOS ANGELES, CA	90046
ALHANTI, JANET	ACTRESS	1308 N HAVENHURST DR #29	LOS ANGELES, CA	90046
ALI, MUHAMMAD	BOXER-ACTOR	POST OFFICE BOX 187	BERRIEN SPRINGS, MI	49103
ALIBI	C & W GROUP	CLOANA, 177 W 7TH, 4TH FLOOR	CANCOUVER, BC V5Y 1KR	CANADA
ALICEA, EDWIN	BASEBALL	POST OFFICE BOX 16683	GREENVILLE, SC	29606
ALICEA, LUIS	BASEBALL	HC-02, BOX 9075	GUAYNABO, PR	00657
ALIFF, LISA	ACTRESS	STONE MANNERS, 9113 SUNSET BL	LOS ANGELES, CA	90069
ALIMENA, CHARLIE	BASEBALL	POST OFFICE BOX 1295	CLINTON, IA	52733
ALINDER, DALLAS	ACTOR	1825 TAFT AVE	HOLLYWOOD, CA	90028
ALL AMERICAN BAND, THE	C & W GROUP	1300 DIVISION ST #103-A	NASHVILLE, TN	37203
ALLAIN, JAYSON "JAKE"	BODYBUILDER	TOO HIP, ROUTE #4, BOX 2967	SANFORD, ME	04073
ALLAIRE, KARL	BASEBALL	POST OFFICE BOX 6212	TOLEDO, OH	43614
ALLAN, ELKAN	WRI-DIR-PROD	3 CRESCENT RD	IPSWICH IP1 2EX	ENGLAND
ALLAN, JED	ACTOR	11759 IOWA AVE	LOS ANGELES, CA	90025
ALLAN, TED	SCREENWRITER	8955 BEVERLY BLVD	WEST HOLLYWOOD, CA	90048
ALLANSON, ANDY	BASEBALL	BREWERS, 201 S 46TH ST	MILWAUKEE, WI	53214
ALLARD, A WAYNE	U S CONGRESSMAN	513 CANNON HOUSE OFFICE BLDG	WASHINGTON, DC	20515
ALLARD, BRIAN	BASEBALL-COACH	110 RICHARD SR	HENRY, IL	61537
ALLARD, JEANNE	ACTRESS	10 RUE PRADIER	PARIS 75019	FRANCE
ALLEGHENY EXPRESS	C & W GROUP	PROCESS, 439 WILEY AVE	FRANKLIN, PA	16323
ALLEN, AL	COMPOSER	MASON, 1299 OCEAN AVE	SANTA MONICA, CA	90401
ALLEN, ALLEN D	COMPOSER-CONDUCTOR	17114 DEVONSHIRE ST	NORTHRIDGE, CA	91325
ALLEN, AMY	ACTRESS	6607 MOORE DR	LOS ANGELES, CA	90048
ALLEN, BECCA	ACTRESS	114 SOUTH PARK AVE	WINTER PARK, FL	32789
ALLEN, BRENDA	SINGER	POST OFFICE BOX 62	GENEVA, NE	68361
ALLEN, BUDDY	TALENT AGENT	65 W 55TH ST #6-C	NEW YORK, NY	10019
ALLEN, CHAD	ACTOR	12049 SMOKEY LN	CERRITOS, CA	90701
ALLEN, CHAD	BASEBALL	2501 ALLEN AVE, SE	CANTON, OH	44707
ALLEN, CHUCK	FOOTBALL EXECUTIVE	SEAHAWKS, 11220 NE 53RD ST	KIRKLAND, WA	98033
ALLEN, COREY	ACT-WRI-DIR	8642 HOLLYWOOD BLVD	LOS ANGELES, CA	90046
ALLEN, CURTIS LYNN	WRITER	22329 KITTRIDGE ST	CANOGA PARK, CA	91303
ALLEN, DEBBIE	ACT-DAN-DIR-SING	607 MARGUERITA AVE	SANTA MONICA, CA	90402
ALLEN, DEBORAH	SINGER-SONGWRITER	10100 SANTA MONICA BLVD #1600	LOS ANGELES, CA	90067
ALLEN, DEDE	FILM EDITOR	ACE, 1041 N FORMOSA AVE	WEST HOLLYWOOD, CA	90046
ALLEN, DOMENICK	ACTOR-SINGER	9165 SUNSET BLVD #202	LOS ANGELES, CA	90069
ALLEN, DONNA	ACTRESS	SELECTED, 3575 W CAHUENGA BLVD	LOS ANGELES, CA	90068
ALLEN, ERIC	FOOTBALL	EAGLES, BROAD ST & PATTISON AVE	PHILADELPHIA, PA	19148
ALLEN, GENE	DIRECTOR	3452 MANDEVILLE CANYON DR	LOS ANGELES, CA	90049
ALLEN, GINGER LYNN	ACTRESS-MODEL	8228 SUNSET BLVD #212	LOS ANGELES, CA	90046
ALLEN, HAROLD	BASEBALL	POST OFFICE BOX 4209	JACKSON, MS	39296
ALLEN, HENRY W	WRITER	4618 LOUISE AVE	ENCINO, CA	91316
ALLEN, INDIA	MODEL	8484 WILSHIRE BLVD #530	BEVERLY HILLS, CA	90211
ALLEN, JONELLE	ACTRESS-SINGER	10351 SANTA MONICA BLVD #211	LOS ANGELES, CA	90025
ALLEN, JULIAN	ARTIST	31 WALKER ST	NEW YORK, NY	10013
ALLEN, KAREN	ACTRESS	122 E 10TH ST	NEW YORK, NY	10013
ALLEN, LEWIS	FILM-TV DIRECTOR	2819 MANDEVILLE CANYON RD	LOS ANGELES, CA	90049
ALLEN, LEWIS M	PRODUCER	1500 BROADWAY	NEW YORK, NY	10036
ALLEN, LINDA	SINGER	POST OFFICE BOX 5881	BELLINGHAM, WA	98227
ALLEN, LINDA-LOU	SINGER-ACTRESS	MILLION, 12 PRAED MEWS	LONDON W2 1QY	ENGLAND
ALLEN, MARCUS	FOOTBALL	1144 RAVOLI DR	PACIFIC PALISADES, CA	90272
ALLEN, MARTY	ACTOR-COMEDIAN	5750 WILSHIRE BLVD #580	LOS ANGELES, CA	90036

ALLEN, MARVIN	FOOTBALL	PATRIOTS, FOXBORO STADIUM, RT #1	FOXBORO, MA	02035
ALLEN, MATT	BASEBALL	POLECATS, 608 N SLAPPEY BLVD	ALBANY, GA	31701
ALLEN, MEL	SPORTSCASTER	N Y YANKEES, YANKEE STADIUM	BRONX, NY	10451
ALLEN, MELVIN F	ACTOR	9864 CAYUGA AVE	PACOIMA, CA	91331
ALLEN, NANCY	ACTRESS	822 S ROBERTSON BLVD #200	LOS ANGELES, CA	90035
ALLEN, NEIL	BASEBALL	1402 ARMSTRONG	KANSAS CITY, KS	66102
ALLEN, PAUL	BASKETBALL EXECUTIVE	700 NE MULTNOMAH ST #600	PORTLAND, OR	97232
ALLEN, PENELOPE	ACTRESS	FLICK EAST-WEST TALENT		
		CARNEGIE HALL STUDIO 110		
		881 7TH AVE	NEW YORK, NY	10019
ALLEN, RAE J	DIRECTOR	1015 GAYLEY AVE #431	LOS ANGELES, CA	90024
ALLEN, RANCE	SINGER	JACKSON, 2405 BOSTON BLVD	DETROIT, MI	48206
ALLEN, REX, JR	SINGER	706 18TH AVE S	NASHVILLE, TN	37203
ALLEN, REX, SR	ACTOR-SINGER	POST OFFICE BOX 430	SONOITA, AZ	85637
ALLEN, RICHIE	BASEBALL	POST OFFICE BOX 204	SELLERSVILLE, PA	18960
ALLEN, RON	BASEBALL	POST OFFICE BOX 10336	CLEARWATER, FL	34617
ALLEN, ROSALIND	ACTRESS	POST OFFICE BOX 5617	BEVERLY HILLS, CA	90213
ALLEN, ROY	TV DIRECTOR-PRODUCER	CBS-TV, 524 W 57TH ST	NEW YORK, NY	10019
ALLEN, SIAN BARBARA	ACTRESS-WRITER	1622 SIERRA BONITA AVE	LOS ANGELES, CA	90046
ALLEN, STEVE	ACT-WRI-COMED-COMP	16185 WOODVALE RD	ENCINO, CA	91436
ALLEN, STEVE	BASEBALL	POST OFFICE BOX 28268	SAN ANTONIO, TX	78228
ALLEN, STUART	TV DIRECTOR-PRODUCER	EAST MIRAMAR, UPPER BONCHURCH		
		VENTNOR	I O WRIGHT PO38 1QB	ENGLAND
ALLEN, TERRY	FOOTBALL	VIKINGS, 9520 VIKING DR	EDEN PRAIRIE, MN	55344
ALLEN, TIM	ACTOR	3633 BELLFIELD WY	STUDIO CITY, CA	91604
ALLEN, TODD	ACTOR	9200 SUNSET BLVD #625	LOS ANGELES, CA	90069
ALLEN, TOM	AUDITOR	STATE CAPITOL BUILDING	SALT LAKE CITY, UT	84114
ALLEN, WOODY	ACT-COMED-WRI-DIR	930 5TH AVE	NEW YORK, NY	10018
ALLEN BROTHERS, THE	C & W GROUP	1001 24TH ST #313	BILLINGS, MT	59102
ALLENDE, FERNANDO	ACTOR	POST OFFICE BOX 4232	ASPEN, CO	81612
ALLENSON, GARY	BASEBALL COACH	FENWAY PARK, 4 YAWKEY WY	BOSTON, MA	02215
ALLEY, KIRSTIE	ACTRESS-SCREENWRITER	MTA, 9320 WILSHIRE BL, 3RD FL	BEVERLY HILLS, CA	90212
ALLGAIER, SIBYLLIE	ACTRESS	8150 BEVERLY BLVD #308	LOS ANGELES, CA	90048
ALLIK, VERA	ACTRESS-SINGER	201 E 87TH ST #11-C	NEW YORK, NY	10128
ALLILUYEVA, SVETLANA (STALIN)	AUTHORESS	ROBERT GRAVES, GENERAL DELIVERY	SPRING GREEN, WI	53588
ALLINSON, MICHAEL	ACTOR	11 KNOLLWOOD DR	LARHCMONT, NY	10538
ALLISON, BOBBY	AUTO RACER	140 CHURCH ST	HUEYTOWN, AL	35020
ALLISON, CHARLES GARY	WRITER-PRODUCER	1302 N ALEXANDRIA AVE	LOS ANGELES, CA	90027
ALLISON, DANA	BASEBALL	POST OFFICE BOX 11087	TACOMA, WA	98411
ALLISON, JERRY	DRUMMER-SONGWRITER	ROUTE #1, BOX 222	LYLES, TN	37098
ALLISON, JUDITH D	WRITER-PRODUCER	8042 WOODROW WILSON DR	LOS ANGELES, CA	90046
ALLISON, MOSE	PIANIST-COMPOSER	34 DOGWOOD ST	SMITHTOWN, NY	11787
ALLISON, SANDY	CASTING DIRECTOR	1759 N ORCHID	HOLLYWOOD, CA	90028
ALLISON, TOM	BASEBALL	POST OFFICE BOX 598	BINGHAMTON, NY	13902
ALLMAN, GREG	SINGER-MUSICIAN	POST OFFICE BOX 4331	MARIETTA, GA	30061
ALLMAN, GREG, BAND	ROCK & ROLL GROUP	POST OFFICE BOX 4331	MARIETTA, GA	30061
ALLMAN, LEE	COMPOSER	POST OFFICE BOX 2588	LOS ANGELES, CA	90077
ALLMAN, P J	SINGER	7100 EXECUTIVE CENTER DR #100	BRENTWOOD, TN	37027
ALLMON, CLINTON	ACTOR	20548 W CALLON DR	TOPANGA, CA	90290
ALLNUTT, WENDY	ACTRESS	CAREY, 64 THORNTON AVE	LONDON W4 1QQ	ENGLAND
ALLOTTA, ALBERT	DIRECTOR	185 E 85TH ST	NEW YORK, NY	10028
ALLPORT, CAROLYN	ACTRESS	145 S FAIRFAX AVE #310	LOS ANGELES, CA	90036
ALLPORT, CHRISTOPHER	ACTOR	SMITH, 121 N SAN VICENTE BLVD	BEVERLY HILLS, CA	90211
ALLRED, BEAU	BASEBALL	4385 TUTT BLVD	COLORADO SPRINGS, CO	80922
ALLRUD, ROMOLA ROBB	ACTRESS	20 WATERSIDE PLAZA #5-A	NEW YORK, NY	10010
ALLSUP, TOMMY D	GUITARIST	113 MEADOWS	BURLESON, TX	76028
ALLYN, WILLIAM	FILM PRODUCER	12031 VENTURA BLVD #3	STUDIO CITY, CA	91604
ALLYSON, JUNE	ACTRESS	ASHROW, 1651 FOOTHILL RD	OJAI, CA	93023
ALM, JEFF	FOOTBALL	OILERS, 6910 FANNIN ST	HOUSTON, TX	77070
ALMARAZ, JOHNNY	BASEBALL SCOUT	REDS, 100 RIVERFRONT STADIUM	CINCINNATI, OH	45202
ALMENDROS, NESTER	CINEMATOGRAPHER	47 RUE AVE MARIE	PARIS 3E	FRANCE
ALMODOVAR, ROBERT	ACTOR	6834 CAMROSE DR	HOLLYWOOD, CA	90068
ALMON, BILL	BASEBALL	88 CLAFLIN CT	WARWICK, RI	02886
ALMOND, PAUL	WRITER-PRODUCER	1272 REDPATH CRESCENT	MONTREAL, QUE H3G 2K1	CANADA
ALMOST NUTS BAND, THE	C & W GROUP	KNIGHT, 1609 CONGRESS RD	EASTOVER, SC	29044
ALOI, CINDY LYNN	DIRECTOR	DGA, 110 W 57TH ST	NEW YORK, NY	10019
ALOMAR, ROBERTO	BASEBALL	SKYDOME, 300 BREMMER BL #3200	TORONTO, ONT M5V 3B3	CANADA
ALOMAR, SANDY	BASEBALL-INSTRUCTOR	1060 W ADDISON ST	CHICAGO, IL	60613
ALOMAR, SANDY, JR	BASEBALL	INDIANS, CLEVELAND STADIUM	CLEVELAND, OH	44114
ALON, RAMI	WRITER	2060 CHARITON ST	LOS ANGELES, CA	90048
ALONI, AMI	COMPOSER-CONDUCTOR	4026 BENEDICT CANYON DR	SHERMAN OAKS, CA	91423
ALONSO, MARIA CONCHITA	ACTRESS	1999 AVE OF THE STARS #2850	LOS ANGELES, CA	90067
ALONZO, JOHN A	CINEMATOGRAPHER	310 AVONDALE AVE	LOS ANGELES, CA	90049
ALOU, FELIPE	BASEBALL-MANAGER	EXPOS, 4545 DE COUBERTIN AVE	MONTREAL, QUE H1V 3P2	CANADA
ALOU, JESUS	BASEBALL-SCOUT	6850 LAWRENCE RD	LANTANA, FL	33462
ALOU, MOISES	BASEBALL	EXPOS, 4545 DE COUBERTIN AVE	MONTREAL, QUE H1V 3P2	CANADA
ALPER, ALLAN M	COMPOSER-CONDUCTOR	128 N SWALL DR #4	LOS ANGELES, CA	90048
ALPERT, DAVID	WRITER-PRODUCER	3900 VENTURA CANYON AVE	SHERMAN OAKS, CA	91423
ALPERT, HERB	MUS-COMP-EXEC	10102 EMPYREAN WY #8-303	LOS ANGELES, CA	90067
ALPERT, HOLLIS	WRITER	POST OFFICE BOX 142	SHELTER ISLAND, NY	11964
ALPERT, LISA	ACTRESS	9229 SUNSET BLVD #311	LOS ANGELES, CA	90069
ALPHIN, GERALD	FOOTBALL	SAINTS, 1500 POYDRAS ST	NEW ORLEANS, LA	90112
ALPINE HARMONAIRES, THE	VOCAL GROUP	FRONTIER, 422 W HIGH AVE	NEW PHILADELPHIA, OH	44663
ALQUIST, JIM	ACTOR	9200 SUNSET BLVD #625	LOS ANGELES, CA	90069
ALSBERG, ARTHUR WILLIAM	WRITER	3816 LONGRIDGE AVE	SHERMAN OAKS, CA	91423

ALSTEAD, JASON	BASEBALL	POST OFFICE BOX 3169	FREDERICK, MD 21701
ALSTON, HOWARD P	TV PRODUCER	10033 VALLEY SPRING LN	NORTH HOLLYWOOD, CA 91602
ALT, CAROL	ACTRESS-MODEL	163 JOHN ST	GREENWICH, CT 06831
ALT, JOHN	FOOTBALL	CHIEFS, 1 ARROWHEAD DR	KANSAS CITY, MO 64129
ALTA MODA	ROCK & ROLL GROUP	366 ADELAIDE ST #437	TORONTO, ONT M5A 3X9 CANADA
ALTAFFER, TODD	BASEBALL	POST OFFICE BOX 611	WATERLOO, IA 50704
ALTER, EDWARD	TREASURER	STATE CAPITOL BUILDING	SALT LAKE CITY, UT 84114
ALTER, ERIC	SCREENWRITER	8955 BEVERLY BLVD	WEST HOLLYWOOD, CA 90048
ALTER, PAUL	TV DIRECTOR-PRODUCER	1030 DELLA DR	BEVERLY HILLS, CA 90210
ALTERS, GERALD	ARRANGER-COMPOSER	301 W 53RD ST #2-G	NEW YORK, NY 10019
ALTFILISH, LINDA	ACTRESS	846 4TH ST #205	SANTA MONICA, CA 90403
ALTMAN, JEFF	COMEDIAN-ACTOR	345 N MAPLE DR #183	BEVERLY HILLS, CA 90210
ALTMAN, JUDY	ACTRESS	8075 W 3RD ST #550	LOS ANGELES, CA 90048
ALTMAN, MILT	DIRECTOR	14889 JADESTONE DR	SHERMAN OAKS, CA 91403
ALTMAN, ROBERT	FINANCIER	5051 KLINGLE ST	WASHINGTON, DC 20016
ALTMAN, ROBERT	WRITER-PRODUCER	502 PARK AVE #15-G	NEW YORK, NY 10022
ALTMAN, STEVE	ACTOR	MTA, 9320 WILSHIRE BL, 3RD FL	BEVERLY HILLS, CA 90212
ALTOBELLI, JOE	BASEBALL-COACH	54 GRECIAN GARDENS DR #B	ROCHESTER, NY 14626
ALTON, BILL	DIRECTOR	435 W 23RD ST #10-B	NEW YORK, NY 10011
ALTSHULER, JOEL	COMPOSER-CONDUCTOR	15420 GAULT ST	VAN NUYS, CA 91406
ALTZ, BARBARA	ACTRESS	8721 SANTA MONICA BLVD #21	WEST HOLLYWOOD, CA 90069
ALU, AL	ACTOR	2001 1/2 CHEREMOYA AVE	LOS ANGELES, CA 90068
ALU, CHERYL	TV WRITER	7109 1/2 HILLSIDE AVE	HOLLYWOOD, CA 90046
ALVARADO, TRINI	ACTRESS	9200 SUNSET BLVD #710	LOS ANGELES, CA 90069
ALVAREZ, CLEMENTE	BASEBALL	POST OFFICE BOX 360007	BIRMINGHAM, AL 35236
ALVAREZ, JORGE	BASEBALL	POST OFFICE BOX 28268	SAN ANTONIO, TX 78228
ALVAREZ, JOSE	BASEBALL	POST OFFICE BOX 23290	NASHVILLE, TN 37202
ALVAREZ, JUAN	BASEBALL	POST OFFICE BOX 842	SALEM, VA 24153
ALVAREZ, LAURA	ACTRESS	822 S ROBERTSON BLVD #200	LOS ANGELES, CA 90035
ALVAREZ, MIKE	BASEBALL COACH	800 HOME RUN LN	MEMPHIS, TN 38104
ALVAREZ, RICHARD	COSTUME DESIGNER	2500 WEBB AVE #1-B	BRONX, NY 10468
ALVAREZ, TAVO	BASEBALL	POST OFFICE BOX 3566	WEST PALM BEACH, FL 33402
ALVAREZ, WILSON	BASEBALL	333 W 35TH ST	CHICAGO, IL 60616
ALVES, JOSEPH	DIRECTOR-PRODUCER	4176 ROSARIO RD	WOODLAND HILLS, CA 91364
ALVI, REBEKAH	COSTUME DESIGNER	2210 WILSHIRE BLVD #523	SANTA MONICA, CA 90403
ALVIN, DAVE	SINGER-SONGWRITER	VISION MGT, 7958 BEVERLY BLVD	LOS ANGELES, CA 90048
ALVIN, PHIL	SINGER-GUITARIST	VISION MGT, 7958 BEVERLY BLVD	LOS ANGELES, CA 90048
ALVINA, ANICEE	ACTRESS	41 RUE DE L'ECHESE	F-78110 LE VISINET FRANCE
ALWOOD, DENNIS	ACTOR	4624 CAHUENGA BLVD #303	NORTH HOLLYWOOD, CA 91602
ALZADO, LYLE	ACTOR-FOOTBALL	1696 VIA CORONEL	PALOS VERDES ESTATES, 90274
AMADILLO FLATS	C & W GROUP	JIMMY ALLEN, 1548 ASHLAND AVE	SAINT PAUL, MN 55104
AMADOR, ANDREW	ACTOR	2072 MOUND ST	LOS ANGELES, CA 90068
AMALFITANO, JOEY	BASEBALL-COACH	1000 ELYSIAN PARK DR	LOS ANGELES, CA 90012
AMANPOUR, CHRISTIANE	NEWS CORRES-PROD	1050 TECHWOOD DR, NW	ATLANTA, GA 30318
AMARAL, RICHARD	BASEBALL	POST OFFICE BOX 3690, STA "B"	CALGARY, ALB T2B 4M4 CANADA
AMARILLO	C & W GROUP	POST OFFICE BOX 86384	PORTLAND, OR 97286
AMARO, RUBEN	BASEBALL-SCOUT	TIGERS, TIGER STADIUM	DETROIT, MI 48216
AMARO, RUBEN, JR	BASEBALL	POST OFFICE BOX 7575	PHILADELPHIA, PA 19101
AMATEAU, CHLOE	ACTRESS	832 1/4 N ALTA VISTA BLVD	LOS ANGELES, CA 90046
AMATEAU, RODNEY	FILM WRITER-DIRECTOR	133 1/2 S LINDEN DR	BEVERLY HILLS, CA 90212
AMATO, JOHN	WRITER	POST OFFICE BOX 55311	SHERMAN OAKS, CA 91423
AMATO, JULIE	ACTRESS	315 N DOHENY DR	BEVERLY HILLS, CA 90211
AMAVISCA, ANDREA	ACTRESS	NATHE, 8281 MELROSE AVE #200	LOS ANGELES, CA 90046
AMBER	C & W GROUP	POST OFFICE BOX 368	NACOGDOCHES, TX 75963
AMBITIOUS LOVERS	ROCK & ROLL GROUP	FAA, 1700 BROADWAY, 5TH FLOOR	NEW YORK, NY 10019
AMBLER, ERIC	WRITER	AVE EUGENE RAMBERT 20	1815 CLARENS IRELAND
AMBOSE, JON	TV PRODUCER	300 E 34TH ST #8-J	NEW YORK, NY 10016
AMBRONN, THERESA	ACTRESS	WHITAKER, 12725 VENTURA BLVD	STUDIO CITY, CA 91604
AMBROSE, BARBARA	ACTRESS	1800 N HIGHLAND AVE #405	LOS ANGELES, CA 90028
AMBROSE, DAVID	WRITER-DIRECTOR	HATTON, 29 ROEHAMPTON GATE	LONDON SW15 5JR ENGLAND
AMECHE, DON	ACTOR	1999 AVE OF THE STARS #2850	LOS ANGELES, CA 90067
AMELON HUDDY, DEBORAH L	WRITER	7875 WILLOW GLEN RD	LOS ANGELES, CA 90046
AMER, NICHOLAS	ACTOR	14 GREAT RUSSELL ST	LONDON WC1 ENGLAND
AMERICA	ROCK & ROLL GROUP	8730 SUNSET BLVD #PH-W	LOS ANGELES, CA 90069
AMERICA'S COUNTRY	C & W GROUP	NADER, 71 LAKE RD	MANHASSET, NY 11030
AMERICAN EXPRESS	C & W GROUP	ALAMO TALENT, 217 ARDEN GROVE	SAN ANTONIO, TX 78215
AMES, DURELLE	SINGER	OUR GANG, 1012 16TH AVE S	NASHVILLE, TN 37212
AMES, ED	SINGER-ACTOR	1457 CLARIDGE DR	BEVERLY HILLS, CA 90210
AMES, GRANVILLE	ACTOR	8831 SUNSET BLVD #304	LOS ANGELES, CA 90069
AMES, LEON	ACTOR	1015 GOLDENROD AVE	CORONA DEL MAR, CA 92625
AMES, LOUIS B	TV PRODUCER	3018 6TH ST #29-H	TUCSON, AZ 85716
AMES, RACHEL	ACTRESS	12711 HACIENDA DR	STUDIO CITY, CA 91604
AMES, TREY	ACTOR	15760 VENTURA BLVD #1730	ENCINO, CA 91436
AMES-REGAN, HARRIETTE	DIRECTOR	POST OFFICE BOX 3680	SANTA MONICA, CA 90403
AMESTOY, JEFFREY L	ATTORNEY GENERAL	PAVILION OFF BLDG, 109 STATE ST	MONTPELIER, VT 05602
AMICK, MADCHEN	ACTRESS	9200 SUNSET BLVD #625	LOS ANGELES, CA 90069
AMIEL, JON	TV DIRECTOR	30 WOLSELEY RD	LONDON N8 8RP ENGLAND
AMIN, IDI	POLITICIAN	POST OFFICE BOX 8948	JIDDA 21492 SAUDI ARABIA
AMIRANTE, DENISE	ACTRESS	14335 SHERMAN WY #326	VAN NUYS, CA 91405
AMIS, KINGSLEY	NOVELIST	CLOWES, 19 JEFFREY'S PL	LONDON NW1 ENGLAND
AMIS, SUZY	ACTRESS	131 S RODEO DR #300	BEVERLY HILLS, CA 90212
AMMACCAPANE, DANIELLE	GOLFER	2750 VOLUSA AVE #B	DAYTON BEACH, FL 32114
AMMERMAN, LORRAINE	ACTRESS	16 ROLLING DR	BROOKVILLE, NY 11545
AMMONDS, JOHN	TV PRODUCER	LWT, KENT HOUSE, UPPER GROUND	LONDON SE1 ENGLAND
AMON, RON	ACTOR	1623 3RD AVE #14-H	NEW YORK, NY 10128

AMOROSI, MICHAEL D	COMPOSER	741 1/4 S BURNSIDE AVE	LOS ANGELES, CA	90036
AMORY, CLEVELAND	WRITER	200 W 57TH ST	NEW YORK, NY	10019
AMOS, JOHN	ACTOR	431 W 162ND ST	NEW YORK, NY	10032
AMOS, PAUL	TX EXECUTIVE	1050 TECHWOOD DR, NW	ATLANTA, GA	30318
AMOS, RICHARD A	TV DIRECTOR	13645 KAMLOOPS ST	ARLETTA, CA	91331
AMOS, WALLY "FAMOUS"	COOKIE ENTREPRENEUR	215 LANIPO DR	KAILUA, HI	96734
AMSLER, GREG	FOOTBALL	POST OFFICE BOX 888	PHOENIX, AZ	85001
AMSTERDAM, MOREY	ACTOR-COMEDIAN	1012 N HILLCREST RD	BEVERLY HILLS, CA	90210
AMY, GEORGE	DIRECTOR-EDITOR	14142 COHASSET ST	VAN NUYS, CA	91405
AMY, GILBERT	COMPOSER-ORCH LEADER	601 E PLANTATION CIR	COURBEVOIE 92400	FRANCE
AMYES, JULIAN	TV DIRECTOR	4 PALLISER CT	LONDON W14 9ED	ENGLAND
ANA-ALICIA	ACTRESS	9744 WILSHIRE BLVD #308	BEVERLY HILLS, CA	90212
ANABLE, THOM	DIRECTOR	13805 CALVERT ST	VAN NUYS, CA	91401
ANACANI	SINGER	9777 WILSHIRE BLVD #707	BEVERLY HILLS, CA	90212
ANASTASI, JOSEPH A	ARTIST	JONES, ANASTASI & MITCHELL		
		40 S 3RD ST	COLUMBUS, OH	43215
ANASTI, RUDOLPH T	WRITER	4225 KLUMP AVE	NORTH HOLLYWOOD, CA	91602
ANAYA, MIKE	BASEBALL	POST OFFICE BOX 7845	COLUMBIA, SC	29202
ANCELL, KENNETH	DIRECTOR	814 MICHIGAN AVE	EVANSTON, IL	60202
ANCICH, HENDI	FOOTBALL REFEREE	NFL, 410 PARK AVE	NEW YORK, NY	10022
ANCIER, GARTH RICHARD	TV EXECUTIVE	NBC, 3000 W ALAMEDA AVE	BURBANK, CA	91523
ANDARIESE, JOHN	SPORTSCASTER	MSG NETWORK, 2 PENNSYLVANIA PLZ	NEW YORK, NY	10001
ANDELMAN, JULIE	ACTRESS	6918 WILLOUGHBY AVE	LOS ANGELES, CA	90038
ANDELSON, SHELDON	DIRECTOR	900 STRADELLA RD	LOS ANGELES, CA	90077
ANDERMAN, MAUREEN	ACTRESS	STE, 888 7TH AVE, 18TH FLOOR	NEW YORK, NY	10106
ANDERS, CHRIS	ACTOR	2700 NEILSON WY #1321	SANTA MONICA, CA	90405
ANDERS, JOHN C	ACTOR	1418 N HIGHLAND AVE #102	LOS ANGELES, CA	90028
ANDERS, KIMBLE	FOOTBALL	CHIEFS, 1 ARROWHEAD DR	KANSAS CITY, MO	64129
ANDERS, KRISTOFFER C	ACTOR	1738 CANYON DR #301	LOS ANGELES, CA	90028
ANDERS, LUANA	ACTRESS-WRITER	12734 WOODRIDGE ST	STUDIO CITY, CA	91604
ANDERS, SUSAN J	ACTRESS	1800 N HIGHLAND AVE #405	LOS ANGELES, CA	90028
ANDERSEN, DANA	ACTRESS	9000 SUNSET BLVD #1200	LOS ANGELES, CA	90069
ANDERSON, ALFRED	FOOTBALL	VIKINGS, 9520 VIKING DR	EDEN PRAIRIE, MN	55344
ANDERSON, ALLAN	BASEBALL	2015 RAINBOW DR NE	LANCASTER, OH	43130
ANDERSON, ARN	WRESTLER	POST OFFICE BOX 105366	ATLANTA, GA	31348
ANDERSON, BARBARA	ACTRESS	4345 ENORO DR	LOS ANGELES, CA	90008
ANDERSON, BILL	SINGER	WORLD CLASS, 1522 DEMONBREUN ST	NASHVILLE, TN	37203
ANDERSON, BRAD	CARTOONIST	422 SANTA MARINA CT	ESCONDIDO, CA	92025
ANDERSON, BRADY	BASEBALL	ORIOLE PARK, 333 W CAMDEN ST	BALTIMORE, MD	21201
ANDERSON, BRYAN J	CINEMATOGRAPHER	921 BUTTERFIELD RD	SAN ANSELMO, CA	94960
ANDERSON, CARL	ACTOR	2924 PACIFIC AVE	VENICE, CA	90291
ANDERSON, CARL	SINGER	CAP MGMT, 1850 MINTWOOD PL, NW	WASHINGTON, DC	20009
ANDERSON, CHARLES SPENCER	ARTIST	THE DUFFY DESIGN GROUP		
		701 4TH AVE S #1660	MINNEAPOLIS, MN	55415
ANDERSON, CHRIS	ACTOR	151 S EL CAMINO DR	BEVERLY HILLS, CA	90212
ANDERSON, DAME JUDITH	ACTRESS	808 SAN YSIDRO LN	SANTA BARBARA, CA	93103
ANDERSON, DARYL	ACTOR	5923 WILBUR AVE	TARZANA, CA	91356
ANDERSON, DAVE	BASEBALL	POST OFFICE BOX 26267	ALBUQUERQUE, NM	87125
ANDERSON, DAVE	FOOTBALL REFEREE	NFL, 410 PARK AVE	NEW YORK, NY	10022
ANDERSON, DAVID E	DIRECTOR-PRODUCER	385 ROSEWOOD AVE	WINNETKA, IL	60093
ANDERSON, DEBBIE	SINGER	POST OFFICE BOX 110423	NASHVILLE, TN	37211
ANDERSON, DION	ACTOR	9744 WILSHIRE BLVD #308	BEVERLY HILLS, CA	90212
ANDERSON, DON	BASEBALL EXECUTIVE	POST OFFICE BOX 7893	EVERETT, WA	98201
ANDERSON, DONALD E	FILM EXECUTIVE	2049 CENTURY PARK E #4170	LOS ANGELES, CA	90067
ANDERSON, EDDIE	FOOTBALL	RAIDERS, 332 CENTER ST	EL SEGUNDO, CA	90245
ANDERSON, ELIZABETH B	WRITER	840 HAVERFORD AVE	PACIFIC PALISADES, CA	90272
ANDERSON, ERIC	SINGER-COMPOSER	50W 34TH ST #11-C-5	NEW YORK, NY	10001
ANDERSON, ERICH	ACTOR	10100 SANTA MONICA BLVD #700	LOS ANGELES, CA	90067
ANDERSON, ERIKA	ACTRESS	11726 SAN VICENTE BLVD #300	LOS ANGELES, CA	90049
ANDERSON, ERNEST	ACTOR	4075 TROOST AVE	STUDIO CITY, CA	91604
ANDERSON, ERNESTINE	SINGER	POST OFFICE BOX 845	CONCORD, CA	94522
ANDERSON, GARRET	BASEBALL	POST OFFICE BOX 1742	PALM SPRINGS, CA	92263
ANDERSON, GARY	FOOTBALL	BUCCANEERS, 1 BUCCANEER PL	TAMPA, FL	33607
ANDERSON, GARY	FOOTBALL	STEELERS, 300 STADIUM CIR	PITTSBURGH, PA	15212
ANDERSON, GEORGE	FILM CRITIC	PITTSBURGH POST-GAZETTE		
		34 BLVD OF ALLIES	PITTSBURGH, PA	15230
ANDERSON, GERRY	FILM PRODUCER	THE ANDERSON BURR PARTNERSHIP		
		CINEMA HOUSE, 93 WARDOUR ST	LONDON W1	ENGLAND
ANDERSON, GLENN	HOCKEY	OILERS, NORTHLANDS COLISEUM	EDMONTON, ALTA T5B 4M9	CANADA
ANDERSON, GLENN M	U S CONGRESSMAN	300 LONG BEACH BLVD	LONG BEACH, CA	90801
ANDERSON, GREG	BASKETBALL	BRADLEY CENTER, 1001 N 4TH ST	MILWAUKEE, WI	53203
ANDERSON, HARRY	ACT-COMED-MAGIC	1420 NW GILMAN BLVD #2123	ISSAQUAH, WA	98027
ANDERSON, HOWARD A	CINEMATOGRAPHER	POST OFFICE BOX 2230	HOLLYWOOD, CA	90078
ANDERSON, JACK	COLUMNIST	1531 "P" ST, NW	WASHINGTON, DC	20005
ANDERSON, JANET	GOLFER	2750 VOLUSA AVE #B	DAYTON BEACH, FL	32114
ANDERSON, JESSE	FOOTBALL	BUCCANEERS, 1 BUCCANEER PL	TAMPA, FL	33607
ANDERSON, JIM	FOOTBALL COACH	BENGALS, 200 RIVERFRONT STADIUM	CINCINNATI, OH	45202
ANDERSON, JOHN	ACTOR	KOHNER, 9169 SUNSET BLVD	LOS ANGELES, CA	90069
ANDERSON, JOHN	SINGER-SONGWRITER	POST OFFICE BOX 2977	HENDERSONVILLE, TN	37077
ANDERSON, JOHN MAXWELL	COMPOSER-ARRANGER	2158 SUNSET PLAZA DR	LOS ANGELES, CA	90069
ANDERSON, JON	TV CRITIC	THE CHICAGO TRIBUNE		
		TRIBUNE TOWER		
		435 N MICHIGAN AVE	CHICAGO, IL	60611
ANDERSON, JON	TV DIRECTOR	150 S BARRINGTON AVE #1	LOS ANGELES, CA	90049
ANDERSON, JOSEF M	TV WRITER	10100 SANTA MONICA BLVD #1600	LOS ANGELES, CA	90067

ANDERSON, JUDY	TV EXECUTIVE	263-A W 19TH ST #739	NEW YORK, NY 10011
ANDERSON, KENT	BASEBALL	10233 96TH AVE	EDMONTON, ALB TK5 0A5 CANADA
ANDERSON, LARRY	ACTOR	STONE MANNERS, 9113 SUNSET BL	LOS ANGELES, CA 90069
ANDERSON, LARRY	BASEBALL	POST OFFICE BOX 2000	SAN DIEGO, CA 92112
ANDERSON, LAURIE	SINGER	10100 SANTA MONICA BLVD #1600	LOS ANGELES, CA 90067
ANDERSON, LEONARD E	DIRECTOR	2924 NW 7TH CT #A	
		RAINBERRY CT	DELRAY BEACH, FL 33445
ANDERSON, LEWIS B	COMPOSER	888 8TH AVE #182	NEW YORK, NY 10019
ANDERSON, LINDSAY	FILM WRITER-DIRECTOR	9 STIRLING MANSIONS	
		CANFIELD GARDENS	LONDON NW6 3JT ENGLAND
ANDERSON, LONI	ACTRESS	1001 INDIANTOWN RD	JUPITER, FL 33458
ANDERSON, LOUIE	COMEDIAN	8033 SUNSET BLVD #605	LOS ANGELES, CA 90046
ANDERSON, LURUTH	CONDUCTOR	2723 VIA VERBENA	SAN CLEMENTE, CA 92672
ANDERSON, LYNN	SINGER	4925 TYNE VALLEY BLVD	NASHVILLE, TN 37220
ANDERSON, MACK B	TV DIRECTOR	DGA, 7920 SUNSET BLVD, 6TH FL	LOS ANGELES, CA 90046
ANDERSON, MARGO	DIRECTOR	DGA, 7920 SUNSET BLVD, 6TH FL	LOS ANGELES, CA 90046
ANDERSON, MARIAN	ACTRESS	2049 CENTURY PARK E #1200	LOS ANGELES, CA 90067
ANDERSON, MARIAN	SINGER	MARIANNA FARMS, JOE'S HILL RD	DANBURY, CT 06811
ANDERSON, MARK	BASEBALL TRAINER	333 W 35TH ST	CHICAGO, IL 60616
ANDERSON, MARK	TRAINER	POST OFFICE BOX 7575	PHILADELPHIA, PA 19101
ANDERSON, MARY	ACTRESS	1127 N NORMAN PL	LOS ANGELES, CA 90049
ANDERSON, MATT	BASEBALL	POST OFFICE BOX 3169	FREDERICK, MD 21701
ANDERSON, MAX W	FILM DIRECTOR	454 SEATON ST #3	LOS ANGELES, CA 90013
ANDERSON, MELISSA SUE	ACTRESS	4160 LAUREL GROVE AVE	STUDIO CITY, CA 91604
ANDERSON, MELODY	ACTRESS	10433 WILSHIRE BLVD #1203	LOS ANGELES, CA 90024
ANDERSON, MICHAEL	FILM DIRECTOR	FILM RIGHTS, 483 SOUTHBANK HOUSE	
		BLACK PRINCE RD	
		ALBERT EMBANKMENT	LONDON SE1 7SJ ENGLAND
ANDERSON, MICHAEL, JR	ACTOR	132 S LASKY DR #B	BEVERLY HILLS, CA 90212
ANDERSON, MITCHELL	ACTOR	POST OFFICE BOX 5617	BEVERLY HILLS, CA 90213
ANDERSON, MORTEN	FOOTBALL	SAINTS, 1500 POYDRAS ST	NEW ORLEANS, LA 90112
ANDERSON, NEAL	FOOTBALL	BEARS, 250 N WASHINGTON RD	LAKE FOREST, IL 60045
ANDERSON, NICK	BASKETBALL	POST OFFICE BOX 76	ORLANDO, FL 32802
ANDERSON, OTIS	FOOTBALL	N Y GIANTS, GIANTS STADIUM	EAST RUTHERFORD, NJ 07073
ANDERSON, PAT	ACTRESS	BDP, 10637 BURBANK BLVD	NORTH HOLLYWOOD, CA 91601
ANDERSON, PAUL	BASEBALL	POST OFFICE BOX 12557	ST PETERSBURG, FL 33733
ANDERSON, PAUL	WRESTLER	1603 MC INTOSH ST	VIDALIA, GAGA 30474
ANDERSON, RANDY	SINGER	MILLETT, 3416 CORONA DEL MAR	LAS VEGAS, NV 89108
ANDERSON, RENEE	ACTRESS	2818 LAUREL CANYON BLVD	LOS ANGELES, CA 90046
ANDERSON, RICHARD	ACTOR	10120 CIELO DR	BEVERLY HILLS, CA 90210
ANDERSON, RICHARD DEAN	ACTOR	ICM, 8899 BEVERLY BLVD	LOS ANGELES, CA 90048
ANDERSON, RICK	BASEBALL	3818 100TH ST SE	EVERETT, WA 98204
ANDERSON, RICK	BASEBALL COACH	POST OFFICE BOX 661	KENOSHA, WI 53141
ANDERSON, RON	BASKETBALL	POST OFFICE BOX 25040	PHILADELPHIA, PA 19147
ANDERSON, RUSS	ACTOR	165 W 46TH ST #1109	NEW YORK, NY 10036
ANDERSON, SAM	ACTOR	2611 N BEACHWOOD DR	LOS ANGELES, CA 90068
ANDERSON, SHERI L	TV WRITER	2611 N BEACHWOOD DR	LOS ANGELES, CA 90068
ANDERSON, SPARKY	BASEBALL-MANAGER	TIGERS, TIGER STADIUM	DETROIT, MI 48216
ANDERSON, STEVE	BASEBALL	POST OFFICE BOX 22093	GREENSBORO, NC 27420
ANDERSON, STEVEN A	ACTOR	12746 HALKIRK ST	STUDIO CITY, CA 91604
ANDERSON, SYLVIA	WRITER-PRODUCER	PINEWOOD STUDIOS, IVER HEATH	IVER, BUCKS SLO ONH ENGLAND
ANDERSON, TERRY	JOURNALIST	438 LAKESHORE DR	CADIZ, KY 42211
ANDERSON, THOMAS S	WRITER	WM MORRIS, 1350 AVE OF AMERICAS	NEW YORK, NY 10019
ANDERSON, TOM	BASEBALL	POST OFFICE BOX 1556	ASHEVILLE, NC 28802
ANDERSON, TOM	TV PRODUCER	151 S EL CAMINO DR	BEVERLY HILLS, CA 90212
ANDERSON, VALERIE	SINGER	POST OFFICE BOX 569	FRANKLIN, PA 16323
ANDERSON, WAYNE	SINGER	BRISTOL, 3722 FAULKNER DR	NASHVILLE, TN 37211
ANDERSON, WILLIAM	FILM EDITOR	ACE, 1041 N FORMOSA AVE	WEST HOLLYWOOD, CA 90046
ANDERSON, WILLIE	BASKETBALL	600 E MARKET ST #102	SAN ANTONIO, TX 78205
ANDERSON, WILLIE	FOOTBALL	RAMS, 2327 W LINCOLN BLVD	ANAHEIM, CA 92801
ANDI & THE BROWNS	C & W GROUP	KENNEDY, 3950 N MOUNT JULIET RD	MOUNT JULIET, TN 37122
ANDOLSEK, ERIC	FOOTBALL	LIONS, 1200 FEATHERSTONE RD	PONTIAC, MI 48432
ANDON, KURT	ACTOR	1725 CAMINO PALMERO	LOS ANGELES, CA 90046
ANDRACKE, GREGORY	CINEMATOGRAPHER	207 W 86TH ST #816	NEW YORK, NY 10024
ANDRADE, BILLY	GOLFER	POST OFFICE BOX 109601	PALM BCH GARDENS, FL 33418
ANDRADE, DANIEL "THE DRIFTER"	SINGER-SONGWRITER	POST OFFICE DRAWER 520	STAFFORD, TX 77477
ANDRE, FELISA	ACTRESS	318 E 70TH ST #1-RW	NEW YORK, NY 10021
ANDRE, JILL	ACTRESS	8075 W 3RD ST #303	LOS ANGELES, CA 90048
ANDRE THE GIANT	WRESTLER	POST OFFICE BOX 3859	STAMFORD, CT 06905
ANDREAS, CHRISTINE	ACTRESS	STE, 888 7TH AVE, 18TH FLOOR	NEW YORK, NY 10106
ANDREEFF, STARR	ACTRESS	345 N MAPLE DR #183	BEVERLY HILLS, CA 90210
ANDREISCHENKO, NATALI	FILM EXECUTIVE	10744 CHALON RD	LOS ANGELES, CA 90077
ANDREOLA, HOWARD	ACTOR	356 S CAMDEN DR	BEVERLY HILLS, CA 90212
ANDREOZZI, GENNARO	TV DIRECTOR	118 E 25TH ST	NEW YORK, NY 10010
ANDRESS, URSULA	ACTRESS	DANIKHOFENWEG 95	3072 OSTERMUNDINGEN SWITZERLAND
ANDRETTA, HOLLY	BASEBALL EXECUTIVE	1325 S MAIN #229	SALT LAKE CITY, UT 84115
ANDRETTI, MARIO	AUTO RACER	53 VICTORY LN	NAZARETH, PA 18064
ANDREW, HRH THE PRINCE	PRINCE	SUNNINGHILL PARK	WINDSOR ENGLAND
ANDREW, RAYMOND	CINEMATOGRAPHER	262 COURT RD	LONDON SE9 4TY ENGLAND
ANDREWS, A BART	WRITER	1321 N STANLEY AVE	LOS ANGELES, CA 90046
ANDREWS, ANDY	COMEDIAN	1514 SHAMROCK DR	HELENA, AL 35080
ANDREWS, ANTHONY	ACTOR	13 MANOR PL	OXFORD, OXON ENGLAND
ANDREWS, BRENT	BASEBALL TRAINER	SKYDOME, 300 BREMMER BL #3200	TORONTO, ONT M5V 3B3 CANADA
ANDREWS, JEFF	BASEBALL COACH	POST OFFICE BOX 4756	JACKSONVILLE, FL 32201
ANDREWS, JULIE	SINGER-ACTRESS	POST OFFICE BOX 666	BEVERLY HILLS, CA 90213

ANDREWS, LEE, & THE HEARTS	VOCAL GROUP	MARS, 168 ORCHID DR	PEARL RIVER, NY	10965
ANDREWS, MARNIE	ACTRESS	230 HAMILTON AVE	STATEN ISLAND, NY	10301
ANDREWS, MAXENE	SINGER-ACTRESS	14200 CARRIAGE OAKS LN	AUBURN, CA	95603
ANDREWS, MICHAEL A	U S CONGRESSMAN	FEDERAL BUILDING		
		515 RUSK ST	HOUSTON, TX	77002
ANDREWS, MICHAEL L A	WRI-DIR-PROD	BBC BROADCASTING HOUSE		
		WHITELADIES RD	BRISTOL	ENGLAND
ANDREWS, NANCY	ACTRESS	302 W 12TH ST #2-G	NEW YORK, NY	10014
ANDREWS, NORMAN J	ACTOR	4619 MELROSE AVE	LOS ANGELES, CA	90029
ANDREWS, PATTI	SINGER	9823 ALDEA AVE	NORTHRIDGE, CA	91325
ANDREWS, PETER	TV DIRECTOR	13-16 CONRAD LN	VIRGINIA BEACH, VA	23454
ANDREWS, PETER L	FILM PRODUCER	14-17 WELLS MEWS, WELLS ST	LONDON W1A 1ET	ENGLAND
ANDREWS, ROBERT E	U S CONGRESSMAN	208 WHITE HORSE PIKE #5	BARRINGTON, NJ	08007
ANDREWS, SHANE	BASEBALL	POLECATS, 608 N SLAPPEY BLVD	ALBANY, GA	31701
ANDREWS, THOMAS	U S CONGRESSMAN	177 COMMERCIAL ST, 2ND FLOOR	PORTLAND, ME	04101
ANDREWS, TIGE	ACTOR-WRITER	4914 ENCINO TERR	ENCINO, CA	91316
ANDREWS, WILLIAM P	TV EXECUTIVE	254 E 68TH ST #6-D	NEW YORK, NY	10021
ANDREYCHUK, DAVE	HOCKEY	SABRES, MEMORIAL AUDITORIUM	BUFFALO, NY	14202
ANDRO, NINA	ACTRESS	1021 12TH ST #102	SANTA MONICA, CA	90403
ANDROSKY, CAROL	ACTRESS	CURTIS BROWN, 10 ASTOR PL	NEW YORK, NY	10003
ANDRUS, CECIL D	GOVERNOR	STATE HOUSE BUILDING	BOISE, ID	83720
ANDRUS, KELLY	ACTRESS	SELECTED, 3575 W CAHUENGA BLVD	LOS ANGELES, CA	90068
ANDUJAR, JOAQUIN	BASEBALL	400 RANDALL WY #106	SPRING, TX	77388
ANDUJAR, JUAN	BASEBALL	POST OFFICE BOX 12557	ST PETERSBURG, FL	33733
ANDUJAR, LUIS	BASEBALL	POST OFFICE BOX 4218	SOUTH BEND, IN	46634
ANELLO, JOHN, JR	SINGER	POST OFFICE BOX 703	PLACENTIA, CA	92670
ANGEL	ROCK & ROLL GROUP	ATI, 888 7TH AVE, 21ST FLOOR	NEW YORK, NY	10106
ANGEL, DAVID R	COMPOSER	357 CRABE BLVD	LOS ANGELES, CA	90065
ANGEL, JACK	ACTOR	5657 WILSHIRE BLVD #290	LOS ANGELES, CA	90036
ANGEL, JOE	SPORTSCASTER	N Y YANKEES, YANKEE STADIUM	BRONX, NY	10451
ANGEL, TIMOTHY	COSTUME DESIGNER	MORRIS ANGEL & SON, LTD		
		119 SHAFTESBURY AVE	LONDON WC2H 8AE	ENGLAND
ANGEL, VANESSA	ACTRESS	853 7TH AVE #9-A	NEW YORK, NY	10019
ANGEL CITY	RHYTHM & BLUES GROUP	10100 SANTA MONICA BLVD #1600	LOS ANGELES, CA	90067
ANGEL TRAIN	C & W GROUP	53 W 87TH ST #4-R	NEW YORK, NY	10024
ANGEL WING	C & W GROUP	BONSWA, 837 TODD PRIES DR	NASHVILLE, TN	37221
ANGELES, JACK	ACTOR	FELBER, 2126 N CAHUENGA BLVD	LOS ANGELES, CA	90068
ANGELICO, JAMES	ACTOR	9255 SUNSET BLVD #401	WEST HOLLYWOOD, CA	90069
ANGELIN, PATRICIA	ACTRESS	114 SOUTH PARK AVE	WINTER PARK, FL	32789
ANGELINI, GEORGE	ARTIST	135 CROTON AVE	OSSINING, NY	10562
ANGELIS, KIM	SINGER-VIOLINIST	POST OFFICE BOX 1027	HERMOSA BEACH, CA	90254
ANGELL, DAVID	TV WRITER	8383 WILSHIRE BLVD #923	BEVERLY HILLS, CA	90211
ANGELL, DAVID L	WRITER	4638 ARCOLA AVE	NORTH HOLLYWOOD, CA	91602
ANGELL, ROBERT	TV PRODUCER	16 ELMSTONE RD	LONDON SW6 5TN	ENGLAND
ANGELS, THE	VOCAL GROUP	324 MAIN AVE #323	NORWALK, CT	06851
ANGELUS, MURIEL	ACTRESS	379 BELDEN HILL RD	WILTON, CT	06897
ANGELYNE	ACTRESS	POST OFFICE BOX 3864	BEVERLY HILLS, CA	90212
ANGER, KENNETH	DIRECTOR	6028 BARTON AVE	LOS ANGELES, CA	90038
ANGERS, AVRIL	ACT-COMED-SING	12 JAMES ST, COVENT GARDEN	LONDON WC2 8BT	ENGLAND
ANGIER, JOSEPH	WRI-DIR-PROD	417 E 70TH ST	NEW YORK, NY	10021
ANGLADE, CATHERINE	TV PRODUCER	10 RUE VILLEHARDOUIN	PARIS 75003	FRANCE
ANGLIM, PHILIP	ACTOR	2404 GRAND CANAL	VENICE, CA	90291
ANGLIN, FLORENCE	ACTRESS	345 W 55TH ST	NEW YORK, NY	10019
ANGLIN, JENNIFER	ACTRESS	3527 PRIMERA AVE	LOS ANGELES, CA	90068
ANGLIN, SONNY	SINGER	POST OFFICE BOX 1104	HARVEY, LA	70058
ANGOTTI, NICK	ACTOR	5329 VANTAGE AVE #5	NORTH HOLLYWOOD, CA	91607
ANGRES, RICHARD D	WRITER	922 19TH ST #E	SANTA MONICA, CA	90403
ANHALT, EDWARD	WRITER-PRODUCER	500 AMALFI DR	PACIFIC PALISADES, CA	90272
ANHOLT, TONY	ACTOR	CAREY, 64 THORNTON AVE	LONDON W4 1QQ	ENGLAND
ANIMOTION	ROCK & ROLL GROUP	1299 OCEAN AVE #PH	SANTA MONICA, CA	90404
ANISTON, JOHN	ACTOR	3307 BONNIE HILL DR	LOS ANGELES, CA	90068
ANKA, PAUL	SINGER-SONGWRITER	140 E TROPICANA AVE	LAS VEGAS, NV	89109
ANKLAM, FRED, JR	COLUMNIST	POST OFFICE BOX 500	WASHINGTON, DC	20044
ANKRUM, DAVID	ACTOR	5707 COSTELLO AVE	VAN NUYS, CA	91401
ANN-MARGRET	ACTRESS-SINGER	2707 BENEDICT CANYON DR	BEVERLY HILLS, CA	90210
ANNABELLA	ACTRESS	1 RUE PIERRET	NEUILLY 92200	FRANCE
ANNAKIN, JANE	TALENT AGENT	WM MORRIS, 31-32 SOHO SQ	LONDON W1V 5DG	ENGLAND
ANNAKIN, KENNETH	FILM WRITER-DIRECTOR	WM MORRIS, 31-32 SOHO SQ	LONDON W1V 5DG	ENGLAND
ANNAUD, JEAN-JACQUES	FILM DIRECTOR	ICM, 8899 BEVERLY BLVD	LOS ANGELES, CA	90048
ANNE, GLORY	SINGER	9940 LOUGHEED HWY #330	BURNABY, BC V3J 1N3	CANADA
ANNE, HRH PRINCESS	PRINCESS	GATCOMBE PARK	GLOUCESTERSHIRE	ENGLAND
ANNE MARIE	SINGER	LEE STOLLER, 120 HICKORY ST	MADISON, TN	37115
ANNENBERG, WALLIS	PUBLISHING EXECUTIVE	10273 CENTURY WOODS PL	LOS ANGELES, CA	90067
ANNENBERG, WALTER	PUBLISHING EXECUTIVE	POST OFFICE BOX 98	RANCHO MIRAGE, CA	92270
ANNESE, FRANK	ACTOR	10600 HOLMAN AVE #1	LOS ANGELES, CA	90024
ANNETT, PAUL	WRITER-PRODUCER	MLR, 200 FULHAM RD	LONDON SW10 9PN	ENGLAND
ANNIE K	SINGER	5625 "O" STREET BLDG #7	LINCOLN, NE	68510
ANNIS, FRANCESCA	ACTRESS	2 VICARAGE CT	LONDON W8	ENGLAND
ANNIS, RICHARD	ACTOR	5418 WILLOW CREST AVE #6	NORTH HOLLYWOOD, CA	91601
ANNO, SAM	FOOTBALL	BUCCANEERS, 1 BUCCANEER PL	TAMPA, FL	33607
ANNON, PAULINE	COSTUME DESIGNER	13949 VENTURA BLVD #309	SHERMAN OAKS, CA	91423
ANNUNZIO, FRANK	U S CONGRESSMAN	230 S DEARBORN ST #3816	CHICAGO, IL	60604
ANQUATTE	RAP GROUP-RAPWRITERS	FAA, 1700 BROADWAY, 5TH FLOOR	NEW YORK, NY	10019
ANSARA, EDWARD	ACTOR	777 E VALLEY BLVD #107	ALHAMBRA, CA	91801
ANSARA, MICHAEL	ACTOR	4624 PARK MIRASOL	CALABASAS, CA	91302

Name	Occupation	Address	City	Zip/Country
ANSARA, MICHAEL, JR	ACTOR	4624 PARK MIRASOL	CALABASAS, CA	91302
ANSEL, JEROME	DIRECTOR	141 5TH AVE	NEW YORK, NY	10010
ANSEN, DAVID	FILM CRITIC	NEWSWEEK, 444 MADISON AVE	NEW YORK, NY	10022
ANSEN, JOHN	TV DIRECTOR	5334 OAK PARK AVE	ENCINO, CA	91316
ANSEN, JOSEPH	WRITER	1950 S BEVERLY GLEN BLVD #302	LOS ANGELES, CA	90025
ANSHUTZ, RICHARD L	CONDUCTOR	1645 SIERRA GARDENS DR #205	ROSEVILLE, CA	95678
ANSLEY, MICHAEL	BASKETBALL	POST OFFICE BOX 76	ORLANDO, FL	32802
ANSLEY, WILLIE	BASEBALL	POST OFFICE BOX 4209	JACKSON, MS	39296
ANSLEY, ZACHARY	ACTOR	1999 AVE OF THE STARS #2850	LOS ANGELES, CA	90067
ANSON, RUTH	ACTRESS-WRITER	9250 WILSHIRE BLVD #208	BEVERLY HILLS, CA	90212
ANSPACH, SUSAN	ACTRESS	473 16TH ST	SANTA MONICA, CA	90420
ANSPAUGH, DAVID	TV DIRECTOR-PRODUCER	7358 W 83RD ST	LOS ANGELES, CA	90045
ANT, ADAM	SINGER-ACTOR	POST OFFICE BOX 866	LONDON SE1 3AP	ENGLAND
ANTHONY, AL	CONDUCTOR	7823 ALLOTT AVE	PANORAMA CITY, CA	91402
ANTHONY, BERYL	U S CONGRESSMAN	100 E 8TH AVE, ROOM 2521	PINE BLUFF, AR	71601
ANTHONY, ERIC	BASEBALL	POST OFFICE BOX 288	HOUSTON, TX	77001
ANTHONY, FRANK S	DIRECTOR	RD #6, BOX 126	MIDDLETOWN, NY	10940
ANTHONY, GERALD	ACTOR	NBC-TV, "ANOTHER WORLD"		
		1268 E 14TH ST	BROOKLYN, NY	11230
ANTHONY, JOHNNY RAY	SINGER	BAKER, 3345 HOLLINS FERRY RD	BALTIMORE, MD	21227
ANTHONY, JOSEPH	ACTOR	6255 SUNSET BLVD #627	LOS ANGELES, CA	90028
ANTHONY, LEE	ACTOR	ATKINS, 303 S CRESCENT HEIGHTS	LOS ANGELES, CA	90048
ANTHONY, LYSETTE	ACTRESS	CONWAY, 18-21 JERMYN ST	LONDON SW1	ENGLAND
ANTHONY, MARK	ACTOR-WRITER	3610 FOOTHILL BLVD	LA CRESCENTA, CA	91214
ANTHONY, MARK	BASEBALL	POST OFFICE BOX 20849	CHARLESTON, SC	29413
ANTHONY, MARK	DIRECTOR	590 N VERMONT AVE	BURBANK, CA	91505
ANTHONY, MARTIN	ACTOR	SNOWSHAFT, 10 CLEVELAND WY	LONDON E1 4TR	ENGLAND
ANTHONY, PEPPER	BASEBALL	POST OFFICE BOX 20849	CHARLESTON, SC	29413
ANTHONY, PETER	COMEDIAN	21243 VENTURA BLVD #243	WOODLAND HILLS, CA	91364
ANTHONY, RAFAEL	ACTRESS	145 S FAIRFAX AVE #310	LOS ANGELES, CA	90036
ANTHONY, RAY	ORCHESTRA LEADER	9288 KINGLET DR	LOS ANGELES, CA	90069
ANTHONY, SAL	COSTUME DESIGNER	13949 VENTURA BLVD #309	SHERMAN OAKS, CA	91423
ANTHONY-KENNEDY, DIANNE	COSTUME DESIGNER	13949 VENTURA BLVD #309	SHERMAN OAKS, CA	91423
ANTILLA, SUSAN	COLUMNIST	POST OFFICE BOX 500	WASHINGTON, DC	20044
ANTIN, STEVE	ACTOR	6909 CLINTON ST	LOS ANGELES, CA	90036
ANTON, JOHN J	DIRECTOR	12027 CREST CT	BEVERLY HILLS, CA	90210
ANTON, SUSAN	ACTRESS	1853 NOEL PL	BEVERLY HILLS, CA	90210
ANTONACCI, GREG	ACTOR-DIRECTOR	14223 GREENLEAF ST	SHERMAN OAKS, CA	91423
ANTONELLI, LAURA	ACTRESS	LUNGOTEVERE MICHELANGELO 9	I-00192 ROME	ITALY
ANTONEN, MEL	SPORTS WRITER	POST OFFICE BOX 500	WASHINGTON, DC	20044
ANTONIO, JIM	ACTOR	1680 N VINE ST #1003	HOLLYWOOD, CA	90028
ANTONIO, LANE	ACTRESS	530 GAYLORD DR	BURBANK, CA	91505
ANTONIO, LOU	ACT-WRI-DIR	530 GAYLORD DR	BURBANK, CA	91505
ANTONIONI, MICHELANGELO	FILM DIRECTOR	VIA VINCENZO TIBERIO 18	ROME	ITALY
ANTONOFSKY, RUTH	ACT-SING-DAN	463 WEST ST #A-205	NEW YORK, NY	10014
ANTONOWSKY, MARVIN	FILM EXECUTIVE	3116 THE STRAND	MANHATTAN BEACH, CA	90266
ANTOON, A J	DIRECTOR	888 7TH AVE #1602	NEW YORK, NY	10019
ANWAR, GABRIELLE	ACTRESS	AIM, 5 DENMARK ST	LONDON WC2H 8LP	ENGLAND
AOKI, ROCKY	FOOD ENTREPRENEUR	8685 NW 53RD TERR	MIAMI, FL	33155
APARICIO, LUIS	BASEBALL	CALLE 67 #26-82	MARACAIBO	VENEZUELA
APOCALYPSE	ROCK & ROLL GROUP	POST OFFICE BOX 942	RAPID CITY, SD	57709
APODACA, BOB	BASEBALL-COACH	POST OFFICE BOX 1211	NORFOLK, VA	23502
APOGEE	C & W GROUP	5625 "O" STREET BLDG #7	LINCOLN, NE	68510
APOLLONIA	ACTRESS	8271 MELROSE AVE #110	LOS ANGELES, CA	90046
APONTE, LUIS	BASEBALL SCOUT	INDIANS, CLEVELAND STADIUM	CLEVELAND, OH	44114
APONTE, RICK	BASEBALL COACH	POST OFFICE BOX 1556	ASHEVILLE, NC	28802
APPEL, ALAN G	WRITER	TV GUIDE, 1290 AVE OF AMERICAS	NEW YORK, NY	10014
APPEL, STANLEY	TV PRODUCER	18 BRAMLEY CRESCENT		
		GANTS HILL, ILFORD	ESSEX	ENGLAND
APPEL, WENDY	DIRECTOR	DGA, 7920 SUNSET BLVD, 6TH FL	LOS ANGELES, CA	90046
APPELBAUM, LAWRENCE	DIRECTOR	508 N CRESCENT DR	BEVERLY HILLS, CA	90210
APPET, LEAH	WRITER	116 N SWEETZER AVE	LOS ANGELES, CA	90048
APPIER, KEVIN	BASEBALL	POST OFFICE BOX 419969	KANSAS CITY, MO	64141
APPLE, JEFFREY D	FILM PRODUCER	116 N ROBERTSON BLVD #402	LOS ANGELES, CA	90048
APPLE, MAX	SCREENWRITER	8955 BEVERLY BLVD	WEST HOLLYWOOD, CA	90048
APPLEBY, PAUL	ACTOR	AIMEE, 13743 VICTORY BLVD	VAN NUYS, CA	91401
APPLEGATE, CHRISTINA	ACTRESS	LYNN, 4527 PARK ALLEGRA	CALABASAS PARK, CA	91302
APPLEGATE, DOUGLAS	U S CONGRESSMAN	OHIO VALLEY TOWER, ROOM 610	STEUBENVILLE, OH	43952
APPLEJACK	C & W GROUP	LANDIS, 1717 LINCOLN HWY E	LANCASTER, PA	17602
APPLEMAN, HERBERT	WRI-DIR-PROD	11 RIVERSAIDE DR #4-FW	NEW YORK, NY	10023
APPLEMAN, SID	COMPOSER	3460 PENINSULA RD #206	OXNARD, CA	93035
APPLETON, VELVY	FILM PRODUCER	COLOSSAL, 2800 3RD ST	SAN FRANCISCO, CA	94107
APPLING, RON	DIRECTOR	555 W SHAW AVE #15	FRESNO, CA	93704
APREA, JOHN	ACTOR	NBC-TV, "ANOTHER WORLD"		
		1268 E 14TH ST	BROOKLYN, NY	11230
APRIL	C & W GROUP	POST OFFICE BOX 15058	FORT WAYNE, IN	46885
APSTEIN, ELLIOTT	WRITER	1000 NORMAN PL	LOS ANGELES, CA	90049
APTED, MICHAEL	FILM DIRECTOR	1051 VILLA VIEW DR	PACIFIC PALISADES, CA	90272
APTER, HAROLD	WRITER	1944 N WHITLEY AVE #310	LOS ANGELES, CA	90068
AQUINO, CORAZON	PHILIPPINE PRESIDENT	MALACANANG PALACE	MANILA	
AQUINO, LUIS	BASEBALL	POST OFFICE BOX 419969	KANSAS CITY, MO	64141
ARACE, PASQUALE	BASEBALL	POST OFFICE BOX 842	SALEM, VA	24153
ARACENA, LUINIS	BASEBALL	POST OFFICE BOX 882	MADISON, WI	53701
ARAFAT, YASSIR	POLITICIAN	ARNESTCONSEIL 17		
		BELEVEDERE 1002	TUNIS	TUNISIA

Name	Occupation	Address	City/State	ZIP/Country
ARAGALL, JAIME	SINGER	LOMBARDO, 30 W 60TH ST	NEW YORK, NY	10023
ARAGON, ART	ACTOR	19050 WELLS DR	TARZANA, CA	91356
ARAGONES, SERGIO	CARTOONIST	MAD MAGAZINE, 485 MADISON AVE	NEW YORK, NY	10022
ARAL, KLYOSHI	BASEBALL	POST OFFICE BOX 4370	SALINAS, CA	93912
ARANHA, RAY	ACTOR-WRITER	KROLL, 390 W END AVE	NEW YORK, NY	10024
ARANZAMENDI, JORGE	BASEBALL SCOUT	250 STADIUM PLAZA	ST LOUIS, MO	63102
ARAR, YARDENA	TV CRITIC	POST OFFICE BOX 51400	LOS ANGELES, CA	90051
ARASKOG, JULIE	ACTRESS	8485 MELROSE PL #E	LOS ANGELES, CA	90069
ARATA, TONY	SINGER	POST OFFICE BOX 5493	HILTON HEAD, SC	29938
ARAZONA	C & W GROUP	JIMMY ALLEN, 1548 ASHLAND AVE	SAINT PAUL, MN	55104
ARBEID, BEN	FILM PRODUCER	ICM, 388-396 OXFORD ST	LONDON W1	ENGLAND
ARBESSIER, LOUIS	ACTOR	33 RUE ARTHUR ROZIER	PARIS 75019	FRANCE
ARBOGAST, ROBERT L	WRITER	629 SUNNYHILL DR	LOS ANGELES, CA	90065
ARBUS, ALLAN	ACTOR	2208 N BEVERLY GLEN	LOS ANGELES, CA	90077
ARBUS, LOREEN J	WRITER-PRODUCER	8841 APPIAN WY	LOS ANGELES, CA	90046
ARBUSTO, DOMENIC	DIRECTOR	333 E 49TH ST #LE	NEW YORK, NY	10017
ARCH ANGELS, THE	ROCK & ROLL GROUP	BASTEIN, 644 WARWICK ST	BROOKLYN, NY	11207
ARCHAMBEAU, LES	FOOTBALL	PACKERS, 1265 LOMBARDI AVE	GREEN BAY, WI	54307
ARCHARD, BERNARD	ACTOR	HOLT BARTON, WITHAM FRAIRY	SOMERSET	ENGLAND
ARCHER, ANNE	ACTRESS	13201 OLD OAK LN	LOS ANGELES, CA	90049
ARCHER, BILL	U S CONGRESSMAN	1003 WIRT RD #311	HOUSTON, TX	77055
ARCHER, GEORGE	GOLFER	PGA SENIORS, 112 T P C BLVD	PONTE VEDRA BEACH, FL	32082
ARCHER, JANICE	BASEBALL EXECUTIVE	2908 ASHLEY ST	KINGSPORT, TN	37664
ARCHER, JOHN	TV PRODUCER-DIRECTOR	BBC-TV, 56 WOOD LN	LONDON W12 7RJ	ENGLAND
ARCHER, KURT	BASEBALL	POST OFFICE BOX 8550	STOCKTON, CA	95208
ARCHER, NICHOLAS	TV EXECUTIVE	ABC-TV, 7 W 66TH ST	NEW YORK, NY	10023
ARCHERD, ARMY	COLUMNIST	442 HILGARD AVE	LOS ANGELES, CA	90024
ARCHERD, EVAN P	WRITER	10124 LA TUNA CANYON RD	SUN VALLEY, CA	91352
ARCHERD, SELMA	ACTRESS	442 HILGARD AVE	LOS ANGELES, CA	90024
ARCHIBALD, DOTTIE	COMEDIENNE-WRITER	10372 TENNESSEE AVE	LOS ANGELES, CA	90064
ARD, BILLY	FOOTBALL	PACKERS, 1265 LOMBARDI AVE	GREEN BAY, WI	54307
ARD, JOHNNY	BASEBALL	5999 E VAN BUREN ST	PHOENIX, AZ	85008
ARDEN, EVE	ACTRESS	9066 SAINT IVES DR	LOS ANGELES, CA	90069
ARDEN, ROBERT	ACTOR	24 NEVILLE ST	LONDON SW7 3AS	ENGLAND
ARDEN, TONI	SINGER	34-34 75TH ST	JACKSON HEIGHTS, NY	11372
ARDOLINO, PAUL	PRODUCER	1807 TAFT AVE #4	LOS ANGELES, CA	90028
ARENA, MAURIZIO	CONDUCTOR	61 W 62ND ST #6-F	NEW YORK, NY	10023
ARENAL, JULIE	CHOREOGRAPHER	205 E 10TH ST	NEW YORK, NY	10003
ARENO, LOIS	ACTRESS-MODEL	9145 CHARLEVILLE BLVD #305	BEVERLY HILLS, CA	90212
ARENS, MOSHE	MILITARY	49 HAGDERAT	SAVYON	ISRAEL
ARGENT, DOUGLAS	TV DIRECTOR-PRODUCER	55 KENTON AVE		
		SUNBURY-ON-THAMES	MIDDLESEX	ENGLAND
ARGENTO, DOMINICK	COMPOSER	MINNESOTA UNIVERSITY		
		MUSIC DEPARTMENT	MINNEAPOLIS, MN	55455
ARGENTO, FRANK	ACTOR	37 88TH ST	BROOKLYN, NY	11209
ARGENZIANO, CARMEN	ACTOR	853 KEMP ST	BURBANK, CA	91505
ARGIRO, JAMES	COMPOSER-CONDUCTOR	11042 AQUA VISTA ST #6	NORTH HOLLYWOOD, CA	91602
ARGO, ALLISON	ACTRESS	54 NAVY ST	VENICE, CA	90291
ARGO, VICTOR	ACTOR	SMITH, 121 N SAN VICENTE BLVD	BEVERLY HILLS, CA	90211
ARIANS, BRUCE	FOOTBALL COACH	CHIEFS, 1 ARROWHEAD DR	KANSAS CITY, MO	64129
ARIAS, ALEX	BASEBALL	CUBS, 2ND & RIVERSIDE DR	DES MOINES, IA	50309
ARIAS, AMADOR	BASEBALL	POST OFFICE BOX 4669	CHARLESTON, WV	25304
ARIAS, OSCAR	POLITICIAN	CASA PRESIDENCIA	SAN JOSE	COSTA RICA
ARIAS, TONY	BASEBALL-SCOUT	ATHLETICS'S, OAKLAND COLISEUM	OAKLAND, CA	94621
ARIOLA, TONY	BASEBALL	POST OFFICE BOX 882	MADISON, WI	53701
ARIS, BEN	ACTOR	BARRY BROWN, 47 WEST SQ	LONDON SE11 4SP	ENGLAND
ARISMAN, MARSHALL	ARTIST	314 W 100TH ST	NEW YORK, NY	10025
ARISON, TED	BASKETBALL EXECUTIVE	MIAMI HEAT, THE MIAMI ARENA	MIAMI, FL	33136
ARIZONA	C & W GROUP	POST OFFICE BOX 256577	CHICAGO, IL	60625
ARIZONA SMOKE REVUE	C & W GROUP	RNJ PRODS, 11514 CALVERT ST	NORTH HOLLYWOOD, CA	91606
ARK VALLEY BOYS, THE	C & W GROUP	HARRY PEEBLES, 24 S 59TH ST	KANSAS CITY, KS	66117
ARKENSTONE, DAVID	COMPOSER-PIANIST	NARADA, 1845 N FARWELL AVE	MILWAUKEE, WI	53202
ARKIN, ADAM	ACTOR-WRITER	50 RIDGE DR	CHAPPAQUE, NY	10514
ARKIN, ALAN	ACTOR-DIRECTOR	31 BANK ST	NEW YORK, NY	10014
ARKIN, JONATHAN	ART DIRECTOR	7 W 22ND ST, 10TH FLOOR	NEW YORK, NY	10010
ARKOFF, SAMUEL Z	FILM PRODUCER	3205 OAKDELL LN	STUDIO CITY, CA	91604
ARKUS, ALBERT	DIRECTOR	2 PADDOCK LN	GREAT NECK, NY	11020
ARKUSH, ALLAN PAUL	DIRECTOR	14134 CHANDLER BLVD	VAN NUYS, CA	91401
ARLEDGE, ROONE	TV DIRECTOR-PRODUCER	535 PARK AVE #13-A	NEW YORK, NY	10021
ARLEN, ALICE A	SCREENWRITER	555 W 57TH ST #1230	NEW YORK, NY	10019
ARLEN, ELIZABETH	ACTRESS	2722 FORRESTER DR	LOS ANGELES, CA	90064
ARLETT, RICHARD	WRITER	9300 SIERRA MAR DR	LOS ANGELES, CA	90069
ARLETTY	ACTRESS	14 RUE DE RIMUSAT	PARIS 75016	FRANCE
ARLIN, JUSTINE	ACTRESS	8271 MELROSE AVE #110	LOS ANGELES, CA	90046
ARLISS, DIMITRA	ACTRESS	9057 NEMO ST #A	WEST HOLLYWOOD, CA	90069
ARLISS, JOEN	ACTRESS	25 CENTRAL PARK W #11-A	NEW YORK, NY	10023
ARLT, LEWIS	ACTOR	165 W 46TH ST #1108	NEW YORK, NY	10036
ARMANI, DEBRA	ACTRESS	5272 BELLINGHAM AVE	NORTH HOLLYWOOD, CA	91607
ARMANI, GIORGIO	FASHION DESIGNER	650 5TH AVE	NEW YORK, NY	10019
ARMAS, MARCOS	BASEBALL	POST OFFICE BOX 2769	HUNTSVILLE, AL	35804
ARMAS, TONY	BASEBALL	LOS MERCEDES #37, P PIRITU	ANZOATEQUI	VENEZUELA
ARMATRADING, JOAN	SINGER-GUITARIST	RUNNING DOG MANAGEMENT		
		27 QUEENSDALE PL	LONDON W11	ENGLAND
ARMBRUSTER, RICHARD	ACTOR	1401 N FULLER AVE #6	LOS ANGELES, CA	90046
ARMEN, MARGARET	WRITER	5707 WALLIS LN	WOODLAND HILLS, CA	91367

Don't Miss Another Issue!

Now Monthly!

AUTOGRAPH COLLECTOR

The Magazine Serving Collectors Worldwide.

Each Issue Features:

- Current prices and trends
- Auction results
- Thousands of offerings from the nation's top dealers
- VIP addresses you can use to write for ***FREE*** autographs.
- Secrets on building a collection for minimal cost.
- ***PLUS***, exciting, in-depth features, and more!

Back Issues

$6.00 Each (Includes Shipping). 3 or more $5.00 Each.

March 1992

AUCTION ACTION: A Market Profile

HOLLYWOOD'S TREASURE On The Block

RUBY AND OSWALD Autographic Review

PROFILE: Joseph Maddalena

May 1992

MICKEY'S MEMORIES Disney Archives

SPORTS: Boxing's Toughest Autographs

PRESERVING HISTORY Legislative Archives

June 1992

SPECIAL REPORT: In Person Autographs

SIGNERS: Who Does, Who Doesn't

July 1992

SPECIAL REPORT: Sports Autographs

Adventures of a Sports Collector

THOMAS JEFFERSON Autographic Profile

☐ **Yes!** Send me one year (12 issues) of **AUTOGRAPH COLLECTOR** so I can keep up on the current prices and trends of autographs and much more!

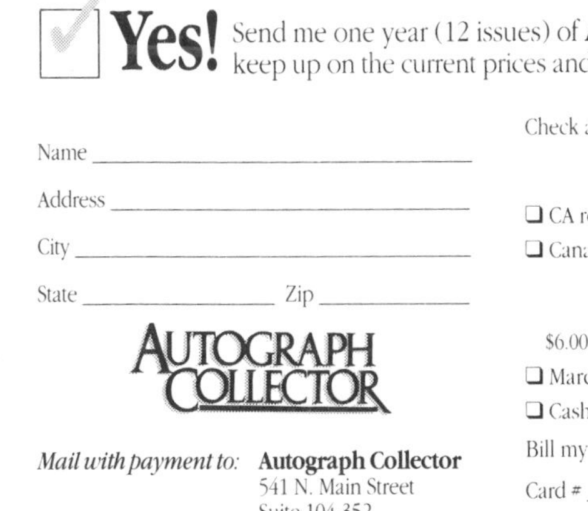

Mail with payment to: **Autograph Collector**
541 N. Main Street
Suite 104-352
Corona, CA 91720
(714) 734-9636

Check appropriate box:

SUBSCRIPTIONS
(CA residents we have added 7¾% sales tax)

❑ CA residents $40.95 ❑ All other U.S. $38.00

❑ Canada/Mexico $72.00 ❑ All other Countries $93.60

BACK ISSUES
(CA residents add 7¾% sales tax)

$6.00 Each (Includes Shipping). 3 or more $5.00 Each.

❑ March '92 ❑ May '92 ❑ June '92 ❑ July '92

❑ Cash, Check or Money Order enclosed

Bill my Credit Card: ❑ VISA ❑ MASTERCARD

Card # ________

Signature ________

Exp. Date ________

August 1992

DETACH AND RETURN COUPON

ARMENTROUT, LEE	DIRECTOR	801 ERIE ST	OAK PARK, IL	60302
ARMER, ALAN A	DIRECTOR-PRODUCER	266 BRONWOOD AVE	LOS ANGELES, CA	90049
ARMEY, RICHARD K	U S CONGRESSMAN	1301 S BOWEN RD #422	ARLINGTON, TX	76013
ARMISTEAD, THOMAS	TV DIRECTOR-PRODUCER	10373 ASHTON AVE	LOS ANGELES, CA	90024
ARMITAGE, GEORGE	WRITER-PRODUCER	1113 N BEVERLY GLEN	LOS ANGELES, CA	90077
ARMOR, JOYCE	TV WRITER	8955 BEVERLY BLVD	WEST HOLLYWOOD, CA	90048
ARMOURY SHOW, THE	ROCK & ROLL GROUP	POST OFFICE BOX 107-A	LONDON N6 5RU	ENGLAND
ARMS, RUSSELL	ACTOR-SINGER	2918 DAVIS WY	PALM SPRINGS, CA	92262
ARMSTRONG, ALUN	ACTOR	MARKHAM AND FROGGATT, LTD		
		JULIAN HOUSE, 4 WINDMILL ST	LONDON W1P 1HF	ENGLAND
ARMSTRONG, B J	BASKETBALL	980 N MICHIGAN AVE #1600	CHICAGO, IL	60611
ARMSTRONG, BARBARA	MAKE-UP ARTIST	401 E 81ST ST #3-F	NEW YORK, NY	10028
ARMSTRONG, BESS	ACTRESS	1518 N DOHENY DR	LOS ANGELES, CA	90069
ARMSTRONG, BILL	TV WRITER	8955 BEVERLY BLVD	WEST HOLLYWOOD, CA	90048
ARMSTRONG, BILLY	SINGER	ROLAND TERRY PRODUCTIONS		
		909 PARKVIEW AVE	LODI, CA	95240
ARMSTRONG, BRAD	WRESTLER	POST OFFICE BOX 105366	ATLANTA, GA	31348
ARMSTRONG, BRUCE	FOOTBALL	PATRIOTS, FOXBORO STADIUM, RT #1	FOXBORO, MA	02035
ARMSTRONG, CURTIS	ACTOR	9200 SUNSET BLVD #710	LOS ANGELES, CA	90069
ARMSTRONG, DOUGLAS	FILM CRITIC	POST OFFICE BOX 661	MILWAUKEE, WI	53201
ARMSTRONG, FRANKIE	SINGER	FOLKLORE, 1671 APPIAN WY	SANTA MONICA, CA	90401
ARMSTRONG, GARNER TED	EVANGELIST-AUTHOR	POST OFFICE BOX 2525	TYLER, TX	75710
ARMSTRONG, GILLIAN	FILM DIRECTOR	151 S EL CAMINO DR	BEVERLY HILLS, CA	90212
ARMSTRONG, HERB	ACTOR	11476 HUSTON ST	NORTH HOLLYWOOD, CA	91601
ARMSTRONG, JACK	BASEBALL	711 HATTON CT	NEPTUNE, NJ	07753
ARMSTRONG, JAMES D	CONDUCTOR	7916 4TH ST	DOWNEY, CA	90241
ARMSTRONG, MICHAEL	ACT-WRI-DIR	8 COLEFORD RD, WANDSWORTH	LONDON SW1	ENGLAND
ARMSTRONG, MOIRA	TV DIRECTOR	10 CEYLON RD	LONDON W14 OPY	ENGLAND
ARMSTRONG, NEIL	ASTRONAUT	1739 N STATE, ROUTE #123	LEBANON, OH	45036
ARMSTRONG, R G	ACTOR	132 S LASKY DR #B	BEVERLY HILLS, CA	90212
ARMSTRONG, RICHARD B	TV DIRECTOR	1910 WINGHAM LN	SILVER SPRING, MD	20902
ARMSTRONG, ROBIN	ACTOR	6101 MORELLA AVE	NORTH HOLLYWOOD, CA	91606
ARMSTRONG, TRACE	FOOTBALL	BEARS, 250 N WASHINGTON RD	LAKE FOREST, IL	60045
ARMSTRONG, VAUGHN	ACTOR	ATKINS, 303 S CRESCENT HEIGHTS	LOS ANGELES, CA	90048
ARMUS, BURTON S	TV WRITER-PRODUCER	2501 CAROB DR	LOS ANGELES, CA	90046
ARNATT, JOHN	ACTOR	3 WARREN COTTAGES, WOODLAND WY		
		KINGSWOOD	SURREY KT20 6NN	ENGLAND
ARNAUD, LEON	COMPOSER-CONDUCTOR	215 BUCK SHOALS RD	HAMPTONVILLE, NC	27020
ARNAZ, DESI, JR	ACTOR	POST OFFICE BOX 60684	BOULDER CITY, NV	89006
ARNAZ, LUCIE	ACTRESS	470-K MAIN ST	RIDGEFIELD, CT	06877
ARNELL, PETER	TV PRODUCER	3750 MAIN ST	BRIDGEPORT, CT	06606
ARNEMANN, DAWN	ACTRESS	6122 DE LONGPRE AVE #1	LOS ANGELES, CA	90028
ARNER, MIKE	BASEBALL	POST OFFICE BOX 3609	PORT CHARLOTTE, FL	33949
ARNESEN, SEDENA	ACTRESS	605 25TH ST	MANHATTAN BEACH, CA	90266
ARNESS, JAMES	ACTOR	POST OFFICE BOX 10480	GLENDALE, CA	91209
ARNETT, JAMES M	FILM DIRECTOR	940 N LA JOLLA AVE	LOS ANGELES, CA	90046
ARNETT, PETER	NEWS CORRESPONDEENT	1050 TECHWOOD DR, NW	ATLANTA, GA	30318
ARNETTE, JEANETTA	ACTRESS	840 N HUNTLEY DR #3	LOS ANGELES, CA	90069
ARNGRIM, ALISON	ACTRESS	1340 N POINSETTIA PL #422	LOS ANGELES, CA	90046
ARNIEL, SCOTT	HOCKEY	JETS, 15-1430 MAROONS RD	WINNIPEG, MAN R3G OL5	CANADA
ARNO, FRANK	ACTOR	5339 NEWCASTLE AVE	ENCINO, CA	91316
ARNOLD, ALAN	SCREENWRITER	20 PEMBRIDGE CRESCENT	LONDON W11	ENGLAND
ARNOLD, CHERYL	SINGER-MODEL	POST OFFICE BOX 189	BOTHELL, WA	98011
ARNOLD, DANNY	WRITER-PRODUCER	1293 SUNSET PLAZA DR	LOS ANGELES, CA	90069
ARNOLD, DEBBIE	ACTRESS	MAY ARNOLD MANAGEMENT		
		12 CAMBRIDGE #2		
		EAST TWICKENHAM	LONDON TW1 2PF	ENGLAND
ARNOLD, EDDY	SINGER	FRANKLKIN, BOX 97	BRENTWOOD, TN	37027
ARNOLD, GARY	FILM CRITIC	5133 N 1ST ST	ARLINGTON, VA	22203
ARNOLD, JACK	DIRECTOR-PRODUCER	4860 NOMAD DR	WOODLAND HILLS, CA	91364
ARNOLD, JAMES	TV DIRECTOR	40 ARAN RD	WESTWOOD, MA	02090
ARNOLD, JIM	FOOTBALL	LIONS, 1200 FEATHERSTONE RD	PONTIAC, MI	48432
ARNOLD, JIM	TV WRITER	8955 BEVERLY BLVD	WEST HOLLYWOOD, CA	90048
ARNOLD, JOHN	ATTORNEY GENERAL	STATE HOUSE BUILDING	CONCORD, NH	03301
ARNOLD, JOHN	DIRECTOR-PRODUCER	GRAPHIC FILMS, 5-46 TITE ST	LONDON SW3 4JA	ENGLAND
ARNOLD, KAY "COOPER"	TV PRODUCER	34 KRAMER DR	PARAMUS, NJ	07652
ARNOLD, KEN	BASEBALL	1524 W NEBRASKA AVE	PEORIA, IL	61604
ARNOLD, MADISON	ACTOR	5750 WILSHIRE BLVD #512	LOS ANGELES, CA	90036
ARNOLD, MARCELLE	ACTOR	60 BLVD SAINT GERMAIN	PARIS 75005	FRANCE
ARNOLD, MARK	ACTOR	BRET ADAMS, 448 W 44TH ST	NEW YORK, NY	10036
ARNOLD, NEIL	SINGER	5625 "O" STREET BLDG #7	LINCOLN, NE	68510
ARNOLD, NEWTON DENNIS	WRITER-PRODUCER	16996 STRAWBERRY DR	ENCINO, CA	91436
ARNOLD, NICK	TV WRITER	R/W/G, 8428 MELROSE PL #C	LOS ANGELES, CA	90069
ARNOLD, RICK	BASEBALL SCOUT	ORIOLE PARK, 333 W CAMDEN ST	BALTIMORE, MD	21201
ARNOLD, ROSEANNE BARR	ACTRESS-COMEDIENNE	14755 VENTURA BLVD #1-170	SHERMAN OAKS, CA	91403
ARNOLD, TAFF	COMEDIAN	TERRY, 909 PARKVIEW AVE	LODI, CA	95240
ARNOLD, TOM	COMEDIAN-ACTOR	14755 VENTURA BLVD #1-170	SHERMAN OAKS, CA	91403
ARNOLD, TONY	BASEBALL COACH	POST OFFICE BOX 483	YAKIMA, WA	98907
ARNOLD, TRACY	ACTRESS	8322 BEVERLY BLVD #200	LOS ANGELES, CA	90048
ARNOTT, ROBERT M	TV WRITER	8955 BEVERLY BLVD	WEST HOLLYWOOD, CA	90048
ARNOUL, FRANCOISE	ACTRESS	24 RUE DAUPHINE	PARIS 75006	FRANCE
ARNSBERG, BRAD	BASEBALL	INDIANS, CLEVELAND STADIUM	CLEVELAND, OH	44114
ARNSTEIN, LARRY	TV WRITER	1601 HILL ST	SANTA MONICA, CA	90405
ARNSTEN, STEFAN	ACTOR	1017 LAUREL WY	BEVERLY HILLS, CA	90210
AROCHA, RENE	BASEBALL	POST OFFICE BOX 36407	LOUISVILLE, KY	40233

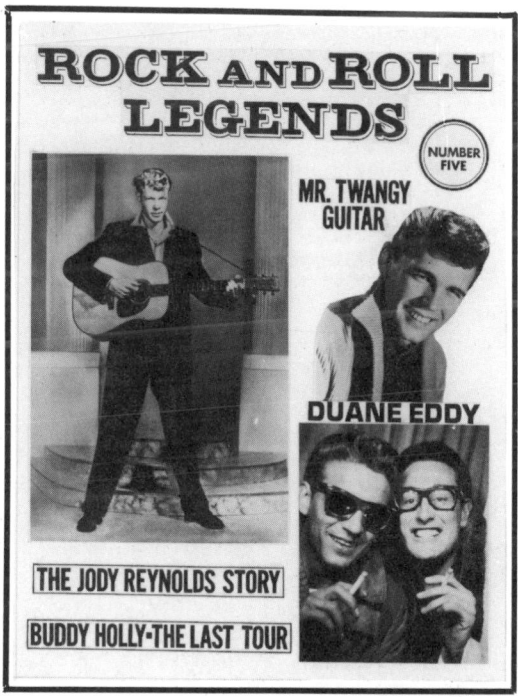

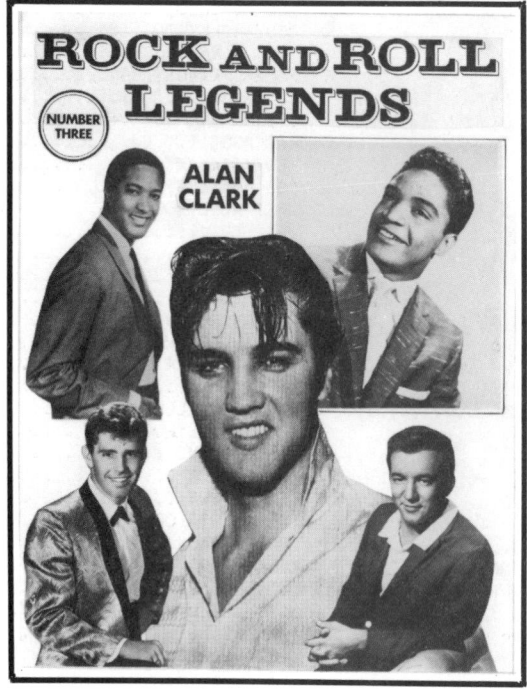

ARONE, JAMES	ACTOR	1809 W CLARK AVE	BURBANK, CA	91506
ARONETZ, CAM	BASEBALL	POST OFFICE BOX 10031	BAKERSFIELD, CA	93389
ARONOWITZ, JOEL	TV DIRECTOR	CBS-TV, 524 W 57TH ST	NEW YORK, NY	10019
ARONSON, BRAD	DIRECTOR	8109 WILLOW GLEN RD	LOS ANGELES, CA	90046
ARONSON, JOSHUA	DIRECTOR	260 5TH AVE	NEW YORK, NY	10001
ARONSON, JUDIE	ACTRESS	280 S BEVERLY DR #400	BEVERLY HILLS, CA	90212
ARQUETTE, DAVID	ACTOR	616 N GOWER ST	LOS ANGELES, CA	90004
ARQUETTE, LEWIS	ACTOR-WRITER	616 N GOWER ST	LOS ANGELES, CA	90004
ARQUETTE, PATRICIA	ACTRESS	POST OFFICE BOX 5617	BEVERLY HILLS, CA	90213
ARQUETTE, ROSANNA	ACTRESS-PRODUCER	1201 ALTA LOMA RD	WEST HOLLYWOOD, CA	90069
ARRANGA, IRENE	ACTRESS	909 N SIERRA BONITA AVE #7	LOS ANGELES, CA	90046
ARRANTS, ROD	ACTOR	STONE MANNERS, 9113 SUNSET BL	LOS ANGELES, CA	90069
ARREDONDO, ROBERTO	BASEBALL	12000 STADIUM RD	ADELANTO, CA	92301
ARRENDELL, EDWARD C, II	TALENT AGENT	POST OFFICE BOX 55398	WASHINGTON, DC	20040
ARRIENDA, GERALDINE J	COMPOSER	1719 GIRVIN RD	JACKSONVILLE, FL	32225
ARRINGTON, STEVE	SINGER	FAA, 1700 BROADWAY, 5TH FLOOR	NEW YORK, NY	10019
ARRIOLA, GUS	CARTOONIST	POST OFFICE BOX 3275	CARMEL, CA	93921
ARROYAVE, KARINA	ACTRESS	CBS-TV, "AS THE WORLD TURNS"		
		524 W 57TH ST #5330	NEW YORK, NY	10019
ARROYO, CARLOS	BASEBALL COACH	POST OFFICE BOX 15050	READING, PA	19612
ARSLANIAN, OSCAR	PRODUCER-MANAGER	6671 SUNSET BLVD #1502	HOLLYWOOD, CA	90028
ART OF NOISE, THE	ROCK & ROLL GROUP	POST OFFICE BOX 119	LONDON W11 4AN	ENGLAND
ARTHUR, BEATRICE	ACTRESS	2000 OLD RANCH RD	LOS ANGELES, CA	90049
ARTHUR, DAVID S	TV WRITER	4330 WINDWARD CIR	DALLAS, TX	75252
ARTHUR, GARFIELD	CINEMATOGRAPHER	POST OFFICE BOX 324	WEST FALMOUTH, MA	02574
ARTHUR, GARY	BASEBALL EXECUTIVE	POST OFFICE BOX 3690, STA "B"	CALGARY, ALB T2B 4M4	CANADA
ARTHUR, JOHN	TV WRITER	8955 BEVERLY BLVD	WEST HOLLYWOOD, CA	90048
ARTHUR, KAREN	TV-FILM DIRECTOR	19130 PACIFIC COAST HWY #8	MALIBU, CA	90265
ARTHUR, MAUREEN	ACTRESS	215 S LA CIENEGA BLVD #200	BEVERLY HILLS, CA	90211
ARTHUR, MIKE	FOOTBALL	BENGALS, 200 RIVERFRONT STADIUM	CINCINNATI, OH	45202
ARTHUR, REBECA	ACTRESS	9255 SUNSET BLVD #515	LOS ANGELES, CA	90069
ARTHUR, SHERWOOD	DIRECTOR	DGA, 110 W 57TH ST	NEW YORK, NY	10019
ARVESEN, NINA	ACTRESS	NBC-TV, "SANTA BARBARA"		
		3000 W ALAMEDA AVE	BURBANK, CA	91523
ASADORIAN, DIANE	ACTOR	SHOWTIME, 1633 BROADWAY	NEW YORK, NY	10019
ASANO, KEISHI	BASEBALL	POST OFFICE BOX 4370	SALINAS, CA	93912
ASCOUGH, STANLEY L	WRITER	11154 AQUA VISTA ST #17	NORTH HOLLYWOOD, CA	91602
ASH, GLENN	SINGER	7837 MASON AVE	CANOGA PARK, CA	91306
ASH, GORD	BASEBALL EXECUTIVE	SKYDOME, 300 BREMMER BL #3200	TORONTO, ONT M5V 3B3	CANADA
ASH, MARY KAY	COSMETIC EXECUTIVE	8787 N STEMMONS FREEWAY	DALLAS, TX	75247
ASH, MONTY	ACTOR	5330 LANKERSHIM BLVD #210	NORTH HOLLYWOOD, CA	91601
ASH, ROD M	TV WRITER	ICM, 8899 BEVERLY BLVD	LOS ANGELES, CA	90048
ASHBROOK, DANA	ACTRESS	2634 N BEACHWOOD DR	LOS ANGELES, CA	90068
ASHBROOK, DAPHNE LEE	ACTRESS	131 S RODEO DR #300	BEVERLY HILLS, CA	90212
ASHBURN, RICHIE	BASEBALL-ANNOUNCER	POST OFFICE BOX 7575	PHILADELPHIA, PA	19101
ASHBY, ANDY	BASEBALL	POST OFFICE BOX 7575	PHILADELPHIA, PA	19101
ASHCROFT, JOHN	GOVERNOR	POST OFFICE BOX 720	JEFFERSON CITY, MO	65102
ASHE, ARTHUR	TENNIS	370 E 76TH ST #A-1402	NEW YORK, NY	10021
ASHE, JENNIFER	ACTRESS	700 W END AVE #11-D	NEW YORK, NY	10025
ASHER, JANE	ACTRESS	CHATTO AND LINNIT, LTD		
		PRINCE OF WALES THEATRE		
		COVENTRY ST	LONDON W1V 7FE	ENGLAND
ASHER, MICHAEL D	CONDUCTOR	10936 1/2 HESBY ST	NORTH HOLLYWOOD, CA	91601
ASHER, MILTON D	CONDUCTOR	1631 LIVONIA AVE	LOS ANGELES, CA	90035
ASHER, PETER	RECORD PROD-AGT	ASHER, 644 N DOHENY DR	LOS ANGELES, CA	90069
ASHER, SCOT	BASEBALL EXECUTIVE	S F GIANTS, CANDLESTICK PARK	SAN FRANICSCO, CA	94124
ASHER, WILLIAM MILTON	WRITER-PRODUCER	2341 CARBON BACK RD	LOS ANGELES, CA	90049
ASHERTON DONAT, RENEE	ACTRESS	28 ELSWORTHY RD	LONDON NW3	ENGLAND
ASHFORD, DAVID	ACTOR	53 MOAT DR, HARROW	MIDDLESEX	ENGLAND
ASHFORD, MATTHEW	ACTOR	10925 HESBY ST	NORTH HOLLYWOOD, CA	91601
ASHFORD & SIMPSON	VOCAL DUO	254 W 72ND ST #1-A	NEW YORK, NY	10023
ASHLEY, BILLY	BASEBALL	POST OFFICE BOX 28268	SAN ANTONIO, TX	78228
ASHLEY, EDWARD	ACTOR	1879 BENECIA AVE	LOS ANGELES, CA	90025
ASHLEY, ELIZABETH	ACTRESS	9010 DORRINGTON AVE	LOS ANGELES, CA	90048
ASHLEY, JENNIFER	ACTRESS-MODEL	200 N ROBERTSON BLVD #219	BEVERLY HILLS, CA	90211
ASHLEY, JOHN	ACTOR-PRODUCER	18067 LAKE ENCINO DR	ENCINO, CA	91316
ASHLEY, LEON	SINGER-GUITARIST	POST OFFICE BOX 567	HENDERSONVILLE, TN	37077
ASHLEY, SHON	BASEBALL	1501 W 16TH ST	INDIANAPOLIS, IN	46202
ASHMAN, CHUCK	WRITER	111 N LAYTON DR	LOS ANGELES, CA	90049
ASHMAN, PENELOPE W	WRITER	322 FITZWATER ST	PHILADELPHIA, PA	19147
ASHMORE, FRANK	ACTOR	6310 SAN VICENTE BLVD #407	LOS ANGELES, CA	90048
ASHTON, BRENT	HOCKEY	JETS, 15-1430 MAROONS RD	WINNIPEG, MAN R3G 0L5	CANADA
ASHTON, DAVID	ACTOR	SIMONS, 9-15 NEAL ST	LONDON WC2H 9PU	ENGLAND
ASHTON, JOHN	ACTOR	22625 TOWN CRIER RD	WOODLAND HILLS, CA	91367
ASHTON, LAURA	ACTRESS	9255 SUNSET BLVD #505	LOS ANGELES, CA	90069
ASHTON, LORI	ACTRESS	8831 SUNSET BLVD #304	LOS ANGELES, CA	90069
ASHTON, PETER	ACTOR	9165 SUNSET BLVD #202	LOS ANGELES, CA	90069
ASHTON, ROY	MAKE-UP ARTIST	"PIPERS", 12 SANDROCK HILL RD		
		WRECCLESHAM, FARNHAM	SURREY GU10 4NS	ENGLAND
ASHTON, VALI	ACTRESS	9300 WILSHIRE BLVD #410	BEVERLY HILLS, CA	90212
ASHTON-GRIFFITHS, ROGER	ACTOR-WRITER-PROD	SPECTACLE FILMS LTD		
		16 CHELMSFORD RD	LONDON E11 1BS	ENGLAND
ASHWORTH, ERNIE	SINGER	38 MUSIC SQUARE E #300	NASHVILLE, TN	37203
ASIA	ROCK & ROLL GROUP	SUN ARTISTES, 9 HILLGATE ST	LONDON W8 7SP	ENGLAND
ASKEW, LUKE	ACTOR	1930 CENTURY PARK W #403	LOS ANGELES, CA	90067

ASKEY, GILBERT A	CONDUCTOR	1309 S REDONDO BLVD	LOS ANGELES, CA 90019
ASKIN, LEON	ACTOR-DIRECTOR	625 N REXFORD DR	BEVERLY HILLS, CA 90210
ASKINS, KEITH	BASKETBALL	MIAMI HEAT, THE MIAMI ARENA	MIAMI, FL 33136
ASKINS, MONROE, SR	DIRECTOR	4560 W HEMLOCK AVE	
		MANALAY BAY	OXNARD, CA 93030
ASKWITH, ROBIN	ACTOR	CHARLESWORTH, 60 OLD BROMPTON	LONDON SW7 3LQ ENGLAND
ASLAKSEN, DUANE	RECORD PRODUCER	POST OFFICE BOX 22129	SAN FRANCISCO, CA 94122
ASLEEP AT THE WHEEL	ROCK & ROLL GROUP	620 CONGRESS AVE #205	AUSTIN, TX 78767
ASMUSSEN, WILLIAM W	DIRECTOR-PRODUCER	21601 ERWIN DR	WOODLAND HILLS, CA 91367
ASNER, EDWARD	ACTOR	POST OFFICE BOX 7407	STUDIO CITY, CA 91604
ASPEL, MICHAEL	RADIO PERSONALITY	BAGENAL, 141-143 DRURY LN	LONDON WC2B ENGLAND
ASPERS, JANET	ACTRESS	12021 WILSHIRE BLVD #230	LOS ANGELES, CA 90025
ASPIN, LES	U S CONGRESSMAN	1661 DOUGLAS AVE	RACINE, WI 53403
ASPINALL, TIM	WRITER-PRODUCER	62 HARTSWOOD RD	LONDON W12 ENGLAND
ASQUITH, DON R	WRITER-PRODUCER	446 SHERMAN CANAL	VENICE, CA 90291
ASSA, RENE	ACTOR	2707 WAVERLY DR	LOS ANGELES, CA 90039
ASSAEL, DAVID	TV WRITER	318 S MANSFIELD AVE	LOS ANGELES, CA 90036
ASSANTE, ARMAND	ACTOR	RD #1, BOX 561	CAMPBELL HALL, NY 10916
ASSELIN, PAUL	DIRECTOR	11668 TERRY HILL PL	LOS ANGELES, CA 90049
ASSENMACHER, PAUL	BASEBALL	1060 W ADDISON ST	CHICAGO, IL 60613
ASSEYEV, TAMARA	FILM PRODUCER	1447 QUEENS RD	LOS ANGELES, CA 90069
ASSOCIATION, THE	ROCK & ROLL GROUP	9000 SUNSET BLVD #1200	LOS ANGELES, CA 90069
AST, PAT	ACTRESS	1336 3/4 N JUNE ST	LOS ANGELES, CA 90028
ASTACIO, PEDRO	BASEBALL	POST OFFICE BOX 26267	ALBUQUERQUE, NM 87125
ASTAIRE, JARVIS	FILM PRODUCER	JARAS ENTERTAINMENTS, LTD	
		21 CAVENDISH PL	LONDON W1M 9DL ENGLAND
ASTIN, JOHN	ACT-WRI-DIR	POST OFFICE BOX 49698	LOS ANGELES, CA 90049
ASTIN, MAC KENZIE	ACTOR	POST OFFICE BOX 385	BEVERLY HILLS, CA 90213
ASTIN, PATTY DUKE	ACTRESS	SEE - DUKE, PATTY	
ASTIN, SEAN	ACTOR	5438 NORWICH AVE	VAN NUYS, CA 91411
ASTOURIAN, JERRY	ACTOR	4302 RAINTREE CIR	CULVER CITY, CA 90230
ASTROW, JO ANNE O	ACTRESS-WRITER	145 S FAIRFAX AVE #310	LOS ANGELES, CA 90036
ASYLEY, RICK	SINGER-SONGWRITER	4-7 THE VINEYARD SANCTUARY	LONDON SE1 1QL ENGLAND
ATCHAFALAYA	C & W GROUP	POST OFFICE BOX 91001	LAFAYETTE, LA 70501
ATHA, STEVE	COSTUME DESIGNER	344 W 38TH ST	NEW YORK, NY 10018
ATHERTON, DAVID	CONDUCTOR	SHAW CONCERTS, 1995 BROADWAY	NEW YORK, NY 10023
ATHERTON, WILLIAM	ACTOR	1527 VETERAN AVE #4	LOS ANGELES, CA 90024
ATKIN, HILLARY C	WRITER	1227 10TH ST #3	SANTA MONICA, CA 90401
ATKINS	ROCK & ROLL GROUP	9454 WILSHIRE BLVD #309	BEVERLY HILLS, CA 90212
ATKINS, CHESTER G	U S CONGRESSMAN	134 MIDDLE ST #320	LOWELL, MA 01852
ATKINS, CHET	GUITARIST	FRED KEWLEY, 1711 18TH AVE S	NASHVILLE, TN 37212
ATKINS, CHRISTOPHER	ACTOR	3751 SUNSWEPT DR	STUDIO CITY, CA 91604
ATKINS, DAVE	FOOTBALL COACH	EAGLES, BROAD ST & PATTISON AVE	PHILADELPHIA, PA 19148
ATKINS, DAVE	SINGER	9271 S WAYNE RD	ROMULUS, MI 48174
ATKINS, DOUG	FOOTBALL	5312 E SUNSET RD	KNOXVILLE, TN 37914
ATKINS, EILEEN	ACTRESS	HEATH, PARAMOUNT HOUSE	
		162-170 WARDOUR ST	LONDON W1V 3AT ENGLAND
ATKINS, GENE	FOOTBALL	SAINTS, 1500 POYDRAS ST	NEW ORLEANS, LA 90112
ATKINS, HANNAH	SECRETARY OF STATE	STATE CAPITOL BUILDING	OKLAHOMA CITY, OK 73105
ATKINS, IRVIN S	TV DIRECTOR	1450 SUNSET PLAZA DR	LOS ANGELES, CA 90069
ATKINS, TOM	ACTOR	9301 WILSHIRE BLVD #312	BEVERLY HILLS, CA 90210
ATKINSON, BEVERLY HOPE	ACTRESS	132 S LASKY DR #B	BEVERLY HILLS, CA 90212
ATKINSON, BUTLER M	WRITER	12659 MOORPARK ST #9	STUDIO CITY, CA 91604
ATKINSON, ROWAN	ACTOR-COMEDIAN	PBJ, 47 DEAN ST	LONDON W1V 5HL ENGLAND
ATKINSON, TERRY	TV CRITIC	LA TIMES, TIMES MIRROR SQ	LOS ANGELES, CA 90053
ATLANTA	VOCAL GROUP	3198 ROYAL LN #204	DALLAS, TX 75229
ATLANTA RHYTHM SECTION	ROCK & ROLL GROUP	MARS, 168 ORCHID DR	PEARL RIVER, NY 10965
ATLANTIC STARR	RHYTHM & BLUES GROUP	4150 RIVERSIDE DR #207	BURBANK, CA 91505
ATLANTICS, THE	VOCAL GROUP	F MUNAO, 113 W 70TH ST	NEW YORK, NY 10023
ATLAS, JACOBA	WRITER	124 S SYRACUSE AVE	LOS ANGELES, CA 90036
ATLAS, TONY	WRESTLER	POST OFFICE BOX 3859	STAMFORD, CT 06905
ATOMIX, THE	ROCK & ROLL GROUP	POST OFFICE BOX 1600	HAVERHILL, MA 01831
ATTARD, TONY	WRITER-PRODUCER	STEEL, 110 GLOUCESTER AVE	LONDON NW1 8JL ENGLAND
ATTAWAY, JERRY	FOOTBALL COACH	S F 49ERS, 4949 CENTENNIAL BL	SANTA CLARA, CA 95054
ATTAWAY, RUTH	ACTRESS	400 W 43RD ST	NEW YORK, NY 10036
ATTEBURY, CLARK M	TV DIRECTOR	19968 LANCASTER	HARPER WOODS, MI 48225
ATTENBOROUGH, DAVID	TV PRODUCER	BBC-TV, 56 WOOD LN	LONDON W12 7RJ ENGLAND
ATTENBOROUGH, SIR RICHARD	ACT-WRI-PROD	OLD FRIARS RICHMOND GREEN	SURREY ENGLAND
ATTERBURY, MALCOLM	ACTOR	605 N CAMDEN DR	BEVERLY HILLS, CA 90210
ATTERBURY, MALCOLM, JR	DIRECTOR	3446 CRANE CT	CLAREMONT, CA 91711
ATTIE, PAULETTE	ACTRESS-SINGER	159 W 53RD ST #18-G	NEW YORK, NY 10019
ATTILA	ROCK & ROLL GROUP	POST OFFICE BOX 5205	BABYLON, NY 11707
ATTLES, AL	BASKETBALL-EXECUTIVE	GOLDEN STATE WARRIORS	
		OAKLAND COLISEUM ARENA	
		NIMITZ FWY & HEGENBERGER RD	OAKLAND, CA 94621
ATTREE, MICHAEL	FILM DIRECTOR	11 MOUNT VIEW RD, ISLINGTON	LONDON N4 ENGLAND
ATTWOOD, JANET DUPONT	ACTRESS	111 W 70TH ST #3-F	NEW YORK, NY 10023
ATWATER, STEVE	FOOTBALL	BRONCOS, 13655 BRONCOS PKWY	ENGLEWOOD, CO 80112
ATWOOD, COLLEEN C	COSTUME DESIGNER	9255 SUNSET BLVD #505	LOS ANGELES, CA 90069
ATWOOD, DAVID	FILM DIRECTOR	SEIFERT, 18 LADBROKE TERR	LONDON W11 3PG ENGLAND
AUBER, BRIGITTE	ACTRESS	56 RUE G MOCQUET	75917 PARIS FRANCE
AUBERJONOIS, RENE	ACTOR	448 S ARDEN BLVD	LOS ANGELES, CA 90020
AUBREY, JAMES T	PRODUCER	16161 VENTURA BLVD #402	ENCINO, CA 91436
AUBREY, SKYE	ACTRESS	1730 N FAIRFAX AVE	LOS ANGELES, CA 90046
AUBUCHON, JACQUES	ACTOR	20978 RIOS ST	WOODLAND HILLS, CA 91364

AUCOIN, DEREK	BASEBALL	POST OFFICE BOX 6748	ROCKFORD, IL	61125
AUCOIN, LES	U S CONGRESSMAN	860 MONTGOMERY PARK		
		2710 VAUGHN ST, NW	PORTLAND, OR	97210
AUCOIN, WILLIAM	DIRECTOR	645 MADISON AVE	NEW YORK, NY	10022
AUDD, RICHARD M	COMPOSER-CONDUCTOR	17400 BURBANK BLVD #206	ENCINO, CA	91316
AUDE, RICH	BASEBALL	POST OFFICE BOX 842	SALEM, VA	24153
AUDIARD, MICHEL	WRITER	ARTMEDIA, 10 AVE GEORGE V	PARIS 75008	FRANCE
AUDIO II	RAP DUO-RAPWRITERS	FAA, 1700 BROADWAY, 5TH FLOOR	NEW YORK, NY	10019
AUDLEY, JIM	BASEBALL	POST OFFICE BOX 3169	FREDERICK, MD	21701
AUDLEY, JOYCE	ACTRESS	7-62 POINT CRESCENT	WHITESTONE, NY	11357
AUDLEY, MAXINE	ACTRESS	EVANS, 221 NEW KINGS RD	LONDON SW6 4XE	ENGLAND
AUDLEY, NANCY	TV WRITER	19761 INSPIRATION TR #2	TOPANGA, CA	90290
AUDRA	VOCAL DUO	TWM, 641 LEXINGTON AVE	NEW YORK, NY	10022
AUER, MILES BOHM	TALENT AGENT	8162 MANITOBA ST #119	PLAYA DEL REY, CA	90291
AUERBACH, ARNOLD "RED"	BASKETBALL EXECUTIVE	151 MERRIMAC ST	BOSTON, MA	02114
AUERBACH, DAVID	TV DIRECTOR	8636 LOOKOUT MOUNTAIN AVE	LOS ANGELES, CA	90046
AUERBACH, GERALD	DIRECTOR	23 MAPLE LN	ESSEX FALLS, NJ	07021
AUERBACH, JANE	TV WRITER-EXECUTIVE	10272 DUNLEER DR	LOS ANGELES, CA	90064
AUERBACH, LARRY	DIRECTOR	32 COUNTRY RD	MAMARONECK, NY	10543
AUERBACH, NORBERT	FILM EXECUTIVE	729 7TH AVE	NEW YORK, NY	10019
AUERBACH, RICHARD	DIRECTOR-PRODUCER	105 SHERMAN AVE W	WHITE PLAINS, NY	10607
AUFZIEN, ALAN L	BASKETBALL EXECUTIVE	N J NETS, MEADOWLANDS ARENA	EAST RUTHERFORD, NJ	07073
AUGER, CLAUDINE	ACTRESS	151 S EL CAMINO DR	BEVERLY HILLS, CA	90212
AUGUST	ROCK & ROLL GROUP	CARURSO, 6 IMPERIAL RD	WORCHESTER, MA	01604
AUGUST, DON	BASEBALL	BREWERS, 201 S 46TH ST	MILWAUKEE, WI	53214
AUGUST, SAM	BASEBALL	POST OFFICE BOX 4209	JACKSON, MS	39296
AUGUSTAIN, IRA	ACTOR	3900 RAMBOZ DR	LOS ANGELES, CA	90063
AULETTA, ROBERT	CONDUCTOR	3844 VALLEYBRINK RD	LOS ANGELES, CA	90039
AULISI, JOSEPH G	COSTUME DESIGNER	802 LEXINGTON AVE	NEW YORK, NY	10021
AULT, DOUG	BASEBALL-MANAGER	POST OFFICE BOX 1110	MYRTLE BEACH, SC	29578
AUMONT, JEAN-PIERRE	ACTOR	27 RUE DE RICHELIEU	75001 PARIS	FRANCE
AURANDT, RICHARD D	COMPOSER-CONDUCTOR	10406 MAGNOLIA BLVD	NORTH HOLLYWOOD, CA	91601
AUREL, JEAN	WRITER	40 RUE LAURISTON	F-75116 PARIS	FRANCE
AUSANIO, JOE	BASEBALL	POST OFFICE BOX 450	BUFFALO, NY	14205
AUSMUS, BRAD	BASEBALL	ALBANY YANKEES, HERITAGE PARK	ALBANY, NY	12211
AUSTIN, COREY	BASEBALL	POST OFFICE BOX 4218	SOUTH BEND, IN	46634
AUSTIN, DARLENE	SINGER	607 ELBA DR	GOODLETTSVILLE, TN	37072
AUSTIN, DAVE	BASEBALL EXECUTIVE	POST OFFICE BOX 661	KENOSHA, WI	53141
AUSTIN, DAVID ARTHUR	ACTOR	8721 SANTA MONICA BLVD #21	WEST HOLLYWOOD, CA	90069
AUSTIN, GERALD	FOOTBALL REFEREE	NFL, 410 PARK AVE	NEW YORK, NY	10022
AUSTIN, JAMES	BASEBALL	2850 W 20TH AVE	DENVER, CO	80211
AUSTIN, JIM	BASEBALL (OUTFIELD)	POST OFFICE BOX 3566	WEST PALM BEACH, FL	33402
AUSTIN, JIM	BASEBALL (PITCHER)	BREWERS, 201 S 46TH ST	MILWAUKEE, WI	53214
AUSTIN, JULIE	ACTRESS	WHITAKER, 12725 VENTURA BLVD	STUDIO CITY, CA	91604
AUSTIN, KAREN	ACTRESS	3356 ROWENA AVE #3	LOS ANGELES, CA	90027
AUSTIN, LEE	CUSTUME DESIGNER	56 W 66TH ST	NEW YORK, NY	10023
AUSTIN, MICHAEL	SCREENWRITER	ICM, 8899 BEVERLY BLVD	LOS ANGELES, CA	90048
AUSTIN, PATTI	SINGER	641 5TH AVE	NEW YORK, NY	10022
AUSTIN, RAY	COMPOSER-CONDUCTOR	1545 GLENOVER DR	PASADENA, CA	91105
AUSTIN, RAY	TV DIRECTOR	8855 HOLLYWOOD BLVD	LOS ANGELES, CA	90068
AUSTIN, RAY	TV WRI-DIR-PROD	190 S CANON DR #201	BEVERLY HILLS, CA	90210
AUSTIN, RICHARD H	SECRETARY OF STATE	STATE CAPITOL BUILDING	LANSING, MI	48953
AUSTIN, RONALD	WRITER-PRODUCER	CAA, 9830 WILSHIRE BLVD	BEVERLY HILLS, CA	90212
AUSTIN, TERI	ACTRESS	4525 LAUREL GROVE AVE	STUDIO CITY, CA	91604
AUTANT-LARA, CLAUDE	DIRECTOR	66 RUE LEPIC	PARIS 75018	FRANCE
AUTOGRAPH	ROCK & ROLL GROUP	FAA, 1700 BROADWAY, 5TH FLOOR	NEW YORK, NY	10019
AUTRY, ALAN	ACTOR	1930 CENTURY PARK W #403	LOS ANGELES, CA	90067
AUTRY, GENE	ACT-SING-BB EXEC	POST OFFICE BOX 710	LOS ANGELES, CA	90078
AUTRY, JACKIE	BASEBALL EXECUTIVE	POST OFFICE BOX 2000	ANAHEIM, CA	92803
AUTUORI, EMILE	ACTOR	15455 GLENOAKS BLVD #441	SYLMAR, CA	91342
AUTY, CHRIS	FILM DISTRIBUTOR	OASIS, 66-68 MARGARET ST	LONDON W1N 7FL	ENGLAND
AVAKIAN, ARAM	DIRECTOR	151 S EL CAMINO DR	BEVERLY HILLS, CA	90212
AVALON, FRANKIE	ACTOR-SINGER	6311 DE SOTO AVE #1	WOODLAND HILLS, CA	91367
AVALON, FRANKIE, JR	DRUMMER	6311 DE SOTO AVE #1	WOODLAND HILLS, CA	91367
AVALON, TONY	GUITARIST	6311 DE SOTO AVE #1	WOODLAND HILLS, CA	91367
AVALOS, LUIS	ACTOR	9744 WILSHIRE BLVD #308	BEVERLY HILLS, CA	90212
AVAN EMAN, CHIP	ACTOR	6430 SUNSET BLVD #701	LOS ANGELES, CA	90069
AVANT, CLARENCE	TALENT AGENT	3850 WILSHIRE BLVD #1820	LOS ANGELES, CA	90011
AVEDIS, HOWARD "HIKMET"	WRITER-DIRECTOR	13521 RAND DR	SHERMAN OAKS, CA	91423
AVEDON, DOE	ACTRESS	4333 HAYVENHURST AVE	ENCINO, CA	91436
AVEDON, RICHARD	PHOTOGRAPHER	407 E 75TH ST	NEW YORK, NY	10021
AVERAGE WHITE BAND, THE	ROCK & ROLL GROUP	BLAU, 6 SLEATOR DR	OSSINING, NY	10562
AVERBACK, HY	FILM-TV DIRECTOR	1015 N KINGS RD #402	LOS ANGELES, CA	90069
AVERSA, JOE	BASEBALL	POST OFFICE BOX 12557	ST PETERSBURG, FL	33733
AVERY, BRIAN	ACTOR	3800 BARHAM BLVD #303	LOS ANGELES, CA	90068
AVERY, JAMES	ACTOR	9200 SUNSET BLVD #625	LOS ANGELES, CA	90069
AVERY, MARGARET	ACTRESS	POST OFFICE BOX 3493	HOLLYWOOD, CA	90078
AVERY, SID	DIRECTOR	3875 BEVERLY RIDGE DR	SHERMAN OAKS, CA	91423
AVERY, STEVE	BASEBALL	POST OFFICE BOX 4064	ATLANTA, GA	30302
AVERY, VAL	ACTOR	84 GROVE ST #9	NEW YORK, NY	10014
AVEZZANO, JOE	FOOTBALL COACH	COWBOYS, 1 COWBOYS PARKWAY	IRVING, TX	75063
AVIAN, BOB	THEATER PRODUCER	QUAD PRODS, 890 BROADWAY	NEW YORK, NY	10003
AVILA, CHRISTINE	ACTRESS	606 N LARCHMONT BLVD #309	LOS ANGELES, CA	90004
AVILA, CYNTHIA	ACTRESS	4329 LAUREL CANYON BLVD	STUDIO CITY, CA	91604
AVILA, STEVE	BASEBALL SCOUT	INDIANS, CLEVELAND STADIUM	CLEVELAND, OH	44114

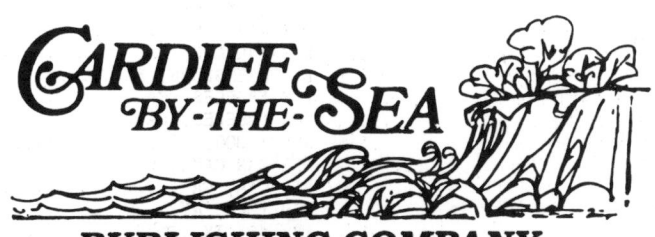

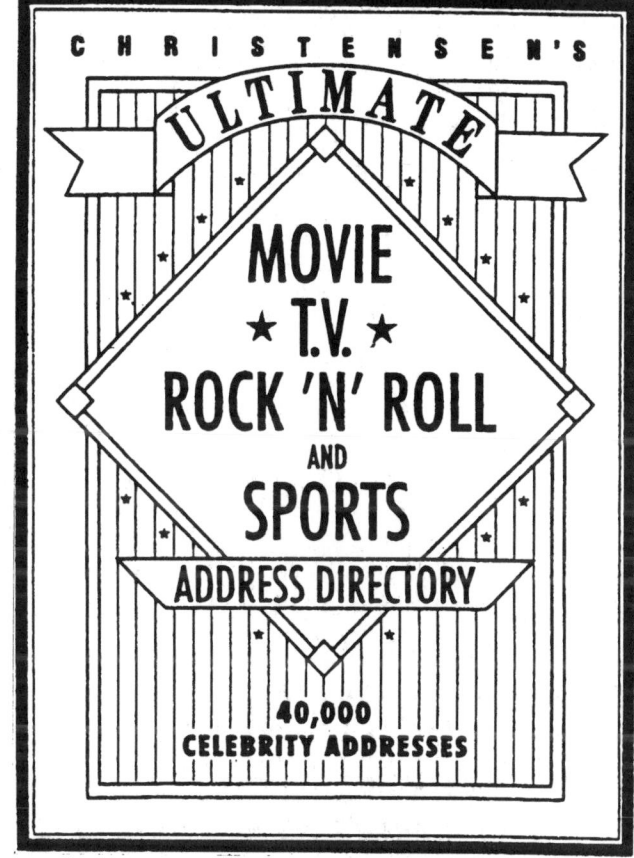

Name	Occupation	Address	City	ZIP/Country
AVILDSEN, JOHN G	FILM WRITER-DIRECTOR	45 E 89TH ST #37-A	NEW YORK, NY	10028
AVILDSEN, THOMAS K	FILM DIRECTOR	7501 TOPEKA DR	RESEDA, CA	91335
AVILDSEN, TOM	FILM DIRECTOR	9200 SUNSET BLVD #201	LOS ANGELES, CA	90069
AVILES, RAMON	BASEBALL MANAGER	POST OFFICE BOX 802	BATAVIA, NY	14021
AVION	ROCK & ROLL GROUP	POST OFFICE BOX 404	PENT HILLS NSW 2RO	AUSTRALIA
AVNET, JONATHAN	FILM-TV DIRECTOR	20911 W COLINA DR	TOPANGA CANYON, CA	90290
AVOLA, ALEXANDER A	COMPOSER-CONDUCTOR	10944 MOORPARK ST	NORTH HOLLYWOOD, CA	91602
AVRAMOV, BOGIDAR V	CONDUCTOR	321 N REXFORD DR	BEVERLY HILLS, CA	90210
AX	WRESTLER	POST OFFICE BOX 3859	STAMFORD, CT	06905
AXE	ROCK & ROLL GROUP	ATI, 888 7TH AVE, 21ST FLOOR	NEW YORK, NY	10106
AXELMAN, ARTHUR	TALENT AGENT	151 S EL CAMINO DR	BEVERLY HILLS, CA	90212
AXELROD, DAVID	COMPOSER-CONDUCTOR	5856 1/2 WOODMAN AVE	VAN NUYS, CA	91401
AXELROD, DAVID	TV WRITER	340 W 55TH ST #1-A	NEW YORK, NY	10019
AXELROD, GEORGE	PLAYWRIGHT	1840 CARLA RIDGE	BEVERLY HILLS, CA	90210
AXELROD, JONATHAN	TV EXECUTIVE-WRITER	1432 ORIOLE DR	LOS ANGELES, CA	90069
AXELROD, NINA	ACTRESS	STONE MANNERS, 9113 SUNSET BL	LOS ANGELES, CA	90069
AXELROD, ROBERT	ACTOR	11443 EMELITA ST #103	NORTH HOLLYWOOD, CA	91601
AXTON, HOYT	SINGER-SONGWRITER	POST OFFICE BOX 614	TAHOE CITY, CA	95730
AYALA, ADAN	BASEBALL	POST OFFICE BOX 20849	CHARLESTON, SC	29413
AYBAR, ANDY	ACTOR	POST OFFICE BOX 69590	LOS ANGELES, CA	90069
AYEROFF, FREDERICK	WRITER	204 S CARSON RD	BEVERLY HILLS, CA	90211
AYERS, CLIFF	SINGER-RECORD PROD	830 GLASTONBURY RD #614	NASHVILLE, TN	37217
AYERS, GERALD	SCREENWRITER	151 S EL CAMINO DR	BEVERLY HILLS, CA	90212
AYERS, THOMAS	BASEBALL EXECUTIVE	1060 W ADDISON ST	CHICAGO, IL	60613
AYKROYD, DAN	ACT-WRI-COMED	3960 LAUREL CANYON BLVD #371	STUDIO CITY, CA	91604
AYKROYD, PETER	ACTOR-WRITER	1717 N HIGHLAND AVE #414	LOS ANGELES, CA	90028
AYLESWORTH, JOHN	WRITER	10970 PALMS BLVD #6	LOS ANGELES, CA	90034
AYLWARD, ROBERT	BASEBALL EXECUTIVE	ORIOLE PARK, 333 W CAMDEN ST	BALTIMORE, MD	21201
AYMONG, KENNETH	TV PRODUCER	30 ROCKEFELLER PLAZA #1719	NEW YORK, NY	10020
AYOUB, SAM	BASEBALL TRAINER	POST OFFICE BOX 6667	RICHMOND, VA	23230
AYRAULT, BOB	BASEBALL	POST OFFICE BOX 3449	SCRANTON, PA	18505
AYRAULT, JOE	BASEBALL	POST OFFICE BOX 4525	MACON, GA	31208
AYRES, EUGENE C	WRITER	3976 MURIETTA AVE	SHERMAN OAKS, CA	91423
AYRES, GERALD	WRITER-PRODUCER	1539 MARMONT AVE	LOS ANGELES, CA	90069
AYRES, LEAH	ACTRESS	SEE - HENDRIX, LEAH AYRES		
AYRES, LENNY	BASEBALL	POST OFFICE BOX 1295	CLINTON, IA	52733
AYRES, LEW	ACTOR	675 WALTHER WY	LOS ANGELES, CA	90049
AYRES, ROSALIND	ACTRESS	WHITEHALL, 125 GLOUCESTER RD	LONDON SW7 4TE	ENGLAND
AZELTON, PHIL	CONDUCTOR	887 CHATTANOOGA AVE	PACIFIC PALISADES, CA	90272
AZEVEDO, HELEN	TV PRODUCER	ESTRADA, 1875 CENTURY PARK E	LOS ANGELES. CA	90067
AZNAVOUR, CHARLES	SINGER	19 CHEMIN DE LA RIPPAZ	CH-1223 COLOGNY	SWITZERLAND
AZOCAR, OSCAR	BASEBALL	POST OFFICE BOX 2000	SAN DIEGO, CA	92112
			UNIVERSAL CITY, CA	91608
AZZARA, CANDICE	ACTRESS	1155 N LA CIENEGA BLVD #307	LOS ANGELES, CA	90069
AZZARI, THOMAS	DIRECTOR	17847 TARZANA ST	ENCINO, CA	91316

Name	Occupation	Address	City	ZIP/Country
B, BUSY	RAPPER-RAPWRITER	SEE - BUSY B		
B, STEADY	RAPPER-RAPWRITER	SEE - STEADY B		
B & RAKIM, ERIC	RAP DUO-RAPWRITERS	SEE - ERIC B & RAKIM		
B A D	ROCK & ROLL GROUP	SEE - BIG AUDIO DYNAMITE		
B G K	ROCK & ROLL GROUP	POST OFFICE BOX 70397	AMSTERDAM 1007 KJ	HOLLAND
B O E	C & W GROUP	5625 "O" STREET BLDG #7	LINCOLN, NE	68510
B PEOPLE	ROCK & ROLL GROUP	POST OFFICE BOX 2428	EL SEGUNDO, CA	90245
B STREET BOMBERS	ROCK & ROLL GROUP	ROCKFEVER, 535 BROADWAY	LAWRENCE, MA	01841
B T EXPRESS	SOUL GROUP	DAVIS, 366 HALSEY ST	BROOKLYN, NY	11216
B T O	ROCK & ROLL GROUP	SEE - BACHMAN-TURNER OVERDRIVE		
B-52'S	ROCK & ROLL GROUP	POST OFFICE BOX 506 (CSS)	NEW YORK, NY	10013
BAAB, MIKE	FOOTBALL	BROWNS, 80 1ST ST	BEREA, OH	44017
BAAR, BRYAN	BASEBALL	POST OFFICE BOX 26267	ALBUQUERQUE, NM	87125
BAAR, TAMARA	ACTRESS	8068 LLOYD AVE	NORTH HOLLYWOOD, CA	91605
BABA, DONALD P	COMPOSER	477 W GAINSBOROUGH RD #106	THOUSAND OAKS, CA	91360
BABBAGE, ROBERT	AUDITOR	STATE CAPITOL BUILDING	FRANKFORT, KY	40601
BABBITT, BRUCE	GOVERNOR	1700 W WASHINGTON	PHOENIX, AZ	85007
BABBITT, HARRY	CONDUCTOR	7 RUE SAINT CLOUD	NEWPORT BEACH, CA	92660
BABBITT, TROY	BASEBALL	POST OFFICE BOX 5566	EUGENE, OR	97405
BABBS, DONNA	SINGER	BROTHERS, 141 DUNBAR AVE	FORDS, NJ	08863
BABCOCK, BARBARA	ACTRESS	530 W CALIFORNIA BLVD	PASADENA, CA	91105
BABCOCK, BRUCE H	COMPOSER	8404 MAMMOTH AVE	PANORAMA CITY, CA	91402
BABCOCK, EDWARD C	COMPOSER-CONDUCTOR	POST OFFICE BOX 44	BRANT LAKE, NY	12815
BABCOCK, PETE	BASKETBALL EXECUTIVE	1 CNN CENTER #405, SOUTH TOWER	ATLANTA, GA	30303
BABER, LA RUE	BASEBALL	POST OFFICE BOX 855	BELOIT, WI	53511
BABER, LARUE	BASEBALL	POST OFFICE BOX 4606	HELENA, MT	59604
BABET, PHILIP	WRITER	POST OFFICE BOX 662	BEVERLY HILLS, CA	90213
BABIC, MILOS	BASKETBALL	POST OFFICE BOX 5000	RICHFIELD, OH	44286
BABILONIA, TAI	ICE SKATER	933 21ST ST #6	SANTA MONICA, CA	90402
BABKA, NANCY	ACTRESS	215 S BARRINGTON AVE #3	LOS ANGELES, CA	90049
BABKI, BLAKE	BASEBALL	POST OFFICE BOX 338	JAMESTOWN, NY	14702

Name	Occupation	Address	City/State	Zip
BABY PEGGY	ACTRESS	MONTGOMERY, 7220 DURANGO CIR	CARLSBAD, CA	92008
BABY SANDY	ACTRESS	SANDRA LEE MAGEE		
		6846 HAYWOOD	TUJUNGA, CA	91042
BABYCH, DAVE	HOCKEY	WHALERS, 1 CIVIC CENTER PLAZA	HARTFORD, CT	06103
BACA, DAVID	COSTUME DESIGNER	13949 VENTURA BLVD #309	SHERMAN OAKS, CA	91423
BACA, DOROTHY	COSTUME DESIGNER	13949 VENTURA BLVD #309	SHERMAN OAKS, CA	91423
BACAL, DAVE	COMPOSER	7850 MORELLA AVE	NORTH HOLLYWOOD, CA	91605
BACAL, HARVEY	COMPOSER	7244 HILLSIDE AVE #309	LOS ANGELES, CA	90046
BACAL, JOE	TV PRODUCER	SUNBOW PRODS, 130 5TH AVE	NEW YORK, NY	10011
BACALL, LAUREN	ACTRESS	1 W 72ND ST #43	NEW YORK, NY	10023
BACALLA, DONNA LEE	ACTRESS	451 SAN VICENTE BLVD #9	SANTA MONICA, CA	90402
BACCHUS, JIM	U S CONGRESSMAN	854 DIXON BLVD	COCOA, FL	32922
BACH, BARBARA	ACTRESS	THE ROCCA BELLA		
		14 AVE PRINCESS GRACE	MONTE CARLO	SPAIN
BACH, CATHERINE	ACTRESS	14000 DAVANA TERR	SHERMAN OAKS, CA	91403
BACH, DANILO	SCREENWRITER	1001 GEORGIA AVE	SANTA MONICA, CA	90402
BACH, JOHNNY	BASKETBALL COACH	980 N MICHIGAN AVE #1600	CHICAGO, IL	60611
BACH, PAMELA	ACTRESS	1930 CENTURY PARK W #403	LOS ANGELES, CA	90067
BACH, STEVEN	FILM WRITER-PRODUCER	746 S ORANGE DR	LOS ANGELES, CA	90036
BACHARACH, BURT	COMPOSER-PIANIST	658 NIMES RD	LOS ANGELES, CA	90077
BACHARDY, DON	WRITER	145 ADELAIDE DR	SANTA MONICA, CA	90402
BACHMAN, MARK	ART DIRECTOR	MESSMORE & DAMON, 530 W 28TH ST	NEW YORK, NY	10001
BACHMANN, CONRAD	ACTOR	8230 SUNSET BLVD #23	LOS ANGELES, CA	90048
BACHMANN, LAWRENCE P	WRITER	9224 ALCOTT ST	LOS ANGELES, CA	90035
BACHNER, ANNETTE	DIRECTOR	360 1ST AVE	NEW YORK, NY	10010
BACK MOUNTAIN STRING BAND	C & W GROUP	POST OFFICE BOX 3124	LINDEN, NJ	07036
BACK ON TRACK	C & W GROUP	38 MUSIC SQUARE E #113	NASHVILLE, TN	37203
BACKER, BRIAN	ACTOR	9200 SUNSET BLVD #625	LOS ANGELES, CA	90069
BACKLIN, HELEN	ACTRESS	POST OFFICE BOX 3207	REDONDO BEACH, CA	90277
BACKMAN, WALLY	BASEBALL	POST OFFICE BOX 7575	PHILADELPHIA, PA	19101
BACKUS, HENNY	ACTRESS	10914 BELLAGIO RD	LOS ANGELES, CA	90077
BACON, ANTHONY	TV DIRECTOR-PRODUCER	FIFYTBEE, CECIL ALDIN DR		
		PURLEY ON THAMES	BERKSHIRE	ENGLAND
BACON, KEVIN	ACTOR	800 W END AVE #7-A	NEW YORK, NY	10025
BACOS, GEORGE	WRITER	1332 N CITRUS AVE #1	LOS ANGELES, CA	90028
BADAT, RANDALL M	WRITER-PRODUCER	14915 WHITFIELD AVE	PACIFIC PALISADES, CA	90272
BADDON, IAN	TV PRODUCER	THE RED COTTAGE		
		EAST TYTHERLY RD		
		LOCKERLEY VILLAGE, NR RAMSEY	HANTS SO51 OLW	ENGLAND
BADEL, SARAH	ACTRESS	PLUNKETT, 4 OVINGTON GARDENS	LONDON SW3 1LS	ENGLAND
BADHAM, JOHN	FILM DIRECTOR	100 UNIVERSAL CITY PLAZA		
		BUILDING 507, RM #3-E	UNIVERSAL CITY, CA	91608
BADIYI, REZA	TV DIRECTOR	3300 WONDER VIEW DR	LOS ANGELES, CA	90068
BADLER, JANE	ACTRESS	10000 SANTA MONICA BLVD #305	LOS ANGELES, CA	90067
BADLWIN, RONALD	ART DIRECTOR	475 RUCKMAN RD	CLOSTER, NJ	07624
BADOREK, MIKE	BASEBALL	80 OTTAWA ST N	HAMILTON, ONT L8H 3Z1	CANADA
BADOREK, MIKE	BASEBALL	POST OFFICE BOX 3004	SPRINGFIELD, IL	62708
BAER, ART	WRITER-PRODUCER	2225 MALAGA RD	LOS ANGELES, CA	90068
BAER, DONALD	DIRECTOR	520 N ARDEN DR	BEVERLY HILLS, CA	9021
BAER, MAX, JR	ACTOR-DIRECTOR	10433 WILSHIRE BLVD #103	LOS ANGELES, CA	90024
BAER, MERIDITH	ACTRESS-WRITER	124 S HARPER AVE	LOS ANGELES, CA	90048
BAER, NEAL	TV WRITER	151 S EL CAMINO DR	BEVERLY HILLS, CA	90212
BAER, PARLEY	ACTOR	4967 BILMOOR AVE	TARZANA, CA	91356
BAER, RANDY CRAIG	WRITER	2604 BERKELEY AVE	LOS ANGELES, CA	90026
BAER, RICHARD	TV WRITER	812 N LINDEN DR	BEVERLY HILLS, CA	90210
BAERE, GEOFFREY C	SCREENWRITER	3000 W OLYMPIC BLVD #138	SANTA MONICA, CA	90404
BAERGA, CARLOS	BASEBALL	INDIANS, CLEVELAND STADIUM	CLEVELAND, OH	44114
BAERWALD, SUSAN	TV DIRECTOR	132 S ANITA AVE	LOS ANGELES, CA	90049
BAERWITZ, JERRY	FILM DIRECTOR	13700 TAHITI WY #351	MARINA DEL REY, CA	90292
BAETZ, PAUL	FOOTBALL REFEREE	NFL, 410 PARK AVE	NEW YORK, NY	10022
BAEZ, DIOGENES	BASEBALL	RED SOX, CHAIN O'LAKES PARK	WINTER HAVEN, FL	33880
BAEZ, FRANCISCO	BASEBALL	POST OFFICE BOX 464	APPLETON, WI	54912
BAEZ, JOAN	SINGER	POST OFFICE BOX 1026	MENLO PARK, CA	94025
BAEZ, KEVIN	BASEBALL	POST OFFICE BOX 1211	NORFOLK, VA	23502
BAFFICO, JAMES A	DIRECTOR	216 MIDLAND AVE	MONTCLAIR, NJ	07042
BAGDASARIAN, CAROL	ACTRESS	627 11TH ST	SANTA MONICA, CA	90402
BAGDASARIAN, ROSS	ACTOR	627 11TH ST	SANTA MONICA, CA	90402
BAGEN, THOMAS GEORGE	WRITER	537 S GRAMERCY PL #12	LOS ANGELES, CA	90020
BAGGETTA, VINCENT	ACTOR	3928 MADELIA AVE	SHERMAN OAKS, CA	91403
BAGGISH, JOY	ACTRESS	7742 LANKERSHIM BLVD #43	NORTH HOLLYWOOD, CA	91605
BAGGOTT, DAVE	BASEBALL EXECUTIVE	1325 S MAIN #229	SALT LAKE CITY, UT	84115
BAGLEY, JOHN	BASKETBALL	151 MERRIMAC ST	BOSTON, MA	02114
BAGNI-DUBOV, GWEN	SCREENWRITER	16272 VIA EMBELESO	SAN DIEGO, CA	92128
BAGWELL, GILLIAN	ACTRESS	12001 VENTURA BLVD #335	STUDIO CITY, CA	91604
BAGWELL, JEFF	BASEBALL	POST OFFICE BOX 288	HOUSTON, TX	77001
BAGWELL, MARCUS ALLEN	WRESTLER	POST OFFICE BOX 105366	ATLANTA, GA	31348
BAHR, FAX	TV WRITER	UTA, 9560 WILSHIRE BL, 5TH FL	BEVERLY HILLS, CA	90212
BAHR, MATT	FOOTBALL	N Y GIANTS, GIANTS STADIUM	EAST RUTHERFORD, NJ	07073
BAILES, DONNIE LEE	SINGER	301 W RIDGE RD	ROCHESTER, NY	14615
BAILES, SCOTT	BASEBALL	POST OFFICE BOX 2000	ANAHEIM, CA	92803
BAILEY, ALLEN	TV PRODUCER	400 E 77TH ST #8-A	NEW YORK, NY	10021
BAILEY, ANNE HOWARD	TV WRITER	8955 BEVERLY BLVD	WEST HOLLYWOOD, CA	90048
BAILEY, BUDDY	BASEBALL MANAGER	POST OFFICE BOX 10213	LYNCHBURG, VA	24506
BAILEY, CARLTON	FOOTBALL	BILLS, 1 BILLS DR	ORCHARD PARK, NJ	14127

BAILEY, CORY	BASEBALL	POST OFFICE BOX 10213	LYNCHBURG, VA	24506
BAILEY, DENNIS	ACTOR	1650 BROADWAY #1005	NEW YORK, NY	10019
BAILEY, DEREK	TV DIRECTOR	HANCOCK, GREENER HOUSE		
		66-68 HAYMARKET	LONDON SW1Y 4AW	ENGLAND
BAILEY, EDWIN	FOOTBALL	SEAHAWKS, 11220 NE 53RD ST	KIRKLAND, WA	98033
BAILEY, F LEE	ATTORNEY	66 LONG WHARF	BOSTON, MA	02110
BAILEY, G W	ACTOR	4972 CALVIN AVE	TARZANA, CA	91356
BAILEY, JEREMY	ACTOR	8075 W 3RD ST #303	LOS ANGELES, CA	90048
BAILEY, JIM	ACTOR-SINGER	1326 N FAIRFAX AVE	LOS ANGELES, CA	90046
BAILEY, JIM	FOOTBALL EXECUTIVE	BROWNS, 80 1ST ST	BEREA, OH	44017
BAILEY, JOEL	ACTOR	6550 MURIETTA AVE	VAN NUYS, CA	91401
BAILEY, JOHN	ACTOR (AMERICAN)	UTA, 9560 WILSHIRE BL, 5TH FL	BEVERLY HILLS, CA	90212
BAILEY, JOHNNY	FOOTBALL	BEARS, 250 N WASHINGTON RD	LAKE FOREST, IL	60045
BAILEY, KATHLEEN	ACTRESS	6310 SAN VICENTE BLVD #407	LOS ANGELES, CA	90048
BAILEY, LARRIE	TREASURER	STATE CAPITOL BUILDING	CHARLESTON, WV	25305
BAILEY, LARRY D	COMPOSER	2223 S 10TH ST	KANSAS CITY, KS	66103
BAILEY, MARK	BASEBALL	5999 E VAN BUREN ST	PHOENIX, AZ	85008
BAILEY, MARVIN LLOYD	DIRECTOR	110 W ILLINOIS ST	CHICAGO, IL	60610
BAILEY, RAZZY	SINGER-SONGWRITER	HATLEY, 520 GEORGETOWN DR	CASSELBERRY, FL	32707
BAILEY, ROB	BASEBALL	POST OFFICE BOX 842	SALEM, VA	24153
BAILEY, ROBIN	ACTOR	WHITEHALL, 125 GLOUCESTER RD	LONDON SW7 4TE	ENGLAND
BAILEY, ROY	BASEBALL	POST OFFICE BOX 3783	SAVANNAH, GA	31414
BAILEY, TERRY & SOUTHERN TRADIT	C & W GROUP	POST OFFICE BOX 4096	TALLAHASSEE, FL	32315
BAILEY, THURL	BASKETBALL	5 TRIAD CENTER #500	SALT LAKE CITY, UT	84180
BAILEY, WENDELL	TREASURER	POST OFFICE BOX 720	JEFFERSON CITY, MO	65102
BAILEY SINGERS & BAND, THE	C & W GROUP	POST OFFICE BOX 6398	CHARLESTON, WV	25302
BAILEY-GATES, CHARLES	ACTOR	CED, 261 S ROBERTSON BLVD	BEVERLY HILLS, CA	90211
BAILLIE & THE BOYS	C & W DUO	MORESS, 1209 16TH AVE S	NASHVILLE, TN	37212
BAILOR, BOB	BASEBALL-MANAGER	15221 TRICIA LN	LA MIRADA, CA	90638
BAIM, HAROLD	WRITER-PRODUCER	12 TUDOR CLOSE, BELSIZE AVE	LONDON NW3 4AB	ENGLAND
BAIN, BARBARA	ACTRESS	23717 LONG VALLEY RD	CALABASAS, CA	91302
BAIN, CONRAD	ACTOR	1230 CHICKORY LN	LOS ANGELES, CA	90049
BAINES, HAROLD	BASEBALL	ATHLETICS'S, OAKLAND COLISEUM	OAKLAND, CA	94621
BAIO, JIMMY	ACTOR	9229 SUNSET BLVD #311	LOS ANGELES, CA	90069
BAIO, SCOTT	ACTOR	11662 DUQUE DR	STUDIO CITY, CA	91604
BAIR, DOUG	BASEBALL	6401 PHEASANT RD	LOVELAND, OH	45140
BAIRD, ALLARD	BASEBALL SCOUT	POST OFFICE BOX 419969	KANSAS CITY, MO	64141
BAIRD, BUTCH	GOLFER	PGA SENIORS, 112 T P C BLVD	PONTE VEDRA BEACH, FL	32082
BAIRD, JEANNE	ACTRESS	3349 W CAHUENGA BLVD #2-B	LOS ANGELES, CA	90068
BAIRD, MIKE L	COMPOSER	2734 MORNINGSIDE ST	PASADENA, CA	91107
BAIRD, ROY	FILM PRODUCER	TRINIFOLD LTD, 48 HARLEY HOUSE		
		MARYLEBOME RD	LONDON NW1 5HL	ENGLAND
BAIRD, STEPHEN	SINGER	276 CAMBRIDGE ST #4	BOSTON, MA	02134
BAIRD, STUART	FILM EDITOR	ACE, 1041 N FORMOSA AVE	WEST HOLLYWOOD, CA	90046
BAIRSTOW, SCOTT	ACTOR	808 GRETNA GREEN WY #7	LOS ANGELES, CA	90049
BAIZER, GAYLE SUSAN	COSTUME DESIGNER	654 PIER AVE #A	SANTA MONICA, CA	90405
BAKALYAN, RICHARD	ACTOR-WRITER	1070 S BEDFORD ST	LOS ANGELES, CA	90035
BAKAY, NICK	ACTOR	301 N CANON DR #305	BEVERLY HILLS, CA	90210
BAKER, ADAM	SINGER	POST OFFICE BOX 627	EDMOND, OK	73083
BAKER, ALAN	TV PRODUCER	344 S LAS PLAMAS AVE	LOS ANGELES, CA	90020
BAKER, ALAN H	DIRECTOR	431 PENN VALLEY RD	NARBERTH, PA	19072
BAKER, ANDY	BASEBALL	POST OFFICE BOX 1886	COLUMBUS, GA	31902
BAKER, ANITA	SINGER-SONGWRITER	BNB ASSOC, 804 N CRESCENT DR	BEVERLY HILLS, CA	90210
BAKER, BENNY	ACTOR	5004 CANOGA AVE	WOODLAND HILLS, CA	91364
BAKER, BILL	BASEBALL SCOUT	REDS, 100 RIVERFRONT STADIUM	CINCINNATI, OH	45202
BAKER, BLANCHE	ACTRESS	70 FLOWER AVE	HASTINGS-ON-HUDSON, NY	10706
BAKER, BOB	FOOTBALL REFEREE	NFL, 410 PARK AVE	NEW YORK, NY	10022
BAKER, BUDDY	COMPOSER-CONDUCTOR	3200 W LA ROTONDA #110	PALOS VERDES, CA	90274
BAKER, BUTCH	SINGER-GUITARIST	QUINN, 2948 FRANKLIN	NASHVILLE, TN	37204
BAKER, CARROLL	ACTRESS	420 MADISON AVE #1400	NEW YORK, NY	10017
BAKER, CARROLL	SINGER	9940 LOUGHEED HWY #330	BURNABY, BC V3J 1N3	CANADA
BAKER, CHRISTOPHER	ACTOR	8075 W 3RD ST #550	LOS ANGELES, CA	90048
BAKER, CLAY & TEXAS HONKY TONK	C & W GROUP	POST OFFICE BOX 448	NEW BRAUNFELS, TX	78130
BAKER, DANNY	TV WRITER	GAY, 24 DENMARK ST	LONDON WC2H 8HJ	ENGLAND
BAKER, DARRELL	ACTOR	A/A/A, 8457 MELROSE PL #200	LOS ANGELES, CA	90069
BAKER, DEBORAH	TV WRITER	555 W 57TH ST #1230	NEW YORK, NY	10019
BAKER, DIANE	ACTRESS-DIRECTOR	10351 SANTA MONICA BLVD #211	LOS ANGELES, CA	90025
BAKER, DOREEN	TV PRODUCER	TRANSWORLD INT'L, 22 E 71ST ST	NEW YORK, NY	10021
BAKER, DOUG	BASEBALL	POST OFFICE BOX 27045	TUCSON, AZ	85726
BAKER, DUSTY	BASEBALL-COACH	S F GIANTS, CANDLESTICK PARK	SAN FRANICSCO, CA	94124
BAKER, ERNIE	BASEBALL	POST OFFICE BOX 12557	ST PETERSBURG, FL	33733
BAKER, FLOYD	BASEBALL SCOUT	TWINS, 501 CHICAGO AVE S	MINNEAPOLIS, MN	55415
BAKER, GENE	BASEBALL-SCOUT	POST OFFICE BOX 7000	PITTSBURGH, PA	15212
BAKER, GEORGE	ACTOR	ICM, 388-396 OXFORD ST	LONDON W1	ENGLAND
BAKER, GEORGI	SINGER	POST OFFICE BOX 211	EAST PRAIRIE, MO	63845
BAKER, HOWARD, JR	U S SENATOR	POST OFFICE BOX 8	HUNTSVILLE, TN	37756
BAKER, JACK	TV DIRECTOR	DGA, 7920 SUNSET BLVD, 6TH FL	LOS ANGELES, CA	90046
BAKER, JAMES	SECRETARY OF STATE	2201 "C" ST, NW	WASHINGTON, DC	20001
BAKER, JOE	ACTOR	12001 VENTURA PL #335	STUDIO CITY, CA	91604
BAKER, JOE DON	ACTOR	23339 HATTERAS ST	WOODLAND HILLS, CA	91367
BAKER, KAI	ACTRESS	6255 SUNSET BLVD #627	LOS ANGELES, CA	90028
BAKER, KIRSTEN	ACTRESS	21757 CASTLEWOOD DR	MALIBU, CA	90265
BAKER, KURT	DIRECTOR	DGA, 7920 SUNSET BLVD, 6TH FL	LOS ANGELES, CA	90046
BAKER, MARTIN	TV DIRECTOR-PRODUCER	77 DEAN ST	LONDON W1V 6LP	ENGLAND
BAKER, OLEDA	MODEL	OLEDA BAKER HAIR VITAMINS CO		

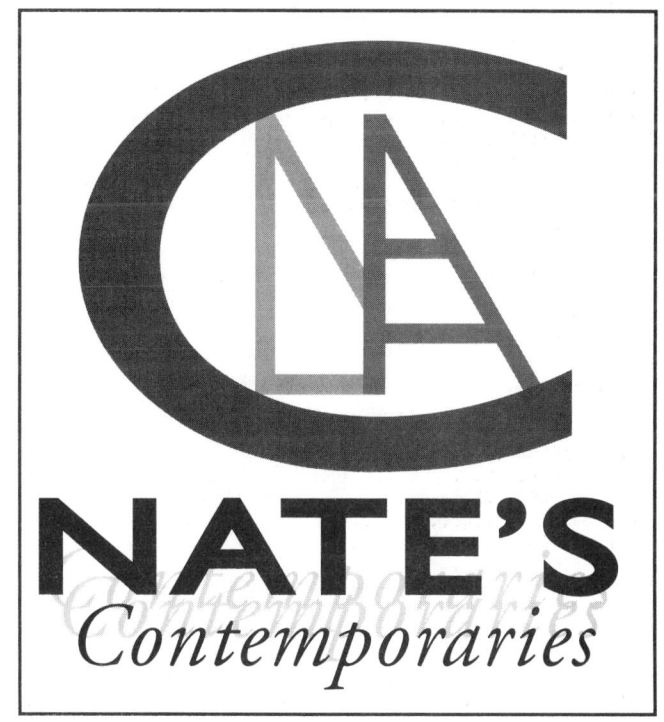

Name	Occupation	Address	City	Zip/Country
		527 3RD AVE	NEW YORK, NY	10016
BAKER, RAYMOND	ACTOR	10100 SANTA MONICA BLVD #1600	LOS ANGELES, CA	90067
BAKER, RICHARD	TV-RADIO PERS	BAGENAL, 141-143 DRURY LN	LONDON WC2B	ENGLAND
BAKER, RICHARD H	U S CONGRESSMAN	5757 CORPORATE BLVD #104	BATON ROUGE, LA	70808
BAKER, ROBERT S	TV DIRECTOR-PRODUCER	GOLDCREST FACILITIES, LTD		
		GOLDCREST ELSTREE STUDIOS		
		SHENLEY RD, BOREHAMWOOD	HERTS WD6 1JG	ENGLAND
BAKER, ROD	TV WRITER	KOHNER, 9169 SUNSET BLVD	LOS ANGELES, CA	90069
BAKER, ROY WARD	FILM DIRECTOR	WHITEHALL, 125 GLOUCESTER RD	LONDON SW7 4TE	ENGLAND
BAKER, SAM	BASEBALL	POST OFFICE BOX 1886	COLUMBUS, GA	31902
BAKER, SCOTT	BASEBALL	POST OFFICE BOX 12557	ST PETERSBURG, FL	33733
BAKER, STEPHEN	FOOTBALL	N Y GIANTS, GIANTS STADIUM	EAST RUTHERFORD, NJ	07073
BAKER, TOM	ACTOR	LONDON MGT, 235-241 REGENT ST	LONDON W1R 4PH	ENGLAND
BAKER, VIRGINIA	ACTRESS	2170 CENTURY PARK E #711	LOS ANGELES, CA	90067
BAKER, WARREN	TV DIRECTOR-EXECUTIVE	29343 FOUNTAINWOOD ST	AGOURA HILLS, CA	91301
BAKER, WARREN A	TV DIRECTOR	16731 BAHAMA ST	SEPULVEDA, CA	91343
BAKER, WILLIAM F	TV EXECUTIVE	GROUP W SATELITE, 90 PARK AVE	NEW YORK, NY	10016
BAKER-FINCH, IAN	GOLFER	POST OFFICE BOX 109601	PALM BCH GARDENS, FL	33418
BAKERMAN, SHEILA	FILM EDITOR	505 LAGUARDIA PL	NEW YORK, NY	10012
BAKEWELL, JOAN	TV HOST-PRODUCER	SUNDAY TIMES, 1 PENNINGTON ST		
		WAPPING	LONDON E1 9XN	ENGLAND
BAKEWELL, WILLIAM	ACTOR	1745 SELBY AVE #16	LOS ANGELES, CA	90024
BAKKE, BRENDA	ACTRESS	BDP, 10637 BURBANK BLVD	NORTH HOLLYWOOD, CA	91601
BAKKER, JIM	TV EVANGELIST	FEDERAL MEDICAL CENTER		
		2110 CENTER ST E	ROCHESTER, MMN	59901
BAKKER, TAMMY FAYE	TV EVANGELIST	POST OFFICE BOX 790788	ORLANDO, FL	32869
BAKSHI, RALPH	ANI-WRI-DIR	1900 AVE OF THE STARS #2270	LOS ANGELES, CA	90067
BAKST, ANN	ARTIST	OLDE FORGE E #V-7	MORRISTOWN, NJ	07960
BAKULA, SCOTT	ACTOR	131 S RODEO DR #300	BEVERLY HILLS, CA	90212
BAL, HENRY KAIMU	ACTOR	FELBER, 2126 N CAHUENGA BLVD	LOS ANGELES, CA	90068
BALABAN, BOB	ACTOR	390 W END AVE	NEW YORK, NY	10024
BALABON, RICK	BASEBALL	POST OFFICE BOX 4756	JACKSONVILLE, FL	32201
BALASH, MURIEL	TV DIRECTOR	421 W 57TH ST #3-G	NEW YORK, NY	10019
BALASKI, BELINDA	ACTRESS	1434 1/2 N CURSON AVE	LOS ANGELES, CA	90046
BALBONI, STEVE	BASEBALL	POST OFFICE BOX 75089	OKLAHOMA CITY, OK	73147
BALDAUFF, PATRIK	ACTOR	POST OFFICE BOX 69405	LOS ANGELES, CA	90069
BALDAVIN, BARBARA	ACTRESS	228 17TH ST	MANHATTAN BEACH, CA	90266
BALDEN, JAMES E	TV DIRECTOR	1879 E ALTADENA DR	ALTADENA, CA	91001
BALDERSON, DICK	BASEBALL EXECUTIVE	1060 W ADDISON ST	CHICAGO, IL	60613
BALDING, REBECCA	ACTRESS	20011 WINNETKA PL	WOODLAND HILLS, CA	91364
BALDINGER, BRIAN	FOOTBALL	POST OFFICE BOX 535000	INDIANPOLIS, IN	46253
BALDINGER, RICH	FOOTBALL	CHIEFS, 1 ARROWHEAD DR	KANSAS CITY, MO	64129
BALDWIN, ADAM	ACTOR	8882 LOOKOUT MOUNTAIN RD	LOS ANGELES, CA	90046
BALDWIN, ALEC	ACTOR	300 CENTRAL PARK W	NEW YORK, NY	10024
BALDWIN, BILL	SINGER	TALENT MASTER AGENCY		
		1019 17TH AVE S	NASHVILLE, TN	37212
BALDWIN, BILLY	ACTOR	9200 SUNSET BLVD #710	LOS ANGELES, CA	90069
BALDWIN, BONNIE	SINGER	PROCESS, 439 WILEY AVE	FRANKLIN, PA	16323
BALDWIN, BRUCE	BASEBALL EXECUTIVE	POST OFFICE BOX 6667	RICHMOND, VA	23230
BALDWIN, DANIEL	ACTOR	10 E 44TH ST #700	NEW YORK, NY	10017
BALDWIN, DAVID	TV EXECUTIVE	HBO, 1100 6TH AVE	NEW YORK, NY	10036
BALDWIN, GERALD	TV PRODUCER	HANNA-BARBERA, 3400 CAHUENGA BL	LOS ANGELES, CA	90068
BALDWIN, JAMES	BASEBALL	POST OFFICE BOX 4218	SOUTH BEND, IN	46634
BALDWIN, JAN MARIE	ACTRESS	301 N CANON DR #305	BEVERLY HILLS, CA	90210
BALDWIN, JANIT	ACTRESS	8508 BRIER DR	LOS ANGELES, CA	90046
BALDWIN, JEFF	BASEBALL (CHARLOTTE)	POST OFFICE DRAWER 1207	ZEBULON, NC	27597
BALDWIN, JEFF	BASEBALL (JACKSON)	POST OFFICE BOX 4209	JACKSON, MS	39296
BALDWIN, JIM	BASEBALL	POST OFFICE BOX 751	UTICA, NY	13503
BALDWIN, JOE	SINGER	GOOD, 2500 NW 39TH ST	OKLAHOMA CITY, OK	73112
BALDWIN, JUDY	ACTRESS	280 S BEVERLY DR #400	BEVERLY HILLS, CA	90212
BALDWIN, PETER D	FILM DIRECTOR	575 N BEVERLY BLVD	LOS ANGELES, CA	90077
BALDWIN, PETER I	SCREENWRITER	9300 WILSHIRE BLVD #410	BEVERLY HILLS, CA	90212
BALDWIN, RANDY	FOOTBALL	VIKINGS, 9520 VIKING DR	EDEN PRAIRIE, MN	55344
BALDWIN, STEPHEN	ACTOR	POST OFFICE BOX 447	CAMILLUS, NY	13031
BALENDA, CARLA	ACTRESS	15848 WOODVALE	ENCINO, CA	91416
BALENTINE, BRIAN	BASEBALL	POST OFFICE BOX 5646	PRINCETON, WV	24740
BALER, LAURA	ACTRESS	CBS-TV, "AS THE WORLD TURNS"		
		524 W 57TH ST #5330	NEW YORK, NY	10019
BALES, CYNTHIA	COSTUME DESIGNER	13949 VENTURA BLVD #309	SHERMAN OAKS, CA	91423
BALHATCHET, BOB	ACTOR	9255 SUNSET BLVD #401	WEST HOLLYWOOD, CA	90069
BALIN, INA	ACTRESS	9000 SUNSET BLVD #801	LOS ANGELES, CA	90069
BALIN, MARTY	SINGER-SONGWRITER	POST OFFICE BOX 347008	SAN FRANCISCO, CA	94134
BALIN, RICHARD	ACTOR	4959 DENNY AVE	NORTH HOLLYWOOD, CA	91601
BALIN, ROCHELLE	ACTRESS	4959 DENNY AVE	NORTH HOLLYWOOD, CA	91601
BALKAN, DAVID H	TV WRITER-PRODUCER	16815 GRESHAM ST	SEPULVEDA, CA	91343
BALL, ERIC	FOOTBALL	BENGALS, 200 RIVERFRONT STADIUM	CINCINNATI, OH	45202
BALL, JEFF	BASEBALL	POST OFFICE BOX 422229	KISSIMMEE, FL	34742
BALL, JERRY	FOOTBALL	LIONS, 1200 FEATHERSTONE RD	PONTIAC, MI	48432
BALL, JOHN	DIRECTOR	BAY CREST, HUNTINGTON	LONG ISLAND, NY	11743
BALL, JOHNNY	TV WRITER	HIGHFILED, BEACONSFIELD RD		
		FARNHAM COMMON	BUCKS	ENGLAND
BALL, LARRY D	CONDUCTOR	19008 COLBECK ST	CARSON, CA	90746
BALL, MARCIA, BAND	SINGER-PIANIST	ATS MGMT, 8306 APPALACHIAN DR	AUSTIN, TX	78759
BALL, MICHAEL	FOOTBALL	POST OFFICE BOX 535000	INDIANPOLIS, IN	46253
BALL, NICHOLAS	ACTOR	WM MORRIS, 31-32 SOHO SQ	LONDON W1V 5DG	ENGLAND

LIGHTS!
CAMERA!
ACTION!

GEORGIA TERRY AUTOGRAPHS

We work actively from your WANT lists.

840 N.E. COCHRAN AVENUE
GRESHAM, OREGON 97030

FREE CATALOG

REASONABLE PRICES

Specializing in the ENTERTAINMENT field.

FAST, FRIENDLY SERVICE

Member U.A.C.C.

Collector since 1952
Dealer since 1978

LIGHTS!
CAMERA!
ACTION!

(503) 667-0950

LIGHTS!
CAMERA!
ACTION!

BALL, RUSS	FOOTBALL COACH	CHIEFS, 1 ARROWHEAD DR	KANSAS CITY, MO	64129
BALL, SHERWOOD	WRITER-MUSICIAN	415 S HAMEL RD	LOS ANGELES, CA	90048
BALLACE, ELAINE	ACTRESS	4265 COLFAX AVE #10	STUDIO CITY, CA	91604
BALLAN, GRANT	SINGER	DUMONT, 1037 S ALAMO ST	SAN ANTONIO, TX	78210
BALLANTINE, CARL	ACTOR-COMEDIAN	10850 RIVERSIDE DR #505	NORTH HOLLYWOOD, CA	91602
BALLARD, CARROLL	FILM DIRECTOR	POST OFFICE BOX 239	CALISTOGA, CA	94515
BALLARD, CHRISTINE	TV WRITER-DIRECTOR	11501 CHANDLER BLVD	NOPRTH HOLLYWOOD, CA	91601
BALLARD, HANK & THE MIDNIGHTERS	SOUL GROUP	MAC NEIL, 11457 HARRISBURG RD	LOS ALAMITOS, CA	90720
BALLARD, HOWARD	FOOTBALL	BILLS, 1 BILLS DR	ORCHARD PARK, NJ	14127
BALLARD, JEFF	BASEBALL	POST OFFICE BOX 36407	LOUISVILLE, KY	40233
BALLARD, KAYE	ACTRESS-SINGER	1204 3RD AVE #152	NEW YORK, NY	10021
BALLARD, LAURA	ACTRESS	8665 WILSHIRE BLVD #208	BEVERLY HILLS, CA	90211
BALLARD, LUCINDA	COSTUME DESIGNER	180 W END AVE	NEW YORK, NY	10028
BALLARD, RAY	ACTOR	4601 WILLIS AVE #101	SHERMAN OAKS, CA	91403
BALLEN, RONNIE Z	ACTOR	267 LA VERNE AVE #1	LONG BEACH, CA	90803
BALLENGER, CASS	U S CONGRESSMAN	POST OFFICE BOX 1830	HICKORY, NC	28603
BALLER, JAY	BASEBALL	POST OFFICE BOX 3449	SCRANTON, PA	18505
BALLHAUS, MICHAEL	CINEMATOGRAPHER	POST OFFICE BOX 2230	HOLLYWOOD, CA	90078
BALLIE & THE BOYS	C & W GROUP	POST OFFICE BOX 2196	WARREN, NJ	37075
BALLIF, VERA	ACTRESS	3869 DEERVALE DR	SHERMAN OAKS, CA	91403
BALLOU, BILL	BASEBALL COACH	POST OFFICE BOX 751	UTICA, NY	13503
BALLUCK, DON	TV WRITER	11566 MORRISON ST	NORTH HOLLYWOOD, CA	91601
BALME, JERRY	TV PRODUCER	3374 WRIGHTWOOD PL	STUDIO CITY, CA	91604
BALOFF, PETER I	SCREENWRITER	5711 MANTON AVE	WOODLAND HILLS, CA	91367
BALSAM, MARTIN	ACTOR	HOTEL OLCOTT, 27 W 72ND ST	NEW YORK, NY	10011
BALSAM, TALIA	ACTRESS	1331 N HAYWORTH AVE #2	LOS ANGELES, CA	90046
BALSLEY, DARREN	BASEBALL COACH	POST OFFICE BOX 1110	MYRTLE BEACH, SC	29578
BALSLEY, PHILIP	SINGER	ROUTE #1, BOX 33-A	SWOOPE, VA	24479
BALTHAZAR, DOYLE	BASEBALL	TIGERS, 89 WHARNCLIFFE RD N	LONDON, ONT N6H 2A7	CANADA
BALTIMORE, DAVID	MICROBIOLOGIST	ROCKEFELLER UNIVERSITY		
		MICROBIOLOGY DEPARTMENT		
		1230 YORK AVE	NEW YORK, NY	10021
BALTZ, BOB	FOOTBALL REFEREE	NFL, 410 PARK AVE	NEW YORK, NY	10022
BALTZ, KIRK	ACTOR	11726 SAN VICENTE BLVD #300	LOS ANGELES, CA	90049
BALZER, GEORGE M	TV WRITER	6616 LANGDON AVE	VAN NUYS, CA	91406
BAMA BAND	C & W GROUP	ENTERTAINMENT ARTISTS, INC		
		819 18TH AVE S	NASHVILLE, TN	37203
BAMBERGER, GEORGE	BASEBALL	455 N BATH CLUB BLVD	NORTH REDINGTON BCH, F	33708
BAMBOO	ROCK & ROLL GROUP	41 BRITAIN ST #200	TORONTO, ONT	CANADA
BAMFORD, GEORGE	ACTOR	BRET ADAMS, 448 W 44TH ST	NEW YORK, NY	10036
BAMFORD, ROGER	TV DIRECTOR-PRODUCER	2 GORDON RD, CHISWICK	LONDON W4	ENGLAND
BANAS, ARLENE M	ACTRESS	718 N KINGS RD #306	LOS ANGELES, CA	90069
BANCELLS, RICHIE	BASEBALL TRAINER	ORIOLE PARK, 333 W CAMDEN ST	BALTIMORE, MD	21201
BANCROFT, ANNE	ACT-WRI-DIR	2301 LA MESA DR	SANTA MONICA, CA	90405
BANCROFT, BOB	ACTOR	9200 SUNSET BLVD #625	LOS ANGELES, CA	90069
BAND, ALBERT	PROD-WRI-DIR	1639 BLUE JAY WY	LOS ANGELES, CA	90069
BAND, CHARLES	FILM PRODUCER	EMPIRE, 1551 N LA BREA AVE	LOS ANGELES, CA	90028
BANDANA	C & W GROUP	POST OFFICE 121089	NASHVILLE, TN	37212
BANDAR AL-SAUND, PRINCE	PRINCE	601 NEW HAMPSHIRE AVE, NW	WASHINGTON, DC	20037
BANDIT	C & W GROUP	355 W PLEASANTVIEW AVE #204	HACKENSACK, NJ	07601
BANDIT BAND, THE	C & W GROUP	KNIGHT, 1609 CONGRESS RD	EASTOVER, SC	29044
BANDO, CHRIS	BASEBALL-MANAGER	POST OFFICE DRAWER 4797	EL PASO, TX	79914
BANDO, SAL	BASEBALL	104 W JUNIPER LN	MEQUON, WI	52092
BANDY, KARROLL M	ACTOR	POST OFFICE BOX 1106	LOS ANGELES, CA	90078
BANDY, MOE	SINGER-SONGWRITER	POST OFFICE BOX 40661	NASHVILLE, TN	37204
BANE, EDDIE	BASEBALL SCOUT	1000 ELYSIAN PARK DR	LOS ANGELES, CA	90012
BANERJEE, VICTOR	ACTOR	WM MORRIS, 31-32 SOHO SQ	LONDON W1V 5DG	ENGLAND
BANGERT, CHARLES A	DIRECTOR-PRODUCER	145 NOD RD	RIDGEFIELD, CT	06877
BANGERTER, MICHAEL	ACTOR	RIGEL, 109-A ALBERT BRIDGE RD	LONDON SW11 4PF	ENGLAND
BANGERTER, NORMAN H	GOVERNOR	STATE CAPITOL BUILDING	SALT LAKE CITY, UT	84114
BANGLES, THE	ROCK & ROLL GROUP	6363 SUNSET BLVD #716	LOS ANGELES, CA	90028
BANGSTON, PAT	BASEBALL	POST OFFICE BOX 5645	ORLANDO, FL	32855
BANISTER, JEFF	BASEBALL	POST OFFICE BOX 450	BUFFALO, NY	14205
BANK, FRANK	ACTOR	42-500 BOB HOPE DR	RANCHO MIRAGE, CA	92270
BANKHEAD, SCOTT	BASEBALL	REDS, 100 RIVERFRONT STADIUM	CINCINNATI, OH	45202
BANKLER-JUKES, STEPHEN	TV PRODUCER	30 MORLEY RD, EAST TWICKENHAM	RICHMOND TW1 2HF	ENGLAND
BANKS, CARL	FOOTBALL	N Y GIANTS, GIANTS STADIUM	EAST RUTHERFORD, NJ	07073
BANKS, CHIP	FOOTBALL	POST OFFICE BOX 535000	INDIANPOLIS, IN	46253
BANKS, DEAN	BASEBALL	1100 ALAMEDA	POCATELLO, ID	83201
BANKS, EMILY	ACTRESS	1800 N HIGHLAND AVE #405	LOS ANGELES, CA	90028
BANKS, ERNIE	BASEBALL	POST OFFICE BOX 24302	LOS ANGELES, CA	90024
BANKS, FRED	FOOTBALL	DOLPHINS, 2269 NW 199TH ST	MIAMI, FL	33056
BANKS, HEIDI	ACTRESS	132 S LASKY DR #B	BEVERLY HILLS, CA	90212
BANKS, JAN	MUSIC EXECUTIVE	BROADCAST MUSIC, 320 W 57TH ST	NEW YORK, NY	10019
BANKS, JONATHAN	ACTOR	909 EUCLID ST #8	SANTA MONICA, CA	90403
BANKS, LANCE	BASEBALL	POST OFFICE BOX 611	WATERLOO, IA	50704
BANKS, LAURA	ACTRESS	FELBER, 2126 N CAHUENGA BLVD	LOS ANGELES, CA	90068
BANKS, WILLIE	BASEBALL	POST OFFICE BOX 1659	PORTLAND, OR	97207
BANKS, WILLIE	BASEBALL	POST OFFICE BOX 1659	PORTLAND, OR	97207
BANKSTON, ARNOLD	ACTOR	1765 N HIGHLAND AVE #568	HOLLYWOOD, CA	90028
BANNEN, IAN	ACTOR	1999 AVE OF THE STARS #2850	LOS ANGELES, CA	90067
BANNER, BOB	DIRECTOR-PRODUCER	2409 BRIARCREST RD	BEVERLY HILLS, CA	90210
BANNICK, LISA A	TV WRITER	ICM, 8899 BEVERLY BLVD	LOS ANGELES, CA	90048
BANNIN, JACQUELINE	TV PRODUCER	100 W 81ST ST	NEW YORK, NY	10024
BANNISTER, ALAN	BASEBALL-COACH	5999 E VAN BUREN ST	PHOENIX, AZ	85008

Name	Occupation	Address	City	Zip/Country
BANNISTER, ALAN	BASKETBALL	5 TRIAD CENTER #500	SALT LAKE CITY, UT	84180
BANNISTER, FLOYD	BASEBALL	POST OFFICE BOX 90111	ARLINGTON, TX	76004
BANNISTER, KEN	BASKETBALL	CLIPPERS, 3939 S FIGUEROA ST	LOS ANGELES, CA	90037
BANNISTER, ROGER	TRACK & FIELD	16 EDWARDS SQUARE	LONDON W8	ENGLAND
BANNON, JACK	ACTOR	5832 NAGLE AVE	VAN NUYS, CA	91401
BANNON, R C	SINGER-SONGWRITER	713 W MAIN ST	HENDERSONVILLE, TN	37075
BANOW, JOEL	DIRECTOR	19 WELLINGTON TERR	WHITE PLAINS, NY	10607
BANSHEES, THE	ROCK & ROLL GROUP	127 ALDERSGATE ST	LONDON WC1	ENGLAND
BANT, GEORGE E	CONDUCTOR	53 OTTER COVE DR	OLD SAYBROOK, CT	06475
BANTA, GLORIA	TV WRITER-PRODUCER	1326 BENEDICT CANYON DR	BEVERLY HILLS, CA	90210
BANTON, SCOTT	BASEBALL	POST OFFICE BOX 3004	SPRINGFIELD, IL	62708
BAPTIST, TRAVIS	BASEBALL	POST OFFICE BOX 465	MED HAT, ALB T1A 7G2	CANADA
BAPTISTE, THOMAS	ACTOR-SINGER	14 KENNETH CRESCENT	LONDON NW2 4PT	ENGLAND
BAR-DAVID, MAURICE	TV DIRECTOR	14705 TUSTIN ST	SHERMAN OAKS, CA	91403
BARACH, SABINA	TV PRODUCER	34-20 32ND ST #1-A	ASTORIA, NY	11106
BARAGONE, TOMMY	ACTOR	2626 KANSAS AVE #1	SANTA MONICA, CA	90404
BARAK, ARI	ACTOR	247 S BEVERLY DR #102	BEVERLY HILLS, CA	90210
BARAKAT, KHALID	FILM PRODUCER	22 SOHO SQ	LONDON W1V 5FJ	ENGLAND
BARAN, JACK	FILM PRODUCER	9200 SUNSET BLVD #402	LOS ANGELES, CA	90069
BARASCH, NORMAN	WRITER	1438 RISING GLEN RD	LOS ANGELES, CA	90069
BARASH, JEAN E	WRITER	825 AMALFI DR	PACIFIC PALISADES, CA	90272
BARASH, OLIVIA	ACTRESS	1123 N ARDMORE AVE	LOS ANGELES, CA	90029
BARBARA, DON	BASEBALL	10233 96TH AVE	EDMONTON, ALB TK5 0A5	CANADA
BARBAROSSA, JOSCIK	ACTOR	BRITISH ACTORS EQUITY		
		8 HARLEY ST	LONDON W1	ENGLAND
BARBASH, BOB	SCREENWRITER	8955 BEVERLY BLVD	WEST HOLLYWOOD, CA	90048
BARBEAU, ADRIENNE	ACTRESS	POST OFFICE BOX 1334	NORTH HOLLYWOOD, CA	91604
BARBEE, CHARLES	CINEMATOGRAPHER	5235 WOODLUKE AVE	WOODLAND HILLS, CA	91367
BARBER, BRIAN	BASEBALL	POST OFFICE BOX 3004	SPRINGFIELD, IL	62708
BARBER, ELLEN	ACTRESS	8150 BEVERLY BLVD #201	LOS ANGELES, CA	90048
BARBER, FRANCES	ACTRESS	SHARKEY, 15 GOLDEN SQ #315	LONDON W1R 3AG	ENGLAND
BARBER, GLYNIS	ACTRESS	MARSH, 19 DENMARK ST	LONDON WC2H 8NA	ENGLAND
BARBER, JERRY	GOLFER	PGA SENIORS, 112 T P C BLVD	PONTE VEDRA BEACH, FL	32082
BARBER, MIKE	FOOTBALL	BENGALS, 200 RIVERFRONT STADIUM	CINCINNATI, OH	45202
BARBER, MILLER	GOLFER	PGA SENIORS, 112 T P C BLVD	PONTE VEDRA BEACH, FL	32082
BARBER, RED	SPORTSCASTER	3013 BROOKMONT DR	TALLAHASSEE, FL	32312
BARBER, ROWLAND	TV WRITER	2216 S BENTLEY AVE #16	LOS ANGELES, CA	90064
BARBERA, JOSEPH R	TV PROD-CARTOONIST	HANNA-BARBERA, 3400 CAHUENGA BL	HOLLYWOOD, CA	90068
BARBERIE, BRET	BASEBALL	EXPOS, 4545 DE COUBERTIN AVE	MONTREAL, QUE H1V 3P2	CANADA
BARBI, SIA & SHANE	MODELS	SECOND GLANCE, 8306 WILSHIRE BL	BEVERLY HILLS, CA	90211
BARBI, VINCENT	ACTOR	1230 COLE AVE #103	LOS ANGELES, CA	90038
BARBIER, CHRISTIAN	ACTOR	LES CHAGRANTS	VALENSOLE 04210	FRANCE
BARBIERI, ERNEST J	DIRECTOR	1777 1ST AVE	NEW YORK, NY	10028
BARBIERI, GATO	SAXOPHONIST	200 W 51ST ST #1410	NEW YORK, NY	10019
BARBOUR, JOHN	WRITER-COMEDIAN	4254 FORMAN AVE	TOLUCA LAKE, CA	91602
BARBOUR, KAREN	ARTIST	51 WARREN ST, 5TH FL	NEW YORK, NY	10007
BARBOUR, KEITH	ACTOR-SINGER	9220 SUNSET BLVD #218	LOS ANGELES, CA	90069
BARBOUR, ROSS	SINGER	17233 RAYEN ST	NORTHRIDGE, CA	91325
BARBOUR, THOMAS	ACTOR	60 PERRY ST	NEW YORK, NY	10014
BARBULEE, MADELEINE	ACTRESS	7 RUE LENTONNETT	PARIS 75009	FRANCE
BARBUTTI, PETE	COMEDIAN	3000 OCEAN PARK BLVD #2006	SANTA MONICA, CA	90405
BARCLAY, DAN	ACTOR	KROLL, 390 W END AVE	NEW YORK, NY	10024
BARCLAY, HUMPHREY	TV PRODUCER	5 ANGLER'S LN	LONDON NW5 3DG	ENGLAND
BARCLAY, RUE	SINGER	VISTONE, 6331 SANTA MONICA BLVD	HOLLYWOOD, CA	90038
BARCUS, STEPHEN J	DIRECTOR	25 DERWEN RD	BALA CYNWYD, PA	19004
BARD, MIKE	BASEBALL	POST OFFICE BOX 6603	BEND, OR	97708
BARD, ROBERT	MUSIC PROD-DIR	168 W 107TH ST #2-C	NEW YORK, NY	10025
BARDACH, ANN L	WRITER	557 WESTMOUNT DR	LOS ANGELES, CA	90048
BARDEUX	ROCK & ROLL GROUP	FAA, 1700 BROADWAY, 5TH FLOOR	NEW YORK, NY	10019
BARDHA, AGIM	GOLFER	PGA SENIORS, 112 T P C BLVD	PONTE VEDRA BEACH, FL	32082
BARDOT, BRIGITTE	ACTRESS	LA MADRIQUE	SAINT TROPEZ 83990	VAR FRANCE
BARDT, HARRY	BASEBALL EXECUTIVE	1000 ELYSIAN PARK DR	LOS ANGELES, CA	90012
BARE, BOBBY	SINGER-SONGWRITER	POST OFFICE BOX 2422	HENDERSONVILLE, TN	37077
BARETTA, PAUL	BASEBALL SCOUT	METS, 126TH ST & ROOSEVELT AVE	FLUSHING, NY	11368
BARFIELD, JESSE	BASEBALL	N Y YANKEES, YANKEE STADIUM	BRONX, NY	10451
BARFIELD, JOHN	BASEBALL	POST OFFICE BOX 90111	ARLINGTON, TX	76004
BARGAS, ROB	BASEBALL	POST OFFICE BOX 3566	WEST PALM BEACH, FL	33402
BARHYDT, FRANK	WRITER	1220 LYNDON ST	SOUTH PASADENA, CA	91030
BARIE, GAIL	ACTRESS	ALLEN, 260 S BEVERLY DR, 2ND FL	BEVERLY HILLS, CA	90212
BARISH, KEITH	FILM PRODUCER	1800 CENTURY PARK E #1100	LOS ANGELES, CA	90067
BARISH, LEORA	SCREENWRITER	151 S EL CAMINO DR	BEVERLY HILLS, CA	90212
BARK, BRIAN	BASEBALL	POST OFFICE BOX 16683	GREENVILLE, SC	29606
BARKAYS, THE	RHYTHM & BLUES GROUP	FAA, 1700 BROADWAY, 5TH FLOOR	NEW YORK, NY	10019
BARKER, BOB	TV HOST	1851 OUTPOST	LOS ANGELES, CA	90068
BARKER, BRYAN	FOOTBALL	CHIEFS, 1 ARROWHEAD DR	KANSAS CITY, MO	64129
BARKER, CURTIS	ACTOR	STAR TALENT, 1050 N MAPLE ST	BURBANK, CA	91505
BARKER, LEO	FOOTBALL	BENGALS, 200 RIVERFRONT STADIUM	CINCINNATI, OH	45202
BARKER, LYNN	TV WRITER	8955 BEVERLY BLVD	WEST HOLLYWOOD, CA	90048
BARKER, STEVE	TV WRITER	8955 BEVERLY BLVD	WEST HOLLYWOOD, CA	90048
BARKER, TIM	BASEBALL	POST OFFICE BOX 28268	SAN ANTONIO, TX	78228
BARKER, WARREN E	COMPOSER-CONDUCTOR	ROUTE #3, BOX 3503	RED BLUFF, CA	96080
BARKEY, DEAN	BASEBALL EXECUTIVE	POST OFFICE BOX 855	BELOIT, WI	53511
BARKIN, ELLEN	ACTRESS	8787 SHOREHAM DR	LOS ANGELES, CA	90069
BARKIN, HASKELL	TV WRITER	11812 LAUREL HILLS RD	STUDIO CITY, CA	91604
BARKLEY, BOYD	BASEBALL SCOUT	1000 ELYSIAN PARK DR	LOS ANGELES, CA	90012

BARKLEY, CHARLES	BASKETBALL	SUNS, 2910 N CENTRAL AVE	PHOENIX, AZ	85012
BARKLEY, ROGER J	ACTOR-WRITER	5435 BURING TREE DR	LA CANADA, CA	91011
BARKWORTH, JOHN	TALENT AGENT	11726 SAN VICENTE BLVD #300	LOS ANGELES, CA	90049
BARKWORTH, PETER	ACTOR	47 FLASK WALK	LONDON NW3	ENGLAND
BARLE, GAIL	ACTRESS	ALLEN, 260 S BEVERLY DR, 2ND FL	BEVERLY HILLS, CA	90212
BARLOW, CLEM	BASEBALL	1316 KING ST	BELLINGHAM, WA	98226
BARLOW, JACK	SINGER	ROUTE #4, BOX 101-B	CAMDEN, TN	38320
BARLOW, MICHAEL W	WRITER-PRODUCER	2237 22ND ST	SANTA MONICA, CA	90405
BARLOW, PATRICK	ACTOR-WRITER	20 ICKBURGH RD	LONDON E5 8AD	ENGLAND
BARLOW, RANDY	SINGER	5514 KELLY RD	BRENTWOOD, TN	37027
BARLOW, RICHARD H	DIRECTOR	411 E 53RD ST	NEW YORK, NY	10022
BARLOW, WILLIAM	DIRECTOR	106 KEITH RD	NEWPORT NEWS, VA	23606
BARMAK, IRA	SCREENWRITER	2711 BOWMONT DR	BEVERLY HILLS, CA	90210
BARNABA, JOSEPH	ACTOR	6919 TOBIAS AVE	VAN NUYS, CA	91405
BARNARD, DOUG, JR	U S CONGRESSMAN	POST OFFICE BOX 10123	AUGUSTA, GA	30903
BARNARD, JERRY	EVANGELIST	POST OFFICE BOX 413	SAN DIEGO, CA	92112
BARNARD, TONY	ACTOR	3345 MENTONE AVE #8	LOS ANGELES, CA	90035
BARNES, BINNIE	ACTRESS	838 N DOHENY DR #B	WEST HOLLYWOOD, CA	90069
BARNES, BRIAN	BASEBALL	1501 W 16TH ST	INDIANAPOLIS, IN	46202
BARNES, GENE	TALENT AGENT	19 W 44TH ST #705	NEW YORK, NY	10036
BARNES, JIMMY	SINGER-SONGWRITER	41 BRITAIN ST #200	TORONTO, ONT	CANADA
BARNES, JOANNA	ACTRESS-WRITER	2160 CENTURY PARK E #210-N	LOS ANGELES, CA	90067
BARNES, JOHN	TV WRITER	8955 BEVERLY BLVD	WEST HOLLYWOOD, CA	90048
BARNES, JON	BASEBALL	POST OFFICE BOX 20849	CHARLESTON, SC	29413
BARNES, LEONARD	ACTOR	6533 HOLLYWOOD BLVD #301	HOLLYWOOD, CA	90028
BARNES, MAX T	GUITARIST-SONGWRITER	448 SAUNDERS FERRY RD	HENDERSONVILLE, TN	37075
BARNES, NANI	ACTRESS	GARRETT, 6525 SUNSET BL, 5TH FL	LOS ANGELES, CA	90028
BARNES, POLITA	ACTRESS	PAT LYNN, 10525 STRATHMORE DR	LOS ANGELES, CA	90024
BARNES, PRISCILLA	ACTRESS	3500 W OLIVE AVE #1400	BURBANK, CA	91505
BARNES, RAYFORD	ACTOR	POST OFFICE BOX 566	JUNE LAKE, CA	93529
BARNES, RON	BASEBALL UMPIRE	2101 E BROADWAY #35	TEMPE, AZ	85282
BARNES, SKEETER	BASEBALL	TIGERS, TIGER STADIUM	DETROIT, MI	48216
BARNES, TOM	FOOTBALL REFEREE	NFL, 410 PARK AVE	NEW YORK, NY	10022
BARNES, WADE	ACTOR	20 BEEKMAN PL	NEW YORK, NY	10022
BARNES-HARPER, GLORIA	ACTRESS	45 E 82ND ST	NEW YORK, NY	10028
BARNET, CHARLIE	CONDUCTOR	1085 MARSHALL WY	PALM SPRINGS, CA	92262
BARNETT, BERT & COLUMBIA	RHYTHM & BLUES GROUP	BLANTON, 2638 TWO NOTCH RD	COLUMBIA, SC	29204
BARNETT, EDWARD A	DIRECTOR	60 E 9TH ST #339	NEW YORK, NY	10003
BARNETT, EILEEN	ACTRESS-SINGER	9255 SUNSET BLVD #515	LOS ANGELES, CA	90069
BARNETT, FRED	FOOTBALL	EAGLES, BROAD ST & PATTISON AVE	PHILADELPHIA, PA	19148
BARNETT, HARLON	FOOTBALL	BROWNS, 80 1ST ST	BEREA, OH	44017
BARNETT, JACK	WRITER-PRODUCER	4151 VIA MARINA #111	MARINA DEL REY, CA	90292
BARNETT, JAMES C, JR	WRITER	13446 ERWIN ST	VAN NUYS, CA	91401
BARNETT, JERRY	CARTOONIST	POST OFFICE BOX 145	INDIANAPOLIS, IN	46206
BARNETT, JOHN M	CONDUCTOR	CALLE SAN ALVARO 1882	RIO PIEDRAS, PR	00926
BARNETT, KAREN M	DIRECTOR	3200 N LAKE SHORE DR #1202	CHICAGO, IL	60657
BARNETT, LARRY	BASEBALL UMPIRE	6464 HUGHES RD	PROSPECT, OH	43342
BARNETT, MARK	ATTORNEY GENERAL	STATE CAPITOL BUILDING	PIERRE, SD	57501
BARNETT, MIKE	BASEBALL COACH	1090 N EUCLID AVE	SARASOTA, FL	34237
BARNETT, OLIVER	FOOTBALL	FALCONS, SUWANEE RD AT I-85	SUWANEE, GA	30174
BARNETT, ROBERT L	TV DIRECTOR	319 ANAPALAU ST	HONOLULU, HI	96825
BARNETT, STEPHEN	FILM DIRECTOR	5231 SAN FELICIANO DR	WOODLAND HILLS, CA	91364
BARNETT, TIM	FOOTBALL	CHIEFS, 1 ARROWHEAD DR	KANSAS CITY, MO	64129
BARNETTE, IRWIN T	WRITER	3333 W 2ND ST #51-118	LOS ANGELES, CA	90004
BARNGROVER, JAMES V, JR	CONDUCTOR	4422 SANBERG WY	IRVINE, CA	92664
BARNHARDT, ROBERLEIGH H	COMPOSER	507 E CYPRESS AVE #C	BURBANK, CA	91501
BARNHARDT, TOMMY	FOOTBALL	SAINTS, 1500 POYDRAS ST	NEW ORLEANS, LA	90112
BARNHART, DON LEWIS	ACTOR-DIRECTOR	3007 WASHINGTON BLVD #220	MARINA DEL REY, CA	90292
BARNHILL, CHARLES	BASEBALL EXECUTIVE	POST OFFICE BOX 882	MADISON, WI	53701
BARNHIZER, DAVID	DIRECTOR	DGA, 110 W 57TH ST	NEW YORK, NY	10019
BARNIAK, JIM	SPORTSCASTER	POST OFFICE BOX 7575	PHILADELPHIA, PA	19101
BARNS, JEFF	BASEBALL	POST OFFICE BOX 2437	MODESTO, CA	95351
BARNUM, H B, III	ACTOR	7300 MULHOLLAND DR	LOS ANGELES, CA	90046
BARNWELL, JOHN	WRITER-PRODUCER	POST OFFICE BOX 1337	BIG BEAR LAKE, CA	92315
BARNWELL, RICHARD	BASEBALL	ALBANY YANKEES, HERITAGE PARK	ALBANY, NY	12211
BARON, ALLEN	WRITER-PRODUCER	407 S SPALDING DR #11	BEVERLY HILLS, CA	90212
BARON, DEBORAH R	TV WRITER	1234 GRANVILLE AVE #4	LOS ANGELES, CA	90025
BARON, LYNDA	ACTRESS	CHARLESWORTH, 60 OLD BROMPTON	LONDON SW7 3LQ	ENGLAND
BARON, MURRAY	HOCKEY	FLYERS, SPECTRUM, PATTISON PL	PHILADELPHIA, PA	19148
BARON, SUZANNE	EDITOR	3 RUE PAUL-FEVAR	PARIS 75018	FRANCE
BARON, VENUS	BASEBALL	5330 LANKERSHIM BLVD #210	NORTH HOLLYWOOD, CA	91601
BARR, ANTHONY	DIRECTOR-PRODUCER	13316 GAULT ST	VAN NUYS, CA	91405
BARR, ART	WRESTLER	8725 N CHAUTAUQUA BLVD	PORTLAND, OR	97217
BARR, BILL	TV WRITER	8955 BEVERLY BLVD	WEST HOLLYWOOD, CA	90048
BARR, DAVE	GOLFER	POST OFFICE BOX 109601	PALM BCH GARDENS, FL	33418
BARR, DAVE	HOCKEY	RED WINGS, 600 CIVIC CENTER DR	DETROIT, MI	48226
BARR, DOUGLAS	ACTOR	515 S IRVING BLVD	LOS ANGELES, CA	90020
BARR, HAYLEY	ACTRESS	CBS-TV, "AS THE WORLD TURNS"		
		524 W 57TH ST #5330	NEW YORK, NY	10019
BARR, JESSE	WRESTLER	8725 N CHAUTAUQUA BLVD	PORTLAND, OR	97217
BARR, JULIA	ACTRESS	888 7TH AVE #602	NEW YORK, NY	10106
BARR, MATTHEW FRANCIS	SCREENWRITER	9200 SUNSET BLVD #531	LOS ANGELES, CA	90069
BARR, STEVE	CARTOONIST	TRIBUNE, 64 E CONCORD ST	ORLANDO, FL	32801
BARR, STEVEN V	ACTOR	132 S LASKY DR #B	BEVERLY HILLS, CA	90212
BARR, TONY	TV EXECUTIVE	CBS-TV, 6121 SUNSET BLVD	LOS ANGELES, CA	90028

BARR, WILLIAM H	TV WRITER-PRODUCER	3690 BARHAM BLVD #G-219	LOS ANGELES, CA 90069
BARR ARNOLD, ROSEANNE	COMEDIENNE-ACTRESS	12916 EVANSTON ST	LOS ANGELES, CA 90049
BARRACLOUGH, JENNY	FILM DIRECTOR	112-A UXBRIDGE RD	LONDON W12 8LR ENGLAND
BARRAULT, JEAN-LOUIS	ACTOR	18 AVE DU PRESIDENT WILSON	PARIS FRANCE
BARRAULT, MARIE-CHRISTINE	ACTRESS	DE LESBONNE 19	F-75008 PARIS FRANCE
BARREIRO, EFRAIN	BASEBALL	POST OFFICE BOX 1556	ASHEVILLE, NC 28802
BARRERA, JOE O	COMPOSER	5038 CAHUENGA BLVD #2	NORTH HOLLYWOOD, CA 91601
BARRERRA, ALBERTO	ARTIST	463 WEST ST #1017-D	NEW YORK, NY 10014
BARRESE, KATHERINE	ACTRESS	7461 BEVERLY BLVD #400	LOS ANGELES, CA 90036
BARRET, EARL	WRITER-PRODUCER	4239 SHERMAN OAKS AVE	SHERMAN OAKS, CA 91403
BARRETT, ALICE	ACTRESS	NBC-TV, "ANOTHER WORLD"	
		1268 E 14TH ST	BROOKLYN, NY 11230
BARRETT, CHRISTOPHER	ACTOR	204 N ROSSMORE AVE	LOS ANGELES, CA 90004
BARRETT, CHRISTOPHER	TALENT AGENT	MTA, 9320 WILSHIRE BL, 3RD FL	BEVERLY HILLS, CA 90212
BARRETT, CLIFFORD	ACTOR-VOICE OVERS	32 FREMONT RD	NORTH TARRYTOWN, NY 10591
BARRETT, JACK E	WRITER	4267 NEOSHO AVE	LOS ANGELES, CA 90066
BARRETT, MAJEL	ACTRESS	10615 BELLAGIO RD	LOS ANGELES, CA 90077
BARRETT, MARTY	BASEBALL	3140 CLAMDIGGER	LAS VEGAS, NV 89117
BARRETT, REGGIE	FOOTBALL	LIONS, 1200 FEATHERSTONE RD	PONTIAC, MI 48432
BARRETT, RONA	TV PERSONALITY	1122 TOWER RD	BEVERLY HILLS, CA 90210
BARRETT, STAN	DIRECTOR	ROLLING "K" RANCH	BISHOP, CA 93514
BARRETT, TIM	SINGER	PENNY, 30 GUINAN ST	WALTHAM, MA 02154
BARRETT, TOM	BASEBALL	POST OFFICE BOX 2365	PAWTUCKET, RI 02861
BARRETT, WILLIAM E "BILL"	U S CONGRESSMAN	1501 2ND AVE #2	SCOTTSBLUFF, NE 69361
BARRETT & SMITH	VOCAL DUO	4111 LINCOLN BLVD #211	MARINA DEL REY, CA 90292
BARRI, STEVE	PRODUCER-SONGWRITER	MOTOWN, 6255 SUNSET BLVD	HOLLYWOOD, CA 90028
BARRIE, BARBARA	ACTRESS	465 W END AVE	NEW YORK, NY 10024
BARRIE, MICHAEL P	WRITER	620 N TRENTON DR	BEVERLY HILLS, CA 90210
BARRIER, ERNESTINE	ACTRESS	2240 STANLEY AVE #3	SIGNAL HILL, CA 90806
BARRIER, MAURICE	ACTOR	18 RUE DE GRAVELLE	F-75012 PARIS FRANCE
BARRINGTON, KRISTARA	ACTRESS-MODEL	POST OFFICE BOX 9786	MARINA DEL REY, CA 90265
BARRIS, CHUCK	TV HOST-PRODUCER	17 E 76TH ST	NEW YORK, NY 10021
BARRON, BARBARA	ACTRESS	711 E ELMWOOD AVE	BURBANK, CA 91501
BARRON, DANA	ACTRESS	151 S EL CAMINO DR	BEVERLY HILLS, CA 90212
BARRON, DOUGLAS MICHAEL	ACTOR	7135 HOLLYWOOD BLVD #PH-2	LOS ANGELES, CA 90046
BARRON, JEFFREY	WRITER	8431 BLACKBURN AVE	LOS ANGELES, CA 90048
BARRON, JOHN	ACTOR	GREEN, 2 CONDUIT ST	LONDON W1R 9TG ENGLAND
BARRON, KENNY	PIANIST	JOANNE KLEIN, 130 W 28TH ST	NEW YORK, NY 10001
BARRON, MARK	BASEBALL UMPIRE	235 MAIN ST #103	TRUSSVILLE, AL 35173
BARRON, RICHARD H	CONDUCTOR	5714 COLUMBUS AVE	VAN NUYS, CA 91411
BARRON, ROBERT V	ACTOR-WRITER	10503 RIVERSIDE DR #7	NORTH HOLLYWOOD, CA 91602
BARRON, STEVE	ACTOR	LIMELIGHT, 3 BROMLEY PL	LONDON W1 ENGLAND
BARRON, STEVE	TEENAGE MUTANT NINJA	151 S EL CAMINO DR	BEVERLY HILLS, CA 90212
BARRON, TONY	BASEBALL	POST OFFICE BOX 28268	SAN ANTONIO, TX 78228
BARRON, WILLIAM A, JR	DIRECTOR	1310 HEULU ST #1901	HONOLULU, HI 96822
BARROS, DANA	BASKETBALL	POST OFFICE BOX C-900911	SEATTLE, WA 98109
BARROW, BERNIE	ACTOR	ABC-TV, "LOVING"	
		320 W 66TH ST, STUDIO 23	NEW YORK, NY 10023
BARROW, CLYDE	SINGER	PROCESS, 439 WILEY AVE	FRANKLIN, PA 16323
BARROWS, DAN	ACTOR	15037 HAMLIN ST	VAN NUYS, CA 91411
BARROWS, GEORGE	ACTOR	6631 ATOLL AVE	NORTH HOLLYWOOD, CA 91606
BARRY, BETTY	ACTRESS	622 N MAPLE DR	BEVERLY HILLS, CA 90210
BARRY, BRUCE STUART	DIRECTOR	2435 YORKTOWN ST	OCEANSIDE, NY 11572
BARRY, CHRISTOPHER C	WRITER-PRODUCER	ALL DIRECTIONS LTD	
		10 WYNDHAM PL	LONDON W1H 1AS ENGLAND
BARRY, DAN	CARTOONIST	KING FEATURES, 216 E 45TH ST	NEW YORK, NY 10017
BARRY, DAVE	COMEDIAN	614 N PALM DR	BEVERLY HILLS, CA 90210
BARRY, DAVE	HUMORIST-COLUMNIST	MIAMI HERALD, 1 HERALD PLAZA	MIAMI, FL 33101
BARRY, DAVID	SCREENWRITER	10000 SANTA MONICA BLVD #305	LOS ANGELES, CA 90067
BARRY, GENE	ACTOR	1930 CENTURY PARK W #403	LOS ANGELES, CA 90067
BARRY, GUERIN	ACTOR	7570 1/2 DE LONGPRE AVE	LOS ANGELES, CA 90046
BARRY, IVOR	ACTOR	3800 BARHAM BLVD #303	LOS ANGELES, CA 90068
BARRY, JEFF	BASEBALL	525 NW PEACOCK BLVD	PORT SAINT LUCIE, FL 34986
BARRY, JEFF	COMPOSER	9100 SUNSET BLVD #200	LOS ANGELES, CA 90069
BARRY, JOHN	COMPOSER	540 CENTER ISLAND RD	OYSTER BAY, NY 11771
BARRY, JULIAN	WRITER	9800 EASTON DR	BEVERLY HILLS, CA 90210
BARRY, JULIE	ACTRESS	12377 LEWIS ST #101	GARDEN GROVE, CA 92640
BARRY, KENNETH	COMPOSER	950 N ARROWHEAD AVE	SAN BERNARDINO, CA 92410
BARRY, LEN	SINGER	CAPE, 1161 NW 76TH AVE	FORT LAUDERDALE, FL 33322
BARRY, LYNDA J	CARTOONIST	THE READER, 635 STATE ST	SAN DIEGO, CA 92101
BARRY, MARION	MAYOR-TEACHER	UNIV OF DISTRICT OF COLUMBIA	
		CRIMINAL JUSTICE DEPARTMENT	
		4200 CONNECTICUT AVE, NW	WASHINGTON, DC 20008
BARRY, PATRICIA	ACTRESS	12742 HIGHWOOD ST	LOS ANGELES, CA 90049
BARRY, PAUL	SINGER	FAA, 1700 BROADWAY, 5TH FLOOR	NEW YORK, NY 10019
BARRY, PHILIP, JR	WRITER-PRODUCER	12742 HIGHWOOD ST	LOS ANGELES, CA 90049
BARRY, RICK	BASKETBALL	POST OFFICE BOX C-900911	SEATTLE, WA 98109
BARRY, SY	CARTOONIST	34 SARATOGA DR	JERICHO, NY 11753
BARRYMORE, DREW	ACTRESS	3960 LAUREL CANYON BLVD #159	STUDIO CITY, CA 91604
BARRYMORE, JOHN BLYTH, III	ACTOR	SIEGEL, 7551 SUNSET BLVD #204	LOS ANGELES, CA 90046
BARRYMORE, MICHAEL	ACTOR-COMEDIAN	NORMAN MURRAY, 235 REGENT ST	LONDON W1R 5DD ENGLAND
BARSACQ, YVES	ACTOR	20 RUE DU CADET, RENE MOUCHO	PARIS 75014 FRANCE
BARSEVICH, MICHAEL	TV DIRECTOR	2524 COLUMBIA AVE #2	PITTSBURGH, PA 15218
BARSOCCHINI, PETER	TV WRITER	11317 VALLEY SPRING LN	NORTH HOLLYWOOD, CA 91602
BARSON, LUCIEN	ACTOR	127 AVE J B CLEMENT	BOULOGNE 92100 FRANCE

BART, LIONEL	LYRICIST-COMPOSER	8-10 BULSTRODE ST	LONDON W1M 6AH	ENGLAND
BARTEL, JEAN	ACTRESS	229 BRONWOOD AVE	LOS ANGELES, CA	90049
BARTEL, PAUL	ACTOR-DIRECTOR	7860 FAREHOLM DR	LOS ANGELES, CA	90068
BARTH, CARL	DIRECTOR	6922 HOLLYWOOD BLVD #621	HOLLYWOOD, CA	90028
BARTH, EDDIE	ACTOR	145 S FAIRFAX AVE #310	LOS ANGELES, CA	90036
BARTH, GENE	FOOTBALL REFEREE	NFL, 410 PARK AVE	NEW YORK, NY	10022
BARTH, HENRY	DIRECTOR	143 CUPSHAW LAKE DR	RINGWOOD, NJ	07456
BARTH, STEVE	BASEBALL EXECUTIVE	POST OFFICE BOX 4370	SALINAS, CA	93912
BARTHOLOMEW, FRED	ACTOR-TV PRODUCER	POST OFFICE BOX 242	BEACH HAVEN, NJ	08008
BARTHOLOMEW, SUMMER	ACTRESS-MODEL	426 W MAIN ST	MERCED, CA	95340
BARTKOWIAK, ANDRZEJ	CINEMATOGRAPHER	DGA, 110 W 57TH ST	NEW YORK, NY	10019
BARTLETT, BONNIE	ACTRESS	3500 W OLIVE AVE #1400	BURBANK, CA	91505
BARTLETT, HALL	WRITER-PRODUCER	861 STONE CANYON RD	LOS ANGELES, CA	90077
BARTLETT, JUANITA LAULEE	TV WRITER-PRODUCER	15970 ROYAL OAK RD	ENCINO, CA	91436
BARTLETT, MARTINE	ACTRESS-WRITER	1560 N LAUREL AVE #107	LOS ANGELES, CA	90046
BARTMAN, BILL	ACTOR	2042 GREEN ST	LOS ANGELES, CA	90024
BARTMAN, WILLIAM	TV DIRECTOR	4247 KESTER AVE	SHERMAN OAKS, CA	91403
BARTO, GORDON	DIRECTOR	320 RIO VISTA PL	SANTA FE, NM	87501
BARTOLD, VIRGINIA	CONDUCTOR	9285 FLICKER PL	LOS ANGELES, CA	90069
BARTOLETTI, BRUNO	CONDUCTOR	LYRIC OPERA, 20 N WACKER DR	CHICAGO, IL	60606
BARTON, CURTIS	SINGER	BUN JAK, 331 PROSPECT ST	BERLIN, NH	03570
BARTON, DAN	ACTOR	14716 WEDDINGTON ST	VAN NUYS, CA	91411
BARTON, DEREK	ACTOR	930 WESTBOURNE DR #400	LOS ANGELES, CA	90069
BARTON, EARL	DIRECTOR	11639 SUNSHINE TERR	STUDIO CITY, CA	91604
BARTON, FRANK	PRODUCER	4000 WARNER BLVD	BURBANK, CA	91522
BARTON, FRANKLIN L	WRITER	9226 SIERRA MAR DR	LOS ANGELES, CA	90069
BARTON, GERALD S	FILM EXECUTIVE	110 N ELM DR	BEVERLY HILLS, CA	90210
BARTON, HARRIS	FOOTBALL	S F 49ERS, 4949 CENTENNIAL BL	SANTA CLARA, CA	95054
BARTON, JEANNIE DIMTER	ACTRESS	110 N ELM DR	BEVERLY HILLS, CA	90210
BARTON, JOE	U S CONGRESSMAN	303 W KNOX #101	ENNIS, TX	75119
BARTON, KENT	ARTIST	11021 LAKEVIEW DR N	PEMBROKE PINES, FL	33026
BARTON, LARRY	ACTOR	4629 FULTON AVE	SHERMAN OAKS, CA	91423
BARTON, LARRY, JR	BASEBALL SCOUT	REDS, 100 RIVERFRONT STADIUM	CINCINNATI, OH	45202
BARTON, PAUL	BASEBALL	POST OFFICE BOX 1088	ST CATH, ONT L2R 3BO	CANADA
BARTON, PETER	ACTOR	2265 WESTWOOD BLVD #2619	LOS ANGELES, CA	90064
BARTON, SHAWN	BASEBALL	POST OFFICE BOX 3690, STA "B"	CALGARY, ALB T2B 4M4	CANADA
BARTOO, MARION	WRITER	3548 CARNATION AVE	LOS ANGELES, CA	90026
BARTOS, MICHAEL	CONDUCTOR	ROSENFIELD, 714 LADD RD	BRONX, NY	10471
BARTOSCH, DAVE	BASEBALL SCOUT	POST OFFICE BOX 2000	SAN DIEGO, CA	92112
BARTRON, HARRY	ACTOR	1714 N IVAR AVE #718	LOS ANGELES, CA	90028
BARTY, BILLY	ACTOR	4502 FARMDALE AVE	NORTH HOLLYWOOD, CA	91602
BARTZ, JAMES	ACTOR	261 S ROBERTSON BLVD	BEVERLY HILLS, CA	90211
BARWOOD, HAL	WRITER-DIRECTOR	123 BOLINAS AVE	SAN ANSELMO, CA	94960
BARYSHNIKOV, MIKHAIL	BALLET DANCER	35 E 12TH ST #5-D	NEW YORK, NY	10003
BARZMAN, NORMA	WRITER	1738 N OGDEN DR	LOS ANGELES, CA	90046
BARZYK, FREDERICK F	DIRECTOR	12 BROOK ST	CHELMSFORD, MA	01824
BASACKER, CATHY	BODYBUILDER	2213 ARNHEM PL	MODESTO, CA	95356
BASACKER, RICK	BODYBUILDER	2213 ARNHEM PL	MODESTO, CA	95356
BASCH, HARRY	ACTOR-WRITER	920 1/2 S SERRANO AVE	LOS ANGELES, CA	90006
BASE, ROB & E-Z ROCK	RAP DUO-RAPWRITERS	FAA, 1700 BROADWAY, 5TH FLOOR	NEW YORK, NY	10019
BASER, MICHAEL S	TV WRITER-PRODUCER	10633 COMMERCE AVE	TUJUNGA, CA	91042
BASEY, JILL	ACTRESS	22552 JAMESON DR	WOODLAND HILLS, CA	91364
BASGALL, MONTY	BASEBALL-COACH	2745 SAINT ANDREWS DR	SIERRA VISTA, AZ	85635
BASH, KEVIN	ACTOR	1800 N VINE ST #120	LOS ANGELES, CA	90028
BASICHIS, GORDON ALLEN	SCREENWRITER	5106 RANCHITO AVE	SHERMAN OAKS, CA	91423
BASIL, TONI	SINGER	9595 WILSHIRE BLVD #505	BEVERLY HILLS, CA	90212
BASILE, NADINE	ACTRESS	15 BLVD LANNES	PARIS 75116	FRANCE
BASILLO, CARMEN	BOXER	67 BOXWOOD DR	ROCHESTER, NY	14617
BASINGER, KIM	ACTRESS-MODEL	3960 LAUREL CANYON BLVD #414	STUDIO CITY, CA	91604
BASINSKI, DAVE	DIRECTOR	920 STRAND	MANHATTAN BEACH, CA	90266
BASKCOMB, JOHN	ACTOR	ROSEAWEN VEAN, SITHNEY GREEN HELSTON	CORNWALL TR13 ORT	ENGLAND
BASKERVILLE, TIMOTHY D	WRITER	2385 ROSCOMARE RD #F-3	LOS ANGELES, CA	90077
BASKIN, JOHN	TV WRITER-PRODUCER	216 N LAYTON DR	LOS ANGELES, CA	90049
BASKIN, LEONARD	ARTIST	AUDUBON RD	LEEDS, MA	01053
BASKIN, SUSAN F	TV WRITER	9242 BEVERLY DR #200	BEVERLY HILLS, CA	90210
BASLER, MOLLY	MODEL-ACTRESS	2215 6TH ST #B	SANTA MONICA, CA	90405
BASQUETTE, LINA	ACTRESS	SHADOW HILL RD #1	WHEELING, WV	26003
BASS, BOB	BASKETBALL EXECUTIVE	600 E MARKET ST #102	SAN ANTONIO, TX	78205
BASS, BOBBY	DIRECTOR-STUNTMAN	POST OFFICE BOX 57	TORRANCE, CA	90507
BASS, CLARENCE	BODYBUILDER	528 NE CHAMA ST	ALBUQUERQUE, NM	87108
BASS, GARY E	DIRECTOR	308 E 85TH ST	NEW YORK, NY	10028
BASS, KEVIN	ACTOR	11901 LAUREL HILLS RD	STUDIO CITY, CA	91604
BASS, KEVIN	BASEBALL	METS, 126TH ST & ROOSEVELT AVE	FLUSHING, NY	11368
BASS, MARVIN	FOOTBALL COACH	BRONCOS, 13655 BRONCOS PKWY	ENGLEWOOD, CO	80112
BASS, RONALD	SCREENWRITER	CAA, 9830 WILSHIRE BLVD	BEVERLY HILLS, CA	90212
BASS, SAUL	DIRECTOR-PRODUCER	337 S LAS PALMAS AVE	LOS ANGELES, CA	90020
BASS MOUNTAIN BOYS	C & W GROUP	POST OFFICE BOX 186	RIVA, MD	21140
BASSE, MIKE	BASEBALL	POST OFFICE BOX 8550	STOCKTON, CA	95208
BASSET, BRIAN	CARTOONIST	UPS, 4900 MAIN ST, 9TH FLOOR	KANSAS CITY, MO	64112
BASSETT, LAURA	ACTRESS	9720 REGENT ST #8	LOS ANGELES, CA	90034
BASSETT, LESLIE	COMPOSER	1618 HARBAL DR	ANN ARBOR, MI	48105
BASSETT, MATT	BASEBALL EXECUTIVE	POST OFFICE BOX 3665	OMAHA, NE	68103
BASSETT, STEVE	ACTOR	200 W 80TH ST #3-S	NEW YORK, NY	10024
BASSETT, WILLIAM H	ACTOR	7924 WOODMAN AVE #66	VAN NUYS, CA	91402

303-778-6462
645 So. Harrison St.
Denver, CO 80209
STAR
SIGNS
JIM LARSON
"The Autograph Man"
Also
Buy & Sell Sheet Music, etc.
• Authentic Signed Pictures
• Movie Stars & Entertainers
• Sports Personalities
• Unsigned 8x10 Photographs

BASSETTI, GIL	BASEBALL SCOUT	1000 ELYSIAN PARK DR	LOS ANGELES, CA	90012
BASSEY, BERNARD	WRITER	254 S ROBERTSON BLVD #200	BEVERLY HILLS, CA	90211
BASSEY, JENNIFER	ACTRESS	CHELSEA HOTEL, 222 W 23RD ST	NEW YORK, NY	10014
BASSEY, SHIRLEY	SINGER	SERGIO NOVAK VILLA CAPRICORN		
		55 VIA CAMPIONE	6816 BISSONE	SWITZERLAND
BASSILL, BARBARA	ACTRESS	3085 MOTOR AVE	LOS ANGELES, CA	90064
BASSING, ROBERT	WRITER	1069 S GENESEE AVE	LOS ANGELES, CA	90019
BASSMAN, GEORGE	COMPOSER-CONDUCTOR	401 S CRESCENT HGTS BLVD	LOS ANGELES, CA	90048
BASSO, MIKE	BASEBALL	STARS, 850 LAS VEGAS BLVD N	LAS VEGAS, NV	89101
BAST, WILLIAM	SCREENWRITER	6691 WHITLEY TERR	LOS ANGELES, CA	90068
BASTABLE, TONY	TV WRITER-DIRECTOR	BURFIELD, 93 CAMBRIDGE ST	LONDON SW1	ENGLAND
BASTIANELLI, LAURA	ACTRESS	4210 SARAH ST #25	BURBANK, CA	91505
BASTONE, RON	WRITER	842 N WILCOX AVE #8	LOS ANGELES, CA	90038
BATANIDES, ARTHUR	ACTOR	3477 BEVERLY GLEN BLVD	SHERMAN OAKS, CA	91423
BATCHELOR, JOY E	CINEMATOGRAPHER	HALAS, 3-7 KEAN ST	LONDON WC2B 4AT	ENGLAND
BATCHELOR, RICH	BASEBALL	ALBANY YANKEES, HERITAGE PARK	ALBANY, NY	12211
BATCHKO, MARK	BASEBALL SCOUT	N Y YANKEES, YANKEE STADIUM	BRONX, NY	10451
BATE, ANTHONY	ACTOR	AL PARKER, 55 PARK LN	LONDON W1Y 3DD	ENGLAND
BATE, BRADLEY G	DIRECTOR	5445 N SHERIDAN RD #141	CHICAGO, IL	60640
BATEMAN, CHARLES	ACTOR	ATKINS, 303 S CRESCENT HEIGHTS	LOS ANGELES, CA	90048
BATEMAN, EARL, III	ARTIST	5401 WESTBARD AVE #1410	BETHESDA, MD	20816
BATEMAN, HERBERT	U S CONGRESSMAN	739 THIMBLE SHOALS BLVD #803	NEWPORT NEWS, VA	23606
BATEMAN, JASON	ACTOR-DIRECTOR	2628 2ND ST	SANTA MONICA, CA	90405
BATEMAN, JUSTINE	ACTRESS	3960 LAUREL CANYON BLVD #193	STUDIO CITY, CA	91604
BATEMAN, KENT	TV DIRECTOR	21931 BURBANK BLVD #21	WOODLAND HILLS, CA	91367
BATEMAN, ROBERT	ARTIST	MILL POND PRESS, INC		
		204 S NASSAU ST	VENICE, FL	33595
BATEMAN, SUZANNE	ACTRESS	8383 WILSHIRE BLVD #649	BEVERLY HILLS, CA	90211
BATES, ALAN	ACTOR	122 HAMILTON TERR	LONDON NW8	ENGLAND
BATES, BILL	FOOTBALL	COWBOYS, 1 COWBOYS PARKWAY	IRVING, TX	75063
BATES, BILLY	BASEBALL	POST OFFICE BOX 23290	NASHVILLE, TN	37202
BATES, JAMES B	COMPOSER	14335 HUSTON ST #210	SHERMAN OAKS, CA	91423
BATES, JEFFREY PETER	WRITER	11157 SARAH ST	NORTH HOLLYWOOD, CA	91602
BATES, KATHY D	ACTRESS	SMITH, 121 N SAN VICENTE BLVD	BEVERLY HILLS, CA	90211
BATES, LINDA	ACTRESS	8721 SANTA MONICA BLVD #21	WEST HOLLYWOOD, CA	90069
BATES, PEG LEG	MUSICIAN	GENERAL DELIVERY	KERKONKSON, NY	12446
BATES, RALPH	ACTOR	HATTON, 29 ROEHAMPTON GATE	LONDON SW15 5JR	ENGLAND
BATES, TOMMY	BASEBALL	POST OFFICE BOX 3452	KINSTON, NC	28502
BATHE, BILL	BASEBALL	11027 KENTUCKY AVE	WHITTIER, CA	90603
BATISTA, MANUEL	BASEBALL SCOUT	POST OFFICE BOX 90111	ARLINGTON, TX	76004
BATISTA, MIGUEL	BASEBALL	POST OFFICE BOX 7000	PITTSBURGH, PA	15212
BATISTA, RAFAEL	BASEBALL-SCOUT	FENWAY PARK, 4 YAWKEY WY	BOSTON, MA	02215
BATISTE, KIM	BASEBALL	POST OFFICE BOX 7575	PHILADELPHIA, PA	19101
BATTA, TOM	FOOTBALL COACH	VIKINGS, 9520 VIKING DR	EDEN PRAIRIE, MN	55344
BATTAGLIA, JANINE	ACTRESS	POST OFFICE BOX 324		
		ANSONIA STATION	NEW YORK, NY	10023
BATTAN, SUSAN	ACTRESS	ABC-TV, "ONE LIFE TO LIVE"		
		56 W 66TH ST	NEW YORK, NY	10023
BATTERBY, ROY	TV DIRECTOR	PETERS, FRASER & DUNLOP, LTD		
		5TH FLOOR, THE CHAMBERS		
		CHELSEA HARBOUR, LOT RD	LONDON SW10 OXF	ENGLAND
BATTIE, HOWARD	BASEBALL	POST OFFICE BOX 1110	MYRTLE BEACH, SC	29578
BATTISTONE, CATHERINE	ACTRESS	5220 BEN AVE	NORTH HOLLYWOOD, CA	91607
BATTLE, ALLEN	BASEBALL	POST OFFICE BOX 3004	SPRINGFIELD, IL	62708
BATTLE, HINTON	ACTOR	420 MADISON AVE #1400	NEW YORK, NY	10017
BATTLE, HOWARD	BASEBALL	POST OFFICE BOX 957	DUNEDIN, FL	34697
BATTLE, JOHN	BASKETBALL	1 CNN CENTER #405, SOUTH TOWER	ATLANTA, GA	30303
BATTLE, KENNY	BASKETBALL	SUNS, 2910 N CENTRAL AVE	PHOENIX, AZ	85012
BATTLECRY	ROCK & ROLL GROUP	POST OFFICE BOX 2896	TORRANCE, CA	90509
BATTOCCHIO, ROY	WRITER	8160 MULHOLLAND TERR	LOS ANGELES, CA	90046
BATTY, PETER	WRITER-PRODUCER	CLAREMONT HOUSE, RENFREW RD		
		KINGSTON	SURREY KT2 7NT	ENGLAND
BATY, GREG	FOOTBALL	DOLPHINS, 2269 NW 199TH ST	MIAMI, FL	33056
BAU, C J	ACTOR	6255 SUNSET BLVD #627	LOS ANGELES, CA	90028
BAUCUS, MAX	U S SENATOR	211 N HIGGINS #102	MISSOULA, MT	59802
BAUDO, SERGE	CONDUCTOR	SHAW CONCERTS, 1995 BROADWAY	NEW YORK, NY	10023
BAUER, BELINDA	ACTRESS	15301 VENTURA BLVD #345	SHERMAN OAKS, CA	91403
BAUER, BRUCE ROGER	ACTOR	12456 VENTURA BLVD #1	STUDIO CITY, CA	91604
BAUER, HANK	BASEBALL	12705 W 108TH ST	OVERLAND PARK, KS	66210
BAUER, JAIME LYN	ACTRESS	KJAR, 10653 RIVERSIDE DR	TOLUCA LAKE, CA	91602
BAUER, MATT	BASEBALL	POST OFFICE BOX 2785	LAKELAND, FL	33806
BAUER, MICHELLE	ACTRESS-MODEL	POST OFFICE BOX 480265	LOS ANGELES, CA	90048
BAUER, PETE	BASEBALL	POST OFFICE BOX 4448	TULSA, OK	74159
BAUER, STEVEN	ACTOR	5233 STROHM AVE	NORTH HOLLYWOOD, CA	91601
BAUGH, SAMMY	FOOTBALL	GENERAL DELIVERY	ROTAN, TX	79546
BAUGHAN, MAXIE	FOOTBALL COACH	VIKINGS, 9520 VIKING DR	EDEN PRAIRIE, MN	55344
BAUGHN, ADELE	ACTRESS	18261 SAN FERNANDO MISSION BL	NORTHRIDGE, CA	91326
BAUGHN, ANADEL	ACTRESS	18261 SAN FERNANDO MISSION BL	NORTHRIDGE, CA	91326
BAUM, BRUCE	COMEDIAN-ACTOR	KARP, 601 N ORANGE DR	LOS ANGELES, CA	90036
BAUM, CAROL	TV PRODUCER	CAA, 9830 WILSHIRE BLVD	BEVERLY HILLS, CA	90212
BAUM, MIRIAM	TALENT AGENT	8230 SUNSET BLVD #23	LOS ANGELES, CA	90048
BAUMAN, CHARLIE	FOOTBALL	DOLPHINS, 2269 NW 199TH ST	MIAMI, FL	33056
BAUMAN, JON "BOWZER"	SINGER-ACTOR-VJ	3168 OAKSHIRE DR	LOS ANGELES, CA	90068
BAUMANN, DAVID	BASEBALL	POST OFFICE BOX 483	YAKIMA, WA	98907
BAUMANN, EVA	ACTRESS	117 W 79TH ST #703	NEW YORK, NY	10024

Announcing

"Celebrity Access-The Directory 1992"

Celebrity Access-The Directory 1992 -- Its like having your own personal address book of today's stars and celebrities. Need to drop a letter to President Bush, Madonna, Mel Gibson, General Schwartzkopf, Whoopie Goldberg, Bishop Tutu, or Reggie Jackson? Look no further. Our hit annual directory, completely revised, now lists over **5000 celebrity addresses --** nearly **double** any of our previous editions.

Why don't **we** list tens of thousands of addresses, like some of the other directories? We have chosen to list only those who have a history of graciously and easily responding to their public in the past. These special listings help one quickly reach the rich and famous, without the disappointment most get from late-released, overstuffed general directories. This book provides information and a resource base for locating celebrities, mainly in film and television, but also in other areas of prominence, such as sports, music, science, military, religion, art, and politics. There are also instructional chapters on many subjects including how to **properly** write celebrities and get a response. There's a handy reference in the back to help locate unsigned photos, vintage magazines and posters, books, fan clubs, and more.

Who uses this book? Professional people in business -- writers, producers, directors, agents, interviewers, realtors, bankers and fund raisers; organizations, newspapers, magazines, fan clubs, and libraries; educators in schools, colleges, and universities, and the celebrities themselves.

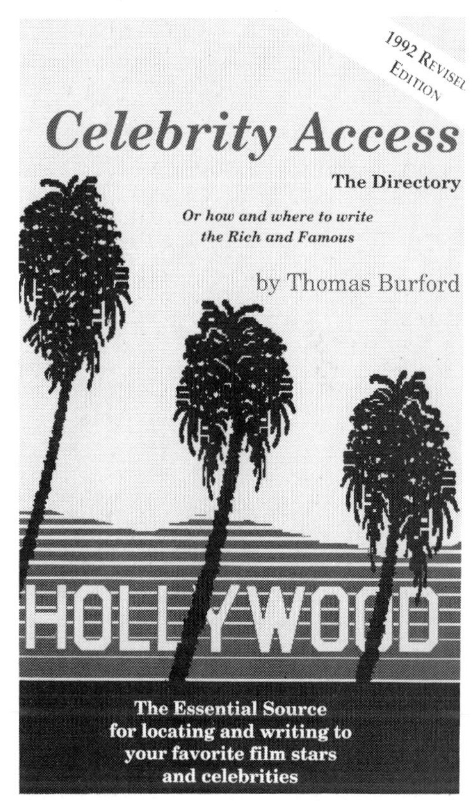

1992 Revised Edition
Celebrity Access
The Directory
Or how and where to write the Rich and Famous
by Thomas Burford
HOLLYWOOD
The Essential Source for locating and writing to your favorite film stars and celebrities

Now only $21.95 (Plus $2.50 Shipping - California add 7.25% sales tax). * Please send check or money order to:

CELEBRITY ACCESS PUBLICATIONS
20 SUNNYSIDE AVE., Ste. A241
MILL VALLEY, CA 94941
(415) 389-8133

WHAT THE REVIEWERS SAID:

"I would be happy to recommend *Celebrity Access-The Directory* now and in the future. Continued good luck with it."
Bill Harris, **Showtime Entertainment Network**

"*Celebrity Access-The Directory*, lists addresses of thousands of stars fans can write to."
Todd Steele, **Asahi Weekly (Japan)**

"When collectors ask me for a celebrity address - I look to *Celebrity Access-The Directory* book. One of the finest address books available. It belongs in every library."
J.W. Morey, **The Autograph Review**

"Whether you want to contact the rich and famous or just out of curiosity's sake know which coast they can be located on, now its easier to do with the help of *Celebrity Access*."
Judy Wiggins, **Book Dealers World**

"*Celebrity Access* is well-researched and a highly respected working tool for any library, fan, fund raiser, or researcher, and has a reputation for its up-to-date listings. Truly your best yet. A must for everyone."
Joe Kraus, **The Autograph Collector's Magazine**

"The most complete CURRENT directory of celebrity names and addresses now available."
Featured Section, **The Movie/Entertainment Book Club**

"Celebrity Access deserves a place on the bookshelves of all who take the time to write their favorite celebrities."
Michael Saks, **The Penn and Quill Magazine**

*******Remember Celebrity Access also buys and sells autographs actively. Do you have a collection or an autograph you want to sell. We also appraise and authenticate autographs for a fee.******

Name	Occupation	Address	City / Zip
BAUMEISTER, LOU	BASKETBALL EXECUTIVE	POST OFFICE BOX 10	INGLEWOOD, CA 90306
BAUMER, JIM	BASEBALL-SCOUT	POST OFFICE BOX 7575	PHILADELPHIA, PA 19101
BAUMES, WILFORD L	WRITER	873 KNOLLWOOD DR	MONTECITO, CA 93108
BAUMGARTEN, CRAIG	TV-FILM PRODUCER	10000 W WASHINGTON BLVD #4900	CULVER CITY, CA 90232
BAUMGARTNER, KEN	HOCKEY	NASSAU VETS MEMORIAL COLISEUM	UNIONDALE, NY 11553
BAUMOHL, MICHAEL	TV PRODUCER	PINEWOOD STUDIOS, IVER HEATH	IVER, BUCKS SLO ONH ENGLAND
BAUTISTA, DAN	BASEBALL	POST OFFICE BOX 64939	FAYETTEVILLE, NC 28306
BAUTISTA, JOSE	BASEBALL	RESTAURACION #26	BANI DOM REP
BAUTISTA, RAMON	BASEBALL	2501 ALLEN AVE, SE	CANTON, OH 44707
BAVARO, DAVID	FOOTBALL	BILLS, 1 BILLS DR	ORCHARD PARK, NJ 14127
BAVASI, BILL	BASEBALL EXECUTIVE	POST OFFICE BOX 2000	ANAHEIM, CA 92803
BAWMANN, TIM	BASEBALL EXECUTIVE	POST OFFICE BOX 422229	KISSIMMEE, FL 34742
BAXLEY, CRAIG R	STUNTMAN-TV DIRECTOR	11429 AWENITA CT	NORTHRIDGE, CA 91311
BAXLEY, GARY	DIRECTOR	12258 HESBY ST	NORTH HOLLYWOOD, CA 91607
BAXLEY, PAUL, JR	DIRECTOR	205 S BEVERLY DR #210	BEVERLY HILLS, CA 90212
BAXTER, BOB	BASEBALL	POST OFFICE BOX 3566	WEST PALM BEACH, FL 33402
BAXTER, BRAD	FOOTBALL	N Y JETS, 1000 FULTON AVE	HEMPSTEAD, NY 11550
BAXTER, C CASH	CASTING DIRECTOR	316 W 79TH ST	NEW YORK, NY 10024
BAXTER, DENNIS	BASEBALL EXECUTIVE	POST OFFICE BOX 418	SAINT CHARLES, IL 60174
BAXTER, ELAINE	SECRETARY OF STATE	STATE CAPITOL BUILDING	DES MOINES, IA 50319
BAXTER, JIM	BASEBALL	800 HOME RUN LN	MEMPHIS, TN 38104
BAXTER, JOHN	BASEBALL EXECUTIVE	POST OFFICE BOX 4218	SOUTH BEND, IN 46634
BAXTER, LES	COMPOSER-CONDUCTOR	6430 SUNSET BLVD #1002	HOLLYWOOD, CA 90028
BAXTER, LYNSEY	ACTRESS	HEATH, PARAMOUNT HOUSE	
		162-170 WARDOUR ST	LONDON W1V 3AT ENGLAND
BAXTER, MEREDITH	ACTRESS	10100 SANTA MONICA BLVD #1600	LOS ANGELES, CA 90067
BAXTER, RICHARD	DIRECTOR	119 E 26TH ST	NEW YORK, NY 10010
BAXTER, RONNIE	DIRECTOR-PRODUCER	INVISION LTD, WARGRAVE RD	HEN-ON-THAMES RG9 3HX ENGLAND
BAXTER, STANLEY	ACTOR-COMEDIAN	WHITE, 2 ORMOND RD, RICHMOND	SURREY TW10 6TH ENGLAND
BAY, SUSAN	ACTRESS-DIRECTOR	801 STONE CANYON RD	LOS ANGELES, CA 90077
BAY, VICTOR	COMPOSER-CONDUCTOR	520 S BURNSIDE AVE #12-E	LOS ANGELES, CA 90036
BAY CITY ROLLERS, THE	ROCK & ROLL GROUP	27 PRESTON GRANGE RD	
		PRESTON PANS, E	LOTHIAN SCOTLAND
BAYER, GARY	ACTOR	280 S BEVERLY DR #400	BEVERLY HILLS, CA 90212
BAYES, JOANNE	ACTRESS	205 W 54TH ST #8-B	NEW YORK, NY 10019
BAYH, BIRCH	U S SENATOR	1 INDIANA SQ #240	INDIANAPOLIS, IN 46204
BAYH, EVAN	GOVERNOR	STATE HOUSE BUILDING	INDIANAPOLIS, IN 46204
BAYLDON, GEOFFREY	ACTOR	8 SHERWOOD CLOSE	LONDON SW13 ENGLAND
BAYLES, MARTHA	TV CRITIC	THE WALL STREET JOURNAL	
		200 LIBERTY ST	NEW YORK, NY 10175
BAYLESS, ANITA	ACTRESS	35-15 78TH ST	JACKSON HEIGHTS, NY 11372
BAYLESS, LEE	COMEDIAN-WRITER	CARMEN, 15456 CABRITO RD	VAN NUYS, CA 91406
BAYLESS, LUSTER	COSTUME DESIGNER	13949 VENTURA BLVD #309	SHERMAN OAKS, CA 91423
BAYLESS, MARTIN	FOOTBALL	POST OFFICE BOX 609609	SAN DIEGO, CA 92160
BAYLIS, JAMES	DIRECTOR-PRODUCER	9 NORTH LN	CHAPPAQUA, NY 10514
BAYLOR, DON	BASEBALL-COACH	BREWERS, 201 S 46TH ST	MILWAUKEE, WI 53214
BAYLOR, DON	BASEBALL-COACH	250 STADIUM PLAZA	ST LOUIS, MO 63102
BAYLOR, ELGIN	BASKETBALL	CLIPPERS, 3939 S FIGUEROA ST	LOS ANGELES, CA 90037
BAYLOR, HAL	ACTOR	15728 HART ST	VAN NUYS, CA 91406
BAYLOR, JOHN	FOOTBALL	POST OFFICE BOX 535000	INDIANPOLIS, IN 46253
BAYLY, STEPHEN	FILM DIRECTOR	RES ROOSTER, 11-13 MACKLIN ST	LONDON WC2B 5NH ENGLAND
BAYNE, TRACY N	COSTUME DESIGNER	1715 CAMDEN AVE #101	LOS ANGELES, CA 90025
BAYNES, RON	FOOTBALL REFEREE	NFL, 410 PARK AVE	NEW YORK, NY 10022
BAYOU	C & W GROUP	POST OFFICE BOX 1259	LAKE DALLAS, TX 75065
BAYS, MICHAEL	ACTOR	5028 SHIRLEY AVE	TARZANA, CA 91356
BAZADONA, MICHAEL	DIRECTOR	23 MOUNTAIN RD	CORNW-ON-HUDSON, NY 12520
BAZELON, IRWIN A	COMPOSER-CONDUCTOR	142 E 71ST ST #4-A	NEW YORK, NY 10021
BB & Q BAND	ROCK & ROLL GROUP	233 W 26TH ST #1-W	NEW YORK, NY 10001
BEACH, ANN	ACTRESS	EDWARDS, 275 KENNINGTON RD	LONDON SE1 6BY ENGLAND
BEACH, BILLIE	ACTRESS	2517 28TH ST	SANTA MONICA, CA 90405
BEACH, PAT	FOOTBALL	POST OFFICE BOX 535000	INDIANPOLIS, IN 46253
BEACH, SANJAY	FOOTBALL	S F 49ERS, 4949 CENTENNIAL BL	SANTA CLARA, CA 95054
BEACH BOYS, THE	ROCK & ROLL GROUP	WEG/CONCERTS WEST MANAGEMENT	
		1111 SANTA MONICA BL, 20TH FL	LOS ANGELES, CA 90025
BEACHAM, STEPHANIE	ACTRESS	31538 BROAD BEACH RD	MALIBU, CA 90265
BEADLE, JEREMY	TV PERSONALITY	MPC, MPC HOUSE, 15-16 MAPEL MEWS	LONDON NW6 5UZ ENGLAND
BEAIRD, JOHN R	SCREENWRITER	POST OFFICE BOX 5617	BEVERLY HILLS, CA 90213
BEAKE, JOHN	FOOTBALL EXECUTIVE	BRONCOS, 13655 BRONCOS PKWY	ENGLEWOOD, CO 80112
BEAL, EDDIE T	COMPOSER-CONDUCTOR	3866 WILLOW CREST AVE #8	STUDIO CITY, CA 91604
BEAL, JOHN	ACTOR	205 W 54TH ST	NEW YORK, NY 10019
BEAL, JOHN E	FILM DIRECTOR	7242 AVENIDA ALTISIMA	PALOS VERDES, CA 90274
BEAL, JOHN EVERETT	MUSICIAN	10918 BLOOMFIELD ST	NORTH HOLLYWOOD, CA 91602
BEALE, PETER	FILM PRODUCER	3939 LANDMARK ST	CULVER CITY, CA 90232
BEALMEAR, ROBERT F	WRITER	2032 BALMER DR	LOS ANGELES, CA 90039
BEALS, GREGORY	BASEBALL	POST OFFICE BOX 7845	COLUMBIA, SC 29202
BEALS, JENNIFER	ACTRESS-DANCER	ICM, 40 W 57TH ST	NEW YORK, NY 10019
BEAME, ABE	MAYOR	1111 20TH ST, NW	WASHINGTON, DC 20575
BEAMS, MICHAEL	BASEBALL	POST OFFICE BOX 1718	NEW BRITAIN, CT 06050
BEAN, ALAN	ASTRONAUT	26 SUGARBERRY CIR	HOUSTON, TX 77024
BEAN, ANDY	GOLFER	POST OFFICE BOX 109601	PALM BCH GARDENS, FL 33418
BEAN, BILLY	BASEBALL	1102 E JOANA	SANTA ANA, CA 92701
BEAN, ED	BASEBALL UMPIRE	235 MAIN ST #103	TRUSSVILLE, AL 35173
BEAN, GERALD	DIRECTOR	840 THAYER AVE	LOS ANGELES, CA 90024
BEAN, HENRY S	SCREENWRITER	1208 PEARL ST	SANTA MONICA, CA 90405
BEAN, ORSON	ACTOR-COMEDIAN	444 CARROLL CANAL	VENICE, CA 90291

Name	Occupation	Address	City	Zip
BEAN, ROBERT B	DIRECTOR	8 HILLTOP RD	NORWALK, CT	06854
BEAN, SIDNEY	SOUND EFFECTS	114-38 201ST ST	SAINT ALBANS, NY	11412
BEAN, STEVE	ACTOR	8831 SUNSET BLVD #304	LOS ANGELES, CA	90069
BEANBLOSSOM, BRAD	BASEBALL	POST OFFICE BOX 5599	LITTLE ROCK, AR	72215
BEANE, BILL	BASEBALL-SCOUT	ATHLETICS'S, OAKLAND COLISEUM	OAKLAND, CA	94621
BEANE, HILARY	ACTRESS	5011 ELMWOOD AVE	LOS ANGELES, CA	90004
BEANES, DAVID L	DIRECTOR	DGA, 7920 SUNSET BLVD, 6TH FL	LOS ANGELES, CA	90046
BEANS, WILFRED W	ACTOR	5631 VENICE BLVD	LOS ANGELES, CA	90019
BEARD, DAVE	BASEBALL	813 E BLOOMINGDALE #284	BRANDON, FL	33511
BEARD, FRANK	GOLFER	PGA SENIORS, 112 T P C BLVD	PONTE VEDRA BEACH, FL	32082
BEARD, GARRETT	BASEBALL	POST OFFICE BOX 2437	MODESTO, CA	95351
BEARD, HENRY	TV WRITER	WM MORRIS, 1350 AVE OF AMERICAS	NEW YORK, NY	10019
BEARDE, CHRIS D	WRITER-PRODUCER	28106 PACIFIC COAST HWY	MALIBU, CA	90265
BEARER, PAUL	WRESTLING MANAGER	POST OFFICE BOX 3859	STAMFORD, CT	06905
BEARNARTH, LARRY	BASEBALL-COACH	EXPOS, 4545 DE COUBERTIN AVE	MONTREAL, QUE H1V 3P2	CANADA
BEARSE, AMANDA	ACTRESS	9000 SUNSET BLVD #1200	LOS ANGELES, CA	90069
BEASCOECHEA, FRANK P	TV DIRECTOR	24612 MALIBU RD	MALIBU, CA	90265
BEASLEY, ALLYCE	ACTRESS	2415 CASTILIAN DR	LOS ANGELES, CA	90068
BEASLEY, ANDY	BASEBALL	POST OFFICE BOX 12557	ST PETERSBURG, FL	33733
BEASLEY, CHRIS	BASEBALL	10233 96TH AVE	EDMONTON, ALB TK5 0A5	CANADA
BEASLEY, TONY	BASEBALL	POST OFFICE BOX 842	SALEM, VA	24153
BEASLEY, WALTER	SAXOPHONIST	POST OFFICE BOX 1187	WHITE PLAINS, NY	10602
BEASOR, TERRENCE	ACTOR	2800 NEILSON WY	SANTA MONICA, CA	90405
BEASTIE BOYS, THE	RAP GROUP	298 ELIZABETH ST #1	NEW YORK, NY	10012
BEAT, THE	ROCK & ROLL GROUP	POST OFFICE BOX 320	BIRMINGHAM B29 7PR	ENGLAND
BEAT FARMERS, THE	ROCK & ROLL GROUP	POST OFFICE BOX 2128	EL CAJON, CA	92021
BEAT TEMPTATION	ROCK & ROLL GROUP	POST OFFICE BOX 570	ROCKVILLE CENTRE, NY	11571
BEATHARD, BOBBY	FOOTBALL EXECUTIVE	POST OFFICE BOX 609609	SAN DIEGO, CA	92160
BEATLEMANIA	ROCK & ROLL GROUP	8665 WILSHIRE BLVD #208	BEVERLY HILLS, CA	90211
BEATON, NORMAN	ACTOR	FRAZER, 34 BRAMERTON ST	LONDON SW3 5LA	ENGLAND
BEATRIX, QUEEN	QUEEN	KASTEEL DRAKESTEI	LAGE VUURSCHE 3744 BA	HOLLAND
BEATTIE, JIM	BASEBALL EXECUTIVE	POST OFFICE BOX 4100	SEATTLE, WA	98104
BEATTIE, LYNDA	ACTRESS	6126 SAINT CLAIR AVE	NORTH HOLLYWOOD, CA	91606
BEATTIE, SHELLEY	BODYBUILDER	POST OFFICE BOX 1111	CORVALIS, OR	97339
BEATTY, BLAINE	BASEBALL	POST OFFICE BOX 1211	NORFOLK, VA	23502
BEATTY, C ROGER	WRITER-PRODUCER	13336 CHANDLER BLVD	VAN NUYS, CA	91401
BEATTY, EDGAR K	DIRECTOR	3932 E COMMERCE RD	MILFORD, MI	48042
BEATTY, NED	ACTOR	2706 N BEACHWOOD DR	LOS ANGELES, CA	90027
BEATTY, WARREN	ACT-WRI-DIR	2029 CENTURY PARK E #300	LOS ANGELES, CA	90067
BEAU, TOBY	ROCK & ROLL GROUP	AUCOIN, 645 MADISON AVE	NEW YORK, NY	10022
BEAUCHAMP, JIM	BASEBALL-COACH	POST OFFICE BOX 4064	ATLANTA, GA	30302
BEAUCHAMP, MARY M	WRITER	23388 MULHOLLAND HIGHWAY	WOODLAND HILLS, CA	91364
BEAUDINE, CRAIG	TV DIRECTOR	2221 PHYLLIS ST	LA CRESCENTA, CA	91214
BEAUDINE, DEKA	ACTRESS	POST OFFICE BOX 69590	LOS ANGELES, CA	90069
BEAUDINE, SKIP	FILM DIRECTOR	4717 POE AVE	WOODLAND HILLS, CA	91367
BEAUDINE, WILLIAM, JR	DIRECTOR-PRODUCER	5461 BOTHWELL RD	TARZANA, CA	91356
BEAUMONT, CHRIS	ACTOR	14746 VALLEY VISTA BLVD	SHERMAN OAKS, CA	91403
BEAUMONT, CHRISTOPHER	TV WRITER	9301 WILSHIRE BLVD #312	BEVERLY HILLS, CA	90210
BEAUMONT, GABRIELLE	TV DIRECTOR-PRODUCER	3456 ALANA DR	SHERMAN OAKS, CA	91403
BEAUMONT, VALERIE	ACTRESS	BIGLEY, 19725 SHERMAN WY #200	CANOGA PARK, CA	91306
BEAUSOLEIL	C & W GROUP	FOLKLORE, 1671 APPIAN WY	SANTA MONICA, CA	90401
BEAUVAIS, GARCELLE	ACTRESS	400 S BEVERLY DR #216	BEVERLY HILLS, CA	90212
BEAVER, DAN	SINGER	POST OFFICE BOX 42613	PORTLAND, OR	97242
BEAVERS, SUSAN	TV PRODUCER	CAA, 9830 WILSHIRE BLVD	BEVERLY HILLS, CA	90212
BEBAN, BOB	BASEBALL EXECUTIVE	POST OFFICE BOX 5566	EUGENE, OR	97405
BECHE, MIKE R	WRITER	18420 LEMARSH ST #27	NORTHRIDGE, CA	91325
BECK, BECK	AUTHOR-TV WRITER	9255 SUNSET BLVD #301	LOS ANGELES, CA	90069
BECK, BRIAN	BASEBALL	POST OFFICE BOX 3746, HILL STA	AUGUSTA, GA	30904
BECK, CHIP	GOLFER	POST OFFICE BOX 109601	PALM BCH GARDENS, FL	33418
BECK, DAVID M	ARTIST	1433 W RASCHER ST #3-W	CHICAGO, IL	60640
BECK, JACK W	CINEMATOGRAPHER	114 E 71ST ST	NEW YORK, NY	10021
BECK, JACKSON	ANNOUNCE-VOICE OVERS	MEDIASCOPE INC, 305 E 86TH ST	NEW YORK, NY	10028
BECK, JEFF	SINGER-GUITARIST	ERNEST CHAPMAN MANAGEMENT		
		11 OLD SQUARE LINCOLN'S INN	LONDON WC2	ENGLAND
BECK, JOHN	ACTOR	NBC-TV, "SANTA BARBARA"		
		3000 W ALAMEDA AVE	BURBANK, CA	91523
BECK, KIMBERLY	ACTRESS-MODEL	9229 SUNSET BLVD #311	LOS ANGELES, CA	90069
BECK, MARILYN	COLUMNIST-CRITIC	2132 EL ROBLE LN	BEVERLY HILLS, CA	90210
BECK, MARK	BASEBALL	POST OFFICE BOX 16683	GREENVILLE, SC	29606
BECK, MICHAEL	ACTOR	1999 AVE OF THE STARS #2850	LOS ANGELES, CA	90067
BECK, NOELLE	ACTRESS	ABC-TV, "LOVING"		
		320 W 66TH ST, STUDIO 23	NEW YORK, NY	10023
BECK, ROD	BASEBALL	S F GIANTS, CANDLESTICK PARK	SAN FRANICSCO, CA	94124
BECK, WYNN	BASEBALL	POST OFFICE BOX 855	BELOIT, WI	53511
BECK-HILTON, KIMBERLY	ACTRESS-MODEL	SEE - BECK, KIMBERLY		
BECKER, ARNOLD	TV EXECUTIVE	CBS-TV, 51 W 52ND ST	NEW YORK, NY	10019
BECKER, BORIS	TENNIS	NUSSLOCHER STR 51	6906 LEIMEN	GERMANY
BECKER, ELIZABETH	ACTRESS	6533 HOLLYWOOD BLVD #201	HOLLYWOOD, CA	90028
BECKER, H W "FRITZ"	CONDUCTOR	1055 E FLAMINGO RD #219	LAS VEGAS, NV	89109
BECKER, HAROLD	FILM DIRECTOR	7722 SENALDA RD	LOS ANGELES, CA	90068
BECKER, JOHN	FOOTBALL COACH	SEAHAWKS, 11220 NE 53RD ST	KIRKLAND, WA	98033
BECKER, LAURA	ACTRESS	150 E OLIVE AVE #111	BURBANK, CA	91502
BECKER, RICHIE	BASEBALL	POST OFFICE BOX 48	VISALIA, CA	93279
BECKER, SUSAN	COSTUME DESIGNER	13949 VENTURA BLVD #309	SHERMAN OAKS, CA	91423
BECKERMAN, ARNOLD	DIRECTOR	153 E 32ND ST	NEW YORK, NY	10016

BECKETT, ANN M	SCREENWRITER	13532 CONTOUR DR	SHERMAN OAKS, CA	91423
BECKETT, ROBBIE	BASEBALL	POST OFFICE BOX 611	WATERLOO, IA	50704
BECKLES, ALBERT	BODYBUILDER	POST OFFICE BOX 5005	MISSION HILLS, CA	91345
BECKLES, IAN	FOOTBALL	BUCCANEERS, 1 BUCCANEER PL	TAMPA, FL	33607
BECKLEY, BARBRA ANN	ACTRESS	2110 MEADOW VALLEY TERR	LOS ANGELES, CA	90039
BECKLUND, ERIC	BASEBALL EXECUTIVE	POST OFFICE BOX 2183	IDAHO FALLS, ID	83402
BECKWITH, ALAN	ACTOR	3928 CARPENTER AVE #102	STUDIO CITY, CA	91604
BECKWITH, DOUGLAS CHARLES	TV WRITER	11852 GORHAM AVE #5	LOS ANGELES, CA	90049
BEDELIA, BONNIE	ACTRESS	1021 GEORGINA AVE	SANTA MONICA, CA	90402
BEDELL, HOWIE	BASEBALL-EXECUTIVE	REDS, 100 RIVERFRONT STADIUM	CINCINNATI, OH	45202
BEDFORD, TERRENCE L	DIRECTOR	PANETH, HABER & ZIMMERMAN		
		TERRY BEDFORD PRODUCTIONS		
		600 3RD AVE, 8TH FLOOR	NEW YORK, NY	10016
BEDFORD, WILLIAM	BASKETBALL	THE PALACE OF AUBURN HILLS		
		2 CHAMPIONSHIP DR	AUBURN HILLS, MI	48326
BEDFORD-LLOYD, JOHN	ACTOR	SMITH, 121 N SAN VICENTE BLVD	BEVERLY HILLS, CA	90211
BEDI, KABIR	ACTOR	SHARKEY, 15 GOLDEN SQ #315	LONDON W1R 3AG	ENGLAND
BEDNAR, RUDY GERARD	DIRECTOR	DGA, 110 W 57TH ST	NEW YORK, NY	10019
BEDROSIAN, STEVE	BASEBALL	5490 CHEISENWOOD DR	DULUTH, GA	30136
BEDWAY, ART	BODYBUILDER	WEST VIRGINIA NPC DISTRICT		
		BOARD OF TRADING BUILDING		
		12TH & CHAPLIN ST	WHEELING, WV	26003
BEE, KATHY	SINGER	12001 WOODRUFF AVE #C	DOWNEY, CA	90241
BEE GEES, THE	ROCK & ROLL GROUP	9220 SUNSET BLVD #320	LOS ANGELES, CA	90069
BEEBE, BARBARA	ACTRESS	23903 RANNEY HOUSE CT	VALENCIA, CA	91355
BEEBE, DON	FOOTBALL	BILLS, 1 BILLS DR	ORCHARD PARK, NJ	14127
BEEBE, PAUL	COLUMNIST	POST OFFICE BOX 500	WASHINGTON, DC	20044
BEECE, DEBBY	TV EXECUTIVE	NICKELODEON, 1775 BROADWAY	NEW YORK, NY	10019
BEECROFT, DAVID	ACTOR	8444 WILSHIRE BLVD #800	BEVERLY HILLS, CA	90211
BEECROFT, GREGORY	ACTOR	247 S BEVERLY DR #102	BEVERLY HILLS, CA	90210
BEEFCAKE, BRUTUS "THE BARBER"	WRESTLER	POST OFFICE BOX 3859	STAMFORD, CT	06905
BEEKER, JEFF	ACTOR	151 N MAPLE ST #207	BURBANK, CA	91505
BEELBY, MALCOLM	COMPOSER-CONDUCTOR	117 S VAN NESS AVE	LOS ANGELES, CA	90004
BEELER, MARIAN	ACTRESS	6132 GLEN HOLLY ST	LOS ANGELES, CA	90068
BEELER, PETE	BASEBALL	POST OFFICE BOX 450	BUFFALO, NY	14205
BEEMAN, GREG	FILM DIRECTOR	9200 SUNSET BLVD #402	LOS ANGELES, CA	90069
BEEN, PATTI	ACTRESS	4943 LAUREL CANYON VLVD #11	NORTH HOLLYWOOD, CA	91607
BEENE, FRED	BASEBALL-SCOUT	BREWERS, 201 S 46TH ST	MILWAUKEE, WI	53214
BEER, HANS L	CONDUCTOR	7225 HOLLYWOOD BLVD #218	LOS ANGELES, CA	90046
BEERMANN, ALLEN	SECRETARY OF STATE	STATE CAPITOL BUILDING	LINCOLN, NE	68509
BEERS, BOB	SINGER	POST OFFICE BOX 655	HUDSON, OH	44236
BEERS, CAROLE A	WRITER	4016 ALTA MESA DR	STUDIO CITY, CA	91604
BEERS, JACK	ACTOR-SINGER	RICHMOND HILL RD	GREENWICH, CT	06830
BEERY, BARBARA	WRITER	3855 VENTURA CANYON AVE	SHERMAN OAKS, CA	91423
BEERY, BUCKLIND	ACTOR	17823 TARZANA ST	ENCINO, CA	91316
BEERY, NOAH, JR	ACTOR	POST OFFICE BOX 108	KEENE, CA	93531
BEESON, JACK	COMPOSER	404 RIVERSIDE DR	NEW YORK, NY	10025
BEESON, PAUL	CINEMATOGRAPHER	TREE HOUSE, HEUDSEN WY		
		GERRARDS CROSS	BUCKS	ENGLAND
BEESTON, PAUL	BASEBALL EXECUTIVE	SKYDOME, 300 BREMMER BL #3200	TORONTO, ONT M5V 3B3	CANADA
BEGA, LESLIE	ACTRESS	6451 DEEP DELL PL	LOS ANGELES, CA	90048
BEGEL, CINDY J	WRITER	14010 CAPTAINS ROW DR #344	MARINA DEL REY, CA	90292
BEGELMAN, DAVID	FILM EXECUTIVE	705 N LINDEN DR	BEVERLY HILLS, CA	90210
BEGHE, JASON	ACTOR	400 S BEVERLY DR #216	BEVERLY HILLS, CA	90212
BEGIN, MARY JANE	ARTIST	124 PELHAMDALE AVE #8	PELHAM, NY	10803
BEGIN, ROGER	LT GOVERNOR	STATE CAPITOL, 320 S MAIN ST	PROVIDENCE, RI	02903
BEGLEITER, RALPH	NEWS CORRESPONDENT	1050 TECHWOOD DR, NW	ATLANTA, GA	30318
BEGLEY, ED, JR	ACTOR	3850 MOUND VIEW AVE	STUDIO CITY, CA	91604
BEGUN, HOWARD J	COMPOSER	4068 TUJUNGA AVE #C	STUDIO CITY, CA	91604
BEHA, TEX	TALENT AGENT	STE, 888 7TH AVE, 18TH FLOOR	NEW YORK, NY	10106
BEHAR, JOSEPH	TV DIRECTOR	22760 FLAMINGO ST	WOODLAND HILLS, CA	91364
BEHLMER, RUDY	DIRECTOR	3972 TROPICAL DR	STUDIO CITY, CA	91604
BEHR, IRA STEVEN	TV WRITER	10100 SANTA MONICA BLVD #1600	LOS ANGELES, CA	90067
BEHR, JACK	WRITER	2460 BEVERLY AVE	SANTA MONICA, CA	90405
BEHREND, JACK	DIRECTOR	918 HINMAN AVE	EVANSTON, IL	60202
BEHRENS, BERNARD	ACTOR	SMITH, 121 N SAN VICENTE BLVD	BEVERLY HILLS, CA	90211
BEHRENS, DIANE	ACTRESS	CED, 261 S ROBERTSON BLVD	BEVERLY HILLS, CA	90211
BEHRENS, KENNETH	JOURNALIST	NO 1 SAINT GEORGE'S FLAT		
		BOURDON ST	LONDON W1X 9JA	ENGLAND
BEHRENS, SAM	ACTOR	10000 SANTA MONICA BLVD #305	LOS ANGELES, CA	90067
BEHRING, LEN	FOOTBALL EXECUTIVE	SEAHAWKS, 11220 NE 53RD ST	KIRKLAND, WA	98033
BEHRMAN, KEVIN M	TV DIRECTOR	109 SEWARD AVE	MINEOLA, NY	11501
BEHRSTOCK, ROGER	ACTOR	212 S LINDEN DR	BEVERLY HILLS, CA	90212
BEIGHTOL, LARRY	FOOTBALL COACH	N Y JETS, 1000 FULTON AVE	HEMPSTEAD, NY	11550
BEILENSON, ANTHONY	U S CONGRESSMAN	11000 WILSHIRE BLVD #12230	LOS ANGELES, CA	90024
BEINFEST, LARRY	BASEBALL EXECUTIVE	POST OFFICE BOX 4100	SEATTLE, WA	98104
BEKINS, RICHARD	ACTOR	225 W 34TH ST #405	NEW YORK, NY	10122
BEL GEDDES, BARBARA	ACTRESS	15 MILL ST	PUTNAM VALLEY, NY	10579
BEL-FIRES, THE	ROCK & ROLL GROUP	POST OFFICE BOX 784	SIERRA MADRE, CA	91024
BELACK, DORIS	ACTRESS	5750 WILSHIRE BLVD #512	LOS ANGELES, CA	90036
BELAFONTE, DAVID	ACTOR	829 S BUNDY DR	LOS ANGELES, CA	90049
BELAFONTE, HARRY	ACTOR-SINGER	888 7TH AVE #1602	NEW YORK, NY	10019
BELAFONTE, SHARI	MODEL-ACTRESS	3546 LONGRIDGE AVE	SHERMAN OAKS, CA	91423
BELANGER, MARK	BASEBALL	2028 POT SPRING RD	TIMONIUM, MD	21093
BELCHER, KEVIN	BASEBALL	POST OFFICE BOX 4448	TULSA, OK	74159

Name	Occupation	Address	City	Zip/Country
BELCHER, TIM	BASEBALL	REDS, 100 RIVERFRONT STADIUM	CINCINNATI, OH	45202
BELEW, BILL	COSTUME DESIGNER	13949 VENTURA BLVD #309	SHERMAN OAKS, CA	91423
BELFORD, CHRISTINA	ACTRESS	10100 SANTA MONICA BLVD #700	LOS ANGELES, CA	90067
BELICH, EMIL	BASEBALL SCOUT	POST OFFICE BOX 7575	PHILADELPHIA, PA	19101
BELICHICK, BILL	FOOTBALL COACH	BROWNS, 80 1ST ST	BEREA, OH	44017
BELIFANTE, GEOFFREY	TV PRODUCER	MAJOR LEAGUE BASEBALL PRODS		
		1212 AVE OF THE AMERICAS	NEW YORK, NY	10036
BELINDA, STAN	BASEBALL	POST OFFICE BOX 7000	PITTSBURGH, PA	15212
BELINSKY, BO	BASEBALL	POST OFFICE BOX 671	WAIALUA, HI	96791
BELITA	ACTRESS-BALLERIA	ROSE COTTAGE, 44 CRABTREE LN	LONDON SW6	ENGLAND
BELKIN, GARY	WRITER	10787 WILSHIRE BLVD #1201	LOS ANGELES, CA	90024
BELKIN, HARRIET	WRITER	516 N LAUREL AVE	LOS ANGELES, CA	90048
BELKIN, NORMAN	WRITER	516 N LAUREL AVE	LOS ANGELES, CA	90048
BELKIN, PEARL	WRITER	10787 WILSHIRE BLVD #1201	LOS ANGELES, CA	90024
BELL, ALAN	WRITER-PRODUCER	CCA, 4 COURT LODGE		
		48 SLOANE SQ	LONDON SW1W 8AT	ENGLAND
BELL, ALAN J W	DIRECTOR-PRODUCER	WM MORRIS, 31-32 SOHO SQ	LONDON W1V 5DG	ENGLAND
BELL, BRADLEY	TV PRODUCER	CBS-TV, "THE BOLD & BEAUTIFUL"		
		7800 BEVERLY BLVD #3371	LOS ANGELES, CA	90036
BELL, BRAND	WRITER	28220 AGOURA RD	AGOURA, CA	91301
BELL, BRENT	BASEBALL	POST OFFICE BOX 3614	MARTINSVILLE, VA	24115
BELL, BUDDY	BASEBALL	6485 HUNTERS TRAIL	CINCINNATI, OH	45243
BELL, BUDDY	BASEBALL-EXECUTIVE	333 W 35TH ST	CHICAGO, IL	60616
BELL, CHARLES ROBERT	DIRECTOR	100 E BROADWAY	ROSLYN, NY	11576
BELL, DAVID	BASEBALL	POST OFFICE BOX 3452	KINSTON, NC	28502
BELL, DAVID A	COMPOSER-CONDUCTOR	1542 HARVARD ST #B	SANTA MONICA, CA	90404
BELL, DEREK	BASEBALL	SKYDOME, 300 BREMMER BL #3200	TORONTO, ONT M5V 3B3	CANADA
BELL, EDWARD	ACTOR	145 S FAIRFAX AVE #310	LOS ANGELES, CA	90036
BELL, ERIC	BASEBALL	INDIANS, CLEVELAND STADIUM	CLEVELAND, OH	44114
BELL, ERIC	TV DIRECTOR	THE ERIC BELL COMPANY		
		310 W 72ND ST	NEW YORK, NY	10023
BELL, FELECIA	ACTRESS	1930 CENTURY PARK W #403	LOS ANGELES, CA	90067
BELL, GEORGE "TACO"	BASEBALL	333 W 35TH ST	CHICAGO, IL	60616
BELL, J D & THE SILVER SPURS	C & W GROUP	ACE PRODS, 3407 GREEN RIDGE DR	NASHVILLE, TN	37214
BELL, JANE UPTON	TV DIRECTOR	12225 SAN VICENTE BLVD	LOS ANGELES, CA	90049
BELL, JAY	BASEBALL	POST OFFICE BOX 7000	PITTSBURGH, PA	15212
BELL, JERRY	BASEBALL EXECUTIVE	TWINS, 501 CHICAGO AVE S	MINNEAPOLIS, MN	55415
BELL, JOHN J	TV DIRECTOR	11-C HERITAGE SOUND	MILFORD, CT	06460
BELL, JUAN	BASEBALL	500 NORTON ST	ROCHESTER, NY	14621
BELL, KAREN	ARTIST	8800 VENICE BLVD	LOS ANGELES, CA	90034
BELL, KENNETH	SINGER	254 W 93RD ST #8	NEW YORK, NY	10025
BELL, LAURALEE	ACTRESS	CBS-TV, "YOUNG & THE RESTLESS"		
		7800 BEVERLY BLVD #3305	LOS ANGELES, CA	90036
BELL, MIKE	BASEBALL	POST OFFICE BOX 16683	GREENVILLE, SC	29606
BELL, TOM	ACTOR	108 TORRIANO AVE	LONDON NW5	ENGLAND
BELL, TOMMY	SINGER	DEAN, 612 HUMBOLDT ST	RENO, NV	89509
BELL, WALLY	BASEBALL UMPIRE	POST OFFICE BOX 608	GROVE CITY, OH	43123
BELL BAND, TIGAR	C & W GROUP	POST OFFICE BOX 4087	MISSOULA, MT	59806
BELLAH, JAMES	WRITER	19030 MIRANDA ST	TARZANA, CA	91356
BELLAK, GEORGE	TV WRITER	CAA, 9830 WILSHIRE BLVD	BEVERLY HILLS, CA	90212
BELLAMY, DAVID	SINGER-SONGWRITER	JIM HALSEY, 24 MUSIC SQUARE W	NASHVILLE, TN	37203
BELLAMY, EARL	DIRECTOR-PRODUCER	6111 EL ESCORPION RD	WOODLAND HILLS, CA	91367
BELLAMY, HOWARD	SINGER-SONGWRITER	JIM HALSEY, 24 MUSIC SQUARE W	NASHVILLE, TN	37203
BELLAMY, NED	ACTOR	2566 OVERLAND AVE #550	LOS ANGELES, CA	90064
BELLAMY BROTHERS, THE	C & W DUO	ROUTE #2, BOX 294	DADE CITY, FL	33525
BELLAVER, HARRY	ACTOR	116 SUMMIT AVE	TAPPAN, NY	10983
BELLE, ALBERT "JOEY"	BASEBALL	4378 THURGOOD CIR	SHREVEPORT, LA	71109
BELLE, BUSTY	DANCER	POST OFFICE BOX 007	GAY MILLS, WI	54631
BELLER, KATHLEEN	ACTRESS	10100 SANTA MONICA BLVD #700	LOS ANGELES, CA	90067
BELLER, MILES	TV CRITIC	6715 SUNSET BLVD	HOLLYWOOD, CA	90028
BELLEROSE, MARK	ARTIST	GUNN ASSOC, 275 NEWBURY ST	BOSTON, MA	02116
BELLI, MELVIN	ATTORNEY	574 PACIFIC AVE	SAN FRANCISCO, CA	94133
BELLIARD, RAFAEL	BASEBALL	POST OFFICE BOX 4064	ATLANTA, GA	30302
BELLIN, GIL	TV DIRECTOR-PRODUCER	175 WESTMINSTER DR	YONKERS, NY	10710
BELLIN, LEWIS	COMPOSER	THE BEACON HOTEL		
		75TH & BROADWAY	NEW YORK, NY	10023
BELLINGER, CLAY	BASEBALL	POST OFFICE BOX 3448	SHREVEPORT, LA	71133
BELLINGHAM, LYNDA	ACTRESS	SARABAND, 265 LIVERPOOL RD	LONDON N1 1LX	ENGLAND
BELLINI, GABRIELE	CONDUCTOR	61 W 62ND ST #6-F	NEW YORK, NY	10023
BELLINO, JOE	BASEBALL SCOUT	REDS, 100 RIVERFRONT STADIUM	CINCINNATI, OH	45202
BELLINO, RAY	BASEBALL SCOUT	REDS, 100 RIVERFRONT STADIUM	CINCINNATI, OH	45202
BELLISARIO, DONALD PAUL	TV PRODUCER	3301 OAKDELL RD	STUDIO CITY, CA	91604
BELLO, STEPHEN	SCREENWRITER	12011 ADDISON ST	NORTH HOLLYWOOD, CA	91607
BELLOMO, KEVIN	BASEBALL	POST OFFICE BOX 7893	EVERETT, WA	98201
BELLOWS, BRIAN	HOCKEY	NORTH STARS, 7901 CEDAR AVE S	BLOOMINGTON, MN	55425
BELLSON, LOUIE	DRUMMER	POST OFFICE BOX 2608	LAKE HAVASU CITY, AZ	86405
BELLWOOD-WHEELER, PAMELA	ACTRESS-PHOTOGRAPHER	7444 WOODROW WILSON DR	LOS ANGELES, CA	90046
BELM, ELIZABETH	ACTRESS	FOLGO, 1502 QUEENS DR	LOS ANGELES, CA	90069
BELMONDO, JEAN-PAUL	ACTOR	77 AVE DONFERT ROCHEREAUX	PARIS 75016	FRANCE
BELMONT, FRANK L	DIRECTOR	18 RICHMOND AVE	PATERSON, NJ	07502
BELMONTE, NICK	BASEBALL MANAGER	1325 S MAIN #229	SALT LAKE CITY, UT	84115
BELSON, JERRY L	FILM WRITER-DIRECTOR	8047 WOODROW WILSON DR	LOS ANGELES, CA	90046
BELTRAN, RIGO	BASEBALL	POST OFFICE BOX 3783	SAVANNAH, GA	31414
BELTRAN, ROBERT	ACTOR	1999 AVE OF THE STARS #2850	LOS ANGELES, CA	90067
BELTRE, ESTEBAN	BASEBALL	CANADIANS, 4601 ONTARIO ST	VANCOUVER, BC V5V 3H4	CANADA

Name	Occupation	Address	City	Zip
BELTZER, YVONNE ROSE	SCREENWRITER	906 UCLAN DR	BURBANK, CA	91504
BELUSHI, JAMES	ACTOR-FILM PRODUCER	CAA, 9830 WILSHIRE BLVD	BEVERLY HILLS, CA	90212
BELYEU, RANDY	BASEBALL	POST OFFICE BOX 4488	WINSTON-SALEM, NC	27115
BELZ, JIM	BASEBALL SCOUT	250 STADIUM PLAZA	ST LOUIS, MO	63102
BELZER, RICHARD	COMEDIAN	151 S EL CAMINO DR	BEVERLY HILLS, CA	90212
BEN, SETH	ARTIST	47 E 3RD ST #3	NEW YORK, NY	10003
BEN-DOR, GISELE BUKA	CONDUCTOR	ROSENFIELD, 714 LADD RD	BRONX, NY	10471
BENAIR, JONATHAN	WRITER	450 N HAYWORTH AVE	LOS ANGELES, CA	90048
BENARD, FRANC M	ACTOR	9300 WILSHIRE BLVD #410	BEVERLY HILLS, CA	90212
BENATAR, PAT	SINGER-SONGWRITER	NEW STAR ENTS, 60 W 70TH ST	NEW YORK, NY	10023
BENAVIDES, ALVARO	BASEBALL	POST OFFICE BOX 21727	SAN FRANCISCO, CA	95151
BENAVIDES, FREDDIE	BASEBALL	REDS, 100 RIVERFRONT STADIUM	CINCINNATI, OH	45202
BENBOW, LOUIS	BASEBALL	POST OFFICE BOX 1088	ST CATH, ONT L2R 3BO	CANADA
BENCH, JOHNNY	BASEBALL	661 REISLING KNOLL	CINCINNATI, OH	45226
BENCHLEY, PETER	AUTHOR	35 BOUDINOT ST	PRINCETON, NJ	08540
BENCIVENGO, RICHARD	DIRECTOR	327 W 89TH ST #5-R	NEW YORK, NY	10024
BENDER, BOB	DIRECTOR	4000 SUNNYSLOPE AVE	SHERMAN OAKS, CA	91423
BENDER, JACK L	TV WRITER-DIRECTOR	1424 ORIOLE DR	LOS ANGELES, CA	90069
BENDER, JOAN	WRITER-DIRECTOR	414 E 52ND ST	NEW YORK, NY	10022
BENDER, JOHANNES P	CONDUCTOR	1619 ALAMITAS AVE	MONROVIA, CA	91016
BENDER, LESLIE MICHAEL	TV DIRECTOR	699 EDGEWOOD DR	MILL VALLEY, CA	94941
BENDER, PHILLIP C	TV DIRECTOR	1283 MUSTANG DR	DANVILLE, CA	94526
BENDER, SHELDON "CHIEF"	BASEBALL-EXECUTIVE	REDS, 100 RIVERFRONT STADIUM	CINCINNATI, OH	45202
BENDER, SID	COMPOSER	11326 CHADWELL	LAKEWOOD, CA	90715
BENDETSON, BOB S	TV WRITER	15128 MARTHA ST	VAN NUYS, CA	91411
BENDETSON, HOWARD M	TV WRITER	5023 SAN FELICIANO DR	WOODLAND HILLS, CA	91364
BENDETT, KATHY	ACTRESS	2431 BRIARCREST RD	BEVERLY HILLS, CA	90210
BENDETTI, MICHAEL	ACTOR	8484 WILSHIRE BLVD #530	BEVERLY HILLS, CA	90211
BENDICK, ROBERT L	TV DIRECTOR	19 SEA VIEW	GUILFORD, CT	06437
BENE, BILL	BASEBALL	POST OFFICE BOX 28268	SAN ANTONIO, TX	78228
BENEDEK, BARBARA	SCREENWRITER	CAA, 9830 WILSHIRE BLVD	BEVERLY HILLS, CA	90212
BENEDEK, LASLO	DIRECTOR	70 BANK ST	NEW YORK, NY	10014
BENEDEK, PETER	TALENT AGENT	UTA, 9560 WILSHIRE BL, 5TH FL	BEVERLY HILLS, CA	90212
BENEDEK, THOMAS R	SCREENWRITER	3472 MANDEVILLE CANYON RD	LOS ANGELES, CA	90049
BENEDETTI, ROBERT	ACTOR	6117 1/2 ROMAINE ST	HOLLYWOOD, CA	90038
BENEDETTO, RICHARD	COLUMNIST	POST OFFICE BOX 500	WASHINGTON, DC	20044
BENEDETTO, ROBERT E	TV WRITER	10100 SANTA MONICA BLVD #1600	LOS ANGELES, CA	90067
BENEDICT, BILLY	ACTOR	1347 N ORANGE GROVE AVE	LOS ANGELES, CA	90046
BENEDICT, BRUCE	BASEBALL	335 QUIET WATER LN	DUNWOODY, GA	30338
BENEDICT, DIRK	ACTOR	1637 WELLESLEY DR	SANTA MONICA, CA	90406
BENEDICT, JAY	ACTOR	18 MARTINDALE RD	LONDON SW12 9PW	ENGLAND
BENEDICT, JIM	BASEBALL COACH	POST OFFICE BOX 186	BUTTE, MT	59703
BENEDICT, JIM	BASEBALL SCOUT	POST OFFICE BOX 90111	ARLINGTON, TX	76004
BENEDICT, NICK	ACTOR	BDP, 10637 BURBANK BLVD	NORTH HOLLYWOOD, CA	91601
BENEDICT, PAUL	ACTOR	POST OFFICE BOX 451	CHILMARK, MA	02535
BENEDICT, ROBERT	ACTOR	13455 VENTURA BLVD #210	SHERMAN OAKS, CA	91423
BENEDICT, SHIRLEY	WRITER	POST OFFICE BOX 155	FOREST HILLS, CA	11375
BENEDICT, WILLIAM	ACTOR	1347 N ORANGE GROVE AVE	LOS ANGELES, CA	90046
BENEDICTUS, DAVID	WRI-DIR-PROD	19 OXFORD RD, TEDDINGTON	MIDDLESEX TW11 OQA	ENGLAND
BENEKE, TEX	ORCHESTRA LEADER	2275 FAUST AVE	LONG BEACH, CA	90815
BENES, ANDY	BASEBALL	POST OFFICE BOX 2000	SAN DIEGO, CA	92112
BENEST, GLEN M	SCREENWRITER	953 11TH ST #1	SANTA MONICA, CA	90403
BENFIELD, DEREK	ACTOR	EDWARDS, 275 KENNINGTON RD	LONDON SE1 6BY	ENGLAND
BENGE, BRETT	BASEBALL	POST OFFICE BOX 418	SAINT CHARLES, IL	60174
BENHARDT, CHRIS	BASEBALL	POST OFFICE BOX 4758	SPOKANE, WA	99202
BENICKES, MILES L	WRITER	3220 PHILO ST	LOS ANGELES, CA	90064
BENING, ANNETTE	ACTRESS	2029 CENTURY PARK E #300	LOS ANGELES, CA	90067
BENIQUEZ, JUAN, SR	BASEBALL	CALLE 99-A BLK 87 #12	CAROLINA, PR	00630
BENITZ, YAMIL	BASEBALL	POLECATS, 608 N SLAPPEY BLVD	ALBANY, GA	31701
BENJAMIN, ANN	TV DIRECTOR	600 W END AVE #1-A-1	NEW YORK, NY	10024
BENJAMIN, BENOIT	BASKETBALL	CLIPPERS, 3939 S FIGUEROA ST	LOS ANGELES, CA	90037
BENJAMIN, BOBBY	BASEBALL	POST OFFICE BOX 8550	STOCKTON, CA	95208
BENJAMIN, BREANNA	TALENT AGENT	1600 BROADWAY #511	NEW YORK, NY	10019
BENJAMIN, CYNTHIA	TV WRITER	555 W 57TH ST #1230	NEW YORK, NY	10019
BENJAMIN, FLOELLA	ACTRESS	TAYLOR, 73 PALANCE RD	LONDON SW2 3LB	ENGLAND
BENJAMIN, KENNETH	ACTOR	7715 SUNSET BLVD #214	LOS ANGELES, CA	90046
BENJAMIN, MIKE	BASEBALL	S F GIANTS, CANDLESTICK PARK	SAN FRANICSCO, CA	94124
BENJAMIN, PAUL	ACTOR	10351 SANTA MONICA BLVD #211	LOS ANGELES, CA	90025
BENJAMIN, RICHARD	ACTOR-DIRECTOR	719 N FOOTHILL RD	BEVERLY HILLS, CA	90210
BENKMAN, HERBERT F	ACTOR	535 S CURSON AVE #8-K	LOS ANGELES, CA	90036
BENN, HARRY	FILM PRODUCER	7 BELLMOUNT WOOD AVE, WATFORD	HERTS WD1 3BN	ENGLAND
BENNEDY, BOB	BASEBALL EXECUTIVE	S F GIANTS, CANDLESTICK PARK	SAN FRANCISCO, CA	94124
BENNER, RICK	BASKETBALL EXECUTIVE	KINGS, 1 SPORTS PARKWAY	SACRAMENTO, CA	95834
BENNETT, AL	BASEBALL	POST OFFICE BOX 1721	SPARTANBURG, SC	29304
BENNETT, ALAN	ACTOR-WRITER	CHATTO AND LINNIT, LTD		
		PRINCE OF WALES THEATRE		
		COVENTRY ST	LONDON W1V 7FE	ENGLAND
BENNETT, ALEXANDRA	TV PRODUCER	CBS-TV, 51 W 52ND ST	NEW YORK, NY	10019
BENNETT, ANDREA "ANDY"	AUDITOR	STATE CAPITOL BUILDING	HELENA, MT	59620
BENNETT, ANNE	FILM EXECUTIVE	UIP HOUSE, 45 BEADON RD		
		HAMMERSMITH	LONDON W6 OEG	ENGLAND
BENNETT, BRUCE	ACTOR	2702 FORESTER RD	LOS ANGELES, CA	90064
BENNETT, CHARLES	WRITER-DIRECTOR	1720 COLDWATER CANYON DR	BEVERLY HILLS, CA	90210
BENNETT, CHARLES E	U S CONGRESSMAN	314 PALMETTO ST	JACKSONVILLE, FL	32202
BENNETT, CORNELIUS	FOOTBALL	BILLS, 1 BILLS DR	ORCHARD PARK, NJ	14127

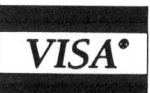

BENNETT, DEREK JAMES	TV DIRECTOR-PRODUCER	THE MEWS, RED LODGE	
		BUSTON RD, DISLEY	CHESHIRE ENGLAND
BENNETT, DOUG	BASEBALL	POST OFFICE BOX 483	YAKIMA, WA 98907
BENNETT, EDWARD	TV DIRECTOR	54 ELMORE ST	LONDON N1 3AL ENGLAND
BENNETT, ERIK	BASEBALL	POST OFFICE BOX 1742	PALM SPRINGS, CA 92263
BENNETT, FRAN	ACTRESS	2125 W SILVER LAKE DR	LOS ANGELES, CA 90039
BENNETT, GARY	BASEBALL	POST OFFICE BOX 3614	MARTINSVILLE, VA 24115
BENNETT, GENE	BASEBALL SCOUT	REDS, 100 RIVERFRONT STADIUM	CINCINNATI, OH 45202
BENNETT, HYWEL	ACTOR-DIRECTOR	SHARKEY, 15 GOLDEN SQ #315	LONDON W1R 3AG ENGLAND
BENNETT, JANET	TV WRITER	MOLLIKO, 16-18 NEW BRIDGE ST	LONDON EC4V 6AU ENGLAND
BENNETT, JOEL	BASEBALL	RED SOX, CHAIN O'LAKES PARK	WINTER HAVEN, FL 33880
BENNETT, JOHN	ACTOR	MARKHAM AND FROGGATT, LTD	
		JULIAN HOUSE, 4 WINDMILL ST	LONDON W1P 1HF ENGLAND
BENNETT, KENNY	SINGER	POST OFFICE BOX 06404	PORTLAND, OR 97206
BENNETT, MARSHALL	TREASURER	POST OFFICE BOX 2000	JACKSON, MS 39215
BENNETT, MATT	ACTOR	4132 TOLUCA LAKE AVE	BURBANK, CA 91505
BENNETT, MEG	ACTRESS-WRITER	8955 BEVERLY BLVD	WEST HOLLYWOOD, CA 90048
BENNETT, PETER	PRODUCER-PROMOTER	POST OFFICE BOX 563	NEW YORK, NY 10036
BENNETT, ROBERT IRWIN	ACTOR	HENRY ONG, 6362 HOLLYWOOD BLVD	LOS ANGELES, CA 90028
BENNETT, SEAN	SINGER	BUN JAK, 331 PROPSECT ST	BERLIN, NH 03570
BENNETT, SEYMOUR	WRITER	6439 MOORE DR	LOS ANGELES, CA 90048
BENNETT, TONY	FOOTBALL	PACKERS, 1265 LOMBARDI AVE	GREEN BAY, WI 54307
BENNETT, TONY	SINGER-ACTOR	101 W 55TH ST #9-A	NEW YORK, NY 10019
BENNETT, WALLACE S	SCREENWRITER	5598 S RIM ST	WESTLAKE VILLAGE, CA 91362
BENNETT, WINSTON	BASKETBALL	POST OFFICE BOX 5000	RICHFIELD, OH 44286
BENNEWITZ, JAMES RICK	TV DIRECTOR	3426 N KNOLL DR	LOS ANGELES, CA 90068
BENNING, BRIAN	HOCKEY	POST OFFICE BOX 17013	INGLEWOOD, CA 90308
BENNINGTON, JEFF	BASEBALL	POST OFFICE BOX 824	BURLINGTON, IA 52601
BENOWITZ, ROY	COMPOSER	464 S BERENDO ST #305	LOS ANGELES, CA 90020
BENRARD, JAMI	FILM CRITIC	N Y POST, 210 SOUTH ST	NEW YORK, NY 10002
BENSCHING, BRUCE	BASEBALL	POST OFFICE BOX 611	WATERLOO, IA 50704
BENSFIELD, RICHARD E	TV WRITER-PRODUCER	8955 BEVERLY BLVD	WEST HOLLYWOOD, CA 90048
BENSINK, JOHN ROBERT	TV WRITER	9000 SUNSET BLVD #1200	LOS ANGELES, CA 90069
BENSON, DEBORAH	ACTRESS	2029 CENTURY PARK E #600	LOS ANGELES, CA 90067
BENSON, DONALD	BASEBALL EXECUTIVE	TWINS, 501 CHICAGO AVE S	MINNEAPOLIS, MN 55415
BENSON, GEORGE	SINGER-GUITARIST	444 S SAN VICENTE BLVD	LOS ANGELES, CA 90048
BENSON, GRAHAM	FILM PRODUCER	PETERS, FRASER & DUNLOP, LTD	
		5TH FLOOR, THE CHAMBERS	
		CHELSEA HARBOUR, LOT RD	LONDON SW10 OXF ENGLAND
BENSON, HUGH	TV PRODUCER	222 N CANON DR	BEVERLY HILLS, CA 90210
BENSON, JAY	TV WRITER-PRODUCER	18628 ROCOSO PL	TARZANA, CA 91356
BENSON, JEFFREY	TALENT AGENT	MTA, 9320 WILSHIRE BL, 3RD FL	BEVERLY HILLS, CA 90212
BENSON, JODI	ACTRESS	11755 WILSHIRE BLVD #2320	LOS ANGELES, CA 90025
BENSON, LINDA	ARTIST	558 7TH ST	BROOKLYN, NY 11215
BENSON, LORRI	TV PRODUCER	"THE DONAHUE SHOW"	
		30 ROCKEFELLER PLAZA, 8TH FL	NEW YORK, NY 10112
BENSON, MITCHELL	FOOTBALL	POST OFFICE BOX 609609	SAN DIEGO, CA 92160
BENSON, NATE	BASEBALL	POST OFFICE BOX 7845	COLUMBIA, SC 29202
BENSON, ROBBY	ACT-WRI-SING	15760 VENTURA BLVD #1730	ENCINO, CA 91436
BENSON, SHEILA	FILM CRITIC	LA TIMES, TIMES MIRROR SQ	LOS ANGELES, CA 90053
BENSON, STEVE	CARTOONIST	POST OFFICE BOX 1950	PHOENIX, AZ 85001
BENSON, TOM	FOOTBALL	RAIDERS, 332 CENTER ST	EL SEGUNDO, CA 90245
BENSON, TOM	FOOTBALL EXECUTIVE	SAINTS, 1500 POYDRAS ST	NEW ORLEANS, LA 90112
BENSON, VERN	BASEBALL-SCOUT	250 STADIUM PLAZA	ST LOUIS, MO 63102
BENSON-GYLES, ANNA	TV DIRECTOR	BBC-TV, 56 WOOD LN	LONDON W12 7RJ ENGLAND
BENTINCK, TIMOTHY	ACTOR	HAMMOND, GOLDEN HOUSE	
		29 GREAT PULTENEY ST	LONDON W1R 3DD ENGLAND
BENTLEY, ALBERT	FOOTBALL	POST OFFICE BOX 535000	INDIANPOLIS, IN 46253
BENTLEY, BLAKE	BASEBALL	POST OFFICE BOX 5646	PRINCETON, WV 24740
BENTLEY, BOB	TV DIRECTOR	7 CHANTRY ST, ISLINGTON	LONDON N1 8NR ENGLAND
BENTLEY, HELEN	U S CONGRESSMAN	115 FULFORD AVE	BEL AIR, MD 21014
BENTLEY, JOHN	ACTOR	WEDGEWORTH HOUSE, PETERWORTH	SURREY ENGLAND
BENTLEY, RAY	FOOTBALL	BILLS, 1 BILLS DR	ORCHARD PARK, NJ 14127
BENTLEY, SAVANNAH	ACTRESS	8225 LOOKOUT MOUNTAIN AVE	LOS ANGELES, CA 90046
BENTON, BARBI	ACTRESS-MODEL	POST OFFICE BOX 549	CARBONDALE, CO 81623
BENTON, DANIEL KING	ACTOR-WRITER	7924 WOODMAN AVE #55	VAN NUYS, CA 91402
BENTON, DOUGLAS CARLTON	WRITER-PRODUCER	4924 CALVIN AVE	TARZANA, CA 91356
BENTON, LEE	ACTRESS	ATKINS, 303 S CRESCENT HEIGHTS	LOS ANGELES, CA 90048
BENTON, SUZANNE	ACTRESS	2360 SUNSET PLAZA DR	LOS ANGELES, CA 90069
BENTSEN, LLOYD	U S SENATOR	1919 SMITH ST #800	HOUSTON, TX 77002
BENVENUTI, JOSEPH	BASKETBALL EXECUTIVE	KINGS, 1 SPORTS PARKWAY	SACRAMENTO, CA 95834
BENZ, GARY	DIRECTOR	12345 VENTURA BLVD #H	STUDIO CITY, CA 91604
BENZINGER, TODD	BASEBALL	1000 ELYSIAN PARK DR	LOS ANGELES, CA 90012
BERADINO, JOHN	ACTOR	1719 AMBASSADOR DR	BEVERLY HILLS, CA 90210
BERARDINO, DICK	BASEBALL-COACH	FENWAY PARK, 4 YAWKEY WY	BOSTON, MA 02215
BERARDINO, JOHN	ACTOR-BASEBALL	1719 AMBASSADOR AVE	BEVERLY HILLS, CA 90210
BERCOV, BRIAN R	COMPOSER-CONDUCTOR	3884 FRANKLIN AVE	LOS ANGELES, CA 90027
BERCOVICI, ERIC	WRITER-PRODUCER	154 S LAYTON DR	LOS ANGELES, CA 90049
BERCOVICI, JULIAN	WRITER	1456 BELFAST DR	LOS ANGELES, CA 90069
BERCOVICI, KAREN	ACTRESS	208 S BEDFORD DR	BEVERLY HILLS, CA 90212
BERCOVICI, LEONARD	WRITER	969 HILGARD AVE	LOS ANGELES, CA 90024
BERCOVICI, LUCA J	ACT-WRI-DIR	2226 PENMAR AVE	VENICE, CA 90291
BERCOVITCH, REUBEN	WRITER-PRODUCER	139 S CARMELINA AVE	LOS ANGELES, CA 90049
BERDIS, BERT	TV WRITER	1100 N ALTA LOMA RD #806	LOS ANGELESLOS ANGELES 90069
BERE, JASON	BASEBALL	1090 N EUCLID AVE	SARASOTA, FL 34237

BERENGER, TOM	ACTOR	POST OFFICE BOX 1842	BEAUFORT, SC	29901
BERENGUER, JUAN	BASEBALL	POST OFFICE BOX 419969	KANSAS CITY, MO	64141
BERENSON, BERRY	ACTRESS	2840 SEATTLE DR	LOS ANGELES, CA	90046
BERENSON, CRAIG	ACTOR	1418 N HIGHLAND AVE #102	LOS ANGELES, CA	90028
BERENSON, MARISA	ACTRESS	80 AVE CHARLES DE GAULLE	NEUILLY 92200	FRANCE
BERENSTEIN, MORT	DIRECTOR	4925 WHITSETT AVE #201	NORTH HOLLYWOOD, CA	91607
BERENYI, BRUCE	BASEBALL	POST OFFICE BOX 133	SHERWOOD, OH	43556
BERESFORD, BRUCE	FILM DIRECTOR	3 MARATHON RD #13		
		DARLING POINT 2027	SYDNEY NSW 2027	AUSTRALIA
BEREUTER, DOUG	U S CONGRESSMAN	1045 "K" ST	LINCOLN, NE	68508
BEREZAN, PERRY	HOCKEY	NORTH STARS, 7901 CEDAR AVE S	BLOOMINGTON, MN	55425
BERG, BILL	HOCKEY	NASSAU VETS MEMORIAL COLISEUM	UNIONDALE, NY	11553
BERG, CURT	COMPOSER	524 N AVON ST	BURBANK, CA	91505
BERG, DANIEL J	DIRECTOR	DGA, 110 W 57TH ST	NEW YORK, NY	10019
BERG, DAVE	ARTIST-WRITER	MAD MAGAZINE, 485 MADISON AVE	NEW YORK, NY	10022
BERG, DICK	TV PRODUCER	WM MORRIS, 31-32 SOHO SQ	LONDON W1V 5DG	ENGLAND
BERG, ILENE AMY	TV PRODUCER	9949 ROBBINS DR #B	BEVERLY HILLS, CA	90212
BERG, JAMES B	TV WRITER	433 N CAMDEN DR #600	BEVERLY HILLS, CA	90210
BERG, JEFF	TALENT AGENT	ICM, 388-396 OXFORD ST	LONDON W1	ENGLAND
BERG, KEN	TV WRITER	2101 KELTON AVE	LOS ANGELES, CA	90045
BERG, PETER	ACTOR	ICM, 8899 BEVERLY BLVD	LOS ANGELES, CA	90048
BERG, PETER	ARTIST	6 ARLINGTON ST	ROCHESTER, NY	14607
BERG, RICHARD	BASEBALL	POST OFFICE BOX 8550	STOCKTON, CA	95208
BERG, RICK	BASEBALL	POST OFFICE DRAWER 4797	EL PASO, TX	79914
BERG, RICK	BASEBALL COACH	POST OFFICE BOX 6667	RICHMOND, VA	23230
BERG, STUART	DIRECTOR	3366 COY DR	SHERMAN OAKS, CA	91423
BERGAN, JUDITH-MARIE	ACTRESS	2458 MICHELTORENA ST	LOS ANGELES, CA	90039
BERGANDI, HECTOR LUIS	ARTIST	ROAD & TRACK MAGAZINE		
		1499 MONROVIA AVE	NEWPORT BEACH, CA	92663
BERGEN, CANDICE	ACTRESS	4000 WARNER BLVD	BURBANK, CA	91522
BERGEN, FRANCES	ACTRESS	1485 CARLA RIDGE DR	BEVERLY HILLS, CA	90210
BERGEN, POLLY	ACTRESS	1400 DEVLIN DR	LOS ANGELES, CA	90069
BERGER, ALAN	ACTOR-WRITER	1127 9TH ST #102	SANTA MONICA, CA	90403
BERGER, FRED W	FILM EDITOR	1560 KELTON AVE	LOS ANGELES, CA	90024
BERGER, GREGG	ACTOR	22061 GRESHAM ST	CANOGA PARK, CA	91304
BERGER, HELMUT	ACTOR	JOVANOVIC PERFALLSTR 6	8000 MUNICH 80	GERMANY
BERGER, LOU	TV WRITER	555 W 57TH ST #1230	NEW YORK, NY	10019
BERGER, MIKE	BASEBALL	POST OFFICE BOX 75089	OKLAHOMA CITY, OK	73147
BERGER, RICHARD L	FILM EXECUTIVE	637 N WILCOX AVE	LOS ANGELES, CA	90004
BERGER, ROBERT BRYAN	ACTOR	4746 VENTURA CANYON AVE	SHERMAN OAKS, CA	91423
BERGER, SENTA	ACTRESS	ROBERT-KOCH-STR 10	GRUNWALD 8022	GERMANY
BERGERE, LEE	ACTOR	2385 CENTURY HILL	LOS ANGELES, CA	90067
BERGERT, NED	BASEBALL TRAINER	POST OFFICE BOX 2000	ANAHEIM, CA	92803
BERGESCH, BILL	BASEBALL EXECUTIVE	N Y YANKEES, YANKEE STADIUM	BRONX, NY	10451
BERGGREN, ARTHUR	ACTOR	611 1/2 OCEAN PARK BLVD	SANTA MONICA, CA	90405
BERGHER, GARY	ACTOR	16814 HART ST	VAN NUYS, CA	91406
BERGLAND, BOND	SINGER	POST OFFICE BOX 20956		
		THOMPSON STATION	NEW YORK, NY	10009
BERGLAND, TIM	HOCKEY	JETS, 15-1430 MAROONS RD	WINNIPEG, MAN R3G 0L5	CANADA
BERGMAN, ALAN	LYRICIST	714 N MAPLE DR	BEVERLY HILLS, CA	90210
BERGMAN, ANDREW	WRITER-PRODUCER	CAA, 9830 WILSHIRE BLVD	BEVERLY HILLS, CA	90212
BERGMAN, ANDREW C	WRITER	ICM, 40 W 57TH ST	NEW YORK, NY	10019
BERGMAN, DAVE	BASEBALL	TIGERS, TIGER STADIUM	DETROIT, MI	48216
BERGMAN, INGMAR	FILM DIRECTOR	BOX 27127, S-10252	STOCKHOLM	SWEDEN
BERGMAN, JERRY	FOOTBALL REFEREE	NFL, 410 PARK AVE	NEW YORK, NY	10022
BERGMAN, MARILYN	LYRICIST	714 N MAPLE DR	BEVERLY HILLS, CA	90210
BERGMAN, PETER	ACTOR	4799 WHITE OAK AVE	ENCINO, CA	91316
BERGMAN, RICHARD	ACTOR	7416 LEMP AVE	NORTH HOLLYWOOD, CA	91605
BERGMAN, RICHARD L	TV WRITER-DIRECTOR	417 GRAND ST #1207	NEW YORK, NY	10002
BERGMAN, SANDAHL	ACTRESS-MODEL	9903 SANTA MONICA BLVD #274	BEVERLY HILLS, CA	90212
BERGMAN, SEAN	BASEBALL	POST OFFICE BOX 2785	LAKELAND, FL	33806
BERGMAN, TED	TV WRITER	11108 OPHIR DR	LOS ANGELES, CA	90024
BERGMAN, YOLANDA	DIET CONSULTANT	YOLANDA ENTERPRISES, INC		
		13915 HESBY ST	SHERMAN OAKS, CA	91423
BERGMANN, ALAN S	TV DIRECTOR	6330 ALLOTT AVE	VAN NUYS, CA	91401
BERGREN, ERIC	SCREENWRITER	1015 GAYLEY AVE #300	LOS ANGELES, CA	90024
BERGSMARK, EDWIN	BASEBALL EXECUTIVE	POST OFFICE BOX 6212	TOLEDO, OH	43614
BERGSTEIN, ELEANOR	SCREENWRITER	555 W 57TH ST #1230	NEW YORK, NY	10019
BERGSTROM, C W	WRESTLER	8725 N CHAUTAUQUA BLVD	PORTLAND, OR	97217
BERGSTROM, CATHERINE	ACTRESS	KATZ, 1168 N DOHENY DR	LOS ANGELES, CA	90069
BERIO, LUCIANO	COMPOSER-CONDUCTOR	11 COLOMBAIG, RADIOCOBDOLI	53100 SIENA,	ITALY
BERJER, BARBARA	ACTRESS	NBC-TV, "ANOTHER WORLD"		
		1268 E 14TH ST	BROOKLYN, NY	11230
BERK, BARRY	TV DIRECTOR	10555 BLYTHE AVE	LOS ANGELES, CA	90064
BERK, HOWARD	SCREENWRITER	2290 STRADELLA RD	LOS ANGELES, CA	90077
BERK, MICHAEL	TV WRITER	9200 SUNSET BLVD #531	LOS ANGELES, CA	90069
BERKE, LESTER W	WRITER-PRODUCER	9200 SUNSET BLVD #909	LOS ANGELES, CA	90069
BERKE, RICKEY	TV EXECUTIVE	POST OFFICE BOX 403	NEW YORK, NY	10028
BERKELEY, CONAN	WRITER	3446 TROY DR	LOS ANGELES, CA	90068
BERKEY, JOHN	ARTIST	LAVATY, 50 E 50TH ST	NEW YORK, NY	10022
BERKLEY, ELIZABETH	ACTRESS	SAVAGE, 6212 BANNER AVE	LOS ANGELES, CA	90038
BERKMAN, AL	COMPOSER-CONDUCTOR	384 N SAN VICENTE BLVD	LOS ANGELES, CA	90048
BERKMAN, JOHN D	COMPOSER	POST OFFICE BOX 1407	LOS ANGELES, CA	90078
BERKOFF, STEVEN	ACTOR	ICM, 388-396 OXFORD ST	LONDON W1	ENGLAND
BERKOFSKY, MICHAEL	DIRECTOR	1026 S CARMELINA AVE	LOS ANGELES, CA	90069

Name	Occupation	Address	City	Zip
BERKOWITZ, BARBARA	TV WRITER	9300 WILSHIRE BLVD #410	BEVERLY HILLS, CA	90212
BERLATSKY, DAVID	TV DIRECTOR	10351 SANTA MONICA BLVD #211	LOS ANGELES, CA	90025
BERLE, MILTON	ACTOR-COMEDIAN	10750 WILSHIRE BLVD #1003	LOS ANGELES, CA	90024
BERLIN, ANN LURIE	TALENT AGENT	350 W 57TH ST #11-A	NEW YORK, NY	10019
BERLIN, PETER R	TV WRITER	9300 WILSHIRE BLVD #410	BEVERLY HILLS, CA	90212
BERLIN, RANDY	BASEBALL	POST OFFICE BOX 3169	FREDERICK, MD	21701
BERLIN, RICK & BERLIN	ROCK & ROLL GROUP	25 HUNTINGTON AVE #420	BOSTON, MA	02116
BERLINGER, WARREN	ACTOR	10642 ARNEL LN	CHATSWORTH, CA	91311
BERMAN, CHRIS	SPORTSCASTER	ESPN PLAZA, 935 MIDDLEST	BRISTOL, CT	06010
BERMAN, DAVID	RECORD EXECUTIVE	CAPITOL RECORDS, 1750 N VINE ST	HOLLYWOOD, CA	90028
BERMAN, DAVID Z	DIRECTOR	530 E 72ND ST	NEW YORK, NY	10021
BERMAN, DOUGLAS	TREASURER	STATE HOUSE BLDG, 125 W STATE ST	TRENTON, NJ	08625
BERMAN, HOWARD	U S CONGRESSMAN	14600 ROSCOE BLVD #506	PANORAMA CITY, CA	91402
BERMAN, LEN	TV PRODUCER	POST OFFICE BOX 86	PORT WASHINGTON, NY	11050
BERMAN, LESTER	TV PRODUCER	55 W 95TH ST #45	NEW YORK, NY	10028
BERMAN, LOIS	TALENT AGENT	THE LITTLE THEATRE BUILDING		
		240 W 44TH ST	NEW YORK, NY	10036
BERMAN, MARTIN	TV PRODUCER	GROUP W, "HOUR MAGAZINE"		
		5746 SUNSET BLVD	LOS ANGELES, CA	90028
BERMAN, SHELLEY	COMEDIAN	268 BELL CANYON RD	BELL CANYON, CA	91307
BERMAN, STEVE	TV EXECUTIVE	CBS-TV, 7800 BEVERLY BLVD	LOS ANGELES, CA	90036
BERMAN, TED	FILM WRITER-DIRECTOR	500 S BUENA VISTA ST	BURBANK, CA	91521
BERMUDEZ, VIVIAN	BODYBUILDER	POST OFFICE BOX 8837	SAN JUAN, PR	00910
BERNABE, SAM	BASEBALL EXECUTIVE	CUBS, 2ND & RIVERSIDE DR	DES MOINES, IA	50309
BERNABEI, JOHN	ACTOR	11583 MAGNOLIA BLVD	NORTH HOLLYWOOD, CA	91601
BERNARD, CRYSTAL	ACTRESS	10100 SANTA MONICA BLVD #1600	LOS ANGELES, CA	90067
BERNARD, DWIGHT	BASEBALL-INSTRUCTOR	TWINS, 501 CHICAGO AVE S	MINNEAPOLIS, MN	55415
BERNARD, ED	ACTOR	18851 BRAEMORE RD	NORTHRIDGE, CA	91326
BERNARD, HERBERT	DIRECTOR	1956 LUCILLE AVE	LOS ANGELES, CA	90039
BERNARD, IAN	SCREENWRITER	8955 BEVERLY BLVD	WEST HOLLYWOOD, CA	90048
BERNARD, JAMES	COMPOSER	LONDON MGT, 235-241 REGENT ST	LONDON W1R 4PH	ENGLAND
BERNARD, JASON	ACTOR	KOHNER, 9169 SUNSET BLVD	LOS ANGELES, CA	90069
BERNARD, PAUL	WRI-DIR-PROD	BRIGHTROSE PRODUCTIONS, LTD		
		37 FENGATES RD, REDHILL	SURREY	ENGLAND
BERNARD, ROBYN	ACTRESS	9300 WILSHIRE BLVD #410	BEVERLY HILLS, CA	90212
BERNARD, SUSAN	ACT-WRI-PROD-MODEL	MILLER, 7089 BIRDVIEW AVE	MALIBU, CA	90265
BERNARDI, JACK	ACTOR	1284 N HAVENHURST DR	LOS ANGELES, CA	90046
BERNAY, LYNETTE D	COSTUME DESIGNER	20095 NE 3RD CT	MIAMI, FL	33179
BERNAZARD, TONY	BASEBALL	SANTA AVE D-25, URB SANTA ELVIRA	CAGUAS, PR	00625
BERNDS, EDWARD L	WRITER	6456 WOODMAN AVE	VAN NUYS, CA	91401
BERNHARD, SANDRA	COMEDIENNE-ACTRESS	151 S EL CAMINO DR	BEVERLY HILLS, CA	90212
BERNHARDI, LEE	DIRECTOR	4475 WHITE OAK PL	ENCINO, CA	91316
BERNHARDT, CARLOS	BASEBALL SCOUT	ORIOLE PARK, 333 W CAMDEN ST	BALTIMORE, MD	21201
BERNHARDT, CESAR	BASEBALL	POST OFFICE BOX 360007	BIRMINGHAM, AL	35236
BERNHARDT, JOSE	BASEBALL SCOUT	333 W 35TH ST	CHICAGO, IL	60616
BERNHARDT, JUAN	BASEBALL-SCOUT	333 W 35TH ST	CHICAGO, IL	60616
BERNHARDT, KEVIN	ACTOR	9300 WILSHIRE BLVD #410	BEVERLY HILLS, CA	90212
BERNHARDT, LAURA	ACTRESS	6362 HOLLYWOOD BLVD #219	HOLLYWOOD, CA	90028
BERNHARDT, MELVIN	DIRECTOR	DURHAM, 123 W 74TH ST	NEW YORK, NY	10023
BERNHAUT, MICHAEL	DIRECTOR	112 W 76TH ST #2-R	NEW YORK, NY	10023
BERNHEIM, ALAIN	FILM PRODUCER	9209 CORDELL DR	LOS ANGELES, CA	90069
BERNI, DENNY	BASEBALL	POST OFFICE BOX 10213	LYNCHBURG, VA	24506
BERNINI, JEFFREY S	SCREENWRITER	15206 LA MAIDA ST	SHERMAN OAKS, CA	91403
BERNS, GERALD	ACTOR	CED, 261 S ROBERTSON BLVD	BEVERLY HILLS, CA	90211
BERNSEN, COLLIN	ACTOR	401 N POINSETTIA PL	LOS ANGELES, CA	90036
BERNSEN, CORBIN	ACTOR	3500 W OLIVE AVE #920	BURBANK, CA	91505
BERNSTEIN, ARMYAN	FILM WRITER-PRODUCER	CAA, 9830 WILSHIRE BLVD	BEVERLY HILLS, CA	90212
BERNSTEIN, BARON	TV EXECUTIVE	36 GOLDEN SQ	LONDON W1R 4AH	ENGLAND
BERNSTEIN, BILL	FILM EXECUTIVE	1875 CENTURY PARK E #300	LOS ANGELES, CA	90067
BERNSTEIN, CAL	TV DIRECTOR	DOVE FILMS, 6387 IVARENE AVE	LOS ANGELES, CA	90068
BERNSTEIN, CARL	WRITER	242 E 62ND ST	NEW YORK, NY	10021
BERNSTEIN, CHARLES	COMPOSER-CONDUCTOR	POST OFFICE BOX 11413	BEVERLY HILLS, CA	90213
BERNSTEIN, ELLIOT	TV EXECUTIVE	315 E 72ND ST	NEW YORK, NY	10021
BERNSTEIN, ELMER	COMPOSER-CONDUCTOR	2121 AVE OF THE STARS #900	LOS ANGELES, CA	90067
BERNSTEIN, ERIC S	TV WRITER	8955 BEVERLY BLVD	WEST HOLLYWOOD, CA	90048
BERNSTEIN, GEORGE J	TV EXECUTIVE	6377 W 6TH ST	LOS ANGELES, CA	90048
BERNSTEIN, GIORA G	CONDUCTOR	755 7TH ST	BOULDER, CO	80302
BERNSTEIN, IRA	CASTING DIRECTOR	1156 SUNSET HILL RD	LOS ANGELES, CA	90069
BERNSTEIN, IRA	THEATER PRODUCER	15 E 48TH ST	NEW YORK, NY	10017
BERNSTEIN, JACK B	DIRECTOR-PRODUCER	KLEIN, 4565 SHERMAN OAKS AVE	SHERMAN OAKS, CA	91403
BERNSTEIN, JAY	DIR-PROD-MGR-AGT	POST OFFICE BOX 1148	BEVERLY HILLS, CA	90213
BERNSTEIN, JERRY	TV DIRECTOR	13127 MORRISON ST	SHERMAN OAKS, CA	91423
BERNSTEIN, JORDAN	DIRECTOR	3716 MALIBU COUNTRY DR	MALIBU, CA	90265
BERNSTEIN, MARK	BASEBALL SCOUT	333 W 35TH ST	CHICAGO, IL	60616
BERNSTEIN, NAN	FILM DIRECTOR	POST OFFICE BOX 43	TYRINGHAM, MA	02164
BERNSTEIN, SIDNEY LEWIS	TV EXECUTIVE	36 GOLDEN SQ	LONDON W1R 4AH	ENGLAND
BERNSTEIN, STEWART K	FILM WRITER-DIRECTOR	13044 HARTSOOK ST	SHERMAN OAKS, CA	91423
BERNSTEIN, WALTER	WRITER-DIRECTOR	320 CENTRAL PARK W	NEW YORK, NY	10025
BERNSTINE, ROD	FOOTBALL	POST OFFICE BOX 609609	SAN DIEGO, CA	92160
BERNUTH, CHARLES P	ACTOR	3989 SUNSWEPT DR	STUDIO CITY, CA	91604
BERRA, YOGI	BASEBALL-MANAGER	19 HIGHLAND AVE	MONTCLAIR, NJ	07042
BERRI, ROBERT	ACTOR	9 RUE DE PAURETTES	CROISSY 78290	FRANCE
BERRIGAN, FRANCES	TV DIRECTOR	108 WESTBOURNE PARK RD	LONDON W2	ENGLAND
BERRIOS, HECTOR	BASEBALL	POST OFFICE BOX 26267	ALBUQUERQUE, NM	87125
BERRIOS, RAY	ACTOR	8150 BEVERLY BLVD #308	LOS ANGELES, CA	90048

R & R ENTERPRISES

Buying and Selling AUTOGRAPHS Since 1980.

P.O. Box 2000 • Amherst, NH 03031 • USA

(603) 672-6611

FAX (603) 672-6442

(All signed photos are 8x10 and not inscribed to anyone)

GUARANTEED AUTHENTIC AUTOGRAPHS

Garth Brooks $85

matted with two color photos $100
Charlie Daniels - Singer. b/w picture signed $20
Marion Davies - Actress from 30's. b/w picture matted w/full signature on album page (11x14) $45
Miles Davis - Vintage signature with "On Green Dolphin Street" 45 single ... $150
Len Dawson - Football. 3x5 card matted w/3 color photos $30
Taylor Dayne - color photo signed $25
Yvonne DeCarlo - As Lily $20
Rebecca DeMornay - Actress. Starred in many popular films like "Risky Business". Beautiful color picture matted with 3x5 card $40
Dempsey & Tunney - Boxers. Two 3x5 card with three boxing poses, one on the famous "long count" (16x20) $250
John Denver - Pop/folk singer. B/w casual portrait signed by this 70's pop/folk artist $20
Laura Dern - Full length pose $25
Danny DeVito - Movie still in coat & tie $25
Thomas Dewey - A one page TLS with a b/w photo $50
Marlene Dietrich - 40's pose $95
Joe DiMaggio - Baseball. 3x5 card matted with array of photos $125
DiMaggio Brothers - Baseball. Three 3x5 cards w/3 photos in uniform (12x16) $200
Dion - Portrait $45
Walt Disney - Producer. Early signature matted with 2 color photos $1250
Divine - Actor. Signature matted with photo in drag $75
Donna Dixon - Low-cut top $15
Fats Domino - Singer. 3x5 card matted with photo and 45 record "Blueberry Hill" $50
James Doohan - As Scotty $25
Tony Dorsett - Football. 3x5 cards matted w/color picture in Dallas Cowboys uniform $30
Kirk Douglas - 50's pose $20
Michael Douglas - 1/2 length of this popular actor $35
Lesley-Anne Down - Actress. 3x5 card w/2 semi-nude color poses . $35
Ann Dvorak - Actress. Page w/40's portrait (12x16) $35
Sheena Easton - Singer. Signed card matted with photo/45 record . $95
Barbara Eden - Actress. Color 8x10 signed in costume from "I Dream of Jeanie" $25
Elvira - In costume $20
Robert Englund - Shoulders up pose in character as "Freddie" $35

Tony & Phil Esposito - Hockey. 2 b/w photos with 3x5's of these brothers $75
Gloria Estefan - Singer. 3x5 card matted with color photo $35
Emilio Estevez - "Young Guns" $35
Maurice Evans - Actor. 3x5 card w/50's phot (12x16) $25
Everly Brothers - Two 3x5's matted with b/w photo and "Wake Up Little Susie" 45 single $100
Everly Brothers - 50's pose $75
Morgan Fairchild - Sensual recent pose of this actress $25
Faith No More - All five $85
Family Ties Cast - TV show. Five signatures matted with color cast photo .. $125
Donna Fargo - Singer. b/w signed photo, matted with single "The Happiest Girl in the Whole USA" $35
James Farley - Politician. 1 pg TLS (1942) sending photo, w/portrait in a straw hat $45
Jamie Farr - From M.A.S.H. $15
Mike Farrell - From M.A.S.H. $20
Hamilton Fish - Politician. Card signed w/formal portrait $35
Elmer Flick - Baseball. 3x5 card w/batting pose (9x12) $50
Errol Flynn - Signature matted with pose as Robin Hood $295
Gerald Ford - President. FDC matted with official color portrait $50
Harrison Ford - From Raiders $150
Lita Ford - Signed photo with 45 of "Kiss Me Deadly" $65
Four Tops - A fabulous b/w signed photo matted with 45 single of "It's All In The Game" $100
Michael J. Fox - Actor. 3x5 card w/2 recent color poses $45
Walt Frazier - Basketball. 3x5 card matted w/photo $35
Ford Frick - Baseball. 3x5 card w/pose at desk (9x12) $45
Robert Frost - Poet. Signature matted with b/w portrait and the poem "The Road Not Taken" $225
Clark Gable - Actor. Signed receipt matted with pose as Rhett Butler $350
Ava Gardner - Actress. Personal signed check matted with portrait . $75
Lucretia Garfield - First Lady. Card signed (1886) w/formal pose ... $100
Judy Garland - Choice signature with photo as Dorothy matted with a single "Over The Rainbow" $495
Dave Garroway - Famous radio and television talk show host, best known for hosting the "Today Show" from 1951-62. ALS w/color portrait (12x16) $25
Horatio Gates - Revolutionary officer, rival of Washington during the war. Signature w/engraving in uniform on horse (11x14) $250
Crystal Gayle - Country/western singer. 3x5 card matted with color photo and single "Don't It Make My Brown Eyes Blue" $45
Janet Gaynor - Actress. 3x5 card w/30's portrait (9x12) $25
Andy Gibb - b/w SP, inscribed, matted with single "Everlasting Love" $75
Cynthia Gibb - Smiling pose $35
Floyd Gibbons - Announcer. Album pg w/pose in front of microphone (9x12) $20
Althea Gibson - A b/w photo with a signature on a card $45
Debbie Gibson - Singer. 3x5 card matted w/color photo $35
Vince Gill - Great casual pose of this popular c/w singer $50
Dizzy Gillespie - With horn $25
Mickey Gilley - Country/Western singer. B/w signed picture matted with 45 record $45
Stephen Girard - Businessman. Clip sig w/engraved portrait at desk (11x14) $50
Lillian Gish - Actress. Signature with beautiful b/w portrait $30
Robin Givens - Sensual pose of model/actress $45
Whoopi Goldberg - Smiling $30
Samuel Gompers - Labor leader. Signed card (1897) matted with portrait ... $175
Benny Goodman - Musician. Album pg, signed in pencil, but firmly,

Fats Domino $50

matted with b/w portrait $30
Jay Gould - Financier. Sig cut from letter w/portrait (9x12) .. $200
Robert Goulet - Singer. 1 pg (1962) AFTRA agreement for appearing on American Bandstand, also signed by Dick Clark $50
Red Grange - Football great. 3x5 card w/action pose from the 20's . $50
Jennifer Gray - matted recent pose $35
Pete Gray - Baseball. Courageous one-armed outfielder, 3x5 ink sig matted w/3 b/w photos (12x16) $50
Lorne Greene - Signature matted with color pose as Ben Cartwright $50
Lee Greenwood - Signed photo matted with 45 record $50
Richard Grieco - shirtless $45
Melanie Griffith - Actress. Movie still, 8x10 signed by actress from"Bonfire" $65
Charlie Grimm - Baseball. Album page with batting pose (11x14) ... $25
Lefty Grove - Baseball. 3x5 sig of this baseball great matted w/4 photos of him pitching in Red Sox uniform $75
Francois Pierre Guillaume Guizot - French historian and politician. Engraving w/cut sig w/closing remarks $45
Sammy Hagar - Singer. Signed 3x5 w/photo and 45 single of "I Don't Need Love" $50
Merle Haggard - Recent pose $10
Larry Hagman - As J.R. $20
Fawn Hall - Beautiful 8x10 color portrait matted w/a 3x5 card $50
Tom T. Hall - Singer. b/w signed photo, matted with single "Faster Horses" .. $35
Hammer - Full length recent pose of popular "rap" artist $50
Daryl Hannah - Actress. Signature matted with three great color photos $50
Mark Harmon - Bare chested $20
Rex Harrison - Actor. FDC w/color pose (12x16) $35
Debbie Harry - Signed photo with "Dreaming" 45 single $50
Lisa Hartman - Actress/singer. Signed 3x5 card matted w/2 color poses of this sexy actress $35
Goldie Hawn - Low-cut top $35
Nathaniel Hawthorne - Author. Clip sig "The Scarlet Letter/The House of Seven Gables" matted with a b/w $450
Gabby Hayes - Actor. Signature matted with western pose $150
Heart - Band. White, 8x10 page signed boldly by all 5 members, matted with group photo $100
Don Henley - Recent pose $45
Jim Henson - Creator of Muppets. Signature matted with two color

Kathleen Turner $50

Bette Davis $50

BERRIS, KEN	FILM DIRECTOR	ELITE FILMS, 31 E 32ND ST	NEW YORK, NY	10016
BERROA, GERONIMO	BASEBALL	POST OFFICE BOX 23290	NASHVILLE, TN	37202
BERRY, BILL	BASKETBALL	KINGS, 1 SPORTS PARKWAY	SACRAMENTO, CA	95834
BERRY, CHUCK	SINGER-SONGWRITER	BERRY FARM, BUCKNER RD	WENTZVILLE, MO	63385
BERRY, FRED	ACTOR	11020 VENTURA BLVD #203	STUDIO CITY, CA	91604
BERRY, HALLE	ACTRESS	9255 SUNSET BLVD #515	LOS ANGELES, CA	90069
BERRY, JAN	SINGER-SONGWRITER	ROUTE 2, BOX 23-W	WINTERS, CA	95694
BERRY, JIM	CARTOONIST	NEWSPAPER ENTERTAINMENT		
		200 PARK AVE	NEW YORK, NY	10017
BERRY, JOHN	WRITER-PRODUCER	299 W 12TH ST	NEW YORK, NY	10014
BERRY, KEN	ACTOR-DANCER	4704 CAHUENGA BLVD	NORTH HOLLYWOOD, CA	91602
BERRY, KEVIN	BASEBALL	POST OFFICE BOX 2001	CEDAR RAPIDS, IA	52406
BERRY, MARK	BASEBALL COACH	POST OFFICE BOX 2001	CEDAR RAPIDS, IA	52406
BERRY, PERRY	BASEBALL	POST OFFICE BOX 824	BURLINGTON, IA	52601
BERRY, RAY	FOOTBALL	VIKINGS, 9520 VIKING DR	EDEN PRAIRIE, MN	55344
BERRY, SEAN	BASEBALL	POST OFFICE BOX 3665	OMAHA, NE	68103
BERRYHILL, DAMON	BASEBALL	POST OFFICE BOX 4064	ATLANTA, GA	30302
BERRYHILL, SHARON	ACTRESS	937 GLEN OAKS BLVD	PASADENA, CA	91105
BERRYMAN, MICHAEL	ACTOR	6735 FOREST LAWN DR #313	HOLLYWOOD, CA	90068
BERSHAD, JAMES	ACTOR	8075 W 3RD ST #550	LOS ANGELES, CA	90048
BERT, LILIAN	ACTRESS	1 RUE JOSEPH GRANIER	PARIS 75007	FRANCE
BERTELSEN, PEGGY	BODYBUILDER	131 CENTRAL AVE	WHITEFISH, MT	59937
BERTELSEN, TROY	BODYBUILDER	131 CENTRAL AVE	WHITEFISH, MT	59937
BERTHAU, TERRELL	BASEBALL	POST OFFICE BOX 186	BUTTE, MT	59703
BERTHEL, DAN	BASEBALL	POST OFFICE BOX 3169	FREDERICK, MD	21701
BERTHELSEN, J C	WRITER	5115 KESTER AVE #13	SHERMAN OAKS, CA	91403
BERTHIAUME, GERRY	BASEBALL EXECUTIVE	POST OFFICE BOX 1718	NEW BRITAIN, CT	06050
BERTHRONG, DEIRDRE	ACTRESS	12121 HERBERT ST	LOS ANGELES, CA	90066
BERTI, DEHL F	ACTOR-WRITER	8230 SUNSET BLVD #23	LOS ANGELES, CA	90048
BERTIL, HRH PRINCE	PRINCE	HERTIGENS AVE HALLAND		
		KUNGL SLOTTET	11130 STOCKHOLM	SWEDEN
BERTINELLI, VALERIE	ACTRESS-TV PRODUCER	12700 VENTURA BLVD #100	STUDIO CITY, CA	91604
BERTISH, SUZANNE	ACTRESS	HEATH, PARAMOUNT HOUSE		
		162-170 WARDOUR ST	LONDON W1V 3AT	ENGLAND
BERTKA, BILL	BASKETBALL COACH	POST OFFICE BOX 10	INGLEWOOD, CA	90306
BERTOLUCCI, BERNARDO	FILM DIRECTOR	VIA DELLA LUNGARA 3	ROME	ITALY
BERTON, MELISSA	ACTRESS	28035 DOROTHY DR #210-A	AGOURA, CA	91301
BERTON, STUART	ACTOR	4026 MARY ELLEN AVE	STUDIO CITY, CA	91604
BERTOTTI, MICHAEL	BASEBALL	POST OFFICE BOX 4218	SOUTH BEND, IN	46634
BERTRAM, C LANIE	TV-COMEDY WRITER	165 W 91ST ST	NEW YORK, NY	10024
BERUBE, CRAIG	HOCKEY	FLYERS, SPECTRUM, PATTISON PL	PHILADELPHIA, PA	19148
BERUMEN, ANDRES	BASEBALL	POST OFFICE BOX 464	APPLETON, WI	54912
BERWICK, IRVIN	TV DIRECTOR	16241 DARCIA PL	ENCINO, CA	91436
BERWICK, JAMES	ACTOR	THE STUDIO, 44 CRABTREE LN	LONDON SW6 6LW	ENGLAND
BERWICK, JOHN	ACTOR	11930 MAYFIELD AVE #12	LOS ANGELES, CA	90049
BERWICK, RAY D	WRITER	32084 CANTERHILL PL	WESTLAKE VILLAGE, CA	91361
BESBAS, PETER	ACTOR	1730 N EDGEMONT ST	LOS ANGELES, CA	90027
BESCH, BIBI	ACTRESS	3500 W OLIVE AVE #1400	BURBANK, CA	91505
BESS, GORDON	CARTOONIST	KING FEATURES, 216 E 45TH ST	NEW YORK, NY	10017
BESSELL, TED	ACTOR-DIRECTOR	1454 STONE CANYON DR	LOS ANGELES, CA	90077
BEST, JANEEN	ACTRESS-DANCER	437 3/4 N GENESEE AVE	LOS ANGELES, CA	90036
BEST, JAYSON	BASEBALL	14100 SIX MILE CYPRESS PKWY	FORT MYERS, FL	33912
BEST, KARL	BASEBALL	11132 SE 129TH	KIRKLAND, WA	98034
BEST, KEN	ACTOR	10100 SANTA MONICA BLVD #1600	LOS ANGELES, CA	90067
BEST, KEVIN	ACTOR	POST OFFICE BOX 1164	HESPERIA, CA	92345
BEST, MARJORIE	COSTUME DESIGNER	13949 VENTURA BLVD #309	SHERMAN OAKS, CA	91423
BEST, PETE	DRUMMER	8 HYMANS GREEN, WEST DERBY	LIVERPOOL 12	ENGLAND
BESWICKE, MARTINE	ACTRESS	BDP, 10637 BURBANK BLVD	NORTH HOLLYWOOD, CA	91601
BETCKE, R D	BASEBALL EXECUTIVE	2850 W 20TH AVE	DENVER, CO	80211
BETHEA, SCOTT	BASEBALL	POST OFFICE BOX 1718	NEW BRITAIN, CT	06050
BETHEA, STEVE	BASEBALL	POST OFFICE BOX 1420	WICHITA, KS	67201
BETHUNE, IVY	ACTRESS	3096 LAKE HOLLYWOOD DR	LOS ANGELES, CA	90068
BETHUNE, ZINA	ACTRESS	3096 LAKE HOLLYWOOD DR	LOS ANGELES, CA	90068
BETLEY, BOB	GOLFER	PGA SENIORS, 112 T P C BLVD	PONTE VEDRA BEACH, FL	32082
BETSY	SINGER	FAA, 1700 BROADWAY, 5TH FLOOR	NEW YORK, NY	10019
BETTENHAUSEN, GARY	AUTO RACER	2550 TREE FARM RD	MARTINSVILLE, IN	46151
BETTENHAUSEN, TONY	AUTO RACER	5234 WILTON WOOD CT	INDIANAPOLIS, IN	46254
BETTI, HENRY	COMPOSER	69 BLVD BINEAU	NEUILLY 92200	FRANCE
BETTIS, JOHN	LYRICIST	3815 W OLIVE AVE #201	BRUBANK, CA	91505
BETTIS, TOM	FOOTBALL COACH	EAGLES, BROAD ST & PATTISON AVE	PHILADELPHIA, PA	19148
BETTMAN, GILBERT, JR	TV DIRECTOR	10521 SELKIRK LN	LOS ANGELES, CA	90077
BETTS, DICKEY	SINGER-GUITARIST	210 25TH AVE N #N-101	NASHVILLE, TN	37203
BETTS, JACK	ACTOR	8831 SUNSET BLVD #304	LOS ANGELES, CA	90069
BETZ, CLAIRE	BASEBALL EXECUTIVE	POST OFFICE BOX 7575	PHILADELPHIA, PA	19101
BETZ, PAT	TV EXECUTIVE	NBC-TV, 3000 W ALAMEDA AVE	BURBANK, CA	91523
BEUERLEIN, ED	BASEBALL	POST OFFICE BOX 1556	ASHEVILLE, NC	28802
BEUERLEIN, STEVE	FOOTBALL	COWBOYS, 1 COWBOYS PARKWAY	IRVING, TX	75063
BEUKEBOOM, JEFF	HOCKEY	OILERS, NORTHLANDS COLISEUM	EDMONTON, ALTA T5B 4M9	CANADA
BEULE, CAROL HELEN	COSTUME DESIGNER	203 W 102ND ST #5-R	NEW YORK, NY	10025
BEUMER, BOB	BASEBALL EXECUTIVE	POST OFFICE BOX 5599	LITTLE ROCK, AR	72215
BEUTEL, BILL	TV COMMENTATOR	1120 PARK AVE	NEW YORK, NY	10128
BEUTH, EUGENE	DIRECTOR	145 E 27TH ST	NEW YORK, NY	10016
BEVACQUA, KURT	BASEBALL-ANNOUNCER	2607 PIRINEOS WY #101	CARLSBAD, CA	92008
BEVEC, BILL	SINGER	PROCESS, 439 WILEY AVE	FRANKLIN, PA	16323
BEVELS, KYLE G	DIRECTOR	131 RIVERSIDE DR	NEW YORK, NY	10024

BEVERLY BROTHERS, THE	WRESTLING TAG TEAM	POST OFFICE BOX 3859	STAMFORD, CT	06905
BEVIL, BRIAN	BASEBALL	POST OFFICE BOX 464	APPLETON, WI	54912
BEVILL, TOM	U S CONGRESSMAN	1710 ALABAMA AVE	JASPER, AL	35501
BEVINGER, TERRY	BASEBALL-COACH	333 W 35TH ST	CHICAGO, IL	60616
BEVINGTON, TERRY	BASEBALL COACH	333 W 35TH ST	CHICAGO, IL	60616
BEVIS, LESLIE	ACTRESS	9229 SUNSET BLVD #311	LOS ANGELES, CA	90069
BEWES, RODNEY	ACTOR	LONDON MGT, 235-241 REGENT ST	LONDON W1R 4PH	ENGLAND
BEXLEY, DON "BUBBA"	ACTOR	6626 HAYVENHURST AVE #108	VAN NUYS, CA	91406
BEY, TURHAN	ACTOR	PARADISGASSE AVE 47	1190 WEIN X1X	AUSTRIA
BEYELER, ARNIE	BASEBALL	TIGERS, 89 WHARNCLIFFE RD N	LONDON, ONT N6H 2A7	CANADA
BEYER, DONALD	LT GOVERNOR	STATE CAPITOL BUILDING	RICHMOND, VA	23219
BEYER, TROY	ACTRESS	3800 BARHAM BLVD #303	LOS ANGELES, CA	90068
BEYERS, TOM	BASEBALL MANAGER	POST OFFICE BOX 10031	BAKERSFIELD, CA	93389
BEYMER, RICHARD	ACTOR-DIRECTOR	9744 WILSHIRE BLVD #308	BEVERLY HILLS, CA	90212
BEYNON, RICHARD	TV WRITER-PRODUCER	14 THE ELMS, BARNES	LONDON SW13 ONF	ENGLAND
BEZZERIDES, A I	TV WRITER	19950 COLLIER ST	WOODLAND HILLS, CA	91364
BHUTTO, BENAZIR	PRIME MINISTER	70 CLIFTON RD	KARACHI	PAKISTAN
BIAGINI, GREG	BASEBALL COACH	ORIOLE PARK, 333 W CAMDEN ST	BALTIMORE, MD	21201
BIALAS, DAVE	BASEBALL MANAGER	POST OFFICE BOX 12557	ST PETERSBURG, FL	33733
BIALIK, MAYIM	ACTRESS	3000 W ALAMEDA AVE	BURBANK, CA	91523
BIANCALANA, BUDDY	BASEBALL	4120 SAN SAVERA DR N	JACKSONVILLE, FL	32217
BIANCAMANO, JOHN	BASEBALL	POST OFFICE BOX 4758	SPOKANE, WA	99202
BIANCHI, AL	BASKETBALL-EXECUTIVE	KNICKS, 4 PENNYLVANIA PLAZA	NEW YORK, NY	10019
BIANCHI, EDWARD	FILM DIRECTOR	36 GRAMMERCY PARK E	NEW YORK, NY	10003
BIANCHINI, JOHN	ACTOR	4613 SAN ANDREAS AVE	LOS ANGELES, CA	90065
BIANCO, ANNETTE	HAIR STYLIST	2720 E 64TH ST	BROOKLYN, NY	11234
BIANCO, FRANK	HAIR STYLIST	1804 BELL BLVD	BAYSIDE, NY	11360
BIANCULLI, DAVID	TV CRITIC	NY POST, 210 SOUTH ST	NEW YORK, NY	10002
BIASUCCI, DEAN	FOOTBALL	POST OFFICE BOX 535000	INDIANPOLIS, IN	46253
BIASUCCI, JOE	BASEBALL	POST OFFICE BOX 4488	WINSTON-SALEM, NC	27115
BIBAS, FRANK P	TV DIRECTOR-PRODUCER	THE KINGSTON SQAUER #I-7		
		9354 SW 77TH AVE	MIAMI, FL	33156
BIBBY, JIM	BASEBALL-COACH	POST OFFICE BOX 10213	LYNCHBURG, VA	24506
BIBERDORF, CAM	BASEBALL	POST OFFICE BOX 2887	VERO BEACH, FL	32961
BIBLE, DANA	FOOTBALL COACH	BENGALS, 200 RIVERFRONT STADIUM	CINCINNATI, OH	45202
BICAT, TONY	TV WRITER-DIRECTOR	LONDON MGT, 235-241 REGENT ST	LONDON W1R 4PH	ENGLAND
BICHETTE, DANTE	BASEBALL	BREWERS, 201 S 46TH ST	MILWAUKEE, WI	53214
BICK, JERRY	FILM PRODUCER	1413 GREENFIELD AVE #201	LOS ANGELES, CA	90025
BICKEL, BUD	BASEBALL EXECUTIVE	POST OFFICE BOX 7005	HUNTINGTON, WV	25775
BICKERSTAFF, BERNIE	BASKETBALL EXECUTIVE	POST OFFICE BOX 4658	DENVER, CO	80204
BICKETT, DUANE	FOOTBALL	POST OFFICE BOX 535000	INDIANPOLIS, IN	46253
BICKHARDT, ERIC	BASEBALL	POST OFFICE BOX 3609	PORT CHARLOTTE, FL	33949
BICKLEY, BILL	PRODUCER	1041 N FORMOSA AVE	LOS ANGELES, CA	90046
BICKLEY, WILLIAM S	TV WRITER	9300 WILSHIRE BLVD #410	BEVERLY HILLS, CA	90212
BICKMAN, EDDIE	BASEBALL SCOUT	POST OFFICE BOX 7575	PHILADELPHIA, PA	19101
BICKNELL, GREG	BASEBALL	POST OFFICE BOX 9194	HAMPTON, VA	23670
BIDASHA, VEENA	ACTRESS	20146 COHASSET ST #2	CANOGA PARK, CA	91306
BIDDICK, GUY M	COMPOSER	18127 ROSCOE BLVD #6	NORTHRIDGE, CA	91324
BIDEN, JOSEPH, JR	U S SENATOR	6 MONTCHAN DR	WILMINGTON, DE	19807
BIDWELL, OLLIE	BASEBALL SCOUT	POST OFFICE BOX 7575	PHILADELPHIA, PA	19101
BIDWELL, WILLIAM V	FOOTBALL EXECUTIVE	POST OFFICE BOX 888	PHOENIX, AZ	85001
BIEDERBECK, DEE	ACTRESS	4001 WITZEL DR	SHERMAN OAKS, CA	91423
BIEHL, ROD	BASEBALL	POST OFFICE BOX 824	BURLINGTON, IA	52601
BIEHN, MICHAEL	ACTOR	14818 VALERIO ST	VAN NUYS, CA	91405
BIELAK, ROBERT S	TV WRITER	860 PRINCETON ST	SANTA MONICA, CA	90403
BIELECKI, MIKE	BASEBALL	POST OFFICE BOX 4064	ATLANTA, GA	30302
BIEN, WALTER N	WRITER	22326 JAMES ALAN CIR	CHATSWORTH, CA	91311
BIENEFELD, DONALD	CINEMATOGRAPHER	3 MILFORD LN #7001	SUFFERN, NY	10901
BIENER, THOMAS J	WRITER	7810 AMESTOY AVE	VAN NUYS, CA	91406
BIENIEMY, ERIC	FOOTBALL	POST OFFICE BOX 609609	SAN DIEGO, CA	92160
BIERBAUER, CHARLES J	NEWS CORRESPONDENT	1050 TECHWOOD DR, NW	ATLANTA, GA	30318
BIERBAUM, TOM	COLUMNIST	5700 WILSHIRE BLVD #120	LOS ANGELES, CA	90036
BIERDZ, THOM	ACTOR	1435 N STANLEY AVE	LOS ANGELES, CA	90046
BIERI, RAMON	ACTOR	19963 ACRE ST	NORTHRIDGE, CA	91324
BIERLEY, BRAD	BASEBALL	CUBS, 2ND & RIVERSIDE DR	DES MOINES, IA	50309
BIERMAN, JIM	BASEBALL SCOUT	POST OFFICE BOX 7575	PHILADELPHIA, PA	19101
BIERY, EDWARD A	FILM EDITOR	ACE, 1041 N FORMOSA AVE	WEST HOLLYWOOD, CA	90046
BIES, DON	GOLFER	PGA SENIORS, 112 T P C BLVD	PONTE VEDRA BEACH, FL	32082
BIESER, STEVE	BASEBALL	POST OFFICE BOX 10336	CLEARWATER, FL	34617
BIG AL & THE HI FI'S	VOCAL GROUP	POST OFFICE BOX 18368	DENVER, CO	80218
BIG BLACK	ROCK & ROLL GROUP	D M RILEY MANAGEMENT		
		3539 N FREMONT ST	CHICAGO, IL	60613
BIG BOSSMAN, THE	WRESTLER	POST OFFICE BOX 3859	STAMFORD, CT	06905
BIG BOYS, THE	ROCK & ROLL GROUP	POST OFFICE BOX 12424	AUSTIN, TX	78711
BIG BROTHER & HOLDING CO	ROCK & ROLL GROUP	FAA, 1700 BROADWAY, 5TH FLOOR	NEW YORK, NY	10019
BIG COUNTRY	ROCK & ROLL GROUP	ATI, 888 7TH AVE, 21ST FLOOR	NEW YORK, NY	10106
BIG DADDY KANE	RAPPER-RAPWRITER	SEE - KANE, BIG DADDY		
BIG E SHOW	C & W GROUP	POST OFFICE BOX 1338	MERCHANTVILLE, NJ	08109
BIG LOU	SINGER	NRB PRODS, 2124 DARBY DR, NW	MASSILLON, OH	44686
BIG SKY MUDD FLAPP	ROCK & ROLL GROUP	9777 HARWIN ST #101	HOUSTON, TX	77036
BIG STREET	ROCK & ROLL GROUP	3 E 54TH ST #1400	NEW YORK, NY	10022
BIGELOW, KATHRYN	FILM WRITER-DIRECTOR	CAA, 9830 WILSHIRE BLVD	BEVERLY HILLS, CA	90212
BIGEN, R C	SINGER	BUN JAK, 331 PROSPECT ST	BERLIN, NH	03570
BIGGERS, BRIAN	BASEBALL	1325 S MAIN #229	SALT LAKE CITY, UT	84115
BIGGERSTAFF, KENT	BASEBALL TRAINER	POST OFFICE BOX 7000	PITTSBURGH, PA	15212

Name	Occupation	Address	City	Zip
BIGGINS, CHRISTOPHER	ACTOR	23 EYOT GARDENS	LONDON W6 9TR	ENGLAND
BIGGIO, CRAIG	BASEBALL	POST OFFICE BOX 288	HOUSTON, TX	77001
BIGGS, GERALD	FOOTBALL	POST OFFICE BOX 17247 (DULLES)	WASHINGTON, DC	20041
BIGGS, RICHARD	ACTOR	728 W 28TH ST	LOS ANGELES, CA	90007
BIGHAM, DAVE	BASEBALL	POST OFFICE BOX 48	VISALIA, CA	93279
BIGLER, JEFF	BASEBALL	POST OFFICE BOX 1721	SPARTANBURG, SC	29304
BIHELLER, ROBERT	WRITER-PRODUCER	614 E 29TH ST	VANCOUVER, WA	98663
BIKALES, ERIC	COMPOSER	14118 ERWIN ST	VAN NUYS, CA	91401
BIKEL, THEODORE	ACTOR	1131 ALTA LOMA RD #523	LOS ANGELES, CA	90069
BILARDELLO, DANN	BASEBALL	POST OFFICE BOX 2000	SAN DIEGO, CA	92112
BILBRAY, JAMES H	U S CONGRESSMAN	1785 E SAHARA AVE #445	LAS VEGAS, NV	89104
BILETNIKOFF, FRED	FOOTBALL COACH	RAIDERS, 332 CENTER ST	EL SEGUNDO, CA	90245
BILIK, JERRY H	COMPOSER-WRITER	7008 ENDICOTT CT	BETHESDA, MD	20817
BILINGSLEY, PETER	ACTOR	11350 VENTURA BLVD #206	STUDIO CITY, CA	91604
BILIRAKIS, MICHAEL	U S CONGRESSMAN	1100 CLEVELAND ST #1600	CLEARWATER, FL	33515
BILL, TONY	ACTOR-DIRECTOR	73 MARKET ST	VENICE, CA	90291
BILLARDELLO, DANN	BASEBALL	836 BLUEBERRY DR	WEST PALM BEACH, FL	33414
BILLECI, CRAIG	BASEBALL	POST OFFICE BOX 802	BATAVIA, NY	14021
BILLETT, STU	TV PRODUCER	RALPH EDWARDS PRODUCTIONS		
		"THE PEOPLE'S COURT"		
		1717 N HIGHLAND AVE, 10TH FLOOR	HOLLYWOOD, CA	90028
BILLINGHAM, JACK	BASEBALL-COACH	POST OFFICE BOX 422229	KISSIMMEE, FL	34742
BILLINGS, DAWN ANN	ACTRESS	FORD MODELS, 344 E 59TH ST	NEW YORK, NY	10022
BILLINGS, EARL	ACTOR	301 N CANON DR #305	BEVERLY HILLS, CA	90210
BILLINGS, JEF	COSTUME DESIGNER	13949 VENTURA BLVD #309	SHERMAN OAKS, CA	91423
BILLINGSLEA, BEAU	ACTOR	1539 SAWTELLE BLVD #10	LOS ANGELES, CA	90025
BILLINGSLEY, ALAN R	COMPOSER	19145 HAYNES ST #2	RESEDA, CA	91335
BILLINGSLEY, BARBARA	ACTRESS	800 SAN LORENZO ST	SANTA MONICA, CA	90402
BILLINGSLEY, PETER	ACTOR	11350 VENTURA BLVD #206	STUDIO CITY, CA	91604
BILLINGTON, KEVIN	FILM DIRECTOR	DAISH, 83 EASTBOURNE MEWS	LONDON W2 6LQ	ENGLAND
BILLMEYER, MICK	BASEBALL	POST OFFICE BOX 12	MIDLAND, TX	79702
BILLONI, MICHAEL	BASEBALL EXECUTIVE	POST OFFICE BOX 450	BUFFALO, NY	14205
BILLOUT, GUY	ARTIST	222 W 15TH ST	NEW YORK, NY	10011
BILLUPS, LEWIS	FOOTBALL	BENGALS, 200 RIVERFRONT STADIUM	CINCINNATI, OH	45202
BILLY & THE BEATERS	ROCK & ROLL GROUP	SCWARTZ, 1015 N FAIRFAX AVE	LOS ANGELES, CA	90046
BILLY BOP	C & W GROUP	GREG, 1288 E 168TH ST	CLEVELAND, OH	44110
BILLY THE KID	ROCK & ROLL GROUP	8255 SUNSET BLVD #100	LOS ANGELES, CA	90046
BILSON, BRUCE	TV DIRECTOR	12505 SARAH ST	STUDIO CITY, CA	91604
BINA, JAN	ACTRESS	14727 COVELLO ST	VAN NUYS, CA	91405
BINDER, JOHN	WRITER-PRODUCER	4084 MANDEVILLE CANYON RD	LOS ANGELES, CA	90049
BINDER, MIKE	COMEDIAN	9000 SUNSET BLVD #1200	LOS ANGELES, CA	90069
BINDER, STEVE	WRITER-PRODUCER	855 S BUNDY DR	LOS ANGELES, CA	90049
BING, MACK	DIRECTOR	8000 WOODROW WILSON DR	LOS ANGELES, CA	90046
BING, SIR RUDOLPH	OPERA EXECUTIVE	160 CENTRAL PARK S	NEW YORK, NY	10019
BINGAMAN, JEFF	U S SENATOR	119 E MARCY #101	SANTA FE, NM	87501
BINGHAM, BARBARA M	ACTRESS	SELECTED, 3575 W CAHUENGA BLVD	LOS ANGELES, CA	90068
BINSFELD, CONNIE	LT GOVERNOR	STATE CAPITOL BUILDING	LANSING, MI	48953
BINYON, CONRAD	ACTOR	17805 S MARGATE ST	ENCINO, CA	91436
BIONDI, MATT	TENNIS	1404 RIMER	MORAGA, CA	94556
BIRCHARD, ROBERT S	WRITER	3207 BROOKHILL ST	LA CRESCENTA, CA	91214
BIRD, BILLIE	ACTRESS	9255 SUNSET BLVD #515	LOS ANGELES, CA	90069
BIRD, CHARLES, JR	CONDUCTOR	POST OFFICE BOX 2908	LOS ANGELES, CA	90028
BIRD, DAVID	BASEBALL	POST OFFICE DRAWER 1218	ZEBULON, NC	27597
BIRD, JOHN	ACTOR-WRITER	CHATTO AND LINNIT, LTD		
		PRINCE OF WALES THEATRE		
		COVENTRY ST	LONDON W1V 7FE	ENGLAND
BIRD, LARRY	BASKETBALL	151 MERRIMAC ST	BOSTON, MA	02114
BIRD, MICHAEL J	TV WRITER-NOVELIST	PETERS, FRASER & DUNLOP, LTD		
		5TH FLOOR, THE CHAMBERS		
		CHELSEA HARBOUR, LOT RD	LONDON SW10 OXF	ENGLAND
BIRD, NORMAN	ACTOR	LONDON MGT, 235-241 REGENT ST	LONDON W1R 4PH	ENGLAND
BIRD, PHILIP	ACTOR	HORNE, 15 EXMOOR ST	LONDON W10 6BA	ENGLAND
BIRD, VICKI	SINGER	38 MUSIC SQUARE E #300	NASHVILLE, TN	37203
BIRDEN, J J	FOOTBALL	CHIEFS, 1 ARROWHEAD DR	KANSAS CITY, MO	64129
BIRDSONG, BOB	BODYBUILDER	POST OFFICE BOX 4333	PALM SPRINGS, CA	92263
BIRDSONG, LORI	ACTRESS	MARX, 11130 HUSTON ST #6	NORTH HOLLYWOOD, CA	91601
BIRK, JOHN	ACTOR	30000 HALSEY CANYON RD #57	CASTAICSAUGUS, CACA	91384
BIRKBECK, MIKE	BASEBALL	POST OFFICE BOX 1211	NORFOLK, VA	23502
BIRKETT, BERNADETTE	ACTRESS	3856 VANTAGE AVE	STUDIO CITY, CA	91604
BIRKIN, JANE	ACTRESS	28 RUE DE LA TOUR	F-75016	FRANCE
BIRKINSHAW, ALAN	WRITER-PRODUCER	ICM, 388-396 OXFORD ST	LONDON W1	ENGLAND
BIRMAN, LEN	ACTOR	8380 MELROSE AVE #207	LOS ANGELES, CA	90069
BIRMKRANT, SAM	THEATER CRITIC	POST OFFICE BOX 1127	MALIBU, CA	90265
BIRN, LAURA BRYAN	ACTRESS	CBS-TV, "YOUNG & THE RESTLESS"		
		7800 BEVERLY BLVD #3305	LOS ANGELES, CA	90036
BIRNBAUM, BERNARD	TV PRODUCER	CBS NEWS, 524 W 57TH ST	NEW YORK, NY	10016
BIRNBAUM, HARVEY	TV DIRECTOR-PRODUCER	535 BROADHOLLOW RD, ROUTE #110	MELVILLE, NY	11747
BIRNBAUM, ROBERT	WRITER-PRODUCER	4048 STONE CANYON AVE	SHERMAN OAKS, CA	91403
BIRNBAUM, STUART	TV WRITER	17200 VENTURA BLVD #340	STUDIO CITY, CA	91604
BIRNEY, DAVID	ACTOR-PRODUCER	20 OCEAN PARK BLVD #11	SANTA MONICA, CA	90405
BIRNEY, FRANK	ACTOR	4941 ALCOVE AVE	NORTH HOLLYWOOD, CA	91607
BIRNEY, MEREDITH BAXTER	ACTRESS	10100 SANTA MONICA BLVD #700	LOS ANGELES, CA	90067
BIRNEY, STUART	ACTOR	310 E 44TH ST #1501	NEW YORK, NY	10017
BIRNKRANT, DON	CINEMATOGRAPHER	3620 GLENRIDGE DR	SHERMAN OAKS, CA	91423
BIROC, JOSEPH	CINEMATOGRAPHER	4427 PETIT AVE	ENCINO, CA	91345

Name	Occupation	Address	City
BIRT, JOHN	TV EXECUTIVE	BBC, BROADCASTING HOUSE	LONDON W1A 1AA ENGLAND
BIRTSAS, TIM	BASEBALL	43 ROBERTSON CT	CLARKSTON, MI 48016
BIRTWISTLE, SUE	TV PRODUCER	BROWN, 162-168 REGENT ST	LONDON W1R 5TB ENGLAND
BISCARDI, JESSICA	ACTRESS	POST OFFICE BOX 38596	LOS ANGELES, CA 90038
BISCHEL, DWIGHT W	WRITER-PRODUCER	2108 EWING AVE	EVANSTON, IL 60201
BISCHOF, LARRY J	WRITER	53700 1/2 HWY 74	MOUNTAIN CENTER, CA 92361
BISH, BRENT	BASEBALL	12000 STADIUM RD	ADELANTO, CA 92301
BISHOFF, ERIC	WRESTLING ANNOUNCER	POST OFFICE BOX 105366	ATLANTA, GA 31348
BISHOP, BILLY	CONDUCTOR	17454 TAM O'SHANTER DR	POWAY, CA 92064
BISHOP, BOB	BASEBALL SCOUT	1000 ELYSIAN PARK DR	LOS ANGELES, CA 90012
BISHOP, DONALD	ACTOR	11319 SUNSHINE TERR	STUDIO CITY, CA 91604
BISHOP, ED	ACTOR	THE GRANARY, VICARAGE RD NAPTON, NEAR RUGBY	WARWICKSHIRE CU23 8NA ENGLAND
BISHOP, FRED	ACTOR	7813 OAKWOOD AVE	LOS ANGELES, CA 90036
BISHOP, GEORGE V	WRITER	14941 HAWK DR	LAKE ELIZABETH, CA 93532
BISHOP, HELEN GARY	TV PRODUCER	BETA PRODS, 56 WASHINGTON MEWS	NEW YORK, NY 10003
BISHOP, JAMES	BASEBALL	POST OFFICE BOX 4370	SALINAS, CA 93912
BISHOP, JENIFER	ACTRESS	9870 VIDOR DR	LOS ANGELES, CA 90035
BISHOP, JIM	BASEBALL	POST OFFICE BOX 360007	BIRMINGHAM, AL 35236
BISHOP, JIM "RIGGIO"	FILM DIRECTOR	POST OFFICE BOX 868	LITCHFIELD, CT 06759
BISHOP, JIMMY & TURNING POINT	ROCK & ROLL GROUP	POST OFFICE BOX 11283	RICHMOND, VA 23230
BISHOP, JOEY	ACTOR-COMEDIAN	534 VIA LIDO NORD	NEWPORT BEACH, CA 92660
BISHOP, JUDITH	TV PRODUCER	WABC-TV, 7 LINCOLN SQ	NEW YORK, NY 10023
BISHOP, LOANNE	ACTRESS	9165 SUNSET BLVD #202	LOS ANGELES, CA 90069
BISHOP, STEPHEN	SINGER-COMPOSER	10100 SANTA MONICA BLVD #1600	LOS ANGELES, CA 90067
BISHOP, TIM	BASEBALL COACH	POST OFFICE BOX 3169	FREDERICK, MD 21701
BISHOP, WESDON	WRITER	12217 TEXAS AVE #101	LOS ANGELES, CA 90025
BISKUP, BILL	ACTOR	POST OFFICE BOX 10854	GLENDALE, CA 91209
BISNO, LESLIE	ACTOR	1108 18TH ST #1	SANTA MONICA, CA 90403
BISOGLIO, VAL	ACTOR	11684 VENTURA BLVD #476	STUDIO CITY, CA 91604
BISSELL, WHIT	ACTOR	23388 MULHOLLAND HIGHWAY	WOODLAND HILLS, CA 91364
BISSET, JACQUELINE	ACTRESS	1815 BENEDICT CANYON DR	BEVERLY HILLS, CA 90210
BISSETT, JOSIE	ACTRESS	KOHNER, 9169 SUNSET BLVD	LOS ANGELES, CA 90069
BITKER, JOE	BASEBALL	POST OFFICE BOX 75089	OKLAHOMA CITY, OK 73147
BITSCH, CHARLES	FILM DIRECTOR	5 PASS DU CHEMIN-VERT	PARIS 75001 FRANCE
BITTIGER, JEFF	BASEBALL	POST OFFICE BOX 2769	HUNTSVILLE, AL 35804
BITTLE, JERRY	CARTOONIST	UPS, 4900 MAIN ST, 9TH FLOOR	KANSAS CITY, MO 64112
BIVENS, ERNIE	SINGER	38 MUSIC SQUARE E #216	NASHVILLE, TN 37203
BIVENS, ERNIE, III	SINGER	38 MUSIC SQUARE E #216	NASHVILLE, TN 37203
BIXBY, BILL	ACTOR-DIRECTOR	200 N ROBERTSON BLVD #223	BEVERLY HILLS, CA 90211
BIZ MARKIE	RAP DUO-RAPWRITERS	FAA, 1700 BROADWAY, 5TH FLOOR	NEW YORK, NY 10019
BIZZELL, CHUCK	BASEBALL SCOUT	333 W 35TH ST	CHICAGO, IL 60616
BJORN, ANNA	MODEL-ACTRESS	KOHNER, 9169 SUNSET BLVD	LOS ANGELES, CA 90069
BJORNSON, CRAIG	BASEBALL	POST OFFICE BOX 1556	ASHEVILLE, NC 28802
BJURMAN, SUSAN	ACTRESS	786 TORTUOSO WY	LOS ANGELES, CA 90077
BLACHE, GREG	FOOTBALL COACH	PACKERS, 1265 LOMBARDI AVE	GREEN BAY, WI 54307
BLACK	ROCK & ROLL GROUP	136-140 NEW KINGS RD	LONDON SW6 4LZ ENGLAND
BLACK, BILL, COMBO	C & W GROUP	BOB TUCKER, 5839 FOX BEND COVE E	MEMPHIS, TN 38115
BLACK, BUD	BASEBALL	S F GIANTS, CANDLESTICK PARK	SAN FRANICSCO, CA 94124
BLACK, CAROL	TV PRODUCER	UTA, 9560 WILSHIRE BL, 5TH FL	BEVERLY HILLS, CA 90212
BLACK, CILLA	SINGER-ACTRESS	HINDWORTH, REGENT HOUSE 235-241 REGENT ST	LONDON W1R 7AG ENGLAND
BLACK, CLINT	SINGER-SONGWRITER	MORESS, 1209 16TH AVE S	NASHVILLE, TN 37212
BLACK, DON	LYRICIST	HANCOCK, GREENER HOUSE 66-68 HAYMARKET	LONDON SW1Y 4AW ENGLAND
BLACK, J D, BAND	C & W GROUP	150 CONSUMERS RD #400	TORONTO, ONT M2J 1P9 CANADA
BLACK, JAY & THE AMERICAN	ROCK & ROLL GROUP	1650 BROADWAY #1410	NEW YORK, NY 10019
BLACK, JOE	BASEBALL	1904 GREYHOUND TOWERS	PHOENIX, AZ 85077
BLACK, JOHN D F	WRITER-PRODUCER	845 KENISTON AVE	LOS ANGELES, CA 90005
BLACK, KAREN	ACTRESS	690 S BURLINGTON AVE	LOS ANGELES, CA 90057
BLACK, KEITH	BASEBALL	80 OTTAWA ST N	HAMILTON, ONT L8H 3Z1 CANADA
BLACK, MICHAEL	TALENT AGENT	ICM, 8899 BEVERLY BLVD	LOS ANGELES, CA 90048
BLACK, NANCY	ACTRESS	ATKINS, 303 S CRESCENT HEIGHTS	LOS ANGELES. CA 90048
BLACK, NOEL	FILM WRITER-DIRECTOR	126 WADSWORTH AVE	SANTA MONICA, CA 90405
BLACK, RICHARD	WRITER-PRODUCER	4020 PACHECO DR	SHERMAN OAKS, CA 91403
BLACK, RONNIE	GOLFER	POST OFFICE BOX 109601	PALM BCH GARDENS, FL 33418
BLACK, ROSALIND	ACTRESS	851 SPRINGFIELD AVE #11-D	SUMMIT, NJ 07901
BLACK, ROYANA	ACTRESS	CARSON/ADLER, 250 W 57TH ST	NEW YORK, NY 10107
BLACK, SHANE	FILM WRITER-PRODUCER	131 S RODEO DR #300	BEVERLY HILLS, CA 90212
BLACK, SHIRLEY TEMPLE	ACTRESS	115 LAKEVIEW DR	WOODSIDE, CA 94062
BLACK, STANLEY	COMPOSER-CONDUCTOR	118-120 WARDOUR ST	LONDON W1V 4BT ENGLAND
BLACK, STEPHEN	TV WRITER	8955 BEVERLY BLVD	WEST HOLLYWOOD, CA 90048
BLACK, TERRY	SCREENWRITER	CAA, 9830 WILSHIRE BLVD	BEVERLY HILLS, CA 90212
BLACK CROWES, THE	ROCK & ROLL GROUP	9016 WILSHIRE BLVD #346	BEVERLY HILLS, CA 90211
BLACK DIAMOND STRINGERS, THE	C & W GROUP	POST OFFICE BOX 156	ROSELLE, NJ 07203
BLACK FLAG	ROCK & ROLL GROUP	POST OFFICE BOX 1	LAWNDALE, CA 90260
BLACK IVORY	ROCK & ROLL GROUP	RALPH MERCADO, 1650 BROADWAY	NEW YORK, NY 10019
BLACK MOUNTAIN STRING BAND, THE	C & W GROUP	POST OFFICE BOX 156	ROSELLE, NJ 07203
BLACK OAK ARKANSAS	ROCK & ROLL GROUP	1487 RED FOX RUN	LILBURN 30247
BLACK ROSE	ROCK & ROLL GROUP	ATI, 888 7TH AVE, 21ST FLOOR	NEW YORK, NY 10106
BLACK SABBATH	ROCK & ROLL GROUP	8730 SUNSET BLVD #200	LOS ANGELES, CA 90069
BLACK SHEED	ROCK & ROLL GROUP	POST OFFICE BOX 2428	EL SEGUNDO, CA 90245
BLACK UHURU	REGGAE GROUP	14011 VENTURA BLVD #215	SHERMAN OAKS, CA 91423
BLACK-STERNE, BARBARA	COSTUME DESIGNER	11532 OTSEGO ST	NORTH HOLLYWOOD, CA 91601
BLACKBURN, CLARICE	TV WRITER	155 E 76TH ST	NEW YORK, NY 10021

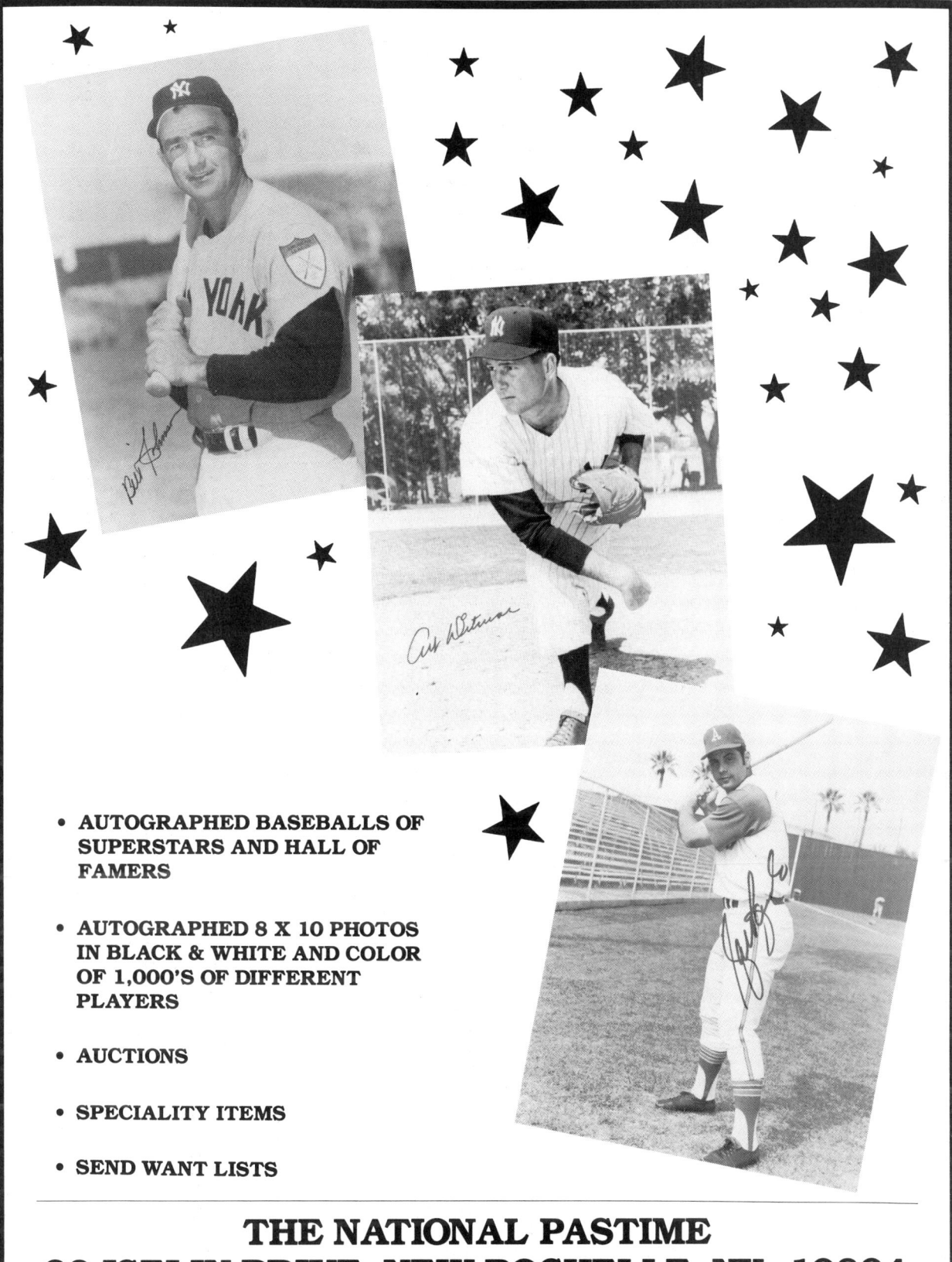

Name	Occupation	Address	City
BLACKBURN, DOROTHY	ACTRESS	903 PARK AVE	NEW YORK, NY 10021
BLACKBURN, GRETA	ACTRESS	11846 VENTURA BLVD #100	STUDIO CITY, CA 91604
BLACKBURN, JANE	ACTRESS	HEATH, PARAMOUNT HOUSE 162-170 WARDOUR ST	LONDON W1V 3AT ENGLAND
BLACKBURN, RICHARD	SCREENWRITER	KOHNER, 9169 SUNSET BLVD	LOS ANGELES, CA 90069
BLACKBURN, WAYNE	BASEBALL SCOUT	TIGERS, TIGER STADIUM	DETROIT, MI 48216
BLACKBYRDS, THE	VOCAL GROUP	527 MADISON AVE #1012	NEW YORK, NY 10022
BLACKCMUN, HARRY A	SUPREME COURT JUDGE	1 1ST ST, NE	WASHINGTON, DC 20543
BLACKFOOT	ROCK & ROLL GROUP	ICM, 40 W 57TH ST	NEW YORK, NY 10019
BLACKFOOT, JAY	SINGER	200 W 51ST ST #1410	NEW YORK, NY 10019
BLACKJACK	ROCK & ROLL GROUP	35 BRENTWOOD	FARMINGVILLE, NY 11738
BLACKJACKS, THE	ROCK & ROLL GROUP	POST OFFICE BOX 205	BROOKLINE, MA 02146
BLACKLEDGE, RON	FOOTBALL COACH	STEELERS, 300 STADIUM CIR	PITTSBURGH, PA 15212
BLACKMAN, CHARLES	CONDUCTOR	10611 STONE CANYON RD	DALLAS, TX 75230
BLACKMAN, HONOR	ACTRESS	11 S WICK MEWS	LONDON 1JG ENGLAND
BLACKMAN, ROBERT	COSTUME DESIGNER	POST OFFICE BOX 1166	PACIFIC PALISADES, CA 90272
BLACKMAN, ROLANDO	BASKETBALL	REUNION ARENA, 777 SPORTS ST	DALLAS, TX 75207
BLACKMAR, PHIL	GOLFER	POST OFFICE BOX 109601	PALM BCH GARDENS, FL 33418
BLACKMON, ANTONIA	TV WRITER	JACK MORTON PRODS, 830 3RD AVE	NEW YORK, NY 10022
BLACKMON, DON	FOOTBALL COACH	PATRIOTS, FOXBORO STADIUM, RT #1	FOXBORO, MA 02035
BLACKMON, ROBERT	FOOTBALL	SEAHAWKS, 11220 NE 53RD ST	KIRKLAND, WA 98033
BLACKMORE, STEPHANIE	ACTRESS	5455 WILSHIRE BLVD #1406	LOS ANGELES, CA 90036
BLACKOFF, EDWARD	ACTOR	13455 VENTURA BLVD #210	SHERMAN OAKS, CA 91423
BLACKSHEAR, THOMAS	ARTIST	108 PROFESSIONAL CTR PKWY #302	SAN RAFAEL, CA 94903
BLACKTON, JAY S	COMPOSER-ARRANGER	9209 MONOGRAM AVE	SEPULVEDA, CA 91343
BLACKWELDER, MYRA	GOLFER	2750 VOLUSA AVE #B	DAYTON BEACH, FL 32114
BLACKWELL, ALAN LEE	SINGER	O & L, 10051 GREENLEAF	SANTA FE SPRINGS, CA 90670
BLACKWELL, BARRY	BASEBALL	2501 ALLEN AVE, SE	CANTON, OH 44707
BLACKWELL, BILL	BASEBALL EXECUTIVE	POST OFFICE BOX 4209	JACKSON, MS 39296
BLACKWELL, EARL "MR"	DESIGNER-PUBLISHER	171 W 57TH ST	NEW YORK, NY 10019
BLACKWELL, EWELL	BASEBALL	20 MOY TOY LN	BREVARD, NC 28712
BLACKWELL, JUAN	BASEBALL	ALBANY YANKEES, HERITAGE PARK	ALBANY, NY 12211
BLACKWELL, KEN	SCREENWRITER	16633 VENTURA BLVD #1421	ENCINO, CA 91436
BLACKWELL, MR	DESIGNER-PUBLISHER	171 W 57TH ST	NEW YORK, NY 10019
BLACKWELL, SAM	WRITER	BRET ADAMS, 448 W 44TH ST	NEW YORK, NY 10036
BLACKWELL, TEDDY	BASEBALL TRAINER	POST OFFICE BOX 1886	COLUMBUS, GA 31902
BLACKWELL, TIM	BASEBALL-MANAGER	POST OFFICE BOX 7845	COLUMBIA, SC 29202
BLACKWOOD, CHRISTIAN	TV PRODUCER	115 BANK ST	NEW YORK, NY 10014
BLACKWOOD, HERMOINE	COMPOSER	2849 ARMCOST AVE	LOS ANGELES, CA 90064
BLACKWOOD, NINA	MUSIC CORRESPONDENT	RUDY TELLEZ, 710 N STEWART ST	LOS ANGELES, CA 90038
BLACKWOOD, R W	SINGER	POST OFFICE BOX 17272	MEMPHIS, TN 38187
BLACKWOOD BROTHERS, THE	C & W GROUP	POST OFFICE BOX 17272	MEMPHIS, TN 38187
BLACKWOOD QUARTET, THE	VOCAL GROUP	POST OFFICE BOX 17272	MEMPHIS, TN 38187
BLACKWOOD SINGERS, THE	GOSPEL GROUP	POST OFFICE BOX 17272	MEMPHIS, TN 38187
BLACQUE, TAUREAN	ACTOR	4207 DON ORTEGA PL	LOS ANGELES, CA 90008
BLADE, RICHARD	ACTOR	KJAR, 10653 RIVERSIDE DR	TOLUCA LAKE, CA 91602
BLADES, BENNIE	FOOTBALL	LIONS, 1200 FEATHERSTONE RD	PONTIAC, MI 48432
BLADES, BRIAN	FOOTBALL	SEAHAWKS, 11220 NE 53RD ST	KIRKLAND, WA 98033
BLADES, RUBEN	SINGER-SONGWRITER	1234 1/2 N CRESCENT HEIGHTS	LOS ANGELES, CA 90046
BLADOS, BRIAN	FOOTBALL	BENGALS, 200 RIVERFRONT STADIUM	CINCINNATI, OH 45202
BLAGDEN, BOB	TV DIRECTOR	BOUNDARY HOUSE, BOUDARY RD TAPLOW	BUCKS ENGLAND
BLAINE, CHARLENE	ACTRESS	7080 HOLLYWOOD BLVD #704	HOLLYWOOD, CA 90028
BLAINE, HAL	DRUMMER	POST OFFICE BOX 6166	SCOTTSDALE, AZ 85261
BLAINE, MARTIN	ACTOR	21458 RAMBLA VISTA	MALIBU, CA 90265
BLAINE, VIVIAN	ACTRESS	20 E 35TH ST	NEW YORK, NY 10016
BLAIR, ALPHA	ACTRESS	L A TALENT, 8335 SUNSET BLVD	LOS ANGELES, CA 90069
BLAIR, BETSY	ACTRESS	11 CHALCOTT GARDENS ENGLAND'S LANE	LONDON NW3 ENGLAND
BLAIR, BILL	BASKETBALL COACH	BULLETS, 1 HARRY S TRUMAN DR	LANDOVER, MD 20785
BLAIR, DENNIS	TV WRITER	555 W 57TH ST #1230	NEW YORK, NY 10019
BLAIR, DIRK	BASEBALL	POST OFFICE BOX 4525	MACON, GA 31208
BLAIR, ISLA	ACTRESS	19 ULLSWATER RD	LONDON SW13 ENGLAND
BLAIR, JANET	ACTRESS	21535 IRWIN ST #126	WOODLAND HILLS, CA 91367
BLAIR, JOHN	WRI-DIR-PROD	20 WILLOW BRIDGE RD	LONDON N1 2LA ENGLAND
BLAIR, JOYCE	ACTRESS	2029 CENTURY PARK E #600	LOS ANGELES, CA 90067
BLAIR, LES	TV DIRECTOR	STEEL, 110 GLOUCESTER AVE	LONDON NW1 8JL ENGLAND
BLAIR, LINDA	ACTRESS-PRODUCER	8033 SUNSET BLVD #204	LOS ANGELES, CA 90046
BLAIR, LIONEL	TV PERS-DANCER	5 BEVERLY RD	LONDON SW13 ENGLAND
BLAIR, PATRICIA	ACTRESS	GILLA ROOS, 16 W 22ND ST, 7TH FL	NEW YORK, NY 10010
BLAIR, WILLIE	BASEBALL	POST OFFICE BOX 27045	TUCSON, AZ 85726
BLAISDELL, BRAD	ACTOR	641 N NAOMI ST	BURBANK, CA 91505
BLAKE, DEBRA	ACTRESS	26-A HIGHCLIFF DR LEIGH-ON-THE-SEA	ESSEX ENGLAND
BLAKE, ELTA	ACTRESS	594 GARFIELD AVE	SOUTH PASADENA, CA 91030
BLAKE, GERALD	TV DIRECTOR	764 THE WHITE HOUSE ALBANY ST	LONDON NW1 3UU ENGLAND
BLAKE, HOWARD	COMPOSER-CONDUCTOR	HEATH, PARAMOUNT HOUSE 162-170 WARDOUR ST	LONDON W1V 3AT ENGLAND
BLAKE, JAY DON	GOLFER	POST OFFICE BOX 109601	PALM BCH GARDENS, FL 33418
BLAKE, JOHN	SINGER	HEARTLAND, 660 DOUGLAS	ALTAMONTE SPRINGS, FL 32714
BLAKE, MERRITT	TALENT AGENT	822 S ROBERTSON BLVD #200	LOS ANGELES, CA 90035
BLAKE, MICHAEL	NOVELIST-SCREENWRITER	9200 SUNSET BLVD #402	LOS ANGELES, CA 90069
BLAKE, PAUL ALAN	DIRECTOR	9300 WILSHIRE BLVD #410	BEVERLY HILLS, CA 90212
BLAKE, PETER	ACTOR	BARRY BROWN, 47 WEST SQ	LONDON SE11 4SP ENGLAND

BLAKE, ROB	HOCKEY	POST OFFICE BOX 17013	INGLEWOOD, CA	90308
BLAKE, ROBERT	ACTOR	11604 DILLING ST	NORTH HOLLYWOOD, CA	91604
BLAKE, SONDRA	ACTRESS	LIGHT, 901 BRINGHAM AVE	LOS ANGELES, CA	90049
BLAKE, SUSIE	ACTRESS	SHARKEY, 15 GOLDEN SQ #315	LONDON W1R 3AG	ENGLAND
BLAKE, TERESA	ACTRESS	ABC-TV, "ALL MY CHILDREN"		
		320 W 66TH ST	NEW YORK, NY	10023
BLAKE, TIMOTHY	ACTRESS	1643 SUNSET PLAZA DR	LOS ANGELES, CA	90069
BLAKE, WHITNEY	ACTRESS	POST OFFICE BOX 6088	MALIBU, CA	90265
BLAKELEY, GORDON	BASEBALL SCOUT	POST OFFICE BOX 4100	SEATTLE, WA	98104
BLAKELY, DON	ACTOR	POST OFFICE BOX 691736	LOS ANGELES, CA	90069
BLAKELY, SUSAN	ACTRESS	1829 FRANKLIN CANYON	BEVERLY HILLS, CA	90210
BLAKEMAN, TODD	BASEBALL	POST OFFICE BOX 661	KENOSHA, WI	53141
BLAKEMORE, MICHAEL	FILM DIRECTOR	11-A SAINT MARTIN'S ALMHOUSES		
		BAYHAM ST	LONDON NW1	ENGLAND
BLAKER, CHARLES R	COMPOSER-CONDUCTOR	1142 S SIERRA BONITA AVE #7	LOS ANGELES, CA	90019
BLAKER, CLAY & TEXAS HONKY TONK	C & W GROUP	POST OFFICE BOX 310448	NEW BRAUNFELS, TX	78131
BLAKLEY, RONEE	SINGER-ACTRESS	8033 SUNSET BLVD #693	LOS ANGELES, CA	90046
BLANC, NOEL BARTON	WRITER	702 N RODEO DR	BEVERLY HILLS, CA	90210
BLANCAS, HOMERO	GOLFER	PGA SENIORS, 112 T P C BLVD	PONTE VEDRA BEACH, FL	32082
BLANCHARD, ELMER	SINGER	PROCESS, 439 WILEY AVE	FRANKLIN, PA	16323
BLANCHARD, NINA	TALENT AGENT	957 N COLE AVE	LOS ANGELES, CA	90028
BLANCHARD, TULLY	WRESTLER	POST OFFICE BOX 105366	ATLANTA, GA	31348
BLANCO, HENRY	BASEBALL	POST OFFICE BOX 10031	BAKERSFIELD, CA	93389
BLANCO, RAY	BASEBALL SCOUT	POST OFFICE BOX 90111	ARLINGTON, TX	76004
BLANCO-HERRERA, JULIO	BASEBALL SCOUT	BREWERS, 201 S 46TH ST	MILWAUKEE, WI	53214
BLAND, BOBBY "BLUE"	SINGER	108 N AUBURNDALE #1010	MEMPHIS, TN	38104
BLAND, LANCE	BASEBALL TRAINER	POST OFFICE BOX 30160	SAN BERNARDINO, CA	92413
BLANDA, GEORGE	FOOTBALL	POST OFFICE BOX 1153	LA QUINTA, CA	92253
BLANDO, CARL	BASEBALL SCOUT	POST OFFICE BOX 419969	KANSAS CITY, MO	64141
BLANE, SALLY	ACTRESS	1114 S ROXBURY DR	LOS ANGELES, CA	90035
BLANEY, CHARLIE	BASEBALL EXECUTIVE	1000 ELYSIAN PARK DR	LOS ANGELES, CA	90012
BLANK, STU	SINGER-SONGWRITER	POST OFFICE BOX 1311	SAN MATEO, CA	94401
BLANK, THOMAS JEFFREY	FILM WRITER-DIRECTOR	1430 MARION DR	GLENDALE, CA	91205
BLANKENSHIP, BRIAN	FOOTBALL	STEELERS, 300 STADIUM CIR	PITTSBURGH, PA	15212
BLANKENSHIP, JOHNNY	SINGER	O & L, 10051 GREENLEAF	SANTA FE SPRINGS, CA	90670
BLANKENSHIP, KEVIN	BASEBALL	POST OFFICE BOX 75089	OKLAHOMA CITY, OK	73147
BLANKENSHIP, LANCE	BASEBALL	ATHLETICS'S, OAKLAND COLISEUM	OAKLAND, CA	94621
BLANKFIELD, MARK	ACTOR	11712 MOORPARK ST #204	STUDIO CITY, CA	91604
BLANKLEY, JONATHAN C	TV DIRECTOR-PRODUCER	82 NEWMAN PL	FAIRFIELD, CT	06430
BLANKS, LANCE	BASKETBALL	THE PALACE OF AUBURN HILLS		
		2 CHAMPIONSHIP DR	AUBURN HILLS, MI	48326
BLANTON, ARELL	ACTOR	4191 GREENBUSH AVE	SHERMAN OAKS, CA	91423
BLANTON, GARRETT	BASEBALL	80 OTTAWA ST N	HAMILTON, ONT L8H 3Z1	CANADA
BLANTON, RICKY	BASKETBALL	SUNS, 2910 N CENTRAL AVE	PHOENIX, AZ	85012
BLASINGAME, DON	BASEBALL-EXECUTIVE	POST OFFICE BOX 7575	PHILADELPHIA, PA	19101
BLASS, BILL	FASHION DESIGNER	550 7TH AVE	NEW YORK, NY	10019
BLASS, STEVE	BASEBALL-ANNOUNCER	POST OFFICE BOX 7000	PITTSBURGH, PA	15212
BLASSIE, FREDDIE	WRESTLER-MANAGER	POST OFFICE BOX 3859	STAMFORD, CT	06905
BLASTERS, THE	ROCK & ROLL GROUP	2667 N BEVERLY GLEN BLVD	LOS ANGELES, CA	90077
BLASUCCI, RICHARD	ACTOR-WRITER	353 1/2 GARDNER	LOS ANGELES, CA	90036
BLATT, DANIEL H	FILM PRODUCER	BLATT/SINGER PRODUCTIONS		
		COLUMBIA PICTURES		
		COLUMBIA PLAZA E	BURBANK, CA	91504
BLATT, DAVID R	TV DIRECTOR	55 E 87TH ST #8-A	NEW YORK, NY	10128
BLATTY, WILLIAM PETER	FILM WRITER-PRODUCER	5841 ROUND MEADOW	WOODLAND HILLS, CA	91364
BLAUSER, JEFF	BASEBALL	POST OFFICE BOX 4064	ATLANTA, GA	30302
BLAUSTEIN, JULIAN	PRODUCER	10126 ANGELO VIEW DR	BEVERLY HILLS, CA	90210
BLAYLOCK, GARY	BASEBALL-SCOUT	POST OFFICE BOX 419969	KANSAS CITY, MO	64141
BLAYLOCK, MOOKIE	BASKETBALL	N J NETS, MEADOWLANDS ARENA	EAST RUTHERFORD, NJ	07073
BLAYLOCK, PEGGY AHERN	ACTRESS	24529 DEEP WELL RD	CALABASAS, CA	91302
BLAZ, BEN	U S DELEGATE	176 SERANO AVE	TAMUNING, GU	96911
BLAZER BROTHERS, THE	C & W GROUP	POST OFFICE BOX 2498	HENDERSONVILLE, TN	37077
BLAZIER, RON	BASEBALL	POST OFFICE BOX 1721	SPARTANBURG, SC	29304
BLEACH, BARRY M	WRITER	8074 FAREHOLM DR #5	LOS ANGELES, CA	90046
BLECHMAN, COREY	TV WRITER	CAA, 9830 WILSHIRE BLVD	BEVERLY HILLS, CA	90212
BLECKNER, JEFF	DIRECTOR	4701 NATOMA AVE	WOODLAND HILLS, CA	91364
BLECKNER, PETER NEIL	TV DIRECTOR	17 W 67TH ST #10-A	NEW YORK, NY	10023
BLEDSOE, TEMPESTT	ACTRESS	8230 BEVERLY BLVD #23	LOS ANGELES, CA	90048
BLEECK, DOUGLAS	DIRECTOR	2120 N BEVERLY GLEN BLVD	LOS ANGELES, CA	90077
BLEES, ROBERT	WRITER-PRODUCER	1373 BECKWITH AVE	LOS ANGELES, CA	90049
BLEETH, YASMINE	ACTRESS	ABC-TV, "ONE LIFE TO LIVE"		
		56 W 66TH ST	NEW YORK, NY	10023
BLEICH, BILL	FILM-TV WRITER	CAA, 9830 WILSHIRE BLVD	BEVERLY HILLS, CA	90212
BLEIER, EDWARD	TV EXECUTIVE	WARNER BROS, 75 ROCKEFELLER PLAZA	NEW YORK, NY	10019
BLEIER, NANCY	ACTRESS	10000 RIVERSIDE DR #6	TOLUCA LAKE, CA	91602
BLEIER, ROCKY	FOOTBALL	580 SQUAW RUN RD #E	PITTSBURGH, PA	15238
BLEMINGS, WILLIAM	BASEBALL EXECUTIVE	POST OFFICE BOX 4488	WINSTON-SALEM, NC	27115
BLENCKSTONE, WINSTON	BASEBALL EXECUTIVE	POST OFFICE BOX 1110	MYRTLE BEACH, SC	29578
BLESER, AL	BASEBALL SCOUT	BREWERS, 201 S 46TH ST	MILWAUKEE, WI	53214
BLESSED, BRIAN	ACTOR	SAINT JAMES'S ST, 22 GROOM PL	LONDON SW1	ENGLAND
BLESSING, BERT	SCREENWRITER	WM MORRIS, 1350 AVE OF AMERICAS	NEW YORK, NY	10019
BLEVINS, GREG	BASEBALL	POST OFFICE BOX 309	GASTONA, NC	28053
BLEVINS, JESSEE	SINGER	HOWARD KNIGHT, 1609 CONGRESS RD	EASTOVER, SC	29044
BLEYER, ROBERT A	TV PRODUCER	J MORTON PRODS, 830 3RD AVE	NEW YORK, NY	10022

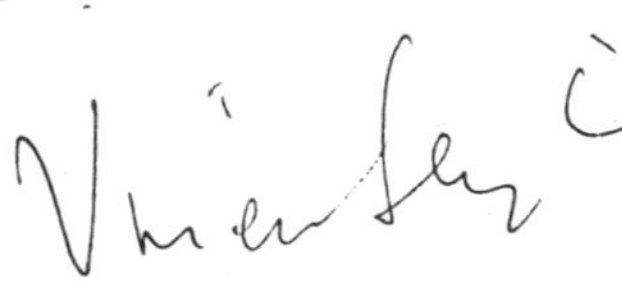

BLICKER, SEYMOUR	WRITER	1501 BROADWAY #2310	NEW YORK, NY	10036
BLILEY, THOMAS J, JR	U S CONGRESSMAN	4914 FITZHUGH AVE #101	RICHMOND, VA	23230
BLINDER, DONNA C	WRITER	10508 CLEARWOOD CT	LOS ANGELES, CA	90077
BLINN, ROGER	ACTOR	264 RUE SAINT-HONORE	PARIS 75001	FRANCE
BLINN, TONY	BODYBUILDER	CAFBB, 53 SUZOR	SAINT HUBERT, QUE J3Y	CANADA
BLINN, WILLIAM FREDERICK	WRITER-PRODUCER	16964 IVADEL PL	ENCINO, CA	91436
BLISS, ALLISON	TV DIRECTOR	2 VISTA VERDE CT	SAN FRANCISCO, CA	94131
BLISS, BILL	BASEBALL	1524 W NEBRASKA AVE	PEORIA, IL	61604
BLITZER, BARRY	TV WRITER	16315 AKRON ST	PACIFIC PALISADES, CA	90272
BLITZER, BILLY	BASEBALL SCOUT	1060 W ADDISON ST	CHICAGO, IL	60613
BLITZER, WOLF	NEWS CORRESPONDENT	1050 TECHWOOD DR, NW	ATLANTA, GA	30318
BLOCH, CHARLES B	FILM PRODUCER	5039 BLUEBELL AVE	NORTH HOLLYWOOD, CA	91607
BLOCH, JOHN W	WRITER-PRODUCER	2248 MANDEVILLE CANYON RD	LOS ANGELES, CA	90049
BLOCH, ROBERT	WRITER	2111 SUNSET CREST DR	LOS ANGELES, CA	90046
BLOCK, BRUCE A	DIRECTOR	POST OFFICE BOX 8743	UNIVERSAL CITY, CA	91608
BLOCK, HERBERT	CARTOONIST	1150 15TH ST, NW	WASHINGTON, DC	20071
BLOCK, HUNT	ACTOR	2216 VANDERBILT LN	REDONDO BEACH, CA	90272
BLOCK, MERVIN A	WRITER	140 W END AVE	NEW YORK, NY	10023
BLOCKER, DIRK	ACTOR	1999 AVE OF THE STARS #2850	LOS ANGELES, CA	90067
BLOCKER, TERRY	BASEBALL	823 PINEY WOODS RD	COLUMBIA, SC	29210
BLODGETT, MICHAEL	ACTOR	10485 NATIONAL BLVD #22	LOS ANGELES, CA	90034
BLOEM, JOANNA	ACTRESS	1243 12TH ST #4	SANTA MONICA, CA	90401
BLOHM, GARY	WRITER-PRODUCER	7259 BIRDVIEW AVE	MALIBU, CA	90265
BLOHM, PETE	BASEBALL	CHIEFS, MAC ARTHUR STADIUM	SYRACUSE, NY	13208
BLOMDAHL, BEN	BASEBALL	POST OFFICE BOX 64939	FAYETTEVILLE, NC	28306
BLOMMAERT, JULIEN	BODYBUILDER	ACB GYM, 9 HOPE LN	B-8200 BRUGGE	BELGIUM
BLOMMAERT, SUSAN	ACTRESS	3115 BROADWAY	NEW YORK, NY	10027
BLOMQUIST, TOM	WRITER-PRODUCER	4769 ELMER AVE	NORTH HOLLYWOOD, CA	91602
BLOODWORTH-THOMASON, LINDA	TV WRITER-PRODUCER	9220 SUNSET BLVD #311	LOS ANGELES, CA	90069
BLOOM, ANNE	ACTRESS-COMEDIENNE	656 W KNOLL DR #303	WEST HOLLYWOOD, CA	90069
BLOOM, ARTHUR	DIRECTOR-PRODUCER	530 W 57TH ST	NEW YORK, NY	10019
BLOOM, BILL ALAN	WRITER	346 N OAKHURST DR #B	BEVERLY HILLS, CA	90210
BLOOM, BRIAN	ACTOR	11 CROYDON CT	DIX HILLS, NY	11746
BLOOM, CLAIRE	ACTRESS	ROSENBERG, 8428 MELROSE PL #C	LOS ANGELES, CA	90069
BLOOM, MAX	SCREENWRITER	UTA, 9560 WILSHIRE BL, 5TH FL	BEVERLY HILLS, CA	90212
BLOOM, STEVEN L	SCREENWRITER	CAA, 9830 WILSHIRE BLVD	BEVERLY HILLS, CA	90212
BLOOM, TOM	ARTIST	235 E 84TH ST	NEW YORK, NY	10028
BLOOM, VERNA	ACTRESS	327 E 82ND ST	NEW YORK, NY	10028
BLOOMBERG, BEVERLY	TV WRITER	8955 BEVERLY BLVD	WEST HOLLYWOOD, CA	90048
BLOOMBERG, RON	TV WRITER	5224 DONNA AVE	TARZANA, CA	91356
BLOOMBERG, STUART J	TV EXECUTIVE	3825 SAN RAFAEL AVE	LOS ANGELES, CA	90065
BLOOMENTHAL, RICHARD	ATTORNEY GENERAL	STATE CAPITOL BUILDING	HARTFORD, CT	06106
BLOOMFIELD, JACK	BASEBALL SCOUT	POST OFFICE BOX 288	HOUSTON, TX	77001
BLOOMGARDEN, JOHN	THEATER PRODUCER	275 CENTRAL PARK W	NEW YORK, NY	10024
BLOOMSTEIN, REX	FILM-TV DIRECTOR	25 WILLOW RD	LONDON NW3	ENGLAND
BLOSSER, GREG	BASEBALL	POST OFFICE BOX 1718	NEW BRITAIN, CT	06050
BLOTTO	ROCK & ROLL GROUP	POST OFFICE BOX 306	MYSTIC, CT	06355
BLOUNT, LISA	ACTRESS	3957 ALBRIGHT AVE	LOS ANGELES, CA	90066
BLOUNT, MEL	FOOTBALL	RD #1, BOX 91	CLAYSVILLE, PA	15323
BLOW, KURTIS	RAPPER-RAPWRITER	201 EASTERN PARKWAY #3-K	BROOKLYN, NY	11238
BLOW MONKEYS, THE	ROCK & ROLL GROUP	370 CITY RD	LONDON EC1V 2QA	ENGLAND
BLOWERS, MIKE	BASEBALL	POST OFFICE BOX 3690, STA "B"	CALGARY, ALB T2B 4M4	CANADA
BLUBAUGH, SUSAN M	ARTIST	416 CLINTON ST	BROOKLYN, NY	11238
BLUE, VIDA	BASEBALL	POST OFFICE BOX 1449	PLEASANTON, CA	94556
BLUE BANDANA COUNTRY BAND	C & W GROUP	CUDE, 519 N HALIFAX AVE	DAYTONA BCH, FL	32018
BLUE BLAZER, THE	WRESTLER	SEE - HART, OWEN "THE ROCKET"		
BLUE IS HEAVEN	ROCK & ROLL GROUP	DESMOND, 23 UPPER SHEPPERD	DUBLIN 1	IRELAND
BLUE MAX	ROCK & ROLL GROUP	POST OFFICE BOX 448	RADFORD, VA	24141
BLUE OYSTER CULT	ROCK & ROLL GROUP	SANDY PEARLMAN, INC		
		888 7TH AVE, 37TH FLOOR	NEW YORK, NY	10106
BLUE RIDGE, THE	C & W GROUP	32500 CONCORD DR #252	MADISON HEIGHTS, MI	48071
BLUE SKY BAND	C & W GROUP	POST OFFICE BOX 684	DES MOINES, IA	50303
BLUE TRAPEZE	ROCK & ROLL GROUP	POST OFFICE BOX 6863	FULLERTON, CA	92631
BLUEBERG, JIM	BASEBALL	ALBANY YANKEES, HERITAGE PARK	ALBANY, NY	12211
BLUEBERRY HELLBELLIES, THE	ROCK & ROLL GROUP	61-71 COLLIER ST	LONDON N1 9BE	ENGLAND
BLUEGRASS CARDINALS, THE	C & W GROUP	POST OFFICE BOX 160	HENDERSONVILLE, TN	37077
BLUEME, DAVID	BASEBALL SCOUT	SKYDOME, 300 BREMMER BL #3200	TORONTO, ONT M5V 3B3	CANADA
BLUESBUSTERS, THE	ROCK & ROLL GROUP	450 14TH ST #201, NW	ATLANTA, GA	30318
BLUESTEIN, STEVE	ACTOR-WRITER	5255 BELLINGAM AVE #205	NORTH HOLLYWOOD, CA	91607
BLUESTONE, BRAD	BASEBALL TRAINER	POST OFFICE BOX 36407	LOUISVILLE, KY	40233
BLUHM, BRANDON	BASEBALL	POST OFFICE BOX 1143	BURLINGTON, NC	27216
BLUM, BILL	WRI-DIR-PROD	300 E 71ST ST	NEW YORK, NY	10021
BLUM, BOB	BASEBALL EXECUTIVE	STARS, 850 LAS VEGAS BLVD N	LAS VEGAS, NV	89101
BLUM, DEBORAH	SCREENWRITER	KOHNER, 9169 SUNSET BLVD	LOS ANGELES, CA	90069
BLUM, EDWIN HARVEY	SCREENWRITER	801 N RODEO DR	BEVERLY HILLS, CA	90210
BLUM, HARRY N	FILM PRODUCER	494 TUALLITAN RD	LOS ANGELES, CA	90049
BLUM, MICHAEL	TV DIRECTOR	423 MADISON AVE	NEW YORK, NY	10017
BLUM, ROBERT P	WRITER	555 W 57TH ST #1230	NEW YORK, NY	10019
BLUM, RON	FOOTBALL REFEREE	NFL, 410 PARK AVE	NEW YORK, NY	10022
BLUM, STANFORD	WRITER-PRODUCER	4222 WOODMAN AVE	SHERMAN OAKS, CA	91423
BLUMBERG, DAVID E	COMPOSER	3309 LAUREL CANYON BLVD	STUDIO CITY, CA	91604
BLUMBERG, ROB	BASEBALL	POST OFFICE BOX 230	HAGERSTOWN, MD	21740
BLUME, HOWARD	DIRECTOR	1501 BROADWAY #2600	NEW YORK, NY	10036
BLUME, JUDY	WRITER	54 RIVERSIDE DR	NEW YORK, NY	10023

BLUMOFE, ROBERT F	FILM PRODUCER	1100 ALTA LOMA RD #1005	LOS ANGELES, CA	90069
BLUNT, CHARLOTTE	ACTRESS	9255 SUNSET BLVD #515	LOS ANGELES, CA	90069
BLUNT, ROY D	SECRETARY OF STATE	POST OFFICE BOX 720	JEFFERSON CITY, MO	65102
BLUTHAL, JOHN	ACTOR	INTERNATIONAL ARTISTES LTD		
		MEZZANINE FL, 235 REGENT ST	LONDON W1R 8AX	ENGLAND
BLUTO, JOHN	ACTOR	7080 HOLLYWOOD BLVD #704	HOLLYWOOD, CA	90028
BLYE, ALLAN	WRITER-PRODUCER	16014 SKYTOP RD	ENCINO, CA	91316
BLYE, MARGARET	ACTRESS	8730 SUNSET BLVD #480	LOS ANGELES, CA	90069
BLYLEVEN, BERT	BASEBALL	18992 CANYON DR	VILLA PARK, CA	92667
BLYSTONE, RICHARD	NEWS CORRESPONDENT	1050 TECHWOOD DR, NW	ATLANTA, GA	30318
BLYTH, ANN	ACTRESS	POST OFFICE BOX 9754	RANCHO SANTE FE, CA	92067
BLYTHE, ARTHUR	SAXOPHONIST	POST OFFICE BOX 7564	NEW YORK, NY	10116
BLYTHE, JOHN	ACTOR	19 BELVEDERE CLOSE, TEDDINGTON	MIDDLESEX	ENGLAND
BLYTHE, PETER	ACTOR	21 ENNISMORE GARDENS	LONDON SW7	ENGLAND
BNARTON, JEFF	BASEBALL SCOUT	REDS, 100 RIVERFRONT STADIUM	CINCINNATI, OH	45202
BOAM, JEFFREY D	SCREENWRITER	17170 KINZIE ST	NORTHRIDGE, CA	91325
BOAN, JOE	COMPOSER	3518 THE STRAND	HERMOSA BEACH, CA	90254
BOARDMAN, CHRISTOPHER E	COMPOSER	13135 ROSE AVE	LOS ANGELES, CA	90066
BOARDMAN, ERIC	TV WRITER	6120 WINANS DR #11	LOS ANGELES, CA	90068
BOARDMAN, TRUE	ACTOR-WRITER	2951 PEISANO RD	PEBBLE BEACH, CA	93953
BOARDMAN, WILLIAM M	TV-RADIO WRITER	555 W 57TH ST #1230	NEW YORK, NY	10019
BOARDO, LIZ	SINGER	PENNY, 30 GUINAN ST	WALTHAM, MA	02154
BOB, BASSEN	HOCKEY	BLUES, 5700 OAKLAND AVE	SAINT LOUIS, MO	63110
BOBBIE	ACTRESS	8235 SANTA MONICA BLVD #202	LOS ANGELES, CA	90046
BOBBY C	SINGER	5625 "O" STREET BLDG #7	LINCOLN, NE	68510
BOBECKER, MARK	SINGER	3125 19TH ST #217	BAKERSFIELD, CA	93301
BOBKER, LEE	DIRECTOR	61 SARA LN	NEW ROCHELLE, NY	10804
BOBO, ELGIN	BASEBALL	POST OFFICE BOX 3496	DAVENPORT, IA	52808
BOBO, JOHN	FOOTBALL COACH	BUCCANEERS, 1 BUCCANEER PL	TAMPA, FL	33607
BOBRICK, NEIL	DIRECTOR	152 FINISTERRE #S-152	LINDENWOLD, NJ	08021
BOBRICK, SAM	TV WRITER-DIRECTOR	5300 OAK PARK AVE	ENCINO, CA	91316
BOBS, THE	ROCK & ROLL GROUP	GREAT AMERICAN MUSIC HALL		
		859 O'FARRELL ST	SAN FRANCISCO, CA	94109
BOCCARDO, JOHN	TV WRITER	21569 PASEO SERRA	MALIBU, CA	90265
BOCCARDO, MASON	ACTOR	CBS-TV, "AS THE WORLD TURNS"		
		524 W 57TH ST #5330	NEW YORK, NY	10019
BOCCHINO, ROBERT	VOICE OVERS	POST OFFICE BOX 99	HAVERFORD, PA	19041
BOCHCO, STEVEN	WRITER-PRODUCER	694 AMALFI DR	PACIFIC PALISADES, CA	90272
BOCHNER, HART	ACTOR	42 HALDEMAN RD	SANTA MONICA, CA	90402
BOCHNER, LLOYD	ACTOR	42 HALDEMAN RD	SANTA MONICA, CA	90402
BOCHTE, BRUCE	BASEBALL	6475 S MAXWELTON RD	CLINTON, WA	98236
BOCHTLER, DOUG	BASEBALL	POST OFFICE BOX 15757	HARRISBURG, PA	17105
BOCHY, BRUCE	BASEBALL-MANAGER	14035 BARRYMORE ST	SAN DIEGO, CA	92129
BOCK, FRED	COMPOSER-CONDUCTOR	5404 TOPEKA DR	TARZANA, CA	91356
BOCK, JERRY	COMPOSER	ASCAP, 1 LINCOLN PLAZA	NEW YORK, NY	10023
BOCKHOLT, ROBERT, JR	COMPOSER	11625 LA MAIDA ST	NORTH HOLLYWOOD, CA	91601
BOCKUS, RANDY	BASEBALL	9313 CHESTNUT ST	EAST SPARTA, OH	44626
BODARD, MEG	FILM PRODUCER	19 RUE MONSTROSIER	NEUILLY 92200	FRANCE
BODDICKER, MIKE	BASEBALL	POST OFFICE BOX 419969	KANSAS CITY, MO	64141
BODENHAMER, GREGORY	AUTHOR	1234 W CHAPMAN AVE #203	ORANGE, CA	92668
BODET, GIB	BASEBALL SCOUT	1000 ELYSIAN PARK DR	LOS ANGELES, CA	90012
BODGER, DOUG	HOCKEY	SABRES, MEMORIAL AUDITORIUM	BUFFALO, NY	14202
BODIE, KEITH	BASEBALL MANAGER	POST OFFICE BOX 3690, STA "B"	CALGARY, ALB T2B 4M4	CANADA
BODWELL, PHILIP	TV DIRECTOR-PRODUCER	1900 OLD BRIAR RD	HIGHLAND PARK, IL	60601
BODY ELECTRIC	ROCK & ROLL GROUP	41 BRITAIN ST #200	TORONTO, ONT	CANADA
BOE	C & W GROUP	5625 "O" STREET BLDG #7	LINCOLN, NE	68510
BOEHLERT, SHERWOOD L	U S CONGRESSMAN	10 BROAD ST, ROOM 200	UTICA, NY	13501
BOEHNER, JOHN	U S CONGRESSMAN	12 S PLUM ST	TROY, OH	45373
BOEHRINGER, BRIAN	BASEBALL	POST OFFICE BOX 4218	SOUTH BEND, IN	46634
BOERSMA, JAMES G	COMPOSER-CONDUCTOR	3910 BROWN ST	OCEANSIDE, CA	92054
BOESKY, IVAN F	STOCK SPECULATOR	BOESKY CO, 650 5TH AVE	NEW YORK, NY	10019
BOETTCHER, KATHY	ACTRESS	12377 LEWIS ST #101	GARDEN GROVE, CA	92640
BOETTICHER, BUDD	FILM DIRECTOR	23969 GREEN HAVEN LN	RAMONA, CA	92065
BOEVER, JOE	BASEBALL	POST OFFICE BOX 288	HOUSTON, TX	77001
BOFILL, ANGELA	SINGER	1385 YORK AVE #6-B	NEW YORK, NY	10021
BOGAR, TIM	BASEBALL	POST OFFICE BOX 1211	NORFOLK, VA	23502
BOGARD, DICK	BASEBALL SCOUT	ATHLETICS'S, OAKLAND COLISEUM	OAKLAND, CA	94621
BOGARDE, DIRK	ACTOR	06 CHATEAUNEUF	DE GRASSE	FRANCE
BOGART, PAUL	TV WRITER-DIRECTOR	1033 CAROL DR #403	LOS ANGELES, CA	90069
BOGART, PETER G	DIRECTOR	202 N LA PEER DR #6	BEVERLY HILLS, CA	90211
BOGAZIANOS, VASILI	ACTOR	STE, 888 7TH AVE, 18TH FLOOR	NEW YORK, NY	10106
BOGDANOVICH, JOSEF	SCREENWRITER	ICM, 8899 BEVERLY BLVD	LOS ANGELES, CA	90048
BOGDANOVICH, PETER	FILM WRITER-DIRECTOR	12250 SHADYBROOK DR	BEVERLY HILLS, CA	90210
BOGDANOVICH STRATTEN, LOUISE	PRODUCER	12250 SHADYBROOK DR	BEVERLY HILLS, CA	90049
BOGGETTO, BRAD	BASEBALL	POST OFFICE BOX 483	YAKIMA, WA	98907
BOGGS, WADE	BASEBALL	FENWAY PARK, 4 YAWKEY WY	BOSTON, MA	02215
BOGGUSS, SUZY	SINGER	1025 16TH AVE S #401	NASHVILLE, TN	37212
BOGOSIAN, ERIC	ACTOR-SCREENWRITER	ICM, 8899 BEVERLY BLVD	LOS ANGELES, CA	90048
BOGUES, TYRONE	BASKETBALL	310 N KINGS DR	CHARLOTTE, NC	28204
BOHANNON, BILL	SINGER	POST OFFICE BOX 18284	SHREVEPORT, LA	71138
BOHANNON, HAMILTON	SINGER	PHASE II, 189 N ORATON PKWY	EAST ORANGE, NJ	07017
BOHANNON, JIM	RADIO PERSONALITY	MUTUAL BROADCASTING SYSTEM		
		1775 S JEFFERSON DAVIS PKWY	ARLINGTON, VA	22202
BOHAY, HEIDI	ACTRESS	4304 FARMDALE AVE	STUDIO CITY, CA	91604
BOHEM, HILDA GORDON	SCREENWRITER	1629 N CRESCENT HGTS BLVD	LOS ANGELES, CA	90069

BOHL, CHARLES	SCREENWRITER	10351 SANTA MONICA BLVD #211	LOS ANGELES, CA	90025
BOHL, DONALD A	DIRECTOR-PRODUCER	634 INTRACOASTAL DR	FORT LAUDERDALE, FL	33304
BOHN, MATT	BASEBALL UMPIRE	235 MAIN ST #103	TRUSSVILLE, AL	35173
BOHRER, ALEXANDER	COMPOSER	7810 LAUREL CANYON BLVD #11	NORTH HOLLYWOOD, CA	91605
BOHRER, CORINNE	ACTRESS	MTA, 9320 WILSHIRE BL, 3RD FL	BEVERLY HILLS, CA	90212
BOHRINGER, HELMS	BASEBALL	POST OFFICE BOX 10031	BAKERSFIELD, CA	93389
BOHROFEN, BRENT	BASEBALL	80 OTTAWA ST N	HAMILTON, ONT L8H 3Z1	CANADA
BOISROND, MICHEL	FILM DIRECTOR	19 RUE DE LISBONNE	PARIS 75008	FRANCE
BOISSET, YVES	FILM DIRECTOR	248 BLVD RASPAIL	PARIS 75014	FRANCE
BOISVERT, RENE	BASEBALL EXECUTIVE	POST OFFICE BOX 4606	HELENA, MT	59604
BOJCUN, PAT	BASEBALL	POST OFFICE BOX 802	BATAVIA, NY	14021
BOKAR, HAL	ACTOR	6723 KRAFT AVE	NORTH HOLLYWOOD, CA	91606
BOKER, MIKE	BASEBALL	POST OFFICE BOX 1295	CLINTON, IA	52733
BOKHOF, EDWARD F	DIRECTOR	POMO TIERRA RANCH	YORKVILLE, CA	95494
BOKOVA, JANA	FILM-TV DIRECTOR	3 HOLLY VILLAS, WELLESLEY AVE	LONDON W6	ENGLAND
BOL, MANUETE	BASKETBALL	POST OFFICE BOX 25040	PHILADELPHIA, PA	19147
BOLAM, JAMES	ACTOR	BURNETT, 42-43 GRAFTON HOUSE		
		2-3 GOLDEN SQ	LONDON W1R 3AD	ENGLAND
BOLAND, EAMON	ACTRESS	76 CHURCH ST, LAVENHAM		
		SUDBURY	SUFFOLK CO10 9QT	ENGLAND
BOLD LIGHTNING	ROCK & ROLL GROUP	POST OFFICE BOX 942	RAPID CITY, SD	57709
BOLDREY, RICHARD	CONDUCTOR	431 DEARBORN ST #1504	CHICAGO, IL	60605
BOLE, CLIFFORD	TV DIRECTOR	2049 CENTURY PARK E #1320	LOS ANGELES, CA	90067
BOLEK, KEN	BASEBALL COACH	INDIANS, CLEVELAND STADIUM	CLEVELAND, OH	44114
BOLES, JOHN	BASEBALL EXECUTIVE	EXPOS, 4545 DE COUBERTIN AVE	MONTREAL, QUE H1V 3P2	CANADA
BOLET, ALBERTO	CONDUCTOR	6328 E 5TH ST	LONG BEACH, CA	90803
BOLGER, JOHN MICHAEL	ACTOR	ICM, 8899 BEVERLY BLVD	LOS ANGELES, CA	90048
BOLICK, FRANK	BASEBALL	POST OFFICE BOX 4756	JACKSONVILLE, FL	32201
BOLINS, CHET	SINGER	POST OFFICE BOX 25	KENDALL PARK, NJ	08824
BOLLEN, ROGER	CARTOONIST	36675 EAGLE RD	WILLOUGHBY HILLS, OH	44094
BOLLING, CLAUDE	SINGER-PIANIST	155 W 72ND ST	NEW YORK, NY	10023
BOLLING, MILT	BASEBALL-SCOUT	FENWAY PARK, 4 YAWKEY WY	BOSTON, MA	02215
BOLLING, TIFFANY	ACTRESS	12483 BRADDOCK DR	LOS ANGELES, CA	90066
BOLO, TERRY	ACTRESS	8949 SUNSET BLVD #203	LOS ANGELES, CA	90069
BOLOGNA, JOSEPH	ACT-WRI-DIR	613 N ARDEN DR	BEVERLY HILLS, CA	90210
BOLOTIN, CRAIG M	SCREENWRITER	CAA, 9830 WILSHIRE BLVD	BEVERLY HILLS, CA	90212
BOLT, ROBERT	SCREENWRITER	14-A GOODWINS, ST MARTIN'S LN	LONDON WC2N 4LL	ENGLAND
BOLTINOFF, HENRY	CARTOONIST	KING FEATURES, 216 E 45TH ST	NEW YORK, NY	10017
BOLTON, EMILY	ACTRESS-SINGER	LONDON MGT, 235-241 REGENT ST	LONDON W1R 4PH	ENGLAND
BOLTON, MICHAEL	SINGER-SONGWRITER	201 W 85TH ST #15-A	NEW YORK, NY	10024
BOLTON, RODNEY	BASEBALL	CANADIANS, 4601 ONTARIO ST	VANCOUVER, BC V5V 3H4	CANADA
BOLTON, TOM	BASEBALL	FENWAY PARK, 4 YAWKEY WY	BOSTON, MA	02215
BOLTZ, BRIAN	BASEBALL	POST OFFICE BOX 16683	GREENVILLE, SC	29606
BOMAN, MALLIE	WRI-DIR-PROD	POST OFFICE BOX 414	JAMAICA, NY	11423
BOMB, ADAM, BAND	ROCK & ROLL GROUP	65 W 55TH ST #306	NEW YORK, NY	10019
BOMBARD, MARC	BASEBALL MANAGER	POST OFFICE BOX 450	BUFFALO, NY	14205
BOMBARD, RICH	BASEBALL COACH	POST OFFICE BOX 2785	LAKELAND, FL	33806
BOMBECK, ERMA	WRITER-TV PERS	UPS, 4900 MAIN ST, 9TH FLOOR	KANSAS CITY, MO	64112
BON JOVI	ROCK & ROLL GROUP	POST OFFICE BOX 326	FORDS, NJ	08863
BONADUCE, DANNY	ACTOR-RADIO PERS	KKFR-FM, 631 N 1ST AVE	PHOENIX, AZ	85003
BONARRIGO, LAURA	ACTRESS	ABC-TV, "ONE LIFE TO LIVE"		
		56 W 66TH ST	NEW YORK, NY	10023
BOND, CHRISTOPHER S	U S SENATOR	510 NE 291 HIGHWAY	LEE'S SUMMIT, MO	64063
BOND, DAVEN	BASEBALL	POST OFFICE BOX 4756	JACKSONVILLE, FL	32201
BOND, GARY	ACTOR	LONDON MGT, 235-241 REGENT ST	LONDON W1R 4PH	ENGLAND
BOND, JULIAN	POLITICIAN	361 W VIEW DR	ATLANTA, GA	30310
BOND, JULIAN	SCREENWRITER	PETERS, FRASER & DUNLOP, LTD		
		5TH FLOOR, THE CHAMBERS		
		CHELSEA HARBOUR, LOT RD	LONDON SW10 OXF	ENGLAND
BOND, LELAND B	COMPOSER	13524 RYE ST #7	SHERMAN OAKS, CA	91423
BOND, LINCOLN	ACTOR	6724 HESPERIA AVE	RESEDA, CA	91355
BOND, MICHAEL	BASEBALL	1316 KING ST	BELLINGHAM, WA	98226
BOND, NANCY S	TV WRITER	1680 N VINE ST #1117	LOS ANGELES, CA	90028
BOND, PHILIP	ACTOR	50 HIGH ST, ABERGWYNFI	WEST GAMORGAN SA13 3YW	ENGLAND
BOND, STEVE	ACTOR	10201 W PICO BLVD, BLDG 54-6	LOS ANGELES, CA	90035
BOND, TIMOTHY	SCREENWRITER	POST OFFICE BOX 5617	BEVERLY HILLS, CA	90213
BOND, TOMMY "BUTCH"	ACTOR	14704 ROAD 36	MADERA, CA	93638
BONDARCHUK, SERGEI	DIRECTOR	GORDY ST, 9-75	MOSCOW 8, RUSSIA	USSR
BONDELLI, PHIL	DIRECTOR	21015 ARMINTA ST	CANOGA PARK, CA	91304
BONDRA, PETER	HOCKEY	JETS, 15-1430 MAROONS RD	WINNIPEG, MAN R3G 0L5	CANADA
BONDS, BARRY	BASEBALL	POST OFFICE BOX 7000	PITTSBURGH, PA	15212
BONDS, BOBBY	BASEBALL	175 LYNDHURST AVE	SAN CARLOS, CA	94070
BONDS, GARY "U S"	SINGER	BROTHERS, 141 DUNBAR AVE	FORDS, NJ	08863
BONERZ, PETER	ACTOR-DIRECTOR	3637 LOWRY RD	LOS ANGELES, CA	90027
BONES, RICKY	BASEBALL	2850 W 20TH AVE	DENVER, CO	80211
BONET, LISA	ACTRESS	6435 BALCOM	RESEDA, CA	91335
BONGIANNI, DREW	ACTOR	9255 SUNSET BLVD #515	LOS ANGELES, CA	90069
BONGOS, THE	ROCK & ROLL GROUP	3 E 54TH ST #1400	NEW YORK, NY	10022
BONHAM CARTER, HELENA	ACTRESS	CONWAY, 18-21 JERMYN ST	LONDON SW1	ENGLAND
BONIFAY, KEN	BASEBALL	POST OFFICE BOX 3746, HILL STA	AUGUSTA, GA	30904
BONIFER, MICHAEL	TV WRITER	8955 BEVERLY BLVD	WEST HOLLYWOOD, CA	90048
BONILLA, BOBBY	BASEBALL	METS, 126TH ST & ROOSEVELT AVE	FLUSHING, NY	11368
BONILLA, JOHNNY	BASEBALL	POST OFFICE BOX 6603	BEND, OR	97708
BONILLA, JUAN	BASEBALL	RURAL ROUTE #3, BOX 262	QUINCY, FL	32351
BONIN, GREG	BASEBALL UMPIRE	101 PROVIDENCE CT	LAFAYETTE, LA	70506

Name	Occupation	Address	City	Zip/Country
BONIOR, DAVID	U S CONGRESSMAN	59 N WALNUT ST #305	MOUNT CLEMENS, MI	48043
BONNELL, TERENCE A	COMPOSER	5985 DOVETAIL DR	AGOURA, CA	91301
BONNEMERE, EDWARD	COMPOSER	FINELL, 155 W 68TH ST	NEW YORK, NY	10023
BONNER, ANTHONY	BASKETBALL	KINGS, 1 SPORTS PARKWAY	SACRAMENTO, CA	95834
BONNER, FRANK	ACTOR-DIRECTOR	10100 SANTA MONICA BLVD #700	LOS ANGELES, CA	90067
BONNER, JEFFRY	BASEBALL	POST OFFICE BOX 21727	SAN FRANCISCO, CA	95151
BONNER, PRISCILLA	ACTRESS	9400 W OLYMPIC BLVD #203	BEVERLY HILLS, CA	90212
BONNER FAMILY, THE	C & W GROUP	POST OFFICE BOX 2686	CYPRESS, CA	90630
BONNER'S, THE	C & W GROUP	POST OFFICE BOX 2686	CYPRESS, CA	90630
BONNET, JAMES	TV WRITER	8955 BEVERLY BLVD	WEST HOLLYWOOD. CA	90048
BONO, CHASTITY	PERSONALITY	BILL SAMMETH ORGANIZATION		
		1888 CENTURY PARK E, 6TH FL	LOS ANGELES, CA	90067
BONO, SONNY	ACT-SING-PROD	1700 N INDIAN AVE	PALM SPRINGS, CA	92262
BONO, STEVE	FOOTBALL	S F 49ERS, 4949 CENTENNIAL BL	SANTA CLARA, CA	95054
BONO-COELHO, SUSIE	ACTRESS-MODEL	SEE - COELHO, SUSIE		
BONOFF, KARLA	SINGER-COMPOSER	1691 N CRESCENT HGTS BLVD	LOS ANGELES, CA	90069
BONOMO, OCTAVE	CONDUCTOR	5023 DELACROIX RD	ROLLING HILLS EST, CA	90274
BONSALL, BRIAN	ACTOR	11712 MOORPARK ST #204	STUDIO CITY, CA	91604
BONSIGNORI, UMBERTO	TV DIRECTOR	115 W 86TH ST #4-D	NEW YORK, NY	10024
BOOGIE BOYS, THE	RAP GROUP	FAA, 1700 BROADWAY, 5TH FLOOR	NEW YORK, NY	10019
BOOGIE DOWN PRODUCTIONS	RAP GROUP-RAPWRITERS	FAA, 1700 BROADWAY, 5TH FLOOR	NEW YORK, NY	10019
BOOKE, SORRELL	ACT-WRI-DIR	POST OFFICE BOX 1105	STUDIO CITY, CA	91604
BOOKER, BOB	TV WRITER-PRODUCER	ABC-TV, 4151 PROPSECT AVE	LOS ANGELES, CA	90027
BOOKER, ERIC	BASEBALL	POST OFFICE BOX 2437	MODESTO, CA	95351
BOOKER, GREG	BASEBALL	9859 SASKATCHEWAN AVE	SAN DIEGO, CA	92120
BOOKER, JANE	ACTRESS	57 MONTGOMERY RD	LONDON W4	ENGLAND
BOOKER, ROD	BASEBALL	POST OFFICE BOX 27045	TUCSON, AZ	85726
BOOKER, SIMON	TV PRODUCER	APRIL YOUNG, THE CLOCKHOUSE		
		6 SAINT CATHERINE'S MEWS		
		MILNER ST	LONDON SW3 2PX	ENGLAND
BOOKER, THOM	ACTOR	26 CAVENDISH RD	LONDON SW12	ENGLAND
BOOKMAN, ROBERT	TV EXECUTIVE	1270 SUNSET PLAZA DR	LOS ANGELES, CA	90069
BOOMTOWN RATS, THE	ROCK & ROLL GROUP	44 SEYMOUR	LONDON W1	ENGLAND
BOONE, ANTONIO	BASEBALL	80 OTTAWA ST N	HAMILTON, ONT L8H 3Z1	CANADA
BOONE, ASHLEY	FILM EXECUTIVE	11955 PINNACLE PL	BEVERLY HILLS, CA	90210
BOONE, BOB	BASEBALL-MANAGER	POST OFFICE BOX 11087	TACOMA, WA	98411
BOONE, BRET	BASEBALL	POST OFFICE BOX 4100	SEATTLE, WA	98104
BOONE, CHERRY	SINGER	904 N BEVERLY DR	BEVERLY HILLS, CA	90210
BOONE, DAN	BASEBALL	POST OFFICE BOX 75089	OKLAHOMA CITY, OK	73147
BOONE, DAVID	SINGER	9940 LOUGHEED HWY #330	BURNABY, BC V3J 1N3	CANADA
BOONE, DEBBY	SINGER	4334 KESTER AVE	SHERMAN OAKS, CA	91403
BOONE, LARRY	SINGER	POST OFFICE BOX 23795	NASHVILLE, TN	37202
BOONE, LESLEY	ACTRESS	5206 NORWICH AVE #206	VAN NUYS, CA	91411
BOONE, LIBBY	ACTRESS	1680 N VINE ST #1003	HOLLYWOOD, CA	90028
BOONE, PAT	SINGER-ACTOR	904 N BEVERLY DR	BEVERLY HILLS, CA	90210
BOONE, RANDY	ACTOR	14250 CALIFA ST	VAN NUYS, CA	91401
BOONE, RAY	BASEBALL-SCOUT	FENWAY PARK, 4 YAWKEY WY	BOSTON, MA	02215
BOONE, RON	BASKETBALL	5 TRIAD CENTER #500	SALT LAKE CITY, UT	84180
BOONSTRA, JOHN	FILM CRITIC	THE HARTFORD ADVOCATE		
		30 ARBOR ST	HARTFORD, CT	06106
BOORMAN, CHARLEY	ACTOR	"THE GLEBE", ANNACOE	COUNTY WICKLOW	IRELAND
BOORMAN, JOHN	FILM DIRECTOR	21 THURLUE SQ	LONDON W1	ENGLAND
BOORSTIN, JONATHAN	FILM DIRECTOR	4007 AVE DEL SOL	STUDIO CITY, CA	91604
BOORSTIN, PAUL TERRY	SCREENWRITER	9915 WESTWANDA DR	BEVERLY HILS, CA	90210
BOORSTIN, SHARON	SCREENWRITER	9915 WESTWANDA DR	BEVERLY HILLS, CA	90210
BOOSLER, ELAYNE	COMEDIENNE	11061 WRIGHTWOOD LN	NORTH HOLLYWOOD, CA	91604
BOOTH, ADRIAN	ACTRESS	3922 GLENRIDGE DR	SHERMAN OAKS, CA	91423
BOOTH, DAVID	ACTOR	AIM, 5 DENMARK ST	LONDON WC2H 8LP	ENGLAND
BOOTH, EARL M	TV WRITER	10526 WYTON DR	LOS ANGELES, CA	90024
BOOTH, GEORGE	CARTOONIST	UPS, 4900 MAIN ST, 9TH FLOOR	KANSAS CITY, MO	64112
BOOTH, JAMES	SCREENWRITER	CAA, 9830 WILSHIRE BLVD	BEVERLY HILLS, CA	90212
BOOTH, SHIRLEY	ACTRESS	POST OFFICE BOX 103	CHATHAM, MA	02633
BOOTHE, POWERS	ACTOR	23629 LONG VALLEY RD	HIDDEN HILLS, CA	91302
BOOTLEG	C & W GROUP	POST OFFICE BOX 40	BANGOR, ME	04401
BOOTY, JOHN	FOOTBALL	EAGLES, BROAD ST & PATTISON AVE	PHILADELPHIA, PA	19148
BOOZER, BRENDA	MEZZO SOPRANO	920 5TH AVE #14-B	NEW YORK, NY	10021
BOP A DIPS	C & W GROUP	POST OFFICE BOX 4087	MISSOULA, MT	59806
BORCHERDING, MARK	BASEBALL	POST OFFICE BOX 2001	CEDAR RAPIDS, IA	52406
BORCHERT, RUDOLPH	WRITER	28856 CLIFFSIDE DR	MALIBU, CA	90265
BORCHERT, SHANE	BASEBALL TRAINER	POST OFFICE BOX 882	MADISON, WI	53701
BORDE, MARK	FILM PRODUCER	1800 N HIGHLAND AVE #600	HOLLYWOOD, CA	90028
BORDEN, DAVID	COMPOSER-MUSICIAN	ROHR & HOWLETT MANAGEMENT		
		425 RIVERSIDE DR	NEW YORK, NY	10025
BORDEN, JASON J	COMPOSER	1001 SPRING ST	LOS ANGELES, CA	90048
BORDEN, LYNN	ACTRESS	16808 OAK VIEW DR	ENCINO, CA	91436
BORDEN, MARSHALL	ACTOR-PLAYWRIGHT	ATKINS, 303 S CRESCENT HEIGHTS	LOS ANGELES, CA	90048
BORDERLINE BAND, THE	C & W GROUP	5625 "O" STREET BLDG #7	LINCOLN, NE	68510
BORDERS, PAT	BASEBALL	SKYDOME, 300 BREMMER BL #3200	TORONTO, ONT M5V 3B3	CANADA
BORDICK, MIKE	BASEBALL	ATHLETICS'S, OAKLAND COLISEUM	OAKLAND, CA	94621
BORDICK, MIKE	BASEBALL	ATHLETICS'S, OAKLAND COLISEUM	OAKLAND, CA	94621
BORDON, PEDRO	BASEBALL (MAJORS)	LAS PALMAS, CORRAZOND DEJESUS #2	SANTA DOMINGO	DOM REP
BORDON, PEDRO	BASEBALL (MINORS)	POST OFFICE BOX 16683	GREENVILLE, SC	29606
BORELLI, CARLA	ACTRESS	8075 W 3RD ST #303	LOS ANGELES, CA	90048
BOREN, DAVID L	U S SENATOR	211 E OAK	SEMINOLE, OK	74868
BORETZ, ALVIN	TV WRITER	8955 BEVERLY BLVD	WEST HOLLYWOOD, CA	90048

Name	Occupation	Address	City	Zip/Country
BORETZ, BENJAMIN	COMPOSER	RIVER RD	BARRYTOWN, NY	12504
BORG, BJORN	TENNIS	VIA ARISTO 10	MILAN	ITALY
BORGE, VICTOR	PIANIST	FIELDPOINT PARK	GREENWICH, CT	06830
BORGES, FRANK	TREASURER	STATE CAPITOL BUILDING	HARTFORD, CT	06106
BORGHESE, BRIGITTE	ACTRESS	CREPIN, 17 RUE BREY	PARIS 75017	FRANCE
BORGMAN, JAMES	CARTOONIST	617 VINE ST	CINCINNATI, OH	45201
BORGNINE, ERNEST	ACTOR	3055 LAKE GLEN DR	BEVERLY HILLS, CA	90210
BORGNINE, TOVE	ACTRESS	3055 LAKE GLEN DR	BEVERLY HILLS, CA	90210
BORIS, ROBERT	FILM WRITER-DIRECTOR	1999 AVE OF THE STARS #2850	LOS ANGELES, CA	90067
BORITZER, ETAN	ACTOR	4942 VINELAND AVE #200	NORTH HOLLYWOOD, CA	91601
BORK, ROBERT	JUDGE	1150 17TH ST, NW	WASHINGTON, DC	20005
BORLAND, CARROLL	ACTRESS	275 LOS RANCHITOS RD #142	SAN RAFAEL, CA	94903
BORLAND, TOBY	BASEBALL	POST OFFICE BOX 3449	SCRANTON, PA	18505
BORLENGHI, MATT	ACTOR	ABC-TV, "ALL MY CHILDREN" 320 W 66TH ST	NEW YORK, NY	10023
BORMAN, FRANK	ASTRONAUT	6628 VISTA HERMOSA	LAS CRUCES, NM	88005
BORMET, GARRY R	TV WRITER	8730 WILSHIRE BLVD #470	LOS ANGELES, CA	90069
BORN, ROSCOE	ACTOR	8444 WILSHIRE BLVD #800	BEVERLY HILLS, CA	90211
BORNE, HAL	COMPOSER-CONDUCTOR	8787 SHOREHAM DR #104	LOS ANGELES, CA	90069
BORNE, JUDITH	ACTRESS	1801 AVE OF THE STARS #1250	LOS ANGELES, CA	90067
BORNING, VERN	BASEBALL SCOUT	TWINS, 501 CHICAGO AVE S	MINNEAPOLIS, MN	55415
BORNSTEIN, HENRY	TV DIRECTOR-PRODUCER	123 E 54TH ST #2-C	NEW YORK, NY	10022
BORNSTEIN, STEVEN	TV EXECUTIVE	ESPN PLAZA, 935 MIDDLEST	BRISTOL, CT	06010
BOROS, JULIUS	GOLFER	2900 NE 40TH ST	FORT LAUDERDALE, FL	33308
BOROS, STEVE	BASEBALL-MGR-EXEC	12121 DECANT	POWAY, CA	92064
BOROWITZ, ANDY S	TV WRITER	289 BELOIT AVE	LOS ANGELES, CA	90049
BOROWSKI, JOE	BASEBALL	POST OFFICE BOX 3169	FREDERICK, MD	21701
BORREGO, JESSE	ACTOR	347 N SWEETZER	LOS ANGELES, CA	90048
BORRELL, NEIL	DIRECTOR	305 RIVERSIDE DR	NEW YORK, NY	10025
BORRELLI, DEAN	BASEBALL	POST OFFICE BOX 2769	HUNTSVILLE, AL	35804
BORRIE, ALEXANDRA	ACTRESS	1320 N MARYLAND AVE	GLENDALE, CA	91207
BORROME, EDMUNDO	BASEBALL SCOUT	6850 LAWRENCE RD	LANTANA, FL	33462
BORRUS, JANET	ACTRESS	1243 N POINSETTIA PL	WEST HOLLYWOOD, CA	90046
BORSKI, JEFFREY	BASEBALL	POST OFFICE BOX 30160	SAN BERNARDINO, CA	92413
BORSKI, ROBERT A, JR	U S CONGRESSMAN	7141 FRANKFORD AVE	PHILADELPHIA, PA	19135
BORTMAN, MICHAEL E	TV WRITER	4365 CHEVY CHASE DR	LA CANADA, CA	91011
BORTOLOTTI, PAUL	BASEBALL UMPIRE	POST OFFICE BOX 608	GROVE CITY, OH	43123
BORTZ, MARK	G	BEARS, 250 N WASHINGTON RD	LAKE FOREST, IL	60045
BORUNE, DAVID	COMPTROLLER	STATE HOUSE BUILDING	AUGUSTA, GA	04333
BORUT, TOM	ACTOR	15534 AQUA VERDE DR	LOS ANGELES, CA	90077
BORY, JEAN-MARL	ACTOR	38 RUE DE LISBONNE	PARIS 75008	FRANCE
BORYER, LUCY	ACTRESS	2116 EWING ST	LOS ANGELES, CA	90039
BOSACKI, JEFFRY B	CONDUCTOR	7985 SANTA MONICA BLVD #109	LOS ANGELES, CA	90046
BOSARGE, SCOTT	BASEBALL	POST OFFICE BOX 9194	HAMPTON, VA	23670
BOSCHETTI, ANTHONY	ACTOR	1340 HUDSON RD	TEANECK, NJ	07666
BOSCHETTI, DESIREE	ACTRESS	STONE MANNERS, 9113 SUNSET BL	LOS ANGELES, CA	90069
BOSCHMAN, LAURIE	HOCKEY	POST OFFICE BOX 504	EAST RUTHERFORD, NJ	07073
BOSCO, PHILIP	ACTOR	337 W 43RD ST #1-B	NEW YORK, NY	10036
BOSE, LUCIA	ACTRESS	RONDE DE CARLA BASSA 5	28043 MADRID	SPAIN
BOSIO, CHRIS	BASEBALL	BREWERS, 201 S 46TH ST	MILWAUKEE, WI	53214
BOSKIE, SHAWN	BASEBALL	1060 W ADDISON ST	CHICAGO, IL	60613
BOSLEY, TOM	ACTOR	2822 ROYSTON PL	BEVERLY HILLS, CA	90210
BOSMAN, DICK	BASEBALL-COACH	ORIOLE PARK, 333 W CAMDEN ST	BALTIMORE, MD	21201
BOSNER, PAUL	TV DIRECTOR-PRODUCER	3327 MOCKINGBIRD LN	DALLAS, TX	75205
BOSO, CAP	FOOTBALL	BEARS, 250 N WASHINGTON RD	LAKE FOREST, IL	60045
BOSS	ROCK & ROLL GROUP	319 PENSHURST ST	WILLOUGHBY NSW 2068	AUSTRALIA
BOSSARD, JERRY	ACTOR	11300 W OLYMPIC BLVD #870	LOS ANGELES, CA	90064
BOSSON, BARBARA	ACTRESS	694 AMLFI DR	PACIFIC PALISADES, CA	90272
BOSTIC, JEFF	FOOTBALL	POST OFFICE BOX 17247 (DULLES)	WASHINGTON, DC	20041
BOSTON	ROCK & ROLL GROUP	SR & D MANAGEMENT 1560 TRAPELO RD	WALTHAM, MA	02154
BOSTON, D J	BASEBALL	POST OFFICE BOX 465	MED HAT, ALB T1A 7G2	CANADA
BOSTON, DARYL	BASEBALL	METS, 126TH ST & ROOSEVELT AVE	FLUSHING, NY	11368
BOSTON, RALPH	RUNNER	3301 WOODBINE AVE	KNOXVILLE, TN	37914
BOSTWICK, BARRY	ACTOR	2770 HUTTON DR	BEVERLY HILLS, CA	90210
BOSUSTOW, NICK	FILM PRODUCER	1156 GALLOWAY ST	PACIFIC PALISADES, CA	90272
BOSUSTOW, STEPHEN	FILM PRODUCER	1649 11TH ST	SANTA MONICA, CA	90404
BOSWALL, JEFFREY	WRI-DIR-PROD	THE LODGE, SANDY	BEDFORDSHIRE SG19 2DL	ENGLAND
BOSWORTH, BRIAN	ACTOR-FOOTBALL	230 PARK AVE #527	NEW YORK, NY	10169
BOTA, FRANCOIS	GRAPHIC DESIGNER	102 RESERVOIR AVE #3	JERSEY CITY, NJ	07307
BOTANA, SAMANTHA	TALENT AGENT	3500 W OLIVE AVE #1400	BURBANK, CA	91505
BOTCHAN, RON	FOOTBALL REFEREE	NFL, 410 PARK AVE	NEW YORK, NY	10022
BOTELHO, DEREK	BASEBALL COACH	POST OFFICE BOX 4669	CHARLESTON, WV	25304
BOTKIN, ALAN	BASEBALL	POST OFFICE BOX 12557	ST PETERSBURG, FL	33733
BOTKIN, CONSTANCE	ACTRESS	8489 W 3RD ST #1105	LOS ANGELES, CA	90048
BOTTALICA, RICK	BASEBALL	POST OFFICE BOX 1721	SPARTANBURG, SC	29304
BOTTENFIELD, KENT	BASEBALL	1501 W 16TH ST	INDIANAPOLIS, IN	46202
BOTTLES, THE	VOCAL GROUP	9025 WILSHIRE BLVD #303	BEVERLY HILLS, CA	90211
BOTTOMS, BENJAMIN	ACTOR	6565 SUNSET BLVD #300	LOS ANGELES, CA	90028
BOTTOMS, JOSEPH	ACTOR	1015 GAYLEY AVE #300	LOS ANGELES, CA	90024
BOTTOMS, SAM	ACTOR	4719 WILLOWCREST AVE	TOLUCA LAKE, CA	91602
BOTTOMS, TIMOTHY	ACTOR	15760 VENTURA BLVD #1730	ENCINO, CA	91436
BOTTS, JACOB	BASEBALL	POST OFFICE BOX 1621	GREAT FALLS, MT	59403
BOTWINICK, AMY	ACTRESS	POST OFFICE BOX 4115	MALIBU, CA	90265
BOTZOW, RUFUS	THEATER PRODUCER	35 W 76TH ST	NEW YORK, NY	10023

Name	Occupation	Address	City/State	Zip/Country
BOUCHARD, RAY	ACTOR	9034 SUNSET BLVD #100	LOS ANGELES, CA	90069
BOUCHE, CLAUDINE	EDITOR	3 RUE NICOLO	PARIS 75016	FRANCE
BOUCHER, DENIS	BASEBALL	4385 TUTT BLVD	COLORADO SPRINGS, CO	80922
BOUCHER, RICK	U S CONGRESSMAN	188 E MAIN ST	ABINGDON, VA	24210
BOUCHER, SAVANNAH SMITH	ACTRESS	9000 SUNSET BLVD #801	LOS ANGELES, CA	90069
BOUDINE, ARTHUR	TV DIRECTOR-PRODUCER	120 VIRGINIA AVE	DOBBS FERRY, NY	10522
BOUDREAU, LOU	BASEBALL	15600 ELLIS AVE	DOLTON, IL	60419
BOUDREAU, PAUL	FOOTBALL COACH	SAINTS, 1500 POYDRAS ST	NEW ORLEANS, LA	90112
BOUDREAU, TOMMY	BASEBALL	1316 KING ST	BELLINGHAM, WA	98226
BOUFFARD-VOGT, JOANNE	TV EXECUTIVE	SHOWTIME, 1633 BROADWAY	NEW YORK, NY	10019
BOUGHTON, EDWARD F	DIRECTOR-PRODUCER	114 GARDEN DR	ALBERTSON, NY	11507
BOUGIE, GARIN	ACTOR	6640 SUNSET BLVD #203	LOS ANGELES, CA	90028
BOULANGER, DANIEL	WRITER	ARTMEDIA, 10 AVE GEORGE V	PARIS 75008	FRANCE
BOULEZ, PIERRE	COMPOSER-CONDUCTOR	POSTFACH 22	BADEN-BADEN	GERMANY
BOULTING, ROY	DIRECTOR-PRODUCER	TWICKENHAM FILM STUDIOS		
		SAINT MARGARET'S, TWICKENHAM	MIDDLESEX TW1 2AW	ENGLAND
BOULTON, DEREK	TV PRODUCER	76 CARLISLE MANSIONS		
		CARLISLE PL	LONDON SW1P 1HZ	ENGLAND
BOULWARE, BILL	TV WRITER	9000 SUNSET BLVD #1200	LOS ANGELES, CA	90069
BOURBON BROTHERS, THE	C & W GROUP	BOB ASH, 2532-D ROYAL PINES CIR	DAYTON BEACH, FL	34623
BOURG, BRYAN	ACTOR	CED, 261 S ROBERTSON BLVD	BEVERLY HILLS, CA	90211
BOURJOS, CHRIS	BASEBALL SCOUT	SKYDOME, 300 BREMMER BL #3200	TORONTO, ONT M5V 3B3	CANADA
BOURNE, STEVEN	ACTOR	1720 PACIFIC AVE #335	VENICE, CA	90291
BOURNIGAL, RAFAEL	BASEBALL	POST OFFICE BOX 26267	ALBUQUERQUE, NM	87125
BOURQUE, PHIL	HOCKEY	PENGUINS, CIVIC ARENA, CENTRE AV	PITTSBURGH, PA	15219
BOURQUE, RAY	HOCKEY	BRUINS, 150 CAUSEWAY ST	BOSTON, MA	02114
BOURSEILLER, ANTOINE	ACTOR	15 RUE DE MIRIMESNI	PARIS 75008	FRANCE
BOUSSON, PATRICE Y	ACTRESS	484 S ROXBURY DR #102	BEVERLY HILLS, CA	90212
BOUTON, JIM	BASEBALL	6 MYRON CT	TEANECK, NJ	07666
BOUTON, TONY	BASEBALL	POST OFFICE BOX 3609	PORT CHARLOTTE, FL	33949
BOUTROSS, THOMAS	DIRECTOR-PRODUCER	1952 N BEACHWOOD DR	HOLLYWOOD, CA	90068
BOUWENS, SHAWN	FOOTBALL	LIONS, 1200 FEATHERSTONE RD	PONTIAC, MI	48432
BOUZON, GWEN	COSTUME DESIGNER	13949 VENTURA BLVD #309	SHERMAN OAKS, CA	91423
BOVEE, MIKE	BASEBALL	POST OFFICE BOX 464	APPLETON, WI	54912
BOVENIZER, N S	BASEBALL EXECUTIVE	POST OFFICE BOX 356	BLUEFIELD, WV	24701
BOWA, LARRY	BASEBALL-COACH	POST OFFICE BOX 7575	PHILADELPHIA, PA	19101
BOWAB, JOHN	TV DIRECTOR	2598 GREENVALLEY RD	LOS ANGELES, CA	90046
BOWDEN, CHARLES	DIRECTOR-PRODUCER	919 3RD AVE	NEW YORK, NY	10022
BOWDEN, MERRITT	BASEBALL	136 S SYCAMORE	ELIZABETHTON, TN	37643
BOWE, SHEILA M	TV DIRECTOR-PRODUCER	54 7TH AVE S	NEW YORK, NY	10014
BOWEN, ANNE	WRITER	555 W 57TH ST #1230	NEW YORK, NY	10019
BOWEN, GARY L	DIRECTOR	74 WILLOW AVE	LARCHMONT, NY	10538
BOWEN, JACK	BASEBALL SCOUT	REDS, 100 RIVERFRONT STADIUM	CINCINNATI, OH	45202
BOWEN, NANCI	GOLFER	2750 VOLUSA AVE #B	DAYTON BEACH, FL	32114
BOWEN, PAMELA	ACTRESS	315 W 57TH ST #4-H	NEW YORK, NY	10019
BOWEN, RYAN	BASEBALL	POST OFFICE BOX 288	HOUSTON, TX	77001
BOWER, ANTOINETTE	ACTRESS	SHERRELL, 1354 LAS ROBLES DR	PALM SPRINGS, CA	92262
BOWERS, BILL	SINGER	POST OFFICE BOX 1025	BOERNE, TX	78006
BOWERS, BRENT	BASEBALL	POST OFFICE BOX 957	DUNEDIN, FL	34697
BOWERS, BRYAN	SINGER	POST OFFICE BOX 800	MAHOPAC, NY	10541
BOWERS, GEORGE A, JR	DIRECTOR-PRODUCER	6417 MARYLAND DR	LOS ANGELES, CA	90048
BOWERS, MARJORIE	COSTUME DESIGNER	1150 LINDA FLORA DR	LOS ANGELES, CA	90049
BOWERS, MICHAEL J	ATTORNEY GENERAL	STATE CAPITOL BUIDLING	ATLANTA, GA	30334
BOWERS, SONNY	BASEBALL SCOUT	FENWAY PARK, 4 YAWKEY WY	BOSTON, MA	02215
BOWIE, DAVID	SINGER-ACTOR	641 5TH AVE #22-Q	NEW YORK, NY	10022
BOWIE, JIM	BASEBALL	POST OFFICE BOX 3690, STA "B"	CALGARY, ALB T2B 4M4	CANADA
BOWIE, SAM	BASKETBALL	N J NETS, MEADOWLANDS ARENA	EAST RUTHERFORD, NJ	07073
BOWKER, JUDI	ACTRESS	WM MORRIS, 31-32 SOHO SQ	LONDON W1V 5DG	ENGLAND
BOWKER, ROBERT E	TV DIRECTOR	2811 LA CUESTA DR	LOS ANGELES, CA	90046
BOWLAN, MARK	BASEBALL	POST OFFICE BOX 5599	LITTLE ROCK, AR	72215
BOWLEN, PAT	FOOTBALL EXECUTIVE	BRONCOS, 13655 BRONCOS PKWY	ENGLEWOOD, CO	80112
BOWLER, ANTON	TV DIRECTOR-PRODUCER	5 CHEYNE PL	LONDON SW3	ENGLAND
BOWLES, KELVIN	BASEBALL EXECUTIVE	POST OFFICE BOX 842	SALEM, VA	24153
BOWLES, PETER	ACTOR	125 GLOUCESTER RD	LONDON SW7	ENGLAND
BOWLES, TODD	FOOTBALL	S F 49ERS, 4949 CENTENNIAL BL	SANTA CLARA, CA	95054
BOWLES, WOODY	TALENT AGENT	POST OFFICE BOX 40661	NASHVILLE, TN	37204
BOWLIN, PAT	FOOTBALL EXECUTIVE	BRONCOS, 13655 BRONCOS PKWY	ENGLEWOOD, CO	80112
BOWMAN, BERNADETTE	ACTRESS	PACIFIC, 515 N LA CIENEGA BLVD	LOS ANGELES, CA	90048
BOWMAN, CHUCK	TV DIRECTOR-PRODUCER	1 UPPER BROOK ST	LA CANADA, CA	91011
BOWMAN, DEREK	TALENT AGENT	109 EASTBOURNE MEWS	LONDON W2	ENGLAND
BOWMAN, GAIL	ACTRESS	5301 LAUREL CANYON BLVD #116	NORTH HOLLYWOOD, CA	91607
BOWMAN, HAROLD	BASEBALL EXECUTIVE	N Y YANKEES, YANKEE STADIUM	BRONX, NY	10451
BOWMAN, JOHN	TV WRITER	151 S EL CAMINO DR	BEVERLY HILLS, CA	90212
BOWSER, KEN	CARTOONIST	TRIBUNE, 64 E CONCORD ST	ORLANDO, FL	32801
BOX, BETTY	FILM PRODUCER	PINEWOOD STUDIOS, IVER HEATH	IVER, BUCKS SLO ONH	ENGLAND
BOX, EUEL	COMPOSER-CONDUCTOR	5930 BEEMAN AVE	NORTH HOLLYWOOD, CA	91607
BOX, JOHN	FILM PRODUCER	41 MEREDYTH RD, BARNES	LONDON SW13	ENGLAND
BOX, THE	ROCK & ROLL GROUP	41 BRITAIN ST #200	TORONTO, ONT	CANADA
BOX TOPS, THE	ROCK & ROLL GROUP	2011 FERRY AVE #U-19	CAMDEN, NJ	08104
BOXCAR WILLIE	SINGER-SONGWRITER	MAJIC, 9265 OLDE EIGHT RD	CLEVELAND, OH	44067
BOXER, BARBARA	U S CONGRESSWOMAN	3301 KERNER BLVD #300	SAN RAFAEL, CA	94901
BOXLEITNER, BRUCE	ACTOR	345 N MAPLE DR #183	BEVERLY HILLS, CA	90210
BOXTOPS, THE	ROCK & ROLL GROUP	2011 FERRY AVE #U-19	CAMDEN, NJ	08104
BOY GEORGE	SINGER-COMPOSER	SEE - GEORGE, BOY		
BOY WHITE	RAPPER-RAPWRITER	FAA, 1700 BROADWAY, 5TH FLOOR	NEW YORK, NY	10019

Name	Occupation	Address	City	Zip/Country
BOYAJIAN, ARAM	WRITER-PRODUCER	50 W 96TH ST	NEW YORK, NY	10025
BOYCE, TOMMY	SINGER-SONGWRITER	1422 LA MAR AVE #614	MEMPHIS, TN	38104
BOYD, DENNIS "OIL CAN"	BASEBALL	1611 20TH ST	MERIDANMERIDIAN, MS	39301
BOYD, DON	DIRECTOR-PRODUCER	PROD ASSOC, 162 WARDOUR ST	LONDON W1	ENGLAND
BOYD, GEORGE D	TV DIRECTOR	30 PALOMA AVE	VENICE, CA	90291
BOYD, HAL H	CONDUCTOR	7234 HIGHWAY #9	FELTON, CA	95018
BOYD, JIMMY	ACTOR-SINGER	LIGHT, 901 BRINGHAM AVE	LOS ANGELES, CA	90049
BOYD, MICHAEL	ACTOR	NBC-TV, "DAYS OF OUR LIVES"		
		3000 W ALAMEDA AVE	BURBANK, CA	91523
BOYD, TANYA	ACTRESS	8271 MELROSE AVE #110	LOS ANGELES, CA	90046
BOYER, CLETE	BASEBALL-COACH	N Y YANKEES, YANKEE STADIUM	BRONX, NY	10451
BOYER, CLOYD	BASEBALL-COACH	POST OFFICE BOX 814	PULASKI, VA	24301
BOYER, MARK	FOOTBALL	N Y JETS, 1000 FULTON AVE	HEMPSTEAD, NY	11550
BOYETT, BOB	TV WRITER-PRODUCER	10124 EMPYREAN WY #201	LOS ANGELES, CA	90067
BOYETT, WILLIAM	ACTOR	LIGHT, 901 BRINGHAM AVE	LOS ANGELES, CA	90049
BOYKIN, TYRONE	BASEBALL	POST OFFICE BOX 3496	DAVENPORT, IA	52808
BOYLAN, JOHN	SINGER	2015 NICHOLS CANYON RD	LOS ANGELES, CA	90046
BOYLE, BARBARA	FILM EXECUTIVE	SOVEREIGN, 11845 W OLYMPIC BLVD	LOS ANGELES, CA	90064
BOYLE, DONALD	WRITER-PRODUCER	3351 OAKDELL RD	STUDIO CITY, CA	91604
BOYLE, LARA FLYNN	ACTRESS	606 N LARCHMONT BLVD #309	LOS ANGELES, CA	90004
BOYLE, PETER	ACTOR	ICM, 40 W 57TH ST	NEW YORK, NY	10019
BOYLES, HARLAN	TREASURER	STATE CAPITOL BUILDING	RALEIGH, NC	27603
BOYLSTON, BOB	FOOTBALL REFEREE	NFL, 410 PARK AVE	NEW YORK, NY	10022
BOYNTON, PETER	ACTOR	419 W 56TH ST #2-B	NEW YORK, NY	10019
BOYRIVEN, PATRICK	TV DIRECTOR	15622 ROYAL OAK RD	ENCINO, CA	91436
BOYS, THE	ROCK & ROLL GROUP	6255 SUNSET BLVD #1700	LOS ANGELES, CA	90028
BOYS BRIGADE, THE	ROCK & ROLL GROUP	ATI, 888 7TH AVE, 21ST FLOOR	NEW YORK, NY	10106
BOYS DON'T CRY	ROCK & ROLL GROUP	3 WANSDOWN PL, FULHAM, BROADWAY	LONDON SW6 1DN	ENGLAND
BOYS FROM INDIANA, THE	C & W GROUP	POST OFFICE BOX 186	RIVA, MD	21140
BOYT, DON	ACTOR	8484 WILSHIRE BLVD #530	BEVERLY HILLS, CA	90211
BOYUM, JOY GOULD	FILM CRITIC	GLAMOUR, 350 MADISON AVE	NEW YORK, NY	10017
BOYUM, STEPHEN M	DIRECTOR	5661 BUSCH DR	MALIBU, CA	90265
BOYZ II MEN	VOCAL GROUP	MOTOWN, 6255 SUNSET BL, 17TH FL	LOS ANGELES, CA	90028
BOYZUIC, MIKE	BASEBALL	POST OFFICE BOX 10031	BAKERSFIELD, CA	93389
BOZE, MARSHALL	BASEBALL	POST OFFICE BOX 855	BELOIT, WI	53511
BOZEK, STEVE	HOCKEY	CANUCKS, 100 N RENFREW ST	VANCOUVER, BC V5K 3N7	CANADA
BOZZUFI, MARCEL	ACTOR	ARTMEDIA, 10 AVE GEORGE V	PARIS 75008	FRANCE
BRABAZON, JAMES	WRITER-PRODUCER	BLAKE, 37-41 GOWER ST	LONDON WC1E 6HH	ENGLAND
BRABEAU, SUSAN	ACTRESS	1627 N PASS AVE	BURBANK, CA	91505
BRACCO, LORRAINE	ACTRESS	POST OFFICE BOX 49	PALISADES, NY	10964
BRACEY, KEN	BASEBALL SCOUT	POST OFFICE BOX 2000	SAN DIEGO, CA	92112
BRACHT, ROLAND	SINGER	CAMI, 165 W 57TH ST	NEW YORK, NY	10019
BRACKEN, CHARLES	BASEBALL EXECUTIVE	POST OFFICE BOX 6212	TOLEDO, OH	43614
BRACKEN, EDDIE	ACTOR	69 DOUGLAS RD	GLEN RIDGE, NJ	07028
BRADBOURNE, LORD	FILM PRODUCER	GW FILMS, 41 MONTPELIER WALK	LONDON SW7	ENGLAND
BRADBURY, JANETTE LANE	ACTRESS-DANCER	5712 LEMP AVE	NORTH HOLLYWOOD, CA	91601
BRADBURY, MIAH	BASEBALL	POST OFFICE BOX 9194	HAMPTON, VA	23670
BRADBURY, RAY	AUTHOR	10265 CHEVIOT DR	LOS ANGELES, CA	90064
BRADEN, BERNARD	ACT-WRI-PROD	ADANAC PRODS, 2 OVINGTON SQ	LONDON SW3	ENGLAND
BRADEN, KIM	ACTRESS	1999 AVE OF THE STARS #2850	LOS ANGELES, CA	90067
BRADEN, MARV	FOOTBALL COACH	BENGALS, 200 RIVERFRONT STADIUM	CINCINNATI, OH	45202
BRADFORD, BARBARA TAYLOR	AUTHORESS	425 E 58TH ST	NEW YORK, NY	10022
BRADFORD, GREG	ACTOR	3752 REDWOOD AVE	LOS ANGELES, CA	90066
BRADFORD, JANE ELLEN	TV PRODUCER	CBS NEWS, 524 W 57TH ST	NEW YORK, NY	10019
BRADFORD, JOHN MILTON	TV WRITER	TREE HOUSE, 104 SKY PINES RD	GRASS VALLEY, CA	95949
BRADFORD, NIKKOLI	MAKEUP ARTIST	9312 PALM ST #208	BELLFLOWER, CA	90706
BRADFORD, RICHARD	ACTOR	SMITH, 121 N SAN VICENTE BLVD	BEVERLY HILLS, CA	90211
BRADFORD, TROY	BASEBALL	POST OFFICE BOX 4488	WINSTON-SALEM, NC	27115
BRADFORD, VINCE	BASEBALL	POST OFFICE BOX 1434	BRISTOL, VA	24203
BRADISH, MIKE	BASEBALL	POST OFFICE BOX 4370	SALINAS, CA	93912
BRADLEE, BENJAMIN	JOURNALIST	1150 15TH ST, NW	WASHINGTON, DC	20071
BRADLEY, BERT	BASEBALL COACH	POST OFFICE BOX 2769	HUNTSVILLE, AL	35804
BRADLEY, BILL	BASKETBALL-SENATOR	1605 VAUXHALL RD	WASHINGTON, DC	90071
BRADLEY, BRIAN	HOCKEY	MAPLE LEAFS, 60 CARLTON ST	TORONTO, ONT M5B 1L1	CANADA
BRADLEY, ED	BROADCAST JOURNALIST	CBS-TV, 524 W 57TH ST	NEW YORK, NY	10019
BRADLEY, ELIZABETH	SCREENWRITER	UTA, 9560 WILSHIRE BL, 5TH FL	BEVERLY HILLS, CA	90212
BRADLEY, ELLEN	ACTRESS	ASKENASE, 6217 GLEN AIRY DR	LOS ANGELES, CA	90068
BRADLEY, GARY	BASKETBALL EXECUTIVE	POST OFFICE BOX 272349	HOUSTON, TX	77277
BRADLEY, HENRY	FOOTBALL	POST OFFICE BOX 23596	SAN DIEGO, CA	92123
BRADLEY, HENRY "KING"	FOOTBALL	POST OFFICE BOX 23596	SAN DIEGO, CA	92193
BRADLEY, LEE	SINGER	PREFERRED, 9701 TAYLORSVILLE RD	LOUISVILLE, KY	40299
BRADLEY, OWEN	PIANIST-COMPOSER	POST OFFICE BOX 120838	NASHVILLE, TN	37212
BRADLEY, PAT	GOLFER	2750 VOLUSA AVE #B	DAYTON BEACH, FL	32114
BRADLEY, PHIL	BASEBALL	207 MEADOW DR	MACOMB, IL	61455
BRADLEY, SCOTT	BASEBALL	POST OFFICE BOX 4100	SEATTLE, WA	98104
BRADLEY, TOM	MAYOR	605 S IRVING BLVD	LOS ANGELES, CA	90005
BRADSHAW, JOHN	TV HOST	1776 YORKTOWN #200	HOUSTON, TX	77056
BRADSHAW, KEVIN	BASEBALL COACH	POST OFFICE BOX 6212	TOLEDO, OH	43614
BRADSHAW, TERRY	ACTOR-FOOTBALL	ROUTE #1, BOX 227	GORDONVILLE, TX	76254
BRADSHAW, TERRY	BASEBALL	POST OFFICE BOX 5599	LITTLE ROCK, AR	72215
BRADY, BRIAN	BASEBALL	67 SCHOOL ST	MALVERNE, NY	11565
BRADY, DOUG	BASEBALL	POST OFFICE BOX 4218	SOUTH BEND, IN	46634
BRADY, ED	FOOTBALL	BENGALS, 200 RIVERFRONT STADIUM	CINCINNATI, OH	45202
BRADY, FRANK	WRITER	175 W 72ND ST	NEW YORK, NY	10023
BRADY, JEFF	FOOTBALL	STEELERS, 300 STADIUM CIR	PITTSBURGH, PA	15212

BRADY, MIKE	BASEBALL (BELOIT)	POST OFFICE BOX 855	BELOIT, WI	53511
BRADY, MIKE	BASEBALL (VERO BEACH)	POST OFFICE BOX 2887	VERO BEACH, FL	32961
BRADY, PAT	BASEBALL	POST OFFICE BOX 10336	CLEARWATER, FL	34617
BRADY, RANDALL	ACTOR	2029 CENTURY PARK E #600	LOS ANGELES, CA	90067
BRADY, SHAWN DANA	ACTOR	6605 HOLLYWOOD BLVD #220	HOLLYWOOD, CA	90028
BRADY, STEPHEN	BASEBALL	POST OFFICE BOX 751	UTICA, NY	13503
BRAEDEN, ERIC	ACTOR	13723 ROMANY DR	PACIFIC PALISADES, CA	90272
BRAFA, TONY	ACTOR	12121 LA MAIDA ST #17	NORTH HOLLYWOOD, CA	91607
BRAGA, SONIA	ACTRESS	210 E 58TH ST	NEW YORK, NY	10022
BRAGAN, JIMMY	BASEBALL EXECUTIVE	235 MAIN ST #103	TRUSSVILLE, AL	35173
BRAGAN, PETER, JR	BASEBALL EXECUTIVE	POST OFFICE BOX 4756	JACKSONVILLE, FL	32201
BRAGAN, PETER, SR	BASEBALL EXECUTIVE	POST OFFICE BOX 4756	JACKSONVILLE, FL	32201
BRAGG, DARREN	BASEBALL	POST OFFICE BOX 9194	HAMPTON, VA	23670
BRAGG, GEORGIA	ACTRESS	212 SAN VICENTE BLVD #E	SANTA MONICA, CA	90402
BRAGG, MELVYN	TV WRITER	12 HAMPSTEAD HILL GARDENS	LONDON NW3	ENGLAND
BRAGGS, GLENN	BASEBALL	REDS, 100 RIVERFRONT STADIUM	CINCINNATI, OH	45202
BRAGGS, STEPHEN	FOOTBALL	BROWNS, 80 1ST ST	BEREA, OH	44017
BRAHA, HERB	ACTOR	1433 N ORANGE GROVE AVE	LOS ANGELES, CA	90046
BRAINARD, MICHAEL	ACTOR	NBC-TV, "SANTA BARBARA" 3000 W ALAMEDA AVE	BURBANK, CA	91523
BRAKEBILL, MARK	BASEBALL	POST OFFICE BOX 3496	DAVENPORT, IA	52808
BRAKELEY, BILL	BASEBALL	2850 W 20TH AVE	DENVER, CO	80211
BRALDS, BRALDT	ARTIST	PINEBALL, 455 W 23RD ST	NEW YORK, NY	10011
BRALEY, JEFF	BASEBALL	TIGERS, 89 WHARNCLIFFE RD N	LONDON, ONT N6H 2A7	CANADA
BRAMAN, BUZZ	BASKETBALL COACH	POST OFFICE BOX 25040	PHILADELPHIA, PA	19147
BRAMAN, NORMAN	FOOTBALL	EAGLES, BROAD ST & PATTISON AVE	PHILADELPHIA, PA	19148
BRANAGAN, LAURA	SINGER-SONGWRITER	641 5TH AVE	NEW YORK, NY	10022
BRANAGH, KENNETH	ACTOR	56 KINGS RD	KINGS-UP-THAMES KT2 5H	ENGLAND
BRANCA, RALPH	BASEBALL	WESTCHESTER COUNTRY CLUB	RYE, NY	10580
BRANCH, WILLIAM	PLAYWRIGHT	53 CORTLANDT AVE	NEW ROCHELLE, NY	10801
BRANCONIER, PAUL	BASEBALL	POST OFFICE BOX 1556	ASHEVILLE, NC	28802
BRAND, ANTHONY	TV DIRECTOR	3253 BENDA ST	LOS ANGELES, CA	90068
BRAND, GIBBY	ACTOR	301 N CANON DR #305	BEVERLY HILLS, CA	90210
BRAND, JOSHUA	TV WRITER-PROUDCER	CAA, 9830 WILSHIRE BLVD	BEVERLY HILLS, CA	90212
BRANDAUER, KLAUS MARIA	ACTRESS	FISCHENDORF 76	8992 ALT-AUSSE	AUSTRIA
BRANDES, JOHN	FOOTBALL	POST OFFICE BOX 17247 (DULLES)	WASHINGTON, DC	20041
BRANDIS, JONATHAN	ACTOR	1800 N VINE ST #120	LOS ANGELES, CA	90028
BRANDO, CHRISTIAN	ACTOR	POST OFFICE BOX 8101	SAN LUIS OBISPO, CA	93409
BRANDO, MARLON	ACTOR-DIRECTOR	POST OFFICE BOX 809	BEVERLY HILLS, CA	90213
BRANDON, CLARK	ACTOR	9000 SUNSET BLVD #801	LOS ANGELES, CA	90069
BRANDON, DAVID	FOOTBALL	BROWNS, 80 1ST ST	BEREA, OH	44017
BRANDON, JOHN	ACTOR	SELECTED, 3575 W CAHUENGA BLVD	LOS ANGELES, CA	90068
BRANDON, MICHAEL	ACTOR	MTA, 9320 WILSHIRE BL, 3RD FL	BEVERLY HILLS, CA	90212
BRANDRETH, GYLES	TV WRITER	INTERNATIONAL ARTISTES LTD MEZZANINE FL, 235 REGENT ST	LONDON W1R 8AX	ENGLAND
BRANDS, X	ACTOR	17171 ROSCOE BLVD #104	NORTHRIDGE, CA	91325
BRANDT, BRANDI	ACTRESS-MODEL	11712 MOORPARK ST #204	STUDIO CITY, CA	91604
BRANDT, ELLEN	ACTRESS	8900 BURTON WY #204	BEVERLY HILLS, CA	90211
BRANDT, HANK	ACTOR	132 S LASKY DR #B	BEVERLY HILLS, CA	90212
BRANDT, MICHAEL	ACT-WRI-DIR	WEALD HOUSE, PLUCKLEY, ASHFORD	KENT TN27 OSN	ENGLAND
BRANDT, SUSIE	ARTIST	205 KAIKUONO PL	HONOLULU, HI	96816
BRANDT, YANNA KROYT	TV WRITER-PRODUCER	KROYT-BRANDT, 12 E 12TH ST	NEW YORK, NY	10028
BRANDWEN, BRUCE	TV PRODUCER	20 W 76TH ST #5-A	NEW YORK, NY	10023
BRANDYWYNNE, MARCIA	BROADCAST JOURNALIST	1438 RISING GLEN RD	LOS ANGELES, CA	90069
BRANIGAN, LAURA	SINGER-SONGWRITER	310 E 65TH ST	NEW YORK, NY	10021
BRANNEN, RALPH	ACTOR	9250 WILSHIRE BLVD #208	BEVERLY HILLS, CA	90212
BRANNON, CLIFF	BASEBALL	POST OFFICE BOX 5599	LITTLE ROCK, AR	72215
BRANNON, PAUL	BASEBALL	POST OFFICE BOX 30160	SAN BERNARDINO, CA	92413
BRANSFORD, MARJORIE	ACTRESS	LIGHT, 901 BRINGHAM AVE	LOS ANGELES, CA	90049
BRANSON, JEFF	BASEBALL	POST OFFICE BOX 23290	NASHVILLE, TN	37202
BRANSTAD, TERRY E	GOVERNOR	STATE CAPITOL BUILDING	DES MOINES, IA	50319
BRANTLEY, CLIFF	BASEBALL	POST OFFICE BOX 7575	PHILADELPHIA, PA	19101
BRANTLEY, JEFF	BASEBALL	S F GIANTS, CANDLESTICK PARK	SAN FRANICSCO, CA	94124
BRANTLEY, MICKEY	BASEBALL	POST OFFICE BOX 27045	TUCSON, AZ	85726
BRANZELL, JOE	BASEBALL SCOUT	POST OFFICE BOX 90111	ARLINGTON, TX	76004
BRASCHLERS COUNTRY MUSIC	C & W GROUP	OZARK PRODS, ROUTE #3, BOX 25	AURORA, MO	65605
BRASCIA, DOMINICK	ACTOR	3500 W OLIVE AVE #1400	BURBANK, CA	91505
BRASCIA, JOHN F	SCREENWRITER	8955 BEVERLY BLVD	WEST HOLLYWOOD, CA	90048
BRASH, PETER	TV WRITER	2025 BROADWAY #8-C	NEW YORK, NY	10023
BRASHER, TOMMY	FOOTBALL COACH	BUCCANEERS, 1 BUCCANEER PL	TAMPA, FL	33607
BRASON, JOHN	TV WRITER	BEWERLEY HOUSE, BEWERLEY	NORTH YORKS	ENGLAND
BRATCHER, BOBBY JOE	SINGER	POST OFFICE BOX 121656	NASHVILLE, TN	37212
BRATKOWSKI, ZEKE	FOOTBALL COACH	BROWNS, 80 1ST ST	BEREA, OH	44017
BRATT, BENJAMIN	ACTOR	STARS AGENCY, 777 DAVIS ST	SAN FRANCISCO, CA	94111
BRAUGHT, MARK	ARTIST	629 CHERRY ST	TERRE HAUTE, IN	47807
BRAUN, BART	BASEBALL SCOUT	POST OFFICE BOX 7000	PITTSBURGH, PA	15212
BRAUN, CLIFFORD H	DIRECTOR	1846 MISSION HILL LN	NORTHBROOK, IL	60062
BRAUN, JOSEF	COMPOSER	500 N MAIN ST	SPRINGDALE, AR	72764
BRAUN, STEVE	BASEBALL-COACH	FENWAY PARK, 4 YAWKEY WY	BOSTON, MA	02215
BRAUN, ZEV	FILM PRODUCER	97 FREMONT PL	LOS ANGELES, CA	90005
BRAUNECKER, DEREK	BASEBALL	POST OFFICE BOX 338	JAMESTOWN, NY	14702
BRAUNER, ASHER	ACTOR	190 S CANON DR #201	BEVERLY HILLS, CA	90210
BRAUNSTEIN, GENE H	TV WRITER	16633 VENTURA BLVD #1421	ENCINO, CA	91436
BRAUNSTEIN, GEORGE G	PRODUCER	1001 N KENTER AVE	LOS ANGELES, CA	90049
BRAUNSTEIN, LAURA M	SCREENWRITER	1001 N KENTER AVE	LOS ANGELES, CA	90049

Name	Occupation	Address	City	Zip/Country
BRAVEMAN, MARSHA	ACTRESS	214 E 24TH ST #5-C	NEW YORK, NY	10010
BRAVERMAN, BART	ACTOR	524 N LAUREL AVE	LOS ANGELES, CA	90048
BRAVERMAN, CHUCK	TV DIRECTOR-PRODUCER	1237 7TH ST	SANTA MONICA, CA	90401
BRAVERMAN, MICHAEL B	TV WRITER-DIRECTOR	3636 DELLVALE PL	ENCINO, CA	91436
BRAVERMAN, ROBERT	DIRECTOR	69 MARION AVE	MERRICK, NY	11556
BRAXTON, ANTHONY	SAXOPHONIST-COMPOSER	2490 CHANNING WY #406	BERKELEY, CA	94704
BRAXTON, DAVID	FOOTBALL	POST OFFICE BOX 888	PHOENIX, AZ	85001
BRAXTON, STEPHANIE	ACTRESS-WRITER	ARCHER II PRODS, 4250 WILSHIRE BL	LOS ANGELES, CA	90010
BRAXTON, TYRONE	FOOTBALL	BRONCOS, 13655 BRONCOS PKWY	ENGLEWOOD, CO	80112
BRAY, THOM	ACTOR	9301 WILSHIRE BLVD #312	BEVERLY HILLS, CA	90210
BRAYFIELD, DOUGLAS	COMPOSER-LYRICIST	3815 W OLIVE AVE #202	BURBANK, CA	91505
BRAYNE, WILLIAM	TV DIRECTOR	31 HOLLAND PARK	LONDON W11 3TA	ENGLAND
BRAZIL, DAVE	FOOTBALL COACH	STEELERS, 300 STADIUM CIR	PITTSBURGH, PA	15212
BRAZZI, ROSSANO	ACTOR	VIA GUISEPPE PERRONE		
		VITLE LIEGI 42	I-00198 ROME	ITALY
BREAKSTONE, BAMBI	COSTUME DESIGNER	POST OFFICE BOX 1166	PACIFIC PALISADES, CA	90272
BREAM, JULIAN	GUITARIST	122 WIGMORE ST	LONDON W1	ENGLAND
BREAM, SCOTT	BASEBALL	POST OFFICE BOX 611	WATERLOO, IA	50704
BREAM, SID	BASEBALL	POST OFFICE BOX 4064	ATLANTA, GA	30302
BREAUX, DON	FOOTBALL COACH	POST OFFICE BOX 17247 (DULLES)	WASHINGTON, DC	20041
BREAUX, JOHN	U S SENATOR	516 HART SENATE OFFICE BLDG	WASHINGTON, DC	20510
BRECK, PETER	ACTOR	238 E 1ST	NO VANC, BC V7L 1B3	CANADA
BRECKER, MICHAEL	SAXOPHONIST	1501 BROADWAY #1506	NEW YORK, NY	10036
BREDE, BRENT	BASEBALL	POST OFFICE BOX 661	KENOSHA, WI	53141
BREECH, JIM	FOOTBALL	BENGALS, 200 RIVERFRONT STADIUM	CINCINNATI, OH	45202
BREEDEN, JOE	BASEBALL MANAGER	POST OFFICE BOX 464	APPLETON, WI	54912
BREEDEN, SCOTT	BASEBALL-INSTRUCTOR	SKYDOME, 300 BREMMER BL #3200	TORONTO, ONT M5V 3B3	CANADA
BREEN, DANNY	ACTOR-COMEDIAN	1801 AVE OF THE STARS #1250	LOS ANGELES, CA	90067
BREEN, JOSEPH	ACTOR	ABC-TV, "LOVING"		
		320 W 66TH ST, STUDIO 23	NEW YORK, NY	10023
BREEZE, THE	C & W GROUP	JIMMY ADAMS, 163 EVERGREEN CIR	HENDERSONVILLE, TN	37075
BREGER, J SUE	TV DIRECTOR-PRODUCER	BREGER VIDEO, 915 BROADWAY	NEW YORK, NY	10010
BREGMAN, BUDDY	DIRECTOR-PRODUCER	11288 VENTURA BLVD #700	STUDIO CITY, CA	91604
BREGMAN, SUZANNE LLOYD	ACTRESS-WRITER	4155 WITZEL DR	SHERMAN OAKS, CA	91423
BREGMAN-RECHT, TRACEY	ACTRESS	10351 SANTA MONICA BLVD #211	LOS ANGELES, CA	90025
BREGONZI, ALEC	ACTOR	36 KNOLL RD, WANDSWORTH	LONDON SW18 2DF	ENGLAND
BREIMAN, VALERI	ACTRESS	280 S BEVERLY DR #400	BEVERLY HILLS, CA	90212
BREMER, DICK	SPORTSCASTER	TWINS, 501 CHICAGO AVE S	MINNEAPOLIS, MN	55415
BREMNER, MELISSA	ACTRESS	23643 CALIFA ST	WOODLAND HILLS, CA	91367
BREMNER, RORY	ACTOR-WRITER	STONE, 25 WHITEHALL	LONDON SW1A 2BS	ENGLAND
BREMSETH, LLOYD L	ACTOR	1217 GREENACRE AVE	LOS ANGELES, CA	90046
BRENDLER, MAGGIE	MODEL	FORD MODELS, 344 E 59TH ST	NEW YORK, NY	10022
BRENLY, BOB	BASEBALL COACH	S F GIANTS, CANDLESTICK PARK	SAN FRANICSCO, CA	94124
BRENLY, BOB	SPORTSCASTER	1060 W ADDISON ST	CHICAGO, IL	60613
BRENNAMAN, MARTY	SPORTSCASTER	REDS, 100 RIVERFRONT STADIUM	CINCINNATI, OH	45202
BRENNAMAN, THOM	SPORTSCASTER	1060 W ADDISON ST	CHICAGO, IL	60613
BRENNAN, BILL	BASEBALL	678 SIOUX DR	MACON, GA	31210
BRENNAN, BRIAN	FOOTBALL	BROWNS, 80 1ST ST	BEREA, OH	44017
BRENNAN, EILEEN	ACTRESS	POST OFFICE BOX 1777	OJAI, CA	93023
BRENNAN, MIKE	FOOTBALL	BENGALS, 200 RIVERFRONT STADIUM	CINCINNATI, OH	45202
BRENNAN, PEGGY LEE	ACTRESS	AGENTS FOR THE ARTS		
		1650 BROADWAY	NEW YORK, NY	10019
BRENNAN, ROBERT E	TV WRITER	12725 VENTURA BLVD #D	STUDIO CITY, CA	91604
BRENNAN, TERRY	BASEBALL UMPIRE	2101 E BROADWAY #35	TEMPE, AZ	85282
BRENNAN, WALTER A, JR	DIRECTOR-PRODUCER	17829 TULSA ST	GRANADA HILLS, CA	91344
BRENNAN, WILLIAM	BASEBALL	POST OFFICE BOX 6212	TOLEDO, OH	43614
BRENNAN, WILLIAM J, JR	SUPREME COURT JUDGE	1 1ST ST, NE	WASHINGTON, DC	20543
BRENNAN REEVES, MELISSA	ACTRESS	9255 SUNSET BLVD #515	LOS ANGELES, CA	90069
BRENNER, DORI	ACTRESS	2106 CANYON DR	LOS ANGELES, CA	90068
BRENNER, HOBY	FOOTBALL	SAINTS, 1500 POYDRAS ST	NEW ORLEANS, LA	90112
BRENNERT, ALAN	TV WRITER	14010 CAPTAINS ROW DR #343	MARINA DEL REY, CA	90292
BRENT, EVE	ACTRESS	200 N ROBERTSON BLVD #214	BEVERLY HILLS, CA	90211
BRESEE, BOBBIE	ACTRESS-MODEL	POST OFFICE BOX 1222	HOLLYWOOD, CA	90028
BRESH, THOM	SINGER-SONGWRITER	ENTERTAINMENT, 819 18TH AVE S	NASHVILLE, TN	37203
BRESLIN, JIMMY	COLUMNIST	220 E 42ND ST	NEW YORK, NY	10017
BRESLOW, JOHN	AUDITOR	STATE CAPITOL BUILDING	LINCOLN, NE	68509
BRESLOW, LOU	SCREENWRITER	825 GRETNA GREEN WY #O	LOS ANGELES, CA	90049
BRESLOW, MARC	DIRECTOR	9454 WILSHIRE BLVD #405	BEVERLY HILLS, CA	90212
BRESNAHAN, TOM	FOOTBALL COACH	BILLS, 1 BILLS DR	ORCHARD PARK, NJ	14127
BRESSLAW, BERNARD	ACTOR	PAYNE, 28 QUEENS RD, WEYBRIDGE	SURREY KT13 9UT	ENGLAND
BRESSON, ROBERT	FILM DIRECTOR	49 QUAI DE BOURBON	PARIS 75004	FRANCE
BREST, MARTIN	FILM WRITER-DIRECTOR	831 PASEO MIRAMAR	PACIFIC PALISADES, CA	90272
BRESTOFF, RICHARD	ACTOR	4621 COUNCIL ST #3	LOS ANGELES, CA	90004
BRETONNIERRE, JEAN	ACTOR	21 RUE DES FOURGERES	PARIS 75020	FRANCE
BRETT, BOBBY	BASEBALL EXECUTIVE	POST OFFICE BOX 4758	SPOKANE, WA	99202
BRETT, GEORGE	BASEBALL-EXECUTIVE	POST OFFICE BOX 419969	KANSAS CITY, MO	64141
BRETT, JEREMY	ACTOR	151 S EL CAMINO DR	BEVERLY HILLS, CA	90212
BRETT, JOHN	BASEBALL EXECUTIVE	POST OFFICE BOX 4758	SPOKANE, WA	99202
BRETT, KEN	SPORTSCASTER	SPORTS CHANNEL, 1545 26TH ST	SANTA MONICA, CA	90404
BRETTSCHNEIDER, MARK	ACTOR	ABC-TV, "ONE LIFE TO LIVE"		
		56 W 66TH ST	NEW YORK, NY	10023
BREUER, RANDY	BASKETBALL	TIMBERWOLVES, 600 1ST AVE N	MINNEAPOLIS, MN	55403
BREWED	ROCK & ROLL GROUP	BIRD, 4905 S ATLANTIC AVE	DAYTONA BEACH, FL	32019
BREWER, BILLY	BASEBALL	POST OFFICE BOX 3566	WEST PALM BEACH, FL	33402

BREWER, COLIN M	FILM PRODUCER	LYNWOOD HOUSE, LYNWOOD HEIGHTS	CHORLEYWOOD, HERTS	ENGLAND
BREWER, GAY	GOLFER	PGA SENIORS, 112 T P C BLVD	PONTE VEDRA BEACH, FL	32082
BREWER, JAMES	ACTOR	AIMEE, 13743 VICTORY BLVD	VAN NUYS, CA	91401
BREWER, JAMESON	SCREENWRITER	8955 BEVERLY BLVD	WEST HOLLYWOOD, CA	90048
BREWER, JIM	BASKETBALL	TIMBERWOLVES, 600 1ST AVE N	MINNEAPOLIS, MN	55403
BREWER, JO	ACTRESS	HANSEN, 2783 LA CASTANA DR	LOS ANGELES, CA	90046
BREWER, MARK	BASEBALL COACH	1325 S MAIN #229	SALT LAKE CITY, UT	84115
BREWER, MATT	BASEBALL	POST OFFICE BOX 21727	SAN FRANCISCO, CA	95151
BREWER, ROD	BASEBALL	POST OFFICE BOX 36407	LOUISVILLE, KY	40233
BREWER, TERESA	SINGER	384 PINEBROOK BLVD	NEW ROCHELLE, NY	10803
BREWSTER, BILL B	U S CONGRESSMAN	123 W 7TH AVE #206	STILLWATER, OK	74074
BREWSTER, D K	SINGER	PAU, RUSTIC ACRES	JASPER, IN	47546
BREWSTER, DIANE	ACTRESS	8322 BEVERLY BLVD #200	LOS ANGELES, CA	90048
BRIAN, DAVID	ACTOR	3922 GLENRIDGE DR	SHERMAN OAKS, CA	91423
BRIAN TOMASSINI, MARY	ACTRESS	4107 TROOST AVE	NORTH HOLLYWOOD, CA	91604
BRIANT, MICHAEL E	FILM-TV DIRECTOR	KRUGER, 121 GLOUCESTER PL	LONDON W1H 3PL	ENGLAND
BRIANT, SHANE	ACTOR	BEDFORD & PEARCE		
		2 PORTMAN CLOSE, 269 ALFRED ST	NORTH SYDNEY	AUSTRALIA
BRICKELL, BETH	WRITER-DIRECTOR	9933 ROBBINS DR #2	BEVERLY HILLS, CA	90212
BRICKERS, THE	C & W GROUP	POST OFFICE BOX 589	CHARLOTTE, MD	20622
BRICKEYS PASS	C & W GROUP	5625 "O" STREET BLDG #7	LINCOLN, NE	68510
BRICKOWSKI, FRANK	BASKETBALL	BRADLEY CENTER, 1001 N 4TH ST	MILWAUKEE, WI	53203
BRICUSSE, LESLIE	COMPOSER-LYRICIST	9903 SANTA MONICA BLVD #112	BEVERLY HILLS, CA	90212
BRIDGES, ALAN J S	TV DIRECTOR	HATTON, 29 ROEHAMPTON GATE	LONDON SW15 5JR	ENGLAND
BRIDGES, BEAU	ACTOR-DIRECTOR	5525 N JED SMITH RD	HIDDEN HILLS, CA	91302
BRIDGES, BETTY	ACTRESS	5000 LANKERSHIM BLVD #7 & 9	NORTH HOLLYWOOD, CA	91601
BRIDGES, JACK	ACTOR	13455 VENTURA BLVD #210	SHERMAN OAKS, CA	91423
BRIDGES, JEFF	ACTOR-PRODUCER	1223 WILSHIRE BLVD #593	SANTA MONICA, CA	90403
BRIDGES, LLOYD	ACTOR	225 LORING AVE	LOS ANGELES, CA	90077
BRIDGES, ROCKY	BASEBALL-INSTRUCTOR	POST OFFICE BOX 7000	PITTSBURGH, PA	15212
BRIDGES, TONY	BASEBALL	800 HOME RUN LN	MEMPHIS, TN	38104
BRIERS, RICHARD	ACTOR	ICM, 388-396 OXFORD ST	LONDON W1	ENGLAND
BRIGGS, JOHNNY	ACTOR	MARTIN, 6-A DANBURY ST	LONDON N1 8JU	ENGLAND
BRIGGS, STONEY	BASEBALL	POST OFFICE BOX 1110	MYRTLE BEACH, SC	29578
BRIGHAM, RED	SINGER	R & J ENTS, 2 HAWKES AVE	OSSINING, NY	10562
BRIGHT, BRIAN	BASEBALL	RED SOX, CHAIN O'LAKES PARK	WINTER HAVEN, FL	33880
BRIGHT, RICHARD	ACTOR	165 W 46TH ST #1109	NEW YORK, NY	10036
BRIGHTON ROCK	ROCK & ROLL GROUP	41 BRITAIN ST #200	TORONTO, ONT M5A 1R7	CANADA
BRIGSTOCKE, DOMINIC	TV DIRECTOR	39 SAINT JULIAN'S RD	LONDON NW6	ENGLAND
BRILES-HINTON, JILL	GOLFER	2750 VOLUSA AVE #B	DAYTON BEACH, FL	32114
BRILEY, GREG	BASEBALL	POST OFFICE BOX 4100	SEATTLE, WA	98104
BRILEY, JOHN	TV WRITER	RAE, CHARING CROSS RD	LONDON WC2H ODB	ENGLAND
BRILEY, JOHN RICHARD	SCREENWRITER	ICM, 8899 BEVERLY BLVD	LOS ANGELES, CA	90048
BRILL, CHARLIE	ACTOR	3635 WRIGHTWOOD DR	STUDIO CITY, CA	91604
BRILL, GEORGE	BASEBALL SCOUT	REDS, 100 RIVERFRONT STADIUM	CINCINNATI, OH	45202
BRILLSTEIN, BERNIE	TALENT AGENT	9200 SUNSET BLVD #428	LOS ANGELES, CA	90069
BRILLSTEIN, LEIGH	TALENT AGENT	9200 SUNSET BLVD #428	LOS ANGELES, CA	90069
BRILZ, DARRICK	FOOTBALL	SEAHAWKS, 11220 NE 53RD ST	KIRKLAND, WA	98033
BRIM, MIKE	FOOTBALL	N Y JETS, 1000 FULTON AVE	HEMPSTEAD, NY	11550
BRIMHALL, BRAD	BASEBALL	POST OFFICE BOX 882	MADISON, WI	53701
BRIMHALL, CYNTHIA	MODEL	9229 SUNSET BLVD #208	LOS ANGELES, CA	90069
BRIMLEY, WILFORD	ACTOR	CAA, 9830 WILSHIRE BLVD	BEVERLY HILLS, CA	90212
BRINCKERHOFF, PETER A	DIRECTOR	WHITEBREAD LTD, 394 W END AVE	NEW YORK, NY	10024
BRIND'AMOUR, ROD	HOCKEY	BLUES, 5700 OAKLAND AVE	SAINT LOUIS, MO	63110
BRINGELSON, MARK	ACTOR	1538 N DERTOIT ST #6	LOS ANGELES, CA	90046
BRINGHAM, RED	SINGER	R & J ENTS, 2 HAWKES AVE	OSSINING, NY	10562
BRINK, BRAD	BASEBALL	POST OFFICE BOX 15050	READING, PA	19612
BRINKLEY, CHRISTIE	MODEL-ACTRESS	344 E 59TH ST	NEW YORK, NY	10022
BRINKLEY, DAVID	TV HOST	NBC-TV, 1717 DE SALES ST, NW	WASHINGTON, DC	20036
BRINKLEY, DONALD	WRITER-PRODUCER	22626 PACIFIC COAST HWY	MALIBU, CA	90265
BRINKMAN, EDDIE	BASEBALL-SCOUT	333 W 35TH ST	CHICAGO, IL	60616
BRINKMAN, JOE	BASEBALL UMPIRE	1021 INDIAN RIVER DR	COCA, FL	32922
BRISCOE, JOHN	BASEBALL	ATHLETICS'S, OAKLAND COLISEUM	OAKLAND, CA	94621
BRISEBOIS, DANIELLE	ACTRESS	8075 W 3RD ST #303	LOS ANGELES, CA	90048
BRISKER, GORDON I	COMPOSER	7 CONCORD SQ #2	BOSTON, MA	02118
BRISKER, MITCHELL	FILM DIRECTOR	3675 FREDONIA DR	LOS ANGELES, CA	90068
BRISKIN, MORT	WRITER-PRODUCER	ICM, 8899 BEVERLY BLVD	LOS ANGELES, CA	90048
BRISTER, BUDDY	FOOTBALL	STEELERS, 300 STADIUM CIR	PITTSBURGH, PA	15212
BRISTOW, ALLAN	BASKETBALL EXECUTIVE	310 N KINGS DR	CHARLOTTE, NC	28204
BRISTOW, RICHIE	BASEBALL	POST OFFICE BOX 7845	COLUMBIA, SC	29202
BRITO, BERNARDO	BASEBALL	POST OFFICE BOX 1659	PORTLAND, OR	97207
BRITO, ENRIQUE	BASEBALL SCOUT	TWINS, 501 CHICAGO AVE S	MINNEAPOLIS, MN	55415
BRITO, JORGE	BASEBALL	POST OFFICE BOX 11087	TACOMA, WA	98411
BRITO, LUIS	BASEBALL	POST OFFICE BOX 1721	SPARTANBURG, SC	29304
BRITO, MARIO	BASEBALL	POST OFFICE BOX 360007	BIRMINGHAM, AL	35236
BRITT, MAI	ACTRESS	POST OFFICE BOX 525	ZEPHYR COVE, NV	89448
BRITT, MELENDY	ACTRESS	551 S PARISH PL	BURBANK, CA	91506
BRITT, ROD	ACTOR	4731 LAUREL CANYON BLVD #5	NORTH HOLLYWOOD, CA	91607
BRITT, RUTH	ACTRESS	200 N ROBERTSON BLVD #214	BEVERLY HILLS, CA	90211
BRITTAIN, GRANT	BASEBALL	POST OFFICE BOX 507	DURHAM, NC	27702
BRITTANY, MORGAN	ACTRESS-MODEL	3434 CORNELL RD	AGOURA HILLS, CA	91301
BRITTON, BILL	GOLFER	POST OFFICE BOX 109601	PALM BCH GARDENS, FL	33418
BRITTON, ROBERT	ACTOR	FELBER, 2126 N CAHUENGA BLVD	LOS ANGELES, CA	90068
BRITTON, TONY	ACTOR	ICM, 388-396 OXFORD ST	LONDON W1	ENGLAND
BRITTON, WAYNE	BASEBALL SCOUT	FENWAY PARK, 4 YAWKEY WY	BOSTON, MA	02215

BROADHURST, KENT	ACTOR	145 W 45TH ST #1204	NEW YORK, NY	10036
BROADIE, RICHARD G	COMPOSER	POST OFFICE BOX 615	PALM SPRINGS, CA	92263
BROCAIL, DOUG	BASEBALL	STARS, 850 LAS VEGAS BLVD N	LAS VEGAS, NV	89101
BROCCO, PETER	ACTOR	GILLY, 8721 SUNSET BLVD #103	LOS ANGELES, CA	90069
BROCCOLI, ALBERT R "CUBBY"	FILM PRODUCER	809 N HILLCREST RD	BEVERLY HILLS, CA	90210
BROCHU, CLAUDE	BASEBALL EXECUTIVE	EXPOS, 4545 DE COUBERTIN AVE	MONTREAL, QUE H1V 3P2	CANADA
BROCHURES, THE	C & W GROUP	5625 "O" STREET BLDG #7	LINCOLN, NE	68510
BROCK, CHRIS	FILM DIRECTOR	THE HIDE, 30 RUSCOMBE GARDENS		
		DATCHET	BERKS	ENGLAND
BROCK, GREG	BASEBALL	201 S 46TH ST	MILWAUKEE, WI	53214
BROCK, LOU	BASEBALL	12155 BRIDGETON SQ	BRIDGETON, MO	63044
BROCK, MATT	FOOTBALL	PACKERS, 1265 LOMBARDI AVE	GREEN BAY, WI	54307
BROCK, RUSS	BASEBALL	POST OFFICE BOX 2437	MODESTO, CA	95351
BROCK, STAN	FOOTBALL	SAINTS, 1500 POYDRAS ST	NEW ORLEANS, LA	90112
BROCK, TARRICK	BASEBALL	POST OFFICE BOX 64939	FAYETTEVILLE, NC	28306
BROCKMAN, MICHAEL S	TV EXECUTIVE	CBS-TV, 6121 SUNSET BLVD	LOS ANGELES, CA	90028
BRODER, ROBERT	TALENT AGENT	9242 BEVERLY DR #200	BEVERLY HILLS, CA	90210
BRODERICK, ALFRED E	TV DIRECTOR	271 ADELPHI ST	BROOKLYN, NY	11205
BRODERICK, LORRAINE	TV WRITER	ABC-TV, "ALL MY CHILDREN"		
		320 W 66TH ST	NEW YORK, NY	10023
BRODERICK, MATTHEW	ACTOR	CAA, 9830 WILSHIRE BLVD	BEVERLY HILLS, CA	90212
BRODHEAD, JAMES E	ACTOR	3642 LONGVIEW VALLEY	SHERMAN OAKS, CA	91423
BRODIE, DON	ACTOR	4410 AVOCADO ST #3	LOS ANGELES, CA	90027
BRODIE, JOHN	FOOTBALL-ANNOUNCER	260 SURRY PL	LOS ALTOS, CA	94022
BRODIE, JOHN	GOLFER	PGA SENIORS, 112 T P C BLVD	PONTE VEDRA BEACH, FL	32082
BRODIE, KEVIN	ACT-WRI-DIR-PROD	4424 MOORPARK WY	NORTH HOLLYWOOD, CA	91602
BRODIE, STEVE	ACTOR	6742 SUNNYBRAE AVE	CANOGA PARK, CA	91306
BRODNEY, OSCAR	WRITER-PRODUCER	450 S MAPLE DR #305	BEVERLY HILLS, CA	90212
BRODSKY, JOE	FOOTBALL COACH	COWBOYS, 1 COWBOYS PARKWAY	IRVING, TX	75063
BRODSKY, STANLEY M	TV PRODUCER	1260 AVE OF THE AMERICAS #604	NEW YORK, NY	10020
BRODY, LANE	SINGER	POST OFFICE BOX 24775	NASHVILLE, TN	37202
BRODY, LARRY	TV WRITER	SHAPIRO, 8827 BEVERLY BLVD	LOS ANGELES, CA	90048
BRODY, RONNIE	ACTOR	21 BARTLE RD	LONDON W11	ENGLAND
BROERSMA, ERIC	BASEBALL SCOUT	METS, 126TH ST & ROOSEVELT AVE	FLUSHING, NY	11368
BROGAN, JIMMY	COMEDIAN	ICM, 8899 BEVERLY BLVD	LOS ANGELES, CA	90048
BROGDON, JOHN CARL	ACTOR	1700 E GARY AVE #113	SANTA ANA, CA	92705
BROGLIATTI, BARBARA	DIRECTOR	15034 MARBLE DR	SHERMAN OAKS, CA	91403
BROGNA, RICO	BASEBALL	POST OFFICE BOX 6212	TOLEDO, OH	43614
BROHN, BILL D	CONDUCTOR	250 W 85TH ST	NEW YORK, NY	10024
BROKAW, JOANNE	TV EXECUTIVE	CBS-TV, 51 W 52ND ST	NEW YORK, NY	10019
BROKAW, NORMAN	TALENT AGENT	530 VICK ST	BEVERLY HILLS, CA	90210
BROKAW, TOM	BROADCAST JOURNALIST	941 PARK AVE #14-C	NEW YORK, NY	10025
BROKE, RICHARD	FILM PRODUCER	PETERS, FRASER & DUNLOP, LTD		
		5TH FLOOR, THE CHAMBERS		
		CHELSEA HARBOUR, LOT RD	LONDON SW10 OXF	ENGLAND
BROKS, CHARLES	CARTOONIST	1612 CRESTHILL RD	BIRMINGHAM, AL	35213
BROLIN, JAMES	ACTOR	2401 COLORADO AVE #160	SANTA MONICA, CA	90404
BROLIN, JOSH	ACTOR	2401 COLORADO AVE #160	SANTA MONICA, CA	90404
BROMBERG, CONRAD	TV WRITER-PRODUCER	ROBERTS, 157 W 57TH ST #PH-A	NEW YORK, NY	10019
BROMBERG, DEBORAH A	WRI-DIR-PROD	11 E 66TH ST #4-C	NEW YORK, NY	10021
BROMFIELD, JOHN	ACTOR	1750 WHITTIER AVE	COSTA MESA, CA	92627
BROMFIELD, LOIS	COMEDIAN	151 S EL CAMINO DR	BEVERLY HILLS, CA	90212
BROMFIELD, REX	DIRECTOR	1237 HOWE ST	VANCOUVER, BC	CANADA
BROMFIELD, VALRI	COMEDIENNE-WRITER	11726 SAN VICENTE BLVD #300	LOS ANGELES, CA	90049
BROMHEAD, MICHAEL	FILM EXECUTIVE	THORN, 9489 DAYTON WY	BEVERLY HILLS, CA	90210
BROMLEY DAVENPORT, HARRY	TV WRITER-DIRECTOR	11 HUNGERFORD RD	LONDON N7 9LA	ENGLAND
BRONDER, WILLIAM	ACTOR	7621 GENTRY AVE	NORTH HOLLYWOOD, CA	91605
BRONKEY, JEFF	BASEBALL	POST OFFICE BOX 4448	TULSA, OK	74159
BRONNER, FRITZ	ACTOR	POST OFFICE BOX 69590	LOS ANGELES, CA	90069
BRONSON, CHARLES	ACTOR	POST OFFICE BOX 2644	MALIBU, CA	90265
BRONSON, HAROLD	RECORD EXECUTIVE	RHINO RECORD COMPANY		
		2225 COLORADO AVE	SANTA MONICA, CA	90404
BRONSON, KIMBERLI	ACTRESS	BURNS TALENT, 478 SEVERN AVE	TAMPA, FL	33606
BRONSON, LILLIAN	ACTRESS	32591 SEVEN SEAS DR	LAGUNA NIGUEL, CA	92677
BRONSON, MICHAEL	OPERA DIRECTOR	MET OPERA, 520 W 27TH ST	NEW YORK, NY	10001
BRONSON, MICHAEL	TV PRODUCER	40 W 77TH ST	NEW YORK, NY	10023
BRONSON, TOM	COSTUME DESIGNER	13949 VENTURA BLVD #309	SHERMAN OAKS, CA	91423
BRONZ	ROCK & ROLL GROUP	BRONZ MGT, 100 CHALK FAR	LONDON NW1 8EH	ENGLAND
BROOD, THE	ROCK & ROLL GROUP	POST OFFICE BOX 34871	LOS ANGELES, CA	90034
BROOK, FAITH	ACTRESS	CONWAY, 18-21 JERMYN ST	LONDON SW1	ENGLAND
BROOK, PETER	DIRECTOR-PRODUCER	C I C T, 9 RUE CIRQUE	PARIS 8	FRANCE
BROOKE, HILLARY	ACTRESS	KLUNE, 40 VIA CASITAS	BONSALL, CA	92003
BROOKE, WALTER	ACTOR	4313 BEN AVE	NORTH HOLLYWOOD, CA	91604
BROOKE-TAYLOR, TIM	ACTOR-WRITER	ROUND COPSE, ALLEYNS LN		
		COOKHAM DEAN	BERKS SL6 9AE	ENGLAND
BROOKENS, JEFF	BASEBALL SCOUT	1060 W ADDISON ST	CHICAGO, IL	60613
BROOKENS, TOM	BASEBALL	120 HILLSIDE DR	FAYETTEVILLE, PA	17222
BROOKER, GARY	SINGER-COMPOSER	5 CRANLEY GARDENS	LONDON SW7	ENGLAND
BROOKES, DIANA	ACTRESS	HPE, 12233 LAUREL TERRACE DR	STUDIO CITY, CA	91604
BROOKES, JACQUELINE	ACTRESS	10100 SANTA MONICA BLVD #1600	LOS ANGELES, CA	90067
BROOKINS, GARY	CARTOONIST	POST OFFICE BOX C-32333	RICHMOND, VA	23293
BROOKLYN BRIDGE, THE	ROCK & ROLL GROUP	BROTHERS, 141 DUNBAR AVE	FORDS, NJ	08863
BROOKMAN, MICHAEL S	TV EXECUTIVE	CBS-TV, 7800 BEVERLY BLVD	LOS ANGELES, CA	90036
BROOKS, ALAN D	DIRECTOR	243 E 93RD ST	NEW YORK, NY	10128
BROOKS, ALBERT	ACT-WRI-DIR	3600 LONGRIDGE AVE	SHERMAN OAKS, CA	91403

The Official Lane Brody

Global Fan Club
P.O. Box 24775
Nashville, TN 37202

BROOKS, ANNABEL	ACTRESS	POST OFFICE BOX 5617	BEVERLY HILLS, CA	90213
BROOKS, AVERY	ACTOR	20 LAYNE RD	SUMMERSET, NJ	08873
BROOKS, BILL	FOOTBALL	POST OFFICE BOX 535000	INDIANPOLIS, IN	46253
BROOKS, DAVID	ACTOR	400 W 43RD ST #40-E	NEW YORK, NY	10036
BROOKS, DAVID	FILM CRITIC	THE WASHINGTON TIMES		
		3600 NEW YORK AVE, NE	WASHINGTON, DC	20002
BROOKS, DONALD	COSTUME DESIGNER	POST OFFICE BOX 5617	BEVERLY HILLS, CA	90213
BROOKS, DWIGHT	FILM DIRECTOR	POST OFFICE BOX 102	GRASS VALLEY, CA	95945
BROOKS, ERIC	ACTOR	215 W 91ST ST #67	NEW YORK, NY	10024
BROOKS, ERIC	BASEBALL	POST OFFICE BOX 957	DUNEDIN, FL	34697
BROOKS, ERIN & DON SHIPLEY	VOCAL DUO	POST OFFICE BOX 42466	TUCSON, AZ	85733
BROOKS, FOSTER	COMEDIAN	18116 CHARDON CIR	ENCINO, CA	91316
BROOKS, GARTH	SINGER-SONGWRITER	DOYLE-LEWIS, 1109 17TH AVE S	NASHVILLE, TN	37212
BROOKS, GEORGE & THE INK SPOTS	C & W GROUP	CAROL SMITH, 3935 CLIFTONDALE PL	COLLEGE PARK, GA	30349
BROOKS, GEORGE W	TV DIRECTOR	20224 SHERMAN WY #41	CANOGA PARK, CA	91306
BROOKS, HAZEL	ACTRESS	ROSS, 754 TORTUOSA WY	LOS ANGELES, CA	90024
BROOKS, HILDY	ACTRESS	5455 WILSHIRE BLVD #1406	LOS ANGELES, CA	90036
BROOKS, HUBIE	BASEBALL	POST OFFICE BOX 2000	ANAHEIM, CA	92803
BROOKS, JACK	U S CONGRESSMAN	201 FEDERAL BUILDING	BEAUMONT, TX	77701
BROOKS, JAMES	CONDUCTOR	GERSHUNOFF, 502 PARK AVE	NEW YORK, NY	10022
BROOKS, JAMES	FOOTBALL	BENGALS, 200 RIVERFRONT STADIUM	CINCINNATI, OH	45202
BROOKS, JAMES L	TV WRITER-PRODUCER	31708 BROAD BEACH RD	MALIBU, CA	90265
BROOKS, JERRY	BASEBALL	POST OFFICE BOX 26267	ALBUQUERQUE, NM	87125
BROOKS, JOSEPH	WRITER-PRODUCER	41-A E 74TH ST	NEW YORK, NY	10021
BROOKS, KATIE	SINGER	COOKE & ROSE, 1601 S QUEEN ST	YORK, PA	17403
BROOKS, KIX	SINGER-SONGWRITER	POST OFFICE BOX 40661	NASHVILLE, TN	37204
BROOKS, LARRY	FOOTBALL COACH	RAMS, 2327 W LINCOLN BLVD	ANAHEIM, CA	92801
BROOKS, LEE	ACTOR	8485 MELROSE PL #E	LOS ANGELES, CA	90069
BROOKS, LOU	ARTIST	415 W 55TH ST	NEW YORK, NY	10019
BROOKS, MARK	GOLFER	POST OFFICE BOX 109601	PALM BCH GARDENS, FL	33418
BROOKS, MARLA	WRITER	7080 HOLLYWOOD BLVD #804	HOLLYWOOD, CA	90028
BROOKS, MARTIN E	ACTOR	ICM, 8899 BEVERLY BLVD	LOS ANGELES, CA	90048
BROOKS, MEL	ACT-WRI-DIR	2301 LA MESA DR	SANTA MONICA, CA	90405
BROOKS, MICHAEL	FOOTBALL	BRONCOS, 13655 BRONCOS PKWY	ENGLEWOOD, CO	80112
BROOKS, NORMAN G	TV PRODUCER	11600 WASHINGTON PL #20	LOS ANGELES, CA	90066
BROOKS, PHYLLIS	ACTRESS	POST OFFICE BOX 14	CAPE NEDDICK, ME	03902
BROOKS, RAND	ACTOR	1701 CAPISTRANO CIR	GLENDALE, CA	91207
BROOKS, RANDI	ACTRESS-WRITER-MODEL	1459 IRVING AVE	GLENDALE, CA	91201
BROOKS, RANDY	ACTOR	KOHNER, 9169 SUNSET BLVD	LOS ANGELES, CA	90069
BROOKS, RAYME	BASEBALL	POST OFFICE BOX 5566	EUGENE, OR	97405
BROOKS, RUTH	ACTRESS	179 E 70TH ST	NEW YORK, NY	10021
BROOKS, SCOTT	BASKETBALL	TIMBERWOLVES, 600 1ST AVE N	MINNEAPOLIS, MN	55403
BROOKS, SYLVIA	ACTRESS	1124 W ANGELENO AVE #M	BURBANK, CA	91506
BROOKS, TERI FOSTER	ACTRESS	18116 CHADRON CIR	ENCINO, CA	91316
BROOKS, TITA	WRITER	5211 VELOZ AVE	TARZANA, CA	91356
BROOKS BROTHERS BAND, THE	VOCAL GROUP	POST OFFICE BOX 111510	NASHVILLE, TN	37211
BROOKSBANK, LES	ANIMATION DIRECTOR	WOOD HOUSE, 500 LEEDS RD	BRADFORD BD3 9RU	ENGLAND
BROOKSHIER, TOM	SPORTSCASTER	CBS SPORTS, 51 W 52ND ST	NEW YORK, NY	10019
BROOM, BOBBY	SINGER	1697 BROADWAY #600	NEW YORK, NY	10019
BROOMFIELD, WILLIAM S	U S CONGRESSMAN	330 PARK ST	BIRMINGHAM, MI	48009
BROPHY, GEORGE	BASEBALL SCOUT	POST OFFICE BOX 288	HOUSTON, TX	77001
BROPHY, KEVIN	ACTOR	15010 HAMLIN ST	VAN NUYS, CA	91411
BROSIUS, SCOTT	BASEBALL	ATHLETICS'S, OAKLAND COLISEUM	OAKLAND, CA	94621
BROSNAN, JASON	BASEBALL	POST OFFICE BOX 26267	ALBUQUERQUE, NM	87125
BROSNAN, PIERCE	ACTOR-MODEL	POST OFFICE BOX 9851	GLENDALE, CA	91206
BROSS, TERRY	BASEBALL	STARS, 850 LAS VEGAS BLVD N	LAS VEGAS, NV	89101
BROSSET, CLAUDE	ACTOR	GEORGES LAMBERT AGENCE		
		13 BIS AVE DE		
		LA MOTTE PIQUET	PARIS 75007	FRANCE
BROSTEK, BEM	FOOTBALL	RAMS, 2327 W LINCOLN BLVD	ANAHEIM, CA	92801
BROSTEN, HARVE	WRI-DIR-PROD	35 W 92ND ST	NEW YORK, NY	10025
BROTEN, AARON	HOCKEY	MAPLE LEAFS, 60 CARLTON ST	TORONTO, ONT M5B 1L1	CANADA
BROTEN, NEAL	HOCKEY	NORTH STARS, 7901 CEDAR AVE S	BLOOMINGTON, MN	55425
BROTEN, PAUL	HOCKEY	POST OFFICE BOX 90111	ARLINGTON, TX	76004
BROTHERS, DR JOYCE	PSYCHOLOGIST	1530 PALISADES AVE	FORT LEE, NJ	07024
BROTHERS, JOHN	BASEBALL	POST OFFICE BOX 5646	PRINCETON, WV	24740
BROTHERS, JULIA ANN	ACTRESS	406 W 48TH ST #2-FE	NEW YORK, NY	10036
BROTHERS FOUR, THE	VOCAL DUO	POST OFFICE BOX 220219	CHARLOTTE, NC	28222
BROTHERS JOHNSON, THE	SOUL DUO	NELSON, 5800 VALLEY OAKS DR	LOS ANGELES, CA	90068
BROTHERS ROSE, THE	C & W GROUP	818 18TH AVE #300	NASHVILLE, TN	37203
BROTMAN, JOYCE	TV WRITER-PRODUCER	2338 1/2 S BEVERLY GLEN BLVD	LOS ANGELES, CA	90064
BROUGH, CANDI	ACTRESS-MODEL	11684 VENTURA BLVD #476	STUDIO CITY, CA	91604
BROUGH, RANDI	ACTRESS-MODEL	11684 VENTURA BLVD #476	STUDIO CITY, CA	91604
BROUGH, WALTER J	WRITER-PRODUCER	STONE MANNERS, 9113 SUNSET BL	LOS ANGELES, CA	90069
BROUGHTON, BRUCE	COMPOSER	3815 W OLIVE AVE #201	BURBANK, CA	91505
BROUN, CHARLES W, JR	TV DIRECTOR-PRODUCER	2238 HILLVIEW DR	SARASOTA, FL	33579
BROUSSARD, REBECCA	ACTRESS	15760 VENTURA BLVD #1730	ENCINO, CA	91436
BROUSSARD, STEVE	ACTOR	CARROLL, 120 S VICTORY BL #104	BURBANK, CA	91502
BROUSSARD, STEVE	FOOTBALL	FALCONS, SUWANEE RD AT I-85	SUWANEE, GA	30174
BROW, SCOTT	BASEBALL	POST OFFICE BOX 957	DUNEDIN, FL	34697
BROWDER, GLEN	U S CONGRESSMAN	115 E NORTHSIDE ST	TUSKEGEE, AL	36083
BROWER, BOB	BASEBALL	2110 GUNNELL FARMS DR	VIENNA, VA	22180
BROWER, STUART	TV EXECUTIVE	995 BRENTAL RD	PASADENA, CA	91105
BROWN, A WHITNEY	TV WRITER	WM MORRIS, 1350 AVE OF AMERICAS	NEW YORK, NY	10019
BROWN, ADAM	BASEBALL	POST OFFICE BOX 28268	SAN ANTONIO, TX	78228

BROWN, ALBERT B	TV DIRECTOR	745 CRANE BLVD	LOS ANGELES, CA 90065
BROWN, ALVIN	BASEBALL	136 S SYCAMORE	ELIZABETHTON, TN 37643
BROWN, ANTHONY B	BASEBALL	POST OFFICE BOX 3746, HILL STA	AUGUSTA, GA 30904
BROWN, ARVIN	DIRECTOR	222 SARGENT DR	NEW HAVEN, CT 06511
BROWN, BAD NEWS	WRESTLER	POST OFFICE BOX 3859	STAMFORD, CT 06905
BROWN, BARRY A	DIRECTOR	DGA, 7920 SUNSET BLVD, 6TH FL	LOS ANGELES, CA 90046
BROWN, BARRY K	DIRECTOR-PRODUCER	BRILLING, 300 CENTRAL PARK W	NEW YORK, NY 10024
BROWN, BARRY M	THEATER PRODUCER	250 W 52ND ST	NEW YORK, NY 10019
BROWN, BILL	SPORTSCASTER	POST OFFICE BOX 288	HOUSTON, TX 77001
BROWN, BILLY RAY	GOLFER	POST OFFICE BOX 109601	PALM BCH GARDENS, FL 33418
BROWN, BLAIR	ACTRESS	434 W 20TH ST #3	NEW YORK, NY 10011
BROWN, BOBBI	MODEL	FLAME MODELS, 6565 SUNSET BLVD	LOS ANGELES, CA 90028
BROWN, BOBBIE	SINGER	POST OFFICE BOX B	CARLISLE, IA 50047
BROWN, BOBBY	SINGER-SONGWRITER	3350 PEACHTREE RD, NE	ATLANTA, GA 30326
BROWN, BRICKHOUSE	WRESTLER	8725 N CHAUTAUQUA BLVD	PORTLAND, OR 97217
BROWN, BRYAN	ACTOR	CAA, 9830 WILSHIRE BLVD	BEVERLY HILLS, CA 90212
BROWN, BRYAN	ACTOR	BELFRAGE, 68 SAINT JAMES'S ST	LONDON SW1A 1LE ENGLAND
BROWN, BRYAN	BASEBALL	RED SOX, CHAIN O'LAKES PARK	WINTER HAVEN, FL 33880
BROWN, CANDY ANN	ACTRESS	13500 RYE ST #5	SHERMAN OAKS, CA 91423
BROWN, CARY	WRITER-PRODUCER	12952 WOODBRIDGE ST	STUDIO CITY, CA 91604
BROWN, CHARLES	SINGER	POST OFFICE BOX 60234	CHICAHO, IL 60660
BROWN, CHARLES CALVIN	PIANIST	436 E LANZIT AVE	LOS ANGELES, CA 90061
BROWN, CHARLIE & THE COASTERS	VOCAL GROUP	JOYCE, 2028 CHESTNUT ST	PHILADELPHIA, PA 19103
BROWN, CHARLOTTE	WRITER-PRODUCER	801 THAYER AVE	LOS ANGELES, CA 90024
BROWN, CHERIE	ACTRESS	1680 N VINE ST #203	HOLLYWOOD, CA 90028
BROWN, CHRIS	BASEBALL	5015 BRIGHTON AVE	LOS ANGELES, CA 90062
BROWN, CHUCKY	BASKETBALL	POST OFFICE BOX 5000	RICHFIELD, OH 44286
BROWN, CLANCY	ACTOR	9301 WILSHIRE BLVD #312	BEVERLY HILLS, CA 90210
BROWN, CLARENCE "GATESMOUTH"	SINGER-GUITARIST	POST OFFICE BOX 958	BOGALUSA, LA 70427
BROWN, CRAIG E	COMPOSER	11708 S FELTON	HAWTHORNE, CA 90250
BROWN, DAN	BASEBALL	POST OFFICE BOX 3614	MARTINSVILLE, VA 24115
BROWN, DANA	BASEBALL	POST OFFICE BOX 15050	READING, PA 19612
BROWN, DAREN	BASEBALL	633 JESSAMINE ST	KNOXVILLE, TN 37917
BROWN, DAVE	HOCKEY	OILERS, NORTHLANDS COLISEUM	EDMONTON, ALTA T5B 4M9 CANADA
BROWN, DAVID	FILM PRODUCER	1 W 81ST ST	NEW YORK, NY 10024
BROWN, DAVID "G B"	TV WRITER	8955 BEVERLY BLVD	WEST HOLLYWOOD, CA 90048
BROWN, DEE	BASKETBALL	151 MERRIMAC ST	BOSTON, MA 02114
BROWN, DENNIS	FOOTBALL	S F 49ERS, 4949 CENTENNIAL BL	SANTA CLARA, CA 95054
BROWN, DENNIS	SINGER	THE MUSIC COMPANY	
		14097 NW 19TH AVE	OPA LOCKA, FL 33054
BROWN, DICK	BASEBALL	POST OFFICE BOX 1886	COLUMBUS, GA 31902
BROWN, DOUG	HOCKEY	POST OFFICE BOX 504	EAST RUTHERFORD, NJ 07073
BROWN, DR BOBBY	BASEBALL EXECUTIVE	AMERICAN LEAGUE, 350 PARK AVE	NEW YORK, NY 10022
BROWN, DUANE	BASEBALL	POST OFFICE BOX 1556	ASHEVILLE, NC 28802
BROWN, DWIER	ACTOR	248 SAN JUAN AVE #B	VENICE, CA 90291
BROWN, EARL	COMPOSER-CONDUCTOR	ICI, 799 BROADWAY	NEW YORK, NY 10003
BROWN, EDDIE	FOOTBALL	BENGALS, 200 RIVERFRONT STADIUM	CINCINNATI, OH 45202
BROWN, EDMUND G "JERRY"	POLITICIAN	3022 WASHINGTON ST	SAN FRANCISCO, CA 94115
BROWN, EDMUND G "PAT"	POLITICIAN	9918 KIP DR	BEVERLY HILLS, CA 90210
BROWN, EDWARD R	CINEMATOGRAPHER	POST OFFICE BOX 2230	HOLLYWOOD, CA 90078
BROWN, ELECTA	TV DIRECTOR-PRODUCER	AIRWORTHY PRODUCTIONS	
		241 AVE OF THE AMERICAS	NEW YORK, NY 10014
BROWN, ELLEN	DIRECTOR	2038 BENEDICT CANYON DR	BEVERLY HILLS, CA 90210
BROWN, ELLSWORTH	BASEBALL SCOUT	TWINS, 501 CHICAGO AVE S	MINNEAPOLIS, MN 55415
BROWN, G MAC	DIRECTOR-PRODUCER	425 E 63RD ST #8-EW	NEW YORK, NY 10021
BROWN, GARRETT M	ACTOR	POST OFFICE BOX 5617	BEVERLY HILLS, CA 90213
BROWN, GARY	FOOTBALL	OILERS, 6910 FANNIN ST	HOUSTON, TX 77070
BROWN, GARY M	TV DIRECTOR	880 W 1ST ST #407	LOS ANGELES, CA 90012
BROWN, GAYE	ACTRESS	94 TANTALLOWN RD	LONDON SW12 ENGLAND
BROWN, GEORG STANFORD	ACTOR-DIRECTOR	ICM, 8899 BEVERLY BLVD	LOS ANGELES, CA 90048
BROWN, GEORGE E, JR	U S CONGRESSMAN	3600 LIME ST #116	RIVERSIDE, CA 92502
BROWN, GEORGIA	ACTRESS	1902 COLDWATER CANYON	BEVERLY HILLS, CA 90210
BROWN, GREG	BASEBALL	POST OFFICE BOX 802	BATAVIA, NY 14021
BROWN, GWENDOLYN	ACTRESS	FELBER, 2126 N CAHUENGA BLVD	LOS ANGELES, CA 90068
BROWN, H ARTHUR	CONDUCTOR-VIOLINIST	5961 CHULA VISTA WY	LOS ANGELES, CA 90068
BROWN, HANK	U S SENATOR	1100 10TH ST #201	GREELEY, CO 80631
BROWN, HEATH	BASEBALL EXECUTIVE	POST OFFICE BOX 2887	VERO BEACH, FL 32961
BROWN, HELEN	ACTRESS	1811 WHITLEY AVE #200	LOS ANGELES, CA 90028
BROWN, HELEN GURLEY	AUTHORESS-EDITOR	1 W 81ST ST #22-D	NEW YORK, NY 10024
BROWN, HERB	BASKETBALL	980 N MICHIGAN AVE #1600	CHICAGO, IL 60611
BROWN, HIMAN	DIRECTOR	221 W 26TH ST	NEW YORK, NY 10001
BROWN, HUBIE	BASKETBALL COACH	6 COBBLEWOOD RD	LIVINGSTON, NJ 07039
BROWN, IVORY LEE	FOOTBALL	POST OFFICE BOX 888	PHOENIX, AZ 85001
BROWN, JACKIE	BASEBALL-COACH	333 W 35TH ST	CHICAGO, IL 60616
BROWN, JAMES	BASEBALL SCOUT	250 STADIUM PLAZA	ST LOUIS, MO 63102
BROWN, JAMES "THE GODFATHER"	SINGER-SONGWRITER	JAMES BROWN ENTERPRISES	
		1217 W MEDICAL PARK RD	AUGUSTA, GA 30909
BROWN, JANET	ACTRESS	BERNARD LEE MANAGEMENT	
		MOORCROFT LODGE, FARLEIGH COMMON	
		WARLINGHAM	SURREY CR3 9PE ENGLAND
BROWN, JANNA	ACTRESS	7080 HOLLYWOOD BLVD #704	HOLLYWOOD, CA 90028
BROWN, JARVIS	BASEBALL	TWINS, 501 CHICAGO AVE S	MINNEAPOLIS, MN 55415
BROWN, JEFF	BASEBALL	POST OFFICE BOX 611	WATERLOO, IA 50704
BROWN, JEFF	HOCKEY	BLUES, 5700 OAKLAND AVE	SAINT LOUIS, MO 63110
BROWN, JEFFREY D	FILM DIRECTOR	719 S LORRAINE BLVD	LOS ANGELES, CA 90005

BROWN, JEROME	FOOTBALL	EAGLES, BROAD ST & PATTISON AVE	PHILADELPHIA, PA	19148
BROWN, JERRY	FOOTBALL COACH	VIKINGS, 9520 VIKING DR	EDEN PRAIRIE, MN	55344
BROWN, JIM	ACTOR-FOOTBALL	1851 SUNSET PLAZA DR	LOS ANGELES, CA	90069
BROWN, JIM ED	SINGER-GUITARIST	4308 KENILWOOD DR	NASHVILLE, TN	37204
BROWN, JIMMY	BASEBALL	1201 HYDE PARK BLVD	NIAGARA FALLS, NY	14301
BROWN, JOCELYN	SINGER	200 W 51ST ST #1410	NEW YORK, NY	10019
BROWN, JOE L	BASEBALL-SCOUT	POST OFFICE BOX 7000	PITTSBURGH, PA	15212
BROWN, JULIE	ACT-SING-WRI-DAN	BYMEL, 723 WESTMOUNT DR	WEST HOLLYWOOD, CA	90069
BROWN, KALE	ACTOR	122 E 10TH ST	NEW YORK, N Y	10013
BROWN, KAT	ACTRESS	BYMEL, 723 WESTMOUNT DR	WEST HOLLYWOOD, CA	90069
BROWN, KATHLEEN	TREASURER	STATE CAPITOL BUILDING	SACRAMENTO, CA	95814
BROWN, KEITH	BASEBALL	POST OFFICE BOX 23290	NASHVILLE, TN	37202
BROWN, KEITH	HOCKEY	BLACKHAWKS, 1800 W MADISON ST	CHICAGO, IL	60612
BROWN, KEVIN	BASEBALL	POST OFFICE BOX 4100	SEATTLE, WA	98104
BROWN, KIM	SINGER	CAA, 9830 WILSHIRE BLVD	BEVERLY HILLS, CA	90212
BROWN, KIMBERLIN	ACTRESS	CBS-TV, "YOUNG & THE RESTLESS"		
		7800 BEVERLY BLVD #3305	LOS ANGELES, CA	90036
BROWN, KIPPY	FOOTBALL COACH	N Y JETS, 1000 FULTON AVE	HEMPSTEAD, NY	11550
BROWN, KURT	BASEBALL	CANADIANS, 4601 ONTARIO ST	VANCOUVER, BC V5V 3H4	CANADA
BROWN, LARRY	BASKETBALL COACH	600 E MARKET ST #102	SAN ANTONIO, TX	78205
BROWN, LARRY	FOOTBALL	COWBOYS, 1 COWBOYS PARKWAY	IRVING, TX	75063
BROWN, LARRY	FOOTBALL	LIONS, 1200 FEATHERSTONE RD	PONTIAC, MI	48432
BROWN, LAWRENCE P	CONDUCTOR-PIANIST	222 MOCKINGBIRD TRAIL	PALM BEACH, FL	33480
BROWN, LES, SR	CONDUCTOR	603 OCEAN AVE #5-S	SANTA MONICA, CA	90405
BROWN, LEWIS	COSTUME DESIGNER	881 10TH AVE #3-H	NEW YORK, NY	10019
BROWN, LISA	ACTRESS	370 LEXINGTON AVE #707	NEW YORK, NY	10017
BROWN, MARCIA	AUTHOR	SCRIBNER'S, 597 5TH AVE	NEW YORK, NY	10017
BROWN, MARTY	BASEBALL	4385 TUTT BLVD	COLORADO SPRINGS, CO	80922
BROWN, MATT	BASEBALL	POST OFFICE BOX 48	VISALIA, CA	93279
BROWN, MAXINE	SINGER	KESSLER, 3960 PEACHTREE RD #418	ATLANTA, GA	30319
BROWN, MEG	ACTRESS	1800 N VINE ST #120	LOS ANGELES, CA	90028
BROWN, MENDE	TV DIRECTOR	39 OLOLA AVE	VAUCLUSE NSW 2030	AUSTRALIA
BROWN, MICHAEL	FOOTBALL EXECUTIVE	BENGALS, 200 RIVERFRONT STADIUM	CINCINNATI, OH	45202
BROWN, MICHAEL DAVID	ARTIST	932 HUNGERFORD DR #24-D	ROCKVILLE, MD	20850
BROWN, MICHAEL G	BASEBALL	8712 PINE NEEDLES CT	VIENNA, VA	22180
BROWN, MICHAEL M	DIRECTOR	10 KENT CT	CLARENDON HILLS, IL	60514
BROWN, MIKE	BASEBALL (AUGUSTA)	POST OFFICE BOX 3746, HILL STA	AUGUSTA, GA	30904
BROWN, MIKE	BASEBALL (GREAT FALL)	POST OFFICE BOX 1621	GREAT FALLS, MT	59403
BROWN, MIKE	BASEBALL COACH	1155 W MOUND ST	COLUMBUS, OH	43223
BROWN, MIKE	BASEBALL MANAGER	POST OFFICE BOX 1886	COLUMBUS, GA	31902
BROWN, MIKE	BASKETBALL	5 TRIAD CENTER #500	SALT LAKE CITY, UT	84180
BROWN, OLIVIA	ACTRESS	8271 MELROSE AVE #110	LOS ANGELES, CA	90046
BROWN, PALMER	COSTUME DESIGNER	13949 VENTURA BLVD #309	SHERMAN OAKS, CA	91423
BROWN, PAUL	TV PRODUCER	CAA, 9830 WILSHIRE BLVD	BEVERLY HILLS, CA	90212
BROWN, PETER	ACTOR	852 CYPRESS AVE	HERMOSA BEACH, CA	90254
BROWN, PETER J	DIRECTOR	706 SKYLINE TRAIL	TOPANGA CANYON, CA	90290
BROWN, RANDY	BASEBALL	RED SOX, CHAIN O'LAKES PARK	WINTER HAVEN, FL	33880
BROWN, REB	ACTOR	5454 LAS VIRGENES RD	CALABASAS, CA	91302
BROWN, RICHARD	BASEBALL EXECUTIVE	POST OFFICE BOX 2000	ANAHEIM, CA	92803
BROWN, RICHARD	FOOTBALL	BROWNS, 80 1ST ST	BEREA, OH	44017
BROWN, ROB	BASEBALL	POST OFFICE BOX 4448	TULSA, OK	74159
BROWN, ROB	HOCKEY	WHALERS, 1 CIVIC CENTER PLAZA	HARTFORD, CT	06103
BROWN, ROBERT	FOOTBALL	PACKERS, 1265 LOMBARDI AVE	GREEN BAY, WI	54307
BROWN, ROGER	FOOTBALL	N Y GIANTS, GIANTS STADIUM	EAST RUTHERFORD, NJ	07073
BROWN, ROGER AARON	ACTOR	400 S BEVERLY DR #216	BEVERLY HILLS, CA	90212
BROWN, ROGER COTTON	DIRECTOR	1055 COTTONWOOD PASS RD	GYPSUM, CO	81637
BROWN, RUTH	SINGER	600 W 165TH ST #4-H	NEW YORK, NY	10032
BROWN, SLADE	THEATER PRODUCER	1175 YORK AVE	NEW YORK, NY	10021
BROWN, STEVE	WRITER-PRODUCER	1650 WESTWOOD BLVD #201	LOS ANGELES, CA	90024
BROWN, SUSAN	ACTRESS	280 S BEVERLY DR #400	BEVERLY HILLS, CA	90212
BROWN, T GRAHAM	SINGER	STARBOUND, 1516 16TH AVE S	NASHVILLE, TN	37212
BROWN, TAB	BASEBALL	POST OFFICE BOX 4525	MACON, GA	31208
BROWN, TED	TV HOST	BECKER & LONDON, 30 LINCOLN PLAZA	NEW YORK, NY	10023
BROWN, TIM	BASEBALL	633 JESSAMINE ST	KNOXVILLE, TN	37917
BROWN, TIM	FOOTBALL	RAIDERS, 332 CENTER ST	EL SEGUNDO, CA	90245
BROWN, TIMOTHY	ACTOR	AIMEE, 13743 VICTORY BLVD	VAN NUYS, CA	91401
BROWN, TONY	BASEBALL	POST OFFICE BOX 12	MIDLAND, TX	79702
BROWN, TONY	BASKETBALL	POST OFFICE BOX 10	INGLEWOOD, CA	90306
BROWN, TY	BASEBALL SCOUT	POST OFFICE BOX 2000	ANAHEIM, CA	92803
BROWN, VANESSA	ACTRESS	14340 MULHOLLAND DR	LOS ANGELES, CA	90077
BROWN, VINCENT	FOOTBALL	PATRIOTS, FOXBORO STADIUM, RT #1	FOXBORO, MA	02035
BROWN, VIRGE	SINGER	PROCESS, 439 WILEY AVE	FRANKLIN, PA	16323
BROWN, WALLY	AUTHOR	POST OFFICE BOX 68	HILLSDALE, NJ	07642
BROWN, WILLIAM	PRODUCER	WORLDWIDE, 2520 W OLIVE AVE	BURBANK, CA	91505
BROWN, WILLIAM	TV EXECUTIVE	SCOTTISH TELEVISION PICTURES		
		COWCADDENS	GLASGOW G2 3PR	SCOTLAND
BROWN, WILLIE L, JR	ASSEMBYMAN	1200 GOUGH ST #200	SAN FRANCISCO, CA	94115
BROWN, WOODY	ACTOR	6548 COLBATH AVE	VAN NUYS, CA	91401
BROWNE, ANGELA	ACTRESS	ESSANAY, 2 CONDUIT ST	LONDON W1R 9TG	ENGLAND
BROWNE, AUTUMN	ACTRESS	DON SCHWARTZ, 8749 SUNSET BLVD	LOS ANGELES, CA	90069
BROWNE, BYRON	BASEBALL	POST OFFICE BOX 855	BELOIT, WI	53511
BROWNE, JACKSON	SINGER-COMPOSER	3208 W CAHUENGA BLVD #108	LOS ANGELES, CA	90068
BROWNE, JERRY	BASEBALL	2-A PRINCE ST	CHRISTIANSTED, VI	00820
BROWNE, JOHN	BASEBALL EXECUTIVE	1090 N EUCLID AVE	SARASOTA, FL	34237
BROWNE, KALE	ACTOR	122 E 10TH ST	NEW YORK, NY	10013

BROWNE, KATE	ACTRESS	DMB & B, 909 3RD AVE	NEW YORK, NY 10022
BROWNE, KENDALL CARLY	ACTRESS	240 N CRESCENT DR #300	BEVERLY HILLS, CA 90210
BROWNE, ROBERT ALAN	ACTOR	2029 CENTURY PARK E #600	LOS ANGELES, CA 90067
BROWNE, ROSCOE LEE	ACT-WRI-DIR	3531 WONDER VIEW DR	LOS ANGELES, CA 90068
BROWNE, SUZANNE SMITH	COSTUME DESIGNER	11420 CHENAULT ST	LOS ANGELES, CA 90049
BROWNELL, BARBARA	ACTRESS	5101 LEDGE AVE	NORTH HOLLYWOOD, CA 91601
BROWNER, JOEY	FOOTBALL	VIKINGS, 9520 VIKING DR	EDEN PRAIRIE, MN 55344
BROWNHOLTZ, JOE	BASEBALL	POST OFFICE BOX 309	GASTONA, NC 28053
BROWNING, KIRK	DIRECTOR	80 CENTRAL PARK W	NEW YORK, NY 10023
BROWNING, TOM	BASEBALL	REDS, 100 RIVERFRONT STADIUM	CINCINNATI, OH 45202
BROWNING, VIRGINIA	ACTRESS	2109 BROADWAY #4131	NEW YORK, NY 10023
BROWNLOW, KEVIN	FILM DIRECTOR	PHOTOPLAY, 21 PRINCESS RD	LONDON NW1 ENGLAND
BROYLES, ROBERT	ACTOR	2311 SCOTT AVE	LOS ANGELES, CA 90026
BRU, SALVADOR	ARTIST	5130 BRADLEY BLVD	CHEVY CHASE, MD 20815
BRUBECK, DAVE	PIANIST	221 MILLSTONE RD	WILTON, CT 06897
BRUCE, ASHLEY	TV DIRECTOR-PRODUCER	156 HIGH ST, BILDESTON	SUFFOLK ENGLAND
BRUCE, AUNDRAY	FOOTBALL	FALCONS, SUWANEE RD AT I-85	SUWANEE, GA 30174
BRUCE, CAROL	ACTRESS	1361 N LAUREL AVE	LOS ANGELES, CA 90046
BRUCE, DAVID	HOCKEY	BLUES, 5700 OAKLAND AVE	SAINT LOUIS, MO 63110
BRUCE, ED	SINGER	POST OFFICE BOX 120694	NASHVILLE, TN 37212
BRUCE, JOHN	TV DIRECTOR	BROWN, 162-168 REGENT ST	LONDON W1R 5TB ENGLAND
BRUCE, KITTY	SINGER	31 HARRISON ST	NEW YORK, NY 10019
BRUCE, ROBERT	TV WRITER	UTA, 9560 WILSHIRE BL, 5TH FL	BEVERLY HILLS, CA 90212
BRUCE, TERRY L	U S CONGRESSMAN	114 W CHESTNUT	OLNEY, IL 62450
BRUCKER, JANE	ACTRESS	151 S EL CAMINO DR	BEVERLY HILLS, CA 90212
BRUDER, PATRICIA	ACTRESS	165 W END AVE	NEW YORK, NY 10023
BRUE, BOB	GOLFER	PGA SENIORS, 112 T P C BLVD	PONTE VEDRA BEACH, FL 32082
BRUESKE, BILLIE	ACTRESS	KAYE, 1006 N LIMA ST	BURBANK, CA 91505
BRUETT, J T	BASEBALL	POST OFFICE BOX 1659	PORTLAND, OR 97207
BRUGNONI, MARC P	TV PRODUCER	POST OFFICE BOX 205	AMAGANSETT, NY 11930
BRUHIN, JOHN	FOOTBALL	BUCCANEERS, 1 BUCCANEER PL	TAMPA, FL 33607
BRUISE BROTHERS, THE	WRESTLING TAG TEAM	8725 N CHAUTAUQUA BLVD	PORTLAND, OR 97217
BRULL, PAMELA	ACTRESS	9255 SUNSET BLVD #515	LOS ANGELES, CA 90069
BRUMBACK, CHARLES	BASEBALL EXECUTIVE	1060 W ADDISON ST	CHICAGO, IL 60613
BRUMEL, VALERYI	ASTRONAUT	LOUJNETZKAYA NAB 8	MOSCOW USSR
BRUMFIELD, JACOB	BASEBALL	REDS, 100 RIVERFRONT STADIUM	CINCINNATI, OH 45202
BRUMLEY, MIKE, JR	BASEBALL	POST OFFICE BOX 2365	PAWTUCKET, RI 02861
BRUMLEY, MIKE, SR	BASEBALL	2621 W VANDALIA ST	BROKEN ARROW, OK 74012
BRUMMER, GLENN	BASEBALL COACH	POST OFFICE BOX 1721	SPARTANBURG, SC 29304
BRUMMETT, GREG	BASEBALL	POST OFFICE BOX 21727	SAN FRANCISCO, CA 95151
BRUNANSKY, TOM	BASEBALL	FENWAY PARK, 4 YAWKEY WY	BOSTON, MA 02215
BRUNDAGE, DAVE	BASEBALL	POST OFFICE BOX 3690, STA "B"	CALGARY, ALB T2B 4M4 CANADA
BRUNDY, STANLEY	BASKETBALL	N J NETS, MEADOWLANDS ARENA	EAST RUTHERFORD, NJ 07073
BRUNEL, LUIS	FILM DIRECTOR	72 AVE DES CHAMPS ELYSE	PARIS 75008 FRANCE
BRUNER, JAMES	SCREENWRITER	8383 WILSHIRE BLVD #923	BEVERLY HILLS, CA 90211
BRUNETTI, ARGENTINA	ACTRESS	2011 HOLLY HILL TERR	HOLLYWOOD, CA 90068
BRUNEY, FRED	FOOTBALL COACH	BUCCANEERS, 1 BUCCANEER PL	TAMPA, FL 33607
BRUNI, CARLA	MODEL	WILHELMINA, 300 PARK AVE	NEW YORK, NY 10010
BRUNNER, DON	ACTOR	2029 CENTURY PARK E #600	LOS ANGELES, CA 90067
BRUNNER, JOHN	FOOTBALL COACH	VIKINGS, 9520 VIKING DR	EDEN PRAIRIE, MN 55344
BRUNO, CHRIS	ACTOR	NBC-TV, "ANOTHER WORLD"	
		1268 E 14TH ST	BROOKLYN, NY 11230
BRUNO, JULIO	BASEBALL	12000 STADIUM RD	ADELANTO, CA 92301
BRUNO, RICHARD	COSTUME DESIGNER	1602 FRANKLIN	PORT TOWNSEND, WA 98368
BRUNS, MONA	ACTRESS	THOMAS, 4140 WARNER BL #210	BURBANK, CA 91522
BRUNS, PHILIP	ACTOR	ATKINS, 303 S CRESCENT HEIGHTS	LOS ANGELES, CA 90048
BRUNT, NATALIE	ACTRESS	8360 MELROSE AVE #203	LOS ANGELES, CA 90069
BRUSH, ROBERT L, JR	TV WRITER	9242 BEVERLY DR #200	BEVERLY HILLS, CA 90210
BRUSHFIRE	C & W GROUP	POST OFFICE BOX 186	RIVA, MD 21140
BRUSKE, JIM	BASEBALL	4385 TUTT BLVD	COLORADO SPRINGS, CO 80922
BRY, ELLEN	ACTRESS	1999 AVE OF THE STARS #2850	LOS ANGELES, CA 90067
BRYAN, MARY	GOLFER	2750 VOLUSA AVE #B	DAYTON BEACH, FL 32114
BRYAN, RICHARD	DIRECTOR	11 CARLISLE MANSIONS	
		CARLISLE PL	LONDON SW1 ENGLAND
BRYAN, RICHARD H	U S SENATOR	300 LAS VEGAS BLVD #140	LAS VEGAS, NV 89101
BRYAN, RICK	FOOTBALL	FALCONS, SUWANEE RD AT I-85	SUWANEE, GA 30174
BRYAN, ZACHARY TY	ACTOR	ABC-TV, 2040 AVE OF THE STARS	LOS ANGELES, CA 90067
BRYAN DART, JANE	ACTRESS	POST OFFICE BOX 1033	PEBBLE BEACH, CA 93953
BRYANT, BART	GOLFER	POST OFFICE BOX 109601	PALM BCH GARDENS, FL 33418
BRYANT, BILL	ACTOR	5000 LANKERSHIM BLVD #7 & 9	NORTH HOLLYWOOD, CA 91601
BRYANT, BRAD	GOLFER	POST OFFICE BOX 109601	PALM BCH GARDENS, FL 33418
BRYANT, CRAIG	BASEBALL	POST OFFICE BOX 30160	SAN BERNARDINO, CA 92413
BRYANT, DAVID	ACTOR	8730 SUNSET BLVD #480	LOS ANGELES, CA 90069
BRYANT, ERWIN	BASEBALL SCOUT	FENWAY PARK, 4 YAWKEY WY	BOSTON, MA 02215
BRYANT, JEFF	FOOTBALL	SEAHAWKS, 11220 NE 53RD ST	KIRKLAND, WA 98033
BRYANT, JOHN	U S CONGRESSMAN	8035 EAST R L THORNTON #518	DALLAS, TX 75228
BRYANT, JOSHUA	ACTOR	9744 WILSHIRE BLVD #308	BEVERLY HILLS, CA 90212
BRYANT, LEE	ACTRESS	CBS-TV, "AS THE WORLD TURNS"	
		524 W 57TH ST #5330	NEW YORK, NY 10019
BRYANT, MARK	BASKETBALL	700 NE MULTNOMAH ST #600	PORTLAND, OR 97232
BRYANT, MICHAEL	ACTOR	WILLOW COTTAGE, KINGTON MAGNA	DORSET SP8 5EW ENGLAND
BRYANT, PAMELA JEAN	ACTRESS-MODEL	2029 CENTURY PARK E #600	LOS ANGELES, CA 90067
BRYANT, PAT	BASEBALL	POST OFFICE BOX 1886	COLUMBUS, GA 31902
BRYANT, RALPH	BASEBALL	RR #4, BOX 374	LEESBURG, GA 31763
BRYANT, SCOTT	BASEBALL	CUBS, 2ND & RIVERSIDE DR	DES MOINES, IA 50309

BRYANT, SHAWN	BASEBALL	POST OFFICE BOX 3452	KINSTON, NC 28502
BRYANT, STEVE .. (MUDCATS)	BASEBALL EXECUTIVE	POST OFFICE DRAWER 1218	ZEBULON, NC 27597
BRYANT, STEVE .. (HORNETS)	BASEBALL EXECUTIVE	POST OFFICE BOX 22093	GREENSBORO, NC 27420
BRYANT, WALTER E	COMPOSER-CONDUCTOR	38 KILLYON RD	GLADSTONE, MO 64118
BRYANT, WEB	ILLUSTRATOR	POST OFFICE BOX 500	WASHINGTON, DC 20044
BRYANT, WINSTON	ATTORNEY GENERAL	STATE CAPITOL BUILDING	LITTLE ROCK, AR 72201
BRYCE, JAMES	SCREENWRITER	555 W 57TH ST #1230	NEW YORK, NY 10019
BRYCE, SCOTT	ACTOR	STE, 888 7TH AVE, 18TH FLOOR	NEW YORK, NY 10106
BRYDEN, BILL	FILM WRITER-DIRECTOR	WM MORRIS, 31-32 SOHO SQ	LONDON W1V 5DG ENGLAND
BRYENTON, GARY	BASEBALL EXECUTIVE	INDIANS, CLEVELAND STADIUM	CLEVELAND, OH 44114
BRYER, MAXIMILLIAN	DIRECTOR	15363 MULHOLLAND DR	LOS ANGELES, CA 90077
BRYERS, PAUL	TV WRITER-DIRECTOR	103-109 WARDOUR ST	LONDON W1 ENGLAND
BRYERS, SHEVAUN	ACTRESS	STRATHAIRD HOUSE	
		LADY MARGARET RD	CAMBRIDGE CB3 OBU ENGLAND
BRYGGMAN, LARRY	ACTOR	CBS-TV, "AS THE WORLD TURNS"	
		524 W 57TH ST #5330	NEW YORK, NY 10019
BRYK, BILL	BASEBALL-SCOUT	POST OFFICE BOX 7000	PITTSBURGH, PA 15212
BRYLAND, RENAY	BASEBALL	POST OFFICE BOX 1420	WICHITA, KS 67201
BRYNE, BARBARA	ACTRESS	11726 SAN VICENTE BLVD #300	LOS ANGELES, CA 90049
BRYSON, PEABO	SINGER-SONGWRITER	FAA, 1700 BROADWAY, 5TH FLOOR	NEW YORK, NY 10019
BRYTTAN, ADRIAN	CONDUCTOR	45 W 60TH ST #4-K	NEW YORK, NY 10023
BRZENK, TED	BASEBALL SCOUT	POST OFFICE BOX 2000	ANAHEIM, CA 92803
BRZEZINSKI, ANTHONY	ARTIST	1609 E TUCKER BLVD	ARLINGTON, TX 76010
BRZEZINSKI, GEORGE	BASEBALL EXECUTIVE	POST OFFICE BOX 2148	WOODBRIDGE, VA 22193
BUBALO, MIKE	BASEBALL COACH	POST OFFICE BOX 7893	EVERETT, WA 98201
BUBALO, RUDOLPH	COMPOSER	333 TAYLOR AVE N #202	SEATTLE, WA 98109
BUBEK, ALBERT	BODYBUILDER	POST OFFICE BOX 800-323	8000 MUNICH 80 GERMANY
BUBOLZ, KERRY	BASEBALL EXECUTIVE	POST OFFICE BOX 3496	DAVENPORT, IA 52808
BUCCHERI, JIM	BASEBALL	POST OFFICE BOX 2769	HUNTSVILLE, AL 35804
BUCCHINO, JOHN J	COMPOSER	527 N LAUREL AVE	LOS ANGELES, CA 90048
BUCHANAN, BOB	BASEBALL	POST OFFICE BOX 3665	OMAHA, NE 68103
BUCHANAN, IAN	ACTOR	345 N MAPLE DR #183	BEVERLY HILLS, CA 90210
BUCHANAN, JAMES D	MUSIC ARRANGER	POST OFFICE BOX 1726	MORGANTON, NC 28655
BUCHANAN, JAMES D	WRITER-PRODUCER	21222 LOPEZ ST	WOODLAND HILLS, CA 91364
BUCHANAN, JENSEN	ACTRESS	NBC-TV, "ANOTHER WORLD"	
		1268 E 14TH ST	BROOKLYN, NY 11230
BUCHANAN, LARRY	FILM WRITER-DIRECTOR	5440 LINDLEY AVE #205	ENCINO, CA 91316
BUCHANAN, PATRICK JOSEPH	TV HOST-COLUMNIST	1017 SAVILE LN N	MC LEAN, WA 22101
BUCHANAN, ROBERT	TV PRODUCER	NBC-TV, 30 ROCKEFELLER PLAZA	NEW YORK, NY 10112
BUCHANAN, SHAWN	BASEBALL	1090 N EUCLID AVE	SARASOTA, FL 34237
BUCHBERGER, KELLY	HOCKEY	OILERS, NORTHLANDS COLISEUM	EDMONTON, ALTA T5B 4M9 CANADA
BUCHER, CMDR LLOYD	U S NAVY	GENERAL DELIVERY	POWAY, CA 92064
BUCHHOLZ, HORST	ACTOR	CLAVADOIRAS	CH-7078 LENZERHEIDE .. SWITZERLAND
BUCHMAN, NANROSE	COSTUME DESIGNER	5018 WILLOW CREST AVE	NORTH HOLLYWOOD, CA 91601
BUCHNER, FEM	MAKE-UP ARTIST	2166 BROADWAY	NEW YORK, NY 10024
BUCHWALD, ART	COLUMNIST	2000 PENNSYLVANIA AVE, NW	WASHINGTON, DC 90036
BUCK, ALEXANDER	BASEBALL EXECUTIVE	POST OFFICE BOX 7575	PHILADELPHIA, PA 19101
BUCK, CRAIG	TV WRITER	16633 VENTURA BLVD #1421	ENCINO, CA 91436
BUCK, DAVID	BASEBALL UMPIRE	2101 E BROADWAY #35	TEMPE, AZ 85282
BUCK, GARY	SINGER	POST OFFICE BOX 4738	NASHVILLE, TN 37216
BUCK, J MAHLON, JR	BASEBALL EXECUTIVE	POST OFFICE BOX 7575	PHILADELPHIA, PA 19101
BUCK, JACK	SPORTSCASTER	250 STADIUM PLAZA	ST LOUIS, MO 63102
BUCK, JOE	SPORTSCASTER	250 STADIUM PLAZA	ST LOUIS, MO 63102
BUCK, MIKE	FOOTBALL	SAINTS, 1500 POYDRAS ST	NEW ORLEANS, LA 90112
BUCK, VINCE	FOOTBALL	SAINTS, 1500 POYDRAS ST	NEW ORLEANS, LA 90112
BUCK, WILLIAM	BASEBALL EXECUTIVE	POST OFFICE BOX 7575	PHILADELPHIA, PA 19101
BUCKAROOS, THE	C & W GROUP	OMAC, 237 W YOSEMITE AVE	MANTECA, CA 95336
BUCKELS, GARY	BASEBALL	10233 96TH AVE	EDMONTON, ALB TK5 0A5 CANADA
BUCKEYE	C & W GROUP	CAM MUSIC, 1423 LEE BLVD	BERKELEY, IL 60163
BUCKHOLZ, STEVE	BASEBALL	POST OFFICE DRAWER 1218	ZEBULON, NC 27597
BUCKINGHAM, LINDSEY	SINGER-SONGWRITER	MICHAEL BROKOW MANAGEMENT	
		3389 CAMINO DE LA CUMBRE	SHERMAN OAKS, CA 91423
BUCKINGHAMS, THE	ROCK & ROLL GROUP	PIPELINE, 620 16TH AVE S	HOPKINS, MN 55343
BUCKLEY, BETTY	ACTRESS	10100 SANTA MONICA BLVD #1600	LOS ANGELES, CA 90067
BUCKLEY, CHRIS	BASEBALL SCOUT	SKYDOME, 300 BREMMER BL #3200	TORONTO, ONT M5V 3B3 CANADA
BUCKLEY, J TAYLOR	NEWS EDITOR	POST OFFICE BOX 500	WASHINGTON, DC 20044
BUCKLEY, KEITH	ACTOR	PETERS, FRASER & DUNLOP, LTD	
		5TH FLOOR, THE CHAMBERS	
		CHELSEA HARBOUR, LOT RD	LONDON SW10 OXF ENGLAND
BUCKLEY, TRAVIS	BASEBALL	POST OFFICE BOX 15757	HARRISBURG, PA 17105
BUCKLEY, TROY	BASEBALL	14100 SIX MILE CYPRESS PKWY	FORT MYERS, FL 33912
BUCKLEY, WILLIAM F, JR	AUTHOR-EDITOR	NATL REVIEW, 150 E 35TH ST	NEW YORK, NY 10016
BUCKMAN, TARA	ACTRESS	8665 WILSHIRE BLVD #208	BEVERLY HILLS, CA 90211
BUCKNER, BETTY	ACTRESS	6000 MONTEREY RD #8	LOS ANGELES, CA 90042
BUCKNER, BILL	BASEBALL	3 MC DONALD CIR	ANDOVER, MA 01810
BUCKNER, BRAD	TV WRITER-PRODUCER	2017 N TAFT AVE	LOS ANGELES, CA 90068
BUCKTON, DAVID	TV DIRECTOR	THE LIACS, SOUTH ST	
		HOCKWOLD, NEAR BRANDON	NORFOLK IP26 4JG ENGLAND
BUCKWALTER, BUCKY	BASKETBALL EXECUTIVE	700 NE MULTNOMAH ST #600	PORTLAND, OR 97232
BUCKWHEAT ZYDECO	CAJUN BAND	CONCERTED, 110 MADISON AVE	NEWTOWNVILLE, MA 02160
BUCZ, BRUCE	BASEBALL EXECUTIVE	POST OFFICE BOX 48	VISALIA, CA 93279
BUDASKA, ROBERT	ACTOR	1418 N HIGHLAND AVE #102	LOS ANGELES, CA 90028
BUDD, JULIE	ACTRESS-SINGER	155 E 68TH ST	NEW YORK, NY 10021
BUDD, ROY	COMPOSER-PIANIST	551 GREEN LANES, PALMER GREEN	LONDON N13 4DR ENGLAND
BUDD, TERENCE	ACTOR	29 RYLETTE RD	LONDON W12 ENGLAND

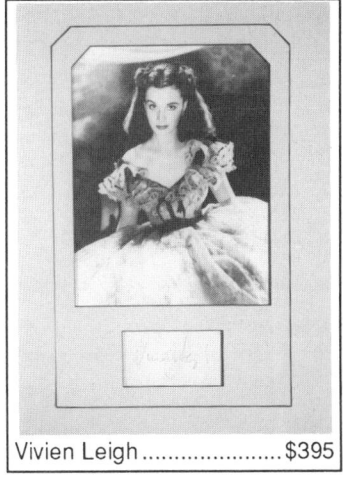

Name	Occupation	Address	City
BUDD, ZOLA	TRACK & FIELD	1 CHURCH ROW, WANDSWORTH PLAIN	LONDON SW18 ENGLAND
BUDGE, DON	TENNIS	POST OFFICE BOX 789	DINGMAN'S FERRY, PA 18328
BUDIN, ELBERT	DIRECTOR	15 HEATHCOTE RD	SCARSDALE, NY 10583
BUDIN, JEFFREY	COMPOSER-CONDUCTOR	3324 BEETHOVEN ST	LOS ANGELES, CA 90066
BUDLEY, CHRIS	BASKETBALL	N J NETS, MEADOWLANDS ARENA	EAST RUTHERFORD, NJ 07073
BUDNER, SCOTT	BASEBALL COACH	POST OFFICE BOX 11363	RENO, NV 89510
BUDREWICZ, TIM	BASEBALL	POST OFFICE BOX 4488	WINSTON-SALEM, NC 27115
BUECHELE, STEVE	BASEBALL	1060 W ADDISON ST	CHICAGO, IL 60613
BUECHLER, JUD	BASKETBALL	N J NETS, MEADOWLANDS ARENA	EAST RUTHERFORD, NJ 07073
BUFFETT, JIMMY	SINGER-SONGWRITER	500 DUVAL ST #B	KEY WEST, FL 33040
BUFFINTON, BRYAN	ACTOR	CBS-TV, "THE GUIDING LIGHT"	
		222 E 44TH ST	NEW YORK, NY 10017
BUFFONE, MICHELE	ACTRESS	371 N GARDNER ST	LOS ANGELES, CA 90036
BUFORD, DAMON	BASEBALL	POST OFFICE BOX 230	HAGERSTOWN, MD 21740
BUFORD, DON	BASEBALL-MANAGER	POST OFFICE BOX 230	HAGERSTOWN, MD 21740
BUFORD, MAURY	FOOTBALL	BEARS, 250 N WASHINGTON RD	LAKE FOREST, IL 60045
BUFORD, R C	BASKETBALL COACH	600 E MARKET ST #102	SAN ANTONIO, TX 78205
BUGDEN, SUE	ACTRESS	6545 SIMPSON AVE #19	NORTH HOLLYWOOD, CA 91606
BUGEL, JOE	FOOTBALL COACH	POST OFFICE BOX 888	PHOENIX, AZ 85001
BUGGLES, THE	ROCK & ROLL GROUP	ISLAND RECORDS COMPANY	
		22 SAINT PETERS SQ	LONDON W69 NW ENGLAND
BUGLIOSI, VINCENT	ATTORNEY-AUTHOR	9300 WILSHIRE BLVD #470	BEVERLY HILLS, CA 90210
BUHAI, JEFF	SCREENWRITER	454 S IRVING BLVD	LOS ANGELES, CA 90020
BUHNER, JAY	BASEBALL	POST OFFICE BOX 4100	SEATTLE, WA 98104
BUHRINGER, MARIAANA	MODEL	L A MODELS, 8335 SUNSET BLVD	HOLLYWOOD, CA 90069
BUHRMAN, DOROTHY	ACTRESS	12800 MOORPARK ST #15	STUDIO CITY, CA 91604
BUICE, DE WAYNE	BASEBALL	1866 PARKCREST DR	COSTA MESA, CA 92627
BUJOLD, GENEVIEVE	ACTRESS	27528 PACIFIC COAST HWY	MALIBU, CA 90265
BUKOWSKI, CHARLES	AUTHOR-SCREENWRITER	BLACK SPARROW, 29 10TH ST	SANTA ROSA, CA 95401
BUKTENICA, RAY	ACTOR	11873 ROCHESTER AVE	LOS ANGELES, CA 90025
BULIFANT, JOYCE	ACTRESS	9300 WILSHIRE BLVD #410	BEVERLY HILLS, CA 90212
BULL, KATIE	ACTRESS	BOB WATERS, 1501 BROADWAY	NEW YORK, NY 10036
BULL, RICHARD	ACTOR	651 N WILCOX #3-G	LOS ANGELES, CA 90036
BULL, SANDY	ACTOR	301 N CANON DR #305	BEVERLY HILLS, CA 90210
BULLARD, JASON	BASEBALL	POST OFFICE DRAWER 1218	ZEBULON, NC 27597
BULLARD, MATT	BASKETBALL	POST OFFICE BOX 272349	HOUSTON, TX 77277
BULLETT, SCOTT	BASEBALL	POST OFFICE DRAWER 1218	ZEBULON, NC 27597
BULLEY, TONY	TV DIRECTOR	BLATT, THE COACH HOUSE	
		1-A LARPENT AVE	LONDON SW15 6UP ENGLAND
BULLING, ERICH	CONDUCTOR	15220 LA MAIDA ST	SHERMAN OAKS, CA 91403
BULLINGER, JIM	BASEBALL	CUBS, 2ND & RIVERSIDE DR	DES MOINES, IA 50309
BULLOCK, BOB	LT GOVERNOR	POST OFFICE BOX 12428	AUSTIN, TX 78711
BULLOCK, CRAIG	BASEBALL	POST OFFICE BOX 7845	COLUMBIA, SC 29202
BULLOCK, DONNA	ACTRESS	111 W 57TH ST #1409	NEW YORK, NY 10019
BULLOCK, EARL	ACTOR	2029 CENTURY PARK E #600	LOS ANGELES, CA 90067
BULLOCK, ERIC	BASEBALL	EXPOS, 4545 DE COUBERTIN AVE	MONTREAL, QUE H1V 3P2 CANADA
BULLOCK, HARVEY	TV WRITER	16633 VENTURA BLVD #1421	ENCINO, CA 91436
BULLOCK, JM J	ACTOR	6210 TEMPLE HILL DR	LOS ANGELES, CA 90069
BULLOCK, SANDRA	ACTRESS	UTA, 9560 WILSHIRE BL, 5TH FL	BEVERLY HILLS, CA 90212
BULLOUGH, HANK	FOOTBALL COACH	PACKERS, 1265 LOMBARDI AVE	GREEN BAY, WI 54307
BULLUCK, VICANGELO	SCREENWRITER	8955 BEVERLY BLVD	WEST HOLLYWOOD, CA 90048
BUMBRY, AL	BASEBALL-COACH	FENWAY PARK, 4 YAWKEY WY	BOSTON, MA 02215
BUMGARNER, JEFF	BASEBALL	POST OFFICE BOX 230	HAGERSTOWN, MD 21740
BUMILLER, WILLIAM	ACTOR	9255 SUNSET BLVD #515	LOS ANGELES, CA 90069
BUMPERS, DALE	U S SENATOR	2527 FEDERAL BUILDING	LITTLE ROCK, AR 72201
BUMSTEAD, J P	ACTOR	10405 FOOTHILL BLVD	LAKE VIEW, CA 91342
BUNCH, JARROD	FOOTBALL	N Y GIANTS, GIANTS STADIUM	EAST RUTHERFORD, NJ 07073
BUNDY, BROOKE	ACTRESS	833 N MARTEL AVE	LOS ANGELES, CA 90046
BUNDY, KING KONG	WRESTLER-ACTOR	POST OFFICE BOX 3859	STAMFORD, CT 06905
BUNDY, LORENZO	BASEBALL MANAGER	POLECATS, 608 N SLAPPEY BLVD	ALBANY, GA 31701
BUNIM, MARY-ELLIS	TV PRODUCER-DIRECTOR	19318 WELLS DR	TARZANA, CA 91356
BUNIN, ELINOR	GRAPHIC DESIGNER	30 E 60TH ST	NEW YORK, NY 10022
BUNKE, JOAN	FILM CRITIC	POST OFFICE BOX 957	DES MOINES, IA 50304
BUNKER, EDWARD	SCREENWRITER	10000 SANTA MONICA BLVD #305	LOS ANGELES, CA 90067
BUNKER, LARRY	COMPOSER	2244 LIVE OAK DR E	LOS ANGELES, CA 90068
BUNKOWSKY, BARB	GOLFER	2750 VOLUSA AVE #B	DAYTON BEACH, FL 32114
BUNN, ELWOOD & DOWN YONDER	C & W GROUP	SPOTFIELD, 84 ELM ST	WESTFIELD, NJ 07090
BUNNING, JIM	BASEBALL-CONGRESSMAN	4 FAIRWAY DR	SOUTHGATE, KY 41071
BUNNYDROMS, THE	ROCK & ROLL GROUP	1704 N 5TH ST	PHILADELPHIA, PA 19122
BUNTING, FINDLAY	WRITER	8955 BEVERLY BLVD	WEST HOLLYWOOD, CA 90048
BUNTING, ROSIE	TV PRODUCER	87 CRESCENT LN	LONDON SW14 ENGLAND
BUNUEL, JOYCE	SCREENWRITER	ROSENBERG, 8428 MELROSE PL #C	LOS ANGELES, CA 90069
BUONO, ROSEMARY	TV DIRECTOR	ABC-TV, 30 W 67TH ST	NEW YORK, NY 10023
BURAS, MILTON	HAIR STYLIST	37-25 CRESCENT ST	LONG ISLAND CITY, NY 11101
BURBA, DAVE	BASEBALL	S F GIANTS, CANDLESTICK PARK	SAN FRANICSCO, CA 94124
BURBANK, DENNIS	BASEBALL	5301 NW 12TH AVE	FORT LAUDERDALE, FL 33309
BURBRINK, NELSON	BASEBALL-SCOUT	BREWERS, 201 S 46TH ST	MILWAUKEE, WI 53214
BURCH, SHERRY WILLIS	ACTRESS	341 1/2 N STANLEY AVE	LOS ANGELES, CA 90036
BURCH, VERNON	SINGER-GUITARIST	6430 SUNSET BLVD #1516	LOS ANGELES, CA 90028
BURCH, WILLIAM JAMES	COMPOSER	777 MARION AVE	PALO ALTO, CA 94301
BURCH SISTERS, THE	C & W GROUP	POST OFFICE BOX 120308	NASHVILLE, TN 37212
BURCHAM, TIM	BASEBALL	10233 96TH AVE	EDMONTON, ALB TK5 0A5 CANADA
BURDEAU, GEORGE	TV DIRECTOR	12330 OSBORNE #34	HANSEN HILLS, CA 91331
BURDEN, JOHN	BASEBALL SCOUT	POST OFFICE BOX 4100	SEATTLE, WA 98104
BURDETTE, LOU	BASEBALL	2019 BENEVA RD	SARASOTA, FL 34232

BURDICK, QUENTIN N	U S SENATOR	657 2ND AVE N, ROOM 266	FARGO, ND 58102
BURDITT, GEORGE	TV WRITER-PRODUCER	1009 E WALNUT AVE	BURBANK, CA 91501
BURDITT, JOYCE	TV WRITER	1009 E WALNUT AVE	BURBANK, CA 91501
BURDON, ERIC	SINGER-SONGWRITER	3575 W CAHUENGA BLVD #435	LOS ANGELES, CA 90068
BUREAU, MARC	HOCKEY	NORTH STARS, 7901 CEDAR AVE S	BLOOMINGTON, MN 55425
BURGE, GREGG	ACTOR	420 MADISON AVE #1400	NEW YORK, NY 10017
BURGE, STUART	FILM-TV DIRECTOR	HARRIET CRUICKSHANK MGMT	
		97 OLD S LAMBETH RD	LONDON SW8 ENGLAND
BURGER, JUSTICE WARREN	JUDGE	3111 N ROCHESTER ST	ARLINGTON, VA 22213
BURGER, WARREN E	SUPREME COURT JUDGE	1 1ST ST, NE	WASHINGTON, DC 20543
BURGESS, ANTHONY	ACTOR	44 RUE GRIMALDI	MONTE CARLO MONACO
BURGESS, BOBBY	ACTOR-DANCER	7752 CHANDELLE PL	LOS ANGELES, CA 90046
BURGESS, CHRISTIAN	ACTOR	33 GASTEIN RD	LONDON W6 8LT ENGLAND
BURGESS, DICK	COMEDIAN	CEE, 193 KONHAUS RD	MECHANICSBURG, PA 17055
BURGESS, KURT	BASEBALL	POST OFFICE BOX 4525	MACON, GA 31208
BURGESS, ROBERT	BASEBALL EXECUTIVE	POST OFFICE BOX 594	WELLAND, ONT L3B 5R3 CANADA
BURGESS, TOMMY	BASEBALL-INSTRUCTOR	POST OFFICE BOX 419969	KANSAS CITY, MO 64141
BURGESS, VIVIENNE	ACTRESS	MORGAN, 1 OLD COMPTON ST	LONDON W1V 5PH ENGLAND
BURGESS, WILMA	SINGER	POST OFFICE BOX DRAWER #1	MADISON, TN 37203
BURGGRAF, PAUL S	DIRECTOR	220 E 54TH ST #6-C	NEW YORK, NY 10022
BURGHOFF, GARY	ACTOR	POST OFFICE BOX 33018-315	SAINT PETERSBURG, FL 33733
BURGON, GEOFFREY	COMPOSER	HEATH, PARAMOUNT HOUSE	
		162-170 WARDOUR ST	LONDON W1V 3AT ENGLAND
BURGOS, CARLOS	BASEBALL	POST OFFICE BOX 464	APPLETON, WI 54912
BURGOS, PACO	BASEBALL	800 HOME RUN LN	MEMPHIS, TN 38104
BURGUILLOS, CARLOS	BASEBALL	POST OFFICE BOX 64939	FAYETTEVILLE, NC 28306
BURKE, CHRIS	ACTOR	9200 SUNSET BLVD #625	LOS ANGELES, CA 90069
BURKE, DAVE	COMPOSER	8211 BOBBYBOYAR AVE	CANOGA PARK, CA 91304
BURKE, DAVID J	TV PRODUCER	CAA, 9830 WILSHIRE BLVD	BEVERLY HILLS, CA 90212
BURKE, DAVID W	TV EXECUTIVE	ABC-TV, 7 W 66TH ST	NEW YORK, NY 10023
BURKE, DELTA	ACTRESS	1290 INVERNESS	PASADENA, CA 91011
BURKE, FRENCHIE	FIDDLER	POST OFFICE BOX 1616	BOERNE, TX 78006
BURKE, GREGORY	ACTOR	CBS-TV, "THE GUIDING LIGHT"	
		222 E 44TH ST	NEW YORK, NY 10017
BURKE, JERRY	TV PRODUCER	30 ROCKEFELLER PLAZA #1169	NEW YORK, NY 10020
BURKE, JOE	BASEBALL EXECUTIVE	POST OFFICE BOX 419969	KANSAS CITY, MO 64141
BURKE, JOHNNY	SINGER	PT & M MANAGEMENT	
		2464 BRASILIA CIR	MISS, ONT L5N 2G1 CANADA
BURKE, JOSEPH	ACTOR	10000 RIVERSIDE DR #6	TOLUCA LAKE, CA 91602
BURKE, MAGGIE	ACTRESS	CBS-TV, "AS THE WORLD TURNS"	
		524 W 57TH ST #5330	NEW YORK, NY 10019
BURKE, ROBERT	ACTOR	10100 SANTA MONICA BLVD #1600	LOS ANGELES, CA 90067
BURKE, SOLOMON	SINGER	CASSIDY, 417 MARAWOOD DR	WOODSTOCK, IL 60098
BURKE, TIM	BASEBALL	METS, 126TH ST & ROOSEVELT AVE	FLUSHING, NY 11368
BURKERT, GEORGE	BASEBALL EXECUTIVE	POST OFFICE BOX 1718	NEW BRITAIN, CT 06050
BURKETT, CHRIS	FOOTBALL	N Y JETS, 1000 FULTON AVE	HEMPSTEAD, NY 11550
BURKETT, JOHN	BASEBALL	S F GIANTS, CANDLESTICK PARK	SAN FRANICSCO, CA 94124
BURKHART, JEFF C	SCREENWRITER	ICM, 8899 BEVERLY BLVD	LOS ANGELES, CA 90048
BURKHART, JOELY	SINGER	SHOWTIME, 120 N SPRINGFIELD	BOLIVAR, MO 65613
BURKLEY, DENNIS	ACTOR	5145 COSTELLO AVE	SHERMAN OAKS, CA 91423
BURKLEY, H LLOYD	DIRECTOR	121 BARTRAM RD	MARLTON, NJ 08053
BURKS, ELLIS	BASEBALL	FENWAY PARK, 4 YAWKEY WY	BOSTON, MA 02215
BURLESON, CAL	BASEBALL EXECUTIVE	1501 W 16TH ST	INDIANAPOLIS, IN 46202
BURLESON, JOE	BASEBALL UMPIRE	2101 E BROADWAY #35	TEMPE, AZ 85282
BURLESON, RICK	BASEBALL-COACH	FENWAY PARK, 4 YAWKEY WY	BOSTON, MA 02215
BURLESON, TOM	BASKETBALL	GENERAL DELIVERY	NEWLAND, NC 28657
BURLINGAME, BEN	BASEBALL	POST OFFICE BOX 4488	WINSTON-SALEM, NC 27115
BURLINGAME, DENNIS	BASEBALL	POST OFFICE BOX 16683	GREENVILLE, SC 29606
BURLISON, HARVEY	SINGER	POST OFFICE BOX 2063	JONESBORO, AR 72402
BURMEISTER, DOUGLAS	ACTOR	124 W 71ST ST	NEW YORK, NY 10023
BURMESTER, BRUCE	TV DIRECTOR	19618 WEEBURN LN	TARZANA, CA 91356
BURN, JONATHAN	ACTOR	FLAT 2, 69 CHIPPENHAM RD	LONDON N9 ENGLAND
BURNETT, BOBBY	COMEDIAN	CEE, 193 KONHAUS RD	MECHANICSBURG, PA 17055
BURNETT, CAROL	ACTRESS	POST OFFICE BOX 1298	SOUTH PASADENA, CA 91031
BURNETT, JIM	CARTOONIST	KING FEATURES, 216 E 45TH ST	NEW YORK, NY 10017
BURNETT, NANCY	ACTRESS	1800 N VINE ST #120	LOS ANGELES, CA 90028
BURNETT, ROB	FOOTBALL	BROWNS, 80 1ST ST	BEREA, OH 44017
BURNETT, ROGER	BASEBALL	POST OFFICE BOX 2148	WOODBRIDGE, VA 22193
BURNETT, T-BONE	SINGER-SONGWRITER	211 20TH ST	SANTA MONICA, CA 90402
BURNETT, WHITNEY	CASTING DIRECTOR	251 W 89TH ST #11-E	NEW YORK, NY 10024
BURNETTE, OLIVIA	ACTRESS	10100 SANTA MONICA BLVD #1600	LOS ANGELES, CA 90067
BURNETTE, ROCKY	SINGER	21009 VALERIO	CANOGA PARK, CA 91303
BURNHAM, EDWARD	TV WRITER	1240 YALE ST	SANTA MONICA, CA 90404
BURNHAM, MALIN	BASEBALL EXECUTIVE	POST OFFICE BOX 2000	SAN DIEGO, CA 92112
BURNHAM, STEPHEN C	SCREENWRITER	729 1/2 N FORMOSA AVE	LOS ANGELES, CA 90046
BURNING SPEAR	RHYTHM & BLUES GROUP	FAST LANE, 4590 MAC ARTHUR BL	WASHINGTON, DC 20007
BURNITZ, JEROMY	BASEBALL	POST OFFICE BOX 1211	NORFOLK, VA 23502
BURNS, ALAN	FILM DIRECTOR	350 WASHINGTON ST #2-B	HEMPSTEAD, NY 11550
BURNS, ALLAN P	WRI-DIR-PROD	1660 MANDEVILLE CANYON BLVD	LOS ANGELES, CA 90049
BURNS, BONNIE	DIRECTOR-PRODUCER	10523 MARS LN	LOS ANGELES, CA 90077
BURNS, BRENDAN	ACTOR	12749 HART ST	NORTH HOLLYWOOD, CA 91605
BURNS, CONRAD	U S SENATOR	575 SUNSET BLVD #101	KALISPELL, MT 59901
BURNS, CONRAD	U S SENATOR	2708 1ST AVE N	BILLINGS, MT 59101
BURNS, EILEEN	ACTRESS	400 W 43RD ST	NEW YORK, NY 10036
BURNS, GEORGE	ACTOR-COMEDIAN	720 N MAPLE DR	BEVERLY HILLS, CA 90210

BURNS, J J	BASEBALL	POST OFFICE BOX 20849	CHARLESTON, SC	29413
BURNS, JACK	ACTOR-COMEDIAN	8955 BEVERLY BLVD	LOS ANGELES, CA	90048
BURNS, JACK	FOOTBALL COACH	POST OFFICE BOX 17247 (DULLES)	WASHINGTON, DC	20041
BURNS, JERE, II	ACTOR	5513 OAKEN CT	AGOURA HILLS, CA	91301
BURNS, JERRY	FOOTBALL COACH	VIKINGS, 9520 VIKING DR	EDEN PRAIRIE, MN	55344
BURNS, JOE A	WRITER-PRODUCER	1155 N BRAND BLVD #802	GLENDALE, CA	91202
BURNS, JOHN F	PRODUCER	30010 ANDROMEDA LN	MALIBU, CA	90265
BURNS, JUDY A	WRITER	SHAPIRO, 8827 BEVERLY BLVD	LOS ANGELES, CA	90048
BURNS, KEITH	WRITER-DIRECTOR	193 N ALISO ST	VENTURA, CA	93001
BURNS, LINDA AMIEL	ACTRESS	450 W 42ND ST #2-E	NEW YORK, NY	10036
BURNS, MARK	ACTOR	44 TEMPERLEY RD	LONDON SW12	ENGLAND
BURNS, MIKE	BASEBALL	POST OFFICE BOX 422229	KISSIMMEE, FL	34742
BURNS, RALPH J	COMPOSER-CONDUCTOR	3815 W OLIVE AVE #201	BRUBANK, CA	91505
BURNS, ROBERT LEWIS	MUSIC ARRANGER	5001 MC LENDON DR	ANTIOCH, TN	37013
BURNS, STAN	TV WRITER	SHAPIRO, 8827 BEVERLY BLVD	LOS ANGELES, CA	90048
BURNS, TED	BASEBALL EXECUTIVE	POST OFFICE BOX 3449	SCRANTON, PA	18505
BURNS, TIMOTHY	TV WRITER	2077 N BEVERLY GLEN BLVD	LOS ANGELES, CA	90077
BURNS, TODD	BASEBALL	POST OFFICE BOX 75089	OKLAHOMA CITY, OK	73147
BURNS, WARREN O	COMPOSER	11714 TERRABELLA ST	LAKE VIEW TERRACE, CA	91342
BURNS, WILFRED	COMPOSER-CONDUCTOR	RONDO, LIME GROVE, WEST CLANDON	SURREY	ENGLAND
BURR, COURTNEY	THEATER PRODUCER	5 TUDOR CITY PL	NEW YORK, NY	10017
BURR, ELIZABETH	ACTRESS	ATKINS, 303 S CRESCENT HEIGHTS	LOS ANGELES, CA	90048
BURR, FRITZI	ACTRESS	1752 PREUSS RD	LOS ANGELES, CA	90035
BURR, GARY	SINGER	217 E 86TH ST #384	NEW YORK, NY	10028
BURR, LONNIE	ACTOR-WRITER	POST OFFICE BOX 69590	LOS ANGELES, CA	90069
BURR, OSCAR	SINGER	POST OFFICE BOX 25371	CHARLOTTE, NC	28212
BURR, RAYMOND	ACTOR-DIRECTOR	POST OFFICE BOX 678	GEYSERVILLE, CA	95441
BURR, ROBERT	ACTOR	OSCARD, 24 W 40TH ST, 17TH FL	NEW YORK, NY	10011
BURR, SHAWN	HOCKEY	RED WINGS, 600 CIVIC CENTER DR	DETROIT, MI	48226
BURR, WALTER S	DIRECTOR	11632 VENTURA BLVD #203	STUDIO CITY, CA	91604
BURRAGE, CHEF DENNIS	EXECUTIVE CHEF	L'ERMITAGE, 9291 BURTON WY	BEVERLY HILLS, CA	90210
BURRELL, GINA EHRLICH	ACTRESS	8927 HOLLY PL	LOS ANGELES, CA	90046
BURRELL, JAN	ACTRESS	6565 SUNSET BLVD #310	HOLLYWOOD, CA	90068
BURRELL, KENNY	GUITARIST	KEANE, 49 E 49TH ST	NEW YORK, NY	10128
BURRELL, KEVIN	BASEBALL	POST OFFICE BOX 3665	OMAHA, NE	68103
BURRELL, MARYEDITH	ACTRESS-WRITER	SMITH, 121 N SAN VICENTE BLVD	BEVERLY HILLS, CA	90211
BURRELL, PETER JOHN	WRITER-PRODUCER	11234 AQUA VISTA ST	NORTH HOLLYWOOD, CA	91602
BURRELL, RUSTY	COURT BAILIFF	RALPH EDWARDS PRODUCTIONS		
		"THE PEOPLE'S COURT"		
		1717 N HIGHLAND AVE, 10TH FLOOR	HOLLYWOOD, CA	90028
BURRELLE, ELIZABETH	ACTRESS	12456 VENTURA BLVD #1	STUDIO CITY, CA	91604
BURRIDGE, RANDY	HOCKEY	BRUINS, 150 CAUSEWAY ST	BOSTON, MA	02114
BURRILL, TIMOTHY	FILM PRODUCER	19 CRANBURY RD	LONDON SW6 2NS	ENGLAND
BURRIS, RAY	BASEBALL-COACH	BREWERS, 201 S 46TH ST	MILWAUKEE, WI	53214
BURRIS, ROWLAND W	ATTORNEY GENERAL	STATE HOUSE BUILDING	SPRINGFIELD, IL	62706
BURROUGHS, BONNIE	ACTRESS	STONE MANNERS, 9113 SUNSET BL	LOS ANGELES, CA	90069
BURROUGHS, JEFF	BASEBALL	6155 LAGUNA CT	LONG BEACH, CA	90803
BURROWS, JAMES	WRITER-PRODUCER	701 N MAPLE DR	BEVERLY HILLS, CA	90210
BURROWS, TERRY	BASEBALL	POST OFFICE BOX 3609	PORT CHARLOTTE, FL	33949
BURROWS, THOMAS	DIRECTOR	5637 OCEAN BLVD	LA CANADA, CA	91011
BURRUD, BILL	FILM PRODUCER	17045 S PACIFIC ST	SUNSET BEACH, CA	90742
BURRUSS, LLOYD	FOOTBALL	CHIEFS, 1 ARROWHEAD DR	KANSAS CITY, MO	64129
BURSKEY, ALLAN	COMEDIAN	ICM, 8899 BEVERLY BLVD	LOS ANGELES, CA	90048
BURSON, CHARLES	ATTORNEY GENERAL	STATE CAPITOL BUILDING	NASHVILLE, TN	37243
BURSTEIN, FRED	ACTOR-DIRECTOR	5122 QUAKERTOWN AVE	WOODLAND HILLS, CA	91364
BURSTEIN, MARC	DIRECTOR	1111 ARLINGTON BLVD	ARLINGTON, VA	22209
BURSTYN, ELLEN	ACTRESS	FERRY HOUSE, BOX 17		
		WASHINGTON SPRING RD		
		SNEDENS LANDING	PALISADES, NY	10964
BURT, ADAM	HOCKEY	WHALERS, 1 CIVIC CENTER PLAZA	HARTFORD, CT	06103
BURT, ANDREW	ACTOR	LONDON MGT, 235-241 REGENT ST	LONDON W1R 4PH	ENGLAND
BURT, CHRIS	DIRECTOR-PRODUCER	46 GRANGE RD	LONDON W4 4DD	ENGLAND
BURT, RODGER	ACTOR	L A TALENT, 8335 SUNSET BLVD	LOS ANGELES, CA	90069
BURTIS, JANET MARIA	ACTRESS	310 GREENWICH ST #38-K	NEW YORK, NY	10013
BURTNETT, LEON	FOOTBALL COACH	POST OFFICE BOX 535000	INDIANPOLIS, IN	46253
BURTNICK, GLEN	SINGER-COMPOSER	E S "BUD" PRAGER MANAGEMENT		
		1790 BROADWAY, PENTHOUSE	NEW YORK, NY	10019
BURTON, AL	WRI-PROD-COMP-EXEC	2300 COLDWATER CANYON DR	BEVERLY HILLS, CA	90210
BURTON, BOB	BASEBALL TRAINER	POST OFFICE BOX 7845	COLUMBIA, SC	29202
BURTON, BRANDIE	GOLFER	2750 VOLUSA AVE #B	DAYTON BEACH, FL	32114
BURTON, CHRIS	BASEBALL	POST OFFICE BOX 16683	GREENVILLE, SC	29606
BURTON, DAN	U S CONGRESSMAN	120 CANNON HOUSE OFFICE BLDG	WASHINGTON, DC	20515
BURTON, DARREN	BASEBALL	300 STADIUM WY	DAVENPORT, FL	33837
BURTON, GARY, QUARTET	JAZZ QUARTET	KURLAND, 173 BRIGHTON AVE	BOSTON, MA	02134
BURTON, GEORGINA	CHOREOGRAPHER	35 STEWART PL #404	MOUNT KISCO, NY	10549
BURTON, HUMPHREY M	DIRECTOR	123 OAKWOOD CT	LONDON W14 8LA	ENGLAND
BURTON, JAY	SCREENWRITER	8955 BEVERLY BLVD	WEST HOLLYWOOD, CA	90048
BURTON, JIM	AUTHOR-BASEBALL	121 CEDAR LN	TEANECK, NJ	07666
BURTON, KATE	ACTRESS	9004 ASHCROFT AVE	LOS ANGELES, CA	90048
BURTON, LEVAR	ACTOR	13601 VENTURA BLVD #209	SHERMAN OAKS, CA	91423
BURTON, MIKE	BASEBALL	POST OFFICE BOX 3609	PORT CHARLOTTE, FL	33949
BURTON, NORMAN	ACTOR	3641 MEADVILLE DR	SHERMAN OAKS, CA	91403
BURTON, PHILIP, JR	WRITER-PRODUCER	CBS-TV, 524 W 57TH ST	NEW YORK, NY	10019
BURTON, SHELLY	SCREENWRITER	8955 BEVERLY BLVD	WEST HOLLYWOOD, CA	90048
BURTON, STEVE	ACTOR	4814 LEMORE AVE	SHERMAN OAKS, CA	91423

Name	Occupation	Address	City	Code
BURTON, STEVE	BASEBALL	POST OFFICE BOX 309	GASTONA, NC	28053
BURTON, TIMOTHY W	FILM DIRECTOR	DGA, 7920 SUNSET BLVD, 6TH FL	LOS ANGELES, CA	90046
BURTON, WARREN	ACTOR	SCHUMER-OUBRE, 1697 BROADWAY	NEW YORK, NY	10019
BURTON, WENDELL	ACTOR	6526 COSTELLO DR	VAN NUYS, CA	91401
BURTON, WILLIE	BASKETBALL	MIAMI HEAT, THE MIAMI ARENA	MIAMI, FL	33136
BURTT, DENNIS	BASEBALL COACH	14100 SIX MILE CYPRESS PKWY	FORT MYERS, FL	33912
BURTT, J DOUGLAS	AUTHOR	400 BUTTERFLY DR	IDAHO FALLS, ID	83401
BURUM, STEPHEN H	CINEMATOGRAPHER	POST OFFICE BOX 1116	PACIFIC PALISADES, CA	90272
BUSBY, MIKE	BASEBALL	POST OFFICE BOX 3783	SAVANNAH, GA	31414
BUSBY, ROBIN	FILM EXECUTIVE	PINEWOOD STUDIOS, IVER HEATH	IVER, BUCKS SLO ONH	ENGLAND
BUSBY, STEVE	BASEBALL-ANNOUNCER	POST OFFICE BOX 90111	ARLINGTON, TX	76004
BUSBY, WAYNE	BASEBALL	POST OFFICE BOX 360007	BIRMINGHAM, AL	35236
BUSCAGLIA, DR LEO	AUTHOR-COLUMNIST	N Y TIMES SYN, 130 5TH AVE	NEW YORK, NY	10011
BUSCAINO, STEVE	CREATURE COPIER	16666 ADDISON ST	ENCINO, CA	91436
BUSCH, AUGUST A, III	BASEBALL EXECUTIVE	250 STADIUM PLAZA	ST LOUIS, MO	63102
BUSCH, COREY	BASEBALL EXECUTIVE	S F GIANTS, CANDLESTICK PARK	SAN FRANICSCO, CA	94124
BUSCH, MIKE	BASEBALL	POST OFFICE BOX 28268	SAN ANTONIO, TX	78228
BUSEY, GARY	ACTOR-SINGER	2914 SEARIDGE ST	MALIBU, CA	90265
BUSFIELD, TIMOTHY	ACTOR	2416 "G" ST #D	SACRAMENTO, CA	95816
BUSH, BARBARA	ACTRESS	9200 SUNSET BLVD #710	LOS ANGELES, CA	90069
BUSH, BARBARA	FIRST LADY	1600 PENNSYLANIA AVE, NW	WASHINGTON, DC	20500
BUSH, BLAIR	FOOTBALL	PACKERS, 1265 LOMBARDI AVE	GREEN BAY, WI	54307
BUSH, CHUCK	BASEBALL	POST OFFICE BOX 8550	STOCKTON, CA	95208
BUSH, DICK	CINEMATOGRAPHER	FLAT 16, 8 GRAND PARADE		
		PLYMOUTH	DEVON PL1 3DF	ENGLAND
BUSH, GEORGE	U S PRESIDENT	1600 PENNSYLANIA AVE, NW	WASHINGTON, DC	20500
BUSH, GEORGE W	BASEBALL EXECUTIVE	POST OFFICE BOX 90111	ARLINGTON, TX	76004
BUSH, GRAND L	ACTOR	1917 W JEFFERSON BLVD	LOS ANGELES, CA	90018
BUSH, HOMER	BASEBALL	POST OFFICE BOX 20849	CHARLESTON, SC	29413
BUSH, JAMES	ACTOR	3270 LAUREL CANYON BLVD	STUDIO CITY, CA	91604
BUSH, JOHNNY	SINGER-SONGWRITER	5420 HOLLYHOCK ST	SAN ANTONIO, TX	78240
BUSH, KATE	SINGER-SONGWRITER	20 MANCHESTER SQ	LONDON W1	ENGLAND
BUSH, NORMAN	ACTOR	311 E 23RD ST	NEW YORK, NY	10011
BUSH, OWEN	ACTOR	POST OFFICE BOX 69590	LOS ANGELES, CA	90069
BUSH, RANDY	BASEBALL	TWINS, 501 CHICAGO AVE S	MINNEAPOLIS, MN	55415
BUSH, REBECCAH	ACTRESS	8271 MELROSE AVE #110	LOS ANGELES, CA	90046
BUSH, STAN	SINGER	ICM, 40 W 57TH ST	NEW YORK, NY	10019
BUSH, WILLIAM	ACTOR	400 W 43RD ST #31-T	NEW YORK, NY	10036
BUSHELMAN, JOHN	FILM DIRECTOR	11972 SUNSHINE TERRACE DR	STUDIO CITY, CA	91604
BUSHING, CHRIS	BASEBALL	POST OFFICE BOX 15050	READING, PA	19612
BUSHNELL, WILLIAM	WRITER-DIRECTOR	2751 PELHAM PL	LOS ANGELES, CA	90068
BUSHWACKERS, THE	WRESTLING TAG TEAM	POST OFFICE BOX 3859	STAMFORD, CT	06905
BUSHWHACK	C & W GROUP	PELLETIER, 36 MARTIN RD	AMESBURY, MA	01913
BUSIA, AKOSUA	ACTRESS	ATHLETES & ARTISTS, 421 7TH AVE	NEW YORK, NY	10001
BUSINO, ORLANDO	CARTOONIST	12 SHADOW HILL RD	RIDGEFIELD, CT	06877
BUSKAS, ROD	HOCKEY	POST OFFICE BOX 17013	INGLEWOOD, CA	90308
BUSS, DR JERRY	BASKETBALL EXECUTIVE	POST OFFICE BOX 10	INGLEWOOD, CA	90306
BUSSA, TODD	BASEBALL	POST OFFICE BOX 64939	FAYETTEVILLE, NC	28306
BUSSARD, STEVEN W	WRITER	10606 KINNARD AVE	LOS ANGELES, CA	90024
BUSTABAD, JUAN	BASEBALL COACH	POST OFFICE BOX 483	YAKIMA, WA	98907
BUSTAMANTE, ALBERT G	U S CONGRESSMAN	FEDERAL BUILDING, ROOM B-146		
		727 E DURANGO ST	SAN ANTONIO, TX	78206
BUSTAMANTE, MELODY	POET	6724 HESPERIA AVE	RESEDA, CA	91355
BUSTANY, DON	RADIO WRITER-PRODUCER	3456 BEN LOMOND PL	LOS ANGELES, CA	90027
BUSTILLOS, ALBERT	BASEBALL	POST OFFICE BOX 28268	SAN ANTONIO, TX	78228
BUSY B	RAPPER-RAPWRITER	FAA, 1700 BROADWAY, 5TH FLOOR	NEW YORK, NY	10019
BUTCHER, ARTHUR	BASEBALL	POST OFFICE BOX 4370	SALINAS, CA	93912
BUTCHER, GARTH	HOCKEY	BLUES, 5700 OAKLAND AVE	SAINT LOUIS, MO	63110
BUTCHER, MIKE	BASEBALL	10233 96TH AVE	EDMONTON, ALB TK5 OA5	CANADA
BUTCHER, PAUL	FOOTBALL	RAMS, 2327 W LINCOLN BLVD	ANAHEIM, CA	92801
BUTCHER, REBECCA	ARTIST	5 CLEMENTINE CT #1-B	BALTIMORE, MD	21237
BUTCHER, STEPHEN	TV DIRECTOR	SEIFERT, 18 LADBROKE TERR	LONDON W11 3PG	ENGLAND
BUTCHER, TED	TV PRODUCER	ABC-TV, 4151 PROSPECT AVE	LOS ANGELES, CA	90027
BUTCHER AXIS, JON	SINGER-GUITARIST	ATI, 888 7TH AVE, 21ST FLOOR	NEW YORK, NY	10106
BUTERA, SAL	BASEBALL-MANAGER	POST OFFICE BOX 422229	KISSIMMEE, FL	34742
BUTKUS, DICK	ACTOR-FOOTBALL	280 S BEVERLY DR #400	BEVERLY HILLS, CA	90212
BUTLER, BILL	CINEMATOGRAPHER	POST OFFICE BOX 2230	HOLLYWOOD, CA	90078
BUTLER, BOBBY	FOOTBALL	FALCONS, SUWANEE RD AT I-85	SUWANEE, GA	30174
BUTLER, BRETT	BASEBALL	1000 ELYSIAN PARK DR	LOS ANGELES, CA	90012
BUTLER, DEAN	ACTOR	6220 ROGERTON DR	LOS ANGELES, CA	90068
BUTLER, GREG	BASKETBALL	CLIPPERS, 3939 S FIGUEROA ST	LOS ANGELES, CA	90037
BUTLER, JERRY	WRITER-PRODUCER	8955 BEVERLY BLVD	WEST HOLLYWOOD, CA	90048
BUTLER, JERRY "THE ICEMAN"	SINGER-SONGWRITER	200 INWOOD DR #510	WHEELING, IL	60090
BUTLER, JONATHAN	GUITARIST-COMPOSER	POST OFFICE BOX 421268	SAN FRANCISCO, CA	94142
BUTLER, KEVIN	FOOTBALL	BEARS, 250 N WASHINGTON RD	LAKE FOREST, IL	60045
BUTLER, LE ROY	FOOTBALL	PACKERS, 1265 LOMBARDI AVE	GREEN BAY, WI	54307
BUTLER, LORI	ACTRESS	NATHE, 8281 MELROSE AVE #200	LOS ANGELES, CA	90046
BUTLER, MICHAEL CHRISTOPHER	CINEMATOGRAPHER	14023 VALLEY VISTA BLVD	SHERMAN OAKS, CA	91423
BUTLER, MICHAEL P	SCREENWRITER	1650 WESTWOOD BLVD #201	LOS ANGELES, CA	90024
BUTLER, RICH	BASEBALL	POST OFFICE BOX 1110	MYRTLE BEACH, SC	29578
BUTLER, RICHARD E, JR	TV DIRECTOR	19447 ROSITA ST	TARZANA, CA	91356
BUTLER, ROB	BASEBALL	POST OFFICE BOX 957	DUNEDIN, FL	34697
BUTLER, ROBERT	TV DIRECTOR	650 CLUB VIEW	LOS ANGELES, CA	90024
BUTLER, SHEA E	TV WRITER	8955 BEVERLY BLVD	WEST HOLLYWOOD, CA	90048
BUTLER, WALTER	TV DIRECTOR	SCHOOL OF FILM & TELEVISION		

		MANCHESTER POLYTECHNIC	
		DIDSBURY	MANCHESTER ENGLAND
BUTLER, WILMER CABLE	DIRECTOR	DGA, 7920 SUNSET BLVD, 6TH FL	LOS ANGELES, CA 90046
BUTTERFIELD, BRIAN	BASEBALL MANAGER	5301 NW 12TH AVE	FORT LAUDERDALE, FL 33309
BUTTERFIELD, CHRIS	BASEBALL	POST OFFICE BOX 598	BINGHAMTON, NY 13902
BUTTERWORTH, ROBERT A	ATTORNEY GENERAL	STATE CAPITOL BUILDING	TALLAHASSEE, FL 32399
BUTTERWORTH, SHANE	ACTRESS	TIFFANY, 23125 PARK CONTESSA	CALABASAS PARK, CA 91302
BUTTERWORTH, SUE	FILM DIRECTOR	119 LINKFIELD RD, ISLEWORTH	MIDDLESEX TW7 6QW ENGLAND
BUTTERWORTH, TYLER	ACTOR	33 BLOEMFONTEIN AVE	LONDON W12 ENGLAND
BUTTERY, JOHN	FILM-TV PRODUCER	DINGLE RD, MIDDLETON	MANCHESTER ENGLAND
BUTTON, CHARLES D	COMPOSER	331 N CALIFORNIA ST	BURBANK, CA 91505
BUTTON, DICK	TV PRODUCER	250 W 57TH ST #1818	NEW YORK, NY 10107
BUTTONS, RED	ACTOR	778 TORTUOSO WY	LOS ANGELES, CA 90077
BUTTRAM, PAT	ACTOR	6430 VARIEL AVE #101	WOODLAND HILLS, CA 91367
BUTTREY, KENNETH	DRUMMER	POST OFFICE BOX 302	HENDERSONVILLE, TN 37075
BUTTS, MARION	FOOTBALL	POST OFFICE BOX 609609	SAN DIEGO, CA 92160
BUTTS, R DALE	COMPOSER-CONDUCTOR	10470 KINNARD 302	LOS ANGELES, CA 90024
BUTZ, BRYAN	BASEBALL TRAINER	POST OFFICE BOX 4525	MACON, GA 31208
BUXTON, FRANK	ACT-WRI-PROD	273 S WESTGATE AVE	LOS ANGELES, CA 90049
BUXTON, SARAH G	ACTRESS	STONE MANNERS, 9113 SUNSET BL	LOS ANGELES, CA 90069
BUXTON, SIMON	TV PRODUCER	THAMES, 149 TOTTENHAM COURT RD	LONDON W1 ENGLAND
BUYSE, EMILE J	FILM EXECUTIVE	1320 CARLA LN	BEVERLY HILLS, CA 90210
BUZARD, BRIAN	BASEBALL	POST OFFICE BOX 1886	COLUMBUS, GA 31902
BUZAS, JOSEPH . (NEW BRITAIN)	BASEBALL EXECUTIVE	POST OFFICE BOX 1718	NEW BRITAIN, CT 06050
BUZAS, JOSEPH . (PORTLAND)	BASEBALL EXECUTIVE	POST OFFICE BOX 1659	PORTLAND, OR 97207
BUZAS, PENNY	BASEBALL EXECUTIVE	POST OFFICE BOX 1659	PORTLAND, OR 97207
BUZAS-DRAHMIS, HILARY	BASEBALL EXECUTIVE	POST OFFICE BOX 1718	NEW BRITAIN, CT 06050
BUZBY, ZANE	ACTRESS-WRITER	4033 HOLLY KNOLL DR	LOS ANGELES, CA 90027
BUZZI, RUTH	ACTRESS	2309 MALAGA RD	LOS ANGELES, CA 90069
BYARS, KEITH	FOOTBALL	EAGLES, BROAD ST & PATTISON AVE	PHILADELPHIA, PA 19148
BYBEE, KLAIR	ACTOR	8250 LANKERSHIM BLVD #6-MAPLE	NORTH HOLLYWOOD, CA 91605
BYERS, BRENDA & NEIGHBORS FOUR	C & W GROUP	32500 CONCORD DR #252	MADISON HEIGHTS, MI 48071
BYERS, RANDY	BASEBALL	POST OFFICE BOX 304	BRIDGETON, NJ 08302
BYERS, WILLIAM	COMPOSER-CONDUCTOR	28822 BONIFACE DR	MALIBU, CA 90265
BYGRAVES, MAX	ACTOR	MAFFINI, 32 STAFFORD MANSIONS	
		STAFFORD PL	LONDON SW1E 6NL ENGLAND
BYLINGTON, JOHN	BASEBALL	POST OFFICE DRAWER 4797	EL PASO, TX 79914
BYLUND, GARY	HOCKEY	NASSAU VETS MEMORIAL COLISEUM	UNIONDALE, NY 11553
BYNER, EARNEST	FOOTBALL	POST OFFICE BOX 17247 (DULLES)	WASHINGTON, DC 20041
BYNER, JOHN	COMEDIAN-WRITER	475 S BEDFORD DR	BEVERLY HILLS, CA 90212
BYNOE, PETER C B	BASKETBALL EXECUTIVE	POST OFFICE BOX 4658	DENVER, CO 80204
BYRAM, STEPHEN	ARTIST-ILLUSTRATOR	CBS RECORDS, 51 W 52ND ST #1018	NEW YORK, NY 10019
BYRD, CHARLIE, TRIO	JAZZ TRIO	1136 PINEMONT PL #3-B	ANNAPOLIS, MD 21403
BYRD, DENNIS	FOOTBALL	N Y JETS, 1000 FULTON AVE	HEMPSTEAD, NY 11550
BYRD, DONALD & 125TH ST BAND	JAZZ GROUP	1501 BROADWAY #2009	NEW YORK, NY 10036
BYRD, GIL	FOOTBALL	POST OFFICE BOX 609609	SAN DIEGO, CA 92160
BYRD, JAMES	BASEBALL	POST OFFICE BOX 1718	NEW BRITAIN, CT 06050
BYRD, JOHN	FILM WRITER-DIRECTOR	61 ARTHUR RD, WIMBLEDON	LONDON SW19 ENGLAND
BYRD, JOSEPH	COMPOSER	13206 DEWEY ST	LOS ANGELES, CA 90066
BYRD, LEVON	ACTOR	2301 CARMONA AVE #111	LOS ANGELES, CA 90016
BYRD, PAUL	BASEBALL	2501 ALLEN AVE, SE	CANTON, OH 44707
BYRD, ROBERT C	U S SENATOR	500 QUARRIER ST #1019	CHARLESTON, WV 25301
BYRD, ROBERT J	ARTIST	409 WARWICK RD	HADDONFIELD, NJ 08033
BYRD, TOM	ACTOR	SMITH, 121 N SAN VICENTE BLVD	BEVERLY HILLS, CA 90211
BYRDE, EDYE	ACTRESS	647 E 227TH ST	BRONX, NY 10466
BYRDS, THE	ROCK & ROLL GROUP	DEAN, 612 HUMBOLDT ST	RENO, NV 89509
BYRGE, DUANE	FILM CRITIC	6715 SUNSET BLVD	LOS ANGELES, CA 90028
BYRNE, CLAYTON	BASEBALL	POST OFFICE BOX 418	SAINT CHARLES, IL 60174
BYRNE, DAVID	SINGER-SONHWRITER	7964 WILLOW GLEN RD	LOS ANGELES, CA 90046
BYRNE, GABRIEL	ACTOR	ICM, 388-396 OXFORD ST	LONDON W1 ENGLAND
BYRNE, JOHNNY	TV WRITER	SEIFERT, 18 LADBROKE TERR	LONDON W11 3PG ENGLAND
BYRNE, JOSEPH P	TV WRITER-PRODUCER	3210 OAKDELL LN	STUDIO CITY, CA 91604
BYRNE, JOSH	ACTOR	ABC-TV, 2040 AVE OF THE STARS	LOS ANGELES, CA 90067
BYRNE, MARTHA	ACTRESS	ICM, 40 W 57TH ST	NEW YORK, NY 10019
BYRNE, MARY	TV EXECUTIVE	30 W 60TH ST	NEW YORK, NY 10023
BYRNE, MICHAEL	ACTOR	CONWAY, 18-21 JERMYN ST	LONDON SW1 ENGLAND
BYRNES, BURKE	ACTOR	3500 W OLIVE AVE #1400	BURBANK, CA 91505
BYRNES, EDD "KOOKIE"	ACTOR	1201 1/2 CABRILLO AVE	VENICE, CA 90292
BYRNES, JAMES	TV WRITER	4820 MULHOLLAND DR	LOS ANGELES, CA 90046
BYRNES, JIM	ACTOR	CANNELL, 7083 HOLLYWOOD BLVD	HOLLYWOOD, CA 90028
BYRNES, MAUREEN	ACTRESS	837 VENICE BLVD	VENICE, CA 90291
BYRNS, ALLAN	ACTOR	11936 BURBANK BLVD #10	NORTH HOLLYWOOD, CA 91607
BYRON, BEVERLY	U S CONGRESSWOMAN	POST OFFICE BOX 3275	CUMBERLAND, MD 21504
BYRON, GARY	ACTOR	8075 W 3RD ST #550	LOS ANGELES, CA 90048
BYRON, JAY	ACTOR	ATKINS, 303 S CRESCENT HEIGHTS	LOS ANGELES, CA 90048
BYRON, JEFFREY	ACTOR	1419 S BENTLEY AVE	LOS ANGELES, CA 90025
BYRON, KATHLEEN	ACTRESS	6 KASSALA RD	LONDON SW11 ENGLAND
BYRON, MICHAEL	ACTOR	807 S CURSON AVE	LOS ANGELES, CA 90036
BYRUM, JOHN	FILM WRITER-DIRECTOR	7435 WOODROW WILSON DR	LOS ANGELES, CA 90046
BYWATERS, TOM SHELTON	TV DIRECTOR-PRODUCER	340 W 57TH ST	NEW YORK, NY 10019
BZDELIK, JEFF	BASKETBALL COACH	BULLETS, 1 HARRY S TRUMAN DR	LANDOVER, MD 20785

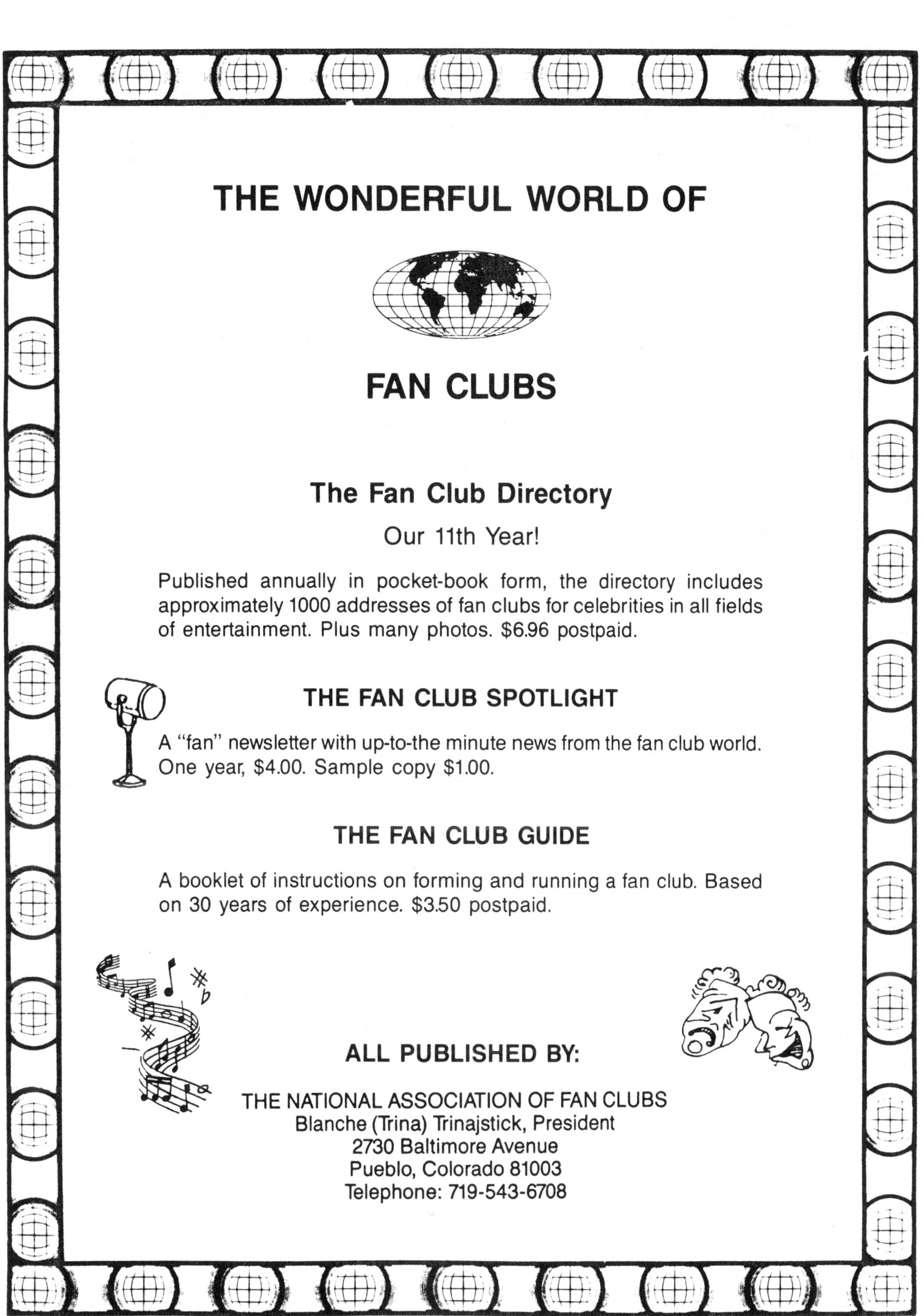
THE WONDERFUL WORLD OF
FAN CLUBS
The Fan Club Directory
Our 11th Year!
Published annually in pocket-book form, the directory includes approximately 1000 addresses of fan clubs for celebrities in all fields of entertainment. Plus many photos. $6.96 postpaid.
THE FAN CLUB SPOTLIGHT
A "fan" newsletter with up-to-the minute news from the fan club world. One year, $4.00. Sample copy $1.00.
THE FAN CLUB GUIDE
A booklet of instructions on forming and running a fan club. Based on 30 years of experience. $3.50 postpaid.
ALL PUBLISHED BY:
THE NATIONAL ASSOCIATION OF FAN CLUBS
Blanche (Trina) Trinajstick, President
2730 Baltimore Avenue
Pueblo, Colorado 81003
Telephone: 719-543-6708

C

CAAN, JAMES	ACTOR-DIRECTOR	1435 STONE CANYON RD	LOS ANGELES, CA	90077
CAAN, SHEILA	ACTRESS	A/A/A, 8457 MELROSE PL #200	LOS ANGELES, CA	90069
CABELL, ENOS	BASEBALL	1002 GOLDFINCH AVE	SUGAR LAND, TX	77478
CABRERA, BASILIO	BASEBALL	TIGERS, 89 WHARNCLIFFE RD N	LONDON, ONT N6H 2A7	CANADA
CABRERA, FRANCISCO	BASEBALL	POST OFFICE BOX 6667	RICHMOND, VA	23230
CABRERA, JOLBERT	BASEBALL	POLECATS, 608 N SLAPPEY BLVD	ALBANY, GA	31701
CABRERA, MIGUEL	BASEBALL	POST OFFICE BOX 1556	ASHEVILLE, NC	28802
CABRERA-RAMIREZ, PABLO A	TV DIR-PROD-CHOREO	210 W 89TH ST #10-A	NEW YORK, NY	10024
CACAVAS, JOHN H	COMPOSER-CONDUCTOR	524 N BEVERLY DR	BEVERLY HILLS, CA	90210
CACAVAS, JOHN MARK	GUITARIST	524 N BEVERLY DR	BEVERLY HILLS, CA	90210
CACCIATORE, FRANK	BASEBALL COACH	POST OFFICE BOX 422229	KISSIMMEE, FL	34742
CACCIOTTI, TONY	TV PRODUCER	616 N MAPLE DR	BEVERLY HILLS, CA	90210
CACERES, ED	BASEBALL	POST OFFICE DRAWER 4797	EL PASO, TX	79914
CACINI, RON	BASEBALL	POST OFFICE BOX 1556	ASHEVILLE, NC	28802
CADARET, GREG	BASEBALL	N Y YANKEES, YANKEE STADIUM	BRONX, NY	10451
CADELL, AVA	ACTRESS-MODEL	POST OFFICE BOX 3673	SANTA MONICA, CA	90403
CADELL, SIMON	ACTOR	MLR, 200 FULHAM RD	LONDON SW10 9PN	ENGLAND
CADEN, FRANK	TV DIRECTOR	80-02 192ND ST	JAMAICA ESTATES, NY	11423
CADIGAN, DAVE	FOOTBALL	N Y JETS, 1000 FULTON AVE	HEMPSTEAD, NY	11550
CADORETTE, MARY	ACTRESS	9000 SUNSET BLVD #801	LOS ANGELES, CA	90069
CADY, CARLY M	TV WRITER	233 S LA FAYETTE PARK PL	LOS ANGELES, CA	90057
CADY, FRANK	ACTOR	110 E 9TH ST #C-1005	LOS ANGELES, CA	90079
CADY, GARY	ACTOR	190 S CANON DR #201	BEVERLY HILLS, CA	90210
CADY, JAMES	DIRECTOR	40 25TH AVE	VEVICE, CA	90291
CAEN, HERB	COLUMNIST	SAN FRANCISCO CHRONICLE 901 MISSION ST	SAN FRANCISCO, CA	94119
CAESAR, HARRY	ACTOR	1112 W 41ST PL	LOS ANGELES, CA	90037
CAESAR, IRVING	LYRICIST-COMPOSER	HOTEL PARK SHERATION 870 7TH AVE	NEW YORK, NY	10019
CAESAR, SID	ACTOR-COMEDIAN	1910 LOMA VISTA DR	BEVERLY HILLS, CA	90210
CAFARELLA, ANTONIO E	COMPOSER	1450 FAIR OAKS BLVD	PASADENA, CA	91103
CAFFARO, CHERI	ACTRESS-WRITER	KOHNER, 9169 SUNSET BLVD	LOS ANGELES, CA	90069
CAFFEY, MICHAEL	DIRECTOR	2049 CENTURY PARK E #1320	LOS ANGELES, CA	90067
CAFFREY, STEPHEN	ACTOR	12338 CANTURA ST	STUDIO CITY, CA	91604
CAGE, JOHN	COMPOSER	101 W 18TH ST	NEW YORK, NY	10011
CAGE, MICHAEL	BASKETBALL	POST OFFICE BOX C-900911	SEATTLE, WA	98109
CAGE, NICOLAS	ACTOR	5647 TRYON RD	LOS ANGELES, CA	90068
CAGGIANO, JOHN JOSEPH	DIRECTOR	DGA, 7920 SUNSET BLVD, 6TH FL	LOS ANGELES, CA	90046
CAGLE, CHARLES	ACTOR	344 W 72ND ST	NEW YORK, NY	10023
CAGNEY, BILL	ACTOR-PRODUCER	2800 BAYSHORE DR	NEWPORT BEACH, CA	92663
CAGNEY, TIM	TV WRITER	7611 S ORANGE BLOSSOM TR #308	ORLANDO, FL	32809
CAGNEY, WILLIAM J	ACTOR	2800 BAYSHORE DR	NEWPORT BEACH, CA	92663
CAHALAN, TERENCE	WRITER	1122 HACIENDA PL	LOS ANGELES, CA	90069
CAHILL, BARRY	ACTOR	12711 HACIENDA DR	NORTH HOLLYWOOD, CA	91604
CAHILL, GERALD M	WRITER	7426 WISH AVE	VAN NUYS, CA	91406
CAHILL, JAMES	ACTOR	400 W 43RD ST #11-G	NEW YORK, NY	10036
CAHILL, TIM	BASEBALL EXECUTIVE	POST OFFICE BOX 3614	MARTINSVILLE, VA	24115
CAHLING, ANDREAS	BODYBUILDER	POST OFFICE BOX 929	VENICE, CA	90291
CAHN, CATHY	ACTRESS	6852 CAMROSE DR	LOS ANGELES, CA	90068
CAHN, DANN	TV DIRECTOR	856 LEONARD RD	LOS ANGELES, CA	90049
CAHN, SAMMY	LYRICIST-COMPOSER	704 N CANON DR	BEVERLY HILLS, CA	90210
CAILLOU, ALAN	ACTOR-TV WRITER	9165 SUNSET BLVD #202	LOS ANGELES, CA	90069
CAIN, CHRISTOPHER	FILM DIRECTOR	5901 CLOVER HEIGHTS	MALIBU, CA	90265
CAIN, JACK	BASEBALL EXECUTIVE	POST OFFICE BOX 6603	BEND, OR	97708
CAIN, JOE	FOOTBALL	SEAHAWKS, 11220 NE 53RD ST	KIRKLAND, WA	98033
CAIN, JOHN	BASEBALL TRAINER	POST OFFICE BOX 6748	ROCKFORD, IL	61125
CAIN, JOHN PAUL	GOLFER	PGA SENIORS, 112 T P C BLVD	PONTE VEDRA BEACH, FL	32082
CAIN, MARY	BASEBALL EXECUTIVE	POST OFFICE BOX 6603	BEND, OR	97708
CAIN, WILLIAM	ACTOR	484 W 43RD ST	NEW YORK, NY	10036
CAINE, HOWARD	ACTOR	6131 COLDWATER CANYON BLVD	NORTH HOLLYWOOD, CA	91606
CAINE, MARTI	COMEDIENNE	ICM, 388-396 OXFORD ST	LONDON W1	ENGLAND
CAINE, MICHAEL	ACTOR	RECTORY FARM HOUSE, NORTHSTROKE	OXFORDSHIRE	ENGLAND
CAINE, RICHARD	ACTOR	11846 VENTURA BLVD #100	STUDIO CITY, CA	91604
CAIRNCROSS, CAMERON	BASEBALL	POST OFFICE BOX 611	WATERLOO, IA	50704
CAIRNS, PAUL	ACTOR	9165 SUNSET BLVD #202	LOS ANGELES, CA	90069
CAIRO, SERGIO	BASEBALL	POST OFFICE BOX 230	HAGERSTOWN, MD	21740
CAJATI, MARIO L	COMPOSER-CONDUCTOR	7735 FLORENCE AVE	DOWNEY, CA	90240
CAKMIS, BILL	ACTOR	POST OFFICE BOX 480361	LOS ANGELES, CA	90048
CALA, JOSEPH MICHAEL	ACTOR	3890 CARPENTER AVE	STUDIO CITY, CA	91604
CALABRESE, PETER ROBERT	TV EXECUTIVE	ICM, 8899 BEVERLY BLVD	LOS ANGELES, CA	90048
CALAWAY, DAVE	BASEBALL SCOUT	REDS, 100 RIVERFRONT STADIUM	CINCINNATI, OH	45202
CALCAGNO, DAN	BASEBALL	POST OFFICE BOX 21727	SAN FRANCISCO, CA	95151
CALCAVECCHIA, MARK	GOLFER	POST OFFICE BOX 109601	PALM BCH GARDENS, FL	33418
CALDE, MARK A	WRITER	7405 OGELSBY AVE	LOS ANGELES, CA	90045
CALDER, DAVID	ACTOR	1 WINTERWELL RD	LONDON SW2 5TB	ENGLAND
CALDER, JOE	BASEBALL	POST OFFICE BOX 3746, HILL STA	AUGUSTA, GA	30904
CALDERON, IVAN	BASEBALL	EXPOS, 4545 DE COUBERTIN AVE	MONTREAL, QUE H1V 3P2	CANADA

CALDERWOOD, ROBERT M	COMPOSER-CONDUCTOR	12208 LOUISE AVE	GRANADA HILLS, CA 91344
CALDWELL, ADRIAN	BASKETBALL	POST OFFICE BOX 272349	HOUSTON, TX 77277
CALDWELL, BOBBY	SINGER-GUITARIST	1995 BROADWAY #501	NEW YORK, NY 10023
CALDWELL, BOBBY LEE & FRIENDS	SINGER-SONGWRITER	2914 BIG BEN	GARLAND, TX 75042
CALDWELL, DAVID	TV DIRECTOR	26934 HALIFAX PL	HAYWARD, CA 94542
CALDWELL, DAVID E	TV DIRECTOR	POST OFFICE BOX 585	CHESTER, CA 96020
CALDWELL, JANETTE	ACTRESS	8383 WILSHIRE BLVD #650	BEVERLY HILLS, CA 90211
CALDWELL, JOHNNY	CONDUCTOR	POST OFFICE BOX 60885	OKLAHOMA CITY, OK 73146
CALDWELL, RAVIN	FOOTBALL	POST OFFICE BOX 17247 (DULLES)	WASHINGTON, DC 20041
CALDWELL, STEPHEN P	TV DIRECTOR-PRODUCER	2285 BEACHWOOD DR	LOS ANGELES, CA 90068
CALDWELL, TAYLOR	AUTHORESS	IVANHOE LN	GREENWICH, CT 06830
CALE, J J	SINGER-GUITARIST	POST OFFICE BOX 210103	NASHVILLE, TN 37202
CALE, JOHN W	SINGER	POST OFFICE BOX 22635	NASHVILLE, TN 37202
CALF, ANTHONY	ACTOR	HAMMOND, GOLDEN HOUSE	
		29 GREAT PULTENEY ST	LONDON W1R 3DD ENGLAND
CALFA, DON	ACTOR	1520 N HAYWORTH AVE #10	LOS ANGELES, CA 90046
CALHOUN, GARY	BASEBALL MANAGER	1201 HYDE PARK BLVD	NIAGARA FALLS, NY 14301
CALHOUN, JEFF	BASEBALL	1212 PARK ST	MC COMB, MS 39648
CALHOUN, JOHN C	SINGER	KNIGHT, 1609 CONGRESS RD	EASTOVER, SC 29044
CALHOUN, RAY	BASEBALL	POST OFFICE BOX 28268	SAN ANTONIO, TX 78228
CALHOUN, ROBERT P	DIRECTOR	1501 BROADWAY #2600	NEW YORK, NY 10036
CALHOUN, RORY	ACTOR	11532 CHIQUITA ST	STUDIO CITY, CA 91604
CALI, JOSEPH	ACTOR	5033 CAMPO RD	WOODLAND HILLS, CA 91364
CALIFANO, ARTHUR	DIRECTOR	DGA, 110 W 57TH ST	NEW YORK, NY 10019
CALIFANO, GARY L	DIRECTOR	COOPER, 28 W 25TH ST	NEW YORK, NY 10010
CALIFANO, JOSEPH	POLITICIAN	1775 PENNSYLVANIA AVE, NW	WASHINGTON, DC 20006
CALIFANO, KEN	BASEBALL SCOUT	BREWERS, 201 S 46TH ST	MILWAUKEE, WI 53214
CALIGUIRE, DEAN	FOOTBALL	S F 49ERS, 4949 CENTENNIAL BL	SANTA CLARA, CA 95054
CALKINS, JOHNNY	ACTOR	5719 COLUMBUS AVE	VAN NUYS, CA 91411
CALL, ANTHONY	ACTOR	305 MADISON AVE #4419	NEW YORK, NY 10165
CALL, BRANDON	ACTOR	5918 VAN NUYS BLVD	VAN NUYS, CA 19401
CALL, KEVIN	FOOTBALL	POST OFFICE BOX 535000	INDIANPOLIS, IN 46253
CALL, THE	ROCK & ROLL GROUP	HEATON, 6858 LOS ALTOS PL	HOLLYWOOD, CA 90068
CALLAGHAN-DIAZ, SHAWN	SET DECORATOR	300 E 74TH ST #8-F	NEW YORK, NY 10021
CALLAHAN, CLAIRE	TV DIRECTOR-PRODUCER	190 WILMOT RD	NEW ROCHELLE, NY 10804
CALLAHAN, GEORGE E	WRITER	10437 ALMAYO AVE	LOS ANGELES, CA 90064
CALLAHAN, GREGORY	ACTOR	7080 HOLLYWOOD BLVD #704	HOLLYWOOD, CA 90028
CALLAHAN, JAMES	ACTOR	2125 21ST ST	SANTA MONICA, CA 90405
CALLAHAN, JOHN	ACTOR	342 N ALFRED ST	LOS ANGELES, CA 90048
CALLAHAN, LEE	ACTRESS	360 CENTRAL PARK W	NEW YORK, NY 10025
CALLAHAN, SONNY	U S CONGRESSMAN	2970 COTTAGE HILL RD #126	MOBILE, AL 36606
CALLAHAN, STEVE	BASEBALL	POST OFFICE BOX 2437	MODESTO, CA 95351
CALLAN, CECILE	ACTRESS	8730 SUNSET BLVD #480	LOS ANGELES, CA 90069
CALLAN, K	ACTRESS-AUTHORESS	4957 MATILIJA AVE	SHERMAN OAKS, CA 91423
CALLAN, MICHAEL	ACTOR	9300 WILSHIRE BLVD #410	BEVERLY HILLS, CA 90212
CALLAS, CHARLIE	COMEDIAN-ACTOR	POST OFFICE BOX 67-B-69	LOS ANGELES, CA 90067
CALLAWAY, NANCY LYNN	TV DIRECTOR	18 BRAYTON ST	ENGLEWOOD, NJ 07631
CALLEI-TREBEK, ELAINE	WRITER	2661 CARMAR DR	LOS ANGELES, CA 90046
CALLEN, CHRIS	ACTRESS	247 S BEVERLY DR #102	BEVERLY HILLS, CA 90210
CALLENDER, COLIN	TV PRODUCER	HBO, 1100 6TH AVE	NEW YORK, NY 10036
CALLENDER, GEORGE S	COMPOSER	8120 CANBY AVE #4	RESEDA, CA 91335
CALLEY, LT WILLIAM	MILITARY	V V VICKS JEWELRY STORE	
		CROSS COUNTRY PLAZA	COLUMBUS, GA 31906
CALLIHAN, C MICHAEL	LT GOVERNOR	STATE CAPITOL BUILDING	DENVER, CO 80203
CALLIHAN, CLAIR C	DIRECTOR	422 CENTRAL AVE	WILMETTE, IL 60091
CALLINAN, DICK	ACTOR	7720 SW 51ST AVE	MIAMI, FL 33143
CALLOW, SIMON	ACTOR	60 FINBOROUGH RD	LONDON SW10 ENGLAND
CALLOWAY, CAB	SINGER-COMPOSER	1040 KNOLLWOOD RD	WHITE PLAINS, NY 10603
CALLOWAY, CHRIS	FOOTBALL	STEELERS, 300 STADIUM CIR	PITTSBURGH, PA 15212
CALLOWAY, KIRK	ACTOR	13619 S BERENDO AVE	GARDENA, CA 90247
CALLOWAY, RICK	BASKETBALL	KINGS, 1 SPORTS PARKWAY	SACRAMENTO, CA 95834
CALMAN, JEFFREY	TV EXECUTIVE	LAUREL ENT, 928 BROADWAY	NEW YORK, NY 10010
CALVE, JEAN-FRANCOIS	ACTOR	1 RUE DE NAVARRE	PARIS 75010 FRANCE
CALVER, DAVE	ARTIST	271 MULBERRY ST	ROCHESTER, NY 14620
CALVERT, HENRY	ACTOR	19 COMMERCE ST	NEW YORK, NY 10014
CALVERT, LUCILE	ACTRESS	1 CHRISTOPHER ST	NEW YORK, NY 10014
CALVET, CORINNE	ACTRESS	BDP, 10637 BURBANK BLVD	NORTH HOLLYWOOD, CA 91601
CALVIN, JOHN	ACTOR	1794 WASHINGTON WY	VENICE, CA 90291
CALVIN, MACK	BASKETBALL COACH	BRADLEY CENTER, 1001 N 4TH ST	MILWAUKEE, WI 53203
CALVINO, WILLIE	BASEBALL SCOUT	POST OFFICE BOX 7575	PHILADELPHIA, PA 19101
CALZADO, JOHNNY	BASEBALL	POST OFFICE BOX 3783	SAVANNAH, GA 31414
CAMACHO, ERNIE	BASEBALL	746 SAINT REGIS	SALINAS, CA 93905
CAMACHO, HECTOR "MACHO"	BOXER	STAR ROUTE, BOX 113	CLEWISTON, FL 33440
CAMAISA, LILINDA	ACTRESS	6362 HOLLYWOOD BLVD #219	HOLLYWOOD, CA 90028
CAMARATA, SALVADOR "TOODIE"	COMPOSER-CONDUCTOR	12141 IREDELL ST	STUDIO CITY, CA 91604
CAMARILLO, RICH	FOOTBALL	POST OFFICE BOX 888	PHOENIX, AZ 85001
CAMBERN, DONN	TV DIRECTOR-FILM ED	11611 AMANDA DR	STUDIO CITY, CA 91604
CAMBOU, DON	WRITER	618 BOCCACCIO WY	VENICE, CA 90291
CAMBRELING, SYLVAIN	CONDUCTOR	ICM, 40 W 57TH ST	NEW YORK, NY 10019
CAMBRIA, CATHY	TV WRITER-DIRECTOR	REEVES ENT, 1697 BROADWAY	NEW YORK, NY 10019
CAMEO	SOUL GROUP	1422 W PEACHTREE ST #816, NW	ATLANTA, GA 30309
CAMERON, CANDACE	ACTRESS	POST OFFICE BOX 80515	CONYERS, GA 30208
CAMERON, CISSE	ACTRESS	POST OFFICE BOX 2012	MALIBU, CA 90265
CAMERON, DAVE	ACTOR	5720 DONNA AVE	TARZANA, CA 91356
CAMERON, DAVID O	ACTOR	2146 1/2 N BEACHWOOD DR	LOS ANGELES, CA 90068

CAMERON, DAVID SCOT	ACTOR	6533 HOLLYWOOD BLVD #201	HOLLYWOOD, CA	90028
CAMERON, DOUG	VIOLINIST	4046 DENNY AVE	STUDIO CITY, CA	91604
CAMERON, GAIL BRYANT	ACTRESS	5319 VICTORIA AVE	LOS ANGELES, CA	90043
CAMERON, JANE	ACTRESS	280 S BEVERLY DR #400	BEVERLY HILLS, CA	90212
CAMERON, JOANNA	ACTRESS-DIRECTOR	POST OFFICE BOX 1400	PEBBLE BEACH, CA	93953
CAMERON, JOHN	COMPOSER-CONDUCTOR	DAVID WILKINSON ASSOCIATES		
		115 HAZELBURY RD	LONDON SW6 2LX	ENGLAND
CAMERON, JOHN ALLAN	SINGER	9940 LOUGHEED HWY #330	BURNABY, BC V3J 1N3	CANADA
CAMERON, KIRK	ACTOR	UTA, 9560 WILSHIRE BL, 5TH FL	BEVERLY HILLS, CA	90212
CAMERON, PATRICK	ACTOR	11846 VENTURA BLVD #100	STUDIO CITY, CA	91604
CAMERON, STANTON	BASEBALL	POST OFFICE BOX 3169	FREDERICK, MD	21701
CAMERON, SUE	TALENT AGENT	POST OFFICE BOX 925	MALIBU, CA	90265
CAMEY, JOHN	FOOTBALL	POST OFFICE BOX 609609	SAN DIEGO, CA	92160
CAMHI, PATRICE	ACTRESS	ICM, 8899 BEVERLY BLVD	LOS ANGELES, CA	90048
CAMIEL, ERIC S	DIRECTOR	210 MIDDLE RIVER RD	DANBURY, CT	06810
CAMILLI, DOUG	BASEBALL-COACH	FENWAY PARK, 4 YAWKEY WY	BOSTON, MA	02215
CAMINITI, KEN	BASEBALL	POST OFFICE BOX 288	HOUSTON, TX	77001
CAMMANN, FREDERIC G	TV DIRECTOR	15 E 91ST ST	NEW YORK, NY	10028
CAMMELL, DONALD	WRITER-PRODUCER	151 S EL CAMINO DR	BEVERLY HILLS, CA	90212
CAMP, BILLY JOE	SECRETARY OF STATE	ALA STATE HOUSE, 11 S UNION ST	MONTGOMERY, AL	36130
CAMP, COLLEEN	ACTRESS	POST OFFICE BOX 5617	BEVERLY HILLS, CA	90213
CAMP, DAVE	U S CONGRESSMAN	135 ASHMAN ST	MIDLAND, MI	48640
CAMP, HAMILTON	ACTOR	205 S BEVERLY DR #210	BEVERLY HILLS, CA	90212
CAMP, JOANNE	ACTRESS	337 W 43RD ST #1-B	NEW YORK, NY	10036
CAMP, JOSEPH M	FILM DIRECTOR	DGA, 110 W 57TH ST	NEW YORK, NY	10019
CAMP, JOSEPH S, JR	WRITER-PRODUCER	2301 14TH ST #720	GULFPORT, MS	39567
CAMP, MARK E	MUSIC ARRANGER	1100 GRANVILLE RD #705	FRANKLIN, TN	37064
CAMPAGNA, DAVID	ACTOR	8450 DE LONGPRE AVE #16	LOS ANGELES, CA	90069
CAMPANELLA, FRANK	ACTOR	151 S EL CAMINO DR	BEVERLY HILLS, CA	90212
CAMPANELLA, JOSEPH	ACTOR	4647 ARCOLA AVE	NORTH HOLLYWOOD, CA	91602
CAMPANELLA, ROY, JR	WRITER-PRODUCER	8383 WILSHIRE BLVD #923	BEVERLY HILLS, CA	90211
CAMPANELLA, ROY, SR	BASEBALL	6213 CAPISTRANO AVE	WOODLAND HILLS, CA	91367
CAMPANERIS, BERT "CAMPY"	BASEBALL	POST OFFICE BOX 8283	SCOTTSDALE, AZ	85252
CAMPANIS, JIM	BASEBALL	POST OFFICE BOX 4756	JACKSONVILLE, FL	32201
CAMPBELL, ARCHIE	COMEDIAN-ACTOR	POST OFFICE BOX 189	BRENTWOOD, TN	37027
CAMPBELL, BEN N	U S CONGRESSMAN	835 2ND AVE #105	DURANGO, CO	81301
CAMPBELL, BILL	ACTOR	ICM, 8899 BEVERLY BLVD	LOS ANGELES, CA	90048
CAMPBELL, BILL	BASEBALL-COACH	2850 W 20TH AVE	DENVER, CO	80211
CAMPBELL, BONNIE	ATTORNEY GENERAL	STATE CAPITOL BUILDING	DES MOINES, IA	50319
CAMPBELL, BRUCE	ACTOR	9200 SUNSET BLVD #630	LOS ANGELES, CA	90069
CAMPBELL, BRUCE KERR	ACTOR	8228 SUNSET BLVD #311	LOS ANGELES, CA	90046
CAMPBELL, BRUCE V	COMPOSER	8322 TOPEKA DR	NORTHRIDGE, CA	91324
CAMPBELL, CARLOS	ACTOR	837 10TH ST #7	SANTA MONICA, CA	90403
CAMPBELL, CARROLL A, JR	GOVERNOR	POST OFFICE BOX 11369	COLUMBIA, SC	29211
CAMPBELL, CHERYL	ACTRESS	WHITEHALL, 125 GLOUCESTER RD	LONDON SW7 4TE	ENGLAND
CAMPBELL, CHIP	ACTOR	4370 TUJUNGA AVE #120	STUDIO CITY, CA	91604
CAMPBELL, CLIFTON	TV PRODUCER	CAA, 9830 WILSHIRE BLVD	BEVERLY HILLS, CA	90212
CAMPBELL, COLIN	ACTOR	3521 GRIFFITH PARK BLVD	LOS ANGELES, CA	90027
CAMPBELL, DARRIN	BASEBALL	CANADIANS, 4601 ONTARIO ST	VANCOUVER, BC V5V 3H4	CANADA
CAMPBELL, DAVE	BASEBALL-ANNOUNCER	9978 WALDGROVE PL	SAN DIEGO, CA	92131
CAMPBELL, DIRK	DIRECTOR-PRODUCER	3 PARLIAMENT HILL	LONDON NW3	ENGLAND
CAMPBELL, DONOVAN	BASEBALL	POST OFFICE BOX 12557	ST PETERSBURG, FL	33733
CAMPBELL, EARL	FOOTBALL	POST OFFICE BOX 7399	AUSTIN, TX	78713
CAMPBELL, ELDEN	BASKETBALL	POST OFFICE BOX 10	INGLEWOOD, CA	90306
CAMPBELL, GLEN	SING-ACT-COMP	5290 EXETER BLVD	PHOENIX, AZ	85018
CAMPBELL, J KENNETH	ACTOR	SMITH, 121 N SAN VICENTE BLVD	BEVERLY HILLS, CA	90211
CAMPBELL, JEFF	FOOTBALL	LIONS, 1200 FEATHERSTONE RD	PONTIAC, MI	48432
CAMPBELL, JIM	BASEBALL	800 HOME RUN LN	MEMPHIS, TN	38104
CAMPBELL, JIM	BASEBALL (CAT-EXEC)	1671 6TH ST	OROVILLE, CA	95965
CAMPBELL, JOE	BASEBALL SCOUT	1000 ELYSIAN PARK DR	LOS ANGELES, CA	90012
CAMPBELL, JULIA	ACTRESS	10100 SANTA MONICA BLVD #1600	LOS ANGELES, CA	90067
CAMPBELL, KEN	ACTOR-DIRECTOR	74 WATERMINT QUAY	LONDON N16	ENGLAND
CAMPBELL, KENNETH L	DIRECTOR-PRODUCER	3704 BARHAM BLVD #E-208	LOS ANGELES, CA	90068
CAMPBELL, KEVIN	BASEBALL	POST OFFICE BOX 11087	TACOMA, WA	98411
CAMPBELL, LOUISE	ACTRESS-SINGER	46 ROWAYTON AVE	ROWAYTON, CT	06853
CAMPBELL, MIKE	BASEBALL	POST OFFICE BOX 75089	OKLAHOMA CITY, OK	73147
CAMPBELL, MOLLY HARRIS	COSTUME DESIGNER	1066 STEARNS DR	LOS ANGELES, CA	90035
CAMPBELL, NICHOLAS	ACTOR	151 S EL CAMINO DR	BEVERLY HILLS, CA	90212
CAMPBELL, NORMAN	FILM DIRECTOR	20 GEORGE HENRY BLVD		
		WILLOWDALE	TORONTO, ONT M2J 1E2	CANADA
CAMPBELL, PAUL	BASEBALL-SCOUT	REDS, 100 RIVERFRONT STADIUM	CINCINNATI, OH	45202
CAMPBELL, SCOTT	BASEBALL	POST OFFICE BOX 3566	WEST PALM BEACH, FL	33402
CAMPBELL, TISHA	ACTRESS	9200 SUNSET BLVD #710	LOS ANGELES, CA	90069
CAMPBELL, TOM	U S CONGRESSMAN	599 N MATHILDA #105	SUNNYVALE, CA	94086
CAMPBELL, TONY	BASKETBALL	TIMBERWOLVES, 600 1ST AVE N	MINNEAPOLIS, MN	55403
CAMPBELL, WILLIAM J	ACTOR	21502 VELICATA ST	WOODLAND HILLS, CA	91364
CAMPEN, JAMES	FOOTBALL	PACKERS, 1265 LOMBARDI AVE	GREEN BAY, WI	54307
CAMPHUIS, RICHARD	ACTOR	4424 WOODMAN AVE #204	SHERMAN OAKS, CA	91423
CAMPION, DR HENRY	TV EXECUTIVE	BBC, BROADCASTING HOUSE	LONDON W1A 1AA	ENGLAND
CAMPO, DAVE	FOOTBALL COACH	COWBOYS, 1 COWBOYS PARKWAY	IRVING, TX	75063
CAMPO, FRANK P	COMPOSER	12336 MILBANK ST	STUDIO CITY, CA	91604
CAMPOS, CYNTHIA	TALENT AGENT	1015 GAYLEY AVE #300	LOS ANGELES, CA	90024
CAMPOS, VICTOR	ACTOR	POST OFFICE BOX 69590	LOS ANGELES, CA	90069
CAMPOS-GREENBERG, CYNTHIA	TALENT AGENT	151 S EL CAMINO DR	BEVERLY HILLS, CA	90212
CAMPUS, MICHAEL	FILM DIRECTOR	2121 KRESS ST	LOS ANGELES, CA	90046

CAMPUSANO, GENARO	BASEBALL	POST OFFICE BOX 842	SALEM, VA	24153
CAMPUSANO, SIL	BASEBALL	POST OFFICE BOX 3449	SCRANTON, PA	18505
CANADA, LINDA	DEPUTY SHERIFF	BROWARD COUNTY SHERIFF'S OFFICE		
		2600 SW 4TH ST	FORT LAUDERDALE, FL	33312
CANALE, GEORGE	BASEBALL	2850 W 20TH AVE	DENVER, CO	80211
CANALES, LAURA	SINGER	ALAMO TALENT, 217 ARDEN GROVE	SAN ANTONIO, TX	78215
CANARY, DAVID	ACTOR	698 W END AVE #1-B	NEW YORK, NY	10025
CANATE, WILLIE	BASEBALL	POST OFFICE BOX 1886	COLUMBUS, GA	31902
CANBY, VINCENT	FILM CRITIC	215 W 88TH ST	NEW YORK, NY	10024
CANCILLA, ELAINE	ACTRESS	232 W 23RD ST	NEW YORK, NY	10011
CANDAD, ROLANDO	BASEBALL	1090 N EUCLID AVE	SARASOTA, FL	34237
CANDAELE, CASEY	BASEBALL	POST OFFICE BOX 288	HOUSTON, TX	77001
CANDELARIA, JOHN	BASEBALL	1000 ELYSIAN PARK DR	LOS ANGELES, CA	90012
CANDIOTTI, TOM	BASEBALL	1000 ELYSIAN PARK DR	LOS ANGELES, CA	90012
CANDIOTTY, MARK	TALENT AGENT	CARROLL, 120 S VICTORY BL #104	BURBANK, CA	91502
CANDLER, BOBBIE	ACTRESS	FELBER, 2126 N CAHUENGA BLVD	LOS ANGELES, CA	90068
CANDOLI, PETER	ACTOR-TRUMPETER	12451 MULHOLLAND DR	BEVERLY HILLS, CA	90210
CANDY, JOHN	ACT-WRI-COMED	ICM, 8899 BEVERLY BLVD	LOS ANGELES, CA	90048
CANE, RIC	ACTOR	11687 WEDDINGTON ST	NORTH HOLLYWOOD, CA	91601
CANETTI, ELIAS	WRITER	FARRAR, 19 UNION SQ W	NEW YORK, NY	10003
CANFIELD, WILLIAM	CARTOONIST	143 WAYSIDE RD	TINTO FALLS, NJ	07724
CANGELOSI, JOHN	BASEBALL	POST OFFICE BOX 90111	ARLINGTON, TX	76004
CANIN, ETHAN	WRITER	HOUGHLIN, 215 PARK AVE S	NEW YORK, NY	10003
CANIPE, DAVID	GOLFER	POST OFFICE BOX 109601	PALM BCH GARDENS, FL	33418
CANNELL, STEPHEN J	TV WRITER-PRODUCER	7083 HOLLYWOOD BLVD	LOS ANGELES, CA	90028
CANNING, LISA	ACTRESS	8383 WILSHIRE BLVD #650	BEVERLY HILLS, CA	90211
CANNISTRACI, JAY	MAKE-UP ARTIST	1790 BROADWAY #130	NEW YORK, NY	10019
CANNON, ACE	SINGER	POST OFFICE BOX 912	CALHOUN CITY, MS	38916
CANNON, DORAN WILLIAM	SCREENWRITER	2671 LA CUESTA DR	LOS ANGELES, CA	90046
CANNON, DYAN	ACTRESS-WRITER	8033 SUNSET BLVD #254	LOS ANGELES, CA	90046
CANNON, FREDDY	SINGER-SONGWRITER	18641 CASSANDRA ST	TARZANA, CA	91356
CANNON, HARRY	ACTOR	15048 GREENLEAF ST	SHERMAN OAKS, CA	91403
CANNON, J D	ACTOR	9255 SUNSET BLVD #515	LOS ANGELES, CA	90069
CANNON, JOHN	ACTOR	110-45 QUEENS BLVD	FOREST HILLS, CA	11375
CANNON, KATHERINE	ACTRESS	10100 SANTA MONICA BLVD #700	LOS ANGELES, CA	90067
CANNON, REUBEN	CAST DIR-TV PROD	1640 S SEPULVEDA BLVD #400	LOS ANGELES, CA	90025
CANNON, TOMMY & BOBBY BALL	COMEDY DUO	ALBERT ST, CHADDERTON, OLDHAM	LANCS OL9 7TR	ENGLAND
CANNONS, THE	C & W GROUP	128 RIVER RD	HENDERSONVILLE, TN	37075
CANO, JOSE	BASEBALL	VILLA DOLORES 2DA #41	SAN PEDRO DE MACORIS	DOM REP
CANO, TERRY J	COMPOSER	18434 COLLINS ST #8	TARZANA, CA	91356
CANON, PETER	ACTOR	1128 N VISTA ST #4	LOS ANGELES, CA	90046
CANONERO, MILENA	COSTUME DESIGNER	13949 VENTURA BLVD #309	SHERMAN OAKS, CA	91423
CANOVA, DIANA	ACTRESS	10351 SANTA MONICA BLVD #211	LOS ANGELES, CA	90025
CANSECO, JOSE	BASEBALL	POST OFFICE BOX 90111	ARLINGTON, TX	76004
CANSECO, OSSIE	BASEBALL	POST OFFICE BOX 36407	LOUISVILLE, KY	40233
CANSINO, RICHARD	ACTOR	1975 N BEACHWOOD DR #307	HOLLYWOOD, CA	90068
CANT, BRIAN	ACTOR	LADKIN, 11 SOUTHWICK MEWS	LONDON W2 1JG	ENGLAND
CANTARELLI, GIUSEPPE	CONDUCTOR	1005 N SWEETZER #24	LOS ANGELES, CA	90069
CANTI, SUZANNE	SINGER-SONGWRITER	MARINA BELICA MANAGEMENT		
		MUSICA INTL, 30 E 23RD ST	NEW YORK, NY	10010
CANTINFLAS	COMEDIAN-ACTOR	AVENUE INSURSENTES SUR 377	MEXICO CITY D F	MEXICO
CANTON, NEIL	FILM PRODUCER	MCA/UNIVERSAL STUDIOS, INC		
		100 UNIVERSAL CITY PLAZA		
		BUILDING #47	UNIVERSAL CITY, CA	91608
CANTONE, VIC	CARTOONIST	DAILY, 220 E 42ND ST	NEW YORK, NY	10017
CANTOR, ARTHUR	THEATER PRODUCER	234 W 44TH ST	NEW YORK, NY	10036
CANTOR, MARILYN	ACTRESS	211 CENTRAL PARK W	NEW YORK, NY	10024
CANTRELL, BYRON	COMPOSER-CONDUCTOR	6831 BOTHWELL RD	RESEDA, CA	91335
CANTRELL, LANA	SINGER	300 E 71ST ST	NEW YORK, NY	10021
CANTY, THOMAS	ARTIST	339 NEWBURY ST	BOSTON, MA	02115
CANUTT, TAP	DIRECTOR	15856 BEAVER RUN RD	CANYON COUNTRY, CA	91351
CANYON	C & W GROUP	POST OFFICE BOX 807	LAKE DALLAS, TX	75065
CANZANO, FRANK	ACTOR	15 CHARLES ST	NEW YORK, NY	10014
CAPALBO, CARMEN	DIRECTOR-PRODUCER	CARPENTER, 254 W 73RD ST	NEW YORK, NY	10023
CAPARROS, ERNESTO	DIRECTOR	DGA, 110 W 57TH ST	NEW YORK, NY	10019
CAPEL, MIKE	BASEBALL	POST OFFICE BOX 27045	TUCSON, AZ	85726
CAPELLAN, CARLOS	BASEBALL	POST OFFICE BOX 5645	ORLANDO, FL	32855
CAPEN, CRIS	ACTOR	6210 WINANS DR	LOS ANGELES, CA	90068
CAPERS, DOM	FOOTBALL COACH	SAINTS, 1500 POYDRAS ST	NEW ORLEANS, LA	90112
CAPERS, VIRGINIA	ACTRESS	390 S HAUSER BLVD	LOS ANGELES, CA	90036
CAPERTON, GASTON	GOVERNOR	STATE CAPITOL BUILDING	CHARLESTON, WV	25305
CAPETANOS, LEON	SCREENWRITER	8431 FOUNTAIN AVE #C	LOS ANGELES, CA	90069
CAPICE, PHILIP	TV PRODUCER	1359 MILLER DR	LOS ANGELES, CA	90069
CAPIZZI, BILL	ACTOR	6147 COLFAX AVE	NORTH HOLLYWOOD, CA	91606
CAPKA, CAROL	ACTRESS	18120 KINZIE ST	NORTHRIDGE, CA	91325
CAPLAIN, ROBERT	WRITER	1033 HILGARD AVE #409	LOS ANGELES, CA	90024
CAPLINGER, ROGER	BASEBALL TRAINER	POST OFFICE BOX 4606	HELENA, MT	59604
CAPO, FERN	ACTRESS-SINGER	PRECISION PRODS, 85-20 167TH ST	JAMAICA, NY	11432
CAPORALE, ESTHER	WRITER	145 S ELM DR	BEVERLY HILLS, CA	90212
CAPOZZOLA, CARMEN	COMPOSER	411 36TH ST	UNION CITY, NJ	07087
CAPPS, BILL	BASEBALL SCOUT	1060 W ADDISON ST	CHICAGO, IL	60613
CAPRA, BUZZ	BASEBALL-COACH	7112 RIVERSIDE DR	BERWYN, IL	60402
CAPRA, FRANK, III	FILM DIRECTOR	14415 BENEFIT ST #301	SHERMAN OAKS, CA	91423
CAPRA, NICK	BASEBALL	POST OFFICE BOX 23290	NASHVILLE, TN	37202
CAPRA, TOM	DIRECTOR-PRODUCER	116 W 78TH ST	NEW YORK, NY	10024

Name	Occupation	Address	City/State	Zip/Country
CAPRI, AHNA	ACTRESS	8227 FOUNTAIN AVE #2	LOS ANGELES, CA	90046
CAPRIATTI, JENNIFER	TENNIS	100 SADDLEBROOK WY	WESLEY CHAPEL, FL	33543
CAPRON, BRIAN	ACTOR	MARKHAM AND FROGGATT, LTD		
		JULIAN HOUSE, 4 WINDMILL ST	LONDON W1P 1HF	ENGLAND
CAPSHAW, KATE	ACTRESS	POST OFFICE BOX 6190	MALIBU, CA	90265
CAPTAIN & TENNILLE, THE	MUSIC DUO	POST OFFICE BOX 262	GLENBROOK, NV	89413
CAPUANO, DAVE	HOCKEY	CANUCKS, 100 N RENFREW ST	VANCOUVER, BC V5K 3N7	CANADA
CAPUTO, PHILIP	AUTHOR	HOLT, 383 MADISON AVE	NEW YORK, NY	10017
CARA, IRENE	ACTRESS-SINGER	8033 SUNSET BLVD #735	LOS ANGELES, CA	90046
CARABALLO, GARY	BASEBALL	300 STADIUM WY	DAVENPORT, FL	33837
CARABALLO, RAMON	BASEBALL	POST OFFICE BOX 16683	GREENVILLE, SC	29606
CARABATSOS, JAMES	SCREENWRITER	SHAPIRO, 8827 BEVERLY BLVD	LOS ANGELES, CA	90048
CARABATSOS, STEVEN	SCREENWRITER	POST OFFICE BOX 753	MALIBU, CA	90265
CARABBA, ROBBIE	BASEBALL	POLECATS, 608 N SLAPPEY BLVD	ALBANY, GA	31701
CARACO, JOE	BASEBALL UMPIRE	POST OFFICE BOX 716	PLAINVILLE, CT	06062
CARAFOTES, PAUL	ACTOR	8033 SUNSET BLVD #3554	LOS ANGELES, CA	90046
CARANGI, JOAN	ACTRESS	928 9TH ST #2	SANTA MONICA, CA	90403
CARAY, CHIP	BASEBALL-ANNOUNCER	250 STADIUM PLAZA	ST LOUIS, MO	63102
CARAY, HARRY	BASEBALL ANNOUNCER	1060 W ADDISON ST	CHICAGO, IL	60613
CARBO, HENRY	ACTOR	5137 WEST BLVD	LOS ANGELES, CA	90043
CARBONE, CARL A	DIRECTOR-PRODUCER	225 E 36TH ST	NEW YORK, NMY	10016
CARBONNEAU, GUY	HOCKEY	CANADIENS, 2313 ST CATHERINE ST	MONTREAL, QUE H3H 1N2	CANADA
CARBY, FANNY	ACTRESS	THE GARDEN FLAT, 3 THURLOW RD		
		HAMPSTEAD	LONDON NW3	ENGLAND
CARCIONE, TOM	BASEBALL	POST OFFICE BOX 2769	HUNTSVILLE, AL	35804
CARD, LAMAR	DIRECTOR-PRODUCER	7318 WOODROW WILSON DR	LOS ANGELES, CA	90046
CARDEA, FRANK, JR	TV WRITER-PRODUCER	1960 LAUGHLIN PARK DR	LOS ANGELES, CA	90027
CARDEN, WILLIAM	ACTOR	165 W 46TH ST #1109	NEW YORK, NY	10036
CARDENAL, JOSE	BASEBALL-COACH	REDS, 100 RIVERFRONT STADIUM	CINCINNATI, OH	45202
CARDENAS, HERNAN	FILM DIRECTOR	201 CRANDON BLVD #1102	KEY BISCAYNE, FL	33149
CARDIFF, JACK	FILM DIRECTOR	L'EPINE SMITH, 10 WYNDHAM PL	LONDON W1H 1AS	ENGLAND
CARDIN, BENJAMIN	U S CONGRESSMAN	540 E BELVEDERE #201	BALTIMORE, MD	21212
CARDIN, PIERRE	FASHION DESIGNER	59 RUE DU FAULBOURG		
		SAINT HONORE	F-75008 PARIS	FRANCE
CARDINAHL, JESSIKA	ACTRESS	VOGELBEERENWEG 4	2000 HAMBURG 60	GERMANY
CARDINAL, CYNDI	ACTRESS	401 1/2 HOWLAND CANAL	VENICE, CA	90291
CARDINALE, CLAUDIA	ACTRESS	SALITA DI CASTEL GIUMBELEO	1-00100 ROME	ITALY
CARDONA, ROBERT	WRITER-PRODUCER	1015 GAYLEY AVE #300	LOS ANGELES, CA	90024
CARDOS, JOHN "BUD"	ACTOR-DIRECTOR	19116 ENADIA WY	RESEDA, CA	91335
CAREW, ALYCE S	PRODUCER	1420 N BEACHWOOD DR #7	LOS ANGELES, CA	90028
CAREW, COLIN A, JR	WRITER	3127 NICHOLS CANYON RD	LOS ANGELES, CA	90046
CAREW, ROD	BASEBALL-COACH	POST OFFICE BOX 2000	ANAHEIM, CA	92803
CAREW, TOPPER	WRITER-PRODUCER	1420 N BEACHWOOD DR	LOS ANGELES, CA	90028
CAREY, CATHERINE	ACTRESS	POST OFFICE BOX 2962	NEW YORK, NY	10185
CAREY, CLARE	ACTRESS	7632 HOLLYWOOD BLVD #3	LOS ANGELES, CA	90046
CAREY, FRANK	BASEBALL	POST OFFICE BOX 21727	SAN FRANCISCO, CA	95151
CAREY, GEORGE E	ACTOR	10701 RIVERSIDE DR #13	TOLUCA LAKE, CA	91602
CAREY, HARRY, JR	ACTOR	14159 DICKENS ST #303	SHERMAN OAKS, CA	91423
CAREY, HUGH	GOVERNOR	9 PROPSECT PL W	BROOKLYN, NY	11215
CAREY, KATHI	ACTRESS	SELECTED, 3575 W CAHUENGA BLVD	LOS ANGELES, CA	90068
CAREY, MAC DONALD	ACTOR-POET	1543 BENEDICT CANYON DR	BEVERLY HILLS, CA	90210
CAREY, MARIAH	SINGER	130 W 57TH ST #12-B	NEW YORK, NY	10019
CAREY, MICHELE	ACTRESS	8019 1/2 MELROSE AVE #3	LOS ANGELES, CA	90046
CAREY, MIKE	FOOTBALL REFEREE	NFL, 410 PARK AVE	NEW YORK, NY	10022
CAREY, MIRIAH	SINGER-SONGWRITER	CAA, 9830 WILSHIRE BLVD	BEVERLY HILLS, CA	90212
CAREY, P J	BASEBALL MANAGER	POST OFFICE BOX 4669	CHARLESTON, WV	25304
CAREY, PAUL	BASEBALL	POST OFFICE BOX 3169	FREDERICK, MD	21701
CAREY, PAUL	SPORTSCASTER	TIGERS, TIGER STADIUM	DETROIT, MI	48216
CAREY, PHILIP	ACTOR	ABC-TV, "ONE LIFE TO LIVE"		
		56 W 66TH ST	NEW YORK, NY	10023
CAREY, RON	ACTOR	10390 SANTA MONICA BLVD #300	LOS ANGELES, CA	90025
CAREY, TIMOTHY AGOGLIA	ACTOR	POST OFFICE BOX 1254	TEMPLE CITY, CA	91780
CARGILL, HENSON	SINGER-SONGWRITER	ACE PRODS, 3407 GREEN RIDGE DR	NASHVILLE, TN	37214
CARGILL, MARK K	COMPOSER	1937 W 94TH ST	LOS ANGELES, CA	90047
CARGILL, PATRICK	ACTOR	MARSH, 19 DENMARK ST	LONDON WC2H 8NA	ENGLAND
CARHART, EILEEN	TV DIRECTOR	11101 1/4 CAMARILLO ST	NORTH HOLLYWOOD, CA	91602
CARIAGA, DANIEL	MUSIC CRITIC	LA TIMES, TIMES MIRROR SQ	LOS ANGELES, CA	90053
CARIBBEAN KNIGHTS, THE	C & W GROUP	CUDE, 519 N HALIFAX AVE	DAYTON BEACH, FL	32018
CARILLO	ROCK & ROLL GROUP	3 E 54TH ST #1400	NEW YORK, NY	10022
CARIOU, LEN	ACTOR	10 E 44TH ST #500	NEW YORK, NY	10017
CARKNER, TERRY	HOCKEY	FLYERS, SPECTRUM, PATTISON PL	PHILADELPHIA, PA	19148
CARL, GEORGE	COMEDIAN	3661 S MARYLAND PKWY #3 - BOX 50	LAS VEGAS, NV	89109
CARLE, FRANKIE	PIANIST-COMPOSER	POST OFFICE BOX 7415	MESA, AZ	85206
CARLEN, CATHERINE	ACTRESS	6310 SAN VICENTE BLVD #407	LOS ANGELES, CA	90048
CARLIN, DANIEL A	CONDUCTOR	6635 SHELTONDALE AVE	CANOGA PARK, CA	91307
CARLIN, GEORGE	COMEDIAN	HAMZA, 901 BRINGHAM AVE	LOS ANGELES, CA	90049
CARLIN, GLORIA	ACTRESS	280 S BEVERLY DR #400	BEVERLY HILLS, CA	90212
CARLIN, JACQUELINE	ACTRESS-MODRL	7684 WOODROW WILSON DR	LOS ANGELES, CA	90046
CARLIN, LYNN	ACTRESS	24504 WINGFIELD RD	CALABASAS, CA	91302
CARLINER, MARK	FILM PRODUCER	11700 LAUREL WOOD DR	STUDIO CITY, CA	91604
CARLINER, MARK P	SCREENWRITER	555 W 57TH ST #1230	NEW YORK, NY	10019
CARLINO, LEWIS JOHN	WRITER-DIRECTOR	68 PENINSULA RD	TIBURON, CA	94920
CARLINO, NIKKI	TV PRODUCER	10 W 16TH ST	NEW YORK, NY	10011
CARLISLE, BELINDA	SINGER-SONGWRITER	3575 W CAHUENGA BLVD #470	LOS ANGELES, CA	90068
CARLISLE, BILL	SINGER	ROUTE #3, BOX 444	GOODLETTSVILLE, TN	37072

CARLISLE, JODI	ACTRESS	7080 HOLLYWOOD BLVD #704	HOLLYWOOD, CA	90028
CARLISLE, KEVIN B	TV DIRECTOR	2022 N SYCAMORE AVE	HOLLYWOOD, CA	90068
CARLISLE, KITTY	ACTRESS	HART, 32 E 64TH ST	NEW YORK, NY	10021
CARLISLE, RICK	BASKETBALL COACH	N J NETS, MEADOWLANDS ARENA	EAST RUTHERFORD, NJ	07073
CARLISLE, ROBERT W	DIRECTOR	45422 INDIAN WELLS LN	INDIAN WELLS, CA	92260
CARLISLE, STEVE	ACTOR	7135 HOLLYWOOD BLVD #PH-2	LOS ANGELES, CA	90046
CARLO, JOHANN	ACTRESS	9000 SUNSET BLVD #1200	LOS ANGELES, CA	90069
CARLON, FRAN	ACTRESS	451 W END AVE	NEW YORK, NY	10024
CARLSEN, BOBBY	BASEBALL	POST OFFICE BOX 4669	CHARLESTON, WV	25304
CARLSEN, DON	FOOTBALL REFEREE	NFL, 410 PARK AVE	NEW YORK, NY	10022
CARLSON, ARNE H	GOVERNOR	STATE CAPTOL BLDG, AURORA AVE	SAINT PAUL, MN	55155
CARLSON, BOB	BASEBALL	POST OFFICE BOX 661	KENOSHA, WI	53141
CARLSON, CODY	FOOTBALL	OILERS, 6910 FANNIN ST	HOUSTON, TX	77070
CARLSON, CRAIG	TV WRITER	HASHAGEN, 157 W 57TH ST	NEW YORK, NY	10019
CARLSON, DAN	BASEBALL	POST OFFICE BOX 3448	SHREVEPORT, LA	71133
CARLSON, DONALD L	DIRECTOR-PRODUCER	1937 NORTH DR	GLENVIEW, IL	60025
CARLSON, GAIL RAE	ACTRESS	11818 RIVERSIDE DR #125	NORTH HOLLYWOOD, CA	91607
CARLSON, JEFF	FOOTBALL	BUCCANEERS, 1 BUCCANEER PL	TAMPA, FL	33607
CARLSON, KAREN	ACTRESS	3700 VENTURA CANYON AVE	SHERMAN OAKS, CA	91423
CARLSON, LENNY	GUITARIST-COMPOSER	249 DIMMICK AVE	VENICE, CA	90291
CARLSON, LYNN	BASEBALL	POST OFFICE BOX 4669	CHARLESTON, WV	25304
CARLSON, PHILIP	TALENT AGENT	SMITH, 121 N SAN VICENTE BLVD	BEVERLY HILLS, CA	90211
CARLSON, ROBERT A	DIRECTOR	1323 HOLMBY AVE	LOS ANGELES, CA	90024
CARLSON, STEVE	ACT-WRI-DIR	10000 RIVERSIDE DR #6	TOLUCA LAKE, CA	91602
CARLTON, BOB	FILM CRITIC	POST OFFICE BOX 2553	BIRMINGHAM, AL	35202
CARLTON, CARL	SINGER	RUBINSON, 827 FOLSOM ST	SAN FRANCISCO, CA	94107
CARLTON, HOPE MARIE	ACTRESS-MODEL	9229 SUNSET BLVD #208	LOS ANGELES, CA	90069
CARLTON, LARRY	GUITARIST-COMPOSER	3208 W CAHUENGA BLVD #42	LOS ANGELES, CA	90068
CARLTON, STEVE	BASEBALL	POST OFFICE BOX 736	DURANGO, CO	81302
CARLTON, TIMOTHY	ACTOR	SARABAND, 265 LIVERPOOL RD	LONDON N1 1LX	ENGLAND
CARLTONS SHOWBAND, THE	C & W GROUP	GASTONI, 3815 BEAUMONT	BROSSARD, PQ J4Z 2N8	CANADA
CARLYLE, AILEEN	ACTRESS	2267 EL CONTENTO DR	LOS ANGELES, CA	90068
CARLYLE, JOHN	ACTOR	9165 SUNSET BLVD #202	LOS ANGELES, CA	90069
CARLYLE, RANDY	HOCKEY	JETS, 15-1430 MAROONS RD	WINNIPEG, MAN R3G 0L5	CANADA
CARLYLE, RICHARD	ACTOR	BARSKIN, 120 S VICTORY BL #104	BURBANK, CA	91502
CARMAN, DON	BASEBALL	REDS, 100 RIVERFRONT STADIUM	CINCINNATI, OH	45202
CARMAN, LINDA RAE	ACTRESS	57 W 84TH ST #2-C	NEW YORK, NY	10024
CARMEN, DON	BASEBALL	6 COOPER RUN DR	CHERRY HILL, NJ	08003
CARMEN, ERIC	SINGER-SONGWRITER	CHATTMAN, 400 ENGINEERS BLDG	CLEVELAND, OH	44114
CARMEN, JOHN	TV CRITIC	S F CHRONICLE, 901 MISSION ST	SAN FRANCISCO, CA	94119
CARMEN, JULIE	ACTRESS	1999 AVE OF THE STARS #2850	LOS ANGELES, CA	90067
CARMICHAEL, IAN	ACTOR-PRODUCER	THE PRIORY, GROSMONT, WHITBY	YORKS YO22 SQT	ENGLAND
CARMICHAEL, ROBERT J	TV DIRECTOR	3419 LOS PINOS DR	SANTA BARBARA, CA	93105
CARMONA, GREG	BASEBALL	POST OFFICE BOX 36407	LOUISVILLE, KY	40233
CARMONA, JESUS	BASEBALL SCOUT	ORIOLE PARK, 333 W CAMDEN ST	BALTIMORE, MD	21201
CARNAHAN, JIM	TALENT AGENT	SMITH, 121 N SAN VICENTE BLVD	BEVERLY HILLS, CA	90211
CARNAHAN, MEL	LT GOVERNOR	POST OFFICE BOX 720	JEFFERSON CITY, MO	65102
CARNE, JEAN	SINGER	REEDER, 1162 E SLOCUM ST	PHILADELPHIA, PA	19150
CARNE, JUDY	ACTRESS	300 W 12TH ST	NEW YORK, NY	10014
CARNEAL, HERB	SPORTSCASTER	TWINS, 501 CHICAGO AVE S	MINNEAPOLIS, MN	55415
CARNER, CHARLES R	SCREENWRITER	8417 HAROLD WY	LOS ANGELES, CA	90069
CARNES, KIM	SINGER-SONGWRITER	CARELL, 3231 BARRY AVE	LOS ANGELES, CA	90066
CARNEVALE, DAN	BASEBALL SCOUT	INDIANS, CLEVELAND STADIUM	CLEVELAND, OH	44114
CARNEY, ART	ACTOR	RURAL ROUTE #20, BOX 911	WESTBROOK, CT	06498
CARNEY, DONALD M	DIRECTOR-PRODUCER	60 CENTRAL AVE	PELHAM, NY	10803
CARNEY, FRED	ACTOR	1429 N HAVENHURST DR	LOS ANGELES, CA	90046
CARNEY, JAMES T	TV DIRECTOR-PRODUCER	PARAGON CABLE, 5120 BROADWAY	NEW YORK, NY	10034
CARNEY, KAY	ACTRESS	396 BLEECKER ST	NEW YORK, NY	10014
CARNEY, SUZANNE	ACTRESS	247 S BEVERLY DR #102	BEVERLY HILLS, CA	90210
CARNOFSKY, MORRIS	ACTOR	422 ROCK HOUSE RD	EASTON, CT	06612
CARO, JOE	BASEBALL SCOUT	POST OFFICE BOX 2000	ANAHEIM, CA	92803
CAROL, JEAN	ACTRESS	CBS-TV, "THE GUIDING LIGHT"		
		222 E 44TH ST	NEW YORK, NY	10017
CAROL, LINDA	ACTRESS	9105 CARMELITA AVE #1	BEVERLY HILLS, CA	90210
CAROL, NANCY	ACTRESS	1801 AVE OF THE STARS #640	LOS ANGELES, CA	90067
CAROLEI, JOSEPH A	TV DIRECTOR	45 W 67TH ST #11-C	NEW YORK, NY	10023
CAROLGEES, BOB	COMEDIAN	158 COLLEGE RD, CROSBY	LIVERPOOL L23 3DP	ENGLAND
CAROLINE, PRINCESS OF MONACO	PRINCESS	LA MAISON DE LA SOURCE	ST REME DE PROVENCE	FRANCE
CAROLL, FRANCINE	SINGER	300 E 56TH ST #25-M	NEW YORK, NY	10022
CAROLLO, BILL	FOOTBALL REFEREE	NFL, 410 PARK AVE	NEW YORK, NY	10022
CARON, GLENN G	TV WRITER-PRODUCER	5474 JED SMITH RD	HIDDEN HILLS, CA	91302
CARON, LESLIE	ACTRESS	6 RUE DE BELLECHASSE		
		7TH DISTRICT	PARIS 75007	FRANCE
CAROTHERS, A J	SCREENWRITER	217 S BURLINGAME AVE	LOS ANGELES, CA	90049
CARPEL, ANDY	DIRECTOR	8618 DISCOVERY BLVD	WALKERSVILLE, IN	21793
CARPENTER, BOBBY	HOCKEY	BRUINS, 150 CAUSEWAY ST	BOSTON, MA	02114
CARPENTER, BUBBA	BASEBALL	ALBANY YANKEES, HERITAGE PARK	ALBANY, NY	12211
CARPENTER, CARLETON	ACTOR	RD #2, CHARDAVOYNE RD	WARWICK, NY	10990
CARPENTER, CHARLOTTE	ACTRESS	6767 FOREST LAWN DR #115	LOS ANGELES, CA	90068
CARPENTER, CRIS	BASEBALL	250 STADIUM PLAZA	ST LOUIS, MO	63102
CARPENTER, DAVID	ACTOR	9255 SUNSET BLVD #515	LOS ANGELES, CA	90069
CARPENTER, DOUG	BASEBALL COACH	POST OFFICE BOX 2785	LAKELAND, FL	33806
CARPENTER, JOE	BASEBALL SCOUT	POST OFFICE BOX 2000	ANAHEIM, CA	92803
CARPENTER, JOHN	ACTOR	HEAVEN-ON-EARTH STABLES	LAKE VIEW TERRACE, CA	91342
CARPENTER, JOHN	FILM WRITER-DIRECTOR	3751 AVENIDA DEL SOL	STUDIO CITY, CA	91604

CARPENTER, JOHN R	AUTHOR-WRITER	2801 MEADOW LARK DR	SAN DIEGO, CA	92123
CARPENTER, KEVIN	BASEBALL EXECUTIVE	POST OFFICE BOX 20849	CHARLESTON, SC	29413
CARPENTER, LEW	FOOTBALL COACH	EAGLES, BROAD ST & PATTISON AVE	PHILADELPHIA, PA	19148
CARPENTER, MARY CHAPIN	SINGER-SONGWRITER	POST OFFICE BOX 5824	BETHESDA, MD	20814
CARPENTER, MICHAEL E	ATTORNEY GENERAL	STATE HOUSE BUILDING	AUGUSTA, GA	04333
CARPENTER, RICHARD	PIANIST-COMPOSER	CARMEN, 15456 CABRITO RD	VAN NUYS, CA	91406
CARPENTER, ROB	FOOTBALL	PATRIOTS, FOXBORO STADIUM, RT #1	FOXBORO, MA	02035
CARPENTER, SCOTT (LT CMDR)	ASTRONAUT	1183 STRADELLA RD	LOS ANGELES, CA	90077
CARPENTIER, ROB	BASEBALL	525 NW PEACOCK BLVD	PORT SAINT LUCIE, FL	34986
CARPER, DON	CONDUCTOR	28303 HAZELRIDGE DR	PALOS VERDES EST, CA	90274
CARPER, JEAN	AUTHOR	1018 W PEACHTREE ST, NW	ATLANTA, GA	30309
CARPER, MARK	BASEBALL	POST OFFICE BOX 230	HAGERSTOWN, MD	21740
CARPER, THOMAS R	U S CONGRESSMAN	131 CANNON OFFICE BUILDING	WASHINGTON, DC	20515
CARPINE, BILL	BASEBALL TRAINER	POST OFFICE BOX 1295	CLINTON, IA	52733
CARR, ALLAN	FILM WRITER-PRODUCER	POST OFFICE BOX 691670	LOS ANGELES, CA	90069
CARR, ANTOINE	BASKETBALL	KINGS, 1 SPORTS PARKWAY	SACRAMENTO, CA	95834
CARR, BOB	U S CONGRESSMAN	2848 E GRAND RIVER #1	EAST LANSING, MI	48823
CARR, CHUCK	BASEBALL	POST OFFICE BOX 5599	LITTLE ROCK, AR	72215
CARR, DARLEEN	ACTRESS	8831 SUNSET BLVD #304	LOS ANGELES, CA	90069
CARR, DIDI	ACTRESS	9105 CARMELITA AVE #1	BEVERLY HILLS, CA	90210
CARR, GORDON	TV PRODUCER-JOURN	9 LYNCROFT GARDENS	LONDON NW6 1LB	ENGLAND
CARR, JANE	ACTRESS	6200 MOUNT ANGELUS DR	LOS ANGELES, CA	90067
CARR, JIMMIE	FOOTBALL COACH	FALCONS, SUWANEE RD AT I-85	SUWANEE, GA	30174
CARR, JOHN	FILM WRITER-DIRECTOR	PAN-AMERICAN PICTURES		
		9033 WILSHIRE BLVD	BEVERLY HILLS, CA	90211
CARR, JUNE	SINGER	3620 CENTRAL AVE	NASHVILLE, TN	37205
CARR, M L	BASKETBALL	151 MERRIMAC ST	BOSTON, MA	02114
CARR, MARCY	SINGER	OVERTON, 10051 GREENLEAF AVE	SANTA FE SPRINGS, CA	90670
CARR, MARTIN	WRITER-PRODUCER	305 W 86TH ST	NEW YORK, NY	10024
CARR, PAUL	ACTOR-WRITER	8019 1/2 MELROSE AVE #3	LOS ANGELES, CA	90046
CARR, THOMAS	FILM DIRECTOR	1365 WEYMOUTH LN	VENTURA, CA	93003
CARR, VICKIE	SINGER	2289 BETTY LN	BEVERLY HILLS, CA	90210
CARR-BOSLEY, PATRICIA	ACTRESS	2822 ROYSTON PL	BEVERLY HILLS, CA	90210
CARRA, MICHAEL	ACTOR	9200 SUNSET BLVD #625	LOS ANGELES, CA	90069
CARRACK, PAUL	SINGER	ICM, 40 W 57TH ST	NEW YORK, NY	10019
CARRADINE, CAROLYN	ACTRESS	2350 SUNSET PLAZA DR	LOS ANGELES, CA	90069
CARRADINE, DAVID	ACTOR	9300 WILSHIRE BLVD #410	BEVERLY HILLS, CA	90212
CARRADINE, KEITH	ACTOR-SINGER	20800 HILLSIDE DR	TOPANGA, CA	90290
CARRADINE, ROBERT	ACTOR	7453 MULHOLLAND DR	LOS ANGELES, CA	90046
CARRAHER, JACK E	COMPOSER	2416 BRYCE CT	LAWRENCE, KS	66044
CARRARA, GIOVANNI	BASEBALL	POST OFFICE BOX 957	DUNEDIN, FL	34697
CARRASCO, HECTOR	BASEBALL	POST OFFICE BOX 1556	ASHEVILLE, NC	28802
CARRASQUEL, EMILIO	BASEBALL SCOUT	6850 LAWRENCE RD	LANTANA, FL	33462
CARRAWAY, STEVE	NEWS CORRESPONDENT	NBC NEWS, 4001 NEBRASKA AV, SW	WASHINGTON, DC	20016
CARREN, DAVID BENNETT	TV WRITER	2458 GLYNDON AVE	VENICE, CA	90291
CARRENO, AMALIO	BASEBALL	POST OFFICE BOX 3449	SCRANTON, PA	18505
CARREON, MARK	BASEBALL	TIGERS, TIGER STADIUM	DETROIT, MI	48216
CARREOW, JACK	TV WRITER	519 S CAMINO REAL	REDONDO BEACH, CA	90277
CARRERA, BARBARA	ACTRESS-MODEL	15301 VENTURA BLVD #345	SHERMAN OAKS, CA	91403
CARRERE, LEON	TV DIRECTOR	220 W CHANNEL RD	SANTA MONICA, CA	90402
CARRERE, TIA	ACTRESS	10000 SANTA MONICA BLVD #305	LOS ANGELES, CA	90067
CARREY, JIM	ACTOR-COMEDIAN	KTTV, 5746 SUNSET BLVD	HOLLYWOOD, CA	90028
CARRICART, ROBERT	ACTOR	205 AVE "G"	REDONDO BEACH, CA	90277
CARRIE, LEN & KRACKERJACKS	C & W GROUP	POST OFFICE BOX 3124	LINDEN, NJ	07036
CARRIER, ALBERT	ACTOR	7640 MULHOLLAND DR	LOS ANGELES, CA	90046
CARRIER, MARK	FOOTBALL (CHICAGO)	BEARS, 250 N WASHINGTON RD	LAKE FOREST, IL	60045
CARRIER, MARK	FOOTBALL (TAMPA)	BUCCANEERS, 1 BUCCANEER PL	TAMPA, FL	33607
CARRIER, MATHIEW	ACTOR	79 BLVD SAINT-MICHEL	PARIS 75009	FRANCE
CARRIGAN, KEVIN	ACTOR	BRET ADAMS, 448 W 44TH ST	NEW YORK, NY	10036
CARRILLO, MATIAS	BASEBALL	2850 W 20TH AVE	DENVER, CO	80211
CARRINGTON, DARREN	FOOTBALL	POST OFFICE BOX 609609	SAN DIEGO, CA	92160
CARRINGTON, DEBBIE LEE	ACTRESS	11500 W OLYMPIC BLVD #400	LOS ANGELES, CA	90064
CARRINGTON, LAURA	ACTRESS	10000 RIVERSIDE DR #6	TOLUCA LAKE, CA	91602
CARRINGTON, ROBERT	SCREENWRITER	10811 WILKINS AVE	LOS ANGELES, CA	90024
CARRION, GERMAN	BASEBALL	POST OFFICE BOX 20849	CHARLESTON, SC	29413
CARROLL, DIAHANN	ACTRESS-SINGER	POST OFFICE BOX 2999	BEVERLY HILLS, CA	90210
CARROLL, DON	BASEBALL	POST OFFICE BOX 1742	PALM SPRINGS, CA	92263
CARROLL, EDDIE	ACTOR	7080 HOLLYWOOD BLVD #704	HOLLYWOOD, CA	90028
CARROLL, GORDON	FILM PRODUCER	9080 SHOREHAM DR #C	LOS ANGELES, CA	90067
CARROLL, J LARRY	SCREENWRITER	8955 BEVERLY BLVD	WEST HOLLYWOOD, CA	90048
CARROLL, JANET	ACTRESS	1999 AVE OF THE STARS #2850	LOS ANGELES, CA	90067
CARROLL, JANICE	ACTRESS	13923 DAVENTRY ST	PACOIMA, CA	91331
CARROLL, KATHLEEN	FILM CRITIC	N Y DAILY NEWS, 220 E 42ND ST	NEW YORK, NY	10017
CARROLL, KEVIN	BASEBALL	POST OFFICE BOX 10213	LYNCHBURG, VA	24506
CARROLL, LARRY	ARTIST	219 GRANT AVE	CLIFFSIDE PARK, NJ	07010
CARROLL, LARRY R	BROADCAST JOURNALIST	8019 1/2 MELROSE AVE #3	LOS ANGELES, CA	90046
CARROLL, LESTER	CARTOONIST	21100 BEACHWOOD DR	ROCKY RIVER, OH	44116
CARROLL, MARTHA	TALENT AGENT	6605 HOLLYWOOD BLVD #220	HOLLYWOOD, CA	90028
CARROLL, PAT	ACTRESS	6523 W OLYMPIC BLVD	LOS ANGELES, CA	90048
CARROLL, PETE	FOOTBALL COACH	N Y JETS, 1000 FULTON AVE	HEMPSTEAD, NY	11550
CARROLL, RAY	MUSIC ARRANGER	ROUTE #8, JEFF DAVIS DR	FRANKLIN, TN	37064
CARROLL, ROBERT G, JR	WRITER-PRODUCER	8141 CORNETT DR	LOS ANGELES, CA	90046
CARROLL, RONNIE	SINGER	LYNCH, 57 DUKE ST	LONDON W1	ENGLAND
CARROLL, VINNETTE	ACT-WRI-DIR	227 W 17TH ST	NEW YORK, NY	10011
CARROLL, WESLEY	FOOTBALL	SAINTS, 1500 POYDRAS ST	NEW ORLEANS, LA	90112

CARROLL COUNTY RAMBLERS, THE	C & W GROUP	BOB ENGLAR, 2466 WILLOW DR	YORK, PA	17403
CARROLL KYSER, GEORGIA	ACTRESS	504 E FRANKLIN ST	CAHPEL HILL, NC	27514
CARRUTHERS, WILLIAM H	DIRECTOR-PRODUCER	506 S BRONSON AVE	LOS ANGELES, CA	90020
CARRY, JULIUS J, III	ACTOR	BDP, 10637 BURBANK BLVD	NORTH HOLLYWOOD, CA	91601
CARS, THE	ROCK & ROLL GROUP	LOOKOUT, 506 SANTA MONICA BLVD	SANTA MONICA, CA	90401
CARSEL, HARRIET	ACTRESS	24520 WELBY WY	WESTHILLS, CA	91307
CARSEY, MARCY	TV PRODUCER	1438 N GOWER ST #376	LOS ANGELES, CA	90028
CARSON, BUD	FOOTBALL COACH	BROWNS, 80 1ST ST	BEREA, OH	44017
CARSON, CAROL	ARTIST	38 E 21ST ST	NEW YORK, NY	10010
CARSON, CRYSTAL	ACTRESS	ABC-TV, "GENERAL HOSPITAL"		
		4151 PROSPECT AVE	BURBANK, CA	91523
CARSON, DARWYN	ACTRESS	5726 CAMELLIA AVE #205	NORTH HOLLYWOOD, CA	91601
CARSON, DAVID	TV DIRECTOR	BROWN, 162-168 REGENT ST	LONDON W1R 5TB	ENGLAND
CARSON, JIM	ARTIST	11 FOCH ST	CAMBRIDGE, MA	02140
CARSON, JIMMY	HOCKEY	RED WINGS, 600 CIVIC CENTER DR	DETROIT, MI	48226
CARSON, JOANNA	PERSONALITY	400 SAINT CLOUD RD	LOS ANGELES, CA	90077
CARSON, JOANNE	CELEBRITY	11001 SUNSET BLVD	LOS ANGELES, CA	90049
CARSON, JOHN DAVID	ACTOR	145 S FAIRFAX AVE #310	LOS ANGELES, CA	90036
CARSON, JOHNNY	TV HOST-COMEDIAN	NBC-TV, 3000 W ALAMEDA AVE	BURBANK, CA	91523
CARSON, KEN	BASEBALL EXECUTIVE	POST OFFICE BOX 957	DUNEDIN, FL	34697
CARSON, L M "KIT"	SCREENWRITER	WM MORRIS, 1350 AVE OF AMERICAS	NEW YORK, NY	10019
CARSON, SONNY	SINGER	POST OFFICE BOX 13	ESTILL SPRINGS, TN	37330
CARTER, AMY	PRESIDENT'S DAUGHTER	1 WOODLAND DR	PLAINS, GA	31780
CARTER, ANDY	BASEBALL	POST OFFICE BOX 15050	READING, PA	19612
CARTER, ANTHONY	FOOTBALL	VIKINGS, 9520 VIKING DR	EDEN PRAIRIE, MN	55344
CARTER, BETTY	SINGER	BET-CAR, 117 SAINT FELIX ST	BROOKLYN, NY	11217
CARTER, BOB	BASEBALL SCOUT	POST OFFICE BOX 419969	KANSAS CITY, MO	64141
CARTER, CARLENE	SINGER-SONGWRITER	1114 17TH AVE S #101	NASHVILLE, TN	37212
CARTER, CHERYL	ACTRESS	12403 MAGNOLIA BLVD	NORTH HOLLYWOOD, CA	91607
CARTER, CLARENCE	SINGER-SONGWRITER	POST OFFICE BOX 4603	MACON, GA	31208
CARTER, CRIS	FOOTBALL	VIKINGS, 9520 VIKING DR	EDEN PRAIRIE, MN	55344
CARTER, DEXTER	FOOTBALL	S F 49ERS, 4949 CENTENNIAL BL	SANTA CLARA, CA	95054
CARTER, DIXIE	ACTRESS	SEE - CARTER HOLBROOK, DIXIE		
CARTER, DONALD	BASKETBALL EXECUTIVE	REUNION ARENA, 777 SPORTS ST	DALLAS, TX	75207
CARTER, FINN	ACTOR	WM MORRIS, 1350 AVE OF AMERICAS	NEW YORK, NY	10019
CARTER, FRED	BASKETBALL COACH	POST OFFICE BOX 25040	PHILADELPHIA, PA	19147
CARTER, FRED "THE FLASH"	GUITARIST	810 DICKERSON RD	GOODLETTSVILLE, TN	37072
CARTER, GARY	BASEBALL	EXPOS, 4545 DE COUBERTIN AVE	MONTREAL, QUE H1V 3P2	CANADA
CARTER, GLENN	BASEBALL	POST OFFICE BOX 8550	STOCKTON, CA	95208
CARTER, HELENA BONHAM	AUTHORESS	1655 GILCREST DR	BEVERLY HILLS, CA	90210
CARTER, HODDING	NEWS CORRESPONDENT	211 S SAINT ASAPH ST	ALEXANDRA, VA	22314
CARTER, JACK	COMEDIAN-ACTOR	1023 CHEVY CHASE DR	BEVERLY HILLS, CA	90210
CARTER, JANICE	ACTRESS	STULMAN, 603 LONGBOAT CLUB RD	LONGBOAT KEY, FL	33548
CARTER, JEFF	BASEBALL (TACOMA)	POST OFFICE BOX 11087	TACOMA, WA	98411
CARTER, JEFF	BASEBALL (VANCOUVER)	CANADIANS, 4601 ONTARIO ST	VANCOUVER, BC V5V 3H4	CANADA
CARTER, JIMMY	PRESIDENT-AUTHOR	1 WOODLAND DR	PLAINS, GA	31780
CARTER, JODY	ACTRESS	5410 WILSHIRE BLVD #243	LOS ANGELES, CA	90036
CARTER, JOE	BASEBALL	SKYDOME, 300 BREMMER BL #3200	TORONTO, ONT M5V 3B3	CANADA
CARTER, JOHN	ACTOR	2535 GREEN VALLEY RD	LOS ANGELES, CA	90046
CARTER, JOHN	HOCKEY	BRUINS, 150 CAUSEWAY ST	BOSTON, MA	02114
CARTER, JUDY	ACTRESS	239 PACIFIC ST #K	SANTA MONICA, CA	90405
CARTER, KENDALL	BASEBALL SCOUT	POST OFFICE BOX 4100	SEATTLE, WA	98104
CARTER, KIT	CASTING DIRECTOR	160 W 95TH ST	NEW YORK, NY	10025
CARTER, LARRY	BASEBALL (PHOENIX)	5999 E VAN BUREN ST	PHOENIX, AZ	85008
CARTER, LARRY	BASEBALL (STOCKTON)	POST OFFICE BOX 8550	STOCKTON, CA	95208
CARTER, LYNDA	ACTRESS-SINGER	9200 HARRINGTON DR	POTOMAC, MD	20854
CARTER, LYNNE	ACTRESS	SHERRELL, 1354 LAS ROBLES DR	PALM SPRINGS, CA	92262
CARTER, MARTY	FOOTBALL	BUCCANEERS, 1 BUCCANEER PL	TAMPA, FL	33607
CARTER, MEL	SINGER-ACTOR	5455 WILSHIRE BLVD #1406	LOS ANGELES, CA	90036
CARTER, MICHAEL	BASEBALL	POST OFFICE BOX 8550	STOCKTON, CA	95208
CARTER, MICHAEL	FOOTBALL	S F 49ERS, 4949 CENTENNIAL BL	SANTA CLARA, CA	95054
CARTER, NELL	ACTRESS-SINGER	512 N CRESCENT DR	BEVERLY HILLS, CA	90210
CARTER, PAT	FOOTBALL	RAMS, 2327 W LINCOLN BLVD	ANAHEIM, CA	92801
CARTER, RANDY	DIRECTOR	6287 VINE WY	HOLLYWOOD, CA	90068
CARTER, ROSALYN	FIRST LADY-AUTHORESS	1 WOODLAND DR	PLAINS, GA	31780
CARTER, RUBIN "HURRICANE"	BOXER	1313 BROOKEDGE DR	HAMLIN, NY	14464
CARTER, RUTH ELAINE	COSTUME DESIGNER	900 S SERRANO AVE	LOS ANGELES, CA	90006
CARTER, SANDRA	TV PRODUCER	44 W 63RD ST	NEW YORK, NY	10023
CARTER, STEVE	BASEBALL	POST OFFICE BOX 6212	TOLEDO, OH	43614
CARTER, STEVE	BASEBALL TRAINER	POST OFFICE BOX 2785	LAKELAND, FL	33806
CARTER, T K	ACTOR	KAMENS, 12831 MULHOLLAND DR	BEVERLY HILLS, CA	90210
CARTER, TERRY	ACTOR	447 9TH ST	SANTA MONICA, CA	90402
CARTER, THOMAS	ACTOR-DIRECTOR	10958 STRATHMORE DR	LOS ANGELES, CA	90024
CARTER, TIM	BASEBALL	POST OFFICE BOX 8550	STOCKTON, CA	95208
CARTER, TOM	BASEBALL	5301 NW 12TH AVE	FORT LAUDERDALE, FL	33309
CARTER CASH, JUNE & THE CARTER	C & W GROUP	11777 SAN VINCENTE BLVD #638	LOS ANGELES, CA	90049
CARTER FAMILY, THE	VOCAL GROUP	POST OFFICE BOX 508	HENDERSONVILLE, TN	37075
CARTER HOLBROOK, DIXIE	ACTRESS	10100 SANTA MONICA BLVD #1600	LOS ANGELES, CA	90067
CARTERET, ANNA	ACTRESS	HIGHCOMBE FARMHOUSE		
		THE DEVIL'S PUNCHBOWL		
		THURSLEY, GODALMING	SURREY GU8 6NS	ENGLAND
CARTERIS, GABRIELLE	ACTRESS	5700 WILSHIRE BLVD #575	LOS ANGELES, CA	90036
CARTEY, SIMEON A T	TV WRITER	45 W 132ND ST #10-C	NEW YORK, NY	10037
CARTHEN, ANDRE E	ACTOR	11712 MOORPARK ST #204	STUDIO CITY, CA	91604
CARTHON, MAURICE	FOOTBALL	N Y GIANTS, GIANTS STADIUM	EAST RUTHERFORD, NJ	07073

Name	Occupation	Address	City	Zip/Country
CARTLAND, BARBARA	NOVELIST	CAMFIELD PL, HATFIELD	HERTFORDSHIRE	ENGLAND
CARTLIDGE, WILLIAM	FILM PRODUCER	22 SAINT HELEN'S CT	SOUTHSEA PO4 ORR	ENGLAND
CARTWRIGHT, ANGELA	ACTRESS	10112 RIVERSIDE DR	TOLUCA LAKE, CA	91602
CARTWRIGHT, BILL	BASKETBALL	980 N MICHIGAN AVE #1600	CHICAGO, IL	60611
CARTWRIGHT, JORCA	ACTRESS	10250 SUNSET BLVD	LOS ANGELES, CA	90024
CARTWRIGHT, JUSTIN	WRITER-PRODUCER	9165 SUNSET BLVD #202	LOS ANGELES, CA	90069
CARTWRIGHT, LIONEL	SINGER-SONGWRITER	33 MUSIC SQUARE W #106-B	NASHVILLE, TN	37203
CARTWRIGHT, LYNN	ACTRESS	3349 W CAHUENGA BLVD #2-B	LOS ANGELES, CA	90068
CARTWRIGHT, NANCY	ACTRESS	3822 LAVELL DR	LOS ANGELES, CA	90065
CARTWRIGHT, VERONICA	ACTRESS	161 W 15TH ST #2-H	NEW YORK, NY	10011
CARUSO, ANTHONY	ACTOR	721 E GRINNELL DR	BURBANK, CA	91501
CARUSO, DAVID	ACTOR	SMITH, 121 N SAN VICENTE BLVD	BEVERLY HILLS, CA	90211
CARUSO, DONALD K	WRITER	11916 SATAIR TERR	LOS ANGELES, CA	90049
CARUSO, JOE	BASEBALL	POST OFFICE BOX 10213	LYNCHBURG, VA	24506
CARUSO, KRISTIN	ACTRESS	1803 N WILTON PL #104	HOLLYWOOD, CA	90028
CARUSO, RICHARD	ACTOR	915 POPPY ST	LOS ANGELES, CA	90042
CARVAJAL, JOVINO	BASEBALL	5301 NW 12TH AVE	FORT LAUDERDALE, FL	33309
CARVEN, MICHAEL	ACTOR	9165 SUNSET BLVD #202	LOS ANGELES, CA	90069
CARVER, JOHNNY	SINGER-SONGWRITER	WILLIAMS, 9 LUCY LN	SHERWOOD, AR	72116
CARVER, MARY	ACTRESS	9200 SUNSET BLVD #710	LOS ANGELES, CA	90069
CARVER, RANDALL	ACTOR	12032 1/2 GUERIN ST	STUDIO CITY, CA	91604
CARVER, RON L	COMPOSER-CONDUCTOR	1637 N VINE ST #713	LOS ANGELES, CA	90028
CARVER, STEVE	FILM DIRECTOR	1010 PACIFIC AVE	VENICE, CA	90291
CARVEY, DANA	COMEDIENNE	9200 SUNSET BLVD #428	LOS ANGELES, CA	90069
CARY, CHRISTOPHER	ACTOR	1930 CENTURY PARK W #403	LOS ANGELES, CA	90067
CARY, CHUCK	BASEBALL	1155 W MOUND ST	COLUMBUS, OH	43223
CARY, LOU	SINGER	64 DIVISION AVE #216	LEVITTOWN, NY	11756
CASADOS, ELOY PHIL	ACTOR	840 N AVE #63	LOS ANGELES, CA	90042
CASADY, CORT	TV WRITER	1543 SUNSET PLAZA DR	LOS ANGELES, CA	90069
CASAGRANDE, ALAN H	COMPOSER	9169 ALCOTT ST #7	LOS ANGELES, CA	90035
CASALAINA, VINCENT	DIRECTOR-PRODUCER	2418 STUART ST	BERKELEY, CA	94705
CASALS, ROSIE	TENNIS	1505 BRIDGEWAY #208	SAUSALITO, CA	94965
CASAMENTO, MARLENE	ACTRESS	1680 N VINE ST #203	HOLLYWOOD, CA	90028
CASANOV, BARON	ACTOR	SNOWSHAFT, WICKHAM HOUSE #10		
		10 CLEVELAND WY	LONDON E1 4TR	ENGLAND
CASAROTTI, RICH	BASEBALL	POST OFFICE BOX 6667	RICHMOND, VA	23230
CASAZZA, JANICE	TV WRITER	132 1/2 N MAPLE ST	BURBANK, CA	91505
CASE, EUGENE L	WRITER-PRODUCER	445 PARK AVE	NEW YORK, NY	10022
CASE, HAROLD	CINEMATOGRAPHER	34 CUNNINGHAM PARK, HARROW	MIDDLESEX HA1 4AL	ENGLAND
CASE, PETER	SINGER-SONGWRITER	10100 SANTA MONICA BLVD #1600	LOS ANGELES, CA	90067
CASE, ROBERT MAXWELL	SINGER	2393 POLEBRIDGE RD	AVON, NY	14414
CASE, SCOTT	FOOTBALL	FALCONS, SUWANEE RD AT I-85	SUWANEE, GA	30174
CASEI, NEDDA	MEZZO SOPRANO	15 W 72ND ST	NEW YORK, NY	10023
CASELLA, MAX	ACTOR	ABC-TV, 2040 AVE OF THE STARS	LOS ANGELES, CA	90067
CASELLI, LAMAR	DIRECTOR	6019 BUFFALO AVE #B	VAN NUYS, CA	91401
CASELOTTI, ADRIANA	VOICE SPECIALIST	201 N LARCHMONT BLVD	LOS ANGELES, CA	90004
CASEY, BERNIE	ACTOR-FOOTBALL	6145 FLIGHT AVE	LOS ANGELES, CA	90056
CASEY, COLLEEN	ACTRESS-SINGER	8831 SUNSET BLVD #304	LOS ANGELES, CA	90069
CASEY, DON	BASKETBALL COACH	151 MERRIMAC ST	BOSTON, MA	02114
CASEY, HARRY "K C"	SINGER-ACTOR	7764 NW 71ST ST	MIAMI, FL	33166
CASEY, JULIE	ACTRESS	3761 LAS FLORES CANYON RD	MALIBU, CA	90265
CASEY, PAUL A	TV WRITER	9100 SUNSET BLVD #340	LOS ANGELES, CA	90069
CASEY, PETER	TV WRITER-PRODUCER	1650 WESTWOOD BLVD #201	LOS ANGELES, CA	90024
CASEY, ROBERT P	GOVERNOR	STATE CAPITOL BUILDING	HARRISBURG, PA	17120
CASEY, SUE	ACTRESS	9255 SUNSET BLVD #401	WEST HOLLYWOOD, CA	90069
CASEY, WARREN	COMPOSER-LYRICIST	ICM, 40 W 57TH ST	NEW YORK, NY	10019
CASH, ANTHONY	DIRECTOR-PRODUCER	7 LILLYVILLE RD	LONDON SW6	ENGLAND
CASH, DAVE	BASEBALL-INSTRUCTOR	POST OFFICE BOX 7575	PHILADELPHIA, PA	19101
CASH, JACK	WRITER	1333 N STANLEY AVE #A-17	LOS ANGELES, CA	90046
CASH, JAMES	ACTOR	FELBER, 2126 N CAHUENGA BLVD	LOS ANGELES, CA	90068
CASH, JIM S	ACTOR	3924 LAUREL CANYON BLVD #4	STUDIO CITY, CA	91604
CASH, JOHN CARTER	SINGER	711 SUMMERFIELD DR	HENDERSONVILLE, TN	37075
CASH, JOHNNY	SINGER-SONGWRITER	711 SUMMERFIELD DR	HENDERSONVILLE, TN	37075
CASH, JUNE CARTER	SINGER-GUITARIST	711 SUMMERFIELD DR	HENDERSONVILLE, TN	37075
CASH, KELLYE	MISS AMERICA (1987)	1935 SUNSET DR #98	ESCONDIDO, CA	92025
CASH, KERRY	FOOTBALL	POST OFFICE BOX 535000	INDIANPOLIS, IN	46253
CASH, PAT	TENNIS	281 CLARENCE ST	SYDNEY NSW 2000	AUSTRALIA
CASH, ROSALIND	ACTRESS	118 PARK PL #D	VENICE, CA	90291
CASH, ROSANNE	SINGER-SONGWRITER	SIDE ONE, 1775 BROADWAY, 7TH FL	NEW YORK, NY	10019
CASH, TOMMY	SINGER-SONGWRITER	1300 DIVISION ST #103-A	NASHVILLE, TN	37203
CASHEN, J FRANK	BASEBALL EXECUTIVE	METS, 126TH ST & ROOSEVELT AVE	FLUSHING, NY	11368
CASHION, RED	FOOTBALL REFEREE	NFL, 410 PARK AVE	NEW YORK, NY	10022
CASHMAN, MICHAEL	ACTOR	DAWSON, 47 COURTFIELD RD #9	LONDON SW7 4DB	ENGLAND
CASIAN, LARRY	BASEBALL	POST OFFICE BOX 1659	PORTLAND, OR	97207
CASILLA, ROBERT	ARTIST	36 HAMILTON AVE	YONKERS, NY	10705
CASILLAS, ADAM	BASEBALL	800 HOME RUN LN	MEMPHIS, TN	38104
CASILLAS, TONY	FOOTBALL	COWBOYS, 1 COWBOYS PARKWAY	IRVING, TX	75063
CASO, PATRICIA	TV PRODUCER	WABC-TV, 7 LINCOLN SQ	NEW YORK, NY	10023
CASON, BARBARA	ACTRESS	5750 WILSHIRE BLVD #512	LOS ANGELES, CA	90036
CASORLA, RICK	ACTOR	850 7TH AVE #1003	NEW YORK, NY	10019
CASPARI, CHERI	ACTRESS	8075 W 3RD ST #550	LOS ANGELES, CA	90048
CASPARY, DENNIS	ACTOR	8465 SAMRA DR	CANOGA PARK, CA	91304
CASPARY, KATRINA "TINA"	ACTRESS	11350 VENTURA BLVD #206	STUDIO CITY, CA	91604
CASPER, BILLY	GOLFER	14 QUIET MEADOW LN	MAPLETON, UT	84663
CASS, CHRISTOPHER	ACTOR	ABC-TV, "LOVING"		

	....	320 W 66TH ST, STUDIO 23	NEW YORK, NY 10023
CASS, DAVID S	DIRECTOR	15021 LARKSPUR ST	SYLMAR, CA 91342
CASS, RONNIE	WRITER-COMPOSER	27-A ELSWORTHY RD	LONDON NW3 3BT .... ENGLAND
CASSADY, HOP	BASEBALL COACH	1155 W MOUND ST	COLUMBUS, OH 43223
CASSAVETES, NICK	ACTOR	22722 CLARENDON ST	WOODLAND HILLS, CA 91367
CASSEL, JEAN-PIERRE	ACTOR	ICM, 388-396 OXFORD ST	LONDON W1 .... ENGLAND
CASSEL, SEYMOUR	ACTOR	POST OFFICE BOX 5617	BEVERLY HILLS, CA 90213
CASSELS, ANDREW	HOCKEY	CANADIENS, 2313 ST CATHERINE ST .	MONTREAL, QUE H3H 1N2 ..... CANADA
CASSERLY, CHARLES	FOOTBALL EXECUTIVE ..	POST OFFICE BOX 17247 (DULLES) ..	WASHINGTON, DC 20041
CASSIDY, BRUCE	COMPOSER	7319 RUBIO AVE	VAN NUYS, CA 91406
CASSIDY, JOANNA	ACTRESS	463 MESA RD	SANTA MONICA, CA 90402
CASSIDY, MIKE	BASEBALL	POST OFFICE BOX 5599	LITTLE ROCK, AR 72215
CASSIDY, PATRICK	ACTOR	10433 WILSHIRE BLVD #605	LOS ANGELES, CA 90024
CASSIDY, RYAN	ACTOR	701 N OAKHURST DR	BEVERLY HILLS, CA 90210
CASSIDY, SHAUN	ACTOR-SINGER	ICM, 8899 BEVERLY BLVD	LOS ANGELES, CA 90048
CASSIDY, WILLIAM	DIRECTOR	DGA, 7920 SUNSET BLVD, 6TH FL ...	LOS ANGELES, CA 90046
CASSINI, OLEG	FASHION DESIGNER	3 W 57TH ST	NEW YORK, NY 10019
CASSITY, JAMES J	FILM WRITER-PRODUCER	10858 DANUBE AVE	GRANADA HILLS, CA 91344
CASSON, PHILIP	TV DIRECTOR	21-E BALCOMBE ST	LONDON NW1 .... ENGLAND
CASSUTT, MICHAEL	TV WRITER-EXECUTIVE .	5523 RANCHITO AVE	VAN NUYS, CA 91401
CAST, EDWARD	ACT-WRI-DIR	SAINT JAMES'S MANAGEMENT	....
	....	4 BANKSIDE DR, THAMES DITTON	SURREY KT7 OAQ .... ENGLAND
CAST, TRICIA	ACTRESS	CBS-TV, "YOUNG & THE RESTLESS" ..	....
	....	7800 BEVERLY BLVD #3305	LOS ANGELES, CA 90036
CASTALDO, VINCE	BASEBALL	POST OFFICE DRAWER 4797	EL PASO, TX 79914
CASTANEDA, NICK	BASEBALL	POST OFFICE BOX 36407	LOUISVILLE, KY 40233
CASTEL, COLLETTE	ACTRESS	36 BIS, QUAI LOUIS BLER	PARIS 75016 .... FRANCE
CASTELLANETA, DAN	ACTOR	328 POQUITO LN	TOPANGA, CA 90290
CASTELLANO, FREDDIE	ACTOR	15 PALOMA AVE #102	VENICE, CA 90291
CASTELLANO, MIGUEL	BASEBALL	POST OFFICE BOX 3609	PORT CHARLOTTE, FL 33949
CASTELLANO, PETE	BASEBALL	CUBS, 2ND & RIVERSIDE DR	DES MOINES, IA 50309
CASTELLANOS, JOHN	ACTOR	CBS-TV, "YOUNG & THE RESTLESS" ..	....
	....	7800 BEVERLY BLVD #3305	LOS ANGELES, CA 90036
CASTELLINO, WILLIAM J	ACTOR	732 N HARPER AVE	LOS ANGELES, CA 90046
CASTELLUCCIO, FEDERICO	ARTIST	345 21ST ST	PATTERON, NJ 07501
CASTELO, MEL	ACTRESS	POST OFFICE BOX 11789	MARINA DEL REY, CA 90295
CASTIGLIONE, JOE	BASEBALL-ANNOUNCER ..	WRKO-AM, 3 FENWAY PLAZA	BOSTON, MA 02215
CASTILE, CHRISTOPHER	ACTOR	ABC-TV, 2040 AVE OF THE STARS ...	LOS ANGELES, CA 90067
CASTILLA, VINNIE	BASEBALL	POST OFFICE BOX 6667	RICHMOND, VA 23230
CASTILLE, HADLEY J	SINGER-SONGWRITER ...	POST OFFICE DRAWER #10	VILLE PLATTE, LA 70586
CASTILLO, ALBERTO "BERT"	BASEBALL	525 NW PEACOCK BLVD	PORT SAINT LUCIE, FL 34986
CASTILLO, BENNY	BASEBALL	POST OFFICE BOX 3609	PORT CHARLOTTE, FL 33949
CASTILLO, BRAULIO	BASEBALL	POST OFFICE BOX 3449	SCRANTON, PA 18505
CASTILLO, CANDY	ACTOR	4216 ARICA AVE	ROSEMEAD, CA 91770
CASTILLO, CARLOS	BASEBALL	POST OFFICE BOX 10031	BAKERSFIELD, CA 93389
CASTILLO, CARMEN	BASEBALL	189 AUDUBON AVE #3-N	NEW YORK, NY 10032
CASTILLO, E J	ACTOR	3627 VALLEY MEADOW RD	SHERMAN OAKS, CA 91403
CASTILLO, FRANK	BASEBALL	1060 W ADDISON ST	CHICAGO, IL 60613
CASTILLO, GERALD	ACTOR	6858 DE LONGPRE AVE #3	HOLLYWOOD, CA 90028
CASTILLO, JUAN	BASEBALL (COLUMBIA) .	525 NW PEACOCK BLVD	PORT SAINT LUCIE, FL 34986
CASTILLO, ROBERTO	BASEBALL	POST OFFICE BOX 1742	PALM SPRINGS, CA 92263
CASTILLO, TONY	BASEBALL (MAJORS) ...	10300 JOYCE CT	SAN JOSE, CA 95127
CASTILLO, TONY	BASEBALL (MINORS) ...	POST OFFICE BOX 6212	TOLEDO, OH 43614
CASTLE, JOHN	ACTOR	DALZELL, 17 BROAD CT #12	LONDON WC2B 5QN .... ENGLAND
CASTLE, MICHAEL N	GOVERNOR	LEGISLATIVE HALL	DOVER, DE 19901
CASTLE, NICK	FILM WRITER-DIRECTOR	8458 RIDPATH DR	LOS ANGELES, CA 90046
CASTLE, ROY	ACTOR	LONDON MGT, 235-241 REGENT ST ...	LONDON W1R 4PH .... ENGLAND
CASTLE FAMILY, THE	MUSICAL GROUP	POST OFFICE BOX 11669	KNOXVILLE, TN 37939
CASTLEBERRY, KEVIN	BASEBALL	1090 N EUCLID AVE	SARASOTA, FL 34237
CASTON, TOBY	FOOTBALL	LIONS, 1200 FEATHERSTONE RD	PONTIAC, MI 48432
CASTOR, JIMMY	SINGER-SONGWRITER ...	1 KINDERKAMACK RD #100	ORADELL, NJ 07649
CASTRO, BILL	BASEBALL-COACH	BREWERS, 201 S 46TH ST	MILWAUKEE, WI 53214
CASTRO, EDUARDO	COSTUME DESIGNER	2026 N ARGYLE AVE	HOLLYWOOD, CA 90068
CASTRO, FIDEL	PRESIDENT	PALACIO DEL GOBIERNO	HAVANA .... CUBA
CASTRO, JOE	COMPOSER-CONDUCTOR ..	2812 COLANTHE AVE	LAS VEGAS, NV 89102
CASTRO, JOSE	BASEBALL COACH	POST OFFICE BOX 6748	ROCKFORD, IL 61125
CASTRO, JUAN	BASEBALL	POST OFFICE BOX 10031	BAKERSFIELD, CA 93389
CASTRO, NELSON	BASEBALL	POST OFFICE BOX 10031	BAKERSFIELD, CA 93389
CASTRO, SHIP, BAND	RHYTHM & BLUES GROUP	POST OFFICE BOX 210103	SAN FRANCISCO, CA 94121
CASTRONOVO, T J	ACTOR	1930 CENTURY PARK W #403	LOS ANGELES, CA 90067
CASWELL, OZZIE	COMPOSER-CONDUCTOR ..	240 ACARI DR	LOS ANGELES, CA 90049
CATALA, MURIEL	ACTRESS	JACQUES ITAH AGENCE	....
	....	15 RUE CHATEAUBRIAND	PARIS 75016 .... FRANCE
CATAREVAS, LUNA	ACTRESS	5900 ARLINGTON AVE	NEW YORK, NY 10471
CATAVOLOS, GEORGE	FOOTBALL COACH	POST OFFICE BOX 535000	INDIANPOLIS, IN 46253
CATCHING, J P "BILL"	DIRECTOR	POST OFFICE BOX AH	SOMERTON, AZ 85350
CATER, JOHN	ACTOR	MARSHALL, 44 PERRYN RD	LONDON W3 7NA .... ENGLAND
CATES, GEORGE	CONDUCTOR	1221 OCEAN AVE #1107	SANTA MONICA, CA 90401
CATES, GILBERT	FILM DIRECTOR	936 HILTS AVE	LOS ANGELES, CA 90024
CATES, JOSEPH	WRITER-PRODUCER	CATES FILMS, 57 E 74TH ST	NEW YORK, NY 10021
CATES, MADELYN	ACTRESS	155 BANK ST	NEW YORK, NY 10014
CATES, PHOEBE	ACTRESS	HAGGERTY, 677 W END AVE	NEW YORK, NY 10025
CATES, RON	TV DIRECTOR	2835 OAKPOINT DR	LOS ANGELES, CA 90068
CATHCART, DICK	COMPOSER	6414 LUBAO AVE	WOODLAND HILLS, CA 91364
CATHCART, JACK W	COMPOSER	2635 WYANDOTTE ST #1	LAS VEGAS, NV 89102

BECOME A VISIBLE FAN!

YOU ARE A FAN...
I KNOW ONE WHEN I SEE ONE...
YOU CAN'T DENY IT
DEATH DOES NOT RELEASE YOU, Y'KNOW

If you are a collector, dealer, publisher, convention organizer, or just an interested fan, you can get a FREE listing of your name, address, and special interests in the **Fandom Directory**.

Get in the listings so that others can find you; fans who share your interests, fanzine editors, movie industry publicity agents who make interesting mailings, and loads of other fascinating people who want to contact fans and fandom.

Fandom Directory is published in March and wants all the names and addresses it can collect in order to increase its usefulness to international fandom.

To be listed free of charge, just fill out the data form below and mail it in today!

DATA FORM

STATUS (Limit 5)

( ) Ad Agency
( ) Amateur Press Assoc.
( ) Artist
( ) Club Officer
( ) Collector
( ) Convention
( ) Convention Organizer
( ) Convention Volunteer
( ) Direct Distributor
( ) Editor
( ) Fan
( ) Game(PBM) Moderator
( ) Library
( ) Mail Order Retailer
( ) Manufacturer
( ) Club
( ) Professional
( ) Publication
( ) Publisher
( ) Subscription Service
( ) Store
( ) System Operator
( ) Translator
( ) Writer

INTERESTS (Limit 10)

( ) Action/Adventure
( ) Alternate Press
( ) Amateur Press Assoc.
( ) Animation
( ) Artzines
( ) Isaac Asimov
( ) Audio Tapes
( ) Autographs
( ) Carl Barks
( ) Baseball Cards
( ) Battlestar Galactica
( ) Beauty & the Beast
( ) Beer Cans
( ) Big Little Books
( ) Blake's 7
( ) Books (Hardcover)
( ) Ray Bradbury
( ) Edgar Rice Burroughs
( ) Classic Comics
( ) Comic Books
( ) Comic Strips/Cartoons
( ) Computers
( ) Costumes
( ) Creative Anacronisms
( ) Dark Shadows
( ) Darkover
( ) DC Comics
( ) Dell Comics
( ) Disney
( ) Doctor Who
( ) Dragons & Unicorns
( ) Dungeons & Dragons
( ) EC Comics
( ) Elfquest
( ) Harlan Ellison
( ) Everything!
( ) Fantasy
( ) Fanzines
( ) Filking
( ) Films
( ) Foreign Comics
( ) Foreign Video/TV
( ) Funny Animals
( ) Gaming Advocacy
( ) Gold Key Comics
( ) Golden Age Comics
( ) Good Girl Art
( ) Robert Heinlein
( ) Horror
( ) Humor
( ) Japanese Animation
( ) H.P. Lovecraft
( ) Magazines
( ) Marvel Comics
( ) Anne McCaffrey
( ) Models/Miniatures
( ) Movie Material
( ) Mystery
( ) Non-sports Cards
( ) Occult
( ) Old Time Radio
( ) Original Art
( ) Paper Collectibles
( ) Paperbacks
( ) Pen Pals
( ) Play-by-mail Games
( ) Porfolios/Prints
( ) Posters
( ) Premiums
( ) Prisoner
( ) Props
( ) Pulps
( ) Rare Books/1st Editions
( ) Regency Dancing
( ) Records
( ) Rock & Roll
( ) Rocky Horror
( ) Role/War Gaming
( ) Science
( ) Science Fiction
( ) Silver Age Comics
( ) Space
( ) Space: 1999
( ) Special Effects
( ) Spies/Espionage
( ) Star Trek
( ) Star Trek: TNG
( ) Star Wars
( ) Storage Supplies
( ) Super Heroes
( ) Sword & Sorcery
( ) Television
( ) Timely Comics
( ) J.R.R. Tolkien
( ) Toys
( ) Trading Cards
( ) Underground Comics
( ) 'V'
( ) Jack Vance
( ) Video Games
( ) Video Tape
( ) War Comics
( ) Warren Magazines
( ) Westerns
( ) Other: ____________
____

Last Name | First Name | Middle | Male | Female

Company/Organization | Year of Birth

Street Address / Post Office Box

USE BLOCK LETTERS. LEAVE SPACES. DO NOT PUNCTUATE.

City | State/Prov. | Zip/Postal Code | Zip+4 | Country

Voice Telephone

FAX Telephone

FANDATA c/o Bill Cole Enterprises
Post Office Box 60
Randolph, MA 02368-0060

Photocopy this form for friends, clubs, newsletters.

Enclose Self-Addressed Stamped Envelope for notice of publication.

CATHERINE, ESCOUDE & LOCKWOOD	JAZZ TRIO	KURLAND, 173 BRIGHTON AVE	BOSTON, MA 02134
CATINGUB, MATTHEW M	COMPOSER-CONDUCTOR	7120 BELLAIRE AVE	NORTH HOLLYWOOD, CA 91605
CATLEDGE, TERRY	BASKETBALL	POST OFFICE BOX 76	ORLANDO, FL 32802
CATLETT, MARY JO	ACTRESS	4375 FARMDALE AVE	NORTH HOLLYWOOD, CA 91604
CATLIN, MICHAEL	ACTOR	3495 LA SOMBRA DR	LOS ANGELES, CA 90068
CATLIN, TOM	FOOTBALL COACH	SEAHAWKS, 11220 NE 53RD ST	KIRKLAND, WA 98033
CATLIN, VICTORIA	ACTRESS	301 N CANON DR #305	BEVERLY HILLS, CA 90210
CATLING, DARREL	WRITER-PRODUCER	TRAVELLERS REST, CHURCH ST	OLD HATFIELD, HERTS ENGLAND
CATON-JONES, MICHAEL	FILM DIRECTOR	ENGIMA FILMS, PINEWOOD STUDIOS	
		IVER HEATH	BUCKS SLO ONH ENGLAND
CATRON, STANLEY R	MUSIC EXECUTIVE	BROADCAST MUSIC, 320 W 57TH ST	NEW YORK, NY 10019
CATT, RICHARD	ACTOR	1327 STANFORD ST #5	SANTA MONICA, CA 90404
CATTANO, JANET	ACTRESS	615 ASHTABULA ST #2	PASADENA, CA 91104
CATTELL, CHRISTINE	ACTRESS	8721 SANTA MONICA BLVD #21	WEST HOLLYWOOD, CA 90069
CATTRALL, KIM	ACTRESS	760 N LA CIENEGA BLVD #200	LOS ANGELES, CA 90069
CAU, JEAN	ACTOR	13 RUE DE SEINE	PARIS 75006 FRANCE
CAUFIELD, JAY	HOCKEY	PENGUINS, CIVIC ARENA, CENTRE AV	PITTSBURGH, PA 15219
CAULFIELD, MAXWELL	ACTOR	4036 FOOTHILL RD	CARPINTERIA, CA 93013
CAUNTER, TONY	ACTOR	HOPESAY, 1 NEW HOUSE YARD	
		SALFORD, CHIPPING NORTON	OXON ENGLAND
CAUSWELL, DUANE	BASKETBALL	KINGS, 1 SPORTS PARKWAY	SACRAMENTO, CA 95834
CAUTHERN, KENNETH	WRITER	13949 WEDDINGTON ST	VAN NUYS, CA 91401
CAUTIOUS DREAMS	ROCK & ROLL GROUP	100 BULIAM LN	AUSTIN, TX 78746
CAVALERI, RAY	TALENT AGENT	6605 HOLLYWOOD BLVD #220	HOLLYWOOD, CA 90028
CAVALIER, CARRIE E	ACTRESS	3200 WYOMING AVE	BURBANK, CA 91505
CAVALIER, JOE	DIRECTOR-PRODUCER	4185 ARCH DR	STUDIO CITY, CA 91604
CAVALIERE, FELIX	SINGER-PIANIST	65 W 55TH ST #306	NEW YORK, NY 10019
CAVALLINI, GINO	HOCKEY	BLUES, 5700 OAKLAND AVE	SAINT LOUIS, MO 63110
CAVALLINI, PAUL	HOCKEY	BLUES, 5700 OAKLAND AVE	SAINT LOUIS, MO 63110
CAVALLO, ROBERT	FILM PRODUCER	11340 W OLYMPIC BLVD #357	LOS ANGELES, CA 90064
CAVANAUGH, JAMES J	CONDUCTOR	1631 SEAL WY	SEAL BEACH, CA 90740
CAVANAUGH, LISA	ACTRESS	6525 SUNSET BLVD #303	HOLLYWOOD, CA 90028
CAVANAUGH, MATT	FOOTBALL	N Y GIANTS, GIANTS STADIUM	EAST RUTHERFORD, NJ 07073
CAVANAUGH, MICHAEL	ACTOR	301 N CANON DR #305	BEVERLY HILLS, CA 90210
CAVAS, CHRISTOPHER P	TV DIRECTOR	5350 MAC ARTHUR BLVD, NW	WASHINGTON, DC 20016
CAVAZZINI, JAMES J	TV EXECUTIVE	ESPN PLAZA, 935 MIDDLEST	BRISTOL, CT 06010
CAVAZZONI, KEN	BASEBALL	POST OFFICE BOX 4669	CHARLESTON, WV 25304
CAVE, NICK & THE BAD SEEDS	ROCK & ROLL GROUP	POST OFFICE BOX 570	ROCKVILLE CENTRE, NY 11571
CAVENDISH, ROBERT	ACTOR	LM AGENCY, 213 EDGWARE RD	LONDON W2 1ES ENGLAND
CAVESTANI, FRANK J	TV WRITER	7120 PACIFIC VIEW DR	LOS ANGELES, CA 90068
CAVETT, DICK	TV HOST-COMEDIAN	2200 FLETCHER AVE	FORT LEE, NJ 07024
CAVETT, MORGAN A	COMPOSER	7923 1/2 NORTON AVE	LOS ANGELES, CA 90046
CAVOLINA, LAWRENCE A	TV DIRECTOR	214-31 38TH AVE	NEW YORK, NY 11361
CAWLFIELD, CONSTANCE	ACTRESS	17009 JEANINE PL	GRANADA HILLS, CA 91344
CAYETANO, BENJAMIN	LT GOVERNOR	STATE CAPITOL BUILDING	HONOLULU, HI 96813
CAYLOR, FLORENCE B	CONDUCTOR	191 ORANGE DR	SAN LUIS OBISPO, CA 93401
CAYLOR, JAMIE	FILM EDITOR	ACE, 1041 N FORMOSA AVE	WEST HOLLYWOOD, CA 90046
CAZDEN, JOANNA	SINGER-GUITARIST	POST OFFICE BOX 36-M-37	LOS ANGELES, CA 90036
CAZENOVE, CHRISTOPHER	ACTOR	KOHNER, 9169 SUNSET BLVD	LOS ANGELES, CA 90069
CEASE, WESLEY J	CONDUCTOR	POST OFFICE BOX 2043	GLENDALE, CA 91209
CEBALLOS, CEDRIC	BASKETBALL	SUNS, 2910 N CENTRAL AVE	PHOENIX, AZ 85012
CECCALDI, DANIEL	ACTOR	81 RUE DE LONGCHAMP	NEUILLY 92200 FRANCE
CECCATO, ALDO	CONDUCTOR	ICM, 40 W 57TH ST	NEW YORK, NY 10019
CECCHETTI, GEORGE	BASEBALL SCOUT	INDIANS, CLEVELAND STADIUM	CLEVELAND, OH 44114
CECHVALA, ALPHONSE A	COMPOSER	1346 VALE VIEW AVE	GLENDORA, CA 91740
CECIL, CHUCK	FOOTBALL	PACKERS, 1265 LOMBARDI AVE	GREEN BAY, WI 54307
CECIL, JANE	ACTRESS	1697 BROADWAY	NEW YORK, NY 10019
CECIL, JONATHAN	ACTOR	43-A PRINCESS RD, REGENTS PK	LONDON NW1 8JS ENGLAND
CECILIA-MENDEZ, ZEIDA E	FILM DIRECTOR	2150 CENTER AVE #3-A	FORT LEE, NJ 07024
CEDAR, JON	ACTOR	2717 LAUREL CANYON BLVD	LOS ANGELES, CA 90046
CEDAR, LARRY	ACTOR	5741 VESPER AVE	VAN NUYS, CA 91411
CEDAR, LOREN	ACTRESS	LAREN/FIELDS, 5119 NAGLE AVE	SHERMAN OAKS, CA 91423
CEDAR, LORRIE	ACTRESS	2717 LAUREL CANYON BLVD	LOS ANGELES, CA 90046
CEDAR, MICHAEL	ACTOR	5119 NAGLE AVE	SHERMAN OAKS, CA 91423
CEDAR CREEK	C & W GROUP	POST OFFICE BOX 1763	HENDERSONVILLE, TN 37075
CEDENO, ANDUJAR	BASEBALL	POST OFFICE BOX 288	HOUSTON, TX 77001
CEDENO, CESAR	BASEBALL	9919 SAGE DOWNE	HOUSTON, TX 77034
CEDENO, DOMINGO	BASEBALL	633 JESSAMINE ST	KNOXVILLE, TN 37917
CEDERSTROM, GARY	BASEBALL UMPIRE	POST OFFICE BOX 608	GROVE CITY, OH 43123
CELENTINO, LUCIANO	WRITER-PRODUCER	ANGLO-FORTUNATO FILMS	
		170 POPES LN	LONDON W5 4NJ ENGLAND
CELESTINO, PETE	BASEBALL UMPIRE	POST OFFICE BOX 716	PLAINVILLE, CT 06062
CELICIA	ACTRESS	41 W 83RD ST	NEW YORK, NY 10024
CELLINO, MARIA ELENA	WRITER	2206 LAS LUNAS ST	PASADENA, CA 91107
CELLUCCI, ARGEO PAUL	LT GOVERNOR	STATE HOUSE BUILDING	BOSTON, MA 02133
CELTIC FROST	ROCK & ROLL GROUP	SECOND DIVISION MGMT	
		5 CROSBY ST	NEW YORK, NY 10013
CENARRUSA, PETE T	SECRETARY OF STATE	STATE HOUSE BUILDING	BOISE, ID 83720
CENTALA, SCOTT	BASEBALL	800 HOME RUN LN	MEMPHIS, TN 38104
CENTENO, HENRI	BASEBALL	POST OFFICE BOX 1556	ASHEVILLE, NC 28802
CENTENO, PEPITO	BASEBALL SCOUT	6850 LAWRENCE RD	LANTANA, FL 33462
CENTERS, LARRY	FOOTBALL	POST OFFICE BOX 888	PHOENIX, AZ 85001
CEPEDA, ORLANDO	BASEBALL	3 SOMMER RIDGE DR #156	ROSEVILLE, CA 95678
CEPICKY, SCOTT	BASEBALL	POST OFFICE BOX 360007	BIRMINGHAM, AL 35236
CERAME, MIKE	BASEBALL TRAINER	POST OFFICE BOX 814	PULASKI, VA 24301

CERES, VELA	ACTRESS	311 CAMPBELL ST	WOODBRIDGE, NJ 07095
CERF, CHRISTOPHER	WRITER	146 E 62ND ST	NEW YORK, NY 10021
CERIO, STEVE	BASEBALL	POST OFFICE BOX 3004	SPRINGFIELD, IL 62708
CERNAN, EUGENE	ASTRONAUT	900 TOWN & COUNTRY LN #210	HOUSTON, TX 77024
CERNY, PAVEL	DIRECTOR	11927 MAGNOLIA BLVD #18	NORTH HOLLYWOOD, CA 91607
CERNY, SCOTT	BASEBALL SCOUT	333 W 35TH ST	CHICAGO, IL 60616
CERONE, RICK	BASEBALL	METS, 126TH ST & ROOSEVELT AVE	FLUSHING, NY 11368
CERRELLA, GINNY	WRITER	1416 N HAVENHURST DR #1	LOS ANGELES, CA 90046
CERRONI, ANGELO	BASEBALL SCOUT	POST OFFICE BOX 2000	ANAHEIM, CA 92803
CERUTTI, JOHN	BASEBALL	POST OFFICE BOX 2365	PAWTUCKET, RI 02861
CERVANTES, GARY	ACTOR	2240 MARDEL AVE	WHITTIER, CA 90601
CERVANTES, MANNY	BASEBALL	POST OFFICE BOX 30160	SAN BERNARDINO, CA 92413
CERVI, BRUCE	ACTOR-WRITER	12042 GERALD AVE	GRANADA HILLS, CA 91344
CESLIK, CAROLYN	TV EXECUTIVE	CBS-TV, 51 W 52ND ST	NEW YORK, NY 10019
CETERA, PETER	SINGER-SONGWRITER	POST OFFICE BOX 326	MALIBU, CA 90265
CEY, RON	BASEBALL	22714 CREOLE RD	WOODLAND HILLS, CA 91364
CHAAPEL, EARL	FILM-TV PRODUCER	DARBO, 9142 CALAHENA BLVD	LOS ANGELES, CA 90016
CHABIDON, RON	ACTOR	FELBER, 2126 N CAHUENGA BLVD	LOS ANGELES, CA 90068
CHABUT, LA REINE	ACTRESS	1930 CENTURY PARK W #403	LOS ANGELES, CA 90067
CHAD & JEREMY	VOCAL DUO	9000 SUNSET BLVD #1200	LOS ANGELES, CA 90069
CHADBON, TOM	ACTOR	LADKIN, 11 SOUTHWICK MEWS	LONDON W2 1JG ENGLAND
CHADBOURNE, EUGENE	SINGER-SONGWRITER	THE OLD COLLARD HOUSE	
		251 RIO CIR	DECATUR, GA 30030
CHADDERTON, JUNE RANDOLPH	WRITER	654 1/2 KELTON AVE	LOS ANGELES, CA 90024
CHADWICK, FLORENCE	SWIMMER	814 ARMADA TERR	SAN DIEGO, CA 92106
CHADWICK, JEFF	FOOTBALL	SEAHAWKS, 11220 NE 53RD ST	KIRKLAND, WA 98033
CHADWICK, JUNE	ACTRESS	9300 WILSHIRE BLVD #410	BEVERLY HILLS, CA 90212
CHAFFEE, JOHN H	U S SENATOR	301 PASTORE FEDERAL BLDG	PROVIDENCE, RI 02903
CHAFFEE, SUZY	TV PERSONALITY	140 HOLLISTER AVE	SANTA MONICA, CA 90405
CHAFFEY, DON	TV DIRECTOR	7020 LA PRESA DR	LOS ANGELES, CA 90068
CHAFFEY, PAT	FOOTBALL	FALCONS, SUWANEE RD AT I-85	SUWANEE, GA 30174
CHAFFIN, KATHY	ACTRESS	200 N ROBERTSON BLVD #219	BEVERLY HILLS, CA 90211
CHAIN, BARBARA	WRITER	835 S HUDSON AVE	LOS ANGELES, CA 90005
CHAIN, MICHAEL	WRITER-COMPOSER	835 S HUDSON AVE	LOS ANGELES, CA 90005
CHAIN LINK FENCE	ROCK & ROLL GROUP	25 HUNTINGTON AVE #420	BOSTON, MA 02116
CHAING KAI-SHEK, MADAME	CELEBRITY	LOCUST VALLEY	LATTINGTOWN, NY 11560
CHAIRMEN OF THE BOARD	SOUL GROUP	INSIGHT TALENT, INC	
		2300 E INDEPENDENCE BLVD	CHARLOTTE, NC 28205
CHAIS, PAMELA HERBERT	WRITER	611 N OAKHURST DR	BEVERLY HILLS, CA 90210
CHAKIRIS, GEORGE	ACTOR	7266 CLINTON ST	LOS ANGELES, CA 90036
CHALK CIRCLE	ROCK & ROLL GROUP	CHRIS PEGG, 163 CRESCENT RD	TORONTO, ONT M4W 1V1 CANADA
CHALLENGERS, THE	C & W GROUP	J S EVANS, 7649 REFUGE RD, SW	PATOSKOLA, OH 43062
CHALLEY, TINA	ACTRESS	KJAR, 10653 RIVERSIDE DR	TOLUCA LAKE, CA 91602
CHALLIS, CHRISTOPHER	CINEMATOGRAPHER	WORLDMARK PRODS, THE OLD STUDIO	
		18 MIDDLE ROW	LONDON W10 5AT ENGLAND
CHALLIS, DRUMMOND	DIRECTOR-PRODUCER	WORLDMARK PRODS, THE OLD STUDIO	
		18 MIDDLE ROW	LONDON W10 5AT ENGLAND
CHALLY, CLIFFORD L	COSTUME DESIGNER	11046 KLING ST	NORTH HOLLYWOOD, CA 91602
CHALMERS, JUDITH	TV PERSONALITY	IMG, 23 EYOT GARDENS	LONDON W6 9TN ENGLAND
CHALOM, MARC	TV EXECUTIVE	THE ARTS & ENTERTAINMENT	
		CABLE NETWORK, 555 5TH AVE	NEW YORK, NY 10019
CHALVET, JACQUES	COMPOSER	221 AVE DE FABRON	NICE 06200 FRANCE
CHAMBARET, CATHERINE	COSTUME DESIGNER	5015 W 8TH ST	LOS ANGELES, CA 90005
CHAMBERLAIN, JEFF	ACTOR	4220 ALLOTT AVE	SHERMAN OAKS, CA 91423
CHAMBERLAIN, JEROME P	TV DIRECTOR	10 LAKE DR W	WAYNE, NJ 07470
CHAMBERLAIN, LACHELLE	ACTRESS	4220 ALLOTT AVE	SHERMAN OAKS, CA 91423
CHAMBERLAIN, RICHARD	ACTOR-PRODUCER	1030 GAYLEY AVE #208	LOS ANGELES, CA 90024
CHAMBERLAIN, WES	BASEBALL	POST OFFICE BOX 7575	PHILADELPHIA, PA 19101
CHAMBERLAIN, WILT	BASKETBALL	15216 ANTELO PL	LOS ANGELES, CA 90077
CHAMBERLIN, BETH	ACTRESS	8150 BEVERLY BLVD #201	LOS ANGELES, CA 90048
CHAMBERLIN, HAP	TV DIRECTOR	3467 PRIMERA DR	HOLLYWOOD, CA 90068
CHAMBERLIN, LEW	BASEBALL EXECUTIVE	POST OFFICE BOX 418	SAINT CHARLES, IL 60174
CHAMBERS, CATHY	SINGER	PEEVER, 2464 BRASILIA CIR	MISSISSAUGA, ONTARIO CANADA
CHAMBERS, DAVID L	TV WRITER-PRODUCER	151 S EL CAMINO DR	BEVERLY HILLS, CA 90212
CHAMBERS, DIANE	ACTRESS	757 S ORANGE GROVE BLVD #1	PASADENA, CA 91105
CHAMBERS, ERNEST	TV WRITER-PRODUCER	1438 N GOWER ST	LOS ANGELES, CA 90028
CHAMBERS, EVERETT	WRITER-PRODUCER	1277 SUNSET PLAZA DR	LOS ANGELES, CA 90069
CHAMBERS, GEORGE	ACTOR	7080 HOLLYWOOD BLVD #704	HOLLYWOOD, CA 90028
CHAMBERS, JEFFREY R	TV DIRECTOR	4726 1/2 FORMAN LN	NORTH HOLLYWOOD, CA 91602
CHAMBERS, MARIE	ACTRESS	1801 AVE OF THE STARS #1250	LOS ANGELES, CA 90067
CHAMBERS, MARILYN	ACTRESS-MODEL	4528 W CHARLESTON BLVD	LAS VEGAS, NV 89102
CHAMBERS, RICHARD O	DIRECTOR	1310 S WESTHOLME AVE	LOS ANGELES, CA 90024
CHAMBERS, SHAWN	HOCKEY	NORTH STARS, 7901 CEDAR AVE S	BLOOMINGTON, MN 55425
CHAMBERS, TERRY	FILM EDITOR	7230 WISH AVE	VAN NUYS, CA 91406
CHAMBERS, TOM	BASKETBALL	SUNS, 2910 N CENTRAL AVE	PHOENIX, AZ 85012
CHAMBERS, WILLIAM GEORGE	FILM EXECUTIVE	1 HONISTER GARDENS, STANMORE	MIDDLESEX ENGLAND
CHAMBLISS, CHRIS	BASEBALL-MANAGER	140 PROSPECT ST #11-N	HACKENSACK, NJ 07601
CHAMCHOUM, GEORGES	FILM WRITER-DIRECTOR	3847 TILDEN AVE	CULVER CITY, CA 90230
CHAMMETTE, FRANCOIS	ACTOR	13 RUE DE TRETAIGNE	PARIS 75018 FRANCE
CHAMORRO, VIOLETTA	PRESIDENT	PRESIDENTIAL PALACE	MANAGUA NICARAGUA
CHAMPA, JO	ACTRESS	ICM, 8899 BEVERLY BLVD	LOS ANGELES, CA 90048
CHAMPION, BILLY	BASEBALL SCOUT	1060 W ADDISON ST	CHICAGO, IL 60613
CHAMPION, DAVID	CONDUCTOR	229 15TH ST	MANHATTAN BEACH, CA 90266
CHAMPION, JOHN	WRITER-PRODUCER	16157 MORRISON ST	ENCINO, CA 91436
CHAMPION, KEITH	BASEBALL MANAGER	POST OFFICE BOX 611	WATERLOO, IA 50704

CHAMPION, KIRK	BASEBALL COACH	1090 N EUCLID AVE	SARASOTA, FL	34237
CHAMPION, MARGE	ACTRESS	484 W 43RD ST	NEW YORK, NY	10036
CHAMPLIN, CHARLES	FILM CRITIC	2169 LINDA FLORA DR	LOS ANGELES, CA	90077
CHAN, ERNIE	ARTIST	4131 VALE AVE	OAKLAND, CA	94619
CHAN, JANET	ACTRESS	SEE - LOUIE, BEBE		
CHAN, KIM	ACTOR	2229 VALENTINE AVE	BRONX, NY	10457
CHAN, MICHAEL PAUL	ACTOR	8235 SANTA MONICA BLVD #202	LOS ANGELES, CA	90046
CHAN, MICHELE B	ACTRESS	3800 BARHAM BLVD #303	LOS ANGELES, CA	90068
CHANCE, DEAN	BASEBALL	9505 W SMITHVILLE WESTERN	WOOSTER, OH	44691
CHANCE, LARRY & THE EARLS	VOCAL GROUP	MARS, 168 ORCHID DR	PEARL RIVER, NY	10965
CHANCE, TONY	BASEBALL	CUBS, 2ND & RIVERSIDE DR	DES MOINES, IA	50309
CHANCELLOR, JOHN	BROADCAST JOURNALIST	NBC NEWS, 4001 NEBRASKA AV, SW	WASHINGTON, DC	20016
CHANDLEE, RICHARD CREEL	WRITER	610 N ROSE ST	BURBANK, CA	91505
CHANDLER, BOB	SPORTSCASTER	POST OFFICE BOX 2000	SAN DIEGO, CA	92112
CHANDLER, CHRIS	FOOTBALL	BUCCANEERS, 1 BUCCANEER PL	TAMPA, FL	33607
CHANDLER, FLOYD	BASEBALL SCOUT	POST OFFICE BOX 419969	KANSAS CITY, MO	64141
CHANDLER, GENE	SINGER	11 N LA SALLE ST #815	CHICAGO, IL	60602
CHANDLER, JOHN (DAVID)	ACTOR	421 N PASS AVE #5	BURBANK, CA	91505
CHANDLER, KAREN MAYO	ACTRESS	3800 BARHAM BLVD #303	LOS ANGELES, CA	90068
CHANDLER, OTIS	ACTOR	1421 EMERSON	OXNARD, CA	93033
CHANDLER, ROD	U S CONGRESSMAN	50 116TH AVE #201, SW	BELLEVUE, WA	98008
CHANDLER, TOM	BASEBALL SCOUT	INDIANS, CLEVELAND STADIUM	CLEVELAND, OH	44114
CHANE, PEGGY	TV PRODUCER	CHANE PRODS, 353 W 57TH ST	NEW YORK, NY	10019
CHANEL, PATRICE	ACTRESS	19216 ANDMARK AVE	CARSON, CA	90746
CHANEL, TALLY	ACTRESS	MARX, 11130 HUSTON ST #6	NORTH HOLLYWOOD, CA	91601
CHANEY, DON	BASKETBALL COACH	POST OFFICE BOX 272349	HOUSTON, TX	77277
CHANEY, HAROLD LEE	SCREENWRITER	13201 ROSCOE BLVD	SUN VALLEY, CA	91352
CHANEY, JEFF	BASEBALL EXECUTIVE	333 W 35TH ST	CHICAGO, IL	60616
CHANG, ALAIN	ARTIST	1625 WALNUT ST #B	BERKELEY, CA	94709
CHANG, CATHY	BODYBUILDER	PHYSIQUE WORLD, INC		
		735 SHERIDAN ST #9	HONOLULU, HI	96814
CHANG, DONALD	BODYBUILDER	PHYSIQUE WORLD, INC		
		735 SHERIDAN ST #9	HONOLULU, HI	96814
CHANG, TISA	ACTRESS	305 RIVERSIDE DR	NEW YORK, NY	10025
CHANIN, JOHN G	DIRECTOR	15 CHRISTY LN	SPARTA, NJ	07871
CHANNING, CAROL	ACTRESS	9301 FLICKER WY	LOS ANGELES, CA	90069
CHANNING, STOCKARD	ACTRESS	10390 SANTA MONICA BLVD #300	LOS ANGELES, CA	90025
CHANTLER, DAVID T	WRITER	14001 PALAWAN WY #PH-18	MARINA DEL REY, CA	90292
CHAO, ROSALIND	ACTRESS	11726 SAN VICENTE BLVD #300	LOS ANGELES, CA	90049
CHAPEL, MAX LEE	ACTOR	6605 HOLLYWOOD BLVD #220	HOLLYWOOD, CA	90028
CHAPIN, DARRIN	BASEBALL	POST OFFICE BOX 3449	SCRANTON, PA	18505
CHAPIN, LAUREN	ACTRESS-AUTHORESS	POST OFFICE BOX 922	KILLEEN, TX	76541
CHAPIN, TOM	SINGER	57 PIERMONT PL	PIERMONT, NY	10968
CHAPLIN, GERALDINE	ACTRESS	6 RUE ASSELINE	75015 PARIS	FRANCE
CHAPLIN, LITA GREY	ACTRESS	8440 FOUNTAIN AVE #302	HOLLYWOOD, CA	90069
CHAPLIN, SYDNEY	ACTOR	69950 FRANK SINATRA DR	RANCHO MIRAGE, CA	92270
CHAPMAN, ALAN	COMPOSER	4853 STRATFORD RD	LOS ANGELES, CA	90042
CHAPMAN, DAN	BASEBALL EXECUTIVE	POST OFFICE BOX 8550	STOCKTON, CA	95208
CHAPMAN, DAVID ELEY	FILM DIRECTOR	650 W END AVE	NEW YORK, NY	10025
CHAPMAN, DENISE	ARTIST	1529 LAWSON ST	HOUSTON, TX	77023
CHAPMAN, GARY	SINGER-SONGWRITER	BLANTON, 2910 POSTON AVE	NASHVILLE, TN	37203
CHAPMAN, JIM	U S CONGRESSMAN	POST OFFICE BOX 538	SULPHUR SPRINGS, TX	74482
CHAPMAN, JUDITH	ACTRESS	67810 MARILYN CIRCLE	CATHEDRAL CITY, CA	92234
CHAPMAN, LEE	FILM DIRECTOR	2359 STANLEY HILLS DR	LOS ANGELES, CA	90046
CHAPMAN, LEIGH	SCREENWRITER	8955 BEVERLY BLVD	WEST HOLLYWOOD, CA	90048
CHAPMAN, LONNY	ACTOR	3973 GOODLAND AVE	STUDIO CITY, CA	91604
CHAPMAN, MARK	BASEBALL	POST OFFICE BOX 15757	HARRISBURG, PA	17105
CHAPMAN, MARK	FILM DIRECTOR	ASPECT, 36 PERCY ST	LONDON W1	ENGLAND
CHAPMAN, MARK LINDSAY	ACTOR	6565 SUNSET BLVD #300	LOS ANGELES, CA	90028
CHAPMAN, MICHAEL	TV WRITER-PRODUCER	MLR, 200 FULHAM RD	LONDON SW10 9PN	ENGLAND
CHAPMAN, MICHAEL C	FILM DIRECTOR	DGA, 7920 SUNSET BLVD, 6TH FL	LOS ANGELES, CA	90046
CHAPMAN, MICHAEL J	ACTOR	12229 VENTURA BLVD #201	STUDIO CITY, CA	91604
CHAPMAN, MIKE	SINGER	FEVER, 50-A E 167TH ST	BRONX, NY	10452
CHAPMAN, PAUL	ACTOR	63 OAKWOOD RD	LONDON NW11 6RJ	ENGLAND
CHAPMAN, PRISCILLA	SCREENWRITER	8955 BEVERLY BLVD	WEST HOLLYWOOD, CA	90048
CHAPMAN, RANDY	SINGER	KNIGHT, 1609 CONGRESS RD	EASTOVER, SC	29044
CHAPMAN, REX	BASKETBALL	310 N KINGS DR	CHARLOTTE, NC	28204
CHAPMAN, RICHARD	TV PRODUCER	MCA/UNIVERSAL STUDIOS, INC		
		100 UNIVERSAL CITY PLAZA	UNIVERSAL CITY, CA	91608
CHAPMAN, STEPHEN	COMMENTATOR	THE CHICAGO TRIBUNE		
		TRIBUNE TOWER		
		435 N MICHIAGN AVE	CHICAGO, IL	60611
CHAPMAN, STEVEN CURTIS	SINGER-SONGWRITER	CAA, 9830 WILSHIRE BLVD	BEVERLY HILLS, CA	90212
CHAPMAN, THOMAS C	SCREENWRITER	8955 BEVERLY BLVD	WEST HOLLYWOOD, CA	90048
CHAPMAN, TRACY	SINGER-SONGWRITER	506 SANTA MONICA BLVD #400	SANTA MONICA, CA	90401
CHAPPEL, TINA	ACTRESS	FELBER, 2126 N CAHUENGA BLVD	LOS ANGELES, CA	90068
CHAPPELL, CRYSTAL	ACTRESS	18261 SAN FERNANDO MISSION BL	NORTHRIDGE, CA	91326
CHARBONNET, MARK	BASEBALL	POST OFFICE BOX 1886	COLUMBUS, GA	31902
CHARISSE, CYD	ACTRESS-DANCER	10390 WILSHIRE BLVD #1507	LOS ANGELES, CA	90024
CHARKHAM, BETH	CASTING DIRECTOR	122 WARDOUR ST	LONDON W1V 3LA	ENGLAND
CHARKHAM, ESTA	FILM PRODUCER	HEATH, PARAMOUNT HOUSE		
		162-170 WARDOUR ST	LONDON W1V 3AT	ENGLAND
CHARLAND, COLIN	BASEBALL	2501 ALLEN AVE, SE	CANTON, OH	44707
CHARLES, BOB	GOLFER	PGA SENIORS, 112 T P C BLVD	PONTE VEDRA BEACH, FL	32082
CHARLES, FRANK	BASEBALL	POST OFFICE BOX 1295	CLINTON, IA	52733

CHARLES, GLEN	WRITER-PRODUCER	1716 WESTRIDGE RD	LOS ANGELES, CA	90049
CHARLES, HARRIET	WRITER	1064 N CATALINA AVE	PASADENA, CA	91104
CHARLES, HRH	PRINCE	PRINCE OF WALES, KENSINGTON PAL	LONDON W8	ENGLAND
CHARLES, KEITH	ACTOR	CBS-TV, "AS THE WORLD TURNS"		
		524 W 57TH ST #5330	NEW YORK, NY	10019
CHARLES, LESLIE D	WRITER	9917 LANCER CT	BEVERLY HILLS, CA	90210
CHARLES, MARIA	ACTRESS	MC REDDIE, 91 REGENT ST	LONDON W1R 7TB	ENGLAND
CHARLES, MARTHA	ACTRESS	MC MILLAN, 126 N DOHENY DR	BEVERLY HILLS, CA	90211
CHARLES, NICK	SPORTSCASTER	CNN, 1050 TECHWOOD DR, NW	ATLANTA, GA	30318
CHARLES, RAY	SINGER-PIANIST	4863 SOUTHRIDGE AVE	LOS ANGELES, CA	90008
CHARLES, SUZETTE	MISS AMERICA-ACTRESS	1930 CENTURY PARK W #403	LOS ANGELES, CA	90067
CHARLES, WALTER	ACTOR	9255 SUNSET BLVD #515	LOS ANGELES, CA	90069
CHARLES, ZACHARY	ACTOR	CARROLL, 120 S VICTORY BL #104	BURBANK, CA	91502
CHARLESON, LESLIE	ACTRESS	2314 LIVE OAK DR E	LOS ANGELES, CA	90068
CHARLSON, CARL	DIRECTOR	DGA, 110 W 57TH ST	NEW YORK, NY	10019
CHARLTON, NORM	BASEBALL	16615 FRONT ROYALS ST	SAN ANTONIO, TX	78247
CHARMOLI, TONY	DIRECTOR-CHOREO	1271 SUNSET PLAZA DR	LOS ANGELES, CA	90069
CHARNAY, LYNNE	ACTRESS-SINGER	75 CENTRAL PARK W	NEW YORK, NY	10023
CHARNEY, JORDAN	ACTOR	9255 SUNSET BLVD #515	LOS ANGELES, CA	90069
CHARNIN, MARTIN	WRITER-PRODUCER	BEAM ONE LTD, 850 7TH AVE	NEW YORK, NY	10019
CHARNOTA, ANTHONY	ACTOR	7250 FRANKLIN AVE #506	LOS ANGELES, CA	90046
CHARNOW, STEVEN	WRITER	143 OCEAN PARK BLVD	SANTA MONICA, CA	90405
CHARNY, SUZANNE	ACTRESS	BARSKIN, 120 S VICTORY BL #104	BURBANK, CA	91502
CHARO	SINGER	POST OFFICE BOX 1007	HANALEI, KAUI, HI	96714
CHARTOFF, MELANIE	ACTRESS	444 S ROXBURY DR #A	BEVERLY HILLS, CA	90212
CHARTOFF, ROBERT	FILM PRODUCER	10125 W WASHINGTON BLVD	CULVER CITY, CA	90230
CHASE, BARRIE	ACTRESS-DANCER	3750 BEVERLY RIDGE DR	SHERMAN OAKS, CA	91423
CHASE, BARRY OLIVER	TV EXECUTIVE	PBS, 475 L'ENFANT PLAZA	WASHINGTON, DC	20024
CHASE, CHANNING	ACTRESS	CARROLL, 120 S VICTORY BL #104	BURBANK, CA	91502
CHASE, CHEVY	ACTOR-WRITER	8436 W 3RD ST #650	LOS ANGELES, CA	90048
CHASE, DAVID	TV WRITER-PRODUCER	CAA, 9830 WILSHIRE BLVD	BEVERLY HILLS, CA	90212
CHASE, DAVID HENRY	WRITER	13215 RIVIERA RANCH RD	LOS ANGELES, CA	90049
CHASE, FRANK	TV WRITER	213 OCEAN AVE	SANTA MONICA, CA	90403
CHASE, GARY J	COMPOSER	7920 MC LAREN AVE	CANOGA PARK, CA	91304
CHASE, LARRY	BASEBALL SCOUT	METS, 126TH ST & ROOSEVELT AVE	FLUSHING, NY	11368
CHASE, LEONARD	TV PRODUCER	5 REGENT SQ	LONDON WC1	ENGLAND
CHASE, LORRAINE	ACTRESS	CHARLESWORTH, 60 OLD BROMPTON	LONDON SW7 3LQ	ENGLAND
CHASE, RAMONA	WRITER	213 OCEAN AVE	SANTA MONICA, CA	90402
CHASE, REBECCA	NEWS CORRESPONDENT	ABC NEWS, 7 W 66TH ST	NEW YORK, NY	10023
CHASE, ROBERT	ACTOR	CASTLE, 1101 S ORLANDO AVE	LOS ANGELES, CA	90035
CHASE, SYLVIA	NEWS CORRESPONDENT	WM MORRIS, 1350 AVE OF AMERICAS	NEW YORK, NY	10019
CHASE, WILLIAM R	TV PRODUCER	152-16 33RD AVE	FLUSHING, NY	11354
CHASIN, PHYLLIS	ACTRESS	2640 1/2 23RD ST	SANTA MONICA, CA	90405
CHASIN, ROBERT	TV EXECUTIVE	COLUMBIA PICTURES TV		
		COLUMBIA PLAZA	BURBANK, CA	91505
CHASIN' THE BLUES	RHYTHM & BLUES GROUP	10 CHESTNUT ST #1105	EXETER, NH	03833
CHASMAN, DAVID	WRITER	1505 CARLA RIDGE DR	BEVERLY HILLS, CA	90210
CHASMAN, JULIA	PRODUCER	ROLLINS/JOFFE, 130 W 57TH ST	NEW YORK, NY	10019
CHASON, MYRA	ACTRESS	1800 N HIGHLAND AVE #405	LOS ANGELES, CA	90028
CHASTAIN, DON	ACTOR	4229 VIA ALONDRA	PALOS VERDES, CA	90274
CHASTAIN, JANE	ACTRESS	3219 CYN LAKE DR	HOLLYWOOD, CA	90068
CHATER, GEOFFREY	ACTOR	HUNTER, 13 SPENCER GARDENS	LONDON SW14	ENGLAND
CHATFIELD, LESLIE	TV DIRECTOR-PRODUCER	BBC-TV, 56 WOOD LN	LONDON W12 7RJ	ENGLAND
CHATFIELD, ROCCINA M	TV WRITER	6639 SUNNYSLOPE AVE	VAN NUYS, CA	91401
CHATINOVER, MARVIN A	ACTOR	22 AVALON RD	GREAT NECK, NY	11021
CHATMAN, DELLE	ACTRESS	5607 LA MIRADA AVE #402	LOS ANGELES, CA	90038
CHATMON, JOHN LEN	SINGER-PIANIST	SEE - MEMPHIS SLIM		
CHAUDHRI, AMIN QAMAR	WRI-DIR-PROD-ED	CONTINENTAL FILM GROUP		
		PARK ST	SHARON, PA	16146
CHAULS, ROBERT N	COMPOSER-CONDUCTOR	3451 VALLEY MEADOW RD	SHERMAN OAKS, CA	91403
CHAUVIN, LILYAN	ACT-WRI-DIR	3841 EUREKA DR	STUDIO CITY, CA	91604
CHAVEZ, CESAR	LABOR LEADER	BOX 62, LA PAZ	KEENE, CA	93531
CHAVEZ, JOHN A	TV EXECUTIVE	ABC-TV, 2040 AVE OF THE STARS	LOS ANGELES, CA	90067
CHAVEZ, RAFAEL	BASEBALL	12000 STADIUM RD	ADELANTO, CA	92301
CHAVEZ, RAUL	BASEBALL	POST OFFICE BOX 1556	ASHEVILLE, NC	28802
CHAVOUS, BARNEY	FOOTBALL COACH	BRONCOS, 13655 BRONCOS PKWY	ENGLEWOOD, CO	80112
CHAW, E CLAY, JR	U S CONGRESSMAN	299 E BROWARD BLVD	FORT LAUDERDALE, FL	33301
CHAYKIN, DANIEL	DIRECTOR	DGA, 110 W 57TH ST	NEW YORK, NY	10019
CHAZAK, GLENN	ACTOR	11726 SAN VICENTE BLVD #300	LOS ANGELES, CA	90049
CHEAP TRICK	ROCK & ROLL GROUP	ADAMANY, 315 W GORHAM ST	MADISON, WI	53703
CHEATHAM, JEAN	SINGER-PIANIST	7836 CAMINO RAPOSA	SAN DIEGO, CA	92122
CHEATHAM, JIMMY	COMPOSER-TRUMPETER	7836 CAMINO RAPOSA	SAN DIEGO, CA	92122
CHEATHAM, MAREE	ACTRESS	3377 CANTON LN	STUDIO CITY, CA	91604
CHECCO, AL	ACTOR	4029 COLDWATER CANYON AVE	STUDIO CITY, CA	91604
CHECK, EDWARD	ART DIRECTOR	255 FORT WASHINGTON AVE	NEW YORK, NY	10032
CHECKER, CHUBBY	SINGER-SONGWRITER	1650 BROADWAY #1011	NEW YORK, NY	10019
CHECKMATES, THE	VOCAL GROUP	8145 E CAMELBACK RD #216	SCOTTSDALE, AZ	85251
CHEEK, DOUGLAS W	WRITER-PRODUCER	DGA, 110 W 57TH ST	NEW YORK, NY	10019
CHEEK, MOLLY	ACTRESS	9200 SUNSET BLVD #625	LOS ANGELES, CA	90069
CHEEK, TOM	SPORTSCASTER	SKYDOME, 300 BREMMER BL #3200	TORONTO, ONT M5V 3B3	CANADA
CHEEKS, MAURICE	BASKETBALL	KNICKS, 4 PENNYLVANIA PLAZA	NEW YORK, NY	10019
CHEER, MAX	ROCK & ROLL GROUP	SEE - MAX CHEER		
CHEETHAM, SEAN	BASEBALL	POST OFFICE BOX 4488	WINSTON-SALEM, NC	27115
CHEEVER, RUSSELL A	COMPOSER	25 MARGARITA	CAMARILLO, CA	93010
CHEFFEY, MARY	ACTRESS	KENNEDY, 2768 WOODWARDIA AVE	LOS ANGELES, CA	90024

CHEHAK, TOM	TV WRITER-PRODUCER	5442 ALLOTT AVE	VAN NUYS, CA	91401
CHELETTE, DANA	ACTOR	6525 SUNSET BLVD #303	HOLLYWOOD, CA	90028
CHELF, WILLIAM DUNBAR	MUSIC ARRANGER	903 RUSSELL ST	NASHVILLE, TN	32206
CHELIOS, CHRIS	HOCKEY	BLACKHAWKS, 1800 W MADISON ST	CHICAGO, IL	60612
CHELSEA	ROCK & ROLL GROUP	BROTHERS, 141 DUNBAR AVE	FORDS, NJ	08863
CHEN, DAVID C	ARTIST	13204 TURNBROOK PKWY #103	ROCKVILLE, MD	20851
CHEN, ERIC	ACTOR	1680 N VINE ST #721	LOS ANGELES, CA	90028
CHEN, TINA	ACTRESS	ICM, 8899 BEVERLY BLVD	LOS ANGELES, CA	90048
CHENAULT, ANNA	AUTHOR	2510 VIRGINIA AVE #1404, NW	WASHINGTON, DC	20005
CHENAULT, CYNTHIA	WRITER	201 W 22ND ST #H-23	SAN PEDRO, CA	90731
CHENAULT, ROBERT	TV DIRECTOR	201 W 22ND ST #H-23	SAN PEDRO, CA	90731
CHENG, LYDIA	BODYBUILDER	POST OFFICE BOX 1490 (RCS)	NEW YORK, NY	10101
CHENG, STEPHEN	ACTOR-WRITER	395 RIVERSIDE DR	NEW YORK, NY	10025
CHENIER, PHIL	BASKETBALL	BULLETS, 1 HARRY S TRUMAN DR	LANDOVER, MD	20785
CHENILLE SISTERS, THE	VOCAL TRIO	POST OFFICE BOX 7023	ANN ARBOR, MI	48107
CHER	SINGER-ACTRESS	10960 WILSHIRE BLVD #938	LOS ANGELES, CA	90024
CHERBAK, CYNTHIA A	TV WRITER	11912 RIVERDALE DR #3	NORTH HOLLYWOOD, CA	91607
CHERELLE	SINGER	FAA, 1700 BROADWAY, 5TH FLOOR	NEW YORK, NY	10019
CHERMAK, CY	WRITER-PRODUCER	20224 DELITA DR	WOODLAND HILLS, CA	91364
CHERNAK, JERALD	TV DIRECTOR-PRODUCER	136 MARGATE MEWS	LONGWOOD, FL	32779
CHERNENKO, TATIANA	ACTRESS	FELBER, 2126 N CAHUENGA BLVD	LOS ANGELES, CA	90068
CHERNIN, PETER	TV EXECUTIVE	10201 W PICO BLVD	LOS ANGELES, CA	90035
CHERNOFF, MICHAEL G	FOOTBALL EXECUTIVE	POST OFFICE BOX 535000	INDIANPOLIS, IN	46253
CHERONES, THOMAS H, JR	WRI-DIR-PROD	3177 LINDO ST	HOLLYWOOD, CA	90068
CHERRILL, DAVID	TV DIRECTOR	52 WOODLAND RISE		
		STUDHAM, NEAR DUNSTABLE	BEDFORDSHIRE	ENGLAND
CHERRY, AL	SINGER	GASTONI, 3815 BEAUMONT	BROSSARD, PQ JAZ 2N8	CANADA
CHERRY, DERON	FOOTBALL	CHIEFS, 1 ARROWHEAD DR	KANSAS CITY, MO	64129
CHERRY, IRVING "GUS"	BASEBALL EXECUTIVE	POST OFFICE BOX 3665	OMAHA, NE	68103
CHERRY, LAMAR	BASEBALL	POST OFFICE BOX 1721	SPARTANBURG, SC	29304
CHERRY, LYNNE	ARTIST	E P DUTTON, 2 PARK AVE	NEW YORK, NY	10016
CHERRY, STANLEY Z	WRITER-PRODUCER	11222 VENTURA BLVD	STUDIO CITY, CA	91604
CHERRY, TOM	MUSIC ARRANGER	2908 DONNA HILL DR	NASHVILLE, TN	37214
CHERTOK, JACK	FILM PRODUCER	515 OCEAN AVE N #305	SANTA MONICA, CA	90402
CHESHE, STEVEN T	COMPOSER	1123 OCEAN PARK BLVD #C	SANTA MONICA, CA	90405
CHESHIRE, DENISE	ACTRESS	1800 N HIGHLAND AVE #405	LOS ANGELES, CA	90028
CHESLEY, HOWARD M	TV WRITER	1908 MONTANA AVE	SANTA MONICA, CA	90403
CHESNEY, RONALD	WRITER-PRODUCER	1 GROSVENOR GARDENS	LONDON NW11 OHH	ENGLAND
CHESS, LISA	ACTRESS	8380 MELROSE AVE #207	LOS ANGELES, CA	90069
CHEST, APRIL	DANCER-MODEL	POST OFFICE BOX 639	SUN VALLEY, CA	91353
CHESTER, COLBY	ACTOR	1245 N ORCHARD DR	BURBANK, CA	91506
CHESTER, EDWARD	ACTOR	8831 SUNSET BLVD #402	LOS ANGELES, CA	90069
CHESTER, GIRAUD	TV EXECUTIVE	GOODSON PRODS, 375 PARK AVE	NEW YORK, NY	10152
CHESTERFIELD KINGS, THE	ROCK & ROLL GROUP	MIRRORS RECORDS, 645 TITUS AVE	ROCHESTER, NY	14617
CHESTNUT, H THOMAS	BASKETBALL EXECUTIVE	POST OFFICE BOX 5000	RICHFIELD, OH	44286
CHETWYND, LIONEL	FILM WRITER-DIRECTOR	2401 S HACIENDA BLVD #311	HACIENDA HGTS, CA	91745
CHEUNG, DAPHNE	ACTRESS	GERALD WOLFF, 10612 CULVER BLVD	CULVER CITY, CA	90232
CHEVILLAT, BRUCE	TV DIRECTOR	1626 CERRO GORDO ST	LOS ANGELES, CA	90026
CHEVRIER, DON	SPORTSCASTER	SKYDOME, 300 BREMMER BL #3200	TORONTO, ONT M5V 3B3	CANADA
CHEVRON, DOLORES	TALENT AGENT	4051 RADFORD AVE #A	STUDIO CITY, CA	91604
CHEW, SAM, JR	ACTOR	8075 W 3RD ST #303	LOS ANGELES, CA	90048
CHI-LITES, THE	SOUL GROUP	640 N LA SALLE ST #545	CHICAGO, IL	60610
CHIAMPARINO, SCOTT	BASEBALL	POST OFFICE BOX 90111	ARLINGTON, TX	76004
CHIASSON, STEVE	HOCKEY	RED WINGS, 600 CIVIC CENTER DR	DETROIT, MI	48226
CHICAGO	ROCK & ROLL GROUP	345 N MAPLE ST #235	BEVERLY HILLS, CA	90210
CHICAGO CITY LIMITS	COMEDY DUO	EAGLES, 305 E 24TH ST	NEW YORK, NY	10010
CHICK, BRUCE	BASEBALL	POST OFFICE BOX 1718	NEW BRITAIN, CT	06050
CHIESA, GORDON	BASKETBALL COACH	5 TRIAD CENTER #500	SALT LAKE CITY, UT	84180
CHIEVOUS, DERRICK	BASKETBALL	POST OFFICE BOX 5000	RICHFIELD, OH	44286
CHIHARA, PAUL	COMPOSER-CONDUCTOR	3815 W OLIVE AVE #202	BURBANK, CA	91505
CHIKLIS, MICHAEL	ACTOR	12424 WILSHIRE BLVD #840	LOS ANGELES, CA	90025
CHILD, JULIA	TV PERS-CHEF	103 IRVING ST	CAMBRIDGE, MA	02138
CHILDERS, BUDDY	COMPOSER	616 N RUSH ST #1611	CHICAGO, IL	60611
CHILDRENN, ROCKY	BASEBALL	5 MEADOWGLEN CT	SANTA ROSA, CA	95404
CHILDRESS, ALICE	PLAYWRIGHT	555 W 57TH ST #1230	NEW YORK, NY	10019
CHILDRESS, BOB	BASEBALL EXECUTIVE	POST OFFICE BOX 1434	BRISTOL, VA	24203
CHILDRESS, FRED	FOOTBALL	PATRIOTS, FOXBORO STADIUM, RT #1	FOXBORO, MA	02035
CHILDRESS, LISA	SINGER	SHOWTIME, 120 N SPRINGFIELD	BOLIVAR, MO	65613
CHILDRESS, RAY	FOOTBALL	OILERS, 6910 FANNIN ST	HOUSTON, TX	77070
CHILDS, ANDY	SINGER	POST OFFICE BOX 23795	NASHVILLE, TN	37202
CHILDS, SUZANNE	ACTRESS	21910 PACIFIC COAST HWY	MALIBU, CA	90265
CHILDS, TED	TV DIRECTOR-PRODUCER	PETERS, FRASER & DUNLOP, LTD		
		5TH FLOOR, THE CHAMBERS		
		CHELSEA HARBOUR, LOT RD	LONDON SW10 OXF	ENGLAND
CHILDS, TONI	SINGER-SONGWRITER	9595 WILSHIRE BLVD #505	BEVERLY HILLS, CA	90212
CHILES, BARRY	BASEBALL	POST OFFICE BOX 507	DURHAM, NC	27702
CHILES, LAWTON	GOVERNOR	STATE CAPITOL BUILDING	TALLAHASSEE, FL	32399
CHILES, LINDEN	ACTOR	2521 TOPANGA SKYLINE	TOPANGA, CA	90290
CHILES, LOIS	ACTRESS	644 SAN LORENZO ST	SANTA MONICA, CA	90402
CHILES, RICH	BASEBALL COACH	POST OFFICE DRAWER 1218	ZEBULON, NC	27597
CHILL, THE	ROCK & ROLL GROUP	BDR, 240 TURNPIKE AVE	DALLAS, TX	75208
CHILLS, THE	C & W GROUP	STARS, INC, 1012 16TH AVE S	NASHVILLE, TN	37212
CHILTON, GENE	FOOTBALL	PATRIOTS, FOXBORO STADIUM, RT #1	FOXBORO, MA	02035
CHILTON, JOHN	ACTOR	2211 OCEAN AVE	SANTA MONICA, CA	90405
CHILVERS, COLIN A	DIRECTOR	DGA, 110 W 57TH ST	NEW YORK, NY	10019

CHIMELIS, JOEL	BASEBALL	POST OFFICE BOX 3448	SHREVEPORT, LA	71133
CHIN, CLINT	ACTOR	91 GROVE ST	PASSIAC, NJ	07055
CHIN, GLEN	ACTOR	3430 3/4 DREW ST	LOS ANGELES, CA	90065
CHIN, MARILYN	ACTRESS	8075 W 3RD ST #303	LOS ANGELES, CA	90048
CHINIQUY, RONALD	WRITER	12021 VALLEY HEART DR #1	STUDIO CITY, CA	91604
CHIPELLO, PAUL W	COMPOSER-CONDUCTOR	6313 PEACH AVE	VAN NUYS, CA	91401
CHISHOLM	C & W GROUP	POST OFFICE BOX 1273	EULESS, TX	76039
CHISHOLM, JOHN	CINEMATOGRAPHER	7715 SUNSET BLVD #150	LOS ANGELES, CA	90046
CHISHOLM, SHIRLEY	POLITICIAN	48 CRESTWOOD LN	WILLIAMSVILLE, NY	14221
CHITI, DOM	BASEBALL COACH	INDIANS, CLEVELAND STADIUM	CLEVELAND, OH	44114
CHITREN, STEVE	BASEBALL	POST OFFICE BOX 11087	TACOMA, WA	98411
CHO, RAYMOND	CONDUCTOR	3123 W 8TH ST #208	LOS ANGELES, CA	90005
CHODERKER, GEORGE	TV DIRECTOR	10282 KINCARDINE AVE	LOS ANGELES, CA	90064
CHODOROV, JEROME	WRITER	131 S MAPLE DR #304	BEVERLY HILLS, CA	90212
CHODOROV, STEPHEN	WRITER-PRODUCER	CAMERA 3, 555 W 57TH ST	NEW YORK, NY	10019
CHODOS, DANIEL	ACTOR	2242 CLIFFORD ST	LOS ANGELES, CA	90026
CHOLAKIS, JOHN E	DIRECTOR	240 CENTRAL PARK S	NEW YORK, NY	10019
CHOLET, BLANCHE	ACTRESS	43 W 93RD ST	NEW YORK, NY	10025
CHOLOWSKY, DAN	BASEBALL	POST OFFICE BOX 3783	SAVANNAH, GA	31414
CHOMSKY, DAVID	TV WRITER	1942 PELHAM AVE #16	LOS ANGELES, CA	90025
CHOMSKY, MARVIN J	DIRECTOR	4707 OCEAN FRONT WALK	VENICE, CA	90291
CHOMYN, JOSEPH K	TV DIRECTOR	6 ARMHERST PL	UPPER MONTCLAIR, NJ	07043
CHONES, JIM	BASKETBALL	WOIO-TV, 2720 VAN AKEN BLVD	CLEVELAND, OH	44120
CHONG, RAE DAWN	ACTRESS	POST OFFICE BOX 181	BEARSVILLE, NY	12409
CHONG, THOMAS	ACT-WRI-DIR	1625 CASALE RD	PACIFIC PALISADES, CA	90272
CHOOLUCK, LEON	DIRECTOR-PRODUCER	6531 RANCHITO AVE	VAN NUYS, CA	91401
CHOROROS, WILLIAM	DIRECTOR	DGA, 110 W 57TH ST	NEW YORK, NY	10019
CHORSKE, TOM	HOCKEY	CANADIENS, 2313 ST CATHERINE ST	MONTREAL, QUE H3H 1N2	CANADA
CHOULNARD, BOBBY	BASEBALL	POST OFFICE BOX 418	SAINT CHARLES, IL	60174
CHOW, RAYMOND	FILM EXECUTIVE	23 BARKER RD		
		CRAIGSIDE MANSIONS #5-B	KOWLOON	HONG KONG
CHRAMOFF, NORMAN	ACTOR	650 WESTMOUNT DR	LOS ANGELES, CA	90069
CHRIS, MARILYN	ACTRESS	BRET ADAMS, 448 W 44TH ST	NEW YORK, NY	10036
CHRISMAN, JIM	BASEBALL	300 STADIUM WY	DAVENPORT, FL	33837
CHRISTEN, PAUL	BASEBALL EXECUTIVE	TWINS, 501 CHICAGO AVE S	MINNEAPOLIS, MN	55415
CHRISTENSEN, BRUCE L	TV EXECUTIVE	NATIONAL ASSOC OF PUBLIC TV		
		955 L'ENFANT PLAZA, SW	WASHINGTON, DC	20024
CHRISTENSEN, JOHN	BASEBALL	20950 VIA CONTENTO	YORBA LINDA, CA	92686
CHRISTENSEN, TODD	FOOTBALL	991 SUNBURST LN	ALPINE, UT	84004
CHRISTIAN, CHRIS	PIANIST-COMPOSER	POST OFFICE BOX 7409	DALLAS, TX	75209
CHRISTIAN, CLAUDIA	ACTRESS	9200 SUNSET BLVD #625	LOS ANGELES, CA	90069
CHRISTIAN, DAVE	HOCKEY	BRUINS, 150 CAUSEWAY ST	BOSTON, MA	02114
CHRISTIAN, H R	SCREENWRITER	CAA, 9830 WILSHIRE BLVD	BEVERLY HILLS, CA	90212
CHRISTIAN, LEIGH	ACTRESS-MODEL	145 S FAIRFAX AVE #310	LOS ANGELES, CA	90036
CHRISTIAN, MARC	PERSONALITY	1801 CENTURY PARK E #1900	LOS ANGELES, CA	90067
CHRISTIAN, MARK	BODYBUILDER	GOLD'S GYM, 360 HAMPTON DR	VENICE, CA	90291
CHRISTIAN, RICHARD S	DIRECTOR	POST OFFICE BOX 3085	PRINCETON, NJ	08540
CHRISTIAN, RICO	BASEBALL	POST OFFICE BOX 36407	LOUISVILLE, KY	40233
CHRISTIAN, S M BOBBY	COMPOSER	531 N EAST AVE	OAK PARK, IL	60302
CHRISTIAN, WILLIAM	ACTOR	ABC-TV, "ALL MY CHILDREN"		
		320 W 66TH ST	NEW YORK, NY	10023
CHRISTIANSEN, CHERYL	ACTRESS	9753 GREGORY WY	BEVERLY HILLS, CA	90212
CHRISTIANSEN, JASON	BASEBALL	POST OFFICE BOX 3746, HILL STA	AUGUSTA, GA	30904
CHRISTIANSON, PEGGY	TV EXECUTIVE	3800 W ALAMEDIA AVE	BURBANK, CA	91505
CHRISTIE, JULIE	ACTRESS	23 LINDEN GARDENS	LONDON W2	ENGLAND
CHRISTIE, KAREN	SINGER	POST OFFICE BOX 111011	NASHVILLE, TN	37211
CHRISTIE, LOU	SINGER	228 W 71ST ST #1-E	NEW YORK, NY	10023
CHRISTIE, STEVE	FOOTBALL	BUCCANEERS, 1 BUCCANEER PL	TAMPA, FL	33607
CHRISTINE, VIRGINIA	ACTRESS	12348 ROCHEDALE LN	LOS ANGELES, CA	90049
CHRISTMAN, KEVIN	BASEBALL SCOUT	BREWERS, 201 S 46TH ST	MILWAUKEE, WI	53214
CHRISTMAS, ERIC	ACTOR	144 S BEVERLY DR #405	BEVERLY HILLS, CA	90212
CHRISTOPHER	ACTOR	MIA GROUP, 2 HINDE ST	LONDON W1	ENGLAND
CHRISTOPHER, ALTA	ACTRESS	5193 CANOGA AVE	WOODLAND HILLS, CA	91364
CHRISTOPHER, DENNIS	ACTOR	2026 3/4 N ARGYLE AVE	HOLLYWOOD, CA	90028
CHRISTOPHER, FAITH	ACTRESS	FELBER, 2126 N CAHUENGA BLVD	LOS ANGELES, CA	90068
CHRISTOPHER, JORDAN	ACTOR	STE, 888 7TH AVE, 18TH FLOOR	NEW YORK, NY	10106
CHRISTOPHER, LOYD	BASEBALL-SCOUT	POST OFFICE BOX 2000	ANAHEIM, CA	92803
CHRISTOPHER, MARC	ACTOR	14027 GARBER ST	ARLETA, CA	91331
CHRISTOPHER, MIKE	BASEBALL	4385 TUTT BLVD	COLORADO SPRINGS, CO	80922
CHRISTOPHER, SYBIL BURTON	ACTRESS	300 CENTRAL PARK W	NEW YORK, NY	10024
CHRISTOPHER, TERRY	BASEBALL	POST OFFICE BOX 855	BELOIT, WI	53511
CHRISTOPHER, THOM	ACTOR	301 N CANON DR #305	BEVERLY HILLS, CA	90210
CHRISTOPHER, WILLIAM	ACTOR-AUTHOR	POST OFFICE BOX 50698	PASADENA, CA	91105
CHRISTOPHERSON, ERIC	BASEBALL	POST OFFICE BOX 3448	SHREVEPORT, LA	71133
CHRISTOPHERSON, GARY	BASEBALL	POST OFFICE BOX 422229	KISSIMMEE, FL	34742
CHRISTOPOULOS, GEORGE	ACTOR	418 REES ST #B	PLAYA DEL REY, CA	90291
CHRISTY, KAREN	SINGER	38 MUSIC SQUARE E #113	NASHVILLE, TN	37203
CHROMCHAK, RUDY	ACTOR	1330 N HARPER AVE #106	LOS ANGELES, CA	90046
CHRONIS, BELLA	ACTRESS	845 S MANSFIELD AVE	LOS ANGELES, CA	90036
CHRONOPOULOS, GENE	ACTOR	1551 MIDVALE AVE	LOS ANGELES, CA	90024
CHUBB, ISABELLA VAN SOEST	COSTUME DESIGNER	1542 N COURTNEY AVE	LOS ANGELES, CA	90046
CHUBB ROCK	RAPPER-RAPWRITER	FAA, 1700 BROADWAY, 5TH FLOOR	NEW YORK, NY	10019
CHUCK WAGON GANG	C & W GROUP	POST OFFICE BOX 140571	NASHVILLE, TN	37214
CHUDNOW, BYRON	TV DIRECTOR-PRODUCER	918 S WESTGATE AVE #4	LOS ANGELES, CA	90049
CHUDNOW, RICHARD G	ACTOR-WRITER	8955 BEVERLY BLVD	WEST HOLLYWOOD, CA	90048

CHULAY, JOHN	TV DIRECTOR	317 MARKHAM PL	PASADENA, CA	91105
CHUMLEY, NORRIS	TV DIRECTOR-PRODUCER	MAGNETIC ARTS, 530 W 23RD ST	NEW YORK, NY	10011
CHUNG, CONNIE	NEWS CORRESPONDENT	CBS-TV, 524 W 75TH ST	NEW YORK, NY	10019
CHUNG, MYUNG-WHUM	CONDUCTOR	ICM, 40 W 57TH ST	NEW YORK, NY	10019
CHURCH, AUSTIN	SINGER	550 HARDING PL #C-108	NASHVILLE, TN	37211
CHURCH, LISA	ACTRESS	L A TALENT, 8335 SUNSET BLVD	LOS ANGELES, CA	90069
CHURCH, NORRIS	ARTIST	MAILER, 142 COLUMBIA HEIGHTS PL	BROOKLYN, NY	11201
CHURCH, WILLIE	BASEBALL EXECUTIVE	136 S SYCAMORE	ELIZABETHTON, TN	37643
CHURLA, SHANE	HOCKEY	NORTH STARS, 7901 CEDAR AVE S	BLOOMINGTON, MN	55425
CHWAST, SEYMOUR	ARTIST	PUSHPIN GROUP, 67 IRVING PL	NEW YORK, NY	10003
CHYCHRUN, JEFF	HOCKEY	FLYERS, SPECTRUM, PATTISON PL	PHILADELPHIA, PA	19148
CHYZOWSKI, DAVE	HOCKEY	NASSAU VETS MEMORIAL COLISEUM	UNIONDALE, NY	11553
CIANFROCCO, ARCI	BASEBALL	EXPOS, 4545 DE COUBERTIN AVE	MONTREAL, QUE H1V 3P2	CANADA
CIANI, SUZANNE	SINGER-SONGWRITER	2400 BROADWAY ST #100	SANTA MONICA, CA	90404
CIARDI, MARK	BASEBALL	21 MITCHELL AVE	PISCATAWAY, NJ	08854
CIARDIELLO, JOE	ARTIST	2182 CLOVE RD	STATEN ISLAND, NY	10305
CIBELLA, ROSS M	DIRECTOR	1711 BEACON ST	WABAN, MA	02168
CIBELLI, HARRIET	PLAYWRIGHT	226 W 47TH ST	NEW YORK, NY	10036
CIBELLI, RENATO	ACTOR	245 W 25TH ST	NEW YORK, NY	10001
CICCANTELLI, PAT	BASEBALL-INSTRUCTOR	INDIANS, CLEVELAND STADIUM	CLEVELAND, OH	44114
CICCARELLA, JOE	BASEBALL	RED SOX, CHAIN O'LAKES PARK	WINTER HAVEN, FL	33880
CICCARELLI, DINO	HOCKEY	JETS, 15-1430 MAROONS RD	WINNIPEG, MAN R3G OL5	CANADA
CIERNY, EGON	SCI-FI EXPERT	MATECHOVA 14	140 00 PRAGUE 4	CZECH
CIGER, ZDENO	HOCKEY	POST OFFICE BOX 504	EAST RUTHERFORD, NJ	07073
CILETTI, MILES	WRITER	12237 LA MAIDA ST	NORTH HOLLYWOOD, CA	91607
CIMETTA, ROB	HOCKEY	MAPLE LEAFS, 60 CARLTON ST	TORONTO, ONT M5B 1L1	CANADA
CIMINO, MICHAEL	WRITER-PRODUCER	9015 ALTA CEDRO DR	BEVERLY HILLS, CA	90210
CIMORELLI, FRANK	BASEBALL	POST OFFICE BOX 3004	SPRINGFIELD, IL	62708
CINARDO, NICK	ACTOR	18625 CLARK ST #101	TARZANA, CA	91356
CINCOTTA, CARMINE	SPORTS PRODUCER	WCBS-TV, 524 W 57TH ST	NEW YORK, NY	10019
CINDERELLA	ROCK & ROLL GROUP	POST OFFICE BOX 543	DREVEL HILL, PA	19026
CINTRON, SHARON	ACTRESS-MODEL	144 S BEVERLY DR #405	BEVERLY HILLS, CA	90212
CIOCCA, ERIC	BASEBALL	POST OFFICE BOX 20849	CHARLESTON, SC	29413
CIOFFI, CHARLES	ACTOR	GLOVER AVE	NORWALK, CT	06850
CIOFFI, LOU	NEWS CORRESPONDENT	ABC NEWS, 7 W 66TH ST	NEW YORK, NY	10023
CIOMBOR, TIM	BASEBALL EXECUTIVE	1090 N EUCLID AVE	SARASOTA, FL	34237
CIPES, ARIANNE ULMER	FILM EXECUTIVE	3651 STONE CANYON RD	LOS ANGELES, CA	90077
CIPPA, STEPHEN H	BASKETBALL EXECUTIVE	KINGS, 1 SPORTS PARKWAY	SACRAMENTO, CA	95834
CIRELLA, JOE	HOCKEY	POST OFFICE BOX 90111	ARLINGTON, TX	76004
CIRILLO, ANTHONY F	DIRECTOR	37 E 28TH ST	NEW YORK, NY	10016
CIRILLO, JEFF	BASEBALL	POST OFFICE BOX 8550	STOCKTON, CA	95208
CIRILLO, LAWRENCE	TV DIRECTOR	412 TIMBER RIDGE DR	LONGWOOD, FL	32779
CIRIMELE, ALBERT	ACTOR	1044 N SWEETZER AVE	LOS ANGELES, CA	90069
CIRKER, IRA	TV DIRECTOR	MITCHON, 235 E 22ND ST	NEW YORK, NY	10010
CISCO, GALEN	BASEBALL-COACH	SKYDOME, 300 BREMMER BL #3200	TORONTO, ONT M5V 3B3	CANADA
CISZCZON, STEVE	BASEBALL TRAINER	4385 TUTT BLVD	COLORADO SPRINGS, CO	80922
CITRON, HERMAN	TALENT AGENT	9255 SUNSET BLVD #910	LOS ANGELES, CA	90069
CITRON, RICHARD D	DIRECTOR-PRODUCER	365 W END AVE	NEW YORK, NY	10024
CITY ON EDGE	ROCK & ROLL GROUP	2256 PEPPERMINT LN	LEMON GROVE, CA	92045
CITYFOLKS COUNTRY BAND	C & W GROUP	CUDE, 519 N HALIFAX AVE	DAYTONA BEACH, FL	32018
CIUPKA, RICHARD	DIRECTOR	71 CORNWALL ST	QUEBEC	CANADA
CIVITA, DIANA	ACTRESS	11846 VENTURA BLVD #100	STUDIO CITY, CA	91604
CIVITELLO, LINDA ANN	WRITER	3741 JASMINE AVE #5	LOS ANGELES, CA	90034
CLAAR, BRIAN	GOLFER	POST OFFICE BOX 109601	PALM BCH GARDENS, FL	33418
CLABOUGH, CHARLES	BASEBALL UMPIRE	235 MAIN ST #103	TRUSSVILLE, AL	35173
CLAIBORNE, LIZ	FASHION DESIGNER	300 E 56TH ST	NEW YORK, NY	10022
CLAIR, BERNICE	ACTRESS	46 EUCALYPTUS KNOLL	MILL VALLEY, CA	94941
CLAIR, ETHLYNE	ACTRESS	FROST, 20174 VILLAGE #2	CAMARILLO, CA	93010
CLAIRE, ADELE	ACTRESS	4051 RADFORD AVE #A	STUDIO CITY, CA	91604
CLAIRE, FRED	BASEBALL EXECUTIVE	1000 ELYSIAN PARK DR	LOS ANGELES, CA	90012
CLAMPETT, BOBBY	GOLFER	POST OFFICE BOX 109601	PALM BCH GARDENS, FL	33418
CLANCY, JIM	BASEBALL	6147 ROBROY ST	OAK FOREST, IL	60452
CLANCY, MARTIN J	TV DIRECTOR-PRODUCER	ABC-TV, 7 W 66TH ST	NEW YORK, NY	10023
CLANCY, SAM	FOOTBALL	POST OFFICE BOX 535000	INDIANPOLIS, IN	46253
CLANCY, TOM	ACTOR	4123 PATRICK HENRY PL	AQUARA, CA	91301
CLANCY BROTHERS, THE	FOLK GROUP	ROTHSCHILD, 330 E 48TH ST	NEW YORK, NY	10017
CLANTON, DARRELL	SINGER	MC FADEN, 48 MUSIC SQUARE E	NASHVILLE, TN	37203
CLAPP, NICHOLAS R	WRITER-PRODUCER	2515 LAUREL PASS AVE	LOS ANGELES, CA	90046
CLAPTON, ERIC	SINGER-GUITARIST	67 BROOK ST	LONDON W1	ENGLAND
CLARDY, LARRY	ACTOR	1203 S LA CIENEGA BLVD #D	LOS ANGELES, CA	90035
CLARIDGE, CHRISTIE	ACTRESS	20541 NORTHRIDGE RD	CHATSWORTH, CA	91311
CLARIDGE, WESTBROOK	WRITER	2210 6TH ST	SANTA MONICA, CA	90405
CLARK, AL	FILM PRODUCER	AUSTRALIAN FILM COMMISISION		
		8 WEST ST	NORTH SYDNEY, NSW 2060	AUSTRALIA
CLARK, ALAN	BASEBALL UMPIRE	16 INDEPENDENCE PL	NEWTOWN, PA	18940
CLARK, ALAN	SINGER-SONGWRITER	POST OFFICE BOX 1062	WEST COVINA, CA	91793
CLARK, ALEXANDER	ACTOR	175 W 79TH ST	NEW YORK, NY	10024
CLARK, BERNARD	FOOTBALL	BENGALS, 200 RIVERFRONT STADIUM	CINCINNATI, OH	45202
CLARK, BOB	FILM WRITER-DIRECTOR	9200 SUNSET BLVD #808	LOS ANGELES, CA	90069
CLARK, BOB	NEWS CORRESPONDENT	ABC NEWS, 7 W 66TH ST	NEW YORK, NY	10023
CLARK, BRIAN	SCREENWRITER	8955 BEVERLY BLVD	WEST HOLLYWOOD, CA	90048
CLARK, BRUCE "B D"	SCREENWRITER	KANT, 233 WILSHIRE BLVD	SANTA MONICA, CA	90401
CLARK, BRYAN	BASEBALL	700 STARKEY RD #511	LARGO, FL	33541
CLARK, BYRON	ACTOR	745 N ALFRED ST #PH	LOS ANGELES, CA	90069
CLARK, CANDY	ACTRESS	5 BRIARHILL RD	MONTCLAIR, NJ	07042

CLARK, CHRISTIE	ACTRESS	3800 BARHAM BLVD #303	LOS ANGELES, CA	90068
CLARK, DANE	ACTOR-DIRECTOR	1680 OLD OAK RD	LOS ANGELES, CA	90049
CLARK, DAVE	BASEBALL	POST OFFICE BOX 450	BUFFALO, NY	14205
CLARK, DERA	BASEBALL	POST OFFICE BOX 3665	OMAHA, NE	68103
CLARK, DICK	SINGER	UTI, 1907 DIVISION ST	NASHVILLE, TN	37202
CLARK, DICK	TV HOST-PRODUCER	3003 W OLIVE AVE	BURBANK, CA	91510
CLARK, DORAN	ACTRESS	9301 WILSHIRE BLVD #312	BEVERLY HILLS, CA	90210
CLARK, DWIGHT	FOOTBALL EXECUTIVE	S F 49ERS, 4949 CENTENNIAL BL	SANTA CLARA, CA	95054
CLARK, GEOFF	BASEBALL TRAINER	POST OFFICE BOX 483	YAKIMA, WA	98907
CLARK, GLORYETTE	FILM EDITOR	3611 WILLOW CREST AVE	STUDIO CITY, CA	91604
CLARK, GREG	FOOTBALL	PACKERS, 1265 LOMBARDI AVE	GREEN BAY, WI	54307
CLARK, GUY	FOOTBALL	POST OFFICE BOX 17247 (DULLES)	WASHINGTON, DC	20041
CLARK, GUY	SINGER-SONGWRITER	ROUTE #4, CROSSWINDS	MOUNT JULIET, TN	37122
CLARK, JACK	BASEBALL	FENWAY PARK, 4 YAWKEY WY	BOSTON, MA	02215
CLARK, JACK	TV ANNOUNCER	MERV GRIFFIN PRODUCTIONS		
		"THE WHEEL OF FORTUNE"		
		3400 RIVERSIDE DR	BURBANK, CA	91505
CLARK, JAMES B	DIRECTOR	10051-5 VALLEY CIRCLE BLVD	CHATSWORTH, CA	91311
CLARK, JERALD	BASEBALL	POST OFFICE BOX 2000	SAN DIEGO, CA	92112
CLARK, JOE	ACTOR	366 S RIDGEWOOD RD	SOUTH ORANGE, NJ	07079
CLARK, JOE	SCHOOL PRINCIPAL	EASTIDE HIGH SCHOOL		
		155 MARKET ST	PATERSON, NJ	07505
CLARK, JOE B	FOOTBALL COACH	PACKERS, 1265 LOMBARDI AVE	GREEN BAY, WI	54307
CLARK, JOHN	TV DIRECTOR	POST OFFICE BOX 1207	TOPANGA CANYON, CA	90290
CLARK, KATHIE	COSTUME DESIGNER	13949 VENTURA BLVD #309	SHERMAN OAKS, CA	91423
CLARK, KEN	FOOTBALL	POST OFFICE BOX 535000	INDIANPOLIS, IN	46253
CLARK, KEN	NEWS REPORTOR	THE CHICAGO TRIBUNE		
		TRIBUNE TOWER		
		435 N MICHIGAN AVE	CHICAGO, IL	60611
CLARK, KERRI	GOLFER	2750 VOLUSA AVE #B	DAYTON BEACH, FL	32114
CLARK, LARRY	COMEDIAN	1022 N PALM AVE #2	LOS ANGELES, CA	90069
CLARK, LOUIS	FOOTBALL	SEAHAWKS, 11220 NE 53RD ST	KIRKLAND, WA	98033
CLARK, LYNN	ACTRESS	247 S BEVERLY DR #102	BEVERLY HILLS, CA	90210
CLARK, MARILYN	ACTRESS	135 CENTRAL PARK W	NEW YORK, NY	10023
CLARK, MARK	BASEBALL	POST OFFICE BOX 36407	LOUISVILLE, KY	40233
CLARK, MARY HIGGINS	TV PRODUCER	210 CENTRAL PARK S	NEW YORK, NY	10019
CLARK, MATT	ACTOR	KOHNER, 9169 SUNSET BLVD	LOS ANGELES, CA	90069
CLARK, MICHELE A	TV EXECUTIVE	HBO, 1100 6TH AVE	NEW YORK, NY	10036
CLARK, MIKE	FILM CRITIC	POST OFFICE BOX 500	WASHINGTON, DC	20044
CLARK, MONTE	FOOTBALL EXECUTIVE	DOLPHINS, 2269 NW 199TH ST	MIAMI, FL	33056
CLARK, PETULA	SINGER-ACTRESS	15 CHEMIN RIEU COLIGNY	GENEVA	SWITZERLAND
CLARK, PHIL	BASEBALL	POST OFFICE BOX 6212	TOLEDO, OH	43614
CLARK, R A "RAC"	TV PRODUCER	3003 W OLIVE AVE	BURBANK, CA	91510
CLARK, RAMSAY	POLITICS	36 E 12TH ST	NEW YORK, NY	10003
CLARK, ROBERT	FOOTBALL	LIONS, 1200 FEATHERSTONE RD	PONTIAC, MI	48432
CLARK, ROBERT C	COMPOSER	POST OFFICE BOX 4121	MALIBU, CA	90265
CLARK, ROBIN S	DIRECTOR	CPB, 1901 AVE OF THE STARS	LOS ANGELES, CA	90067
CLARK, RON	BASEBALL COACH	INDIANS, CLEVELAND STADIUM	CLEVELAND, OH	44114
CLARK, RONALD	WRITER	151 S EL CAMINO DR	BEVERLY HILLS, CA	90212
CLARK, ROSS	ACTOR	336 HERMITAGE LN	AZUSA, CA	91702
CLARK, ROY	SINGER-GUITARIST	104 CUMBERLAND TRACE	NASHVILLE, TN	37214
CLARK, ROYDON E	DIRECTOR	9483 WHEATLAND AVE	SUNLAND, CA	91040
CLARK, SUSAN	ACTRESS	7943 WOODROW WILSON DR	LOS ANGELES, CA	90046
CLARK, TEDDY	SINGER	SHOWTIME, 120 N SPRINGFIELD	BOLIVAR, MO	65613
CLARK, TEECI	SINGER	POST OFFICE BOX 5412	BUENA PARK, CA	90620
CLARK, TERRY	BASEBALL	4385 TUTT BLVD	COLORADO SPRINGS, CO	80922
CLARK, VINNIE	FOOTBALL	PACKERS, 1265 LOMBARDI AVE	GREEN BAY, WI	54307
CLARK, WENDEL	HOCKEY	MAPLE LEAFS, 60 CARLTON ST	TORONTO, ONT M5B 1L1	CANADA
CLARK, WILL	BASEBALL	S F GIANTS, CANDLESTICK PARK	SAN FRANICSCO, CA	94124
CLARK, WILLIAM G	ACTOR	4908 FRAN PL #203	ALEXANDRIA, VA	22312
CLARK SISTERS, THE	GOSPEL TRIO	330 W 56TH ST #18-M	NEW YORK, NY	10019
CLARKE, ANGELA	ACTRESS	7557 MULHOLLAND DR	LOS ANGELES, CA	90046
CLARKE, ARTHUR C	AUTHOR	4715 GREGORY'S RD	COLOMBO 7	CEYLON
CLARKE, BOB	CARTOONIST	MAD MAGAZINE, 485 MADISON AVE	NEW YORK, NY	10022
CLARKE, BRIAN D	DIRECTOR	DGA, 110 W 57TH ST	NEW YORK, NY	10019
CLARKE, BRIAN PATRICK	ACTOR-FOOTBALL	333 N KENWOOD ST #D	BURBANK, CA	91505
CLARKE, CAITLIN	ACTRESS	ICM, 8899 BEVERLY BLVD	LOS ANGELES, CA	90048
CLARKE, DAVID	ACTOR	225 CENTRAL PARK W	NEW YORK, NY	10024
CLARKE, JEFF	BASEBALL	POST OFFICE BOX 464	APPLETON, WI	54912
CLARKE, JOHN	ACTOR	NBC-TV, "DAYS OF OUR LIVES"		
		3000 W ALAMEDA AVE	BURBANK, CA	91523
CLARKE, JORDAN	ACTOR	CBS-TV, "THE GUIDING LIGHT"		
		222 E 44TH ST	NEW YORK, NY	10017
CLARKE, KEN	FOOTBALL	VIKINGS, 9520 VIKING DR	EDEN PRAIRIE, MN	55344
CLARKE, MALCOLM	TV DIRECTOR	314 E 41ST ST #805	NEW YORK, NY	10017
CLARKE, RICHARD	ACTOR	40 STUYVESANT ST	NEW YORK, NY	10003
CLARKE, RICHARD W	ACTOR	350 E 57TH ST	NEW YORK, NY	10022
CLARKE, ROBERT	ACTOR	4841 GENTRY AVE	NORTH HOLLYWOOD, CA	91607
CLARKE, STANLEY	GUITARIST-COMPOSER	POST OFFICE BOX 25863	LOS ANGELES, CA	90025
CLARKE, WILLIAM, BLUES BAND	RHYTYM & BLUES BAND	POST OFFICE BOX 1848	ORANGE, CA	92668
CLARKSON, CHANNING	ACTOR	POST OFFICE BOX 441	PACIFIC PALISADES, CA	90272
CLARKSON, PATRICIA	ACTRESS	ICM, 8899 BEVERLY BLVD	LOS ANGELES, CA	90048
CLARKSON, WILLIAM C	TV DIRECTOR	1449 W GEORGE ST	CHICAGO, IL	60614
CLARY, ELLIS	BASEBALL-SCOUT	SKYDOME, 300 BREMMER BL #3200	TORONTO, ONT M5V 3B3	CANADA
CLARY, JULIAN	ACTOR-COMEDIAN	ADDISON CRESWELL, THE OLD BAKERY		

Name	Occupation	Address	City	Zip/Country
		6-A PHILLIP WALK	LONDON SE15 3BH	ENGLAND
CLARY, MARTY	BASEBALL	254 PARE	CLAWSON, MI	48017
CLARY, ROBERT	ACTOR	10001 SUNDIAL LN	BEVERLY HILLS, CA	90210
CLASH, THE	ROCK & ROLL GROUP	268 CAMDEN RD	LONDON NW1	ENGLAND
CLASSICS IV	ROCK & ROLL GROUP	POST OFFICE BOX 53664	INDIANAPOLIS, IN	46253
CLAUDIO, ANDREA	ACTRESS	3644 BARCELONA ST	LAS VEGAS, NV	89121
CLAUS, TODD	BASEBALL	POST OFFICE BOX 3496	DAVENPORT, IA	52808
CLAUSEN, ALF H	COMPOSER-CONDUCTOR	3853 ROYAL WOODS DR	SHERMAN OAKS, CA	91403
CLAUSEN, ALIS	ACTRESS	1208 E AVE "R" #2	PALMDALE, CA	93550
CLAVEL, ROBERT	COMPOSER	2024 RUE EMILE-DUBOIS	PARIS 75014	FRANCE
CLAVELL, JAMES	WRITER-PRODUCER	2006 THAYER AVE	LOS ANGELES, CA	90025
CLAVER, BOB	DIRECTOR-PRODUCER	22244 PACIFIC COAST HWY	MALIBU, CA	90265
CLAWSON, TIM	SCREENWRITER	8955 BEVERLY BLVD	WEST HOLLYWOOD, CA	90048
CLAXTON, WILLIAM F	TV DIRECTOR-PRODUCER	1065 NAPOLI DR	PACIFIC PALISADES, CA	90272
CLAXTON, WILLIAM J	DIRECTOR	1368 ANGELO DR	BEVERLY HILLS, CA	90210
CLAY, ANDREW "DICE"	COMEDIAN-ACTOR	48 E 50TH ST #400	NEW YORK, NY	10022
CLAY, MARCELLO R	ACTOR	4845 CLELAND AVE	LOS ANGELES, CA	90065
CLAY, WILLIAM "BILL"	U S CONGRESSMAN	12263 BELLEFONTAINE RD	SAINT LOUIS, MO	63138
CLAYBORN, RAYMOND	FOOTBALL	BROWNS, 80 1ST ST	BEREA, OH	44017
CLAYBORNE, ROY	SINGER	POST OFFICE BOX 740368	HOUSTON, TX	77274
CLAYBURGH, JILL	ACTRESS	225 MC LAIN ST	MOUNT KISCO, NY	10549
CLAYMAN, RICHARD	ACTOR	STEVENS, 11524 AMANDA DR	STUDIO CITY, CA	91604
CLAYTON, CRAIG	BASEBALL	POST OFFICE BOX 30160	SAN BERNARDINO, CA	92413
CLAYTON, JACK	FILM DIRECTOR	THE HERON'S FLIGHT		
		HIGHFIELD PARK, MARLOW	BUCKS	ENGLAND
CLAYTON, MARK	FOOTBALL	DOLPHINS, 2269 NW 199TH ST	MIAMI, FL	33056
CLAYTON, MELISSA	ASTRESS	KJAR, 10653 RIVERSIDE DR	TOLUCA LAKE, CA	91602
CLAYTON, MERRY	ACTRESS-SINGER	10351 SANTA MONICA BLVD #211	LOS ANGELES, CA	90025
CLAYTON, MILES	ACTOR	918 MALTMAN AVE	LOS ANGELES, CA	90026
CLAYTON, ROY & CLAYTON COUNTRY	C & W GROUP	ATLAS MGMT, 217 E CEDAR ST	GOODLETTSVILLE, TN	37072
CLAYTON, ROYAL	BASEBALL	1155 W MOUND ST	COLUMBUS, OH	43223
CLAYTON, ROYCE	BASEBALL	S F GIANTS, CANDLESTICK PARK	SAN FRANICSCO, CA	94124
CLAYTON, STAN	FOOTBALL	PATRIOTS, FOXBORO STADIUM, RT #1	FOXBORO, MA	02035
CLAYWORTH, JUNE	ACTRESS	1641 VETERAN AVE	LOS ANGELES, CA	90024
CLEAMONS, JIM	BASKETBALL COACH	980 N MICHIGAN AVE #1600	CHICAGO, IL	60611
CLEAR, BOB	BASEBALL-INSTRUCTOR	POST OFFICE BOX 2000	ANAHEIM, CA	92803
CLEAR, MARK	BASEBALL	15821 W 127TH TERR	OLATHE, KS	66062
CLEARLIGHT	ROCK & ROLL GROUP	41 BRITAIN ST #200	TORONTO, ONT M5A 1R7	CANADA
CLEARWATER, KEITH	GOLFER	POST OFFICE BOX 109601	PALM BCH GARDENS, FL	33418
CLEARY, DANIEL J	MUSIC ARRANGER	810 BELLEVUE RD #100	NASHVILLE, TN	37221
CLEARY, MARTIN	BASEBALL EXECUTIVE	INDIANS, CLEVELAND STADIUM	CLEVELAND, OH	44114
CLEAVES, ROBERT	ACTOR	5432 LA MIRADA AVE	LOS ANGELES, CA	90029
CLEESE, JOHN	ACTOR-WRITER	82 LADBROKE RD	LONDON W11 3NU	ENGLAND
CLEFTONES, THE	VOCAL GROUP	MARS, 168 ORCHID DR	PEARL RIVER, NY	10965
CLEIN, HAROLD	WRITER	8836 LOOKOUT MOUNTAIN AVE	LOS ANGELES, CA	90046
CLELAND, MAX	SECRETARY OF STATE	STATE CAPITOL BUIDLING	ATLANTA, GA	30334
CLELLAND, RICKY	BASEBALL	POLECATS, 608 N SLAPPEY BLVD	ALBANY, GA	31701
CLEMENS, ROGER	BASEBALL	FENWAY PARK, 4 YAWKEY WY	BOSTON, MA	02215
CLEMENS, TROY	BASEBALL	POST OFFICE BOX 21727	SAN FRANCISCO, CA	95151
CLEMENT, BOB	U S CONGRESSMAN	2701 JEFFERSON ST #103	NASHVILLE, TN	37208
CLEMENT, JACK	GUITARIST	POST OFFICE BOX 120477	NASHVILLE, TN	37212
CLEMENTE, JOHN R	DIRECTOR	1955 MONON ST	LOS ANGELES, CA	90027
CLEMENTS, BOOTS	SINGER-RECORD EXEC	POST OFFICE BOX 8875	UNIVERSAL CITY, CA	91608
CLEMENTS, CAL	PRODUCER	MCA/UNIVERSAL STUDIOS, INC		
		100 UNIVERSAL CITY PLAZA	UNIVERSAL CITY, CA	91608
CLEMENTS, CALVIN J, SR	TV WRITER	18796 PASADERO DR	TARZANA, CA	91356
CLEMENTS, CALVIN, JR	TV WRITER	23050 CASS AVE	WOODLAND HILLS, CA	91364
CLEMENTS, PAT	BASEBALL	POST OFFICE BOX 2000	SAN DIEGO, CA	92112
CLEMENTS, RICHARD	COMPOSER-CONDUCTOR	5000 CALATRANA DR	WOODLAND HILLS, CA	91364
CLEMENTS, ZEKE	MANDOLINIST	POST OFFICE BOX 22035	NASHVILLE, TN	37202
CLEMMONS HERITAGE GOSP SING, TH	GOSPEL GROUP	CLEMMONS, 1203 E ETHEL ST	DOUGLAS, GA	31533
CLEMONS, CLARENCE	SINGER-SAXOPHONIST	SANFORD NEIMAN, 701 IVY ST	PITTSBURGH, PA	15232
CLEMONS, DON	FOOTBALL COACH	LIONS, 1200 FEATHERSTONE RD	PONTIAC, MI	48432
CLENNON, DAVID	ACTOR	954 20TH ST #B	SANTA MONICA, CA	90403
CLEVELAND, ODESSA	ACTRESS	6058 FAIR AVE	NORTH HOLLYWOOD, CA	91606
CLEVELAND, PATIENCE	ACTRESS	21321 PROVIDENCIA ST	WOODLAND HILLS, CA	91364
CLEVELAND, REGGIE	BASEBALL-COACH	POST OFFICE BOX 465	MED HAT, ALB T1A 7G2	CANADA
CLIBURN, STAN	BASEBALL-COACH	POST OFFICE BOX 309	GASTONA, NC	28053
CLIBURN, STU	BASEBALL COACH	POST OFFICE BOX 1742	PALM SPRINGS, CA	92263
CLIBURN, VAN	PIANIST	455 WILDER PL	SHREVEPORT, LA	71104
CLIFF, JIMMY	SINGER	611 BROADWAY #822	NEW YORK, NY	10012
CLIFFORD, CLARK M	POLITICIAN	9421 ROCKVILLE PIKE	BETHESDA, MD	20814
CLIFFORD, GRAEME	DIRECTOR	21750 CASTLEWOOD DR	MALIBU, CA	90265
CLIFFORD, LINDA	SINGER	BORZOI MUSIC, 222 DUNCAN ST	SAN FRANCISCO, CA	94131
CLIFFORD, ROBERT J	COMPOSER	14114 GLADESIDE DR	LA MIRADA, CA	90638
CLIFT, RALPH M	ACTOR	5111 DENNY AVE #6	NORTH HOLLYWOOD, CA	91601
CLIFT, W BROOKS	DIRECTOR	5455 30TH ST, NW	WASHINGTON, DC	20015
CLIFTON, DAVID	AUTHOR	POST OFFICE BOX 1941	BRENTWOOD, TN	37027
CLIFTON, GEORGE	ACTOR	9469 BEACHY AVE	ARLETA, CA	91331
CLIFTON, KYLE	FOOTBALL	N Y JETS, 1000 FULTON AVE	HEMPSTEAD, NY	11550
CLINE, HAROLD "DICK"	TV DIRECTOR	64 TURTLE BAY DR	BRANFORD, CT	06405
CLINE, STEVE	BASEBALL COACH	POST OFFICE BOX 3448	SHREVEPORT, LA	71133
CLINES, GENE	BASEBALL-COACH	POST OFFICE BOX 4100	SEATTLE, WA	98104
CLINGER, DEBRA	ACTRESS	4415 AUCKLAND AVE	HOLLYWOOD, CA	91602
CLINGER, WILLIAM	U S CONGRESSMAN	PENNSYLVANIA BANK & TRUST BLDG		

		ROOM 605	WARREN, PA	16365
CLINTON, BILL	GOVERNOR	1800 CENTER ST	LITTLE ROCK, AR	72206
CLINTON, GEORGE	SINGER	EGMITT INC, ARCHIE IVY		
		2418 W THOREAU ST	INGLEWOOD, CA	90303
CLINTON, JAMES	BASEBALL	POST OFFICE BOX 3609	PORT CHARLOTTE, FL	33949
CLINTON, LAWRENCE	BASEBALL	POST OFFICE BOX 3609	PORT CHARLOTTE, FL	33949
CLINTON, MILDRED	ACTRESS	68-36 108TH ST	FOREST HILLS, NY	11375
CLIQUE, THE	R & B GROUP	MEIER, 511 W 3RD ST	HAZLETON, PA	18201
CLIVE, JOHN	ACTOR-WRITER	CCA, 4 COURT LODGE		
		48 SLOANE SQ	LONDON SW1W 8AT	ENGLAND
CLOAN, BRAD	BASEBALL SCOUT	POST OFFICE BOX 2000	SAN DIEGO, CA	92112
CLOEREC, RENE	COMPOSER	7 RUE DU PRES-V-PAUCHET	VAUCRESSON 92420	FRANCE
CLOKE, JOHN	ACTOR	HUDSON HOUSE, BOX 7082	ARDSLEY-ON-HUDSON, NY	10503
CLONES, THE	ROCK & ROLL GROUP	POST OFFICE BOX 158486	NASHVILLE, TN	37215
CLONINGER, TONY	BASEBALL-COACH	N Y YANKEES, YANKEE STADIUM	BRONX, NY	10451
CLOONEY, GEORGE	ACTOR	11655 LAURELCREST DR	STUDIO CITY, CA	91604
CLOONEY, ROSEMARY	SINGER	1019 N ROXBURY DR	BEVERLY HILLS, CA	90210
CLOOSE, ROBERT	DIRECTOR	454 HOT SPRING RD	SANTA BARBARA, CA	93108
CLOSE, GLENN	ACTRESS	CAA, 9830 WILSHIRE BLVD	BEVERLY HILLS, CA	90212
CLOTHIER, BARRY	BODYBUILDER	1456 GUERRERO ST	SAN FRANCISCO, CA	94110
CLOTWORTHY, ROBERT	ACTOR	122 S HARPER AVE	LOS ANGELES, CA	90048
CLOUD, HAMILTON S, II	TV EXECUTIVE	NBC-TV, 3000 W ALAMEDA AVE	BURBANK, CA	91523
CLOUGH, ALAN	TV DIRECTOR-PRODUCER	170 W 23RD ST #4-D	NEW YORK, NY	10011
CLOUSE, ROBERT	FILM WRITER-DIRECTOR	32356 W MULHOLLAND WY	MALIBU, CA	90265
CLOVER, DAVID	ACTOR	KJAR, 10653 RIVERSIDE DR	TOLUCA LAKE, CA	91602
CLOWER, JERRY	COMEDIAN	POST OFFICE BOX 121089	NASHVILLE, TN	37212
CLUCK, BOB	BASEBALL COACH	POST OFFICE BOX 288	HOUSTON, TX	77001
CLUESS, CHRISTOPHER J	WRITER	1112 MAPLE ST	SANTA MONICA, CA	90405
CLURMAN, HAROLD	FILM CRITIC	205 W 57TH ST	NEW YORK, NY	10019
CLUTE, CHARLES	COSTUME DESIGNER	ABC-TV, 101 W 67TH ST	NEW YORK, NY	10023
CLUTTERBUCK, GRAHAM	FILM PRODUCER	FILMFAIR, JACOBS WELL MEWS	LONDON W1	ENGLAND
CLYMER, ROY	FOOTBALL REFEREE	NFL, 410 PARK AVE	NEW YORK, NY	10022
COACHMAN, BOBBY	BASEBALL	POST OFFICE BOX 44	COTTONWOOD, AL	36320
COACHMAN, PETE	BASEBALL	5999 E VAN BUREN ST	PHOENIX, AZ	85008
COANE, JAMES B	DIRECTOR	240 CENTRAL PARK S	NEW YORK, NY	10019
COASTERS, THE	VOCAL GROUP	4484 PENNWOOD #233	LAS VEGAS, NV	89102
COATES, BEN	FOOTBALL	PATRIOTS, FOXBORO STADIUM, RT #1	FOXBORO, MA	02035
COATES, PHYLLIS	ACTRESS	711 MEADOWCREST DR #15	CORTE MADERA, CA	94925
COATES-WEST, CAROLE	TV EXECUTIVE	NBC-TV, 3000 W ALAMEDA AVE	BURBANK, CA	91523
COATS, DAN	U S SENATOR	1300 S MARRISON ST #3158	FORT WAYNE, IN	46802
COBB, JULIE	ACTRESS	4433 BERGAMMO DR	ENCINO, CA	91436
COBB, MARVIN	BASEBALL	POST OFFICE BOX 12	MIDLAND, TX	79702
COBB, RANDALL "TEX"	ACTOR-BOXER	SELECTED, 3575 W CAHUENGA BLVD	LOS ANGELES, CA	90068
COBB, VINCENT	ACTOR	1935 LIVONIA AVE	LOS ANGELES, CA	90034
COBER, ALAN E	ARTIST	95 CORTON DAM RD	OSSINING, NY	10562
COBERT, ROBERT	COMPOSER	10800 HOLMAN AVE	LOS ANGELES, CA	90024
COBHAM, BILLY	DRUMMER	POST OFFICE BOX 396	BEVERLY, MA	01915
COBLE, DREW	BASEBALL UMPIRE	3554 BOY WOOD RD	GRAHAM, NC	27253
COBLE, HOWARD	U S CONGRESSMAN	POST OFFICE BOX 1813	LEXINGTON, NC	27293
COBLENZ, WALTER	FILM-TV PRODUCER	2348 APOLLO DR	LOS ANGELES, CA	90046
COBOS, MARCO	BASEBALL SCOUT	POST OFFICE BOX 90111	ARLINGTON, TX	76004
COBURN, JAMES	ACTOR-DIRECTOR	3930 HOLLYLINE AVE	SHERMAN OAKS, CA	91423
COBURN, WILLIAM J	CONDUCTOR	3855 BROADVIEW DR	LOS ANGELES, CA	90068
COCA, IMOGENE	ACTRESS	200 E 66TH ST #1803-D	NEW YORK, NY	10021
COCANOWER, JAIME	BASEBALL	1609 STONEHENGE	LITTLE ROCK, AR	72212
COCEK, CHRISTINA	ACTRESS	1017 HANCOCK AVE	WEST HOLLYWOOD, CA	90069
COCHARIO, DANNY	ACTOR	11751 HORTENSE ST	NORTH HOLLYWOOD, CA	91607
COCHRAN, BOBBYE	ARTIST	730 N FRANKLIN ST	CHICAGO, IL	60610
COCHRAN, CHUCK	PIANIST	1011 MANLEY LN	BRENTWOOD, TN	37027
COCHRAN, GARLAND	SONGWRITER	ROUTE #2, BOX 448, LATTAMER LN	HENDERSONVILLE, TN	37505
COCHRAN, HANK	SINGER-SONGWRITER	ROUTE #2, BOX 438, HUNTERS LN	HENDERSONVILLE, TN	37075
COCHRAN, JOHN	NEWS CORRESPONDENT	NBC NEWS, 4001 NEBRASKA AV, SW	WASHINGTON, DC	20016
COCHRAN, RUSS	GOLFER	POST OFFICE BOX 109601	PALM BCH GARDENS, FL	33418
COCHRAN, THAD	U S SENATOR	188 E CAPITOL ST #614	JACKSON, MS	39201
COCHRAN, TODD T	COMPOSER	5731 TOPANGA CANYON BLVD	WOODLAND HILLS, CA	92367
COCHRANE, DAVE	BASEBALL	POST OFFICE BOX 4100	SEATTLE, WA	98104
COCK ROBIN	ROCK & ROLL GROUP	32 E 76TH ST #605	NEW YORK, NY	10021
COCKBURN, BRUCE	SINGER-SONGWRITER	151 JOHN ST #301	TORONTO, ONT M5V 2T2	CANADA
COCKBURN, LESLIE C	WRITER-PRODUCER	DGA, 110 W 57TH ST	NEW YORK, NY	10019
COCKER, JOE	SINGER	476 BROOME ST #6-A	NEW YORK, NY	10013
COCKRELL, ALAN	BASEBALL	4385 TUTT BLVD	COLORADO SPRINGS, CO	80922
COCKRELL, FRANK	ACTOR	13408 CHANDLER BLVD	VAN NUYS, CA	91401
COCKS, JAY	MUSIC CRITIC-WRITER	TIME/TIME & LIFE BLDG		
		ROCKEFELLER CENTER	NEW YORK, NY	10020
COCODRIL, FELICIAN	COMEDIAN	333 SAINT CHARLES AVE #500	NEW ORLEANS, LA	70130
COCONIS, TED	ARTIST	2244 SANTA ANA ST	PALO ALTO, CA	94303
COCTEAU TWINS, THE	ROCK & ROLL TRIO	10100 SANTA MONICA BLVD #1600	LOS ANGELES, CA	90067
CODIROLI, CHRIS	BASEBALL	5421 SILVERLODE DR	PLACERVILLE, CA	95667
CODY, BUCK	SINGER	POST OFFICE BOX 13	ESTILL SPRINGS, TN	37330
CODY, IRON EYES	ACTOR	2013 GRIFFITH PARK BLVD	LOS ANGELES, CA	90039
COE, BERNICE	TV EXECUTIVE	65 E 96TH ST	NEW YORK, NY	10128
COE, BOYER	BODYBUILDER	POST OFFICE BOX 5877	HUNTINGTON BEACH, CA	92646
COE, DAVID ALLAN	SINGER-SONGWRITER	ROUTE #3, BOX 549	DICKSON, TN	37055
COE, LIZ	TV WRITER	1511 SUNSET PLAZA DR	LOS ANGELES, CA	90069
COE, VIVIAN	ACTRESS	SEE - AUSTIN, VIVIAN		

COEHLO, TONY	U S CONGRESSMAN	787 7TH AVE	NEW YORK, NY	10036
COELHO, SUSIE	ACTRESS-MODEL	2814 HUTTON DR	BEVERLY HILLS, CA	90210
COEN, ETHAN	FILM PRODUCER	UTA, 9560 WILSHIRE BL, 5TH FL	BEVERLY HILLS, CA	90212
COEN, JOEL	FILM PRODUCER	UTA, 9560 WILSHIRE BL, 5TH FL	BEVERLY HILLS, CA	90212
COFER, BRIAN	BASEBALL	POST OFFICE BOX 3452	KINSTON, NC	28502
COFER, MICHAEL	FOOTBALL	LIONS, 1200 FEATHERSTONE RD	PONTIAC, MI	48432
COFER, MIKE	FOOTBALL	S F 49ERS, 4949 CENTENNIAL BL	SANTA CLARA, CA	95054
COFFEY, DENNIS	GUITARIST-COMPOSER	19631 W 8 MILE RD	DETROIT, MI	48219
COFFEY, EDWARD HOPE, III	WRITER	9442 SIERRA MAR PL	LOS ANGELES, CA	90069
COFFEY, JOHN L	TV DIRECTOR	54 HAVERFORD RD	HICKSVILLE, NY	11801
COFFEY, JOSEPH F	DIRECTOR	112 E 17TH ST	NEW YORK, NY	10003
COFFEY, MICHAEL	SINGER	PROCESS, 439 WILEY AVE	FRANKLIN, PA	16323
COFFEY, PAUL	HOCKEY	PENGUINS, CIVIC ARENA, CENTRE AV	PITTSBURGH, PA	15219
COFFEY, RICHARD	BASKETBALL	TIMBERWOLVES, 600 1ST AVE N	MINNEAPOLIS, MN	55403
COFFEY, SCOTT	ACTOR	1999 AVE OF THE STARS #2850	LOS ANGELES, CA	90067
COFFIELD, KELLY	ACTRESS	GEDDES, 8457 MELROSE PL #200	LOS ANGELES, CA	90069
COFFIELD, PETER	ACTOR	333 E 13TH ST	NEW YORK, NY	10003
COFFIN, STANTON	ACTOR	1217 1/8 N FAIRFAX AVE	LOS ANGELES, CA	90046
COFFMAN, KEVIN	BASEBALL	POST OFFICE BOX 16683	GREENVILLE, SC	29606
COGAN, DAVID	THEATER PRODUCER	350 5TH AVE	NEW YORK, NY	10001
COGGIN, W ROY	DIRECTOR	64 W 21ST ST	NEW YORK, NY	10010
COGHILL, JACK	LT GOVERNOR	POST OFFICE BOX A	JUNEAU, AK	99811
COGHLAN, FRANK "JUNIOR"	ACTOR	12522 ARGYLE AVE	LOS ALAMITOS, CA	90720
COGLIANO, PHILIP A	COMPOSER	36 WOODLAND RD	JAMAICA PLAIN, MA	02130
COHAN, MARTIN	WRITER-PRODUCER	5693 SPREADING OAK DR	LOS ANGELES, CA	90068
COHEN, ALAN N	BASKETBALL EXECUTIVE	151 MERRIMAC ST	BOSTON, MA	02114
COHEN, ALEXANDER H	THEATER-TV PRODUCER	25 W 54TH ST #5-F	NEW YORK, NY	10019
COHEN, ANNETTE	DIRECTOR	77 ROXBOROUGH DR	TORONTO, ONT M4W 1X2	CANADA
COHEN, BARBARA S	TV EXEC-NEWS CORRES	2617 WOODLEY PL, NW	WASHINGTON, DC	20008
COHEN, BERNARD I	TV PRODUCER	ABC-TV, 7 W 66TH ST	NEW YORK, NY	10023
COHEN, CHARLES Z	SCREENWRITER	8955 BEVERLY BLVD	WEST HOLLYWOOD, CA	90048
COHEN, ELLIS	COSTUME DESIGNER	645 N LA JOLLA AVE	LOS ANGELES, CA	90048
COHEN, ELLIS A	TV WRITER-PRODUCER	920 N KINGS RD #226	LOS ANGELES, CA	90069
COHEN, FRED H	TV DIRECTOR	8509 PATTON RD	WYNDMOOR, PA	19118
COHEN, GARY	SPORTSCASTER	METS, 126TH ST & ROOSEVELT AVE	FLUSHING, NY	11368
COHEN, GERRY	DIRECTOR	250 W 85TH ST	NEW YORK, NY	10024
COHEN, GERRY	TV DIRECTOR	3825 SHANNON RD	LOS ANGELES, CA	90027
COHEN, HAROLD D	CINEMATOGRAPHER	847 COMMONWEALTH AVE	VENICE, CA	90291
COHEN, HARVEY R	COMPOSER	14066-7 VAN NUYS BLVD	ARLETA, CA	91331
COHEN, HILDY PARKS	WRITER-PRODUCER	DGA, 110 W 57TH ST	NEW YORK, NY	10019
COHEN, JERRY L	BASKETBALL EXECUTIVE	N J NETS, MEADOWLANDS ARENA	EAST RUTHERFORD, NJ	07073
COHEN, JOSEPH	DIRECTOR-CHOREO	484 W 43RD ST	NEW YORK, NY	10036
COHEN, LARRY	WRITER-PRODUCER	2111 COLDWATER CANYON DR	BEVERLY HILLS, CA	90210
COHEN, LAWRENCE D	SCREENWRITER	151 S EL CAMINO DR	BEVERLY HILLS, CA	90212
COHEN, LEONARD	SINGER-SONGWRITER	3 E 54TH ST #1400	NEW YORK, NY	10022
COHEN, MARTY	COMEDIAN	KARP, 601 N ORANGE DR	LOS ANGELES, CA	90036
COHEN, MITCHELL WAYNE	TV WRITER	8383 WILSHIRE BLVD #923	BEVERLY HILLS, CA	90211
COHEN, PAUL	DIRECTOR	15 HIGHLAND RD	WESTPORT, CT	06880
COHEN, RICHARD M	DIRECTOR	585 W END AVE #12-G	NEW YORK, NY	10024
COHEN, ROB	FILM PRODUCER	1800 CENTURY PARK E #1100	LOS ANGELES, CA	90067
COHEN, ROB	WRITER-PRODUCER	1383 MILLER PL	LOS ANGELES, CA	90069
COHEN, ROBERT	BASEBALL EXECUTIVE	POST OFFICE BOX 11363	RENO, NV	89510
COHEN, ROBERT CARL	SCREENWRITER	401 S CAMDEN DR	LOS ANGELES, CA	90035
COHEN, RONALD M	WRITER	2446 N COMMONWEALTH AVE	LOS ANGELES, CA	90027
COHEN, SONA ROBBINS	TV WRITER-PRODUCER	36 E 36TH ST #7-H	NEW YORK, NY	10016
COHEN, STEVE E	DIRECTOR	6448 1/2 W OLYMPIC BLVD	LOS ANGELES, CA	90048
COHEN, STEVEN A	CINEMATOGRAPHER	21 FIREPLACE DR	KINGS PARK, NY	11754
COHEN, THOMAS A	DIRECTOR-PRODUCER	FREELAND-COPPER, WHITE & COOPER 100 CALIFORNIA ST	SAN FRANCISCO, CA	94111
COHEN, WILLIAM	THEATER PRODUCER	THEATRE NOW, 1515 BROADWAY	NEW YORK, NY	10036
COHEN, WILLIAM S	U S SENATOR	202 HARLOW ST #204	BANGOR, ME	04401
COHEN-ROSS, JUDITH L	WRITER	29606 MEADOWMIST WY	AGOURA HILLS, CA	91301
COHENOUR, LOU	BASEBALL SCOUT	BREWERS, 201 S 46TH ST	MILWAUKEE, WI	53214
COHICK, EMMITT	BASEBALL	POST OFFICE BOX 1742	PALM SPRINGS, CA	92263
COHN, BRUCE	SCREENWRITER	ICM, 8899 BEVERLY BLVD	LOS ANGELES, CA	90048
COHN, DAVID	ACTOR	10524 MONOGRAM AVE	GRANADA HILLS, CA	91344
COHN, DAVID	CASTING DIRECTOR	12023 1/2 VENTURA BLVD	STUDIO CITY, CA	91604
COHN, LAWRENCE	COLUMNIST	VARIETY, 475 PARK AVE S	NEW YORK, NY	10016
COHN, MARC	SINGER	CAA, 9830 WILSHIRE BLVD	BEVERLY HILLS, CA	90212
COHN, MINDY	ACTRESS	9606 YOAKUM DR	BEVERLY HILLS, CA	90210
COHN, ROY B	TV-COMEDY WRITER	205 PARK PL #6	BROOKLYN, NY	11754
COHN, SAM	TALENT AGENT	ICM, 40 W 57TH ST	NEW YORK, NY	10019
COHOON, CHRIS S	WRITER	1823 12TH ST #3	SANTA MONICA, CA	90404
COHOON, DIANNE	COSTUME DESIGNER	13949 VENTURA BLVD #309	SHERMAN OAKS, CA	91423
COIT, MARGARET	WRITER	386 PARK AVE	RUTHERFORD, NJ	07070
COKER, KATHERINE E	TV WRITER	978 WELLESLEY AVE	LOS ANGELES, CA	90049
COKER, PAUL	CARTOONIST	MAD MAGAZINE, 485 MADISON AVE	NEW YORK, NY	10022
COLANGELO, BRYAN	BASKETBALL	SUNS, 2910 N CENTRAL AVE	PHOENIX, AZ	85012
COLANGELO, JERRY	BASKETBALL EXECUTIVE	SUNS, 2910 N CENTRAL AVE	PHOENIX, AZ	85012
COLARUSSO, CHARLES A	WRITER	2225 MALAGA RD	LOS ANGELES, CA	90048
COLARUSSO, FRANK	BASEBALL EXECUTIVE	POST OFFICE BOX 11087	TACOMA, WA	98411
COLBERT, CLAUDETTE	ACTRESS	BELLERIVE SAINT PETER	BARBADOS	
COLBERT, CRAIG	BASEBALL	S F GIANTS, CANDLESTICK PARK	SAN FRANICSCO, CA	94124
COLBERT, EARL	ACTOR	8051 WILLOW GLEN RD	LOS ANGELES, CA	90046
COLBERT, IVY	ACTRESS	2239 GREENFIELD AVE	LOS ANGELES, CA	90064

COLBERT, JIM	GOLFER	PGA SENIORS, 112 T P C BLVD	PONTE VEDRA BEACH, FL 32082
COLBERT, RICK	BASEBALL MANAGER	80 OTTAWA ST N	HAMILTON, ONT L8H 3Z1 CANADA
COLBERT, ROBERT	ACTOR	151 OCEAN PARK BLVD	SANTA MONICA, CA 90405
COLBERT, VERDELL & OFFSPRIN	GOSPEL GROUP	POST OFFICE BOX 2095	PHILADELPHIA, PA 19103
COLBRUNN, GREG	BASEBALL	1501 W 16TH ST	INDIANAPOLIS, IN 46202
COLBY, PHIL	ACTOR	1401 VALLEY VIEW RD #21	GLENDALE, CA 91202
COLCORD, RAY, III	WRITER-MUSICIAN	5453 AGNES AVE	NORTH HOLLYWOOD, CA 91607
COLDER, BEN	SINGER	CIRCUIT, 123 WALTON FERRY RD	HENDERSONVILLE, TN 37075
COLE, ALEX	BASEBALL	POST OFFICE BOX 7000	PITTSBURGH, PA 15212
COLE, ALEX	COMEDIAN	POST OFFICE BOX 9532	MADISON, WI 53715
COLE, BRENDA	SINGER	ARTIST NETWORK, 13749 RIVERSIDE	SHERMAN OAKS, CA 91403
COLE, BUTCH	BASEBALL	300 STADIUM WY	DAVENPORT, FL 33837
COLE, CHARLES E	ATTORNEY GENERAL	POST OFFICE BOX A	JUNEAU, AK 99811
COLE, DANNY LEE	TV WRITER	16633 VENTURA BLVD #1421	ENCINO, CA 91436
COLE, DANTON	HOCKEY	JETS, 15-1430 MAROONS RD	WINNIPEG, MAN R3G 0L5 CANADA
COLE, DENNIS	ACTOR	2160 CENTURY PARK E #1712	LOS ANGELES, CA 90067
COLE, EVAN	ACTOR	6843 WILLIS AVE	VAN NUYS, CA 91405
COLE, GARY	ACTOR	10390 SANTA MONICA BLVD #300	LOS ANGELES, CA 90025
COLE, GEORGE	ACTOR	"DONNELLY", NEWNHAM HILL BOTTOM, NETTLEFORD	OXFORDSHIRE ENGLAND
COLE, JOHN	BASEBALL SCOUT	SKYDOME, 300 BREMMER BL #3200	TORONTO, ONT M5V 3B3 CANADA
COLE, MARK	BASEBALL	POST OFFICE BOX 8550	STOCKTON, CA 95208
COLE, MARVIN	BASEBALL	POST OFFICE BOX 4488	WINSTON-SALEM, NC 27115
COLE, MICHAEL	ACTOR	6332 COSTELLO AVE	VAN NUYS, CA 91401
COLE, NATALIE	SINGER	19218 WELLS DR	TARZANA, CA 91356
COLE, OLIVIA	ACTRESS	9744 WILSHIRE BLVD #308	BEVERLY HILLS, CA 90212
COLE, ROYAL	WRITER	16754 E AVE "X" #33	LLANO, CA 93544
COLE, SANDY	COSTUME DESIGNER	13949 VENTURA BLVD #309	SHERMAN OAKS, CA 91423
COLE, STU	BASEBALL	POST OFFICE BOX 3665	OMAHA, NE 68103
COLE, TINA	ACTRESS	FELBER, 2126 N CAHUENGA BLVD	LOS ANGELES, CA 90068
COLE, VICTOR	BASEBALL (BUFFALO)	POST OFFICE BOX 450	BUFFALO, NY 14205
COLE, VICTOR	BASEBALL (CAROLINA)	POST OFFICE DRAWER 1218	ZEBULON, NC 27597
COLEMAN, BILLY	BASEBALL	POST OFFICE BOX 22093	GREENSBORO, NC 27420
COLEMAN, CY	PIANIST-COMPOSER	NOTABLE MUSIC, 161 W 54TH ST	NEW YORK, NY 10023
COLEMAN, DABNEY	ACTOR	715 NAPOLI DR	PACIFIC PALISADES, CA 90272
COLEMAN, DERRICK	BASKETBALL	N J NETS, MEADOWLANDS ARENA	EAST RUTHERFORD, NJ 07073
COLEMAN, DESIREE	SINGER	PAZ MANAGMENT (L A EDWARDS) 526 S 3RD ST	PHILADELPHIA, PA 19147
COLEMAN, DON	ACTOR	POST OFFICE BOX 567	WILLITS, CA 95490
COLEMAN, E THOMAS	U S CONGRESSMAN	POST OFFICE & FEDERAL BLDG 8TH AND EDMOND	SAINT JOSEPH, MO 64501
COLEMAN, GARY	ACTOR	9000 SUNSET BLVD #1200	LOS ANGELES, CA 90069
COLEMAN, GORDY	BASEBALL-EXECUTIVE	REDS, 100 RIVERFRONT STADIUM	CINCINNATI, OH 45202
COLEMAN, HERBERT	FILM DIRECTOR	687 SAN MORITZ DR FOREST LAKES	BAYFIELD, CO 81122
COLEMAN, JACK	ACTOR	7358 WOODROW WILSON DR	LOS ANGELES, CA 90046
COLEMAN, JERRY	BASEBALL-ANNOUNCER	1004 HAVENHURST DR	LA JOLLA, CA 92037
COLEMAN, JOE	BASEBALL-COACH	250 STADIUM PLAZA	ST LOUIS, MO 63102
COLEMAN, JOHN	TV EXECUTIVE	2840 MOUNT WILKINSON PARKWAY	ATLANTA, GA 30339
COLEMAN, JOHN W	DIRECTOR	4524 RHODELLA AVE	CLAREMONT, CA 91711
COLEMAN, KEN	BASEBALL	1090 N EUCLID AVE	SARASOTA, FL 34237
COLEMAN, MONTE	FOOTBALL	POST OFFICE BOX 17247 (DULLES)	WASHINGTON, DC 20041
COLEMAN, NANCY	ACTRESS	484 W 43RD ST #42-G	NEW YORK, NY 10036
COLEMAN, ORNETTE	MUSICIAN	POST OFFICE BOX 106	NEW YORK, NY 10013
COLEMAN, PAT	FOOTBALL	OILERS, 6910 FANNIN ST	HOUSTON, TX 77070
COLEMAN, PAUL	BASEBALL	POST OFFICE BOX 5599	LITTLE ROCK, AR 72215
COLEMAN, RONALD D	U S CONGRESSMAN	FEDERAL BUILDING, ROOM C-723 700 E SAN ANTONIO	EL PASO, TX 79901
COLEMAN, SIDNEY	FOOTBALL	POST OFFICE BOX 888	PHOENIX, AZ 85001
COLEMAN, VINCE	BASEBALL	METS, 126TH ST & ROOSEVELT AVE	FLUSHING, NY 11368
COLEMAN, WALT	FOOTBALL REFEREE	NFL, 410 PARK AVE	NEW YORK, NY 10022
COLENBACK, JOHN	ACTOR	8560 RIDPATH DR	LOS ANGELES, CA 90046
COLES, ANDREA	ACTRESS	4 WASHINGTON SQUARE VILLAGE	NEW YORK, NY 10012
COLES, BIMBO	BASKETBALL	MIAMI HEAT, THE MIAMI ARENA	MIAMI, FL 33136
COLES, CHARLES "HONI"	ACTOR	24-40 94TH ST	EAST ELMHURST, NY 11369
COLES, DARNELL	BASEBALL	POST OFFICE BOX 23290	NASHVILLE, TN 37202
COLESBERRY, ROBERT F	FILM PRODUCER	CAA, 9830 WILSHIRE BLVD	BEVERLY HILLS, CA 90212
COLEY, RAY	BASEBALL SCOUT	POST OFFICE BOX 2000	SAN DIEGO, CA 92112
COLGAN, DR MICHAEL	FITNESS AUTHORITY	531 ENCINITAS BLVD #101	ENCINITAS, CA 92024
COLICK, LEWIS A	WRITER	416 N VISTA ST	LOS ANGELES, CA 90036
COLIN, MARGARET	ACTRESS	366 W 11TH ST #PH-C	NEW YORK, NY 10014
COLITTI, RIK	ACTOR	215 SEBONAC RD	SOUTHAMPTON, NY 11968
COLLA, RICHARD	DIRECTOR	2533 GREENVALLEY RD	LOS ANGELES, CA 90046
COLLAMORE, JEROME	ACTOR	147-05 SANFORD AVE	FLUSHING, NY 11355
COLLEARY, ROBERT J	TV WRITER	10537 VALLEY SPRING LN	NORTH HOLLYWOOD, CA 91602
COLLEARY, ROBERT M	TV WRITER	10537 VALLEY SPRING LN	NORTH HOLLYWOOD, CA 91602
COLLERAN, WILLIAM	WRITER-PRODUCER	1535 N LAS PALMAS AVE #32	LOS ANGELES, CA 90028
COLLEY, PETER M	PLAYWRIGHT	250 W 57TH ST	NEW YORK, NY 10107
COLLIE, MARK	SINGER-SONGWRITER	POST OFFICE BOX 120308	NASHVILLE, TN 37212
COLLIER, ANTHONY	BASEBALL	POST OFFICE BOX 2887	VERO BEACH, FL 32961
COLLIER, BOB	ACTOR	1560 BROADWAY #509	NEW YORK, NY 10036
COLLIER, EARL W	COMPOSER	7745 ETON AVE	CANOGA PARK, CA 91304
COLLIER, HELEN M	CASTING DIRECTOR	1560 BROADWAY #509	NEW YORK, NY 10036
COLLIER, JOEL	FOOTBALL COACH	BUCCANEERS, 1 BUCCANEER PL	TAMPA, FL 33607
COLLIER, JOHN	ARTIST	2309 WILLOW CREEK LN	LAWRENCE, KS 66044

COLLIN, MARGARET H	COMPOSER	6250 TELEGRAPH RD #109	VENTURA, CA 93003
COLLINS, ALANA	ACTRESS	SEE - HAMILTON, ALANA	
COLLINS, ANDRE	FOOTBALL	POST OFFICE BOX 17247 (DULLES)	WASHINGTON, DC 20041
COLLINS, BARBARA-ROSE	U S CONGRESSWOMAN	1543 E LAFAYETTE AVE	DETROIT, MI 48207
COLLINS, BILL	GOLFER	PGA SENIORS, 112 T P C BLVD	PONTE VEDRA BEACH, FL 32082
COLLINS, BURTON	ACTOR	1803 CARNEGIE LN	REDONDO BEACH, CA 90278
COLLINS, C T	ACTOR	7616 HOLLYWOOD BLVD #304	LOS ANGELES, CA 90046
COLLINS, CARDISS	U S CONGRESSMAN	230 S DEARBORN ST #3880	CHICAGO, IL 60605
COLLINS, CARRIE	TV PRODUCER	400 N CAPITOL ST #155, NW	WASHINGTON, DC 20001
COLLINS, CYNTHIA	COMPOSER	100 COOPER ST #3-H	NEW YORK, NY 10034
COLLINS, DAVE	BASEBALL-COACH	250 STADIUM PLAZA	ST LOUIS, MO 63102
COLLINS, DAVID	TV PRODUCER	8 TIVOLI TERRACE SOUTH	DUN LOAGHAIRE, DUBLIN IRELAND
COLLINS, DOUG	ACTOR	2230 S BEVERLY GLEN BLVD #208	LOS ANGELES, CA 90064
COLLINS, DOUG	BODYGUARD	EVENT MANAGEMENT CO	
		3662 KATELLA AVE	LOS ALAMITOS, CA 90720
COLLINS, ERNIE	ACTOR	14144 DICKENS ST	SHERMAN OAKS, CA 91423
COLLINS, ERNIE L	MUSIC ARRANGER	1515 DENISE CT	ANTIOCH, TN 37013
COLLINS, GARY	ACTOR-TV HOST	2751 HUTTON DR	BEVERLY HILLS, CA 90210
COLLINS, GUNTHER	WRITER-PRODUCER	21917 GRANT AVE	TORRANCE, CA 90503
COLLINS, IAN DAVID	TV DIRECTOR	304 W 88TH ST #3-C	NEW YORK, NY 10024
COLLINS, JACKIE	AUTHORESS	13701 RIVERSIDE DR #608	SHERMAN OAKS, CA 91423
COLLINS, JAY	MUSIC ARRANGER	POST OFFICE BOX 815	BRENTWOOD, TN 37027
COLLINS, JESSICA	ACTRESS	ABC-TV, "LOVING"	
		320 W 66TH ST, STUDIO 23	NEW YORK, NY 10023
COLLINS, JIM	SINGER	POST OFFICE BOX 57291	DALLAS, TX 75207
COLLINS, JIMMY	SINGER	POST OFFICE BOX 120308	NASHVILLE, TN 37212
COLLINS, JOAN	ACTRESS-PRODUCER	19 EATON PL, FLAT #2	LONDON SW1 ENGLAND
COLLINS, JOHN	ACTOR	6525 SUNSET BLVD #303	HOLLYWOOD, CA 90028
COLLINS, JOHNNIE, III	ACTOR	MALIBU LAKE MOUNTATIN CLUB	
		29033 WESTLAKE VISTA DR	AGOURA, CA 92301
COLLINS, JUDY	SINGER-SONGWRITER	POST OFFICE BOX 1296	NEW YORK, NY 10025
COLLINS, KATE	ACTRESS	ABC-TV, "ALL MY CHILDREN"	
		320 W 66TH ST	NEW YORK, NY 10023
COLLINS, MARK	FOOTBALL	N Y GIANTS, GIANTS STADIUM	EAST RUTHERFORD, NJ 07073
COLLINS, MAX	CARTOONIST	TRIBUNE, 64 E CONCORD ST	ORLANDO, FL 32801
COLLINS, MICHAEL C	ACTOR	1974 HILLCREST RD	LOS ANGELES, CA 90068
COLLINS, MONICA	TV CRITIC	POST OFFICE BOX 500	WASHINGTON, DC 20044
COLLINS, PAT	FILM CRITIC	WWOR-TV, 140 BROADWAY	NEW YORK, NY 10018
COLLINS, PETER	NEWS CORRESPONDENT	ABC-TV, 7 W 66TH ST	NEW YORK, NY 10019
COLLINS, PHIL	SINGER-DRUMMER	LOCKSWOOD	SUSSEX ENGLAND
COLLINS, RICHARD J	WRITER	200 ACARI DR	LOS ANGELES, CA 90049
COLLINS, ROBERT	CINEMATOGRAPHER	7715 SUNSET BLVD #150	LOS ANGELES, CA 90046
COLLINS, ROBERTA	ACTRESS	8831 SUNSET BLVD #402	LOS ANGELES, CA 90069
COLLINS, SHAWN	FOOTBALL	FALCONS, SUWANEE RD AT I-85	SUWANEE, GA 30174
COLLINS, STEPHEN	ACTOR	7920 SUNSET BLVD #350	LOS ANGELES, CA 90046
COLLINS, TERRY	BASEBALL COACH	POST OFFICE BOX 7000	PITTSBURGH, PA 15212
COLLINS, TOMMY	SINGER	ACE PRODS, 3407 GREEN RIDGE DR	NASHVILLE, TN 37214
COLLINS, TYLER	SINGER	8380 MELROSE AVE #310	WEST HOLLYWOOD, CA 90069
COLLINS, WILLIAM "BOOTSY"	SINGER-GUITARIST	FAA, 1700 BROADWAY, 5TH FLOOR	NEW YORK, NY 10019
COLLINSWORTH, MILLICENT	ACTRESS	205 S BEVERLY DR #210	BEVERLY HILLS, CA 90212
COLLOFF, ROGER D	TV EXECUTIVE	WCBS-TV, 524 W 57TH ST	NEW YORK, NY 10019
COLMAN, BOOTH	ACTOR	8024 W NORTON AVE	LOS ANGELES, CA 90046
COLMAN, HENRY	TV WRITER-PRODUCER	423 LINNIE CANAL	VENICE, CA 90291
COLMAN, JOEL	DIRECTOR	755 BROOKTREE RD	PACIFIC PALISADES, CA 90272
COLMERAUER, DANIEL M	TV WRITER	3518 W CAHUENGA BLVD #318	LOS ANGELES, CA 90068
COLMES, WALTER	FILM DIRECTOR	5425 SW 77TH CT #1080	MIAMI, FL 33155
COLODNY, LESTER	DIRECTOR	DORCHER, 15 E 48TH ST	NEW YORK, NY 10017
COLODZIN, ROBERT S	DIRECTOR	7 WAKE ROBIN LN	STAMFORD, CT 06903
COLOMBIER, MICHAEL	COMPOSER-MUSICIAN	POST OFFICE BOX 779	MILL VALLEY, CA 94942
COLOMBINO, CARLO	BASEBALL	2501 ALLEN AVE, SE	CANTON, OH 44707
COLOMBO, PATTI	ACTRESS	8228 SUNSET BLVD #212	LOS ANGELES, CA 90046
COLOMBU, FRANCO	BODYBUILDER	2389 WESTWOOD BLVD	LOS ANGELES, CA 90025
COLOMBY, HARRY	TV WRITER-PRODUCER	4139 WOODCLIFF RD	SHERMAN OAKS, CA 91403
COLOMBY, ROBERT "BOBBY"	MUSICIAN-RECORD EXEC	CBS RECORDS, 1801 CENTURY PK W	LOS ANGELES, CA 90067
COLOMBY, SCOTT	ACTOR	8730 SUNSET BLVD #480	LOS ANGELES, CA 90069
COLON, ALEX	ACTOR	POST OFFICE BOX 1221	STUDIO CITY, CA 91604
COLON, CHRIS	BASEBALL	POST OFFICE BOX 4448	TULSA, OK 74159
COLON, DAVID	BASEBALL	POST OFFICE BOX 1742	PALM SPRINGS, CA 92263
COLON, DENNIS	BASEBALL	POST OFFICE BOX 824	BURLINGTON, IA 52601
COLON, HARY	FOOTBALL	PATRIOTS, FOXBORO STADIUM, RT #1	FOXBORO, MA 02035
COLON, MIRIAM	ACTRESS	EISEN, 154 E 61ST ST	NEW YORK, NY 10021
COLOR ME BADD	RAP GROUP	345 N MAPLE DR #205	BEVERLY HILLS, CA 90210
COLPITTS, CISSY	ACTRESS	SEE - CAMERON, CISSE	
COLPMAN, NORA	ACTRESS	250 W 94TH ST #10-H	NEW YORK, NY 10025
COLSON, CHARLES	AUTHOR	POST OFFICE BOX 40562	WASHINGTON, DC 20016
COLT, MARSHALL	ACTOR-WRITER	923 OCEAN AVE #5	SANTA MONICA, CA 90403
COLTER, JESSI	SINGER-SONGWRITER	1117 17TH AVE S	NASHVILLE, TN 37203
COLTER, STEVE	BASKETBALL	KINGS, 1 SPORTS PARKWAY	SACRAMENTO, CA 95834
COLTON, BARBARA	ACTRESS	117 W 13TH ST	NEW YORK, NY 10011
COLTON, CHEVI	ACTRESS	SILVER, 300 CENTRAL PARK W	NEW YORK, NY 10024
COLTON, JACQUE LYNN	ACTRESS	4116 W VERDUGO AVE	BURBANK, CA 91505
COLTRANE, CHI	SINGER-SONGWRITER	5955 TUXEDO TERR	LOS ANGELES, CA 90068
COLUMBU, FRANCO	ACTOR-BODYBUILDER	POST OFFICE BOX 1250	SANTA MONICA, CA 90406
COLUMBUS, CHRIS	SCREENWRITER	290 W END AVE	NEW YORK, NY 10023
COLVARD, BENNY	BASEBALL	POST OFFICE BOX 11002	CHATTANOOGA, TN 37401

COLVIN, JACK L	ACTOR-DIRECTOR	3404 LARISSA DR	LOS ANGELES, CA 90026
COLVIN, ROB	ARTIST	POST OFFICE BOX 17193	SALT LAKE CITY, UT 84117
COMA, AGIM	ACTOR	5330 LANKERSHIM BLVD #210	NORTH HOLLYWOOD, CA 91601
COMBA, FRED W	COMPOSER	54 CRAGMONT AVE	SAN FRANCISCO, CA 94116
COMBEST, LARRY	U S CONGRESSMAN	FEDERAL BUILDING, ROOM 613	
		1205 TEXAS AVE	LUBBOCK, TX 79401
COMBIER, ELIZABETH	TV PRODUCER	315 E 65TH ST #4-C	NEW YORK, NY 10021
COMBS, FREDERICK	ACTOR	1152 N HOOVER ST	LOS ANGELES, CA 90029
COMBS, PAT	BASEBALL	POST OFFICE BOX 3449	SCRANTON, PA 18505
COMBS, RAY	GAME SHOW HOST	CBS-TV, "THE FAMILY FEUD"	
		7800 BEVERLY BLVD	LOS ANGELES, CA 90036
COMDEN, BETTY	WRITER	117 E 95TH ST	NEW YORK, NY 10028
COMEAUX, DARREN	FOOTBALL	SEAHAWKS, 11220 NE 53RD ST	KIRKLAND, WA 98033
COMENETZ, LEWIS D	SOUND EDITOR	6700 192ND ST	FRESH MEADOWS, NY 11365
COMER, ANJANETTE	ACTRESS	2357 KIMBRIDGE RD	BEVERLY HILLS, CA 90210
COMERFORD, CLINTON P	WRITER	528 E FOOTHILL BLVD	GLENDORA, CA 91740
COMI, PAUL	ACTOR	1665 OAK KNOLL AVE	SAN MARINO, CA 91108
COMICI, ELIZABETH L	TV WRITER	15415 MILLDALE DR	LOS ANGELES, CA 90077
COMICI, LUCIANO	TV WRITER	15415 MILLDALE DR	LOS ANGELES, CA 90077
COMINOS, NICHOLAS	WRITER-PRODUCER	THE CAMBRIDGE TOWER	
		1801 LAVACA ST	AUSTIN, TX 78701
COMISKEY, ROBERT J	TV DIRECTOR	WCVB-TV, 5 TV PL	NEEDHAM, MA 02192
COMISSIONA, SERGIU	CONDUCTOR	ICM, 40 W 57TH ST	NEW YORK, NY 10019
COMISSIONG, LYDIA NICOLE	ACTRESS	3800 BARHAM BLVD #303	LOS ANGELES, CA 90068
COMMANDER CODY BAND	ROCK & ROLL GROUP	150 5TH AVE #1103	NEW YORK, NY 10011
COMMANDER MARK	TV HOST	SEE - KISTLER, COMMANDER MARK	
COMMIRE, ANNE	PLAYWRIGHT	81-R OSWEGATCHIE RD	WATERFORD, CT 06385
COMMODORES, THE	SOUL GROUP	3151 W CAHUENGA BLVD #235	LOS ANGELES, CA 90068
COMMONS, DAVID	WRITER-PRODUCER	1835 CAMINO PALMERO ST	LOS ANGELES, CA 90046
COMO, DARLENE	ACTRESS	1124 W ANGELENO AVE #M	BURBANK, CA 91506
COMO, PERRY	SINGER	305 NORTHERN BLVD #3-A	GREAT NECK, NY 11021
COMORA, BETTY	SINGER	POST OFFICE BOX C	RIVER EDGE, NJ 07661
COMPRES, FIDEL	BASEBALL	POST OFFICE BOX 5599	LITTLE ROCK, AR 72215
COMPTON, ANN	NEWS CORRESPONDENT	ABC NEWS, 1717 DE SALES ST, NW	WASHINGTON, DC 20036
COMPTON, CLINT	BASEBALL	POST OFFICE BOX 20849	CHARLESTON, SC 29413
COMPTON, CRAIG	BASEBALL UMPIRE	2101 E BROADWAY #35	TEMPE, AZ 85282
COMPTON, FORREST	ACTOR	CED, 118 E 25TH ST, 6TH FLOOR	NEW YORK, NY 10010
COMPTON, JOYCE	ACTRESS	23388 MULHOLLAND DR	WOODLAND HILLS, CA 91364
COMPTON, KEN	BASEBALL SCOUT	POST OFFICE BOX 4100	SEATTLE, WA 98104
COMPTON, RICHARD	WRITER-PRODUCER	9000 SUNSET BLVD #1200	LOS ANGELES, CA 90069
COMSTOCK, FRANK G	COMPOSER-CONDUCTOR	3966 ALADDIN DR	HUNTINGTON HARBOUR, CA 92649
CONACHER, PAT	HOCKEY	POST OFFICE BOX 504	EAST RUTHERFORD, NJ 07073
CONAWAY, JEFF	ACTOR	10351 SANTA MONICA BLVD #211	LOS ANGELES, CA 90025
CONBOY, JOHN J	TV DIRECTOR-PRODUCER	NEW WORLD, 1440 S SEPULVEDA BL	LOS ANGELES, CA 90025
CONCEPCION, DAVE	BASEBALL	URB LOS CAOBOS BOTALON 5D	5 PISO-MARACAY VENEZUELA
CONDE, RAMON	BASEBALL-SCOUT	INDIANS, CLEVELAND STADIUM	CLEVELAND, OH 44114
CONDIT, GARY	U S CONGRESSMAN	415 W 18TH ST	MERCED, CA 95340
CONDON, MAGGIE MC GRAW	DIRECTOR	20 5TH AVE	NEW YORK, NY 10011
CONDON, WILLIAM	SCREENWRITER	CAA, 9830 WILSHIRE BLVD	BEVERLY HILLS, CA 90212
CONDOS, DIMO	ACTOR	75 BANK ST	NEW YORK, NY 10014
CONDRA, JULIE	ACTRESS	NBC-TV, 3000 W ALAMEDA AVE	BURBANK, CA 91523
CONE, DAVE	BASEBALL	SKYDOME, 300 BREMMER BL #3200	TORONTO, ONT M5V 3B3 CANADA
CONE, DWIGHT	BASEBALL	METS, 126TH ST & ROOSEVELT AVE	FLUSHING, NY 11368
CONE, TOM	CARTOONIST	TRIBUNE, 64 E CONCORD ST	ORLANDO, FL 32801
CONER, LEONARD	ACTOR-ANNOUNCER	POST OFFICE BOX 26087	LAS VEGAS, NV 89102
CONEY HATCH	ROCK & ROLL GROUP	1505 W 2ND AVE #200	VANCOUVER, BC V6H 3Y4 CANADA
CONFER, MITCHELL	ARTIST	229 BAY ST #2	JERSEY CITY, NJ 07302
CONFORTI, GINO	ACTOR	132 S LASKY DR #B	BEVERLY HILLS, CA 90212
CONFORTI, JOE	DIRECTOR	49 PARK AVE	NEW YORK, NY 10011
CONGDON, JAMES	ACTOR	340 RIVERSIDE DR	NEW YORK, NY 10025
CONGE, BOB	ARTIST	28 HARPER ST	ROCHESTER, NY 14607
CONGER, ERIC	ACTOR	484 W 43RD ST #37-F	NEW YORK, NY 10036
CONGER, JEFF	BASEBALL	POST OFFICE BOX 3746, HILL STA	AUGUSTA, GA 30904
CONIFF, RAY	COMPOSER	2154 HERCULES DR	LOS ANGELES, CA 90046
CONIN, AL	SPORTSCASTER	POST OFFICE BOX 710	LOS ANGELES, CA 90028
CONINE, JEFF	BASEBALL	POST OFFICE BOX 3665	OMAHA, NE 68103
CONKIN, MARK	BASEBALL SCOUT	ATHLETICS'S, OAKLAND COLISEUM	OAKLAND, CA 94621
CONKLIN, PEGGY	ACTRESS	THOMPSON, 142 E 71ST ST	NEW YORK, NY 10021
CONKWRIGHT, LYNN	BODYBUILDER	POST OFFICE BOX 4235	VIRGINIA BEACH, CA 23454
CONLAN, JOHN	BASEBALL	7810 E MARIPOSA DR	SCOTTSDALE, AZ 85251
CONLAN, SHANE	FOOTBALL	BILLS, 1 BILLS DR	ORCHARD PARK, NJ 14127
CONLEE, JOHN	SINGER-SONGWRITER	38 MUSIC SQUARE E #117	NASHVILLE, TN 37203
CONLEY, DARLENE	ACTRESS	CBS-TV, "THE BOLD & BEAUTIFUL"	
		7800 BEVERLY BLVD #3371	LOS ANGELES, CA 90036
CONLEY, DAVID M	DIRECTOR	DGA, 110 W 57TH ST	NEW YORK, NY 10019
CONLEY, EARL THOMAS	SINGER-SONGWRITER	POST OFFICE BOX 23552	NASHVILLE, TN 37202
CONLEY, GENE	BASEBALL-BASKETBALL	12 RIDGE RD	FOXBORO, MA 02035
CONLEY, JOE	ACTOR	10332 CHRISTINE PL	CHATSWORTH, CA 91311
CONLEY, MATT	BASEBALL	POLECATS, 608 N SLAPPEY BLVD	ALBANY, GA 31701
CONLEY, RENIE	COSTUME DESIGNER	1080 RAVOLI DR	PACIFIC PALISADES, CA 90272
CONLIN, NOEL	ACTOR	4317 CROWNFIELD CT	WESTLAKE VILLAGE, CA 91361
CONLIN, NOREEN P	TV PRODUCER	13577 VALLEYHEART DR N	SHERMAN OAKS, CA 91423
CONN, BILLY	BOXER	544 GETTYSBURG ST	PITTSBURGH, PA 15206
CONN, DIDI	ACTRESS	14820 VALLEY VISTA BLVD	SHERMAN OAKS, CA 91403
CONN, TONY	COMPOSER	5503 BECK AVE #B	NORTH HOLLYWOOD, CA 91601

Name	Occupation	Address	City
CONNALLY, CONNIE	ARTIST	7818 RIDGEMAR DR	DALLAS, TX 75231
CONNALLY, JOHN	VICE PRESIDENT	600 CONGRESS AVE #1630	AUSTIN, TX 78701
CONNALLY, MARY	ACTRESS-SINGER	142 E 33RD ST #6-C	NEW YORK, NY 10016
CONNELL, DAVID D	TV WRITER-EXECUTIVE	CHILDREN'S TV WORKSHOP	
		1 LINCOLN PLAZA	NEW YORK, NY 10023
CONNELL, KATHLEEN	ACTRESS	ANDERSON, 5923 WILBUR AVE	TARZANA, CA 91356
CONNELL, KATHLEEN	SECRETARY OF STATE	STATE CAPITOL, 320 S MAIN ST	PROVIDENCE, RI 02903
CONNELLS, THE	ROCK & ROLL GROUP	5 W HARGETT ST #407	RALEIGH, NC 27601
CONNELLY, JENNIFER	ACTRESS	ICM, 8899 BEVERLY BLVD	LOS ANGELES, CA 90048
CONNELLY, LARRY E	COMPOSER	824 N LINCOLN ST	BURBANK, CA 91506
CONNER, DARION	FOOTBALL	FALCONS, SUWANEE RD AT I-85	SUWANEE, GA 30174
CONNER, DENNIS	YACHTSMAN	DENNIS CONNER SPORTS	
		720 GATEWAY CENTER DR #E	SAN DIEGO, CA 92102
CONNER, LESTER	BASKETBALL	N J NETS, MEADOWLANDS ARENA	EAST RUTHERFORD, NJ 07073
CONNERY, JASON	ACTOR	22 BISHOPS RD	LONDON SW6 7AB ENGLAND
CONNERY, SEAN	ACTOR	FUENTE DEL RODEO	
		CASA MALIBU, NUEVA	
		ANDALUSIA	MALAGA SPAIN
CONNICK, HARRY, JR	SINGER-PIANIST	298 MULBERRY ST	NEW YORK, NY 10012
CONNIE	COMEDIENNE	3661 S MARYLAND PKWY #3 - BOX 50	LAS VEGAS, NV 89109
CONNOCK, JIM	FILM EDITOR-PRODUCER	28 SUSSEX MANSIONS	
		OLD BROMPTON RD	LONDON SW7 ENGLAND
CONNOLLY, BILLY	ACTOR-COMEDIAN	151 S EL CAMINO DR	BEVERLY HILLS, CA 90212
CONNOLLY, CRAIG	BASEBALL	POST OFFICE BOX 11363	RENO, NV 89510
CONNOLLY, JAMES G	DIRECTOR	DGA, 110 W 57TH ST	NEW YORK, NY 10019
CONNOLLY, MATT	BASEBALL	POST OFFICE BOX 48	VISALIA, CA 93279
CONNOLLY, MICHAEL JOSEPH	SEC OF COMMONWEALTH	STATE HOUSE BUILDING	BOSTON, MA 02133
CONNOLLY, NORMA	ACTRESS	ABC-TV, "GENERAL HOSPITAL"	
		4151 PROSPECT AVE	BURBANK, CA 91523
CONNOLLY, RAY	TV WRITER	LEMON, 24 POTTERY, HOLLAND PK	LONDON W11 4LZ ENGLAND
CONNOR, HAYDEN	ACTRESS	1800 N HIGHLAND AVE #405	LOS ANGELES, CA 90028
CONNOR, KEVIN G	WRITER-PRODUCER	MERRILL, 4260 ARCOLA AVE	TOLUCA LAKE, CA 91602
CONNOR, MARK	BASEBALL-COACH	N Y YANKEES, YANKEE STADIUM	BRONX, NY 10451
CONNOR, MICHAEL	ACTOR	1416 N HAVENHURST DR	LOS ANGELES, CA 90046
CONNOR, MICHAEL	TV DIRECTOR-PRODUCER	OLD POPLARS FARM HOUSE	
		EASTGATE, HORNTON, BANBURY	OXON ENGLAND
CONNOR, MICHAEL	TV PRODUCER	THE WALL STREET JOURNAL	
		200 LIBERTY ST	NEW YORK, NY 10281
CONNOR, PATRICK	ACTOR	3 SPRING BANK, NEW MILLS	VIA STOCKPORT SK12 4AS.... ENGLAND
CONNOR, WHITFIELD	ACTOR	5 LADDER HILL RD S	WESTON, CT 06883
CONNORS, BILL	BASEBALL-INSTRUCTOR	1060 W ADDISON ST	CHICAGO, IL 60613
CONNORS, BILLY	BASEBALL COACH	1060 W ADDISON ST	CHICAGO, IL 60613
CONNORS, CAROL	SONGWRITER	1709 FERRARI DR	BEVERLY HILLS, CA 90210
CONNORS, CHUCK	ACTOR-BASEBALL	HC 99, BOX 4440-73	TEHACHAPI, CA 93561
CONNORS, JIMMY	TENNIS	200 S REFUGIO RD	SANTA YNEZ, CA 93460
CONNORS, MIKE	ACTOR	4810 LOUISE AVE	ENCINO, CA 91316
CONNORS, SUSAN	ACTRESS	1757 N KINGSLEY DR #211	HOLLYWOOD, CA 90027
CONNORS, THOMAS J, III	DIRECTOR	13371 PHILLIPPI AVE	SYLMAR, CA 91342
CONOVER, FRANK	FOOTBALL	BROWNS, 80 1ST ST	BEREA, OH 44017
CONOVER, SCOTT	FOOTBALL	LIONS, 1200 FEATHERSTONE RD	PONTIAC, MI 48432
CONRAD, CHRISTIAN	ACTOR	15301 VENTURA BLVD #345	SHERMAN OAKS, CA 91403
CONRAD, CONSTANCE	ACTRESS	KEY, 45 BURLINGTON AVE	LEONARDO, NJ 07737
CONRAD, DEREK	WRITER-PRODUCER	26 BELLS HILL, BARNET	HERTS EN5 2RY ENGLAND
CONRAD, JEFF	RADIO PERSONALITY	KVSD-AM, 550 LAGUNA DR	CARLSBAD, CA 92008
CONRAD, JON J	DIRECTOR	9224 MARMORA	MORTON GROVE, IL 66053
CONRAD, KENDALL	ACTRESS	9255 SUNSET BLVD #515	LOS ANGELES, CA 90069
CONRAD, KENT	U S SENATOR	FEDERAL BUILDING, ROOM 228	
		3RD & ROSSER	BISMARCK, ND 58501
CONRAD, KIM	ACTRESS	1350 N HIGHLAND AVE #24	LOS ANGELES, CA 90028
CONRAD, KIMBERLY	ACTRESS-MODEL	10236 CHARING CROSS RD	LOS ANGELES, CA 90024
CONRAD, NANCY	ACTRESS	11666 GOSHEN AVE #305	LOS ANGELES, CA 90049
CONRAD, PAUL	CARTOONIST	28649 CRESTRIDGE RD	PALOS VERDES, CA 90274
CONRAD, PAULA	TV PRODUCER	ROUTE #1, BOX 174-2	CARYVILLE, FL 32427
CONRAD, ROBERT	ACT-WRI-DIR-PROD	21316 PACIFIC COAST HIGHWAY	MALIBU, CA 9265
CONRAD, SHANE	ACTOR	21355 PACIFIC COAST HIGHWAY	MALIBU, CA 90265
CONRAD, SID	ACTOR	18954 STRATHERN ST	RESEDA, CA 91335
CONRAD, SIMA	ACTRESS	31377 PACIFIC COAST HWY	MALIBU, CA 90265
CONRAD, WILLIAM	ACTOR-RADIO PERS	4031 LONGRIDGE AVE	SHERMAN OAKS, CA 91403
CONROY, BRIAN	BASEBALL	POST OFFICE BOX 2365	PAWTUCKET, RI 02861
CONROY, DAVID	FILM WRITER-PRODUCER	16 WOODLANDS RD	LONDON SW13 ENGLAND
CONROY, KEVIN	ACTOR	9301 WILSHIRE BLVD #312	BEVERLY HILLS, CA 90210
CONROY, LARRY	ACTOR	140 E 95TH ST #1-E	NEW YORK, NY 10128
CONROY, TIM	BASEBALL	416 LUZERNE DR	MONROEVILLE, PA 15146
CONS, CARL	WRITER-PRODUCER	6622 LINDLEY AVE	RESDEDA, CA 91335
CONSIDINE, DENNIS J	TV EXECUTIVE	11541 LAUREL CREST DR	STUDIO CITY, CA 91604
CONSIDINE, JOHN	ACTOR-WRITER	16 1/2 RED COAT LN	GREENWICH, CT 06830
CONSIDINE, TIM	ACT-WRI-DIR	10328 VIRETTA LN	LOS ANGELES, CA 90077
CONSOLO, BILLY	BASEBALL-COACH	TIGERS, TIGER STADIUM	DETROIT, MI 48216
CONSTANT, GEORGE	ACTOR	23-30 NEWTOWN AVE #1-EW	ASTORIA, NY 11102
CONSTANTE, ENRIQUE	BASEBALL SCOUT	REDS, 100 RIVERFRONT STADIUM	CINCINNATI, OH 45202
CONSTANTIN, GAVRAS	WRITER-PRODUCER	244 RUE SAINT JACQUES	PARIS FRANCE
CONSTANTINE, KAREN	ACTRESS	11-24 46TH AVE	LONG ISLAND CITY, NY 11101
CONSTANTINE, KING	KING	4 LINNELL DR, HAMPSTEAD WY	LONDON NW11 ENGLAND
CONSTANTINE, MICHAEL	ACTOR	1476 S SHERNANDOAH ST #301	LOS ANGELES, CA 90035
CONTE, JOHN	ACTOR	75600 BERYL DR	INDIAN WELLS, CA 92260

R&R ENTERPRISES

WE WILL PAY YOU THESE PRICES FOR THE FOLLOWING AUTOGRAPHS

Below are the guaranteed prices (in dollars) we are paying for high-quality signatures and signed 8x10 photos of various personalities.

P.O. Box 2000 Amherst, NH 03031 (603) 672-6611

Name	8x10	Sig
3 Stooges (w. Curly),	$1,000	$500
3 Stooges (w. Shemp),	$700	$350
Aames, Willie	—	$2
Abbott, Bud	$125	$50
Abbott & Costello,	$500	$200
Abdul-Jabber, Kareem	—	$10
Ackroyd, Dan	—	$3
Adams, John	—	$600
Adams, John Quincy	—	$150
Adams, Samuel	—	$250
Alcott, Louisa May	—	$50
Alda, Alan	—	$5
Aldrin, Buzz	$35	$15
Alexander, Grover C.	$300	$100
Ali, Muhammad	—	$10
Ally, Kirstie	—	$5
Anderson, Herbers	—	$75
Andretti, Mario	—	$1
Andrews, Julie	—	$5
Andrews, Tige	—	$3
Anthony, Susan B.	$250	$100
Apollo 11 (all 3),	$350	$150
Applegate, Christina	—	$5
Arbuckle, Roscoe	$300	$100
Armour, Tommy	$100	$50
Armstrong, Henry	$75	$25
Armstrong, Louis	$150	$50
Armstrong, Neil	$100	$50
Arnaz, Desi	$50	$35
Arness, James	—	$3
Arthur, Jean	$75	$25
Astaire, Fred	$50	$20
Astaire & Rogers,	$125	$50
Astin, John	—	$2
Audubon, John J.	—	
Bach, Catherine	—	$2
Baer, Max	$75	$25
Bailey, Raymond	—	$50
Bain, Barbara	—	$1
Baker, Josephine	$250	$100
Ball, Lucille	$125	$50
Banner, John	$75	$50
Bara, Theda	$150	$100
Barnum, P.T.	$200	$50
Barrymore, John	$125	$50
Barton, Clara	$150	$50
Basinger, Kim	—	$5
Bateman, Justine	—	$5
Baum, Frank L.	—	$300
Bavier, Frances	—	$15
Baxter-Birney, Meridith	—	$3
Beatles (all 4),	$1,750	$1,250
Beatty, Warren	—	$10
Beauregard, P.G.T.	—	$125
Becker, Boris	—	$10
Bel Geddes, Barbara	—	$1
Bell, Alexander G.	$750	$250
Bellwood, Pamela	—	$2
Belushi, John	$275	$150
Benatar, Pat	—	$10
Bench, Johnny	—	$10
Benny, Jack	$50	$20
Benton, Barbi	—	$5
Bergman, Ingrid	$75	$25
Beringer, Tom	—	$2
Berry, Chuck	—	$35
Bessell, Ted	—	$5
Bird, Larry	—	$20
Birney, David	—	$2
Bixby, Bill	—	$3
Bledsoe, Tempestt	—	$3
Bogart, Humphrey	$1,750	$375
Bonaduce, Danny	—	$5
Bonaparte, Napoleon	—	$500
Bono, Sonny	—	$10
Boone, Daniel	—	$1,250
Booth, John Wilkes	—	$1,500
Borg, Bjorn	—	$5
Bow, Clara	$125	$50
Boyd, William	$100	$40
Boyer, Clete	—	$2
Bradley, Ed	—	$2
Bradley, Omar	$25	$10
Bradshaw, Terry	—	$5
Brandeis, Louis	$100	$50
Brando, Marlon	$200	$100
Breck, Peter	—	$5
Brennan, Walter	$50	$20
Bridges, Jerr	—	$3
Brinkley, Christie	—	$10
Bronson, Charles	—	$5

Name	8x10	Sig
Brown, Jim	—	$5
Browne, Jackson	—	$5
Browning, Elizabeth Barrett	—	$300
Browning, Robert	—	$100
Bruce, Nigel	$200	$100
Buick, David	—	$100
Bull, Sitting	—	$1,000
Burke, Billie	—	$75
Burns, Tommy	$250	$150
Burns & Allen,	$100	$35
Burr, Aaron	—	$200
Burr, Raymond	—	$5
Burroughs, Edgar R.	$200	$100
Bush, George	$150	$100
Cady, Frank	—	$2
Cagney, James	$50	$35
Camera, Primo	$125	$100
Camp, Walter	—	$35
Capone, Al	$2,500	$1,000
Capriati, Jennifer	—	$5
Carey, Mariah	—	$10
Carne, Judy	—	$3
Carpenter, Scott	—	$10
Carson, Johnny	—	$10
Carter, Jimmy	—	$15
Cartwright, Angela	—	$3
Cassidy, David	—	$3
Cassidy, Ted	$75	$50
Castro, Fidel	$200	$100
Ceasar, Sid	—	$1
Chaffee, Roger	$150	$100
Chamberlain, Joshua L.	—	$100
Chamberlain, Richard	—	$3
Chamberlain, Wilt	—	$10
Chandler, Raymond	$350	$250
Chaney, Jr., Lon	$150	$125
Chaney, Sr., Lon	$800	$500
Chaplin, Charlie	$175	$100
Chase, Chevy	—	$3
Cher,	—	$5
Christie, Agatha	$125	$50
Christin, Marta	—	$5
Chrysler, Walter	—	$100
Churchill, Winston	$1,500	$450
Cicotte, Eddie	$150	$50
Clary, Robert	—	$1
Clemens, Roger	—	$10
Clemente, Roberto	$200	$150
Clift, Montgomery	$275	$100
Cline, Patsy	$350	$200
Close, Glenn	—	$3
Cobb, Ty	$650	$250
Coburn, James	—	$2
Cochrane, Eddie	$300	$150
Coco, Imogene	—	$1
Cody, Buffalo Bill	$500	$300
Cole, Michael	—	$3
Collins, Joan	—	$2
Collins, Michael	$50	$25
Collins, Ray	—	$5
Colt, Samuel	—	$200
Comaneci, Nadia	—	$10
Conigliaro, Tony	$50	$30
Connery, Sean	—	$35
Connery, Sean	—	$10
Connors, Chuck	—	$2
Connors, Jimmy	—	$5
Cooke, Sam	$175	$100
Coolidge, Calvin	$100	$50
Cooper, Alice	—	$10
Cooper, Gary	$200	$50
Copland, Aaron	$75	$25
Corbett, Jas. J.	—	$250
Cosby, Bill	—	$5
Costello, Lou	$150	$60
Costner, Kevin	—	$15
Costner, Kevin	—	$10
Cousy, Bob	—	$5
Crawford, Cindy	—	$15
Crawford, Johnny	—	$2
Crosby, Bing	$40	$20
Crowley, Jim	—	$20
Cruise, Tom	—	$20
Cruise, Tom	—	$10
Cunningham, Randell	—	$5
Curtin, Jane	—	$15
Curtiss, Glenn	$200	$75
Custer, George	—	$1,800
Daily, Bill	—	$2
Dalton, Emmett	—	$250
Dalton, Timothy	—	$20

Name	8x10	Sig
Danson, Ted	—	$5
Darrow, Clarence	$500	$200
Darwin, Charles	—	$375
Davis, Ann B.	—	$2
Davis, Jefferson	—	$250
Davis, Miles	—	$20
Dawson, Richard	—	$1
Dean, James	$2,000	$1,250
Dean, Paul Daffy	$50	$25
Debs, Eugene	$50	$25
DeCarlo, Yvonne	—	$2
Decatur, Stephen	—	$400
deGaulle, Charles	$300	$100
DeHavilland, Olivia	—	$5
Demerest, William	—	$3
Dempsey, Jack	$100	$30
DeNiro, Robert	—	$10
Denver, Bob	—	$3
Derek, Bo	—	$5
DeVito, Danny	—	$5
Dickens, Charles	—	$250
DiMaggio, Joe	$50	$35
Disney, Walt	$1,000	$500
Dodgson, C.L.	—	$200
Dodson, Jack	—	$20
Dolenz, Mickey	—	$15
Doubleday, Abner	—	$275
Douglas, Buster	—	$5
Douglas, Donna	—	$2
Douglas, Michael	—	$5
Douglass, Frederick	—	$50
Doyle, Arthur Conan	$500	$200
Draper, Polly	—	$2
Dressler, Marie	$75	$25
Drysdale, Don	—	$2
Duffy, Patrick	—	$5
Duncan, Isadora	$400	$150
Earhart, Amelia	$500	$225
Early, Jubal	—	$100
Eastman, George	$150	$50
Easton, Sheena	—	$10
Eddy, Mary Baker	—	$350
Eden, Barbara	—	$2
Edison, Thomas	$750	$250
Einstein, Albert	$2,000	$600
Eisenhower, Dwight	$150	$100
Ekberg, Anita	$50	$25
Eliot, T.S.	$200	$100
Ellington, Duke	$100	$20
Emerson, Ralph W.	$150	$75
Erving, Julius	—	$5
Estefan, Gloria	—	$5
Estevez, Emilo	—	$3
Ewing, Patrick	—	$5
Fairbanks, Sr., Douglas	$75	$20
Falk, Peter	—	$3
Fargo, William	—	$100
Farmer, Frances	$100	$50
Faulkner, William	$400	$225
Faustino, David	—	$3
Fawcett, Farrah	—	$3
Fawcett, Farrah	—	$5
Ferrari, Enzo	—	$150
Fields, W.C.	$400	$150
Fillmore, Milliard	—	$100
Fine, Larry	$175	$50
Firestone, Sr., Harvey	$250	$75
Fisher, Carrie	—	$2
Fisher, Carrie	—	$3
Fisk, Carlton	—	$5
Fitzgerald, F. Scott	$2,000	$350
Fitzsimmons, Bob	—	$250
Flynn, Errol	$200	$75
Fonda, Peter	—	$2
Ford, Harrison	—	$35
Ford, Henry	$800	$400
Foreman, George	—	$10
Forest, Nathan Bedford	—	$300
Foster, Jodie	—	$35
Foster, Phil	—	$3
Fox, Michael J.	—	$10
Fox, Michael J.	—	$10
Fox, Nellie	—	$40
Foxx, Jimmie	$200	$100
Foyt, AJ	—	$3
Franklin, Benjamin	—	$1,750
Frawley, William	$100	$75
Freud, Sigmund	$1,500	$750
Frid, Jonathan	—	$5
Fried, Jonathon	—	$3
Frost, Robert	$350	$100

Name	8x10	Sig
Fulton, Robert	—	$200
Gable, Clark	$300	$150
Gabor, Eva	—	$3
Gagarin, Yuri	—	$75
Gandhi, Mahatma	—	$500
Garbo, Greta	$2,000	$750
Garfield, James	—	$100
Garfield, John	$100	$25
Garland, Judy	$250	$200
Geer, Will	—	$5
Gehrig, Lou	$1,500	$600
Gere, Richard	—	$15
Geronimo,	—	$1,500
Gershwin, George	$2,000	$400
Getty, J. Paul	$100	$50
Gibson, Henry	—	$3
Gibson, Hoot	$75	$25
Gibson, Mel	—	$10
Gipp, George	—	$250
Gleason, Jackie	$25	$10
Glenn, John	—	$5
Glenn, Scott	—	$5
Glover, Danny	—	$10
Goddard, Mark	—	$3
Goddard, Robert	$250	$150
Goering, Herman	—	$250
Goldblum, Jeff	—	$2
Goodeve, Grant	—	$2
Goodyear, Charles	—	$100
Gorcey, Leo	$50	$25
Gorshin, Frank	—	$10
Grable, Betty	$40	$25
Grady, Don	—	$3
Graf, Steffi	—	$10
Grange, Red	$50	$20
Grant, Cary	$125	$50
Grant, U.S.	—	$250
Gray, Billy	—	$2
Gray, Linda	—	$1
Greenstreet, Sydney	$200	$100
Gretsky, Wayne	—	$20
Griffith, Andy	—	$3
Griffith, Melanie	—	$15
Grissom, Gus	$150	$100
Gross, Michael	—	$3
Guiness, Alec	—	$3
Gwyne, Fred	—	$15
Hagen, Jean	—	$5
Hagen, Walter	$150	$75
Hagler, Marvin	—	$10
Hagman, Larry	—	$3
Hale, Jr, Alan	—	$25
Haley, Jack	$75	$50
Hamill, Mark	—	$2
Hamill, Mark	—	$3
Hamilton, Alexander	—	$350
Hamilton, Margaret	$50	$25
Hammer, Rusty	—	$40
Hammett, Dashiell	—	$200
Hampton, Wade	—	$100
Hancock, John	—	$1,250
Harding, Warren G.	$150	$50
Hardy, Oliver	$200	$125
Hardy, Thomas	$300	$100
Harlow, Jean	$1,250	$500
Harris, Mel	—	$2
Harrison, George	$100	$75
Harrison, Wm. Henry	—	$225
Harry, Debby	—	$10
Hart, Marvin	$350	$250
Hartman, Lisa	—	$5
Hauptmann, Bruno R.	—	$150
Havilcek, John	—	$5
Hawn, Goldie	—	$5
Hawthorne, Nathaniel	—	$200
Hayes, Gabby	$125	$75
Hayes, Rutherford B.	—	$75
Hayward, Susan	$125	$75
Hayworth, Rita	$125	$50
Hearns, Thomas	—	$5
Hearst, Wm. Randolph	—	$100
Heifitz, Jascha	$75	$35
Hemingway, Ernest	$1,500	$500
Henderson, Ricky	—	$5
Hendrix, Jimi	$500	$300
Henner, Marilu	—	$10
Henry, Gloria	—	$10
Henry, Patrick	—	$300
Hepburn, Audrey	$20	$10
Hepburn, Katharine	$250	$50
Hershiser, Orel	—	$5

Name	8x10	Sig
Hitchcock, Alfred	$150	$75
Hitler, Adolf	$1,500	$950
Hodges, Gil	$75	$50
Hoffman, Dustin	—	$5
Hogan, Ben	$65	$30
Holiday, Billie	$600	$250
Holiday, Judy	$100	$25
Holly, Buddy	$1,500	$750
Holmes, Jr., Oliver W.	—	$50
Hopkins, Anthony	—	$10
Hopper, Dennis	—	$5
Hopper, William	—	$25
Horton, Peter	—	$2
Houdini, Harry	$700	$400
Houston, Sam	—	$275
Hovis, Larry	—	$2
Howard, Curly	$500	$200
Howard, Leslie	$100	$75
Howard, Moe	$175	$75
Howard, Shemp	$300	$200
Howe, Gordie	—	$5
Huggins, Miller	$300	$200
Hughes, Howard	—	$750
Hugo, Victor	—	$50
Hull, Brett	—	$5
Hunter, Rachel	—	$10
Hurt, William	—	$15
Ireland, Cathy	—	$10
jackson, Andrew	—	$300
Jackson, Bo	—	$10
Jackson, Kate	—	$5
Jackson, Kate	—	$5
Jackson, Michael	—	$40
Jackson, Reggie	—	$15
Jackson, Stonewall	—	$800
Jagger, Mick	—	$35
Jarvis, Greg	—	$40
Jasen, Rick	—	$10
Jay, John	—	$200
Jefferson, Thomas	—	$1,000
Jeffries, Jim	$300	$150
Joel, Billy	—	$10
John, Elton	—	$25
Johnson, Arte	—	$2
Johnson, Don	—	$20
Johnson, Don	—	$10
Johnson, Jack	$600	$400
Johnson, Russell	—	$2
Johnson, Walter	$500	$200
Jolson, Al	$125	425
Jones, Bobby	$600	$250
Jones, Buck	$100	$35
Jones, Carolyn	—	$25
Jones, Carolyn	$25	$15
Jones, Davey	—	$20
Jones, Jennifer	$75	$40
Jones, Shirley	—	$2
Joplin, Janis	$500	$350
Jordon, Michael	—	$10
Kane, Carol	—	$5
Kaplan, Gabe	—	$5
Karloff, Boris	$150	$100
Keaton, Buster	$150	$75
Keeler, Wee Willie	—	$150
Keller, Helen	$175	$50
Kelly, Grace	$125	$75
Kennedy, Jacqueline	$175	$100
Kennedy, John F.	$1,000	$450
Kennedy, Ted	—	$10
Kern, Jerome	$300	$150
Kerouac, Jack	$375	$250
Key, Francis Scott	—	$400
King, Stephen	—	$25
King, Jr, Martin Luther	$850	$450
Klemper, Werner	—	$3
Kline, Kevin	—	$3
Knight, Christopher	—	$5
Knight, Ted	—	$5
Knight Pulliam, Keshia	—	$3
Knox, Terence	—	$2
Korbut, Olga	—	$5
Koufax, Sandy	—	$5
Kovacs, Ernie	$200	$100
Kulp, Nancy	—	$20
Ladd, Cheryl	—	$5
Lafayette,	—	$150
Lahr, Bert	—	$150
Lajoie, Larry	—	$100
Lake, Veronica	$85	$35
LaMaar, Hedy	—	$15
Landau, Martin	—	$2

R&R ENTERPRISES

WE WILL PAY YOU THESE PRICES FOR THE FOLLOWING AUTOGRAPHS

Below are the guaranteed prices (in dollars) we are paying for high-quality signatures and signed 8x10 photos of various personalities.

P.O. Box 2000 Amherst, NH 03031 (603) 672-6611

Name	8x10	Sig
Lanza, Mario	$125	$50
Laural, Stan	$125	$50
Laural & Hardy,	$500	$250
Layden, Elmer	—	$25
Leahy, Frank	$100	$50
LeBrock, Kelly	—	$5
Lee, Robert E.	—	$1,750
Leigh, Vivien	$250	$150
Lemieux, Mario	—	$5
Lennon, John	$500	$375
Leonard, Benny	—	$50
Lewis, Carl	—	$10
Lewis, Jerry Lee	—	$10
Light, Judith	—	$5
Lincoln, Abraham	—	$1,800
Lindbergh, Charles	$700	$450
Linden, Hal	—	$5
Linville, Larry	—	$2
Lipton, Peggy	—	$2
Liston, Sonny	$150	$100
Little, Richard	—	$35
Livingston, Barry	—	$2
Lloyd, Christopher	—	$15
Lloyd, Harold	$100	$40
Lloyd, Norman	—	$2
Locklear, Heather	—	$3
Locklear, Heather	—	$5
Lombard, Carole	$350	$100
Lombardi, Vince	$300	$100
London, Jack	—	$125
Long, Richard	—	$15
Long, Shelly	—	$5
Long, Shelly	—	$3
Longstreet, James	—	$100
Lookingland, Mike	—	$3
Lords, Traci	—	$10
Loring, Lisa	—	$10
Lorre, Peter	$125	$50
Louis, Joe	$200	$75
Lugosi, Bela	$350	$200
MacArthur, Douglas	$150	$75
MacLaine, Shirley	—	$3
Macnee, Patrick	—	$10
MacPherson, Elle	—	$10
Madden, David	—	$1
Madison, James	—	$225
Madonna,	—	$50
Magic, Johnson	—	$15
Majors, Lee	—	$2
Mandel, Howie	—	$2
Manilow, Barry	—	$10
Mansfield, Jayne	$150	$100
Manson, Charles	$125	$50
Mantle, Mickey	—	$25
Maples, Marla	—	$10
Marciano, Rocky	$200	$125
Marconi, Guglielmo	$200	$75
Maris, Roger	$100	$40
Mark Twain, S. Clemens	$2,000	$750
Marshall, George	$65	$35
Marshall, John	—	$200
Marshall, Penny	—	$5
Martin, Dick	—	$2
Martin, Pamela Sue	—	$3
Martin, Steve	—	$3
Marx, Chico	$200	$75
Marx, Groucho	$100	$75
Marx, Harpo	$200	$75
Marx, Karl	—	$500
Marx, Zeppo	$75	$50
Marx Brothers (all),	$750	$300
Mathewson, Christy	$1,000	$600
Mays, Willie	—	$15
McAuliffe, Christa	$375	$200
McCartney, Paul	$150	$100
McClellan, George	—	$75
McCord, Kent	—	$3
McCormick, Maureen	—	$5
McDaniel, Hattie	$350	$225
McEnroe, John	—	$5
McNair, Ron	—	$25
McNear, Howard	—	$15
McQueen, Steve	$150	$100
Meade, George	—	$75
Mellencamp, John C.	—	$10
Melville, Herman	—	$400

Name	8x10	Sig
Meredith, Burgess	—	$10
Meyers, Ari	—	$3
Miken, George	—	$2
Miller, Glenn	$200	$75
Mills, Donna	—	$3
Milner, Martin	—	$5
Mitchell, Margaret	—	$300
Mix, Tom	$125	$40
Monroe, James	—	$150
Monroe, Marilyn	$2,000	$1,000
Montana, Joe	—	$15
Moon, Warren	—	$5
Moore, Clayton	—	$5
Moore, Roger	—	$15
Moore, Roger	—	$5
Morgan, Frank	—	$150
Morris, Garrett	—	$5
Morris, Greg	—	$2
Morse, Samuel	$275	$125
Mosby, John	—	$250
Mosley, Roger E.	—	$3
Most, Donny	—	$5
Mulligan, Richard	—	$2
Muni, Paul	$65	$20
Munro, Caroline	—	$5
Munson, Ona	$50	$25
Murphy, Audie	$50	$20
Murray, Bill	—	$10
Mussolini, Benito	$450	$275
Namath, Joe	—	$10
Navratilova, Martina	—	$10
Needham, Connie	—	$1
Nelson, David	—	$3
Nelson, Ricky	$100	$50
Nesmith, Michael	—	$20
Newman, Loraine	—	$5
Newton-John, Olivia	—	$5
Nichols, Nichol	—	$5
Nicklaus, Jack	$25	$20
Nicks, Stevie	—	$10
Nimitz, Chester	$40	$20
Nimoy, Leonard	—	$25
Nimoy, Leonard	—	$5
Nixon, Richard	$75	$35
Normand, Mabel	$125	$50
North, Jay	—	$3
Norton-Taylor, Judy	—	$2
Oakley, Annie	$900	$500
Oland, Warner	$75	$35
Oldfield, Barney	—	$25
Olds, Ransom	—	$100
Olin, Ken	—	$2
Olsen, Susan	—	$3
Oppenheimer, J. Robert	—	$100
Orizuka, Ellison	—	$25
Orr, Bobby	—	$5
Ott, Mel	$175	$75
Ouimet, Francis	—	$75
Ouspenskaya, Maria	$100	$50
Owen, Beverly	—	$5
Owens, Gary	—	$3
Owens, Jesse	$65	$25
O'Connor, Carroll	—	$10
O'Grady, Lan	—	$3
O'Neal, Ed	—	$3
O'Neil, Barbara	$100	$45
O'Neill, Eugene	$200	$100
O'Sullivan, Maureen	—	$3
Pacasso, Pablo	—	$150
Paige, Satchel	$50	$25
Pasteur, Louis	—	$150

Name	8x10	Sig
Patton, George	$850	$500
Peary, Robert	$150	$50
Pele,	—	$5
Penney, J.C.	—	$25
Pfeiffer, Michelle	—	$10
Pfieffer, Michelle	—	$15
Phillips, Lou Diamond	—	$3
Pickerton, Allan	—	$150
Pickett, George	—	$250
Place, MaryKay	—	$5
Plumb, Eve	—	$5
Poriskova, Paulina	—	$15
Porter, Cole	$200	$75
Post, Wiley	$300	$100
Potter, Beatrix	—	$100
Powell, Colin	—	$20
Power, Tyrone	$100	$25
Presley, Elvis	$400	$275
Presley, Priscilla	—	$5
Priest, Pat	—	$20
Principle, Victoria	—	$5
Puckett, Kirby	—	$5
Ramis, Harold	—	$3
Rand, Ayn	$250	$50
Rashay, Phylcia	—	$3
Rathbone, Basil	$150	$75
Ratzenberger, John	—	$3
Reagan, Ronald	$100	$50
Reasonor, Harry	—	$5
Reed, Robert	—	$3
Reeve, Christopher	—	$5
Reeves, George	—	$400
Remington, Frederic	—	$250
Repp, Stafford	—	$25
Resnik, Judy	—	$50
Revere, Paul	—	$1,500
Reynolds, Burt	—	$5
Rich, Adam	—	$5
Richardson, Susan	—	$2
Rickard, Tex	$150	$75
Rickey, Branch	$125	$75
Rigg, Dianna	—	$10
Roberts, Julia	—	$35
Robertson, Oscar	—	$5
Robinson, Brooks	—	$2
Robinson, Jackie	$250	$125
Rock, Blossom	—	$40
Rockefeller, John D.	—	$300
Rockne, Knute	$650	$350
Rockwell, Norman	$100	$20
Rodgers, Wayne	—	$2
Roebuck, A.C.	—	$200
Rogers, Roy	—	$3
Rogers, Wilt	$375	$150
Roosevelt, Franklin	$250	$125
Roosevelt, Theodore	$400	$150
Rorke, Hayden	—	$10
Rose, Pete	—	$10
Ross, Joe E.	—	$20
Rowen, Dan	—	$10
Ruby, Jack	—	$150
Russell, Bertrand	$150	$30
Russell, Bill	$125	$50
Ruth, Babe	$1,500	$500
Ryan, Irene	$50	$20
Ryan, Meg	—	$10
Sabatini, Gabriella	—	$5
Sagel, Katy	—	$3
Sandburg, Carl	$75	$35
Sanders, Richard	—	$2
Sater, Morey	—	$2

Name	8x10	Sig
Sawyer, Diane	—	$2
Sayers, Gale	—	$3
Schaffer, Natalie	—	$5
Schirra, Wally	—	$5
Schulz, Charles	—	$20
Schwarzenegger, Arnold	—	$35
Scobee, Dick	—	$25
Scott, George C.	—	$10
Sears, Richard W.	—	$300
Seaver, Tom	—	$10
Segal, Steven	—	$10
Selby, David	—	$3
Selleck, Tom	—	$10
Sellers, Peter	$75	$50
Serling, Rod	$125	$50
Seymour, Stephanie	—	$15
Sharkey, Jack	—	$10
Shatner, William	—	$10
Shaw, George B.	$250	$50
Shaw, Wilbur	$100	$50
Sheen, Charlie	—	$5
Shepard, Alan	—	$5
Sheridan, Nicolette	—	$15
Sheridan, Phillip	—	$85
Sherman, Wm. T.	—	$100
Shoemaker, Willie	—	$10
Short, Martin	—	$2
Simon, Carly	—	$5
Simpson, O.J.	—	$10
Sinatra, Frank	$100	$75
Smith, Jaclyn	—	$3
Smith, Michael	—	$25
Solzhenitsyn, A.	$125	$50
Somers, Suzanne	—	$5
Sousa, John Phillip	—	$50
Speaker, Tris	$200	$100
Speilberg, Steven	—	$20
Spitz, Mark	—	$5
St. James, Susan	—	$5
Stagg, Amos A.	—	$50
Stallone, Sly	—	$25
Stanton, Elizabeth Cady	—	$50
Starr, Ringo	$100	$50
Staubach, Roger	—	$5
Steinbeck, John	$250	$75
Steirs, David Ogden	—	$20
Stevens, Cat	—	$25
Stevenson, McClean	—	$3
Stevenson, Robert L.	—	$200
Stewart, Rod	—	$10
Stowe, Harriet Beecher	—	$50
Stravinsky, Igor	$225	$100
Streep, Meryl	—	$10
Streisand, Barbara	$50	$35
Stualdreher, Harry	—	$25
Stuart, J.E.B.	—	$800
Sullivan, John L.	$750	$300
Swayze, Patrick	—	$10
Talman, William	—	$50
Taylor, Elizabeth	$150	$100
Taylor, Lawrence	—	$10
Thomas, Dylan	—	$200
Thomas, George	—	$50
Thomas, Phillip Michael	—	$5
Thomas, Richard	—	$2
Thorpe, Jim	$650	$400
Tilden, Bill	$100	$50
Tilley, Meg	—	$5
Tilton, Charlene	—	$2
Tolkien, J.R.R.	—	$150
Tolstoy, Leo	—	$300

Name	8x10	Sig
Tork, Peter	—	$20
Tracy, Spencer	$150	$50
Travis, Mary	—	$2
Travis, Randy	—	$5
Travolta, John	—	$3
Truman, Harry	$125	$75
Tunney, Gene	$100	$50
Turner, Kathleen	—	$3
Turner, Lana	—	$5
Tyler, John	—	$150
Tyler Moore, Mary	—	$5
Tyson, Mike	—	$20
Valens, Richie	$500	$250
Valentino, Rudolph	$750	$375
Van Dyke, Dick	—	$3
Vance, Vivian	$125	$100
Vanderbilt, Comelius	—	$100
Verne, Jules	—	$125
Victoria I,	—	$100
Von Stroheim, Erich	$150	$75
Wagner, Honus	$350	$150
Waite, Ralph	—	$3
Walker, Harry	—	$10
Wallace, Mike	—	$2
Walston, Ray	—	$2
Warner, Glenn Pop	—	$40
Warner, Malcolm J.	—	$2
Washington, Denzel	—	$5
Washington, George	—	$2,500
Wayne, John	$150	$100
Weatherwax, Ken	—	$10
Weaver, Sigourney	—	$5
Webster, Daniel	—	$50
Weissmuller, Johnny	$50	$20
Wendt, George	—	$3
West, Jerry	—	$3
Westinghouse, George	—	$100
Wetting, Patricia	—	$2
White, Edward	$200	$100
Whitman, Walt	—	$250
Whitney, Eli	—	$200
Wilde, Oscar	—	$300
Willard, Jess	$75	$35
Williams, Andy	—	$2
Williams, Anson	—	$2
Williams, Barry	—	$2
Williams, Cindy	—	$5
Williams, Guy	—	$40
Williams, JoBeth	—	$3
Williams, Ted	—	$25
Williams, Tennessee	$60	$35
Williams III, Clarence	—	$10
Williams, Sr., Hank	$750	$450
Winger, Debra	—	$5
Witt, Katarina	—	$10
Wolfe, Thomas	—	$200
Wood, Natalie	$75	$35
Woolworth, Frank	—	$100
Wray, Fay	—	$10
Wright, Frank Lloyd	$400	$275
Wright, Orville	$750	$300
Wright, Wilbur	—	$1,000
X, Malcolm	$500	$250
Yastrzemski, Carl	—	$10
Yeats, Wm. Butler	—	$100
York, Alvin	—	$50
York, Dick	—	$15
Yothers, Tina	—	$2
Young, Cy	$350	$150
Young, Robert	—	$2
Zola, Emile	—	$75

HIGHEST PRICES PAID!

PLEASE USE ONE OF THE FOLLOWING PROCEDURES WHEN OFFERING ITEM(S) FOR SALE

- ☞ Send copies of the item(s) to R&R Enterprises, P.O. Box 2000, Amherst, NH 03031.
- ☞ Fax copies to us at (603) 672-6442 and we will get back to you as soon as possible.
- ☞ Call 1-603-672-6611 and speak directly to our purchaser, Bob Eaton.
- ☞ Send us the actual item(s) via insured mail or Federal Express.
- ☞ At certain times, we become "overstocked" on a particular signature, because of this we reserve the right to refuse some purchases.
We will call you upon receipt of the package to arrange payment.

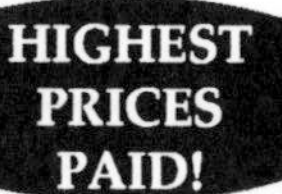

CONTE, JOSEPH A	DIRECTOR	860 NORTH ST	GREENWICH, CT 06830
CONTE, MIKE	BASEBALL	POST OFFICE BOX 2769	HUNTSVILLE, AL 35804
CONTI, BILL	COMPOSER-ARRANGER	117 FREMONT PL W	LOS ANGELES, CA 90005
CONTI, GUY	BASEBALL COACH	POST OFFICE BOX 1621	GREAT FALLS, MT 59403
CONTI, ROBERT J	COMPOSER	518 N JUANITA AVE	REDONDO BEACH, CA 90277
CONTI, TOM	ACTOR-DIRECTOR	CHATTO AND LINNIT, LTD	
		PRINCE OF WALES THEATRE	
		COVENTRY ST	LONDON W1V 7FE ENGLAND
CONTNER, JAMES A	CINEMATOGRAPHER	7460 MANDARIN DR	BOCA RATON, FL 33433
CONTRERAS, NADRI	BASEBALL COACH	1501 W 16TH ST	INDIANAPOLIS, IN 46202
CONTROLLERS, THE	R & B GROUP	POST OFFICE BOX 4603	MACON, GA 31208
CONVERSE, JIM	BASEBALL	POST OFFICE BOX 4756	JACKSONVILLE, FL 32201
CONVERSE, MELISSA	ACTRESS	368 GRENOLA ST	PACIFIC PALISADES, CA 90272
CONVERSE, PEGGY	ACTRESS	2525 BRIARCREST RD	BEVERLY HILLS, CA 90210
CONVY, ANNE	SCREENWRITER	11737 CRESCENDA ST	LOS ANGELES, CA 90049
CONVY, JENNIFER	ACTRESS	6255 SUNSET BLVD #627	LOS ANGELES, CA 90028
CONWAY, AL	FOOTBALL REFEREE	NFL, 410 PARK AVE	NEW YORK, NY 10022
CONWAY, GARY	ACTOR	2035 MANDEVILLE CANYON RD	LOS ANGELES, CA 90049
CONWAY, JAMES L	WRITER-PRODUCER	4300 COQUETTE PL	TARZANA, CA 91356
CONWAY, KEVIN	ACTOR	9301 WILSHIRE BLVD #312	BEVERLY HILLS, CA 90210
CONWAY, TIM	ACTOR-DIRECTOR	POST OFFICE BOX 17047	ENCINO, CA 91416
CONWAY-SACHI, KARLA	MODEL	POST OFFICE BOX 1619	KEALA KEKUA, HI 96750
CONWELL, CAROLYN	ACTRESS	CBS-TV, "YOUNG & THE RESTLESS"	
		7800 BEVERLY BLVD #3305	LOS ANGELES, CA 90036
CONWELL, JOHN	CASTING DIRECTOR	2542 BENEDICT CANYON DR	BEVERLY HILLS, CA 90210
CONWELL, TOMMY & YOUNG RUMBLERS	ROCK & ROLL GROUP	CORNERSTONE, 23 E LANCASTER AVE	ARDMORE, PA 19003
CONY, EDWARD	JOURNALIST	7 GULL'S COVE	MANHASSET, NY 11030
CONYERS, JOHN, JR	U S CONGRESSMAN	231 W LAFAYETTE #669	DETROIT, MI 48226
COODER, RY	GUITARIST-SONGWRITER	326 ENTRADA DR	SANTA MONICA, CA 90402
COODY, CHARLES	GOLFER	PGA SENIORS, 112 T P C BLVD	PONTE VEDRA BEACH, FL 32082
COOGAN, KEITH	ACTOR	3500 W OLIVE AVE #1400	BURBANK, CA 91505
COOK, ANCEL	ACTRESS	25844 LUCILLE AVE	LOMITA, CA 90717
COOK, ANTHONY	BASKETBALL	POST OFFICE BOX 4658	DENVER, CO 80204
COOK, BOB A	BASKETBALL EXECUTIVE	KINGS, 1 SPORTS PARKWAY	SACRAMENTO, CA 95834
COOK, CAROLE	ACTRESS	8829 ASHCROFT AVE	LOS ANGELES, CA 90022
COOK, CHRISTOPHER	TV DIRECTOR-PRODUCER	23-A WARWICK AVE	LONDON W9 2PS ENGLAND
COOK, DENNIS	BASEBALL	INDIANS, CLEVELAND STADIUM	CLEVELAND, OH 44114
COOK, DORIA	ACTRESS	9246 SIERRA MAR DR	LOS ANGELES, CA 90069
COOK, ELISHA, JR	ACTOR	POST OFFICE BOX 335	BISHOP, CA 93514
COOK, FIELDER	TV DIRECTOR-PRODUCER	180 CENTRAL PARK S	NEW YORK, NY 10019
COOK, FRED	ACTOR	7 E 14TH ST	NEW YORK, NY 10003
COOK, GENE	BASEBALL EXECUTIVE	POST OFFICE BOX 6212	TOLEDO, OH 43614
COOK, GLEN	TV CRITIC	CHRONICLE, 801 TEXAS AVE	HOUSTON, TX 77002
COOK, JOHN	GOLFER	POST OFFICE BOX 109601	PALM BCH GARDENS, FL 33418
COOK, JOHN P	FILM EDITOR	WABC-TV, 7 LINCOLN SQ	NEW YORK, NY 10023
COOK, LINDA	ACTRESS	BRET ADAMS, 448 W 44TH ST	NEW YORK, NY 10036
COOK, MARV	FOOTBALL	PATRIOTS, FOXBORO STADIUM, RT #1	FOXBORO, MA 02035
COOK, MIKE	BASEBALL	POST OFFICE BOX 36407	LOUISVILLE, KY 40233
COOK, NORMAN W	DIRECTOR	17130 BURBANK BLVD #204	ENCINO, CA 91316
COOK, PATRICK M	DIRECTOR	139 BELL AVE	HASBROUCK HEIGHTS, NJ 07604
COOK, PETER	ACTOR-COMEDIAN	24 PERRRINE WALK	LONDON NW3 ENGLAND
COOK, ROBIN	SCREENWRITER	22 PRINCE ALBERT RD	LONDON NW1 7ST ENGLAND
COOK, RODERICK	THEATER PRODUCER	425 E 51ST ST	NEW YORK, NY 10022
COOK, ROGER-SONGWRITER	PIANIST	4006 ESTES RD	NASHVILLE, TN 37215
COOK, RON	ACTOR	HEATH, PARAMOUNT HOUSE	
		162-170 WARDOUR ST	LONDON W1V 3AT ENGLAND
COOK, STANTON	BASEBALL EXECUTIVE	1060 W ADDISON ST	CHICAGO, IL 60613
COOK, SUE	TV HOST	BROWN, 162-168 REGENT ST	LONDON W1R 5TB ENGLAND
COOK, THOMAS S	SCREENWRITER	5950 FOOTHILL DR	LOS ANGELES, CA 90068
COOK, TOI	FOOTBALL	SAINTS, 1500 POYDRAS ST	NEW ORLEANS, LA 90112
COOK, TOM	TV PRODUCER	MCA/UNIVERSAL STUDIOS, INC	
		100 UNIVERSAL CITY PLAZA	UNIVERSAL CITY, CA 91608
COOK, TOMMY	ACTOR	4572 VIA MARINA #307	MARINA DEL REY, CA 90292
COOKE, ALAN	TV DIRECTOR	7670 WOODROW WILSON DR	LOS ANGELES, CA 90046
COOKE, ALAN	WRITER-PRODUCER	2 CARDIGAN RD, RICHMOND	SURREY ENGLAND
COOKE, ALISTAIR	AUTHOR	NASSAU POINT	CUTCHOGUE, NY 11935
COOKE, BRIAN	TV WRITER	PETERS, FRASER & DUNLOP, LTD	
		5TH FLOOR, THE CHAMBERS	
		CHELSEA HARBOUR, LOT RD	LONDON SW10 OXF ENGLAND
COOKE, JACK KENT	FOOTBALL EXECUTIVE	POST OFFICE BOX 17247 (DULLES)	WASHINGTON, DC 20041
COOKE, JOHN	CABLE EXECUTIVE	2951 E 28TH ST #2000	SANTA MONICA, CA 90405
COOKE, JOHN BYRNE	NOVELIST	POST OFFICE BOX 68	TETON VILLAGE, WY 83025
COOKE, JOHN KENT	FOOTBALL EXECUTIVE	POST OFFICE BOX 17247 (DULLES)	WASHINGTON, DC 20041
COOKE, STEVE	BASEBALL	POST OFFICE DRAWER 1218	ZEBULON, NC 27597
COOKE, SUSAN	PRODUCER	101 OCEAN AVE #D-8	SANTA MONICA, CA 90402
COOKS, JOHNIE	FOOTBALL	N Y GIANTS, GIANTS STADIUM	EAST RUTHERFORD, NJ 07073
COOKSEY, DANNY	SINGER	9255 SUNSET BLVD #706	LOS ANGELES, CA 90069
COOKSON, BRENT	BASEBALL	POST OFFICE BOX 1295	CLINTON, IA 52733
COOKSON, GARY	ACTOR	54 W 70TH ST	NEW YORK, NY 10023
COOKSON, GEORGINA	ACTRESS	APARTADO 62, SANTA EULA	IBIZA SPAIN
COOKSON, PETER	ACTOR	30 NORFOLK RD	SOUTHFIELD, MA 01259
COOLBAUGH, SCOTT	BASEBALL	STARS, 850 LAS VEGAS BLVD N	LAS VEGAS, NV 89101
COOLEY, FRED	BASEBALL	POST OFFICE BOX 5645	ORLANDO, FL 32855
COOLIDGE, MARTHA	FILM DIRECTOR	1305 PARK AVE	BEVERLY HILLS, CA 90210
COOLIDGE, RITA	SINGER-ACTRESS	9200 SUNSET BLVD #706	LOS ANGELES, CA 90069

COOMBS, PAT	ACTRESS	5 WENDELA CT	
		HARROW-ON-THE-HILL	MIDDLESEX ENGLAND
COOMER, RON	BASEBALL	CANADIANS, 4601 ONTARIO ST	VANCOUVER, BC V5V 3H4 CANADA
COONEY, JOAN GANZ	TV PRODUCER	CHILDREN'S TV WORKSHOP	
		1 LINCOLN PLAZA	NEW YORK, NY 10023
COONEY, MIKE	SECRETARY OF STATE	STATE CAPITOL BUILDING	HELENA, MT 59620
COONEY, TERRY	BASEBALL	4860 N WOODROW AVE #101	FRESNO, CA 93726
COOPER, ADRIAN	FOOTBALL	STEELERS, 300 STADIUM CIR	PITTSBURGH, PA 15212
COOPER, ALICE	SINGER-SONGWRITER	4135 E KEIM ST	PARADISE VALLEY, AZ 85253
COOPER, BEN	ACTOR	20838 EXHIBIT CT	WOODLAND HILLS, CA 91367
COOPER, BOB	COMPOSER	3548 STONEWOOD DR	SHERMAN OAKS, CA 91403
COOPER, CAMILLE	ACTRESS	ABC-TV, "GENERAL HOSPITAL"	
		4151 PROSPECT AVE	BURBANK, CA 91523
COOPER, CECIL	BASEBALL	1431 MISTY BEND	KATY, TX 77450
COOPER, CRAIG	BASEBALL	2501 ALLEN AVE, SE	CANTON, OH 44707
COOPER, DAN	WRITER-PRODUCER	1060 PARK AVE	NEW YORK, NY 10128
COOPER, DON	BASEBALL COACH	POST OFFICE BOX 360007	BIRMINGHAM, AL 35236
COOPER, EDWIN	ACTOR	RURAL FARM DELIVERY #5	
		PARMALEE HILL RD	NEWTON, CT 06470
COOPER, GARY	BASEBALL	POST OFFICE BOX 27045	TUCSON, AZ 85726
COOPER, GEORGE A	ACTOR	PETERS, FRASER & DUNLOP, LTD	
		5TH FLOOR, THE CHAMBERS	
		CHELSEA HARBOUR, LOT RD	LONDON SW10 OXF ENGLAND
COOPER, GUY	TV DIRECTOR	600 E OLIVE AVE	BURBANK, CA 91501
COOPER, HAL	WRITER-PRODUCER	2651 HUTTON DR	BEVERLY HILLS, CA 90210
COOPER, HENRY	TV PERSONALITY	36 BRAMPTON GROVE	LONDON NW4 ENGLAND
COOPER, JACKIE	ACTOR-DIRECTOR	9621 ROYALTON DR	BEVERLY HILLS, CA 90210
COOPER, JAMIE	BASEBALL	5999 E VAN BUREN ST	PHOENIX, AZ 85008
COOPER, JAY L	COMPOSER	9465 WILSHIRE BLVD #800	BEVERLY HILLS, CA 90212
COOPER, JEANNE	ACTRESS	2472 COLDWATER CANYON DR	BEVERLY HILLS, CA 90210
COOPER, JEFF	BASEBALL TRAINER	POST OFFICE BOX 7575	PHILADELPHIA, PA 19101
COOPER, JIM	U S CONGRESSMAN	210 E DEPOT ST	SHELBYVILLE, TN 37160
COOPER, JOHN	DIRECTOR-PRODUCER	18 PELHAM CRESCENT	
		THE PARK	NOTTINGHAM NG1 6GN ENGLAND
COOPER, JOHN GARY	DIRECTOR	26675 HUMBER AVE	HUNTINGTON WOODS, MI 48070
COOPER, JOHN KAYE	TV DIRECTOR-PRODUCER	HANCOCK, GREENER HOUSE	
		66-68 HAYMARKET	LONDON SW1Y 4AW ENGLAND
COOPER, L GORDON	ASTRONAUT	5011 WOODLEY AVE	ENCINO, CA 91436
COOPER, LOUIS	FOOTBALL	DOLPHINS, 2269 NW 199TH ST	MIAMI, FL 33056
COOPER, NATALIE	SCREENWRITER	8955 BEVERLY BLVD	WEST HOLLYWOOD, CA 90048
COOPER, PAT	COMEDIAN	9200 SUNSET BLVD #620	LOS ANGELES, CA 90069
COOPER, PETER H	DIRECTOR	28 W 25TH ST	NEW YORK, NY 10010
COOPER, RAY	MUSICIAN-FILM PROD	HAND MADE, 26 CADOGAN SQ	LONDON SW1X OJP ENGLAND
COOPER, RICHARD	FOOTBALL	SAINTS, 1500 POYDRAS ST	NEW ORLEANS, LA 90112
COOPER, ROBERT	FILM PRODUCER	11500 W OLYMPIC BLVD #300	LOS ANGELES, CA 90064
COOPER, ROBERT	FILM PRODUCER	78 SCOLLARD ST	TORONTO, ONT M5R 1GA CANADA
COOPER, ROY	ACTOR	202 SOUNDVIEW AVE #29	STAMFORD, CT 06902
COOPER, SCOTT	BASEBALL	FENWAY PARK, 4 YAWKEY WY	BOSTON, MA 02215
COOPER, STUART	TV DIRECTOR	R/W/G, 8428 MELROSE PL #C	LOS ANGELES, CA 90069
COOPER, SUSAN	WRITER	ICM, 8899 BEVERLY BLVD	LOS ANGELES, CA 90048
COOPER, TABI	ACTRESS	1717 N HIGHLAND AVE #701	LOS ANGELES, CA 90028
COOPER, TAMAR	ACTRESS	2265 N BEVERLY GLEN PL	LOS ANGELES, CA 90077
COOPER, TIM	BASEBALL	POST OFFICE BOX 22093	GREENSBORO, NC 27420
COOPER, WAYNE	BASKETBALL	700 NE MULTNOMAH ST #600	PORTLAND, OR 97232
COOPER, WILLIAM L, JR	TV PRODUCER	420 LEXINGTON AVE #2009	NEW YORK, NY 10170
COOPER, WILMA LEE & CLINCH	BLUEGRASS GROUP	POST OFFICE BOX 809	GOODLETTSVILLE, TN 37072
COOPER, WILMA LEE	SINGER-GUITARIST	606 DAVIS DR	BRENTWOOD, TN 37027
COOPER, ZACKIE C	COMPOSER	1634 N WESTERLY TERR	LOS ANGELES, CA 90026
COOPER-SEALY, JUDI	HAIR STYLIST	JCS TV, 191 SEATON ST	TORONTO, ONT M5A 2T5 CANADA
COOPERMAN, ALVIN	TV WRITER-PRODUCER	146 CENTRAL PARK W	NEW YORK, NY 10023
COOPERMAN, JACK	FILM DIRECTOR	POST OFFICE BOX 5118	BEVERLY HILLS, CA 90210
COOPERSTEIN, EDWIN	TV DIRECTOR	7745 N TATUM BLVD	PARADISE VALLEY, AZ 85253
COOPLE, TY	ACTOR	429 W 45TH ST #4-FW	NEW YORK, NY 10036
COPAGE, MARC	ACTOR	POST OFFICE BOX 461677	LOS ANGELES, CA 90067
COPELAND, ALAN	CONDUCTOR	POST OFFICE BOX 393	AGOURA, CA 91301
COPELAND, DANNY	FOOTBALL	POST OFFICE BOX 17247 (DULLES)	WASHINGTON, DC 20041
COPELAND, JOAN	ACTRESS	88 CENTRAL PARK W	NEW YORK, NY 10023
COPELAND, JOHNNY CLYDE	SINGER-GUITARIST	2000 S DAIRY ASHFORD ST #150	HOUSTON, TX 77077
COPELAND, KAREN LEE	TV EXECUTIVE	WNBC-TV, 30 ROCKEFELLER PLZ	NEW YORK, NY 10020
COPELAND, KENNETH	EVANGELIST	POST OFFICE BOX 2908	FORT WORTH, TX 76113
COPELAND, MARK	BASEBALL TRAINER	POST OFFICE BOX 651	AUBURN, NY 13021
COPELAND, MARTIN W	SCREENWRITER	10351 SANTA MONICA BLVD #211	LOS ANGELES, CA 90025
COPELAND, MAURICE	ACTOR	47 ROCKWOOD DR	LARCHMONT, NY 10538
COPELAND, STEWART	DRUMMER-SONGWRITER	9313 DOHENY RD	BEVERLY HILLS, CA 90210
COPLEY, PAUL	ACTOR	43-A PRINCESS RD, REGENTS PK	LONDON NW1 8JS ENGLAND
COPLEY, TERI	ACTRESS-MODEL	3500 W OLIVE AVE #920	BURBANK, CA 91505
COPPERFIELD, DAVID	MAGICIAN	15456 VENTURA BLVD #300	SHERMAN OAKS, CA 91403
COPPETTA, GREG	BASEBALL	POST OFFICE BOX 2785	LAKELAND, FL 33806
COPPOLA, ALICIA	ACTRESS	151 S EL CAMINO DR	BEVERLY HILLS, CA 90212
COPPOLA, FRANCIS FORD	WRITER-PRODUCER	916 KEARNY ST	SAN FRANCISCO, CA 91433
COPPOLA, FRANK	ACTOR	573 N WINDSOR BLVD	LOS ANGELES, CA 90004
COPPOLA, SOFIA	ACTRESS	916 KEARNEY ST	SAN FRANCISCO, CA 94133
COPPOLA, SOPHIE	ACTRESS	781 5TH AVE	NEW YORK, NY 10022
CORA, JOEY	BASEBALL	333 W 35TH ST	CHICAGO, IL 60616
CORA, MANNY	BASEBALL	POST OFFICE BOX 20849	CHARLESTON, SC 29413

CORBETT, GLENN	ACTOR	15010 VENTURA BLVD #219	SHERMAN OAKS, CA 91403
CORBETT, GRETCHEN	ACTRESS	9229 SUNSET BLVD #311	LOS ANGELES, CA 90069
CORBETT, MICHAEL	ACTOR	1434 N SPALDING #A	LOS ANGELES, CA 90046
CORBETT, RAY	BASEBALL SCOUT	REDS, 100 RIVERFRONT STADIUM	CINCINNATI, OH 45202
CORBETT, RONNIE	COMEDIAN	INTERNATIONAL ARTISTES LTD	
		MEZZANINE FL, 235 REGENT ST	LONDON W1R 8AX ENGLAND
CORBETT, SHERMAN	BASEBALL	10233 96TH AVE	EDMONTON, ALB TK5 0A5 CANADA
CORBIN, ALBERT	ACTOR	714 GREENWICH ST	NEW YORK, NY 10014
CORBIN, ARCHIE	BASEBALL	800 HOME RUN LN	MEMPHIS, TN 38104
CORBIN, BARRY	ACTOR	4529 TYRONE AVE	SHERMAN OAKS, CA 91423
CORBIN, TYRONE	BASKETBALL	TIMBERWOLVES, 600 1ST AVE N	MINNEAPOLIS, MN 55403
CORBIN/HANNER BAND	C & W GROUP	1018 17TH AVE S #8	NASHVILLE, TN 37212
CORBY, ELLEN	ACTRESS	9024 HARRATT ST	LOS ANGELES, CA 90069
CORCORAN, BRIAN	ACTOR	2502 1/2 CHANDLER BLVD	BURBANK, CA 91505
CORCORAN, KERRY	ACTOR	350 S MADISON AVE #126	PASADENA, CA 91101
CORCORAN, KEVIN	ACTOR	8617 BALCOM AVE	NORTHRIDGE, CA 91325
CORCORAN, NOREEN	ACTRESS	5926 JAMIESON AVE	ENCINO, CA 91316
CORCORAN, TIM	BASEBALL SCOUT	ATHLETICS'S, OAKLAND COLISEUM	OAKLAND, CA 94621
CORD, ALEX	ACTOR	7387 WOODROW WILSON DR	LOS ANGELES, CA 90046
CORD, ERIK	DIRECTOR	4987 CALDERON RD	WOODLAND HILLS, CA 91364
CORDAY, BARBARA	TV WRITER-PRODUCER	532 N CHEROKEE	LOS ANGELES, CA 90004
CORDAY, KEN	TV PRODUCER	10343 VALLEY SPRING LN	TOLUCA LAKE, CA 91602
CORDAY, MARA	ACTRESS-MODEL	25932 MENDOZE DR	VALENCIA, CA 91355
CORDAY, MRS TED	TV PRODUCER	4000 WARNER BLVD #8-139	BURBANK, CA 91522
CORDAY, THEODORE	TV PRODUCER	1925 CENTURY PARK E #650	LOS ANGELES, CA 90067
CORDELL, CATHLEEN	ACTOR	1850 N WHITLEY AVE #419	LOS ANGELES, CA 90028
CORDELL, MELINDA	ACTRESS	8322 BEVERLY BLVD #200	LOS ANGELES, CA 90048
CORDEN, HENRY	ACTOR	3697 GOODLAND AVE	STUDIO CITY, CA 91604
CORDERO, MARIA-ELENA	ACTRESS	17240 REVELLO DR	PACIFIC PALISADES, CA 90272
CORDERO, WILFREDO	BASEBALL	1501 W 16TH ST	INDIANAPOLIS, IN 46202
CORDES, KATHRYN	ACTRESS	195 W 10TH ST #2-B	NEW YORK, NY 10014
CORDIC, REGIS J	ACTOR	8410 ALLENWOOD RD	LOS ANGELES, CA 90046
CORDOVA, MARTY	BASEBALL	POST OFFICE BOX 48	VISALIA, CA 93279
CORDOVA, PAMELA	ACTRESS	723 N BEDFORD DR	BEVERLY HILLS, CA 90210
CORDY, ANNIE	ACTRESS	LA ROSERAIE	BIEVRES 91570 FRANCE
COREA, CHICK	MUSICIAN	2635 GRIFFITH PARK BLVD	LOS ANGELES, CA 90039
COREA, NICHOLAS JOHN	WRITER-PRODUCER	14101 DICKENS ST #6	SHERMAN OAKS, CA 91423
COREY, JEFF	ACTOR-DIRECTOR	29445 BLUEWATER RD	MALIBU, CA 90265
COREY, PROF IRWIN	COMEDIAN	58 NASSAU	GREAT NECK, NY 11022
COREY, WALT	FOOTBALL COACH	BILLS, 1 BILLS DR	ORCHARD PARK, NJ 14127
CORGIAT, GARRY	ACTOR	8400 DE LONGPRE AVE #315	LOS ANGELES, CA 90069
CORINIS, DIMITRI	WRITER-PRODUCER	27 SANDERSTEAD AVE	LONDON NW2 1SE ENGLAND
CORIO, ANN	BURLESQUE	CARUSO, 721 E GRINNEL DR	BURBANK, CA 91501
CORLESS, MIKE	SINGER	KNIGHT, 1609 CONGRESS RD	EASTOVER, SC 29044
CORLEY, AL	SINGER	3330 PURDUE AVE	LOS ANGELES, CA 90066
CORLEY, PAT	ACTOR	9000 SUNSET BLVD #1200	LOS ANGELES, CA 90069
CORLISS, RICHARD	FILM CRITIC-WRITER	TIME/TIME & LIFE BLDG	
		ROCKEFELLER CENTER	NEW YORK, NY 10020
CORMAN, EUGENE H	FILM PRODUCER	615 N ALTA DR	BEVERLY HILLS, CA 90210
CORMAN, JULIE	FILM PRODUCER	TRINITY PRODUCTIONS CO	
		11600 SAN VICENTE BLVD	LOS ANGELES, CA 90049
CORMAN, ROGER	WRITER-PRODUCER	NEW HORIZON PICTURES CO	
		11600 SAN VICENTE BLVD	LOS ANGELES, CA 90049
CORMIER, RHEAL	BASEBALL	POST OFFICE BOX 36407	LOUISVILLE, KY 40233
CORNELIUS, BRIAN	BASEBALL	TIGERS, 89 WHARNCLIFFE RD N	LONDON, ONT N6H 2A7 CANADA
CORNELIUS, DON	TV PRODUCER	9255 SUNSET BLVD #420	LOS ANGELES, CA 90069
CORNELIUS, HELEN	SINGER	724 STATE ST	HANNIBAL, MO 63401
CORNELL, DON	SINGER	100 BAYVIEW DR #1521	NORTH MIAMI, FL 33160
CORNELL, LYDIA	ACTRESS-MODEL-AUTHOR	12456 VENTURA BLVD #1	STUDIO CITY, CA 91604
CORNELLUS, REID	BASEBALL	POST OFFICE BOX 15757	HARRISBURG, PA 17105
CORNING, JOY	LT GOVERNOR	STATE CAPITOL BUILDING	DES MOINES, IA 50319
CORNISH, DOUG	DIRECTOR	11266 DORLAND ST	WHITTIER, CA 90606
CORNISH, EDWARD	COLUMNIST	7720 EL CAMINO REAL #2-C	RANCHO LA COSTA, CA 92008
CORNISH, FRANK	FOOTBALL	POST OFFICE BOX 609609	SAN DIEGO, CA 92160
CORNS, GREG	BASEBALL EXECUTIVE	5999 E VAN BUREN ST	PHOENIX, AZ 85008
CORNTHWAITE, ROBERT	ACTOR	11656 JACARANDA AVE	HESPERIA, CA 92345
CORNWELL, JUDY	ACTRESS	MC REDDIE, 91 REGENT ST	LONDON W1R 7TB ENGLAND
CORONA, JOHN	BASEBALL	POST OFFICE BOX 12557	ST PETERSBURG, FL 33733
CORPORA, THOMAS	TV EXECUTIVE	POST OFFICE BOX 467	ATLANTA, GA 30301
CORPORON, JOHN R	TV EXECUTIVE	INN, 11 WPIX PLAZA	NEW YORK, NY 10017
CORRADO, GUS	ACTOR	1626 S WOOSTER ST	LOS ANGELES, CA 90035
CORRALES, PAT	BASEBALL-COACH	POST OFFICE BOX 4064	ATLANTA, GA 30302
CORRALES, PILITA	SINGER	POST OFFICE BOX 63	ORINDA, CA 94563
CORREA, AMILCAR	BASEBALL	POST OFFICE BOX 4488	WINSTON-SALEM, NC 27115
CORREA, RAMSER	BASEBALL	POST OFFICE BOX 8550	STOCKTON, CA 95208
CORREIA, ROD	BASEBALL	POST OFFICE BOX 12	MIDLAND, TX 79702
CORRELL, CHARLES	CINEMATOGRAPHER	MTA, 9320 WILSHIRE BL, 3RD FL	BEVERLY HILLS, CA 90212
CORRENTI, CHRIS	BASEBALL TRAINER	POST OFFICE BOX 824	BURLINGTON, IA 52601
CORRIGAN, DOUGLAS	ACTOR	2828 N FLOWER ST	SANTA ANA, CA 92706
CORRIGAN, JACK	SPORTSCASTER	INDIANS, CLEVELAND STADIUM	CLEVELAND, OH 44114
CORRIN, GEORGE, JR	ART DIRECTOR	303 W 42ND ST	NEW YORK, NY 10036
CORRONS, JIM	SINGER	5625 "O" STREET BLDG #7	LINCOLN, NE 68510
CORRY, EARLE	CONDUCTOR	130 W PITKIN AVE	PUEBLO, CO 81004
CORSARO, FRANK	OPERA DIRECTOR	33 RIVERSIDE DR	NEW YORK, NY 10023
CORSI, JIM	BASEBALL	POST OFFICE BOX 11087	TACOMA, WA 98411

Name	Occupation	Address	City	Zip/Country
CORSON, SHAYNE	HOCKEY	CANADIENS, 2313 ST CATHERINE ST	MONTREAL, QUE H3H 1N2	CANADA
CORT, BUD	ACTOR	606 N LARCHMONT BLVD #309	LOS ANGELES, CA	90004
CORTES, ROBERT	PRODUCER	MCA/UNIVERSAL STUDIOS, INC		
		100 UNIVERSAL CITY PLAZA	UNIVERSAL CTIY, CA	91608
CORTESE, JOE	ACTOR	4724 POE AVE	WOODLAND HILLS, CA	91364
CORTESE, VALENTINA	ACTRESS	PRETTA S ERASMO 6	MILAN	ITALY
CORTEZ, STACEY	ACTRESS	ABC-TV, "GENERAL HOSPITAL"		
		4151 PROSPECT AVE	BURBANK, CA	91523
CORTEZ, STANLEY	CINEMATOGRAPHER	1512 SUNSET PLAZA DR	LOS ANGELES, CA	90069
CORTINO, ANTHONY	HAIR STYLIST	415 W 23RD ST	NEW YORK, NY	10011
CORVO, DAVID	WRITER	3870 RAMBLA ORIENTA	MALIBU, CA	90265
CORWIN, BRUCE	BASEBALL EXECUTIVE	POST OFFICE BOX 2000	SAN DIEGO, CA	92112
CORWIN, BRUCE	BASEBALL EXECUTIVE	POST OFFICE BOX 1742	PALM SPRINGS, CA	92263
CORWIN, M J	TV EXECUTIVE	NBC-TV, 3000 W ALAMEDA AVE	BURBANK, CA	91523
CORWIN, MARK ROBERT	TV DIRECTOR	5748 HILLVIEW PARK AVE	VAN NUYS, CA	91401
CORWIN, NORMAN	WRITER-PRODUCER	1840 FAIRBURN AVE #302	LOS ANGELES, CA	90025
CORWIN, RAYMOND A	DIRECTOR	370 RIVERSIDE DR	NEW YORK, NY	10025
CORWIN, SHERRILL	ACTOR	838 N DOHENRY DR #PH-C	LOS ANGELES, CA	90069
CORWIN, VANESSA	WRI-DIR-PROD	CHILDREN'S TV WORKSHOP		
		1 LINCOLN PLAZA	NEW YORK, NY	10023
CORYELL, LARRY	MUSICIAN	5 WATCHILL RD	WESTPORT, CT	06880
CORZINE, DAVE	BASKETBALL	POST OFFICE BOX C-900911	SEATTLE, WA	98109
COSAND, LARRY	ACTOR	1214 N CLARK ST #9	LOS ANGELES, CA	90069
COSBY, BILL	ACTOR-COMEDIAN	POST OFFICE BOX 69646	LOS ANGELES, CA	90069
COSCARELLI, DAC	FILM PRODUCER	15445 VENTURA BLVD #10	SHERMAN OAKS, CA	91413
COSCARELLI, DONALD	FILM DIRECTOR	4132 FULTON AVE	SHERMAN OAKS, CA	91423
COSCIA, JOSEPH	HAIR STYLIST	8 CHARNWOOD DR	SUFFERN, NY	10901
COSEL, WILLIAM N	DIRECTOR	335 HURON AVE	CAMBRIDGE, MA	02138
COSELL, HOWARD	SPORTSCASTER	150 E 69TH ST	NEW YORK, NY	10021
COSGROVE, DAN	ARTIST	405 N WABASH AVE #2914	CHICAGO, IL	60611
COSGROVE, JOHN	DIRECTOR	546 N CHEROKEE AVE	LOS ANGELES, CA	90004
COSLET, BRUCE	FOOTBALL COACH	N Y JETS, 1000 FULTON AVE	HEMPSTEAD, NY	11550
COSMATOS, GEORGE P	FILM WRI-DIR-PROD	1875 CENTURY PARK E #2200	LOS ANGELES, CA	90067
COSMIDIS, ALEX	BASEBALL SCOUT	333 W 35TH ST	CHICAGO, IL	60616
COSS, MIKE	BASEBALL	POST OFFICE BOX 3169	FREDERICK, MD	21701
COSSETT, PIERRE	PRODUCER	8899 BEVERLY BLVD #900	LOS ANGELES, CA	90048
COSSINS, JAMES	ACTOR	BELFRAGE, 68 SAINT JAMES'S ST	LONDON SW1A 1LE	ENGLAND
COSSON, PIERRE	FILM DIRECTOR	RUE DU PRESSOIR	EPISRHUS 95810	FRANCE
COST, THOMAS M	WRITER	5800 SHIRLEY AVE	TARZANA, CA	91356
COSTA, COSIE	ACTOR	2816 N FREDERICK ST	BURBANK, CA	91504
COSTA, JOSEPH	PHOTOGRAPHER	25301 OUTLOOK DR	CARMEL, CA	93923
COSTA-GAVRAS, HENRI CONSTANTIN	FILM WRITER-DIRECTOR	244 RUE SAINT JACQUES	PARIS 75005	FRANCE
COSTAPERARIA, BARBARA M	WRITER	12308 EMELITA ST	NORTH HOLLYWOOD, CA	91607
COSTAS, BOB	SPORTSCASTER	NBC-TV, 30 ROCKEFELLER PLAZA	NEW YORK, NY	10112
COSTELLO, ELVIS & ATTRACTIONS	ROCK & ROLL GROUP	GLOBAL RIVIIERA, WESTERN HOUSE		
		9028 GREAT GUEST RD	MIDDLESEX TW8 9EW	ENGLAND
COSTELLO, FRED	BASEBALL	POST OFFICE BOX 422229	KISSIMMEE, FL	34742
COSTELLO, JERRY	U S CONGRESSMAN	1316 NIEDRINGHAUS AVE	GRANITE CITY, IL	62040
COSTELLO, JOHN	BASEBALL	POST OFFICE BOX 2000	SAN DIEGO, CA	92112
COSTELLO, PERRY	BASEBALL UMPIRE	POST OFFICE BOX 608	GROVE CITY, OH	43123
COSTELLO, ROBERT E	TV PRODUCER-DIRECTOR	NARWAL PRODS, 161 W 54TH ST	NEW YORK, NY	10019
COSTELLO, WARD	ACTOR	247 S BEVERLY DR #102	BEVERLY HILLS, CA	90210
COSTER, CANDACE	ACTRESS	345 N PALM DR #8	BEVERLY HILLS, CA	90210
COSTER, NICOLAS	ACTOR	1930 CENTURY PARK W #403	LOS ANGELES, CA	90067
COSTI, AL R	COMPOSER	9838 WHEATLAND	SUNLAND, CA	91040
COSTIGAN, JAMES	SCREENWRITER	8955 BEVERLY BLVD	WEST HOLLYWOOD, CA	90048
COSTIKYAN, ANDREW M	DIRECTOR	567 HAPP RD	NORTHFIELD, IL	60093
COSTNER, KEVIN	ACT-DIR-PROD	POST OFFICE BOX 275	MONTROSE, CA	91021
COSTON, SUZANNE	TV PRODUCER	ICM, 8899 BEVERLY BLVD	LOS ANGELES, CA	90048
COTE, SUZY	ACTRESS	CBS-TV, "THE GUIDING LIGHT"		
		222 E 44TH ST	NEW YORK, NY	10017
COTE, SYLVAIN	HOCKEY	WHALERS, 1 CIVIC CENTER PLAZA	HARTFORD, CT	06103
COTHRAN, WILLIAM	ACTOR-WRITER	3850 WAWONA ST	LOS ANGELES, CA	90065
COTLER, ALAN B	SCREENWRITER	8955 BEVERLY BLVD	WEST HOLLYWOOD, CA	90048
COTRONEO, VINCE	SPORTSCASTER	POST OFFICE BOX 288	HOUSTON, TX	77001
COTTEN, JOSEPH	ACTOR	1993 MESA DR	PALM SPRINGS, CA	92264
COTTIER, CHUCK	BASEBALL-COACH	1060 W ADDISON ST	CHICAGO, IL	60613
COTTLE, GRAHAM DAVID	DIRECTOR	8261 MARMONT LN	LOS ANGELES, CA	90069
COTTO, HENRY	BASEBALL	POST OFFICE BOX 4100	SEATTLE, WA	98104
COTTON, GENE	SINGER-GUITARIST	ROUTE #3, SWEENEY HOLLOW RD	FRANKLIN, TN	37064
COTTON, JACK	GUITARIST	5141 LANA RENEE CT	HERMITAGE, TN	37076
COTTON, JAMES, BAND	JAZZ GROUP	BACKROOM, 1450 N CLEVELAND AVE	CHICAGO, IL	60610
COTTON, JOHN	BASEBALL	POST OFFICE BOX 3452	KINSTON, NC	28502
COTTON, MARCUS	FOOTBALL	SEAHAWKS, 11220 NE 53RD ST	KIRKLAND, WA	98033
COTTON, OLIVER	ACTOR	CONWAY, 18-21 JERMYN ST	LONDON SW1	ENGLAND
COTTON, PAUL	SINGER-SONGWRITER	4804 KELVIN AVE	WOODLAND HILLS, CA	91364
COTTON-ATES, CAROLINA	SINGER	POST OFFICE BOX 730	BAKERSFIELD, CA	93302
COTTRELL, PADDY	BASEBALL SCOUT	POST OFFICE BOX 90111	ARLINGTON, TX	76004
COTTRELL, PORTER	BOLDYBUILDER	3099 BRECKINRIDGE LN	LOUISVILLE, KY	40220
COTTRELL, TED	FOOTBALL COACH	POST OFFICE BOX 888	PHOENIX, AZ	85001
COTTS, GERALD VOSS	DIRECTOR	627 W END AVE	NEW YORK, NY	10024
COUCH, CHARLES EDWARD	DIRECTOR	DGA, 7920 SUNSET BLVD, 6TH FL	LOS ANGELES, CA	90046
COUCH, JACK	ACTOR	2901 AVENUE "J"	BROOKLYN, NY	11210
COUFFER, JACK	WRITER-PRODUCER	ICM, 8899 BEVERLY BLVD	LOS ANGELES, CA	90048
COUGAR, JOHN	SINGER-SONGWRITER	SEE - MELLENCAMP, JOHN COUGAR		

COUGHLAN, FRANK "JUNIOR"	ACTOR-AUTHOR	12522 ARGYLE AVE	LOS ALAMITOS, CA	90720
COUGHLIN, KEVIN	BASEBALL	1090 N EUCLID AVE	SARASOTA, FL	34237
COUGHLIN, LAWRENCE	U S CONGRESSMAN	6813 RIDGE AVE	PHILADELPHIA, PA	19128
COUGHLIN, TOM	FOOTBALL COACH	N Y GIANTS, GIANTS STADIUM	EAST RUTHERFORD, NJ	07073
COUKART, ED	FOOTBALL REFEREE	NFL, 410 PARK AVE	NEW YORK, NY	10022
COULIER, DAVE	ACTOR	ABC-TV, 2040 AVE OF THE STARS	LOS ANGELES, CA	90067
COULIER, DAVID	ACTOR	259 20TH ST	SANTA MONICA, CA	90401
COULSON, PETER	DIRECTOR-PRODUCER	15 EYOT GARDENS	LONDON W6 9TN	ENGLAND
COULTER, CHRISTOPHER	BASEBALL	POST OFFICE BOX 1886	COLUMBUS, GA	31902
COUNTRY BELLES, THE	C & W GROUP	POST OFFICE BOX 4553	CAMP HILL, PA	17011
COUNTRY CLASS	C & W GROUP	OPERATION MUSIC ENTERPRISES		
		233 W WOODLAND AVE	OTTUMWA, IA	52501
COUNTRY CREEK	C & W GROUP	JIMMY ALLEN, 1548 ASHLAND AVE	SAINT PAUL, MN	55104
COUNTRY FREEDOM	C & W GROUP	ANJOLI, 24 CENTER SQUARE RD	LEOLA, PA	17540
COUNTRY GAZETTE	VOCAL GROUP	FOLKLORE, 1671 APPIAN WY	SANTA MONICA, CA	90401
COUNTRY GENTLEMEN, THE	VOCAL GROUP	LENDEL, ROUTE #5, BOX 19-A	WARRENTON, VA	22186
COUNTRY PRIDE	C & W GROUP	5625 "O" STREET BLDG #7	LINCOLN, NE	68510
COUNTRY RHYTHM BOYS, THE	C & W GROUP	POST OFFICE BOX 263	CENTRE VALLEY, PA	18034
COUNTRY WITH A TOUCH OF BRASS	C & W GROUP	DEAN SHORT, 1203 S 62ND ST	OMAHA, NE	68106
COUNTRY WITH CLASS	C & W GROUP	OPERATION MUSIC ENTERPRISES		
		233 W WOODLAND AVE	OTTUMWA, IA	52501
COUNTRYMAN, JOHN R	SINGER-SONGWRITER	SEE - RUSSELL, JOHNNY		
COUNTS, MEL	BASKETBALL	1581 MATHENY RD	GERVALIS, OR	97026
COUPE'DE'VILLE	C & W GROUP	POST OFFICE BOX 4087	MISSOULA, MT	59806
COUPLES, FRED	GOLFER	POST OFFICE BOX 109601	PALM BCH GARDENS, FL	33418
COUPPEE, ED	ACTOR	12168 OXNARD ST	NORTH HOLLYWOOD, CA	91606
COURAGE, ALEXANDER	COMPOSER-CONDUCTOR	23344 PALOMA BLANCA	MALIBU, CA	90265
COURAGE, CAROLYN	ACTRESS	GREEN, 2 CONDUIT ST	LONDON W1R 9TG	ENGLAND
COURCEL, NICOLE	ACTRESS	G BEAUME, 3 QUAI MALAQUAIS	PARIS 75006	FRANCE
COURIC, KATIE	BROADCAST JOURNALIST	NBC-TV, 30 ROCKEFELLER PLAZA	NEW YORK, NY	10112
COURT, GERALDINE	ACTRESS	8150 BEVERLY BLVD #201	LOS ANGELES, CA	90048
COURT, HAZEL	ACTRESS	TAYLOR, 1111 SAN VICENTE BLVD	SANTA MONICA, CA	90402
COURTENAY, MARGARET	ACTRESS	HEATH, PARAMOUNT HOUSE		
		162-170 WARDOUR ST	LONDON W1V 3AT	ENGLAND
COURTENAY, TOM	ACTOR	30 CHARLYWOOD RD	LONDON SW15	ENGLAND
COURTLAND, JEROME	DIRECTOR	27354 LANDON PL	VALENCIA, CA	91354
COURTLAND, JOHN C	DIRECTOR	4909 BELLAIRE AVE	NORTH HOLLYWOOD, CA	91607
COURTLEIGH, BOB	ACTOR	3321 LANDA ST	LOS ANGELES, CA	90039
COURTNALL, GEOFF	HOCKEY	CANUCKS, 100 N RENFREW ST	VANCOUVER, BC V5K 3N7	CANADA
COURTNALL, RUSS	HOCKEY	CANADIENS, 2313 ST CATHERINE ST	MONTREAL, QUE H3H 1N2	CANADA
COURTNEY, ALEX	ACTOR	3351 OAK GLEN DR	LOS ANGELES, CA	90068
COURTNEY, JACQUELINE	ACTRESS	10 E 44TH ST #700	NEW YORK, NY	10017
COURTRIGHT, JOHN	BASEBALL	POST OFFICE BOX 4669	CHARLESTON, WV	25304
COURY, DICK	BASEBALL SCOUT	POST OFFICE BOX 90111	ARLINGTON, TX	76004
COURY, DICK	FOOTBALL COACH	RAMS, 2327 W LINCOLN BLVD	ANAHEIM, CA	92801
COUSIN BRUCIE	RADIO PERSONALITY	POST OFFICE BOX 50	NEW YORK, NY	10101
COUSIN BUBBA	SINGER	BRODY, 4086 ROYAL CREST DR	MEMPHIS, TN	38115
COUSINS, CHRISTOPHER	ACTOR	ABC-TV, "ONE LIFE TO LIVE"		
		56 W 66TH ST	NEW YORK, NY	10023
COUSINS, DERRYL	BASEBALL UMPIRE	702 4TH ST	HERMOSA BEACH, CA	90254
COUSTEAU, JACQUES	OCEANOGRAPHER	425 E 52ND ST	NEW YORK, NY	10022
COUSTEAU, JEAN-MICHEL	OCEANOGRAPHER	425 E 52ND ST	NEW YORK, NY	10022
COUSTON, TOM	BASEBALL SCOUT	INDIANS, CLEVELAND STADIUM	CLEVELAND, OH	44114
COUSY, BOB	BASKETBALL	459 SALISBURY ST	WORCESTER, MA	01609
COUTARD, RAOUL	FILM DIRECTOR	138 BLVD MURAT	PARIS 75016	FRANCE
COUTURE, MIKE	BASEBALL	POST OFFICE BOX 855	BELOIT, WI	53511
COVAN, DE FOREST	DANCER	5545 CARLSON WY #301	LOS ANGELES, CA	90028
COVENEY, JIM	BASEBALL-INSTRUCTOR	POST OFFICE BOX 288	HOUSTON, TX	77001
COVER, FRANKLIN	ACTOR	11726 SAN VICENTE BLVD #300	LOS ANGELES, CA	90049
COVER GIRLS, THE	SOUL GROUP	BROTHERS, 141 DUNBAR AVE	FORDS, NJ	08863
COVERT, DAVE	SINGER	POST OFFICE BOX 171132	NASHVILLE, TN	37217
COVINGTON, HILBURN	DIRECTOR	2816 NICHOLS CANYON RD	LOS ANGELES, CA	90046
COVINGTON, TONY	FOOTBALL	BUCCANEERS, 1 BUCCANEER PL	TAMPA, FL	33607
COWAN, CLAYTON L	COMPOSER	15749 MERCED AVE	CHINO, CA	91710
COWAN, DAVID	SCREENWRITER	FILM RIGHTS, 483 SOUTHBANK HOUSE		
		BLACK PRINCE RD		
		ALBERT EMBANKMENT	LONDON SE1 7SJ	ENGLAND
COWAN, FRED	ATTORNEY GENERAL	STATE CAPITOL BUILDING	FRANKFORT, KY	40601
COWAN, GARY	GOLFER	PGA SENIORS, 112 T P C BLVD	PONTE VEDRA BEACH, FL	32082
COWAN, MICHAEL A	TV DIRECTOR	3756 EFFINGHAM PL	LOS ANGELES, CA	90027
COWAN, THEO	TV EXECUTIVE	NAMARA HOUSE, 45 POLAND ST	LONDON W1V 4AU	ENGLAND
COWAN, WILL	FILM DIRECTOR	9140 BROOKSHIRE AVE	DOWNEY, CA	90240
COWBOY JAZZ	C & W GROUP	LONE STAR, 13987 W ANNAPOLIS CT	MOUNT AIRY, MD	21771
COWBOY JUNKIES, THE	ROCK & ROLL GROUP	143 W 69TH ST #2-A	NEW YORK, NY	10023
COWELL, STANLEY	PIANIST	KURLAND, 173 BRIGHTON AVE	BOSTON, MA	02134
COWEN, DONNA	ACTRESS	340 S OCEAN BLVD	PALM BEACH, FL	33480
COWEN, FRANK	COMPOSER	POST OFFICE BOX 395	ROSAMOND, CA	93560
COWEN, RON	TV WRITER	620 VIA DE LA PAZ	PACIFIC PALISADES, CA	90272
COWHER, BILL	FOOTBALL COACH	CHIEFS, 1 ARROWHEAD DR	KANSAS CITY, MO	64129
COWL, DARRYL	ACTOR	3 RUE EDOUARD NORTIER	NEUILLY 92200	FRANCE
COWLES, MATHEW	ACTOR	50 DELANCY ST	NEW YORK, NY	10002
COWLEY, WILLIAM M, III	WRITER	2544 HUTTON DR	BEVERLY HILLS, CA	90210
COX, AARON	FOOTBALL	RAMS, 2327 W LINCOLN BLVD	ANAHEIM, CA	92801
COX, ARCHIBALD	ATTORNEY	GLESEN LN	WAYLAND, MA	01778
COX, ARTHUR	FOOTBALL	POST OFFICE BOX 609609	SAN DIEGO, CA	92160

COX, ASHLEY	ACTRESS-MODEL	100 E ARLINGTON DR	CLAREMONT, CA	91711
COX, BARRY	TV DIRECTOR-PRODUCER	LONDON WEEKEND TELEVISION		
		SOUTH BANK TV CENTRE, UPPER GR	LONDON SE1	ENGLAND
COX, BETSY	COSTUME DESIGNER	13949 VENTURA BLVD #309	SHERMAN OAKS, CA	91423
COX, BOBBY	BASEBALL MANAGER	POST OFFICE BOX 4064	ATLANTA, GA	30302
COX, BOYCE	BASEBALL EXECUTIVE	POST OFFICE BOX 1434	BRISTOL, VA	24203
COX, BRYAN	FOOTBALL	DOLPHINS, 2269 NW 199TH ST	MIAMI, FL	33056
COX, CHRISTOPHER	U S CONGRESSMAN	4000 MAC ARTHUR BLVD #430	NEWPORT BEACH, CA	92660
COX, COURTENEY	ACTRESS	9016 WILSHIRE BLVD #500	BEVERLY HILLS, CA	90211
COX, CRAWFORD	ACTOR	8640 HILLROSE ST #E-12	SUNLAND, CA	91040
COX, DANNY	BASEBALL	POST OFFICE BOX 7000	PITTSBURGH, PA	15212
COX, DEANNA	SINGER	MC FADDEN, 818 18TH AVE S	NASHVILLE, TN	37203
COX, ELIZABETH	ACTRESS	8484 WILSHIRE BLVD #530	BEVERLY HILLS, CA	90211
COX, FRANK	TV DIRECTOR-PRODUCER	63 ELERS RD	LONDON W13 9QB	ENGLAND
COX, GREG	FOOTBALL	S F 49ERS, 4949 CENTENNIAL BL	SANTA CLARA, CA	95054
COX, JAMES	COLUMNIST	POST OFFICE BOX 500	WASHINGTON, DC	20044
COX, JAMES RUSSELL	TV DIRECTOR	1872 W TEDMAR AVE	ANAHEIM, CA	92804
COX, JEFF	BASEBALL-MANAGER	2727 VANDERHOOF DR	WEST COVINA, CA	91791
COX, JOHN	BASEBALL SCOUT	ORIOLE PARK, 333 W CAMDEN ST	BALTIMORE, MD	21201
COX, JOHN W, JR	U S CONGRESSMAN	POST OFFICE BOX 252	GALENA, IL	61036
COX, MARY	SCREENWRITER	8955 BEVERLY BLVD	WEST HOLLYWOOD, CA	90048
COX, MICHAEL GRAHAM	ACTOR	32 CLIFTON GARDENS	LONDON W9	ENGLAND
COX, MICHAEL STEPHEN	TV DIRECTOR-PRODUCER	WM MORRIS, 31-32 SOHO SQ	LONDON W1V 5DG	ENGLAND
COX, NELL	WRITER-PRODUCER	1629 GEORGINA AVE	SANTA MONICA, CA	90403
COX, RICHARD	ACTOR	ABC-TV, "LOVING"		
		320 W 66TH ST, STUDIO 23	NEW YORK, NY	10023
COX, RICHARD M	DIRECTOR	933 TOWLSTON RD	MC LEAN, VA	22102
COX, RON	FOOTBALL	BEARS, 250 N WASHINGTON RD	LAKE FOREST, IL	60045
COX, RONNY	ACTOR-FILM PRODUCER	13948 MAGNOLIA BLVD	SHERMAN OAKS, CA	91423
COXX, JEFF	BASEBALL MANAGER	800 HOME RUN LN	MEMPHIS, TN	38104
COYLE, HARRY J	TV DIRECTOR	70 ALPINE DR	WAYNE, NJ	07470
COYLE, PAUL ROBERT	TV WRITER	8383 WILSHIRE BLVD #1039	BEVERLY HILLS, CA	90211
COYLE, RANDO	BODYBUILDER	1446-2 EDWIN MILLER BLVD	MARTINSBURG, WV	25401
COYLE, SUSAN	ACTRESS	1042 E WALNUT AVE	BURBANK, CA	91501
COYNE, WILLIAM J	U S CONGRESSMAN	2009 FEDERAL BUILDING		
		1009 LIBERTY AVE	PITTSBURGH, PA	15222
COYOTE	C & W GROUP	POST OFFICE BOX 40	BANGOR, ME	04401
COYOTE, PETER	ACTOR	SMITH, 121 N SAN VICENTE BLVD	BEVERLY HILLS, CA	90211
COZENS, VIVIENNE	TV DIRECTOR	3 ROSEHART MEWS, WESTBOURNE GR	LONDON W11 3JN	ENGLAND
COZZENS, MIMI	ACTRESS	12456 VENTURA BLVD #1	STUDIO CITY, CA	91604
COZZI, MIKE	TV DIRECTOR	8508 CASABA AVE	CANOGA PARK, CA	91306
CRABBE, BRUCE	BASEBALL	CHIEFS, MAC ARTHUR STADIUM	SYRACUSE, NY	13208
CRABBE, CUFFY	ACTOR	11216 N 74TH ST	SCOTTSDALE, AZ	85260
CRADDOCK, BILLY "CRASH"	SINGER-SONGWRITER	1020 E WENDOVER AVE #202	GREENSBORO, NC	27405
CRADDOCK, MALCOLM	TV DIRECTOR-PRODUCER	13 RANDOLPH RD	LONDON W9	ENGLAND
CRADDOCK, RON	TV DIRECTOR-PRODUCER	WOODSTONE, KIDMORE END		
		READING	BERKS	ENGLAND
CRAFT, CHRISTINE	NEWSCASTER-AUTHORESS	500 MEDIA PL	SACRAMENTO, CA	95815
CRAFT, HARRY	BASEBALL-MGR-SCOUT	S F GIANTS, CANDLESTICK PARK	SAN FRANICSCO, CA	94124
CRAFT, KINUKO Y	ARTIST	BROCKLEBANK, RDF #1, BOX 167	NORFOLK, CT	06058
CRAFT, ROBERT J	WRITER	23279 WELBY WY	CANOGA PARK, CA	91307
CRAFT, TERRY	BASEBALL UMPIRE	POST OFFICE BOX 608	GROVE CITY, OH	43123
CRAFTS, RITA	ACTRESS	2541 6TH ST	SANTA MONICA, CA	90405
CRAGG, STEPHEN	TV DIRECTOR	12415 VALLEYHEART DR	STUDIO CITY, CA	91604
CRAGG, STEVEN	PRODUCER	MCA/UNIVERSAL STUDIOS, INC		
		100 UNIVERSAL CITY PLAZA	UNIVERSAL CITY, CA	91608
CRAGGS, JULIAN	DIRECTOR	1419 DAUPHINE ST	NEW ORLEANS, LA	70116
CRAIG, CARL	ACTOR	3281 N FAIR OAKS AVE	ALTADENA, CA	91001
CRAIG, CATHERINE	ACTRESS	PRESTON, 1035 FAIRWAY DR	MONTECITO, CA	93108
CRAIG, DAVID	COLUMNIST	POST OFFICE BOX 500	WASHINGTON, DC	20044
CRAIG, JENNY	DIETICIAN	445 MARINE VIEW DR #300	DEL MAR, CA	92014
CRAIG, JOHN	ARTIST	ROUTE #2, BOX 81	SOLDIERS GROVE, WI	54655
CRAIG, JOHN	BASEBALL EXECUTIVE	SKYDOME, 300 BREMMER BL #3200	TORONTO, ONT M5V 3B3	CANADA
CRAIG, LARRY E	U S SENATOR	304 N 8TH ST #149	BOISE, ID	83701
CRAIG, MICHAEL	ACTOR	CHATTO AND LINNIT, LTD		
		PRINCE OF WALES THEATRE		
		COVENTRY ST	LONDON W1V 7FE	ENGLAND
CRAIG, MIKE	HOCKEY	NORTH STARS, 7901 CEDAR AVE S	BLOOMINGTON, MN	55425
CRAIG, MORRIS	BASEBALL	1524 W NEBRASKA AVE	PEORIA, IL	61604
CRAIG, ROGER	BASEBALL-MANAGER	S F GIANTS, CANDLESTICK PARK	SAN FRANICSCO, CA	94124
CRAIG, ROGER	FOOTBALL	RAIDERS, 332 CENTER ST	EL SEGUNDO, CA	90245
CRAIG, TOMMY	BASEBALL TRAINER	SKYDOME, 300 BREMMER BL #3200	TORONTO, ONT M5V 3B3	CANADA
CRAIG, W SCOTT	DIRECTOR-PRODUCER	1924 A N MOHAWK ST #11	CHICAGO, IL	60614
CRAIG, WENDY	ACTRESS	HATTON, 29 ROEHAMPTON GATE	LONDON SW15 5JR	ENGLAND
CRAIG, YVONNE	ACTRESS	1221 OCEAN AVE #202	SANTA MONICA, CA	90401
CRAIN, JEANNE	ACTRESS	354 HILGARD AVE	LOS ANGELES, CA	90024
CRAIN, WILLIAM	FILM DIRECTOR	POST OFFICE BOX 744	BEVERLY HILLS, CA	90213
CRAIS, ROBERT	WRITER	12829 LANDALE ST	STUDIO CITY, CA	91604
CRAM, JERRY	BASEBALL-INSTRUCTOR	POST OFFICE BOX 419969	KANSAS CITY, MO	64141
CRAMER, BUD	U S CONGRESSMAN	408 FRANKLIN ST	HUNTSVILLE, AL	35801
CRAMER, DOUGLAS A	TV WRITER-PRODUCER	738 SARBONNE RD	LOS ANGELES, CA	90077
CRAMER, FLOYD	PIANIST	5109 OLD HAVEN LN	TAMPA, FL	33617
CRAMER, ROSS G	DIRECTOR	MAYHEW, 581 6TH AVE	NEW YORK, NY	10011
CRAMPTON, BARBARA	ACTRESS	10000 SANTA MONICA BLVD #305	LOS ANGELES, CA	90067

CRAMPTON, BRUCE	GOLFER	7107 SPANKY RANCH DR	DALLAS, TX 75248
CRANDALL, CECIL A	COMPOSER	1441 MERRIMAN DR	GLENDALE, CA 91202
CRANDELL, DEL	BASEBALL-COACH	BREWERS, 201 S 46TH ST	MILWAUKEE, WI 53214
CRANE, CHERYL	AUTHORESS	1271 OZETA TERR	LOS ANGELES, CA 90069
CRANE, DAVID H	COMPOSER	3725 S TOPANGA BLVD	MALIBU, CA 90265
CRANE, FRED	ACTOR	803 S SPALDING	LOS ANGELES, CA 90036
CRANE, HARRY	WRITER	9014 ALTO CEDRO DR	BEVERLY HILLS, CA 90210
CRANE, KENNETH	FILM DIRECTOR	6627 LINDENHURST AVE	LOS ANGELES, CA 90048
CRANE, MATT	ACTOR	NBC-TV, "ANOTHER WORLD"	
		1268 E 14TH ST	BROOKLYN, NY 11230
CRANE, PETER MAURICE	DIRECTOR-PRODUCER	333 W 86TH ST	NEW YORK, NY 10024
CRANE, PHILIP M	U S CONGRESSMAN	3719 W ELM ST	MC HENRY, IL 60050
CRANFILL, DAVID	DIRECTOR	445 W ERIE ST	CHICAGO, IL 60610
CRANHAM, KENNETH	ACTOR	MARKHAM AND FROGGATT, LTD	
		JULIAN HOUSE, 4 WINDMILL ST	LONDON W1P 1HF ENGLAND
CRANSHAW, PATRICK	ACTOR	8165 KATHERINE AVE	PANORAMA CITY, CA 91402
CRANSTON, ALAN	U S SENATOR	2024 CAMDEN AVE	LOS ANGELES, CA 90025
CRANSTON, BRYAN	ACTOR	POST OFFICE BOX 69405	LOS ANGELES, CA 90069
CRAVEN, CAROL	TV DIRECTOR	137 E 66TH ST	NEW YORK, NY 10021
CRAVEN, GARTH	DIRECTOR	21751 AZURELEE DR	MALIBU, CA 90265
CRAVEN, GEMMA	ACTRESS	RICHARDS, 42 HAZLEBURY RD	LONDON SW6 2ND ENGLAND
CRAVEN, MIMI	ACTRESS	1930 CENTURY PARK W #403	LOS ANGELES, CA 90067
CRAVEN, MURRAY	HOCKEY	FLYERS, SPECTRUM, PATTISON PL	PHILADELPHIA, PA 19148
CRAVEN, PEGGY	ACTRESS	LLOYD, 1813 OLD RANCH RD	LOS ANGELES, CA 90049
CRAVEN, RICHARD	DIRECTOR	137 E 66TH ST	NEW YORK, NY 10021
CRAVEN, RICHARD	FILM PRODUCER	LOCATION, 16 BROADWICK ST	LONDON W1 ENGLAND
CRAVEN, THOMAS	DIRECTOR	83 HEWLETT AVE	POINT LOOKOUT, NY 11569
CRAVEN, WESLEY	WRITER-PRODUCER	2015 NAVY ST	SANTA MONICA, CA 90405
CRAVER, AARON	FOOTBALL	DOLPHINS, 2269 NW 199TH ST	MIAMI, FL 33056
CRAVIOTTE, DARLENE	SCREENWRITER	LEVIEN, 1202 N POINSETTIA DR	LOS ANGELES, CA 90046
CRAW FISH BAND	C & W GROUP	POST OFFICE BOX 5412	BUENA PARK, CA 90620
CRAWFORD, CARLOS	BASEBALL	POST OFFICE BOX 1886	COLUMBUS, GA 31902
CRAWFORD, CHERYL	THEATER PRODUCER	400 E 52ND ST	NEW YORK, NY 10022
CRAWFORD, CHRISTINA	AUTHORESS	3530 PINE VALLEY DR	SARASOTA, FL 34239
CRAWFORD, CINDY	MODEL	ELITE MODELS, 111 E 22ND ST	NEW YORK, NY 10010
CRAWFORD, ELBERT	FOOTBALL	PATRIOTS, FOXBORO STADIUM, RT #1	FOXBORO, MA 02035
CRAWFORD, FRANK B, JR	DIRECTOR-PRODUCER	7838 SHOSONE AVE	NORTHRIDGE, CA 91325
CRAWFORD, GERRY	BASEBALL UMPIRE	1 PINZON AVE	HAVERTON, PA 19083
CRAWFORD, GUY	WRITER-DIRECTOR	704 SEACLIFF WY	OCEANSIDE, CA 92056
CRAWFORD, HARRIET B	COMPOSER	5505 TOPEKA DR	TARZANA, CA 91356
CRAWFORD, JOANNA	TV WRITER	151 S EL CAMINO DR	BEVERLY HILLS, CA 90212
CRAWFORD, JOE	BASEBALL	525 NW PEACOCK BLVD	PORT SAINT LUCIE, FL 34986
CRAWFORD, JOHN	ACTOR	3800 BARHAM BLVD #303	LOS ANGELES, CA 90068
CRAWFORD, JOHNNY	ACTOR	2440 EL CONTENTO DR	LOS ANGELES, CA 90068
CRAWFORD, JOSEPH A	ACTOR	8800 KITTYHAWK AVE	LOS ANGELES, CA 90045
CRAWFORD, MICHAEL	ACTOR	HEATH, PARAMOUNT HOUSE	
		162-170 WARDOUR ST	LONDON W1V 3AT ENGLAND
CRAWFORD, RANDY	SINGER	911 SW PARK ST	GRAND RAPIDS, MI 49504
CRAWFORD, ROBERT	ARTIST	340 E 93RD ST #9-I	NEW YORK, NY 10128
CRAWFORD, ROBERT	FILM PRODUCER	PAN-ARTS PRODUCTIONS	
		4000 WARNER BLVD	BURBANK, CA 91522
CRAWFORD, STEVE	BASEBALL	RR #2, BOX 7-8	SALINA, OK 74365
CRAWFORD, WAYNE	FILM PRODUCER	9220 SUNSET BLVD #311	LOS ANGELES, CA 90069
CRAWFORD, WAYNE	SCREENWRITER	8955 BEVERLY BLVD	WEST HOLLYWOOD, CA 90048
CRAY, ROBERT, BAND	RHYTHM & BLUES GROUP	POST OFFICE BOX 210103	SAN FRANCISCO, CA 94121
CRAYNE, DIAN GIRARD	SCI-FI AUTHOR	POST OFFICE BOX 987	MANHATTAN BEACH, CA 90266
CRAYS, DURRELL ROYCE	WRITER-PRODUCER	11650 MAYFIELD AVE #1	LOS ANGELES, CA 90049
CREACH, EVERETT	STUNT DIRECTOR	9355 NOBLE AVE	SEPULVEDA, CA 91343
CREACH, PAPA JOHN	SINGER-GUITARIST	SYLVAKIAN, 1122 S LA JOLLA AVE	LOS ANGELES, CA 90035
CREASY, WILLIAM N, JR	DIRECTOR	8 OAK BEND	BRONXVILLE, NY 10708
CRECHALES, ANTHONY	WRITER	12031 HOFFMAN ST #6	STUDIO CITY, CA 91604
CREDLE, GARY	TV PRODUCER	WARNER BROTHERS TV	
		4000 WARNER BLVD	BURBANK, CA 91522
CREECH, ED	BASEBALL MGR-SCOUT	6850 LAWRENCE RD	LANTANA, FL 33462
CREED, DICK	FOOTBALL REFEREE	NFL, 410 PARK AVE	NEW YORK, NY 10022
CREEK, DOUG	BASEBALL	POST OFFICE BOX 5599	LITTLE ROCK, AR 72215
CREEK, MORGAN	FILM PRODUCER	1875 CENTURY PARK E #200	LOS ANGELES, CA 90067
CREEL, JOY BETH	ACTRESS	9744 WILSHIRE BLVD #308	BEVERLY HILLS, CA 90212
CREEL, LEANNA JOY	ACTRESS	9744 WILSHIRE BLVD #308	BEVERLY HILLS, CA 90212
CREEL, MONICA JOY	ACTRESS	9744 WILSHIRE BLVD #308	BEVERLY HILLS, CA 90212
CREGEEN, PETER	TV DIRECTOR-PRODUCER	38 STRAWBERRY HILL RD	
		TWICKENHAM	MIDDLESEX ENGLAND
CREIGHTON, ADAM	HOCKEY	BLACKHAWKS, 1800 W MADISON ST	CHICAGO, IL 60612
CREIGHTON, GEORGIA	ACTRESS-SINGER	73 W 68TH ST #3	NEW YORK, NY 10023
CREME, LOL	SINGER	JOHN GAYDON, MEDIALAB, LTD	
		CHELSEA WHARF, 15 LOTS RD	LONDON SW10 OQH ENGLAND
CRENNA, RICHARD	ACTOR-DIRECTOR	3951 VALLEY MEADOW RD	ENCINO, CA 91436
CRENNELL, ROMEO	FOOTBALL COACH	N Y GIANTS, GIANTS STADIUM	EAST RUTHERFORD, NJ 07073
CRENSHAW, BEN	GOLFER	1811 W 35TH ST	AUSTIN, TX 78703
CRENSHAW, KEN	BASEBALL TRAINER	POST OFFICE BOX 594	WELLAND, ONT L3B 5R3 CANADA
CRENSHAW, MARSHALL	SINGER-SONGWRITER	200 W 57TH ST #1403	NEW YORK, NY 10019
CRENSHAW, RANDEL L	COMPOSER	913 1/2 S OLIVE AVE	ALHAMBRA, CA 91803
CRESPO, FELIPE	BASEBALL	POST OFFICE BOX 1110	MYRTLE BEACH, SC 29578
CRESPO, MICHAEL	BASEBALL	POST OFFICE BOX 309	GASTONA, NC 28053
CRESSE, MARK	BASEBALL-COACH	1000 ELYSIAN PARK DR	LOS ANGELES, CA 90012

CRESSON, JAMES	THEATER PRODUCER	4001 AVENIDA DEL SOL	STUDIO CITY, CA	91604
CREW CUTS, THE	VOCAL GROUP	BROWN, 29 CEDAR ST	CRESKILL, NJ	07626
CREWS, TIM	BASEBALL	1000 ELYSIAN PARK DR	LOS ANGELES, CA	90012
CRIBBINS, BERNARD	ACTOR	HAMM CT, WEYBRIDGE	SURREY	ENGLAND
CRICHTON, CHARLES	FILM DIRECTOR	MLR, 200 FULHAM RD	LONDON SW10 9PN	ENGLAND
CRICHTON, MICHAEL	FILM WRITER-DIRECTOR	7605 SANTA MONICA BLVD #644	LOS ANGELES, CA	90046
CRICHTON, ROBIN	TV DIRECTOR-PRODUCER	EDINBURGH FILM PRODUCTIONS		
		9 MILE BURN, BY PENICUIK	MIDLOTHIAN EH26 9LT	SCOTLAND
CRICKETS, THE	ROCK & ROLL GROUP	BYRD, 1222 16TH AVE S	NASHVILLE, TN	37212
CRIGGER, HARRY	ACTOR	5709 SILVA ST	LAKEWOOD, CA	90713
CRIM, CHUCK	BASEBALL	POST OFFICE BOX 2000	ANAHEIM, CA	92803
CRIPPS, ERIK	DIRECTOR	POST OFFICE BOX 321	QUEEN ANNE, MD	21657
CRIQUI, DON	SPORTSCASTER	NBC SPORTS, 30 ROCKEFELLER PLZ	NEW YORK, NY	10112
CRISAFULLI, V JAMES	COMPOSER	245 N MANHATTAN PL	LOS ANGELES, CA	90004
CRISCI, EUGENE W	WRITER	1339 WESLEYAN AVE	WALNUT, CA	91789
CRISMAN, RONALD	TREASURER	PAVILION OFF BLDG, 109 STATE ST	MONTPELIER, VT	05602
CRISP, QUENTIN	ACTOR	46 E 3RD ST	NEW YORK, NY	10003
CRISP, TRACEY	ACTRESS	40 CENTRAL PARK S	NEW YORK, NY	10023
CRISPELL, EDDIE	ACTRESS	536 N LA CIENEGA BLVD #A	LOS ANGELES, CA	90048
CRIST, CLARK	BASEBALL COACH-SCOUT	POST OFFICE BOX 651	AUBURN, NY	13021
CRIST, JUDITH	FILM CRITIC	180 RIVERSIDE DR	NEW YORK, NY	10024
CRISTAL, LINDA	ACTRESS	9129 HAZEN DR	BEVERLY HILLS, CA	90210
CRISTOFER, MICHAEL	SCREENWRITER	151 S EL CAMINO DR	BEVERLY HILLS, CA	90212
CRISWELL, JEFF	FOOTBALL	N Y JETS, 1000 FULTON AVE	HEMPSTEAD, NY	11550
CRITCHFIELD, JAMES F	WRITER-PRODUCER	22 THORNTON AVE	VENICE, CA	90291
CROCE, ANTHONY SANTA	FILM-TV PRODUCER	ASCATO, 6650 SANTA MONICA BLVD	HOLLYWOOD, CA	90038
CROCKER, JAMES S	WRITER	15746 MORRISON ST	ENCINO, CA	91436
CROCKER, ROBERT R	CONDUCTOR	POST OFFICE BOX 5192	HACIENDA HEIGHTS, CA	91745
CROCKETT, BILLY	MUSIC ARRANGER	6576 CABOT DR	NASHVILLE, TN	37209
CROCKETT, GIBSON	CARTOONIST	4713 GREAT OAK RD	ROCKVILLE, MD	20853
CROCKETT, KARLENE	ACTRESS	4408 CAHUENGA BLVD	NORTH HOLLYWOOD, CA	91602
CROCKETT, RAY	FOOTBALL	LIONS, 1200 FEATHERSTONE RD	PONTIAC, MI	48432
CROCKETT, RUSTY	BASEBALL	POST OFFICE DRAWER 1207	ZEBULON, NC	27597
CROCKETT, UNCLE STEVE & LOG CAB	C & W GROUP	MUSKRAT, 44 N CENTRAL AVE	ELMSFORD, NY	10523
CROEL, MIKE	FOOTBALL	BRONCOS, 13655 BRONCOS PKWY	ENGLEWOOD, CO	80112
CROFT, MARY JANE	ACTRESS	POST OFFICE BOX 416	GLENEDEN BEACH, OR	97388
CROFT, SANDY	SINGER	BIRDSONG, 2714 WESTWOOD DR	NASHVILLE, TN	37204
CROFWELL, JAMES	ACTOR	4237 LONGRIDGE AVE	STUDIO CITY, CA	91604
CROGHAN, ANDY	BASEBALL	POST OFFICE BOX 22093	GREENSBORO, NC	27420
CROLL, MARK	TV DIRECTOR-PRODUCER	934 8TH AVE #2-B	NEW YORK, NY	10019
CROMARTIE, WARREN	BASEBALL	POST OFFICE BOX 419969	KANSAS CITY, MO	64141
CROME, JOHN	DIRECTOR	FLAT 4, THE WHITFIELDS		
		120 WHITFIELD ST	LONDON W1P 5RZ	ENGLAND
CROMELIN, CAREY	ACTRESS	CBS-TV, "THE GUIDING LIGHT"		
		222 E 44TH ST	NEW YORK, NY	10017
CROMER, ROY	BASEBALL SCOUT	250 STADIUM PLAZA	ST LOUIS, MO	63102
CROMER, TRIPP	BASEBALL	POST OFFICE BOX 5599	LITTLE ROCK, AR	72215
CROMMIE, KAREN	WRITER-PRODUCER	DGA, 7920 SUNSET BLVD, 6TH FL	LOS ANGELES, CA	90046
CROMWELL, NATE	BASEBALL	633 JESSAMINE ST	KNOXVILLE, TN	37917
CRON, CHRIS	BASEBALL	CANADIANS, 4601 ONTARIO ST	VANCOUVER, BC V5V 3H4	CANADA
CRON, CLAUDIA	ACTRESS	11300 W OLYMPIC BLVD #610	LOS ANGELES, CA	90064
CRONAN, MICHAEL	CARTOONIST	POST OFFICE BOX 191	SAN DIEGO, CA	92112
CRONE, RAY ..... (ORIOLES)	BASEBALL SCOUT	ORIOLE PARK, 333 W CAMDEN ST	BALTIMORE, MD	21201
CRONE, RAY ..... (ANGELS)	BASEBALL-SCOUT	POST OFFICE BOX 2000	ANAHEIM, CA	92803
CRONENBERG, DAVID	FILM WRITER-DIRECTOR	184 COTTINGHAM ST	TORONTO, ONT M4V 7C7	CANADA
CRONENWETH, JORDAN	CINEMATOGRAPHER	2276 S BEVERLY GLEN BLVD	LOS ANGELES, CA	90064
CRONIN, KEVIN	SINGER-SONGWRITER	17145 RANCHO ST	ENCINO, CA	91316
CRONIN, PATRICK	ACTOR	131 S ARDEN BLVD	LOS ANGELES, CA	90004
CRONIN, SHAWN	HOCKEY	JETS, 15-1430 MAROONS RD	WINNIPEG, MAN R3G 0L5	CANADA
CRONKITE, KATHY	ACTRESS-AUTHORESS	DMI, 250 W 57TH ST	NEW YORK, NY	10107
CRONKITE, WALTER	BROADCAST JOURNALIST	519 E 84TH ST	NEW YORK, NY	10028
CRONYN, HUME	ACTOR	63-23 CARLTON ST	REGO PARK, NY	11374
CRONYN, TANDY	ACTRESS	WM MORRIS, 1350 AVE OF AMERICAS	NEW YORK, NY	10019
CROOK, EDDY	MUSIC ARRANGER	107 CHIPPENDALE DR	HENDERSONVILLE, TN	37075
CROOKHAM, WADE	ACTOR	7100 HILLSIDE AVE #502	HOLLYWOOD, CA	90046
CROOM, CARL ERSKINE	ACTOR	813 W 103RD ST	LOS ANGELES, CA	90044
CROOM, SYLVESTER	FOOTBALL COACH	BUCCANEERS, 1 BUCCANEER PL	TAMPA, FL	33607
CROSBIE, ANNETTE	ACTRESS	23 WILTON CRESCENT, WIMBLEDON	LONDON SW19	ENGLAND
CROSBY, BOB	MUSICIAN	939 COAST BLVD	LA JOLLA, CA	92037
CROSBY, CATHY LEE	ACTRESS-MODEL	1223 WILSHIRE BLVD #404	SANTA MONICA, CA	90403
CROSBY, DAVID	SINGER-SONGWRITER	17351 RANCHO ST	ENCINO, CA	91316
CROSBY, DENISE	ACTOR	POST OFFICE BOX 5617	BEVERLY HILLS, CA	90213
CROSBY, ED	BASEBALL SCOUT	INDIANS, CLEVELAND STADIUM	CLEVELAND, OH	44114
CROSBY, GEORGE	PRODUCER	MCA/UNIVERSAL STUDIOS, INC		
		100 UNIVERSAL CITY PLAZA	UNIVERSAL CITY, CA	91608
CROSBY, JOAN	ACTRESS-WRITER	5036 STROHM AVE	NORTH HOLLYWOOD, CA	91601
CROSBY, KATHRYN GRANT	ACTRESS	POST OFFICE BOX 85	GANDA, NV	89411
CROSBY, LUCINDA	ACTRESS	4942 VINELAND AVE #200	NORTH HOLLYWOOD, CA	91601
CROSBY, MARY	ACTRESS	2875 S BARRYMORE DR	MALIBU, CA	90265
CROSBY, NORM	COMEDIAN-ACTOR	1400 LONDONDERRY PL	LOS ANGELES, CA	90069
CROSBY, PEGGY JOYCE	ACTRESS	13329 MAGNOLIA BLVD	SHERMAN OAKS, CA	91423
CROSBY, PHILIP	ACTOR	21801 PROVIDENCIA ST	WOODLAND HILLS, CA	91364
CROSBY, STEVE	FOOTBALL COACH	PATRIOTS, FOXBORO STADIUM, RT #1	FOXBORO, MA	02035
CROSBY, TODD	BASEBALL	POST OFFICE BOX 3448	SHREVEPORT, LA	71133
CROSBY, STILLS & NASH	ROCK & ROLL GROUP	THE RASCOFF/ZYSBLAT ORG, INC		

		110 W 57TH ST	NEW YORK, NY	10019
CROSETTI, FRANK	BASEBALL-CAOCH	65 W MONTEREY AVE	STOCKTON, CA	95204
CROSLAND, CHERYL	ACTRESS	518 N FAIRVIEW ST	BURBANK, CA	91505
CROSLAND, STEVEN JAY	WRITER	1426 1/2 PORTIA ST	LOS ANGELES, CA	90026
CROSNOE, CORY	BASEBALL	POST OFFICE BOX 4525	MACON, GA	31208
CROSS, ALISON	SCREENWRITER-TV PROD	1148 SIERRA ALTA WY	LOS ANGELES, CA	90069
CROSS, BEN	ACTOR	CONEJO LA PERDIZ		
		BARRIADA DE CONCELADA	MALAGA	SPAIN
CROSS, CHARLES	SINGER	BUN JAK, 331 PROSPECT ST	BERLING, NH	03570
CROSS, CHRISTOPHER	SINGER-SONGWRITER	POST OFFICE BOX 23021	SANTA BARBARA, CA	93103
CROSS, HOWARD	FOOTBALL	N Y GIANTS, GIANTS STADIUM	EAST RUTHERFORD, NJ	07073
CROSS, JAMES R	DIRECTOR-PRODUCER	WISTERIA PATH	SANDS POINT, NY	11050
CROSS, JEFF	FOOTBALL	DOLPHINS, 2269 NW 199TH ST	MIAMI, FL	33056
CROSS, JESSE	BASEBALL	CHIEFS, MAC ARTHUR STADIUM	SYRACUSE, NY	13208
CROSS, JUNE	TV PRODUCER	CBS NEWS, 524 W 57TH ST	NEW YORK, NY	10019
CROSS, MIKE	SINGER	POST OFFICE BOX 1556	GAINESVILLE, FL	32602
CROSS, WENDY	ACTRESS	FOX-ALBERT MGMT, 1697 BROADWAY	NEW YORK, NY	10019
CROSSFIELD, HENRY H	TV-COMEDY WRITER	TELE-TELE PRODS, 1158 5TH AVE	NEW YORK, NY	10029
CROSSMAN, DAVID	DIRECTOR	58 WICKHAM RD, BECKENHAM	KENT	ENGLAND
CROSSMAN, DOUG	HOCKEY	RED WINGS, 600 CIVIC CENTER DR	DETROIT, MI	48226
CROTTY, DANIEL	ACTOR	708 BAY ST #B	SANTA MONICA, CA	90405
CROUCH, BRYON	TV DIRECTOR	11450 BOLAS ST	LOS ANGELES, CA	90049
CROUCH, COLLEEN ZENK	ACTRESS	SEE - ZENK, COLLEEN		
CROUCH, ZACHARY	BASEBALL	3122 TORY ST	SACRAMENTO, CA	95827
CROUSE, LINDSAY	ACTRESS	ROSENBERG, 8428 MELROSE PL #C	LOS ANGELES, CA	90069
CROW, BILL	BASEBALL EXECUTIVE	136 S SYCAMORE	ELIZABETHTON, TN	37643
CROWDED HOUSE	ROCK & ROLL GROUP	POST OFFICE BOX 333	PRAHRAN, VIC 3181	AUSTRALIA
CROWDER, JOHN	ACTOR	7727 ORION AVE	VAN NUYS, CA	91406
CROWDER, TROY	HOCKEY	POST OFFICE BOX 504	EAST RUTHERFORD, NJ	07073
CROWE, CAMERON	FILM WRITER-PRODUCER	151 S EL CAMINO DR	BEVERLY HILLS, CA	90212
CROWE, CHRISTOPHER	WRITER-PRODUCER	11922 IREDELL ST	STUDIO CITY, CA	91604
CROWE, GORDON	THEATER PRODUCER	30 E 40TH ST	NEW YORK, NY	10016
CROWE, J D	CARTOONIST	POST OFFICE BOX 191	SAN DIEGO, CA	92112
CROWE, J D & THE NEW SOUTH	BLUEGRASS GROUP	POST OFFICE BOX 1210	HAMILTON, OH	45012
CROWE, RON	BASEBALL	POST OFFICE BOX 3448	SHREVEPORT, LA	71133
CROWE, SUSAN	SINGER	DELICATE ARTIST MANAGEMENT		
		1379 LA MARCHANT ST, HALIFAX	NOVA SCOTIA B3J 3K6	CANADA
CROWE, TONYA	ACTRESS	13030 MINDANAO WY #4	MARINA DEL REY, CA	90291
CROWELL, RODNEY	SINGER-SONGWRITER	1114 17TH AVE S #101	NASHVILLE, TN	37212
CROWELL, ROSANNE CASH	SINGER	SEE - CASH, ROSANNE		
CROWIN, TANYA NITA	ACTRESS	330 E 58TH ST #4-F	NEW YORK, NY	10022
CROWLEY, ED	ACTOR	142 W END AVE	NEW YORK, NY	10023
CROWLEY, JIM	BASEBALL	POST OFFICE BOX 10213	LYNCHBURG, VA	24506
CROWLEY, KATHLEEN	ACTRESS	9000 SUNSET BLVD #1200	LOS ANGELES, CA	90069
CROWLEY, KRISTIN	ACTRESS	POST OFFICE BOX 691736	LOS ANGELES, CA	90069
CROWLEY, PATRICIA	ACTRESS	150 W 56TH ST #4603	NEW YORK, NY	10019
CROWLEY, TERRY, SR	BASEBALL-COACH	TWINS, 501 CHICAGO AVE S	MINNEAPOLIS, MN	55415
CROWN, DANIEL	BASEBALL EXECUTIVE	N Y YANKEES, YANKEE STADIUM	BRONX, NY	10451
CROWN, JAMES	BASEBALL EXECUTIVE	N Y YANKEES, YANKEE STADIUM	BRONX, NY	10451
CROWN, LESTER	BASEBALL EXECUTIVE	N Y YANKEES, YANKEE STADIUM	BRONX, NY	10451
CROWNER, STUART W	WRITER-PRODUCER	4821 WESTPARK DR	NORTH HOLLYWOOD, CA	91601
CROWTHER, JOHN	SCREENWRITER	13900 PANAY WY #DN-15	MARINA DEL REY, CA	90292
CROWTHER, LESLIE	ACTOR-COMEDIAN	MARSH, 19 DENMARK ST	LONDON WC2H 8NA	ENGLAND
CROY, GEORGE E, JR	COMPOSER	20449 ACRE ST	CANOGA PARK, CA	91306
CROYDON, JOAN	ACTRESS	2 BEEKMAN PL	NEW YORK, NY	10022
CRUDUP, DERRICK	FOOTBALL	RAIDERS, 332 CENTER ST	EL SEGUNDO, CA	90245
CRUICKSHANKS, REID	ACTOR	4201 VIA MARINA	MARINA DEL REY, CA	90292
CRUISE, TOM	ACTOR	CAA, 9830 WILSHIRE BLVD	BEVERLY HILLS, CA	90212
CRUM, JAMES	TV DIRECTOR	5075 WESTSLOPE LN	LA CANADA, CA	91011
CRUMB, GEORGE	COMPOSER	240 KIRK LN	MEDIA, PA	19063
CRUMP, OWEN	WRITER-PRODUCER	9015 ELEVADO AVE	LOS ANGELES, CA	90069
CRUSADERS, THE	JAZZ GROUP	9034 SUNSET BLVD #250	LOS ANGELES, CA	90069
CRUSE	GOSPEL GROUP	2201 RIDGELY	FLINT, TX	75762
CRUSETURNER, WAYNE	WRITER	5345 SEPULVEDA BLVD #242	VAN NUYS, CA	91411
CRUSH	WRESTLER	POST OFFICE BOX 3859	STAMFORD, CT	06905
CRUTCHER, BRETT	DIRECTOR	DGA, 7920 SUNSET BLVD, 6TH FL	LOS ANGELES, CA	90046
CRUTCHLEY, ANTHONY	TV WRITER	103 N END AVE, FITZ JAMES AVE	LONDON W14	ENGLAND
CRUTCHLEY, ROSALIE	ACTRESS	LONDON MGT, 235-241 REGENT ST	LONDON W1R 4PH	ENGLAND
CRUZ, FAUSTO	BASEBALL	POST OFFICE BOX 11363	RENO, NV	89510
CRUZ, GREGORY NORMAN	ACTOR	1119 S ORME AVE	LOS ANGELES, CA	90023
CRUZ, IVAN	BASEBALL	TIGERS, 89 WHARNCLIFFE RD N	LONDON, ONT N6H 2A7	CANADA
CRUZ, JOSE	BASEBALL	B-15 JARDINES LAFAYETTE	ARROYO, PR	00615
CRUZ, JUAN	BASEBALL	POST OFFICE BOX 20849	CHARLESTON, SC	29413
CRUZ, JULIO	BASEBALL-INSTRUCTOR	40 ORCAS KEY	BELLEVUE, WA	98006
CRUZ, NICKY	AUTHOR	POST OFFICE BOX 25070	COLORADO SPRINGS, CO	80936
CRUZ, PABLO	BASEBALL SCOUT	POST OFFICE BOX 7000	PITTSBURGH, PA	15212
CRUZ, RUBEN	BASEBALL	POST OFFICE BOX 422229	KISSIMMEE, FL	34742
CRUZ, TOMMY	BASEBALL COACH	POST OFFICE BOX 9194	HAMPTON, VA	23670
CRUZADOS, THE	ROCK & ROLL GROUP	GERBER, 5260 SOUTHRIDGE AVE	LOS ANGELES, CA	90043
CRWIN, ELLIOT	BASEBALL EXECUTIVE	500 NORTON ST	ROCHESTER, NY	14621
CRYER, JON	ACTOR	10000 W WASHINGTON BLVD #3018	CULVER CITY, CA	90232
CRYSTAL, BILLY	ACTOR-COMEDIAN	MORRA, 801 WESTMOUNT DR	LOS ANGELES, CA	90069
CRYSTAL, RICHARD	ACTOR-WRITER	737 N MC CADDEN PL	LOS ANGELES, CA	90038
CRYSTALS, THE	VOCAL GROUP	MARS, 168 ORCHID DR	PEARL RIVER, NY	10965
CSENCSITS, CANDY	BODYBUILDER	RURAL DELIVERY #1, BOX 746	LENHARTSVILLE, PA	19534

Name	Occupation	Address	City/State	Zip/Country
CSICKO, DAVID	ARTIST	19 E PEARSON ST #33	CHICAGO, IL	60611
CSIKI, ANTHONY	TV DIRECTOR	6926 PACIFIC VIEW DR	LOS ANGELES, CA	90068
CUA, RICK	SINGER	NRC, 2901 HUNTWICK CT	RICHMOND, VA	23233
CUAN, SERGIO E	ARTIST	92 EDGEMONT PL	TEANECK, NJ	07666
CUBBAGE, MIKE	BASEBALL-COACH	METS, 126TH ST & ROOSEVELT AVE	FLUSHING, NY	11368
CUCUMBERS, THE	ROCK & ROLL GROUP	611 BROADWAY #526	NEW YORK, NY	10012
CUDDEBACK, ALEC RICHARD	WRITER	10757 HORTENSE ST #407	NORTH HOLLYWOOD, CA	91602
CUELLAR, BOBBY	BASEBALL	705 E 6TH ST	ALICE, TX	78332
CUELLER, BOBBY	BASEBALL-COACH	POST OFFICE BOX 4756	JACKSONVILLE, FL	32201
CUERVO, CARLOS	BASEBALL SCOUT	POST OFFICE BOX 7575	PHILADELPHIA, PA	19101
CUESTA, ANGEL M	DIRECTOR	5 RANDOLPH DR	DIX HILLS, NY	11746
CUEVAS, JOHNNY	BASEBALL	POST OFFICE BOX 507	DURHAM, NC	27702
CUEVAS, JOSE LUIS	ARTIST	BALEANA 109 SAN ANGEL	MEXICO CITY 20	MEXICO
CUEVAS; NELSON D	ACTOR	7674 OAKDALE AVE	CANOGA PARK, CA	91306
CUGAT, CHARO	SINGER	SEE - CHARO		
CULBERSON, CALVAIN	BASEBALL	POST OFFICE BOX 2001	CEDAR RAPIDS, IA	52406
CULBERSON, DON	BASEBALL	POST OFFICE BOX 4218	SOUTH BEND, IN	46634
CULBERTSON, DIANE	WRITER-EDITOR	POST OFFICE BOX 500	WASHINGTON, DC	20044
CULBERTSON, FRED W	WRITER	10975 PEORIA ST	SUN VALLEY, CA	91352
CULBRETH, FIELD	BASEBALL UMPIRE	235 MAIN ST #103	TRUSSVILLE, AL	35173
CULEA, MELINDA	ACTRESS	5504 CALHOUN AVE	VAN NUYS, CA	91401
CULHANE, DAVID	NEWS CORRESPONDENT	CBS NEWS, 524 W 57TH ST	NEW YORK, NY	10019
CULHANE, SHAMUS	DIRECTOR	325 W END AVE	NEW YORK, NY	10023
CULKIN, MACAULAY	ACTOR	ICM, 40 W 57TH ST	NEW YORK, NY	10019
CULLBERG, BIRGIT	CHOREOGRAPHER	SVENSKA RIKSTEATERN		
		RASUNDAVAGEN 150	S-171 30 SOLNA	SWEDEN
CULLEN, ALMA	TV WRITER	WRITERS GUILD, 430 EDGWARE RD	LONDON W2 1EH	ENGLAND
CULLEN, IAN	ACTOR-WRITER	STONE, 25 WHITEHALL	LONDON SW1A 2BS	ENGLAND
CULLEN, JOHN	HOCKEY	WHALERS, 1 CIVIC CENTER PLAZA	HARTFORD, CT	06103
CULLEN, PATRICIA	ACTRESS	150 E OLIVE AVE #111	BURBANK, CA	91502
CULLEN, PATRICIA	COMPOSER	6404 WILSHIRE BLVD #900	LOS ANGELES, CA	90048
CULLINANE, RUTH	ACTRESS	FELBER, 2126 N CAHUENGA BLVD	LOS ANGELES, CA	90068
CULLINGHAM, G MARK	TV DIRECTOR	POST OFFICE BOX 694	CENTER MORICHES, NY	11934
CULLITON, CAROLYN	TV WRITER	ICM, 40 W 57TH ST	NEW YORK, NY	10019
CULLITON, RICHARD	TV WRITER	ICM, 40 W 57TH ST	NEW YORK, NY	10019
CULLLEN, EDWARD F	DIRECTOR	250 W 57TH ST	NEW YORK, NY	10019
CULLUM, JOHN	ACTER-SINGER	ICM, 40 W 57TH ST	NEW YORK, NY	10019
CULLUM, KIMBERLY	ACTRESS	1717 N HIGHLAND AVE #414	LOS ANGELES, CA	90028
CULP, JASON	ACTOR	NBC-TV, "ANOTHER WORLD"		
		1268 E 14TH ST	BROOKLYN, NY	11230
CULP, JOE BILL	SINGER	ROUTE #9, BOX 340	BENTON, KY	42025
CULP, JOSEPH	ACTOR	9332 READCREST DR	BEVERLY HILLS, CA	90210
CULP, JOSH	ACTOR	9332 READCREST DR	BEVERLY HILLS, CA	90210
CULP, RACHEL	ACTRESS	9332 READCREST DR	BEVERLY HILLS, CA	90210
CULT, THE	ROCK & ROLL GROUP	30 PRIDSTOW PL	LONDON W2 5AE	ENGLAND
CULT JAM	ROCK & ROLL GROUP	2135 E 3RD ST	BROOKLYN, NY	11223
CULVER, CARMEN	TV WRITER	9046 SUNSET BLVD #202	LOS ANGELES, CA	90069
CULVER, GEORGE	BASEBALL-INSTRUCTOR	POST OFFICE BOX 7575	PHILADELPHIA, PA	19101
CULVER, MICHAEL	ACTOR	5 CLANCARTY RD	LONDON SW6	ENGLAND
CULVERHOUSE, HUGH F	FOOTBALL EXECUTIVE	BUCCANEERS, 1 BUCCANEER PL	TAMPA, FL	33607
CULVERHOUSE, JOY	FOOTBALL EXECUTIVE	BUCCANEERS, 1 BUCCANEER PL	TAMPA, FL	33607
CUMBERLAND, JOHN	BASEBALL COACH	POST OFFICE BOX 1420	WICHITA, KS	67201
CUMBERLAND GAP, THE	C & W GROUP	159 MADISON AVE #2-G	NEW YORK, NY	10016
CUMMING, MERVYN	FILM-TV DIRECTOR	45 HANGER VIEW WY, EALING	LONDON W3 OEY	ENGLAND
CUMMINGS, BOB	BASEBALL SCOUT	S F GIANTS, CANDLESTICK PARK	SAN FRANICSCO, CA	94124
CUMMINGS, BRIAN	ACTOR	25020 AVE BALITA	VALENCIA, CA	91355
CUMMINGS, CLYDE FOLEY	SINGER	POST OFFICE BOX 1793	KANSAS CITY, KS	66117
CUMMINGS, CONSTANCE	ACTRESS	66 OLD CHURCH ST	LONDON SW3	ENGLAND
CUMMINGS, DICK	BASEBALL TRAINER	POST OFFICE BOX 402	GENEVA, NY	14456
CUMMINGS, DREW	DIRECTOR	1528 NORTHVIEW DR	WESTLAKE VGE, CA	91362
CUMMINGS, IRVING, JR	WRITER	11516 MOORPARK ST #9	NORTH HOLLYWOOD, CA	91602
CUMMINGS, JOHN	BASEBALL	POST OFFICE BOX 9194	HAMPTON, VA	23670
CUMMINGS, MARILYN A	TV DIRECTOR	34 ANNAPOLIS RD	MILTON, MA	02186
CUMMINGS, MIDRE	BASEBALL	POST OFFICE BOX 842	SALEM, VA	24153
CUMMINGS, PARKE	WRITER	178 COMPO RD S	WESTPORT, CT	06880
CUMMINGS, QUINN	ACTRESS	SMITH, 121 N SAN VICENTE BLVD	BEVERLY HILLS, CA	90211
CUMMINGS, STEVE	BASEBALL	POST OFFICE BOX 6212	TOLEDO, OH	43614
CUMMINGS, TERRY	BASKETBALL	600 E MARKET ST #102	SAN ANTONIO, TX	78205
CUMMINS, BRIAN KENNAWAY	WRITER-PRODUCER	2372 CANYON DR	LOS ANGELES, CA	90068
CUMMINS, CLYDE FOLEY	GUITARIST	1310 TARRYWOOD LN	NASHVILLE, TN	37217
CUMMINS, JULIETTE, JR	ACTRESS	145 S FAIRFAX AVE #310	LOS ANGELES, CA	90036
CUNDEY, DEAN	CINEMATOGRAPHER	POST OFFICE BOX 2230	HOLLYWOOD, CA	90078
CUNDIFF, MEG	ARTIST	10500 LEE BLVD	LEAWOOD, KS	66206
CUNLIFFE, DAVID	TV DIRECTOR-PRODUCER	BRYAN DREW, MEZANNINE FLOOR		
		QUADRANT HOUSE, 80-82 REGENT ST	LONDON W1R 6AU	ENGLAND
CUNNEFF, RAY	SCREENWRITER	8955 BEVERLY BLVD	WEST HOLLYWOOD, CA	90048
CUNNEYWORTH, RANDY	HOCKEY	WHALERS, 1 CIVIC CENTER PLAZA	HARTFORD, CT	06103
CUNNIFF, HERB	TV DIRECTOR	NBC-TV, 3000 W ALAMEDA AVE	BURBANK, CA	91523
CUNNING & 20-20	C & W GROUP	2108-A WESTMOUNT RD, NW	CALGARY AB T2N 3N2	CANADA
CUNNINGHAM, BILLY	BASKETBALL EXECUTIVE	MIAMI HEAT, THE MIAMI ARENA	MIAMI, FL	33136
CUNNINGHAM, CORNELIUS	TV DIRECTOR	23 MITCHELL RD	PORT WASHINGTON, NY	11050
CUNNINGHAM, DEBRA	ACTRESS	2160 S BEVERLY GLEN BLVD	LOS ANGELES, CA	90025
CUNNINGHAM, EARL	BASEBALL	POST OFFICE BOX 4488	WINSTON-SALEM, NC	27115
CUNNINGHAM, GLENN	RUNNER	8 ROSEWOOD	CONWAY, AR	72032
CUNNINGHAM, GUNTHER	FOOTBALL COACH	POST OFFICE BOX 609609	SAN DIEGO, CA	92160

CUNNINGHAM, NEIL	TV PRODUCER	NBC-TV, 30 ROCKEFELLER PLAZA	NEW YORK, NY	10112
CUNNINGHAM, RANDALL	FOOTBALL	EAGLES, BROAD ST & PATTISON AVE	PHILADELPHIA, PA	19148
CUNNINGHAM, RANDALL "DUKE"	U S CONGRESSMAN	430 DAVIDSON ST #A	CHULA VISTA, CA	91910
CUNNINGHAM, ROBERT M	ARTIST	177 WAVERLY PL #4-F	NEW YORK, NY	10014
CUNNINGHAM, SEAN	BASEBALL TRAINER	POST OFFICE BOX 3566	WEST PALM BEACH, FL	33402
CUNNINGHAM, SEAN S	DIRECTOR-PRODUCER	155 LONG LOTS RD	WESTPORT, CT	06880
CUNNINGHAM, WALT	MUSIC ARRANGER	5292 EDMONDSON PL #1314	NASHVILLE, TN	37211
CUNNINGHAM, WALTER R	ASTRONAUT	520 POST OAK BLVD #130	HOUSTON, TX	77027
CUOMO, MARIO M	GOVERNOR	2 WORLD TRADE CTR #5700	NEW YORK, NY	10047
CURB, MIKE	RECORD PRODUCER	1820 CARLA RIDGE	BEVERLY HILLS, CA	90210
CURI, ALEX	ACTOR	2028 STEWART ST #B	SANTA MONICA, CA	90404
CURLESS, DICK	SINGER	TESSIER, 505 CANTON PASS	MADISON, TN	37115
CURLEY, GEORGE	ACTOR	415 W 50TH ST	NEW YORK, NY	10019
CURLEY, JOHN J	PUBLISHING EXECUTIVE	POST OFFICE BOX 500	WASHINGTON, DC	20044
CURLEY, THOMAS	PUBLISHING EXECUTIVE	POST OFFICE BOX 500	WASHINGTON, DC	20044
CURRAN, J JOSEPH, JR	ATTORNEY GENERAL	STATE HOUSE BUILDING	ANNAPOLIS, MD	21401
CURRAN, KEVIN P	TV WRITER	555 W 57TH ST #1230	NEW YORK, NY	10019
CURRAN, PAT	FOOTBALL EXECUTIVE	POST OFFICE BOX 609609	SAN DIEGO, CA	92160
CURRAN, ROBERT M	TV DIRECTOR-PRODUCER	MAC MILLAN PUB, 866 3RD AVE	NEW YORK, NY	10022
CURRENT, MATT	BASEBALL	POST OFFICE BOX 10336	CLEARWATER, FL	34617
CURRIE, AINSLIE	ACTRESS	SAVAGE, 6212 BANNER AVE	LOS ANGELES, CA	90038
CURRIE, CHERIE	ACTRESS	6512 CORBIN AVE	RESEDA, CA	91335
CURRIE, LOUISE	ACTRESS	GOOD, 1317 DELRESTO DR	BEVERLY HILLS, CA	90210
CURRIE, SONDRA	ACTRESS	LEVI, 3951 LONGRIDGE AVE	SHERMAN OAKS, CA	91423
CURRIER, LAUREN	SCREENWRITER	8955 BEVERLY BLVD	WEST HOLLYWOOD, CA	90048
CURRIER, TERRENCE P	ACTOR	1602 N MC KINLEY RD	ARLINGTON, VA	22205
CURRY, ANNE	ACTRESS	KOHNER, 9169 SUNSET BLVD	LOS ANGELES, CA	90069
CURRY, DAVID	WRITER-MUSICIAN	10514 WIPPLE ST	NORTH HOLLYWOOD, CA	91602
CURRY, DELL	BASKETBALL	310 N KINGS DR	CHARLOTTE, NC	28204
CURRY, JACK	TV CRITIC	POST OFFICE BOX 500	WASHINGTON, DC	20044
CURRY, JULIAN	ACTOR	MARTIN, 6-A DANBURY ST	LONDON N1 8JU	ENGLAND
CURRY, SHANE	FOOTBALL	POST OFFICE BOX 535000	INDIANPOLIS, IN	46253
CURRY, STEVE	BASEBALL	800 HOME RUN LN	MEMPHIS, TN	38104
CURRY, TIM	ACTOR	2401 WILD OAK DR	LOS ANGELES, CA	90068
CURRY, TOM	ARTIST	309 E LIVE OAK ST	AUSTIN, TX	78704
CURTEIS, IAN	WRITER-PRODUCER	THE MILL HOUSE, COIN ST ALDWYNS		
		CIRENCESTER	GLOS	ENGLAND
CURTICE, PATRICIA	TV PRODUCER	222 W 83RD ST	NEW YORK, NY	10024
CURTIN, HOYT	COMPOSER-MUSIC EXEC	3706 CAPSTAN CIR	WESTLAKE VILLAGE, CA	91361
CURTIN, JANE	ACTRESS	35 W 11TH ST	NEW YORK, NY	10011
CURTIN, JIM "E"	SINGER	JOYCE, 2028 CHESTNUT ST	PHILADELPHIA, PA	19103
CURTIN, VALERIE	ACTRESS-WRITER	15622 MEADOWGATE RD	ENCINO, CA	91316
CURTIS, CHAD	BASEBALL	POST OFFICE BOX 2000	ANAHEIM, CA	92803
CURTIS, CHRIS	BASEBALL	POST OFFICE BOX 309	GASTONA, NC	28053
CURTIS, CRAIG	BASEBALL	POST OFFICE BOX 824	BURLINGTON, IA	52601
CURTIS, DAN	DIRECTOR-PRODUCER	DGA, 7920 SUNSET BLVD, 6TH FL	LOS ANGELES, CA	90046
CURTIS, JAMIE LEE	ACTRESS	POST OFFICE BOX 2358	RUNNING SPRINGS, CA	92382
CURTIS, JOHN	MUSIC ARRANGER	1973 SUNNYSIDE DR	BRENTWOOD, TN	37027
CURTIS, JUDITH BREWER	COSTUME DESIGNER	2616 PURDUE AVE	LOS ANGELES, CA	90064
CURTIS, KEENE	ACTOR	6363 IVARENE AVE	HOLLYWOOD, CA	90068
CURTIS, KELLY	ACTRESS	GOLAN, 651 N KILKEA DR	LOS ANGELES, CA	90048
CURTIS, LIANE	ACTRESS	8730 SUNSET BLVD #220-W	LOS ANGELES, CA	90069
CURTIS, PHYLLIS	SINGER	80 HIGH ST	NEW HAVEN, CT	06511
CURTIS, RANDY	BASEBALL	POST OFFICE BOX 7845	COLUMBIA, SC	29202
CURTIS, ROBERT	DIRECTOR	3018 BENTLEY CT #2	SANTA MONICA, CA	90405
CURTIS, ROBERT ALLEN	TV WRI-DIR-PROD	POST OFFICE BOX 6188	MALIBU, CA	90265
CURTIS, ROBERT L	DIRECTOR	6143 PASEO CANYON DR	MALIBU, CA	90265
CURTIS, ROBIN	ACTRESS	10000 SANTA MONICA BLVD #305	LOS ANGELES, CA	90067
CURTIS, SHELLEY	TV DIRECTOR-PRODUCER	9315 LLOYDCREST DR	BEVERLY HILLS, CA	90210
CURTIS, SONNY	SINGER-SONGWRITER	ROUTE #2, BOX 61	DICKSON, TN	37055
CURTIS, TODD	ACTOR	2046 14TH ST #10	SANTA MONICA, CA	90405
CURTIS, TONY	ACTOR-PAINTER	11831 FOLKSTONE LN	LOS ANGELES, CA	90077
CURTIZ, GABRIEL	ACTOR	3625 LAUREL CANYON BLVD	NORTH HOLLYWOOD, CA	91604
CURTOLA, BOBBY	SINGER	576 WOLF WILLOW RD	EDMONDTON, ALB T5T 1E5	CANADA
CURWICK, STEPHEN J	SCREENWRITER	1402 9200 SUNSET BLVD #909 ST	LOS ANGELES, CA	90069
CURY, IVAN	TV DIRECTOR	2620 11TH ST #13	SANTA MONICA, CA	90405
CUSACK, BELINDA	TV DIRECTOR	202 E 35TH ST	NEW YORK, NY	10016
CUSACK, CYRIL	ACTOR	30 LOWER HATCH ST	DUBLIN 2	IRELAND
CUSACK, JOAN	ACTRESS	GEDDES, 8457 MELROSE PL #200	LOS ANGELES, CA	90069
CUSACK, JOHN	ACTOR	GEDDES, 8457 MELROSE PL #200	LOS ANGELES, CA	90069
CUSACK, SINEAD	ACTRESS	HUTTON, 200 FULHAM RD	LONDON SW14 7AH	ENGLAND
CUSEY, LEE	BASEBALL	POST OFFICE BOX 882	MADISON, WI	53701
CUSHING, PETER	ACTOR	SEASALTER, WHITSTABLE	KENT	ENGLAND
CUSTANCE, MICHAEL	TV DIRECTOR	BASE INTL, 13-14 GOLDEN SQ	LONDON W1R 3AG	ENGLAND
CUSTE, WILLIAM J, JR	ATTORNEY GENERAL	POST OFFICE BOX 94004	BATON ROUGE, LA	70804
CUTCHLOW, GAIL	ACTRESS	1693 E CALAVERAS ST	ALTADENA, CA	91001
CUTELL, LOU	ACTOR	1923 N CRESCENT HGTS BLVD	LOS ANGELES, CA	90069
CUTHBERTSON, IAIN	ACTOR-DIRECTOR	FRENCH'S, 52 HOLLAND PARK MEWS	LONDON W11	ENGLAND
CUTLER, BARRY	ACTOR	310 S KENMORE AVE #1	LOS ANGELES, CA	90020
CUTLER, BRIAN	ACTOR	5505 CLYBOURN AVE	NORTH HOLLYWOOD, CA	91601
CUTLER, DEVORAH	WRITER	1888 CENTURY PARK E #815	LOS ANGELES, CA	90067
CUTLER, JIM	BASEBALL EXECUTIVE	POST OFFICE BOX 936	BELOIT, WI	53511
CUTLER, LESLIE B	ACTOR-DIRECTOR	344 W 72ND ST	NEW YORK, NY	10023
CUTLER, RON "ROLAND"	WRITER	MARKSON, 44 GREENWICH AVE	NEW YORK, NY	10011
CUTLER, STAN	WRITER	BDP, 10637 BURBANK BLVD	NORTH HOLLYWOOD, CA	91601

CUTLER, WILLIAM	BASEBALL EXECUTIVE	2101 E BROADWAY #35	TEMPE, AZ	85282
CUTTER, LISE	ACTRESS	1423 NADEAU DR	LOS ANGELES, CA	90019
CUYLER, MILT	BASEBALL	1795 CHRISTIAN AVE	MACON, GA	31204
CUZZI, PHIL	BASEBALL UMPIRE	POST OFFICE BOX 608	GROVE CITY, OH	43123
CYNKO, CYNTHIA	ACTRESS	4740 VANTAGE AVE #2	NORTH HOLLYWOOD, CA	91607
CYPHER, JON	ACTOR	4053 SAN RAFAEL AVE	LOS ANGELES, CA	90065
CYPHERS, CHARLES	ACTOR	10949 FRUITLAND DR #17	STUDIO CITY, CA	91604
CYR, PAUL	HOCKEY	WHALERS, 1 CIVIC CENTER PLAZA	HARTFORD, CT	06103
CYRUS, BILLY RAY	SINGER-SONGWRITER	MC FADDEN, 818 18TH AVE S	NASHVILLE, TN	37203
CYTRON, SAMUEL D	COMPOSER	1620 N STANLEY AVE	LOS ANGELES, CA	90046
CZAJKOWSKI, JIM	BASEBALL	POST OFFICE DRAWER 4797	EL PASO, TX	79914
CZARKOWSKI, MARK	BASEBALL	POST OFFICE BOX 4756	JACKSONVILLE, FL	32201
CZONKA, LARRY	FOOTBALL	37256 HUNTER CAMP RD	LISBON, OH	44128
CZYS, KENNETH E	DIRECTOR	424 STAPLES AVE	SAN FRANCISCO, CA	94112

D O A	ROCK & ROLL GROUP	1505 W 2ND AVE #200	VANCOUVER, BC V6H 3Y4	CANADA
D'ABO, MARYAM	ACTRESS	9301 WILSHIRE BLVD #312	BEVERLY HILLS, CA	90210
D'ABO, OLIVIA	ACTRESS	335 N MAPLE DR #360	BEVERLY HILLS, CA	90210
D'ALESSIO, CLEMENTE	TV PRODUCER	271 MADISON AVE #700	NEW YORK, NY	10016
D'AMATO, ALFONSE M	U S SENATOR	520 HART SENATE OFFICE BLDG	WASHINGTON, DC	20510
D'AMATO, BRIAN	BASEBALL	POST OFFICE BOX 20849	CHARLESTON, SC	29413
D'AMATO, LARRY	BASEBALL-SCOUT	POST OFFICE BOX 7000	PITTSBURGH, PA	15212
D'AMBOISE, JACQUES	CHOREOGRAPHER	DANCE INSTITUTE, 244 W 71ST ST	NEW YORK, NY	10023
D'AMBROSIO, EUGENIA MARIA	ACTRESS-SINGER	142 BOND ST	BROOKLYN, NY	11217
D'ANGELO, BEVERLY	ACTRESS	ADDIS, 8444 WILSHIRE BL, 5TH FL	BEVERLY HILLS, CA	90211
D'ANGELO, JOSEPH F	TV PRODUCER	KING FEATURES, 216 E 45TH ST	NEW YORK, NY	10017
D'ANGELO, MIRELLA	ACTRESS	CAROL LEVY, VIA GIOSUE CARDUCCI	00187 ROME	ITALY
D'ANGELO, WILLIAM	PRODUCER	GROSSO, 767 3RD AVE, 15TH FL	NEW YORK, NY	10017
D'ANJOLELL, RICHARD M	DIRECTOR	140 SYCAMORE MILLS RD	MEDIA, PA	19063
D'ANTONI, PHILIP	WRITER-PRODUCER	8 E 63RD ST	NEW YORK, NY	10021
D'ARBANVILLE, PATTI	ACTRESS	432 15TH ST	SANTA MONICA, CA	90403
D'ARBY, TERENCE TRENT	SINGER-SONGWRITER	POST OFFICE BOX 910-L	LONDON NW1 9AQ	ENGLAND
D'ARCY, CATHLEEN	ACTRESS	RICHARD CATALDI, 180 7TH AVE	NEW YORK, NY	10011
D'ARNAL, DAVID	ACTOR	350 N GENESEE AVE #2	LOS ANGELES, CA	90036
D'MORAIS, JOSEPH	FILM EXECUTIVE	BLUE DOLPHIN FILM DISTRIBUTORS		
		15-17 OLD COMPTON ST	LONDON W1V 6JN	ENGLAND
D'ONOFRIO, VINCENT PHILLIP	ACTOR	4249 E BLVD 6	LOS ANGELES, CA	90066
D'USSEAU, LORING	DIRECTOR-PRODUCER	8420 KIRKWOOD DR	HOLLYWOOD, CA	90046
DA PRON, LOUIS	ACTOR-DANCER	5743 LAKE LINDERO DR	AGOURA, CA	91301
DA SILVA, MARIO	BODYBUILDER	POST OFFICE BOX 36643	LOS ANGELES, CA	90036
DA-KOTA	C & W GROUP	POST OFFICE BOX 9377	ASHEVILLE, NC	28815
DAAL, OMAR	BASEBALL	POST OFFICE BOX 28268	SAN ANTONIO, TX	78228
DAB, BARBARA	ACTRESS	5429 NEWCASTLE AVE #318	ENCINO, CA	91316
DABBS, HENRY	DIRECTOR-PRODUCER	24 WHITTIER DR	ENGLISHTOWN, NJ	07726
DABNEY, AUGUSTA	ACTRESS	NORTH MOUNTAIN DR	DOBBS FERRY, NY	10522
DABNEY, FRED	BASEBALL	POST OFFICE BOX 360007	BIRMINGHAM, AL	35236
DACQMINE, JACQUES	ACTOR	49 RUE DE VERSAILLES		
		DE MESNIL	SAINT-DENNIS 78320	FRANCE
DACYS, MILDA	ACTRESS	943 7TH ST #2	SANTA MONICA, CA	90403
DADARIO, JEAN L	TV DIRECTOR	1661 WILLIAMBRIDGE RD	BRONX, NY	10461
DADISMAN, E KING	COMPOSER	4384 LEMP AVE	STUDIO CITY, CA	91604
DAFFRON, TOM	BASEBALL TRAINER	ORIOLE PARK, 333 W CAMDEN ST	BALTIMORE, MD	21201
DAFOE, WILLEM	ACTOR	POST OFFICE BOX 654 (CANAL STA)	NEW YORK, NY	10013
DAGHE, NOELLE	GOLFER	2750 VOLUSA AVE #B	DAYTON BEACH, FL	32114
DAHEIM, JOHN J	DIRECTOR	937 S PACIFIC ST	OCEANSIDE, CA	92054
DAHL, ARLENE	ACTRESS	POST OFFICE BOX 116	SPARKILL, NY	10976
DAHLEN, ULF	HOCKEY	NORTH STARS, 7901 CEDAR AVE S	BLOOMINGTON, MN	55425
DAHLIA, RICHARD	ACTOR	400 W 43RD ST #26-J	NEW YORK, NY	10036
DAHLQUIST, CHRIS	HOCKEY	NORTH STARS, 7901 CEDAR AVE S	BLOOMINGTON, MN	55425
DAIGNEAULT, J J	HOCKEY	CANADIENS, 2313 ST CATHERINE ST	MONTREAL, QUE H3H 1N2	CANADA
DAILEY, IRENE	ACTRESS	NBC-TV, "ANOTHER WORLD"		
		1268 E 14TH ST	BROOKLYN, NY	11230
DAILEY, QUINTON	BASKETBALL	POST OFFICE BOX C-900911	SEATTLE, WA	98109
DAILEY, ROBERT	TV DIRECTOR	521 N RIVERSIDE DR #PH-1207	POMPANO BEACH, FL	33062
DAILY, BILL	ACTOR	5245 E COLDWATER CANYON AVE	VAN NUYS, CA	91401
DAILY, DON	ARTIST	57 ACADEMY RD	BALA CYNWYD, PA	19004
DAILY, ELIZABETH "E G "	ACT-SING-WRI-PROD	9595 WILSHIRE BLVD #3811	BEVERLY HILLS, CA	90212
DAILY, WILLIAM E	DIRECTOR	DGA, 7920 SUNSET BLVD, 6TH FL	LOS ANGELES, CA	90046
DAINES, DARREL R	COMPTROLLER	STATE CAPITOL BUILDING	CARSON CITY, NV	89710
DALBEY, DIANE	WRITER	4700 NATICK AVE #311	SHERMAN OAKS, CA	91403
DALE, CARROLL	FOOTBALL	109 SOUTHWOOD LN	BRISTOL, TN	37620
DALE, DICK	SINGER-GUITARIST	909 PARKVIEW AVE	LODI, CA	95240
DALE, DUCHESS	ACTRESS	11653 ACAMA ST	STUDIO CITY, CA	91604
DALE, FELICA	ACTRESS	10000 RIVERSIDE DR #6	TOLUCA LAKE, CA	91602
DALE, GROVER	DIRECTOR	12758 MULHOLLAND DR	BEVERLY HILLS, CA	90210
DALE, JIM	ACTOR	26 PEMBRIDGE VILLAS	LONDON W11	ENGLAND
DALE, JOHN R "JACK"	COMPOSER-CONDUCTOR	6836 ALDEA AVE	VAN NUYS, CA	91406

DALENA, PETE	BASEBALL-COACH	4951 N THORNE	FRESNO, CA	93704
DALESANDRO, JAMES	ACTOR	12926 RIVERSIDE DR #C	STUDIO CITY, CA	91423
DALESANDRO, MARK	BASEBALL	POST OFFICE BOX 1742	PALM SPRINGS, CA	92263
DALEY, RICHARD M	MAYOR	121 N MAIN ST	CHICAGO, IL	60602
DALEY, ROBERT A	FILM PRODUCER	POST OFFICE BOX 8509	UNIVERSAL CITY, CA	91608
DALEY, WILLIAM A	WRITER	19317 STARE ST	NORTHRIDGE, CA	91324
DALGARNO, BRAD	HOCKEY	NASSAU VETS MEMORIAL COLISEUM	UNIONDALE, NY	11553
DALLAS, GERSHON	BASEBALL	POST OFFICE BOX 1886	COLUMBUS, GA	31902
DALLENBACH, WALTER	WRITER	2682 WOODSTOCK RD	LOS ANGELES, CA	90046
DALLESANDRO, JOE	ACTOR	711 N FORMOSA AVE	LOS ANGELES, CA	90046
DALLIN, LEON	COMPOSER	POST OFFICE BOX 2400	SEAL BEACH, CA	90740
DALLIS, DR NICHOLAS P	CARTOON WRITER	7315 E MC LELLAN BLVD	SCOTTSDALE, AZ	85253
DALPHONSE, LORI	SINGER	BUN JAK, 331 PROSPECT ST	BERLING, NH	03570
DALRYMPLE, JEAN	THEATER PRODUCER	150 W 55TH ST	NEW YORK, NY	10019
DALTON, ABBY	ACTRESS	10000 SANTA MONICA BLVD #305	LOS ANGELES, CA	90067
DALTON, HARRY	BASEBALL EXECUTIVE	BREWERS, 201 S 46TH ST	MILWAUKEE, WI	53214
DALTON, LACY J	SINGER-SINGER	TBA MGMT, 147 BELL CANYON RD	BELL CANYON, CA	91307
DALTON, MIKE	BASEBALL	POST OFFICE BOX 450	BUFFALO, NY	14205
DALTON, ROBIN	FILM PRODUCER	127 HAMILTON TERR	LONDON NW8 9QR	ENGLAND
DALTON, TIMOTHY	ACTOR	SHARKEY, 15 GOLDEN SQ #315	LONDON W1R 3AG	ENGLAND
DALTON, WALTER	ACTOR-WRITER	4011 STONE CANYON AVE	SHERMAN OAKS, CA	91403
DALTRY, ROGER	SINGER-ACTOR	48 HARLEY HOUSE, MARLEBONE RD	LONDON NW1 5HL	ENGLAND
DALUISO, BRAD	FOOTBALL	FALCONS, SUWANEE RD AT I-85	SUWANEE, GA	30174
DALVA, ROBERT	WRITER-PRODUCER	THE ZOETROPE STUDIOS		
		1040 N LAS PALMAS AVE	HOLLYWOOD, CA	90038
DALVAN, ROBERT	ACTOR	58 RUE MICHEL-ANGE	PARIS 75017	FRANCE
DALY, CHUCK	BASKETBALL COACH	THE PALACE OF AUBURN HILLS		
		2 CHAMPIONSHIP DR	AUBURN HILLS, MI	48326
DALY, FRANK	ACTOR	400 W 43RD ST #10-P	NEW YORK, NY	10036
DALY, JOHN	FILM PRODUCER	HEMDALE, 7960 BEVERLY BLVD	LOS ANGELES, CA	90048
DALY, JOHN	GOLFER	POST OFFICE BOX 109601	PALM BCH GARDENS, FL	33418
DALY, JOYCE S	TV WRITER	630 1ST AVE	NEW YORK, NY	10016
DALY, PATRICK	BASEBALL EXECUTIVE	POST OFFICE BOX 6748	ROCKFORD, IL	61125
DALY, RAD	ACTOR	4258 BEVERLY GLEN BLVD	SHERMAN OAKS, CA	91423
DALY, ROBERT	FILM-TV EXECUTIVE	444 LORING AVE	LOS ANGELES, CA	90024
DALY, TIMOTHY	ACTOR	401 E 88TH ST #11-G	NEW YORK, NY	10128
DALY, TYNE	ACTRESS	2934 1/2 BEVERLY GLEN CIR #404	LOS ANGELES, CA	90077
DALZELL, JEFFREY	SINGER-GUITARIST	POST OFFICE BOX 158332	NASHVILLE, TN	37215
DALZIEL, DOUG	GOLFER	PGA SENIORS, 112 T P C BLVD	PONTE VEDRA BEACH, FL	32082
DAMANTE-SHAW, SUSAN	ACTRESS	8075 W 3RD ST #303	LOS ANGELES, CA	90048
DAMES, ROBERT L	WRITER-PRODUCER	5329 TOPEKA DR	TARZANA, CA	91356
DAMIAN, LEO	ACTOR	303 S CRESCENT HEIGHTS	LOS ANGELES, CA	90048
DAMIAN, MICHAEL	ACTOR-SINGER	24337 MULHOLLAND HWY	CALABASAS, CA	91302
DAMIAN DAME	RAP DUO	1627 W PEACHTREE RD		
		HILL TOP TOWERS #39-N	ATLANTA, GA	30312
DAMIANI, LEO G	CONDUCTOR	1909 MANNING ST	BURBANK, CA	91505
DAMMANN, APRIL A	WRITER	7065 HILLSIDE AVE	HOLLYWOOD, CA	90068
DAMMANN, JOE	ACTOR	1450 BELFAST DR	LOS ANGELES, CA	90069
DAMMANN, SARAH	ACTRESS	1450 BELFAST DR	LOS ANGELES, CA	90069
DAMMETT, BLACKIE	ACTOR	1004 N LA JOLLA AVE	LOS ANGELES, CA	90046
DAMON, MARK	ACTOR-FILM EXEC	2781 BENEDICT CANYON DR	BEVERLY HILLS, CA	90210
DAMON, STUART	ACTOR	367 N VAN NESS AVE	LOS ANGELES, CA	90004
DAMONE, VIC	SINGER	POST OFFICE BOX 2999	BEVERLY HILLS, CA	90213
DAMPHOUSSE, VINCENT	HOCKEY	MAPLE LEAFS, 60 CARLTON ST	TORONTO, ONT M5B 1L1	CANADA
DAMRON, DIRK	SINGER	MAGNUM, 8607 12TH AVE	EDMONTON, AB T5E 0G3	CANADA
DAMSKI, MELVIN	WRITER-PRODUCER	10533 DUNLEER DR	LOS ANGELES, CA	90064
DANA, BARBARA	ACTRESS-WRITER	ARKIN, 50 RIDGE DR	CHAPPAQUE, NY	10514
DANA, BILL	ACTOR-COMEDIAN	5965 PEACOCK RIDGE #563	RANCHO PLS VERDES, CA	90274
DANA, DEREK	BASEBALL	POST OFFICE BOX 1295	CLINTON, IA	52733
DANA, JUSTIN	ACTOR	16830 VENTURA BLVD #300	ENCINO, CA	91436
DANAHER, KAREN	TV DIRECTOR-PRODUCER	NBC-TV, 3000 W ALAMEDA AVE	BURBANK, CA	91523
DANAHY, MICHAEL	ACTOR	2235 1/2 N CAHUENGA BLVD	HOLLYWOOD, CA	90068
DANCE, CHARLES	ACTOR	DAWSON, 47 COURTFIELD RD #9	LONDON SW7 4DB	ENGLAND
DANCY, BILL	BASEBALL MANAGER	POST OFFICE BOX 10336	CLEARWATER, FL	34617
DANCY, JOHN	NEWS CORRESPONDENT	NBC NEWS, 4001 NEBRASKA AV, SW	WASHINGTON, DC	20016
DANDES, JONATHAN	BASEBALL EXECUTIVE	POST OFFICE BOX 450	BUFFALO, NY	14205
DANDO, PAT	BASEBALL	300 STADIUM WY	DAVENPORT, FL	33837
DANDREA, RONALD	FILM EXECUTIVE	8 HAMMER HILL RD	KOWLOON	HONG KONG
DANDRIDGE, DON	ACTOR	1527 S OGDEN DR	LOS ANGELES, CA	90019
DANDRIDGE, FRANK	TV WRITER	16633 VENTURA BLVD #1421	ENCINO, CA	91436
DANDRIDGE, RUBY	ACTRESS	BALDWIN HILLS CARE CENTER		
		3737 DON FELIPE DR	LOS ANGELES, CA	90008
DANE, HOLLY	ACTOR	13906 FIJI WY #344	MARINA DEL REY, CA	90292
DANE, LAWRENCE	ACTOR	1930 CENTURY PARK W #403	LOS ANGELES, CA	90067
DANEMAN, PAUL	ACTOR-WRITER	CHATTO AND LINNIT, LTD		
		PRINCE OF WALES THEATRE		
		COVENTRY ST	LONDON W1V 7FE	ENGLAND
DANESE, SHERA	ACTRESS	1004 N ROXBURY DR	BEVERLY HILLS, CA	90210
DANEYKO, KEN	HOCKEY	POST OFFICE BOX 504	EAST RUTHERFORD, NJ	07073
DANFORTH, DOUGLAS	BASEBALL EXECUTIVE	POST OFFICE BOX 7000	PITTSBURGH, PA	15212
DANFORTH, JOHN	U S SENATOR	ROUTE 1, BOX 91	NEWBURG, MO	65550
DANFORTH, JOHN C	U S SENATOR	1736 E SUNSHINE #705	SPRINGFIELD, MO	65804
DANGERFIELD, RODNEY	COMEDIAN-ACTOR	530 E 76TH ST	NEW YORK, NY	10021
DANGLE, DAVID	COSTUME DESIGNER	315 S RIDGLELEY DR	LOS ANGELES, CA	90036
DANIAS, STARR	ACTRESS-DANCER	30 W 63RD ST #30-K	NEW YORK, NY	10023

DANIEL, ANN	FILM-TV PRODUCER	PARAMOUNT TV, 5555 MELROSE AVE	LOS ANGELES, CA	90038
DANIEL, BETH	GOLFER	1350 ECHO DR	JUPITER, FL	33458
DANIEL, CLAY	BASEBALL SCOUT	REDS, 100 RIVERFRONT STADIUM	CINCINNATI, OH	45202
DANIEL, ELIOT H	CONDUCTOR	FAIR PLAY RD	SOMERSET, CA	95684
DANIEL, EUGENE	FOOTBALL	POST OFFICE BOX 535000	INDIANPOLIS, IN	46253
DANIEL, GERALD	COMPOSER-CONDUCTOR	1850 CARFAX	LONG BEACH, CA	90815
DANIEL, JAY	TV DIRECTOR	5933 ROD AVE	WOODLAND HILLS, CA	91367
DANIEL, JIM	BASEBALL TRAINER	12000 STADIUM RD	ADELANTO, CA	92301
DANIEL, MARGARET TRUMAN	AUTHORESS	830 PARK AVE	NEW YORK, NY	10028
DANIEL, MIKE	BASEBALL	POST OFFICE BOX 3566	WEST PALM BEACH, FL	33402
DANIEL, ROD	FILM DIRECTOR	19414 OLIVOS DR	TARZANA, CA	91356
DANIEL, TAMARA	ACTRESS	149 W 13TH ST	NEW YORK, NY	10011
DANIEL'S, MR JACK, ORIGINAL	C & W GROUP	POST OFFICE BOX 667418	NASHVILLE, TN	37202
DANIELEWSKI, TAD	TV DIRECTOR	3263 N SHADOWBROOK CIR	PROVO, UT	84604
DANIELLE	ACTRESS	17029 DEVONSHIRE ST #155	NORTHRIDGE, CA	91325
DANIELS, BILL	COLUMNIST	5700 WILSHIRE BLVD #120	LOS ANGELES, CA	90036
DANIELS, CHARLIE, BAND	C & W GROUP	POST OFFICE BOX 882	MOUNT JULIET, TN	37122
DANIELS, DAVID	FOOTBALL	SEAHAWKS, 11220 NE 53RD ST	KIRKLAND, WA	98033
DANIELS, DONNA	MUSIC PRODUCER	320 W 108TH ST #5-B	NEW YORK, NY	10025
DANIELS, FAITH	TV HOST	30 ROCKEFELLER PLAZA #333	NEW YORK, NY	10112
DANIELS, GARY HUGH	ACTOR	420 N ONTARIO ST	BURBANK, CA	91505
DANIELS, IRWIN	TV EXECUTIVE	COLUMBIA PICTURES CORP		
		50-30 NORTHERN BLVD	LONG ISLAND CITY, NY	11101
DANIELS, JACK B	DIRECTOR	349 N OAKHURST DR	BEVERLY HILLS, CA	90210
DANIELS, JOE	FOOTBALL COACH	N Y JETS, 1000 FULTON AVE	HEMPSTEAD, NY	11550
DANIELS, KAL	BASEBALL	1060 W ADDISON ST	CHICAGO, IL	60613
DANIELS, MEL	BASKETBALL	PACERS, 300 E MARKET ST	INDIANAPOLIS, IN	46204
DANIELS, PAUL	MAGICIAN	140 BECKETT RD, DONCASTER	SOUTH YORKSHIRE	ENGLAND
DANIELS, PHIL	ACTOR	HOPE, 108 LEONARD ST	LONDON EC2A 4RH	ENGLAND
DANIELS, RUDY	ACTOR	5811 VALLEY OAK DR	HOLLYWOOD, CA	90068
DANIELS, STANLEY E	WRITER-PRODUCER	4754 ALONZO AVE	ENCINO, CA	91316
DANIELS, WILLIAM	ACTOR	10000 SANTA MONICA BLVD #305	LOS ANGELES, CA	90067
DANIELSON, ROCKY	CINEMATOGRAPHER	7715 SUNSET BLVD #150	LOS ANGELES, CA	90046
DANIELSON, SHELL	ACTRESS	ABC-TV, "GENERAL HOSPITAL"		
		4151 PROSPECT AVE	BURBANK, CA	91523
DANILOFF, NICHOLAS	NEWS CORRESPONDENT	2400 "N" ST, NW	WASHINGTON, DC	20037
DANILOVA, ALEXANDRA	BALLERINA	100 W 57TH ST	NEW YORK, NY	10019
DANK, HARRY	TV PRODUCER	CBS NEWS, 524 W 57TH ST	NEW YORK, NY	10019
DANKWORTH, JOHN	MUSICIAN-COMPOSER	THE OLD RECTORY, WAVENDON	MILTON KEYNES MK17 8LT	ENGLAND
DANNE, TERRY D	CONDUCTOR	10681 VALLEYHEART DR	STUDIO CITY, CA	91604
DANNEMEYER, WILLIAM E	U S CONGRESSMAN	1235 N HARBOR BLVD #100	FULLERTON, CA	92632
DANNER, BLYTHE	ACTRESS	304 21ST ST	SANTA MONICA, CA	90402
DANNER, DEON	BASEBALL	POST OFFICE BOX 3746, HILL STA	AUGUSTA, GA	30904
DANNING, SYBIL	ACTRESS-MODEL	3575 W CAHUENGA BLVD #200	LOS ANGELES, CA	90068
DANNIS, RAY	ACTOR	965 LAKE ST	VENICE, CA	90291
DANNY & THE JUNIORS	VOCAL GROUP	POST OFFICE BOX 1987	STUDIO CITY, CA	91604
DANO, LINDA	ACTRESS-TV HOST	NBC-TV, "ANOTHER WORLD"		
		1268 E 14TH ST	BROOKLYN, NY	11230
DANO, ROYAL	ACTOR	517 20TH ST	SANTA MONICA, CA	90402
DANSBY, SUSAN	TV DIRECTOR	CBS-TV, "THE GUIDING LIGHT"		
		222 E 44TH ST	NEW YORK, NY	10017
DANSKA, DOLORES F	TV DIRECTOR-PRODUCER	711 AMSTERDAM AVE	NEW YORK, NY	10025
DANSKA, HERBERT	WRITER-PRODUCER	9601 WILSHIRE BLVD #642	BEVERLY HILLS, CA	90210
DANSON, TED	ACTOR	31504 VICTORIA POINTE RD	MALIBU, CA	90265
DANTE, DANELLO	TV DIRECTOR-PRODUCER	2 W 32ND ST #200	NEW YORK, NY	10001
DANTE, JOE	FILM DIRECTOR	2321 HOLLY DR	HOLLYWOOD, CA	90068
DANTE, MICHAEL	ACTOR	9827 BURGEN AVE	LOS ANGELES, CA	90034
DANTINE, NIKI	ACTRESS	707 N PALM DR	BEVERLY HILLS, CA	90210
DANTZSCHER, BARRY C	WRITER	13414 OXNARD ST	VAN NUYS, CA	91401
DANUS, BONNIE BENOV	WRITER	400 N OAKHURST DR #101	BEVERLY HILLS, CA	90210
DANUS, RICHARD CHRISTIAN	WRITER	432 N PALM DR	BEVERLY HILLS, CA	90210
DANYLUK, KELLY	ACTRESS	8228 SUNSET BLVD #311	LOS ANGELES, CA	90046
DANZA, JOHN	DIRECTOR	140 GLENWOOD AVE	LEONIA, NJ	07605
DANZA, TONY	ACTOR	19722 TRULL BROOK DR	TARZANA, CA	91356
DANZIG, MICHAEL H	WRITER	1920 HILLCREST RD #9	LOS ANGELES, CA	90068
DANZIGER, DENNIS JAY	TV WRITER	10549 NORTHVALE RD	LOS ANGELES, CA	90064
DANZY, ROSCOE, JR	COMPOSER	13120 VICTORY BLVD #11	VAN NUYS, CA	91401
DAOPOULOS, JIM	FOOTBALL REFEREE	NFL, 410 PARK AVE	NEW YORK, NY	10022
DAPAR, JOSEPHINE N	COMPOSER	6910 DAY ST	TUJUNGA, CA	91042
DAPRATO, WILLIAM J	ACTOR	220 E 27TH ST	NEW YORK, NY	10016
DARBO, PATRIKA	ACTRESS	346 N AVON ST	BURBANK, CA	91505
DARBY, DAVID	TV DIRECTOR-PRODUCER	235 W 108TH ST #63	NEW YORK, NY	10025
DARBY, KIM	ACTRESS	4255 LAUREL GROVE AVE	STUDIO CITY, CA	91604
DARCY, GEORGINE	ACTRESS	7044 LOS TILOS RD	HOLLYWOOD, CA	90068
DARDEN, GEORGE "BUDDY"	U S CONGRESSMAN	376 POWDER SPRINGS STREET	MARIETTA, GA	30064
DARDEN, SEVERN	ACTOR	3220 LAUREL CANYON BLVD	STUDIO CITY, CA	91604
DARENSBERT, JOE	MUSICIAN	22233 AVE SAN LUIS	WOODLAND HILLS, CA	91364
DARGET, CHANTAL	ACTRESS	15 RUE DE MIROMESNIL	PARIS 75008	FRANCE
DARIAN, ANITA	ACTRESS-SOPRANO	800 W END AVE	NEW YORK, NY	10025
DARION, JOE	LYRICIST	PINNACLE RD	LYME, NH	03768
DARION, SIDNEY	TV EXECUTIVE-WRITER	276 RIVERSIDE DR	NEW YORK, NY	10025
DARK, ALVIN	BASEBALL	103 CRANBERRY WY	EASLEY, SC	29640
DARK, GREGORY	FILM DIRECTOR	158-A SOUTHFIELD RD	CHISWICK W4 1AN	ENGLAND
DARK, JOHN	FILM PRODUCER	ROLLINS, BURDOCK, HUNTER, LTD		
		BRAINTREE HOUSE, BRAINTREE RD		

	....	RUISLIP	MIDDLESEX HA4 OYA .... ENGLAND
DARKROOM	ROCK & ROLL GROUP ...	1505 W 2ND AVE #200	VANCOUVER, BC V6H 3Y4 ..... CANADA
DARLEY, CHRIS	DIRECTOR	4092 DEERVALE DR	SHERMAN OAKS, CA 91403
DARLEY, DICK	TV DIRECTOR	3383 TARECO DR	HOLLYWOOD, CA 90068
DARLING, GARY	BASEBALL UMPIRE	319 S ABILENE	GILBERT, AZ 85234
DARLING, JENNIFER	ACTRESS	606 N LARCHMONT BLVD #309	LOS ANGELES, CA 90004
DARLING, JOAN	WRITER-DIRECTOR	POST OFFICE BOX 6700	TESUQUE, NM 87574
DARLING, KERRI ANNE	ACTRESS	NBC-TV, "ANOTHER WORLD"	....
	....	1268 E 14TH ST	BROOKLYN, NY 11230
DARLING, RON	BASEBALL	ATHLETICS'S, OAKLAND COLISEUM ...	OAKLAND, CA 94621
DARLOW, MICHAEL	WRITER-PRODUCER	THE PRODUCTION CENTRE	....
	....	40-44 CLIPSTONE ST	LONDON W1P 7EA .... ENGLAND
DARNELL, CYTHIA	TV WRITER	9100 SUNSET BLVD #340	LOS ANGELES, CA 90069
DARNELL, DEEDE	ACTRESS-DANCER	175 W 12TH ST	NEW YORK, NY 10011
DARNELL, JAY	BASEBALL EXECUTIVE ..	POST OFFICE BOX 3566	WEST PALM BEACH, FL 33402
DARNEY, TONI	ACTRESS	7 W 16TH ST	NEW YORK, NY 10011
DARR, CHERIE	ACTRESS	KJAR, 10653 RIVERSIDE DR	TOLUCA LAKE, CA 91602
DARR, DEBORAH	ACTRESS	275 W 96TH ST #9-G	NEW YORK, NY 10025
DARR, LISA	ACTRESS	SHAPIRO, 2147 N BEACHWOOD DR #2 .	LOS ANGELES, CA 90068
DARRELL, DAVID	ACTOR	7309 FRANKLIN AVE #102	LOS ANGELES, CA 90046
DARRELL, JOHNNY	SINGER	TOM HALEY, ROUTE #2, BOX 309-B ..	WINSLOW, AR 72959
DARREN, JAMES	ACTOR-SINGER	POST OFFICE BOX 1088	BEVERLY HILLS, CA 90213
DARRID, WILLIAM	WRITER	4035 MADELIA AVE	SHERMAN OAKS, CA 91403
DARRIEUX, DANIELLE	ACTRESS	3 QUAI MALAIVAIS	75006 PARIS .... FRANCE
DARROW, HENRY	ACTOR	KOHNER, 9169 SUNSET BLVD	LOS ANGELES, CA 90069
DARROW, WHITNEY, JR	CARTOONIST	331 NEWTOWN TURNPIKE	WILTON, CT 06897
DART, IRIS RAINER	AUTHORESS	SEE - RAINER DART, IRIS	....
DART, JUSTIN	ACTOR	8480 BEVERLY BLVD	LOS ANGELES, CA 90048
DART, STEPHEN M	WRITER	3555 BEVERLY GLEN BLVD	SHERMAN OAKS, CA 91423
DARTLAND, DOTTIE	TV WRITER	151 S EL CAMINO DR	BEVERLY HILLS, CA 90212
DARVAS, TEDDY	FILM EDITOR	1 ROTHWELL ST	LONDON NW1 8YH .... ENGLAND
DARWIN, BOB	BASEBALL-SCOUT	1000 ELYSIAN PARK DR	LOS ANGELES, CA 90012
DARWIN, DANNY	BASEBALL	FENWAY PARK, 4 YAWKEY WY	BOSTON, MA 02215
DARWIN, JEFF	BASEBALL	POST OFFICE BOX 9194	HAMPTON, VA 23670
DARWISH, TIFFANY	SINGER-SONGWRITER ...	SEE - TIFFANY	....
DASCENZO, DOUG	BASEBALL	1060 W ADDISON ST	CHICAGO, IL 60613
DASCHLE, THOMAS A	U S SENATOR	615 S MAIN ST	ABERDEEN, SD 57401
DASH, SAM	ATTORNEY	110 NEWLANDS	CHEVY CHASE, MD 20015
DASH, STACEY	ACTRESS	8730 SUNSET BLVD #220-W	LOS ANGELES, CA 90069
DASPIT, JIM	BASEBALL	POST OFFICE BOX 2887	VERO BEACH, FL 32961
DASSIN, JULES	ACTOR-DIRECTOR	25 ANAGNOSTOPOULON ST	ATHENS .... GREECE
DASTOR, SAM	ACTOR	45 CHOUMERT RD	LONDON SE15 4AR .... ENGLAND
DATTILO, KRISTIN	ACTRESS	MTA, 9320 WILSHIRE BL, 3RD FL ...	BEVERLY HILLS, CA 90212
DATTOLA, KEVIN	BASEBALL	POST OFFICE BOX 2769	HUNTSVILLE, AL 35804
DATZ, DAVID	ACTOR	1066 CONCHA ST	ALTADENA, CA 91001
DATZ, JEFF	BASEBALL	86 S MAIN ST	MULLICA HILL, NJ 08062
DAUBER, PHILIP	WRITER-PRODUCER	1454 CEDAR ST	BERKELEY, CA 94702
DAUER, RICH	BASEBALL-COACH	POST OFFICE BOX 418	SAINT CHARLES, IL 60174
DAUGHERTY, BRAD	BASKETBALL	POST OFFICE BOX 5000	RICHFIELD, OH 44286
DAUGHERTY, HERSCHEL	TV DIRECTOR	925 SANTE FE DR	ENCINITAS, CA 92024
DAUGHERTY, JACK	BASEBALL	POST OFFICE BOX 90111	ARLINGTON, TX 76004
DAUGHERTY, PAT	BASEBALL SCOUT	6850 LAWRENCE RD	LANTANA, FL 33462
DAUGHTON, JAMES	ACTOR	415 N SYCAMORE AVE #102	LOS ANGELES, CA 90036
DAUGHTRY, MIKE	BASEBALL SCOUT	POST OFFICE BOX 90111	ARLINGTON, TX 76004
DAULTON, DARREN	BASEBALL	POST OFFICE BOX 7575	PHILADELPHIA, PA 19101
DAUPHIN, PHIL	BASEBALL	POST OFFICE DRAWER 1207	ZEBULON, NC 27597
DAUPHIN, RUDA	FILM PRODUCER	401-E 80TH ST	NEW YORK, NY 10021
DAVALILLO, POMPEYO	BASEBALL-SCOUT	POST OFFICE BOX 2000	ANAHEIM, CA 92803
DAVALOS, ELYSSA	ACTRESS	1958 VESTAL AVE	LOS ANGELES, CA 90026
DAVALOS, RICHARD	ACTOR	1958 VESTAL AVE	LOS ANGELES, CA 90026
DAVE & SUGAR	C & W GROUP	POST OFFICE BOX 2977	HENDERSONVILLE, TN 37077
DAVENALL, ANTHONY	TV DIRECTOR	37 RANDOLPH CRESCENT	LONDON W9 .... ENGLAND
DAVENPORT, ADELL	BASEBALL	POST OFFICE BOX 3448	SHREVEPORT, LA 71133
DAVENPORT, CLAIRE	ACTRESS	27 ROYAL CRESCENT	LONDON W11 .... ENGLAND
DAVENPORT, JIM	BASEBALL (MAJORS) ...	TIGERS, TIGER STADIUM	DETROIT, MI 48216
DAVENPORT, JIM	BASEBALL (MINORS) ...	80 OTTAWA ST N	HAMILTON, ONT L8H 3Z1 ..... CANADA
DAVENPORT, MARY	ACTRESS	215 E 68TH ST	NEW YORK, NY 10021
DAVENPORT, NIGEL	ACTOR	5 ANN'S CLOSE, KINNERTON ST	LONDON SW1 .... ENGLAND
DAVENPORT, RALPH W	TV WRITER	1221 N KINGS RD #PH-405	LOS ANGELES, CA 90069
DAVEY, DON	FOOTBALL	PACKERS, 1265 LOMBARDI AVE	GREEN BAY, WI 54307
DAVI, ROBERT	ACTOR	11448 GERALD AVE	GRANADA HILLS, CA 91344
DAVIAU, ALLEN	CINEMATOGRAPHER	2249 BRONSON HILL DR	LOS ANGELES, CA 90069
DAVICH, MARTIN A	COMPOSER	3480 BARHAM BLVD #215	LOS ANGELES, CA 90068
DAVICH, MARTY	ACTOR	530 S GREENWOOD LN	PASADENA, CA 91107
DAVID, ANDRE	BASEBALL MANAGER	2908 ASHLEY ST	KINGSPORT, TN 37664
DAVID, ART	ACTOR	POST OFFICE BOX 11	BLOOMBURG, TX 75556
DAVID, B J	DIRECTOR	POST OFFICE BOX 2175	TOLUCA LAKE, CA 91602
DAVID, BOWEN	CONDUCTOR	379 GRANT PARK PL, SE	ATLANTA, GA 30315
DAVID, CLIVE	RECORD EXECUTIVE	88 CENTRAL PARK W	NEW YORK, NY 10019
DAVID, CYNTHIA	ACTRESS	928 1/2 S SERRANO AVE	LOS ANGELES, CA 90006
DAVID, DAVID H	COMPOSER-CONDUCTOR ..	POST OFFICE BOX 24-B30	LOS ANGELES, CA 90024
DAVID, GREG	BASEBALL	800 HOME RUN LN	MEMPHIS, TN 38104
DAVID, HAL	LYRICIST	5253 LANKERSHIM BLVD	NORTH HOLLYWOOD, CA 91061
DAVID, HUGH	ACT-WRI-DIR	WILDACRE, 10 PARSONAGE, WINDSOR .	BERKSHIRE SL4 5EN .... ENGLAND
DAVID, HUMPHREY	ACTOR	16 ARLINGTOPN TERR	EDGEWATER, NJ 07020

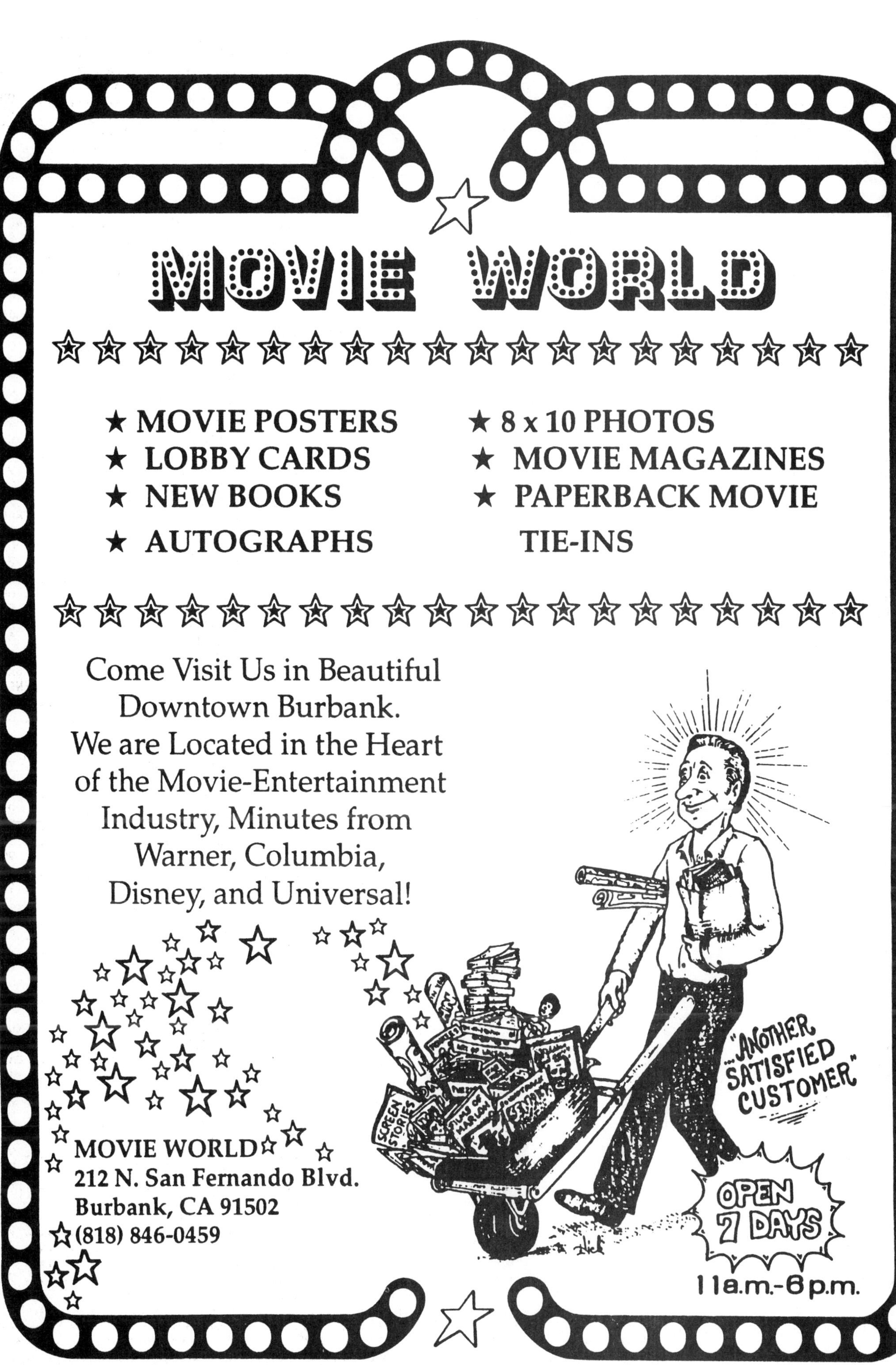
MOVIE WORLD
★ MOVIE POSTERS
★ LOBBY CARDS
★ NEW BOOKS
★ AUTOGRAPHS
★ 8 x 10 PHOTOS
★ MOVIE MAGAZINES
★ PAPERBACK MOVIE TIE-INS
Come Visit Us in Beautiful Downtown Burbank. We are Located in the Heart of the Movie-Entertainment Industry, Minutes from Warner, Columbia, Disney, and Universal!
"ANOTHER ...SATISFIED CUSTOMER"
SCREEN STORIES
MOVIE WORLD
212 N. San Fernando Blvd.
Burbank, CA 91502
(818) 846-0459
OPEN 7 DAYS
11a.m.-6p.m.

DAVID, JERRY	WRITER-PRODUCER	1250 LA COLLINA DR	BEVERLY HILLS, CA	90210
DAVID, JOANNA	ACTRESS	25 MAIDA AVE	LONDON W2	ENGLAND
DAVID, LARRY	TV WRITER	UTA, 9560 WILSHIRE BL, 5TH FL	BEVERLY HILLS, CA	90212
DAVID, LOLITA	ACTRESS	SEE - DAVIDOVICH, LOLITA		
DAVID, MACK	COMPOSER	1575 TOLEDO CIR	PALM SPRINGS, CA	92262
DAVID, MARJORIE S	WRITER	ICM, 8899 BEVERLY BLVD	LOS ANGELES, CA	90048
DAVID, MARK	BASEBALL	10233 96TH AVE	EDMONTON, ALB TK5 0A5	CANADA
DAVID, MICHAEL ROBERT	WRITER	10442 GLORIA AVE	GRANADA HILLS, CA	91344
DAVID, PIERRE	FILM PRODUCER	9000 SUNSET BLVD #915	LOS ANGELES, CA	90069
DAVID, SAUL	WRITER	13216 CUMPSTON ST	VAN NUYS, CA	91401
DAVID & DAVID	ROCK & ROLL GROUP	1830 S ROBERTSON BLVD #201	LOS ANGELES, CA	90035
DAVID & THE GIANTS	GOSPEL GROUP	POST OFFICE BOX 723591	ATLANTA, GA	30339
DAVIDOFF, LOLITA	ACTRESS	1030 N STATE ST #4C	CHICAGO, IL	60610
DAVIDOWITZ, LENNY	VIDEOTAPE EDITOR	EMPIRE VIDEO, 216 E 45TH ST	NEW YORK, NY	10017
DAVIDS, HOLLACE G	WRITER	1880 CENTURY PARK E #618	LOS ANGELES, CA	90067
DAVIDS, PAUL	SCREENWRITER	435 HOLLAND AVE	LOS ANGELES, CA	90042
DAVIDSON, ARLENE	SCREENWRITER	R/W/G, 8428 MELROSE PL #C	LOS ANGELES, CA	90069
DAVIDSON, BILL	BASEBALL EXECUTIVE	POST OFFICE BOX 11002	CHATTANOOGA, TN	37401
DAVIDSON, BOAZ	DIRECTOR	CANNON, 9911 W PICO BLVD	LOS ANGELES, CA	90035
DAVIDSON, BOB	BASEBALL	POST OFFICE BOX 36407	LOUISVILLE, KY	40233
DAVIDSON, DOUG	ACTOR	3641 E CHEVY CHASE DR	GLENDALE, CA	91206
DAVIDSON, EILEEN	ACTRESS	620 VOLLAMBROSA DR	PASADENA, CA	91107
DAVIDSON, EMIL G	WRITER	12125 HOLLYGLEN PL	STUDIO CITY, CA	91604
DAVIDSON, GORDON	DIRECTOR	165 MABERY RD	SANTA MONICA, CA	90402
DAVIDSON, JEFF	FOOTBALL	BRONCOS, 13655 BRONCOS PKWY	ENGLEWOOD, CO	80112
DAVIDSON, JERRY	TALENT AGENT	3800 BARHAM BLVD #303	LOS ANGELES, CA	90068
DAVIDSON, JOHN, JR	ACTOR	21243 VENTURA BLVD #101	WOODLAND HILLS, CA	91364
DAVIDSON, JOHN, SR	SINGER-ACTOR	6051 SPRING VALLEY RD	HIDDEN HILLS, CA	91302
DAVIDSON, JOY	MEZZO SOPRANO	5751 SW 74TH AVE	MIAMI, FL	33143
DAVIDSON, KENNY	FOOTBALL	STEELERS, 300 STADIUM CIR	PITTSBURGH, PA	15212
DAVIDSON, MARK	BASEBALL	4385 TUTT BLVD	COLORADO SPRINGS, CO	80922
DAVIDSON, MARTIN	FILM WRITER-DIRECTOR	1505 VIEWSITE TERR	LOS ANGELES, CA	90069
DAVIDSON, MONTY	SINGER	POST OFFICE BOX 1987	STUDIO CITY, CA	91604
DAVIDSON, ROD	ACTOR	10359 MONTE MAR DR	LOS ANGELES, CA	90064
DAVIDSON, SANDY	COSTUME DESIGNER	13949 VENTURA BLVD #309	SHERMAN OAKS, CA	91423
DAVIDSON, SATCH	BASEBALL UMPIRE	2400 WESTHEIMER ST #209-W	HOUSTON, TX	77098
DAVIDSON, WILLIAM J	WRITER	1666 THAYER AVE #202	LOS ANGELES, CA	90024
DAVIDSON, WILLIAM M	BASKETBALL EXECUTIVE	THE PALACE OF AUBURN HILLS		
		2 CHAMPIONSHIP DR	AUBURN HILLS, MI	48326
DAVIDSON, ZEKE	ACTOR	POST OFFICE BOX 347	ANNA, IL	62906
DAVIES, BRIAN	ACTOR	6355 N LEMON AVE	SAN GABRIEL, CA	91775
DAVIES, DANIEL	ACTOR	4558 CAMELLIA AVE	NORTH HOLLYWOOD, CA	91602
DAVIES, FREDRICK	ACTOR	30 LINCOLN PLAZA #26-W	NEW YORK, NY	10023
DAVIES, GAIL	SINGER-SONGWRITER	246 CHEROKEE RD	NASHVILLE, TN	37205
DAVIES, GARETH	TV PRODUCER	MTM, 4024 RADFORD AVE	STUDIO CITY, CA	91604
DAVIES, JACK	SCREENWRITER	8955 BEVERLY BLVD	WEST HOLLYWOOD, CA	90048
DAVIES, JANICE	ACTRESS	4558 CAMELLIA AVE	NORTH HOLLYWOOD, CA	91602
DAVIES, JOHN RHYS	ACTOR	CCA MGMT, 4 CT LODGE		
		48 SLOANE SQ	LONDON SW1	ENGLAND
DAVIES, KAREN	GOLFER	2750 VOLUSA AVE #B	DAYTON BEACH, FL	32114
DAVIES, LANE	ACTOR	9220 SUNSET BLVD #625	LOS ANGELES, CA	90069
DAVIES, LAURA	GOLFER	2750 VOLUSA AVE #B	DAYTON BEACH, FL	32114
DAVIES, RICHARD B	TV DIRECTOR	6939 MAMMOTH AVE	LOS ANGELES, CA	90026
DAVIES, WILLIAM C	CONDUCTOR	5548 ELMER AVE	NORTH HOLLYWOOD, CA	91601
DAVILA, JOSE	BASEBALL	POST OFFICE BOX 611	WATERLOO, IA	50704
DAVINS, JIM	BASEBALL	2850 W 20TH AVE	DENVER, CO	80211
DAVIS, AL	FOOTBALL EXECUTIVE	RAIDERS, 332 CENTER ST	EL SEGUNDO, CA	90245
DAVIS, ALLAN	DIRECTOR	ICM, 388-396 OXFORD ST	LONDON W1	ENGLAND
DAVIS, ALTOVISE	ACTRESS-MODEL	279 S BEVERLY DR #1006	BEVERLY HILLS, CA	90212
DAVIS, ALVIN	BASEBALL	POST OFFICE BOX 2000	ANAHEIM, CA	92803
DAVIS, ANDREW	FILM DIRECTOR	BLOOM/DEKOM, 9255 SUNSET BLVD	LOS ANGELES, CA	90069
DAVIS, ANGELA	AUTHOR-LECTURER	SAN FRANCISCO STATE UNIV		
		ETHNIC STUDIES DEPT		
		1600 HOLLOWAY AVE	SAN FRANCISCO, CA	94132
DAVIS, ANN B	ACTRESS	1427 BEAVER RD	AMBRIDGE, PA	15003
DAVIS, ANTONE	FOOTBALL	EAGLES, BROAD ST & PATTISON AVE	PHILADELPHIA, PA	19148
DAVIS, B J	DIRECTOR	712 WILSHIRE BLVD #50	SANTA MONICA, CA	90401
DAVIS, BALOS	BASEBALL SCOUT	POST OFFICE BOX 419969	KANSAS CITY, MO	64141
DAVIS, BENJAMIN	LT GENERAL	1001 WILSON BLVD #906	ARLINGTON, VA	22209
DAVIS, BILL	TV DIRECTOR	CAA, 9830 WILSHIRE BLVD	BEVERLY HILLS, CA	90212
DAVIS, BILLY NEWTON	SINGER	157 PRINCESS ST #300	TORONTO, ONT M5A 4M4	CANADA
DAVIS, BILLY, JR	SINGER	POST OFFICE BOX 7905	BEVERLY HILLS, CA	90212
DAVIS, BRAD	BASKETBALL	REUNION ARENA, 777 SPORTS ST	DALLAS, TX	75207
DAVIS, BRANDY	BASEBALL-SCOUT	N Y YANKEES, YANKEE STADIUM	BRONX, NY	10451
DAVIS, BRIAN	FOOTBALL	SEAHAWKS, 11220 NE 53RD ST	KIRKLAND, WA	98033
DAVIS, BUTCH	BASEBALL	CHIEFS, MAC ARTHUR STADIUM	SYRACUSE, NY	13208
DAVIS, BUTCH	FOOTBALL COACH	COWBOYS, 1 COWBOYS PARKWAY	IRVING, TX	75063
DAVIS, BYRON M	CONDUCTOR	1236 CEDAREDGE CT	LOS ANGELES, CA	90041
DAVIS, CHARLIE	FOOTBALL COACH	PACKERS, 1265 LOMBARDI AVE	GREEN BAY, WI	54307
DAVIS, CHILI	BASEBALL	TWINS, 501 CHICAGO AVE S	MINNEAPOLIS, MN	55415
DAVIS, CHRIS	BASEBALL	RED SOX, CHAIN O'LAKES PARK	WINTER HAVEN, FL	33880
DAVIS, CLIFTON	ACTOR-CLERGYMAN	500 N ROSSMORE AVE #502	LOS ANGELES, CA	90004
DAVIS, CLINT	BASEBALL	POST OFFICE BOX 3783	SAVANNAH, GA	31414
DAVIS, CLIVE	RECORD EXECUTIVE	ARISTA RECORDS, 6 W 57TH ST	NEW YORK, NY	10019
DAVIS, CRITT	ACTOR	9235 1/2 DOHENY RD	LOS ANGELES, CA	90069

DAVIS, DANGEROUS DANNY	WRESTLING REFEREE	POST OFFICE BOX 3859	STAMFORD, CT 06905
DAVIS, DANIEL	ACTOR	500 E 85TH ST #22-G	NEW YORK, NY 10028
DAVIS, DANNY	TRUMPETER	550 PHARR RD #620	ATLANTA, GA 30505
DAVIS, DARREL "MOUSE"	FOOTBALL COACH	LIONS, 1200 FEATHERSTONE RD	PONTIAC, MI 48432
DAVIS, DARRELL	FOOTBALL	N Y JETS, 1000 FULTON AVE	HEMPSTEAD, NY 11550
DAVIS, DAVID	WRITER-PRODUCER	DGA, 7920 SUNSET BLVD, 6TH FL	LOS ANGELES, CA 90046
DAVIS, DAVID M	FILM-TV PROD-EXEC	AMERICAN, 1776 BROADWAY, 9TH FL	NEW YORK, NY 10019
DAVIS, DEXTER	FOOTBALL	POST OFFICE BOX 888	PHOENIX, AZ 85001
DAVIS, DON	COMPOSER-CONDUCTOR	4146 LANKERSHIM BLVD #300	NORTH HOLLYWOOD, CA 91602
DAVIS, DON G	DIRECTOR	POST OFFICE BOX 1127	NEW YORK, NY 10023
DAVIS, DONALD I	DIRECTOR	34 CRYSTAL COVE	LAGUNA BEACH, CA 92651
DAVIS, DOUG	BASEBALL	POST OFFICE BOX 75089	OKLAHOMA CITY, OK 73147
DAVIS, EARLENE	ACTRESS	KJAR, 10653 RIVERSIDE DR	TOLUCA LAKE, CA 91602
DAVIS, ED	THEATER PRODUCER	THEATRE NOW, 1515 BROADWAY	NEW YORK, NY 10036
DAVIS, ELIAS S	TV WRITER	3311 LEDGEWOOD DR	LOS ANGELES, CA 90068
DAVIS, ELLEN S	WRITER	10 COLUMBUS CIR #1300	NEW YORK, NY 10019
DAVIS, ERIC	BASEBALL	1000 ELYSIAN PARK DR	LOS ANGELES, CA 90012
DAVIS, ERIC	FOOTBALL	S F 49ERS, 4949 CENTENNIAL BL	SANTA CLARA, CA 95054
DAVIS, ERIK	ACTOR	2820 3RD ST #3	SANTA MONICA, CA 90405
DAVIS, GEENA	ACTRESS	6201 SUNSET BLVD #7	LOS ANGELES, CA 90028
DAVIS, GENE A	WRITER-PRODUCER	ESSENCE COMM, 1500 BROADWAY	NEW YORK, NY 10036
DAVIS, GEORGE BUD	DIRECTOR	DGA, 7920 SUNSET BLVD, 6TH FL	LOS ANGELES, CA 90046
DAVIS, GERRY	BASEBALL UMPIRE	616 CAMELLIA LN	APPLETON, WI 54915
DAVIS, GLENN	BASEBALL	ORIOLE PARK, 333 W CAMDEN ST	BALTIMORE, MD 21201
DAVIS, GRAY	COMPTROLLER	STATE CAPITOL BUILDING	SACRAMENTO, CA 95814
DAVIS, GREG	FOOTBALL	POST OFFICE BOX 888	PHOENIX, AZ 85001
DAVIS, GWEN	TV WRITER-NOVELIST	LITTLE, BROWN & COMPANY	
		205 LEXINGTON AVE	NEW YORK, NY 10016
DAVIS, H FREDERICK	CONDUCTOR	5738 SIMPSON AVE	NORTH HOLLYWOOD, CA 91607
DAVIS, HAL	DIRECTOR	441 E 20TH ST	NEW YORK, NY 10010
DAVIS, IVOR	COLUMNIST	N Y TIMES SYN, 130 5TH AVE	NEW YORK, NY 10011
DAVIS, J RODNEY	DIRECTOR	HARMONY, 2921 W ALAMEDA AVE	BURBANK, CA 91505
DAVIS, JACK	CARTOONIST	MAD MAGAZINE, 485 MADISON AVE	NEW YORK, NY 10022
DAVIS, JAMES H	SINGER-COMPOSER	POST OFFICE BOX 15826	BATON ROUGE, LA 70895
DAVIS, JAY	BASEBALL	525 NW PEACOCK BLVD	PORT SAINT LUCIE, FL 34986
DAVIS, JIM	CARTOONIST	UNITED FEATURE, 200 PARK AVE	NEW YORK, NY 10166
DAVIS, JIM	GOVERNOR-SONGWRITER	POST OFFICE BOX 15826	BATON ROUGE, LA 70895
DAVIS, JIM	WRITER	10960 WILSHIRE BLVD #924	LOS ANGELES, CA 90024
DAVIS, JOAN	ACTRESS	9057 NEMO ST #A	WEST HOLLYWOOD, CA 90069
DAVIS, JODY	BASEBALL	RR #1, BEN HILL DR	OAKWOOD, GA 30566
DAVIS, JOEL	WRITER	DAVIES, 3518 W CAHUENGA BLVD	LOS ANGELES, CA 90068
DAVIS, JOHN	BASEBALL EXECUTIVE	1060 W ADDISON ST	CHICAGO, IL 60613
DAVIS, JOHN	FOOTBALL	BILLS, 1 BILLS DR	ORCHARD PARK, NJ 14127
DAVIS, JOHN	TV DIRECTOR-PRODUCER	20 BROCKLEY AVE, STANMORE	MIDDLESEX ENGLAND
DAVIS, JOHN E	COMPOSER	5105 VARNA AVE	SHERMAN OAKS, CA 91423
DAVIS, JOHNNY	BASKETBALL COACH	1 CNN CENTER #405, SOUTH TOWER	ATLANTA, GA 30303
DAVIS, JUDY	ACTRESS (AMERICAN)	ICM, 8899 BEVERLY BLVD	LOS ANGELES, CA 90048
DAVIS, JUDY	ACTRESS (ENGLISH)	CHATTO AND LINNIT, LTD	
		PRINCE OF WALES THEATRE	
		COVENTRY ST	LONDON W1V 7FE ENGLAND
DAVIS, JULIE	TV PRODUCER	290 W END AVE	NEW YORK, NY 10023
DAVIS, KAREN L	WRITER	WILLIAM M CAUTHERN	
		13949 WEDDINGTON ST	VAN NUYS, CA 91401
DAVIS, KENNETH	FOOTBALL	BILLS, 1 BILLS DR	ORCHARD PARK, NJ 14127
DAVIS, LARRY	BASEBALL TRAINER	ATHLETICS'S, OAKLAND COLISEUM	OAKLAND, CA 94621
DAVIS, LARRY M	DIRECTOR	714 N SWEETZER AVE #5	LOS ANGELES, CA 90069
DAVIS, LINDSAY W	COSTUME DESIGNER	13949 VENTURA BLVD #309	SHERMAN OAKS, CA 91423
DAVIS, LOWELL	ARTIST	FLATLANDER GALL	
		107 E 3RD ST	CARTHAGE, MO 64836
DAVIS, LUTHER	WRITER	LANTZ, 888 7TH AVE, 25TH FLOOR	NEW YORK, NY 10106
DAVIS, LUTHER	WRITER-PRODUCER	PICTURES, 18 W 55TH ST	NEW YORK, NY 10019
DAVIS, MAC	SINGER-ACTOR	759 NIMES RD	LOS ANGELES, CA 90077
DAVIS, MADELYN MARTIN	TV WRITER	142 N BRIGHTON ST	BURBANK, CA 91506
DAVIS, MARIPAT	SINGER	4219 W OLIVE AVE #245	BURBANK, CA 91505
DAVIS, MARK	BASEBALL (ANGELS)	POST OFFICE BOX 2000	ANAHEIM, CA 92803
DAVIS, MARK	BASEBALL (ROYALS)	POST OFFICE BOX 4064	ATLANTA, GA 30302
DAVIS, MARTHA	SINGER-SONGWRITER	NEECE, 10513 CUSHDON AVE	LOS ANGELES, CA 90064
DAVIS, MARVIN	FILM EXECUTIVE	1120 SCHUYLER RD	BEVERLY HILLS, CA 90210
DAVIS, MATT	BASEBALL	POST OFFICE BOX 21727	SAN FRANCISCO, CA 95151
DAVIS, MIKE	BASEBALL	1501 W 16TH ST	INDIANAPOLIS, IN 46202
DAVIS, MIKE	SPORTS WRITER	POST OFFICE BOX 500	WASHINGTON, DC 20044
DAVIS, OSSIE	ACT-WRI-DIR	44 CORTLAND AVE	NEW ROCHELLE, NY 10801
DAVIS, PATTI	ACTRESS	959 22ND ST	SANTA MONICA, CA 90403
DAVIS, PAUL	ARTIST	14 E 4TH ST	NEW YORK, NY 10012
DAVIS, PAUL	SINGER-SONGWRITER	POST OFFICE BOX 7308	CARMEL, CA 93921
DAVIS, PAUL E	TV DIRECTOR	PARDO, 121 W 72ND ST #14-C	NEW YORK, NY 10023
DAVIS, PESHA PAUL	DIRECTOR	8242 HILLSIDE AVE	LOS ANGELES, CA 90069
DAVIS, PETER	FILM-TV PRODUCER	1438 N GOWER ST #401	LOS ANGELES, CA 90028
DAVIS, PETER	TV WRITER-PRODUCER	320 CENTRAL PARK W	NEW YORK, NY 10025
DAVIS, PHYLLIS	ACTRESS	HERA, 3575 W CAHUENGA, 2ND FL	LOS ANGELES, CA 90068
DAVIS, RICHARD	BASEBALL EXECUTIVE	POST OFFICE BOX 1211	NORFOLK, VA 23502
DAVIS, RICK	BASEBALL	STARS, 850 LAS VEGAS BLVD N	LAS VEGAS, NV 89101
DAVIS, ROBERT P	SCREENWRITER	555 W 57TH ST #1230	NEW YORK, NY 10019
DAVIS, ROBERT W	U S CONGRESSMAN	144 S 2ND ST	ALPENA, MI 49707
DAVIS, RUBY DEE	ACTRESS-WRITER	44 CORTLAND AVE	NEW ROCHELLE, NY 10801

DAVIS, RUEBEN	FOOTBALL	BUCCANEERS, 1 BUCCANEER PL	TAMPA, FL 33607
DAVIS, RUSS	BASEBALL	ALBANY YANKEES, HERITAGE PARK	ALBANY, NY 12211
DAVIS, SAMMI	ACTRESS	COULSON, 37 BERWICK ST	LONDON W1V 3RF ENGLAND
DAVIS, SCOTT	FOOTBALL	RAIDERS, 332 CENTER ST	EL SEGUNDO, CA 90245
DAVIS, SKEETER	SINGER-SONGWRITER	508 SEWARD RD	BRENTWOOD, TN 37027
DAVIS, SPENCER, GROUP	ROCK & ROLL GROUP	1 KINDERKAMACK RD #100	ORADELL, NJ 07649
DAVIS, STANLEY	MUSIC EDITOR	4378 CAHUENGA BLVD	NORTH HOLLYWOOD, CA 91602
DAVIS, STEVE	BASEBALL TRAINER	1090 N EUCLID AVE	SARASOTA, FL 34237
DAVIS, STORM	BASEBALL	ORIOLE PARK, 333 W CAMDEN ST	BALTIMORE, MD 21201
DAVIS, SYLVIA	ACTRESS	484 W 43RD ST #14-F	NEW YORK, NY 10036
DAVIS, TERRY	BASKETBALL	MIAMI HEAT, THE MIAMI ARENA	MIAMI, FL 33136
DAVIS, TIM	BASEBALL	RED SOX, CHAIN O'LAKES PARK	WINTER HAVEN, FL 33880
DAVIS, TODD	ACTOR	RAPER, 159 N SHOSHONE ST	FLAGSTAFF, AZ 86001
DAVIS, TOM	BASEBALL SCOUT	1060 W ADDISON ST	CHICAGO, IL 60613
DAVIS, TRAVIS	FOOTBALL	POST OFFICE BOX 535000	INDIANPOLIS, IN 46253
DAVIS, TYRONE	SINGER-SONGWRITER	POST OFFICE BOX 4603	MACON, GA 31208
DAVIS, VERONICA	ACTRESS	11712 MOORPARK ST #204	STUDIO CITY, CA 91604
DAVIS, VIVEKA	ACTRESS	11712 MOORPARK ST #204	STUDIO CITY, CA 91604
DAVIS, WALTER	BASKETBALL	POST OFFICE BOX 4658	DENVER, CO 80204
DAVIS, WALTER HALSEY	SCREENWRITER	433 N CAMDEN DR #600	BEVERLY HILLS, CA 90210
DAVIS, WENDELL	FOOTBALL	BEARS, 250 N WASHINGTON RD	LAKE FOREST, IL 60045
DAVIS, WILLIE	BASEBALL	4419 BUENA VISTA #203	DALLAS, TX 75202
DAVISON, BRUCE	ACTOR	POST OFFICE BOX 57593	SHERMAN OAKS, CA 91403
DAVISON, DAVEY	ACTRESS	10000 RIVERSIDE DR #6	TOLUCA LAKE, CA 91602
DAVISON, JON	FILM PRODUCER	POST OFFICE BOX 5617	BEVERLY HILLS, CA 90213
DAVISON, MICHELLE	ACTRESS	CBS-TV, "THE BOLD & BEAUTIFUL"	
		7800 BEVERLY BLVD #3371	LOS ANGELES, CA 90036
DAVISON, PETER S	COMPOSER	1924 EUCLID ST	SANTA MONICA, CA 90404
DAVITT, MARK	ACTOR	8831 SUNSET BLVD #402	LOS ANGELES, CA 90069
DAVRO, BOBBY	COMEDIAN	TVS STUDIO	SOUTHAMPTON ENGLAND
DAW, TERENCE	TV DIRECTOR	DALZELL, 17 BROAD CT #12	LONDON WC2B 5QN ENGLAND
DAWBER, PAM	ACTRESS	WEBER, 9738 ARBY DR	BEVERLY HILLS, CA 90210
DAWES, AMY	COLUMNIST	5700 WILSHIRE BLVD #120	LOS ANGELES, CA 90036
DAWKINS, DALE	FOOTBALL	N Y JETS, 1000 FULTON AVE	HEMPSTEAD, NY 11550
DAWKINS, JOHNNY	BASKETBALL	POST OFFICE BOX 25040	PHILADELPHIA, PA 19147
DAWLEY, BILL	BASEBALL	RR #2, KENDALL RD EXT	LISBON, CT 06417
DAWSEY, LAWRENCE	FOOTBALL	BUCCANEERS, 1 BUCCANEER PL	TAMPA, FL 33607
DAWSON, ANDRE "THE HAWK"	BASEBALL	1060 W ADDISON ST	CHICAGO, IL 60613
DAWSON, ATNHONY	ACTOR-WRI-PROD	VIA RICCIONE 6	FREGENE 00050, ROME ITALY
DAWSON, CARROLL	BASKETBALL COACH	POST OFFICE BOX 272349	HOUSTON, TX 77277
DAWSON, CATHY HUGHART	TV PRODUCER	8200 KIRKWOOD DR	LOS ANGELES, CA 90046
DAWSON, CLIFF	SINGER	BROADWALK, 200 W 58TH ST	NEW YORK, NY 10019
DAWSON, DEBORAH ZOE	TV WRITER-PRODUCER	10000 SANTA MONICA BLVD #305	LOS ANGELES, CA 90067
DAWSON, DERMONTTI	FOOTBALL	STEELERS, 300 STADIUM CIR	PITTSBURGH, PA 15212
DAWSON, DOUG	FOOTBALL	OILERS, 6910 FANNIN ST	HOUSTON, TX 77070
DAWSON, DOUGLAS	BASEBALL EXECUTIVE	TIGERS, TIGER STADIUM	DETROIT, MI 48216
DAWSON, GORDON T	WRITER-PRODUCER	10100 SANTA MONICA BLVD #1600	LOS ANGELES, CA 90067
DAWSON, JANE	TV DIRECTOR	515 N SPAULDING AVE	LOS ANGELES, CA 90036
DAWSON, JAY THOMAS	MUSIC ARRANGER	4421 BRUSH HILL RD	NASHVILLE, TN 37216
DAWSON, JOHN S	DIRECTOR	1505 SAN FELIPE DR	BOULDER CITY, NV 89005
DAWSON, LE	COSTUME DESIGNER	2915 SEARIDGE DR	MALIBU, CA 90265
DAWSON, LEN	SPORTSCASTER	NBC SPORTS, 30 ROCKEFELLER PLZ	NEW YORK, NY 10112
DAWSON, LESLIE	ACTOR-COMEDIAN	LONDON MGT, 235-241 REGENT ST	LONDON W1R 4PH ENGLAND
DAWSON, MARCO	GOLFER	POST OFFICE BOX 109601	PALM BCH GARDENS, FL 33418
DAWSON, RICHARD	ACTOR	1117 ANGELO DR	BEVERLY HILLS, CA 90210
DAWSON, THOMAS	COSTUME DESIGNER	7258 WOODVALE CT	WEST HILLS, CA 91307
DAWSON, ZEKE	MUSIC ARRANGER	ROUTE #2, BOX 95	DICKSON, TN 37055
DAY, ADAM	SINGER	POST OFFICE BOX 18284	SHREVEPORT, LA 71138
DAY, BILL	CARTOONIST	THE DETROIT FREE PRESS	
		321 W LAFAYETTE BLVD	DETROIT, MI 48231
DAY, BILLY	SINGER	POST OFFICE BOX 1875	GRETNA, LA 70054
DAY, BOB	BASEBALL TRAINER	POST OFFICE BOX 2000	SAN DIEGO, CA 92112
DAY, BOOTS	BASEBALL-SCOUT	N Y YANKEES, YANKEE STADIUM	BRONX, NY 10451
DAY, CHON	CARTOONIST	22 CROSS ST	WESTERLY, RI 02891
DAY, CLIFF	DIRECTOR-PRODUCER	CJD PRODS, 12 MOOR ST	LONDON W1 ENGLAND
DAY, CORA LEE	ACTRESS	1823 S COCHRAN AVE	LOS ANGELES, CA 90019
DAY, DENNIS	SINGER	2401 MANDEVILLE CANYON RD	LOS ANGELES, CA 90049
DAY, DINAH	ACTRESS	51 W 69TH ST	NEW YORK, NY 10036
DAY, DORIS	ACTRESS (COMEDIES)	POST OFFICE BOX 223163	CARMEL, CA 93922
DAY, DORIS	ACTRESS (WESTERNS)	RENNA, 16222 MONTEREY LN #279	HUNTINGTON HARBOR, CA 92649
DAY, GERRY	TV WRITER	1546 N FAIRFAX AVE	LOS ANGELES, CA 90046
DAY, JAMES	TV EXECUTIVE	1 LINCOLN PLAZA #300	NEW YORK, NY 10023
DAY, JERRY	ACTOR	5735 VINELAND AVE	NORTH HOLLYWOOD, CA 91601
DAY, LARAINE	ACTRESS	GRILIKHES, 10313 LAURISTON AVE	LOS ANGELES, CA 90025
DAY, LINDA GAIL	TV DIRECTOR	3335 COY DR	SHERMAN OAKS, CA 91423
DAY, LYNDA	ACTRESS	SEE - GEORGE, LYNDA DAY	
DAY, MORRIS & TYME	R & B GROUP	8730 SUNSET BLVD #PH-W	LOS ANGELES, CA 90069
DAY, OTIS & THE KNIGHTS	SOUL GROUP	AMERICAN ENTS, 239 W OLIVE AVE	BURBANK, CA 91502
DAY, RICHARD	U S CONGRESSMAN	200 CARL VINSON PKWY	WARNER ROBINS, GA 31088
DAY, ROBERT	CARTOONIST	ROUTE #1	GRAVETTE, AR 72736
DAY-LEWIS, DANIEL	ACTOR	BELFRAGE, 68 SAINT JAMES'S ST	LONDON SW1A 1LE ENGLAND
DAY-NYE, SHARON	COSTUME DESIGNER	13949 VENTURA BLVD #309	SHERMAN OAKS, CA 91423
DAYETT, BRIAN	BASEBALL	10 HEMLOCK TERRACE EXT	DEEP RIVER, CT 06417
DAYLEY, KEN	BASEBALL	SKYDOME, 300 BREMMER BL #3200	TORONTO, ONT M5V 3B3 CANADA
DAYNE, TAYLOR	SINGER-SONGWRITER	ABBATE, 2288 JERUSALEM AVE	NORTH BELLMORE, NY 11710

DAYTON, DAN	DIRECTOR	1449 LAUREL WY	BEVERLY HILLS, CA	90210
DAYTON, HOWARD	ACTOR	11237 BRADDOCK DR	CULVER CITY, CA	90230
DAYTON, LYMAN	DIRECTOR-PRODUCER	SANTA CLARA HEIGHTS	SAINT GEORGE, UT	84770
DAYTON, MARK	AUDITOR	STATE CAPTOL BLDG, AURORA AVE	SAINT PAUL, MN	55155
DAZZ BAND, THE	RHYTHM & BLUES GROUP	6255 SUNSET BLVD #917	LOS ANGELES, CA	90028
DE ALMEIDA, ANTONIO J	CONDUCTOR	13210 SAINT-REMY-DE PROVEN	MAS DE ROMANIN	FRANCE
DE ANDA, PETER	ACTOR	929 N LARRABEE ST #10	LOS ANGELES, CA	90069
DE ANGELIS, ANGELINA	HAIR STYLIST	2807 QUENTIN RD	BROOKLYN, NY	11229
DE ANGELIS, ROSEMARY	ACTRESS	817 W END AVE	NEW YORK, NY	10025
DE ARMAS, ROLLIE	BASEBALL MANAGER	POST OFFICE BOX 3614	MARTINSVILLE, VA	24115
DE ARMOND, LOIS	COSTUME DESIGNER	415 N OGDEN DR #3	LOS ANGELES, CA	90036
DE AZEVEDO, ALEXIS K	COMPOSER-CONDUCER	POST OFFICE BOX 2228	NORTH HOLLYWOOD, CA	91602
DE BAKEY, DR MICHAEL	SUREGON	BAYLOR COLLEGE OF MEDICINE		
		1200 MOURSUND AVE	HOUSTON, TX	77030
DE BARGE, CHICO	SINGER-WRITER	POST OFFICE BOX 491423	LOS ANGELES, CA	90049
DE BARGE, EL	SINGER	6255 SUNSET BLVD #624	LOS ANGELES, CA	90028
DE BARI, IRENE	ACTRESS	2425 MEADOW VALLEY TERR	LOS ANGELES, CA	90039
DE BARTOLO, EDWARD J, JR	FOOTBALL EXECUTIVE	S F 49ERS, 4949 CENTENNIAL BL	SANTA CLARA, CA	95054
DE BECKER, GAVIN	SECURITY CONSULTANT	11684 VENTURA BLVD #440	STUDIO CITY, CA	91604
DE BEER, GENE	ACTOR	5086 MARMOL DR	WOODLAND HILLS, CA	91364
DE BEERS, COLONEL	WRESTLER	8725 N CHAUTAUQUA BLVD	PORTLAND, OR	97217
DE BENEDETTI, ED	BASEBALL SCOUT	REDS, 100 RIVERFRONT STADIUM	CINCINNATI, OH	45202
DE BENEDICTIS, RICHARD	COMPOSER	1430 GEORGINA AVE	SANTA MONICA, CA	90402
DE BENNING, BURR	ACTOR	4235 KINGFISHER RD	CALABASAS, CA	91302
DE BERG, STEVE	FOOTBALL	CHIEFS, 1 ARROWHEAD DR	KANSAS CITY, MO	64129
DE BERRY, JOE	BASEBALL	POST OFFICE BOX 2001	CEDAR RAPIDS, IA	52406
DE BLASIO, EDWARD P	TV WRITER-PRODUCER	8955 BEVERLY BLVD	WEST HOLLYWOOD, CA	90048
DE BLOIS, LUCIEN	HOCKEY	MAPLE LEAFS, 60 CARLTON ST	TORONTO, ONT M5B 1L1	CANADA
DE BOER, GENE	BASEBALL SCOUT	TWINS, 501 CHICAGO AVE S	MINNEAPOLIS, MN	55415
DE BONO, JERRY	WRITER	4653 W 1ST ST	LOS ANGELES, CA	90004
DE BORBA, DOROTHY	ACTRESS	1810 MONTECITO CIR	LIVERMORE, CA	94550
DE BROUX, LEE	ACTOR	8646 CASABA AVE	CANOGA PARK, CA	91306
DE BRUIN, SANDRA M	ACTRESS-WRITER	6605 HOLLYWOOD BLVD #220	HOLLYWOOD, CA	90028
DE BURGE, CHRIS	SINGER-SONGWRITER	BARGY CASTLE	TONHAGGARD, WESXORD	IRELAND
DE BUTCH, MIKE	BASEBALL	TIGERS, 89 WHARNCLIFFE RD N	LONDON, ONT N6H 2A7	CANADA
DE CAMP, ROSEMARY	ACTRESS	317 CAMINO DE LOS COLIN	REDONDO BEACH, CA	90277
DE CAPRIO, AL	DIRECTOR	203 E CHESTER ST	VALLEY STREAM, NY	11580
DE CARL, NANCY	ACTRESS	4615 WINNETKA AVE	WOODLAND HILLS, CA	91364
DE CARLO, THOMAS	ACTOR	470 W END AVE	NEW YORK, NY	10024
DE CARLO, YVONNE	ACTRESS	4 MARTINE AVE #501	WHITE PLAINS, NY	10606
DE CHAINE, JULIANNE	COSTUME DESIGNER	13949 VENTURA BLVD #309	SHERMAN OAKS, CA	91423
DE CHELLIS, TARYN	COSTUME DESIGNER	1219 N HOWARD ST	GLENDALE, CA	91207
DE CLAMECY, DREE	WRITER	28312 RIDGEFALLS CT	RCHO PALOS VERDES, CA	90274
DE COIT, DICK	ACTOR	652 VERNON AVE #4	VENICE, CA	90291
DE CONCINI, DENNIS	U S SENATOR	40 N CENTER ST #100	MESA, AZ	85201
DE CORDOVA, FREDERICK	FILM-TV DIRECTOR	1875 CARLA RIDGE	BEVERLY HILLS, CA	90210
DE CUELLAR, JAVIER PEREZ	UN SECRETARY GENERAL	3 SUTTON PL	NEW YORK, NY	10022
DE CUIR, GABRIELLE	ACTRESS	208 ADELAIDE DR	SANTA MONICA, CA	90402
DE DERIAN, BABBIE	AUTHORESS	331 W 57TH ST #133	NEW YORK, NY	10019
DE FARIA, WALT	WRITER-PRODUCER	1515 LINDACREST DR	BEVERLY HILLS, CA	90210
DE FARRA, LOUIS	ACTOR	1621 W 221ST ST	TORRANCE, CA	90501
DE FAZIO, PETER A	U S CONGRESSMAN	POST OFFICE BOX 2460	ROSEBERG, OR	97470
DE FAZIO, SAM	ACTOR	7632 HOLLYWOOD BLVD #4	LOS ANGELES, CA	90046
DE FELITTA, FRANK	WRITER-PRODUCER	3008 PAULCREST DR	LOS ANGELES, CA	90046
DE FERRO, GREG	BODYBUILDER	POST OFFICE BOX 8427	CHERRY HILL, NJ	08002
DE FILIPPI, AMEDEO	COMPOSER-CONDUCTOR	4101 WILKINSON AVE	STUDIO CITY, CA	91604
DE FINA, MARIANNA ASTROM	COSTUME DESIGNER	123 UNION ST	SAN RAFAEL, CA	94901
DE FORD, FRANK	TV WRITER	STERLING LORD, 1 MADISON AVE	NEW YORK, NY	10020
DE FORE, DON	ACTOR	2496 MANDEVILLE CANYON RD	LOS ANGELES, CA	90049
DE FRANCESCO, TONY	BASEBALL	POST OFFICE BOX 11363	RENO, NV	89510
DE FRANCO, B F	COMPOSER	POST OFFICE BOX 252	SUNNYSIDE, FL	32461
DE FRANCO, BUDDY, QUARTET	JAZZ QUARTET	CASSIDY, 417 MARAWOOD DR	WOODSTOCK, IL	60098
DE FRANK, ROBERT	ACTOR	241 W 15TH ST	NEW YORK, NY	10011
DE GENERES, ELLEN	COMEDIENNE	9000 SUNSET BLVD #1200	LOS ANGELES, CA	90069
DE GRASSI, ALEX	GUITARIST	POST OFFICE BOX 9188	COLORADO SPRINGS, CO	80932
DE GROOT, TED E	DIRECTOR	708 FORESTDALE RD	ROYAL OAK, MI	48067
DE GRUNWALD, ALEXANDER	TV PRODUCER	4 HOWLEY PL	LONDON W2 1XA	ENGLAND
DE GUERE, PHILIP	WRI-DIR-PROD	5315 YARMOUTH AVE #111	ENCINO, CA	91316
DE GUZMAN, MICHAEL	WRITER	1557 N ORANGE GROVE AVE	LOS ANGELES, CA	90046
DE HART, RICHARD "WHITEY"	BASEBALL SCOUT	6850 LAWRENCE RD	LANTANA, FL	33462
DE HART, RICK	BASEBALL	POLECATS, 608 N SLAPPEY BLVD	ALBANY, GA	31701
DE HAVEN, BRUCE	FOOTBALL COACH	BILLS, 1 BILLS DR	ORCHARD PARK, NJ	14127
DE HAVEN, CARTER, III	DIRECTOR-PRODUCER	5170 W 2ND ST	LOS ANGELES, CA	90004
DE HAVEN, GLORIA	ACTRESS	73 DEVONSHIRE RD	CEDAR GROVE, NH	07009
DE HAVEN, PENNY	SINGER	POST OFFICE BOX 83	BRENTWOOD, TN	37027
DE HAVILLAND, OLIVIA	ACTRESS	BOITE POSTALE 156-16	F-PARIS CEDEX 16-75764	FRANCE
DE JARDIN, BOBBY	BASEBALL	1155 W MOUND ST	COLUMBUS, OH	43223
DE JARNATT, STEVE	WRITER-PRODUCER	8955 BEVERLY BLVD	WEST HOLLYWOOD, CA	90048
DE JESUS, CARLOS	TV DIRECTOR	55 W 11TH ST	NEW YORK, NY	10011
DE JESUS, IVAN	BASEBALL-MANAGER	POST OFFICE BOX 30160	SAN BERNARDINO, CA	92413
DE JESUS, JOSE	BASEBALL	POST OFFICE BOX 7575	PHILADELPHIA, PA	19101
DE JOHN, MARK	BASEBALL MANAGER	TIGERS, 89 WHARNCLIFFE RD N	LONDON, ONT N6H 2A7	CANADA
DE JOHNETTE, JACK	MUSICIAN	SILVER HOLLOW RD	WILLOW, NY	11201
DE KNEEF, MIKE	BASEBALL	POST OFFICE BOX 1718	NEW BRITAIN, CT	06050
DE KORTE, PAUL D	CONDUCTOR	HANNA, 3400 W CAHUENGA BLVD	LOS ANGELES, CA	90068

DE KOVEN, LENORE	TV DIRECTOR	229 E 79TH ST	NEW YORK, NY	10021
DE KOVEN, ROGER	ACTOR	360 W CENTRAL PARK W	NEW YORK, NY	10025
DE LA CROIX, RAVEN	ACTRESS-MODEL	MARX, 11130 HUSTON ST #6	NORTH HOLLYWOOD, CA	91601
DE LA CRUZ, MARCELINO	BASEBALL	POST OFFICE BOX 20849	CHARLESTON, SC	29413
DE LA FUENTE, ALFRED	ACTOR	1362 OCEAN AVE	BROOKLYN, NY	11230
DE LA GARZA, KIKA	U S CONGRESSMAN	1418 BEECH ST	MC ALLEN, TX	78509
DE LA PENA, GILBERT	ACTOR	15632 LE MARSH ST	SEPULVEDA, CA	91343
DE LA RENTA, OSCAR	FASHION DESIGNER	BROOK HILL FARM		
		SKIFF MOUNTAIN RD	KENT, CT	06757
DE LA ROSA, FRANCISCO	BASEBALL	1155 W MOUND ST	COLUMBUS, OH	43223
DE LA ROSA, JUAN	BASEBALL	633 JESSAMINE ST	KNOXVILLE, TN	37917
DE LA TOUR, FRANCES	ACTRESS	SHARKEY, 15 GOLDEN SQ #315	LONDON W1R 3AG	ENGLAND
DE LANCIE, JOHN	ACTOR	1313 BRUNSWICK AVE	SOUTH PASADENA, CA	91030
DE LANEY, STEVE	NEWS CORRESPONDENT	NBC NEWS, 4001 NEBRASKA AV, SW	WASHINGTON, DC	20016
DE LANO, LEE	ACTOR	13615 VALERIO ST #B	VAN NUYS, CA	91405
DE LANO, MICHAEL	ACTOR	13671 DRONFIELD AVE	SYLMAR, CA	91342
DE LAURENTIIS, DINO	FILM PRODUCER	VIA POUNTINA KU 23270	ROME	ITALY
DE LAURENTIS, ROBERT J	SCREENWRITER	8955 BEVERLY BLVD	WEST HOLLYWOOD, CA	90048
DE LAURENTIS, SEMINA	ACTRESS	9229 SUNSET BLVD #311	LOS ANGELES, CA	90069
DE LAURO, ROSA L	U S CONGRESSWOMAN	256 CHURCH ST	NEW HAVEN, CT	06510
DE LAWDER FAMILY, THE	GOSPEL GROUP	POST OFFICE BOX 2145	MORGANTOWN, WV	26507
DE LAY, DOROTHY	VIOLINIST	349 N BROADWAY	UPPER NYACK, NY	10960
DE LAY, TOM	U S CONGRESSMAN	500 N CHENAGO ST #312	ANGELTON, TX	77515
DE LEO, MIKE	BASEBALL TRAINER	POST OFFICE BOX 64939	FAYETTEVILLE, NC	28306
DE LEON, JOSE	BASEBALL	250 STADIUM PLAZA	ST LOUIS, MO	63102
DE LEON, YOBANNE	BASEBALL	POST OFFICE BOX 464	APPLETON, WI	54912
DE LIAGRE, ALFRED, JR	DIRECTOR-PRODUCER	245 W 52ND ST	NEW YORK, NY	10019
DE LON, NATHALIE	ACTRESS	GEORGES BEAUME AGENCE		
		3 QUAI MALAQUAIS	PARIS 75006	FRANCE
DE LONG, KEITH	FOOTBALL	S F 49ERS, 4949 CENTENNIAL BL	SANTA CLARA, CA	95054
DE LONGIS, ANTHONY	ACTOR	2042 N HIGHLAND AVE	LOS ANGELES, CA	90068
DE LOREAN, JOHN Z	CELEBRITY	834 5TH AVE	NEW YORK, NY	10028
DE LORENZO, MICHAEL	ACTOR	118 W ELK AVE	GLENDALE, CA	91204
DE LORME, DANIEL	ACTOR	16 RUE DE MARIGNAN	PARIS 75008	FRANCE
DE LOS SANTOS, ALBERTO	BASEBALL	POST OFFICE DRAWER 1218	ZEBULON, NC	27597
DE LOS SANTOS, LUIS	BASEBALL	575 W 172ND ST	NEW YORK, NY	10032
DE LOS SANTOS, MARIANO	BASEBALL	POST OFFICE BOX 3746, HILL STA	AUGUSTA, GA	30904
DE LOS SANTOS, RAMON	BASEBALL SCOUT	POST OFFICE BOX 4100	SEATTLE, WA	98104
DE LUCA, RUDY	WRITER-PRODUCER	POST OFFICE BOX 5617	BEVERLY HILLS, CA	90213
DE LUCIA, ERIK	BASEBALL	POST OFFICE BOX 4100	SEATTLE, WA	98104
DE LUCIA, RICH	BASEBALL	POST OFFICE BOX 4100	SEATTLE, WA	98104
DE LUGG, MILTON	ACCORDIONIST-ARRANGER	2740 CLARAY AVE	LOS ANGELES, CA	90077
DE LUGO, RON	U S DELEGATE	FEDERAL BUILDING #256	SAINT THOMAS, VI	00801
DE LUISE, DOM	ACTOR-DIRECTOR	1186 CORISCA DR	PACIFIC PALISADES, CA	90272
DE LUISE, MICHAEL	ACTOR	1186 CORSICA DR	PACIFIC PALISADES, CA	90272
DE LUISE, PETER	ACTOR	5643 BURNETT ST	VAN NUYS, CA	91411
DE MAIO, RICHARD R	DIRECTOR	2451 WEBB AVE	NEW YORK, NY	10468
DE MANN, ROBERT	ACTOR	894 1/2 W KNOLL DR	LOS ANGELES, CA	90069
DE MARCO, JOHN G	SCREENWRITER	9300 WILSHIRE BLVD #410	BEVERLY HILLS, CA	90212
DE MARCO, NICHOLAS	DIRECTOR	560 SUMMIT AVE	ORADELL, NJ	07649
DE MARRAIS, JOAN	ACTRESS	33 W 67TH ST #4-FW	NEW YORK, NY	10023
DE MAVE, JACK	ACTOR	4329 COLFAX AVE	STUDIO CITY, CA	91604
DE MAY, SALLY	ACTRESS	325 W 45TH ST	NEW YORK, NY	10036
DE MEO, FRANK	CINEMATOGRAPHER	FJD PRODS, 261 BROADWAY	NEW YORK, NY	10007
DE MEO, PAUL J	WRITER	721 N LA JOLLA AVE	LOS ANGELES, CA	90046
DE MEY, BERRY	BODYBUILDER	POST OFFICE BOX 1236	VENICE, CA	90294
DE MICHELE, RAYNER "REMO"	CONDUCTOR	1637 N VINE ST #414	LOS ANGELES, CA	90028
DE MILLA, WAYNE	BODYBUILDER	POST OFFICE BOX 1490	NEW YORK, NY	10019
DE MILLE, AGNES	CHOREOGRAPHER	25 E 9TH ST	NEW YORK, NY	10003
DE MILO, VENUS	ACTRESS	3500 W OLIVE AVE #1400	BURBANK, CA	91505
DE MORA, ROBERT	COSTUME DESIGNER	13949 VENTURA BLVD #309	SHERMAN OAKS, CA	91423
DE MORAES, RON	TV DIRECTOR	17250 SUNSET BLVD #303	PACIFIC PALISADES, CA	90272
DE MORNAY, REBECCA	ACTRESS	JPM, 760 N LA CIENEGA BL #200	LOS ANGELES, CA	90069
DE MOSS, DARCY	ACTRESS	9300 WILSHIRE BLVD #410	BEVERLY HILLS, CA	90212
DE MOSS, FRANK	BASEBALL SCOUT	1060 W ADDISON ST	CHICAGO, IL	60613
DE NEUT, RICHARD	WRITER	8476 FOUNTAIN AVE	LOS ANGELES, CA	90069
DE NIRO, DJ DRENA	MODEL-DEEJAY	MARS DANCE CLUB, 28 10TH AVE	NEW YORK, NY	10014
DE NIRO, DRENA	MODEL-DEEJAY	SEE - DE NIRO, DJ DRENA		
DE NIRO, ROBERT	ACTOR	375 GREENWICH ST	NEW YORK, NY	10013
DE NOIA, NICK	TV DIRECTOR	4319 LAUREL GROVE AVE	STUDIO CITY, CA	91604
DE NUCCI, A JOSEPH	AUDITOR	STATE HOUSE BUILDING	BOSTON, MA	02133
DE ORE, BILL	CARTOONIST	POST OFFICE BOX 225537	DALLAS, TX	75265
DE OSSIE, STEVE	FOOTBALL	N Y GIANTS, GIANTS STADIUM	EAST RUTHERFORD, NJ	07073
DE PAIVA, JAMES	ACTOR	880 GREENLEAF CANYON	TOPANGA, CA	90290
DE PALMA, BRIAN	WRITER-PRODUCER	270 N CANON DR #1195	BEVERLY HILLS, CA	90210
DE PAOLA, ALESSIO	DIRECTOR	3800 E LINCOLN DR	PHOENIX, AZ	85018
DE PARDIEU, GERALD	ACTOR	4 PLACE DE LA CHAPELLE	BOUGIVAL	FRANCE
DE PASS, STEVE	SINGER	EAGLES, 305 E 24TH ST	NEW YORK, NY	10010
DE PASSE, SUZANNE	RECORD EXEC-TV WRITER	270 N CANON DR #1195	BEVERLY HILLS, CA	90210
DE PAUL, BOBBY	FOOTBALL COACH	POST OFFICE BOX 17247 (DULLES)	WASHINGTON, DC	20041
DE PAUL, GENE	COMPOSER	9607 CALVIN AVE	NORTHRIDGE, CA	91324
DE PAUL, LYNSEY	SINGER-SONGWRITER	LONDON MGT, 235-241 REGENT ST	LONDON W1R 4PH	ENGLAND
DE PEW, JOSEPH	DIRECTOR	15316 SKY HIGH DR	ESCONDIDO, CA	92025
DE PRIEST, JAMES	CONDUCTOR	142 W END AVE #3	NEW YORK, NY	10023
DE RITA, CURLY JOE	ACTOR	545 N MYERS ST	BURBANK, CA	91506

DE ROSA, PAT	TV PRODUCER	PDR PRODS, 747 3RD AVE, 8TH FL	NEW YORK, NY 10017
DE ROSE, CHRISTOPHER	ACTOR	9040 HARRAIT ST #4	LOS ANGELES, CA 90069
DE ROY, JAMIE	ACTRESS	175 W 72ND ST #11-G	NEW YORK, NY 10023
DE ROY, RICHARD	WRITER	334 S CANYON VIEW DR	LOS ANGELES, CA 90049
DE SAILLY, JEAN	ACTOR	53 QUAI DES GRANDS AUGUSTINS	PARIS 75006 FRANCE
DE SALES, FRANCIS A	ACTOR	5729 MAMMOTH AVE	VAN NUYS, CA 91401
DE SALVO, STEVE	BASEBALL EXECUTIVE	POST OFFICE BOX 16683	GREENVILLE, SC 29606
DE SANTOS, DOM	BASEBALL	POST OFFICE BOX 1721	SPARTANBURG, SC 29304
DE SHANNON, JACKIE	SINGER-SONGWRITER	7626 SUNNYWOOD LN	LOS ANGELES, CA 90046
DE SHIELDS, ANDRE	ACTOR	256 W 21ST ST	NEW YORK, NY 10011
DE SHIELDS, DELINO	BASEBALL	EXPOS, 4545 DE COUBERTIN AVE	MONTREAL, QUE H1V 3P2 CANADA
DE SILVA, JOHN	BASEBALL	POST OFFICE BOX 6212	TOLEDO, OH 43614
DE SOUZA, RON	FOOTBALL REFEREE	NFL, 410 PARK AVE	NEW YORK, NY 10022
DE SOUZA, STEVEN E	SCREENWRITER	16476 REFUGIO RD	ENCINO, CA 91436
DE TITTA, ARTHUR	PHOTOGRAPHER	74 VIA MINORCA	CATHEDRAL CITY, CA 92234
DE TOTH, ANDRE	WRITER-PRODUCER	3690 BARHAM BLVD #6-307	LOS ANGELES, CA 90068
DE VALLY, RAYMOND	TV DIRECTOR	600 E CAMBRIDGE DR	BURBANK, CA 91504
DE VANY, EDWARD H	WRITER-PRODUCER	312 W WEATHERSPOON	SANFORD, NC 27330
DE VARONA, DONNA	SPORTS ANALYST	30 LINCOLN PLAZA #1300	NEW YORK, NY 10023
DE VASQUEZ, DEVIN	ACTRESS-MODEL	9229 SUNSET BLVD #208	LOS ANGELES, CA 90069
DE VERE COLE, TRISTAN	TV DIRECTOR-PRODUCER	ODSTOCK MANOR, SALIBURY	WILTS SP5 4JA ENGLAND
DE VILLE, MICHEL	FILM DIRECTOR	32 RUE REINHARDT	BOULOGNE 92100 FRANCE
DE VILLE, MINK	ROCK & ROLL GROUP	SEE - MINK DEVILLE	
DE VINNEY, JAMES A	TV PRODUCER	WONDERWORKS, 4802 5TH AVE	PITTSBURGH, PA 15213
DE VITO, ALBERT	ACTOR	361 PIN OAK LN	WESTBURY, NY 11590
DE VITO, DANNY	ACT-WRI-DIR	POST OFFICE BOX 491246	LOS ANGELES, CA 90049
DE VITO, KARLA	ACTRESS	POST OFFICE BOX 1305	WOODLAND HILLS, CA 91364
DE VITT, TIMOTHY	DIRECTOR	18 STUYVESANT OVAL	NEW YORK, NY 10009
DE VORE, ANN	AUDITOR	STATE HOUSE BUILDING	INDIANAPOLIS, IN 46204
DE VORZON, BARRY	COMPOSER-MUSICIAN	1323 E VALLEY RD	SANTA BARBARA, CA 93108
DE VOTO, JOSEPH	DIRECTOR	318 SPINNAKER WY	NEPTUNE, NJ 07753
DE VRIES, DAVID	DIRECTOR	100 RIVERSIDE DR	NEW YORK, NY 10024
DE WAART, EDO	CONDUCTOR	107 WAR MEMORIAL VETS BLDG	SAN FRANCISCO, CA 94102
DE WINE, MICHAEL	LT GOVERNOR	STATE CAPITOL BUILDING	COLUMBUS, OH 43266
DE WINTER, JO	ACTRESS	5750 WILSHIRE BLVD #512	LOS ANGELES, CA 90036
DE WIT, LEW	SONGWRITER	312 BALDWIN DR	STAUNTON, VA 24401
DE WITT, CHRISTOPHER	SCREENWRITER	4765 MAYTEN CT	OCEANSIDE, CA 92057
DE WITT, FAY	ACTRESS	2012 LA BREA TERR	LOS ANGELES, CA 90046
DE WITT, JOYCE	ACTRESS	101 OCEAN AVE #L-4	SANTA MONICA, CA 90402
DE WITT, ROGER	COMPOSER	3347 PASEO-HALCON	SAN CLEMENTE, CA 92672
DE YOUNG, CLIFF	ACTOR	766 KINGMAN AVE	SANTA MONICA, CA 90402
DEA, JANE	SINGER	POST OFFICE BOX 25371	CHARLOTTE, NC 28212
DEACON, BRIAN	ACTOR	85 GLADSTONE RD	LONDON SW19 ENGLAND
DEACON, ERIC	ACTOR	EDWARDS, 275 KENNINGTON RD	LONDON SE1 6BY ENGLAND
DEACY, JANE	TALENT AGENT	181 REVOLUTIONARY RD	SCARBOROUGH, NY 10510
DEAD OR ALIVE	ROCK & ROLL GROUP	370 CITY RD	LONDON EC1V 2QA ENGLAND
DEADLY ERNEST	ROCK & ROLL GROUP	GREG, 1288 E 168TH ST	CLEVELAND, OH 44110
DEADRICK, GAIL R	CONDUCTOR	POST OFFICE BOX 69281	LOS ANGELES, CA 90069
DEADRICK, VINCENT PAUL, JR	ACTOR	18012 RAYMER ST	NORTHRIDGE, CA 91325
DEAK, BRIAN	BASEBALL	POST OFFICE BOX 6667	RICHMOND, VA 23230
DEAKINS, ROGER	CINEMATOGRAPHER	23 TAVISTOCK TERR	LONDON N19 4BZ ENGLAND
DEAL, BILL & THE RHONDELLS	ROCK & ROLL GROUP	1604 W HILLTOP SQ #308	VIRGINIA BEACH, VA 23451
DEAL, JIM	SINGER	PROCESS, 439 WILEY AVE	FRANKLIN, PA 16323
DEAN, BARTON	WRITER	1117 EUCLID ST #7	SANTA MONICA, CA 90403
DEAN, EDDIE	ACTOR-SINGER	32161 SAILVIEW LN	WESTLAKE VILLAGE, CA 91360
DEAN, FELICITY	ACTRESS	ICM, 388-396 OXFORD ST	LONDON W1 ENGLAND
DEAN, G R, JR	FILM CRITIC	POST OFFICE BOX 23596	SAN DIEGO, CA 92193
DEAN, HAZEL	ACTRESS	7 KENTISH TOWN RD	LONDON NW1 84N ENGLAND
DEAN, HOWARD	LT GOVERNOR	PAVILION OFF BLDG, 109 STATE ST	MONTPELIER, VT 05602
DEAN, ISABEL	ACTRESS	43-A PRINCESS RD, REGENTS PK	LONDON NW1 8JS ENGLAND
DEAN, JIMMY	SINGER-FOOD EXEC	28035 DOROTHY DR #210-A	AGOURA, CA 91301
DEAN, JOHN	AUTHOR	9496 REMBERT LN	BEVERLY HILLS, CA 90210
DEAN, KEVIN	BASEBALL	POST OFFICE BOX 4209	JACKSON, MS 39296
DEAN, LOREN	ACTOR	151 S EL CAMINO DR	BEVERLY HILLS, CA 90212
DEAN, MORTON	NEWS CORRESPONDENT	CBS NEWS, 524 W 57TH ST	NEW YORK, NY 10019
DEAR, WILLIAM	FILM DIRECTOR	POST OFFICE BOX 22345	CARMEL, CA 93922
DEARDEN, JAMES	FILM WRITER-DIRECTOR	77 ELLERBY ST	LONDON SW6 6EU ENGLAND
DEARDEN, ROBIN	ACTRESS	9000 SUNSET BLVD #801	LOS ANGELES, CA 90069
DEARIE, BLOSSOM	SINGER	POST OFFICE BOX 21	EAST DURHAM, NY 12423
DEARING, JO ANN	ACTRESS	280 S BEVERLY DR #400	BEVERLY HILLS, CA 90212
DEARWATER, ANDY	ARTIST	2801 WALNUT BEND LN #128	HOUSTON, TX 77042
DEAS, MICHAEL J	ARTIST	39 SIDNEY PL	BROOKLYN, NY 11201
DEASON, PAUL	WRITER-PRODUCER	10550 OHIO AVE	LOS ANGELES, CA 90024
DEAVEN, JOHN	ACTOR	5217 3/4 VIRGINIA AVE	LOS ANGELES, CA 90029
DEBARTOLO, DICK	WRITER	MAD MAGAZINE, 485 MADISON AVE	NEW YORK, NY 10022
DEBBIE SUE	SINGER	PROCESS, 439 WILEY AVE	FRANKLIN, PA 16323
DEBIN, DAVID	TV WRITER	5613 VALLEY OAK DR	LOS ANGELES, CA 90068
DEBIN, JOHN	PRODUCER	1119 N MC CADDEN PL	LOS ANGELES, CA 90038
DEBNEY, JOHN C	COMPOSER	2722 N BRIGHTON ST	BURBANK, CA 91504
DEBUS, JON	BASEBALL COACH	POST OFFICE BOX 2887	VERO BEACH, FL 32961
DEBUSSCHERE, DAVE	BASEBALL-BASKETBALL	90 3RD ST	GARDEN CITY, NY 11530
DECHTER, BRADLEY G	COMPOSER	641 27TH ST	MANHATTAN BEACH, CA 90266
DECHTER, TED	COMPOSER	22921 CALIFA ST	WOODLAND HILLS, CA 91367
DECILLIS, DEAN	BASEBALL	POST OFFICE BOX 6212	TOLEDO, OH 43614
DECKER, FRANK	BASEBALL EXECUTIVE	POST OFFICE BOX 2785	LAKELAND, FL 33806

DECKER, JOE	BASEBALL COACH	POST OFFICE BOX 1434	BRISTOL, VA 24203
DECKER, LANE	BASEBALL SCOUT	ORIOLE PARK, 333 W CAMDEN ST	BALTIMORE, MD 21201
DECKER, PAUL	CASTING DIRECTOR	3000 W ALAMEDA AVE #233	BURBANK, CA 91523
DECKER, STEVE	BASEBALL	5999 E VAN BUREN ST	PHOENIX, AZ 85008
DECKER SLANEY, MARY	RUNNER	2923 FLINTLOCK ST	EUGENE, OR 97402
DEDEAUX, ROD	BASEBALL-COACH	1430 S EASTMAN AVE	LOS ANGELES, CA 90023
DEDINI, ELDON	CARTOONIST	POST OFFICE BOX 1630	MONTEREY, CA 93940
DEDIO, JOEY	ACTOR	9171 WILSHIRE BLVD #300	BEVERLY HILLS, CA 90210
DEDRICK, JAMES	BASEBALL	POST OFFICE BOX 3169	FREDERICK, MD 21701
DEE, DAVID	DIRECTOR	14 E 52ND ST	NEW YORK, NY 10022
DEE, JOEY & THE STARLIGHTERS	VOCAL GROUP	BROTHERS, 141 DUNBAR AVE	FORDS, NJ 08863
DEE, JOHNNY & THE ROCKET 88'S	ROCK & ROLL GROUP	4407-B MEDICAL PARKWAY	AUSTIN, TX 78756
DEE, RUBY	ACTRESS-WRITER	44 CORTLAND AVE	NEW ROCHELLE, NY 10801
DEE, SANDRA	ACTRESS	10351 SANTA MONICA BLVD #211	LOS ANGELES, CA 90025
DEE, SIMON	ACTOR-TV PERS	17 VICTORIA RD	LONDON SW14 ENGLAND
DEE MC CREA, FRANCES	ACTRESS	ROUTE #1	CAMARILLO, CA 93010
DEEGAN, MARY JANE	ACTRESS	5055 WILLOW CREST AVE	NORTH HOLLYWOOD, CA 91601
DEEL, SANDRA	ACTRESS	1717 N STANLEY AVE	LOS ANGELES, CA 90046
DEELE, THE	RHYTHM & BLUES GROUP	SOLAR, 1635 N CAHUENGA BLVD	LOS ANGELES, CA 90028
DEELEY, MICHAEL	FILM PRODUCER	CONSOLIDATED FILMS & TV 5 JUBILEE PL	LONDON SW3 ENGLAND
DEEMS, MICKEY	ACTOR-DIRECTOR	13114 WEDDINGTON ST	VAN NUYS, CA 91401
DEEP PURPLE	ROCK & ROLL GROUP	POST OFFICE BOX 254	SHEFFIELD S6 1DF ENGLAND
DEER, ROB	BASEBALL	TIGERS, TIGER STADIUM	DETROIT, MI 48216
DEES, JULIE	COMEDIENNE	8730 SUNSET BLVD #PH-W	LOS ANGELES, CA 90069
DEES, RICK	RADIO-TV PERSONALITY	8 TOLUCA ESTATES DR	TOLUCA LAKE, CA 91602
DEEZEN, EDDIE	ACTOR	1570 N EDGEMONT ST #602	LOS ANGELES, CA 90027
DEF LEPPARD	ROCK & ROLL GROUP	80 WARWICK GARDENS	LONDON W14 8PR ENGLAND
DEFFENBAUGH, JO ELLA	ACTRESS	6310 W 5TH ST	LOS ANGELES, CA 90048
DEFINA, BARBARA	FILM PRODUCER	CAA, 9830 WILSHIRE BLVD	BEVERLY HILLS, CA 90212
DEFORD, F H "JUG"	BASEBALL SCOUT	POST OFFICE BOX 288	HOUSTON, TX 77001
DEFREITAS, SCOTT	ACTOR	CBS-TV, "AS THE WORLD TURNS" 524 W 57TH ST #5330	NEW YORK, NY 10019
DEGAS, BRIAN	WRITER-PRODUCER	POLYMUSE, 2000 FULHAM RD	LONDON SW10 ENGLAND
DEGATINA, JOHN	COMPOSER	570 N ROSSMORE AVE	LOS ANGELES, CA 90004
DEGHY, GUY	ACTOR-WRITER	41 FILMER RD	LONDON SW6 7JJ ENGLAND
DEHDASHTIAN, DEREK	BASEBALL	POST OFFICE BOX 6748	ROCKFORD, IL 61125
DEHRAN, BERNARD	ACTOR	82 AVE DE VILLIERS	PARIS 75017 FRANCE
DEICHMAN, DAVID C	CONDUCTOR	14834 WYANDOTTE ST	VAN NUYS, CA 91405
DEICHMAN, JOHN CHARLES	CONDUCTOR	1640 SUNNYSIDE TERR	SAN PEDRO, CA 90732
DEIGHTON, LEN	WRITER	FAIRYMOUNT, BLACKROCK DUNDALK	COUNTY LOUTH IRELAND
DEITCH, DONNA	FILM DIRECTOR	ROSENBERG, 8428 MELROSE PL #C	LOS ANGELES, CA 90069
DEJA BU	ROCK & ROLL GROUP	1 TOUCHSTONE LN, CHARD	SOMERSET TA20 1RF ENGLAND
DEKLE, BILL	MUSIC ARRANGER	1605 16TH AVE S #8	NASHVILLE, TN 37212
DEKTOR, LESLIE MICHAEL	FILM-TV DIRECTOR	3923 GOODLAND AVE	STUDIO CITY, CA 91604
DEL BARBA, BRAD	BASEBALL SCOUT	REDS, 100 RIVERFRONT STADIUM	CINCINNATI, OH 45202
DEL BARRIO, GEORGE G	COMPOSER-CONDUCTOR	5826 CANTALOUPE AVE	VAN NUYS, CA 91401
DEL CANTON, BRUCE	BASEBALL-COACH	POST OFFICE BOX 6667	RICHMOND, VA 23230
DEL CASTILLO, LLOYD G	COMPOSER	2008 PREUSS RD	LOS ANGELES, CA 90034
DEL CASTILLO MORANTE, MARK	ACTOR	4120 MONROE ST	LOS ANGELES, CA 90029
DEL FOSS, RAOUL	ACTOR	3 RUE DE VERDUN	VIARMES 95270 FRANCE
DEL GRANDE, LOUIS	ACTOR-WRITER	32 N SHERBOURNE ST	TORONTO, ONT M4W 2T3 CANADA
DEL LORDS, THE	ROCK & ROLL GROUP	188 1ST AVE #6	NEW YORK, NY 10009
DEL MAR, MARCIA	ACTRESS	329 N WETHERLY DR #101	BEVERLY HILLS, CA 90211
DEL PAPA, FRANKIE SUE	ATTORNEY GENERAL	STATE CAPITOL BUILDING	CARSON CITY, NV 89710
DEL POZO, PAUL C	TV DIRECTOR	WNJU-TV, 1020 BROAD ST	NEWARK, NJ 07102
DEL RAY, SANDRA	SINGER	ROSEWOOD, ROUTE #7, BOX 285	LAKE CITY, FL 32055
DEL RIO, JACK	FOOTBALL	COWBOYS, 1 COWBOYS PARKWAY	IRVING, TX 75063
DEL RUSSO, JOSEPH	MAKE-UP ARTIST	127 E 39TH ST	NEW YORK, NY 10016
DEL RUTH, THOMAS	CINEMATOGRAPHER	POST OFFICE BOX 2230	HOLLYWOOD, CA 90078
DEL TREDICI, DAVID	COMPOSER-PIANIST	463 WEST ST #G-121	NEW YORK, NY 10014
DEL TUFO, ROBERT	ATTORNEY GENERAL	STATE HOUSE BLDG, 125 W STATE ST	TRENTON, NJ 08625
DEL-VIKINGS, THE	VOCAL GROUP	1001 W CYPRESS CREEK RD #314	FORT LAUDERDALE, FL 33309
DELAHOYA, JAVIER	BASEBALL	POST OFFICE BOX 2887	VERO BEACH, FL 32961
DELANEY, ETHEL	SINGER	POST OFFICE BOX 655	HUDSON, OH 44236
DELANEY, JAMES ROBERT	TV DIRECTOR	292 SPOOK ROCK RD	SUFFERN, NY 10901
DELANEY, KIM	ACTRESS	4724 POE AVE	WOODLAND HILLS, CA 91364
DELANEY, PAT	ACTRESS	280 S BEVERLY DR #400	BEVERLY HILLS, CA 90212
DELANUEZ, REX	BASEBALL	POST OFFICE BOX 5645	ORLANDO, FL 32855
DELANY, DANA	ACTRESS	2521 6TH ST	SANTA MONICA, CA 90405
DELARWELLE, CHRIS	BASEBALL	POST OFFICE BOX 5645	ORLANDO, FL 32855
DELFIN, KIMBERLY B	ACTRESS	7461 BEVERLY BLVD #400	LOS ANGELES, CA 90036
DELFINO, FRANK	ACTOR	1441 PASO REAL AVE #270	ROWLAND HEIGHTS, CA 91748
DELFONICS, THE	VOCAL GROUP	2011 FERRY AVE #U-19	CAMDEN, NJ 08104
DELFONT, LORD	FILM EXECUTIVE	7 SOHO ST, SOHO SQ	LONDON W1V 5FA ENGLAND
DELGADO, CARLOS	BASEBALL	POST OFFICE BOX 957	DUNEDIN, FL 34697
DELGADO, FELIX	BASEBALL SCOUT	BREWERS, 201 S 46TH ST	MILWAUKEE, WI 53214
DELGADO, LUIS	BASEBALL-SCOUT	FENWAY PARK, 4 YAWKEY WY	BOSTON, MA 02215
DELGADO, MARGARITA	COSTUME DESIGNER	327 E 89TH ST #4-E	NEW YORK, NY 10128
DELGADO, ROBERTO	BASEBALL	POST OFFICE BOX 1295	CLINTON, IA 52733
DELGADO, TIM	BASEBALL	POST OFFICE BOX 4488	WINSTON-SALEM, NC 27115
DELIMA, RAFAEL	BASEBALL	POST OFFICE BOX 5645	ORLANDO, FL 32855
DELIN, BARBARA	ACTRESS	21-36 33RD RD #4-B	ASTORIA, NY 11106
DELIRIOUS PINK	ROCK & ROLL GROUP	POST OFFICE BOX 4429	AUSTIN, TX 78765

DELK, JOAN	GOLFER	2750 VOLUSA AVE #B	DAYTON BEACH, FL 32114
DELL, MYRNA	ACTRESS	12958 VALLEYHEART DR	STUDIO CITY, CA 91604
DELL, TIM	BASEBALL	POST OFFICE DRAWER 4797	EL PASO, TX 79914
DELLA PIETRA, CARLINA F	TV WRITER	A M C WRITERS, 33 W 60TH ST	NEW YORK, NY 10023
DELLA PIETRA, STEPHEN J	TV DIRECTOR	711 W END AVE	NEW YORK, NY 10025
DELLA SORTE, JOSEPH	ACTOR	1422 1/2 N SIERRA BONITA AVE	LOS ANGELES, CA 90046
DELLAR, MELVIN	FILM DIRECTOR	125 TURQUOISE AVE	BALBOA ISLAND, CA 92662
DELLENBACH, JEFF	FOOTBALL	DOLPHINS, 2269 NW 199TH ST	MIAMI, FL 33056
DELLER, ROBERT	BASEBALL	5301 NW 12TH AVE	FORT LAUDERDALE, FL 33309
DELLINGER, ROBERT	TV WRITER-PRODUCER	21 WESTMINSTER AVE #201	VENICE, CA 90291
DELLO JOIO, NORMAN	COMPOSER	POST OFFICE BOX 154	EAST HAMPTON, NY 11937
DELLS, DOROTHY	ACTRESS	1026 TIVERTON AVE #207	LOS ANGELES, CA 90024
DELLS, THE	VOCAL GROUP	200 INWOOD DR #510	WHEELING, IL 60090
DELLUMS, RONALD	U S CONGRESSMAN	3732 MOUNT DIABLE BLVD #160	LAFAYETTE, CA 94549
DELON, ALAIN	ACTOR	4 CHAMBIGES, TROIS ETAGE	F-75008 PARIS FRANCE
DELPINO, ROBERT	FOOTBALL	RAMS, 2327 W LINCOLN BLVD	ANAHEIM, CA 92801
DELSING, JAY	GOLFER	POST OFFICE BOX 109601	PALM BCH GARDENS, FL 33418
DELU, YVONNE BRONOWICZ	COSTUME DESIGNER	1560 SANBORN AVE	LOS ANGELES, CA 90027
DELUCCA, JOE	BASEBALL SCOUT	INDIANS, CLEVELAND STADIUM	CLEVELAND, OH 44114
DEMBECKI, STAN	ACTOR	220 MARKET ST #7	VENICE, CA 90291
DEMBERG, LISA	TV WRITER	345 S COCHRAN AVE #7	LOS ANGELES, CA 90036
DEMERS, DONALD	ARTIST	POST OFFICE BOX 4009	PORTSMOUTH, NH 03801
DEMERSON, TIM	BASEBALL	5301 NW 12TH AVE	FORT LAUDERDALE, FL 33309
DEMETER, STEVE	BASEBALL-SCOUT	POST OFFICE BOX 7000	PITTSBURGH, PA 15212
DEMETRAL, CHRIS	ACTOR	9171 WILSHIRE BLVD #300	BEVERLY HILLS, CA 90210
DEMETRAL, CHRIS	BASEBALL	POST OFFICE BOX 10031	BAKERSFIELD, CA 93389
DEMIAN, MARCUS	WRITER	1850 N WHITLEY AVE	HOLLYWOOD, CA 90028
DEMING, ROLF	GOLFER	PGA SENIORS, 112 T P C BLVD	PONTE VEDRA BEACH, FL 32082
DEMMAS, ART	FOOTBALL REFEREE	NFL, 410 PARK AVE	NEW YORK, NY 10022
DEMME, EVELYN PURCELL	DIRECTOR-PRODUCER	9000 SUNSET BLVD #1115	LOS ANGELES, CA 90069
DEMME, JONATHAN	FILM WRITER-DIRECTOR	1355 MILLER PL	LOS ANGELES, CA 90069
DEMOLITION	WRESTLING TAG TEAM	POST OFFICE BOX 3859	STAMFORD, CT 06905
DEMONBREUN, DAVID	BASEBALL EXECUTIVE	POST OFFICE BOX 2769	HUNTSVILLE, AL 35804
DEMPSEY, JOHN	BASEBALL	POST OFFICE BOX 3783	SAVANNAH, GA 31414
DEMPSEY, JOHN	COLUMNIST	5700 WILSHIRE BLVD #120	LOS ANGELES, CA 90036
DEMPSEY, PATRICK	ACTOR	431 LINCOLN BLVD	SANTA MONICA, CA 90402
DEMPSEY, RICK	BASEBALL	ORIOLE PARK, 333 W CAMDEN ST	BALTIMORE, MD 21201
DEMPSTER, NIGEL	WRITER	10 BUCKINGHAM ST	LONDON WC2 ENGLAND
DEMUS, JOE	BASEBALL	POST OFFICE BOX 1718	NEW BRITAIN, CT 06050
DEMUTH, DANA	BASEBALL UMPIRE	8388 VIA AIROSA	RANCHO CUCAMONGA, CA 91730
DENBO, GARY	BASEBALL COACH	1155 W MOUND ST	COLUMBUS, OH 43223
DENBY, DAVID	FILM CRITIC	N Y MAGAZINE, 755 2ND AVE	NEW YORK, NY 10017
DENCH, JUDI	ACTRESS	BELFRAGE, 68 SAINT JAMES'S ST	LONDON SW1A 1LE ENGLAND
DENCINCES, DOUG	BASEBALL	2 LEESBURG CT	NEWPORT BEACH, CA 92660
DENERSTEIN, ROBERT	FILM CRITIC	POST OFFICE BOX 719	DENVER, CO 80204
DENEUVE, CATHERINE	ACTRESS	76 RUE BONAPARTE	75016 PARIS FRANCE
DENHAM, MAURICE	ACTOR	44 BRUNSWICK GARDENS #2	LONDON W8 ENGLAND
DENHART, THOMAS E	DIRECTOR	OGILVY, 2 E 48TH ST	NEW YORK, NY 10017
DENIER, LYDIE	ACTRESS	8485 MELROSE PL #E	LOS ANGELES, CA 90069
DENIS, CHRISTOPHER	WRI-DIR-PROD	3840 GREYSTONE AVE	NEW YORK, NY 10463
DENISE MARIE	SINGER	POST OFFICE BOX 500	ROBINSON CREEK, KY 41560
DENISON, MICHAEL	ACTOR	ICM, 388-396 OXFORD ST	LONDON W1 ENGLAND
DENISON, ROBERT G	ACTOR	7449 ALDEA AVE	VAN NUYS, CA 91406
DENKER, HENRY	PLAYWRIGHT	241 CENTRAL PARK W	NEW YORK, NY 10024
DENKINGER, DON	BASEBALL UMPIRE	3322 DORAL DR	WATERLOO, IA 50701
DENN, MARIE	ACTRESS	22831 NADINE CIR #B	TORRANCE, CA 90505
DENNEHY, AL	FILM DIRECTOR	20360 HAYNES ST	WINNETKA, CA 91306
DENNEHY, BRIAN	ACTOR	SMITH, 121 N SAN VICENTE BLVD	BEVERLY HILLS, CA 90211
DENNEHY, KATHLEEN	ACTRESS	SMITH, 121 N SAN VICENTE BLVD	BEVERLY HILLS, CA 90211
DENNETT, JIM	DIRECTOR	20575 CHENEY DR	TOPANGA CANYON, CA 90290
DENNEY, AL B, JR	CINEMATOGRAPHER	8635 YOLANDA AVE #3	NORTHRIDGE, CA 91324
DENNEY, CHARLES	ACTOR	1 W 67TH ST	NEW YORK, NY 10023
DENNIS, ALFRED	ACTOR	312 N LOUISE ST #212	GLENDALE, CA 91206
DENNIS, ALLAN	DIRECTOR	461 PARK AVE S	NEW YORK, NY 10016
DENNIS, CHARLES	SCREENWRITER	9000 SUNSET BLVD #1200	LOS ANGELES, CA 90069
DENNIS, DIANA	BODYBUILDER	POST OFFICE BOX 15042	NEWPORT BEACH, CA 92663
DENNIS, MARK	FOOTBALL	DOLPHINS, 2269 NW 199TH ST	MIAMI, FL 33056
DENNIS, RICHARD	ART DIRECTOR	240 E 13TH ST #28	NEW YORK, NY 10003
DENNIS, ROBERT C	WRITER	8082 MULHOLLAND DR	HOLLYWOOD, CA 90046
DENNIS, SANDY	ACTRESS	853 7TH AVE #9-A	NEW YORK, NY 10019
DENNISON, BRIAN	BASEBALL	POST OFFICE BOX 855	BELOIT, WI 53511
DENNISON, JIM	BASEBALL	POST OFFICE BOX 10213	LYNCHBURG, VA 24506
DENNISON, RACHEL PARTON	ACTRESS	9255 SUNSET BLVD #1115	LOS ANGELES, CA 90069
DENNISON, SCOTT	BASEBALL	POST OFFICE BOX 6748	ROCKFORD, IL 61125
DENNY, BIRCH	SINGER	RAY RUFF, 156 CARLIN DR	WEST COLUMBIA, SC 29169
DENNY, J WILLIAM	MUSIC PUBLISHER	800 CALDWELL LN	NASHVILLE, TN 37204
DENNY, MARTIN	COMPOSER	4080 BLACK POINT RD	HONOLULU, HI 96816
DENNY & KRISTINA	C & W DUO	5625 "O" STREET BLDG #7	LINCOLN, NE 68510
DENOFF, SAMUEL	TV WRITER-PRODUCER	428 N CARMELINA AVE	LOS ANGELES, CA 90049
DENSHAM, PEN	FILM WRITER-DIRECTOR	1875 CENTURY PARK E #700	LOS ANGELES, CA 90067
DENSMORE, JOHN	DRUMMER-AUTHOR	927 BERKELEY ST	SANTA MONICA, CA 90403
DENSON, ANDREW	BASEBALL	1718 AVONLEA AVE	CINCINNATI, OH 45237
DENSON, DREW	BASEBALL	POST OFFICE BOX 360007	BIRMINGHAM, AL 35236
DENSON, FRANK	COMPOSER	846 WILADONDA DR	LA CANADA, CA 91011
DENT, BUCKY	BASEBALL-COACH	250 STADIUM PLAZA	ST LOUIS, MO 63102

DENT, BURNELL	FOOTBALL	PACKERS, 1265 LOMBARDI AVE	GREEN BAY, WI 54307
DENT, JIM	GOLFER	PGA SENIORS, 112 T P C BLVD	PONTE VEDRA BEACH, FL 32082
DENT, RICHARD	FOOTBALL	BEARS, 250 N WASHINGTON RD	LAKE FOREST, IL 60045
DENTON, DONNA	ACTRESS	MAPLE ENT, 1440 S SEPULVEDA BL	LOS ANGELES, CA 90025
DENTON, JACK	ACTOR	8256 CANTERBURY AVE	SUN VALLEY, CA 91352
DENTON, JOE	ARTIST	1351 OCEAN PARK WALK #106	SANTA MONICA, CA 90405
DENTON, KATHY BELL	ACTRESS	1339 FEDERAL AVE #3	LOS ANGELES, CA 90025
DENVER, BOB	ACTOR	POST OFFICE BOX 196	BEARSVILLE, NY 12409
DENVER, JOHN	SINGER-SONGWRITER	POST OFFICE BOX 1587	ASPEN, CO 81612
DENVER BILL	SINGER	PROCESS, 439 WILEY AVE	FRANKLIN, PA 16323
DENZIEN, RICK	SINGER	POST OFFICE BOX 314	AMBER, PA 19002
DEODATO, EUMIR	COMPOSER	565 5TH AVE #600	NEW YORK, NY 10017
DEPARDIEU, GERARD	ACTOR	4 PLACE DE LA CHAPELE	BOUGIVAL FRANCE
DEPECHE MODE	ROCK & ROLL GROUP	429 HARROW RD	LONDON W10 4RE ENGLAND
DEPEW, ART	CONDUCTOR	11530 HUSTON ST	NORTH HOLLYWOOD, CA 91601
DEPP, JOHNNY	ACTOR	1636 N BEVERLY DR	BEVERLY HILLS, CA 90210
DER MARDEROSIAN, ALAN DICKRAN	COMPOSER	12547 CHANDLER BLVD #4	NORTH HOLLYWOOD, CA 91607
DERDIVANIS, KENT	SPORTSCASTER	POST OFFICE BOX 7000	PITTSBURGH, PA 15212
DEREK, BO	ACTRESS-MODEL	3625 ROBLAR	SANTA YNEZ, CA 93460
DEREK, JOHN	ACT-WRI-DIR	3625 ROBLAR	SANTA YNEZ, CA 93460
DERFNER, DORI	WRITER	1223 AMALFI DR	PACIFIC PALISADES, CA 90272
DERKSEN, ROB	BASEBALL COACH	POST OFFICE DRAWER 4797	EL PASO, TX 79914
DERLOSHON, GERALD B	SCREENWRITER	8955 BEVERLY BLVD	WEST HOLLYWOOD, CA 90048
DERMAN, RICHARD	TV DIRECTOR-PRODUCER	875 W END AVE #11-E	NEW YORK, NY 10025
DERN, BRUCE	ACTOR	23430 MALIBU COLONY RD	MALIBU, CA 90265
DERN, LAURA	ACTRESS	131 S RODEO DR #300	BEVERLY HILLS, CA 90212
DERNIER, BOB	BASEBALL	9509 E 77TH ST	RAYTOWN, MO 64138
DEROSA, FRANCO	ACTOR	L'EPINE SMITH, 10 WYNDHAM PL	LONDON W1H 1AS ENGLAND
DERR, RICHARD	ACTOR	8965 CYNTHIA ST	LOS ANGELES, CA 90069
DERRICK, BUTLER C, JR	U S CONGRESSMAN	POST OFFICE BOX 4126	ANDERSON, SC 29622
DERRICKS, CLEAVANT	ACTOR	533 W END AVE #3-A	NEW YORK, NY 10024
DERRINGER, RICK	SINGER-SONGWRITER	60 W 68TH ST	NEW YORK, NY 10023
DERRIS, STEVE	TV DIRECTOR	325 E 64TH ST	NEW YORK, NY 10036
DERRY, CHARLES	TV DIRECTOR	8660 MERKEL RD	DEXTER, MI 48130
DERSHOWITZ, ALAN	ATTORNEY	2 TUDOR CITY PL	NEW YORK, NY 10017
DERVAL, LAMYA	ACTRESS	49 AVENUE FOCH	75116 PARIS FRANCE
DERWIN, JORDAN	ACTOR	305 E 86TH ST	NEW YORK, NY 10028
DERWIN, MARK	ACTOR	CBS-TV, "THE GUIDING LIGHT"	
		222 E 44TH ST	NEW YORK, NY 10017
DES BARRES, MICHAEL	SINGER-SONGWRITER	3575 W CAHUENGA BLVD #470	LOS ANGELES, CA 90028
DES BARRES, PAMELA	ACTRESS	814 10TH ST	SANTA MONICA, CA 90403
DESATOFF, PAUL	TV DIRECTOR	2944 MARIQUITA ST	LONG BEACH, CA 90803
DESBY, FRANK H	COMPOSER-CONDUCTOR	6234 SCENIC AVE	LOS ANGELES, CA 90068
DESCHANEL, CALEB	CINEMATOGRAPHER	844 CHAUTAUQUA BLVD	PACIFIC PALISADES, CA 90272
DESCHANEL, MARY JO	ACTRESS	844 CHAUTAUQUA BLVD	PACIFIC PALISADES, CA 90272
DESCRIERES, GEORGES	ACTOR	15 PLACE DU MARCHE	SAINT MONORE 75001 FRANCE
DESERT ROSE BAND, THE	C & W GROUP	POST OFFICE BOX 1053	ARVADA, CO 80001
DESERT SKY	C & W GROUP	5625 "O" STREET BLDG #7	LINCOLN, NE 68510
DESHAIES, JIM	BASEBALL	POST OFFICE BOX 2000	SAN DIEGO, CA 92112
DESIDERIO, ROBERT	ACTOR	3960 LAUREL CANYON #280	STUDIO CITY, CA 91604
DESJARDINS, ERIC	HOCKEY	CANADIENS, 2313 ST CATHERINE ST	MONTREAL, QUE H3H 1N2 CANADA
DESMARETS, SOPHIE	ACTRESS	GEORGES BEAUME AGENCE	
		3 QUAI MALAQUAIS	PARIS 75006 FRANCE
DESMOND, DICK	SCREENWRITER	8955 BEVERLY BLVD	WEST HOLLYWOOD, CA 90048
DESMOND, JOHN J	DIRECTOR	165 E 66TH ST	NEW YORK, NY 10021
DESMOND CHILD	ROCK & ROLL GROUP	1780 BROADWAY #1208	NEW YORK, NY 10019
DESMONI-HORNE, MADDY	TV EXECUTIVE	CBS-TV, 7800 BEVERLY BLVD	LOS ANGELES, CA 90036
DESPRES, LORAINE	WRITER	6403 SEASTAR DR	MALIBU, CA 90265
DESROCHER, JACK	ARTIST	176 LEE AVE	SAN FRANCISCO, CA 94112
DESTINE, JEAN-LEON	CHOREOGRAPHER-DANCER	676 RIVERSIDE DR	NEW YORK, NY 10031
DESTRUCTION	ROCK & ROLL GROUP	10100 SANTA MONICA BLVD #1600	LOS ANGELES, CA 90067
DETERS, THOMAS C, MD	BODYBUILDER	POST OFFICE BOX 666	VENICE, CA 90294
DETMER, TY	FOOTBALL	BRIGHAM YOUNG UNIVERSITY	
		ATHLETIC DEPARTMENT	
		500 CAMPUS DR	PROVO, UT 84602
DETORO, KATHLEEN	COSTUME DESIGNER	13949 VENTURA BLVD #309	SHERMAN OAKS, CA 91423
DETTORE, TOM	BASEBALL COACH	POST OFFICE DRAWER 1218	ZEBULON, NC 27597
DEUBEL, ROBERT	DIRECTOR-PRODUCER	CONCEPTS, 315 W 57TH ST	NEW YORK, NY 10019
DEUCE	C & W GROUP	JVS PRODS, 147 12TH ST #C	PACIFIC GROVE, CA 93950
DEUTSCH, DAVID	FILM PRODUCER	26-B THORNEY CRES	LONDON SW11 3TR ENGLAND
DEUTSCH, DAVID GEORGE	SCREENWRITER	2311 CHEREMOYA AVE	LOS ANGELES, CA 90068
DEUTSCH, DAVID S	TV DIRECTOR	1243 "C" ST, SE	WASHINGTON, DC 20003
DEUTSCH, DOUG	BASEBALL SCOUT	POST OFFICE BOX 288	HOUSTON, TX 77001
DEUTSCH, HELEN	SCREENWRITER	1185 PARK AVE	NEW YORK, NY 10128
DEUTSCH, JOHN	BASEBALL	POST OFFICE BOX 28268	SAN ANTONIO, TX 78228
DEUTSCH, PATTI	ACTRESS	9255 SUNSET BLVD #603	LOS ANGELES, CA 90069
DEVANE, WILLIAM	ACTOR	11567 ACAMA ST	STUDIO CITY, CA 91604
DEVANEY, BILLY	FOOTBALL EXECUTIVE	POST OFFICE BOX 609609	SAN DIEGO, CA 92160
DEVANEY, DAN	CINEMATOGRAPHER	JERSEY COAST VIDEO PRODS	
		15 N WOOD AVE	LINDEN, NJ 07036
DEVARES, CESAR	BASEBALL	POST OFFICE BOX 230	HAGERSTOWN, MD 21740
DEVENISH, ROSS	FILM DIRECTOR	LEMON, 24 POTTERY, HOLLAND PK	LONDON W11 4LZ ENGLAND
DEVER, TOM	ACTOR	5953 1/4 CARLTON WY	LOS ANGELES, CA 90028
DEVERAUX, SUZI	C & W GROUP	154 CHIPPENDALE DR	HENDERSONVILLE, TN 37075
DEVEREAUX, DAVID EARL	TV DIRECTOR	2870 DERBY RD	BIRMINGHAM, MI 48008

DEVEREAUX, MIKE	BASEBALL	ORIOLE PARK, 333 W CAMDEN ST	BALTIMORE, MD	21201
DEVEREUX, ROBERT	FILM PRODUCER	VIRGIN FILMS, 328 KENSAL RD	LONDON W10	ENGLAND
DEVERY, LOUISE	ACTRESS	25 82ND ST	SEA ISLE CITY, NJ	08243
DEVINE, BING	BASEBALL-SCOUT	POST OFFICE BOX 7575	PHILADELPHIA, PA	19101
DEVINE, DEBORAH	CASTING DIRECTOR	EUE/SCREEN GEMS, 222 E 44TH ST	NEW YORK, NY	10017
DEVLIN, BRIGID	ACTRESS	7135 HOLLYWOOD BLVD #PH-2	LOS ANGELES, CA	90046
DEVLIN, BRUCE	GOLFER	PGA SENIORS, 112 T P C BLVD	PONTE VEDRA BEACH, FL	32082
DEVLIN, DON	WRITER	8577 BRIER DR	LOS ANGELES, CA	90046
DEVO	ROCK & ROLL GROUP	LOOKOUT, 506 SANTA MONICA BLVD	SANTA MONICA, CA	90401
DEVON, RICHARD	ACTOR	5727 CANOGA AVE	WOODLAND HILLS, CA	91367
DEVON, TONY	ACTOR	101 W 57TH ST	NEW YORK, NY	10019
DEVON, VALERIE	ACTRESS	FELBER, 2126 N CAHUENGA BLVD	LOS ANGELES, CA	90068
DEVONNES, THE	VOCAL GROUP	DEANGELIS, 79 KINGSLAND AVE	BROOKLYN, NY	11211
DEVONSHIRE, DUKE & DUCHESS	DUKE & DUCHESS	CHATSWORTH, BAKEWELL	DERBYSHIRE	ENGLAND
DEVORE, GARY M	SCREENWRITER	1403 MARINETTE RD	PACIFIC PALISADES, CA	90272
DEVORE, TED	BASEBALL	12000 STADIUM RD	ADELANTO, CA	92301
DEVROY, ANN	WRITER-EDITOR	1150 15TH ST, NW	WASHINGTON, DC	20071
DEWBERRY, DEAN & PENNY	GOSPEL DUO	POST OFFICE BOX 302	KEYSTONE HEIGHTS, FL	32656
DEWEY, MARK	BASEBALL	POST OFFICE BOX 1211	NORFOLK, VA	23502
DEWEY, RAY	COMPOSER-CONDUCTOR	3641 CROWNRIDGE DR	SHERMAN OAKS, CA	91403
DEWHURST, COLLEEN	ACTRESS	STE, 888 7TH AVE, 18TH FLOOR	NEW YORK, NY	10106
DEWINDT, ANGELIQUE	ACTRESS	1680 N VINE ST #1003	HOLLYWOOD, CA	90028
DEWITT, LOU	SINGER	STARS, INC, 1012 16TH AVE S	NASHVILLE, TN	37212
DEXTER, MAURY	TV DIRECTOR	1384 CAMINO MAGENTA	THOUSAND OAKS, CA	91360
DEXTER, RON P	DIRECTOR	8675 EDWIN DR	LOS ANGELES, CA	90046
DEXTER, VON	COMPOSER	73-680 ROADRUNNER CT	PALM DESERT, CA	92260
DEY, JANET	ACTRESS	5330 LANKERSHIM BLVD #210	NORTH HOLLYWOOD, CA	91601
DEY, SUSAN	ACTRESS	MTA, 9320 WILSHIRE BL, 3RD FL	BEVERLY HILLS, CA	90212
DEYELL, PETER R J	TV DIRECTOR	10742 CAMARILLO ST	TOLUCA LAKE, CA	91602
DEZELAN, JOHN	BASEBALL UMPIRE	POST OFFICE BOX 716	PLAINVILLE, CT	06062
DI BENEDETTO, THOMAS	BASEBALL EXECUTIVE	FENWAY PARK, 4 YAWKEY WY	BOSTON, MA	02215
DI BIASE, TED	WRESTLER	POST OFFICE BOX 3859	STAMFORD, CT	06905
DI BONA, VINCENT J	DIRECTOR-PRODUCER	1912 THAYER AVE	LOS ANGELES, CA	90025
DI CARLO, JOE	BASEBALL SCOUT	N Y YANKEES, YANKEE STADIUM	BRONX, NY	10451
DI CENZO, GEORGE	ACTOR	RD #1, BOX 728		
		STONE HOLLOW FARM	PIPERSVILLE, PA	18947
DI CIANNI, RON	ARTIST	340 THOMPSON BLVD	BUFFALO GROVE, IL	60089
DI LELLO, RICHARD	SCREENWRITER	1420 BEL AIR RD	LOS ANGELES, CA	90077
DI LEO, MARIO	CINEMATOGRAPHER	7617 KESTER AVE	VAN NUYS, CA	91405
DI LEVA, ANTHONY J	ACTOR	160 W 73RD ST	NEW YORK, NY	10023
DI LORENZO, CATHERINE	ACTRESS	KRUGLOV, 8282 SUNSET BLVD	LOS ANGELES, CA	90046
DI MAGGIO, DOM	BASEBALL	162 POINT RD	MARION, MA	02738
DI MAGGIO, JOE	BASEBALL	POST OFFICE BOX 590	COPPERSTOWN, NY	13326
DI MAGGIO, LOU	COMEDIAN	151 S EL CAMINO DR	BEVERLY HILLS, CA	90212
DI MARCO, SALVATORE C	PHOTOGRAPHER	1002 COBBS ST	DREXEL HILL, PA	19026
DI MASSA, ERNANI V, JR	TV WRITER-PRODUCER	23237 KESWICK ST	CANOGA PARK, CA	91304
DI MEOLA, AL	GUITARIST	POST OFFICE BOX 68	TENAFLY, NJ	07670
DI MISCIO, ANTHONY	COMPOSER	1045 N BUENA VISTA ST	BURBANK, CA	91505
DI MORA, SHANE	BODYBUILDER	POST OFFICE BOX 15454	SAINT PETERSBURG, FL	33733
DI MUCCI, DION	SINGER	2639 NW 42ND ST	BOCA RATON, FL	33434
DI NALLO, GREGORY S	WRITER	958 24TH ST	SANTA MONICA, CA	90403
DI PASQUALE, JAMES	COMPOSER-LYRICIST	4058 WOODMAN AVE	SHERMAN OAKS, CA	91423
DI PEGO, GERALD	WRITER-PRODUCER	610 MARGUERITA AVE	SANTA MONICA, CA	90402
DI PINO, FRANK	BASEBALL	250 STADIUM PLAZA	ST LOUIS, MO	63102
DI POTO, JERRY	BASEBALL	4385 TUTT BLVD	COLORADO SPRINGS, CO	80922
DI RAMIO, ED	BASEBALL SCOUT	1060 W ADDISON ST	CHICAGO, IL	60613
DI RE, FLO	ACTRESS	1092 LOMA DR	HERMOSA BEACH, CA	90254
DI SALVO, PIO	BASEBALL TRAINER	TIGERS, TIGER STADIUM	DETROIT, MI	48216
DI SARCINA, GARY	BASEBALL	POST OFFICE BOX 2000	ANAHEIM, CA	92803
DI SARCINA, GLENN	BASEBALL	POST OFFICE BOX 4218	SOUTH BEND, IN	46634
DI SHELL, WALTER D, MD	TV WRITER	4610 AZALIA DR	TARZANA, CA	91356
DI STEFANO, DANIEL M	TV WRITER	9431 BIANCA AVE	NORTHRIDGE, CA	91325
DI TILLIO, LAWRENCE GABRIEL	WRITER	1441 1/2 S HOLT AVE	LOS ANGELES, CA	90035
DI TOSTI, BEN	COMPOSER-CONDUCTOR	1645 CAMINO DE VILLAS	BURBANK, CA	91501
DI ZENZO, CHARLES	TV WRITER	420 VIA ALMAR	PALOS VERDES, CA	90274
DI ZENZO, PATRICIA	TV WRITER	420 VIA ALMAR	PALOS VERDES, CA	90274
DIAL, DICK	DIRECTOR	3220 COLONY VIEW CIR	MALIBU, CA	90265
DIAL, WILLIAM ALLEN	ACTOR-WRITER	4171 WITZEL DR	SHERMAN OAKS, CA	91423
DIAMOND, BOB	DIRECTOR	680 W END AVE	NEW YORK, NY	10025
DIAMOND, BOBBY	ACTOR-ATTORNEY	633 CALLE ARROYO	THOUSAND OAKS, CA	91360
DIAMOND, DAVID	COMPOSER	249 EDGERTON ST	ROCHESTER, NY	14607
DIAMOND, G WILLIAM	SECRETARY OF STATE	STATE HOUSE BUILDING	AUGUSTA, GA	04333
DIAMOND, I A L	SCREENWRITER	313 EL CAMINO DR	BEVERLY HILLS, CA	90212
DIAMOND, JILL RENEE	COMPOSER-MUSIC EXEC	60 W 76TH ST #1-B	NEW YORK, NY	10024
DIAMOND, KATHERINE	ACTOR	127 W 82ND ST #9-D	NEW YORK, NY	10024
DIAMOND, MATTHEW	CHOREOGRAPHER	29 W 21ST ST, 4TH FLOOR	NEW YORK, NY	10010
DIAMOND, NEIL	SINGER-SONGWRITER	POST OFFICE BOX 3357	LOS ANGELES, CA	90028
DIAMOND, PAUL	TV WRITER	R/W/G, 8428 MELROSE PL #C	LOS ANGELES, CA	90069
DIAMOND, ROBERT R	TV DIRECTOR	680 W END AVE	NEW YORK, NY	10025
DIAMOND, VERNON K	TV DIRECTOR	5 DUXBURY RD	GREAT NECK, NY	11023
DIAMONDS, THE	C & W GROUP	IN TUNE MGMT, 1503 16TH AVE S	NASHVILLE, TN	37212
DIAMONDS, THE	VOCAL GROUP	PAR-PAR PRODS, 9560 WILSHIRE BL	BEVERLY HILLS, CA	90212
DIAMONT, DON	ACTOR	15045 SHERVIEW PL	SHERMAN OAKS, CA	91403
DIAMONT, KATHI	ACTRESS-TV HOST	4660 LA JOLLA VILLAGE DR #500	SAN DIEGO, CA	92122
DIANA	SINGER	7100 EXECUTIVE CENTER DR #100	BRENTWOOD, TN	37027

DIANA, HRH PRINCESS	PRINCESS	KENSINGTON PALACE	LONDON W8 ENGLAND
DIAZ, ALEX	BASEBALL	2850 W 20TH AVE	DENVER, CO 80211
DIAZ, CARLOS	BASEBALL	800 HOME RUN LN	MEMPHIS, TN 38104
DIAZ, CESAR	BASEBALL	POST OFFICE BOX 7845	COLUMBIA, SC 29202
DIAZ, EDDY	BASEBALL	POST OFFICE BOX 30160	SAN BERNARDINO, CA 92413
DIAZ, EDITH	ACTRESS	POST OFFICE BOX 8775	NORTH HOLLYWOOD, CA 91608
DIAZ, JUSTINO	SINGER	140 W END AVE	NEW YORK, NY 10023
DIAZ, MARIO	BASEBALL	POST OFFICE BOX 3690, STA "B"	CALGARY, ALB T2B 4M4 CANADA
DIAZ, MIKE	BASEBALL	1032 BANYAN WY	PACIFICA, CA 94044
DIAZ, RALPH	BASEBALL	POST OFFICE BOX 3566	WEST PALM BEACH, FL 33402
DIAZ, ROBERTO	BASEBALL SCOUT	250 STADIUM PLAZA	ST LOUIS, MO 63102
DIAZ, SANDY	BASEBALL	POST OFFICE BOX 661	KENOSHA, WI 53141
DIBBLE, ROB	BASEBALL	REDS, 100 RIVERFRONT STADIUM	CINCINNATI, OH 45202
DIBIE, GEORGE	TV DIRECTOR	14537 HESBY ST	SHERMAN OAKS, CA 91403
DICAPRIO, LEONARDO	ACTOR	WARNER TV, 4000 WARNER BLVD	BURBANK, CA 91522
DICHTER, LEE	FILM SOUND MIXER	3042 SHORE DR	MERRICK, NY 11566
DICK, DOUGLAS	ACTOR	604 GRETNA GREEN WY	LOS ANGELES, CA 90049
DICK, PEGGY CHANTLER	WRITER	604 GRETNA GREEN WY	LOS ANGELES, CA 90049
DICK, RALPH	BASEBALL-INSTRUCTOR	POST OFFICE BOX 4100	SEATTLE, WA 98104
DICK & DEE DEE	VOCAL DUO	17530 VENTURA BLVD #108	ENCINO, CA 91316
DICKENS, LITTLE JIMMY	SINGER-MUSICIAN	510 W CONCORD	BRENTWOOD, TN 37027
DICKERSON, BOBBY	BASEBALL	500 NORTON ST	ROCHESTER, NY 14621
DICKERSON, CHUCK	FOOTBALL COACH	BILLS, 1 BILLS DR	ORCHARD PARK, NJ 14127
DICKERSON, ERIC	FOOTBALL	RAIDERS, 332 CENTER ST	EL SEGUNDO, CA 90245
DICKERSON, ERNEST	CINEMATOGRAPHER	POST OFFICE BOX 2230	HOLLYWOOD, CA 90078
DICKERSON, NANCY	BROADCAST JOURNALIST	1811 KALORAMA SQ, NW	WASHINGTON, DC 20008
DICKEY, BILL	BASEBALL	7611 CHOCTAW RD	LITTLE ROCK, AR 72205
DICKEY, GLENN	COLUMNIST-WRITER	120 FLORENCE AVE	OAKLAND, CA 94618
DICKEY, JAMES	POET-NOVELIST	4620 LELIA'S CT, LAKE KATHERINE	COLUMBIA, SC 29206
DICKEY, LUCINDA	ACTRESS	9300 WILSHIRE BLVD #410	BEVERLY HILLS, CA 90212
DICKIES, THE	ROCK & ROLL GROUP	11116 AQUA VISTA ST #39	STUDIO CITY, CA 91602
DICKINSON, ANGIE	ACTRESS	9580 LIME ORCHARD RD	BEVERLY HILLS, CA 90210
DICKINSON, BOB	CINEMATOGRAPHER	7715 SUNSET BLVD #150	LOS ANGELES, CA 90046
DICKINSON, JUDY	GOLFER	2750 VOLUSA AVE #B	DAYTON BEACH, FL 32114
DICKINSON, WILLIAM	U S CONGRESSMAN	CITY HALL BLDG, MAIN ST	OPP, AL 36467
DICKMAN, CAROL	DIRECTOR	1552 NE QUAYSIDE TERR	MIAMI, FL 33138
DICKS, NORMAN D	U S CONGRESSMAN	500 PACIFIC AVE #301	BREMERTON, WA 98310
DICKSON, BRENDA	ACTRESS	10366 WILSHIRE BLVD #5	LOS ANGELES, CA 90024
DICKSON, DAVID A	COMPOSER	382 E DEL MAR BLVD #3	PASADENA, CA 91101
DICKSON, LANCE	BASEBALL	CUBS, 2ND & RIVERSIDE DR	DES MOINES, IA 50309
DICOPOULOS, FRANK	ACTOR	CBS-TV, "THE GUIDING LIGHT"	
		222 E 44TH ST	NEW YORK, NY 10017
DIDDLEY, BO	SINGER-GUITARIST	3697 ANDREAS HILLS DR #A	PALM SPRINGS, CA 92262
DIDIER, BOB	BASEBALL-INSTRUCTOR	544 SW 335TH ST	FEDERAL WAY, WA 98023
DIDION, JOAN	SCREENWRITER	ICM, 8899 BEVERLY BLVD	LOS ANGELES, CA 90048
DIDUCK, GERALD	HOCKEY	CANUCKS, 100 N RENFREW ST	VANCOUVER, BC V5K 3N7 CANADA
DIEHENN, ART	DIRECTOR	5817 PACKARD ST	LOS ANGELES, CA 90019
DIEHL, DIGBY R	FILM CRITIC-WRITER	788 S LAKE AVE	PASADENA, CA 91106
DIEHL, JOHN	ACTOR	15758 HARTLAND ST	VAN NUYS, CA 91405
DIEKHAUS, GRACE	TV WRITER-PRODUCER	CBS-TV, 524 W 57TH ST	NEW YORK, NY 10019
DIERKER, LARRY	BASEBALL-ANNOUNCER	POST OFFICE BOX 288	HOUSTON, TX 77001
DIERKOP, CHARLES	ACTOR	7845 TUJUNGA AVE	NORTH HOLLYWOOD, CA 91605
DIERKS, DONALD	MUSIC CRITIC	POST OFFICE BOX 191	SAN DIEGO, CA 92112
DIETHER, ANTON	SCREENWRITER	POST OFFICE BOX 1982	LOS ANGELES, CA 90028
DIETRICH, DENA	ACTRESS	1228 N LA CIENEGA BLVD #303	LOS ANGELES, CA 90069
DIETRICH, JAMES	CONDUCTOR	11547 HESBY ST	NORTH HOLLYWOOD, CA 91601
DIETRICH, RAY	DIRECTOR	3047 S KENNEWICK DR	LAS VEGAS, NV 89121
DIETRICK, GARTH	DIRECTOR	166 HARBOURSIDE CIR	JUPITER, FL 33477
DIETZ, DICK	BASEBALL COACH	POST OFFICE BOX 3448	SHREVEPORT, LA 71133
DIETZ, EILEEN	ACTRESS	2036 VISTA DEL MAR AVE	LOS ANGELES, CA 90068
DIETZ, HOWARD	LYRICIST-WRITER	180 E END AVE	NEW YORK, NY 10028
DIFFIE, JOE	SINGER-SONGWRITER	34 MUSIC SQUARE E	NASHVILLE, TN 37203
DIFFRING, ANTON	ACTOR	WM MORRIS, 31-32 SOHO SQ	LONDON W1V 5DG ENGLAND
DIGBY, GEORGE	BASEBALL SCOUT	FENWAY PARK, 4 YAWKEY WY	BOSTON, MA 02215
DIGGINS, PETER	BALLET EXECUTIVE	133 W 71ST ST	NEW YORK, NY 10023
DIGGS, DAVID H	COMPOSER	POST OFFICE BOX 1834	STUDIO CITY, CA 91604
DIGGS, TONY	BASEBALL	POST OFFICE DRAWER 4797	EL PASO, TX 79914
DIGITAL UNDERGROUND	ROCK & RILL GROUP	151 S EL CAMINO DR	BEVERLY HILLS, CA 90212
DIKE, MATT	RECORD EXECUTIVE	DELICIOUS VINYL RECORDS	
		7471 MELROSE AVE	WEST HOLLYWOOD, CA 90046
DIKEOU, JOHN, JR	BASEBALL EXECUTIVE	2850 W 20TH AVE	DENVER, CO 80211
DILBERT, BERNARD	TV WRITER	8955 BEVERLY BLVD	WEST HOLLYWOOD, CA 90048
DILG, LARRY	ACTOR	2439 IVANHOE DR	LOS ANGELES, CA 90039
DILL, SCOTT	FOOTBALL	BUCCANEERS, 1 BUCCANEER PL	TAMPA, FL 33607
DILL, TERRY	GOLFER	PGA SENIORS, 112 T P C BLVD	PONTE VEDRA BEACH, FL 32082
DILLARD, ANNIE	AUTHOR	GREGORY, 2 TUDOR PL	NEW YORK, NY 10017
DILLARD, GORDON	BASEBALL	1290 RIDER AVE	SALINAS, CA 93905
DILLARD, STEVE	BASEBALL-INSTRUCTOR	POST OFFICE BOX 288	HOUSTON, TX 77001
DILLARDS, THE	BLUEGRASS GROUP	CASE, 1016 16TH AVE S	NASHVILLE, TN 37212
DILLE, KARREN	ACTRESS	6457 MAMMOTH AVE	VAN NUYS, CA 91401
DILLE, ROBERT N	WRITER	1400 KELTON AVE #203	LOS ANGELES, CA 90024
DILLER, BARRY	FILM EXECUTIVE	1940 COLDWATER CANYON DR	BEVERLY HILLS, CA 90210
DILLER, JOHN C	BASKETBALL EXECUTIVE	KNICKS, 4 PENNYLVANIA PLAZA	NEW YORK, NY 10019
DILLER, JULIE	ACTRESS	163 S ROCKINGHAM AVE	LOS ANGELES, CA 90049
DILLER, PHYLLIS	ACTRESS-COMEDIENNE	163 S ROCKINGHAM AVE	LOS ANGELES, CA 90049

DILLINDER, ERMA	COMPOSER	5864 HARCO ST	LONG BEACH, CA 90808
DILLMAN, BRADFORD	ACTOR	770 HOT SPRINGS RD	SANTA BARBARA, CA 93103
DILLMAN BAND, THE	ROCK & ROLL GROUP	POST OFFICE BOX O	MINNEAPOLIS, MN 55331
DILLON, BILL	SINGER	POST OFFICE BOX 16540	PLANTATION, FL 33318
DILLON, DANIEL	TV DIRECTOR	14 CROSSWINDS	OLIVETTE, MO 63132
DILLON, DAVID D	ACTOR	612 BRANCH AVE	LITTLE RIVER, NJ 07739
DILLON, DEAN	SINGER-SONGWRITER	MC FADEN, 48 MUSIC SQUARE E	NASHVILLE, TN 37203
DILLON, DIANE	ARTIST	221 KANE ST	BROOKLYN, NY 11231
DILLON, JAMES	FILM DIRECTOR	9579 OLYMPIC BLVD	BEVERLY HILLS, CA 90212
DILLON, JIM	BASEBALL	POST OFFICE BOX 2437	MODESTO, CA 95351
DILLON, JOHN JOSEPH	TV DIRECTOR	241 PENNSYLVANIA AVE	CRESTWOOD, NY 10707
DILLON, KEVIN	ACTOR	49 W 9TH ST #5-B	NEW YORK, NY 10010
DILLON, MARK	DIRECTOR	18644 VINTAGE ST	NORTHRIDGE, CA 91324
DILLON, MATT	ACTOR	49 W 9TH ST #5-B	NEW YORK, NY 10010
DILLON, MELINDA	ACTRESS	3949 RAMBLA ORIENTA	MALIBU, CA 90265
DILLON, MIA	ACTRESS	606 N LARCHMONT BLVD #309	LOS ANGELES, CA 90004
DILLON, ROBERT	SCREENWRITER	CAA, 9830 WILSHIRE BLVD	BEVERLY HILLS, CA 90212
DILTZ, HENRY	SINGER-PHOTOGRAPHER	8777 LOOKOUT MOUNTAIN AVE	LOS ANGELES, CA 90046
DIMBLEBY, DAVID	REPORTER-PUBLISHER	14 KING ST	RICHMOND, SURREY ENGLAND
DIMBLEBY, JONATHAN	AUTHOR	ROSEMAN, 8 POLAND ST	LONDON W1 ENGLAND
DIMICHELE, FRANK	BASEBALL	812 TASKER ST	PHILADELPHIA, PA 19148
DIMRY, CHARLES	FOOTBALL	BRONCOS, 13655 BRONCOS PKWY	ENGLEWOOD, CO 80112
DIMSDALE, HOWARD	WRITER	2662 CARMAR DR	LOS ANGELES, CA 90046
DINEEN, KEVIN	HOCKEY	WHALERS, 1 CIVIC CENTER PLAZA	HARTFORD, CT 06103
DINEHART, ALAN	WRITER	5040 TUJUNGA AVE #16	NORTH HOLLYWOOD, CA 91601
DINGELL, JOHN D	U S CONGRESSMAN	214 E ELM AVE #105	MONROE, MI 48161
DINKINS, DAVID	MAJOR	GRACIE MANSION, 888 9TH AVE	NEW YORK, NY 10010
DINMAN, DICK	ACTOR	5255 BELLINGHAM AVE #215	NORTH HOLLYWOOD, CA 91607
DINNERSTEIN, HARVEY	ARTIST	933 PRESIDENT ST	BROOKLYN, NY 11215
DINOTA, PAT	ACTRESS	1951 1/2 N ARGYLE AVE	HOLLYWOOD, CA 90068
DINSDALE, REECE	ACTOR	HAMMOND, GOLDEN HOUSE	
		29 GREAT PULTENEY ST	LONDON W1R 3DD ENGLAND
DINYER, ERIC	ARTIST	1 E 2ND ST	BROOKLYN, NY 11218
DINZAY, AMADO	BASEBALL EXECUTIVE	POST OFFICE BOX 90111	ARLINGTON, TX 76004
DIO	ROCK & ROLL GROUP	NIJI MGMT, 5937 DONNA AVE	TARZANA, CA 91356
DIOGUARDI, PAUL C	COMPOSER-CONDUCTOR	11517 CUMPSTON ST #1	NORTH HOLLYWOOD, CA 91601
DION	SINGER-SONGWRITER	SEE - DI MUCCI, DION	
DION, COLLEEN	ACTRESS-SINGER	CBS-TV, "THE BOLD & BEAUTIFUL"	
		7800 BEVERLY BLVD #3371	LOS ANGELES, CA 90036
DIONNE, DANNY	SINGER	CUDE, 519 N HALIFAX AVE	DAYTONA BEACH, FL 32018
DIOS, KELLY	TV DIRECTOR	1234 WESTGATE AVE #2	LOS ANGELES, CA 90025
DIRE STRAITS, THE	ROCK & ROLL GROUP	10 SOUTHWICK MEWS	LONDON W2 ENGLAND
DIRK, ROBERT	HOCKEY	CANUCKS, 100 N RENFREW ST	VANCOUVER, BC V5K 3N7 CANADA
DIRKSON, DOUGLAS	ACTOR	740 W 24TH ST #10	SAN PEDRO, CA 90731
DIRT, PHIL & THE DOZERS	ROCK & ROLL GROUP	DENNIS, 1002 18TH AVE S	NASHVILLE, TN 37212
DIRT BAND, THE	C & W GROUP	SEE - NITTY GRITTY DIRT BAND, THE	
DISHMAN, CRIS	FOOTBALL	OILERS, 6910 FANNIN ST	HOUSTON, TX 77070
DISHY, BOB	ACTOR-WRITER	20 E 9TH ST	NEW YORK, NY 10003
DISKIN, JOY MATTHEWS	ACTRESS	4225 GLEN ALBYN DR	LOS ANGELES, CA 90065
DISMUKE, JAMIE	BASEBALL	POST OFFICE BOX 4669	CHARLESTON, WV 25304
DISNEY, ROY E	WRITER-PRODUCER	500 S BUENA VISTA ST	BURBANK, CA 91521
DISNEY, ROY P	ANIMATOR	11650 SUNSHINE TERR	STUDIO CITY, CA 91604
DISTAL, SACHA	SINGER	3 QUAI MALAQUAIS	PARIS 75006 FRANCE
DISTANCE, THE	C & W GROUP	POST OFFICE BOX 4087	MISSOULA, MT 59806
DISTEFANO, BENNY	BASEBALL	POST OFFICE BOX 27045	TUCSON, AZ 85726
DITKA, MIKE	FOOTBALL-COACH	BEARS, 250 N WASHINGTON RD	LAKE FOREST, IL 60045
DITTRICH, JOHN	BASEBALL EXECUTIVE	POST OFFICE BOX 1886	COLUMBUS, GA 31902
DIVAC, VLADE	BASKETBALL	POST OFFICE BOX 10	INGLEWOOD, CA 90306
DIVINE	ROCK & ROLL GROUP	2025 BROADWAY #28-C	NEW YORK, NY 10023
DIVINYLS	ROCK & ROLL GROUP	POST OFFICE BOX 1524	POTTS POINT, NSW 2011 AUSTRALIA
DIVISEK, BARBARA	CASTING DIRECTOR	2741 WOODHAVERN DR	LOS ANGELES, CA 90068
DIVISEK, KAREN	CASTING DIRECTOR	2741 WOODHAVEN DR	LOS ANGELES, CA 90068
DIXIE	SINGER	5625 "O" STREET BLDG #7	LINCOLN, NE 68510
DIXIE DOUGHBOYS, THE	C & W GROUP	MUSKRATS, 44 N CENTRAL AVE	ELMSFORD, NY 10523
DIXIE DREGS, THE	ROCK & ROLL GROUP	5775 PEACHTREE DUNWOODY	ATLANTA, GA 30342
DIXIE HUMMINGBIRDS, THE	VOCAL GROUP	CASE, 1016 16TH AVE S	NASHVILLE, TN 37212
DIXIELAND RHYTHM KINGS, THE	JAZZ GROUP	POST OFFICE BOX 12403	ATLANTA, GA 30355
DIXIT, NORMA	ACTRESS	TROLAN, 30 BURRARD RD	LONDON NW6 1DB ENGLAND
DIXON, ALAN J	U S SENATOR	230 S DEARBORN ST #3996	CHICAGO, IL 60604
DIXON, ALICIA	ACTRESS	4185 ARCH DR #316	STUDIO CITY, CA 91604
DIXON, BEVERLY	ACTRESS	4919 COLDWATER CANYON AVE #6	SHERMAN OAKS, CA 91423
DIXON, CHRISTOPHER P	TV DIRECTOR-PRODUCER	116 E 63RD ST	NEW YORK, NY 10021
DIXON, COLIN	BASEBALL	POST OFFICE BOX 1718	NEW BRITAIN, CT 06050
DIXON, DICKIE	BASEBALL	POST OFFICE BOX 48	VISALIA, CA 93279
DIXON, DON	SINGER-SONGWRITER	SIMMONS, 5 W HARGETT ST, 10TH FR	RALEIGH, NC 27601
DIXON, DONNA	ACTRESS	RICH, 2400 WHITMAN PL	LOS ANGELES, CA 90068
DIXON, EDDIE	BASEBALL	POST OFFICE BOX 450	BUFFALO, NY 14205
DIXON, FITZ EUGENE, JR	BASEBALL EXECUTIVE	POST OFFICE BOX 7575	PHILADELPHIA, PA 19101
DIXON, FLOYD	FOOTBALL	FALCONS, SUWANEE RD AT I-85	SUWANEE, GA 30174
DIXON, IVAN	ACTOR-DIRECTOR	3432 N MARGENGO AVE	ALTADENA, CA 91001
DIXON, JEANNE	PSYCHIC	1225 CONECTICUT AVE #411, NW	WASHINGTON, DC 20036
DIXON, JESSY	SINGER	2008 S YALE ST #F	SANTA ANA, CA 92704
DIXON, JOHN ROBERT	ACTOR	3800 BARHAM BLVD #303	LOS ANGELES, CA 90068
DIXON, JULIAN C	U S CONGRESSMAN	5100 W GOLDLEAF CIR #208	LOS ANGELES, CA 90056
DIXON, MASON	C & W GROUP	SEE - MASON DIXON	

R & R ENTERPRISES

Buying and Selling AUTOGRAPHS Since 1980.

P.O. Box 2000 • Amherst, NH 03031 • USA

(603) 672-6611

FAX (603) 672-6442

(All signed photos are 8x10 and not inscribed to anyone)

GUARANTEED AUTHENTIC AUTOGRAPHS

Sam Snead $65

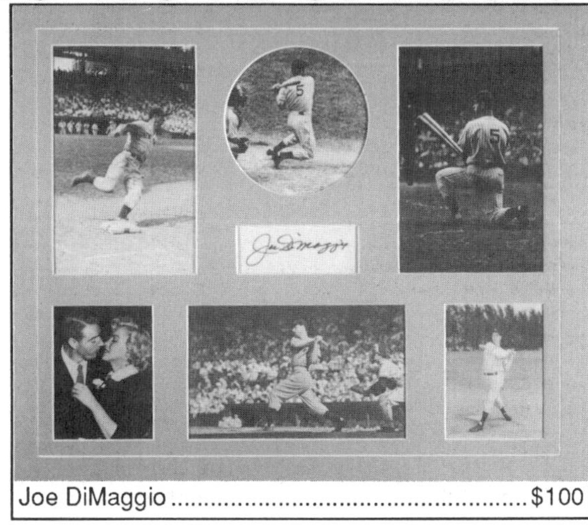

Joe DiMaggio $100

photos of Henson and the muppets $125
Audrey Hepburn - 50's pose $60
Jean Hersholt - Actor. Album pg w/portrait (11x14) $25
Charlton Heston - As Ben Hur $20
Alger Hiss - Ink sig matted with b/w photo (9x12) $45
Dustin Hoffman - Actor. Signature matted with three color photos $45
The Hollies - 2 album pages w/entire band signatures with b/w photo (11x14) $150
The Honeymooners - TV cast. Four 3x5 cards matted with color photo of the group $200
Anthony Hopkins - 8x10 signed by star of "Silence of the Lambs" in character movie still as "Hannibal Lector" $65
Miriam Hopkins - Actress. Album pg w/40's pose (11x14) $25
Bob Hoskins - With Roger Rabbit $35
Harry Houdini - Magician. Signed endorsed check (1922) .. $750
Whitney Houston - Signature matted with great color photo and a "45" of the "Greatest Love of All" $95
Elston Howard - Baseball. 3x5 card w/color photos (11x14) . $50
Moe Howard - Stooge. Envelope signed, matted with b/w photo $100
William D. Howells - Writer. 1 pg ANS (1873) w/formal portrait $45
Carl Hubbell - Baseball. 3x5 matted w/array of pitching action photos $50
Victor Hugo - Author. "Les Miserables" clip signature matted with b/w portrait $350
Brett Hull - Hockey. 2 3x5 cards w/2 b/w photos of this legendary hockey player $50
Hubert Humphrey - A TLS with a small b/w portrait $45
Jim "Catfish" Hunter - Baseball player. 3x5 matted with two color photos in uniform $35
Rachel Hunter - In Swim Suit $65
Billy Idol - Signed close-up matted with "White Wedding" 45 $65
Indigo Girls - On Stage $75
Kathy Ireland - Nice pose of beautiful model $75
Jeremy Irons - Recent pose $35
Alan Jackson - Singer. Recent color picture signed $40
Kate Jackson - Facial pose $25
LaToya Jackson - Sexy pose $50
Michael Jackson - Recent pose of this talented muscian/dancer $395
Victoria Jackson - Pretty pose $20
Harry James - Signed real estate assessment dated 1968 with b/w picture $75
Tony Dow & Jerry Mathers - Actors. B/w portrait signed by both of the Cleaver brothers from "Leave It To Beaver" TV show $35
Joan Jett - Musician. Signed 3x5 card matted w/color picture $45
Billy Joel - Singer. b/w photo signed, matted w/45 "It's still Rock & Roll To Me" (12x18.5) $50
Elton John - 8x10 photo matted w/45 record of "Goodbye Yellow Brick Road" $100
Al Jolsen - Actor. Beautiful signature of the actor w/2 b/w photos, one in black face $150
Buck Jones - Cowboy. Album page matted with 2 b/w photos $200
George Jones - Singer. 3x5 card matted with 2 b/w younger photos $35
Jennifer Jones - Actress. 1 pg contract, signed, matted w/nice color photo of actress (12x16) $150
Helen Kane - Album page matted with b/w photo (9x12) $295
Boris Karloff - Actor. Album page matted with photo as Frankenstein $250

Michael Keaton - Beetlejuice $35
Gene Kelly - Dancer and actor. 3x5 card matted with array of photos $50
Jack Kemp - Football, politician. 3x5 matted with photos as QB and as Congressman $45
Kay Kendall - Actress. Album pg w/studio portrait from the 50's $35
Robert Kennedy - Signature matted w/portrait $350
Rose Kennedy - Signature matted with 70's portrait $75
Margot Kidder - Portrait $20
B.B. King - Musician. Sig matted w/photo of musician $50
Billie Jean King - 60's tennis $20
Stephen King - Author. 3x5 card matted with portrait $50
Tawny Kitaen - Model. Lovely signature on 3x5 card matted with picture $35
Kevin Kline - Portrait $15
Jack Klugman - As Oscar $20
Fuzzy Knight - Actor. Album page with western photo (11x14) $25
Sandy Koufax - Baseball. Signed card matted with 4 consecutive action photos starting with the wind up $50
Fritz Kreisler - American violinist and composer. 3x5 signed card matted with b/w photo $50
Kris Kristoferson - Casual close-up of this musician/actor $30
LA Guns - Rock group. b/w photo signed $45
Bert Lahr - Actor. Album page matted with photo as the Lion $250
Arthur Lake - Album pg matted with b/w photo (11x14) $50
Veronica Lake - Deceased actress. Signed album page matted with alluring b/w photo $95
Jake LaMotta - Fight pose $30
Elisa Landi - Actress. Pg w/30's pose (11x14) $35
Diane Lane - Actress. 3x5 matted w/photos of actress $35
Harry Langdon - Actor. 1 pg TLS (1932) cancelling his contract with Mascot Pictures Corp $150
Don Larson - Final pitch $20
Cyndi Lauper - In costume pose of this "fun" pop star $35
Kelly LeBrock - Actress/Model. 3x5 matted w/2 color photos of this gorgeous model (12x16) $35
Robert E Lee - Portion of document matted with two photos $2800
Tommy Lee - 1/2 length pose of musician $50
Janet Leigh - 50's pose $10
Vivien Leigh - Signature matted with Scarlett photo $450
Al Lewis - as Grandpa $20
Carl Lewis - Track star. 3x5 card matted with two color photos $50
Jerry Lee Lewis - Picture of pianist at the keyboards, full length $75
Heather Locklear - Actress/model. 3x5 matted w/2 color photos $35
Gina Lollabrigida - Actress. Sig attractively matted w/color sexy photo $35
Traci Lords - Sexy actress in steamy pose $65
Greg Louganis - Swimmer. Signature matted with action photos $45
Bessie Love - Actress. Signed album pg matted with photo .. $35
Love Boat - All five $50
Carey Lowell - from Bond $35
J.R. Lowell - Poet. Signed card with engraved portrait (9x12) $25
Bela Lugosi - Album page matted with two photos as Dracula $495
Dolph Lundgren - Shirtless pose $35
Kelly Lynch - sexy pose $50
Carol Lynley - 50's pose $20
Loretta Lynn - Signed b/w photo w/single of "Coal Miner's Daughter" $40
Louise L'Amour - Author. 3x5 card matted with portrait at typewriter $100

Douglas MacArthur - Signed Waldorf Astoria memorandum w/a b/w photo $200
Virginia Madsen - Actress. 3x5 matted with two color portraits $35
Boom Boom Mancini - Fight pose $25
Manfred Mann - Rock band. Card signed by all 5 members. Matted with b/w photo $95
Manfred Mann Band - Band. Popular in 60's album page signed by all 5 members matted with photo $125
Barry Manilow - portrait $50
Thomas Mann - Author. 1 pg note (1925) signed, matted with b/w portrait .. $200
Mickey Mantle - Baseball. HOF card signed, matted with 2 color photos $75
Marla Maples - Leggy pose $45
Marion Marsh - Actress. Album page signed in ink, matted with b/w portrait $45
Dean Martin - Singer/actor. Signed check w/color performing photo $95
Mary Martin - Actress. 3x5 card w/pose as Peter Pan "flying" $35
Pamela Sue Martin - Portrait $15
Steve Martin - A favorite comedian in serious pose in suit $25
Martin & Lewis - Comedians. Two 3x5 cards matted w/a color photograph ... $50
Raymond Massey - Actor. Card w/portrait (11x14) $25
Johnny Mathis - Singer. Signed card matted w/attractive color photo and "Chances Are" single $50
Kathy Mattea - Musician. 8x10 color photo of popular singer matted with signed 3x5 card $35
Don Mattingly - Baseball. 3x5 card signed, matted with color photo in Yankees uniform $35
Willie Mays - HOF plaque signed, matted with b/w portrait ... $65
Christa McAuliffe - Teacher in space. Lovely signature matted with four color photos $750
George B McClellan - American army officer important in the civil war. Signed receipt matted with b/w portrait $200
Tim McCoy - Actor. Signature matted with western photo ... $100
Reba McEntire - 3x5 card matted with photo and single "Whoever's in New England" $50
Elle McPherson - Model. 3x5 card w/2 color poses, one semi-nude $40
Butterfly McQueen - Actress. Signed check with b/w photo as "Prissy" from "GWTW" $75
John Mellencamp - Singer. Signed 3x5 card matted w/color picture and "Jack & Diane" single $50
Andrew Mellon - Financier. Sig w/portrait (9x12) $50
Yehudi Menuhin - Violinist. 3x5 matted with b/w of this famous violinist in action (11x14) $45
George Michael - Casual pose of this rock star in leather jeacket $85
Alyssa Milano - Actress. 3x5 matted with two color poses $40
Marilyn Miller - Dancer/singer. She died of poisoning in 1937. Album page (1933) w/dancing pose (12x16) $50
Donna Mills - pretty pose $20
Ronnie Milsap - Signed photo matted w/single "Lost in the Fifties Tonight" $50
Yvette Mimieux - Actress. Signature matted with two color poses ... $35
Liza Minelli - Singer & actress. 2 pg (1979) United Artist agreement for the delivery of one 16mm print of the film "New York, New York" solely for her private use $200
Tom Mix - Album page matted with black and white western pose $150
Marilyn Monroe - Actress. Signed playbill on front cover, matted with two color photos $2250
Ashley Montana - swim suit $65

Name	Occupation	Address	City / Zip
DIXON, PENNY C	WRITER-PRODUCER	555 W 57TH ST #1230	NEW YORK, NY 10019
DIXON, PETER	ACTOR	1350 EDGECLIFFE DR #10	LOS ANGELES, CA 90026
DIXON, PETER LEE	TV WRITER	31875 SEA LEVEL DR	MALIBU, CA 90265
DIXON, RANDY	FOOTBALL	POST OFFICE BOX 535000	INDIANPOLIS, IN 46253
DIXON, RICKEY	FOOTBALL	BENGALS, 200 RIVERFRONT STADIUM	CINCINNATI, OH 45202
DIXON, ROB & LOST COWBOY BAND	C & W GROUP	POST OFFICE BOX 57291	DALLAS, TX 75207
DIXON, SARAH H	WRITER-PRODUCER	31875 SEA LEVEL DR	MALIBU, CA 90265
DIXON, STEVE	BASEBALL	POST OFFICE BOX 5599	LITTLE ROCK, AR 72215
DIXON, WALT	BASEBALL SCOUT	N Y YANKEES, YANKEE STADIUM	BRONX, NY 10451
DIXON, WILLIE	GUITARIST	CAMERON, 2001 W MAGNOLIA BLVD	BURBANK, CA 91506
DIZON, JESSE	ACTOR-WRITER	POST OFFICE BOX 8933	UNIVERSAL CITY, CA 91608
DJ JAZZY JEFF & FRESH PRINCE	RAP DUO	298 ELIZABETH ST #1	NEW YORK, NY 10012
DLUGOZIMA, ROB	BASEBALL EXECUTIVE	POST OFFICE BOX 507	DURHAM, NC 27702
DMYTRYK, EDWARD	DIRECTOR	8729 LOOKOUT MOUNTAIN AVE	LOS ANGELES, CA 90046
DMYTRYK, MICHAEL	DIRECTOR	3637 AVENIDA DEL SOL	STUDIO CITY, CA 91604
DO'QUI, ROBERT	ACTOR	1529 S ELLSMERE AVE	LOS ANGELES, CA 90019
DOANE, SAMANTHA	ACTRESS	20550 STAGG ST	CANOGA PARK, CA 91306
DOBBINS, BILL	WRITER-BODYBUILDER	2012 VETERAN AVE	LOS ANGELES, CA 90025
DOBBINS, SCOTT	TV DIRECTOR-PRODUCER	162 W 13TH ST #54	NEW YORK, NY 10011
DOBBS, CHARLOTTE M	TV WRITER	1818 FAIRBURN AVE #303	LOS ANGELES, CA 90025
DOBBS, SHELIA	SINGER	BUN JAK, 331 PROSPECT ST	BERLIN, NH 03570
DOBBS, WILLIAM ARTHUR	TV DIRECTOR	2007 HILEMAN RD	FALLSS CHURCH, VA 22043
DOBIE, ALAN	ACTOR	PONTUS, MOLASH	KENT CT4 8HW ENGLAND
DOBKIN, LAWRENCE	ACT-WRI-DIR	1787 OLD RANCH RD	LOS ANGELES, CA 90049
DOBKOWITZ, ROGER	TV PRODUCER	CBS-TV, "THE PRICE IS RIGHT"	
		7800 BEVERLY BLVD	LOS ANGELES, CA 90036
DOBRO, CARRIE	ACTRESS	8665 WILSHIRE BLVD #208	BEVERLY HILLS, CA 90211
DOBROFSKY, NEAL H	WRITER	839 19TH ST	SANTA MONICA, CA 90403
DOBROLSKY, BILL	BASEBALL	POST OFFICE BOX 855	BELOIT, WI 53511
DOBROW, JOELLE	TV DIRECTOR-PRODUCER	1615 REDCLIFF AVE	LOS ANGELES, CA 90026
DOBSON, BRIDGET	TV WRITER-PRODUCER	221 E CONSTANCE AVE	SANTA BARBARA, CA 93105
DOBSON, DR JAMES C	AUTHOR-RADIO PERS	"FOCUS ON THE FAMILY"	
		420 N CASCADE AVE	COLRORADO SPRINGS, CO 80903
DOBSON, JAMES	ACTOR	8464 COLE CREST DR	LOS ANGELES, CA 90046
DOBSON, JEROME	TV WRITER-PRODUCER	221 E CONSTANCE AVE	SANTA BARBARA, CA 93105
DOBSON, KEVIN	ACTOR-DIRECTOR	11930 IREDELL ST	STUDIO CITY, CA 91604
DOBSON, MARIAH	ACTRESS	11930 IREDELL ST	STUDIO CITY, CA 91604
DOBSON, PAT	BASEBALL-COACH	5318 SW 26TH AVE	CAPE CORAL, FL 33914
DOBTCHEFF, VERNON	ACTOR	MC REDDIE, 91 REGENT ST	LONDON W1R 7TB ENGLAND
DOBY, LARRY	BASEBALL	NISHUANA RD #45	MONTCLAIR, NJ 07042
DOCHERTY, JAMES J	SCREENWRITER	8955 BEVERLY BLVD	WEST HOLLYWOOD, CA 90048
DOCHERTY, RICH	DIRECTOR	40 W 86TH ST #2-D	NEW YORK, NY 10024
DOCHTERMANN, RUDOLPH	WRITER-PRODUCER	12801 MARTHA ST	NORTH HOLLYWOOD, CA 91607
DOCHTERMANN, WOLFRAM J	DIRECTOR	46 SANTO DOMINGO DR	RANCHO MIRAGE, CA 92270
DOCKSTADER, DONNA	CASTING DIRECTOR	MCA/UNIVERSAL STUDIOS, INC	
		100 UNIVERSAL CITY PLAZA	UNIVERSAL CITY, CA 91608
DOCTOR & THE MEDICS	ROCK & ROLL GROUP	53 GREEK ST	LONDON W1 ENGLAND
DOCTOROW, E L	SCREENWRITER	RANDOM HOUSE, 201 E 50TH ST	NEW YORK, NY 10022
DODA, CAROL	DANCER	POST OFFICE BOX 387	FREMONT, CA 94537
DODD, CHRISTOPHER J	U S SENATOR	444 RUSSELL SENATE OFFICE BLDG	WASHINGTON, DC 20510
DODD, ED	CARTOONIST	POST OFFICE BOX 76	ORLANDO, FL 32802
DODEZ, RAY	FOOTBALL REFEREE	NFL, 410 PARK AVE	NEW YORK, NY 10022
DODGE, RICHARD	DIRECTOR	2254 N GOWER ST	LOS ANGELES, CA 90068
DODGE, SUE ELLEN	SINGER	6750 W 75TH ST, BLDG #2-A	OVERLAND PARK, KS 66204
DODGE, TOM	BASEBALL	POST OFFICE BOX 1742	PALM SPRINGS, CA 92263
DODSON, BO	BASEBALL	POST OFFICE DRAWER 4797	EL PASO, TX 79914
DODSON, PAT	BASEBALL	844 GLENWAY DR	INGLEWOOD, CA 90302
DODSON, RICHARD E	NEWS CORRESPONDENT	NBC NEWS, 4001 NEBRASKA AV, SW	WASHINGTON, DC 20016
DOE, KELLY	CARTOONIST	POST OFFICE BOX 5533	SAN JOSE, CA 95190
DOEL, FRANCES M	WRITER	11611 CHENAULT ST #219	LOS ANGELES, CA 90049
DOELGER, FRANK G	TV EXECUTIVE	GROUP W, 90 PARK AVE	NEW YORK, NY 10016
DOERR, BOBBY	BASEBALL	33705 ILLAMO AGNESS RD	AGNESS, OR 97406
DOFFEK, SCOTT	BASEBALL	POST OFFICE BOX 28268	SAN ANTONIO, TX 78228
DOHENY, LAWRENCE	TV DIRECTOR	38 COLGATE DR	PLAINVIEW, NY 11803
DOHERTY, JOHN	BASEBALL (COACH)	FENWAY PARK, 4 YAWKEY WY	BOSTON, MA 02215
DOHERTY, JOHN	BASEBALL (PITCHER)	TIGERS, TIGER STADIUM	DETROIT, MI 48216
DOHERTY, PETER M	NEWS CORRES-WRITER	ABC NEWS, 1717 DE SALES ST, NW	WASHINGTON, DC 20036
DOHERTY, SHANNEN	ACTRESS	5700 WILSHIRE BLVD #575	LOS ANGELES, CA 90036
DOKKEN	ROCK & ROLL GROUP	Q TIME, 80 WARWICK GARDENS	LONDON W14 8PR ENGLAND
DOKOFF, BARRY M	CINEMATOGRAPHER	31770 BROAD BEACH RD	MALIBU, CA 90265
DOKTOR, PAUL	MUSICIAN	215 W 88TH ST	NEW YORK, NY 10024
DOLACK, DICK	FOOTBALL REFEREE	NFL, 410 PARK AVE	NEW YORK, NY 10022
DOLAN, ANTHONY	JOURNALIST	1600 PENNSYLVANIA AVE, NW	WASHINGTON, DC 20500
DOLAN, DON	ACTOR	14228 EMELITA ST	VAN NUYS, CA 91401
DOLAN, ELLEN	ACTRESS	CBS-TV, "AS THE WORLD TURNS"	
		524 W 57TH ST #5330	NEW YORK, NY 10019
DOLAN, JULIE	ACTRESS	2029 CENTURY PARK E #600	LOS ANGELES, CA 90067
DOLAN, MARY ANNE	COLUMNIST	UPS, 4900 MAIN ST, 9TH FLOOR	KANSAS CITY, MO 64112
DOLAN, TRENT	ACTOR	1408 RISING GLEN RD	LOS ANGELES, CA 90069
DOLBY, THOMAS	SINGER-SONGWRITER	20 MANCHESTER SQ	LONDON W1 ENGLAND
DOLE, ELIZABETH	POLITICIAN	2510 VIRGINIA AVE #112, NW	WASHINGTON, DC 20037
DOLE, ROBERT	U S SENATOR	2510 VIRGINIA AVE #112, NW	WASHINGTON, DC 20037
DOLEMAN, CHRIS	FOOTBALL	VIKINGS, 9520 VIKING DR	EDEN PRAIRIE, MN 55344
DOLENZ, AMI	ACTRESS	6058 SAINT CLAIR AVE	NORTH HOLLYWOOD, CA 91607
DOLENZ, MICKEY	ACT-MUS-PROD	2921 W ALAMEDA AVE	BURBANK, CA 91505

DOLIN, GERALD	COMPOSER	5961 CHULA VISTA WY #5	LOS ANGELES, CA	90068
DOLL, CHRISTOPHER	TV PRODUCER	WHITE BRIARS, SLINFOLD, HORSHAM	SUSSEX RH13 7RP	ENGLAND
DOLL, STEVE	WRESTLER	8725 N CHAUTAUQUA BLVD	PORTLAND, OR	97217
DOLL, VICKI LYNN	SINGER	830 GLASTONBURY RD #614	NASHVILLE, TN	37217
DOLLAS, BOBBY	HOCKEY	RED WINGS, 600 CIVIC CENTER DR	DETROIT, MI	48226
DOLLINGER, STEPHEN	DIRECTOR	24017 PARK GRANADA	CALABASAS, CA	91302
DOLMAN, ROBERT H	TV WRITER	4716 INDIANOLA WY	LA CANADA, CA	91011
DOLMATCH, HANK	TV PRODUCER	228 W 71ST ST #14-J	NEW YORK, NY	10023
DOLNY, JOSEPH J	COMPOSER	5116 CAROLI LN	LA CANADA, CA	91011
DOLPHIN, JOSEPH	ACTOR	698 W END AVE	NEW YORK, NY	10025
DOMBASLE, ARIELLE	ACTRESS	31 AVE DE CHAMPS-ELYSSES	F-75008 PARIS	FRANCE
DOMBROWSKI, DAVID	BASEBALL EXECUTIVE	EXPOS, 4545 DE COUBERTIN AVE	MONTREAL, QUE H1V 3P2	CANADA
DOMBROWSKI, JIM	FOOTBALL	SAINTS, 1500 POYDRAS ST	NEW ORLEANS, LA	90112
DOMECQ, RAY	BASEBALL	POST OFFICE BOX 1721	SPARTANBURG, SC	29304
DOMENICI, PETE	U S SENATOR	625 SILVER #120, SW	ALBUQUERQUE, NM	87102
DOMI, TIE	HOCKEY	POST OFFICE BOX 90111	ARLINGTON, TX	76004
DOMINELLO, LAWRENCE A	COMPOSER	1219 N COLUMBUS AVE #C	GLENDALE, CA	91202
DOMINGO, PLACIDO	TENOR	10601 WILSHIRE BLVD #1502	LOS ANGELES, CA	90024
DOMINGUEZ, JAY & STONEY RIDGE	C & W GROUP	ALAMO TALENT, 217 ARDEN GROVE	SAN ANTONIO, TX	78215
DOMINGUEZ, KEN	BASEBALL COACH	POST OFFICE BOX 2148	WOODBRIDGE, VA	22193
DOMINO, CHUCK	BASEBALL EXECUTIVE	POST OFFICE BOX 15050	READING, PA	19612
DOMINO, FATS	SINGER-PIANIST	5525 MARAIS ST	NEW ORLEANS, LA	70117
DOMOKOS, CHARLES A	WRITER	21205 LESSEN ST #4	CHATSWORTH, CA	91311
DON, CARL	ACTOR	333 W 57TH ST	NEW YORK, NY	10019
DONAHOE, TERRY	ACTRESS	WM MORRIS, 1350 AVE OF AMERICAS	NEW YORK, NY	10019
DONAHUE, BARBARA L S	TV DIRECTOR	GRAND PRIX, 35 MEAD AVE	COS COB, CT	06807
DONAHUE, ELINOR	ACTRESS	4525 LEMP AVE	NORTH HOLLYWOOD, CA	91602
DONAHUE, JAMES	ACTOR	BALDWIN, 501 5TH AVE	NEW YORK, NY	10017
DONAHUE, MITCH	FOOTBALL	S F 49ERS, 4949 CENTENNIAL BL	SANTA CLARA, CA	95054
DONAHUE, PHIL	TV HOST-AUTHOR	420 E 54TH ST #22-F	NEW YORK, NY	10022
DONAHUE, TIM	BASEBALL	POST OFFICE BOX 3452	KINSTON, NC	28502
DONAHUE, TROY	ACTOR	1022 EUCLID AVE #1	SANTA MONICA, CA	90403
DONALD, TREMAYNE	BASEBALL	POST OFFICE BOX 12557	ST PETERSBURG, FL	33733
DONALDSON, HERBERT	COMPOSER	14409 VALLEY VISTA BLVD	SHERMAN OAKS, CA	91403
DONALDSON, JAMES	BASKETBALL	REUNION ARENA, 777 SPORTS ST	DALLAS, TX	75207
DONALDSON, JEFF	FOOTBALL	FALCONS, SUWANEE RD AT I-85	SUWANEE, GA	30174
DONALDSON, NORMA	ACTRESS	CBS-TV, "YOUNG & THE RESTLESS"		
		7800 BEVERLY BLVD #3305	LOS ANGELES, CA	90036
DONALDSON, RAY	FOOTBALL	POST OFFICE BOX 535000	INDIANPOLIS, IN	46253
DONALDSON, SAM	JOURNALIST	4452 VOLTA PL, NW	WASHINGTON, DC	20007
DONATELL, ED	FOOTBALL COACH	N Y JETS, 1000 FULTON AVE	HEMPSTEAD, NY	11550
DONATI, WILLIAM	COMPOSER	11550 KLING ST	NORTH HOLLYWOOD, CA	91602
DONATI, WILLIAM R	DIRECTOR	POST OFFICE BOX 63, CANAL ST	NEW YORK, NY	10013
DONATO, JUDITH A	TV WRITER	619 MILLARD RD	WAYNE, PA	19087
DONDERO, PAUL	MUSICIAN	POST OFFICE BOX 9388	STANFORD, CA	94305
DONEN, STANLEY	FILM DIRECTOR	300 STONE CANYON RD	LOS ANGELES, CA	90077
DONFELD	COSTUME DESIGNER	2900 HUTTON DR	BEVERLY HILLS, CA	90210
DONIAN, BRIAN	TV CRITIC	POST OFFICE BOX 500	WASHINGTON, DC	20044
DONIGER, WALTER	WRI-DIR-PROD	555 HUNTLEY DR	LOS ANGELES, CA	90048
DONIZETTI, MARIO	ARTIST	VIA ROCCA 13, 24100	BELGAMO	ITALY
DONLAN, YOLANDE	ACTRESS-WRITER	LONDON MGT, 235-241 REGENT ST	LONDON W1R 4PH	ENGLAND
DONLEY, JOHN	NEWS CORRESPONDENT	NBC NEWS, 4001 NEBRASKA AV, SW	WASHINGTON, DC	20016
DONLEY, JOHN	TV WRITER	127 S LARCHMONT BLVD	LOS ANGELES, CA	90004
DONNA-MARIE	ACTRESS	7080 HOLLYWOOD BLVD #704	HOLLYWOOD, CA	90028
DONNALLEY, KEVIN	FOOTBALL	OILERS, 6910 FANNIN ST	HOUSTON, TX	77070
DONNELL, KATHY	SCREENWRITER	1340 SANBORN AVE	LOS ANGELES, CA	90027
DONNELLEY, ALEXANDRIA	ACTRESS-MODEL	9744 WILSHIRE BLVD #308	BEVERLY HILLS, CA	90212
DONNELLY, BRIAN	U S CONGRESSMAN	47 HANCOCK ST	QUINCY, MA	02169
DONNELLY, DENNIS	DIRECTOR	17751 SABBIADORO WY	PACIFIC PALISADES, CA	90272
DONNELLY, GORD	HOCKEY	JETS, 15-1430 MAROONS RD	WINNIPEG, MAN R3G OL5	CANADA
DONNELLY, MIKE	HOCKEY	POST OFFICE BOX 17013	INGLEWOOD, CA	90308
DONNELLY, RICH	BASEBALL-COACH	POST OFFICE BOX 7000	PITTSBURGH, PA	15212
DONNELLY, RICK	FOOTBALL	SEAHAWKS, 11220 NE 53RD ST	KIRKLAND, WA	98033
DONNELLY, THOMAS MICHEL	SCREENWRITER	UTA, 9560 WILSHIRE BL, 5TH FL	BEVERLY HILLS, CA	90212
DONNELS, CHRIS	BASEBALL	POST OFFICE BOX 1211	NORFOLK, VA	23502
DONNER, CLIVE	FILM DIRECTOR	1466 N KINGS RD	LOS ANGELES, CA	90069
DONNER, JILL SHERMAN	TV WRITER	9300 WILSHIRE BLVD #410	BEVERLY HILLS, CA	90212
DONNER, JORN	DIRECTOR	POHJOISRANTA 12	00170 HELSINKI 17	FINLAND
DONNER, REBECCA	ACTRESS	11712 MOORPARK ST #204	STUDIO CITY, CA	91604
DONNER, RICHARD	FILM DIRECTOR	4000 WARNER BLVD, BLDG #102	BURBANK, CA	91522
DONNER, ROBERT	ACTOR	3828 GLENRIDGE DR	SHERMAN OAKS, CA	91423
DONNETT, JACQUELINE	TV PRODUCER	302 W 12TH ST	NEW YORK, NY	10014
DONNO, EDDY	DIRECTOR	5051 BILOXI AVE	NORTH HOLLYWOOD, CA	91601
DONOGHUE, MARY AGNES	WRITER	427 ALTA AVE	SANTA MONICA, CA	90402
DONOHUE, AMANDA	ACTRESS	HEATH, PARAMOUNT HOUSE		
		162-170 WARDOUR ST	LONDON W1V 3AT	ENGLAND
DONOVAN	SINGER-SONGWRITER	POST OFFICE BOX 472	LONDON SW7 2QB	ENGLAND
DONOVAN, ARLENE	FILM PRODUCER	ICM, 40 W 57TH ST	NEW YORK, NY	10019
DONOVAN, ART	FOOTBALL	1512 JEFFERS RD	BALTIMORE, MD	21204
DONOVAN, BRETT	BASEBALL	RED SOX, CHAIN O'LAKES PARK	WINTER HAVEN, FL	33880
DONOVAN, ERIN	ACTRESS	15055 MC KENDREE AVE	PACIFIC PALISADES, CA	90272
DONOVAN, JACK	BASEBALL EXECUTIVE	1325 S MAIN #229	SALT LAKE CITY, UT	84115
DONOVAN, JOHN, JR	BASEBALL EXECUTIVE	FENWAY PARK, 4 YAWKEY WY	BOSTON, MA	02215
DONOVAN, KING	ACTOR-DIRECTOR	200 E 66TH ST	NEW YORK, NY	10021
DONOVAN, LISA ANN	SINGER-COMPOSER	927 18TH ST #E	SANTA MONICA, CA	90403

DONOVAN, LISA L	ACTRESS	10707 CAMARILLO ST #308	NORTH HOLLYWOOD, CA 91602
DONOVAN, MARTIN	WRITER	10871 VICENZA WY	LOS ANGELES, CA 90077
DONOVAN, TOM	DIRECTOR-PRODUCER	650 PARK AVE	NEW YORK, NY 10021
DONOVAN, WARDE	ACTOR	10850 RIVERSIDE DR #505	NORTH HOLLYWOOD, CA 91602
DONOVAN, WENDELL & EASTCOAST RI	C & W GROUP	9940 LOUGHEED HWY #330	BURNABY, BC V3J 1N3 CANADA
DONSKOI, MARK	DIRECTOR	UNION OF CINEMATOGRAPHISTS	
		USSR, 14 VASSILIEVSKAYA UL	MOSCOW USSR
DONTZIG, GARY	TV PRODUCER	8383 WILSHIRE BLVD #923	BEVERLY HILLS, CA 90211
DOOBIE BROTHERS, THE	ROCK & ROLL GROUP	15140 SONOMA HWY	GLEN ELLEN, CA 95442
DOODY, ALISON	ACTRESS	BELFRAGE, 68 SAINT JAMES'S ST	LONDON SW1A 1LE ENGLAND
DOOHAN, JAMES	ACTOR	POST OFFICE BOX 1100	BURBANK, CA 91507
DOOLAN, TRISH	ACTRESS	419 WINDSOR PL	OCEANSIDE, NY 11572
DOOLEY, CALVIN M, JR	U S CONGRESSMAN	711 N COURT ST #E	VISALIA, CA 93291
DOOLEY, PAUL	SCREENWRITER	484 W 43RD ST #43-N	NEW YORK, NY 10036
DOOLEY, PAUL	SINGER-SONGWRITER	MORGAN, 301 W 53RD ST	NEW YORK, NY 10019
DOOLEY, RAE	ACTRESS	HARRIS AVE, RD #1	LINCOLN, RI 02865
DOOLEY, TOM	FOOTBALL REFEREE	NFL, 410 PARK AVE	NEW YORK, NY 10022
DOOLITTLE, JAMES H	LT GENERAL	8545 CARMEL VALLEY RD	CARMEL, CA 93923
DOOLITTLE, JOHN T	U S CONGRESSMAN	1624 SANTA CLARA DR #260	ROSEVILLE, CA 95661
DOOLITTLE, ROBERT	ACTOR	1021 N EDINBURGH AVE #2	LOS ANGELES, CA 90046
DOPPELT, MARGERY	WRITER	2325 HOLLYRIDGE DR	LOS ANGELES, CA 90068
DOPSON, JOHN	BASEBALL	FENWAY PARK, 4 YAWKEY WY	BOSTON, MA 02215
DOR, KARIN	ACTRESS	TSINTAUERSTRASSE 80	D-8000 MUNICH 82 GERMANY
DORAN, ANN	ACTRESS	1610 N ORANGE GROVE AVE	LOS ANGELES, CA 90046
DORAN, BILL	BASEBALL	REDS, 100 RIVERFRONT STADIUM	CINCINNATI, OH 45202
DORAN, MATT H	COMPOSER	11432 CHENAULT ST	LOS ANGELES, CA 90049
DORAN, PHILLIP G	TV WRITER	311 OCEAN AVE #302	SANTA MONICA, CA 90402
DORAN, TAKAYO	ACTRESS	10590 WILSHIRE BLVD #1601	LOS ANGELES, CA 90024
DORE, BONNY	TV PRODUCER	11300 W OLYMPIC BLVD #870	LOS ANGELES, CA 90064
DORFF, MATTHEW	SCREENWRITER	SMITH, 121 N SAN VICENTE BLVD	BEVERLY HILLS, CA 90211
DORFMAN, HARVEY	BASEBALL-INSTRUCTOR	ATHLETICS'S, OAKLAND COLISEUM	OAKLAND, CA 94621
DORFMAN, STANLEY	DIRECTOR-PRODUCER	2556 DEARBORN DR	LOS ANGELES, CA 90068
DORFMAN, STEVEN	TV WRITER	151 S EL CAMINO DR	BEVERLY HILLS, CA 90212
DORFSMAN, LOUIS	BROADCAST EXECUTIVE	80 STATION RD	GREAT NECK, NY 11023
DORGAN, BYRON	U S CONGRESSMAN	358 FEDERAL BUILDING	BISMARCK, ND 58502
DORIN, PHOEBE	ACTRESS-WRITER	8857 WONDERLAND AVE	LOS ANGELES, CA 90046
DORKIN, MICHAEL	ACTOR	530 PARK AVE	NEW YORK, NY 10021
DORKOWSKI, DON	FOOTBALL REFEREE	NFL, 410 PARK AVE	NEW YORK, NY 10022
DORLEAC, JEAN PIERRE	COSTUME DESIGNER	13949 VENTURA BLVD #309	SHERMAN OAKS, CA 91423
DORMAN, ROBERT K	U S CONGRESSMAN	300 ALICANTE PLAZA #360	GARDEN GROVE, CA 92642
DORN, CHRIS	BASEBALL	POST OFFICE BOX 598	BINGHAMTON, NY 13902
DORN, DOLORES	ACTRESS	7461 BEVERLY BLVD #400	LOS ANGELES, CA 90036
DORN, MICHAEL	ACTOR	3751 MULTIVIEW DR	LOS ANGELES, CA 90068
DORN, RUDI	TV DIRECTOR	31 ASHGROVE PL	DON MILLS, ONT CANADA
DORN, TORIN	FOOTBALL	RAIDERS, 332 CENTER ST	EL SEGUNDO, CA 90245
DORNAN, DON	TV DIRECTOR	15459 DICKENS ST	SHERMAN OAKS, CA 91403
DORNISCH, WILLIAM PAUL	FILM EDITOR	150 S BARRINGTON AVE #1	LOS ANGELES, CA 90049
DORR, DAVID	ACTOR	LEWIS, 110 W 40TH ST	NEW YORK, NY 10018
DORRIS, DAVID	MUSIC ARRANGER	5028 REGENT DR	NASHVILLE, TN 37220
DORSETT, BRIAN	BASEBALL	POST OFFICE BOX 450	BUFFALO, NY 14205
DORSETT, TONY	FOOTBALL	COWBOYS, 1 COWBOYS PARKWAY	IRVING, TX 75063
DORSEY, BOB	ARTIST	107 N HOOPES AVE	AUBURN, NY 13021
DORSEY, ERIC	FOOTBALL	N Y GIANTS, GIANTS STADIUM	EAST RUTHERFORD, NJ 07073
DORSEY, JOHN	DIRECTOR-PRODUCER	11912 RIVERSIDE DR #11	NORTH HOLLYWOOD, CA 91607
DORSEY, LOUISE	ACTRESS	151 S EL CAMINO DR	BEVERLY HILLS, CA 90212
DORSEY, REGINALD T	ACTOR	SCHWARTZ, 935 N CROFT AVE	LOS ANGELES, CA 90069
DORSO, RICHARD J	WRITER	1100 N ALTA LOMA RD	LOS ANGELES, CA 90069
DORTORT, DAVID	WRITER-PRODUCER	133 UDINE WY	LOS ANGELES, CA 90077
DORWARD, KENNETH L	SCREENWRITER	8955 BEVERLY BLVD	WEST HOLLYWOOD, CA 90048
DOSS, JASON	BASEBALL	POST OFFICE BOX 4488	WINSTON-SALEM, NC 27115
DOSS, TERRI LYNN	ACTRESS-MODEL	6605 HOLLYWOOD BLVD #220	HOLLYWOOD, CA 90028
DOSS FAMILY, THE	C & W GROUP	POST OFFICE BOX 13	ESTILL SPRINGS, TN 37330
DOSSOR, ALAN	TV DIRECTOR	PETERS, FRASER & DUNLOP, LTD	
		5TH FLOOR, THE CHAMBERS	
		CHELSEA HARBOUR, LOT RD	LONDON SW10 OXF ENGLAND
DOSTAL, BRUCE	BASEBALL	POST OFFICE BOX 3449	SCRANTON, PA 18505
DOTEL, ANGEL	BASEBALL	POST OFFICE BOX 10031	BAKERSFIELD, CA 93389
DOTEL, MARIANO	BASEBALL	POST OFFICE BOX 957	DUNEDIN, FL 34697
DOTOLO, CHRIS	BASEBALL	POST OFFICE BOX 1295	CLINTON, IA 52733
DOTRICE, MICHELE	ACTRESS	GLASS, 28 BERKELEY SQ	LONDON W1X 6HD ENGLAND
DOTRICE, ROY	ACTOR	TALBOT HOUSE, SAINT MARTINS LN	LONDON WC2 ENGLAND
DOTSON, RICH	BASEBALL	HICKS, 4240 PALOMINO CIR	RENO, NV 89509
DOTY, CURT	ARTIST	115 WOOSTER ST #2-B	NEW YORK, NY 10012
DOTY, SEAN	BASEBALL	POST OFFICE BOX 2001	CEDAR RAPIDS, IA 52406
DOUBET, STEVE	ACTOR	1629 CALIFORNIA AVE	SANTA MONICA, CA 90403
DOUBLE DARE	ROCK & ROLL GROUP	1505 W 2ND AVE #200	VANCOUVER, BC V6H 3Y4 CANADA
DOUBLE EAGLE	C & W GROUP	DIRECTION FOUR MANAGEMENT	
		301-140 BABBATYNE AVE	WINNIPEG, MB R3B 3C5 CANADA
DOUBLEDAY, FRANK	ACTOR	5061 ELMWOOD AVE	LOS ANGELES, CA 90004
DOUBLEDAY, NELSON	BASEBALL EXECUTIVE	METS, 126TH ST & ROOSEVELT AVE	FLUSHING, NY 11368
DOUCETTE, J DUKE	ACTOR	POST OFFICE BOX 657	MONTAUK, NY 11954
DOUCETTE, JEFF	ACTOR	1315 N SIERRA BONITA AVE	LOS ANGELES, CA 90046
DOUCETTE, JOHN	ACTOR	POST OFFICE BOX 252	CABAZON, CA 92230
DOUCHETTE, GENE	COSTUME DESIGNER	13949 VENTURA BLVD #309	SHERMAN OAKS, CA 91423
DOUG & THE SLUGS	ROCK & ROLL GROUP	1505 W 2ND AVE #200	VANCOUVER, BC V6H 3Y4 CANADA

DOUGAN, MICHAEL	CRITIC	110 5TH ST	SAN FRANCISCO, CA	94103
DOUGHERTY, DOUG	TV DIRECTOR	4219 W OLIVE AVE #327	BURBANK, CA	91505
DOUGHERTY, ED	GOLFER	POST OFFICE BOX 109601	PALM BCH GARDENS, FL	33418
DOUGHERTY, JACK	BASEBALL	POST OFFICE BOX 90111	ARLINGTON, TX	76004
DOUGHERTY, JEANNE	ACTRESS	3239 BENNETT DR	LOS ANGELES, CA	90068
DOUGHERTY, JIM	BASEBALL	POST OFFICE BOX 422229	KISSIMMEE, FL	34742
DOUGHERTY, JOSEPH	TV PRODUCER	151 S EL CAMINO DR	BEVERLY HILLS, CA	90212
DOUGHTY, LARRY	BASEBALL EXECUTIVE	POST OFFICE BOX 7000	PITTSBURGH, PA	15212
DOUGLAS, ANGELA	ACTRESS	ICM, 388-396 OXFORD ST	LONDON W1	ENGLAND
DOUGLAS, BARRY "BERRY"	TV WRITER	151 S EL CAMINO DR	BEVERLY HILLS, CA	90212
DOUGLAS, CHARLIE	SINGER	TAYLOR, 2401 12TH AVE S	NASHVILLE, TN	37204
DOUGLAS, CHUCK	BASKETBALL	BULLETS, 1 HARRY S TRUMAN DR	LANDOVER, MD	20785
DOUGLAS, DIANA	ACTRESS	250 W 57TH ST #2223	NEW YORK, NY	10019
DOUGLAS, DONNA	ACTRESS-SINGER	POST OFFICE BOX 49455	LOS ANGELES, CA	90049
DOUGLAS, ERIC	ACTOR	9000 SUNSET BLVD #405	LOS ANGELES, CA	90069
DOUGLAS, GORDON	FILM DIRECTOR	6600 W 6TH ST	LOS ANGELES, CA	90048
DOUGLAS, JAMES "BUSTER"	BOXER	2525 OAKSTONE DR #C	COLUMBUS, OH	43231
DOUGLAS, JAMES H	SECRETARY OF STATE	PAVILION OFF BLDG, 109 STATE ST	MONTPELIER, VT	05602
DOUGLAS, JERRY	ACTOR	8600 HILLSIDE AVE	LOS ANGELES, CA	90069
DOUGLAS, JERRY	SINGER	CASE, 1016 16TH AVE S	NASHVILLE, TN	37212
DOUGLAS, KIRK	ACTOR-DIRECTOR	805 N REXFORD DR	BEVERLY HILLS, CA	90210
DOUGLAS, KYM	ACTRESS	1930 CENTURY PARK W #403	LOS ANGELES, CA	90067
DOUGLAS, LEE	BASKETBALL EXECUTIVE	1 CNN CENTER #405, SOUTH TOWER	ATLANTA, GA	30303
DOUGLAS, MERRILL	FOOTBALL REFEREE	NFL, 410 PARK AVE	NEW YORK, NY	10022
DOUGLAS, MICHAEL	ACT-DIR-PROD	POST OFFICE BOX 49054	LOS ANGELES, CA	90049
DOUGLAS, MIKE	TV HOST-SINGER	602 N ARDEN DR	BEVERLY HILLS, CA	90210
DOUGLAS, PAMELA	TV WRITER	1650 WESTWOOD BLVD #201	LOS ANGELES, CA	90024
DOUGLAS, PAULETTE	TV DIRECTOR	112 W 76TH ST #1-R	NEW YORK, NY	10023
DOUGLAS, PETER	SCREENWRITER	CAA, 9830 WILSHIRE BLVD	BEVERLY HILLS, CA	90212
DOUGLAS, PRESTON	BASEBALL SCOUT	333 W 35TH ST	CHICAGO, IL	60616
DOUGLAS, ROBERT	ACTOR-DIRECTOR	SEA BLUFF, 1810 PARLIAMENT RD	LEUCADIA, CA	92024
DOUGLAS, SARAH	ACTRESS	STONE MANNERS, 9113 SUNSET BL	LOS ANGELES, CA	90069
DOUGLAS, SHERMAN	BASKETBALL	MIAMI HEAT, THE MIAMI ARENA	MIAMI, FL	33136
DOUGLASS, DALE	GOLFER	PGA SENIORS, 112 T P C BLVD	PONTE VEDRA BEACH, FL	32082
DOUGLASS, MAURICE	FOOTBALL	BEARS, 250 N WASHINGTON RD	LAKE FOREST, IL	60045
DOUGNAC, FRANCE	ACTRESS	BABETTE POUGE, 6 SQUARE		
		VILLARET DE JOYEUSE	PARIS 75017	FRANCE
DOUR, BRIAN	BASEBALL	POST OFFICE BOX 21727	SAN FRANCISCO, CA	95151
DOURIF, BRAD	ACTRESS	213 1/2 S ARNAZ DR	BEVERLY HILLS, CA	90211
DOURIS, PETER	HOCKEY	BRUINS, 150 CAUSEWAY ST	BOSTON, MA	02114
DOUTHIT, RANDALL	TV PRODUCER	2133 WISCONSIN AVE, NW	WASHINGTON, DC	20007
DOVE, BILLIE	ACTRESS	POST OFFICE BOX 5005	RANCHO MIRAGE, CA	92270
DOVE, RONNIE	SINGER-SONGWRITER	107 DORAL DR	FRANKLIN, TN	37064
DOVE, ULYSSES	DANCER-CHOREOGRAPHER	272 W 84TH ST	NEW YORK, NY	10024
DOVELLS, THE	VOCAL GROUP	BROTHERS, 141 DUNBAR AVE	FORDS, NJ	08863
DOVEY, TROY	BASEBALL	POST OFFICE BOX 422229	KISSIMMEE, FL	34742
DOW, DAVID	NEWS CORRESPONDENT	CBS-TV, NEWS DEPARTMENT		
		7800 BEVERLY BLVD	LOS ANGELES, CA	90036
DOW, HAROLD	NEWS CORRESPONDENT	CBS NEWS, 524 W 57TH ST	NEW YORK, NY	10019
DOW, PEGGY	ACTRESS	HELMERICH, 3003 S ROCKFORD RD	TULSA, OK	74114
DOW, TONY	ACTOR	DIAMOND, 215 N BARRINGTON AVE	LOS ANGELES, CA	90049
DOWD, CHARLIE	BASEBALL EXECUTIVE	POST OFFICE BOX 12	MIDLAND, TX	79702
DOWD, M'EL	ACTRESS	325 E 80TH ST	NEW YORK, NY	10021
DOWD, NANCY	SCREENWRITER	6310 HEATHER DR	LOS ANGELES, CA	90068
DOWDELL, ROBERT	ACTOR	BDP, 10637 BURBANK BLVD	NORTH HOLLYWOOD, CA	91601
DOWELL, KEN	BASEBALL	2720 CASTRO WY	SACRAMENTO, CA	95818
DOWHOWER, ROD	FOOTBALL COACH	POST OFFICE BOX 17247 (DULLES)	WASHINGTON, DC	20041
DOWIE, FREDA	ACTRESS	PTA, BUGLE HOUSE, 21-A NOEL ST	LONDON W1V 3PD	ENGLAND
DOWLING, DORIS	ACTRESS	9026 ELEVADO AVE	LOS ANGELES, CA	90069
DOWN, LESLEY-ANNE	ACTRESS	6509 WANDERMERE RD	MALIBU, CA	90265
DOWN, RENA	WRITER-PRODUCER	834 LINCOLN BLVD #5	SANTA MONICA, CA	90403
DOWN, RICK	BASEBALL MANAGER	1155 W MOUND ST	COLUMBUS, OH	43223
DOWNCHILD BLUES BAND	BLUES BAND	1505 W 2ND AVE #200	VANCOUVER, BC V6H 3Y4	CANADA
DOWNE, EDWARD R, JR	THEATER PRODUCER	824 5TH AVE	NEW YORK, NY	10021
DOWNES, BARRY E	TV WRITER	ONE TO ONE COMMINCATIONS		
		319 E 85TH ST	NEW YORK, NY	10023
DOWNEY, MORTON, JR	TV HOST-SINGER	8121 GEORGIA AVE	SILVER SPRING, MD	20910
DOWNEY, ROBERT	FILM DIRECTOR	8497 CRESCENT DR	HOLLYWOOD, CA	90046
DOWNEY, ROBERT, JR	ACTOR	1494 N KINGS RD	LOS ANGELES, CA	90049
DOWNEY, ROGER LEE	TV DIRECTOR-PRODUCER	PBS, 1320 BRADDOCK PL	ALEXANDRIA, VA	22314
DOWNEY, THOMAS J	U S CONGRESSMAN	4 UDALL RD	WEST ISLIP, NY	11795
DOWNING, BIG AL	BASEBALL-SINGER	2800 NEILSON WAY #412	SANTA MONICA, CA	90405
DOWNING, BRIAN	BASEBALL	POST OFFICE BOX 90111	ARLINGTON, TX	76004
DOWNING, DAVID	ACTOR	23938 HAMLIN ST	CANOGA PARK, CA	91307
DOWNS, HUGH	TV HOST-JOURNALIST	POST OFFICE BOX 1132	CAREFREE, AZ	85331
DOWNS, KELLY	BASEBALL	S F GIANTS, CANDLESTICK PARK	SAN FRANICSCO, CA	94124
DOWNS, M A	ACTOR	10701 RIVERSIDE DR #13	TOLUCA LAKE, CA	91602
DOWNS, RICHARD	ARTIST	1347 E TOPEKA ST	PASADENA, CA	91104
DOYEL, DAN	BASEBALL TRAINER	POST OFFICE BOX 5599	LITTLE ROCK, AR	72215
DOYEN, JACQUELINE	ACTRESS	3 RUE DE REGARD	PARIS 75006	FRANCE
DOYLE, DAVID	ACTOR-DIRECTOR	4731 NOELINE AVE	ENCINO, CA	91436
DOYLE, DENNIS	SINGER	POST OFFICE BOX 06404	PORTLAND, OR	97206
DOYLE, DENNY	BASEBALL-SCOUT	FENWAY PARK, 4 YAWKEY WY	BOSTON, MA	02215
DOYLE, ENOS LYNN	ACTOR	1933 N BEACHWOOD DR #20	LOS ANGELES, CA	90068
DOYLE, IAN	BASEBALL	POST OFFICE BOX 1886	COLUMBUS, GA	31902

DOYLE, JIM	ATTORNEY GENERAL	STATE CAPITOL BUILDING	MADISON, WI	53702
DOYLE, PATRICIA	ACTRESS-MODEL	1175 YORK AVE	NEW YORK, NY	10021
DOYLE, RON	ACTOR	11137 ARCHWOOD ST	NORTH HOLLYWOOD, CA	91606
DOYLE-MURRAY, BRIAN	ACTOR-SCREENWRITER	555 W 57TH ST #1230	NEW YORK, NY	10019
DOZIER, LAMONT	SINGER-SONGWRITER	4175 STANSBURY AVE	SHERMAN OAKS, CA	91423
DOZLER, D J	BASEBALL	POST OFFICE BOX 1211	NORFOLK, VA	23502
DR DEMENTO	RADIO PERSONALITY	LEVEY, 925 WESTMOUNT AVE	LOS ANGELES, CA	90069
DR JOHN	SINGER-SONGWRITER	ENCORE PRODS, 76 MARYLAND DR	NEW ORLEANS, LA	70124
DR K & THE SHANTAYS	ROCK & ROLL GROUP	POST OFFICE BOX 222	BLACK HAWK, SD	57718
DRABEK, DOUG	BASEBALL	POST OFFICE BOX 7000	PITTSBURGH, PA	15212
DRABINSKY, GARTH	FILM PRODUCER	CINEPLEX, 214 KING STREET W	TORONTO, ONT M5H 1K4	CANADA
DRABOWSKY, MOE	BASEBALL-COACH	530 AUDUBON PL	HIGHLAND PARK, IL	60035
DRAGO, BILLY	ACTOR	4270 CAMILLIA AVE	STUDIO CITY, CA	91604
DRAGON	ROCK & ROLL GROUP	122 MC EVOY ST	ALEXANDRIA MSW 2015	AUSTRALIA
DRAGON, TONI	SINGER	SEE - CAPTAIN & TENNILLE, THE		
DRAGONI, CARLA	ACTRESS	939 CANDLEWOOD LAKE RD	NEW MILFORD, CT	06776
DRAGOTI, STAN	WRITER-PRODUCER	755 STRADELLA RD	LOS ANGELES, CA	90077
DRAHAM, BRIAN	BASEBALL	CANADIANS, 4601 ONTARIO ST	VANCOUVER, BC V5V 3H4	CANADA
DRAI, VICTOR	FILM PRODUCER	1201 DELRESTO DR	BEVERLY HILLS, CA	90210
DRAKE, ALAN	COMEDIAN	21243 VENTURA BLVD #243	WOODLAND HILLS, CA	91364
DRAKE, ALFRED	ACTOR	50 E 89TH ST #26-A	NEW YORK, NY	10128
DRAKE, ALLAN	ACTOR	22038 VANOWEN ST #106	CANOGA PARK, CA	91303
DRAKE, BUD	CARTOONIST	KING FEATURES, 216 E 45TH ST	NEW YORK, NY	10017
DRAKE, DONA	ACTRESS	425 N OAKHURST DR #213	BEVERLY HILLS, CA	90210
DRAKE, ELLIOTT R	WRITER-PRODUCER	67 HILTON AVE	GARDEN CITY, NJ	11530
DRAKE, FRANCES	ACTRESS	1511 SUMMITRIDGE DR	BEVERLY HILLS, CA	90210
DRAKE, JIM	TV DIRECTOR	5145 CALVIN AVE	TARZANA, CA	91356
DRAKE, LARRY	ACTOR	2293 BRONSON HILL DR	LOS ANGELES, CA	90069
DRAKE, MICHELE	ACTRESS-MODEL	MARX, 11130 HUSTON ST #6	NORTH HOLLYWOOD, CA	91601
DRAKE, PAUL	ACTOR	9301 WILSHIRE BLVD #312	BEVERLY HILLS, CA	90210
DRAKE, PETE	DOBROIST	809 18TH AVE S	NASHVILLE, TN	37203
DRAKE, RONALD	ACTOR	ABC-TV, "ALL MY CHILDREN"		
		320 W 66TH ST	NEW YORK, NY	10023
DRAKE, STANLEY	CARTOONIST	46 POST RD E	WESTPORT, CT	06880
DRAKE, SYLVIE	THEATER CRITIC	701 "B" ST #501	SAN DIEGO, CA	92101
DRAKE, THOMAS Y	SCREENWRITER	8955 BEVERLY BLVD	WEST HOLLYWOOD, CA	90048
DRANE, DWIGHT	FOOTBALL	BILLS, 1 BILLS DR	ORCHARD PARK, NJ	14127
DRAPER, EMILY	COSTUME DESIGNER	13949 VENTURA BLVD #309	SHERMAN OAKS, CA	91423
DRAPER, MIKE	BASEBALL	1155 W MOUND ST	COLUMBUS, OH	43223
DRAPER, NATALIE	ACTRESS	GOFF, 86 MALIBU COLONY DR	MALIBU, CA	90265
DRAPER, PETER	TV-FILM WRITER	18-A MARLBOROUGH RD	EXETER EX2 4TJ	ENGLAND
DRAPER, POLLY	ACTRESS	11487 LAUREL CREST DR	STUDIO CITY, CA	91604
DRAPER, ROBERT	CINEMATOGRAPHER	POST OFFICE BOX 2230	HOLLYWOOD, CA	90078
DRASNIN, IRV	WRITER-PRODUCER	180 E 79TH ST #10-D	NEW YORK, NY	10021
DRASNIN, ROBERT J	COMPOSER-CONDUCTOR	17115 NANETTE ST	GRANADA HILLS, CA	91344
DRAVECKY, DAVE	BASEBALL	POST OFFICE BOX 3505	BOARDMAN, OH	44513
DRAYCOTT, PHILIP	FILM DIRECTOR	SHARKEY, 15 GOLDEN SQ #315	LONDON W1R 3AG	ENGLAND
DRAYTON, LESLIE C	COMPOSER	3441 S DUNSMUIR AVE	LOS ANGELES, CA	90016
DREAPER, JENNIFER	SINGER	POST OFFICE BOX 689	PUTNAM VALLEY, NY	10579
DREES, TOM	BASEBALL	POST OFFICE BOX 75089	OKLAHOMA CITY, OK	73147
DREESEN, TOM	COMEDIAN	14570 BENEFIT ST #201	SHERMAN OAKS, CA	91403
DREIDAME, DANA	ACTRESS	4141 ELENDA ST #3	CULVER CITY, CA	90230
DREIER, DAVID	U S CONGRESSMAN	112 N 2ND AVE	COVINACA, CA	91723
DREIFUSS, ARTHUR	WRITER-PRODUCER	3950 LOS FELIZ BLVD #210	LOS ANGELES, CA	90027
DREILING, GREG	BASKETBALL	PACERS, 300 E MARKET ST	INDIANAPOLIS, IN	46204
DREISPAN, HOWARD C	TV PRODUCER	257 ESSEX ST #7	HACKENSACK, NJ	07601
DREITH, BEN	FOOTBALL REFEREE	NFL, 410 PARK AVE	NEW YORK, NY	10022
DREITH, DENNIS J	COMPOSER	4820 1/2 CLEON AVE	NORTH HOLLYWOOD, CA	91601
DRELL, TOM	BASEBALL	POST OFFICE BOX 2785	LAKELAND, FL	33806
DRENNAN, NOEL	ACTOR-SINGER	81 DOWNTON AVE	LONDON SW2	ENGLAND
DRESCHER, FRAN	ACTRESS	RICH, 2400 WHITMAN PL	LOS ANGELES, CA	90068
DRESDEN, JOHN	ACTOR	950 N KINGS RD #137	LOS ANGELES, CA	90069
DRESNER, HAL	SCREENWRITER	1569 BENEDICT CANYON DR	BEVERLY HILLS, CA	90210
DRESS, SAMUEL	DIRECTOR	1114 15TH ST	SANTA MONICA, CA	90403
DRESSEL, CHRIS	FOOTBALL	N Y JETS, 1000 FULTON AVE	HEMPSTEAD, NY	11550
DRESSENDORFER, KIRK	BASEBALL	ATHLETICS'S, OAKLAND COLISEUM	OAKLAND, CA	94621
DRESSER, LEE & THE KRAZY CATS	ROCK & ROLL GROUP	17530 VENTURA BLVD #108	ENCINO, CA	91316
DRESSER, NORINE S	WRITER	3093 SAINT GEORGE ST	LOS ANGELES, CA	90027
DREW, CAMERON	BASEBALL	31 HIGHBRIDGE RD	YARDVILLE, NJ	08620
DREW, KIM	ARTIST	4 LEXINGTON AVE #9-D	NEW YORK, NY	10010
DREW, LARRY	BASKETBALL	POST OFFICE BOX 10	INGLEWOOD, CA	90306
DREW, ROBERT J	ACTOR	6 SUNSET LN	PORT WASHINGTON, NY	11050
DREW, ROLAND	ACTOR	1117 6TH ST #A-12	SANTA MONICA, CA	90403
DREW, RUE FARIS	TV PRODUCER	177 E 77TH ST, COTTAGE #E	NEW YORK, NY	10021
DREWREY, WILLIE	FOOTBALL	BUCCANEERS, 1 BUCCANEER PL	TAMPA, FL	33607
DREXLER, CLYDE	BASKETBALL	700 NE MULTNOMAH ST #600	PORTLAND, OR	97232
DREXLER, ROSALYN	PLAYWRIGHT	ROSENSTONE, 3 E 48TH ST	NEW YORK, NY	10017
DREYER, JIM	BASEBALL SCOUT	POST OFFICE BOX 90111	ARLINGTON, TX	76004
DREYER, STEVE	BASEBALL	POST OFFICE BOX 3609	PORT CHARLOTTE, FL	33949
DREYFUSS, DAVID	DIRECTOR-PRODUCER	3977 SEDGEWICK AVE #12-C	BRONX, NY	10463
DREYFUSS, DAVID HANS	DIRECTOR-PRODUCER	320 E 57TH ST	NEW YORK, NY	10022
DREYFUSS, LORIN	SCREENWRITER	8955 BEVERLY BLVD	WEST HOLLYWOOD, CA	90048
DREYFUSS, RICHARD	ACTOR	2809 NICHOLS CANYON RD	LOS ANGELES, CA	90046
DRIESSEN, DAN	BASEBALL	POST OFFICE BOX 1001	HILTON HEAD ISLAND, SC	29928
DRIFTERS, THE	VOCAL GROUP	324 MAIN AVE #333	NORWALK, CT	06851

Name	Occupation	Address	City	Code
DRIFTING COWBOYS BAND	C & W GROUP	38 MUSIC SQUARE E #300	NASHVILLE, TN	37203
DRIFTWOOD, JIMMY	SINGER	FEGAN, 6638 MAPLE AVE	DALLAS, TX	75235
DRIGGERS, LEE	BASEBALL MANAGER	POST OFFICE BOX 594	WELLAND, ONT L3B 5R3	CANADA
DRIGGS, DENNIS L	COMPOSER	1351 N ORANGE DR #207	LOS ANGELES, CA	90028
DRIMMER, JOHN A	SCREENWRITER	151 S EL CAMINO DR	BEVERLY HILLS, CA	90212
DRISCOLL, LAWRASON	ACTOR	837 VENICE BLVD	VENICE, CA	90291
DRISCOLL, RICHARD	ACTOR	EAA, 84 WARDOUR ST, 1ST FLOOR	LONDON W1V 3LF	ENGLAND
DRISI, MOHAMED	ARTIST	100 W MAIN ST	GLENWOOD, IL	60425
DRISKILL, WILLIAM	SCREENWRITER	8955 BEVERLY BLVD	WEST HOLLYWOOD, CA	90048
DRIVER, BRUCE	HOCKEY	POST OFFICE BOX 504	EAST RUTHERFORD, NJ	07073
DRIVER, DONALD	TV DIRECTOR	OSCARD, 24 W 40TH ST, 17TH FL	NEW YORK, NY	10011
DRIVER, JOHN S	TV WRITER-DIRECTOR	ASKENASE, 6217 GLEN AIRY DR	LOS ANGELES, CA	90068
DROMGOOLE, PATRICK	TV DIRECTOR-PRODUCER	HTV CENTRE, 99 BAKER ST	LONDON W1M 2AJ	ENGLAND
DROTT, JOAN	ACTRESS	24 SUMMIT PL	NEWBURY PORT, MA	01950
DRU, JOANNE	ACTRESS	1459 CARLA RIDGE	BEVERLY HILLS, CA	90210
DRUCE, JEFFRY	ACTOR	4117 MICHAEL AVE	LOS ANGELES, CA	90066
DRUCE, JOHN	HOCKEY	JETS, 15-1430 MAROONS RD	WINNIPEG, MAN R3G 0L5	CANADA
DRUCE, OLGA	ACTRESS	152 E 94TH ST	NEW YORK, NY	10028
DRUCK, MARK	COMEDY WRITER	300 E 40TH ST #32-E	NEW YORK, NY	10016
DRUCKER, BRUCE	TV DIRECTOR	WCVB-TV, 5 TV PL	NEEDHAM, MA	02192
DRUCKER, JEROLD P	WRITER	5560 RANTHOM AVE	WOODLAND HILLS, CA	91367
DRUCKER, MORT	CARTOONIST	MAD MAGAZINE, 485 MADISON AVE	NEW YORK, NY	10022
DRUGSTORE COWBOYS, THE	C & W GROUP	ENCORE TALENT, 2137 ZERCHER RD	SAN ANTONIO, TX	78209
DRULEY, TOM	SINGER-GUITARIST	POST OFFICE BOX 73	GOODLETTSVILLE, TN	37072
DRUMMOND, ALICE	ACTRESS	242 E 26TH ST	NEW YORK, NY	10010
DRUMMOND, GEOFFREY	TV WRITER-PRODUCER	262 E 78TH ST	NEW YORK, NY	10021
DRUMMOND, RANDY	CINEMATOGRAPHER	220 E 25TH ST #4-B	NEW YORK, NY	10010
DRUMMOND, ROBERT	FOOTBALL	EAGLES, BROAD ST & PATTISON AVE	PHILADELPHIA, PA	19148
DRUMMOND, TIM	BASEBALL	POST OFFICE BOX 23290	NASHVILLE, TN	37202
DRUMMY, SAM	CINEMATOGRAPHER	7715 SUNSET BLVD #150	LOS ANGELES, CA	90046
DRURY, DAVID	FILM DIRECTOR	JAC PR LTD, 113 WARDOUR ST	LONDON W1V 3TD	ENGLAND
DRURY, JAMES	ACTOR	12755 MILL RIDGE #622	CYPRESS, TX	77429
DRURY, MARK	ARTIST	EISENBERG, 3311 OAK LAWN AVE	DALLAS, TX	75219
DRUSKY, ROY	SINGER-SONGWRITER	131 TRIVETT DR	PORTLAND, TN	37148
DRY BRANCH FIRE SQUAD	C & W GROUP	POST OFFICE BOX 506	LEMONT, PA	16851
DRYDEN, DON	COMPTROLLER	LEGISLATIVE HALL	DOVER, DE	19901
DRYDEN, MACK L	WRITER	POST OFFICE BOX 34384	LOS ANGELES, CA	90034
DRYDEN, PATTY	ARTIST	575 W END AVE	NEW YORK, NY	10024
DRYER, DAVID CARL	DIRECTOR	16140 MOORPARK ST	ENCINO, CA	91346
DRYER, FRED	ACTOR-FOOTBALL	1722 FERRAI DR	BEVERLY HILLS, CA	90210
DRYHURST, ANNA	MAKE-UP ARTIST	258 S CARMELINA AVE	LOS ANGELES, CA	90048
DRYHURST, MICHAEL	FILM PRODUCER	21 BROADLANDS AVE	SHEP-ON-THAMES	ENGLAND
DRYSDALE, DON	BASEBALL-ANNOUNCER	1488 RUTHERFORD DR	PASADENA, CA	91103
DU ARTE, STEVE	BASEBALL EXECUTIVE	POST OFFICE BOX 1457	MEDFORD, OR	97501
DU BAIN, DONNA	ACTRESS	1231 FLANDERS RD	LA CANADA, CA	91011
DU BARRY, DENISE	ACTRESS	3083 1/2 RAMBLA PACIFICA	MALIBU, CA	90265
DU BOIS, BRIAN	BASEBALL	159 RIDGE ST	BRAIDWOOD, IL	60402
DU BOIS, JA'NET	ACTRESS	405 W IVY ST #204	GLENDALE, CA	91204
DU BOIS, MARTA	ACTRESS	6255 SUNSET BLVD #627	LOS ANGELES, CA	90028
DU BOST, PAULETTE	ACTRESS	23 RUE DE BELVEDERE	BOULOGNE 92100	FRANCE
DU BROCK, NEAL	THEATER PRODUCER	STUDIO ARENA, 681 MAIN ST	BUFFALO, NY	14203
DU MONT, MIKE	BASEBALL UMPIRE	POST OFFICE BOX 608	GROVE CITY, OH	43123
DU PLESSIS, DAVE	BASEBALL	POST OFFICE BOX 4370	SALINAS, CA	93912
DU PONT, PIERRE	GOVERNOR	PATTERNS	ROCKLAND, DE	19732
DU PONT, WILLIAM, III	BASKETBALL EXECUTIVE	POST OFFICE BOX 76	ORLANDO, FL	32802
DU PREE, DAVID	SPORTS WRITER	POST OFFICE BOX 500	WASHINGTON, DC	20044
DU VALL, BRAD	BASEBALL	POST OFFICE BOX 36407	LOUISVILLE, KY	40233
DU VALL, ELIZABETH	ACTRESS	13455 VENTURA BLVD #210	SHERMAN OAKS, CA	91423
DUBBINS, DON	ACTOR	17020 SUNSET BLVD #9	PACIFIC PALISADES, CA	90272
DUBEE, RICH	BASEBALL COACH	1501 W 16TH ST	INDIANAPOLIS, IN	46202
DUBELMAN, RICHARD S	WRITER-PRODUCER	1 LAURIE DR	ENGLEWOOD CLIFFS, NJ	07632
DUBIN, CHARLES S	TV DIRECTOR	651 LORNA LN	LOS ANGELES, CA	90049
DUBIN, JAY	TV DIRECTOR	260 W BROADWAY	NEW YORK, NY	10013
DUBIN, LAURENCE	DIRECTOR	POST OFFICE BOX 78	LIVINGSTON, NY	12541
DUBIN, MORTON	DIRECTOR	63 W 83RD ST	NEW YORK, NY	10024
DUBOSE, BRIAN	BASEBALL	POST OFFICE BOX 64939	FAYETTEVILLE, NC	28306
DUBOV, ADAM	TV WRITER	5700 RHODES AVE	NORTH HOLLYWOOD, CA	91607
DUBS, THE	VOCAL GROUP	BROTHERS, 141 DUNBAR AVE	FORDS, NJ	08863
DUBY, JACQUES	ACTOR	4 RUE ST-ROCH	PARIS 75001	FRANCE
DUCEY, BOB	BASEBALL	47 ELGIN ST N	CAMBRIDGE, ONT N1R 5H1	CANADA
DUCHESNE, GAETAN	HOCKEY	NORTH STARS, 7901 CEDAR AVE S	BLOOMINGTON, MN	55425
DUCHESNE, STEVE	HOCKEY	POST OFFICE BOX 17013	INGLEWOOD, CA	90308
DUCHIN, DAVE	BASEBALL TRAINER	POST OFFICE BOX 10213	LYNCHBURG, VA	24506
DUCHIN, PETER	PIANIST	305 MADISON AVE #956	NEW YORK, NY	10165
DUCHOW, PETER	TV PRODUCER	29500 HEATHCLIFF RD #292	MALIBU, CA	90265
DUCHOWNY, ROGER	DIRECTOR	POST OFFICE BOX 302	CREST PARK, CA	92326
DUCKHAM, GRAEME	TV-FILM DIRECTOR	NOBLE GATE PRODUCTIONS		
		21 LOTHAIR RD	LONDON W5 4TA	ENGLAND
DUCKSWORTH, KEVIN	BASKETBALL	700 NE MULTNOMAH ST #600	PORTLAND, OR	97232
DUCKWORTH, DORTHA	ACTRESS	200 W 54TH ST	NEW YORK, NY	10019
DUCLON, DAVID W	TV WRITER-PRODUCER	NBC-TV, 3000 W ALAMEDA AVE	BURBANK, CA	91523
DUCLOUX, WALTER	CONDUCTOR	2 WILDWIND POINT	AUSTIN, TX	78746
DUCOMMUN, RICK	ACTOR-COMEDIAN	7967 WOODROW WILSON DR	LOS ANGELES, CA	90046
DUDA, MATTHEW A	TV EXECUTIVE	SHOWTIME, 10 UNIVERSAL CITY PLZ	UNIVERSAL CITY, CA	91608
DUDASH, MICHAEL	ARTIST	ROXBURY MOUNTAIN RD	EAST WARREN, VT	05674

DUDIKOFF, MICHAEL	ACTOR	8485 MELROSE PL #E	LOS ANGELES, CA	90069
DUDLEY, DAVE	SINGER-SONGWRITER	TESSIER, 505 CANTON PASS	MADISON, TN	37115
DUDLEY, JONATHAN	CONDUCTOR	121 WAVERLY PL	NEW YORK, NY	10011
DUDZINSKI, ANDRZEJ	ARTIST	52 E 81ST ST #4	NEW YORK, NY	10028
DUELL, D WILLIAM	ACTOR	4 PARK AVE	NEW YORK, NY	10016
DUERR, ROBERT KENNETH	CONDUCTOR	80 N EUCLID AVE #401	PASADENA, CA	91101
DUEY, KYLE	BASEBALL	POST OFFICE BOX 957	DUNEDIN, FL	34697
DUFAULT, MONTE	BASEBALL	POST OFFICE BOX 661	KENOSHA, WI	53141
DUFF, DENICE MARIE	ACTRESS	279 S BEVERLY DR #708	BEVERLY HILLS, CA	90212
DUFF, SCOTT	BASEBALL	POST OFFICE BOX 2001	CEDAR RAPIDS, IA	52406
DUFFEK, PATTY	MODEL	9229 SUNSET BLVD #208	LOS ANGELES, CA	90069
DUFFELL, PETER	TV WRITER-DIRECTOR	HATTON, 29 ROEHAMPTON GATE	LONDON SW15 5JR	ENGLAND
DUFFY, DARRIN	BASEBALL	POST OFFICE DRAWER 1207	ZEBULON, NC	27597
DUFFY, JAMES STUART	ACTOR	4345 OCEAN VIEW DR	MALIBU, CA	90265
DUFFY, JOHN	COMPOSER-CONDUCTOR	MEET THE COMPOSER, 2112 BROADWAY	NEW YORK, NY	10023
DUFFY, JULIA	ACTRESS-DIRECTOR	10100 SANTA MONICA BLVD #700	LOS ANGELES, CA	90067
DUFFY, MIKE	TV CRITIC	FREE PRESS, 321 W LAFAYETTE BLVD	DETROIT, MI	48231
DUFFY, PATRICK	ACTOR-DIRECTOR	POST OFFICE BOX D	TARZANA, CA	91356
DUFFY, ROGER	FOOTBALL	N Y JETS, 1000 FULTON AVE	HEMPSTEAD, NY	11550
DUFFY BROTHERS, THE	C & W GROUP	3198 ROYAL LN #204	DALLAS, TX	75229
DUFOUR, VAL	ACTOR	40 W 22ND ST	NEW YORK, NY	10010
DUFRESNE, DONALD	HOCKEY	CANADIENS, 2313 ST CATHERINE ST	MONTREAL, QUE H3H 1N2	CANADA
DUGAN, DENNIS	ACTOR	2072 1/2 N COMMONWEALTH AVE	LOS ANGELES, CA	90027
DUGAN, MARY	COMPOSER	2560 "D" HWY #273	ANDERSON, CA	96007
DUGAN, MICHAEL	FILM DIRECTOR	77765 CALIFORNIA DR	PALM DESERT, CA	92260
DUGGAN, ANDREW	ACTOR	711 S BEVERLY GLEN BLVD	LOS ANGELES, CA	90024
DUGGAN, HACKSAW JIM	WRESTLER	POST OFFICE BOX 3859	STAMFORD, CT	06905
DUGGAN, RICHARD	ACTOR	711 S BEVERLY GLEN BLVD	LOS ANGELES, CA	90024
DUGGER, CARMON	BASEBALL EXECUTIVE	136 S SYCAMORE	ELIZABETHTON, TN	37643
DUGGER, KEITH	BASEBALL TRAINER	POST OFFICE BOX 4758	SPOKANE, WA	99202
DUGUAY, RON	ACTOR	150 E 58TH ST #2610	NEW YORK, NY	10021
DUIN, DEREK	BASEBALL EXECUTIVE	POST OFFICE BOX 1556	ASHEVILLE, NC	28802
DUKAKIS, KITTY	AUTHORESS	85 PERRY ST	BROOKLINE, MA	02146
DUKAKIS, MICHAEL	GOVERNOR	85 PERRY ST	BROOKLINE, MA	02146
DUKAKIS, OLYMPIA	ACTRESS	222 UPPER MOUNTAIN RD	MONTCLAIR, NJ	07043
DUKANE, SY	ACTOR	610 N ORLANDO AVE #204	LOS ANGELES, CA	90048
DUKAS, JAMES G	ACTOR	39 W 67TH ST	NEW YORK, NY	10023
DUKE, BILL	ACTOR-DIRECTOR	8306 WILSHIRE BLVD #438	BEVERLY HILLS, CA	90211
DUKE, CHRIS	ARTIST	LAVATY, 50 E 50TH ST	NEW YORK, NY	10022
DUKE, DARYL	FILM DIRECTOR	1153 LILLOOET RD	NORTH VANCOUVER, BC	CANADA
DUKE, DAVID	POLITICIAN	500 N ARNOULT RD	METAIRIE, LA	70001
DUKE, DAVID A	COMPOSER	831 TEAKWOOD RD	LOS ANGELES, CA	90049
DUKE, GEORGE	MUSICIAN-PRODUCER	HERB COHEN, 740 N LA BREA AVE	LOS ANGELES, CA	90038
DUKE, KYLE	BASEBALL	POST OFFICE BOX 30160	SAN BERNARDINO, CA	92413
DUKE, PATTY	ACTRESS	326 N FOREST DR	COEUR D'ALENE, ID	83814
DUKE OF PADUCAH	BANJOIST	625 FARRELL PARKWAY	NASHVILLE, TN	37220
DUKES, DAVID	ACTOR	255 S LORRAINE BLVD	LOS ANGELES, CA	90004
DUKES, JAMIE	FOOTBALL	FALCONS, SUWANEE RD AT I-85	SUWANEE, GA	30174
DUKESMEN, THE	JAZZ GROUP	3003 VAN NESS ST #W-205, NW	WASHINGTON, DC	20008
DUKORE, LAWRENCE	SCREENWRITER	RLR ASSOC, LTD, 7 W 51ST ST	NEW YORK, NY	10019
DULIN, DAN	ACTOR	38 W 31ST ST #403	NEW YORK, NY	10001
DULLEA, KEIR	ACTOR	151 CENTRAL PARK W	NEW YORK, NY	10023
DUMARS, JOE	BASKETBALL	THE PALACE OF AUBURN HILLS		
		2 CHAMPIONSHIP DR	AUBURN HILLS, MI	48326
DUMAS, ANDRE	ACTOR	19 AVE DE CHATEAU	MAUDON 92190	FRANCE
DUMAS, JERRY	CARTOONIST	KING FEATURES, 216 E 45TH ST	NEW YORK, NY	10017
DUMAS, JOHN	FILM DIRECTOR	2601 MARLU DR	LOS ANGELES, CA	90046
DUMAS, JOHN J	FILM EDITOR	ACE, 1041 N FORMOSA AVE	WEST HOLLYWOOD, CA	90046
DUMAS, MIKE	FOOTBALL	OILERS, 6910 FANNIN ST	HOUSTON, TX	77070
DUMAS, ROGER	ACTOR	GEORGES LAMBERT AGENCE		
		13 BIS AVE LA MOTTE PIQUET	F-PARIS 75007	FRANCE
DUMM, JOHN RICKLEY	TV WRITER-PRODUCER	2056 BEL AIRE DR	GLENDALE, CA	91201
DUMPTRUCK	ROCK & ROLL GROUP	POST OFFICE BOX 551	BROOKLINE, MA	02146
DUMROSE, BOYD	ART DIRECTOR	ABC, 2040 BROADWAY	NEW YORK, NY	10023
DUNAS, RONALD S	WRITER	10643 SOMMA WY	LOS ANGELES, CA	90077
DUNAVAN, PATRICK	DIRECTOR-PRODUCER	2315 KENILWORTH AVE	LOS ANGELES, CA	90039
DUNAWAY, DON CARLOS	SCREENWRITER	UTA, 9560 WILSHIRE BL, 5TH FL	BEVERLY HILLS, CA	90212
DUNAWAY, FAYE	ACTRESS-MODEL	1435 LINDA CREST DR	BEVERLY HILLS, CA	90210
DUNBAR, ADRIAN	ACTOR	HEATH, PARAMOUNT HOUSE		
		162-170 WARDOUR ST	LONDON W1V 3AT	ENGLAND
DUNBAR, JEFFERSON, JR	WRITER	UBELL, 13443 MULHOLLAND DR	BEVERLY HILLS, CA	90210
DUNBAR, MATT	BASEBALL	POST OFFICE BOX 2148	WOODBRIDGE, VA	22193
DUNBAR, TOMMY	BASEBALL	558 S PALM DR	AIKEN, SC	29801
DUNCAN, ANDRES	BASEBALL	POST OFFICE BOX 21727	SAN FRANCISCO, CA	95151
DUNCAN, CHIP	BASEBALL	800 HOME RUN LN	MEMPHIS, TN	38104
DUNCAN, CURTIS	FOOTBALL	OILERS, 6910 FANNIN ST	HOUSTON, TX	77070
DUNCAN, DAVE	BASEBALL-COACH	ATHLETICS'S, OAKLAND COLISEUM	OAKLAND, CA	94621
DUNCAN, HERB	ACTOR	SUNNYRIDGE RD	HARRISON, NY	10528
DUNCAN, JEFF	BASEBALL	POST OFFICE BOX 882	MADISON, WI	53701
DUNCAN, JOHN J, JR	U S CONGRESSMAN	318 POST OFFICE BUILDING	KNOXVILLE, TN	37902
DUNCAN, JOHNNY	SINGER	ROUTE #2, BOX 356	STEPHENVILLE, TX	76401
DUNCAN, JUDITH	TV DIRECTOR	554 FOREST HILL RD	LAKE FOREST, IL	60045
DUNCAN, LANNY	ACTOR	336 N ISABEL ST	GLENDALE, CA	91206
DUNCAN, LINDSAY	ACTRESS	MC REDDIE, 91 REGENT ST	LONDON W1R 7TB	ENGLAND
DUNCAN, MARIANO	BASEBALL	POST OFFICE BOX 7575	PHILADELPHIA, PA	19101

Name	Occupation	Address	City	Zip/Country
DUNCAN, MARLA	BODYBUILDER	POST OFFICE BOX 417614	SACRAMENTO, CA	95841
DUNCAN, MEREDITH	ACTRESS	4257 CLYBOURN AVE	NORTH HOLLYWOOD, CA	91602
DUNCAN, PATRICK	SCREENWRITER	16633 VENTURA BLVD #1421	ENCINO, CA	91436
DUNCAN, PETER	ACTOR	MARKHAM AND FROGGATT, LTD		
		JULIAN HOUSE, 4 WINDMILL ST	LONDON W1P 1HF	ENGLAND
DUNCAN, RACHEL	ACTRESS	150 E OLIVE AVE #111	BURBANK, CA	91502
DUNCAN, ROBERT B	WRITER-PRODUCER	4360 TROOST AVE	STUDIO CITY, CA	91604
DUNCAN, SANDY	ACTRESS	10390 SANTA MONICA BLVD #300	LOS ANGELES, CA	90025
DUNCAN, WAYNE	ACTOR	8701 DELGANY AVE #215	PLAYA DEL REY, CA	90291
DUNDEE, ANGELO	BOXING REFEREE	1700 WASHINGTON AVE	MIAMI BEACH, FL	33141
DUNGAN, ELLIS	BASEBALL SCOUT	SKYDOME, 300 BREMMER BL #3200	TORONTO, ONT M5V 3B3	CANADA
DUNGY, TONY	FOOTBALL COACH	CHIEFS, 1 ARROWHEAD DR	KANSAS CITY, MO	64129
DUNIGAN, TIM	ACTOR	4277 MURIETTA AVE	SHERMAN OAKS, CA	91423
DUNING, GEORGE W	COMPOSER	13455 VENTURA BLVD #207	SHERMAN OAKS, CA	91423
DUNKLIN, BUD	BASEBALL UMPIRE	235 MAIN ST #103	TRUSSVILLE, AL	35173
DUNLAP, CARLA	BODYBUILDER	DIAMOND, 732 IRVINGTON AVE	MAPLEWOOD, NJ	07040
DUNLAP, GEOFF	TV DIRECTOR	3 WHITEHALL GARDENS	LONDON W4 3LT	ENGLAND
DUNLAP, LESLIE	ACTRESS	STONE, 9 NEWBURGH ST	LONDON W1V 1LH	ENGLAND
DUNLAP, MARGOT R	NEWS CORRESPONDENT	NBC NEWS, 4001 NEBRASKA AV, SW	WASHINGTON, DC	20016
DUNLAP, PAGE	GOLFER	2750 VOLUSA AVE #B	DAYTON BEACH, FL	32114
DUNLAP, RICHARD D	TV DIRECTOR	POST OFFICE BOX 336	MONTEREY, MA	01245
DUNLAP, TRAVIS	BASEBALL	POST OFFICE BOX 4525	MACON, GA	31208
DUNLEAVY, MIKE	BASKETBALL COACH	POST OFFICE BOX 10	INGLEWOOD, CA	90306
DUNLOP, HARRY	BASEBALL-MANAGER	POST OFFICE BOX 4606	HELENA, MT	59604
DUNN, ALDEN B	COMPOSER-CONDUCTOR	1918 COLLEGE VISTA AVE	WALNUT, CA	91789
DUNN, BOB	CARTOONIST	KING FEATURES, 216 E 45TH ST	NEW YORK, NY	10017
DUNN, BRIAN	BASEBALL	525 NW PEACOCK BLVD	PORT SAINT LUCIE, FL	34986
DUNN, CAL	DIRECTOR	RT #3, BOX 86-L, SUNLIT HILLS	SANTE FE, NM	87505
DUNN, ELI	DIRECTOR	8565 FALLBROOK CIR #D-718	HUNTINGTON BEACH, CA	92646
DUNN, HOLLY	SINGER-SONGWRITER	POST OFFICE BOX 128037	NASHVILLE, TN	37212
DUNN, JAMES	DIRECTOR	POST OFFICE BOX 64761	DALLAS, TX	75206
DUNN, JOHN	FOOTBALL COACH	POST OFFICE BOX 609609	SAN DIEGO, CA	92160
DUNN, RICHARD	CONDUCTOR	27 SKYLINE CIR	SANTA BARBARA, CA	93109
DUNN, RON	FILM-TV DIRECTOR	4627 ALLOTT AVE	SHERMAN OAKS, CA	91423
DUNN, STEVE	BASEBALL	POST OFFICE BOX 48	VISALIA, CA	93279
DUNN, T R	BASKETBALL	POST OFFICE BOX 4658	DENVER, CO	80204
DUNN, WILLIAM	COLUMNIST	POST OFFICE BOX 500	WASHINGTON, DC	20044
DUNNAGAN, MICHAEL	ACTOR	685 W GRANDVIEW AVE	SIERRA MADRE, CA	91024
DUNNE, DOMINICK	ACTOR-NOVELIST	155 E 49TH ST	NEW YORK, NY	10017
DUNNE, GRIFFIN	ACTOR-PRODUCER	40 W 12TH ST	NEW YORK, NY	10011
DUNNE, JAMES PATRICK	COMPOSER	3030 DURAND DR	LOS ANGELES, CA	90068
DUNNE, MIKE	BASEBALL	CANADIANS, 4601 ONTARIO ST	VANCOUVER, BC V5V 3H4	CANADA
DUNNE, MURPHY	ACTOR	1850 1/2 N VISTA ST	LOS ANGELES, CA	90046
DUNNE, PETER	TV PRODUCER	MTA, 9320 WILSHIRE BL, 3RD FL	BEVERLY HILLS, CA	90212
DUNNE, PHILIP	WRITER-PRODUCER	24708 PACIFIC COAST HWY	MALIBU, CA	90265
DUNNELL, RAN	DIRECTOR	5800 KELVIN AVE	WOODLAND HILLS, CA	91367
DUNNICK, REGAN	ARTIST	1135 HAMPTON RD	SARASOTA, FL	33577
DUNNING, BRUCE	NEWS CORRESPONDENT	CBS NEWS, 524 W 57TH ST	NEW YORK, NY	10019
DUNPHY, JERRY	BROADCAST JOURNALIST	KCAL-TV, 5515 MELROSE AVE	LOS ANGELES, CA	90038
DUNSMORE, BARRIE	NEWS CORRESPONDENT	ABC NEWS, 1717 DE SALES ST, NW	WASHINGTON, DC	20036
DUNSMUIR, THOMAS D	WRITER	567 RADCLIFFE AVE	PACIFIC PALISADES, CA	90272
DUNSTAN, PAUL	TV PRODUCER	YORKSHIRE TV, KIRKSTALL RD	LEEDS	ENGLAND
DUNSTAN, TOM	ACTOR	3533 KEYSTONE AVE #2	LOS ANGELES, CA	90034
DUNSTON, SHAWON	BASEBALL	1060 W ADDISON ST	CHICAGO, IL	60613
DUPER, MARK "SUPER"	FOOTBALL	DOLPHINS, 2269 NW 199TH ST	MIAMI, FL	33056
DUPREE, PAUL R	BASKETBALL EXECUTIVE	151 MERRIMAC ST	BOSTON, MA	02114
DUPREE, ROBBIE	SINGER-SONGWRITER	TWENTIETH CENTURY PROMOTIONS		
		1775 BROADWAY, 7TH FLOOR	NEW YORK, NY	10019
DUPREES, THE	VOCAL GROUP	MARS, 168 ORCHID DR	PEARL RIVER, NY	10965
DUQUETTE, DAN	BASEBALL EXECUTIVE	EXPOS, 4545 DE COUBERTIN AVE	MONTREAL, QUE H1V 3P2	CANADA
DUQUETTE, TONY	COSTUME DESIGNER	13949 VENTURA BLVD #309	SHERMAN OAKS, CA	91423
DURAL, JEFFREY P	COMPOSER	149 E 120TH ST	LOS ANGELES, CA	90061
DURAL, STANLEY, JR	SINGER-SONGWRITER	SEE - ZYDECO, BUCKWHEAT		
DURALIA, DARLENE	ACTRESS	3935 VINELAND AVE #6	NORTH HOLLYWOOD, CA	91604
DURAN, FELIPE	BASEBALL	POST OFFICE BOX 1886	COLUMBUS, GA	31902
DURAN, IGNACIO	BASEBALL	POST OFFICE BOX 3783	SAVANNAH, GA	31414
DURAN, ROBERTO	BOXER	ELETA, BOX 157, ARENA COLON	PANAMA CITY	PANAMA
DURAND, JOSEPH	DIRECTOR	729 CLEARVIEW AVE	WOODBURY HEIGHTS, NJ	08097
DURAND, RUDY	WRITER-PRODUCER	KOALA, 361 N CANON DR	BEVERLY HILLS, CA	90210
DURANT, HEIDI	ACTRESS	2049 CENTURY PARK E #1200	LOS ANGELES, CA	90067
DURANT, JOHN	WRITER	350 10TH AVE S	NAPLES, FL	33940
DURANT, MIKE	BASEBALL	POST OFFICE BOX 48	VISALIA, CA	93279
DURBIN, DEANNA	ACTRESS	B P 767	75123 PARIS CEDEX 03	FRANCE
DURBIN, RICHARD	U S CONGRESSMAN	525 S 8TH ST	SPRINGFIELD, IL	62703
DURENBERGER, DAVE	U S SENATOR	12 S 6TH ST #1020	MINNEAPOLIS, MN	20510
DURENBURGER, DAVID	SENATOR	7732 CANAL ST	MC LEAN, VA	22101
DURHAM, CHRISTOPHER	ACTOR	POST OFFICE BOX 982	NEW YORK, NY	10023
DURHAM, EARL	TV WRITER-PRODUCER	3500 W OLIVE AVE #500	BURBANK, CA	91505
DURHAM, JOE	BASEBALL-COACH	POST OFFICE BOX 230	HAGERSTOWN, MD	21740
DURHAM, LEON "BULL"	BASEBALL	3932 DICKSON AVE	CINCINNATI, OH	45229
DURHAM BROTHERS, THE	C & W GROUP	742-B LINDEN GREEN DR	HERMITAGE, TN	37076
DURKIN, CHRIS	BASEBALL	POST OFFICE BOX 1556	ASHEVILLE, NC	28802
DURKIN, ED	BASEBALL SCOUT	BREWERS, 201 S 46TH ST	MILWAUKEE, WI	53214
DURNING, CHARLES	ACTOR	10590 WILSHIRE BLVD #506	LOS ANGELES, CA	90024
DURSLAG, MELVIN	COLUMNIST	523 DALEHURST AVE	LOS ANGELES, CA	90024

DURST, DAN	BASEBALL SCOUT	TWINS, 501 CHICAGO AVE S	MINNEAPOLIS, MN	55415
DURUSSEL, SCOTT	BASEBALL	POST OFFICE BOX 64939	FAYETTEVILLE, NC	28306
DUSAY, DEBRA	ACTRESS	9000 SUNSET BLVD #1200	LOS ANGELES, CA	90069
DUSAY, MARJ	ACTRESS	6310 SAN VICENTE BLVD #407	LOS ANGELES, CA	90048
DUSBABEK, MARK	FOOTBALL	VIKINGS, 9520 VIKING DR	EDEN PRAIRIE, MN	55344
DUSENBERRY, ANN	ACTRESS	9200 SUNSET BLVD #710	LOS ANGELES, CA	90069
DUSENBERRY, PHILIP B	SCREENWRITER	555 W 57TH ST #1230	NEW YORK, NY	10019
DUSKIN, KENNETH	DIRECTOR	RURAL DELIVERY #5, BOX 256		
		PRIMROSE ST	KATONAH, NY	10536
DUSSAULT, NANCY	ACTRESS	12211 IREDELL ST	NORTH HOLLYWOOD, CA	91604
DUTCH, DEBORAH	ACTRESS	801 S WOOSTER ST #2	LOS ANGELES, CA	90035
DUTEIL, JEFFREY	TV WRITER	9122 AMBOY AVE	SUN VALLEY, CA	91352
DUTFIELD, RAYMOND	FILM EXECUTIVE	TECHNICOLOR LTD, BATH RD		
		HARMONSWORTH	MIDDLESEX	ENGLAND
DUTTINE, JOHN	ACTOR	PEBRO HOUSE, 13 SAINT MARTIN RD	LONDON SW9	ENGLAND
DUTTON, CHARLES S	ACTOR	CAA, 9830 WILSHIRE BLVD	BEVERLY HILLS, CA	90212
DUTTON, JOHN	DIRECTOR	1289 N CRESCENT HGTS BLVD #A	LOS ANGELES, CA	90046
DUVAL, CHARLES	ACTOR	78 BEDFORD ST	NEW YORK, NY	10014
DUVALIER, JEAN-CLAUDE	PRESIDENT	HOTEL DE L'ABBAYE	TALLOIRES	FRANCE
DUVALL, ROBERT	ACTOR-SCREENWRITER	257 W 86TH ST	NEW YORK, NY	10024
DUVALL, SHELLEY	ACTRESS-PRODUCER	12725 VENTURA BLVD #J	STUDIO CITY, CA	91604
DUX, PIERRE	ACTOR	ARTMEDIA, 10 AVE GEORGE V	PARIS 75008	FRANCE
DUZICH, KEN	BASEBALL SCOUT	INDIANS, CLEVELAND STADIUM	CLEVELAND, OH	44114
DVENSING, LARRY	BASEBALL TRAINER	STARS, 850 LAS VEGAS BLVD N	LAS VEGAS, NV	89101
DVORAK, WAYNE C	ACTOR	1308 N HAVENHURST DR #5	LOS ANGELES, CA	90046
DVORE, SANDY	ARTIST	9255 SUNSET BLVD #713	LOS ANGELES, CA	90069
DVORE, SANDY	TV DIRECTOR	840 N LARRABEE ST	LOS ANGELES, CA	90069
DWAN, ROBERT	DIRECTOR	229 AMALFI DR	SANTA MONICA, CA	90402
DWIGGINS, DAVID	PRODUCER	RIVER RUN, 650 N BRONSON AVE	LOS ANGELES, CA	90004
DWORET, LAURENCE	WRITER	6726 MILNER RD	LOS ANGELES, CA	90068
DWORSKI, DAVID	WRITER	31840 SEAFIELD DR	MALIBU, CA	90265
DWORSKI, SUSAN B	WRITER	31840 SEAFIELD DR	MALIBU, CA	90265
DWORSKY, RICHARD	MUSICIAN	POST OFFICE BOX 9388	STANFORD, CA	94305
DWORSKY, ROBERT	FILM EDITOR	95 INDIA ST	BROOKLYN, NY	11222
DWYER, BERNARD	U S CONGRESSMAN	86 BAYARD ST	NEW BRUNSWICK, NJ	08901
DWYER, EDWARD	BASEBALL EXECUTIVE	POST OFFICE BOX 802	BATAVIA, NY	14021
DWYER, FRANK	ACTOR	243 W 4TH ST #5	NEW YORK, NY	10014
DWYER, JIM	BASEBALL-MANAGER	7607 W 159TH PL	TINLEY PARK, IL	60477
DYBAS, JAMES	ACTOR	14350 ADDISON ST #220	SHERMAN OAKS, CA	91423
DYE, BRAD	LT GOVERNOR	POST OFFICE BOX 2000	JACKSON, MS	39215
DYE, CAMERON	ACTOR	9000 SUNSET BLVD #1200	LOS ANGELES, CA	90069
DYER, CHARLES CORNELIUS	DIRECTOR	670 WHITE ASH DR	LANGHORNE, PA	19047
DYER, DUFFY	BASEBALL-COACH	BREWERS, 201 S 46TH ST	MILWAUKEE, WI	53214
DYER, GEORGE	FOOTBALL COACH	SEAHAWKS, 11220 NE 53RD ST	KIRKLAND, WA	98033
DYER, JAYE F	FOOTBALL EXECUTIVE	VIKINGS, 9520 VIKING DR	EDEN PRAIRIE, MN	55344
DYER, MIKE	BASEBALL	POST OFFICE BOX 1659	PORTLAND, OR	97207
DYKE, BILL	BASEBALL EXECUTIVE	633 JESSAMINE ST	KNOXVILLE, TN	37917
DYKE, GREG	TV PRODUCER	TVS, TELEVISION CENTRE	SOUTHAMPTON SO9 5HZ	ENGLAND
DYKINGA, JACK	PHOTOJOURNALIST	POST OFFICE BOX 26807	TUCSON, AZ	85726
DYKMAN, JOAN DAY	ACTRESS	WEBB, 7500 DEVISTA DR	LOS ANGELES, CA	90046
DYKSTRA, JOHN	DIRECTOR	6842 VALJEAN AVE	VAN NUYS, CA	91406
DYKSTRA, LEN	BASEBALL	POST OFFICE BOX 7575	PHILADELPHIA, PA	19101
DYLAN, BOB	SINGER-SONGWRITER	LOOKOUT, 506 SANTA MONICA BLVD	SANTA MONICA, CA	90401
DYMALLY, AMENTHA V	ACTRESS	2366 W 23RD ST	LOS ANGELES, CA	90018
DYMALLY, MERVYN	U S CONGRESSMAN	306 W COMPTON BLVD	COMPTON, CA	90220
DYNATONES, THE	ROCK & ROLL GROUP	POST OFFICE BOX 22372	SAN FRANCISCO, CA	94122
DYRECTOR, JOYCE	WRITER	756 1/2 N CROFT AVE	LOS ANGELES, CA	90069
DYRECTOR, STANLEY	ACTOR-WRITER	756 1/2 N CROFT AVE	LOS ANGELES, CA	90069
DYRENFORTH, DR H O	ACTOR	3489 ASHWOOD AVE	LOS ANGELES, CA	90066
DYRSTAD, JOANELL	LT GOVERNOR	STATE CAPTOL BLDG, AURORA AVE	SAINT PAUL, MN	55155
DYSART, RICHARD A	ACTOR	654 COPELAND CT	SANTA MONICA, CA	90405
DYSERT, ALAN	ACTOR	304 W 88TH ST	NEW YORK, NY	10024
DYSON, NOEL	ACTRESS	18 PETHERTON RD, GARDEN FLAT	LONDON N5	ENGLAND
DZIADKOWIEC, ANDY	BASEBALL	POST OFFICE BOX 598	BINGHAMTON, NY	13902
DZUNDZA, GEORGE	ACTOR	151 S EL CAMINO DR	BEVERLY HILLS, CA	90212

E, SHEILA	SINGER-MUSICIAN	9665 WILSHIRE BLVD #850	BEVERLY HILLS, CA	90212
EAGAN, SHERMAN G	TV DIRECTOR	23 HOLLOW TREE RIDGE	DARIEN, CT	06820
EAGLE, JACK	ACTOR	63 CONTINENTAL AVE	FOREST HILLS, NY	11375
EAGLE, JEFF	ACTOR	13455 VENTURA BLVD #210	SHERMAN OAKS, CA	91423
EAGLE, MARY	PRODUCER	MCA/UNIVERSAL STUDIOS, INC		
		100 UNIVERSAL CITY PLAZA	UNIVERSAL CITY, CA	91608
EAGLES, MIKE	HOCKEY	JETS, 15-1430 MAROONS RD	WINNIPEG, MAN R3G 0L5	CANADA
EAGLETON, THOMAS F	ATTORNEY-U S SENATOR	THOMPSON & MITCHELL LAW FIRM		
		1 MERCANTILE CTR	ST LOUIS, MO	68101
EAKES, BOBBIE	ACTRESS	4320 VAN NUYS BLVD #114	SHERMAN OAKS, CA	91403
EALY, TOM	BASEBALL	POST OFFICE BOX 2785	LAKELAND, FL	33806

EARHART, JOHN	BASEBALL EXECUTIVE	POST OFFICE BOX 2000	SAN DIEGO, CA	92112
EARL, ELIZABETH	ACTRESS	5226 BECKFORD AVE	TARZANA, CA	91356
EARLEY, BILL	BASEBALL COACH	POST OFFICE DRAWER 1207	ZEBULON, NC	27597
EARLEY, CANDICE	ACTRESS	ABC-TV, "ALL MY CHILDREN"		
		320 W 66TH ST	NEW YORK, NY	10023
EARLL, ROBERT	WRITER	16633 VENTURA BLVD #1421	ENCINO, CA	91346
EARLY, JOSEPH D	U S CONGRESSMAN	34 MECHANIC ST #203	WORCESTER, MA	01608
EARLY, QUINN	FOOTBALL	SAINTS, 1500 POYDRAS ST	NEW ORLEANS, LA	90112
EARNHARDT, DAVID	TV DIRECTOR-PRODUCER	902 RUSSELL ST	NASHVILLE, TN	37206
EARNHART, BILL	BASEBALL SCOUT	POST OFFICE BOX 90111	ARLINGTON, TX	76004
EARTH, WIND & FIRE	SOUL GROUP	1990 WESTWOOD BLVD #210	LOS ANGELES, CA	90025
EASLER, MIKE	BASEBALL-COACH	BREWERS, 201 S 46TH ST	MILWAUKEE, WI	53214
EASLEY, DAMION	BASEBALL	10233 96TH AVE	EDMONTON, ALB TK5 0A5	CANADA
EASLEY, DOUGLAS	ACTOR	200 W 16TH ST	NEW YORK, NY	10011
EASLEY, HOLMES	SET DECORATOR	CBS-TV, 524 W 57TH ST	NEW YORK, NY	10023
EASLEY, JAMES LAVELL	SINGER	POST OFFICE BOX 30166	MEMPHIS, TN	38130
EASLEY, MIKE	BASEBALL	POST OFFICE BOX 3448	SHREVEPORT, LA	71133
EASON, TOMMY	BASEBALL	POST OFFICE BOX 1721	SPARTANBURG, SC	29304
EAST, JADE	ACTRESS-MODEL	POST OFFICE BOX 9786	MARINA DEL REY, CA	90265
EAST, JEFF	ACTOR	5521 RAINBOW CREST DR	AGOURA, CA	91301
EASTBURN, JOSEPH	ACTOR	85 CHRISTOPHER ST #6-B	NEW YORK, NY	10014
EASTERBROOK, LESLIE	ACTRESS-SINGER	17352 SUNSET BLVD #401-D	PACIFIC PALISADES, CA	90272
EASTHAM, RICHARD	ACTOR	1529 ORIOLE LN	LOS ANGELES, CA	90069
EASTMAN, CAROL J	SCREENWRITER	8955 BEVERLY BLVD	WEST HOLLYWOOD, CA	90048
EASTMAN, CHARLES	WRITER-PRODUCER	113 27TH ST #B	MANHATTAN BEACH, CA	90266
EASTMAN, EDDIE	SINGER	NEW DIRECTIONS, 706 18TH AVE S	NASHVILLE, TN	37203
EASTMAN, PETER A	ACTOR	112 GREENE ST	NEW YORK, NY	10012
EASTON, ELLIOT	SINGER-SONGWRITER	LOOKOUT, 506 SANTA MONICA BLVD	SANTA MONICA, CA	90401
EASTON, JACK	COMPOSER-CONDUCTOR	295 CENTRAL PARK W	NEW YORK, NY	10024
EASTON, JOE	BASEBALL EXECUTIVE	POST OFFICE BOX 5566	EUGENE, OR	97405
EASTON, MICHAEL	ACTOR	NBC-TV, "DAYS OF OUR LIVES"		
		3000 W ALAMEDA AVE	BURBANK, CA	91523
EASTON, ROBERT	ACTOR	KOHNER, 9169 SUNSET BLVD	LOS ANGELES, CA	90069
EASTON, SHEENA	SINGER-SONGWRITER	WASSERMAN, 5954 WILKINSON AVE	NORTH HOLLYWOOD, CA	91607
EASTWOOD, ALISON	ACTRESS	4000 WARNER BLVD #16	BURBANK, CA	91522
EASTWOOD, CLINT	ACTOR-DIRECTOR	4000 WARNER BLVD #16	BURBANK, CA	91522
EASTWOOD, KYLE	ACTOR	4000 WARNER BLVD #16	BURBANK, CA	91522
EASY MONEY	C & W GROUP	BGM NETWORK, 10450 SENTINEL ST	SAN ANTONIO, TX	78217
EATINGER, MIKE	BASEBALL	1090 N EUCLID AVE	SARASOTA, FL	34237
EATMAN, IRV	FOOTBALL	N Y JETS, 1000 FULTON AVE	HEMPSTEAD, NY	11550
EATON, BEAUTIFUL BOBBY	WRESTLER	POST OFFICE BOX 105366	ATLANTA, GA	31348
EATON, DIAN	ACTRESS	12320 CHANDLER BLVD #12	NORTH HOLLYWOOD, CA	91607
EATON, MARK	BASKETBALL	5 TRIAD CENTER #500	SALT LAKE CITY, UT	84180
EATON, SHIRLEY	ACTRESS	8 HARLEY ST	LONDON W1N 2AB	ENGLAND
EATON, TRACEY	FOOTBALL	FALCONS, SUWANEE RD AT I-85	SUWANEE, GA	30174
EAVE, GARY	BASEBALL	POST OFFICE BOX 3690, STA "B"	CALGARY, ALB T2B 4M4	CANADA
EAZY E	RAP GROUP-RAPWRITERS	FAA, 1700 BROADWAY, 5TH FLOOR	NEW YORK, NY	10019
EBB, FRED	COMPOSER-LYRICIST	146 CENTRAL PARK W #14-D	NEW YORK, NY	10023
EBEL, BRIAN	BASEBALL TRAINER	POST OFFICE BOX 230	HAGERSTOWN, MD	21740
EBEL, DINO	BASEBALL COACH	POST OFFICE BOX 10031	BAKERSFIELD, CA	93389
EBER, JOSE	HAIR STYLIST	JOSE EBER SALON, BEVERLY CENTER		
		121 N LA CIENEGA BLVD	LOS ANGELES, CA	90048
EBERHARDT, RICHARD	POET	5 WEBSTER TERR	HANOVER, NH	03755
EBERHARDT, THOM	WRITER-DIRECTOR	9200 SUNSET BLVD #402	LOS ANGELES, CA	90069
EBERLE, MIKE	BASEBALL	500 NORTON ST	ROCHESTER, NY	14621
EBERSOLE, CHRISTINE	ACT-SING-COMED	1244-A 11TH ST	SANTA MONICA, CA	90401
EBERT, ALAN M	TV WRITER	353 W 56TH ST	NEW YORK, NY	10019
EBERT, ROGER	FILM CRITIC	509 W DICKENS AVE	CHICAGO, IL	60614
EBERTS, JAKE	TV PRODUCER	KATEVALE PRODUCTIONS, LTD		
		3-A WALMER COURTYARD		
		225-227 WALMER RD	LONDON W11 43Y	ENGLAND
EBONEE, WEBB	SINGER	POST OFFICE BOX 161076	MEMPHIS, TN	38116
EBRAHIM, GRETCHEN	TV WRITER	630 BIENVENEDA AVE	PACIFIC PALISADES, CA	90272
EBRIGHT, CHRIS	BASEBALL	POST OFFICE DRAWER 1207	ZEBULON, NC	27597
EBSEN, BONNIE	ACTRESS	POST OFFICE BOX 356	AGOURA, CA	91301
EBSEN, BUDDY	ACTOR	605 VIA HORQUILLA	PALOS VERDES ESTATES,	90274
EBSON, ROD	CINEMATOGRAPHER	19 HIGH CLIFF DR	LIEGH-ON-SEA, ESSEX	ENGLAND
EBY, GEORGE	ENTERTAINMENT EXEC	11679 DONA ALICIA PL	STUDIO CITY, CA	91604
EBY, JOHN	ACTOR	733 N SEWARD ST	LOS ANGELES, CA	90038
ECHO HAWK, LARRY	ATTORNEY GENERAL	STATE HOUSE BUILDING	BOISE, ID	83720
ECKARD, PAUL	BASEBALL TRAINER	POST OFFICE BOX 7893	EVERETT, WA	98201
ECKART, DENNIS E	U S CONGRESSMAN	5970 HEISLEY RD #220	MENTOR, OH	44060
ECKELS, NANCY D	WRITER	5100 RIVERTON AVE #4	NORTH HOLLYWOOD, CA	91601
ECKERSLEY, DENNIS	BASEBALL	ATHLETICS'S, OAKLAND COLISEUM	OAKLAND, CA	94621
ECKHARDT, SARAH	ACTRESS	STONE MANNERS, 9113 SUNSET BL	LOS ANGELES, CA	90069
ECKHOUSE, JAMES	ACTOR	5817 BUFFALO AVE	VAN NUYS, CA	91401
ECKLES, AIMEE	ACTRESS	SEE - ECKLES-BAKER, AIMEE		
ECKSTEIN, GEORGE	WRITER-PRODUCER	MTA, 9320 WILSHIRE BL, 3RD FL	BEVERLY HILLS, CA	90212
ECKSTINE, BILLY	SINGER	1118 15TH ST #4	SANTA MONICA, CA	90403
EDDIE, JOHN	SINGER	130 W 57TH ST #2-A	NEW YORK, NY	10019
EDDINGTON, PAUL	ACTOR	ICM, 388-396 OXFORD ST	LONDON W1	ENGLAND
EDDINS, JAMES DONALD	TV DIRECTOR	420 BROOKSHIRE DR	COLUMBIA, SC	29210
EDDO, NANCY	TV WRITER	5516 CORTEEN PL #15	NORTH HOLLYWOOD, CA	91607
EDDY, DUANE	SINGER-GUITARIST	200 W 57TH ST #910	NEW YORK, NY	10019
EDDY, JIM	BASEBALL	POST OFFICE BOX 3566	WEST PALM BEACH, FL	33402

BARBARA EDEN

INTERNATIONAL FAN CLUB

c/o Kenneth A. Bealer
1332 North Ulster Street
Allentown, PA 18103

Bi-monthly newsletter
Color photo in every issue.
A 6-issue (1 year) subscription
is only $8.00

Started in 1977, I took over the operation of the Fan Club in 1979 and we published a Quarterly newsletter until January 1984 at which time we went Bi-monthly, due in great part to Barbara's continued popularity and increasingly busy career, and my desire to give everyone more timely, up-to-date news on her activities.

Each of our newsletters varies in size from 5-10 pages, with each issue containing a color print of Barbara and all the latest news on her future activities, tours, photos and clippings covering Barbara's past and present career.

New members receive a 6-page TV/Credit listing and a 1-page Filmography. Both are updated yearly in the June issue.

I have personally traveled to Lake Tahoe, NV, Atlanta GA, Hot Springs, AK, Reno, NV, etc. to see Barbara's nightclub act and give her our support, as well as seeing all of her plays in which she has toured in the past five years.

In early 1986 we were contacted by Barbara to help supply photographs for her upcoming autobiography and we sent over 200 photos for her consideration, and many will be used in the book when published.

Barbara is certainly one actress who deserves the support of her fans from around the world. Merv Griffin and Bob Hope are counted among our Honorary members and we are a member of NAFC (National Association of Fan Clubs). Help us support entertainment's most beautiful and talented actress. Yearly dues are $8.00 per year for 6-issues for the Bi-Monthly newsletter. Just send us your full name and address along with a No. 10 SASE for more information to address listed above. Renewal notices are sent out with the last issue prior to expiration. Thank you for your interest.

Kenneth Bealer

Kenneth A. Bealer
International President

EDDY, JIM	FOOTBALL COACH	OILERS, 6910 FANNIN ST	HOUSTON, TX	77070
EDELMAN, HERB	ACTOR	147 N OLD TOPANGA CANYON RD	TOPANGA, CA	90290
EDELMAN, JONATHAN	SCREENWRITER	2419 BEVERLY AVE #1	SANTA MONICA, CA	90405
EDELMAN, JULIUS	DIRECTOR	21-15 34TH AVE	LONG ISLAND, CA	11106
EDELMAN, RICHARD	TV DIRECTOR	1 SHERIDAN SQ	NEW YORK, NY	10014
EDELMAN HOLT, NORAH J	SCREENWRITER	495 W END AVE #8-D	NEW YORK, NY	10024
EDELSTEIN, RICK	WRITER-PRODUCER	747 GAYLEY AVE	LOS ANGELES, CA	90024
EDEN, BARBARA	ACTRESS-PRODUCER	9816 DENBIGH	BEVERLY HILLS, CA	90210
EDEN, DIANA	COSTUME DESIGNER	4141 WESLIN AVE	SHERMAN OAKS, CA	91423
EDEN, RICHARD	ACTOR	RINI MGMT, 9000 SUNSET BLVD	LOS ANGELES, CA	90069
EDENFIELD, KEN	BASEBALL	POST OFFICE BOX 1742	PALM SPRINGS, CA	92263
EDENS, TOM	BASEBALL	TWINS, 501 CHICAGO AVE S	MINNEAPOLIS, MN	55415
EDERLE, GERTRUDE	SWIMMER	4465 SW 37TH AVE	FORT LAUDERDALE, FL	33312
EDGAR, JIM	GOVERNOR	STATE HOUSE BUILDING	SPRINGFIELD, IL	62706
EDGAR, ROBERTA	WRITER	703 N FOOTHILL RD	BEVERLY HILLS, CA	90210
EDGAR, WILLIAM ALFRED	WRITER	703 N FOOTHILL RD	BEVERLY HILLS, CA	90210
EDGE, GREG	BASEBALL	POST OFFICE DRAWER 1218	ZEBULON, NC	27597
EDGE, MITZI	GOLFER	2750 VOLUSA AVE #B	DAYTON BEACH, FL	32114
EDGE, TIM	BASEBALL	POST OFFICE BOX 842	SALEM, VA	24153
EDLUND, RICHARD	CINEMATOGRAPHER	POST OFFICE BOX 2230	HOLLYWOOD, CA	90078
EDMANS, ANDREW	ACTOR	EAA, 84 WARDOUR ST, 1ST FLOOR	LONDON W1V 3LF	ENGLAND
EDMISTEN, RUFUS	SECRETARY OF STATE	STATE CAPITOL BUILDING	RALEIGH, NC	27603
EDMONDS, BERNARD M	TV-COMEDY WRITER	163 GARFIELD PL	BROOKLYN, NY	11215
EDMONDS, JIM	BASEBALL	POST OFFICE BOX 12	MIDLAND, TX	79702
EDMONDS, LOUIS	ACTOR	250 W 57TH ST #2317	NEW YORK, NY	10107
EDMONDS, NOEL	TV-RADIO PERS	BBC-TV, 56 WOOD LN	LONDON W12 7RJ	ENGLAND
EDMONDS, ROBERT J	DIRECTOR	1132 W LUNT AVE #9-D	CHICAGO, IL	60626
EDMONDSON, ADRIAN	ACTOR-COMEDIAN	LONDON MGT, 235-241 REGENT ST	LONDON W1R 4PH	ENGLAND
EDMONDSON, CHUCK	BASEBALL SCOUT	POST OFFICE BOX 288	HOUSTON, TX	77001
EDMONSON, BRIAN	BASEBALL	POST OFFICE BOX 64939	FAYETTEVILLE, NC	28306
EDMONSTON, MARY-KATE	ACTRESS	438 N SWEETZER AVE	LOS ANGELES, CA	90048
EDMUNDS, DAVE	SINGER-GUITARIST	MONARCH, 7 N MOUNTAIN AVE	MONTCLAIR, NJ	07042
EDMUNDS, MALCOLM	DIRECTOR	19243 CASTLEBAY LN	NORTHRIDGE, CA	91326
EDNEY, BEATIE	ACTRESS	MC REDDIE, 91 REGENT ST	LONDON W1R 7TB	ENGLAND
EDSON, ERIC	SCREENWRITER	ICM, 8899 BEVERLY BLVD	LOS ANGELES, CA	90048
EDWARDS, AL	FOOTBALL	BILLS, 1 BILLS DR	ORCHARD PARK, NJ	14127
EDWARDS, ANTHONY	ACTOR	8820 LOOKOUT MOUNTAIN AVE	LOS ANGELES, CA	90046
EDWARDS, BLAKE	WRITER-PRODUCER	9336 W WASHINGTON BLVD	CULVER CITY, CA	90230
EDWARDS, BLUE	BASKETBALL	5 TRIAD CENTER #500	SALT LAKE CITY, UT	84180
EDWARDS, BRAD	FOOTBALL	POST OFFICE BOX 17247 (DULLES)	WASHINGTON, DC	20041
EDWARDS, CASH	WRITER	SAMURAI, 4672 QUEBEC ST	VANCOUVER, BC VSV 3MI	CANADA
EDWARDS, CHET	U S CONGRESSMAN	425 CANNON HOUSE OFFICE BLDG	WASHINGTON, DC	20515
EDWARDS, DAVID	GOLFER	POST OFFICE BOX 109601	PALM BCH GARDENS, FL	33418
EDWARDS, DOC	BASEBALL-COACH	POST OFFICE BOX 450	BUFFALO, NY	14205
EDWARDS, DON	U S CONGRESSMAN	1042 W HEDDING ST #100	SAN JOSE, CA	95126
EDWARDS, EDWARD	ACTOR	726 IDAHO AVE #105	SANTA MONICA, CA	90403
EDWARDS, GAIL	ACTRESS	2321 21ST ST	SANTA MONICA, CA	90405
EDWARDS, GEOFF	FILM EDITOR	1034 N LA JOLLA AVE	LOS ANGELES, CA	90046
EDWARDS, GEOFFREY B	SCREENWRITER	16530 VENTURA BLVD #202	ENCINO, CA	91436
EDWARDS, GEORGE	PRODUCER	650 N BRONSON AVE	LOS ANGELES, CA	90004
EDWARDS, GEORGE L	SCREENWRITER	8955 BEVERLY BLVD	WEST HOLLYWOOD, CA	90048
EDWARDS, GLYNN	ACTOR	EDWARDS, 275 KENNINGTON RD	LONDON SE1 6BY	ENGLAND
EDWARDS, HANLEY E	COMPOSER	2131 3RD AVE	LOS ANGELES, CA	90018
EDWARDS, JAMES	BASKETBALL	THE PALACE OF AUBURN HILLS 2 CHAMPIONSHIP DR	AUBURN HILLS, MI	48326
EDWARDS, JENNIFER BLAKE	ACTRESS	6805 DUME DR	MALIBU, CA	90265
EDWARDS, JEROME	BASEBALL	POST OFFICE BOX 1721	SPARTANBURG, SC	29304
EDWARDS, JOHN	TV PRODUCER	THAMES TV, TEDDINGTON LOCK TEDDINGTON	MIDDLESEX TW11 9NT	ENGLAND
EDWARDS, JOHN H	ACTOR	3129 HIGHLAND VIEW DR	BURBANK, CA	91504
EDWARDS, JONATHAN	SINGER-SONGWRITER	ROBERTSON, 1030 16TH AVE	NASHVILLE, TN	37212
EDWARDS, KEVIN	BASKETBALL	MIAMI HEAT, THE MIAMI ARENA	MIAMI, FL	33136
EDWARDS, LYDIA JUSTICE	TREASURER	STATE HOUSE BUILDING	BOISE, ID	83720
EDWARDS, MEREDITH	ACTRESS	TY COCH, CILCAIN	MOLD	WALES
EDWARDS, MICKEY	U S CONGRESSMAN	900 NW 63RD ST #105	OKLAHOMA CITY, OK	73116
EDWARDS, MIKE	BASEBALL	POST OFFICE BOX 309	GASTONA, NC	28053
EDWARDS, PAUL F	TV WRITER-DIRECTOR	16812 CHARMEL LN	PACIFIC PALISADES, CA	90272
EDWARDS, RANDALL	ACTRESS	1930 CENTURY PARK W #403	LOS ANGELES, CA	90067
EDWARDS, RYAN	BASEBALL	POST OFFICE BOX 2001	CEDAR RAPIDS, IA	52406
EDWARDS, STACY	ACTRESS	11726 SAN VICENTE BLVD #300	LOS ANGELES, CA	90049
EDWARDS, STEPHANIE	ACTRESS	533 18TH ST	SANTA MONICA, CA	90402
EDWARDS, STEVE	TV HOST	3980 ROYAL OAK PL	ENCINO, CA	91436
EDWARDS, VINCENT	ACT-WRI-DIR	POST OFFICE BOX 642	MALIBU, CA	90265
EDWARDS, WAYNE	BASEBALL	9738 AQUEDUCT AVE	SEPULVEDA, CA	91343
EDWING, DON	WRITER	MAD MAGAZINE, 485 MADISON AVE	NEW YORK, NY	10022
EELLS, GEORGE	NOVELIST	514 N RODEO DR	BEVERLY HILLS, CA	90210
EELLS, PAMELA	TV WRITER	9242 BEVERLY DR #200	BEVERLY HILLS, CA	90210
EENHOORN, ROBERT	BASEBALL	5301 NW 12TH AVE	FORT LAUDERDALE, FL	33309
EGAN, DICK	BASEBALL-SCOUT	POST OFFICE BOX 90111	ARLINGTON, TX	76004
EGAN, PETER	ACTOR	SHARKEY, 15 GOLDEN SQ #315	LONDON W1R 3AG	ENGLAND
EGAN, SAM	TV WRITER-DIRECTOR	521 12TH ST	SANTA MONICA, CA	90402
EGER, DENNIS	MAKE-UP ARTIST	80 MAGNAW PL	WEST BABYLON, NY	11704
EGER, JOSEPH	CONDUCTOR	40 W 67TH ST	NEW YORK, NY	10023
EGGAR, SAMANTHA	ACTRESS	8485 MELROSE PL #E	LOS ANGELES, CA	90069
EGGART, HARRY R	DIRECTOR	41 SPICER RD	WESTPORT, CT	06880

EGGELING, DALE	GOLFER	2750 VOLUSA AVE #B	DAYTON BEACH, FL	32114
EGGERS, ROBERT	DIRECTOR	6345 FOUNTAIN AVE	LOS ANGELES, CA	90028
EGGERT, NICOLE	ACTRESS	20591 QUEENS PARK	HUNTINGTON BEACH, CA	92646
EGIELSKI, RICHARD	ARTIST	55 BETHUNE ST	NEW YORK, NY	10014
EGLEE, CHARLES	SCREENWRITER	1023 17TH ST #C	SANTA MONICA, CA	90403
EGLOFF, BRUCE	BASEBALL	4385 TUTT BLVD	COLORADO SPRINGS, CO	80922
EGNATZ, GARY A	COMPOSER	6076 FRANKLIN AVE	LOS ANGELES, CA	90028
EHLERS, BETH	ACTRESS	CBS-TV, "THE GUIDING LIGHT"		
		222 E 44TH ST	NEW YORK, NY	10017
EHLO, CRAIG	BASKETBALL	POST OFFICE BOX 5000	RICHFIELD, OH	44286
EHRLICH, AARON	DIRECTOR	414 E 52ND ST	NEW YORK, NY	10022
EHRLICH, KEN	WRITER-PRODUCER	17200 OAK VIEW DR	ENCINO, CA	91316
EHRLICH, MAX	WRITER	10459 WILSHIRE BLVD	LOS ANGELES, CA	90024
EHRLICH, SOL	DIRECTOR	49 W 53RD ST	NEW YORK, NY	10019
EHRLICHMAN, JOHN	AUTHOR	POST OFFICE BOX 5559	SANTE FE, NM	87502
EICH, JOSEPH F	CONDUCTOR	1301 N GENESEE AVE	LOS ANGELES, CA	90046
EICHEL, PAUL	ACTOR-SINGER	350 W 57TH ST	NEW YORK, NY	10019
EICHELBERGER, JUAN	BASEBALL	14674 SILVERSET ST	POWAY, CA	92064
EICHER, MIKE	BASEBALL	POST OFFICE BOX 3004	SPRINGFIELD, IL	62708
EICHERN, CHERI	ACTRESS-SINGER	747 S DUNSMUIR AVE	LOS ANGELES, CA	90036
EICHHORN, LISA	ACTRESS	19 W 44TH ST #1000	NEW YORK, NY	10036
EICHHORN, MARK	BASEBALL	POST OFFICE BOX 2000	ANAHEIM, CA	92803
EICHLER, UDI	DIRECTOR-PRODUCER	BROOKS PRODS, 21-24 BRUGES PL		
		RANDOLPH ST	LONDON NW1 OTF	ENGLAND
EIDELMAN, CLIFF	COMPOSER	6525 SUNSET BLVD #402	HOLLYWOOD, CA	90028
EIDSVOOG, JOHN C	CONDUCTOR	12305 HARTSOOK ST	NORTH HOLLYWOOD, CA	91607
EIERMAN, JOHN	BASEBALL	POST OFFICE BOX 10213	LYNCHBURG, VA	24506
EIFFERT, LEO J, JR	SINGER	POST OFFICE BOX 5412	BUENA VISTA, CA	90620
EIKENBERRY, JILL	ACTRESS	2183 MANDEVILLE CANYON RD	LOS ANGELES, CA	90049
EIKENBERRY, KENNETH	ATTORNEY GENERAL	STATE LEGISLATIVE BUILDING	OLYMPIA, WA	98504
EILAND, DAVE	BASEBALL	POST OFFICE BOX 2000	SAN DIEGO, CA	92112
EILAND, KENNETH S	ACTOR	5756 CRANER AVE	NORTH HOLLYWOOD, CA	91601
EILBACHER, CYNTHIA	ACTRESS	11051 OPHIR DR	LOS ANGELES, CA	90024
EILBACHER, KIM	ACTRESS	7080 HOLLYWOOD BLVD #704	HOLLYWOOD, CA	90028
EILBACHER, LISA	ACTRESS	2949 DEEP CANYON DR	BEVERLY HILLS, CA	90210
EILBAUM, MICHAEL A	TV DIRECTOR	Q ME PRODS, 23 VISTA RD	PLAINVIEW, NY	11803
EILBER, JANET	ACTRESS	LIGHT, 901 BRINGHAM AVE	LOS ANGELES, CA	90049
EILERS, PAT	FOOTBALL	VIKINGS, 9520 VIKING DR	EDEN PRAIRIE, MN	55344
EILERSON POSEY, PAMELA	DIRECTOR	6320 TRANCAS CANYON RD	MALIBU, CA	90265
EINBERG, FRANNE	WRITER	10524 BLYTHE AVE	LOS ANGELES, CA	90064
EINFRANK, BOB	ACTOR	5020 TUJUNGA AVE #211	NORTH HOLLYWOOD, CA	91601
EINHORN, EDDIE	BASEBALL EXECUTIVE	333 W 35TH ST	CHICAGO, IL	60616
EINHORN, LAWRENCE	TV DIRECTOR	5001 OAKDALE AVE	WOODLAND HILLS, CA	91364
EINHORN, MARVIN D	TV DIRECTOR	150 W 79TH ST #6-A	NEW YORK, NY	10024
EINSEL, NAIAD	ARTIST	26 S MORNINGSIDE DR	WESTPORT, CT	06880
EINSTEIN, BOB	TV WRITER	9915 GIRLA WY	LOS ANGELES, CA	90064
EISCHEN, JOEY	BASEBALL	POST OFFICE BOX 3566	WEST PALM BEACH, FL	33402
EISELE, ROBERT	SCREENWRITER	9255 SUNSET BLVD #505	LOS ANGELES, CA	90069
EISENBERG, AVNER	ACTOR	POST OFFICE BOX 3819	LA MESA, CA	91944
EISENBERG, IRA	WRITER-PRODUCER	30 BERRY ST	SAN FRANCISCO, CA	94107
EISENBERG, MAX	WRITER	6356 MARYLAND DR	LOS ANGELES, CA	90048
EISENBERG, NAT	DIRECTOR-PRODUCER	202 E 35TH ST	NEW YORK, NY	10016
EISENMAN, ROBIN G	ACTRESS	14006 RUNNYMEDE ST	VAN NUYS, CA	91405
EISENMANN, GUSTAVE W	DIRECTOR	375 HIGHLAND AVE	SAN FRANCISCO, CA	94110
EISENREICH, JIM	BASEBALL	POST OFFICE BOX 419969	KANSAS CITY, MO	64141
EISENSON, ARTHUR M	TV WRITER	12737 INDIANAPOLIS ST	LOS ANGELES, CA	90035
EISENSTAEDT, ALFRED	PHOTOGRAPHER	TIME/TIME & LIFE BLDG		
		ROCKEFELLER CENTER	NEW YORK, NY	10020
EISENSTOCK, ALAN	TV WRITER	533 N MC CADDEN PL	LOS ANGELES, CA	90004
EISMAN, HY	CARTOONIST	KING FEATURES, 216 E 45TH ST	NEW YORK, NY	10017
EISNER, ARTHUR	ACTOR	13336 EBELL ST	VAN NUYS, CA	91402
EISNER, DAVID	ACTOR	260 RIVERSIDE DR #10-G	NEW YORK, NY	10025
EISNER, JANE B	WRITER	283 BEL AIR RD	LOS ANGELES, CA	90077
EISNER, MICHAEL	FILM-TV EXECUTIVE	500 S BUENA VISTA ST	BURBANK, CA	91521
EITERMAN, TOM	BASEBALL	2501 ALLEN AVE, SE	CANTON, OH	44707
EITNER, DON	ACTOR-DIRECTOR	10915 HESBY ST	NORTH HOLLYWOOD, CA	91601
EKINS, DONNA	ACTRESS	1841 COURTNEY AVE	HOLLYWOOD, CA	90046
EKLAND, BRITT	ACTRESS	1744 N DOHENY DR	LOS ANGELES, CA	90069
EKLUND, PELLE	HOCKEY	FLYERS, SPECTRUM, PATTISON PL	PHILADELPHIA, PA	19148
EKSTRAND, BRADFORD L	ACTOR	1750 1/2 LUCRETIA AVE	LOS ANGELES, CA	90026
EL CHICANO	ROCK & ROLL GROUP	AKO PRODS, 20531 PLUMMER ST	CHATSWORTH, CA	91311
ELAM, JACK	ACTOR	POST OFFICE BOX 5718	SANTA BARBARA, CA	93108
ELANJIAN, GEORGE, JR	TV DIRECTOR	8312 MAPLE DR	LOS ANGELES, CA	90046
ELCAR, DANA	ACTOR-DIRECTOR	22920 HATTERAS ST	WOODLAND HILLS, CA	91367
ELCAR, NORA	ACTRESS	22920 HATTERAS ST	WOODLAND HILLS, CA	91367
ELDER, ANN W	TV WRITER	1811 COURTNEY AVE	LOS ANGELES, CA	90046
ELDER, DONNIE	FOOTBALL	POST OFFICE BOX 609609	SAN DIEGO, CA	92160
ELDER, JANE	ACTRESS	3195 SHERIDAN BLVD	LINCOLN, NB	68502
ELDER, JUDITH	ACTRESS	320 S CAMAC ST	PHILADELPHIA, CA	19107
ELDER, LEE	BASEBALL SCOUT	N Y YANKEES, YANKEE STADIUM	BRONX, NY	10451
ELDER, LEE	GOLFER	PGA SENIORS, 112 T P C BLVD	PONTE VEDRA BEACH, FL	32082
ELDER, LONNE, III	SCREENWRITER	7615 GLADE AVE #110	CANOGA PARK, CA	91304
ELDRED, CAL	BASEBALL	2850 W 20TH AVE	DENVER, CO	80211
ELEAZAR, ROSE	ACTRESS-MODEL	2801 MEADOW LARK DR	SAN DIEGO, CA	92123
ELEGANTS, THE	VOCAL GROUP	KNIGHT, 185 CLINTON AVE	STATEN ISLAND, NY	10301

ELENIAK, ERIKA	ACTRESS-MODEL	1999 AVE OF THE STARS #2850	LOS ANGELES, CA 90067
ELES, SANDOR	ACTOR	KRUGER, 121 GLOUCESTER PL	LONDON W1H 3PL ENGLAND
ELFAND, MARTIN	FILM PRODUCER	9486 LLOYDCREST DR	BEVERLY HILLS, CA 90210
ELFERING, KEVIN	BASEBALL SCOUT	N Y YANKEES, YANKEE STADIUM	BRONX, NY 10451
ELFERMAN, GEORGE	BODYBUILDER	953 E SAHARA AVE #11-A	LAS VEGAS, NV 89104
ELFMAN, BLOSSOM	TV WRITER	476 GREENCRAIG RD	LOS ANGELES, CA 90049
ELFMAN, DANNY	COMPOSER	19668 GRAND VIEW DR	TOPANGA, CA 90290
ELFORD, JENNIE	WRITER	10536 MOORPARK ST	NORTH HOLLYWOOD, CA 91602
ELGAR, AVRIL	ACTRESS	FRENCH'S, 52 HOLLAND PARK MEWS	LONDON W11 ENGLAND
ELGART, LARRY	ORCHESTRA LEADER	55 E 74TH ST	NEW YORK, NY 10021
ELIA, LEE	BASEBALL-MANAGER	POST OFFICE BOX 3449	SCRANTON, PA 18505
ELIANO, RICHARD J	CINEMATOGRAPHER	15 E 71ST #4-A	NEW YORK, NY 10021
ELIAS, HECTOR	ACTOR	828 N MANSFIELD AVE	LOS ANGELES, CA 90038
ELIAS, MICHAEL	SCREENWRITER	10036 REEVESBURY DR	BEVERLY HILLS, CA 90210
ELIASBERG, JAN P	FILM DIRECTOR	8515 WALNUT DR	LOS ANGELES, CA 90046
ELIASON, JOHN	TV WRITER	10960 WILSHIRE BLVD #922	LOS ANGELES, CA 90024
ELIASON, JOYCE	SCREENWRITER	8955 BEVERLY BLVD	WEST HOLLYWOOD, CA 90048
ELIC, JOSIP	ACTOR	POST OFFICE BOX 793	NEW YORK, NY 10022
ELIK, TODD	HOCKEY	POST OFFICE BOX 17013	INGLEWOOD, CA 90308
ELIKANN, LARRY	TV-FILM DIRECTOR	100 S DOHENY DR	LOS ANGELES, CA 90048
ELINSON, JACK	TV WRITER-PRODUCER	3313 BUTLER AVE	LOS ANGELES, CA 90066
ELIOT, MIKE	FILM EDITOR	ACE, 1041 N FORMOSA AVE	WEST HOLLYWOOD, CA 90046
ELIOT, TAMARA	ACTRESS	545 MESA LILA RD	GLENDALE, CA 91208
ELIZABETH, HM	QUEEN MOTHER	CLARENCE HOUSE	LODNON SW1 ENGLAND
ELIZABETH, MISS	WRESTLING MANAGER	SEE - MISS ELIZABETH	
ELIZABETH II, HM QUEEN	QUEEN	BUCKINGHAM PALACE	LONDON SW1 ENGLAND
ELIZONDO, HECTOR	ACTOR	5040 NOBLE AVE	SHERMAN OAKS, CA 91403
ELKINGTON, STEVE	GOLFER	POST OFFICE BOX 109601	PALM BCH GARDENS, FL 33418
ELKINS, HILLARD	PRODUCER-TALENT AGT	6515 WILSHIRE BLVD #205	HOLLYWOOD, CA 90028
ELKINS, SAUL	WRITER	1230 EDRIS DR	LOS ANGELES, CA 90035
ELKOUBY, DAVID	PHOTOGRAPHER	STARWORLD, 6655 HOLLYWOOD BLVD	HOLLYWOOD, CA 90028
ELLARD, HENRY	FOOTBALL	RAMS, 2327 W LINCOLN BLVD	ANAHEIM, CA 92801
ELLENSTEIN, DAVID	ACTOR	5525 COSTELLO AVE	VAN NUYS, CA 91401
ELLENSTEIN, ROBERT	ACTOR-DIRECTOR	5215 SEPULVEDA BLVD #23-F	CULVER CITY, CA 90230
ELLERBE, HARRY	ACTOR	1896 WYCLIFF RD, NW	ATLANTA, GA 30309
ELLERBEE, LINDA	BROADCAST JOURNALIST	17 SAINT LUKES PL	NEW YORK, NY 10014
ELLERING, PAUL	WRESTLING MANAGER	POST OFFICE BOX 3859	STAMFORD, CT 06905
ELLETT, DAVE	HOCKEY	MAPLE LEAFS, 60 CARLTON ST	TORONTO, ONT M5B 1L1 CANADA
ELLINGSEN, MARIA	ACTRESS	NBC-TV, "SANTA BARBARA"	
		3000 W ALAMEDA AVE	BURBANK, CA 91523
ELLINGTON, MERCER	MUSICIAN	DOCTOR JAZZ RECORDS COMPANY	
		1414 AVE OF THE AMERICAS	NEW YORK, NY 10019
ELLIOT, DAVID	DIRECTOR	200 W 90TH ST	NEW YORK, NY 10024
ELLIOT, JANE	ACTRESS	606 N LARCHMONT BLVD #309	LOS ANGELES, CA 90004
ELLIOT, MICHAEL	DIRECTOR	15 W 72ND ST	NEW YORK, NY 10023
ELLIOT, NEIL	ACTOR	807 HYPERION AVE #1	LOS ANGELES, CA 90029
ELLIOT, RICHARD	SAXOPHONIST	MATT KRAMER, AT MY PLACE	
		1026 WILSHIRE BLVD	SANTA MONICA, CA 90401
ELLIOT, ROBERT	DIRECTOR	DGA, 110 W 57TH ST	NEW YORK, NY 10019
ELLIOT, STEPHEN	TV DIRECTOR	239 E 79TH ST	NEW YORK, NY 10021
ELLIOT, STEPHEN B	DIRECTOR	120 W 97TH ST	NEW YORK, NY 10025
ELLIOT, SUSAN	TV WRITER	8955 BEVERLY BLVD	WEST HOLLYWOOD, CA 90048
ELLIOTT, ALICE	ACTRESS	107 BEDFORD ST	NEW YORK, NY 10014
ELLIOTT, BARRY	DIRECTOR	932 N LA BREA AVE	HOLLYWOOD, CA 90038
ELLIOTT, CHRIS	ACTOR-TV WRITER	9000 SUNSET BLVD #1200	LOS ANGELES, CA 90069
ELLIOTT, DAVID	FILM CRITIC	POST OFFICE BOX 191	SAN DIEGO, CA 92112
ELLIOTT, DEAN	COMPOSER-CONDUCTOR	22410 MARTHA ST	WOODLAND HILLS, CA 91364
ELLIOTT, DENHOLM	ACTOR	LONDON MGT, 235-241 REGENT ST	LONDON W1R 4PH ENGLAND
ELLIOTT, DON "DORIS"	TV PRODUCER	67 PARK AVE	NEW YORK, NY 10016
ELLIOTT, DONNIE	BASEBALL	POST OFFICE BOX 10336	CLEARWATER, FL 34617
ELLIOTT, GLENN	SINGER	POST OFFICE BOX 50729	OXNARD, CA 90301
ELLIOTT, JACK	CONDUCTOR	9312 SANTA MONICA BLVD	BEVERLY HILLS, CA 90210
ELLIOTT, JOHN	FOOTBALL	N Y GIANTS, GIANTS STADIUM	EAST RUTHERFORD, NJ 07073
ELLIOTT, LANG	DIRECTOR-PRODUCER	POST OFFICE BOX 7419	THOUSAND OAKS, CA 91359
ELLIOTT, MARIANNA	COSTUME DESIGNER	POST OFFICE BOX 5617	BEVERLY HILLS, CA 90213
ELLIOTT, PATRICIA	ACTRESS	SEM & M, 156 5TH AVE	NEW YORK, NY 10010
ELLIOTT, PAUL C	SCREENWRITER	8955 BEVERLY BLVD	WEST HOLLYWOOD, CA 90048
ELLIOTT, PETER	FILM EDITOR	OAKLEY, EVELYN WY, STOKE	
		STOKE D'ABERNON	SURREY ENGLAND
ELLIOTT, RAMBLIN' JACK	SINGER-SONGWRITER	DAY PRODS, 300 W 55TH ST	NEW YORK, NY 10019
ELLIOTT, RON	GUITARIST	3991 DICKERSON RD	NASHVILLE, TN 37207
ELLIOTT, ROSS	ACTOR	5702 GRAVES AVE	ENCINO, CA 91316
ELLIOTT, SAM	ACTOR	33050 PACIFIC COAST HWY	MALIBU, CA 90265
ELLIOTT, SEAN	BASKETBALL	600 E MARKET ST #102	SAN ANTONIO, TX 78205
ELLIOTT, STACEY	ACTRESS	7461 BEVERLY BLVD #400	LOS ANGELES, CA 90036
ELLIOTT, STEPHEN	ACTOR	3948 WOODFIELD DR	SHERMAN OAKS, CA 91403
ELLIS, ARTHUR	FILM WRITER-DIRECTOR	16 GRANVILLE MANSIONS	
		SHEPHERDS BUSH GREEN	LONDON W12 ENGLAND
ELLIS, DALE	BASKETBALL	POST OFFICE BOX C-900911	SEATTLE, WA 98109
ELLIS, DAVID RICHARD	DIRECTOR	6587 TAMARIND ST	AGOURA, CA 91301
ELLIS, DONALD E	DIRECTOR	404 NOBLE CREEK DR, NW	ATLANTA, GA 30327
ELLIS, HAROLD E	COMPOSER-CONDUCTOR	1861 WHITLEY AVE	LOS ANGELES, CA 90028
ELLIS, HERB	GUITARIST	CASSIDY, 417 MARAWOOD DR	WOODSTOCK, IL 60098
ELLIS, JEFFREY	SCREENWRITER	9301 WILSHIRE BLVD #312	BEVERLY HILLS, CA 90210
ELLIS, JON	ARTIST	81 GRAND AVE #2-L	ENGLEWOOD, NJ 07631

ELLIS, KENNETH R	WRITER-PRODUCER	3200 BURDECK DR	OAKLAND, CA	94602
ELLIS, MATT	BASEBALL EXECUTIVE	1316 KING ST	BELLINGHAM, WA	98226
ELLIS, PAUL	BASEBALL	POST OFFICE BOX 12557	ST PETERSBURG, FL	33733
ELLIS, PERRY	FASHION DESIGNER	575 7TH AVE	NEW YORK, NY	10018
ELLIS, PETER	DIRECTOR	HEATH, PARAMOUNT HOUSE		
		162-170 WARDOUR ST	LONDON W1V 3AT	ENGLAND
ELLIS, RAMEY	ACTRESS	1239 WASHINGTON BLVD	VENICE, CA	90291
ELLIS, RAYMOND S	CONDUCTOR	12821 MOORPARK ST #8	STUDIO CITY, CA	91604
ELLIS, RICHARD	DIRECTOR	345 E 69TH ST #16-D	NEW YORK, NY	10021
ELLIS, ROBERT	BASEBALL	POST OFFICE BOX 751	UTICA, NY	13503
ELLIS, ROGER	ACTOR	POST OFFICE BOX 543	ENCINO, CA	91426
ELLIS, SAMMY	BASEBALL-COACH	1060 W ADDISON ST	CHICAGO, IL	60613
ELLIS, SIDNEY	WRITER	238 ENTRADA DR	SANTA MONICA, CA	90402
ELLIS, TERRY	AUDITOR	ALA STATE HOUSE, 11 S UNION ST	MONTGOMERY, AL	36130
ELLIS, TOTTIE	COLUMNIST	POST OFFICE BOX 500	WASHINGTON, DC	20044
ELLISON, HARLAN	AUTHOR-FUTURIST	3484 COY DR	SHERMAN OAKS, CA	91423
ELLISON, JAMES S	TV DIRECTOR	101 GEDNEY ST	NYACK, NY	10960
ELLISON, PERVIS	BASKETBALL	BULLETS, 1 HARRY S TRUMAN DR	LANDOVER, MD	20785
ELLISON, RIKI	FOOTBALL	RAIDERS, 332 CENTER ST	EL SEGUNDO, CA	90245
ELLISON, ROBERT J	WRITER	11474 BELLAGIO RD	LOS ANGELES, CA	90049
ELLSBERG, DANIEL	AUTHOR	90 NORWOOD AVE	KENSINGTON, CA	94707
ELLSWORTH, BEN	BASEBALL	POST OFFICE BOX 3783	SAVANNAH, GA	31414
ELLSWORTH, STEVE	BASEBALL	1099 W MORRIS	FRESNO, CA	93705
ELMAN, EUGENE	ACTOR	540 N ORLANDO AVE #6	LOS ANGELES, CA	90048
ELMAN, IRVING	WRITER-PRODUCER	430 PUERTO DEL MAR	PACIFIC PALISADES, CA	90272
ELMAN, LOUIS	TV DIRECTOR	ANVIL STUDIOS, DENHAM		
		NEAR UXBRIDGE	MIDDLESEX UB9 5HH	ENGLAND
ELMAN, MILDRED M	WRITER	430 PUERTO DEL MAR	PACIFIC PALISADES, CA	90272
ELMES, FRED	ACTOR	438 NORWICH DR	HOLLYWOOD, CA	90048
ELMORE, DAVE	BASEBALL EXECUTIVE	POST OFFICE BOX 28268	SAN ANTONIO, TX	78228
ELMORE, DAVE	BASEBALL EXECUTIVE	POST OFFICE BOX 483	YAKIMA, WA	98907
ELPHICK, MICHAEL	ACTOR	37 DENNINGTON PARK RD	LONDON NW6	ENGLAND
ELRIDGE, ROD	BASEBALL	POST OFFICE BOX 12557	ST PETERSBURG, FL	33733
ELSENBACH, JOHN	CINEMATOGRAPHER	POST OFFICE BOX 2230	HOLLYWOOD, CA	90078
ELSON, DONALD	ACTOR	2456 HIDALGO AVE	LOS ANGELES, CA	90039
ELSTAD, LINDA BARRIC	TV WRITER	788 BROOKTREE RD	PACIFIC PALISADES, CA	90272
ELSTEIN, DAVID	TV DIRECTOR-PRODUCER	THAMES TV, 306 EUSTON RD	LONDON SW 1	ENGLAND
ELSTER, KEVIN	BASEBALL	METS, 126TH ST & ROOSEVELT AVE	FLUSHING, NY	11368
ELTERMAN, JUDI	TV DIRECTOR	4265 MARINA CITY DR	MARINA DEL REY, CA	90292
ELTON, BEN	WRITER-COMEDIAN	JAN MC INTYRE MANAGEMENT		
		LONDON HOUSE #70, 271 KING ST	LONDON W6 9LZ	ENGLAND
ELTON, WILLIAM	COMPOSER-CONDUCTOR	431 N CITRUS AVE	LOS ANGELES, CA	90036
ELVIRA	ACTRESS	SEE - PETERSON, CASSANDRA		
ELVIRA, NARCISO	BASEBALL	POST OFFICE BOX 75089	OKLAHOMA CITY, OK	73147
ELVIS BROTHERS, THE	ROCK & ROLL TRIO	ADAMANY, 315 W GORHAM ST	MADISON, WI	53703
ELWAY, JOHN	FOOTBALL	BRONCOS, 13655 BRONCOS PKWY	ENGLEWOOD, CO	80112
ELWES, CASSIAN	FILM PRODUCER	SMOKING GUN, 935 SAN VICENTE BL	WEST HOLLYWOOD, CA	90069
ELY, JOE	SINGER-SONGWRITER	CROWLEY, 122 LONGWOOD AVE	AUSTIN, TX	78734
ELY, RON	ACTOR	4161 MARIPOSA DR	SANTA BARBARA, CA	93110
ELYNUIK, PAT	HOCKEY	JETS, 15-1430 MAROONS RD	WINNIPEG, MAN R3G 0L5	CANADA
EMANUEL	FASHION DESIGNER	1406 GEORGETTE ST	SANTURCE, PR	00910
EMBER, MAX	WRITER	2331 OUTPOST DR	LOS ANGELES, CA	90068
EMBERG, KELLY	MODEL	1608 N POINSETTIA	MANHATTAN BEACH, CA	90266
EMBLEN, CLOVIS	ACTRESS	19816 GRAND VIEW DR #A	TOPANGA CANYON, CA	90290
EMBREE, ALAN	BASEBALL	POST OFFICE BOX 3452	KINSTON, NC	28502
EMBRY, JOAN	ANIMAL TRAINER	SAN DIEGO ZOO, PARK BLVD	SAN DIEGO, CA	92104
EMBRY, WAYNE	BASKETBALL EXECUTIVE	POST OFFICE BOX 5000	RICHFIELD, OH	44286
EMERICK, ROBERT J	TV DIRECTOR	CHILDREN'S TV WORKSHOP		
		1 LINCOLN PLAZA, 4TH FLOOR	NEW YORK, NY	10023
EMERSON, BILL	U S CONGRESSMAN	FEDERAL BLDG, 339 BROADWAY	CAPE GIRARDEAU, MO	63701
EMERSON, DOUGLAS	ACTOR	1450 BELFAST DR	LOS ANGELES, CA	90069
EMERSON, GLORIA	TV CRITIC	LA TIMES, TIMES MIRROR SQ	LOS ANGELES, CA	90053
EMERSON, KARRIE	ACTRESS-MODEL	BLANCHARD, 957 N COLE AVE	LOS ANGELES, CA	90038
EMERSON, LAKE & POWELL	ROCK & ROLL TRIO	ALEX GROB, THEATERSTRASSE	POSTFACH 8024	
EMERY, CAL	BASEBALL-SCOUT	333 W 35TH ST	CHICAGO, IL	60616
EMERY, RALPH	TV HOST	2806 OPRYLAND DR	NASHVILLE, TN	37213
EMES, IAN	FILM DIRECTOR	HEATH, PARAMOUNT HOUSE		
		162-170 WARDOUR ST	LONDON W1V 3AT	ENGLAND
EMHARDT, ROBERT	ACTOR	POST OFFICE BOX 303	OJAI, CA	93023
EMMANS, KATHLEEN	TV PRODUCER	323 W 76TH ST #2-F	NEW YORK, NY	10023
EMMICH, CLIFF	ACTOR	5312 BELLINGHAM AVE #2	NORTH HOLLYWOOD, CA	91607
EMOTIONS, THE	SOUL GROUP	1995 BROADWAY #501	NEW YORK, NY	10023
EN VOGUE	R & B GROUP	10100 SANTA MONICA BLVD #1600	LOS ANGELES, CA	90067
ENBERG, DICK	SPORTSCASTER	NBC SPORTS, 30 ROCKEFELLER PLZ	NEW YORK, NY	10112
ENCARNACION, ANGELO	BASEBALL	POST OFFICE BOX 3746, HILL STA	AUGUSTA, GA	30904
ENCARNACION, LUIS	BASEBALL	POST OFFICE BOX 3665	OMAHA, NE	68103
ENCELL, ARLENE	COSTUME DESIGNER	13949 VENTURA BLVD #309	SHERMAN OAKS, CA	91423
ENCHANTMENT	VOCAL GROUP	STAR-VEST, 102 RYDERS LN	EAST BRUNSWICK, NJ	08816
ENDARA, GUILLERMO	PRESIDENT	PRESIDENTIAL PALACE	PANAMA CITY, CA	PANAMA
ENDE, MICHAEL	AUTHOR	VIA MONTEGIOVE 13	00045 GENZANO DI ROMA	ITALY
ENDERS, HOWARD	WRITER-PRODUCER	19 FOREST PARK AVE	LARCHMONT, NY	10538
ENDERS, ROBERT	WRITER-PRODUCER	1110 BENEDICT CANYON DR	BEVERLY HILLS, CA	90210
ENDERSBY, CLIVE	TV WRITER	9200 SUNSET BLVD #531	LOS ANGELES, CA	90069
ENDES, JOE	ACTOR	1352 N LAS PALMAS AVE #1	HOLLYWOOD, CA	90028
ENDEWELT, JACK	ARTIST	50 RIVERSIDE DR	NEW YORK, NY	10024

ENDICOTT, JAMES	ARTIST	ROUTE #1, BOX 27-B	NEWBURG, OR	97132
ENDLER, ESTELLE	FILM PRODUCER	3920 SUNNY OAK RD	SHERMAN OAKS, CA	91403
ENDLER, MICHAEL	FILM WRITER-PRODUCER	3920 SUNNY OAK RD	SHERMAN OAKS, CA	91403
ENDO, AKIRA	CONDUCTOR	8853 MOUNTAIN RIDGE CIR	AUSTIN, TX	78759
ENEVOLDSEN, ROBERT M	COMPOSER	20621 AETNA ST	WOODLAND HILLS, CA	91367
ENG, RICHARD	ACTOR	433 W 24TH ST #1-E	NEW YORK, NY	10011
ENG, STEVE	SINGER-SONGWRITER	POST OFFICE BOX 110423	NASHVILLE, TN	37211
ENGEL, ART	BASEBALL EXECUTIVE	POST OFFICE BOX 2000	SAN DIEGO, CA	92112
ENGEL, ELIOT L	U S CONGRESSMAN	177 DREISER LOOP #3	BRONX, NY	10475
ENGEL, GEORGIA	ACTRESS	350 W 57TH ST #10-E	NEW YORK, NY	10019
ENGEL, LAWRENCE B	TV PRODUCER	51 GRANDVIEW AVE	GLEN ROCK, NJ	07452
ENGEL, MARY	ACTRESS	8900 BOULEVARD EAST	NORTH BERGEN, NJ	07047
ENGEL, SUSAN	ACTRESS	43-A PRINCESS RD, REGENTS PK	LONDON NW1 8JS	ENGLAND
ENGELBACH, DAVID	SCREENWRITER	12 24TH AVE #9	VENICE, CA	90291
ENGELHARDT, DEAN	DIRECTOR	404 N DANEHURST AVE	COVINA, CA	91724
ENGELHARDT, THOMAS	CARTOONIST	900 N 12TH BLVD	SAINT LOUIS, MO	63101
ENGELS, ROBERT	TV PRODUCER	CAA, 9830 WILSHIRE BLVD	BEVERLY HILLS, CA	90212
ENGELSON, GEORGE J	ACTOR	11640 HAMLIN ST	NORTH HOLLYWOOD, CA	91606
ENGLAND, HAL	ACTOR	BREWIS, 12429 LAUREL TERRACE DR	STUDIO CITY, CA	91604
ENGLANDER, ROGER	DIRECTOR-PRODUCER	15 SAINT LUKES PL	NEW YORK, NY	10014
ENGLE, BOB	BASEBALL SCOUT	SKYDOME, 300 BREMMER BL #3200	TORONTO, ONT M5V 3B3	CANADA
ENGLE, DAVE	BASEBALL-COACH	5343 CASTLE HILLS DR	SAN DIEGO, CA	92019
ENGLE, NITA	ARTIST	177 COUNTY RD #550	MARQUETTE, MI	49855
ENGLE, TOD	ACTOR	155 E 96TH ST #5-H	NEW YORK, NY	10128
ENGLE, TOM	BASEBALL	POST OFFICE BOX 7845	COLUMBIA, SC	29202
ENGLEHART	CARTOONIST	HARTFORD COURANT, 285 BROAD ST	HARTFORD, CT	06115
ENGLER, JOHN M	GOVERNOR	STATE CAPITOL BUILDING	LANSING, MI	48953
ENGLER, LORI-NAN	ACTRESS	145 W 45TH ST #1204	NEW YORK, NY	10036
ENGLISH, A J	BASKETBALL	BULLETS, 1 HARRY S TRUMAN DR	LANDOVER, MD	20785
ENGLISH, ALEX	BASKETBALL-ACTOR	REUNION ARENA, 777 SPORTS ST	DALLAS, TX	75207
ENGLISH, ARTHUR	ACTOR	FREEMAN, 4 CROMWELL GROVE		
		HAMMERSMITH	LONDON W6 7RG	ENGLAND
ENGLISH, BRAD	ACTOR	11494 DELLMONT DR	TUJUNGA, CA	91042
ENGLISH, GLENN	U S CONGRESSMAN	POST OFFICE BOX 1927	WOODWARD, OK	73802
ENGLISH, KERRY SHERMAN	ACTRESS	SEE - SHERMAN ENGLISH, KERRY		
ENGLISH, M JOHN	ARTIST	101 E WINTROPE RD	KANSAS CITY, MO	64113
ENGLISH, PRISCILLA	SCREENWRITER	9941 YOUNG DR #A	BEVERLY HILLS, CA	90212
ENGLUND, GEORGE H	DIRECTOR-PRODUCER	201 OCEAN AVE #907-P	SANTA MONICA, CA	90402
ENGLUND, GEORGE H	MUSICIAN	2041 MANDEVILLE CANYON RD	LOS ANGELES, CA	90049
ENGLUND, MORGAN	ACTOR	CBS-TV, "THE GUIDING LIGHT"		
		222 E 44TH ST	NEW YORK, NY	10017
ENGLUND, ROBERT	ACTOR-DIRECTOR	2451 HORSESHOE CANYON RD	LOS ANGELES, CA	90046
ENNIS, CARMENE	SINGER	289 S BARRINGTON AVE #101	LOS ANGELES, CA	90049
ENO, BRIAN	SINGER-PRODUCER	OPAL, 330 HARROW RD	LONDON W9 2HP	ENGLAND
ENO, ROGER	SINGER-MUSICIAN	OPAL, 330 HARROW RD	LONDON W9 2HP	ENGLAND
ENOCH, RUSSELL	ACTOR	43-A PRINCESS RD, REGENTS PK	LONDON NW1 8JS	ENGLAND
ENOS, BILL	BASEBALL SCOUT	FENWAY PARK, 4 YAWKEY WY	BOSTON, MA	02215
ENRICH, EDWARD	ACTOR	20884 TIARA ST	WOODLAND HILLS, CA	91367
ENRICO, ROBERT	FILM DIRECTOR	ARTMEDIA, 10 AVE GEORGE V	PARIS 75008	FRANCE
ENRIGHT, DAN	TV PRODUCER	201 WILSHIRE BLVD, 2ND FLOOR	SANTA MONICA, CA	90401
ENRIGHT, DON	SCREENWRITER	1253 AMALFI DR	PACIFIC PALISADES, CA	90272
ENRIGHT, ERICA	ACTRESS-WRITER	1253 AMALFI DR	PACIFIC PALISADES, CA	90272
ENRIQUEZ, GRACIANO	BASEBALL	POST OFFICE BOX 855	BELOIT, WI	53511
ENSLEY, ANNETTE	ACTRESS	1865 3/4 S SYCAMORE AVE	LOS ANGELES, CA	90019
ENSOR, TONY	BASEBALL EXECUTIVE	POST OFFICE BOX 360007	BIRMINGHAM, AL	35236
ENTNER, WARREN	MUSICIAN-TAL AGT	1021 S STEARNS DR	LOS ANGELES, CA	90035
ENTON-FRIEDKIN, GREGORY	ACTOR-WRITER	1811 VETERAN AVE	LOS ANGELES, CA	90025
ENTWHISTLE, JOHN	SINGER-SONGWRITER	1704 QUEEN CT	LOS ANGELES, CA	90069
EP MD	RAP DUO-RAPWRITERS	FAA, 1700 BROADWAY, 5TH FLOOR	NEW YORK, NY	10019
EPHRON, AMY	FILM EXECUTIVE	8439 KIRKWOOD DR	LOS ANGELES, CA	90046
EPHRON, DELIA	WRITER	1464 GLENVILLE DR	LOS ANGELES, CA	90035
EPHRON, HENRY	SCREENWRITER	176 E 71ST ST	NEW YORK, NY	10021
EPHRON, NORA	SCREENWRITER	2211 BROADWAY	NEW YORK, NY	10024
EPLEY, DAREN	BASEBALL	4385 TUTT BLVD	COLORADO SPRINGS, CO	80922
EPLIN, COURTNEY	ACTOR	ABC-TV, "ALL MY CHILDREN"		
		320 W 66TH ST	NEW YORK, NY	10023
EPLIN, TOM	ACTOR	NBC-TV, "ANOTHER WORLD"		
		1268 E 14TH ST	BROOKLYN, NY	11230
EPPARD, JIM	BASEBALL	332 ASHBY ST	AZUSA, CA	91702
EPPERSON, BRENDA	ACTRESS	11712 MOORPARK ST #204	STUDIO CITY, CA	91604
EPPS, JACK, JR	SCREENWRITER	425 SKEWIAY RD	LOS ANGELES, CA	90049
EPPS, TORY	FOOTBALL	FALCONS, SUWANEE RD AT I-85	SUWANEE, GA	30174
EPSTEIN, ALLEN	TV PRODUCER	10100 SANTA MONICA BLVD #1600	LOS ANGELES, CA	90067
EPSTEIN, DASHA	THEATER PRODUCER	720 PARK AVE	NEW YORK, NY	10021
EPSTEIN, DAVID SCHAFFER	DIRECTOR	315 CENTRAL PARK W	NEW YORK, NY	10025
EPSTEIN, JACOB	TV WRITER	ICM, 8899 BEVERLY BLVD	LOS ANGELES, CA	90048
EPSTEIN, JON	TV WRITER-PRODUCER	1988 COLDWATER CANYON DR	BEVERLY HILLS, CA	90210
EPSTEIN, JULIUS J	SCREENWRITER	10556 FONTENELLE WY	LOS ANGELES, CA	90077
EPSTEIN, MITCH	COMPOSER-PRODUCER	ICM, 40 W 57TH ST	NEW YORK, NY	10019
EPSTEIN, STANLEY	DIRECTOR	310 W 72ND ST	NEW YORK, NY	10023
ERASURE	ROCK GROUP	POST OFFICE BOX 899	LONDON NEW3 1TU	ENGLAND
ERB, MIKE	BASEBALL	10233 96TH AVE	EDMONTON, ALB TK5 0A5	CANADA
ERBA, ELI	BASEBALL-COACH	POST OFFICE BOX 3614	MARTINSVILLE, VA	24115
ERCH, NIELS	WRITER	732 1/2 N DETROIT ST	LOS ANGELES, CA	90046
ERDMAN, BRAD	BASEBALL	POST OFFICE BOX 4488	WINSTON-SALEM, NC	27115

ERDMAN, RICHARD	ACTOR-DIRECTOR	12256 DEHOUGE ST	NORTH HOLLYWOOD, CA	91605
ERDREICH, BEN	U S CONGRESSMAN	305 VANCE FEDERAL BLDG	BIRMINGHAM, AL	35203
ERHARDT, RON	FOOTBALL COACH	N Y GIANTS, GIANTS STADIUM	EAST RUTHERFORD, NJ	07073
ERHART, THOMAS, JR	ACTOR	862 W NEWPORT AVE	CHICAGO, IL	60657
ERHLER, BREMER	SECRETARY OF STATE	STATE CAPITOL BUILDING	FRANKFORT, KY	40601
ERIC B & RAKIM	RAP DUO-RAPWRITERS	RUSH, 298 ELIZABETH ST	NEW YORK, NY	10012
ERICKS, JOHN	BASEBALL	POST OFFICE BOX 5599	LITTLE ROCK, AR	72215
ERICKSON, BOB	GOLFER	PGA SENIORS, 112 T P C BLVD	PONTE VEDRA BEACH, FL	32082
ERICKSON, BUTSY	HOCKEY	JETS, 15-1430 MAROONS RD	WINNIPEG, MAN R3G 0L5	CANADA
ERICKSON, GREG	BASEBALL	5301 NW 12TH AVE	FORT LAUDERDALE, FL	33309
ERICKSON, HOWARD	BASEBALL EXECUTIVE	POST OFFICE BOX 855	BELOIT, WI	53511
ERICKSON, ROGER	BASEBALL COACH	2506 ARROWHEAD DR	SPRINGFIELD, IL	62702
ERICKSON, ROKY	SINGER-WRITER	POST OFFICE BOX 22129	SAN FRANCISCO, CA	94122
ERICKSON, SCOTT	BASEBALL	TWINS, 501 CHICAGO AVE S	MINNEAPOLIS, MN	55415
ERICKSON, TRICIA	AGENT-MODEL	ERICKSON MODELING AGENCY		
		1483 CHAIN BRIDGE RD	MC LEAN, VA	22101
ERICSON, JOHN	ACTOR	12659 MOORPARK ST #12	STUDIO CITY, CA	91604
ERICSON, KAREN	ACTRESS	12659 MOORPARK ST #12	STUDIO CITY, CA	91604
ERICSON, MIKE	BASEBALL	POST OFFICE BOX 48	VISALIA, CA	93279
ERIKSEN, NAIMA	ACTRESS-SINGER	436 W 22ND ST #1-B	NEW YORK, NY	10011
ERIXON, JAN	HOCKEY	POST OFFICE BOX 90111	ARLINGTON, TX	76004
ERKENBECK, JIM	FOOTBALL COACH	CHIEFS, 1 ARROWHEAD DR	KANSAS CITY, MO	64129
ERLANGER, DAVID MICHAEL	COMPOSER	6200 CANTERBURY DR #205	CULVER CITY, CA	90230
ERLICH, KEN	PRODUCER	17200 OAKVIEW DR	ENCINO, CA	91316
ERMAN, JOHN	TV-FILM DIRECTOR	978 CASIANO RD	LOS ANGELES, CA	90049
ERMER, CAL	BASEBALL-COACH-SCOUT	TWINS, 501 CHICAGO AVE S	MINNEAPOLIS, MN	55415
ERMEY, R LEE	ACTOR-DRILL SARGEANT	1999 AVE OF THE STARS #2850	LOS ANGELES, CA	90067
ERNEST, ROGER CRAIG	WRITER	266 WISCONSIN AVE	LONG BEACH, CA	90803
ERRAIR, KENDALL	COSTUME DESIGNER	13949 VENTURA BLVD #309	SHERMAN OAKS, CA	91423
ERREY, BOB	HOCKEY	PENGUINS, CIVIC ARENA, CENTRE AV	PITTSBURGH, PA	15219
ERRICKSON, KRISTA	ACTRESS	9000 SUNSET BLVD #1200	LOS ANGELES, CA	90069
ERSKINE, CARL	BASEBALL	6214 S MADISON AVE	ANDERSON, IN	46013
ERSKINE, CHRIS M	TV DIRECTOR	330 W RUSSELL	BARRINGTON, IL	60610
ERTEGUN, AHMET	RECORD EXECUTIVE	75 ROCKEFELLER PLAZA	NEW YORK, NY	10019
ERTMANN, JOHN	TV DIRECTOR-PRODUCER	VISUAL INFORMATION SYSTEMS		
		1 HARMON PLAZA	SECAUCUS, NJ	07094
ERVIN, CHRIS	BASEBALL TRAINER	POST OFFICE BOX 855	BELOIT, WI	53511
ERVING, JULIUS "DR J"	BASKETBALL EXECUTIVE	POST OFFICE BOX 25040	PHILADELPHIA, PA	19147
ERVINS, RICKY	FOOTBALL	POST OFFICE BOX 17247 (DULLES)	WASHINGTON, DC	20041
ERWIN, BILL	ACTOR	12324 MOORPARK ST	STUDIO CITY, CA	91604
ERWIN, SCOTT	BASEBALL	POST OFFICE BOX 2769	HUNTSVILLE, AL	35804
ESASKY, NICK	BASEBALL	1048 JUMPERS RIDGE	MARIETTA, GA	30064
ESCALERA, NINO	BASEBALL-SCOUT	S F GIANTS, CANDLESTICK PARK	SAN FRANICSCO, CA	94124
ESCALONA, JUDITH ROSE	TV DIRECTOR	1540 VAN SICLEN AVE	BROOKLYN, NY	11239
ESCH, DAVID	ACTOR	14214 COHASSET ST	VAN NUYS, CA	91405
ESCHELBACHER, DAVID	TV PRODUCER	ABC-TV, 38 W 66TH ST	NEW YORK, NY	10023
ESCOBAR, JOHN	BASEBALL	POST OFFICE BOX 15050	READING, PA	19612
ESCOVEDO, PETE	MUSICIAN	2490 CHANNING WY #418	BERKELEY, CA	94704
ESCOVEDO, SHEILA	SINGER-MUSICIAN	SEE - E, SHEILA		
ESFORMES, NATE	ACTOR-WRITER	7266 FRANKLIN AVE #16	LOS ANGELES, CA	90046
ESHBACH, CHARLES	BASEBALL EXECUTIVE	POST OFFICE BOX 716	PLAINVILLE, CT	06062
ESHBACH, LLOYD ARTHUR	WRITER	220 S RAILROAD ST	MEYERSTOWN, PA	17067
ESHELMAN, VAUGHN	BASEBALL	POST OFFICE BOX 418	SAINT CHARLES, IL	60174
ESIASON, BOOMER	FOOTBALL	BENGALS, 200 RIVERFRONT STADIUM	CINCINNATI, OH	45202
ESKEL, BEVERLY	SINGER	RAB, 158 S BROADWAY	LAWRENCE, MA	01843
ESLIN, JAMES	ACTOR	7406 ENFIELD AVE	RESEDA, CA	91335
ESMOND, CARL	ACTOR	576 TIGERTAIL RD	LOS ANGELES, CA	90049
ESMONDE, JOHN	TV WRITER	LEMON, 24 POTTERY, HOLLAND PK	LONDON W11 4LZ	ENGLAND
ESPARZA, MONTESUMA	WRITER-PRODUCER	2036 LEMOYNE ST	LOS ANGELES, CA	90026
ESPINO, JUAN	BASEBALL-INSTRUCTOR	POST OFFICE BOX 7000	PITTSBURGH, PA	15212
ESPINOSA, MANUEL	BASEBALL SCOUT	250 STADIUM PLAZA	ST LOUIS, MO	63102
ESPINOZA, ALVARO	BASEBALL	4385 TUTT BLVD	COLORADO SPRINGS, CO	80922
ESPOSITO, JOSEPH	DRUMMER	416 N OAKHURST DR #105	BEVERLY HILLS, CA	90210
ESPOSITO, MARTY	BASEBALL SCOUT	TWINS, 501 CHICAGO AVE S	MINNEAPOLIS, MN	55415
ESPY, CECIL	BASEBALL	POST OFFICE BOX 7000	PITTSBURGH, PA	15212
ESPY, DUANE	BASEBALL-MANAGER	5999 E VAN BUREN ST	PHOENIX, AZ	85008
ESPY, MIKE	U S CONGRESSMAN	300 S MAIN ST	YAZOO CITY, MS	39194
ESPY, WILLIAM GRAY	ACTOR	205 W 54TH ST #3-D	NEW YORK, NY	10019
ESSEX, DAVID	SINGER-ACTOR	LAMPLIGHT, 109 EASTBOURNE MEWS	LONDON W2	ENGLAND
ESSEX, HARRY J	WRITER-PRODUCER	9303 READCREST DR	BEVERLY HILLS, CA	90210
ESSIAN, JIM	BASEBALL-MANAGER	134 ECKFORD	TROY, MI	48098
ESTEFAN, GLORIA & MIAMI SOUND	ROCK & ROLL GROUP	8390 SW 4TH ST	MIAMI, FL	33144
ESTEP, CHRIS	BASEBALL	POST OFFICE DRAWER 1218	ZEBULON, NC	27597
ESTES, BARRY H	ACTOR	8270 W NORTON AVE #8	HOLLYWOOD, CA	90046
ESTES, BOB	GOLFER	POST OFFICE BOX 109601	PALM BCH GARDENS, FL	33418
ESTES, ROB	ACTOR	151 S EL CAMINO DR	BEVERLY HILLS, CA	90212
ESTEVEZ, CARLOS	BASEBALL	POST OFFICE BOX 661	KENOSHA, WI	53141
ESTEVEZ, EMILIO	ACT-WRI-DIR	31709 SEA LEVEL DR	MALIBU, CA	90265
ESTEVEZ, ORLANDO	BASEBALL SCOUT	POST OFFICE BOX 288	HOUSTON, TX	77001
ESTEVEZ, RAMON	ACTOR	837 OCEAN AVE #101	SANTA MONICA, CA	90402
ESTEVEZ, RENEE	ACTRESS	9000 SUNSET BLVD #1200	LOS ANGELES, CA	90069
ESTILL, MICHELLE	GOLFER	2750 VOLUSA AVE #B	DAYTON BEACH, FL	32114
ESTRADA, ERIK	ACTOR-FILM PRODUCER	3768 EUREKA DR	STUDIO CITY, CA	91604
ESTRADA, LEE	SINGER	POST OFFICE BOX 263	HASBROUCK HEIGHTS, NJ	07604
ESTRADA, MANNY	BASEBALL-SCOUT	6850 LAWRENCE RD	LANTANA, FL	33462

Name	Occupation	Address	City/State	Zip
ESTRADA, PETER	BASEBALL	POST OFFICE BOX 10213	LYNCHBURG, VA	24506
ESTRIN, JONATHAN	ACTOR-WRITER	2919 GRAND CANAL	VENICE, CA	90291
ESTROM, JACK	ACTOR	1310 N JUNE ST	LOS ANGELES, CA	90028
ESZTERHAS, JOSEPH A	SCREENWRITER	ICM, 8899 BEVERLY BLVD	LOS ANGELES, CA	90048
ETCHEBARREN, ANDY	BASEBALL-COACH	BREWERS, 201 S 46TH ST	MILWAUKEE, WI	53214
ETCHISON, DENNIS W	WRITER	2041 N BEVERLY GLEN BLVD	LOS ANGELES, CA	90077
ETERNITY	GOSPEL GROUP	6750 W 75TH ST, BLDG #2-A	OVERLAND PARK, KS	66204
ETHERIDGE, MELISSA	SINGER	3800 BARHAM BLVD #309	LOS ANGELES, CA	90068
ETTINGER, RICHARD B	TV DIRECTOR	3238 BEECHWOOD BLVD	PITTSBURGH, PA	15217
ETTLES, MARK	BASEBALL	POST OFFICE BOX 1420	WICHITA, KS	67201
ETTLINGER, JOHN	DIRECTOR-PRODUCER	520 HAYNES AVE	BEVERLY HILLS, CA	90210
EU, MARCH FONG	SECRETARY OF STATE	STATE CAPITOL BUILDING	SACRAMENTO, CA	95814
EUBANKS, BOB	TV HOST	23801 CALABASAS RD #2050	CALABASAS, CA	91302
EUBANKS, KEVIN	GUITARIST	55 W 14TH ST #11-D	NEW YORK, NY	10011
EUBANKS, RACHEL	COMPOSER	4928 CRENSHAW BLVD	LOS ANGELES, CA	90043
EUNSON, DALE	WRITER	2707 6TH ST	SANTA MONICA, CA	90405
EURE, WESLEY	ACTOR	POST OFFICE BOX 69405	LOS ANGELES, CA	90069
EUROGLIDERS, THE	ROCK & ROLL GROUP	POST OFFICE BOX 979		
		BONDI JUNCTION	SYDNEY 2022	AUSTRALIA
EUROPE	ROCK & ROLL GROUP	BOX 22036, S-104-22	STOCKHOLM	SWEDEN
EURYTHMICS, THE	ROCK & ROCK DUO	POST OFFICE BOX 245	LONDON N8	ENGLAND
EUSEBIO, TONY	BASEBALL	POST OFFICE BOX 4209	JACKSON, MS	39296
EUSTIS, RICHARD	SCREENWRITER	CAA, 9830 WILSHIRE BLVD	BEVERLY HILLS, CA	90212
EVANGELISTA, GEORGE	BASEBALL	14100 SIX MILE CYPRESS PKWY	FORT MYERS, FL	33912
EVANGELISTA, LINDA	MODEL	ELITE MODELS, 10 AVE DE L'OPERA	PARIS	FRANCE
EVANIER, MARK	TV WRITER	6282 DREXEL AVE	LOS ANGELES, CA	90048
EVANS, ALISON	ACTRESS	4225 ETHEL AVE #20	STUDIO CITY, CA	91604
EVANS, ANDREA	ACTRESS	STONE MANNERS, 9113 SUNSET BL	LOS ANGELES, CA	90069
EVANS, ART J	ACTOR-DIRECTOR	280 S BEVERLY DR #400	BEVERLY HILLS, CA	90212
EVANS, BRUCE A	WRITER-PRODUCER	8218 HOLLYWOOD BLVD	LOS ANGELES, CA	90069
EVANS, BYRON	FOOTBALL	EAGLES, BROAD ST & PATTISON AVE	PHILADELPHIA, PA	19148
EVANS, CHICK	GOLFER	PGA SENIORS, 112 T P C BLVD	PONTE VEDRA BEACH, FL	32082
EVANS, CRISPIN	TV DIRECTOR-PRODUCER	DIRECTORS GUILD OF GREAT BRITAIN		
		125 TOTTENHAM COURT RD	LONDON W1P 9HN	ENGLAND
EVANS, DALE	ACTRESS	ROGERS, 15650 SENECA RD	VICTORVILLE, CA	92392
EVANS, DANIEL	BASEBALL EXECUTIVE	333 W 35TH ST	CHICAGO, IL	60616
EVANS, DARRELL	BASEBALL-COACH	31918 FOXFIELD DR	WESTLAKE VILLAGE, CA	91361
EVANS, DAVID	BASEBALL	POST OFFICE BOX 4756	JACKSONVILLE, FL	32201
EVANS, DONALD	FOOTBALL	STEELERS, 300 STADIUM CIR	PITTSBURGH, PA	15212
EVANS, DOUG	HOCKEY	JETS, 15-1430 MAROONS RD	WINNIPEG, MAN R3G 0L5	CANADA
EVANS, DWIGHT "DEWEY"	BASEBALL	ORIOLE PARK, 333 W CAMDEN ST	BALTIMORE, MD	21201
EVANS, EDWARD R	DIRECTOR	403 BRECKENRIDGE DR #2	HUNTSVILLE, AL	35802
EVANS, ERNEST	SINGER-SONGWRITER	SEE - CHECKER, CHUBBY		
EVANS, EVANS	ACTRESS	3114 ABINGTON DR	BEVERLY HILLS, CA	90210
EVANS, GENE	ACTOR	POST OFFICE BOX 93	MEDON, TN	38356
EVANS, GEOFFREY	TV DIRECTOR-PRODUCER	CASTLE COACH HOUSE, MARKET LN		
		LAUGHARNE	DYFED SA33 4SB	ENGLAND
EVANS, GEORGE	CARTOONIST	KING FEATURES, 216 E 45TH ST	NEW YORK, NY	10017
EVANS, GERAINT	SINGER	SEE - EVANS, SIR GERAINT		
EVANS, GLENN	BASEBALL	POST OFFICE BOX 661	KENOSHA, WI	53141
EVANS, JAMIE	BASEBALL	POST OFFICE BOX 1556	ASHEVILLE, NC	28802
EVANS, JEANMARIE	SINGER	400 E 52ND ST	NEW YORK, NY	10022
EVANS, JERRY	TV DIRECTOR	1 SUNSET DR	SUMMIT, NJ	07901
EVANS, JIM	BASEBALL UMPIRE	9302 SCENIC BLUFF DR	AUSTIN, TX	78733
EVANS, JIMMY	ATTORNEY GENERAL	ALA STATE HOUSE, 11 S UNION ST	MONTGOMERY, AL	36130
EVANS, JOAN V	COSTUME DESIGNER	171 W 12TH ST	NEW YORK, NY	10011
EVANS, JOSH	ACTOR	1032 N BEVERLY DR	BEVERLY HILLS, CA	90210
EVANS, JOSHUA	ACTOR	27040 MALIBU COVE COLONY DR	MALIBU, CA	90265
EVANS, JUDI	ACTRESS	20955 WARNER CENTER LN	WOODLAND HILLS, CA	91367
EVANS, JUDY	COSTUME DESIGNER	13949 VENTURA BLVD #309	SHERMAN OAKS, CA	91423
EVANS, LANE	U S CONGRESSMAN	1535 47TH AVE #5	MOLINE, IL	61265
EVANS, LAURENCE	TALENT AGENT	ICM, 388-396 OXFORD ST	LONDON W1	ENGLAND
EVANS, LINDA	ACTRESS	6015 W 6TH ST	LOS ANGELES, CA	90036
EVANS, LLOYD RANNEY	ART DIRECTOR	CBS-TV, 524 W 57TH ST	NEW YORK, NY	10019
EVANS, MARTIN A	DIRECTOR	4235 KESTER AVE	SHERMAN OAKS, CA	91403
EVANS, MARTY	DIRECTOR	11112 VENTURA BLVD	STUDIO CITY, CA	91604
EVANS, MARY BETH	ACTRESS	106 N GRAND AVE	PASADENA, CA	91103
EVANS, MICHAEL	ACTOR-WRITER	12530 COLLINS ST	NORTH HOLLYWOOD, CA	91605
EVANS, MIKE	BASEBALL TRAINER	POST OFFICE BOX 3004	SPRINGFIELD, IL	62708
EVANS, MIKE	BASKETBALL COACH	POST OFFICE BOX 4658	DENVER, CO	80204
EVANS, MIKE	EVANGELIST-AUTHOR	POST OFFICE BOX 709	BEDFORD, TX	76021
EVANS, RICHARD	TV WRITER-PRODUCER	15 THE GREEN, SOUTHWICK	WEST SUSSEX	ENGLAND
EVANS, RICHARD H	BASKETBALL EXECUTIVE	KNICKS, 4 PENNYLVANIA PLAZA	NEW YORK, NY	10019
EVANS, ROBERT	PRODUCER-ACTOR	10033 WOODLAWN DR	BEVERLY HILLS, CA	90210
EVANS, ROLAND	JOURNALIST	1750 PENNSYLVANIA AVE #1312, NW	WASHINGTON, DC	20006
EVANS, ROXIE	TV DIRECTOR	11733 MONTANA AVE #207	LOS ANGELES, CA	90049
EVANS, SEAN	BASEBALL	POST OFFICE BOX 3746, HILL STA	AUGUSTA, GA	30904
EVANS, SIR GERAINT	SINGER	17 HIGHCLIFFE		
		32 ALBEMARLE ST, BECKENHAM	KENT	ENGLAND
EVANS, STEVEN LEE	COMPOSER	2377 MALCOM AVE	LOS ANGELES, CA	90064
EVANS, TENNIEL	ACTOR	CANDLEMAS, JORDANS	BUCKS	ENGLAND
EVANS, VINCE	FOOTBALL	RAIDERS, 332 CENTER ST	EL SEGUNDO, CA	90245
EVASON, DEAN	HOCKEY	WHALERS, 1 CIVIC CENTER PLAZA	HARTFORD, CT	06103
EVE, TREVOR	ACTOR	BELFRAGE, 68 SAINT JAMES'S ST	LONDON SW1A 1LE	ENGLAND
EVERETT, BILL	TV DIRECTOR-PRODUCER	17 HARTLEY AVE	LONDON E6 1NU	ENGLAND

EVERETT, CARL	BASEBALL	5301 NW 12TH AVE	FORT LAUDERDALE, FL	33309
EVERETT, CHAD	ACTOR	19901 NORTHRIDGE RD	CHATSWORTH, CA	91311
EVERETT, ELAINE	ACTRESS	1421 N AVE 47	LOS ANGELES, CA	90042
EVERETT, JIM	FOOTBALL	RAMS, 2327 W LINCOLN BLVD	ANAHEIM, CA	92801
EVERETT, KENNY	TV-RADIO PERSONALITY	GURNETT, 2 NEW KINGS RD	LONDON SW6 4SA	ENGLAND
EVERETT, RUPERT	ACTOR	HEATH, PARAMOUNT HOUSE		
		162-170 WARDOUR ST	LONDON W1V 3AT	ENGLAND
EVERETT, SHELBY GRANT	ACTRESS	19901 NORTHRIDGE RD	CHATSWORTH, CA	91311
EVERETT, THOMAS	FOOTBALL	STEELERS, 300 STADIUM CIR	PITTSBURGH, PA	15212
EVERETT, TOM	SINGER-ACTOR	8721 SANTA MONICA BLVD #21	WEST HOLLYWOOD, CA	90069
EVERHARD, NANCY	ACTRESS	LIGHT, 901 BRINGHAM AVE	LOS ANGELES, CA	90049
EVERHART, BOB	SINGER-SONGWRITER	106 NAVAJO	COUNCIL BLUFFS, IA	51501
EVERHART, REX	ACTOR	42 N COMPO RD	WESTPORT, CT	06880
EVERING, JAMES V	TV WRITER	2438 N BEACHWOOD DR	LOS ANGELES, CA	90068
EVERITT, RICHARD	TV PRODUCER	LAUREL MOUNT, RICHMOND RD		
		BOWDEN	CHESHIRE	ENGLAND
EVERLY, DAVID	BASEBALL	POST OFFICE BOX 855	BELOIT, WI	53511
EVERLY, DON	SINGER-SONGWRITER	10100 SANTA MONICA BLVD #1600	LOS ANGELES, CA	90067
EVERLY, PATRICIA	ACTRESS	2175 CENTURY WOODS WY	LOS ANGELES, CA	90067
EVERLY, PHIL	SINGER-SONGWRITER	10414 CAMARILLO ST	NORTH HOLLYWOOD, CA	91602
EVERLY, TRISH	ACTRESS	SEE - EVERLY, PATRICIA		
EVERLY BROTHERS, THE	VOCAL DUO	10100 SANTA MONICA BLVD #1600	LOS ANGELES, CA	90067
EVERS, BILL	BASEBALL MANAGER	5999 E VAN BUREN ST	PHOENIX, AZ	85008
EVERS, WALTER "HOOT"	BASEBALL-SCOUT	TIGERS, TIGER STADIUM	DETROIT, MI	48216
EVERSGERD, BRYAN	BASEBALL	POST OFFICE BOX 12557	ST PETERSBURG, FL	33733
EVERSON, CORY	BODYBUILDER	7324 RESEDA BLVD #208	RESEDA, CA	91335
EVERSON, JEFF	BODYBUILDER	7324 RESEDA BLVD #208	RESEDA, CA	91335
EVERT-LLOYD, CHRIS	TENNIS	500 NE 25TH ST	WILTON MANORS, FL	33305
EVERTON, DEBORAH	COSTUME DESIGNER	1999 AVE OF THE STARS #2850	LOS ANGELES, CA	90067
EVERYTHING BUT GIRL	ROCK & ROCK DUO	200 W 57TH ST #104	NEW YORK, NY	10019
EVIGAN, GREG	ACTOR-SINGER	1765 N HIGHLAND AVE #560	HOLLYWOOD, CA	90028
EWBANK, WEBB	FOOTBALL COACH	7 PATRICK DR	OXFORD, OH	45056
EWELL, TOM	ACTOR	53 ASPEN ST	ROLLING HILLS EST, CA	90274
EWEN, LINDA	ACTRESS	262 1/2 S SPALDING DR #6	BEVERLY HILLS, CA	90212
EWEN, TODD	HOCKEY	CANADIENS, 2313 ST CATHERINE ST	MONTREAL, QUE H3H 1N2	CANADA
EWING, DIANA	WRITER	407 SAN VICENTE BLVD	SANTA MONICA, CA	90402
EWING, GORDON	ACTOR	3502 ST ELIZABETH RD	GLENDALE, CA	91206
EWING, JOHN CHRISTY	ACTOR	368 GRENOLA ST	PACIFIC PALISADES, CA	90272
EWING, MARTY	FILM DIRECTOR	170 MISTY LAKE CT	WOOD RANCH, CA	93065
EWING, PATRICK	BASKETBALL	KNICKS, 4 PENNYLVANIA PLAZA	NEW YORK, NY	10019
EWING, ROGER	ACTOR	7733 HAMPTON AVE #4	LOS ANGELES, CA	90046
EWING, SKIP	SINGER-SONGWRITER	POST OFFICE BOX 17087	NASHVILLE, TN	37217
EXILE	C & W GROUP	POST OFFICE BOX 23341	LEXINGTON, KY	40523
EXON, J JAMES	U S SENATOR	528 HART SENATE OFFICE BLDG	WASHINGTON, DC	20510
EXPOSE	VOCAL TRIO	PANTERA, 13644 SW 142ND AVE	MIAMI, FL	33186
EXTON, CLIVE	TV WRITER	PETERS, FRASER & DUNLOP, LTD		
		5TH FLOOR, THE CHAMBERS		
		CHELSEA HARBOUR, LOT RD	LONDON SW10 OXF	ENGLAND
EYE EYE	ROCK & ROLL GROUP	1505 W 2ND AVE #200	VANCOUVER, BC V6H 3Y4	CANADA
EYEN, JIM	BASKETBALL COACH	POST OFFICE BOX 10	INGLEWOOD, CA	90306
EYMAN, SCOTT	FILM CRITIC	MIAMI NEWS, 1 HERALD PLAZA	MIAMI, FL	33101
EYRE, DAVID M, JR	SCREENWRITER	10000 SANTA MONICA BLVD #305	LOS ANGELES, CA	90067
EYRE, RICHARD	TV DIRECTOR-PRODUCER	ROYAL NATIONAL THEATRE		
		SOUTH BANK	LONDON SE1 9PX	ENGLAND
EZELL, GLENN	BASEBALL-COACH	POST OFFICE BOX 419969	KANSAS CITY, MO	64141
EZRA, MARK	SCREENWRITER	HEATH, PARAMOUNT HOUSE		
		162-170 WARDOUR ST	LONDON W1V 3AT	ENGLAND

F/X	ROCK & ROLL GROUP	POST OFFICE BOX 260501	TAMPA, FL	33685
FABARES, SHELLEY	ACTRESS	POST OFFICE BOX 6010-85	SHERMAN OAKS, CA	91413
FABEL, BRAD	GOLFER	POST OFFICE BOX 109601	PALM BCH GARDENS, FL	33418
FABER, GEORGE D	AUTHOR-EXECUTIVE	VIACOM COMMUNICATIONS		
		10900 WILSHIRE BLVD	LOS ANGELES, CA	90024
FABER, MORT	CONDUCTOR	1123 GARFIELD AVE	MARINA DEL REY, CA	90292
FABER, ROBERT	WRITER-PRODUCER	1524 STRADELLA RD	LOS ANGELES, CA	90077
FABIAN	ACTOR-SINGER	SEE - FORTE, FABIAN		
FABIANI, JOEL	ACTOR	5750 WILSHIRE BLVD #512	LOS ANGELES, CA	90036
FABRAY, NANETTE	ACTRESS	14360 SUNSET BLVD	PACIFIC PALISADES, CA	90272
FABREGAS, JORGE	BASEBALL	POST OFFICE BOX 1742	PALM SPRINGS, CA	92263
FABRIQUE, TINA	SINGER	360 CENTRAL PARK W #16-G	NEW YORK, NY	10025
FABRY, JOHN	FOOTBALL EXECUTIVE	PACKERS, 1265 LOMBARDI AVE	GREEN BAY, WI	54307
FABULOUS THUNDERBIRDS, THE	ROCK & ROLL GROUP	POST OFFICE BOX 17006	AUSTIN, TX	78760
FACCIO, LUIS	BASEBALL	POST OFFICE BOX 5599	LITTLE ROCK, AR	72215
FACTOR, ALAN JAY	FILM DIRECTOR	404 N ROXBURY DR #800	BEVERLY HILLS, CA	90210
FAER, STANLEY	TV DIRECTOR	301 E 62ND ST	NEW YORK, NY	10021
FAGA, GARY	ACTOR	31637 SEA LEVEL DR	MALIBU, CA	90265
FAGAN, ANDREW H	DIRECTOR	PEACHTREE, 3900 W ALAMEDA AVE	BURBANK, CA	91505

FAGAN, JIM	ACTOR	TUSH, 119 W 57TH ST	NEW YORK, NY	10019
FAGAN, KEVIN	CARTOONIST	UNITED FEATURE, 200 PARK AVE	NEW YORK, NY	10166
FAGAN, KEVIN	FOOTBALL	S F 49ERS, 4949 CENTENNIAL BL	SANTA CLARA, CA	95054
FAGAN, PETE	BASEBALL TRAINER	POST OFFICE BOX 12557	ST PETERSBURG, FL	33733
FAGAN, RONALD J	FILM EDITOR	ACE, 1041 N FORMOSA AVE	WEST HOLLYWOOD, CA	90046
FAGEN, DONALD	SINGER-SONGWRITER	24109 MALIBU RD	MALIBU, CA	90265
FAGEN, FRED	ACTOR	2074 20TH LN #4-C	BROOKLYN, NY	11214
FAHEY, BILL	BASEBALL-COACH	S F GIANTS, CANDLESTICK PARK	SAN FRANICSCO, CA	94124
FAHEY, JEFF	ACTOR	250 N ROBERTSON BLVD #518	BEVERLY HILLS, CA	90211
FAHEY, JOHN	GUITARIST	4230 SW VIEWPOINT TERR #12	PORTLAND, OR	97201
FAHN, MELISSA	ACTRESS	1717 N HIGHLAND AVE #414	LOS ANGELES, CA	90028
FAICHNEY, JAMES B	WRITER-PRODUCER	75-C LAKESIDE DR	MONSON, MA	01057
FAIN, JOHNNY	ACTOR	25154 MALIBU RD #1	MALIBU, CA	90265
FAIN, SAMMY	COMPOSER	1640 SAN YSIDRO DR	BEVERLY HILLS, CA	90210
FAIRBAIRN, BRUCE	ACTOR	9744 WILSHIRE BLVD #308	BEVERLY HILLS, CA	90212
FAIRBANKS, DOUGLAS, JR	ACTOR	575 PARK AVE #608	NEW YORK, NY	10021
FAIRBANKS, JERRY	DIRECTOR-PRODUCER	826 N COLE AVE	HOLLYWOOD, CA	90038
FAIRCHILD, BARBARA	SINGER	CARROLL, RT #2, LEWISBURG PIKE	FRANKLIN, TN	37064
FAIRCHILD, MORGAN	ACTRESS-MODEL	3321 DIXIE CANYON LN	BEVERLY HILLS, CA	90210
FAIRCHILD, WILLIAM	TV WRITER-DIRECTOR	A M HEATH, 79 SAINT MATINS LN	LONDON WC2N 4AA	ENGLAND
FAIREY, JIM	BASEBALL-SCOUT	S F GIANTS, CANDLESTICK PARK	SAN FRANICSCO, CA	94124
FAIRFIELD, HEATHER	ACTRESS	280 S BEVERLY DR #400	BEVERLY HILLS, CA	90212
FAIRLY, RON	BASEBALL-ANNOUNCER	S F GIANTS, CANDLESTICK PARK	SAN FRANICSCO, CA	94124
FAIRMAN, ANDY	BASEBALL	POST OFFICE BOX 855	BELOIT, WI	53511
FAIRMAN, MICHAEL	ACT-WRI-DIR	6615 FRANKLIN AVE #220	LOS ANGELES, CA	90028
FAIRS, ERIC	FOOTBALL	OILERS, 6910 FANNIN ST	HOUSTON, TX	77070
FAISA, PRINCESS	PRINCESS	10747 WILSHIRE BLVD #E-1504	LOS ANGELES, CA	90024
FAISON, MATTHEW	ACTOR	13701 KAGEL CANYON RD	SYLMAR, CA	91342
FAISON, SANDY	ACTRESS	STE, 888 7TH AVE, 18TH FLOOR	NEW YORK, NY	10106
FAITH, ADAM	SINGER-ACTOR	CROCKHAM HILL, EDENBRIDGE	KENT	ENGLAND
FAITH NO MORE	ROCK & ROLL GROUP	5550 WILSHIRE BLVD #202	LOS ANGELES, CA	90036
FAITHFULL, MARIANNE	SINGER-SONGWRITER	YEW TREE COTTAGE, ALDRIDGE	BERKS	ENGLAND
FAJARDO, HECTOR	BASEBALL	POST OFFICE BOX 90111	ARLINGTON, TX	76004
FALANA, LOLA	SINGER-ACTRESS	POST OFFICE BOX 50369	HENDERSON, NV	89016
FALCO	SINGER-SONGWRITER	MOHLSTR 16	D-8000 MUNICH 80	GERMANY
FALCO, CHRIS	BASEBALL	POST OFFICE BOX 6748	ROCKFORD, IL	61125
FALCO, MICHAEL ANTHONY	ACTOR	MINE HILL RD	CORNWALL, NY	12518
FALCON, BILLY	SINGER	POST OFFICE BOX 602	WOODCLIFF LAKE, NJ	07675
FALCON, ELLEN	TV DIRECTOR	14924 GREENLEAF ST	SHERMAN OAKS, CA	91403
FALCON, ERROL	DIRECTOR	133 ARAGON AVE	CORAL GABLES, FL	33134
FALCONER, THEODORE E	WRITER	6139 BLUEBELL AVE	NORTH HOLLYWOOD, CA	91606
FALDO, NICK	GOLFER	POST OFFICE BOX 109601	PALM BCH GARDENS, FL	33418
FALEOMAVAEGA, ENI F H	U S DELEGATE	POST OFFICE BOX X	PAGO PAGO, AS	96799
FALK, HARRY	DIRECTOR	1289 SUNSET PLAZA DR	LOS ANGELES, CA	90069
FALK, LAURA NELSON	SCREENWRITER	6360 ORANGE DR	LOS ANGELES, CA	90048
FALK, LEE	CARTOONIST	KING FEATURES, 216 E 45TH ST	NEW YORK, NY	10017
FALK, LISANNE	ACTRESS	POST OFFICE BOX 5617	BEVERLY HILLS, CA	90213
FALK, PETER	ACTOR-DIRECTOR	1004 N ROXBURY DR	BEVERLY HILLS, CA	90210
FALK, QUENTIN S	JOURNALIST	OLD BARN COTTAGE, LITTLE MARLOW	BUCKS	ENGLAND
FALK, TOM	WRITER	6360 ORANGE DR	LOS ANGELES, CA	90048
FALKENBERG, KORT	ACTOR	20831 BURBANK BLVD	WOODLAND HILLS, CA	91367
FALKENBERG, PAUL	DIRECTOR	15 W 67TH ST	NEW YORK, NY	10023
FALKENBURG, JINX	ACTRESS	10 SHELTER ROCK RD	MANHASSET, LI, NY	11030
FALLICK, MORTON	DIRECTOR	23885 KILLION ST	WOODLAND HILLS, CA	91367
FALLON, JOEL R	WRITER	426 S GRIFFITH PARK DR	BURBANK, CA	91506
FALOTICO, CREIGHTON	ACTOR	5431 JED SMITH RD	CALABASAS, CA	91302
FALSEY, JOHN	TV PRODUCER	BRAND-FALSEY, 3000 OLYMPIC BL	SANTA MONICA, CA	90404
FALWELL, CALVIN	BASEBALL EXECUTIVE	POST OFFICE BOX 10213	LYNCHBURG, VA	24506
FALWELL, REV JERRY	EVANGELIST	701 THOMAS RD	LYNCHBURG, VA	24502
FAMILY BROWN, THE	C & W GROUP	SPARLING, 71 BIRCHVIEW RD	NEPEAN, ONT K2G 3G3	CANADA
FANARO, BARRY P	TV WRITER	13914 BORA BORA WY #318	MARINA DEL REY, CA	90292
FANEYTE, RIKKERT	BASEBALL	POST OFFICE BOX 21727	SAN FRANCISCO, CA	95151
FANGIO, VIC	FOOTBALL COACH	SAINTS, 1500 POYDRAS ST	NEW ORLEANS, LA	90112
FANN, AL	ACTOR	19649 CITRONIA ST	NORTHRIDGE, CA	91324
FANNING, GEORGE	BASEBALL EXECUTIVE	POST OFFICE BOX 356	BLUEFIELD, WV	24701
FANNING, JIM	BASEBALL-EXECUTIVE	EXPOS, 4545 DE COUBERTIN AVE	MONTREAL, QUE H1V 3P2	CANADA
FANNING, STEVE	BASEBALL	POST OFFICE BOX 5599	LITTLE ROCK, AR	72215
FANSLER, STAN	BASEBALL	POST OFFICE DRAWER 1218	ZEBULON, NC	27597
FANT, LESA	ACTRESS	19602 LANARK ST	RESEDA, CA	91335
FANT, LOU	ACTOR	19602 LANARK ST	RESEDA, CA	91335
FARACY, STEPHANIE	ACTRESS	8765 LOOKOUT MOUNTAIN RD	LOS ANGELES, CA	90046
FARAGO, JOE	ACTOR	835 HOPKINS WY #313	REDONDO BEACH, CA	90277
FARALLA, WILLIAM	DIRECTOR	16530 14TH AVE SE	MILL CREEK, WA	98012
FARBER, STEPHEN	WRITER	10611 WILKINS AVE #6	LOS ANGELES, CA	90024
FARBMAN, PAUL	ACTOR	2832 EXPOSITION BLVD	SANTA MONICA, CA	90404
FARENHEIT	ROCK & ROLL GROUP	DOUBLE EAGLE, 280 LINCOLN ST	BOSTON, MA	02134
FARENTINO, DEBRAH	ACTRESS	586 LORNA LN	LOS ANGELES, CA	90049
FARENTINO, JAMES	ACTOR	1340 LONDONDERRY PL	LOS ANGELES, CA	90069
FARGO, DONNA	SINGER	POST OFFICE BOX 150527	NASHVILLE, TN	37215
FARGO, LOUIS JAMES	DIRECTOR	2419 OCEAN FRONT WALK #3	VENICE, CA	90291
FARIES, PAUL	BASEBALL	STARS, 850 LAS VEGAS BLVD N	LAS VEGAS, NV	89101
FARINA, DENNIS	ACTOR	GEDDES, 8457 MELROSE PL #200	LOS ANGELES, CA	90069
FARINA, MICHAEL	TV DIRECTOR	2060 MOUND ST	HOLLYWOOD, CA	90068
FARINA, MIMI	SINGER	BREAD, 78 THROCKMORTON AVE	MILL VALLEY, CA	94941
FARISS, MONTY	BASEBALL	POST OFFICE BOX 90111	ARLINGTON, TX	76004

FARLEIGH, LYNN	ACTRESS	CONWAY, 18-21 JERMYN ST	LONDON SW1	ENGLAND
FARLOW, KEVIN	BASEBALL	POST OFFICE BOX 611	WATERLOO, IA	50704
FARMER, ART, QUARTET	JAZZ QUARTET	KEANE, 49 E 96TH ST	NEW YORK, NY	10128
FARMER, DON	BROADCAST JOURNALIST	MARTIN KRALL, 1800 "M" ST, NW	WASHINGTON, DC	20036
FARMER, ED	BASEBALL SCOUT	333 W 35TH ST	CHICAGO, IL	60616
FARMER, HOWARD	BASEBALL	1501 W 16TH ST	INDIANAPOLIS, IN	46202
FARMER, JOHN A	ACTOR-WRITER	5542 SUNNYSLOPE AVE	VAN NUYS, CA	91401
FARMER, MARK	ACTOR	ANNA SCHER THEATRE MANAGEMENT		
		70-72 BARNSBURY RD	LONDON N1 OES	ENGLAND
FARMER, MICHAEL	BASEBALL	POST OFFICE BOX 10336	CLEARWATER, FL	34617
FARMER, RANDY	BASEBALL	POST OFFICE BOX 7845	COLUMBIA, SC	29202
FARMER, REGINALD H	WRITER	POST OFFICE BOX 1040	STUDIO CITY, CA	91604
FARNON, SHANNON	ACTRESS	12743 MILBANK ST	STUDIO CITY, CA	91604
FARNSWORTH, MARK	BASEBALL TRAINER	POST OFFICE BOX 3665	OMAHA, NE	68103
FARNSWORTH, RICHARD	ACTOR	3219 ELLINGTON DR	LOS ANGELES, CA	90068
FARNSWORTH, ROSS	BASEBALL	POST OFFICE BOX 10031	BAKERSFIELD, CA	93389
FARQUHAR, RALPH	TV WRITER	1300 1/2 N SYCAMORE AVE	LOS ANGELES, CA	90028
FARR, BERNARD	CONDUCTOR	300 N RAMPART ST #158	ORANGE, CA	92667
FARR, FELICIA	ACTRESS	141 S EL CAMINO DR #201	BEVERLY HILLS, CA	90212
FARR, GORDON	WRITER-PRODUCER	8161 LAUREL VIEW DR	LOS ANGELES, CA	90069
FARR, JAMIE	ACTOR-DIRECTOR	53 RANCHERO, BELL CANYON	BELL CANYON, CA	91307
FARR, MIKE	FOOTBALL	LIONS, 1200 FEATHERSTONE RD	PONTIAC, MI	48432
FARR, STEVE	BASEBALL	NY YANKEES, YANKEE STADIUM	BRONX, NY	10451
FARRAKHAN, LOUIS	MINISTER	813 E BROADWAY	PHOENIX, AZ	85501
FARRANT, TREVOR A	SCREENWRITER	8955 BEVERLY BLVD	WEST HOLLYWOOD, CA	90048
FARRAR, TERRY	BASEBALL	POST OFFICE BOX 3169	FREDERICK, MD	21701
FARREL, BRIONI	ACTRESS	12456 VENTURA BLVD #1	STUDIO CITY, CA	91604
FARRELL, BRIAN	ACTOR	18432 LINNET ST	TARZANA, CA	91356
FARRELL, CHARLES	ACTOR (ENGLISH)	GREEN ROOM CLUB, 9 ADAMS ST	LONDON WC2	ENGLAND
FARRELL, COLIN	ACTOR	DALZELL, 17 BROAD CT #12	LONDON WC2B 5QN	ENGLAND
FARRELL, GAIL	ACTRESS	16022 MEADOWCREST RD	SHERMAN OAKS, CA	91403
FARRELL, JOHN	BASEBALL	12 HIGHLAND AVE	MONMOUTH BEACH, NJ	07750
FARRELL, JON	BASEBALL	POST OFFICE BOX 3746, HILL STA	AUGUSTA, GA	30904
FARRELL, MARTY	TV-COMEDY WRITER	301 E 64TH ST	NEW YORK, NY	10021
FARRELL, MIKE	ACT-WRI-DIR	POST OFFICE BOX 5961-306	SHERMAN OAKS, CA	91413
FARRELL, MIKE	BASEBALL	POST OFFICE BOX 8550	STOCKTON, CA	95208
FARRELL, PETER	TV DIRECTOR	8 GROVE LODGE, CROSS DEEP		
		TWICKENHAM	MIDDLESEX	ENGLAND
FARRELL, SEAN	FOOTBALL	BRONCOS, 13655 BRONCOS PKWY	ENGLEWOOD, CO	80112
FARRELL, SHARON	ACTRESS	11846 VENTURA BLVD #100	STUDIO CITY, CA	91604
FARRELL, SHEA	ACTOR	125 S BOWLING GREEN WY	LOS ANGELES, CA	90049
FARRELL, TOMMY	ACTOR	5225 RIVERTON AVE	NORTH HOLLYWOOD, CA	91601
FARRELL, WILLIAM PATRICK	DIRECTOR	518 E 80TH ST #2-P	NEW YORK, NY	10021
FARREN, PAUL	FOOTBALL	BROWNS, 80 1ST ST	BEREA, OH	44017
FARRER, TINA	ACTRESS-MODEL	13 ORLOP ST, GREENWICH	LONDON SE10 9AB	ENGLAND
FARRER, TRACY	ACTRESS-MODEL	13 ORLOP ST, GREENWICH	LONDON SE10 9AB	ENGLAND
FARRINGTON, HUGH	ACTRESS	SCHWARTZ, 935 N CROFT AVE	LOS ANGELES, CA	90069
FARRISH, KEOKI	BASEBALL	POST OFFICE BOX 2887	VERO BEACH, FL	32961
FARROW, DAVID M	FILM DIRECTOR	1915 CERRO GORDO ST	LOS ANGELES, CA	90039
FARROW, LAWRENCE G	COMPOSER-CONDUCTOR	373 N WESTERN AVE #18	LOS ANGELES, CA	90004
FARROW, MIA	ACTRESS	135 CENTRAL PARK W	NEW YORK, NY	10018
FARYNIAK, KAREN	ARTIST	1406 E WASHINGTON ST	ALLENTOWN, PA	18103
FARYNIARZ, BRETT	FOOTBALL	RAMS, 2327 W LINCOLN BLVD	ANAHEIM, CA	92801
FASCALL, DANTE B	U S CONGRESSMAN	7855 SW 104TH ST #220	MIAMI, FL	33156
FASCIANO, DEBRA J	WRITER	5914 W 85TH PL	LOS ANGELES, CA	90045
FASH, MIKE	CINEMATOGRAPHER	10 BERMUDA RD	WESTPORT, CT	06880
FASHION, THE	ROCK & ROLL GROUP	POST OFFICE BOX 1000	WINDSOR, VT	05089
FASOLINO, TERESA	ARTIST	233 E 21ST ST	NEW YORK, NY	10010
FASSERO, JEFF	BASEBALL	EXPOS, 4545 DE COUBERTIN AVE	MONTREAL, QUE H1V 3P2	CANADA
FAST, HOWARD	TV WRITER	2 PARK ST	BOSTON, MA	02107
FAT AMMON'S BAND	ROCK & ROLL GROUP	210 81ST ST #4	VIRGINIA BEACH, VA	23451
FAT BOYS, THE	RAP GROUP	250 W 57TH ST #1723	NEW YORK, NY	10107
FAT CITY BAND, THE	ROCK & ROLL GROUP	ASA PRODS, 36 MYRTLE ST	NORTH QUINCY, MA	02171
FATBACK	ROCK & ROLL GROUP	POST OFFICE BOX 151	SAINT ALBANS, NY	11412
FATBURGER	JAZZ GROUP	9157 SUNSET BLVD #200	LOS ANGELES, CA	90069
FATES WARNING	ROCK & ROLL GROUP	1133 BROADWAY #204	NEW YORK, NY	10010
FATOVICH, PETER	TV DIRECTOR	156 HOLLYWOOD AVE	TUCKAHOE, NY	10707
FAUBUS, ORVAL	GOVERNOR	POST OFFICE BOX 488	LITTLE ROCK, AR	72203
FAUER, JONATHAN	TV DIRECTOR	500 E 83RD ST #14-B	NEW YORK, NY	10028
FAULDS, ANDREW	ACTOR	14 ALBEMARLE ST	LONDON W1	ENGLAND
FAULK, PAUL	BASEBALL SCOUT	REDS, 100 RIVERFRONT STADIUM	CINCINNATI, OH	45202
FAULKINER, MIKE	FOOTBALL COACH	BROWNS, 80 1ST ST	BEREA, OH	44017
FAULKNER, CAROLINE	ACTRESS	161 E 89TH ST	NEW YORK, NY	10028
FAULKNER, CRAIG	BASEBALL	POST OFFICE DRAWER 4797	EL PASO, TX	79914
FAULKNER, GUY	ACTOR	HUTTON, 200 FULHAM RD	LONDON SW14 7AH	ENGLAND
FAULKNER, JACK	FOOTBALL EXECUTIVE	RAMS, 2327 W LINCOLN BLVD	ANAHEIM, CA	92801
FAULKNER, JAMES	ACTOR	HATTON, 18 JERMYN ST	LONDON SW1	ENGLAND
FAULKNER, JEFF	FOOTBALL	POST OFFICE BOX 888	PHOENIX, AZ	85001
FAULKNER, LEO	ACTOR	HUTTON, 200 FULHAM RD	LONDON SW14 7AH	ENGLAND
FAULKNER, STEPHANIE	ACTRESS	2010 S SPAULDING AVE	LOS ANGELES, CA	90016
FAULKNER, TIM	ACTOR	COULSON, 37 BERWICK ST	LONDON W1V 3RF	ENGLAND
FAULKNER, TRADER	ACTOR	21 LEXHAM GARDENS #15	LONDON W8 5JJ	ENGLAND
FAURE, RENEE	ARTIST	600 2ND ST	NEPTUNE NEACH, FL	32233
FAUST, CLIFF	ARTIST	322 W 57TH ST	NEW YORK, NY	10019
FAUSTINO, DAVID	ACTOR	1320 N MAPLE ST	BURBANK, CA	91505

FAUSTINO, MICHAEL	ACTOR	11350 VENTURA BLVD #206	STUDIO CITY, CA	91604
FAVIA, PHIL	BASEBALL SCOUT	METS, 126TH ST & ROOSEVELT AVE	FLUSHING, NY	11368
FAVRE, BRETT	FOOTBALL	FALCONS, SUWANEE RD AT I-85	SUWANEE, GA	30174
FAVREAUX, LOU	ACTOR	438 N SWEETZER AVE	LOS ANGELES, CA	90048
FAW, BRIAN	BASEBALL	5301 NW 12TH AVE	FORT LAUDERDALE, FL	33309
FAWCETT, ALLEN	ACTOR-TV HOST	STONE MANNERS, 9113 SUNSET BLVD	LOS ANGELES, CA	90069
FAWCETT, FARRAH	ACTRESS-MODEL	3130 ANTELO RD	LOS ANGELES, CA	90077
FAWELL, HARRIS	U S CONGRESSMAN	115 W 55TH ST #100	CLARENDON HILLS, IL	60514
FAXON, BRAD	GOLFER	POST OFFICE BOX 109601	PALM BCH GARDENS, FL	33418
FAY, DEIDRE	TV WRITER-PRODUCER	8955 BEVERLY BLVD	WEST HOLLYWOOD, CA	90048
FAY, DOROTHY	ACTRESS	RITTER, 14151 VALLEY VISTA BL	SHERMAN OAKS, CA	91423
FAY, EDDY	ACTOR	330 E 49TH ST	NEW YORK, NY	10017
FAYE, ALICE	ACTRESS-SINGER	49400 JOHN F KENNEDY TRAIL	PALM DESERT, CA	92260
FAYMAN, WILLIAM	FILM PRODUCER	FGH FILM CONSORTIUM		
		74 BRIDPORT ST, ALBERT PARK	VICTORIA 3206	AUSTRALIA
FAYNE, JEFF	BASEBALL	POST OFFICE BOX 3783	SAVANNAH, GA	31414
FAZIO, FOGE	FOOTBALL COACH	N Y JETS, 1000 FULTON AVE	HEMPSTEAD, NY	11550
FAZIO, VIC	U S CONGRESSMAN	2525 NATOMAS PARK DR #330	SACRAMENTO, CA	95833
FEAGLES, JEFF	FOOTBALL	EAGLES, BROAD ST & PATTISON AVE	PHILADELPHIA, PA	19148
FEAR	ROCK & ROLL GROUP	POST OFFICE BOX 2428	EL SEGUNDO, CA	90245
FEARS, TOM	FOOTBALL	41470 WOODHAVEN DR W	PALM DESERT, CA	92260
FEASEL, DARLENE	ACTRESS	5812 WHITSETT AVE	NORTH HOLLYWOOD, CA	91607
FEASEL, GRANT	FOOTBALL	SEAHAWKS, 11220 NE 53RD ST	KIRKLAND, WA	98033
FEATHER, JACQUELINE M	TV WRITER	10351 SANTA MONICA BLVD #211	LOS ANGELES, CA	90025
FEATHER, LEONARD	AUTHOR-JAZZ CRITIC	13833 RIVERSIDE DR	SHERMAN OAKS, CA	91423
FEATHERS, CHARLIE	SINGER	POST OFFICE BOX 242	HORSESHOE BEND, AR	72512
FEATHERSTONE, GLEN	HOCKEY	BLUES, 5700 OAKLAND AVE	SAINT LOUIS, MO	63110
FEAZELL, JIM	SCREENWRITER	8955 BEVERLY BLVD	WEST HOLLYWOOD, CA	90048
FEDDERSON, DON	TV PRODUCER	16071 ROYAL OAK	ENCINO, CA	91436
FEDER, DAVID L	FILM WRITER-PRODUCER	5800 OWENSMOUTH AVE #32	WOODLAND HILLS, CA	91367
FEDER, DON	COLUMNIST	BOSTON HERALD, 1 HERALD SQ	BOSTON, MA	02106
FEDER, MIKE	BASEBALL EXECUTIVE	POST OFFICE BOX 27045	TUCSON, AZ	85726
FEDER, ROBERT	TV-RADIO REPORTER	SUN-TIMES, 401 N WABASH AVE	CHICAGO, IL	60611
FEDERBUSH, ARNOLD	WRITER	840 S SERRANO AVE #305	LOS ANGELES, CA	90005
FEDOROV, SERGEI	HOCKEY	RED WINGS, 600 CIVIC CENTER DR	DETROIT, MI	48226
FEDUKE, MICHAEL	TV WRITER	301 E 79TH ST #34-F	NEW YORK, NY	10021
FEDYK, BRENT	HOCKEY	RED WINGS, 600 CIVIC CENTER DR	DETROIT, MI	48226
FEE, MELINDA	ACTRESS	8019 1/2 MELROSE AVE #3	LOS ANGELES, CA	90046
FEELIES, THE	ROCK & ROLL GROUP	BALLFIELD PRODS, 9 BERNARD AVE	HALEDIN, NJ	07508
FEELY, TERENCE	PLAYWRIGHT	RAE, CHARING CROSS RD	LONDON WC2H ODB	ENGLAND
FEENER, PAMELA	ACTRESS	1758 N ORANGE DR #17	HOLLYWOOD, CA	90028
FEES, JARRE-BETH	ACTRESS	6406 FRANKLIN AVE #5	LOS ANGELES, CA	90028
FEHR, KAJA	FILM EDITOR	POST OFFICE BOX 5617	BEVERLY HILLS, CA	90213
FEHR, RICK	GOLFER	POST OFFICE BOX 109601	PALM BCH GARDENS, FL	33418
FEHR, RUDI	EXECUTIVE PRODUCER	3410 LA SOMBRA DR	LOS ANGELES, CA	90068
FEHRLE, PHILIP D	WRITER	691 COUNTRY CLUB DR	BURBANK, CA	91501
FEIBLEMAN, PETER	SCREENWRITER	263 LOMA AVE	LONG BEACH, CA	90803
FEIERMAN, JACK W	CONDUCTOR	13120 HARTSOOK ST	SHERMAN OAKS, CA	91423
FEIFFER, JULES	WRITER	325 W END AVE	NEW YORK, NY	10023
FEIGENBAUM, JOEL J	TV WRITER-DIRECTOR	151 S EL CAMINO DR	BEVERLY HILLS, CA	90212
FEIGHAN, EDWARD	U S CONGRESSMAN	FEDERAL OFFICE BUILDING #2951		
		1240 E 9TH ST	CLEVELAND, OH	44199
FEIL, GERALD	DIRECTOR	JACKSON AGENCY, 250 W 57TH ST	NEW YORK, NY	10107
FEIN, BRUCE	COLUMNIST	THE WASHINGTON TIMES		
		3600 NEW YORK AVE, NE	WASHINGTON, DC	20002
FEIN, IRVING	TV EXECUTIVE	1100 N ALTA LOMA RD	LOS ANGELES, CA	90069
FEINBERG, RONALD	ACTOR	220 S REEVES DR	BEVERLY HILLS, CA	90212
FEINGOLD, SUSAN	TV PRODUCER	TURNSTYLE PRODS, 130 W 25TH ST	NEW YORK, NY	10001
FEINGOLD, VIRGINIA	ACTRESS	612 WESTBOURNE DR #8	LOS ANGELES, CA	90069
FEININGER, ANDREAS	PHOTOGRAPHER	18 ELIZABETH LN	NEW MILFORD, CT	06776
FEINSTEIN, ALAN	ACTOR	432 S OGDEN DR	LOS ANGELES, CA	90036
FEINSTEIN, DIANE	MAYOR	30 PRESIDIO TERR	SAN FRANCISCO, CA	94102
FEINSTEIN, MERYLL R	CASTING DIRECTOR	49 HEATHERFIELD RD	VALLEY STREAM, NY	11581
FEINSTEIN, MICHAEL	ACTOR	2233 CHEREMOYA AVE	LOS ANGELES, CA	90068
FEIRSTEIN, BRUCE J	AUTHOR-WRITER	DELL-DELTA, 666 5TH AVE	NEW YORK, NY	10103
FEIST, KEN	BASEBALL	POST OFFICE BOX 1295	CLINTON, IA	52733
FEITL, DAVE	BASKETBALL	POST OFFICE BOX 272349	HOUSTON, TX	77277
FEJER, TIBOR	COMPOSER-CONDUCTOR	8440 DE LONGPRE AVE	LOS ANGELES, CA	90069
FEKE, STEPHEN JAMES	WRITER	11719 EL CERRO LN	STUDIO CITY, CA	91604
FELD, FRITZ	ACTOR	12348 ROCHEDALE LN	LOS ANGELES, CA	90049
FELD, JOEL D	TV DIRECTOR-PRODUCER	200 E 90TH ST #19-E	NEW YORK, NY	10023
FELD, JOHN C	TV PRODUCER	CBS-TV, "THE GUIDING LIGHT"		
		222 E 44TH ST	NEW YORK, NY	10017
FELD, PHILIP	DIRECTOR	1001 91ST ST	BAY HARBOR ISLAND, FL	33154
FELDER, CLARENCE	ACTOR	606 N LARCHMONT BLVD #309	LOS ANGELES, CA	90004
FELDER, DON	SINGER-SONGWRITER	POST OFFICE BOX 6051	MALIBU, CA	90265
FELDER, MIKE	BASEBALL	S F GIANTS, CANDLESTICK PARK	SAN FRANICSCO, CA	94124
FELDER, WILTON	MUSICIAN	4485 MYRTLE AVE	LONG BEACH, CA	90807
FELDINGER, FRANK A	WRITER	7960 SELMA AVE #303	LOS ANGELES, CA	90046
FELDMAN, CHARLES	TV DIRECTOR	355 S END AVE #1-A	NEW YORK, NY	10280
FELDMAN, CHESTER	DIRECTOR	304 CASTLE DR	ENGLEWOOD, NJ	07632
FELDMAN, COREY	ACTOR	9000 SUNSET BLVD #1200	LOS ANGELES, CA	90069
FELDMAN, DANIEL M	TV DIRECTOR	451 BROOME ST #5-E	NEW YORK, NY	10013
FELDMAN, DENNIS	SCREENWRITER	8955 BEVERLY BLVD	WEST HOLLYWOOD, CA	90048
FELDMAN, EDWARD S	FILM PRODUCER	9454 WILSHIRE BLVD #903	BEVERLY HILLS, CA	90212

Name	Occupation	Address	City	Zip/Country
FELDMAN, JACK L	DIRECTOR-PRODUCER	FORDHAM, 6430 SUNSET BLVD	HOLLYWOOD, CA	90028
FELDMAN, JUDITH B	TV WRITER	11726 SAN VICENTE BLVD #300	LOS ANGELES, CA	90049
FELDMAN, MAXINE	SINGER	POST OFFICE BOX 114	BOSTON, MA	02117
FELDMAN, RANDOLPH ROBERT	SCREENWRITER	6946 CAMROSE DR	LOS ANGELES, CA	90068
FELDMAN, SY	MUSIC EXECUTIVE	265 SECAUCUS RD	SEACAUCUS, NJ	07094
FELDON, BARBARA	ACTRESS-MODEL	14 E 74TH ST	NEW YORK, NY	10021
FELDSHER, PAUL	TALENT AGENT	11726 SAN VICENTE BLVD #300	LOS ANGELES, CA	90049
FELDSHUH, TOVAH	ACTRESS	110 RIVERSIDE DR #16-F	NEW YORK, NY	10024
FELICE, JACK	TV DIRECTOR	75 CLIFFORD AVE	PELHAM, NY	10803
FELICIANO, JOSE	SINGER-GUITARIST	266 LYONS PLAIN RD	WESTON, CT	06883
FELIX, JOE	CONDUCTOR	2117 POWER ST	HERMOSA BEACH, CA	90254
FELIX, JUNIOR	BASEBALL	POST OFFICE BOX 2000	ANAHEIM, CA	92803
FELIX, MARIA	ACTRESS	SCHATZ, MELCHOR OCAMPO 309-403	MEXICO 7 DF	MEXICO
FELIX, NICK	BASEBALL	POST OFFICE BOX 3609	PORT CHARLOTTE, FL	33949
FELIX, OTTO	ACTOR	2147 N BEVERLY GLEN BLVD	LOS ANGELES, CA	90077
FELL, HERMAN	TV DIRECTOR	434 ROSCOE ST	CHICAGO, IL	60657
FELL, NORMAN	ACTOR	113 N SAN VICENTE BLVD #202	BEVERLY HILLS, CA	90211
FELLER, BOB	BASEBALL	POST OFFICE BOX 157	GATES MILLS, OH	44040
FELLER, SIDNEY H	CONDUCTOR	4216 VILLAGE 4, LEISURE VILLAGE	CAMARILLO, CA	93010
FELLINI, FEDERICO	WRITER-PRODUCER	141A VIA MARGUTTA 110	ROME	ITALY
FELLNER, ERIC	FILM PRODUCER	INITIAL FILMS & TV LTD		
		10-16 RATHBONE ST #12	LONDON W1P 1AH	ENGLAND
FELLOWS, EDITH	ACTRESS	2016 1/2 VISTA DEL MAR	LOS ANGELES, CA	90068
FELTHAM, KERRY	DIRECTOR-PRODUCER	16131 SUNSET BLVD #7	PACIFIC PALISADES, CA	90272
FELTHEIMER, JON	FILM EXECUTIVE	1440 S SEPULVEDA BLVD	LOS ANGELES, CA	90025
FELTMAN, JOEL	TV PRODUCER	411 BRONX RIVER RD	YONKERS, NY	10704
FELTON, NORMAN	TV WRITER-PRODUCER	22146 PACIFIC COAST HWY	MALIBU, CA	90265
FELTS, NARVEL	SINGER-SONGWRITER	2005 NARVEL FELTS AVE	MALDEN, MO	63863
FEMIA, JOHN	SINGER	1650 BROADWAY #714	NEW YORK, NY	10019
FENADY, ANDREW J	FILM WRITER-PRODUCER	126 N ROSSMERE AVE	LOS ANGELES, CA	90004
FENADY, GEORG	TV DIRECTOR	602 N CHEROKEE AVE	LOS ANGELES, CA	90004
FENDEL, DAN L	TV WRITER	1951 SELBY AVE #5	LOS ANGELES, CA	90025
FENDER, FREDDY	SINGER-SONGWRITER	SHD MGMT, 706 18TH AVE	NASHVILLE, TN	37203
FENDRICK, DAVID	ACTOR	360 CENTRAL PARK W #16-G	NEW YORK, NY	10025
FENEMORE, HILDA	ACTRESS	MAHONEY, SOUTH BANK HOUSE #105		
		BLACK PRINCE ROAD	LONDON SE1	ENGLAND
FENERTY, GILL	FOOTBALL	SAINTS, 1500 POYDRAS ST	NEW ORLEANS, LA	90112
FENHOLT, JEFF	SINGER-SONGWRITER	7201 ARCHIBALD AVE #494	ALTA LOMA, CA	91701
FENICHEL, JAY	ACTOR	4076 ALBRIGHT AVE	LOS ANGELES, CA	90066
FENMORE, TANYA	ACTRESS	3018 HUTTON PL	BEVERLY HILLS, CA	90210
FENN, SHERILYN	ACTRESS	7266 FRANKLIN AVE #310	LOS ANGELES, CA	90046
FENNEMAN, CLIFFORD	TV DIRECTOR	13007 DEBBY ST	VAN NUYS, CA	91401
FENNEMAN, GEORGE	TV HOST	13214 MOORPARK ST #206	SHERMAN OAKS, CA	91423
FENNER, DERRICK	FOOTBALL	SEAHAWKS, 11220 NE 53RD ST	KIRKLAND, WA	98033
FENSKE, MARK	ACTOR	4150 ARCH DR #2	STUDIO CITY, CA	91604
FENTON, GEORGE	COMPOSER	HEATH, PARAMOUNT HOUSE		
		162-170 WARDOUR ST	LONDON W1V 3AT	ENGLAND
FENTON, MIKE	CASTING DIRECTOR	100 UNIVERSAL CITY PLAZA		
		BUNGALOW #477	UNIVERSAL CITY, CA	91608
FENTON, NORMAN	TV DIRECTOR	WAVENDON, MANOR PARK, ILKLEY	YORKSHIRE	ENGLAND
FENTON, PAUL	HOCKEY	POST OFFICE BOX 1540, STA "M"	CALGARY, ALTA T2P 3BP	CANADA
FENTON, ROBERT L	PRODUCER	MCA/UNIVERSAL STUDIOS, INC		
		100 UNIVERSAL CITY PLAZA	UNIVERSAL CITY, CA	91608
FENTON, THOMAS T	NEWS CORRESPONDENT	CBS NEWS, 524 W 57TH ST	NEW YORK, NY	10019
FENYVES, DAVE	HOCKEY	FLYERS, SPECTRUM, PATTISON PL	PHILADELPHIA, PA	19148
FERA, GREG	TV DIRECTOR	7019 WOODSTONE PL	CANOGA PARK, CA	91307
FERACO, SCOTT	ACTOR	467 CENTRAL PARK W #6-F	NEW YORK, NY	10025
FERBER, BRUCE	TV WRITER	13526 MORRISON ST	SHERMAN OAKS, CA	91423
FERBER, MEL	DIRECTOR-PRODUCER	5141 ENCINO AVE	ENCINO, CA	91316
FERDIN, PAMELYN	ACTRESS	727 ESPLANADE #203	REDONDO BEACH, CA	90277
FERE, TAWNY	ACTRESS	9057 NEMO ST #A	WEST HOLLYWOOD, CA	90069
FERESTEN, SPIKE	TV WRITER	WM MORRIS, 1350 AVE OF AMERICAS	NEW YORK, NY	10019
FERGON, VICKI	GOLFER	2750 VOLUSA AVE #B	DAYTON BEACH, FL	32114
FERGUS, TOM	HOCKEY	MAPLE LEAFS, 60 CARLTON ST	TORONTO, ONT M5B 1L1	CANADA
FERGUSON, ALLYN	CONDUCTOR	12941 MOORPARK ST #4	STUDIO CITY, CA	91604
FERGUSON, BIANCA	ACTRESS	17401 ARMINTA ST	NORTHRIDGE, CA	91325
FERGUSON, BOB	FOOTBALL EXECUTIVE	BILLS, 1 BILLS DR	ORCHARD PARK, NJ	14127
FERGUSON, FRANCES	ACTRESS	6054 FRANKLIN AVE	LOS ANGELES, CA	90028
FERGUSON, GRAEME	FILM DIRECTOR	417 CARLTON ST	TORONTO, ONT M5A 2M3	CANADA
FERGUSON, IAN	TV DIRECTOR	WILLOW BROOK, KETTLESING		
		HARROWGATE	NO YORKSHIRE HG3 2LS	ENGLAND
FERGUSON, J DON	ACTOR	1 CHANTILLY CT	SAVANNAH, GA	31406
FERGUSON, JAY	ACTOR	4024 RADFORD AVE #5-104	STUDIO CITY, CA	91604
FERGUSON, JIM	BASEBALL	POLECATS, 608 N SLAPPEY BLVD	ALBANY, GA	31701
FERGUSON, JOE	BASEBALL-COACH	1000 ELYSIAN PARK DR	LOS ANGELES, CA	90012
FERGUSON, JOHNNY	SINGER-SONGWRITER	POST OFFICE BOX 24970	NASHVILLE, TN	37202
FERGUSON, LARRY	SCREENWRITER	8955 BEVERLY BLVD	WEST HOLLYWOOD, CA	90048
FERGUSON, MAYNARD	TRUMPETER	POST OFFICE BOX 716	OJAI, CA	93023
FERGUSON, MICHAEL	TV DIRECTOR-PRODUCER	FLICKERING IMAGES, LTD		
		8 THE CAUSEWAY, TEDDINGTON	MIDDLESEX TW11 OHE	ENGLAND
FERGUSON, NANCYE	ACTRESS	8383 WILSHIRE BLVD #649	BEVERLY HILLS, CA	90211
FERGUSON, ROGER	BASEBALL SCOUT	POST OFFICE BOX 2000	ANAHEIM, CA	92803
FERGUSON, THOMAS	AUDITOR	STATE CAPITOL BUILDING	COLUMBUS, OH	43266
FERGUSON, THOMAS	BASEBALL SCOUT	POST OFFICE BOX 7575	PHILADELPHIA, PA	19101
FERGUSON, WILLIAM	BASEBALL EXECUTIVE	SKYDOME, 300 BREMMER BL #3200	TORONTO, ONT M5V 3B3	CANADA

FERLENDA, GREG	BASEBALL COACH	POST OFFICE BOX 802	WATERTOWN, NY	13601
FERMAN, JAMES	FILM EXECUTIVE	3 SOHO SQ	LONDON W8 5DE	ENGLAND
FERMIN, FELIX	BASEBALL	INDIANS, CLEVELAND STADIUM	CLEVELAND, OH	44114
FERMIN, RAMON	BASEBALL	POST OFFICE BOX 882	MADISON, WI	53701
FERNAN, ANGELA	ANIMATOR	NBC-TV, 30 ROCKEFELLER PLAZA	NEW YORK, NY	10112
FERNANDEZ, ALEX	BASEBALL	333 W 35TH ST	CHICAGO, IL	60616
FERNANDEZ, CHICO	BASEBALL-INSTRUCTOR	1000 ELYSIAN PARK DR	LOS ANGELES, CA	90012
FERNANDEZ, DAN	BASEBALL	POST OFFICE BOX 3448	SHREVEPORT, LA	71133
FERNANDEZ, JOEY	BASEBALL	POST OFFICE BOX 36407	LOUISVILLE, KY	40233
FERNANDEZ, JOSE	BASEBALL	POST OFFICE BOX 36407	LOUISVILLE, KY	40233
FERNANDEZ, JUAN	ACTOR	200 N ROBERTSON BLVD #219	BEVERLY HILLS, CA	90211
FERNANDEZ, JULIO	BASEBALL	POST OFFICE BOX 30160	SAN BERNARDINO, CA	92413
FERNANDEZ, MERVYN	FOOTBALL	RAIDERS, 332 CENTER ST	EL SEGUNDO, CA	90245
FERNANDEZ, MIKE	BASEBALL	136 S SYCAMORE	ELIZABETHTON, TN	37643
FERNANDEZ, ROLANDO	BASEBALL	POST OFFICE BOX 4488	WINSTON-SALEM, NC	27115
FERNANDEZ, SID	BASEBALL	METS, 126TH ST & ROOSEVELT AVE	FLUSHING, NY	11368
FERNANDEZ, TONY	BASEBALL	POST OFFICE BOX 2000	SAN DIEGO, CA	92112
FERNBACH, ALEXANDER	DIRECTOR	UPPER SHAD RD	POUND RIDGE, NY	10576
FERRAGAMO, VINCE	FOOTBALL	6715 HORSESHOE RD	ORANGE, CA	92669
FERRANDINI, DEAN	DIRECTOR	POST OFFICE BOX 6201	BEVERLY HILLS, CA	90212
FERRANO, DOLORES MARIE	DIRECTOR	727 WESTBOURNE DR #307	LOS ANGELES, CA	90069
FERRANTE & TEICHER	PIANO DUO	210 W 100TH TERR #306	KANSAS CITY, KS	64114
FERRARE, ASHLEY	ACTRESS	7060 HOLLYWOOD BLVD #1216	HOLLYWOOD, CA	90028
FERRARE, CRISTINA	ACTRESS-MODEL-TV HOST	1280 STONE CANYON RD	LOS ANGELES, CA	90077
FERRARI, ANTONELLA	MODEL	VIA WASHINGTON 11	MILAN 20146	ITALY
FERRARI, DAVID	AUDITOR	STATE CAPITOL BUILDING	CHEYENNE, WY	82002
FERRARI, TINA	DANCER-WRESTLER	2901 S LAS VEGAS BLVD	LAS VEGAS, NV	89109
FERRARO, GERALDINE	POLITICIAN	22 DEEPDENE RD	FOREST HILLS, CA	11375
FERRARO, MIKE	BASEBALL-COACH	NY YANKEES, YANKEE STADIUM	BRONX, NY	10451
FERRARO, RALPH	COMPOSER	467 W RUSTIC RD	SANTA MONICA, CA	90402
FERRARO, RAY	HOCKEY	NASSAU VETS MEMORIAL COLISEUM	UNIONDALE, NY	11553
FERRARO, TONY G	CONDUCTOR	2122 GRIFFITH PARK BLVD	LOS ANGELES, CA	90039
FERRATTI, REBECCA	ACTRESS-MODEL	7461 BEVERLY BLVD #400	LOS ANGELES, CA	90036
FERREE, JIM	GOLFER	PGA SENIORS, 112 T P C BLVD	PONTE VEDRA BEACH, FL	32082
FERREIRA, FRED	BASEBALL SCOUT	REDS, 100 RIVERFRONT STADIUM	CINCINNATI, OH	45202
FERREIRA, TONY	BASEBALL	RED SOX, CHAIN O'LAKES PARK	WINTER HAVEN, FL	33880
FERRELL, CONCHATA	ACTRESS	1347 N SEWARD ST	LOS ANGELES, CA	90028
FERRELL, RICK	BASEBALL	2199 GOLFVIEW DR	TROY, MI	48084
FERRENTINO, HENRY	ACTOR	405 BROAD ST	BLOOMFIELD, NJ	07003
FERRER, MARIA	ACTRESS	1019 N ROXBURY DR	BEVERLY HILLS, CA	90210
FERRER, MEL	ACTOR	6590 CAMINO CARRETA	CARPINTERIA, CA	93013
FERRER, MIGUEL	ACTOR	4334 KESTER AVE	SHERMAN OAKS, CA	91403
FERRER, RAFAEL	ACTOR	1019 N ROXBURY DR	BEVERLY HILLS, CA	90210
FERRETTI, ROBERT A	FILM EDITOR	ACE, 1041 N FORMOSA AVE	WEST HOLLYWOOD, CA	90046
FERRETTI, SAM	BASEBALL	POST OFFICE BOX 230	HAGERSTOWN, MD	21740
FERRICK, TOM	BASEBALL-SCOUT	POST OFFICE BOX 419969	KANSAS CITY, MO	64141
FERRIGNO, CARLA	ACTRESS	621 17TH ST	SANTA MONICA, CA	90402
FERRIGNO, LOU	ACTOR-BODYBUILDIER	621 17TH ST	SANTA MONICA, CA	90402
FERRIN, RALPH	DIRECTOR	22410 HATTERAS ST	WOODLAND HILLS, CA	91367
FERRIN, RICHARD R	CONDUCTOR	220 S MICHIGAN AVE	CHICAGO, IL	60604
FERRIS, IRENA	ACTRESS	SEE - WARD, IRENA FERRIS		
FERRIS, JOHN	SCREENWRITER	9200 SUNSET BLVD #531	LOS ANGELES, CA	90069
FERRIS, ROBERT N	RADIO WRITER	222 5TH AVE	VENICE, CA	90291
FERRITER, THOMAS	ACTOR	234 E 14TH ST #4-E	NEW YORK, NY	10003
FERRO, TALYA	ACTRESS	ATKINS, 303 S CRESCENT HEIGHTS	LOS ANGELES, CA	90048
FERRONE, DAN	ACTOR	22605 MULHOLLAND DR	WOODLAND HILLS, CA	92364
FERRY, APRIL	COSTUME DESIGNER	1615 SHELL AVE	VENICE, CA	90291
FERRY, BRYAN	SINGER-SONGWRITER	321 FULHAM RD	LONDON SW10 9QL	ENGLAND
FERRY, DANNY	BASKETBALL	POST OFFICE BOX 5000	RICHFIELD, OH	44286
FERRY, MIKE	BASEBALL	POST OFFICE BOX 2001	CEDAR RAPIDS, IA	52406
FERTIK, BILL	CINEMATOGRAPHER	251 W 89TH ST	NEW YORK, NY	10024
FESTINGER, FRED	ACTOR	17830 SHERMAN WY #280	RESEDA, CA	91335
FETCHICK, MIKE	GOLFER	PGA SENIORS, 112 T P C BLVD	PONTE VEDRA BEACH, FL	32082
FETISOV, VIACHESLAV	HOCKEY	POST OFFICE BOX 504	EAST RUTHERFORD, NJ	07073
FETNER, MARK	TV DIRECTOR	50 BULAIRE RD	EAST ROCKWAY, NY	11518
FETTA, FRANK	CONDUCTOR	5843 EUCALYPTUS LN	LOS ANGELES, CA	90042
FETTERS, MIKE	BASEBALL	BREWERS, 201 S 46TH ST	MILWAUKEE, WI	53214
FETTY, DARRELL	ACTOR	4423 VANTAGE AVE	STUDIO CITY, CA	91604
FETTY, PAT	BASEBALL	POST OFFICE BOX 855	BELOIT, WI	53511
FEUER, CY	THEATER DIR-PROD	502 PARK AVE	NEW YORK, NY	10022
FEUER, DEBRA	ACTRESS	1778 OLD RANCH RD	LOS ANGELES, CA	90049
FEUER, JULIE	ACTRESS	108-02 72ND ST #4-A	FOREST HILLS, NY	11375
FEUILLERE, EDWIGE	ACTOR	19 RUE EUGENE MANUEL	PARIS 75016	FRANCE
FEVES, RICHARD	CONDUCTOR	3432 WONDERVIEW DR	LOS ANGELES, CA	90068
FFREY, PETER	ARTIST	141 2ND AVE #16	NEW YORK, NY	10003
FIALA, RICK	BASEBALL SCOUT	REDS, 100 RIVERFRONT STADIUM	CINCINNATI, OH	45202
FIANDER, LEWIS	ACTOR	CANN, 1 RIDGE ST	NORTH SYDNEY	AUSTRALIA
FICALORA, ANTHONY	DIRECTOR	28 E 29TH ST	NEW YORK, NY	10016
FICHMAN, MAL	BASEBALL MANAGER	POST OFFICE BOX 11363	RENO, NV	89510
FICHTNER, WILLIAM	ACTOR	59 CARMINE ST #4-F	NEW YORK, NY	10014
FICKAS, MARSHA	ACTRESS	5011 STONEY CREEK RD #326	CULVER CITY, CA	90230
FICKETT, MARY	ACTRESS	ABC-TV, "ALL MY CHILDREN"		
		320 W 66TH ST	NEW YORK, NY	10023
FIDANQUE, DEL	ACTOR	ALBANY POST RD	GARRISON, NY	10524
FIDLER, JIMMY	ACTOR	POST OFFICE BOX 4027	WESTLAKE VILLAGE, CA	91359

FIDRYCH, MARK	BASEBALL	260 WEST ST	NORTHBORO, MA 01532
FIEDEL, BRAD	SINGER-COMPOSER	11726 LAURELWOOD DR	STUDIO CITY, CA 91604
FIEDLER, E ROBERT	TV DIRECTOR	13959 LA MAIDA ST	SHERMAN OAKS, CA 91423
FIEDLER, JOHN	ACTOR	225 ADAMS ST #10-B	BROOKLYN, NY 11201
FIEDLER, PETER	DIRECTOR-PRODUCER	173 HERRICK RD	BOXFORD, MA 01921
FIEDLER, TOM	NEWS REPORTER	MIAMI HERALD, 1 HERALD PLAZA	MIAMI, FL 33101
FIEGEL, TODD	BASEBALL	POST OFFICE BOX 7845	COLUMBIA, SC 29202
FIELD, CAROLE H	ACTRESS	11030 AQUA VISTA ST	NORTH HOLLYWOOD, CA 91602
FIELD, CHELSEA	ACTRESS	10390 SANTA MONICA BLVD #300	LOS ANGELES, CA 90025
FIELD, FERN	WRITER-PRODUCER	13935 TAHITI WY #147	MARINA DEL REY, CA 90292
FIELD, FREDERICK "TED"	FILM PRODUCER	10900 WILSHIRE BLVD #1400	LOS ANGELES, CA 90024
FIELD, HOWARD O	WRITER	1516 1/2 SUNSET PLAZA DR	LOS ANGELES, CA 90069
FIELD, LEONARD S	TV-THEATER PRODUCER	1697 BROADWAY	NEW YORK, NY 10019
FIELD, PATRICIA	COSTUME DESIGNER	10 E 8TH ST	NEW YORK, NY 10003
FIELD, PAUL L	WRITER-PRODUCER	119 WHITE PLAINS RD	BRONXVILLE, NY 10708
FIELD, ROY	FILM DIRECTOR	REDROFF COTTAGE, TEMPLEWOOD LN	
		FARNHAM COMMON	BUCKS SL2 3HA ENGLAND
FIELD, SALLY	ACTRESS	825 S BARRINGTON AVE #204	LOS ANGELES, CA 90049
FIELD, SHIRLEY ANNE	ACTRESS	4260 ARCOLA AVE	TOLUCA LAKE, CA 91602
FIELD, SIDNEY	WRITER	2440 S BARRINGTON AVE #1	LOS ANGELES, CA 90064
FIELD, SYLVIA	ACTRESS	3263 VIA ALTA MIRA	FALLBROOK, CA 92028
FIELDER, CECIL	BASEBALL	TIGERS, TIGER STADIUM	DETROIT, MI 48216
FIELDER, JOHN	PRODUCER	1518 N DOHENY DR	LOS ANGELES, CA 90069
FIELDER, PAT P	TV WRITER	10040 REEVESBURY DR	BEVERLY HILLS, CA 90210
FIELDER, RICHARD	TV WRITER-PRODUCER	MTA, 9320 WILSHIRE BL, 3RD FL	BEVERLY HILLS, CA 90212
FIELDING, DOROTHY	ACTRESS	8271 MELROSE AVE #110	LOS ANGELES, CA 90046
FIELDS, BRANDON	SAXOPHONIST	9570 WILSHIRE BLVD #260	BEVERLY HILLS, CA 90212
FIELDS, BRUCE	BASEBALL-COACH	TIGERS, 89 WHARNCLIFFE RD N	LONDON, ONT N6H 2A7 CANADA
FIELDS, DEBBIE	COOKIE ENTREPRENEUR	POST OFFICE BOX 680370	PARK CITY, UT 84068
FIELDS, FREDDIE	FILM PRODUCER	1005 BENEDICT CANYON DR	BEVERLY HILLS, CA 90210
FIELDS, HOLLY	ACTRESS	3800 BARHAM BLVD #303	LOS ANGELES, CA 90068
FIELDS, JACK M, JR	U S CONGRESSMAN	108 CANNON HOUSE OFFICE BLDG	WASHINGTON, DC 20515
FIELDS, KIM	ACTRESS	2437 E WASHINGTON BLVD	PASADENA, CA 91104
FIELDS, MARJORIE	TALENT AGENT	165 W 46TH ST	NEW YORK, NY 10036
FIELDS, MRS	COOKIE ENTREPRENEUR	SEE - FIELDS, DEBBIE	
FIELDS, SIMON	TEENAGE MUTANT NINJA	151 S EL CAMINO DR	BEVERLY HILLS, CA 90212
FIELDS, TARA	ACTRESS	9052 LLOYD PL	LOS ANGELES, CA 90069
FIELDS, THOMAS G	DIRECTOR	POST OFFICE BOX 14371	ORLANDO, FL 32857
FIERMAN, DENNIS	FILM EDITOR	400 E 85TH ST #21-E	NEW YORK, NY 10028
FIERRO, JOHN	BASEBALL TRAINER	1060 W ADDISON ST	CHICAGO, IL 60613
FIERRO, PAUL	ACTOR	8618 APPIAN WY	LOS ANGELES, CA 90046
FIFE, RANDY	FILM DIRECTOR	5521 GREENVILLE AVE #104	DALLAS, TX 75206
FIFFICK, ED	FOOTBALL REFEREE	NFL, 410 PARK AVE	NEW YORK, NY 10022
FIFTH DIMENSION, THE	VOCAL GROUP	1900 AVE OF THE STARS #739	LOS ANGELES, CA 90067
FIGGA, MICHAEL	BASEBALL	POST OFFICE BOX 2148	WOODBRIDGE, VA 22193
FIGUEROA, ANGEL	BASEBALL SCOUT	POST OFFICE BOX 7000	PITTSBURGH, PA 15212
FIGUEROA, BIEN	BASEBALL	POST OFFICE BOX 36407	LOUISVILLE, KY 40233
FIGUEROA, EFRAIN	ACTOR	9744 WILSHIRE BLVD #308	BEVERLY HILLS, CA 90212
FIGUEROA, FERNANDO	BASEBALL	POST OFFICE BOX 4756	JACKSONVILLE, FL 32201
FIGUEROA, RUBEN	ACTOR	826 COLUMBUS AVE	NEW YORK, NY 10026
FIGUS, LISA	ACTRESS	9165 SUNSET BLVD #202	LOS ANGELES, CA 90069
FIKE, DAN	FOOTBALL	BROWNS, 80 1ST ST	BEREA, OH 44017
FILER, THOMAS	BASEBALL	9748 SUSAN RD	PHILADELPHIA, PA 19115
FILERMAN, MICHAEL	TV WRITER-PRODUCER	7533 WOODROW WILSON DR	LOS ANGELES, CA 90046
FILI, PATRICIA D	TV EXECUTIVE	HBO, 1100 6TH AVE	NEW YORK, NY 10036
FILICE, ERNEST	COMPOSER	5500-1-E PASEO DEL LAGO	LAGUNA HILLS, CA 92653
FILIPPO, JUDY	ARTIST	120 BROOK ST #1	BROOKLINE, MA 02146
FILKIN, DAVID	TV PRODUCER	29 BLOOMFIELD RD	
		KINGSTON UPON THAMES	SURREY ENGLAND
FILOSA, BRIAN	BASEBALL	POST OFFICE BOX 4218	SOUTH BEND, IN 46634
FILPI, CARMEN	ACTOR	6569 DE LONGPRE AVE	LOS ANGELES, CA 90028
FILSON, PETE	BASEBALL COACH	300 STADIUM WY	DAVENPORT, FL 33837
FIMPLE, DENNIS	ACTOR	200 N ROBERTSON BLVD #214	BEVERLY HILLS, CA 90211
FINCH, JON	ACTOR	NEASRADER, 135 NEW KINGS RD	LONDON SW6 4SL ENGLAND
FINCH, MARTINA	ACTRESS	9255 SUNSET BLVD #515	LOS ANGELES, CA 90069
FINCH, NIGE;	TV DIRECTOR	80 CULVERDEN RD	LONDON SW12 ENGLAND
FINCKEN, TOM	FOOTBALL REFEREE	NFL, 410 PARK AVE	NEW YORK, NY 10022
FINE, BILLY	FILM PRODUCER	9229 SUNSET BLVD #320	LOS ANGELES, CA 90069
FINE, DELIA	TV PRODUCER	WABC-TV, 7 LINCOLN SQ	NEW YORK, NY 10023
FINE, PAUL R	DIRECTOR	2300 CHAIN BRIDGE RD, NW	WASHINGTON, DC 20016
FINE, SYLVIA	TV WRITER	KAYE, 1103 SAN YSIDRO DR	BEVERLY HILLS, CA 90210
FINE YOUNG CANNIBALS, THE	ROCK & ROLL GROUP	1680 N VINE ST #1101	HOLLYWOOD, CA 90028
FINELL, ALYCE	TV WRITER-PRODUCER	301 E 79TH ST	NEW YORK, NY 10021
FINEMAN, JOSEPH	WRITER	9351 W OLYMPIC BLVD	BEVERLY HILLS, CA 90212
FINESTRA, CARMEN	WRITER	404 S COCHRAN AVE	LOS ANGELES, CA 90036
FINGERS, ROLLIE	BASEBALL	1268 HIDDEN MOUNTAIN DR	EL CAJON, CA 92020
FINIZZA, EILEEN	ACTRESS	130 S CARSON RD	BEVERLY HILLS, CA 90211
FINK, MARK	TV WRITER	13040 WOODBRIDGE ST	STUDIO CITY, CA 91604
FINK, MITCHELL	FILM CRITIC	FOX TV, 5746 SUNSET BLVD	HOLLYWOOD, CA 90028
FINKEL, FYVUSH	ACTOR	155 E 50TH ST	NEW YORK, NY 10022
FINKEL, GEORGE	TV DIRECTOR-PRODUCER	110 BRENTWOOD DR	MOUNT LAUREL, NJ 08054
FINKEL, HOWARD "THE FINK"	RING ANNOUCER	POST OFFICE BOX 3859	STAMFORD, CT 06905
FINKEL, ROBERT	WRITER-PRODUCER	12560 THE VISTA	LOS ANGELES, CA 90049
FINKELMAN, WAYNE A	COSTUME DESIGNER	13949 VENTURA BLVD #309	SHERMAN OAKS, CA 91423
FINKELSTEIN, JULIAN	TV DIRECTOR	54 BLISS AVE	TENAFLY, NJ 07670

FINKELSTEIN, WILLIAM M	TV WRITER	UTA, 9560 WILSHIRE BLVD, 5TH FL	BEVERLY HILLS, CA	90212
FINKLEMAN, KENNETH C	WRITER-PRODUCER	151 S EL CAMINO DR	BEVERLY HILLS, CA	90212
FINKS, JIM	FOOTBALL EXECUTIVE	SAINTS, 1500 POYDRAS ST	NEW ORLEANS, LA	90112
FINLAY, FRANK	ACTOR	AL PARKER, 55 PARK LN	LONDON W1Y 3DD	ENGLAND
FINLAYSON, ALEX	ACTOR	6605 HOLLYWOOD BLVD #220	HOLLYWOOD, CA	90028
FINLAYSON, KATE	ACTRESS	2029 CENTURY PARK E #600	LOS ANGELES, CA	90067
FINLEY, CHARLES	BASEBALL EXECUTIVE	151 N MICHIGAN AVE	CHICAGO, IL	60605
FINLEY, CHUCK	BASEBALL	POST OFFICE BOX 2000	ANAHEIM, CA	92803
FINLEY, KENNETH Q	WRITER-PRODUCER	908 E HARVARD RD	BURBANK, CA	91501
FINLEY, STEVE	BASEBALL	POST OFFICE BOX 288	HOUSTON, TX	77001
FINLEY, WILLIAM FRANKLYN	SCREENWRITER	STONE MANNERS, 9113 SUNSET BLVD	LOS ANGELES, CA	90069
FINN, HERBERT	TV WRITER	4058 CAMELLIA AVE	STUDIO CITY, CA	91604
FINN, JOHN	BASEBALL	POST OFFICE DRAWER 4797	EL PASO, TX	79914
FINN, MARILYN	BASEBALL EXECUTIVE	POST OFFICE BOX 1088	ST CATH, ONT L2R 3BO	CANADA
FINN, STEVEN	HOCKEY	NORDIQUES, 2205 AVE DU COLISEE	QUEBEC, QUE G1L 4W7	CANADA
FINN, TERRY	ACTRESS	8665 WILSHIRE BLVD #208	BEVERLY HILLS, CA	90211
FINNANE, DANIEL F	BASKETBALL EXECUTIVE	GOLDEN STATE WARRIORS		
		OAKLAND COLISEUM ARENA		
		NIMITZ FWY & HEGENBERGER RD	OAKLAND, CA	94621
FINNEGAN, J P	ACTOR	9639 VIA RIMINI	BURBANK, CA	91504
FINNEGAN, JACK	ACTOR	435 E 85TH ST	NEW YORK, NY	10028
FINNEGAN, PATRICIA	TV PRODUCER	4225 COLDWATER CANYON DR	STUDIO CITY, CA	91604
FINNEGAN, WILLIAM P	FILM WRITER-PRODUCER	4225 COLDWATER CANYON DR	STUDIO CITY, CA	91604
FINNEGAN, WILLIAM R	FILM WRITER-PRODUCER	3074 FRANKLIN CANYON DR	BEVERLY HILLS, CA	90210
FINNELL, MICHAEL	FILM PRODUCER	4000 WARNER BLVD, BLDG #103-1	BURBANK, CA	91522
FINNERMAN, GERALD	CINEMATOGRAPHER	3211 OAKDELL LN	STUDIO CITY, CA	91604
FINNEY, ALBERT	ACTOR	ICM, 388-396 OXFORD ST	LONDON W1	ENGLAND
FINNEY, JOAN	GOVERNOR	STATE CAPITOL BUILDING	TOPEKA, KS	66617
FINNEY, SARA V	TV WRITER	1233 1/2 S CITRUS AVE	LOS ANGELES, CA	90019
FINNVOLD, GAR	BASEBALL	POST OFFICE BOX 1718	NEW BRITAIN, CT	06050
FINSTERWALD, DOW	GOLFER	1 LAKE CIR	COLORADO SPRINGS, CO	80906
FINUCANE, TOM	ACTOR	11175 HUSTON ST #29	NORTH HOLLYWOOD, CA	91601
FIONA	SINGER-SONGWRITER	10100 SANTA MONICA BLVD #1600	LOS ANGELES, CA	90067
FIONDELLA, JAY	WRITER	1657 OCEAN AVE #3	SANTA MONICA, CA	90401
FIORE, ALBERT	DIRECTOR	128 MALLORY AVE	JERSEY CITY, NJ	07304
FIORE, FRANK	CONDUCTOR	243 E WILBUR RD #320	THOUSAND OAKS, CA	91360
FIORE, PETER M	ARTIST	10-11 162ND ST #7-D	WHITESTONE, NY	11357
FIORE, ROBERT	WRITER-PRODUCER	141 GARDEN CITY AVE	POINT LOOKOUT, NY	11569
FIORENTINO, JACQUES	PRODUCER	933 N CROFT AVE	LOS ANGELES, CA	90069
FIORENTINO, LINDA	ACTRESS	9200 SUNSET BLVD #PH-25	LOS ANGELES, CA	90069
FIORENTINO, TONY	BASKETBALL COACH	MIAMI HEAT, THE MIAMI ARENA	MIAMI, FL	33136
FIORI, ED	GOLFER	POST OFFICE BOX 109601	PALM BCH GARDENS, FL	33418
FIRBANK, ANN	ACTRESS	HEATH, PARAMOUNT HOUSE		
		162-170 WARDOUR ST	LONDON W1V 3AT	ENGLAND
FIREFALL	ROCK & ROLL GROUP	2980 BEVERLY GLEN CIR #302	LOS ANGELES, CA	90077
FIREHOUSE	C & W GROUP	POST OFFICE BOX O	EXCELSIOR, MN	55331
FIREMAN, MARVIN	DIRECTOR	DGA, 110 W 57TH ST	NEW YORK, NY	10019
FIREOVID, STEVE	BASEBALL	POST OFFICE BOX 75089	OKLAHOMA CITY, OK	73147
FIRESTEIN, LES	TV WRITER	CAA, 9830 WILSHIRE BLVD	BEVERLY HILLS, CA	90212
FIRESTONE, EDDIE	ACTOR	303 S CRESCENT HEIGHTS	LOS ANGELES, CA	90048
FIRESTONE, ROY	SPORTSCASTER	ESPN PLAZA, 935 MIDDLEST	BRISTOL, CT	06010
FIRSICH, STEVE	BASEBALL	POST OFFICE BOX 418	SAINT CHARLES, IL	60174
FIRST LIGHT	ROCK & ROLL GROUP	GREG, 1288 E 168TH ST	CLEVELAND, OH	44110
FIRSTENBERG, SAM	FILM DIRECTOR	467 N ALMONT DR	BEVERLY HILLS, CA	90211
FIRTH, COLIN	ACTOR	BELFRAGE, 68 SAINT JAMES'S ST	LONDON SW1A 1LE	ENGLAND
FIRTH, PETER	ACTOR	MARKHAM AND FROGGATT, LTD		
		JULIAN HOUSE, 4 WINDMILL ST	LONDON W1P 1HF	ENGLAND
FISCHER, BILL	BASEBALL-COACH	FENWAY PARK, 4 YAWKEY WY	BOSTON, MA	02215
FISCHER, BOBBY	CHEST	186 RT 9-W	NEW WINDSOR, NY	12550
FISCHER, BRAD	BASEBALL-INSTRUCTOR	ATHLETICS'S, OAKLAND COLISEUM	OAKLAND, CA	94621
FISCHER, BRENT	COMPOSER	3832 LAUREL CANYON BLVD	STUDIO CITY, CA	91604
FISCHER, BRUCE M	ACTOR	6000 COCOS DR #4	LOS ANGELES, CA	90068
FISCHER, CARL	TV DIRECTOR	121 E 83RD ST	NEW YORK, NY	10028
FISCHER, CLARE	COMPOSER-CONDUCTOR	3832 LAUREL CANYON BLVD	STUDIO CITY, CA	91604
FISCHER, FREDERIC	TV DIRECTOR-PRODUCER	28 VERANDAH PL	BROOKLYN, NY	11201
FISCHER, JEFF	BASEBALL	124 GREGORY PL	WEST PALM BEACH, FL	33405
FISCHER, PETER S	TV WRITER-PRODUCER	MCA/UNIVERSAL STUDIOS, INC		
		100 UNIVERSAL CITY PLAZA	UNIVERSAL CITY, CA	91608
FISCHER, STEWART R	COMPOSER-CONDUCTOR	19112 FRIENDLY VALLEY PARKWAY	NEWHALL, CA	91321
FISCHER, TOM	BASEBALL	POST OFFICE BOX 2365	PAWTUCKET, RI	02861
FISCHER, WILLIAM P	TV PRODUCER	1977 N DRACENA DR	LOS ANGELES, CA	90027
FISCHMANN, RUEL	TV WRITER	4637 MAYTIME LN	CULVER CITY, CA	90230
FISCHOFF, GEORGE	COMPOSER-PIANIST	MM GROUP, 48 W 38TH ST	NEW YORK, NY	10018
FISCHOFF, STUART P	WRITER	5911 CANYON HEIGHTS LN	LOS ANGELES, CA	90068
FISH, HAMILTON, JR	U S CONGRESSMAN	70 GLENEIDA AVE	CARMEL, NY	10512
FISHEL, JOHN	BASEBALL	2957 SHAMROCK AVE	BREA, CA	92621
FISHER, ALBERT C	DIRECTOR-PRODUCER	333 W 86TH ST #PH-2006	NEW YORK, NY	10024
FISHER, AMEEL J	TV WRITER	6 STUYVESANT OVAL	NEW YORK, NY	10009
FISHER, ARTHUR	WRI-DIR-PROD	324 N CROFT AVE	BEVERLY HILLS, CA	90048
FISHER, BILL	BASEBALL UMPIRE	POST OFFICE BOX 716	PLAINVILLE, CT	06062
FISHER, BRIAN	BASEBALL	2850 W 20TH AVE	DENVER, CO	80211
FISHER, CARRIE	ACTRESS-AUTHORESS	KAUFMAN, 1201 ALTA LOMA RD	WEST HOLLYWOOD, CA	90069
FISHER, CINDY	ACTRESS	3641 E CHEVY CHASE DR	GLENDALE, CA	91206
FISHER, CRAIG	FILM-TV EXECUTIVE	233 E 52ND ST	NEW YORK, NY	10022
FISHER, EDDIE	SINGER-ACTOR	1000 NORTH POINT ST #1802	SAN FRANCISCO, CA	94109

Name	Occupation	Address	City	Zip/Country
FISHER, GAIL	ACTRESS	1150 S HAYWORTH AVE	LOS ANGELES, CA	90035
FISHER, GAIL LESLIE	SCREENWRITER	CAA, 9830 WILSHIRE BLVD	BEVERLY HILLS, CA	90212
FISHER, GERRY	CINEMATOGRAPHER	PEBBLE COTTAGE, RIVER BANK		
		HURSTFIELD RD, WEST MOLESEY	SURREY	ENGLAND
FISHER, JEFF	FOOTBALL COACH	EAGLES, BROAD ST & PATTISON AVE	PHILADELPHIA, PA	19148
FISHER, JOELY	ACTRESS	STEVENS, 9551 CHEROKEE LN	BEVERLY HILLS, CA	90210
FISHER, JOHN C	TV PRODUCER	227 INWOOD AVE	UPPER MONTCLAIR, NJ	07043
FISHER, JULES	THEATER PRODUCER	126 5TH AVE	NEW YORK, NY	10011
FISHER, KYLE	BASEBALL EXECUTIVE	POST OFFICE BOX 3746, HILL STA	AUGUSTA, GA	30904
FISHER, LEE	ATTORNEY GENERAL	STATE CAPITOL BUILDING	COLUMBUS, OH	43266
FISHER, LEE	COMM OF REVENUE	POST OFFICE BOX A	JUNEAU, AK	99811
FISHER, LINDA	COSTUME DESIGNER	139 W 82ND ST	NEW YORK, NY	10024
FISHER, LOLA	ACTRESS	1768 S SHERBOURNE DR	LOS ANGELES, CA	90035
FISHER, M F K	WRITER	13935 SONOMA HWY	GLEN ELLEN, CA	95442
FISHER, ROBERT J	DIRECTOR	4283 COLDWATER CANYON AVE #2	STUDIO CITY, CA	91604
FISHER, ROBERT S	ACTOR	1426 N HOOVER ST #4	LOS ANGELES, CA	90027
FISHER, RUSS	COMEDIAN	CLOUSHER, 193 KONHAUS RD	MECHANICSBURG, PA	17055
FISHER, SANFORD H	TV EXECUTIVE	CORPORATION FOR ENTERTAINMENT		
		AND LEARNING		
		515 MADISON AVE	NEW YORK, NY	10022
FISHER, TERRY LOUISE	TV WRITER-PRODUCER	FISHER ENT, 500 S BUENA VISTA	BURBANK, CA	91521
FISHER, TODD	ACTOR	9555 OAK PASS RD	BEVERLY HILLS, CA	90210
FISHER, TRICIA LEIGH	ACTRESS	11712 MOORPARK ST #204	STUDIO CITY, CA	91604
FISHER-LUMPKIN, JIMMIE LOU	TREASURER	STATE CAPITOL BUILDING	LITTLE ROCK, AR	72201
FISHKO, ROBERT S	THEATER PRODUCER	1501 BROADWAY	NEW YORK, NY	10036
FISHMAN, JANET	DIRECTOR-PRODUCER	305 E 40TH ST	NEW YORK, NY	10016
FISHMAN, NEIL	ACTOR-SINGER	355 W 41ST ST #5-FE	NEW YORK, NY	10036
FISHMAN, ROBERT A	TV DIRECTOR	101 GROVE POINT RD	WESTPORT, CT	06880
FISK, CARLTON	BASEBALL	333 W 35TH ST	CHICAGO, IL	60616
FISK, JACK	FILM DIRECTOR	BEAU VAL FARM, BOX #7	COBHAM, VA	22929
FISKIN, JEFFREY A	SCREENWRITER	6107 TEMPLE HILL DR	LOS ANGELES, CA	90068
FITCH, BILL	BASKETBALL COACH	N J NETS, MEADOWLANDS ARENA	EAST RUTHERFORD, NJ	07073
FITSGERALD, NEIL	ACTOR	32 GRAMERCY PARK S	NEW YORK, NY	10003
FITTS, RICK	ACTOR	2054 1/2 RODNEY DR	LOS ANGELES, CA	90027
FITZ, ALEXANDER	ACTOR	26 1/2 18TH AVE	VENICE, CA	90291
FITZ PATRICK, JAMES	FOOTBALL	RAIDERS, 332 CENTER ST	EL SEGUNDO, CA	90245
FITZALAN, MARSHA	ACTRESS	PETERS, FRASER & DUNLOP, LTD		
		5TH FLOOR, THE CHAMBERS		
		CHELSEA HARBOUR, LOT RD	LONDON SW10 OXF	ENGLAND
FITZER, DOUG	BASEBALL	POST OFFICE BOX 9194	HAMPTON, VA	23670
FITZER, JOHN	COMPOSER	3156 KALLIN AVE	LONG BEACH, CA	90808
FITZGERALD, ANNE	CARTOONIST	KING FEATURES, 216 E 45TH ST	NEW YORK, NY	10017
FITZGERALD, DAN L	DIRECTOR	1410 1/2 HAVENHURST DR	HOLLYWOOD, CA	90046
FITZGERALD, DAVE	BASEBALL (EL PASO)	POST OFFICE DRAWER 4797	EL PASO, TX	79914
FITZGERALD, ELLA	SINGER	908 WHITTIER DR	BEVERLY HILLS, CA	90210
FITZGERALD, FERN	ACTRESS	8485 MELROSE PL #E	LOS ANGELES, CA	90069
FITZGERALD, GERALDINE	ACTRESS	50 E 79TH ST	NEW YORK, NY	10019
FITZGERALD, JAMES F	BASKETBALL EXECUTIVE	GOLDEN STATE WARRIORS		
		OAKLAND COLISEUM ARENA		
		NIMITZ FWY & HEGENBERGER RD	OAKLAND, CA	94621
FITZGERALD, JEFF	FOOTBALL COACH	BUCCANEERS, 1 BUCCANEER PL	TAMPA, FL	33607
FITZGERALD, MICHAEL	PRODUCER	MCA/UNIVERSAL STUDIOS, INC		
		100 UNIVERSAL CITY PLAZA	UNIVERSAL CITY, CA	91608
FITZGERALD, MIKE	BASEBALL	POST OFFICE BOX 2000	ANAHEIM, CA	92803
FITZGERALD, NEIL	ACTOR	32 GRAMERCY PARK S	NEW YORK, NY	10003
FITZGERALD, RAYMOND	DIRECTOR	546 E 87TH ST	NEW YORK, NY	10028
FITZGERALD, TOM	HOCKEY	NASSAU VETS MEMORIAL COLISEUM	UNIONDALE, NY	11553
FITZGERALD, WAYNE R	DIRECTOR	1878 LAUREL CANYON BLVD	LOS ANGELES, CA	90046
FITZGERLAD, MICHAEL L	TREASURER	STATE CAPITOL BUILDING	DES MOINES, IA	50319
FITZPATRICK, MICHAEL	ACTOR	MANSON, 288 MUNSTER RD	LONDON SW6 6BQ	ENGLAND
FITZPATRICK, ROB	BASEBALL	POST OFFICE BOX 3566	WEST PALM BEACH, FL	33402
FITZSIMMONS, COTTON	BASKETBALL COACH	SUNS, 2910 N CENTRAL AVE	PHOENIX, AZ	85012
FITZSIMMONS, TOM	ACTOR	247 S BEVERLY DR #102	BEVERLY HILLS, CA	90210
FITZSTEPHENS, JOHN J	FILM DIRECTOR-EDITOR	235 W 76TH ST #10-C	NEW YORK, NY	10023
FITZWATER, MARLIN	PRESS SECRETARY	2001 SWAN TERR	ALEXANDRIA, VA	22307
FIVE PLATTERS, THE	VOCAL GROUP	POST OFFICE BOX 39	LAS VEGAS, NV	89101
FIVE SATINS, THE	VOCAL GROUP	MARTINELLI MGMT, 888 8TH AVE	NEW YORK, NY	10019
FIVE STAR	VOCAL GROUP	POST OFFICE BOX 29, ROMFORD	ESSEX RM7 OST	ENGLAND
FIVESON, ROBERT S	WRITER	2365 TEVOIT ST	LOS ANGELES, CA	90039
FIXX, THE	ROCK & ROLL GROUP	POST OFFICE BOX 4XN	LONDON W1A 4XN	ENGLAND
FIZDALE, JONATHAN	WRITER	14230 MULHOLLAND DR	LOS ANGELES, CA	90077
FIZZINOGLIA, DONALD	WRI-DIR-PROD	809 3RD ST	EAST NORTHPORT, NY	11731
FJELL, JUDY	SINGER-GUITARIST	POST OFFICE BOX 56	CORVALLIS, OR	97339
FLACK, ROBERTA	SINGER-SONGWRITER	THE DAKOTA, 1 W 72ND ST	NEW YORK, NY	10023
FLAGG, DON	FILM DIRECTOR	11847 RIVERSIDE DR	NORTH HOLLYWOOD, CA	91607
FLAGG, FANNIE	ACTRESS	1520 WILLINA LN	MONTECITO, CA	93108
FLAHERTY, EDWARD	DIRECTOR	9594 NEWFAME CIR	FOUNTAIN VALLEY, CA	92708
FLAHERTY, JOE	ACT-WRI-PROD	SCTV, 110 LOMBARD ST	TORONTO, ONT M5C 1M3	CANADA
FLAHERTY, JOHN	BASEBALL	POST OFFICE BOX 2365	PAWTUCKET, RI	02861
FLAHERTY, MAUREEN	ACTRESS	5455 WILSHIRE BLVD #1406	LOS ANGELES, CA	90036
FLAHERTY, PETER	COSTUME DESIGNER	13949 VENTURA BLVD #309	SHERMAN OAKS, CA	91423
FLAHERTY, THOMAS	COMPOSER	5151 EL RIO AVE	LOS ANGELES, CA	90041
FLAIR, RIC	WRESTLER	POST OFFICE BOX 3859	STAMFORD, CT	06905
FLAKE, FLOYD	U S CONGRESSMAN	114-60 MERRICK BLVD	JAMAICA, NY	11434
FLAMBEAU, PERE ANTOINE	COMEDIAN	333 SAINT CHARLES AVE #500	NEW ORLEANS, LA	70130

FLAMIN GROOVIES, THE	ROCK & ROLL GROUP	POST OFFICE BOX 287	NEWPORT BEACH, NSW 210.. AUSTRALIA
FLAMINGOS, THE	VOCAL GROUP	2375 E TROPICANA AVE #304	LAS VEGAS, NV 89119
FLANAGAN, DAN	BASEBALL	POST OFFICE BOX 21727	SAN FRANCISCO, CA 95151
FLANAGAN, FIONNULA	ACTRESS	10000 SANTA MONICA BLVD #305	LOS ANGELES, CA 90067
FLANAGAN, JUDITH	ACTRESS	301 N CANON DR #305	BEVERLY HILLS, CA 90210
FLANAGAN, MIKE	BASEBALL	ORIOLE PARK, 333 W CAMDEN ST	BALTIMORE, MD 21201
FLANDERS, ED	ACTOR	POST OFFICE BOX 210	WILLOW CREEK, CA 95573
FLANNELLY, TIMOTHY	BASEBALL	POST OFFICE BOX 22093	GREENSBORO, NC 27420
FLANNERY, JOHN	FOOTBALL	OILERS, 6910 FANNIN ST	HOUSTON, TX 77070
FLANNERY, SUSAN	ACTRESS	480 PIMIENTO LN	SANTA BARBARA, CA 93108
FLANNERY, THOMAS	CARTOONIST	911 DARTMOUTH GLEN WY	BALTIMORE, MD 21212
FLANNERY, TIM	BASEBALL	KFMB-TV, 7677 ENGINEER RD	SAN DIEGO, CA 92111
FLANNIGAN, MAUREEN	ACTRESS	11100 HORTENSE ST	NORTH HOLLYWOOD, CA 91602
FLASH CADILLAC	ROCK & ROLL GROUP	POST OFFICE BOX 6588	SAN ANTONIO, TX 78209
FLATLEY, PATRICK	HOCKEY	NASSAU VETS MEMORIAL COLISEUM	UNIONDALE, NY 11553
FLATLEY, WILLIAM	ACTOR	10845 LINDBROOK DR #3	LOS ANGELES, CA 90024
FLATT, ERNEST	DIRECTOR-CHOREORAPHER	POST OFFICE BOX 40	VALLEY CENTER, CA 92082
FLATT, LESTER	BANJOIST	POST OFFICE BOX 647	HENDERSONVILLE, TN 37215
FLAUM, MARSHALL	WRITER-PRODUCER	301 S RODEO DR	BEVERLY HILLS, CA 90212
FLAVIN, JENNIFER	CELEBRITY	7271 ANGELA AVE	CANOGA PARK, CA 91307
FLAX, PHYLLIS	ACTRESS	8831 SUNSET BLVD #402	LOS ANGELES, CA 90069
FLECK, BELA	MUSICIAN	10100 SANTA MONICA BLVD #1600	LOS ANGELES, CA 90067
FLECK, JACK	GOLFER	PGA SENIORS, 112 T P C BLVD	PONTE VEDRA BEACH, FL 32082
FLECK, MICHAEL	ACTOR	1617 POINT VIEW ST	LOS ANGELES, CA 90035
FLEER, ALICIA	ACTRESS	5035 CATALON AVE	WOODLAND HILLS, CA 91364
FLEER, HARRY	ACTOR	5035 CATALON AVE	WOODLAND HILLS, CA 91364
FLEET, JOE	BASEBALL	POST OFFICE BOX 1886	COLUMBUS, GA 31902
FLEETWOOD, MICK	DRUMMER-SONGWRITER	29169 W HEATHERCLIFF RD #574	MALIBU, CA 90265
FLEETWOOD MAC	ROCK & ROLL GROUP	2899 AGOURA RD #562	WESTLAKE, CA 91361
FLEETWOODS, THE	VOCAL GROUP	POST OFFICE BOX 262	CARTERET, NJ 07008
FLEISCHER, CHARLES	ACTOR	749 N CRESCENT HEIGHTS BLVD	LOS ANGELES, CA 90048
FLEISCHER, RICHARD	FILM DIRECTOR	169 S ROCKINGHAM AVE	LOS ANGELES, CA 90049
FLEISCHMAN, ALBERT S	TV WRITER	305 10TH ST	SANTA MONICA, CA 90402
FLEISCHMAN, STEPHEN	WRITER-PRODUCER	33 W 93RD ST	NEW YORK, NY 10025
FLEISCHNER, MORTON	NEWS WRITER	WABC-TV, 7 LINCOLN SQ	NEW YORK, NY 10023
FLEISHER, BRUCE	GOLFER	POST OFFICE BOX 109601	PALM BCH GARDENS, FL 33418
FLEISHER, SUSAN	TV DIRECTOR-PRODUCER	144 WILLOW ST #1-F	BROOKLYN HEIGHTS, NY 11201
FLEITA, ONERI	BASEBALL COACH	POST OFFICE BOX 3169	FREDERICK, MD 21701
FLEMING, B B	SINGER	POST OFFICE BOX 11321	MIAMI, FL 33101
FLEMING, DAVE	BASEBALL	POST OFFICE BOX 4100	SEATTLE, WA 98104
FLEMING, JIM	BASEBALL COACH-SCOUT	6850 LAWRENCE RD	LANTANA, FL 33462
FLEMING, PEGGY	SKATER	16387 AZTEC RIDGE	LOS GATOS, CA 95030
FLEMING, RHONDA	ACTRESS	MANN, 2129 CENTURY WOODS WY	LOS ANGELES, CA 90067
FLEMING, ROBERT	WRITER-PRODUCER	ARGO PRODUCTIONS, LTD	
		5 S VILLAS, CAMDEN SQ	LONDON NW1 9BS ENGLAND
FLEMING, STEVE	BASEBALL-SCOUT	POST OFFICE BOX 7000	PITTSBURGH, PA 15212
FLEMING, THOMAS	WRITER	315 E 72ND ST	NEW YORK, NY 10021
FLEMING, VERN	BASKETBALL	PACERS, 300 E MARKET ST	INDIANAPOLIS, IN 46204
FLEMYNG, GORDON	TV DIRECTOR	ACTT, 111 WARDOUR ST	LONDON W1 ENGLAND
FLEMYNG, ROBERT	ACTOR	4 NETHERBOURNE RD	LONDON SW4 ENGLAND
FLENER, HUCK	BASEBALL	POST OFFICE BOX 957	DUNEDIN, FL 34697
FLENNIKEN, SHARY	CARTOONIST-WRITER	555 W 57TH ST #1230	NEW YORK, NY 10019
FLESER, APRIL	ACTRESS	24235 BURBANK BLVD	WOODLAND HILLS, CA 91367
FLESHER, VIVIENNE	ARTIST	23 E 10TH ST #1204	NEW YORK, NY 10003
FLETCHER, BRAMWELL	ACTOR	ROUTE #1	MARLBOROUGH, NH 03455
FLETCHER, DARRIN	BASEBALL	EXPOS, 4545 DE COUBERTIN AVE	MONTREAL, QUE H1V 3P2 CANADA
FLETCHER, DENNIS	BASEBALL	POST OFFICE BOX 12557	ST PETERSBURG, FL 33733
FLETCHER, DEXTER	ACTOR	1 KINGSWAY HOUSE, ALBION RD	LONDON N16 ENGLAND
FLETCHER, HERB	TV EXECUTIVE	8701 WILSHIRE BLVD	BEVERLY HILLS, CA 90211
FLETCHER, JACK	ACTOR	569 N ROSSMORE AVE #609	LOS ANGELES, CA 90004
FLETCHER, LESTER C	ACTOR	9028 LLOYD PL	LOS ANGELES, CA 90069
FLETCHER, LOUISE	ACTRESS	10390 SANTA MONICA BLVD #300	LOS ANGELES, CA 90025
FLETCHER, PATRICIA	TV PRODUCER	AMERICAN TV PRODS, 521 5TH AVE	NEW YORK, NY 10017
FLETCHER, ROBERT	COSTUME DESIGNER	13949 VENTURA BLVD #309	SHERMAN OAKS, CA 91423
FLETCHER, SCOTT	BASEBALL	BREWERS, 201 S 46TH ST	MILWAUKEE, WI 53214
FLETCHER, SIMON	FOOTBALL	BRONCOS, 13655 BRONCOS PKWY	ENGLEWOOD, CO 80112
FLETT, ANNE	TV PRODUCER	R/W/G, 8428 MELROSE PL #C	LOS ANGELES, CA 90069
FLEURY, THRO	HOCKEY	POST OFFICE BOX 1540, STA "M"	CALGARY, ALTA T2P 3BP CANADA
FLICK, BOB	TV WRITER	ENTERTAINMENT TONIGHT	
		PARAMOUNT TELEVISION	
		5555 MELROSE AVE	LOS ANGELES, CA 90038
FLICK, VICTOR H	COMPOSER-CONDUCTOR	1385 N GILBERT ST #145	FULLERTON, CA 92633
FLICKER, TED	TV WRITER-PRODUCER	FREEDMAN, KINZELBERG & BRODER	
		2121 AVE OF THE STARS	LOS ANGELES, CA 90067
FLICKINGER, CHARLES E	ACTOR	435 W WILSON AVE	GLENDALE, CA 91203
FLINT, CAROL	TV PRODUCER	CAA, 9830 WILSHIRE BLVD	BEVERLY HILLS, CA 90212
FLINT, ROGER	DIRECTOR	1015 N ORLANDO AVE	LOS ANGELES, CA 90069
FLIPPIN, LUCY LEE	ACTRESS	1753 CANFIELD AVE	LOS ANGELES, CA 90035
FLIRTS, THE	ROCK & ROLL GROUP	1776 BROADWAY #1801	NEW YORK, NY 10019
FLOCK, JEFF	TV WRITER-PRODUCER	CHICAGO MERCHANDISE MART #409	CHICAGO, IL 60634
FLOCK, JOHN	FILM EXECUTIVE	3619 MOTOR AVE #300	LOS ANGELES, CA 90034
FLOCK OF SEAGULLS	ROCK & ROLL GROUP	POST OFFICE BOX 145, HARROW	MIDDLESEX HA2 ORT ENGLAND
FLON, SUZANNE	ACTRESS	NORA STERN	VANEUA 75007 FRANCE
FLOOD, ANN	ACTRESS	15 E 91ST ST	NEW YORK, NY 10128
FLOOD, CURT	BASEBALL	4139 CLOVERDALE AVE	LOS ANGELES, CA 90008

FLORA, JANET	MAKE-UP ARTIST	170 2ND AVE	NEW YORK, NY	10003
FLORA, KEVIN	BASEBALL	10233 96TH AVE	EDMONTON, ALB TK5 0A5	CANADA
FLOREA, JOHN	DIRECTOR-PRODUCER	11730 MOORPARK ST #B	STUDIO CITY, CA	91604
FLOREN, MYRON	COMPOSER	26 GEORGEFF RD	RCHO PALOS VERDES, CA	90274
FLORENCE, ANTHONY	FOOTBALL	BROWNS, 80 1ST ST	BEREA, OH	44017
FLORENCE, DONALD	BASEBALL	POST OFFICE BOX 1718	NEW BRITAIN, CT	06050
FLORENCE, JOSEPH	ACTOR	112 S AVE 66 #2	LOS ANGELES, CA	90042
FLORES, JESS	BASEBALL-SCOUT	333 W 35TH ST	CHICAGO, IL	60616
FLORES, JESSE	BASEBALL-SCOUT	POST OFFICE BOX 7000	PITTSBURGH, PA	15212
FLORES, JOSE	BASEBALL	POST OFFICE BOX 1556	ASHEVILLE, NC	28802
FLORES, MIGUEL	BASEBALL	2501 ALLEN AVE, SE	CANTON, OH	44707
FLORES, MIKE	FOOTBALL	EAGLES, BROAD ST & PATTISON AVE	PHILADELPHIA, PA	19148
FLORES, STEVE	BASEBALL SCOUT	POST OFFICE BOX 419969	KANSAS CITY, MO	64141
FLORES, TIM	BASEBALL	POST OFFICE BOX 1295	CLINTON, IA	52733
FLORES, TOM	FOOTBALL COACH-EXEC	SEAHAWKS, 11220 NE 53RD ST	KIRKLAND, WA	98033
FLORES, TONY	BASEBALL EXECUTIVE	POST OFFICE BOX 12557	ST PETERSBURG, FL	33733
FLORIE, BRYCE	BASEBALL	12000 STADIUM RD	ADELANTO, CA	92301
FLORIMONTE, LOUIS	WRITER	25376 N AVE CAPPELA	VALENCIA, CA	91355
FLORIO, ANDY	COMPOSER	1634 WESTERLY TERR	LOS ANGELES, CA	90026
FLORIO, JIM	GOVERNOR	STATE HOUSE BLDG, 125 W STATE ST	TRENTON, NJ	08625
FLORIO, ROBERT	FILM EDITOR	ACE, 1041 N FORMOSA AVE	WEST HOLLYWOOD, CA	90046
FLORY, MED	ACTOR	6044 ENSIGN AVE	NORTH HOLLYWOOD, CA	91606
FLORY, VERDON	ARTIST	141 E 62ND ST	NEW YORK, NY	10021
FLOTSAM AND JETSAM	ROCK & ROLL GROUP	SHOCKIN MANAGEMENT, BOX 6	RUSHCUTTERS BAY NSW	AUSTRALIA
FLOWER, GEORGE "BUCK"	ACTOR	11812 PENDLETON ST	SUN VALLEY, CA	91352
FLOWER, ROBIN	SINGER-GUITARIST	POST OFFICE BOX 3505	BERKELEY, CA	94703
FLOWERS, DOUG	BASEBALL	POST OFFICE BOX 3169	FREDERICK, MD	21701
FLOYD, BOBBY	BASEBALL EXECUTIVE	METS, 126TH ST & ROOSEVELT AVE	FLUSHING, NY	11368
FLOYD, CLIFF	BASEBALL	POLECATS, 608 N SLAPPEY BLVD	ALBANY, GA	31701
FLOYD, EDDIE	SINGER	2272 DEADRICK AVE	MEMPHIS, TN	38114
FLOYD, ERIC	FOOTBALL	POST OFFICE BOX 609609	SAN DIEGO, CA	92160
FLOYD, RAY	GOLFER	POST OFFICE BOX 109601	PALM BCH GARDENS, FL	33418
FLOYD, SLEEPY	BASKETBALL	POST OFFICE BOX 272349	HOUSTON, TX	77277
FLUEGEL SMALL, DARLANNE	ACTRESS	1999 AVE OF THE STARS #2850	LOS ANGELES, CA	90067
FLUELLEN, JOEL	ACTOR	1253 S WILTON PL	LOS ANGELES, CA	90019
FLUTIE, DOUG	FOOTBALL	21 SPRING VALLEY RD	NATICK, MA	01760
FLYNN, BARBARA	ACTRESS	MARKHAM AND FROGGATT, LTD		
		JULIAN HOUSE, 4 WINDMILL ST	LONDON W1P 1HF	ENGLAND
FLYNN, DARCY	ACTRESS	3-A GILSTON RD, THE BOLTONS	LONDON SW10 9SJ	ENGLAND
FLYNN, F PERSHING	DIRECTOR	13701 RIVERSIDE DR	SHERMAN OAKS, CA	91423
FLYNN, GERTRUDE	ACTRESS	9009 WONDERLAND AVE	LOS ANGELES, CA	90046
FLYNN, JAMES	ACTOR	POST OFFICE BOX 1115	CANYON CITY, CA	91351
FLYNN, JOHN	FILM WRITER-DIRECTOR	574 LATIMER RD	SANTA MONICA, CA	90402
FLYNT, LARRY	PUBLISHER	9211 ROBIN DR	LOS ANGELES, CA	90069
FM	ROCK & ROLL GROUP	1505 W 2ND AVE #200	VANCOUVER, BCV6H 3Y4	CANADA
FOCA-RODI, GEORGE	PIANIST-COMPOSER	POST OFFICE BOX 20072	NEW YORK, NY	10001
FOCH, NINA	ACTRESS	POST OFFICE BOX 1884	BEVERLY HILLS, CA	90213
FOGARTY, BRENDA J	ACTRESS	10831 HUSTON ST	NORTH HOLLYWOOD, CA	91601
FOGARTY, BRYAN	HOCKEY	NORDIQUES, 2205 AVE DU COLISEE	QUEBEC, QUE G1L 4W7	CANADA
FOGARTY, JACK PATRICK	ACTOR	294 HIGHWOOD ST	TEANECK, NJ	07666
FOGARTY, JACK V	TV WRITER	12432 SANFORD ST	LOS ANGELES, CA	90066
FOGEL, IRA	TV DIRECTOR	15 W 72ND ST	NEW YORK, NY	10023
FOGELBERG, DAN	SINGER-SONGWRITER	MOUNTAIN BIRD RANCH, BOX 824	PAGOSA SPRINGS, CO	81147
FOGERTY, JOHN	SINGER-SONGWRITER	CAA, 9830 WILSHIRE BLVD	BEVERLY HILLS, CA	90212
FOGHAT	ROCK & ROLL GROUP	SKYLINE, 85 FAIRHAVEN LN	MARSTONS MILLS, MA	02648
FOGLE, ELLEN L	TV WRITER	UTA, 9560 WILSHIRE BLVD, 5TH FL	BEVERLY HILLS, CA	90212
FOGLIETTA, THOMAS M	U S CONGRESSMAN	600 ARCH ST #10402	PHILADELPHIA, PA	19106
FOLB, JAY	TV WRITER	1652 COMSTOCK AVE	LOS ANGELES, CA	90024
FOLEY, ELLEN	ACTRESS	130 W 42ND ST #1804	NEW YORK, NY	10036
FOLEY, JAMES	WRITER-PRODUCER	CAA, 9830 WILSHIRE BLVD	BEVERLY HILLS, CA	90212
FOLEY, MARV	BASEBALL MANAGER	POST OFFICE DRAWER 1207	ZEBULON, NC	27597
FOLEY, THOMAS S	U S CONGRESSMAN	1228 E 29TH AVE	SPOKANE, WA	99202
FOLEY, TOM	ACTOR	36 W 73RD ST	NEW YORK, NY	10023
FOLEY, TOM	BASEBALL	EXPOS, 4545 DE COUBERTIN AVE	MONTREAL, QUE H1V 3P2	CANADA
FOLGER, EDWARD	WRITER-PRODUCER	POST OFFICE BOX 124	FROBISHER BAY NWT XOA	CANADA
FOLI, TIM	BASEBALL-COACH	BREWERS, 201 S 46TH ST	MILWAUKEE, WI	53214
FOLIGNO, MIKE	HOCKEY	MAPLE LEAFS, 60 CARLTON ST	TORONTO, ONT M5B 1L1	CANADA
FOLK, ROBERT	COMPOSER-CONDUCTOR	35218 PACIFIC COAST HWY	MALIBU, CA	90265
FOLLETT, JAMES	TV WRITER	SCHEHALLIEN, WOODSIDE RD		
		CHIDDINGFOLD	SURREY	ENGLAND
FOLLOWS, MEGAN	ACTRESS	ICM, 8899 BEVERLY BLVD	LOS ANGELES, CA	90048
FOLOOWELL, VERN	BASEBALL SCOUT	TWINS, 501 CHICAGO AVE S	MINNEAPOLIS, MN	55415
FOLSEY, GEORGE, JR	ACTOR-DIRECTOR	350 N CLIFFWOOD AVE	LOS ANGELES, CA	90049
FOLSOM, AL	WRITER-PRODUCER	13856 BORA BORA WY #11	MARINA DEL REY, CA	90292
FOLSOM, ALLAN R	TV WRITER	22545 CARBON MESA RD	MALIBU, CA	90265
FOLSOM, JIM	LT GOVERNOR	ALA STATE HOUSE, 11 S UNION ST	MONTGOMERY, AL	36130
FONDA, BRIDGET	ACTRESS	UTA, 9560 WILSHIRE BL, 5TH FL	BEVERLY HILLS, CA	90212
FONDA, JANE	ACTRESS-WRITER	POST OFFICE BOX 1198	SANTA MONICA, CA	90406
FONDA, PETER	ACT-WRI-DIR	RURAL ROUTE #38	LIVINGSTON, MT	59047
FONDY, DEE	BASEBALL-COACH	BREWERS, 201 S 46TH ST	MILWAUKEE, WI	53214
FONER, NAOMI	TV WRITER	226 S NORTON AVE	LOS ANGELES, CA	90004
FONG, BENSON	ACTOR	7236 OUTPOST COVE	LOS ANGELES, CA	90068
FONG, KAM	ACTOR	9430 W WASHINGTON BLVD #5	CULVER CITY, CA	90230
FONTAINE, BOB	BASEBALL SCOUT	S F GIANTS, CANDLESTICK PARK	SAN FRANICSCO, CA	94124
FONTAINE, BOB, JR	BASEBALL EXECUTIVE	POST OFFICE BOX 2000	ANAHEIM, CA	92803

FONTAINE, CHAR	ACTRESS	200 N ROBERTSON BLVD #219	BEVERLY HILLS, CA	90211
FONTAINE, JOAN	ACTRESS	POST OFFICE BOX 222600	CARMEL, CA	93922
FONTAINE, LUTHER	ACTOR	36 W 90TH ST	NEW YORK, NY	10024
FONTAINE, MOLLY	ACTRESS	3500 W OLIVE AVE #1400	BURBANK, CA	91505
FONTANA, D J	DRUMMER	493 BRENT LAWN DR	NASHVILLE, TN	37220
FONTANA, DOROTHY C	WRITER	11862 MOORPARK ST #D	STUDIO CITY, CA	91604
FONTANA, TOM	TV WRITER-PRODUCER	THE PALTROW GROUP, PIER 62		
		W 23RD ST & HUDSON RIVER, 3RD FL	NEW YORK, NY	10011
FONTANA, WAYNE & THE MINDBENDER	ROCK & ROLL GROUP	BRIAN CANNON MANAGEMENT		
		BOX 81, RUYTON, OLDHAM	MANCHESTER OL2 5DG	ENGLAND
FONTENOT, JERRY	FOOTBALL	BEARS, 250 N WASHINGTON RD	LAKE FOREST, IL	60045
FONTES, LEN	FOOTBALL COACH	LIONS, 1200 FEATHERSTONE RD	PONTIAC, MI	48432
FONTES, WAYNE	FOOTBALL COACH	LIONS, 1200 FEATHERSTONE RD	PONTIAC, MI	48432
FONVIELLE, LLOYD	SCREENWRITER	8955 BEVERLY BLVD	WEST HOLLYWOOD, CA	90048
FOOLS, THE	ROCK & ROLL GROUP	137 SOUTH ST #2	BOSTON, MA	02111
FOOS, RICHARD	RECORD EXECUTIVE	RHINO, 2225 COLORADO AVE	SANTA MONICA, CA	90404
FOOTE, BARRY	BASEBALL-COACH	METS, 126TH ST & ROOSEVELT AVE	FLUSHING, NY	11368
FOOTE, CHRIS	FOOTBALL	9520 VIKING DR	EDEN PRAIRIE, MN	55344
FOOTE, DOROTHY COOPER	SCREENWRITER	219 WILD HORSE DR	PALM DESERT, CA	92260
FOOTE, HORTON	SCREENWRITER	95 HORATIO ST #332	NEW YORK, NY	10014
FORAY, JUNE	ACTRESS	22745 ERWIN ST	WOODLAND HILLS, CA	91367
FORBERT, STEVE	SINGER	TRILLON, 301 W 53RD ST	NEW YORK, NY	10019
FORBES, BART	ARTIST	2706 FAIRMOUNT ST	DALLAS, TX	75201
FORBES, BRENDA	ACTRESS	430 E 57TH ST	NEW YORK, NY	10022
FORBES, BRYAN	WRITER-DIRECTOR	7 PINES, WENTWORTH	SURREY	ENGLAND
FORBES, CHRIS	ACTRESS	12060 LAUREL TERR DR	STUDIO CITY, CA	91604
FORBES, DON	TV DIRECTOR	1347 MILLER DR	LOS ANGELES, CA	90069
FORBES, GORDON	SPORTS WRITER	POST OFFICE BOX 500	WASHINGTON, DC	20044
FORBES, JERRY	SPORTS WRITER	POST OFFICE BOX 500	WASHINGTON, DC	20044
FORBES, P J	BASEBALL	POST OFFICE BOX 3496	DAVENPORT, IA	52808
FORCE, THE	ROCK & ROLL GROUP	POST OFFICE BOX 272	LONDON N20 0B4	ENGLAND
FORCE M D'S	RAP GROUP	FAA, 1700 BROADWAY, 5TH FLOOR	NEW YORK, NY	10019
FORD, BETTE	ACTRESS	1999 AVE OF THE STARS #2850	LOS ANGELES, CA	90067
FORD, BETTY	FIRST LADY-AUTHOR	2100 CENTURY PARK W	LOS ANGELES, CACA	90067
FORD, CHRIS	BASKETBALL COACH	151 MERRIMAC ST	BOSTON, MA	02114
FORD, CONSTANCE	ACTRESS	244 E 53RD ST	NEW YORK, NY	10022
FORD, CURT	BASEBALL	POST OFFICE BOX 6212	TOLEDO, OH	43614
FORD, DALE	BASEBALL UMPIRE	RURAL ROUTE 5, BOX 1260	JONESBORO, TN	37659
FORD, DOROTHY	ACTRESS	BANE, 13906 FIJI WY #344	MARINA DEL REY, CA	90292
FORD, DOUG	GOLFER	PGA SENIORS, 112 T P C BLVD	PONTE VEDRA BEACH, FL	32082
FORD, EILEEN	TALENT AGENT	FORD MODELS, 344 E 59TH ST	NEW YORK, NY	10022
FORD, FAITH	ACTRESS	WM MORRIS, 1350 AVE OF AMERICAS	NEW YORK, NY	10019
FORD, FRANKIE	SINGER-SONGWRITER	POST OFFICE BOX 1830	NEW ORLEANS, LA	70053
FORD, GERALD R	PRESIDENT-AUTHOR	POST OFFICE BOX 927	RANCHO MIRAGE, CA	92270
FORD, GLENN	ACTOR	911 OXFORD WY	BEVERLY HILLS, CA	90210
FORD, GRAHAM	TV PRODUCER	10201 MASON AVE #13	CHATSWORTH, CA	91311
FORD, HAROLD E	U S CONGRESSMAN	193 W MITCHELL RD	MEMPHIS, TN	38109
FORD, HARRISON	ACTOR	3555 N MOOSE WILSON RD	JACKSON HOLE, WY	83001
FORD, JOE	BASEBALL SCOUT	SKYDOME, 300 BREMMER BL #3200	TORONTO, ONT M5V 3B3	CANADA
FORD, LOUIS	DIRECTOR	2111 JEFFERSON DAVIS HW	ARLINGTON, VA	22202
FORD, MELISSA MATHISON	SCREENWRITER	SEE - MATHESON, MELISSA FORD		
FORD, MICK	ACTOR	47 GLENGARRY RD, DULWICH	LONDON SE22 8QA	ENGLAND
FORD, NANCY	TV WRITER	711 W END AVE	NEW YORK, NY	10025
FORD, REBAKKAH S	WRITER	1949 BUCKINGHAM RD	LOS ANGELES, CA	90016
FORD, ROBERT C	WRITER-PRODUCER	281 LAMBERT RD	NEW CANAAN, CT	06840
FORD, RUTH	ACTRESS	THE DAKOTA, 1 W 72ND ST	NEW YORK, NY	10023
FORD, STEPHEN	ACTOR	ROUTE #1, BOX 90	SAN LUIS OBISPO, CA	93401
FORD, STEVE	BASEBALL EXECUTIVE	POST OFFICE BOX 483	YAKIMA, WA	98907
FORD, THOMAS I	WRITER-PRODUCER	PARK DR S	RYE, NY	10580
FORD, WENDELL H	U S SENATOR	172-C NEW FEDERAL PL	LOUISVILLE, KY	40202
FORD, WHITEY	BASEBALL	38 SCHOOLHOUSE LN	LAKE SUCCESS, NY	11020
FORD, WILLIAM CLAY	FOOTBALL EXECUTIVE	LIONS, 1200 FEATHERSTONE RD	PONTIAC, MI	48432
FORD, WILLIAM D	U S CONGRESSMAN	31 S HURON	YPSILANTI, MI	48197
FORDE, BRIAN	FOOTBALL	SAINTS, 1500 POYDRAS ST	NEW ORLEANS, LA	90112
FORDYCE, BROOK	BASEBALL	525 NW PEACOCK BLVD	PORT SAINT LUCIE, FL	34986
FOREIGNER	ROCK & ROLL GROUP	E S "BUD" PRAGER MANAGEMENT		
		1790 BROADWAY, PENTHOUSE	NEW YORK, NY	10019
FOREMAN, DEBORAH	ACTRESS	1341 OCEAN AVE #213	SANTA MONICA, CA	90401
FOREMAN, GEORGE	BOXER	7639 PINE OAK DR	HUMBLE, TX	77397
FOREMAN, JOHN	FILM PRODUCER	TVI, 517 W 35TH ST	NEW YORK, NY	10001
FOREMAN, STEPHEN H	WRITER-PRODUCER	405 E 54TH ST #9-D	NEW YORK, NY	10022
FOREMAN, TOBY	BASEBALL	POST OFFICE BOX 30160	SAN BERNARDINO, CA	92413
FORER, DANIEL H	TV PRODUCER	CBS SPORTS, 51 W 52ND ST	NEW YORK, NY	10023
FOREST, MICHAEL	ACTOR	POST OFFICE BOX 69590	LOS ANGELES, CA	90069
FORESTER, DAVID	CONDUCTOR	11593 KLING ST	NORTH HOLLYWOOD, CA	91602
FORESTER SISTERS, THE	C & W GROUP	128 VOLUNTEER DR	HENDERSONVILLE, TN	37075
FORESTIERI, SUSANNE	ARTIST	535 W 110TH ST	NEW YORK, NY	10025
FORGIONE, BOB N	DIRECTOR	12 W 37TH ST	NEW YORK, NY	10018
FORMAN, JOHN	FILM PRODUCER	ICM, 40 W 57TH ST	NEW YORK, NY	10019
FORMAN, MILOS	FILM DIRECTOR	THE HAMPSHIRE HOUSE		
		150 CENTRAL PARK S	NEW YORK, NY	10019
FORMAN, SIR DENIS	FILM EXECUTIVE	GRANADA GROUP, 36 GOLDEN SQ	LONDON W1	ENGLAND
FORMAN, STANLEY	TV DIRECTOR-PRODUCER	247-A UPPER ST	LONDON N1 QRU	ENGLAND
FORMAN, TOM	CARTOONIST	5755 RAINBOW HILL	AGOURA, CA	91301
FORMICA, SALVATORE EDWARD	DIRECTOR	12704 MONTCLAIR DR	SILVER SPRING, MD	20904

FORMICOLA, FIL	ACTOR	6000 COCOS DR	LOS ANGELES, CA	90068
FORNES, MARIA	PLAYWRIGHT	1 SHERIDAN SQ	NEW YORK, NY	10014
FORNEY, RICK	BASEBALL	POST OFFICE BOX 418	SAINT CHARLES, IL	60174
FORONJY, RICHARD	ACTOR	137 N SWEETZER AVE	LOS ANGELES, CA	90048
FORREST, ARTHUR	DIRECTOR-PRODUCER	10366 HOLMAN AVE	LOS ANGELES, CA	90024
FORREST, FREDERIC	ACTOR	11100 HORTENSE ST	NORTH HOLLYWOOD, CA	91602
FORREST, HELEN	SINGER	1870 CAMINITO DEL CIELO	GLENDALE, CA	91208
FORREST, PHIL	MUSIC ARRANGER	2207 CABIN HILL RD	NASHVILLE, TN	37214
FORREST, SALLY	ACTRESS	1125 ANGELO DR	BEVERLY HILLS, CA	90210
FORREST, STEVE	ACTOR	1065 MICHAEL LN	PACIFIC PALISADES, CA	90272
FORSBERG, ROLF	WRITER-PRODUCER	380 TOYON RD	SIERRA MADRE, CA	91024
FORSCH, BOB	BASEBALL	1532 HIGHLAND VALLEY CIR	CHESTERFIELD, MO	63005
FORSLUND, CONSTANCE	ACTRESS	165 W 46TH ST #1109	NEW YORK, NY	10036
FORSMAN, DAN	GOLFER	POST OFFICE BOX 109601	PALM BCH GARDENS, FL	33418
FORSTATER, MARK	FILM PRODUCER	8-A TREBECK ST	LONDON W1	ENGLAND
FORSTER, ROBERT	ACTOR	8550 HOLLOWAY DR #402	LOS ANGELES, CA	90069
FORSYTH, BILL	FILM DIRECTOR	LAKE FILM PRODS, 20 WINTON DR	GLASGOW G-12	SCOTLAND
FORSYTH, BRIGIT	ACTRESS	CONWAY, 18-21 JERMYN ST	LONDON SW1	ENGLAND
FORSYTH, BRUCE	TV PERSONALITY	MARSH, 19 DENMARK ST	LONDON WC2H 8NA	ENGLAND
FORSYTH, DAVID	ACTOR	205 W 89TH ST #PH-9	NEW YORK, NY	10024
FORSYTH, ROSEMARY	ACTRESS	1591 BENEDICT CANYON DR	BEVERLY HILLS, CA	90210
FORSYTHE, CHARLES	THEATER PRODUCER	1841 BROADWAY	NEW YORK, NY	10023
FORSYTHE, ERIC	ACTOR	152 SHAWNEE RD	ARDMORE, PA	19003
FORSYTHE, JOHN	ACTOR	14215 SUNSET BLVD	PACIFIC PALISADES, CA	90272
FORTE, CHET	TV DIRECTOR	POST OFFICE BOX 8030	RANCHO SANTE FE, CA	92067
FORTE, FABIAN	ACTOR-SINGER	6671 SUNSET BLVD #1502	HOLLYWOOD, CA	90028
FORTE, MO	FOOTBALL COACH	BRONCOS, 13655 BRONCOS PKWY	ENGLEWOOD, CO	80112
FORTENSKY, LARRY	CELEBRITY	700 NIMES RD	LOS ANGELES, CA	90077
FORTIN, ROMAN	FOOTBALL	LIONS, 1200 FEATHERSTONE RD	PONTIAC, MI	48432
FORTSON, EDWIN B, JR	WRITER	400 S JUNE ST	LOS ANGELES, CA	90020
FORTUGNO, TIM	BASEBALL	10233 96TH AVE	EDMONTON, ALB TK5 0A5	CANADA
FORTUNE, LOIS	TV PRODUCER	91 PAYSON AVE	NEW YORK, NY	10034
FORWARD, ROBERT H, SR	WRITER-PRODUCER	550 S BARRINGTON AVE	LOS ANGELES, CA	90049
FORWARD, WILLIAM	ACTOR	550 S BARRINGTON AVE	LOS ANGELES, CA	90049
FOSHKO, ALLAN	DIRECTOR	STUDIO, 305 W 52ND ST	NEW YORK, NY	10019
FOSHKO, ROBERT	WRITER	3710 HAYVENHURST AVE	ENCINO, CA	91316
FOSS, GENERAL JOE	FOOTBALL	POST OFFICE BOX 566	SCOTTSDALE, AZ	85252
FOSSA, RICHARD	BASEBALL UMPIRE	POST OFFICE BOX 25010	LITTLE ROCK, AZ	72221
FOSSAS, TONY	BASEBALL	FENWAY PARK, 4 YAWKEY WY	BOSTON, MA	02215
FOSSE, RAY	BASEBALL-ANNOUNCER	ATHLETICS'S, OAKLAND COLISEUM	OAKLAND, CA	94621
FOSSEY, BRIGITTE	ACTRESS	18 RUE TROYON	75017 PARIS	FRANCE
FOSTER, BARRY	ACTOR	AL PARKER, 55 PARK LN	LONDON W1Y 3DD	ENGLAND
FOSTER, BARRY	FOOTBALL	STEELERS, 300 STADIUM CIR	PITTSBURGH, PA	15212
FOSTER, BILL R	TV DIRECTOR	12325 MOORPARK ST	STUDIO CITY, CA	91604
FOSTER, CASSANDRA	ACTRESS	11574 IOWA AVE #105	LOS ANGELES, CA	90025
FOSTER, DAN, JR	SINGER-GUITARIST	ROUTE #1, BOX 104	SUMMERTOWN, TN	38483
FOSTER, DAVID	FILM PRODUCER	719 N PALM DR	BEVERLY HILLS, CA	90210
FOSTER, DAVID	TV DIRECTOR-PRODUCER	KINGS COTTAGE, THE SQUARE		
		COSTOCK, NEAR LOUGHBOROUGH	LEICS LE12 6XG	ENGLAND
FOSTER, DAVID W	COMP-ARR-PROD-PIANO	6173 BONSALL DR	MALIBU, CA	90265
FOSTER, DICK	BASEBALL SCOUT	BREWERS, 201 S 46TH ST	MILWAUKEE, WI	53214
FOSTER, FLOYD L, JR	ACTOR	1830 S SAINT ANDREWS PL #8	LOS ANGELES, CA	90019
FOSTER, FRANCES	ACTRESS	146 E 49TH ST	NEW YORK, NY	10019
FOSTER, GEORGE	BASEBALL (EXEC-A'S)	POST OFFICE BOX 11087	TACOMA, WA	98411
FOSTER, GEORGE	BASEBALL (REDS-METS)	POST OFFICE BOX 11098	GREENWICH, CT	06830
FOSTER, GILES	TV DIRECTOR	PETERS, FRASER & DUNLOP, LTD		
		5TH FLOOR, THE CHAMBERS		
		CHELSEA HARBOUR, LOT RD	LONDON SW10 0XF	ENGLAND
FOSTER, GREG	BASKETBALL	BULLETS, 1 HARRY S TRUMAN DR	LANDOVER, MD	20785
FOSTER, JEAN RENEE	ACTRESS	431 N SYCAMORE AVE #103	LOS ANGELES, CA	90036
FOSTER, JIM	SINGER	1505 W 2ND AVE #200	VANCOUVER, BCV6H 3Y4	CANADA
FOSTER, JODIE	ACTRESS-DIRECTOR	ICM, 8899 BEVERLY BLVD	LOS ANGELES, CA	90048
FOSTER, KIMBERLY	ACTRESS	BLANCHARD, 957 N COLE AVE	LOS ANGELES, CA	90038
FOSTER, LINDSAY	BASEBALL	POST OFFICE BOX 360007	BIRMINGHAM, AL	35236
FOSTER, LLOYD DAVID	SINGER	POST OFFICE BOX 1373	LEWISVILLE, TX	75067
FOSTER, MARTIN	BASEBALL UMPIRE	235 MAIN ST #103	TRUSSVILLE, AL	35173
FOSTER, MEG	ACTRESS	9301 WILSHIRE BLVD #312	BEVERLY HILLS, CA	90210
FOSTER, NORAH	ACTRESS	4301 KLING ST #25	BURBANK, CA	91505
FOSTER, ORVILLE	COMPOSER	334 E OCEAN BLVD #305	LONG BEACH, CA	90802
FOSTER, ROBERT W	WRITER-PRODUCER	1005 N CROFT AVE #6	LOS ANGELES, CA	90069
FOSTER, ROY	FOOTBALL	S F 49ERS, 4949 CENTENNIAL BL	SANTA CLARA, CA	95054
FOSTER, SUSANNA	ACTRESS	11255 MORRISON ST #F	NORTH HOLLYWOOD, CA	91601
FOSTER & LLOYD	C & W DUO	POST OFFICE BOX 128037	NASHVILLE, TN	37212
FOTRE, VINCENT G	WRITER	1227 ROBERTO LN	LOS ANGELES, CA	90077
FOUCAULT, STEVE	BASEBALL COACH	POST OFFICE BOX 855	BELOIT, WI	53511
FOULK, ROBERT	ACTOR	9 WILLIAMSBURG LN	ROLLING HILLS, CA	90274
FOUNTAIN, ALAN	DIRECTOR	76 FLORENCE RD	LONDON N4	ENGLAND
FOUNTAIN, PETE	CLARINETIST	237 N PETERS ST #400	NEW ORLEANS, LA	70130
FOUR FRESHMAN, THE	VOCAL GROUP	POST OFFICE BOX 34397	SAN DIEGO, CA	92103
FOUR GUYS, THE	VOCAL GROUP	POST OFFICE BOX 7859	NASHVILLE, TN	37217
FOUR LADS, THE	VOCAL GROUP	5 GLEN ST # 106	GREENWICH, CT	06830
FOUR TOPS, THE	VOCAL GROUP	FAA, 1700 BROADWAY, 5TH FLOOR	NEW YORK, NY	10019
FOURNIER, RIFT	WRITER-PRODUCER	10535 WILSHIRE BLVD #610	LOS ANGELES, CA	90024
FOUSER, DONALD B	DIRECTOR-PRODUCER	19 N MAIN ST	IPSWICH, MA	01938
FOUST, NINA	GOLFER	2750 VOLUSA AVE #B	DAYTON BEACH, FL	32114

FOUTS, DAN	FOOTBALL	POST OFFICE BOX 609609	SAN DIEGO, CA 92160
FOUTS, KENNETH	TV DIRECTOR	5499 BELFAST RD	BATAVIA, OH 45103
FOWLDS, DEREK	ACTOR	CDA, 47 COURTFIELD RD #20	LONDON SW7 4DB ENGLAND
FOWLER, BOB	BASEBALL EXECUTIVE	POST OFFICE BOX 751	UTICA, NY 13503
FOWLER, CHRISTINA	ACTRESS	10118 ALDEA AVE	NORTHRIDGE, CA 91325
FOWLER, ERIC	ARTIST	122 N UNION ST	LAMBERTVILLE, NJ 08530
FOWLER, GENE, JR	FILM DIRECTOR	7261 OUTPOST COVE DR	HOLLYWOOD, CA 90068
FOWLER, HARRY	ACTOR	ESSANAY, 2 CONDUIT ST	LONDON W1R 9TG ENGLAND
FOWLER, JAMES EMMET	ACTOR	10118 ALDEA AVE	NORTHRIDGE, CA 91325
FOWLER, MARJORIE	TV WRITER	9200 SUNSET BLVD #531	LOS ANGELES, CA 90069
FOWLER, MARK S	COMMUNICATIONS EXEC	FCC, 1919 "M" ST, NW	WASHINGTON, DC 20554
FOWLER, ROBERT	FILM DIRECTOR	HAROLD GREENE, 8455 SUNSET BLVD	LOS ANGELES, CA 90048
FOWLER, WILLIAM R	ACTOR-VOICE OVERS	253 E 77TH ST #2-G	NEW YORK, NY 10023
FOWLER, WYNCHE, JR	U S SENATOR	10 PARK PL S #501	ATLANTA, GA 30303
FOWLES, JOHN	NOVELIST	ASA, 52 FLORAL ST	LONDON WC2 ENGLAND
FOWLEY, DOUGLAS V	ACTOR	38510 GLEN ABBEY LN	MURIETTA, CA 92362
FOX, ANDY	BASEBALL	POST OFFICE BOX 2148	WOODBRIDGE, VA 22193
FOX, BARRY	FILM DIR-PROD	FOX TV, 10-12 FITZROY MEWS	LONDON W1P 5DQ ENGLAND
FOX, BERTIL	BODYBUILDER	POST OFFICE BOX 531	CANOGA PARK, CA 91305
FOX, CHARLES	COMPOSER-CONDUCTOR	4601 VANALDEN AVE	TARZANA, CA 91356
FOX, CHARLIE	BASEBALL SCOUT	POST OFFICE BOX 288	HOUSTON, TX 77001
FOX, DAN	BASEBALL TRAINER	POST OFFICE BOX 661	KENOSHA, WI 53141
FOX, DAVID	TV DIRECTOR	46 W 65TH ST	NEW YORK, NY 10023
FOX, EDWARD	ACTOR	25 MAIDA AVE	LONDON W2 ENGLAND
FOX, ERIC	BASEBALL	POST OFFICE BOX 11087	TACOMA, WA 98411
FOX, FRED, S, JR	TV WRITER	4217 EMPRESS AVE	ENCINO, CA 91436
FOX, HOWARD, JR	BASEBALL EXECUTIVE	TWINS, 501 CHICAGO AVE S	MINNEAPOLIS, MN 55415
FOX, IRWIN SONNY	TV PRODUCER	1969 GLENCOE WY	LOS ANGELES, CA 90068
FOX, JAMES	ACTOR	WHITEHALL, 125 GLOUCESTER RD	LONDON SW7 4TE ENGLAND
FOX, JOHN	FOOTBALL COACH	STEELERS, 300 STADIUM CIR	PITTSBURGH, PA 15212
FOX, JOHN G	DIRECTOR-PRODUCER	215 W 91ST ST	NEW YORK, NY 10023
FOX, JUDY SCOTT	TALENT AGENT	151 S EL CAMINO DR	BEVERLY HILLS, CA 90212
FOX, KENT	SINGER	POST OFFICE BOX 2271	PALM SPRINGS, CA 92263
FOX, M BERNARD	WRITER-PRODUCER	DGA, 7920 SUNSET BL, 6TH FL	LOS ANGELES, CA 90046
FOX, MAXINE	THEATER PRODUCER	1501 BROADWAY	NEW YORK, NY 10036
FOX, MICHAEL	ACTOR (SOAPS)	CBS-TV, "THE BOLD & BEAUTIFUL"	
FOX, MICHAEL	ACTOR (SOAPS-2)	7800 BEVERLY BLVD #3371	LOS ANGELES, CA 90036
FOX, MICHAEL	TV DIRECTOR	6425 NAGLE AVE	VAN NUYS, CA 91401
FOX, MICHAEL A	ACTOR	SEE - FOX, MICHAEL J	
FOX, MICHAEL J	ACTOR-DIRECTOR	12828 VICTORY BLVD #344	NORTH HOLLYWOOD, CA 91606
FOX, MICHAEL S	WRITER	10356 ASHTON AVE	LOS ANGELES, CA 90024
FOX, MIKE	FOOTBALL	N Y GIANTS, GIANTS STADIUM	EAST RUTHERFORD, NJ 07073
FOX, NANCY	ACTRESS	8665 WILSHIRE BLVD #208	BEVERLY HILLS, CA 90211
FOX, PETER	ACTOR	228 23RD ST	MANHATTAN BEACH, CA 90266
FOX, SAMANTHA	SINGER-MODEL	11 MOUNT PLEASANT WILLAS	LONDON 4HH ENGLAND
FOX, SONNY	TV PRODUCER	1447 N KINGS RD	LOS ANGELES, CA 90069
FOX, VIVICA	ACTRESS	250 W 57TH ST #2223	NEW YORK, NY 10019
FOX, WALTER	SCREENWRITER	ICM, 8899 BEVERLY BLVD	LOS ANGELES, CA 90048
FOX BROTHERS, THE	GOSPEL GROUP	ROUTE #6, BENDING CHESTNUT	FRANKLIN, TN 37064
FOXWELL, IVAN	FILM PRODUCER	CLEMENT HOUSE, 99 ALDWYCH	LONDON WC2 B4JY ENGLAND
FOXWORTH, ROBERT	ACTOR	1230 BENEDICT CANYON DR	BEVERLY HILLS, CA 90210
FOXWORTHY, M W	SET DECORATOR	CBS-TV, 530 W 57TH ST #2220	NEW YORK, NY 10019
FOXX, ELIZABETH	ACTRESS	3907 W ALAMDEA AVE #101	BURBANK, CA 91505
FOY, NANCY	ACTRESS	3424 TROY DR	LOS ANGELES, CA 90068
FOY, NANCY	CASTING DIRECTOR	6565 SUNSET BLVD #306	LOS ANGELES, CA 90028
FOYT, A J	AUTO RACER	6415 TOLEDO ST	HOUSTON, TX 77008
FRABOTTA, DON	ACTOR	5036 RIVERTON AVE #2	NORTH HOLLYWOOD, CA 91601
FRADON, RAMONA	CARTOONIST	TRIBUNE, 64 E CONCORD ST	ORLANDO, FL 32801
FRAENKEL, WOLFGANG	COMPOSER-CONDUCTOR	143 S LAPEER DR	LOS ANGELES, CA 90048
FRAKER, WILLIAM A	CINEMATOGRAPHER	POST OFFICE BOX 2230	HOLLYWOOD, CA 90078
FRAKES, JONATHAN	ACTOR	5062 CALVIN AVE	TARZANA, CA 91356
FRALEY, JOSEPH REX	SCREENWRITER	8955 BEVERLY BLVD	WEST HOLLYWOOD, CA 90048
FRALIC, BILL	FOOTBALL	FALCONS, SUWANEE RD AT I-85	SUWANEE, GA 30174
FRALICK, BOB	BASEBALL COACH	POST OFFICE BOX 726	POMPANO BEACH, FL 33064
FRAMPTON, DAVID	ARTIST	RURAL FARM DELIVERY #3	RICHMOND, NH 03470
FRAMPTON, MARC	KEYBOARDIST	POST OFFICE BOX 12403	
		NORTH SIDE STATION	ATLANTA, GA 30355
FRAMPTON, PETER	SINGER-GUITARIST	2669 LARMAR RD	LOS ANGELES, CA 90068
FRANCATORE, JOHN	BASEBALL	POST OFFICE BOX 3783	SAVANNAH, GA 31414
FRANCE, MARIE	COSTUME DESIGNER	POST OFFICE BOX 5617	BEVERLY HILLS, CA 90213
FRANCES, MARY	ACTRESS	SEE - FRANN, MARY	
FRANCESCA, ALBA	ACTRESS	4455 LOS FELIZ BLVD #802	LOS ANGELES, CA 90027
FRANCESCHETTI, LOU	HOCKEY	SABRES, MEMORIAL AUDITORIUM	BUFFALO, NY 14202
FRANCHINI, BRUCE	TV DIRECTOR	4600 VIA MARINA #107	MARINA DEL REY, CA 90292
FRANCHOT, RICHARD	DIRECTOR	1146 HACIENDA PL	LOS ANGELES, CA 90069
FRANCHUK, ORV	BASEBALL COACH	HAWKS, 5600 N GLENWOOD	BOISE, ID 83714
FRANCIOSA, TONY	ACTOR	567 TIGERTAIL RD	LOS ANGELES, CA 90049
FRANCIS, AL	CINEMATOGRAPHER	POST OFFICE BOX 2230	HOLLYWOOD, CA 90078
FRANCIS, ANNE	ACTRESS	POST OFFICE BOX 5417	SANTA BARBARA, CA 93103
FRANCIS, ARLENE	ACTRESS	112 CENTRAL PARK S	NEW YORK, NY 10019
FRANCIS, BEV	BODYBUILDER	POST OFFICE BOX 250	GLEN OAKS, NY 11004
FRANCIS, CLIVE	ACTOR	MC REDDIE, 91 REGENT ST	LONDON W1R 7TB ENGLAND
FRANCIS, CLIVE	SINGER-SONGWRITER	MORESS, 1209 16TH AVE S	NASHVILLE, TN 37212
FRANCIS, CONNIE	SINGER-ACTRESS	11 POMPTON AVE	VERONA, NJ 07044
FRANCIS, FREDDIE	FILM-TV DIRECTOR	12 THE CHESTNUTS	

Name	Occupation	Address	City	Postal Code / Country
		JERSEY RD, OSTERLEY	MIDDLESEX	ENGLAND
FRANCIS, GENIE	ACTRESS	ABC-TV, "ALL MY CHILDREN"		
		320 W 66TH ST	NEW YORK, NY	10023
FRANCIS, JAMES	FOOTBALL	BENGALS, 200 RIVERFRONT STADIUM	CINCINNATI, OH	45202
FRANCIS, JAN	ACTRESS	BELFRAGE, 68 SAINT JAMES'S ST	LONDON SW1A 1LE	ENGLAND
FRANCIS, JEFF	FOOTBALL	BROWNS, 80 1ST ST	BEREA, OH	44017
FRANCIS, KEVIN	FILM PRODUCER	TYBURN PRODS, PINEWOOD STUDIOS		
		IVER HEATH	BUCKS	ENGLAND
FRANCIS, MISSY	ACTRESS	1800 N VINE ST #120	LOS ANGELES, CA	90028
FRANCIS, RON	HOCKEY	PENGUINS, CIVIC ARENA, CENTRE AV	PITTSBURGH, PA	15219
FRANCIS, RYAN	ACTOR	9171 WILSHIRE BLVD #300	BEVERLY HILLS, CA	90210
FRANCIS, WILLIAM V, JR	DIRECTOR	POST OFFICE BOX 1352	NEW YORK, NY	10185
FRANCISCO, JAMES	LT GOVERNOR	STATE CAPITOL BUILDING	TOPEKA, KS	66617
FRANCISCO, VINCENTE	BASEBALL	POST OFFICE BOX 882	MADISON, WI	53701
FRANCK, EDWARD A	DIRECTOR-PRODUCER	136 SICKELTOWN RD	WEST NYACK, NY	10994
FRANCO, GIUSEPPE "JOEY"	HAIR STYLIST	GIUSEPPE FRANCO SALON		
		350 N CANON DR	BEVERLY HILLS, CA	90210
FRANCO, JOHN	BASEBALL	METS, 126TH ST & ROOSEVELT AVE	FLUSHING, NY	11368
FRANCO, JULIO	BASEBALL	POST OFFICE BOX 90111	ARLINGTON, TX	76004
FRANCO, MATT	BASEBALL	POST OFFICE DRAWER 1207	ZEBULON, NC	27597
FRANCONA, TERRY	BASEBALL MANAGER	POST OFFICE BOX 4218	SOUTH BEND, IN	46634
FRANGAKIS, NICHOLAS	SCREENWRITER	8721 SUNSET BLVD #103	WEST HOLLYWOOD, CA	90069
FRANK, ALAN G	DIRECTOR	127 W 79TH ST	NEW YORK, NY	10024
FRANK, ASTRID	ACTOR-DIRECTOR	CCA, 4 COURT LODGE		
		48 SLOANE SQ	LONDON SW1W 8AT	ENGLAND
FRANK, BARNEY	U S CONGRESSMAN	437 CHERRY ST	WEST NEWTON, MA	02165
FRANK, BOBBI	PRODUCER	569 N ROSSMORE AVE #206	LOS ANGELES, CA	90004
FRANK, CHARLES	ACTOR	9744 WILSHIRE BLVD #308	BEVERLY HILLS, CA	90212
FRANK, DAVID M	CONDUCTOR	2971 BRIAR KNOLL DR	LOS ANGELES, CA	90046
FRANK, DEBRA	TV WRITER	9300 WILSHIRE BLVD #410	BEVERLY HILLS, CA	90212
FRANK, DONALD	FOOTBALL	POST OFFICE BOX 609609	SAN DIEGO, CA	92160
FRANK, GAIL E	DIRECTOR-PRODUCER	360 E 55TH ST	NEW YORK, NY	10022
FRANK, GARY	ACTOR	323 S ANITA AVE	LOS ANGELES, CA	90049
FRANK, HARRIET, JR	SCREENWRITER	8955 BEVERLY BLVD	WEST HOLLYWOOD, CA	90048
FRANK, JOANNA	ACTRESS	1274 CAPRI DR	PACIFIC PALISADES, CA	90272
FRANK, MILO	WRITER-PRODUCER	1125 ANTELO DR	BEVERLY HILLS, CA	90210
FRANK, SELIG	TV DIRECTOR	10331 RIVERSIDE DR #103	NORTH HOLLYWOOD, CA	91602
FRANK, SHERMAN	CONDUCTOR	47 MARGARET CT	TOMS RIVER, NJ	08753
FRANKAU, JOHN	TV DIRECTOR-PRODUCER	HANCOCK, GREENER HOUSE		
		66-68 HAYMARKET	LONDON SW1Y 4AW	ENGLAND
FRANKEL, CYRIL	ACTOR	KRUGER, 121 GLOUCESTER PL	LONDON W1H 3PL	ENGLAND
FRANKEL, DORIS C	TV WRITER	158-18 RIVERSIDE DR W #7-B	NEW YORK, NY	10032
FRANKEL, ERNEST	WRITER-PRODUCER	19501 ROSITA ST	TARZANA, CA	91536
FRANKEL, MAX	COLUMNIST	N Y TIMES, 229 W 43RD ST	NEW YORK, NY	10036
FRANKEN, AL	COMEDIAN-WRITER	10000 SANTA MONICA BLVD #305	LOS ANGELES, CA	90067
FRANKEN, STEVE	ACTOR	3704 WHITESPEAK DR	SHERMAN OAKS, CA	91403
FRANKENHEIMER, JOHN	DIRECTOR-PRODUCER	3114 ABINGTON DR	BEVERLY HILLS, CA	90210
FRANKFATHER, WILLIAM	ACTOR	1246 VICTORIA AVE	LOS ANGELES, CA	90019
FRANKHAUSER, MERRELL	SINGER-GUITARIST	POST OFFICE BOX 1504	ARROYO GRANDE, CA	93420
FRANKLIN, ARETHA	SINGER-SONGWRITER	POST OFFICE BOX 12137	BIRMINGHAM, MI	48012
FRANKLIN, BONNIE	ACTRESS	15745 ROYAL OAK RD	ENCINO, CA	91436
FRANKLIN, CARL	ACTOR	4402 VICTORIA PARK DR	LOS ANGELES, CA	90019
FRANKLIN, CECIL	SINGER	16919 STANSBURY ST	DETROIT, MI	48235
FRANKLIN, DANIEL JAY	FILM-TV WRITER	8955 BEVERLY BLVD	WEST HOLLYWOOD, CA	90048
FRANKLIN, DIANE	ACTRESS	1999 AVE OF THE STARS #2850	LOS ANGELES, CA	90067
FRANKLIN, GARY	FILM CRITIC	KABC-TV, 4151 PROSPECT AVE	LOS ANGELES, CA	90027
FRANKLIN, GRETCHEN	ACTRESS	50 BOILEAU RD	LONDON SW13	ENGLAND
FRANKLIN, HARRY S	FILM WRITER-DIRECTOR	10118 EMPYREAN WY #304	LOS ANGELES, CA	90067
FRANKLIN, JEFF	SCREENWRITER	8955 BEVERLY BLVD	WEST HOLLYWOOD, CA	90048
FRANKLIN, JOE	TV HOST	9 BROADCAST PLAZA	SECAUCUS, NJ	07094
FRANKLIN, LAWRENCE	CONDUCTOR	28500 BRADLEY RD #183	SUN CITY, CA	92381
FRANKLIN, LOUISE	ACTRESS	2425 7TH AVE	LOS ANGELES, CA	90018
FRANKLIN, PAMELA	ACTRESS	1280 SUNSET PLAZA DR	LOS ANGELES, CA	90069
FRANKLIN, RICHARD B	FILM DIRECTOR	11726 SAN VICENTE BLVD #300	LOS ANGELES, CA	90049
FRANKLIN, RODNEY	PIANIST-COMPOSER	1995 BROADWAY #501	NEW YORK, NY	10023
FRANKLIN, TONY	BASEBALL MANAGER	POST OFFICE BOX 360007	BIRMINGHAM, AL	35236
FRANKLIN, WENDELL JAMES	TV DIRECTOR	3401 VIA DOLCE #609-A	MARINA DEL REY, CA	90292
FRANKLYN, SABINA	ACTRESS	LADKIN, 11 SOUTHWICK MEWS	LONDON W2 1JG	ENGLAND
FRANKLYN, WILLIAM	ACTOR-DIRECTOR	REDWAY (AIM), 5 DENMARK ST	LONDON WC2H 8LP	ENGLAND
FRANKLYN-ROBBINS, JOHN	ACTOR	CONWAY, 18-21 JERMYN ST	LONDON SW1	ENGLAND
FRANKOVICH, PETER	TV EXECUTIVE	CBS-TV, 6121 SUNSET BLVD	LOS ANGELES, CA	90028
FRANKS, GARY A	U S CONGRESSMAN	135 GRAND ST #210	WATERBURY, CT	06701
FRANKS, MICHAEL	SINGER-GUITARIST	9000 SUNSET BLVD #1200	LOS ANGELES, CA	90069
FRANN, MARY	ACTRESS	250 N ROBERTSON BLVD #518	BEVERLY HILLS, CA	90211
FRANTZ, EARNIE	FOOTBALL REFEREE	NFL, 410 PARK AVE	NEW YORK, NY	10022
FRANZ, ARTHUR	ACTOR	32960 PACIFIC COAST HWY	MALIBU, CA	90265
FRANZ, CAROLINE J	TV WRITER	5530 E GLEN ARM RD	GLEN ARM, MD	21057
FRANZ, DENNIS	ACTOR	11805 BELLAGIO RD	LOS ANGELES, CA	90049
FRANZ, ELIZABETH	ACTRESS	1650 BROADWAY #1005	NEW YORK, NY	10019
FRANZ, ROBERT	DIRECTOR	45 W 45TH ST	NEW YORK, NY	10036
FRANZONI, DAVID H	WRITER	2 SEA COLONY DR	SANTA MONICA, CA	90405
FRASCO, KAREN ANN	ACTRESS	424 W END AVE #3-K	NEW YORK, NY	10024
FRASE, PAUL	FOOTBALL	N Y JETS, 1000 FULTON AVE	HEMPSTEAD, NY	11550
FRASER, BOB	ACTOR-WRITER	8955 BEVERLY BLVD	WEST HOLLYWOOD, CA	90048
FRASER, IAN	COMPOSER-CONDUCTOR	2386 SUNSET HEIGHTS DR	LOS ANGELES, CA	90046

Name	Occupation	Address	City
FRASER, JILL	COMPOSER	15209 VALERIO ST	VAN NUYS, CA 91405
FRASER, LIZ	ACTRESS	MC REDDIE, 91 REGENT ST	LONDON W1R 7TB ENGLAND
FRASER, PATRICIA	ACTRESS	289 SAINT ALBANS AVE	SOUTH PASADENA, CA 91030
FRASER, PHYLLIS	ACTRESS	R F WAGNER, 425 PARK AVE	NEW YORK, NY 10022
FRASER, RONALD	ACTOR	12 CAROLINE TERR, SLOANE SQ	LONDON SW1 ENGLAND
FRASER, TOM	DIRECTOR	3337 SCADLOCK LN	SHERMAN OAKS, CA 91403
FRASER, WILLIE	BASEBALL	10233 96TH AVE	EDMONTON, ALB TK5 0A5 CANADA
FRATES, ROBIN	ACTRESS	8228 SUNSET BLVD #311	LOS ANGELES, CA 90046
FRATTARE, LANNY	SPORTSCASTER	POST OFFICE BOX 7000	PITTSBURGH, PA 15212
FRAWLEY, JIMMY B	FILM DIRECTOR	8439 SUNSET BLVD #402	LOS ANGELES, CA 90069
FRAYN, MICHAEL	WRITER	PETERS, FRASER & DUNLOP, LTD	
		5TH FLOOR, THE CHAMBERS	
		CHELSEA HARBOUR, LOT RD	LONDON SW10 OXF ENGLAND
FRAZER, DAN	ACTOR	CBS-TV, "AS THE WORLD TURNS"	
		524 W 57TH ST #5330	NEW YORK, NY 10019
FRAZER, LIZ	ACTRESS	AM MGMT, 23 HAYMARKET, 4TH FL	LONDON SW1V 4DG ENGLAND
FRAZER, RUPERT	ACTOR	MARKHAM AND FROGGATT, LTD	
		JULIAN HOUSE, 4 WINDMILL ST	LONDON W1P 1HF ENGLAND
FRAZER-JONES, PETER	TV PRODUCER	THAMES TELEVISION, TEDDINGTON	MIDDLESEX TW11 9NT ENGLAND
FRAZIER, BRUCE	CONDUCTOR	2927 N MYERS ST	BURBANK, CA 91504
FRAZIER, CRAIG	ARTIST	173 7TH ST	SAN FRANCISCO, CA 94103
FRAZIER, DALLAS	SINGER-SONGWRITER	ROUTE 5, BOX 133, LH PIKE	GALLATIN, TN 37066
FRAZIER, HARRY	ACTOR	5152 LA VISTA CT	LOS ANGELES, CA 90004
FRAZIER, JIMMY B	FILM EDITOR	842 E CAMBRIDGE DR	BURBANK, CA 91504
FRAZIER, JOE	BOXER-SINGER	2917 N BROAD ST	PHILADELPHIA, PA 19132
FRAZIER, L D	SINGER	2528-A W JEROME AVE	CHICAGO, IL 60645
FRAZIER, LOU	BASEBALL	TIGERS, 89 WHARNCLIFFE RD N	LONDON, ONT N6H 2A7 CANADA
FRAZIER, RON	BASEBALL	POST OFFICE BOX 2148	WOODBRIDGE, VA 22193
FRAZIER, SHEILA A	ACTRESS	9300 WILSHIRE BLVD #410	BEVERLY HILLS, CA 90212
FRAZIER, WALT	BASKETBALL	WFAN-AM, 34-12 36TH ST	LONG ISLAND CITY, CA 11106
FREBERG, STAN	ACTOR-DIRECTOR	DGA, 7920 SUNSET BL, 6TH FL	LOS ANGELES, CA 90046
FRECHETTE, PETER	ACTOR	38 PARK PL	BROOKLYN, NY 11217
FREDERICK, VICKI	ACTRESS	10000 SANTA MONICA BLVD #305	LOS ANGELES, CA 90067
FREDERICKS, FRED	CARTOONIST	BRIDGE RD, BOX 475	EASTHAM, MA 02642
FREDERICKS, KEITH	SINGER	45 TUDOR CITY PL #911	NEW YORK, NY 10016
FREDERICKSON, MARK A	ARTIST	5285 N STONEHOUSE PL	TUCSON, AZ 85715
FREDIANI, PAUL	ACTOR	1200 N 6TH ST	BURBANK, CA 91504
FREDMAN, DAVID	BASKETBALL COACH	5 TRIAD CENTER #500	SALT LAKE CITY, UT 84180
FREDRICKSON, SCOTT	BASEBALL	POST OFFICE BOX 1420	WICHITA, KS 67201
FREDRIK, BURRY	THEATER PRODUCER	165 W 46TH ST	NEW YORK, NY 10036
FREDRIX, PAUL MORGAN	ACTOR	802 HILLDALE AVE #7	LOS ANGELES, CA 90069
FREEBAIRN-SMITH, IAN	COMPOSER	4362 LEMP AVE	STUDIO CITY, CA 91604
FREED, BERT	ACTOR	418 N BOWLING GREEN WY	LOS ANGELES, CA 90049
FREED, DAN	BASEBALL	TIGERS, 89 WHARNCLIFFE RD N	LONDON, ONT N6H 2A7 CANADA
FREED, HERB	WRITER-DIRECTOR	120 N ORANGE DR	LOS ANGELES, CA 90036
FREEDA, WILLIAM	FILM EDITOR	58 RUTH CT	WANTAGH, NY 11793
FREEDMAN, GORDON	FILM PRODUCER	1145 N MC CADDEN PL	LOS ANGELES, CA 90036
FREEDMAN, JERROLD	DIRECTOR	9220 SUNSET BLVD #206	LOS ANGELES, CA 90069
FREEDMAN, LEWIS	TV DIRECTOR-PRODUCER	THE CORPORATION FOR	
		PUBLIC BROADCASTING	
		1111 16TH ST, NW	WASHINGTON, DC 20036
FREEDMAN, MIKE	TV DIRECTOR	5 N WAGON RD	BELL CANYON, CA 91307
FREEDMAN, ROB	DIRECTOR	DGA, 110 W 57TH ST	NEW YORK, NY 10019
FREEDMAN, STEVEN ALLAN	DIRECTOR	DGA, 7920 SUNSET BL, 6TH FL	LOS ANGELES, CA 90046
FREEMAN, AL, JR	ACTOR-DIRECTOR	10 W 66TH ST #14-K	NEW YORK, NY 10023
FREEMAN, ALLYN I	TV WRITER	1239 N SWEETZER AVE	LOS ANGELES, CA 90069
FREEMAN, ARNY	ACTOR	70 GROVE ST	NEW YORK, NY 10014
FREEMAN, BEA	ACTRESS	120 W 3RD ST	NEW YORK, NY 10012
FREEMAN, CARRIE	ACTRESS	15900 SUNSET BLVD #2	PACIFIC PALISADES, CA 90272
FREEMAN, DAMITA JO	ACTRESS	9012 7TH AVE	INGLEWOOD, CA 90305
FREEMAN, DAVID	SCREENWRITER	8955 BEVERLY BLVD	WEST HOLLYWOOD, CA 90048
FREEMAN, DEVERY	SCREENWRITER	9481 CHEROKEE LN	BEVERLY HILLS, CA 90210
FREEMAN, DICK	BASEBALL EXECUTIVE	POST OFFICE BOX 129000	SAN DIEGO, CA 92112
FREEMAN, DICK	COMEDIAN	MAGNAN, 1121 NORTHRUP DR, NW	GRAND RAPIDS, MI 49504
FREEMAN, DON	COLUMNIST	POST OFFICE BOX 191	SAN DIEGO, CA 92112
FREEMAN, ED	CONDUCTOR-ARRANGER	8439 RIDPATH DR	LOS ANGELES, CA 90046
FREEMAN, FRED	TV WRITER	602 25TH ST	SANTA MONICA, CA 90402
FREEMAN, JOAN	ACT-WRI-DIR	3349 W CAHUENGA BLVD #2-B	LOS ANGELES, CA 90068
FREEMAN, JOAN TERRY	FILM DIRECTOR	151 S EL CAMINO DR	BEVERLY HILLS, CA 90212
FREEMAN, KATHLEEN	ACTRESS	6247 ORION AVE	VAN NUYS, CA 91411
FREEMAN, LAVEL	BASEBALL	2501 GARDENDALE RD	SACRAMENTO, CA 95822
FREEMAN, LISA	ACTRESS	1930 CENTURY PARK W #403	LOS ANGELES, CA 90067
FREEMAN, LISA M	ACTRESS	1440 23RD ST #314	SANTA MONICA, CA 90404
FREEMAN, LOREN	VENTRILOQUIST	8831 SUNSET BLVD #304	LOS ANGELES, CA 90069
FREEMAN, MARION C	TV WRITER	11906 GOSHEN AVE #1	LOS ANGELES, CA 90049
FREEMAN, MARVIN	BASEBALL	POST OFFICE BOX 4064	ATLANTA, GA 30302
FREEMAN, MICKEY	ACTOR	433 W 34TH ST	NEW YORK, NY 10120
FREEMAN, MONA	ACTOR	608 N ALPINE DR	BEVERLY HILLS, CA 90210
FREEMAN, MORGAN	ACTOR	340 E 87 TH ST #1-A	NEW YORK, NY 10128
FREEMAN, ORRIN	BASEBALL SCOUT	6850 LAWRENCE RD	LANTANA, FL 33462
FREEMAN, ORVILLE	POLITICIAN	1800 "M" ST #300-S, NW	WASHINGTON, DC 20036
FREEMAN, PAUL	ACTOR (AMERICAN)	301 N CANON DR #305	BEVERLY HILLS, CA 90210
FREEMAN, PAUL	ACTOR (ENGLISH)	MC REDDIE, 91 REGENT ST	LONDON W1R 7TB ENGLAND
FREEMAN, PAUL	TV DIRECTOR	330 E 49TH ST	NEW YORK, NY 10017
FREEMAN, SANDY	ACTRESS	KJAR, 10653 RIVERSIDE DR	TOLUCA LAKE, CA 91602

FREEMAN, SCOTT	BASEBALL	POST OFFICE BOX 10031	BAKERSFIELD, CA	93389
FREEMAN, SETH	WRITER-PRODUCER	1465 CAPRI DR	PACIFIC PALISADES, CA	90272
FREEMANS, THE	C & W GROUP	POST OFFICE BOX 2514	HENDERSONVILLE, TN	37077
FREER, MIKE	BASEBALL TRAINER	POST OFFICE BOX 422229	KISSIMMEE, FL	34742
FREGOSI, JIM	BASEBALL-MANAGER	POST OFFICE BOX 7575	PHILADELPHIA, PA	19101
FREHM, WALTER	CARTOONIST	KING FEATURES, 216 E 45TH ST	NEW YORK, NY	10017
FREI, SALLY	ACTRESS	3544 JASMINE AVE #9	LOS ANGELES, CA	90034
FREIBERGER, FRED	TV WRITER	10390 WILSHIRE BLVD	LOS ANGELES, CA	90024
FREIDUS, LLOYD S	CINEMATOGRAPHER	236 W 10TH ST	NEW YORK, NY	10014
FREILICH, JEFFREY	TV WRITER-PRODUCER	10594 HOLMAN AVE	LOS ANGELES, CA	90024
FREILING, HOWIE	BASEBALL COACH	POST OFFICE BOX 7845	COLUMBIA, SC	29202
FREITAG, DOROTHEA	COMPOSER	2 LINCOLN SQ	NEW YORK, NY	10023
FREITAG, DUSTY	BASEBALL	POST OFFICE BOX 6748	ROCKFORD, IL	61125
FREITAS, MIKE	BASEBALL	525 NW PEACOCK BLVD	PORT SAINT LUCIE, FL	34986
FREITAS, RICHARD	COMPOSER-ARRANGER	127 W 92ND ST, DUPLEX #2	NEW YORK, NY	10025
FRELENG, FRIZ	DIRECTOR-PRODUCER	10551 WILSHIRE BLVD #701	LOS ANGELES, CA	90024
FRELICH, PHYLLIS	ACTRESS	139 SPRING ST	NEW YORK, NY	10012
FREMIN, JOURDAN	ACTOR	128 1/2 N HAMILTON DR	BEVERLY HILLS, CA	90211
FRENCH, ARTHUR T	ACTOR	233 E 80TH ST	NEW YORK, NY	10021
FRENCH, LEIGH	ACTRESS	1850 N VISTA ST	LOS ANGELES, CA	90046
FRENCH, LISA	ARTIST	1069 GARDENIA AVE	LONG BEACH, CA	90813
FRENCH, SUSAN S	MUSICIAN	11934 RIVERSIDE DR #110	NORTH HOLLYWOOD, CA	91607
FRENCH, VALERIE	ACTRESS	309 W 57TH ST	NEW YORK, NY	10019
FRENKE, EUGENE	FILM WRITER-DIRECTOR	2022 COLDWATER CANYON DR	BEVERLY HILLS, CA	90210
FREROTTE, MITCH	FOOTBALL	BILLS, 1 BILLS DR	ORCHARD PARK, NJ	14127
FRESCO, DAVID	ACTOR	7960 SELMA AVE #304	LOS ANGELES, CA	90046
FRESCO, JOHN	COMPOSER	4567 WHITE OAK PL	ENCINO, CA	91316
FRESH, DOUG E & GET FRESH CREW	RAPPERS-RAPWRITERS	CITY SLICKER, 579 W 215TH ST	NEW YORK, NY	10019
FREUD, EMMA	TV HOST	GAY, 24 DENMARK ST	LONDON WC2H 8HJ	ENGLAND
FREUDBERG, FRANK	COLUMNIST	POST OFFICE BOX 500	WASHINGTON, DC	20044
FREUDBERG, JUDITH	TV WRITER	CHILDREN'S TV WORKSHOP		
		1 LINCOLN PLAZA	NEW YORK, NY	10023
FREUDENBERGER, DANIEL N	TV WRITER-DIRECTOR	10486 LORENZO PL	LOS ANGELES, CA	90064
FREWER, MATT "MAX HEADROOM"	ACTOR	5007 ROMA CT	MARINA DEL REY, CA	90292
FREY, CHRISTOPHER	ACTOR	THE TOFT, EAST DEA		
		NEAR CHICHESTER	SUSSEX	ENGLAND
FREY, GLENN	SINGER-SONGWRITER	345 N MAPLE DR #205	BEVERLY HILLS, CA	90210
FREY, JIM	BASEBALL-EXECUTIVE	1060 W ADDISON ST	CHICAGO, IL	60613
FREY, JOHN	BASEBALL EXECUTIVE	POST OFFICE BOX 22093	GREENSBORO, NC	27420
FREY, K ALLEY	WRESTLING EXECUTIVE	POST OFFICE BOX 105366	ATLANTA, GA	31348
FREY, LEONARD	ACTOR	180 WAVERLY PL	NEW YORK, NY	10014
FREY, STEVE	BASEBALL	10233 96TH AVE	EDMONTON, ALB TK5 OA5	CANADA
FREYTAG, ARNY	PHOTOGRAPHER	22735 MAC FARLANE DR	WOODLAND HILLS, CA	91364
FRIAS, PEPE	BASEBALL	POST OFFICE BOX 21727	SAN FRANCISCO, CA	95151
FRIBERG, CARL	CONDUCTOR	3334 BONNIE HILL DR	LOS ANGELES, CA	90068
FRICK, STEVE	BASEBALL EXECUTIVE	5301 NW 12TH AVE	FORT LAUDERDALE, FL	33309
FRICKE, JANIE	SINGER	POST OFFICE BOX 680785	SAN ANTONIO, TX	78268
FRICKER, BRENDA	ACTRESS	11726 SAN VICENTE BLVD #300	LOS ANGELES, CA	90049
FRID, JONATHAN	ACTOR	157 E 18TH ST #5-J	NEW YORK, NY	10003
FRIDAY, NANCY	AUTHORESS	ICM, 40 W 57TH ST	NEW YORK, NY	10019
FRIDELL, SQUIRE	ACTOR	7080 HOLLYWOOD BLVD #704	LOS ANGELES, CA	90028
FRIDLEY, ROD	BASEBALL SCOUT	333 W 35TH ST	CHICAGO, IL	60616
FRIED, GERALD	COMPOSER-CONDUCTOR	4146 LANKERSHIM BLVD #300	NORTH HOLLYWOOD, CA	91602
FRIEDAN, BETTY	AUTHORESS	USC SWMS DEPT, TAPER HALL #331-M	LOS ANGELES, CA	90089
FRIEDBERG, RICK	WRITER-PRODUCER	439 S PALM DR	BEVERLY HILLS, CA	90212
FRIEDENBERG, RICHARD	WRITER-PRODUCER	5847 KEOKUK AVE	WOODLAND HILLS, CA	91367
FRIEDER, SOL	ACTOR	POST OFFICE BOX 235	NEW YORK, NY	10003
FRIEDGEN, BUD	FILM EDITOR	ACE, 1041 N FORMOSA AVE	WEST HOLLYWOOD, CA	90046
FRIEDKIN, WILLIAM	FILM WRITER-DIRECTOR	668 PERUGIA WY	LOS ANGELES, CA	90077
FRIEDL, CINDY	ACTRESS	8228 SUNSET BLVD #311	LOS ANGELES, CA	90046
FRIEDL, ROBERT J	WRITER	10022 MELVIN AVE	NORTHRIDGE, CA	91324
FRIEDLANDER, HOWARD	TV WRITER	10351 SANTA MONICA BLVD #211	LOS ANGELES, CA	90025
FRIEDMAN, ALAN	ACTOR-SINGER	POST OFFICE BOX 11749	MARINA DEL REY, CA	90295
FRIEDMAN, BARBARA	TV DIRECTOR	35 E 75TH ST	NEW YORK, NY	10021
FRIEDMAN, BARBARA B	ACTRESS-SINGER	MANGO SOUND, 729 7TH AVE	NEW YORK, NY	10036
FRIEDMAN, BONNIE	TV DIRECTOR	4327 LOWER HONOAPIILANI	LAHAINA, HI	96761
FRIEDMAN, BRUCE JAY	SCREENWRITER	CAA, 9830 WILSHIRE BLVD	BEVERLY HILLS, CA	90212
FRIEDMAN, BUDD	TV-COMEDY PRODUCER	IMPROV, 8162 MELROSE AVE	LOS ANGELES, CA	90046
FRIEDMAN, DAVID JERROLD	AUTHOR	8939 CANBY AVE	NORTHRIDGE, CA	91325
FRIEDMAN, FAIGY	ACTOR	145 W 67TH ST #14-A	NEW YORK, NY	10023
FRIEDMAN, JASON	BASEBALL	POST OFFICE BOX 10213	LYNCHBURG, VA	24506
FRIEDMAN, JOSEPH	DIRECTOR	11 KEELER	ROWAYTON, CT	06854
FRIEDMAN, JUDITH	DIRECTOR	1872 N CLYBOURN AVE	CHICAGO, IL	60614
FRIEDMAN, KENNETH	SCREENWRITER	1015 GAYLEY AVE #300	LOS ANGELES, CA	90024
FRIEDMAN, KIM H	TV DIRECTOR	POST OFFICE BOX 5617	BEVERLY HILLS, CA	90213
FRIEDMAN, KIM PAUL	DIRECTOR-PRODUCER	4425 BABCOCK AVE	STUDIO CITY, CA	91604
FRIEDMAN, KINKY	SINGER	POST OFFICE BOX 160668	AUSTIN, TX	78716
FRIEDMAN, MARVIN	TV DIRECTOR	283 HENRY ST	BROOKLYN HEIGHTS, NY	11201
FRIEDMAN, MEL	WRITER	9000 SUNSET BLVD #1200	LOS ANGELES, CA	90069
FRIEDMAN, MICHAEL	BASEBALL EXECUTIVE	NY YANKEES, YANKEE STADIUM	BRONX, NY	10451
FRIEDMAN, PAUL L	TV WRITER	10000 SANTA MONICA BLVD #305	LOS ANGELES, CA	90067
FRIEDMAN, RONALD	TV WRITER	1280 COLDWATER CANYON DR	BEVERLY HILLS, CA	90210
FRIEDMAN, SEYMOUR	FILM DIRECTOR	1960 COLDWATER CANYON DR	BEVERLY HILLS, CA	90210
FRIEDMAN, SONYA	TV HOST	208 HARRISTOWN RD	GLEN ROCK, NJ	07452
FRIEDMAN, STANLEY	COMPOSER	187 S MARENGO AVE #6	PASADENA, CA	91101

FRIEDMANN, ANTHONY	FILM WRITER-DIRECTOR	PANTHEON FILMS, 38 MT PLEASANT	LONDON WC1X OAP	ENGLAND
FRIEND, MARTYN	TV DIRECTOR	PETERS, FRASER & DUNLOP, LTD		
		5TH FLOOR, THE CHAMBERS		
		CHELSEA HARBOUR, LOT RD	LONDON SW10 OXF	ENGLAND
FRIEND, ROBERT	FILM DIRECTOR	932 N LARRABEE ST #307	LOS ANGELES, CA	90069
FRIENDLY, ANDY	TV WRITER	1472 RISING GLEN RD	LOS ANGELES, CA	90069
FRIENDLY, ED	TV PRODUCER	1110 BEL AIR PL	LOS ANGELES, CA	90077
FRIENDLY, FRED W	COMMUNICATIONS EXEC	NAB, 1771 "N" ST, NW	WASHINGTON, DC	20036
FRIES, CHARLES	TV PRODUCER-EXECUTIVE	971 N ALPINE DR	BEVERLY HILLS, CA	90210
FRIES, SANDY	TV WRITER	SHAPIRO, 8827 BEVERLY BLVD	LOS ANGELES, CA	90048
FRIESEN, DAVID	SINGER-SONGWRITER	POST OFFICE BOX 29242	OAKLAND, CA	94604
FRIESEN, EUGENE	CELLIST	POST OFFICE BOX 9388	STANFORD, CA	94305
FRIESEN, KEVIN	BASEBALL EXECUTIVE	POST OFFICE BOX 465	MED HAT, ALB T1A 7G2	CANADA
FRIESZ, JOHN	FOOTBALL	POST OFFICE BOX 609609	SAN DIEGO, CA	92160
FRIMEL, RUDE V	COMPOSER	MCA/UNIVERSAL STUDIOS, INC		
		100 UNIVERSAL CITY PLAZA	UNIVERSAL CITY, CA	91608
FRIPP, ROBERT	SINGER-SONGWRITER	ROUTE #1, BOX 279	CHARLESTON, WV	25414
FRISBIE, ALEX	DIRECTOR	275 BUNKER HILL ST #2	CHARLESTOWN, MA	02129
FRISCHMAN, DAN	ACTOR	717 N ONTARIO ST	BURBANK, CA	91505
FRISHBERG, DAVE	MUSICIAN	POST OFFICE BOX C	RIVER EDGE, NJ	07661
FRISHMAN, EARL	BASEBALL SCOUT	TWINS, 501 CHICAGO AVE S	MINNEAPOLIS, MN	55415
FRISINA, JOE	BASEBALL SCOUT	6850 LAWRENCE RD	LANTANA, FL	33462
FRISTOE, ALLEN	TV DIRECTOR	35 HORIZON DR	CHATHAM, MA	02633
FRITH, MICHAEL	ART DIRECTOR	HENSON ASSOC, 117 E 69TH ST	NEW YORK, NY	10021
FRITSCH, GUNTHER	TV DIRECTOR	265 MARGUERITA LN	PASADENA, CA	91106
FRITZ, GREGORY	BASEBALL	POST OFFICE BOX 4370	SALINAS, CA	93912
FRITZ, JOHN	BASEBALL	POST OFFICE BOX 3496	DAVENPORT, IA	52808
FRITZ, RICHARD	COMPOSER-CONDUCTOR	7709 HOSFORD AVE	LOS ANGELES, CA	90045
FRITZHAND, JAMES	TV WRITER	1645 WOODS DR	LOS ANGELES, CA	90069
FRIZZELL, DAVID	SINGER-SONGWRITER	SMITH, 228 MC KAY'S CT	BRENTWOOD, TN	37027
FRIZZELL, WILLIAM	FOOTBALL	BUCCANEERS, 1 BUCCANEER PL	TAMPA, FL	33607
FROEBER, RICHARD	COMPOSER	POST OFFICE BOX 2166	LOS ANGELES, CA	90028
FROEHLICH, GUSTAV	ACTOR	CASA AL MURO, CH-6614 BRISSAGO	TESSIN	
FROEMMING, BRUCE	BASEBALL UMPIRE	5045 ELK CT	MILWAUKEE, WI	53223
FROGLEY, LOUISE	COSTUME DESIGNER	13949 VENTURA BLVD #309	SHERMAN OAKS, CA	91423
FROHMAN, CLAYTON	SCREENWRITER	UTA, 9560 WILSHIRE BLVD, 5TH FL	BEVERLY HILLS, CA	90212
FROHMAN, MELVYN	SCREENWRITER	2051 PELHAM AVE	LOS ANGELES, CA	90025
FROHNMAYER, DAVE	ATTORNEY GENERAL	STATE CAPITOL BUILDING	SALEM, OR	97310
FROHWIRTH, TODD	BASEBALL	ORIOLE PARK, 333 W CAMDEN ST	BALTIMORE, MD	21201
FROLOV, DIANE	TV WRITER-PRODUCER	3148 WAVERLY DR	LOS ANGELES, CA	90027
FROMMERT, PETER	TV DIRECTOR	9235 SILVERSIDE DR	SOUTH LYON, MI	48178
FROMSON, CAROLYN	ACTRESS	1230 HORN AVE #100	LOS ANGELES, CA	90069
FRONS, BRIAN	TV EXECUTIVE	NBC-TV, 3000 W ALAMEDA AVE	BURBANK, CA	91523
FRONTIERE, DOMINIC	COMPOSER-CONDUCTOR	3815 W OLIVE AVE #202	BURBANK, CA	91505
FRONTIERE, GEORGIA	FOOTBALL EXECUTIVE	RAMS, 2327 W LINCOLN BLVD	ANAHEIM, CA	92801
FROST, BOBBY JEAN	MUSIC ARRANGER	2137 JUNE DR	NASHVILLE, TN	37214
FROST, DAVID	GOLFER	POST OFFICE BOX 109601	PALM BCH GARDENS, FL	33418
FROST, DAVID	TV HOST	130 W 57TH ST	NEW YORK, NY	10019
FROST, JEAN SARAH	ACTRESS	2341 SCARFF ST	LOS ANGELES, CA	90007
FROST, LINDSAY	ACTRESS	9200 SUNSET BLVD #625	LOS ANGELES, CA	90069
FROST, LINDSAY	ACTRESS	151 S EL CAMINO DR	BEVERLY HILLS, CA	90212
FROST, MARK	TV WRITER-PRODUCER	CAA, 9830 WILSHIRE BLVD	BEVERLY HILLS, CA	90212
FROST, MARTIN	U S CONGRESSMAN	1319 NCNB OAK CLIFF TOWER		
		400 S ZANG BLVD	DALLAS, TX	75208
FROST, RALPH L	FILM WRITER-DIRECTOR	7813 HILLSIDE AVE	LOS ANGELES, CA	90046
FROUG, WILLIAM	WRITER-PRODUCER	3419 WOODCLIFF RD	SHERMAN OAKS, CA	91403
FRUCHTMAN, MILTON	TV DIRECTOR-PRODUCER	180 MADISON AVE #1407	NEW YORK, NY	10016
FRUEH, MARK	ARTIST	PHASE 2, 155 N MICHIGAN AVE	CHICAGO, IL	60601
FRUET, WILLIAM	DIRECTOR	51 OLIVE ST	TORONTO, ONT M6G 1T7	CANADA
FRUITMAN, SHEVA	ART DIRECTOR	73 ORCHARD ST #8	NEW YORK, NY	10002
FRY, DEBBIE	SINGER	5625 "O" STREET BLDG #7	LINCOLN, NE	68510
FRY, ED	ACTOR	9301 WILSHIRE BLVD #312	BEVERLY HILLS, CA	90210
FRY, GARY	COMPOSER-CONDUCTOR	3950 LYONS ST	EVANSTON, IL	60203
FRY, MICHAEL	CARTOONIST	THE WASHINGTON POST		
		WRITERS GROUP		
		1150 15TH ST, NW	WASHINGTON, DC	20071
FRY, STEPHEN	ACTOR-WRITER	GAY, 24 DENMARK ST	LONDON WC2H 8HJ	ENGLAND
FRYAR, IRVING	FOOTBALL	PATRIOTS, FOXBORO STADIUM, RT #1	FOXBORO, MA	02035
FRYE, JEFF	BASEBALL	POST OFFICE BOX 75089	OKLAHOMA CITY, OK	73147
FRYE, ROBERT	DIRECTOR	6006 GRACIOSA DR	LOS ANGELES, CA	90068
FRYE, SEAN	ACTOR	1930 CENTURY PARK W #403	LOS ANGELES, CA	90067
FRYE, SOLEIL MOON	ACTRESS	POST OFFICE BOX 5164	GLENDALE, CA	91201
FRYE, STUART	DIRECTOR	1404 S BAY FRONT	BALBOA ISLAND, CA	92662
FRYER, PAUL	BASEBALL SCOUT	ORIOLE PARK, 333 W CAMDEN ST	BALTIMORE, MD	21201
FRYER, ROBERT	THEATER PRODUCER	PRODUCERS CIRCLE COMPANY		
		1350 AVE OF THE AMERICAS	NEW YORK, NY	10019
FRYMAN, NICHOLAS	COMPOSER	310 N VAN NESS AVE #6	LOS ANGELES, CA	90004
FRYMAN, TRAVIS	BASEBALL	TIGERS, TIGER STADIUM	DETROIT, MI	48216
FRYMAN, TROY	BASEBALL	POST OFFICE BOX 4218	SOUTH BEND, IN	46634
FUCCI, WILLIAM	DIRECTOR	12 W 37TH ST	NEW YORK, NY	10018
FUCHS, BERNIE	ARTIST	3 TANGLEWOOD LN	WETSPORT, CT	06880
FUCHS, C EMIL	COMPOSER	455 N CRESCENT HEIGHTS BLVD	LOS ANGELES, CA	90048
FUCHS, DICK	ACTOR	1412 N GORDON ST	HOLLYWOOD, CA	90028
FUCHS, LEO	ACTOR	609 N KILKEA DR	LOS ANGELES, CA	90048
FUCHS, MICHAEL J	CABLE EXECUTIVE	1100 6TH AVE #8-27	NEW YORK, NY	10036

Name	Occupation	Address	City
FUCHS, THOMAS	WRITER	1427 N HAYWORTH AVE #D	LOS ANGELES, CA 90046
FUDGE, ALAN	ACTOR	355 S REXFORD DR	BEVERLY HILLS, CA 90212
FUDGE, GEORGIA ANN	BODYBUILDER	10113 N 14TH ST #110	SAINT PETERSBURG, FL 33702
FUDPUCKER, ELMER	SINGER	POST OFFICE BOX 120223	NASHVILLE, TN 37212
FUENTES, DAISY	ACTRESS	ABC-TV, "LOVING"	
		320 W 66TH ST, STUDIO 23	NEW YORK, NY 10023
FUENTES, ERNIE	ACTOR	16636 RUNNYMEDE ST	VAN NUYS, CA 91406
FUENTES, LUIS	COMPOSER	98 RUE LEPIC	PARIS 75018 FRANCE
FUENTES, PAUL	WRITER-PRODUCER	12345 CALIFA ST	NORTH HOLLYWOOD, CA 91607
FUJI, MR	WRESTLER-MANAGER	POST OFFICE BOX 3859	STAMFORD, CT 06905
FUJIMORI, WARREN	ACTOR	10800 WESCOTT AVE	SUNLAND, CA 91040
FUJIWARA, HARRY	WRESTLER-MANAGER	SEE - FUJI, MR	
FULBRIGHT, J WILLIAM	U S SENATOR	2527 BELMONT RD, NW	WASHINGTON, DC 20005
FULCHER, DAVID	FOOTBALL	BENGALS, 200 RIVERFRONT STADIUM	CINCINNATI, OH 45202
FULHAGE, SCOTT	FOOTBALL	FALCONS, SUWANEE RD AT I-85	SUWANEE, GA 30174
FULHAM, MARY	ACTRESS	156 BERGEN ST	NEW YORK, NY 11217
FULL HOUSE	ROCK & ROLL GROUP	332 S MICHIGAN AVE #1847	CHICAGO, IL 60604
FULLENWIDER, FRAN	ACTRESS	JAMES, 22 WESTBERE RD	LONDON NW2 3SR ENGLAND
FULLER, CHARLES	SCREENWRITER	WM MORRIS, 1350 AVE OF AMERICAS	NEW YORK, NY 10019
FULLER, CHRISTA	ACTRESS	7628 WOODROW WILSON DR	LOS ANGELES, CA 90046
FULLER, DAVE	SCREENWRITER	9200 SUNSET BLVD #402	LOS ANGELES, CA 90069
FULLER, EDDIE	FOOTBALL	BILLS, 1 BILLS DR	ORCHARD PARK, NJ 14127
FULLER, ERWIN	ACTOR	122 S SYCAMORE AVE	LOS ANGELES, CA 90036
FULLER, GAIL	ART DIRECTOR	24 MINETTA LN #4-R	NEW YORK, NY 10012
FULLER, JERRY	SINGER-SONGWRITER	WILLIAMS ARTISTS MANAGEMENT	
		816 N LA CIENEGA BLVD	LOS ANGELES, CA 90069
FULLER, JOE	FOOTBALL	PACKERS, 1265 LOMBARDI AVE	GREEN BAY, WI 54307
FULLER, JOHNNY	BODYBUILDER	3002 E 20TH ST	TUCSON, AZ 85716
FULLER, JON	BASEBALL	POST OFFICE BOX 2001	CEDAR RAPIDS, IA 52406
FULLER, KURT	ACTOR	9255 SUNSET BLVD #515	LOS ANGELES, CA 90069
FULLER, LANCE	ACTOR	8831 SUNSET BLVD #402	LOS ANGELES, CA 90069
FULLER, LARRY	CHOREOGRAPHER	BECKER/LONDON, 30 LINCOLN PLAZA	NEW YORK, NY 10023
FULLER, LESLIE	COMPOSER-LYRICIST	151 S EL CAMINO DR	BEVERLY HILLS, CA 90212
FULLER, MICHAEL	WRITER	2565 1/2 GLEN GREEN ST	LOS ANGELES, CA 90068
FULLER, NIKKI	BODYBUILDER	JUNGLE GYM, 4624 SE 67TH AVE	PORTLAND, OR 97206
FULLER, PARMER	COMPOSER-CONDUCTOR	911 MALCOLM AVE	LOS ANGELES, CA 90024
FULLER, PENNY	ACTRESS	12428 HESBY ST	NORTH HOLLYWOOD, CA 91607
FULLER, ROBERT	ACTOR	1930 CENTURY PARK W #403	LOS ANGELES, CA 90067
FULLER, SAMUEL	FILM WRITER-PRODUCER	7628 WOODROW WILSON DR	LOS ANGELES, CA 90046
FULLER, WILLIAM	FOOTBALL	OILERS, 6910 FANNIN ST	HOUSTON, TX 77070
FULLERTON, FIONA	ACTRESS	LONDON MGT, 235-241 REGENT ST	LONDON W1R 4PH ENGLAND
FULLERTON, RICHARD S	ACTOR	431 N SPAULDING AVE	LOS ANGELES, CA 90036
FULLERTON, SANDI	TV DIRECTOR	8264 GOULD AVE	LOS ANGELES, CA 90046
FULLINGTON, DARRELL	FOOTBALL	PATRIOTS, FOXBORO STADIUM, RT #1	FOXBORO, MA 02035
FULLMER, GENE	BOXER	9250 S 2200 WEST	WEST JORDAN, UT 84084
FULLY, EDWARDS	BASEBALL	525 NW PEACOCK BLVD	PORT SAINT LUCIE, FL 34986
FULMORE, CHUCK, TRIO	GOSPEL GROUP	4031 FORNI RD	PLACERVILLE, CA 95667
FULTON, ED	BASEBALL	POST OFFICE BOX 5599	LITTLE ROCK, AR 72215
FULTON, EILEEN	ACTRESS	301 W 57TH ST	NEW YORK, NY 10019
FULTON, GREG	BASEBALL	POST OFFICE BOX 15757	HARRISBURG, PA 17105
FULTON, WENDY	ACTRESS	12700 VENTURA BLVD #350	STUDIO CITY, CA 91604
FULTS, RICHARD J	ACTOR	4763 NOBLE AVE	SHERMAN OAKS, CA 91403
FULTZ, FRANK	BASEBALL-INSTRUCTOR	POST OFFICE BOX 7000	PITTSBURGH, PA 15212
FULTZ, VINCE	BASEBALL	POLECATS, 608 N SLAPPEY BLVD	ALBANY, GA 31701
FUMOSO, DONNA	MAKE-UP ARTIST	485 COLUMBUS AVE #1-A	NEW YORK, NY 10024
FUNDERBURK, MARK	BASEBALL COACH	POST OFFICE BOX 5645	ORLANDO, FL 32855
FUNDIS, GARTH	GUITARIST-SONGWRITER	POST OFFICE BOX 120715	NASHVILLE, TN 37212
FUNICELLO, ANNETTE	ACTRESS	16202 SANDY LN	ENCINO, CA 91436
FUNK, DANIEL	TV DIRECTOR	636 E HARVARD RD #D	BURBANK, CA 91501
FUNK, FRANK	BASEBALL-MANAGER	4452 E BELLVIEW ST	PHOENIX, AZ 85008
FUNK, FRED	GOLFER	POST OFFICE BOX 109601	PALM BCH GARDENS, FL 33418
FUNT, ALLEN	TV HOST-DIRECTOR	2359 NICHOLS CANYON	LOS ANGELES, CA 90046
FUNT, DAVID	DIRECTOR	SUNTREE, 400 E 85TH ST	NEW YORK, NY 10028
FURCAL, MANNY	BASEBALL	POST OFFICE BOX 30160	SAN BERNARDINO, CA 92413
FUREY, JOHN	ACTOR	10000 SANTA MONICA BLVD #305	LOS ANGELES, CA 90067
FURIA, JOHN, JR	TV WRITER	17147 OAK VIEW DR	ENCINO, CA 91316
FURIE, SIDNEY J	WRITER-PRODUCER	1191 ANGELO DR	BEVERLY HILLS, CA 90210
FURINO, FRANK	WRITER-PRODUCER	3900 GLENRIDGE DR	SHERMAN OAKS, CA 91423
FURLAN, ALAN	ACTOR	665 ELM GROVE RD	ELM GROVE, WI 53122
FURLONG, EDDIE	ACTOR	SMITH, 121 N SAN VICENTE BLVD	BEVERLY HILLS, CA 90211
FURLONG, JOHN	ACTOR	5250 WOODMAN AVE	VAN NUYS, CA 91401
FURLONG, SHIRLEY	GOLFER	2750 VOLUSA AVE #B	DAYTON BEACH, FL 32114
FURMAN, MARY ANN	ACTRESS	505 AVONDALE AVE #A	LOS ANGELES, CA 90049
FURMSTON, DAVID	COMPOSER-CONDUCTOR	804 N LINDEN DR	BEVERLY HILLS, CA 90210
FURNAD, V R "BOB"	TV EXECUTIVE	1050 TECHWOOD DR, NW	ATLANTA, GA 30318
FURNELL, BILL	ACTOR	1134 9TH ST #H	SANTA MONICA, CA 90403
FURNESS, DEBORRA-LEE	ACTRESS	10100 SANTA MONICA BLVD #1600	LOS ANGELES, CA 90067
FURR, CLARE	BODYBUILDER	1250 POYDRAS ST #200	NEW ORLEANS, LA 70012
FURST, ANTON	ART DIRECTOR	CAA, 9830 WILSHIRE BLVD	BEVERLY HILLS, CA 90212
FURST, JONATHAN	SCREENWRITER	17514 VENTURA BLVD #205	ENCINO, CA 91316
FURST, STEPHEN	ACTOR	3900 HUNTERCREST CT	MOORPARK, CA 93021
FURTH, GEORGE	ACTOR-WRITER	307 W 4TH ST	NEW YORK, NY 10014
FUSARI, LOUIS	DIRECTOR	10084 ROSCOE BLVD	SUN VALLEY, CA 91352
FUSCO, CARMEN	BASEBALL SCOUT	POST OFFICE BOX 129000	SAN DIEGO, CA 92112
FUSCO, PAUL	PHOTOGRAPHER	7 MELODY LN	MILL VALLEY, CA 94941

FUSCO, TOM	BASEBALL	POST OFFICE BOX 3783	SAVANNAH, GA	31414
FUSELIER, OLIVER	ACTOR	323 VETERAN AVE	LOS ANGELES, CA	90024
FUSON, GRADY	BASEBALL MANAGER	POST OFFICE BOX 1457	MEDFORD, OR	97501
FUSTER, JAIME B	U S COMMISSIONER	POST OFFICE BOX 4751	SAN JUAN, PR	00902
FUTRELL, MICHELE	DIRECTOR	505 N LAKESHORE DR #1915	CHICAGO, IL	60611
FYHRIE, MIKE	BASEBALL	300 STADIUM WY	DAVENPORT, FL	33837
FYSON, CAROLYN	ACTRESS	15605 WOODFIELD PL	SHERMAN OAKS, CA	91403

G, KENNY	SAXOPHONIST	SEE - KENNY G		
G B H	ROCK & ROLL GROUP	149-03 GUY R BREWER BLVD	JAMAICA, NY	11434
G G SHINN	RHYTHM & BLUES GROUP	KINGSLAND, 108 SHARON DR	WEST MONROE, LA	71291
GAARE, HOWARD	BASEBALL EXECUTIVE	POST OFFICE BOX 1621	GREAT FALLS, MT	59403
GABAI, RICHARD	ACTOR-FILM DIRECTOR	6310 SAN VICENTE BLVD #407	LOS ANGELES, CA	90048
GABBANI, MIKE	BASEBALL	POST OFFICE BOX 4488	WINSTON-SALEM, NC	27115
GABEL, CYPRIENNE	ACTRESS	321 DARTMOUTH ST	BOSTON, MA	02116
GABELLA, JIM	BASEBALL COACH	2501 ALLEN AVE, SE	CANTON, OH	44707
GABLE, CHRISTOPHER	ACTOR	MC REDDIE, 91 REGENT ST	LONDON W1R 7TB	ENGLAND
GABLER, CARL	WRITER	5730 LEMONA AVE	VAN NUYS, CA	91411
GABOR, EVA	ACTRESS	9255 SUNSET BLVD #1115	LOS ANGELES, CA	90069
GABOR, JOLIE	ACTRESS	17 CAHUILLA HILLS DR	PALM SPRINGS, CA	92264
GABOR, ZSA ZSA	ACTRESS-PRINCESS	1001 BEL AIR RD	LOS ANGELES, CA	90024
GABRIEL, JOHN	ACTOR	100 W 57TH ST #5-Q	NEW YORK, NY	10019
GABRIEL, JOHN	BASKETBALL COACH	POST OFFICE BOX 76	ORLANDO, FL	32802
GABRIEL, PETER	SINGER-SONGWRITER	GALIFORCE MANAGEMENT		
		81-83 WALTON ST	LONDON SW3 2HP	ENGLAND
GABRIELLE, MONIQUE	ACTRESS-MODEL	MONIQUE GABRIELLE FAN CLUB		
		4520 VAN NUYS BLVD #538	SHERMAN OAKS, CA	91403
GADDY, MIKE	BASEBALL TRAINER	POST OFFICE BOX 1535	JOHNSON CITY, TN	37605
GADDY, ROBERT	BASEBALL	POST OFFICE BOX 10336	CLEARWATER, FL	34617
GAETANO, NICK	ARTIST	821 BROADWAY	NEW YORK, NY	10003
GAETTI, GARY	BASEBALL	POST OFFICE BOX 2000	ANAHEIM, CA	92803
GAFFNEY, FREDRICKA	DIRECTOR	12306 MONTANA AVE	LOS ANGELES, CA	90049
GAFFNEY, GEORGE	CONDUCTOR	5902 COLFAX AVE	NORTH HOLLYWOOD, CA	91601
GAFFNEY, RICKIE	TV WRITER-PRODUCER	7225 SHOUP AVE	LOS ANGELES, CA	91307
GAGE, BETH	SCREENWRITER	150 POLECAT LN	TELLURIDE, CO	81435
GAGE, GEORGE	FILM DIRECTOR	150 POLECAT LN	TELLURIDE, CO	81435
GAGE, JACK	DIRECTOR	948 CHANNEL DR	SANTA BARBARA, CA	93108
GAGE, LOUTZ	ACTOR	2455 CUMBERLAND RD	SAN MARINO, CA	91108
GAGLIANO, BOB	FOOTBALL	POST OFFICE BOX 609609	SAN DIEGO, CA	92160
GAGLIARDI, JOSEPH	BASEBALL EXECUTIVE	POST OFFICE BOX 26400	SAN JOSE, CA	95125
GAGNE, GREG	BASEBALL	TWINS, 501 CHICAGO AVE S	MINNEAPOLIS, MN	55415
GAGNER, DAVE	HOCKEY	NORTH STARS, 7901 CEDAR AVE S	BLOOMINGTON, MN	55425
GAGNIER, HOLLY	ACTRESS	59 W 76TH ST #3-D	NEW YORK, NY	10023
GAGNIER, HUGH	DIRECTOR	4250 VIA MARINA #49	MARINA DEL REY, CA	90292
GAGNON, ANDRE-PHILIPPE	COMEDIAN	89 RUE ALEXANDRA	GRANBY, QUE J2C 2P4	CANADA
GAGO, JENNY	ACTRESS	KOHNER, 9169 SUNSET BLVD	LOS ANGELES, CA	90069
GAHL, FRANK	BASEBALL EXECUTIVE	POST OFFICE BOX 7005	HUNTINGTON, WV	25775
GAILE, JERI	ACTRESS	606 N LARCHMONT BLVD #309	LOS ANGELES, CA	90004
GAILEY, CHAN	FOOTBALL COACH	BRONCOS, 13655 BRONCOS PKWY	ENGLEWOOD, CO	80112
GAILEY, SUSAN	ACTRESS	22233 FLANCO RD	WOODLAND HILLS, CA	91364
GAINER, GLEN B	AUDITOR	STATE CAPITOL BUILDING	CHARLESTON, WV	25305
GAINER, JAY	BASEBALL	POST OFFICE BOX 1420	WICHITA, KS	67201
GAINES, ALBERT	FILM EDITOR	75 HENRY ST #32-B	BROOKLYN, NY	11201
GAINES, AMBROSE, III	TV DIRECTOR	430 W ERIE	CHICAGO, IL	60610
GAINES, BOYD	ACTOR	1999 AVE OF THE STARS #2850	LOS ANGELES, CA	90067
GAINES, COREY	BASKETBALL	POST OFFICE BOX 4658	DENVER, CO	80204
GAINES, JACK	TV DIRECTOR-PRODUCER	USIA-TV, 26 FEDERAL PLZ #30-100	NEW YORK, NY	10278
GAINES, LA DONNA	SINGER-ACTRESS	SEE - SUMMER, DONNA		
GAINES, SMOKEY	BASKETBALL	10475 SAN DIEGO MISSION RD	SAN DIEGO, CA	92120
GAINOR, PAT	ACTRESS	TIFFANY, 23125 PARK CONTESSA	CALABASAS PARK, CA	91302
GAINS, COURTNEY	ACTOR	4125 S FIGUEROA ST #408	LOS ANGELES, CA	90037
GAINSBOURG, SERGE	ACTOR	ARTMEDIA, 10 AVE GEORGE V	PARIS 75008	FRANCE
GAISER, GERALD	WRITER	17411 TILFORD CT	GRANADA HILLS, CA	91344
GAKELER, DAN	BASEBALL	TIGERS, TIGER STADIUM	DETROIT, MI	48216
GALAN, PAUL	DIRECTOR-PRODUCER	10 PINE RD	SUFFERN, NY	10901
GALANOY, TERRY I	WRITER	220 24TH ST	SANTA MONICA, CA	90402
GALANTE, BEN	BASEBALL SCOUT	POST OFFICE BOX 288	HOUSTON, TX	77001
GALANTE, MATT	BASEBALL-COACH	POST OFFICE BOX 288	HOUSTON, TX	77001
GALANTLE, GEORGE	TALENT AGENT	112 21ST AVE S #204	NASHVILLE, TN	37203
GALANTY, SIDNEY	TV DIRECTOR	1272 LACHMAN LN	PACIFIC PALISADES, CA	90272
GALARNO, BILL	ACTOR	400 W 43RD ST #17-0	NEW YORK, NY	10036
GALARRAGE, ANDRES	BASEBALL	250 STADIUM PLAZA	ST LOUIS, MO	63102
GALATI, FRANK	SCREENWRITER	151 S EL CAMINO DR	BEVERLY HILLS, CA	90212
GALBRAITH, BILL	TV EXECUTIVE	CBS NEWS, 2020 "M" ST, NW	WASHINGTON, DC	20036
GALBRAITH, JANE	COLUMNIST	5700 WILSHIRE BLVD #120	LOS ANGELES, CA	90036
GALBRAITH, SCOTT	FOOTBALL	BROWNS, 80 1ST ST	BEREA, OH	44017
GALE, BOB	FILM WRITER-PRODUCER	CAA, 9830 WILSHIRE BLVD	BEVERLY HILLS, CA	90212

GALE, CYNTHIA	ACTRESS	8360 MELROSE AVE #203	LOS ANGELES, CA 90069
GALE, DAVID	ACTOR	102 GREENWICH AVE	NEW YORK, NY 10011
GALE, ERIC	GUITARIST-COMPOSER	POST OFFICE BOX 741074	LOS ANGELES, CA 90004
GALE, RICH	BASEBALL-COACH	3 YORK DR	DURHAM, NH 03824
GALEHOUSE, DENNY	BASEBALL-SCOUT	POST OFFICE BOX 2000	SAN DIEGO, CA 92112
GALFAS, TIMOTHY	WRITER-PRODUCER	1366 SAN YSIDRO DR	BEVERLY HILLS, CA 90210
GALIK, DENISE	ACTRESS	12456 VENTURA BLVD #1	STUDIO CITY, CA 91604
GALIMIR, FELIX	VIOLINIST	225 E 74TH ST	NEW YORK, NY 10021
GALINDEZ, LUIS	BASEBALL	12000 STADIUM RD	ADELANTO, CA 92301
GALLA-RINI, ANTHONY	COMPOSER-CONDUCTOR	971 BORDEN RD #104	SAN MARCOS, CA 92069
GALLAGHER	COMEDIAN	12164 EMELITA ST	NORTH HOLLYWOOD, CA 91607
GALLAGHER, BRIAN	WRITER-EDITOR	POST OFFICE BOX 500	WASHINGTON, DC 20044
GALLAGHER, DAVE	BASEBALL	METS, 126TH ST & ROOSEVELT AVE	FLUSHING, NY 11368
GALLAGHER, JIM, JR	GOLFER	POST OFFICE BOX 109601	PALM BCH GARDENS, FL 33418
GALLAGHER, JOHN P	NEWS CORRES-WRITER	CBS NEWS, 2020 "M" ST, NW	WASHINGTON, DC 20036
GALLAGHER, LEO	COMEDIAN	SEE - GALLAGHER	
GALLAGHER, MARGARET	ACTRESS	1310 WARNALL AVE	LOS ANGELES, CA 90024
GALLAGHER, MARY LYNN	SINGER	POST OFFICE BOX 1338	MERCHANTVILLE, NJ 08109
GALLAGHER, MEGAN	ACTRESS	442 LANDFAIR AVE	LOS ANGELES, CA 90024
GALLAGHER, OLIVE	ACTRESS	13827 SUNSET BLVD	PACIFIC PALISADES, CA 90272
GALLAGHER, PAT	BASEBALL EXECUTIVE	S F GIANTS, CANDLESTICK PARK	SAN FRANICSCO, CA 94124
GALLAGHER, PETER	ACTOR	151 S EL CAMINO DR	BEVERLY HILLS, CA 90212
GALLAGHER, SARAH WOODSIDE	TV WRITER	11726 SAN VICENTE BLVD #300	LOS ANGELES, CA 90049
GALLAGHER, SUSAN	ARTIST	3624 AMARYLLIS DR	SAN DIEGO, CA 92106
GALLAGHER, TOM	TREASURER	STATE CAPITOL BUILDING	TALLAHASSEE, FL 32399
GALLANT, GERARD	HOCKEY	RED WINGS, 600 CIVIC CENTER DR	DETROIT, MI 48226
GALLARDO, LUIS	BASEBALL	5301 NW 12TH AVE	FORT LAUDERDALE, FL 33309
GALLARDO, SILVANA	ACTRESS	4270 CAMILLIA AVE	STUDIO CITY, CA 91604
GALLAY, PETER M	TV WRITER	621 GEORGINA AVE	SANTA MONICA, CA 90402
GALLEGLY, ELTON	U S CONGRESSMAN	200 N WESTLAKE BLVD #207	THOUSAND OAKS, CA 91362
GALLEGO, GINA	ACTRESS	6550 MURIETTA AVE	VAN NUYS, CA 91401
GALLEGO, MIKE	BASEBALL	N Y YANKEES, YANKEE STADIUM	BRONX, NY 10451
GALLERY, MICHELE	TV WRITER	11906 SUNSHINE TERR	STUDIO CITY, CA 91604
GALLEY, GARRY	HOCKEY	BRUINS, 150 CAUSEWAY ST	BOSTON, MA 02114
GALLIN, SANDY	TALENT AGENT-TV PROD	8730 SUNSET BLVD #PH-W	LOS ANGELES, CA 90069
GALLISON, JOE	ACTOR	3760 GREEN VISTA DR	ENCINO, CA 91436
GALLO, BOB	ACTOR	12619 VANDOWEN ST	NORTH HOLLYWOOD, CA 91605
GALLO, DEAN	U S CONGRESSMAN	101 GIBRALTER DR #2-D	MORRIS PLAINS, NJ 07950
GALLO, GEORGE	SCREENWRITER	CAA, 9830 WILSHIRE BLVD	BEVERLY HILLS, CA 90212
GALLO, GLORIA	TV EXECUTIVE	PRIMETIME ENTERPRISES, INC	
		444 MADISON AVE, 32ND FLOOR	NEW YORK, NY 10022
GALLO, GUY	SCREENWRITER	ICM, 8899 BEVERLY BLVD	LOS ANGELES, CA 90048
GALLO, LEW	DIRECTOR-PRODUCER	915 N BEVERLY DR	BEVERLY HILLS, CA 90210
GALLO, LILLIAN	FILM PRODUCER	915 N BEVERLY DR	BEVERLY HILLS, CA 90210
GALLO, WILLIAM	CARTOONIST	1 MAYFLOWER DR	YONKERS, NY 10710
GALLOWAY, DON	ACTOR	BDP, 10637 BURBANK BLVD	NORTH HOLLYWOOD, CA 91601
GALLOWAY, JAMES	ACTOR	22327 HART ST	CANOGA PARK, CA 91303
GALLOWAY, JAMES U, JR	FILM EDITOR	ACE, 1041 N FORMOSA AVE	WEST HOLLYWOOD, CA 90046
GALLOWAY, JANE	ACTRESS	10351 SANTA MONICA BLVD #211	LOS ANGELES, CA 90025
GALLOWAY, LINDA	ACTRESS	BDP, 10637 BURBANK BLVD	NORTH HOLLYWOOD, CA 91601
GALLUN, RAYMOND Z	WRITER	110-20 71ST AVE	FOREST HILLS, CA 11375
GALTON, RAY	RADIO-TV WRITER	LE BARS, 18 QUEEN ANNE	LONDON W1M 9LB ENGLAND
GALVEZ, BALVINO	BASEBALL	POST OFFICE BOX 28268	SAN ANTONIO, TX 78228
GALVIN, JOHN	GOLFER	2750 VOLUSA AVE #B	DAYTON BEACH, FL 32114
GALVIN, RAY	ACTOR	5529 HAZELBROOK AVE	LAKEWOOD, CA 90712
GAM, RITA	ACTRESS	180 W 58TH ST #8-B	NEW YORK, NY 10019
GAMBARELLI, MARIA	ACTRESS	50 CENTRAL PARK W	NEW YORK, NY 10023
GAMBETTA, VERN	BASEBALL-INSTRUCTOR	333 W 35TH ST	CHICAGO, IL 60616
GAMBLE, DUNCAN	ACTOR	1080 NOWITA PL	VENICE, CA 90291
GAMBLE, ED	CARTOONIST	POST OFFICE BOX 1949-F	JACKSONVILLE, FL 32231
GAMBLE, HARRY	FOOTBALL	EAGLES, BROAD ST & PATTISON AVE	PHILADELPHIA, PA 19148
GAMBLE, JOHN	TV EXECUTIVE	1245 N CRESCENT HEIGHTS BLVD	LOS ANGELES, CA 90046
GAMBLE, KENNETH	RECORD PRODUCER	309 S BROAD ST	PHILADELPHIA, PA 19107
GAMBLE, KEVIN	BASKETBALL	151 MERRIMAC ST	BOSTON, MA 02114
GAMBLE, OSCAR	BASEBALL	108 TENSAW RD	MONTGOMERY, AL 36117
GAMBOA, TOM	BASEBALL EXECUTIVE	POST OFFICE BOX 2000	SAN DIEGO, CA 92112
GAMBON, MICHAEL	ACTOR	DALZELL, 17 BROAD CT #12	LONDON WC2B 5QN ENGLAND
GAMBS, CHRIS	BASEBALL	POST OFFICE BOX 1295	CLINTON, IA 52733
GAMBS, CRAIG	BASEBALL SCOUT	REDS, 100 RIVERFRONT STADIUM	CINCINNATI, OH 45202
GAME THEORY	ROCK & ROLL GROUP	POST OFFICE BOX 578190	CHICAGO, IL 60657
GAMEZ, FRANCISCO	BASEBALL	POST OFFICE BOX 8550	STOCKTON, CA 95208
GAMEZ, ROBERT	GOLFER	POST OFFICE BOX 109601	PALM BCH GARDENS, FL 33418
GAMEZ, ROBERT "BOBBY"	BASEBALL	POST OFFICE BOX 1742	PALM SPRINGS, CA 92263
GAMMELL, ROBIN	ACTOR	822 S ROBERTSON BLVD #200	LOS ANGELES, CA 90035
GAMMON, JAMES	ACTOR	641 N POINSETTA PL	LOS ANGELES, CA 90036
GAMPEL, CHRIS	ACTOR	400 W 43RD ST	NEW YORK, NY 10036
GAMSON, CHERYL	ACTRESS	6116 ALCOVE AVE	NORTH HOLLYWOOD, CA 91605
GANDOLPH, DAVID	BASEBALL	POST OFFICE BOX 309	GASTONA, NC 28053
GANIS, GLENDA	COSTUME DESIGNER	8447 BRIER DR	LOS ANGELES, CA 90046
GANIS, GLENDA	WRITER	8745 WONDERLAND AVE	LOS ANGELES, CA 90046
GANKEMA, LINDSAY	ACTRESS	NBC-TV, "SANTA BARBARA"	
		3000 W ALAMEDA AVE	BURBANK, CA 91523
GANKEMA, PAIGE	ACTRESS	NBC-TV, "SANTA BARBARA"	
		3000 W ALAMEDA AVE	BURBANK, CA 91523
GANN, ERNEST	AUTHOR	RED MILL FARM	SAN JUAN ISLAND, WA 98250

Name	Occupation	Address	City/State	Zip/Country
GANN, MIKE	FOOTBALL	FALCONS, SUWANEE RD AT I-85	SUWANEE, GA	30174
GANNON, JOSEPH M	TV WRITER	STONE MANNERS, 9113 SUNSET BL	LOS ANGELES, CA	90069
GANNON, RICH	FOOTBALL	VIKINGS, 9520 VIKING DR	EDEN PRAIRIE, MN	55344
GANOTE, JOE	BASEBALL	POST OFFICE BOX 1110	MYRTLE BEACH, SC	29578
GANS, DANNY	IMPRESSIONIST	2153 LYANS DR	LA CANADA-FLINTRIDGE,	91011
GANSZ, FRANK	FOOTBALL COACH	LIONS, 1200 FEATHERSTONE RD	PONTIAC, MI	48432
GANT, KENNETH	FOOTBALL	COWBOYS, 1 COWBOYS PARKWAY	IRVING, TX	75063
GANT, RON	BASEBALL	POST OFFICE BOX 4064	ATLANTA, GA	30302
GANTNER, JIM	BASEBALL	BREWERS, 201 S 46TH ST	MILWAUKEE, WI	53214
GANZ, JEFFREY JAY	DIRECTOR-PRODUCER	2136 NICHOLS CANYON RD	LOS ANGELES, CA	90046
GANZ, LOWELL	TV WRITER-DIRECTOR	3950 LONGRIDGE AVE	SHERMAN OAKS, CA	91423
GANZ, TONY	FILM PRODUCER	ITC PRODS, 12711 VENTURA BLVD	STUDIO CITY, CA	91604
GANZEL, MARK	ACT-WRI-PROD	1145 S FORMOSA AVE #3	LOS ANGELES, CA	90046
GANZEL, TERESA	ACTRESS	6500 HAYES DR	LOS ANGELES, CA	90048
GANZER, ALVIN	FILM-TV DIRECTOR	31673 W FOXFIELD DR	WESTLAKE VILLAGE, CA	91367
GAONA, ROBERT	GOLFER	PGA SENIORS, 112 T P C BLVD	PONTE VEDRA BEACH, FL	32082
GARAGIOLA, JOE	RADIO-TV PERSONALITY	6221 E HUNTRESS DR	PARADISE VALLEY, AZ	85253
GARAGOZZO, KEITH	BASEBALL	POST OFFICE BOX 22093	GREENSBORO, NC	27420
GARAS, KAZ	ACTOR-DIRECTOR	31276 BAILARD RD	MALIBU, CA	90265
GARAY, VAL C	RECORD PRODUCER	13200 CHELTENHAM DR	SHERMAN OAKS, CA	91413
GARBAREK, JAN	SAXOPHONIST	KURLAND, 173 BRIGHTON AVE	BOSTON, MA	02134
GARBER, DAVID M	WRITER-PRODUCER	13469 GALEWOOD ST	SHERMAN OAKS, CA	91423
GARBER, GENE	BASEBALL	771 STONEMILL DR	ELIZABETHTOWN, PA	17022
GARBER, HARRIET M	NEWS CORRES-WRITER	4409 RANDALE CT	OLNEY, MD	20832
GARBER, JEFF	BASEBALL	800 HOME RUN LN	MEMPHIS, TN	38104
GARBER, TERRI	ACTRESS	NBC-TV, "SANTA BARBARA"		
		3000 W ALAMEDA AVE	BURBANK, CA	91523
GARCES, RICH	BASEBALL	POST OFFICE BOX 5645	ORLANDO, FL	32855
GARCIA, ANASTACIO	BASEBALL	POST OFFICE BOX 1110	MYRTLE BEACH, SC	29578
GARCIA, ANDY	ACTOR	4519 VARNA AVE	SHERMAN OAKS, CA	91423
GARCIA, APOLINAR	BASEBALL	14100 SIX MILE CYPRESS PKWY	FORT MYERS, FL	33912
GARCIA, CARLOS	BASEBALL	POST OFFICE BOX 450	BUFFALO, NY	14205
GARCIA, CHEO	BASEBALL	POST OFFICE BOX 1659	PORTLAND, OR	97207
GARCIA, DANNY	BASEBALL COACH	POST OFFICE BOX 1420	WICHITA, KS	67201
GARCIA, DAVE	BASEBALL-COACH-SCOUT	BREWERS, 201 S 46TH ST	MILWAUKEE, WI	53214
GARCIA, FERMIN	BASEBALL	POST OFFICE BOX 4669	CHARLESTON, WV	25304
GARCIA, JAMIE	BASEBALL COACH	POST OFFICE BOX 4218	SOUTH BEND, IN	46634
GARCIA, JOHN CARLOS	COMPOSER	POST OFFICE BOX 733	POMONA, CA	91766
GARCIA, JULIO	BASEBALL COACH	POST OFFICE BOX 3746, HILL STA	AUGUSTA, GA	30904
GARCIA, LEO	BASEBALL	POST OFFICE BOX 3665	OMAHA, NE	68103
GARCIA, LUIS	BASEBALL	POST OFFICE BOX 661	KENOSHA, WI	53141
GARCIA, MARCOS	BASEBALL	POST OFFICE BOX 4756	JACKSONVILLE, FL	32201
GARCIA, MIKE	BASEBALL	TIGERS, 89 WHARNCLIFFE RD N	LONDON, ONT N6H 2A7	CANADA
GARCIA, OMAR	BASEBALL	POST OFFICE BOX 7845	COLUMBIA, SC	29202
GARCIA, RAMON	BASEBALL	CANADIANS, 4601 ONTARIO ST	VANCOUVER, BC V5V 3H4	CANADA
GARCIA, RAPHAEL	BASEBALL	POST OFFICE BOX 957	DUNEDIN, FL	34697
GARCIA, RICH	BASEBALL UMPIRE	2633 FIRESTONE DR	CLEARWATER, FL	33519
GARCIA, RON	CINEMATOGRAPHER	1999 AVE OF THE STARS #2850	LOS ANGELES, CA	90067
GARCIA, RONQUITO	BASEBALL SCOUT	POST OFFICE BOX 2000	SAN DIEGO, CA	92112
GARCIA, RUSSELL	COMPOSER-CONDUCTOR	6836 WOODMAN AVE #7	VAN NUYS, CA	91405
GARCIA, VICTOR	BASEBALL	2501 ALLEN AVE, SE	CANTON, OH	44707
GARD-WORNSON, CHERYL	WRITER	1421 N LAUREL AVE #5	LOS ANGELES, CA	90046
GARDE, BETTY	ACTRESS	3928 CARPENTER AVE #202	STUDIO CITY, CA	91604
GARDELLA, KAY	TV CRITIC	N Y DAILY NEWS, 220 E 42ND ST	NEW YORK, NY	10017
GARDELLA, MIKE	BASEBALL	ALBANY YANKEES, HERITAGE PARK	ALBANY, NY	12211
GARDEN, GRAEME	ACTOR-WRITER	HANCOCK, GREENER HOUSE		
		66-68 HAYMARKET	LONDON SW1Y 4AW	ENGLAND
GARDENER, HERB	TV DIRECTOR-PRODUCER	1390 MARTINE AVE	SCOTCH PLAINS, NJ	07076
GARDENHIRE, RON	BASEBALL-COACH	TWINS, 501 CHICAGO AVE S	MINNEAPOLIS, MN	55415
GARDENIA, VINCENT	ACTOR	WM MORRIS, 1350 AVE OF AMERICAS	NEW YORK, NY	10019
GARDINER, MIKE	BASEBALL	FENWAY PARK, 4 YAWKEY WY	BOSTON, MA	02215
GARDNER, ANN	ACTRESS	201 W 86TH ST #PH W-17	NEW YORK, NY	10024
GARDNER, ARTHUR	PRODUCER	9570 WILSHIRE BLVD #400	BEVERLY HILLS, CA	90212
GARDNER, ARTHUR H	SCREENWRITER	300 N SWALL DR	BEVERLY HILLS, CA	90211
GARDNER, BILL, JR	BASEBALL COACH	525 NW PEACOCK BLVD	PORT SAINT LUCIE, FL	34986
GARDNER, BOB	BASEBALL SCOUT	POST OFFICE BOX 2000	ANAHEIM, CA	92803
GARDNER, BOBBY	BASEBALL SCOUT	1060 W ADDISON ST	CHICAGO, IL	60613
GARDNER, BUDDY	GOLFER	POST OFFICE BOX 109601	PALM BCH GARDENS, FL	33418
GARDNER, CARWELL	FOOTBALL	BILLS, 1 BILLS DR	ORCHARD PARK, NJ	14127
GARDNER, CHRIS	BASEBALL	POST OFFICE BOX 27045	TUCSON, AZ	85726
GARDNER, DARREL	CONDUCTOR	1158 LEEWARD WY	ANAHEIM, CA	92801
GARDNER, GENE	BASEBALL EXECUTIVE	POST OFFICE BOX 36407	LOUISVILLE, KY	40233
GARDNER, GERALD	SCREENWRITER	466 S 822 S ROBERTSON BLVD #200 D	LOS ANGELES, CA	90035
GARDNER, HY	TV-RADIO PERSONALITY	5601 N BAYSHORE DR	MIAMI, FL	33137
GARDNER, JAMES C	LT GOVERNOR	STATE CAPITOL BUILDING	RALEIGH, NC	27603
GARDNER, JEAN	FILM PRODUCER	1445 N BEVERLY GLEN BLVD	LOS ANGELES, CA	90077
GARDNER, JEFF	BASEBALL	STARS, 850 LAS VEGAS BLVD N	LAS VEGAS, NV	89101
GARDNER, JERRY	BASEBALL SCOUT	POST OFFICE BOX 7000	PITTSBURGH, PA	15212
GARDNER, JOHN	BASEBALL	CUBS, 2ND & RIVERSIDE DR	DES MOINES, IA	50309
GARDNER, MARK	BASEBALL	EXPOS, 4545 DE COUBERTIN AVE	MONTREAL, QUE H1V 3P2	CANADA
GARDNER, MOE	FOOTBALL	FALCONS, SUWANEE RD AT I-85	SUWANEE, GA	30174
GARDNER, RANDY	SKATER	4640 GLENCOVE AVE #6	MARINA DEL REY, CA	90291
GARDNER, ROSEMARIE	MAKE-UP ARTIST	280 CROCKER PL	HAWORTH, NJ	07641
GARDNER, WES	BASEBALL	305 RUTH ST	BENTON, AR	72015
GARDNER, WILLIAM	SECRETARY OF STATE	STATE HOUSE BUILDING	CONCORD, NH	03301

GARDNER, WILLIAM BOOTH	GOVERNOR	STATE LEGISLATIVE BUILDING	OLYMPIA, WA	98504
GARDNER, WINNIE	ACTRESS	10350 WILSHIRE BLVD #502	LOS ANGELES, CA	90024
GARDONYI, FRANK	DIRECTOR	1299 OCEAN AVE #720	SANTA MONICA, CA	90401
GAREN, LEO	TV WRITER	2417 WILSON AVE	VENICE, CA	90291
GAREN, SCOTT	TV DIRECTOR-PRODUCER	617 9TH ST	SANTA MONICA, CA	90402
GARFEIN, JACK	DIRECTOR-PRODUCER	ACTORS & DIRECTORS LAB		
		412 W 42ND ST	NEW YORK, NY	10036
GARFIELD, ALLEN	ACTOR	9973 DURANT DR	BEVERLY HILLS, CA	90212
GARFIELD, BRIAN	SCREENWRITER	MTA, 9320 WILSHIRE BL, 3RD FL	BEVERLY HILLS, CA	90212
GARFINKEL, LEE	COMEDY WRITER	LEVINE HUNTLEY SCHMIDT		
		250 PARK AVE	NEW YORK, NY	10177
GARFINKLE, LOUIS A	SCREENWRITER	14127 MARGATE ST	VAN NUYS, CA	91401
GARFUNKEL, ART	SING-ACT-COMP	9 E 79TH ST	NEW YORK, NY	10021
GARGAN, LESLIE H	TV WRITER	6816 WOODROW WILSON DR	LOS ANGELES, CA	90068
GARGANO, BILL	BASEBALL EXECUTIVE	POST OFFICE BOX 7575	PHILADELPHIA, PA	19101
GARGARO, WILLIAM, JR	WRITER	6226 SCENIC AVE	LOS ANGELES, CA	90068
GARGIULO, MICHAEL R	TV DIRECTOR-PRODUCER	301 E 21ST ST	NEW YORK, NY	10010
GARIBALDI, MARCO	WRITER-DIRECTOR	PRESLEY, 1167 SUMMIT DR	BEVERLY HILLS, CA	90210
GARLAND, BEVERLY	ACTRESS	8014 BRIAR SUMMIT DR	LOS ANGELES, CA	90046
GARLAND, CARRINGTON	ACTRESS	2029 CENTURY PARK E #600	LOS ANGELES, CA	90067
GARLAND, CHAON	BASEBALL	POST OFFICE BOX 2437	MODESTO, CA	95351
GARLAND, GEOFF	ACTOR	340 W 11TH ST	NEW YORK, NY	10014
GARLAND, GRACE	ACTRESS-SINGER	250 W 54TH ST #800	NEW YORK, NY	10019
GARLAND, HANK	GUITARIST	ROUTE #1, BOX 370, TWIN BROOKS	INMAN, SC	29347
GARLAND, MICHAEL	ARTIST	78 COLUMBIA AVE	HARTSDALE, NY	10530
GARLAND, ROBERT	SCREENWRITER	CAA, 9830 WILSHIRE BLVD	BEVERLY HILLS, CA	90212
GARLAND, TIM	BASEBALL	POST OFFICE BOX 2148	WOODBRIDGE, VA	22193
GARLAND, TRISH	ACTRESS	12223 CALIFA ST	NORTH HOLLYWOOD, CA	91607
GARLAND, WINSTON	BASKETBALL	CLIPPERS, 3939 S FIGUEROA ST	LOS ANGELES, CA	90037
GARN, JAKE	U S SENATOR	4225 W F BENNETT FEDERAL BLDG	SALT LAKE CITY, UT	84138
GARNER, ANTHONY	TV DIRECTOR	HEATH, PARAMOUNT HOUSE		
		162-170 WARDOUR ST	LONDON W1V 3AT	ENGLAND
GARNER, GIGI	SINGER	33 OAKMONT DR	LOS ANGELES, CA	90049
GARNER, HAL	FOOTBALL	BILLS, 1 BILLS DR	ORCHARD PARK, NJ	14127
GARNER, JACK	ACTOR	11820 CHANDER BLVD #5	NORTH HOLLYWOOD, CA	91607
GARNER, JAMES	ACT-DIR-PROD	33 OAKMONT DR	LOS ANGELES, CA	90049
GARNER, KATINA HELENA	ACTRESS	11827 ARMINTA ST	NORTH HOLLYWOOD, CA	91605
GARNER, KEVIN	BASEBALL	POST OFFICE BOX 360007	BIRMINGHAM, AL	35236
GARNER, PAUL "MOUSIE"	ACTOR	7220 HOLLYWOOD BLVD #230	LOS ANGELES, CA	90046
GARNER, PHIL	BASEBALL-MANAGER	BREWERS, 201 S 46TH ST	MILWAUKEE, WI	53214
GARNER, ROBERT L	COMPOSER	10 LAWSON PL #6	YELLOW SPRINGS, OH	45387
GARNES, LEE	CINEMATOGRAPHER	POST OFFICE BOX 2230	HOLLYWOOD, CA	90078
GARNETT, RICHARD	COMPOSER	2429 N BEACHWOOD DR #2	LOS ANGELES, CA	90068
GARNITZ, BERNARD	COMPOSER	538 PIER ST #6-A	SANTA MONICA, CA	90405
GAROFALO, ROBERT	WRITER-DIRECTOR	CRANBOURNE HALL, DRIFT RD		
		WINKFIELD ROW, WINDSOR	BERKSHIRE SL4 4TY	ENGLAND
GAROFALO, TONY	TV WRITER-PRODUCER	16205 MORRISON ST	ENCINO, CA	91436
GARPENLOV, JOHAN	HOCKEY	RED WINGS, 600 CIVIC CENTER DR	DETROIT, MI	48226
GARR, LISA	ACTRESS	6255 SUNSET BLVD #627	LOS ANGELES, CA	90028
GARR, MICHAEL L	WRITER-PRODUCER	2008 1/2 VISTA DEL MAR ST	LOS ANGELES, CA	90068
GARR, TERI	ACTRESS	9200 SUNSET BLVD #428	LOS ANGELES, CA	90069
GARRELTS, SCOTT	BASEBALL	S F GIANTS, CANDLESTICK PARK	SAN FRANICSCO, CA	94124
GARRETT, ADRIAN	BASEBALL-COACH	POST OFFICE BOX 419969	KANSAS CITY, MO	64141
GARRETT, BRAD	COMEDIAN	9243 1/2 DOHENY RD	LOS ANGELES, CA	90069
GARRETT, CLIFTON	BASEBALL	POST OFFICE BOX 1742	PALM SPRINGS, CA	92263
GARRETT, GINGER	ACTRESS	346 E 63RD ST #4-A	NEW YORK, NY	10021
GARRETT, HANK	ACTOR	LIGHT, 901 BRINGHAM AVE	LOS ANGELES, CA	90049
GARRETT, JOY	ACTRESS	11552 HESBY ST	NORTH HOLLYWOOD, CA	91601
GARRETT, LEIF	ACTOR-SINGER	5750 WILSHIRE BLVD #580	LOS ANGELES, CA	90037
GARRETT, LILA	WRITER-PRODUCER	1356 LAUREL WY	BEVERLY HILLS, CA	90210
GARRETT, LIN	BASEBALL SCOUT	1000 ELYSIAN PARK DR	LOS ANGELES, CA	90012
GARRETT, MAUREEN	ACTRESS	CBS-TV, "THE GUIDING LIGHT"		
		222 E 44TH ST	NEW YORK, NY	10017
GARRETT, SNUFF	TALENT AGENT	4121 1/2 RADFORD AVE	STUDIO CITY, CA	91604
GARRICK, EDWARD	FILM DIRECTOR	1827 JEWETT DR	LOS ANGELES, CA	90046
GARRICK, STEVEN	COMPOSER	23739 SANDALWOOD ST	CANOGA PARK, CA	91307
GARRICK, TOM	BASKETBALL	CLIPPERS, 3939 S FIGUEROA ST	LOS ANGELES, CA	90037
GARRIDO, GIL	BASEBALL COACH	POST OFFICE BOX 507	DURHAM, NC	27702
GARRIGAN, PAT	BASEBALL	POST OFFICE BOX 30160	SAN BERNARDINO, CA	92413
GARRISON, DAVID	ACTOR	1999 AVE OF THE STARS #2850	LOS ANGELES, CA	90067
GARRISON, GREG	DIRECTOR	3400 W ALAMEDA AVE	BURBANK, CA	91523
GARRISON, LARRY	PRODUCER	4432 AGNES AVE	NORTH HOLLYWOOD, CA	91607
GARRISON, WEBSTER	BASEBALL	POST OFFICE BOX 11087	TACOMA, WA	98411
GARRON, BARRY	TV CRITIC	K C STAR, 1729 GRAND AVE	KANSAS CITY, MO	64108
GARRONI, ANDREW	FILM EXECUTIVE	9301 WILSHIRE BLVD #602	BEVERLY HILLS, CA	90210
GARRONI, WILLIAM	DIRECTOR	11 ALLISON DR	ENGLEWOOD CLIFFS, NJ	07632
GARROW, DAVID	BASEBALL	POST OFFICE BOX 661	KENOSHA, WI	53141
GARRY	SINGER	POST OFFICE BOX 470874	BROOKLYN, NY	11247
GARSON, GREER	ACTRESS	2400 REPUBLIC BANK TOWER #11	DALLAS, TX	75201
GARSON, HENRY	WRITER	411 N PALM DR #3	BEVERLY HILLS, CA	90210
GARSON, JOHN	ACTOR	415 E 71ST ST	NEW YORK, NY	10021
GARSON, MORT	CONDUCTOR	11824 MOORPARK ST #H	STUDIO CITY, CA	91604
GARTH, JENNIE	ACTRESS	5700 WILSHIRE BLVD #575	LOS ANGELES, CA	90036
GARTIN, SANDY RUSSEL	TV EXECUTIVE	151 W 86TH ST	NEW YORK, NY	10024
GARTNER, MIKE	HOCKEY	POST OFFICE BOX 90111	ARLINGTON, TX	76004

GARVER, KATHY	ACTRESS	170 WOODBRIDGE RD	HILLSBOROUGH, CA 94010
GARVER, LLOYD	TV WRITER-PRODUCER	10474 ILONA AVE	LOS ANGELES, CA 90064
GARVEY, CYNTHIA	TV HOST	3516 MALIBU COUNTRY RD	MALIBU, CA 90265
GARVEY, STEVE	BASEBALL	13162 CAMINITO POINTE DEL MAR	DEL MAR, CA 92014
GARVIN, CLINTON	MUSIC ARRANGER	916 MESA ST	MORRO BAY, CA 93442
GARVIN, RONNIE	WRESTLER	POST OFFICE BOX 3859	STAMFORD, CT 06905
GARWOOD, JOHN	ACTOR	8628 FONTANA ST	DOWNEY, CA 90241
GARY, A PETER	COMPOSER-CONDUCTOR	1328 S BUNDY DR #9	LOS ANGELES, CA 90025
GARY, CLEVELAND	FOOTBALL	RAMS, 2327 W LINCOLN BLVD	ANAHEIM, CA 92801
GARY, HAROLD	ACTOR	2109 BROADWAY	NEW YORK, NY 10023
GARY, JOHN	SINGER	32500 CONCORD DR #252	MADISON HEIGHTS, MI 48071
GARY, LORRAINE	ACTRESS	1158 TOWER RD	BEVERLY HILLS, CA 90210
GARY, SAM	TV DIRECTOR	8770 CRESCENT DR	LOS ANGELES, CA 90046
GARY O	SINGER-COMPOSER	1505 W 2ND AVE #200	VANCOUVER, BC V6H 3Y4 CANADA
GARZA, JANISS	ACTRESS	1750 CAMINO PALMERO #52	LOS ANGELES, CA 90046
GASBARRO, MARK	COMPOSER	17540 HIAWATHA ST	GRANADA HILLS, CA 91344
GASCO, ERNESTO	ACTOR	55-41 96TH ST	ELMHURST, NY 11368
GASCOINE, JILL	ACTRESS	MARTIN, 6-A DANBURY ST	LONDON N1 8JU ENGLAND
GASH, DARIUS	BASEBALL	12000 STADIUM RD	ADELANTO, CA 92301
GASKILL, RED	BASEBALL SCOUT	POST OFFICE BOX 2000	ANAHEIM, CA 92803
GASPARD-HUIT, PIERRE	FILM DIRECTOR	25 BIS RUE JASMIN	PARIS 75016 FRANCE
GASPARI, RICHARD	BODYBUILDER	POST OFFICE BOX 29	MILLTOWN, NJ 08850
GASS, MARC	DIRECTOR	8501 BRIER DR	HOLLYWOOD, CA 90046
GASSAWAY, DOUG	BASEBALL SCOUT	POST OFFICE BOX 90111	ARLINGTON, TX 76004
GAST, HAROLD	TV WRITER-PRODUCER	281 LORING AVE	LOS ANGELES, CA 90024
GASTON, CITO	BASEBALL-MANAGER	1421 GLEN BURNIE RD	MISSISSA, ONT L5G 3C7 CANADA
GASTON, DON F	BASKETBALL EXECUTIVE	151 MERRIMAC ST	BOSTON, MA 02114
GATES, BRENT	BASEBALL	POST OFFICE BOX 2437	MODESTO, CA 95351
GATES, JAMES S	TV DIRECTOR	24952 KIT CARSON RD	HIDDEN HILLS, CA 91302
GATES, LARRY	ACTOR	CBS-TV, "THE GUIDING LIGHT"	
		222 E 44TH ST	NEW YORK, NY 10017
GATES, MAUREEN L	COSTUME DESIGNER	2015 PIER AVE	SANTA MONICA, CA 90405
GATES, NANCY	ACTRESS	HAYES, 200 CONWAY AVE	LOS ANGELES, CA 90024
GATES, PHYLLIS	ACTRESS	POST OFFICE BOX 6965	BEVERLY HILLS, CA 90212
GATES, RICHARD	ACTOR	2055 N LAS PALMAS AVE	LOS ANGELES, CA 90068
GATES, TUDOR	WRITER-PRODUCER	DRUMBEAT, 17-A MERCER ST	LONDON WC2H 9QJ ENGLAND
GATEWOOD, JOHNNY	SINGER	ROUTE #2, BOX 73	INMAN, KS 67546
GATI, KATHLEEN	ACTRESS	250 W 57TH ST #2317	NEW YORK, NY 10107
GATLIN, LARRY	SINGER-SONGWRITER	7003 CHADWICK DR #360	BRENTWOOD, TN 37037
GATLIN, LARRY & GATLIN BROS	C & W GROUP	7003 CHADWICK DR #360	BRENTWOOD, TN 37037
GATTISON, KENNY	BASKETBALL	310 N KINGS DR	CHARLOTTE, NC 28204
GATTO, PETER	ACTOR	RAGLYN, 60 E 42ND ST	NEW YORK, NY 10165
GATWARD, JAMES	TV EXECUTIVE	TVS FILMS TV CENTRE	SOUTHAMPTON SO9 5HZ ENGLAND
GAUBERT, JAMES	BODYBUILDER	POST OFFICE BOX 2343	LAFAYETTE, LA 70502
GAUDUCHON, NICOLE	FILM EDITOR	11 AVE GEORGES-BIZET	LE VESINET 78110 FRANCE
GAUGHAN, MICHAEL P	TV PRODUCER	81 OCEAN PARKWAY #6-A	BROOKLYN, NY 11218
GAUL, PATRICIA	ACTRESS	13205 CHELTENHAM DR	SHERMAN OAKS, CA 91423
GAULT, CHARLIE	BASEBALL SCOUT	TIGERS, TIGER STADIUM	DETROIT, MI 48216
GAULT, JENNY	ACTRESS	333 E 49TH ST	NEW YORK, NY 10017
GAULT, MARILYN	FILM-TV DIR-PROD	120 PRINCE OF WALES RD	LONDON NW5 3NE ENGLAND
GAULT, WILLIAM	ACTOR-DIRECTOR	MAC DERMOT, 14 LEAMORE ST	LONDON W6 0JZ ENGLAND
GAULT, WILLIE	FOOTBALL	RAIDERS, 332 CENTER ST	EL SEGUNDO, CA 90245
GAUTHIER, JACK	ACTOR	19 RUE JEAN-LECLAIRE	PARIS 75017 FRANCE
GAVALA, YULA	ACT-WRI-PROD	651 LORNA LN	LOS ANGELES, CA 90049
GAVIATI, RONALD M	TV DIRECTOR	3159 W BLACK HILLS CT	WESTLAKE VILLAGE, CA 91362
GAVIN, DELANE "MIKE"	TV DIRECTOR	4660 WILLIS AVE	SHERMAN OAKS, CA 91403
GAVIN, JOHN	ACTOR	2415 CENTURY HILL	LOS ANGELES, CA 90067
GAVITT, DAVE	BASKETBALL EXECUTIVE	151 MERRIMAC ST	BOSTON, MA 02114
GAVRAS-COSTA	FILM DIRECTOR	SA AU CAPITAL DE 300.00	
		244 RUE SAINT-JACQUES	PARIS 75005 FRANCE
GAY, JOHN	TV WRITER	1636 SAN ONOFRE DR	PACIFIC PALISADES, CA 90272
GAY, MICHAEL	ACTOR	JARRETT, 220 E 63RD ST	NEW YORK, NY 10021
GAYBIS, ANNIE	ACTRESS-SINGER	999 N DOHENY DR #1005	LOS ANGELES, CA 90069
GAYDOES, STEVEN M	WRITER	1680 N VINE ST #1117	LOS ANGELES, CA 90028
GAYDOS, JOSEPH	U S CONGRESSMAN	318 5TH AVE	MC KEESPORT, PA 15132
GAYLE, CRYSTAL	SINGER	51 MUSIC SQUARE E	NASHVILLE, TN 37203
GAYLE, JACKIE	COMEDIAN	13109 CHANDLER BLVD	VAN NUYS, CA 91401
GAYLE, ROZELLE	ACTOR	1766 S STEARNS DR	LOS ANGELES, CA 90035
GAYLIN, GEORGE	PHOTOGRAPHER	1101 BAHAMA BEND #F-2	COCONUT CREEK, FL 33066
GAYLORD, MITCH	ACTOR-GYMNAST	100 N WOODBURN DR	LOS ANGELES, CA 90049
GAYNES, GEORGE	ACTOR-DIRECTOR	3344 CAMPANIL DR	SANTA BARBARA, CA 93109
GAYNES, LLOYD	TV DIRECTOR	6918 OPORTO DR	HOLLYWOOD, CA 90068
GAYNOR, GLORIA	SINGER	POST OFFICE BOX 374	FAIRVIEW, NJ 07010
GAYNOR, GRACE	ACTRESS	9850 YOAKUM DR	BEVERLY HILLS, CA 90210
GAYNOR, JOCK	ACTOR	9850 YOAKUM DR	BEVERLY HILLS, CA 90210
GAYNOR, MITZI	ACTRESS-DANCER	610 N ARDEN DR	BEVERLY HILLS, CA 90210
GAYTON, BILL	BASEBALL SCOUT	ATHLETICS'S, OAKLAND COLISEUM	OAKLAND, CA 94621
GAYTON, JOE	SCREENWRITER	131 S RODEO DR #300	BEVERLY HILLS, CA 90212
GAZNICK, TONY	ACTOR	843 TIPTON TERR	LOS ANGELES, CA 90042
GAZZANIGA, DON	ACTOR-DIRECTOR	14758 MORRISON ST	SHERMAN OAKS, CA 91403
GAZZARA, BEN	ACTOR-DIRECTOR	1080 MADISON AVE	NEW YORK, NY 10028
GAZZO, MICHAEL V	ACTOR	2047 MALCOLM AVE	LOS ANGELES, CA 90025
GEARON, J MICHAEL	BASKETBALL EXECUTIVE	1 CNN CENTER #405, SOUTH TOWER	ATLANTA, GA 30303
GEARY, CYNTHIA	ACTRESS	10351 SANTA MONICA BLVD #211	LOS ANGELES, CA 90025
GEARY, TONY	ACTOR	7010 PACIFIC VIEW DR	LOS ANGELES, CA 90068

Name	Occupation	Address	City/State	Zip/Country
GEATHERS, JAMES	FOOTBALL	POST OFFICE BOX 17247 (DULLES)	WASHINGTON, DC	20041
GEBHARD, BOB	BASEBALL EXECUTIVE	TWINS, 501 CHICAGO AVE S	MINNEAPOLIS, MN	55415
GEBHART, COURTNEY	ACTRESS	STONE MANNERS, 9113 SUNSET BL	LOS ANGELES, CA	90069
GECKS, NICHOLAS	ACTOR	CONWAY, 18-21 JERMYN ST	LONDON SW1	ENGLAND
GEDDES, AL	BASEBALL SCOUT	BREWERS, 201 S 46TH ST	MILWAUKEE, WI	53214
GEDDES, BETH R	TV WRITER	12039 WEDDINGTON ST	NORTH HOLLYWOOD, CA	91607
GEDDES, BRUCE	FILM DIRECTOR	4988 VINCENT AVE	LOS ANGELES, CA	90041
GEDDIE, WANDA GAYLE	MODEL	FORD MODELS, 344 E 59TH ST	NEW YORK, NY	10022
GEDMAN, RICH	BASEBALL	250 STADIUM PLAZA	ST LOUIS, MO	63102
GEDRICK, JASON	ACTOR	UTA, 9560 WILSHIRE BL, 5TH FL	BEVERLY HILLS, CA	90212
GEE, CHRISTOPHER LYNDON	CONDUCTOR	111 W 57TH ST #1203	NEW YORK, NY	10019
GEE, LAURA	ACTRESS	POST OFFICE BOX 66	MONMOUTH BEACH, NJ	07750
GEE, PRUNELLA	ACTRESS	CROUCH, 59 FIRTH ST	LONDON W1V 5TA	ENGLAND
GEER, ELLEN	ACTRESS	21418 W ENTRADA RD	TOPANGA, CA	90290
GEER, HAROLD	DIRECTOR-PRODUCER	776 BENNETT ST	SIMI VALLEY, CA	93065
GEER, STEPHEN	NEWS CORRESPONDENT	ABC NEWS, 7 W 66TH ST	NEW YORK, NY	10023
GEER, THAD	ACTOR	1419 N TOPANGA CANYON BLVD	TOPANGA, CA	90290
GEESON, JUDY	ACTRESS	MLR, 200 FULHAM RD	LONDON SW10 9PN	ENGLAND
GEEVE, DAVE	BASEBALL	POST OFFICE BOX 3609	PORT CHARLOTTE, FL	33949
GEFFEN, DAVID	RECORD-FILM EXECUTIVE	9130 SUNSET BLVD	LOS ANGELES, CA	90069
GEFSKY, HAL	TALENT AGENT	8650 PINE TREE PL	LOS ANGELES, CA	90069
GEHR, CAROL	BASEBALL EXECUTIVE	POST OFFICE BOX 230	HAGERSTOWN, MD	21740
GEHRINGER, CHARLIE	BASEBALL	32301 LAHSER RD	BIRMINGHAM, MI	48010
GEIBERGER, AL	GOLFER	PGA SENIORS, 112 T P C BLVD	PONTE VEDRA BEACH, FL	32082
GEIGER, GEORGE	TV WRITER-PRODUCER	151 S EL CAMINO DR	BEVERLY HILLS, CA	90212
GEIGER, MIRIAM	WRITER	7676 HOLLYWOOD BLVD #7	LOS ANGELES, CA	90046
GEIS, BUDDY	FOOTBALL COACH	PACKERS, 1265 LOMBARDI AVE	GREEN BAY, WI	54307
GEISINGER, ELLIOT	DIRECTOR	RALEIGH, 650 N BRONSON AVE	HOLLYWOOD, CA	90004
GEISLER, PHIL	BASEBALL	POST OFFICE BOX 10336	CLEARWATER, FL	34617
GEISS, TONY	TV WRITER	CHILDREN'S TV WORKSHOP		
		1 LINCOLN PLAZA	NEW YORK, NY	10023
GEJDENSON, SAM	U S CONGRESSMAN	POST OFFICE BOX 2000	NORWICH, CT	06360
GEKAS, GEORGE	U S CONGRESSMAN	POST OFFICE BOX 606	WILLIAMSPORT, PA	17703
GELBART, LARRY	WRITER-PRODUCER	807 N ALPINE DR	BEVERLY HILLS, CA	90210
GELBER, CHARLES	TV DIRECTOR-PRODUCER	14 E 40TH ST #701	NEW YORK, NY	10022
GELBMANN, LARRY	ACTOR	5235 VIRGINIA AVE	LOS ANGELES, CA	90029
GELBRETIE, HENRY	BASEBALL EXECUTIVE	POST OFFICE BOX 1886	COLUMBUS, GA	31902
GELD, KARYL	WRITER	14455 DUNBAR PL	SHERMAN OAKS, CA	91423
GELDOF, BOB	SINGER-HUMANITARIAN	DAVINGTON PRIORY	LONDON	ENGLAND
GELFOND, BERYL	DIRECTOR	3217 FRYMAN RD	STUDIO CITY, CA	91604
GELIN, DANIEL	FILM DIRECTOR	92 BLVD MURAT	75016 PARIS	FRANCE
GELIN, XAVIER	ACTOR	16 RUE DE MARIGNAN	PARIS 75008	FRANCE
GELINAS, MARTIN	HOCKEY	OILERS, NORTHLANDS COLISEUM	EDMONTON, ALTA T5B 4M9	CANADA
GELLER, HERBERT	COMPOSER	JULIUS VOSSELERSTRASSE	2000 HAMBURG 54 566-78	GERMANY
GELLER, MATT	TV WRITER	10982 ROEBLIND AVE #438	LOS ANGELES, CA	90024
GELLER, NANCY	TV PRODUCER	10100 SANTA MONICA BLVD #1600	LOS ANGELES, CA	90067
GELLER, NORM	CONDUCTOR	1418 N HIGHLAND AVE #102	LOS ANGELES, CA	90028
GELLER, ROBERT	TV PRODUCER-EXECUTIVE	LEARNING IN FOCUS		
		310 MADISON AVE	NEW YORK, NY	10017
GELLER, URI	PSYCHIC	SONNING-ON-THAMES	BERKSHIRE	ENGLAND
GELLINGER, MIKE	BASEBALL MANAGER	POST OFFICE BOX 751	UTICA, NY	13503
GELLMAN, ALEXANDER	ACTOR	3 E MOUNT AIRY RD	CROTON-ON-HUDSON, NY	10520
GELLMAN, MICHAEL	ACTOR-WRITER	8955 BEVERLY BLVD	WEST HOLLYWOOD, CA	90048
GELMAN, LARRY	ACTOR	5121 GREENBUSH AVE	SHERMAN OAKS, CA	91423
GELMAN, LAURIE	TV WRITER	12232 HUSTON ST	NORTH HOLLYWOOD, CA	91607
GELMAN, MORRIE	COLUMNIST	5700 WILSHIRE BLVD #120	LOS ANGELES, CA	90036
GELMIS, JOSEPH	FILM CRITIC	1500 BROADWAY #2201	NEW YORK, NY	10036
GELSEY, ERWIN S	WRITER	9160 BEVERLY BLVD #302	BEVERLY HILLS, CA	90210
GENELIN, ALAN MICHAEL	WRITER	13169 CHELTENHAM DR	SHERMAN OAKS, CA	91423
GENERATION X	ROCK & ROLL GROUP	JOSEPH, 184 GLOUCESTER	LONDON NW1	ENGLAND
GENESIS	ROCK & ROLL TRIO	HIT & RUN MUSIC, LTD		
		81-83 WALTON ST	LONDON SW3 2HR	ENGLAND
GENET, MICHAEL	ACTOR	CBS-TV, "AS THE WORLD TURNS"		
		524 W 57TH ST #5330	NEW YORK, NY	10019
GENGE, PAUL	ACTOR	5607 LA MIRADA AVE #406	LOS ANGELES, CA	90038
GENISE, LIVIA	ACTRESS	7050 FLORAMORGAN TRAIL	TUJUNGA, CA	91042
GENNARELLI, CHARLES	DIRECTOR	7 PHILLIPS LN	RYE, NY	10580
GENOVESE, GEORGE	BASEBALL-SCOUT	S F GIANTS, CANDLESTICK PARK	SAN FRANICSCO, CA	94124
GENSON, DON	WRITER	144 S MC CARTHY DR	BEVERLY HILLS, CA	90212
GENTEEL, LINDA	PIANIST	822 S ROBERTSON BLVD #200	LOS ANGELES, CA	90035
GENTRY, ALVIN	BASKETBALL COACH	CLIPPERS, 3939 S FIGUEROA ST	LOS ANGELES, CA	90037
GENTRY, DENNIS	FOOTBALL	BEARS, 250 N WASHINGTON RD	LAKE FOREST, IL	60045
GENUS, KARL	TV DIRECTOR	533 BEACHWALK CIR	NAPLES, FL	33963
GEOGHAN, JIM	TV WRITER-PLAYWRIGHT	804 MANSFIELD AVE	LOS ANGELES, CA	90038
GEORGE, ANTHONY	ACTOR	6216 MONERO DR	RCHO PALOS VERDES, CA	90274
GEORGE, BARBARA	ACTRESS-WRITER	1437 N HAVENHURST DR	LOS ANGELES, CA	90046
GEORGE, BOY	SINGER-COMPOSER	34-A GREEN LN, NORTHWOOD	MIDDLESEX	ENGLAND
GEORGE, CHRIS	BASEBALL (DENVER)	2850 W 20TH AVE	DENVER, CO	80211
GEORGE, EARL	ACTOR	4445 POST RD	RIVERDALE, NY	10471
GEORGE, GEORGE L	DIRECTOR-PRODUCER	685 W END AVE	NEW YORK, NY	10025
GEORGE, GEORGE W	THEATER PRODUCER	60 W 55TH ST	NEW YORK, NY	10019
GEORGE, HOWARD	ACTOR-WRITER	1746 N ORANGE DR #1002	LOS ANGELES, CA	90028
GEORGE, JEFF	FOOTBALL	POST OFFICE BOX 535000	INDIANAPOLIS, IN	46253
GEORGE, JOE	ACTOR	1422 N SWEETZER AVE	LOS ANGELES, CA	90069
GEORGE, JON A	SCREENWRITER	8955 BEVERLY BLVD	WEST HOLLYWOOD, CA	90048

GEORGE, LYNDA DAY	ACTRESS	10310 RIVERSIDE DR #104	TOLUCA LAKE, CA 91602
GEORGE, NANCY	TALENT AGENT	MTA, 9320 WILSHIRE BL, 3RD FL	BEVERLY HILLS, CA 90212
GEORGE, PHYLLIS	TV PERSONALITY	SEE - GEORGE BROWN, PHYLLIS	
GEORGE, SUSAN	ACTRESS	BOX 428, MAIDENHEAD	BERKS SL6 4EW ENGLAND
GEORGE, TATE	BASKETBALL	N J NETS, MEADOWLANDS ARENA	EAST RUTHERFORD, NJ 07073
GEORGE, WALLY	TV HOST	14155 MAGNOLIA BLVD #127	SHERMAN OAKS, CA 91423
GEORGE, WILL	BASEBALL COACH	2501 ALLEN AVE, SE	CANTON, OH 44707
GEORGE BROWN, PHYLLIS	TV PERSONALITY	CAVE HILL LN, BOX 4308	LEXINGTON, KY 40511
GEORGER, JOE	BASEBALL COACH	POST OFFICE BOX 3496	DAVENPORT, IA 52808
GEORGEVICH, DEJAN	DIRECTOR	42 CROTON AVE	HASTINGS-ON-HUDSON, NY 10706
GEORGIADE, NICHOLAS	ACTOR	3429 COUNTRY CLUB DR	LOS ANGELES, CA 90019
GEPHARDT, RICHARD	U S CONGRESSMAN	9959 GRAVOIS	SAINT LOUIS, MO 63123
GERACE, LOIS	ACTRESS	6767 IRONDALE AVE	CANOGA PARK, CA 91306
GERAGHTY, MAURY	TV WRITER-DIRECTOR	1557 S RIVERSIDE DR	PALM SPRINGS, CA 92262
GERALD, ED	BASEBALL	POST OFFICE BOX 464	APPLETON, WI 54912
GERARD, ANNE	SCREENWRITER	PLESHETTE, 2700 N BEACHWOOD DR	LOS ANGELES, CA 90068
GERARD, DANNY	ACTOR	SAPERSTEIN, 160 W 72ND ST	NEW YORK, NY 10023
GERARD, GIL	ACTOR	32 HURRICANE ST	MARINA DEL REY, CA 90292
GERARD, MERWIN	TV WRITER	857 BURNSIDE AVE	LOS ANGELES, CA 90036
GERARD, NORA	TV DIRECTOR	CBS-TV, 524 W 57TH ST	NEW YORK, NY 10019
GERARDI, BOB	ACTOR-SINGER	160 W 73RD ST	NEW YORK, NY 10023
GERARDO	SINGER-SONGWRITER	20912 DELPHINE DR	WALNUT, CA 91789
GERATY, FRANK	CINEMATOGRAPHER	7715 SUNSET BLVD #150	LOS ANGELES, CA 90046
GERBER, DAISY	FILM DIRECTOR	9617 OAK PASS RD	BEVERLY HILLS, CA 90210
GERBER, DAVID	TV PRODUCER	10800 CHALON RD	LOS ANGELES, CA 90077
GERBER, EDWARD	CONDUCTOR	12406 CHERRY	KANSAS CITY, MO 64145
GERBER, ELLA	ACTRESS	329 E 58TH ST	NEW YORK, NY 10022
GERBER, JAY	ACTOR	16732 MC CORMICK ST	ENCINO, CA 91436
GERDAU, RICHARD	TV WRITER-DIRECTOR	9200 SUNSET BLVD #808	LOS ANGELES, CA 90069
GERE, RICHARD	ACTOR	9115 CORDELL	LOS ANGELES, CA 90069
GEREB, NEIL	FOOTBALL REFEREE	NFL, 410 PARK AVE	NEW YORK, NY 10022
GEREN, BOB	BASEBALL	2710 BAY CANYON CT	SAN DIEGO, CA 92117
GEREN, TOM	CINEMATOGRAPHER	7715 SUNSET BLVD #150	LOS ANGELES, CA 90046
GERHART, BERT	BASEBALL	POST OFFICE BOX 309	GASTONA, NC 28053
GERHART, KEN	BASEBALL	707 ELLIOT ST	MURFREESBORO, TN 37130
GERICKE, THOMAS J	WRITER	2322 LYRIC AVE	LOS ANGELES, CA 90027
GERKEN, ELLEN	ACTRESS	646 S BARRINGTON AVE #213	LOS ANGELES, CA 90049
GERMANN, MARK	BASEBALL SCOUT	INDIANS, CLEVELAND STADIUM	CLEVELAND, OH 44114
GERNERT, DICK	BASEBALL-SCOUT	METS, 126TH ST & ROOSEVELT AVE	FLUSHING, NY 11368
GERO, FRANK	THEATER PRODUCER	1140 BROADWAY	NEW YORK, NY 10001
GERO, MARK	THEATER PRODUCER	214 E 89TH ST	NEW YORK, NY 10028
GEROLMO, CHRIS	SCREENWRITER	CAA, 9830 WILSHIRE BLVD	BEVERLY HILLS, CA 90212
GERONIMI, CLYDE	ANIMATOR-DIRECTOR	1069 BUCKINGHAM LN	NEWPORT BEACH, CA 92660
GERRITY, DANIEL	ACTOR	1752 N SERRANO AVE #604	LOS ANGELES, CA 90027
GERSHBERG, HOWIE	BASEBALL COACH	HAWKS, 5600 N GLENWOOD	BOISE, ID 83714
GERSHE, LEONARD	TV WRITER	9400 EDEN DR	BEVERLY HILLS, CA 90210
GERSHMAN, BEN	WRITER	451 SAN VICENTE BLVD #1	SANTA MONICA, CA 90402
GERSHON, GINA	ACTRESS	11726 SAN VICENTE BLVD #300	LOS ANGELES, CA 90049
GERSON, KEN	ACTOR	HERA, 3575 W CAHUENGA BL, 2ND FL	LOS ANGELES, CA 90068
GERSON, PHILIP	ACTOR-WRITER	1310 N VISTA ST	LOS ANGELES, CA 90046
GERSTEIN, DANNY	ACTOR	49 W 88TH ST #3	NEW YORK, NY 10024
GERSTEIN, DAVID B	BASKETBALL EXECUTIVE	N J NETS, MEADOWLANDS ARENA	EAST RUTHERFORD, NJ 07073
GERSTEIN, RON	BASEBALL	POST OFFICE BOX 6748	ROCKFORD, IL 61125
GERSTEN, BERNARD	THEATER PRODUCER	QUAD PRODS, 890 BROADWAY	NEW YORK, NY 10003
GERSTEN, GERRY	CARTOONIST	MAD MAGAZINE, 485 MADISON AVE	NEW YORK, NY 10022
GERTZ, IRVING	COMPOSER-CONDUCTOR	351 VETERAN AVE	LOS ANGELES, CA 90024
GERTZ, JAMI	ACTRESS	151 S EL CAMINO DR	BEVERLY HILLS, CA 90212
GERULAITAS, VITAS	TENNIS	200 E END AVE #15-P	NEW YORK, NY 10028
GERVIN, DERRICK	BASKETBALL	N J NETS, MEADOWLANDS ARENA	EAST RUTHERFORD, NJ 07073
GESCHWIND, JOE	ACTOR	226 GRUBER CT	WEST HEMPSTEAD, NY 11552
GESEK, JOHN	FOOTBALL	COWBOYS, 1 COWBOYS PARKWAY	IRVING, TX 75063
GESSELL, GERHARD	JUDGE	UNITED STATES COURTHOUSE	
		3RD ST & CONSTITUTION AVE, NW	WASHINGTON, DC 20001
GESSLER, JOAN E	WRITER	13416 RAMONA PARKWAY	BALDWIN PARK, NY 91706
GESSNER, HAL	TV DIRECTOR-PRODUCER	30 W 15TH ST	NEW YORK, NY 10011
GETCHELL, FRANKLIN	TV WRITER	CHILDREN'S TV WORKSHOP	
		1 LINCOLN PLAZA	NEW YORK, NY 10023
GETCHELL, ROBERT L	SCREENWRITER	8730 HOLLYWOOD HILLS RD	LOS ANGELES, CA 90046
GETHERS, ERIC	TV WRITER	2759 WOODSHIRE DR	LOS ANGELES, CA 90068
GETHERS, STEVEN	TV WRITER-DIRECTOR	9100 HAZEN DR	BEVERLY HILLS, CA 90210
GETLIN, SCOTT	ACTOR	183 N MARTEL AVE #260	LOS ANGELES, CA 90036
GETTENGER, BRAD	ACTOR	101 W 69TH ST #3-B	NEW YORK, NY 10023
GETTINGER, DON	ACTOR	330 W END AVE #7-A	NEW YORK, NY 10023
GETTY, BALTHAZER	ACTOR	1535 N BEVERLY DR	BEVERLY HILLS, CA 90210
GETTY, ESTELLE	ACTRESS	GETTLEMAN, 68-85 218TH ST	BAYSIDE, NY 11364
GETTY, GORDON	COMPOSER	1199 PARK AVE #1-E	NEW YORK, NY 10028
GETTY, GORDON P	PHILANTHROPIST	THE JOHN PAUL GETTY MUSEUM	
		17985 PACIFIC COAST HWY	MALIBU, CA 90265
GETZ, DON	FILM EXECUTIVE	PLAYPONT FILMS, 1/2 RAMILLES ST	LONDON W1V 1DF ENGLAND
GETZ, JOHN	ACTOR	402 21ST PL	SANTA MONICA, CA 90402
GETZ, ROBERT	TV PRODUCER	CBS-TV, 524 W 57TH ST	NEW YORK, NY 10019
GEWIRTZ, HOWARD	TV WRITER	12301 ROCHEDALE LN	LOS ANGELES, CA 90049
GEYER, GEORGIE ANNE	JOURNALIST	1271 AVE OF THE AMERICAS #3717	NEW YORK, NY 10020
GEYER, STEPHEN	COMPOSER	118 PACIFIC ST	SANTA MONICA, CA 90405
GHERTNER, CAROLE	ACTRESS	11429 YOLANDA AVE	NORTHRIDGE, CA 91326

Name	Occupation	Address	City
GHIAZZA, GIACOMO	ARTIST	1351 OCEAN PARK WALK #106	SANTA MONICA, CA 90405
GHOSTLEY, ALICE	ACTRESS	3800 REKLAW DR	NORTH HOLLYWOOD, CA 91604
GIACHETTI, RICHIE	ACTOR-BOXING TRAINER	ROUND 15, 10400 LORRAINE AVE	CLEVELAND, OH 44136
GIAMBALVO, LOUIS	ACTOR	606 N LARCHMONT BLVD #309	LOS ANGELES, CA 90004
GIANNELLI, RAY	BASEBALL	CHIEFS, MAC ARTHUR STADIUM	SYRACUSE, NY 13208
GIANNINI, GIANCARLO	ACTOR	VIA MERCALLI 46	ROME ITALY
GIARDINO, MARK	ACTOR	4545 TALOFA AVE	NORTH HOLLYWOOD, CA 91602
GIBB, BARRY	SINGER-SONGWRITER	3088 S MANN ST	LAS VEGAS, NV 89102
GIBB, CYNTHIA	ACTRESS	151 S EL CAMINO DR	BEVERLY HILLS, CA 90212
GIBB, MAURICE	SINGER-SONGWRITER	9220 SUNSET BLVD #320	LOS ANGELES, CA 90069
GIBB, ROBIN	SINGER-SONGWRITER	9220 SUNSET BLVD #320	LOS ANGELES, CA 90069
GIBB, TOM	CARTOONIST	HERITAGE FEATURES SYNDICATE	
		214 MASSACHUSETTS AVE, NE	WASHINGTON, DC 20002
GIBBON, MIKE	TV DIRECTOR	7 ALTON RD	LONDON SW15 ENGLAND
GIBBON, SAMUEL YOUNG, JR	DIRECTOR	CHILDREN'S TV WORKSHOP	
		1 LINCOLN PLAZA	NEW YORK, NY 10023
GIBBONS, BRIAN	BASEBALL UMPIRE	POST OFFICE BOX 25010	LITTLE ROCK, AZ 72221
GIBBONS, JOHN	BASEBALL-INSTRUCTOR	METS, 126TH ST & ROOSEVELT AVE	FLUSHING, NY 11368
GIBBONS, LEEZA	NEWS CORRESPONDENT	ENTERTAINMENT TONIGHT	
		PARAMOUNT TELEVISION	
		5555 MELROSE AVE	LOS ANGELES, CA 90038
GIBBONS, SAM	U S CONGRESSMAN	101 E KENNEDY BLVD #1425	TAMPA, FL 33602
GIBBS, ALAN R	DIRECTOR	3518 W CAHUENGA BLVD #300	LOS ANGELES, CA 90068
GIBBS, ALEX	FOOTBALL COACH	POST OFFICE BOX 609609	SAN DIEGO, CA 92160
GIBBS, GEORGIA	SINGER	GERVASI, 965 5TH AVE	NEW YORK, NY 10021
GIBBS, JOE	FOOTBALL COACH	POST OFFICE BOX 17247 (DULLES)	WASHINGTON, DC 20041
GIBBS, MARLA	ACTRESS-SINGER	2323 W MARTIN LUTHER KING BLVD	LOS ANGELES, CA 90008
GIBBS, MICHAEL	CONDUCTOR	KURLAND, 173 BRIGHTON AVE	BOSTON, MA 02134
GIBBS, RICHARD	COMPOSER	7921 AURA AVE	RESEDA, CA 91335
GIBBS, SCOTT	DIRECTOR	1911 ALAMEDA AVE	ALAMEDA, CA 94501
GIBBS, TERRI	SINGER-SONGWRITER	110 30TH AVE N	NASHVILLE, TN 37203
GIBBS, TIM	ACTOR	23740 PARK ANTIQUEA	CALABASAS, CA 91302
GIBERTI, DAVE	BASEBALL	14100 SIX MILE CYPRESS PKWY	FORT MYERS, FL 33912
GIBLIN, JOHN J	ACTOR	1056 1/4 N OXFORD AVE	LOS ANGELES, CA 90029
GIBRALTER, STEVE	BASEBALL	POST OFFICE BOX 2001	CEDAR RAPIDS, IA 52406
GIBS, GARY	TV PRODUCER	444 3RD AVE #15	NEW YORK, NY 10016
GIBSON, ALEXANDER	CONDUCTOR	SEE - GIBSON, SIR ALEXANDER	
GIBSON, ALTHEA	TRACK & FIELD	DARBEU, 275 PROSPECT SR #768	EAST ORANGE, NJ 07017
GIBSON, BOB	BASEBALL	215 BELLEVIEW BLVD S	BELLEVIEW, NE 68005
GIBSON, DEBBIE	SINGER	POST OFFICE BOX 489	MERRICK, NY 11566
GIBSON, DENNIS	FOOTBALL	LIONS, 1200 FEATHERSTONE RD	PONTIAC, MI 48432
GIBSON, DEREK	FILM-TV EXECUTIVE	1118 N WETHERLY DR	LOS ANGELES, CA 90069
GIBSON, DON	SINGER-GUITARIST	POST OFFICE BOX 50474	NASHVILLE, TN 37205
GIBSON, ELLIE	GOLFER	2750 VOLUSA AVE #B	DAYTON BEACH, FL 32114
GIBSON, HARRIETT	FILM PRODUCER	843 21ST ST #1	SANTA MONICA, CA 90403
GIBSON, HENRY	ACTOR	26740 LATIGO SHORE DR	MALIBU, CA 90265
GIBSON, JACK	RADIO PERSONALITY	BILLYE LOVE, JACK THE RAPPER	
		2637 BARKWATER DR	ORLANDO, FL 32809
GIBSON, JEAN LEWIS	COMPOSER	4108 TUJUNGA AVE	STUDIO CITY, CA 91604
GIBSON, KENT	DIRECTOR	1508 N CRESCENT HEIGHTS BLVD	HOLLYWOOD, CA 90046
GIBSON, KIRK	BASEBALL	POST OFFICE BOX 7000	PITTSBURGH, PA 15212
GIBSON, MEL	ACTOR-WRITER	SHANAHAN MANAGEMNET	
		129 BOURKE ST	WOOLLOOMOOLOO NSW 2011.. AUSTRALIA
GIBSON, PAUL	BASEBALL	METS, 126TH ST & ROOSEVELT AVE	FLUSHING, NY 11368
GIBSON, RUSS	ACTOR	BURLEWS #5, HWY 71	BRIELLE, NJ 08730
GIBSON, SIR ALEXANDER	CONDUCTOR	ICM, 40 W 57TH ST	NEW YORK, NY 10019
GIBSON, TOBE	TALENT AGENT	301 E 62ND ST #2-C	NEW YORK, NY 10021
GIBSON, TOM	FOOTBALL	EAGLES, BROAD ST & PATTISON AVE	PHILADELPHIA, PA 19148
GIBSON, WILLIAM	TV DIRECTOR	POST OFFICE BOX 188	CONNER, MT 59827
GIDDENS, JAMES	DIRECTOR	GMS, 7025 SANTA MONICA BLVD	HOLLYWOOD, CA 90038
GIDDING, NELSON	WRITER	234 VANCE ST	PACIFIC PALISADES, CA 90272
GIDEON, BRETT	BASEBALL	2501 ALLEN AVE, SE	CANTON, OH 44707
GIDEON, LOUAN	ACTOR	SAVAGE, 6212 BANNER AVE	LOS ANGELES, CA 90038
GIDEON, RAYMOND	SCREENWRITER	3524 MULTIVIEW DR	LOS ANGELES, CA 90068
GIDEON, RON	BASEBALL COACH	POST OFFICE BOX 598	BINGHAMTON, NY 13902
GIDLEY, PAMELA	ACTRESS	ICM, 8899 BEVERLY BLVD	LOS ANGELES, CA 90048
GIEGLER, MARK	BASEBALL SCOUT	TIGERS, TIGER STADIUM	DETROIT, MI 48216
GIEGLING, MATT	BASEBALL	POST OFFICE BOX 2001	CEDAR RAPIDS, IA 52406
GIELGUD, SIR JOHN	ACTOR	SOUTH PAVILLION, WOTTEN	
		UNDERWOOD, AYLESBURY	BUCKINGHAMSHIRE ENGLAND
GIERASCH, STEFAN	ACTOR	9301 WILSHIRE BLVD #312	BEVERLY HILLS, CA 90210
GIERE, GLENN	TV DIRECTOR	208 W SHORE TRAIL	SPARTA, NJ 07871
GIERKE, TERRY	FOOTBALL REFEREE	NFL, 410 PARK AVE	NEW YORK, NY 10022
GIES, CHRIS	BASEBALL	POST OFFICE BOX 3609	PORT CHARLOTTE, FL 33949
GIESECKE, ROB	BASEBALL TRAINER	POST OFFICE BOX 2887	VERO BEACH, FL 32961
GIESEKE, MARK	BASEBALL	POST OFFICE BOX 1420	WICHITA, KS 67201
GIESELMANN, GENE	BASEBALL TRAINER	250 STADIUM PLAZA	ST LOUIS, MO 63102
GIETZEN, PETER	BASEBALL	POST OFFICE BOX 22093	GREENSBORO, NC 27420
GIFFEN, RALPH R	DIRECTOR	633 HERITAGE VILLAGE #B	SOUTHBURY, CT 06488
GIFFORD, FRANCES	ACTRESS	940 E COLORADO BLVD #306	PASADENA, CA 91106
GIFFORD, FRANK	SPORTSCASTER-FOOTBALL	625 MADISON AVE #1200	NEW YORK, NY 10022
GIFFORD, GLORIA	ACTRESS	8228 SUNSET BLVD #212	LOS ANGELES, CA 90046
GIFFORD, HAZEN	ACTOR	5 PETER COOPER RD	NEW YORK, NY 10010
GIFFORD, KATHIE LEE	SINGER-TV HOST	625 MADISON AVE #1200	NEW YORK, NY 10022

Buying and Selling AUTOGRAPHS Since 1980.

P.O. Box 2000 • Amherst, NH 03031 • USA

(603) 672-6611

FAX (603) 672-6442

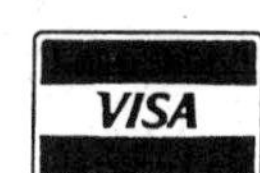

(All signed photos are 8x10 and not inscribed to anyone)

GUARANTEED AUTHENTIC AUTOGRAPHS

Hank Aaron - Baseball Player. Signature with photos of #715$75
Paula Abdul - Singer/dancer. 3x5 card matted w/color picture and single "Promise of a New Day" $100
AC/DC - all five members $100
Ansel Adams - Photographer. Signed card w/a b/w photo $95
Charles Francis Adams - Diplomat. Slip of paper with formal portrait (11x14) $50
Andre Aggasi - Tennis. In action, full length sp 8x10 .... $40
Buzz Aldrin - standing on moon $75
Kim Alexis - smiling pose $20
Muhammad Ali - Boxer. 3x5 card w/2 color action poses (12x16) $50
Alice Cast - 3 waitresses $50
Woody Allen - Comedian. 3x5 card matted with two color photos $45
Carol Alt - in swimsuit $20
Ian Anderson - recent pose $45
Mario Andretti - Race car driver. Signature on 3x5 card, matted with 2 photos $45
Julie Andrews - Actress. 3x5 card color photos from Sound of Music and Mary Poppins (12x16) $35
The Animals - Nicely matted color magazine photo signed by all five members $250
Susan Anton - Supermodel in sexy bathing suit $20
Eddie Arcaro - 3x5 w/an array of photos of this famous jockey $50
Edward Arnold - Actor. Signature on album page matted with b/w photo (11x14) $30
Rosanne Arquette - Actress. Casual color 8x10 signed by star of "Desperately Seeking Susan" $25
Neils Astor - Actor. Album page w/studio portrait from the 40's (11x14) $35
Hoyt Axton - b/w photo signed $10
Jim Backus - Actor. Famous voice of cartoon's "Mr. Magoo" 3x5 card matted with a picture of Backus & Magoo $35
Josephine Baker - Singer. Album page with color 20's pose $150
Alec Baldwin - shirtless holding gun $35
William Baldwin - Actor. Two color photos matted with a 3x5 card $50
Wm Baldwin - from "Backdraft" $50
Severino Ballesteros - Golf. Color photo w/a 3x5 .... $35
The Bangles - Large white card signed by all 4 members, matted w/ color picture. Hit song, "Manic Monday" $95
Theda Bara - Actress. Lg pg w/signed quote with b/w photo $150
Brigette Bardot - Actress. 8x10 color pose of this beautiful actress from her heyday $50
Brigitte Bardot - Actress/model. Signature matted with pictures $50
Lex Barker - Actor. Album page matted w/color picture $50
Ellen Barkin - Signed close-up color 8x10 of actress $50
Charles Barkley - Basketball. 3x5 card, matted with 3 color action photos $40
Diana Barrymore - Actress. Album page w/full length 40's pose (11x14) $35
Clara Barton - Founder of american Red Cross. Card signed w/ original engraved portrait (9x12) $175
Kim Basinger - Actress. 8x10 color signed photo of this steamy actress from "91/2 Weeks" $50
Beach Boys - Music. Five excellent signatures and 2 color photos make this a great display item $450
Beach Boys - Vocal group. They are credited with igniting the surf music craze. Five excellent signatures and 2 color photos make this a great display item $450
The Beatles - Music group. Album page signed by all, matted with a selection of three color photos $2000
Warren Beatty - as Clyde Barrow $65
Warren Beatty - as Dick Tracy $65
The Bee Gees - Singers. Signed card w/70's color pose (12x16) $95
David Ben-Gurion - Israeli statesmen. 3x5 card w/later in life portrait (9x12) $200
Johnny Bench - Baseball player. Signature matted with three color photos in Reds uniform $50
Annette Bening - Actress. In casual recent pose $45
Tony Bennett - Singer. 1 pg (1961) AFTRA contract signed by Bennett and Dick Clark for American Bandstand. Matted with full length color photo $75
Busby Berkely - Producer & choreographer. Known for lavish production techniques $100
David Berkowitz - Son of Sam killer. ALS in pencil recognizing his "Horrible sins" and giving directions to a church he attended (12x16) $250
Milton Berle - Comedian. 1 pg TLS, matted w/young color picture of this memorable funnyman (12x16) $95
Irving Berlin - Signature matted with b/w 40's portrait at piano $150
Sarah Bernhardt - Actress. Signature with portrait $150
Leonard Bernstein - Composer and conductor. 3x5 card w/photo of him conducting (11x14) $75
Chuck Berry - Signature matted w/"Johnny B. Good" single and picture $200
The Big Valley - TV show. Five signatures, matted photo of the cast $200
Jacqueline Bisset - 60's pose $15
Clint Black - Signed color photo matted with single of "Killin' Time" . $75

FREE
CATALOG!
R&R ENTERPRISES
CATALOG 121
Subscriptions $25 per year
Our fully-illustrated monthly sales catalog contains thousands of autographed items of famous personalities in all fields, including TV, movies, sports, music, history, art, and science.
Call today to receive a FREE copy of our current issue while supply lasts!

James Blaine - Politician. Card w/portrait (11x14) $35
Joan Blondell - Actress. Album page matted with b/w photo (11x14) $40
Ray Bolger - 3x5 card matted with poses as the Scarecrow from Oz $75
Michael Bolton - Casual pose of this popular music star $95
Gary U.S. Bonds - Singer. 1 pg (1961) AFTRA contract signed in his legal name Gary Levohn Anderson and Dick Clark. Matted with two b/w photos $75
Pat Boone - Singer. 1 pg (1961) AFTRA agreement to perform on American Bandstand, also signed by Dick Clark $95
David Bowie - Actress. Large sig. attractively matted w/2 full length and 2 smaller photos in b/w $100
Jimmy Braddock - Boxer. Album page matted with b/w photo of 1935-1937 heavy weight champion $95
Omar Bradley - Military. Album pg matted with b/w photo $75
Frankie Brimsek - Hockey. 1 pg ALS w/photo in hockey gear (11x14) $45
Christie Brinkley - "Cover Girl" in beautiful pose $45
Charles Bronson - Actor. Check signed, matted with b/w photo $75
Garth Brooks - Singer. Signed photo with 45 single "The Thunder Rolls" $85
Jackson Browne - Singer. 3x5 card matted w/photo $40
William Cullen Bryant - American poet and editor. Card signed and dated Dec. 4, 1877, matted with b/w portrait $50
Yul Brynner - Actor. 3x5 card matted w/color photo in costume from "The King and I" (12x16) $50
Luther Burbank - Horticulturist. Large and w/full-length portrait (11x14) $50
Billie Burke - Signature matted with photo as the "good witch" $150

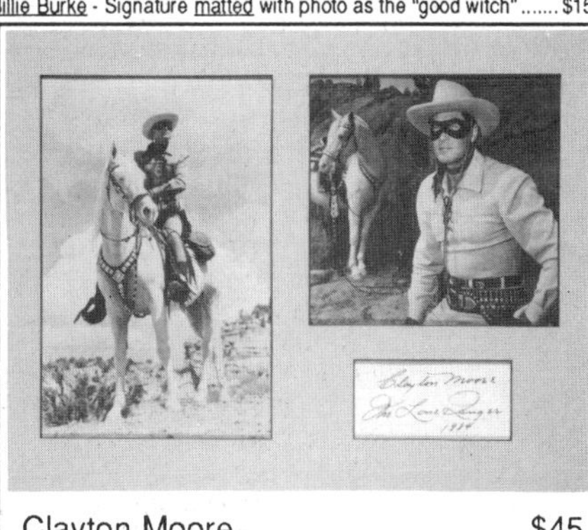

Clayton Moore $45

Burns & Allen - Comedy. Album page signed by both, matted with great picture of this unforgettable team $100
Edgar Rice Burroughs - Creator of Tarzan. Signature w/photo at his desk (11x14) $200
Charles Butterworth - Comic actor. Album pg w/comical portrait (11x14) $25
Hector Camacho - Boxer. Signature with b/w photo (11x14) . $30
Kim Cantrell - Actress. Casual color 8x10 signed of this beautiful actress $45
Yakima Canutt - Stuntman. Nicely signed 3x5 card w/western photo (11x14) $35
Frank Capra - Producer. Signature matted with b/w portrait $150
Jennifer Capriati - Tennis. Color action photo matted with a signature on 3x5 card $50
Mariah Carey - Tight, short dress $95
Max Carey - Baseball star of the 20's. 3x5 matted with b/w photo $25
Belinda Carlisle - Smiling pose $45
Art Carney - Actor. 1 pg TLS (1958) matted with color picture of the Honeymooners (11x171/2) $75
Carney & Meadows - 50's pose $25
Leo Carrillo - Actor. Page w/photo as Pancho (11x14) $50
Madeline Carroll - Actress. Page w/30's portrait (11x14) $35
Sunset Carson - Actor. Two western poses (12x16) $35
Jimmy & Rosalyn Carter - recent $100
Lynda Carter - as Wonder Women $30
Johnny Cash - Singer. Lyrics of "Ragged Old Flag" signed, matted with b/w photo $50
David Cassidy - Picture from "Partridge Family" era $30
Jack Cassidy - Actor. TV actor sig matted w/60's portrait (11x14) $25
Ted Cassidy - Actor. 3x5 matted w/photo as "Lurch" from "The Adams Family" (12x16) $200
Phoebe Cates - Smiling and sexy pose from this young actress $45
Wilt Chamberlain - 3x5 matted with two color action poses $50
Lon Chaney, Jr - Signature with photo as "wolfman" matted $300
Carrie Chapman Catt - Reformer. Portrait (12x16) $45
Ruth Chatterton - 30's film actress. Sig on album page matted with b/w portrait (11x14) $35
Chubby Checker - Formal portrait from 50's signed recently . $50
Cher - recent sexy pose $45
Agatha Christie - Author. Signature matted with portrait $200
Eric Clapton - Great full length pose with guitar $85
Lone Ranger/ Clayton Moore - Actor. B/w signed picture in character on his horse "Silver" $50
Francis Cleveland - Clip signature dated 1899 w/formal portrait of this 1st lady $95
Montgomery Clift - Actor. Popular big screen actor, ablum page matted with color portrait $250
Lee J. Cobb - Lawyer. Check signed, matted with b/w photo $60
Phil Collins - signed photo $65
Earle Combs - Baseball player. B/w photo in uniform, matted with 3x5 card $45
Jimmy Conners - 3x5 card matted with color action pose $50
Sean Connery - Actor. Signed personal check matted with three color photos as James Bond $200
Harry Connick, Jr - Singer. b/w portrait $95
Jennifer Connolly - Casual pose of this young actress $45
Jackie Coogen - Actor. Signature matted with photo as youngster .. $25
Jay Cooke - Banker. Slip w/engraved portrait. (9x12) $75
Alice Cooper - Singer. 3x5 card matted w/color picture $45
Gary Cooper - Actor. Album page matted with western pose $250
Jackie Cooper - Actor. Album page, matted w/ b/w portrait of Cooper as a young boy (11x14) $25
Bob Cousy - Basketball great. 3x5 card w/2 color action photos $40
Broderick Crawford - Actor. Signature matted with pose from "Highway Patrol" $35
Joan Crawford - Signature matted with 40's portrait $75
Creedence Clearwater Revival - Music group. Album page signed by all four members matted with photo $395
Joe Cronin - Baseball player. Signed uniform agreement for the assignment for the Assignment of a Players contract by a Major League Club - matted with b/w photo in Red Sox uniform $50
Cathy Lee Crosby - Actress. Sexy swimsuit pose (11x14) $35
Crosby & Hope - Hope on album pg, Crosby on card, matted with b/w photo of them together $100
Crosby, Stills & Nash - Music group. Three signatures matted with color photo of the group $250
Larry Csonka - 3x5 w/photo $50
Macauley Culkin - Portrait $75
G.W. Curtis - Aviator. Rival to the Wright Bros. sig with photos $195
Beverly D'Angelo - Recent pose $35
Salvador Dali - Artist. Formal portrait. He has signed a 4x6 reproduction $125
Roger Daltry - Smiling pose $35
Roger Daltry & Pete Townshend - Musicians. Two signatures

GIFFORD, LEWIS	DIRECTOR	134 SISSON RD	HARWICHPORT, MA	02646
GIFFORD, THOMAS	SCREENWRITER	555 W 57TH ST #1230	NEW YORK, NY	10019
GIFFORD, WENDY	ACTRESS	CONWAY, 18-21 JERMYN ST	LONDON SW1	ENGLAND
GIFT, ROLAND	SINGER-SONGWRITER	SEE - FINE YOUNG CANNIBALS, THE		
GIFTOS, ELAINE	ACTRESS	10351 SANTA MONICA BLVD #211	LOS ANGELES, CA	90025
GIGANTINO, ARTIE	FOOTBALL COACH	RAMS, 2327 W LINCOLN BLVD	ANAHEIM, CA	92801
GIGLI, ORMOND	DIRECTOR	327 E 58TH ST	NEW YORK, NY	10022
GIGUERE, RALPH	ARTIST	322 S 11TH ST	PHILADELPHIA, PA	19107
GIL, BENJI	BASEBALL	POST OFFICE BOX 309	GASTONA, NC	28053
GIL, GUS	BASEBALL-MANAGER	POST OFFICE BOX 356	BLUEFIELD, WV	24701
GILAD, YEHUDA	CONDUCTOR	953 N LAUREL AVE	LOS ANGELES, CA	90046
GILBEAUX, EUGENE	COMPOSER	1020 GIRARD ST	SAN FRANCISCO, CA	94134
GILBERT, ADAM HILL	TV WRITER-PRODUCER	1590 SUNSET PLAZA DR	LOS ANGELES, CA	90069
GILBERT, ALLEN	BASEBALL EXECUTIVE	POST OFFICE BOX 1742	PALM SPRINGS, CA	92263
GILBERT, BRENT	BASEBALL	POST OFFICE BOX 2148	WOODBRIDGE, VA	22193
GILBERT, BRUCE	FILM-TV PRODUCER	3 LATIMER RD	SANTA MONICA, CA	90402
GILBERT, CHARLES	ACTOR	400 W 43RD ST #42-N	NEW YORK, NY	10036
GILBERT, DON	BASEBALL	POST OFFICE BOX 418	SAINT CHARLES, IL	60174
GILBERT, ELSIE	ACTRESS	1016 N ORANGE GROVE #4	LOS ANGELES, CA	90046
GILBERT, GALE	FOOTBALL	BILLS, 1 BILLS DR	ORCHARD PARK, NJ	14127
GILBERT, GIBBY	GOLFER	PGA SENIORS, 112 T P C BLVD	PONTE VEDRA BEACH, FL	32082
GILBERT, GREG	HOCKEY	BLACKHAWKS, 1800 W MADISON ST	CHICAGO, IL	60612
GILBERT, HERSCHEL BURKE	COMPOSER-CONDUCTOR	2451 NICHOLS CANYON PL	LOS ANGELES, CA	90046
GILBERT, JAMES	DIRECTOR-PRODUCER	THAMES TV, BROIOM RD, TEDDINGTON	MIDDLESEX	ENGLAND
GILBERT, JIM	BASEBALL SCOUT	ORIOLE PARK, 333 W CAMDEN ST	BALTIMORE, MD	21201
GILBERT, JIMMIE	CONDUCTOR	1771 KENNETH WY	PASADENA, CA	91103
GILBERT, KENNETH C	DIRECTOR	KENANN, 6111 W 75TH ST	LOS ANGELES, CA	90045
GILBERT, LEWIS	WRITER-PRODUCER	BAKER ROOKE, CLEMENT HOUSE		
		99 ALDWYCH	LONDON WC2 BJY	ENGLAND
GILBERT, MICKEY	DIRECTOR	4170 LA LADERA RD	SANTA BARBARA, CA	93110
GILBERT, RON	FILM-TV PRODUCER	HILL FILMS, 320 N LARCHMONT BL	LOS ANGELES, CA	90004
GILBERT, RUTH	ACTRESS	1070 PARK AVE	NEW YORK, NY	10028
GILBERT, SARA	ACTRESS	16254 HIGH VALLEY DR	ENCINO, CA	91436
GILBERT, SHAWN	BASEBALL	POST OFFICE BOX 1659	PORTLAND, OR	97207
GILBERT, STANLEY E	CINEMATOGRAPHER	DGA, 7920 SUNSET BLVD, 6TH FL	LOS ANGELES, CA	90046
GILBERT, TAYLOR	ACTRESS-MODEL	400 S BEVERLY DR #216	BEVERLY HILLS, CA	90212
GILBERT-BRINKMAN, MELISSA	ACTRESS	3960 LAUREL CANYON BLVD #370	STUDIO CITY, CA	91604
GILBRIDE, KEVIN	FOOTBALL COACH	OILERS, 6910 FANNIN ST	HOUSTON, TX	77070
GILCHREST, WAYNE	U S CONGRESSMAN	POST OFFICE BOX 2076	WALDORF, MD	20601
GILCHRIST, BRENT	HOCKEY	CANADIENS, 2313 ST CATHERINE ST	MONTREAL, QUE H3H 1N2	CANADA
GILDER, BOB	GOLFER	POST OFFICE BOX 109601	PALM BCH GARDENS, FL	33418
GILDER, ROSAMOND	DRAMA CRITIC	24 GRAMERCY PARK	NEW YORK, NY	10003
GILDNER, BARBARA	ACTRESS	1217 S WESTGATE AVE #H	LOS ANGELES, CA	90025
GILER, DAVID	WRITER-PRODUCER	7874 WOODROW WILSON DR	LOS ANGELES, CA	90046
GILER, LYNNE D	WRITER	609 SAINT CLOUD RD	LOS ANGELES, CA	90077
GILES, BILL	BASEBALL EXECUTIVE	POST OFFICE BOX 7575	PHILADELPHIA, PA	19101
GILES, BRIAN	BASEBALL	2501 ALLEN AVE, SE	CANTON, OH	44707
GILES, CURT	HOCKEY	NORTH STARS, 7901 CEDAR AVE S	BLOOMINGTON, MN	55425
GILES, JOHNNY	COMPOSER-CONDUCTOR	POST OFFICE BOX 244	APTOS, CA	95003
GILES, LEONARD	MUSIC ARRANGER	488 LEMONT DR #1-182	NASHVILLE, TN	37216
GILES, NANCY	ACTRESS	433 SHIRLEY PL #4	BEVERLY HILLS, CA	90212
GILES, SANDRA	ACTRESS	3500 W OLIVE AVE #1400	BURBANK, CA	91505
GILFORD, GWYNNE	ACTOR-WRITER	11846 VENTURA BLVD #100	STUDIO CITY, CA	91604
GILHEN, RANDY	HOCKEY	PENGUINS, CIVIC ARENA, CENTRE AV	PITTSBURGH, PA	15219
GILHOUSEN, ROSEY	BASEBALL SCOUT	POST OFFICE BOX 2000	ANAHEIM, CA	92803
GILKEY, BERNARD	BASEBALL	250 STADIUM PLAZA	ST LOUIS, MO	63102
GILKEY, OTIS	BASEBALL	7895 TRENTON	UNIVERSITY CITY, MO	63130
GILL, CHRIS	BASEBALL	POST OFFICE BOX 2001	CEDAR RAPIDS, IA	52406
GILL, DEREK	WRITER	700 ESPLANADE ST #34	REDONDO BEACH, CA	90277
GILL, ELIZABETH	TV WRITER	959 GALLOWAY ST	PACIFIC PALISADES, CA	90272
GILL, JACK	STUNTMAN	18060 BORIS DR	ENCINO, CA	91316
GILL, JOHNNY	SINGER-PIANIST	MUSKRAT, 44 N CENTRAL AVE	ELMSFORD, NY	10523
GILL, KENDALL	BASKETBALL	310 N KINGS DR	CHARLOTTE, NC	28204
GILL, MICHAEL	TV DIRECTOR	MALONE-GILL, 16 NEWMAN PASS	LONDON W1R 3LD	ENGLAND
GILL, STEVE	BASEBALL	12000 STADIUM RD	ADELANTO, CA	92301
GILL, TODD	HOCKEY	MAPLE LEAFS, 60 CARLTON ST	TORONTO, ONT M5B 1L1	CANADA
GILL, VINCE	SINGER-SONGWRITER	TRIAD, 1114 17TH AVE S	NASHVILLE, TN	37212
GILLARD, STUART	WRITER-PRODUCER	9744 WILSHIRE BLVD #308	BEVERLY HILLS, CA	90212
GILLASPY, RICHARD	TV PRODUCER	POST OFFICE BOX 430667	SOUTH MIAMI, FL	33143
GILLERAN, TOM	ACTOR	574 GREENCRAIG RD	LOS ANGELES, CA	90049
GILLES, GENEVIEVE	ACTRESS	THE DAKOTA, 1 W 72ND ST	NEW YORK, NY	10023
GILLES, NICHOLAS	TV EXECUTIVE	1111 PARK AVE	NEW YORK, NY	10028
GILLES, THOMAS	BASEBALL	RURAL ROUTE 1, BOX 87-A	KICKAPOO, IL	61528
GILLESPIE, DIZZY	TRUMPETER	477 N WOODLANDS ST	ENGLEWOOD, NJ	07631
GILLESPIE, JEAN	ACTRESS	135 S CANON DR	BEVERLY HILLS, CA	90212
GILLESPIE, ROBERT	ACTOR-DIRECTOR	10 IRVING RD	LONDON W14 OJS	ENGLAND
GILLETT, JOHN	FILM CRITIC	BRITISH FILM INSTITUTE		
		21 STEPHEN ST	LONDON W1P 1PL	ENGLAND
GILLETTE, ANITA	ACTRESS	10000 SANTA MONICA BLVD #305	LOS ANGELES, CA	90067
GILLETTE, MIKE	BASEBALL	TIGERS, 89 WHARNCLIFFE RD N	LONDON, ONT N6H 2A7	CANADA
GILLETTE, STEVE	SINGER-SONGWRITER	4 JOHN ST #301	TARRYTOWN, NY	10591
GILLEY, MICKEY	SINGER-SONGWRITER	POST OFFICE BOX 23162	NASHVILLE, TN	37202
GILLGAN, SONJA CARL	TV DIRECTOR-PRODUCER	HUDSON RIVER FILM & VIDEO		
		INDIAN BROOK RD	GARRISON, NY	10524
GILLIAM, ARMON	BASKETBALL	310 N KINGS DR	CHARLOTTE, NC	28204

Name	Occupation	Address	City
GILLIAM, BABE	ACTRESS	SEE - EVANS, BABE	
GILLIAM, BO	BASEBALL	5301 NW 12TH AVE	FORT LAUDERDALE, FL 33309
GILLIAM, BURTON	ACTOR	825 N BEACHWOOD DR	BURBANK, CA 91506
GILLIAM, TERRY	ANI-DIR-ACT	THE OLD WALL, SO GROVE, HIGHGATE	LONDON N6 ENGLAND
GILLICK, PAT	BASEBALL EXECUTIVE	SKYDOME, 300 BREMMER BL #3200	TORONTO, ONT M5V 3B3 CANADA
GILLIES, CHUCK	ARTIST	SKIDMORE SAHARATIN & MINDOLA	
		2100 W BIG RIVER	TROY, MI 48084
GILLIGAN, JOHN P	TV WRITER	3120 SCOTLAND ST #A	LOS ANGELES, CA 90039
GILLILAND, RICHARD	ACTOR	4545 NOELINE AVE	ENCINO, CA 91346
GILLIS, ANN	ACTRESS	OOSTRATIESTRAAT 187	2550 KONTICH BELGIUM
GILLIS, JACK	BASEBALL MGR-SCOUT	95 RIVER ST	ONEONTA, NY 13820
GILLIS, JACKSON C	TV WRITER	4980 VANALDEN AVE	TARZANA, CA 91356
GILLIS, JOHN	CINEMATOGRAPHER	7715 SUNSET BLVD #150	LOS ANGELES, CA 90046
GILLIS, MARY	ACTRESS	1975 N BEACHWOOD DR #31	LOS ANGELES, CA 90068
GILLIS, PAUL	HOCKEY	BLACKHAWKS, 1800 W MADISON ST	CHICAGO, IL 60612
GILLIS, TIM	BASEBALL	POST OFFICE BOX 507	DURHAM, NC 27702
GILLMOR, PAUL E	U S CONGRESSMAN	120 JEFFERSON ST, 2ND FLOOR	PORT CLINTON, OH 43452
GILLOTT, NICK	TV PRODUCER	169 QUEENSGATE #8-A	LONDON SW7 5EH ENGLAND
GILLSON, CAROL A	TV WRITER-PRODUCER	4519 GLORIA AVE	ENCINO, CA 91436
GILLUM, K C	BASEBALL	POST OFFICE BOX 4669	CHARLESTON, WV 25304
GILLUM, VERN	DIRECTOR	8640 PINETREE PL	HOLLYWOOD, CA 90069
GILMAN, BENJAMIN A	U S CONGRESSMAN	POST OFFICE BOX 358	MIDDLETOWN, NY 10940
GILMAN, KENNETH	ACTOR	3516 MULTIVIEW DR	LOS ANGELES, CA 90068
GILMER, ROBERT W	TV WRITER-PRODUCER	13308 CHELTENHAM DR	SHERMAN OAKS, CA 91423
GILMORE, BO-DEAN	SINGER-GUITARIST	500 SADDLE DR	NASHVILLE, TN 37221
GILMORE, JOEL	BASEBALL	POST OFFICE BOX 1721	SPARTANBURG, SC 29304
GILMORE, PETER	ACTOR	WM MORRIS, 31-32 SOHO SQ	LONDON W1V 5DG ENGLAND
GILMORE, ROBERT	TV DIRECTOR	685 INGLENOOK DR	LAS VEGAS, NV 89123
GILMORE, TONY	BASEBALL	POST OFFICE BOX 422229	KISSIMMEE, FL 34742
GILMORE, WALTER L, JR	TV DIRECTOR	345 S SPARKS ST	BURBANK, CA 91506
GILMOUR, BILL	TV DIRECTOR	12 LANSDOWNE RD, SALE	CHESHIRE M33 1PF ENGLAND
GILMOUR, DOUG	HOCKEY	POST OFFICE BOX 1540, STA "M"	CALGARY, ALTA T2P 3BP CANADA
GILROY, DAN	COLUMNIST	5700 WILSHIRE BLVD #120	LOS ANGELES, CA 90036
GILSON, BOB	BASEBALL EXECUTIVE	TIGERS, 89 WHARNCLIFFE RD N	LONDON, ONT N6H 2A7 CANADA
GILYARD, CLARENCE, JR	ACTOR	556 W AVE 46	LOS ANGELES, CA 90065
GIMBEL, NORMAN	LYRICIST-SONGWRITER	1172 CENTINELA AVE #3	SANTA MONICA, CA 90403
GIMBEL, PETER	DIRECTOR-PRODUCER	BLUE GANDER, 10 E 63RD ST	NEW YORK, NY 10021
GIMBEL, ROGER	TV PRODUCER	8439 SUNSET BLVD #201	LOS ANGELES, CA 90069
GIMBLE, JOHNNY	FIDDLER	1204 CLUB CIR	SALADO, TX 76571
GIMPEL, ERICA	ACTRESS	STE, 888 7TH AVE, 18TH FLOOR	NEW YORK, NY 10106
GIMPEL, SANDRA	DIRECTOR	11944 OTSEGO ST	NORTH HOLLYWOOD, CA 91607
GINDES, MARK	SCREENWRITER	1584 PALISADES DR	PACIFIC PALISADES, CA 90272
GINDOFF, BRYAN	SCREENWRITER	2820 DELL AVE	VENICE, CA 90291
GING, JACK	ACTOR	25234 MALIBU RD	MALIBU, CA 90265
GINGOLD, DAN	DIRECTOR	3540 BEVERLY RIDGE DR	SHERMAN OAKS, CA 91403
GINGRICH, NEWT	U S CONGRESSMAN	19 E WASHINGTON ST	NEWMAN, GA 30263
GINNANE, ANTONY I	FILM PRODUCER	IFM FILM ASSOCIATES PTY, LTD	
		LEVEL 4, 63 STEAD ST	
		SOUTH MELBOURNE	VICTORIA 3025 AUSTRALIA
GINNES, ABRAM	TV WRITER	9713 SANTA MONICA BLVD	BEVERLY HILLS, CA 90210
GINNES, JUDITH BINDER	WRITER	326 S BENTLEY AVE	LOS ANGELES, CA 90049
GINSBERG, ALLEN	POET	POST OFFICE BOX 582	NEW YORK, NY 10019
GINSBERG, SUSAN	MAKE-UP ARTIST	102-30 67TH AVE #6-G	FOREST HILLS, NY 11375
GINSBURG, MAX	ARTIST	40 W 77TH ST	NEW YORK, NY 10024
GINSBURG, ROBIN	ACTRESS	1307 15TH ST #1	SANTA MONICA, CA 90404
GINTY, ROBERT	ACTOR-DIRECTOR	9834 WANDA PARK DR	BEVERLY HILLS, CA 90210
GIODANO, TOM	BASEBALL-SCOUT	INDIANS, CLEVELAND STADIUM	CLEVELAND, OH 44114
GIORDANO, TONY	DIRECTOR	40 W 74TH ST	NEW YORK, NY 10023
GIOVANNINI, CAESAR	COMPOSER	POST OFFICE BOX 1503	SEDONA, AZ 86336
GIOVI, MARLENE	ACTRESS	9900 DURANT DR #C	BEVERLY HILLS, CA 90212
GIPS, ROBERT	DIRECTOR-PRODUCER	POST OFFICE BOX 23345	VENTURA, CA 93002
GIR, FRANCOIS	FILM DIRECTOR	95810 GRISY-LES-PLATRES	PARIS FRANCE
GIRALDI, ROBERT	DIRECTOR	GIRALDI SUAREZ, 581 6TH AVE	NEW YORK, NY 10011
GIRARD, LOUIS	ACTOR	POST OFFICE BOX 476	BRANCHVILLE, NJ 07826
GIRARD, STEPHEN	TV EXECUTIVE	4705 LAUREL CANYON #PH	NORTH HOLLYWOOD, CA 91607
GIRARD, WENDY	ACTRESS	1173 N ARDMORE AVE #3	LOS ANGELES, CA 90029
GIRARDI, JOE	BASEBALL	1060 W ADDISON ST	CHICAGO, IL 60613
GIRARDOT, ANNIE	ACTRESS	J NAINCHRIC, 31 CHAMPS-ELYSEES	PARIS 75008 FRANCE
GIRLS NEXT DOOR, THE	C & W GROUP	POST OFFICE BOX 2977	HENDERSONVILLE, TN 37077
GIRONDA, VINCE	BODYBUILDER	VINCE'S GYM, 11262 VENTURA BL	NORTH HOLLYWOOD, CA 91604
GIROUX RAILSBACK, JACKELYN	ACTRESS	4503 BAKMAN AVE	NORTH HOLLYWOOD, CA 91602
GISEL, WILLIAM, JR	BASEBALL EXECUTIVE	POST OFFICE BOX 450	BUFFALO, NY 14205
GISH, ANNABETH	ACTRESS	POST OFFICE BOX 5617	BEVERLY HILLS, CA 90213
GISH, LILLIAN	ACTRESS	430 E 57TH ST	NEW YORK, NY 10022
GISH, SHEILA	ACTRESS	BELFRAGE, 68 SAINT JAMES'S ST	LONDON SW1A 1LE ENGLAND
GISMONTI, EGBERTO	GUITARIST	POST OFFICE BOX 411	MILL VALLEY, CA 94941
GIST, ROBERT	DIRECTOR	4675 WILLIS AVE	SHERMAN OAKS, CA 91403
GITOMER, MICHAEL	ACTOR	239 N ORCHARD DR	BURBANK, CA 91506
GITTELMAN, PHIL	WRI-DIR-PROD	112 E 36TH ST	NEW YORK, NY 10016
GITTLIN, JOYCE	ACTRESS-WRITER	6234 W 6TH ST	LOS ANGELES, CA 90048
GIUFFRE, JAMES	COMPOSER	STONE MILL, BOX 302	WEST STOCKBRIDGE, MA 01266
GIULI, ANN MARION	CASTING DIRECTOR	16 W 76TH ST #2-RW	NEW YORK, NY 10023
GIULIANI, ANGELO	BASEBALL-SCOUT	TWINS, 501 CHICAGO AVE S	MINNEAPOLIS, MN 55415
GIULINI, CARLO MARIA	CONDUCTOR	LOS ANGELES PHILHARMONIC	
		135 N GRAND AVE	LOS ANGELES, CA 90012

Name	Occupation	Address	City/State	Zip/Country
GIUSTI, ROBERT	ARTIST	350 E 52ND ST	NEW YORK, NY	10022
GIVENS, BRIAN	BASEBALL	POST OFFICE BOX 3690, STA "B"	CALGARY, ALB T2B 4M4	CANADA
GIVENS, JIM	BASEBALL	POST OFFICE BOX 2785	LAKELAND, FL	33806
GIVENS, ROBIN	ACTRESS	8818 THRASHER AVE	LOS ANGELES, CA	90069
GIVINS, ERNEST	FOOTBALL	OILERS, 6910 FANNIN ST	HOUSTON, TX	77070
GLADDEN, DAN	BASEBALL	TIGERS, TIGER STADIUM	DETROIT, MI	48216
GLADDING, FRED	BASEBALL-COACH	POST OFFICE BOX 1886	COLUMBUS, GA	31902
GLADSTON, JENNIFER	WRITER	1221 OCEAN AVE #401	SANTA MONICA, CA	90401
GLADSTONE, BERNARD	COLUMNIST	N Y TIMES, 229 W 43RD ST	NEW YORK, NY	10036
GLADSTONE, DANA	ACTOR	1336 N ALTA VISTA BLVD	LOS ANGELES, CA	90046
GLADWELL, DAVID	FILM DIRECTOR	7 CALDERVALE RD	LONDON SW4	ENGLAND
GLAISTER, GERARD	TV PRODUCER	SPRINGFIELD GROVE		
		SUNBURY-ON-THAMES	MIDDLESEX TW16 6NT	ENGLAND
GLANDBARD, MAX	DIRECTOR	195 MOHAWK DR	RIVER EDGE, NJ	07661
GLANVILLE, DOUG	BASEBALL	POST OFFICE BOX 4488	WINSTON-SALEM, NC	27115
GLANVILLE, JERRY	FOOTBALL COACH	FALCONS, SUWANEE RD AT I-85	SUWANEE, GA	30174
GLANZ, BETHANY	ACTRESS	8228 SUNSET BLVD #311	LOS ANGELES, CA	90046
GLASAUER, WILLI	ARTIST	SAINT PAUL DE FENOUILLET	VIRA 66220	FRANCE
GLASELL, DON LEON	WRITER-PRODUCER	331 KEDZIE ST	EVANSTON, IL	60202
GLASER, CHUCK	SINGER-GUITARIST	916 19TH AVE S	NASHVILLE, TN	37212
GLASER, JIM	SINGER-SONGWRITER	TAYLOR, 2401 12TH AVE S	NASHVILLE, TN	37204
GLASER, JOSEPH R	COMPOSER	639 HILL ST #C	SANTA MONICA, CA	90405
GLASER, MILTON	ARTIST	207 E 32ND ST	NEW YORK, NY	10016
GLASER, PAUL MICHAEL	ACTOR-DIRECTOR	317 GEORGINA AVE	SANTA MONICA, CA	90402
GLASER, SHERI	ACTRESS	9000 SUNSET BLVD #1200	LOS ANGELES, CA	90069
GLASER, SIOMA	CASTING DIRECTOR	B'WAY ARTISTS, 99-46 64TH AVE	REGO PARK, NY	11374
GLASGOW, DALE	ILLUSTRATOR	POST OFFICE BOX 500	WASHINGTON, DC	20044
GLASGOW, NESBY	FOOTBALL	SEAHAWKS, 11220 NE 53RD ST	KIRKLAND, WA	98033
GLASS, BAMA	FOOTBALL REFEREE	NFL, 410 PARK AVE	NEW YORK, NY	10022
GLASS, CHARLES	BODYBUILDER	742 E 88TH PL	LOS ANGELES, CA	90002
GLASS, GERALD	BASKETBALL	TIMBERWOLVES, 600 1ST AVE N	MINNEAPOLIS, MN	55403
GLASS, JERALYN	ACTRESS	1733 PASEO DEL MAR	PALOS VERDES, CA	90274
GLASS, PHILIP	COMPOSER	231 2ND AVE	NEW YORK, NY	10003
GLASS, RON	ACTOR	2485 WILD OAK DR	LOS ANGELES, CA	90068
GLASS, SANFORD	SCREENWRITER	8955 BEVERLY BLVD	WEST HOLLYWOOD, CA	90048
GLASS, SEAMON	ACTOR	814 6TH ST #4	SANTA MONICA, CA	90403
GLASS, STEPHEN	TALENT AGENT	761 JANE ST #15	TORONTO, ONT M6N 4B4	CANADA
GLASS, SYDNEY A	TV WRITER	2004 MILAN AVE	SOUTH PASADENA, CA	91030
GLASS PYRAMID	ROCK & ROLL GROUP	GOOD, 2500 NW 39TH ST	OKLAHOMA CITY, OK	73112
GLASS TIGER	ROCK & ROLL GROUP	MGMT WEST, 14 SUMACH ST	TORONTO, ON M5A 3JA	CANADA
GLASSER, ALBERT	COMPOSER-CONDUCTOR	11812 BELLAGIO RD	LOS ANGELES, CA	90049
GLASSER, BARRY H	WRITER	1417 PEARL ST #6	SANTA MONICA, CA	90405
GLASSER, BERNARD	DIRECTOR	POST OFFICE BOX 67635	LOS ANGELES, CA	90067
GLASSER, HAROLD L	TV PRODUCER	1 GROVE ISLE DR #1002	COCONUT GROVE, FL	33133
GLASSER, KERRY	DIRECTOR	400 E 54TH ST	NEW YORK, NY	10022
GLASSER, LEONARD	DIRECTOR-PRODUCER	8109 GLADE AVE	CANOGA PARK, CA	91304
GLASSMAN, PAULETTE M	WRITER-PRODUCER	DGA, 110 W 57TH ST	NEW YORK, NY	10019
GLASSMAN, SETH	TV DIRECTOR	484 W 43RD ST #19-B	NEW YORK, NY	10036
GLATTES, WOLFGANG	FILM DIRECTOR	3801 RHODES AVE	NORTH HOLLYWOOD, CA	91604
GLAUBERG, JOE	TV WRITER	12570 ROSY CIR	LOS ANGELES, CA	90066
GLAVINE, TOM	BASEBALL	POST OFFICE BOX 4064	ATLANTA, GA	30302
GLAZER, BARRY	TV DIRECTOR-PRODUCER	1227 SUNSET PLAZA DR	LOS ANGELES, CA	90069
GLAZER, DAVID	CLARINETIST	25 CENTRAL PARK W	NEW YORK, NY	10023
GLAZER, VICTOR	COMPOSER-CONDUCTOR	1304 WOODLOW CT	WESTLAKE VILLAGE, CA	91361
GLEASON, JOANNA	ACTRESS	ICM, 8899 BEVERLY BLVD	LOS ANGELES, CA	90048
GLEASON, PAUL	ACTOR	1999 AVE OF THE STARS #2850	LOS ANGELES, CA	90067
GLEATON, JERRY	BASEBALL	106 BROADMOOR CIR	BROWNWOOD, TX	76801
GLEDHILL, CHANCE	BASEBALL	POST OFFICE BOX 3496	DAVENPORT, IA	52808
GLEN, IAIN	ACTOR	HEATH, PARAMOUNT HOUSE		
		162-170 WARDOUR ST	LONDON W1V 3AT	ENGLAND
GLEN, JOHN	FILM DIRECTOR	9-A BARKSTON GARDENS	LONDON SW5	ENGLAND
GLEN, TOM	BASEBALL EXECUTIVE	POST OFFICE BOX 402	GENEVA, NY	14456
GLENISTER, JOHN	TV DIRECTOR	BROWN, 162-168 REGENT ST	LONDON W1R 5TB	ENGLAND
GLENN, BILL	TV DIRECTOR	230 W 55TH ST #17-D	NEW YORK, NY	10019
GLENN, CHARLES	TV EXECUTIVE	2247 STRADELLA RD	LOS ANGELES, CA	90077
GLENN, CHRISTOPHER	BROADCAST JOURNALIST	CBS-TV, 51 W 52ND ST	NEW YORK, NY	10019
GLENN, DENNIS	DIRECTOR	1410 N STATE PARKWAY	CHICAGO, IL	60610
GLENN, JOHN	ASTRONAUT-US SENATOR	1000 URLIN AVE	COLUMBUS, OH	43212
GLENN, KERRY	FOOTBALL	DOLPHINS, 2269 NW 199TH ST	MIAMI, FL	33056
GLENN, LEON	BASEBALL	POST OFFICE BOX 8550	STOCKTON, CA	95208
GLENN, SCOTT	ACTOR	126 E DE VARGAS ST	SANTA FE, NM	87501
GLENN, VENCIE	FOOTBALL	SAINTS, 1500 POYDRAS ST	NEW ORLEANS, LA	90112
GLENNDENING, ED	ARTIST	8285 SUNSET BLVD #3	LOS ANGELES, CA	90046
GLENVILLE, PETER	DIRECTOR	LEFKOWITZ, 641 LEXINGTON AVE	NEW YORK, NY	10022
GLENWOOD, TERRY	FILM EXECUTIVE	GLINWOOD FILMS LIMITED		
		SWAN HOUSE, 52 POLAND ST	LONDON W1V 3DF	ENGLAND
GLESS, SHARON	ACTRESS	CAA, 9830 WILSHIRE BLVD	BEVERLY HILLS, CA	90212
GLICK, BARBARA	ACTRESS-SINGER	65-05 YELLOWSTONE BLVD	FOREST HILLS, CA	11375
GLICK, PAMELA	ARTIST	2914 MERIDA AVE	FORT WORTH, TX	76109
GLICKENHAUS, JAMES W	WRITER-PRODUCER	1619 BROADWAY #303	NEW YORK, NY	10019
GLICKMAN, DAN	U S CONGRESSMAN	401 N MARKET #134	WICHITA, KS	67201
GLICKMAN, HARRY	BASKETBALL EXECUTIVE	700 NE MULTNOMAH ST #600	PORTLAND, OR	97232
GLICKMAN, SUSAN	CASTING DIRECTOR	ABC-TV, 2040 AVE OF THE STARS	LOS ANGELES, CA	90067
GLIDDEN, DAN	ARTIST	FLAT LIZARD GRAPHICS		
		1 CHELSEA PL	HOUSTON, TX	77006

Name	Occupation	Address	City/State	Zip/Country
GLINATSIS, GEORGE	BASEBALL	POST OFFICE BOX 30160	SAN BERNARDINO, CA	92413
GLINER, STEVE	BASEBALL EXECUTIVE	POST OFFICE BOX 20849	CHARLESTON, SC	29413
GLINN, BURTON	PHOTOGRAPHER	41 CENTRAL PARK W	NEW YORK, NY	10023
GLITTER, GARY	SINGER-SONGWRITER	37 BLACKSMITHS LN	RAINHAM RM13 7AD	ENGLAND
GLOBUS, YORAM	PRODUCER-EXECUTIVE	PATHE INT'L-CANNON CINEMAS		
		PATHE HOUSE, 76 HAMMERSMITH RD	LONDON W14 8YR	ENGLAND
GLOSSER, DANIEL	CONDUCTOR	750 S SPAULDING AVE #31	LOS ANGELES, CA	90036
GLOUNER, RICHARD C	CINEMATOGRAPHER	POST OFFICE BOX 2230	HOLLYWOOD, CA	90078
GLOVANOLA, ED	BASEBALL	POST OFFICE BOX 16683	GREENVILLE, SC	29606
GLOVER, ANDREW	FOOTBALL	RAIDERS, 332 CENTER ST	EL SEGUNDO, CA	90245
GLOVER, BRIAN	ACTOR	DE WOLFE, 376-378 THE STRAND	LONDON WC2RN OLR	ENGLAND
GLOVER, BRUCE	ACTOR	11449 WOODBINE ST	LOS ANGELES, CA	90066
GLOVER, BRUCE E	CONDUCTOR	POST OFFICE BOX 10413	MARINA DEL REY, CA	90295
GLOVER, CRISPIN	ACTOR	1811 WHITLEY AVE #1400	LOS ANGELES, CA	90028
GLOVER, DANNY	ACTOR-PRODUCER	POST OFFICE BOX 1648	SAN FRANCISCO, CA	94101
GLOVER, JOHN	ACTOR	2417 MICHELTORENA ST	LOS ANGELES, CA	90039
GLOVER, JULIAN	ACTOR	19 ULLSWATER RD	LONDON SW13	ENGLAND
GLOVER, KEVIN	FOOTBALL	LIONS, 1200 FEATHERSTONE RD	PONTIAC, MI	48432
GLOVER, WILLIAM	THEATER CRITIC	4 E 88TH ST	NEW YORK, NY	10028
GLOVITZ, LINDA	TV DIRECTOR-PRODUCER	360 E 65TH ST	NEW YORK, NY	10021
GLUCK, MARVIN A	TV WRITER	19988 OBSERVATION DR	TOPANGA CANYON, CA	90290
GLUCK, STEPHEN HENRY	DIRECTOR	DGA, 110 W 57TH ST	NEW YORK, NY	10019
GLUECKMAN, ALAN JAY	SCREENWRITER	SHAPIRO, 8827 BEVERLY BLVD	LOS ANGELES, CA	90048
GLUM, GARY L, MD	BODYBUILDER	5250 W CENTURY BLVD #614	LOS ANGELES, CA	90045
GLUSKIN, MICHAEL	ACTOR	619 N HOLLISTON AVE #4	PASADENA, CA	91106
GLUT, DONALD F	WRITER	2805 N KEYSTONE ST	BURBANK, CA	91504
GLYNN, BRIAN	HOCKEY	NORTH STARS, 7901 CEDAR AVE S	BLOOMINGTON, MN	55425
GLYNN, GENE	BASEBALL MANAGER	POST OFFICE BOX 4758	SPOKANE, WA	99202
GLYNN, JEANNE DAVIS	TV WRITER	70 PARK TERRACE W	NEW YORK, NY	10034
GLYNN, MICHAEL	TV PRODUCER	4 BERMUDA HOUSE, MOUNT PARK RD		
		HARROW-ON-THE-HILL	MIDDLESEX HA1 3XH	ENGLAND
GLYNN, VICTOR	FILM PRODUCER	92 KINGSTON RD	OXFORD	ENGLAND
GLYTTOV, BRIENNE	COSTUME DESIGNER	3906 WITZEL DR	SHERMAN OAKS, CA	91423
GMINSKI, CHARLES	BASKETBALL	POST OFFICE BOX 25040	PHILADELPHIA, PA	19147
GNSWOLD, DOUG	ARTIST	695 S 11TH ST #16	SAN JOSE, CA	95112
GO WEST	ROCK & ROLL DUO	BLUE PRINT MANAGEMENT		
		81 HARLEY HOUSE		
		MARYLEBONE RD	LONDON NW1	ENGLAND
GOAD, TIM	FOOTBALL	PATRIOTS, FOXBORO STADIUM, RT #1	FOXBORO, MA	02035
GOALBY, BOB	GOLFER	PGA SENIORS, 112 T P C BLVD	PONTE VEDRA BEACH, FL	32082
GOBERMAN, JOHN	TV PRODUCER	140 W 65TH ST	NEW YORK, NY	10023
GOBETTI, MARIA	ACTRESS	12833 LANDALE ST	NORTH HOLLYWOOD, CA	91604
GOBRON, JEAN-NOEL	FILM DIRECTOR	RUE BOURE, 14	1050 BRUSSELS	BELGIUM
GOCKE, JUSTIN	ACTOR	6763 PISTACHIO PL	PALMDALE, CA	93551
GODAR, GODFREY	CINEMATOGRAPHER	23 SAINT PETERS CL, BURNHAM	BUCKS SL1 7HS	ENGLAND
GODARD, JEAN-LUC	FILM DIRECTOR	15 RUE DU NORD	1180 ROULLE	
GODDARD, GARY	SCREENWRITER	CAA, 9830 WILSHIRE BLVD	BEVERLY HILLS, CA	90212
GODDARD, JIM	TV DIRECTOR	7 CHISWICK QUAY	LONDON W4 3UR	ENGLAND
GODDARD, JOHN	ACTOR	5125 FULTON AVE	SHERMAN OAKS, CA	91423
GODDARD, LIZA	ACTRESS	BURNETT, 42-43 GRAFTON HOUSE		
		2-3 GOLDEN SQ	LONDON W1R 3AD	ENGLAND
GODDARD, PAULINE	DIRECTRESS-PRODUCER	EUROPEAN SCHOOL OF DANCE		
		853 AMBOY AVE	EDISON, NJ	08837
GODDARD, SCOTT	SINGER	2250 N ONTARIO ST	BURBANK, CA	91504
GODFREY, TYSON	BASEBALL	1524 W NEBRASKA AVE	PEORIA, IL	61604
GODIN, STEVE	BASEBALL	POST OFFICE BOX 3169	FREDERICK, MD	21701
GODLEY, KEVIN	TV DIRECTOR-SINGER	CHELSEA WHARF, 15 LOTS RD	LONDON SW10 OQH	ENGLAND
GODUNOV, ALEXANDER	DANCER-ACTOR	8787 SHOREHAM DR #1001	LOS ANGELES, CA	90069
GODWIN, FRANK	WRITER-PRODUCER	77 DEAN ST	LONDON W1V 6LP	ENGLAND
GODYNUK, ALEXANDER	HOCKEY	MAPLE LEAFS, 60 CARLTON ST	TORONTO, ONT M5B 1L1	CANADA
GOEAS, LEO	FOOTBALL	POST OFFICE BOX 609609	SAN DIEGO, CA	92160
GOEBEL, BRAD	FOOTBALL	EAGLES, BROAD ST & PATTISON AVE	PHILADELPHIA, PA	19148
GOEN, BOB	TV HOST	3400 RIVERSIDE DR	BURBANK, CA	91505
GOERGEN, TODD	BASEBALL	POST OFFICE BOX 10336	CLEARWATER, FL	34617
GOETZ, BARRY	BASEBALL	POST OFFICE BOX 3609	PORT CHARLOTTE, FL	33949
GOETZ, BERNHARD	CELEBRITY	55 W 14TH ST	NEW YORK, NY	10011
GOETZ, THEODORE	DIRECTOR	13457 CHANDLER BLVD	VAN NUYS, CA	91401
GOETZMAN, GARY	ACTOR	11558 RIVERSIDE DR	NORTH HOLLYWOOD, CA	91602
GOFF, IVAN CLAYTON	TV WRITER-PRODUCER	86 MALIBU COLONY DR	MALIBU, CA	90265
GOFF, JERRY	BASEBALL	1501 W 16TH ST	INDIANAPOLIS, IN	46202
GOFF, MIKE	BASEBALL COACH	POST OFFICE BOX 4756	JACKSONVILLE, FL	32201
GOFF, ROBERT	FOOTBALL	SAINTS, 1500 POYDRAS ST	NEW ORLEANS, LA	90112
GOFFIN, GERRY	SONGWRITER	8062 WOODROW WILSON DR	LOS ANGELES, CA	90046
GOGAN, KEVIN	FOOTBALL	COWBOYS, 1 COWBOYS PARKWAY	IRVING, TX	75063
GOGOLEWSKI, DOUG	BASEBALL	5301 NW 12TH AVE	FORT LAUDERDALE, FL	33309
GOHR, GREG	BASEBALL	POST OFFICE BOX 6212	TOLEDO, OH	43614
GOINS, TIM	BASEBALL	POST OFFICE BOX 611	WATERLOO, IA	50704
GOLAN, MENAHEM	PRODUCER-EXECUTIVE	CANNON FILM GROUP		
		640 S SAN VICENTE BLVD	LOS ANGELES, CA	90048
GOLAND, ALAN	TV DIRECTOR-PRODUCER	1024 STEARNS DR	LOS ANGELES, CA	90035
GOLD, ANDREW	SINGER-SONGWRITER	2565 ZORADA DR	LOS ANGELES, CA	90046
GOLD, AVRAM D	WRITER	146 N ARNAZ DR #D	BEVERLY HILLS, CA	90211
GOLD, DAVID	WRESTLER	POST OFFICE BOX 3859	STAMFORD, CT	06905
GOLD, ERNEST	COMPOSER	269 N BELLINO DR	PACIFIC PALISADES, CA	90272
GOLD, FAY	ACTRESS	POST OFFICE BOX 256, TSS	NEW YORK, NY	10108

GOLD, JACK	FILM-TV DIRECTOR	18 AVENUE RD	LONDON N6 5DW ENGLAND
GOLD, JEFF	TV DIRECTOR-PRODUCER	300 E 51ST ST	NEW YORK, NY 10022
GOLD, MICK	FILM-TV DIRECTOR	6 OAKFORD RD	LONDON NW5 ENGLAND
GOLD, MISSY	ACTRESS	3500 W OLIVE AVE #1400	BURBANK, CA 91505
GOLD, PAUL H	DIRECTOR	401 E 74TH ST	NEW YORK, NY 10021
GOLD, SYLVIA	TALENT AGENT	ICM, 8899 BEVERLY BLVD	LOS ANGELES, CA 90048
GOLD, TRACEY	ACTRESS	12631 ADDISON ST	NORTH HOLLYWOOD, CA 91607
GOLD CITY	C & W GROUP	365 GREAT CIRCLE DR	NASHVILLE, TN 37228
GOLDBERG, BETTY	TV WRITER-DIRECTOR	1042 CORNING ST	LOS ANGELES, CA 90035
GOLDBERG, DIEGO	PHOTOGRAPHER	75 E END AVE	NEW YORK, NY 10028
GOLDBERG, ESTHER	COMPOSER-LYRICIST	67 MANHATTAN AVE	BROOKLYN, NY 11206
GOLDBERG, GARY DAVID	TV WRITER-PRODUCER	POST OFFICE BOX 84168	LOS ANGELES, CA 90077
GOLDBERG, HOWARD S	WRITER	1358 N ALTA VISTA BLVD	LOS ANGELES, CA 90046
GOLDBERG, JEANNE	DIETITIAN-COLUMNIST	THE WASHINGTON POST	
		WRITERS GROUP	
		1150 15TH ST, NW	WASHINGTON, DC 20071
GOLDBERG, JOANN	TV WRITER-DIRECTOR	POST OFFICE BOX 8523 (FDR)	NEW YORK, NY 10150
GOLDBERG, LEONARD	TV-FILM PRODUCER	235 LADERA DR	BEVERLY HILLS, CA 90210
GOLDBERG, LYNNE P	ACTRESS	YOUNG/RUBICAM, 285 MADISON AVE	NEW YORK, NY 10017
GOLDBERG, SHARON	ACTRESS	2269 N BEACHWOOD DR #203	LOS ANGELES, CA 90068
GOLDBERG, SHARON	CHOREOGRAPHER	2106 MOUNT OLYMPUS DR	LOS ANGELES, CA 90046
GOLDBERG, SUSAN S	TV WRITER	9300 WILSHIRE BLVD #410	BEVERLY HILLS, CA 90212
GOLDBERG, WHOOPI	COMEDIENNE-ACTRESS	33012 PACIFIC COAST HIGHWAY	MALIBU, CA 90265
GOLDBLATT, STEPHEN	DIRECTOR	POST OFFICE BOX 2230	HOLLYWOOD, CA 90078
GOLDBLUM, JEFF	ACTOR	8033 SUNSET BLVD #367	LOS ANGELES, CA 90046
GOLDEMBERG, ROSE LEIMAN	TV WRITER-PRODUCER	61 JANE ST #15-M	NEW YORK, NY 10014
GOLDEN, ALEX	ACTOR-DIRECTOR	8286 PRESSON PL	LOS ANGELES, CA 90069
GOLDEN, ALEXANDER	CONDUCTOR	8286 PRESSON PL	LOS ANGELES, CA 90069
GOLDEN, HERB	TV WRITER-PRODUCER	4108 SAUGUS AVE	SHERMAN OAKS, CA 91403
GOLDEN, JOY	COMEDY WRITER	60 W 57TH ST	NEW YORK, NY 10019
GOLDEN, LAURA	SONGWRITER	11554 1/2 HUSTON ST	NORTH HOLLYWOOD, CA 91601
GOLDEN, NORMA DARWIN	ACTRESS	200 E 66TH ST #B-406	NEW YORK, NY 10021
GOLDEN, OLIVE FULLER	ACTRESS	SEE - CAREY, OLIVE FULLER	
GOLDEN, WILLIAM LEE	SINGER-SONGWRITER	POST OFFICE BOX 1795	HENDERSONVILLE, TN 37075
GOLDEN EARRING	ROCK & ROLL GROUP	DMA, 21182 EASTFARM	NORTHFIELD, MI 48167
GOLDENBERG, BILLY	COMPOSER	10037 VALLEY SPRING LN	NORTH HOLLYWOOD, CA 91602
GOLDENBERG, HARVEY J	ACTOR	1807 N CHEROKEE AVE	LOS ANGELES, CA 90028
GOLDENS, THE	C & W GROUP	POST OFFICE BOX 1795	HENDERSONVILLE, TN 37075
GOLDFARB, PETER	DIRECTOR	781 5TH AVE	NEW YORK, NY 10021
GOLDHOR, DAVID	DIRECTOR	EAGLE EYE, 4019 TUJUNGA AVE	STUDIO CITY, CA 91604
GOLDIN, MARILYN	WRITER	534 WESTMOUNT DR	LOS ANGELES, CA 90048
GOLDIN, RICKY PAULL	ACTOR	356 BROADWAY #2-D	NEW YORK, NY 10013
GOLDING, LOUISE DIANA	ACTRESS	367 N SIERRA BONITA AVE	LOS ANGELES, CA 90036
GOLDING, PAUL	TV WRITER	5007 STONEY CREEK RD #433	CULVER CITY, CA 90230
GOLDKLANG, MARVIN	BASEBALL EXECUTIVE	POST OFFICE BOX 75089	OKLAHOMA CITY, OK 73147
GOLDMAN, ALBERT	AUTHOR	WILLIAM MORROW & CO, INC	
		105 MADISON AVE	NEW YORK, NY 10016
GOLDMAN, BO	SCREENWRITER	ICM, 8899 BEVERLY BLVD	LOS ANGELES, CA 90048
GOLDMAN, BYRON	THEATER PRODUCER	1270 AVE OF THE AMERICAS	NEW YORK, NY 10020
GOLDMAN, CAROLE	ACTRESS	1030 N STATE ST #4C	CHICAGO, IL 60610
GOLDMAN, DANNY	ACTOR	1625 N STANLEY AVE	LOS ANGELES, CA 90046
GOLDMAN, DONALD	DIRECTOR	9759 SOPHIA AVE	SEPULVEDA, CA 91343
GOLDMAN, ERWIN	WRITER	2800 NEILSON WY #902	SANTA MONICA, CA 90405
GOLDMAN, GINA	WRITER	8250 FOUNTAIN AVE #C	LOS ANGELES, CA 90046
GOLDMAN, GREGORY	WRITER-PRODUCER	2016 OCEAN DR	MANHATTAN BEACH, CA 90266
GOLDMAN, HAROLD I	TV WRITER	2341 DONELLA CIR	LOS ANGELES, CA 90077
GOLDMAN, JACK	COMPOSER	11317 HERBERT ST	LOS ANGELES, CA 90066
GOLDMAN, JAMES	PLAYWRIGHT	ICM, 40 W 57TH ST	NEW YORK, NY 10019
GOLDMAN, LESLIE	CINEMATOGRAPHER	330 W 55TH ST	NEW YORK, NY 10019
GOLDMAN, LORRY	ACTOR	1310 N SWEETZER AVE #205	LOS ANGELES, CA 90069
GOLDMAN, MARCY	ACTRESS	116 N GALE DR #22	BEVERLY HILLS, CA 90211
GOLDMAN, MARGARET A	TV WRITER	9633 BEVERLYWOOD ST	LOS ANGELES, CA 90034
GOLDMAN, MARTIN	FILM DIRECTOR	POST OFFICE BOX 370	WILSON, WY 83014
GOLDMAN, MAURICE	COMPOSER-CONDUCTOR	23001 BIGLER ST	WOODLAND HILLS, CA 91364
GOLDMAN, PAMELA B	COSTUME DESIGNER	POST OFFICE BOX 636	NEW ROCHELLE, NY 10580
GOLDMAN, PEGGY	TV WRITER	SEE - GOLDMAN, MARGARET A	
GOLDMAN, RICK	ACTOR	GEDDES, 8457 MELROSE PL #200	LOS ANGELES, CA 90069
GOLDMAN, ROY	ACTOR	1713 BRYN MAWN AVE	SANTA MONICA, CA 90405
GOLDMAN, RUDI	PRODUCER	400 S BEVERLY DR #214	BEVERLY HILLS, CA 90212
GOLDMAN, SHEPARD	WRITER	COHN, GLICKSTEIN & LURIE	
		1370 AVE OF THE AMERICAS	NEW YORK, NY 10019
GOLDMAN, SHERWIN	THEATER PRODUCER	1501 BROADWAY	NEW YORK, NY 10036
GOLDMAN, STUART	WRI-DIR-PROD	4 GREAT JONES ST	NEW YORK, NY 10012
GOLDMAN, WILLIAM	SCREENWRITER	50 E 77TH ST #30	NEW YORK, NY 10021
GOLDMAN, WILLIAM	TV DIRECTOR	4 INDIANCREEK RD	MATAWAN, NJ 07747
GOLDONI, LELIA	ACTRESS	15459 WYANDOTTE ST	VAN NUYS, CA 91406
GOLDSBERRY, GORDON	BASEBALL-EXECUTIVE	ORIOLE PARK, 333 W CAMDEN ST	BALTIMORE, MD 21201
GOLDSBORO, BOBBY	SINGER-SONGWRITER	POST OFFICE BOX 5250	OCALA, FL 32678
GOLDSCHMIDT, ERNST	FILM EXECUTIVE	11845 W OLYMPIC BLVD #1055	LOS ANGELES, CA 90064
GOLDSCHMIDT, JOHN	TV DIRECTOR	46 CASCADE AVE	LONDON N10 3PU ENGLAND
GOLDSMITH, BRUCE LEIGH	WRITER-PRODUCER	9722 OAK PASS RD	BEVERLY HILLS, CA 90210
GOLDSMITH, GLORIA	WRITER	8440 DE LONGPRE AVE #10	LOS ANGELES, CA 90069
GOLDSMITH, JERRY	COMPOSER-CONDUCTOR	6525 SUNSET BLVD #402	HOLLYWOOD, CA 90028
GOLDSMITH, JOEL	COMPOSER	10100 SANTA MONICA BLVD #1600	LOS ANGELES, CA 90067
GOLDSMITH, JONATHAN	ACTOR	POST OFFICE BOX 9464	MARINA DEL REY, CA 90292

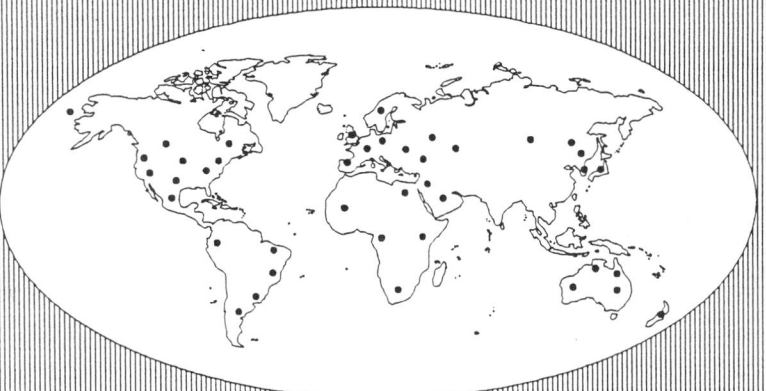

GOLDSMITH, LYNN	DIRECTOR	241 W 36TH ST	NEW YORK, NY	10018
GOLDSMITH, MALISSA	ACTRESS	POST OFFICE BOX 75	DEMAREST, NJ	07627
GOLDSMITH, MARTIN M	TV WRITER	13643 OAK CANYON AVE	SHERMAN OAKS, CA	91423
GOLDSMITH, MERWIN	ACTOR	66 W 88TH ST	NEW YORK, NY	10024
GOLDSMITH, RAYMOND	TV PRODUCER	RETAIL MEDIA GROUP, 5 PETO PL		
		REGENTS PARK	LONDON NW1 4DT	ENGLAND
GOLDSMITH, RUSSELL	BASEBALL EXECUTIVE	POST OFFICE BOX 2000	SAN DIEGO, CA	92112
GOLDSON, BENNY	COMPOSER	1140 BROADWAY #1006	NEW YORK, NY	10001
GOLDSTEIN, CHARLES	TV EXECUTIVE	19463 HATTON ST	RESEDA, CA	91335
GOLDSTEIN, JEFFREY	TV DIRECTOR	DGA, 7920 SUNSET BLVD, 6TH FL	LOS ANGELES, CA	90046
GOLDSTEIN, JENETTE	ACTRESS	1999 AVE OF THE STARS #2850	LOS ANGELES, CA	90067
GOLDSTEIN, LEE	TV WRITER	14058 DAVANA TERR	SHERMAN OAKS, CA	91423
GOLDSTEIN, LOUIS L	COMPTROLLER	STATE HOUSE BUILDING	ANNAPOLIS, MD	21401
GOLDSTEIN, MARTIN M	TV WRITER	151 S EL CAMINO DR	BEVERLY HILLS, CA	90212
GOLDSTEIN, MITCHELL	DIRECTOR	706 POLO CIR	BRYN MAWR, PA	19010
GOLDSTEIN, NEIL	TV DIRECTOR-PRODUCER	1930 CATHEDRAL RD	HUNTINGTON VALLEY, PA	19006
GOLDSTEIN, NORMAN	DIRECTOR	KATZ, 109 E 29TH ST	NEW YORK, NY	10016
GOLDSTEIN, PATRICK	FILM CRITIC	LA TIMES, TIMES MIRROR SQ	LOS ANGELES, CA	90053
		TIME MIRROR SQUARE	LOS ANGELES, CA	90053
GOLDSTEIN, REBECCA	ACTRESS-WRITER	6121 1/2 GLEN TOWER ST	LOS ANGELES, CA	90068
GOLDSTEIN, RONALD	COMPOSER-CONDUCTOR	9740 DONNA AVE	NORTHRIDGE, CA	91324
GOLDSTEIN, WILLIAM	COMPOSER-CONDUCTOR	8521 ALLENWOOD RD	LOS ANGELES, CA	90046
GOLDSTEIN-HOPKINS, SUELLEN	TV DIRECTOR	317 W 87TH ST	NEW YORK, NY	10024
GOLDSTONE, DEENA	TV WRITER	5672 TYRON RD	LOS ANGELES, CA	90068
GOLDSTONE, DUKE	DIRECTOR	351 N PALM DR #120	BEVERLY HILLS, CA	90210
GOLDSTONE, JAMES	FILM WRITER-DIRECTOR	344 CONWAY AVE	LOS ANGELES, CA	90024
GOLDSTONE, JOHN	FILM PRODUCER	8-A BRUNSWICK GARDENS	LONDON W8 4AJ	ENGLAND
GOLDSTONE, RAYMOND E	TV WRITER	14128 EMELITA ST	VAN NUYS, CA	91401
GOLDSTONE, RICHARD	DIRECTOR	LEVINSON, 12 1/2 E 82ND ST	NEW YORK, NY	10028
GOLDSTROM, ROBERT	ARTIST	471 5TH ST	BROOKLYN, NY	11215
GOLDTHWAIT, BOBCAT	ACTOR-COMEDIAN	3950 FREDONIA DR	LOS ANGELES, CA	90068
GOLDWASSER, LAWRENCE	DIRECTOR	686 QUAKER ST	CHAPPAQUA, NY	10514
GOLDWATER, BARRY	U S SENATOR	6250 HOGAHN	PARADISE VALLEY, AZ	85253
GOLDWYN, SAMUEL, JR	DIRECTOR-PRODUCER	10203 SANTA MONICA BLVD #500	LOS ANGELES, CA	90067
GOLDWYN, TONY	ACTOR	751 OZONE ST	SANTA MONICA, CA	90405
GOLIC, BOB	FOOTBALL	RAIDERS, 332 CENTER ST	EL SEGUNDO, CA	90245
GOLIC, MIKE	FOOTBALL	EAGLES, BROAD ST & PATTISON AVE	PHILADELPHIA, PA	19148
GOLINO, VALERIA	ACTRESS	MICKELSON, 1707 CLEARVIEW DR	BEVERLY HILLS, CA	90210
GOLITZEN, ALEXANDER	ART DIRECTOR	14880 VALLEY VISTA BLVD	VAN NUYS, CA	91403
GOLLANCE, RICHARD	TV WRITER	2686 WOODSTOCK RD	LOS ANGELES, CA	90046
GOLONKA, ARLENE	ACTRESS	1835 PANDORA AVE #3	LOS ANGELES, CA	90025
GOMAVITZ, LEWIS	DIRECTOR	10831 SYLVIA AVE	NORTHRIDGE, CA	91326
GOMBERG, SY L	SCREENWRITER	13233 RIVIERA RANCH RD	LOS ANGELES, CA	90049
GOMES, GEORGE	DIRECTOR	217 E 49TH ST	NEW YORK, NY	10017
GOMEZ, ALLEN	TV DIRECTOR	2071 SYDNEY DR	NORTH MERRICK, NY	11566
GOMEZ, CARLOS	ACTOR	12456 VENTURA BLVD #1	STUDIO CITY, CA	91604
GOMEZ, FABIO	BASEBALL	POST OFFICE BOX 11363	RENO, NV	89510
GOMEZ, JOSE	BASEBALL SCOUT	POST OFFICE BOX 2000	ANAHEIM, CA	92803
GOMEZ, LEO	BASEBALL	ORIOLE PARK, 333 W CAMDEN ST	BALTIMORE, MD	21201
GOMEZ, LUIS	BASEBALL SCOUT	S F GIANTS, CANDLESTICK PARK	SAN FRANICSCO, CA	94124
GOMEZ, ORLANDO	BASEBALL COACH-SCOUT	POST OFFICE BOX 90111	ARLINGTON, TX	76004
GOMEZ, PANCHITO	ACTOR	POST OFFICE BOX 7016	BURBANK, CA	91510
GOMEZ, PAT	BASEBALL	POST OFFICE BOX 6667	RICHMOND, VA	23230
GOMEZ, PRESTON	BASEBALL-EXECUTIVE	POST OFFICE BOX 2000	ANAHEIM, CA	92803
GOMEZ, RUDY	BASEBALL	POST OFFICE BOX 4488	WINSTON-SALEM, NC	27115
GOMPERTZ, ROLF	WRITER	6516 BEN AVE	NORTH HOLLYWOOD, CA	91606
GONSHER, DEBRA A	TV EXECUTIVE	DIVA COMM, 304 E 45TH ST	NEW YORK, NY	10017
GONYEA, DALE	ACTOR-SINGER	7916 1/8 W NORTON AVE	LOS ANGELES, CA	90046
GONZALES, BEN	BASEBALL	POST OFFICE BOX 422229	KISSIMMEE, FL	34742
GONZALES, FRANK	BASEBALL	TIGERS, 89 WHARNCLIFFE RD N	LONDON, ONT N6H 2A7	CANADA
GONZALES, JIM	BASEBALL	POST OFFICE BOX 824	BURLINGTON, IA	52601
GONZALES, KEN	BASEBALL SCOUT	POST OFFICE BOX 419969	KANSAS CITY, MO	64141
GONZALES, LARRY	BASEBALL	10233 96TH AVE	EDMONTON, ALB TK5 0A5	CANADA
GONZALES, MARY	TV DIRECTOR	519 N ELECTRIC AVE #7	ALHAMBRA, CA	91801
GONZALES, MICHAEL	ARTIST	CBS RECORD COMPANY		
		1801 CENTURY PARK W	LOS ANGELES, CA	90067
GONZALES, RENE	BASEBALL	10233 96TH AVE	EDMONTON, ALB TK5 0A5	CANADA
GONZALEZ, ALEX	BASEBALL	POST OFFICE BOX 1110	MYRTLE BEACH, SC	29578
GONZALEZ, ANGEL	BASEBALL	POST OFFICE BOX 23290	NASHVILLE, TN	37202
GONZALEZ, CLIFF	BASEBALL	POST OFFICE BOX 4370	SALINAS, CA	93912
GONZALEZ, ERNESTO	ACTOR	195 PRINCE ST	NEW YORK, NY	10012
GONZALEZ, FREDDY	BASEBALL	POST OFFICE BOX 28268	SAN ANTONIO, TX	78228
GONZALEZ, FREDI	BASEBALL-MANAGER	POST OFFICE BOX 726	POMPANO BEACH, FL	33064
GONZALEZ, HENRY B	U S CONGRESSMAN	FEDERAL BUILDING, B-124		
		727 E DURANGO BLVD	SAN ANTONIO, TX	78206
GONZALEZ, JAVIER	BASEBALL	POST OFFICE BOX 1211	NORFOLK, VA	23502
GONZALEZ, JOHN MICHAEL	DIRECTOR	DGA, 110 W 57TH ST	NEW YORK, NY	10019
GONZALEZ, JOSE	BASEBALL	10233 96TH AVE	EDMONTON, ALB TK5 0A5	CANADA
GONZALEZ, JUAN	BASEBALL	POST OFFICE BOX 90111	ARLINGTON, TX	76004
GONZALEZ, LUIS	BASEBALL	POST OFFICE BOX 288	HOUSTON, TX	77001
GONZALEZ, PAUL	BASEBALL	POST OFFICE BOX 1420	WICHITA, KS	67201
GONZALEZ, PEDRO	BASEBALL	POST OFFICE BOX 64939	FAYETTEVILLE, NC	28306
GONZALEZ, RAUL	BASEBALL	POST OFFICE BOX 464	APPLETON, WI	54912
GONZALEZ, STEPHANIE	SECRETARY OF STATE	SATE CAPITOL BUILDING	SANTE FE, NM	87503
GONZALEZ-GONZALEZ, PETER	ACTOR	4153 CHARLES AVE	CULVER CITY, CA	90230

Name	Occupation	Address	City/State	ZIP/Country
GOOD, ART	RADIO PERSONALITY	KIFM RADIO 98, 5125 CONVOY ST	SAN DIEGO, CA	92111
GOOD, LARRY	SINGER	627 COUNTRY VIEW ESTATE	COLUMBUS, NE	68601
GOOD BROTHERS, THE	C & W GROUP	POST OFFICE BOX 33	AURORA, ONT L4G 3H1	CANADA
GOOD COMPANY	MUSICAL GROUP	GOOD, 2500 NW 39TH ST	OKLAHOMA CITY, OK	73112
GOODACRE, JILL	MODEL	ELITE MODELS, 111 E 22ND ST	NEW YORK, NY	10010
GOODALE, PETER	ACTOR	39 E 19TH ST	NEW YORK, NY	10003
GOODALL, JACK	BASEBALL EXECUTIVE	POST OFFICE BOX 2000	SAN DIEGO, CA	92112
GOODBURN, KELLY	FOOTBALL	POST OFFICE BOX 17247 (DULLES)	WASHINGTON, DC	20041
GOODE, CHRIS	FOOTBALL	POST OFFICE BOX 535000	INDIANPOLIS, IN	46253
GOODE, DIANE	ARTIST	E P DUTTON/CHILDREN'S BOOKS		
		2 PARK AVE	NEW YORK, NY	10016
GOODE, FRITZ	DIRECTOR	6249 RODGERTON DR	HOLLYWOOD, CA	90068
GOODE, MARK	DIRECTOR	1600 N OAK ST #1219	ARLINGTON, VA	22209
GOODELL, GREGORY	WRITER-PRODUCER	1228 N FLORES ST	LOS ANGELES, CA	90069
GOODELL, HAROLD	ACTOR	1633 VISTA DEL MAR ST #201	LOS ANGELES, CA	90028
GOODEN, DWIGHT "DOC"	BASEBALL	METS, 126TH ST & ROOSEVELT AVE	FLUSHING, NY	11368
GOODEN, ROBERT	ACTOR-WRITER	3407 WARNER BLVD #B	BURBANK, CA	91505
GOODENOUGH-BARTON, GAY	ACTRESS	13827 E FOSTER AVE	BALDWIN PARK, CA	91706
GOODEVE, GRANT	ACTOR	21416 NE 68TH CT	REDMOND, WA	98053
GOODFORD, JACK	DIRECTOR	295 CARLTON ST	TORONTO, ONT M5A 2L6	CANADA
GOODFRIEND, LYNDA	ACTRESS	5700 ETIWANA AVE #150	TARZANA, CA	91356
GOODHART, JOANNE	TV DIRECTOR	136 W 16TH ST	NEW YORK, NY	10011
GOODHART, WILLIAM M	SCREENWRITER	555 W 57TH ST #1230	NEW YORK, NY	10019
GOODING, CUBA, JR	ACTOR	4789 VINELAND AVE #100	NORTH HOLLYWOOD, CA	91602
GOODLING, WILLIAM F	U S CONGRESSMAN	140 BALTIMORE ST #210	GETTYSBURG, PA	17325
GOODMAN, ALBERT M	TV WRITER	CAA, 9830 WILSHIRE BLVD	BEVERLY HILLS, CA	90212
GOODMAN, DODY	ACTRESS	10144 CULVER BLVD #21	CULVER CITY, CA	90232
GOODMAN, ELLEN	COLUMNIST	BOSTON GLOBE, 135 MORRISSEY RD	BOSTON, MA	02107
GOODMAN, EVELYN	WRITER	1123 N FULLER AVE #302	LOS ANGELES, CA	90046
GOODMAN, FRED	BASEBALL SCOUT	N Y YANKEES, YANKEE STADIUM	BRONX, NY	10451
GOODMAN, JOHN	ACTOR	2412 JUPITER DR	LOS ANGELES, CA	90046
GOODMAN, JOHNNY	FILM PRODUCER	9 TUDOR WELL CLOSE		
		OLD CHURCH LN, STANMORE	MIDDLESEX	ENGLAND
GOODMAN, JON W	WRITER	19252 LUDLOW ST	NORTHRIDGE, CA	91326
GOODMAN, LEE	DIRECTOR	3105 GULF OF MEXICO DR	LONGBOAT KEY, FL	33548
GOODMAN, MAURICE	WRITER-PRODUCER	11179 BERTRAND AVE	GRANADA HILLS, CA	91344
GOODMAN, MILES	COMPOSER	11812 SAN VICENTE BLVD #200	LOS ANGELES, CA	90049
GOODMAN, ROBERT	TV DIRECTOR-PRODUCER	545 W END AVE #16-D	NEW YORK, NY	10024
GOODMAN, ROGER	TV DIRECTOR-PRODUCER	ABC NEWS, 77 W 66TH ST	NEW YORK, NY	10023
GOODMAN, STUART	DIRECTOR	170 W 73RD ST #12-D	NEW YORK, NY	10023
GOODMAN, WALTER	WRITER	N Y TIMES, 229 W 43RD ST	NEW YORK, NY	10036
GOODMAN, WILLARD	WRITER-PRODUCER	6200 VISTA DEL MAR	PLAYA DEL REY, CA	90291
GOODNOFF, SOL	DIRECTOR	HALLOCKVILLE RD, ROUTE #8-A	PLAINFIELD, MA	01070
GOODRICH, DEBORAH	ACTRESS	335 N MAPLE DR #360	BEVERLY HILLS, CA	90210
GOODRICH, ROBERT	DIRECTOR	47 W 66TH ST	NEW YORK, NY	10023
GOODROW, MICHAEL	ACTOR	49 BREEZE AVE #1	VENICE, CA	90291
GOODRUM, CHARLES	TV DIRECTOR	1702 SAN MIGUEL DR	SAINT CHARLES, MO	63301
GOODSON, JOSEPH	TV DIRECTOR	858 RIDGE RD	LAKE ARROWHEAD, CA	92352
GOODSON, MARK	TV PRODUCER	375 PARK AVE	NEW YORK, NY	10152
GOODWIN, CURTIS	BASEBALL	POST OFFICE BOX 418	SAINT CHARLES, IL	60174
GOODWIN, DOUG	COMPOSER	24758 HERMOSILLA CT	CALABASAS, CA	91302
GOODWIN, GEENA	ACTRESS	143 PRINCE ST	NEW YORK, NY	10012
GOODWIN, GERALD	COMEDIAN	1007 BUCKINGHAM RD	GARNER, NC	27529
GOODWIN, HAROLD	ACTOR	21 ALBERT RD, TWICKENHAM	MIDDLESEX	ENGLAND
GOODWIN, JAMES M	ACTOR	NBC-TV, "ANOTHER WORLD"		
		1268 E 14TH ST	BROOKLYN, NY	11230
GOODWIN, JIM	BASEBALL EXECUTIVE	POST OFFICE BOX 4756	JACKSONVILLE, FL	32201
GOODWIN, JOHN M, III	ACTOR	706 N BUSHNELL AVE	ALHAMBRA, CA	91801
GOODWIN, MICHAEL	ACTOR	8271 MELROSE AVE #110	LOS ANGELES, CA	90046
GOODWIN, RICHARD	FILM PRODUCER	SANDS FILMS, GRICE'S WHARF		
		119 ROTHERHITHE ST	LONDON SE16 4NF	ENGLAND
GOODWIN, ROBERT WILLIAM	TV WRITER-PRODUCER	33267 W DECKER SCHOOL RD	MALIBU, CA	90265
GOODWIN, RONALD ALFRED	COMPOSER-CONDUCTOR	BLACK NEST COTTAGE		
		HOCKFORD LN, BRIMPTON COMMON	READING RG7 4RP	ENGLAND
GOODWIN, TOM	BASEBALL	POST OFFICE BOX 26267	ALBUQUERQUE, NM	87125
GOOLAGOND CAWLEY, EVONNE	TENNIS	80 DUNTROON AVE	ROSEVILLE NSW	AUSTRALIA
GOOSIE, J C	GOLFER	PGA SENIORS, 112 T P C BLVD	PONTE VEDRA BEACH, FL	32082
GOOTSAN, GEORGE	DIRECTOR	529 N MICHIGAN AVE	CHICAGO, IL	60611
GORBACHEV, MIKHAIL S	SOVIET PRESIDENT	LENINGRADSKY PROSPEKT 49	MOSCOW,	RUSSIA
GORBATY, NORMAN	ARTIST	14 E 38TH ST	NEW YORK, NY	10016
GORDEAN, WILLIAM	DIRECTOR	19517 BOWER DR	TOPANGA, CA	90290
GORDON, AARON SONNY	TV WRITER	3752 TRACY ST	LOS ANGELES, CA	90027
GORDON, AL	BASEBALL EXECUTIVE	POST OFFICE BOX 418	SAINT CHARLES, IL	60174
GORDON, ALVIN LAWRENCE	TV WRITER	789 WESTHOLME AVE	LOS ANGELES, CA	90024
GORDON, ANTHONY	BASEBALL	300 STADIUM WY	DAVENPORT, FL	33837
GORDON, BARRY	ACTOR	7065 HOLLYWOOD BLVD	LOS ANGELES, CA	90028
GORDON, BART	U S CONGRESSMAN	POST OFFICE BOX 1986	MURFREESBORO, TN	37133
GORDON, BERNARD	SCREENWRITER	1383 LONDONDERRY PL	LOS ANGELES, CA	90069
GORDON, BERT	WRITER-PRODUCER	9640 ARBY DR	BEVERLY HILLS, CA	90210
GORDON, BRUCE	ACTOR	ROUTE #4, BOX 247	SANTA FE, NM	87501
GORDON, BRYAN	ACTOR-WRITER	854 19TH ST	SANTA MONICA, CA	90403
GORDON, CHARLES A	TV WRITER	10518 CHEVIOT DR	LOS ANGELES, CA	90064
GORDON, CLARKE	ACTOR	13429 CANTARA ST	VAN NUYS, CA	91402
GORDON, CLAUDE	CONDUCTOR	19522 LEADWELL ST	RESEDA, CA	91335
GORDON, DAN	SCREENWRITER	CAA, 9830 WILSHIRE BLVD	BEVERLY HILLS, CA	90212

GORDON, DANIEL	ACTOR	32-40 91ST ST	JACKSON HEIGHTS, NY 11369
GORDON, DANIEL H	ACTOR	205 E 63RD ST	NEW YORK, NY 10021
GORDON, DENISE A	WRITER-PRODUCER	31 MERCER ST #3-C	NEW YORK, NY 10013
GORDON, DON	ACTOR	8485 MELROSE PL #E	LOS ANGELES, CA 90069
GORDON, DON	BASEBALL	CHIEFS, MAC ARTHUR STADIUM	SYRACUSE, NY 13208
GORDON, DOUGLAS	ACTOR	100 LA SALLE ST	NEW YORK, NY 10027
GORDON, EDITH	CONDUCTOR	5458 BEAUMONT	LA JOLLA, CA 92037
GORDON, EDWIN	SCREENWRITER	8955 BEVERLY BLVD	WEST HOLLYWOOD, CA 90048
GORDON, EVE	ACTRESS	9301 WILSHIRE BLVD #312	BEVERLY HILLS, CA 90210
GORDON, EVERETT	CONDUCTOR	8819 EVANVIEW DR	LOS ANGELES, CA 90069
GORDON, GALE	ACTOR	POST OFFICE BOX 179	BORREGO SPRINGS, CA 92004
GORDON, GEOFFREY	ACTOR	4181 KLING ST #4	BURBANK, CA 91505
GORDON, HAROLD	WRITER	25253 MALIBU RD	MALIBU, CA 90265
GORDON, JILL	TV WRITER	131 S RODEO DR #300	BEVERLY HILLS, CA 90212
GORDON, JOHN	SPORTSCASTER	TWINS, 501 CHICAGO AVE S	MINNEAPOLIS, MN 55415
GORDON, JUDITH ANN	THEATER PRODUCER	7 E 84TH ST	NEW YORK, NY 10028
GORDON, KEITH	BASEBALL	POST OFFICE BOX 2001	CEDAR RAPIDS, IA 52406
GORDON, LAWRENCE	FILM PRODUCER	LARGO, 10201 W PICO BLVD	LOS ANGELES, CA 90035
GORDON, LAWRENCE D, SR	COMPOSER	4257 SHADYGLADE AVE	STUDIO CITY, CA 91604
GORDON, LEO V	ACTOR-WRITER	9977 WORNOM AVE	SUNLAND, CA 91040
GORDON, MARC	TALENT AGENT	1244 OZETA TERR	LOS ANGELES, CA 90069
GORDON, MARIANNE	ACTRESS	ROGERS, BOX 100, ROUTE #1	COLBERT, GA 30628
GORDON, MARK	TV DIRECTOR	323 W 83RD ST	NEW YORK, NY 10024
GORDON, MICHAEL	FILM DIRECTOR	550 VETERAN AVE #204	LOS ANGELES, CA 90024
GORDON, NEIL	DIRECTOR	1321 WELLESLEY AVE	LOS ANGELES, CA 90025
GORDON, REGINA	TV DIRECTOR	13342 CROCKER ST	LOS ANGELES, CA 90061
GORDON, RICHARD	FILM PRODUCER	119 W 57TH ST #319	NEW YORK, NY 10019
GORDON, RICHARD	WRITER	1 CRAVEN HILL	LONDON W2 3EP ENGLAND
GORDON, STEVE	WRITER-PRODUCER	151 S EL CAMINO DR	BEVERLY HILLS, CA 90212
GORDON, STEVEN A	CONDUCTOR	11821 MAGNOLIA BLVD #5	NORTH HOLLYWOOD, CA 91607
GORDON, THOMAS	BASEBALL	1052 HIGHLANDS AVE	AVON PARK, FL 33828
GORDON, TIM	FOOTBALL	PATRIOTS, FOXBORO STADIUM, RT #1	FOXBORO, MA 02035
GORDON, TOM	BASEBALL	POST OFFICE BOX 419969	KANSAS CITY, MO 64141
GORDON-CLARK, LAWRENCE	TV DIRECTOR	BOKELLY, SAINT KEW, BODMIN	CORNWALL ENGLAND
GORDON-SINCLAIR, JOHN	ACTOR	HEATH, PARAMOUNT HOUSE	
		162-170 WARDOUR ST	LONDON W1V 3AT ENGLAND
GORDONE, CHARLES	PLAYWRIGHT	BOBBS-MERRILL COMPANY	
		4300 W 62ND ST	INDIANPOLIS, IN 46206
GORDY, BERRY	RECORD EXECUTIVE	878 STRADELLA RD	LOS ANGELES, CA 90077
GORDY, FULLER	RECORD EXECUTIVE	2378 ACHILLES DR	LOS ANGELES, CA 90046
GORE, ALBERT, JR	U S SENATOR	ROUTE #2	CARTHAGE, TN 37030
GORE, BRYAN	BASEBALL	POST OFFICE BOX 4448	TULSA, OK 74159
GORE, DENNIS	COMPOSER-CONDUCTOR	355 NW 189TH ST	SEATTLE, WA 98177
GORE, LESLEY	SINGER-ACTRESS	170 E 77TH ST #2-A	NEW YORK, NY 10021
GORE, MICHAEL	COMPOSER	310 W END AVE #12-C	NEW YORK, NY 10023
GORE, TIPPER	POLITICIAN	ROUTE #2	CARTHAGE, TN 37030
GORECKI, RICK	BASEBALL	POST OFFICE BOX 10031	BAKERSFIELD, CA 93389
GORELICK, KENNY	SAXOPHONIST	SEE - KENNY G	
GOREN, ROWBY	TV WRITER	17514 VENTURA BLVD #205	ENCINO, CA 91316
GORES, JOSEPH N	TV WRITER	9200 SUNSET BLVD #531	LOS ANGELES, CA 90069
GORFAIN, LOUIS H	TV WRITER	888 7TH AVE #602	NEW YORK, NY 10106
GORG, GALYN	ACTRESS	420 S SEPULVEDA BLVD #18	LOS ANGELES, CA 90049
GORI, KATHLEEN	SCREENWRITER	1127 9TH ST #102	SANTA MONICA, CA 90403
GORING, MARIUS	ACTOR	MIDDLECOURT, THE GREEN	
		HAMPTON CT	SURREY ENGLAND
GORKA, JOHN	SINGER-SONGWRITER	POST OFFICE BOX 4044	SAINT PAUL, MN 55104
GORMAN, BRIAN	BASEBALL UMPIRE	POST OFFICE BOX 608	GROVE CITY, OH 43123
GORMAN, CLIFF	ACTOR	333 W 57TH ST	NEW YORK, NY 10019
GORMAN, LOU	BASEBALL EXECUTIVE	FENWAY PARK, 4 YAWKEY WY	BOSTON, MA 02215
GORMAN, MARI	ACTRESS	117 1/2 N SYCAMORE AVE	LOS ANGELES, CA 90036
GORME, EYDIE	SINGER	820 GREENWAY DR	BEVERLY HILLS, CA 90210
GORMLEY, ROBERT	ACTOR	543 N SYCAMORE AVE #11	LOS ANGELES, CA 90036
GORNEL, RANDY	ACTOR	1525 MONTANA AVE #A	SANTA MONICA, CA 90403
GORNEY, KAREN LYNN	ACTRESS	KROLL, 390 W END AVE	NEW YORK, NY 10024
GOROG, LASZLO	SCREENWRITER	5124 WILKINSON AVE	NORTH HOLLYWOOD, CA 91607
GOROKHOVSKY, ZINOVY	COMPOSER	1005 N STANLEY AVE #206	LOS ANGELES, CA 90046
GOROW, RONALD F	COMPOSER	POST OFFICE BOX 1131	LOS ANGELES, CA 90078
GORRELL, BOB	CARTOONIST	POST OFFICE BOX C-32333	RICHMOND, VA 23293
GORRIE, JOHN	TV DIRECTOR	139-141 HOLLAND PARK LN #7	LONDON W11 4UT ENGLAND
GORRIN, MICHAEL	ACTOR	160 W 77TH ST	NEW YORK, NY 10024
GORSHIN, FRANK	ACTOR-COMEDIAN	75 S MORNINGSIDE DR	WESTPORT, CT 06880
GORTON, SLADE	U S SENATOR	3206 JACKSON FEDERAL BUILDING	SEATTLE, WA 98174
GORYL, JOHNNY	BASEBALL-SCOUT	INDIANS, CLEVELAND STADIUM	CLEVELAND, OH 44114
GOSA, JAMES	ACTOR	5727 OSO AVE	WOODLAND HILLS, CA 91367
GOSDIN, VERN	SINGER-SONGWRITER	151 TRAILS CIR	NASHVILLE, TN 37214
GOSE, DULCINDA	WRITER	9039 PHYLLIS AVE	LOS ANGELES, CA 90069
GOSEY, DAVID	TV DIRECTOR	9 BROOKFIELD CIR	FRAMINGHAM, MA 01701
GOSS, PORTER	U S CONGRESSMAN	224 CANNON HOUSE OFFICE BLDG	WASHINGTON, DC 20515
GOSSAGE, RICH "GOOSE"	BASEBALL	ATHLETICS'S, OAKLAND COLISEUM	OAKLAND, CA 94621
GOSSELAAR, MARK-PAUL	ACTOR	NBC-TV, 3000 W ALAMEDA AVE	BURBANK, CA 91523
GOSSETT, CYNDI JAMES	ACTRESS	1801 AVE OF THE STARS #1250	LOS ANGELES, CA 90067
GOSSETT, JEFF	FOOTBALL	RAIDERS, 332 CENTER ST	EL SEGUNDO, CA 90245
GOSSETT, LOUIS, JR	ACTOR-DIRECTOR	POST OFFICE BOX 6187	MALIBU, CA 90265
GOTHARD, MICHAEL	ACTOR	18 SHIRLOCK RD	LONDON NW3 ENGLAND
GOTT, JIM	BASEBALL	1000 ELYSIAN PARK DR	LOS ANGELES, CA 90012

GOTTFRIED, MARTIN	DRAMA CRITIC	17 96TH ST E	NEW YORK, NY	10020
GOTTLICHER, ERHARD	ARTIST	2082 UETERSEN	NEUWEG 5	GERMANY
GOTTLIEB, BERNARD	CONDUCTOR	1237 CRESTBROOK PL	ANAHEIM, CA	92805
GOTTLIEB, CARL	WRITER-DIRECTOR	8328 FOUNTAIN AVE #C	LOS ANGELES, CA	90069
GOTTLIEB, DAVID	DIRECTOR	1406 N TOPANGA CANYON BLVD	TOPANGA CANYON, CA	90290
GOTTLIEB, LARRY	TV WRITER-PRODUCER	2133 REDLOCK CT	LOS ANGELES, CA	90039
GOTTLIEB, MICHAEL	DIRECTOR	2436 WASHINGTON AVE	SANTA MONICA, CA	90403
GOTTLIEB, MORTON	THEATER PRODUCER	165 W 46TH ST	NEW YORK, NY	10036
GOTTLIEB, RICHARD	TV DIRECTOR	1717 N HIGHLAND AVE #1000	LOS ANGELES, CA	90028
GOTTSCHALK, ROBERT	DIRECTOR	18618 OXNARD ST	TARZANA, CA	91356
GOUGH, MICHAEL	ACTOR	8281 MELROSE AVE #200	LOS ANGELES, CA	90046
GOUGHAN, BOB	BASEBALL EXECUTIVE	4385 TUTT BLVD	COLORADO SPRINGS, CO	80922
GOULD, BERNI	WRITER	126 MABERY RD	SANTA MONICA, CA	90402
GOULD, CAROL	TV WRITER	WARE, 19-C JOHN SPENCER SQ		
		CANONBURY	LONDON N1 2LZ	ENGLAND
GOULD, DANNY	COMPOSER-CONDUCTOR	12315 RYE ST	STUDIO CITY, CA	91604
GOULD, DIANA	TV WRITER	267 MABERRY RD	SANTA MONICA, CA	90402
GOULD, DOROTHY	ACTRESS	CORWIN, 838 N DOHENY DR	LOS ANGELES, CA	90069
GOULD, ELEANOR CODY	ACTRESS	360 W 22ND ST	NEW YORK, NY	10011
GOULD, ELLIOTT	ACTOR	21250 CALIFA #201	WOODLAND HILLS, CA	91367
GOULD, HAROLD	ACTOR	912 EL MEDIO AVE	PACIFIC PALISADES, CA	90272
GOULD, HEYWOOD	SCREENWRITER	CAA, 9830 WILSHIRE BLVD	BEVERLY HILLS, CA	90212
GOULD, JACK	BASEBALL EXECUTIVE	333 W 35TH ST	CHICAGO, IL	60616
GOULD, JASON	ACTOR	446 N ORLANDO AVE	LOS ANGELES, CA	90048
GOULD, KENNETH	ACTOR-SINGER	25 CENTRAL PARK W	NEW YORK, NY	10023
GOULD, MARTY	CONDUCTOR	THE SARTINI PLAZA		
		900 BRUSH ST #418	LAS VEGAS, NV	89107
GOULD, MORTON	COMPOSER-CONDUCTOR	231 SHOREWARD DR	GREAT NECK, NY	10201
GOULD BRYSON, NANCY	ACTRESS	12 E 62ND ST	NEW YORK, NY	10021
GOULDING, RAY	ACT-WRI-COMED	420 LEXINGTON AVE	NEW YORK, NY	10017
GOULET, MICHEL	HOCKEY	BLACKHAWKS, 1800 W MADISON ST	CHICAGO, IL	60612
GOULET, NICOLETTE	ACTRESS	OSCARD, 24 W 40TH ST, 17TH FL	NEW YORK, NY	10011
GOULET, ROBERT	SINGER	3110 MONTE ROSA AVE	LAS VEGAS, NV	89120
GOURDINE, LITTLE ANTHONY	SINGER	POST OFFICE BOX 3032	PALOS VERDES PENN, CA	90274
GOURSAUD, ANNE	CINEMATOGRAPHER	POST OFFICE BOX 2230	HOLLYWOOD, CA	90078
GOUTMAN, CHRISTOPHER PAUL	TV DIRECTOR	10 W 66TH ST	NEW YORK, NY	10023
GOUVEIA, KURT	FOOTBALL	POST OFFICE BOX 17247 (DULLES)	WASHINGTON, DC	20041
GOUX, MARV	FOOTBALL COACH	RAMS, 2327 W LINCOLN BLVD	ANAHEIM, CA	92801
GOVER, DOUGLAS	TV DIRECTOR	7803 VIA FOGGIA	BURBANK, CA	91504
GOWAN	ROCK & ROLL GROUP	SRO MGMT, 189 CARLTON ST	TORONTO, ONT M5A 2K7	CANADA
GOWAN, CAROLINE	GOLFER	2750 VOLUSA AVE #B	DAYTON BEACH, FL	32114
GOWANS, JOHN	ACTOR	12456 VENTURA BLVD #1	STUDIO CITY, CA	91604
GOWDY, CURT	SPORTCASTER-TV HOST	9 PIERCE RD	WELLESLEY HILLS, MA	02181
GOWER, ANDRE	ACTOR	POST OFFICE BOX 7277	NORTHRIDGE, CA	91327
GOWERS, BRUCE	DIRECTOR	2153 KRESS ST	LOS ANGELES, CA	90046
GOYETTE, DESIREE	COMPOSER-ACTRESS	POST OFFICE BOX 10622	BEVERLY HILLS, CA	90213
GOZ, HARRY	ACTOR	SCHAPIRO, 122 E 42ND ST	NEW YORK, NY	10168
GOZZO, MAURO	BASEBALL	POST OFFICE BOX 1659	PORTLAND, OR	97207
GRAAS, JOHN CHRISTIAN	ACTOR	SAVAGE, 6212 BANNER AVE	LOS ANGELES, CA	90038
GRABER, KATHY	ACTRESS	11846 VENTURA BLVD #100	STUDIO CITY, CA	91604
GRABLE, ROB	BASEBALL	POST OFFICE BOX 64939	FAYETTEVILLE, NC	28306
GRACE, MARK	BASEBALL	1060 W ADDISON ST	CHICAGO, IL	60613
GRACE, MICHAEL L	WRITER	4520 RUSSELL AVE	LOS ANGELES, CA	90027
GRACE, MIKE	BASEBALL	POST OFFICE DRAWER 1207	ZEBULON, NC	27597
GRACE, NIKOLAS	ACTOR	HUTTON, 200 FULHAM RD	LONDON SW14 7AH	ENGLAND
GRACE, NORMAN	ARTIST	7516 LAMAR #81	PRAIRIE VILLAGE, KS	66208
GRACEN, ELIZABETH	ACTRESS	9000 SUNSET BLVD #1200	LOS ANGELES, CA	90069
GRACIO, JOHN	BASEBALL SCOUT	1060 W ADDISON ST	CHICAGO, IL	60613
GRAD, PETER	TV EXECUTIVE	MTM, 4024 RADFORD AVE	STUDIO CITY, CA	91604
GRADDY, SAM	FOOTBALL	RAIDERS, 332 CENTER ST	EL SEGUNDO, CA	90245
GRADE, LORD LEW	FILM EXECUTIVE	EMBASSY HOUSE, 8 QUEEN ST	LONDON W1X 7PH	ENGLAND
GRADE, MICHAEL	TV EXECUTIVE	CHANNEL 4, 60 CHARLOTTE ST	LONDON W1	ENGLAND
GRADISON, WILLIS D, JR	U S CONGRESSMAN	FEDERAL OFFICE BUILDING		
		550 MAIN ST	CINCINNATI, OH	45202
GRADUS, BEN	TV WRITER-DIRECTOR	161 GREENWAY S	FOREST HILLS GARDENS,	11375
GRADY, DON	ACTOR	4537 SIMPSON AVE	NORTH HOLLYWOOD, CA	91607
GRADY, ELLEN	ACTRESS	150 E OLIVE AVE #111	BURBANK, CA	91502
GRADY, MARY	TALENT AGENT	150 E OLIVE AVE #111	BURBANK, CA	91502
GRADY, MIKE	ACTOR	122 QUEENS RD	LONDON SW19 8LS	ENGLAND
GRADY, WAYNE	GOLFER	POST OFFICE BOX 109601	PALM BCH GARDENS, FL	33418
GRAEF, ROGER	FILM DIRECTOR	72 WESTBOURNE PARK VILLAS	LONDON W2	ENGLAND
GRAEF, VICKI	COSTUME DESIGNER	13949 VENTURA BLVD #309	SHERMAN OAKS, CA	91423
GRAF, DAVID	ACTOR	10000 SANTA MONICA BLVD #305	LOS ANGELES, CA	90067
GRAF, ELLY	TV DIRECTOR	457 W 57TH ST	NEW YORK, NY	10019
GRAF, RICK	FOOTBALL	OILERS, 6910 FANNIN ST	HOUSTON, TX	77070
GRAF, WILLIAM N	FILM PRODUCER	1100 N ALTA LOMA RD #603	LOS ANGELES, CA	90069
GRAFA, JULIE	SINGER	GOOD, 2500 NW 39TH ST	OKLAHOMA CITY, OK	73112
GRAFF, ILENE	ACTRESS	11455 SUNSHINE TERR	STUDIO CITY, CA	91604
GRAFF, RANDY	ACTRESS	ROSENBERG, 8428 MELROSE PL #C	LOS ANGELES, CA	90069
GRAFF, ROBERT	DIRECTOR	116 E 68TH ST	NEW YORK, NY	10021
GRAFF, THOMAS	DIRECTOR	50 W 96TH ST #1-A	NEW YORK, NY	10025
GRAFF, TODD	ACTOR	547 HUDSON ST	NEW YORK, NY	10014
GRAFFAGNINO, TONY	BASEBALL	POST OFFICE BOX 4525	MACON, GA	31208
GRAFFIUS, JOHN	DIRECTOR	515 UNIVERSITY PL	GROSSE POINTE CITY, MI	48230
GRAFTON, SUE	TV WRITER-PRODUCER	1015 GAYLEY AVE #300	LOS ANGELES, CA	90024

GRAHAM, BILL	ROCK PROMOTER	POST OFFICE BOX 1994	SAN FRANCISCO, CA	94101
GRAHAM, BILLY	EVANGELIST	SEE - GRAHAM, REV BILLY		
GRAHAM, BOB	FILM DIRECTOR	1926 HILLCREST RD	LOS ANGELES, CA	90068
GRAHAM, BOB	U S SENATOR	44 W FLAGER ST #1715	MIAMI, FL	33130
GRAHAM, BRIAN	BASEBALL MANAGER	2501 ALLEN AVE, SE	CANTON, OH	44707
GRAHAM, BRUCE	TRAINER	5999 E VAN BUREN ST	PHOENIX, AZ	85008
GRAHAM, BRUCE	TV PRODUCER	KAUFMAN ASTORIA, 34-12 36TH ST	ASTORIA, NY	11106
GRAHAM, BRUCE	WRITER	GOLDSTEIN, 99 PARK AVE	NEW YORK, NY	10016
GRAHAM, CAROLE	BODYBUILDER	288 THE GRAND PARADE	RAMSGATE BEACH	AUSTRALIA
GRAHAM, DERRICK	FOOTBALL	CHIEFS, 1 ARROWHEAD DR	KANSAS CITY, MO	64129
GRAHAM, DIRK	HOCKEY	BLACKHAWKS, 1800 W MADISON ST	CHICAGO, IL	60612
GRAHAM, DONALD	TV DIRECTOR	6425 PINECROFT	WEST BLOOMFIELD, MI	48322
GRAHAM, FRED	LAW-NEWS CORRES	2149 CALIFORNIA ST, NW	WASHINGTON, DC	20008
GRAHAM, GARY	ACTOR	183 N MARTEL AVE #260	LOS ANGELES, CA	90036
GRAHAM, GERRIT	ACTOR-WRITER	5601 PARK OAK PL	LOS ANGELES, CA	90068
GRAHAM, GREG	BASEBALL	POST OFFICE BOX 1718	NEW BRITAIN, CT	06050
GRAHAM, HEATHER	ACTRESS	11726 SAN VICENTE BLVD #300	LOS ANGELES, CA	90049
GRAHAM, IRVIN	ACTOR-WRITER	360 E 55TH ST	NEW YORK, NY	10022
GRAHAM, JANICE LEE	SCREENWRITER	8955 BEVERLY BLVD	WEST HOLLYWOOD, CA	90048
GRAHAM, JEFF	FOOTBALL	STEELERS, 300 STADIUM CIR	PITTSBURGH, PA	15212
GRAHAM, JOHN	BASEBALL EXECUTIVE	POST OFFICE BOX 651	AUBURN, NY	13021
GRAHAM, JOHN MICHAEL	ACTOR	14955 OTSEGO ST	SHERMAN OAKS, CA	91403
GRAHAM, JOHN W	BASKETBALL EXECUTIVE	POST OFFICE BOX 5000	RICHFIELD, OH	44286
GRAHAM, KATHARINE	PUBLISH EXECUTIVE	NEWSWEEK, 444 MADISON AVE	NEW YORK, NY	10022
GRAHAM, KENNETH F	ACTOR	1746 N ORANGE DR #803	LOS ANGELES, CA	90028
GRAHAM, LARRY	SINGER-GUITARIST	MISTER I MOUSE, LTD		
		920 DICKSON ST	MARINA DEL REY, CA	90292
GRAHAM, LOU	GOLFER	PGA SENIORS, 112 T P C BLVD	PONTE VEDRA BEACH, FL	32082
GRAHAM, MICHAEL	WRITER	MALIS, 12417 HESBY ST	NORTH HOLLYWOOD, CA	91607
GRAHAM, PAUL	BODYBUILDER	288 THE GRAND PARADE	RAMSGATE BEACH	AUSTRALIA
GRAHAM, REV BILLY	EVANGELIST	1300 HARMON PL	MINNEAPOLIS, MN	55403
GRAHAM, ROBERT V	AUDITOR	STATE LEGISLATIVE BUILDING	OLYMPIA, WA	98504
GRAHAM, RONNIE	ACTOR	R/W/G, 8428 MELROSE PL #C	LOS ANGELES, CA	90069
GRAHAM, TIM	BASEBALL	POST OFFICE BOX 10213	LYNCHBURG, VA	24506
GRAHAM, TIMOTHI-JANE	ACTRESS	KOHNER, 9169 SUNSET BLVD	LOS ANGELES, CA	90069
GRAHAM, VIRGINIA	TV HOST-AUTHORESS	WEBB, 7500 DEVISTA DR	LOS ANGELES, CA	90046
GRAHAM, WILLIAM	DIRECTOR	21510 CALLE DEL BARCO	MALIBU, CA	90265
GRAHAN, NANCY	ACTRESS	4910 AGNES AVE	NORTH HOLLYWOOD, CA	91607
GRAHE, JOE	BASEBALL	POST OFFICE BOX 2000	ANAHEIM, CA	92803
GRAHN, NANCY	ACTRESS	4910 AGNES AVE	NORTH HOLLYWOOD, CA	91607
GRAHOVAC, MIKE	BASEBALL	POST OFFICE BOX 3448	SHREVEPORT, LA	71133
GRAIMAN, JACK	COMEDIAN	5455 WILSHIRE BLVD #1406	LOS ANGELES, CA	90036
GRAIS, MICHAEL	SCREENWRITER	683 HAMPDEN PL	PACIFIC PALISADES, CA	90272
GRAMALIA, ROSE	WRITER	6057 BECK AVE	NORTH HOLLYWOOD, CA	91606
GRAMM, LOU	SINGER-SONGWRITER	E S "BUD" PRAGER MANAGEMENT		
		1790 BROADWAY, PENTHOUSE	NEW YORK, NY	10019
GRAMM, PHIL	U S SENATOR	2323 BRYAN #1500	DALLAS, TX	75201
GRAMMAS, ALEX	BASEBALL-COACH	3432 OAKDALE DR	BIRMINGHAM, AL	35223
GRAMMER, BILLY	SINGER-GUITARIST	ROUTE #1	NOLENSVILLE, TN	37135
GRAMMER, KELSEY	ACTOR	13539 HART ST	VAN NUYS, CA	91405
GRANAT, STEVEN B	TV WRITER	17514 VENTURA BLVD #205	ENCINO, CA	91316
GRANATO, TONY	HOCKEY	POST OFFICE BOX 17013	INGLEWOOD, CA	90308
GRANBY, NICHOLAS	WRI-DIR-PROD	ACTT, 111 WARDOUR ST	LONDON W1	ENGLAND
GRANDQUIST, KEN	BASEBALL EXECUTIVE	CUBS, 2ND & RIVERSIDE DR	DES MOINES, IA	50309
GRANDY, FRED	ACTOR-CONGRESSMAN	5904 MOUNT EAGLE DR #1118	ALEXANDRIA, VA	22303
GRANER, GERTRUDE	ACTRESS	7072 HAWTHORN AVE	LOS ANGELES, CA	90028
GRANET, BERT	WRITER	350 ENTRADA DR	SANTA MONICA, CA	90402
GRANET, IRMA	ACTRESS	4448 TYRONE AVE	SHERMAN OAKS, CA	91423
GRANEY, SARA	ACTRESS	CBS-TV, "AS THE WORLD TURNS"		
		524 W 57TH ST #5330	NEW YORK, NY	10019
GRANGE, ROGER T, III	CINEMATOGRAPHER	350 CABRINI BLVD #2-F	NEW YORK, NY	10040
GRANGER, BRIAN	BASEBALL SCOUT	POST OFFICE BOX 2000	SAN DIEGO, CA	92112
GRANGER, DEREK	TV PRODUCER	82 PALACE GARDENS	LONDON W8	ENGLAND
GRANGER, DOROTHY	ACTRESS	HILDER, 11903 W PICO BLVD	LOS ANGELES, CA	90064
GRANGER, FARLEY	ACTOR	18 W 72ND ST #25-D	NEW YORK, NY	10023
GRANGER, PERCY	TV WRITER	165 W 46TH ST #409	NEW YORK, NY	10036
GRANGER, SHANTON	ACTOR	450 E 84TH ST	NEW YORK, NY	10028
GRANGER, STEWART	ACTOR	8485 MELROSE PL #E	LOS ANGELES, CA	90069
GRANIK, RUSSELL R	BASKETBALL	NBA, OLYMPIC TOWER, 545 5TH AVE	NEW YORK, NY	10022
GRANITO, LIVIA	DIRECTOR	130 W 67TH ST #9-D	NEW YORK, NY	10023
GRANT, ALAN	FOOTBALL	POST OFFICE BOX 535000	INDIANPOLIS, IN	46253
GRANT, AMY	SINGER-SONGWRITER	BLANTON, 2910 POSTON AVE	NASHVILLE, TN	37203
GRANT, ARMAND	TV WRITER-PRODUCER	2270 BOWMONT DR	BEVERLY HILLS, CA	90210
GRANT, BARRA	TV WRITER-DIRECTOR	453 7TH ST	SANTA MONICA, CA	90402
GRANT, BETH	ACTRESS	12456 VENTURA BLVD #1	STUDIO CITY, CA	91604
GRANT, BILL	BODYBUILDER	POST OFFICE BOX 1493	SANTA MONICA, CA	90406
GRANT, DAVID	FOOTBALL	BENGALS, 200 RIVERFRONT STADIUM	CINCINNATI, OH	45202
GRANT, DR TONI	RADIO PERSONALITY	610 S ARDMORE AVE	LOS ANGELES, CA	90005
GRANT, FAYE	ACTRESS	322 W 20TH ST	NEW YORK, NY	10011
GRANT, GARY	BASKETBALL	CLIPPERS, 3939 S FIGUEROA ST	LOS ANGELES, CA	90037
GRANT, GIL	TV WRITER-PRODUCER	MTA, 9320 WILSHIRE BL, 3RD FL	BEVERLY HILLS, CA	90212
GRANT, GOGI	SINGER	10323 ALAMO AVE #202	LOS ANGELES, CA	90064
GRANT, GORDON W	ACTOR	3414 1/2 S SEPULVEDA BLVD	LOS ANGELES, CA	90034
GRANT, GREG	BASKETBALL	KNICKS, 4 PENNYLVANIA PLAZA	NEW YORK, NY	10019
GRANT, HANK	WRITER	6715 SUNSET BLVD	HOLLYWOOD, CA	90028

GRANT, HARVEY	BASKETBALL	BULLETS, 1 HARRY S TRUMAN DR	LANDOVER, MD	20785
GRANT, HORACE	BASKETBALL	980 N MICHIGAN AVE #1600	CHICAGO, IL	60611
GRANT, HUGH	ACTOR	HEATH, PARAMOUNT HOUSE		
		162-170 WARDOUR ST	LONDON W1V 3AT	ENGLAND
GRANT, JANA	ACTRESS	8033 SUNSET BLVD #4053	HOLLYWOOD, CA	90046
GRANT, JERRY	COMPOSER	6040 VANTAGE AVE	NORTH HOLLYWOOD, CA	91606
GRANT, JOHNNY	TV HOST	KTLA-TV, 5800 SUNSET BLVD	HOLLYWOOD, CA	90028
GRANT, LEE	ACTRESS-DIRECTOR	21243 VENTURA BLVD #101	WOODLAND HILLS, CA	91364
GRANT, LEE H	TV WRITER	962 1ST ST #D	HERMOSA BEACH, CA	90006
GRANT, LEE J	WRITER	5417 ENCINO AVE	ENCINO, CA	91316
GRANT, MARK	BASEBALL	123 FAIRLANE DR	JOLIET, IL	60435
GRANT, MARK ALLEN	ACTOR	12713 CASWELL AVE #1	LOS ANGELES, CA	90066
GRANT, MARSHALL	GUITARIST-TAL AGT	POST OFFICE BOX 492	HERNANDO, MS	38632
GRANT, MERRILL	TV WRITER-PRODUCER	6 CAYUGA RD	SCARSDALE, NY	10583
GRANT, MICKI	ACTRESS-SINGER	250 W 94TH ST #6-G	NEW YORK, NY	10025
GRANT, PERRY	TV WRITER-PRODUCER	727 OCAMPO DR	PACIFIC PALISADES, CA	90272
GRANT, RICHARD E	ACTOR	HEATH, PARAMOUNT HOUSE		
		162-170 WARDOUR ST	LONDON W1V 3AT	ENGLAND
GRANT, RON	RECORDING ENGINEER	3815 W OLIVE AVE #202	BURBANK, CA	91505
GRANT, RUSSELL	TV ASTROLOGER	11-A SAINT JOHN'S WOOD HIGH ST	LONDON NW8	ENGLAND
GRANT, SHELBY	ACTRESS	SEE - EVERETT, SHELBY GRANT		
GRANT, TOM	KEYBOARDIST-COMPOSER	BRAD SIMON, 122 E 57TH ST	NEW YORK, NY	10022
GRANT, TONI	RADIO PERSONALITY	SEE - GRANT, DR TONI		
GRANTHAM, LESLIE	ACTOR	265 LIVERPOOL RD	LONDON N1 1LX	ENGLAND
GRANTS, MAURICE	CONDUCTOR	11319 ALETHEA DR	SUNLAND, CA	91040
GRANZ, NORMAN	RECORD PRODUCER	1110 DOLORITA AVE	GLENDALE, CA	91208
GRAPPELLI, STEPHANE	VIOLINIST	HOFFER, 233 1/2 E 48TH ST	NEW YORK, NY	10017
GRAPPLER, THE	WRESTLER	8725 N CHAUTAUQUA BLVD	PORTLAND, OR	97217
GRASS ROOTS, THE	ROCK & ROLL GROUP	ETA, INC, 214 W ALISO ST	OJAI, CA	93023
GRASSHOFF, ALEX	WRI-DIR-PROD	7845 TORREYSON DR	LOS ANGELES, CA	90046
GRASSIE, JOHN E	DIRECTOR	1120 DENNIS CT	SILVER SPRING, MD	20901
GRASSLE, KAREN	ACTRESS	9744 WILSHIRE BLVD #308	BEVERLY HILLS, CA	90212
GRASSLEY, CHARLES E	U S SENATOR	135 HART SENATE OFFICE BLDG	WASHINGTON, DC	20510
GRATEFUL DEAD	ROCK & ROLL GROUP	POST OFFICE BOX 1073	SAN RAFAEL, CA	94915
GRATER, MARK	BASEBALL	POST OFFICE BOX 36407	LOUISVILLE, KY	40233
GRAU, JAMES W, III	TV DIRECTOR-PRODUCER	CHARISMA, 32 E 57TH ST #PH	NEW YORK, NY	10022
GRAU, SHIRLEY ANN	WRITER	BRANDT & BRANDT, 1501 BROADWAY	NEW YORK, NY	10036
GRAUL, EWALD	COMPOSER-CONDUCTOR	528 S RAMPART BLVD #2	LOS ANGELES, CA	90057
GRAUMAN, WALTER	TV DIRECTOR-PRODUCER	9329 DOHENY RD	BEVERLY HILLS, CA	90210
GRAVAGE, BOB	ACTOR	8250 LANKERSHIM BLVD PARK #14	NORTH HOLLYWOOD, CA	91605
GRAVER, FRED	TV WRITER	WM MORRIS, 1350 AVE OF AMERICAS	NEW YORK, NY	10019
GRAVES, ADAM	HOCKEY	OILERS, NORTHLANDS COLISEUM	EDMONTON, ALTA T5B 4M9	CANADA
GRAVES, AMANDA LEE	ACTRESS	660 E CHANNEL RD	SANTA MONICA, CA	90402
GRAVES, BILL	SECRETARY OF STATE	STATE CAPITOL BUILDING	TOPEKA, KS	66617
GRAVES, ERNEST	ACTOR	323 W 83RD ST	NEW YORK, NY	10024
GRAVES, PETER (AMERICAN)	ACTOR-DIRECTOR	660 E CHANNEL RD	SANTA MONICA, CA	90402
GRAVES, PETER (ENGLISH)	ACTOR	ICM, 388-396 OXFORD ST	LONDON W1	ENGLAND
GRAVES, RORY	FOOTBALL	RAIDERS, 332 CENTER ST	EL SEGUNDO, CA	90245
GRAVES, TERESA	ACTRESS	3437 W 78TH PL	LOS ANGELES, CA	90043
GRAVLIN, VIRGINIA	ACTRESS	425 RIVERSIDE DR	NEW YORK, NY	10025
GRAY, BARTON	COMPOSER	5129 ALTA DR	LAS VEGAS, NV	89107
GRAY, BILLY	ACTOR	19612 GRAND VIEW DR	TOPANGA CANYON, CA	90290
GRAY, BRUCE	ACTOR	2029 CENTURY PARK E #600	LOS ANGELES, CA	90067
GRAY, CECIL	FOOTBALL	EAGLES, BROAD ST & PATTISON AVE	PHILADELPHIA, PA	19148
GRAY, CHARLES	ACTOR	LONDON MGT, 235-241 REGENT ST	LONDON W1R 4PH	ENGLAND
GRAY, COLEEN	ACTRESS	1432 N KENWOOD ST	BURBANK, CA	91505
GRAY, DANIEL	BASEBALL	POST OFFICE BOX 2887	VERO BEACH, FL	32961
GRAY, DAVID	ACTOR	DAVID GRAHAM MANAGEMENT		
		DESIGNER LINER, BECKETT'S WHARF		
		OFF LOWER TEDDINGTON RD		
		HAMPTON WICK	SURREY KT1 4ER	ENGLAND
GRAY, DENNIS	BASEBALL	POST OFFICE BOX 1110	MYRTLE BEACH, SC	29578
GRAY, DOBIE	SINGER-SONGWRITER	POST OFFICE BOX 121682	NASHVILLE, TN	37212
GRAY, DOLORES	ACTRESS	8485 MELROSE PL #E	LOS ANGELES, CA	90069
GRAY, ELIOTT	BASEBALL	POST OFFICE BOX 10336	CLEARWATER, FL	34617
GRAY, ELMER	BASEBALL SCOUT	POST OFFICE BOX 7000	PITTSBURGH, PA	15212
GRAY, ERIN	ACTRESS	11300 W OLYMPIC BLVD #610	LOS ANGELES, CA	90064
GRAY, JEFF	BASEBALL	FENWAY PARK, 4 YAWKEY WY	BOSTON, MA	02215
GRAY, JERRY	FOOTBALL	RAMS, 2327 W LINCOLN BLVD	ANAHEIM, CA	92801
GRAY, LINDA	ACTRESS-DIRECTOR	UTA, 9560 WILSHIRE BL, 5TH FL	BEVERLY HILLS, CA	90212
GRAY, MALCOLM	ACTOR	400 W 43RD ST #33-K	NEW YORK, NY	10036
GRAY, MARK	SINGER	33 MUSIC SQUARE W #104-B	NASHVILLE, TN	37203
GRAY, MEL	FOOTBALL	LIONS, 1200 FEATHERSTONE RD	PONTIAC, MI	48432
GRAY, MIKE	WRITER-PRODUCER	20373 EVERDING LN	TOPANGA CANYON, CA	90290
GRAY, NICK	TV DIRECTOR-PRODUCER	76 BROADGATE LN, HORSFORTH	LEEDS	ENGLAND
GRAY, NORM	DIRECTOR	11138 AQUA VISTA ST #25	STUDIO CITY, CA	91602
GRAY, PETE	BASEBALL	203 PHILLIPS ST	NATICOKE, PA	18634
GRAY, QUINTON	GOLFER	PGA SENIORS, 112 T P C BLVD	PONTE VEDRA BEACH, FL	32082
GRAY, RUDY	SCREENWRITER	KLAUSNER, 71 PARK AVE	NEW YORK, NY	10016
GRAY, SPALDING	WRITER-ACTOR	PROGRAM, 136 E 65TH ST	NEW YORK, NY	10021
GRAY, STANLEY LEROY	WRITER	401 W WELLS ST	SAN GABRIEL, CA	91776
GRAY, STUART	BASKETBALL	KNICKS, 4 PENNYLVANIA PLAZA	NEW YORK, NY	10019
GRAY, THOMAS	FILM EXECUTIVE	GOLDEN HARVEST PICTURES		
		9884 SANTA MONICA BLVD	BEVERLY HILLS, CA	90212
GRAY, WILLIAM	SCREENWRITER	POST OFFICE BOX 5617	BEVERLY HILLS, CA	90213

GRAY, WILLIAM H, III	U S CONGRESSMAN	2316 CECIL B MOORE AVE	PHILADELPHIA, PA 19121
GRAYDON, JAY	COMPOSER	POST OFFICE BOX 1507	STUDIO CITY, CA 91604
GRAYER, JEFF	BASKETBALL	BRADLEY CENTER, 1001 N 4TH ST	MILWAUKEE, WI 53203
GRAYSON, KATHRYN	ACTRESS-SINGER	2009 LA MESA DR	SANTA MONICA, CA 90402
GRAZER, BRIAN	FILM PRODUCER	20434 ROCA CHICA DR	MALIBU, CA 90265
GRAZIER, JOHN	MUSIC ARRANGER	4121 ABERDEEN RD	NASHVILLE, TN 37205
GRDNIC, JOY	COMEDIENNE	16565 SAN FERNANDO MISSION BLVD	GRANADA HILLS, CA 91344
GREASON, STACI	ACTRESS	NBC-TV, "DAYS OF OUR LIVES"	
		3000 W ALAMEDA AVE	BURBANK, CA 91523
GREAT PRETENDERS, THE	VOCAL GROUP	32500 CONCORD DR #252	MADISON HEIGHTS, MI 48071
GREAT WHITE	ROCK & ROLL GROUP	3 E 54TH ST #1400	NEW YORK, NY 10022
GREAVES, WILLIAM	WRITER-PRODUCER	230 W 55TH ST #26-D	NEW YORK, NY 10019
GREBECK, BRIAN	BASEBALL	POST OFFICE BOX 1742	PALM SPRINGS, CA 92263
GREBECK, CRAIG	BASEBALL	333 W 35TH ST	CHICAGO, IL 60616
GRECO, BUDDY	SINGER-PIANIST	9200 SUNSET BLVD #621	LOS ANGELES, CA 90069
GRECO, JOSE	CHOREOGRAPHER	SOCIETY OF STAGE DIRECTORS	
		AND CHOREOGRAPGERS, INC	
		1501 BROADWAY, 31ST FLOOR	NEW YORK, NY 10036
GRECO, KRISTINE	ACTRESS	14225 RIVERSIDE DR	SHERMAN OAKS, CA 91423
GREEDY, ALLAN	DIRECTOR	28647 VISCO CT	SAUGUS, CA 91350
GREEK, JANET C	WRITER	25136 MALIBU RD	MALIBU, CA 90265
GREEN, A C	BASKETBALL	POST OFFICE BOX 10	INGLEWOOD, CA 90306
GREEN, ADOLPH	ACTOR-WRITER	529 W 42ND ST #7-F	NEW YORK, NY 10036
GREEN, AL	SINGER-PREACHER	3208 WINCHESTER RD	MEMPHIS, TN 38118
GREEN, ALAN	DIRECTOR	2554 LINCOLN BLVD #644	MARINA DEL REY, CA 90291
GREEN, ALLAN	DIRECTOR	110 PASCACK RD	PEARL RIVER, NY 10965
GREEN, ALLEN	TV DIRECTOR	13 CHAPEL LN	RIVERSIDE, CT 06878
GREEN, BILL	U S CONGRESSMAN	60 E 42ND ST #2306	NEW YORK, NY 10165
GREEN, BRIAN	ACTOR	11557 HESBY ST	NORTH HOLLYWOOD, CA 91601
GREEN, BRIAN AUSTIN	ACTOR	5700 WILSHIRE BLVD #575	LOS ANGELES, CA 90036
GREEN, BRUCE SETH	TV DIRECTOR	1729 BRYN MAWR AVE	SANTA MONICA, CA 90405
GREEN, CAROL L	FILM DIRECTOR	11575 MOORPARK AVE #207	STUDIO CITY, CA 91602
GREEN, CHIC	DIRECTOR	POST OFFICE BOX 1527	EAST HAMPTON, NY 11937
GREEN, CHRIS	FOOTBALL	DOLPHINS, 2269 NW 199TH ST	MIAMI, FL 33056
GREEN, DARRELL	FOOTBALL	POST OFFICE BOX 17247 (DULLES)	WASHINGTON, DC 20041
GREEN, DAVID	FILM DIRECTOR	HEATH, PARAMOUNT HOUSE	
		162-170 WARDOUR ST	LONDON W1V 3AT ENGLAND
GREEN, DICK	BASEBALL-SCOUT	POST OFFICE BOX 2000	ANAHEIM, CA 92803
GREEN, ERIC	FOOTBALL	STEELERS, 300 STADIUM CIR	PITTSBURGH, PA 15212
GREEN, FRANCIS	CONDUCTOR	1970 N NEW HAMPSHIRE AVE	LOS ANGELES, CA 90027
GREEN, GARY	BASEBALL	POST OFFICE BOX 23290	NASHVILLE, TN 37202
GREEN, GASTON	FOOTBALL	BRONCOS, 13655 BRONCOS PKWY	ENGLEWOOD, CO 80112
GREEN, GERALD	TV WRITER	WM MORRIS, 1350 AVE OF AMERICAS	NEW YORK, NY 10019
GREEN, GUY M	DIRECTOR	POST OFFICE BOX 5617	BEVERLY HILLS, CA 90213
GREEN, HAROLD	BASEBALL EXECUTIVE	POST OFFICE BOX 309	GASTONA, NC 28053
GREEN, HAROLD	FOOTBALL	BENGALS, 200 RIVERFRONT STADIUM	CINCINNATI, OH 45202
GREEN, I BERNARD	DIRECTOR	24 STAFFIRE DR	SCHAUMBURG, IL 60194
GREEN, JACOB	FOOTBALL	SEAHAWKS, 11220 NE 53RD ST	KIRKLAND, WA 98033
GREEN, JAY	BASEBALL SCOUT	INDIANS, CLEVELAND STADIUM	CLEVELAND, OH 44114
GREEN, JIM	FILM-TV PRODUCER	4400 COLDWATER CANYON #300	STUDIO CITY, CA 91604
GREEN, KATHERINE D	TV WRITER	13616 VALLEY VISTA BLVD	SHERMAN OAKS, CA 91423
GREEN, KEN	GOLFER	POST OFFICE BOX 109601	PALM BCH GARDENS, FL 33418
GREEN, KEN	TV EXECUTIVE	THE MORTIMER HOUSE	
		37-41 MORTIMER ST	LONDON W1A 2JL ENGLAND
GREEN, KERRI	ACTRESS	ICM, 8899 BEVERLY BLVD	LOS ANGELES, CA 90048
GREEN, KEVIN	BASEBALL EXECUTIVE	500 NORTON ST	ROCHESTER, NY 14621
GREEN, KIM MORGAN	ACTRESS	KOHNER, 9169 SUNSET BLVD	LOS ANGELES, CA 90069
GREEN, LES	FILM EDITOR	ACE, 1041 N FORMOSA AVE	WEST HOLLYWOOD, CA 90046
GREEN, LESLIE	DIRECTOR	2445 EL CONTENTO DR	LOS ANGELES, CA 90068
GREEN, MARC E	WRITER	10341 KESWICK AVE	LOS ANGELES, CA 90064
GREEN, MARK	FOOTBALL	BEARS, 250 N WASHINGTON RD	LAKE FOREST, IL 60045
GREEN, MARSHALL	DIRECTOR	POST OFFICE BOX 415	BALBOA ISLAND, CA 92662
GREEN, MARTIN	TV WRI-DIR-PROD	DGA, 7920 SUNSET BLVD, 6TH FL	LOS ANGELES, CA 90046
GREEN, MARVIN HOWE, JR	TV PRODUCER	REEVES COMM, 708 3RD AVE	NEW YORK, NY 10017
GREEN, MICHAEL C	FILM PRODUCER	4020 TOWHEE DR	CALABASAS, CA 91302
GREEN, MORT	WRITER-PRODUCER	320 S ELM DR #1	BEVERLY HILLS, CA 90212
GREEN, NORMAN	ARTIST	JERRY ANTON, 107 E 38TH ST	NEW YORK, NY 10016
GREEN, OTIS	BASEBALL	2850 W 20TH AVE	DENVER, CO 80211
GREEN, PATRICIA M	TV WRITER	451 RIVERSIDE DR	BURBANK, CA 91506
GREEN, PAULA	DIRECTOR	145 W 86TH ST	NEW YORK, NY 10024
GREEN, PETE	U S CONGRESSMAN	100 E 15TH ST #500	FORT WORTH, TX 76102
GREEN, RICK	HOCKEY	RED WINGS, 600 CIVIC CENTER DR	DETROIT, MI 48226
GREEN, RICKEY	BASKETBALL	POST OFFICE BOX 25040	PHILADELPHIA, PA 19147
GREEN, SHAWN	BASEBALL	POST OFFICE BOX 957	DUNEDIN, FL 34697
GREEN, SIDNEY	BASKETBALL	600 E MARKET ST #102	SAN ANTONIO, TX 78205
GREEN, SYLVIA	COMPOSER	153 S MAPLE DR	BEVERLY HILLS, CA 90212
GREEN, TERRY	TV DIRECTOR	EUSTON FILMS, 365 EUSTON RD	LONDON NW1 ENGLAND
GREEN, TIM	FOOTBALL	FALCONS, SUWANEE RD AT I-85	SUWANEE, GA 30174
GREEN, TOM	BASEBALL	POST OFFICE BOX 842	SALEM, VA 24153
GREEN, TOM	TV CRITIC	POST OFFICE BOX 500	WASHINGTON, DC 20044
GREEN, TRUDY	TALENT AGENT	345 N MAPLE ST #235	BEVERLY HILLS, CA 90210
GREEN, TYLER	BASEBALL	POST OFFICE BOX 15050	READING, PA 19612
GREEN, WALON	WRITER-PRODUCER	3089 SEAHORSE AVE	VENTURA, CA 93001
GREEN, WILLIE	FOOTBALL	LIONS, 1200 FEATHERSTONE RD	PONTIAC, MI 48432
GREEN RIVER	ROCK & ROLL GROUP	41 BRITAIN ST #200	TORONTO, ONT M5A 1R7 CANADA

GREENAWAY, PETER	FILM DIRECTOR	STONE, HALINAN & MC DONALD		
		100 EBURY ST	LONDON SW1W 9QD	ENGLAND
GREENBAUM, EVERETT	TV WRITER	4507 NOELINE AVE	ENCINO, CA	91436
GREENBERG, ADAM	CINEMATOGRAPHER	POST OFFICE BOX 2230	HOLLYWOOD, CA	90078
GREENBERG, BOB	TV WRITER	151 S EL CAMINO DR	BEVERLY HILLS, CA	90212
GREENBERG, BURTON	TV DIRECTOR	28 E 10TH ST	NEW YORK, NY	10003
GREENBERG, CHUCK	LYRICONIST	POST OFFICE BOX 9388	STANFORD, CA	94305
GREENBERG, HENRY F	SCREENWRITER	8955 BEVERLY BLVD	WEST HOLLYWOOD, CA	90048
GREENBERG, JEFF	ACTOR	1280 N LAUREL AVE #18	LOS ANGELES, CA	90046
GREENBERG, MITCHELL	ART DIRECTOR	48 W 21ST ST, 10TH FLOOR	NEW YORK, NY	10010
GREENBERG, PAUL	TV WRITER-DIRECTOR	DGA, 110 W 57TH ST	NEW YORK, NY	10019
GREENBERG, RICHARD	DIRECTOR	240 MADISON AVE	NEW YORK, NY	10016
GREENBERG, SHELDON	ARTIST	304 E 20TH ST #PH-H	NEW YORK, NY	10003
GREENBURG, DR MARTIN	PSYCHOLOGIST-AUTHOR	2801 MEADOW LARK DR	SAN DIEGO, CA	92123
GREENBURG, EARL	TV DIRECTOR-PRODUCER	1807 NICHOLS CANYON RD	LOS ANGELES, CA	90046
GREENE, ALLEN	TALENT AGENT	11726 SAN VICENTE BLVD #300	LOS ANGELES, CA	90049
GREENE, ARTHUR	COMPOSER-CONDUCTOR	529 W 42ND ST	NEW YORK, NY	10036
GREENE, BARNEY	COMPOSER	12619 HORTENSE ST	STUDIO CITY, CA	91604
GREENE, BOB	COLUMNIST	THE CHICAGO TRIBUNE		
		TRIBUNE TOWER		
		435 N MICHIGAN AVE	CHICAGO, IL	60611
GREENE, CARL	BASEBALL SCOUT	POST OFFICE BOX 288	HOUSTON, TX	77001
GREENE, CHARLIE	BASEBALL	POST OFFICE BOX 20849	CHARLESTON, SC	29413
GREENE, CLARENCE	SCREENWRITER	8955 BEVERLY BLVD	WEST HOLLYWOOD, CA	90048
GREENE, DANIEL	ACTOR	2121 AVE OF THE STARS #950	LOS ANGELES, CA	90067
GREENE, DAVID	WRI-DIR-PROD	4225 COLDWATER CANYON AVE	STUDIO CITY, CA	91604
GREENE, EDWARD	COMPOSER	11033 FRUITLAND DR #6	STUDIO CITY, CA	91604
GREENE, ELLEN	ACTRESS-SINGER	151 S EL CAMINO DR	BEVERLY HILLS, CA	90212
GREENE, GRAHAM	AUTHOR	59 DAWN VALLEY DR	TORONTO, ONT MYK 2J1	CANADA
GREENE, HERBERT	TV DIRECTOR	4176 ARCH DR	STUDIO CITY, CA	91604
GREENE, JACK	SINGER	38 MUSIC SQUARE E #213	NASHVILLE, TN	37203
GREENE, JAMES	ACTOR	60 POPES GROVE, TWICKENHAM	MIDDLESEX	ENGLAND
GREENE, JAVOTTE SUTTON	ACTRESS	225 HAMILTON AVE	NEW ROCHELLE, NY	10801
GREENE, JERI-ANN	ACTRESS	1710 MONTE CIELO DR	BEVERLY HILLS, CA	90210
GREENE, JOE	FOOTBALL COACH	STEELERS, 300 STADIUM CIR	PITTSBURGH, PA	15212
GREENE, KELLIE	COMPOSER	12301 VIEWCREST RD	STUDIO CITY, CA	91604
GREENE, KEVIN	FOOTBALL	RAMS, 2327 W LINCOLN BLVD	ANAHEIM, CA	92801
GREENE, KIM MORGAN	ACTRESS	KOHNER, 9169 SUNSET BLVD	LOS ANGELES, CA	90069
GREENE, LARRY	COMPOSER-CONDUCTOR	1151 SUNSET HILLS RD	LOS ANGELES, CA	90069
GREENE, MATT	ACTOR	360 S ELM DR	BEVERLY HILLS, CA	90212
GREENE, MICHAEL	ACTOR	1999 AVE OF THE STARS #2850	LOS ANGELES, CA	90067
GREENE, MICHELE	ACTRESS	2281 HOLLY DR	LOS ANGELES, CA	90068
GREENE, MILTON	CONDUCTOR	2149 HERCULES DR	LOS ANGELES, CA	90046
GREENE, MILTON H	DIRECTOR	244 LAKE MERCED HILLS ST	SAN FRANCISCO, CA	94132
GREENE, NOEL	TV DIRECTOR-PRODUCER	36-A GRAFTON SQ	LONDON SW4 ODB	ENGLAND
GREENE, OTIS GARY	ACTOR	990 PALM AVE #A-12	LOS ANGELES, CA	90069
GREENE, SARAH	BROADCAST JOURNALIST	LADKIN, 11 SOUTHWICK MEWS	LONDON W2 1JG	ENGLAND
GREENE, SHECKY	COMEDIAN	1220 SHADOW LN	LAS VEGAS, NV	89102
GREENE, SPARKY	DIRECTOR	TITAL FILMS, 73 MARKET ST	VENICE, CA	90291
GREENE, STEVEN S	SCREENWRITER	8955 BEVERLY BLVD	WEST HOLLYWOOD, CA	90048
GREENE, TOM	WRITER-PRODUCER	2049 CENTURY PARK E #13	LOS ANGELES, CA	90067
GREENE, TOMMY	BASEBALL	POST OFFICE BOX 224	BRUNSWICK, NC	28424
GREENE, WALTER	COMPOSER-CONDUCTOR	15175 KINAI RD	APPLE VALLEY, CA	92307
GREENE, WILLIE	BASEBALL	POST OFFICE BOX 3566	WEST PALM BEACH, FL	33402
GREENFELD, JOSH	SCREENWRITER	14637 BESTER BLVD	PACIFIC PALISADES, CA	90272
GREENFIELD, BARRY	DIRECTOR	3301 SHORELINE DR	LAS VEGAS, NV	89101
GREENFIELD, BARRY	WRITER	632 PACIFIC ST #2	SANTA MONICA, CA	90405
GREENFIELD, JEFF	WRITER-COLUMNIST	UPS, 4900 MAIN ST, 9TH FLOOR	KANSAS CITY, MO	64112
GREENFIELD, LEO	FILM EXECUTIVE	1811 RISING GLEN RD	LOS ANGELES, CA	90069
GREENGRASS, KEN	TV PRODUCER	16 E 48TH ST	NEW YORK, NY	10017
GREENHILL, AMY	ACTRESS	14 WASHINGTON PL	NEW YORK, NY	10003
GREENHILL, MITCH	SINGER	FOLKLORE, 1671 APPIAN WY	SANTA MONICA, CA	90401
GREENHOUSE, MARTHA	ACTRESS	1230 PARK AVE	NEW YORK, NY	10028
GREENHUNT, ROBERT	FILM PRODUCER	ROLLINS/JOFFE, 130 W 57TH ST	NEW YORK, NY	10019
GREENIER, MARK	BASEBALL EXECUTIVE	STARS, 850 LAS VEGAS BLVD N	LAS VEGAS, NV	89101
GREENLAW, REBECCA	TV DIRECTOR-PRODUCER	13201 BLOOMFIELD ST	SHERMAN OAKS, CA	91423
GREENLUND, ALYS	COMPOSER	659 GRETNA GREEN WY	LOS ANGELES, CA	90049
GREENSPAN, BUD	WRITER-PRODUCER	33 E 68TH ST	NEW YORK, NY	10021
GREENWALD, HANK	SPORTSCASTER	S F GIANTS, CANDLESTICK PARK	SAN FRANICSCO, CA	94124
GREENWALD, NANCY	TV WRITER	3633 MOUNTAIN VIEW AVE	LOS ANGELES, CA	90066
GREENWALD, ROBERT	FILM-TV DIRECTOR	10510 CULVER BLVD	CULVER CITY, CA	90232
GREENWALT, DAVID	SCREENWRITER	417 SYCAMORE RD	SANTA MONICA, CA	90402
GREENWELL, MIKE	BASEBALL	FENWAY PARK, 4 YAWKEY WY	BOSTON, MA	02215
GREENWICH, ELLIE	SONGWRITER	315 W 57TH ST #16-H	NEW YORK, NY	10019
GREENWOOD, DAVID	BASKETBALL	600 E MARKET ST #102	SAN ANTONIO, TX	78205
GREENWOOD, GILLIAN	TV DIRECTOR	12 HILLMARTON RD	LONDON N7 90W	ENGLAND
GREENWOOD, JANE	COSTUME DESIGNER	13949 VENTURA BLVD #309	SHERMAN OAKS, CA	91423
GREENWOOD, LEE	SINGER-SONGWRITER	1311 ELM HILL PIKE	NASHVILLE, TN	37210
GREENWOOD, MICHAEL	ACTOR	14 KINGSTON HOUSE EAST		
		PRINCES GATE	LONDON SW7 1LJ	ENGLAND
GREER, BRODIE	ACTOR	5840 SHIRLEY AVE	TARZANA, CA	91356
GREER, DABS	ACTOR	284 S MADISON AVE	PASADENA, CA	91101
GREER, DARRELL	ACTOR	180 S AVE 53	LOS ANGELES, CA	90042
GREER, GEORGE	WRITER	8468 HATILLO AVE	CANOGA PARK, CA	91306
GREER, JANE "BETTY"	ACTRESS	966 MORAGA DR	LOS ANGELES, CA	90049

GREER, KATHLEEN	WRITER-PRODUCER	4422 BEN AVE	NORTH HOLLYWOOD, CA	91607
GREER, KEN	BASEBALL	POST OFFICE BOX 2148	WOODBRIDGE, VA	22193
GREER, RICHARD	DIRECTOR	RURAL DELIVERY #1, CENTER RD	SCIPIO CENTER, NY	13147
GREER, ROBIN	ACTRESS	280 S BEVERLY DR #400	BEVERLY HILLS, CA	90212
GREER, RUSTY	BASEBALL	POST OFFICE BOX 4448	TULSA, OK	74159
GREFE, WILLIAM	DIRECTOR-PRODUCER	14390 MUSTANG TRAIL	FORT LAUDERDALE, FL	33330
GREGG, COLIN	TV DIRECTOR-PRODUCER	COLIN GREGG FILMS, FLOOR 2		
		1/6 FALCONBERG CT	LONDON W1	ENGLAND
GREGG, ERIC	BASEBALL UMPIRE	2635 MIMI CIR	PHILADELPHIA, PA	19131
GREGG, JUDD	GOVERNOR	STATE HOUSE BUILDING	CONCORD, NH	03301
GREGG, JULIE	ACTRESS	8019 1/2 MELROSE AVE #3	LOS ANGELES, CA	90046
GREGG, TOMMY	BASEBALL	POST OFFICE BOX 4064	ATLANTA, GA	30302
GREGG, WALTER	DIRECTOR	236 E 33RD ST	NEW YORK, NY	10016
GREGGORY, DAVID	WRITER	1737 VIEWMONT DR	LOS ANGELES, CA	90069
GREGOINE, JULIE	BODYBUILDER	THE FITNESS FACTORY		
		2852 DELAWARE AVE	KENMORE, NY	14127
GREGORIO, ROSE	ACTRESS	KOHNER, 9169 SUNSET BLVD	LOS ANGELES, CA	90069
GREGORY, ARTHUR	TV PRODUCER	11548 ACAMA ST	NORTH HOLLYWOOD, CA	91604
GREGORY, CONSTANTINE	ACTOR	172 CLONMORE ST	LONDON SW10	ENGLAND
GREGORY, DEBBIE	ACTRESS	8228 SUNSET BLVD #212	LOS ANGELES, CA	90046
GREGORY, DICK	COMEDIAN-ACTIVIST	BOX 3266, TOWER HILL FARM	PLYMOUTH, MA	02361
GREGORY, DON	THEATER PRODUCER	9200 SUNSET BLVD	LOS ANGELES, CA	90069
GREGORY, JAMES	ACTOR	55 CATHEDRAL ROCK DR #33	SEDONA, AZ	86336
GREGORY, MICHAEL	ACTOR	7461 BEVERLY BLVD #400	LOS ANGELES, CA	90036
GREGORY, MOLLIE	SCREENWRITER	3278 WILSHIRE BLVD #401	LOS ANGELES, CA	90010
GREGORY, PAUL	FILM PRODUCER	POST OFFICE BOX 38	PALM SPRINGS, CA	92262
GREGORY, RUTH	ACTRESS	400 W 43RD ST #32-A	NEW YORK, NY	10036
GREGSON, GOOSE	BASEBALL COACH	POST OFFICE BOX 10031	BAKERSFIELD, CA	93389
GREIF, STEPHEN	ACTOR	CAREY, 64 THORNTON AVE	LONDON W4 1QQ	ENGLAND
GREISE, BOB	FOOTBALL	3250 MARY ST	MIAMI, FL	33133
GREISMAN, ALAN	FILM PRODUCER	2121 AVE OF THE STARS #1700	LOS ANGELES, CA	90067
GREISMAN, GORDON JAMES	SCREENWRITER	1845 CALGARY LN	LOS ANGELES, CA	90024
GREIST, KIM	ACTRESS	CAA, 9830 WILSHIRE BLVD	BEVERLY HILLS, CA	90212
GRENESKO, DONALD	BASEBALL EXECUTIVE	1060 W ADDISON ST	CHICAGO, IL	60613
GRESH, THEODORE	CONDUCTOR	8118 TILDEN AVE	PANORAMA CITY, CA	91402
GRESHAM, GLORIA	COSTUME DESIGNER	POST OFFICE BOX 5617	BEVERLY HILLS, CA	90213
GRESHAM, KRIS	BASEBALL	POST OFFICE BOX 418	SAINT CHARLES, IL	60174
GRESSETT, LISA	ACTRESS	6255 SUNSET BLVD #627	LOS ANGELES, CA	90028
GRETZKY, WAYNE	HOCKEY	POST OFFICE BOX 17013	INGLEWOOD, CA	90308
GREWAL, RANBIR	BASEBALL	POST OFFICE BOX 3566	WEST PALM BEACH, FL	33402
GREY, ARLYNE	ACTRESS	484 W 43RD ST #39-L	NEW YORK, NY	10036
GREY, JENNIFER	ACTRESS	CAA, 9830 WILSHIRE BLVD	BEVERLY HILLS, CA	90212
GREY, JOEL	ACTOR-SINGER	130 W 42ND ST #1804	NEW YORK, NY	10036
GREY, LARRY	ACTOR	35 W 90TH ST	NEW YORK, NY	10024
GREY, NAN	ACTRESS	LAINE, 352 SAN GORGONIO ST	SAN DIEGO, CA	92106
GREY, VIRGINIA	ACTRESS	15101 MAGNOLIA BLVD #5-H	SHERMAN OAKS, CA	91403
GREYHOSKY, BABS	TV WRITER-PRODUCER	9046 SUNSET BLVD #202	LOS ANGELES, CA	90069
GREYN, CLINTON	ACTOR	14 GARWAY RD	LONDON W2	ENGLAND
GREYSON, KAREN	ACTRESS	12433 MOORPARK ST #213	STUDIO CITY, CA	91604
GRIBA, KATE	ACTRESS	KRUGLOV, 8282 SUNSET BLVD	LOS ANGELES, CA	90046
GRICH, BOBBY	BASEBALL	206 PROPSETC AVE	LONG BEACH, CA	90803
GRIDNEFF, EVGENY	TV PRODUCER	35 MIDHURST RD, EARING	LONDON W13 9XS	ENGLAND
GRIECO, RICHARD	ACTOR	15263 MULHOLLAND DR	LOS ANGELES, CA	90077
GRIEF, JIM	BASEBALL SCOUT	REDS, 100 RIVERFRONT STADIUM	CINCINNATI, OH	45202
GRIER, BOBBY	FOOTBALL COACH	PATRIOTS, FOXBORO STADIUM, RT #1	FOXBORO, MA	02035
GRIER, JOHNNY	FOOTBALL REFEREE	NFL, 410 PARK AVE	NEW YORK, NY	10022
GRIER, PAM	ACTRESS	9000 SUNSET BLVD #1200	LOS ANGELES, CA	90069
GRIER, ROD	ACTOR	6546 SEPULVEDA BLVD #207	VAN NUYS, CA	91411
GRIER, ROSEY	ACTOR	11656 MONTANA AVE #301	LOS ANGELES, CA	90049
GRIES, JONATHAN	ACTOR	827 4TH ST #306	SANTA MONICA, CA	90403
GRIEVE, ANDREW	FILM DIRECTOR	2 DARTMOUTH PARK AVE	LONDON NW5	ENGLAND
GRIEVE, TOM	BASEBALL-EXECUTIVE	POST OFFICE BOX 90111	ARLINGTON, TX	76004
GRIFF, BARBARA	TV WRITER-PRODUCER	710 BROADWAY	NEW YORK, NY	10003
GRIFF, RAY	SINGER-SONGWRITER	POST OFFICE BOX 158925	NASHVILLE, TN	37215
GRIFFEN, LEONARD	BASEBALL	POST OFFICE BOX 2001	CEDAR RAPIDS, IA	52406
GRIFFEN, STUART	TALENT AGENT	CAA, 9830 WILSHIRE BLVD	BEVERLY HILLS, CA	90212
GRIFFETH, SIMONE	ACTRESS-MODEL	POST OFFICE BOX 148	BLUFFTON, GA	29910
GRIFFEY, KEN, JR	BASEBALL	POST OFFICE BOX 4100	SEATTLE, WA	98104
GRIFFEY, KEN, SR	BASEBALL	5385 CROSS BRIDGE RD	WESTCHESTER, OH	45069
GRIFFIN, ALFREDO	BASEBALL	SKYDOME, 300 BREMMER BL #3200	TORONTO, ONT M5V 3B3	CANADA
GRIFFIN, CHRISTOPHER	TV DIRECTOR-PRODUCER	THE OLD POST HOUSE, WILMCOTE	STRATFORD-UPON-AVON	ENGLAND
GRIFFIN, DICK	COMPOSER	POST OFFICE BOX 284	TEANECK, NJ	07666
GRIFFIN, DON	FOOTBALL	S F 49ERS, 4949 CENTENNIAL BL	SANTA CLARA, CA	95054
GRIFFIN, JAMES	SINGER-SONGWRITER	25 PAULSON DR	BURLINGTON, MA	01803
GRIFFIN, JAMES M	TALENT AGENT	WM MORRIS, 1350 AVE OF AMERICAS	NEW YORK, NY	10019
GRIFFIN, JOHNNY, QUARTET	JAZZ QUARTET	HOFFER, 233 1/2 E 48TH ST	NEW YORK, NY	10017
GRIFFIN, KEN	TV PRODUCER	TV-VIDEO PRODUCTIONS		
		LITTLE OWLSWYCK, CHURCH LN		
		SIDESHAM, CHICHESTER	WEST SUSSEX PO20 7RH	ENGLAND
GRIFFIN, LARRY	FOOTBALL	STEELERS, 300 STADIUM CIR	PITTSBURGH, PA	15212
GRIFFIN, LEONARD	FOOTBALL	CHIEFS, 1 ARROWHEAD DR	KANSAS CITY, MO	64129
GRIFFIN, LORIE	ACTRESS	10000 SANTA MONICA BLVD #305	LOS ANGELES, CA	90067
GRIFFIN, MARK	BASEBALL	POST OFFICE BOX 15757	HARRISBURG, PA	17105
GRIFFIN, MERV	SINGER-HOST-PRODUCER	1541 N VINE ST	LOS ANGELES, CA	90028
GRIFFIN, MIKE	BASEBALL COACH	POST OFFICE BOX 11002	CHATTANOOGA, TN	37401

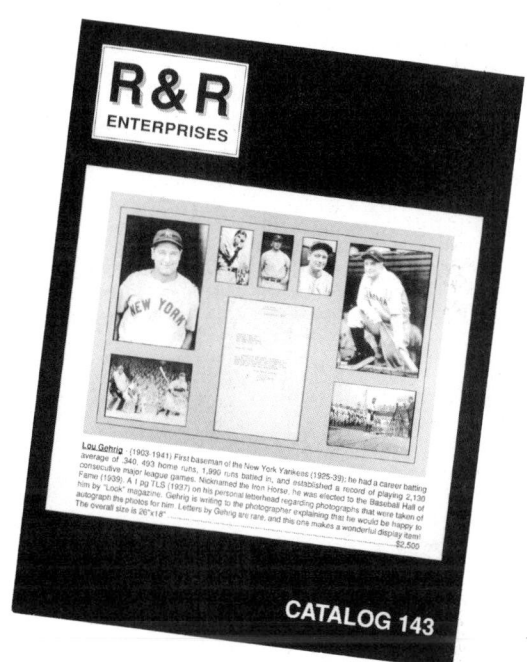

GRIFFIN, RICK	BASEBALL TRAINER	POST OFFICE BOX 4100	SEATTLE, WA 98104
GRIFFIN, THOMAS L	TV PRODUCER	SUNBOW PRODS, 130 5TH AVE	NEW YORK, NY 10011
GRIFFIN, TIM	BASEBALL	POST OFFICE BOX 2887	VERO BEACH, FL 32961
GRIFFIN, TONY	ACTOR-WRITER	9300 WILSHIRE BLVD #410	BEVERLY HILLS, CA 90212
GRIFFITH, ANDY	ACTOR	10500 CAMARILLO	NORTH HOLLYWOOD, CA 91602
GRIFFITH, BILL	CARTOONIST	KING FEATURES, 216 E 45TH ST	NEW YORK, NY 10017
GRIFFITH, CHARLES B	WRITER-PRODUCER	1650 WESTWOOD BLVD #201	LOS ANGELES, CA 90024
GRIFFITH, DARRELL	BASKETBALL	5 TRIAD CENTER #500	SALT LAKE CITY, UT 84180
GRIFFITH, GEORGE	BASEBALL EXECUTIVE	TIGERS, TIGER STADIUM	DETROIT, MI 48216
GRIFFITH, JAMES	ACTOR	POST OFFICE BOX 351	AVILA BEACH, CA 93424
GRIFFITH, KENNETH	ACT-WRI-DIR-PROD	ICM, 388-396 OXFORD ST	LONDON W1 ENGLAND
GRIFFITH, MELANIE	ACTRESS	9555 HEATHER RD	BEVERLY HILLS, CA 90210
GRIFFITH, NANCI	SINGER-SONGWRITER	POST OFFICE BOX 128037	NASHVILLE, TN 37212
GRIFFITH, THOMAS IAN	ACTOR	5444 AGNES AVE	NORTH HOLLYWOOD, CA 91607
GRIFFITH, TRACY LEE	ACTRESS	9100 SUNSET BLVD #300	LOS ANGELES, CA 90069
GRIFFITH, WILLIAM	WRITER	234 5TH AVE	NEW YORK, NY 10001
GRIFFITH-JOYNER, FLORENCE	RUNNER	11444 W OLYMPIC BLVD, 10TH FL	LOS ANGELES, CA 90064
GRIFFITHS, BRIAN	BASEBALL	POST OFFICE BOX 4209	JACKSON, MS 39296
GRIFFITHS, DEREK	ACTOR-COMEDIAN	AZA, 652 FINCHLEY RD	LONDON NW11 7NT ENGLAND
GRIFFITHS, DEWI	WRI-DIR-PROD	EAA, 84 WARDOUR ST, 1ST FLOOR	LONDON W1V 3LF ENGLAND
GRIFFITHS, LEON	TV WRITER	PETERS, FRASER & DUNLOP, LTD	
		5TH FLOOR, THE CHAMBERS	
		CHELSEA HARBOUR, LOT RD	LONDON SW10 OXF ENGLAND
GRIFFITHS, MARK	FILM WRITER-DIRECTOR	10945 AYRES AVE	LOS ANGELES, CA 90064
GRIFFITHS, RICHARD	ACTOR	WHITEHALL, 125 GLOUCESTER RD	LONDON SW7 4TE ENGLAND
GRIFOL, PEDRO	BASEBALL	14100 SIX MILE CYPRESS PKWY	FORT MYERS, FL 33912
GRIGGS, DAVID	FOOTBALL	DOLPHINS, 2269 NW 199TH ST	MIAMI, FL 33056
GRIGSBY, DEAN	COMPOSER	ROUTE #1, BOX 363-A-9	FOREST GROVE, OR 97116
GRILIKHES, MICHEL M	WRITER	463 S ELM DR	BEVERLY HILLS, CA 90212
GRILLO, DENNIS	COMPOSER	245 E 62ND ST	NEW YORK, NY 10021
GRILLO, JOANN	MEZZO SOPRANO	1550 75TH ST	BROOKLYN, NY 10018
GRILLO, JOHN	ACTOR	HOWES, 66 BERKELEY HO, HAY HILL	LONDON W1X 7LH ENGLAND
GRILLO, MICHAEL	FILM DIRECTOR	11533 KELSEY ST	STUDIO CITY, CA 91604
GRILO, BETH A	ARTIST	5942 CHERRY ST	KANSAS CITY, MO 64110
GRIM REAPER	ROCK & ROLL GROUP	DMA, 21182 EASTFARM	NORTHFIELD, MI 48167
GRIMALDI, ALBERTO	FILM PRODUCER	9320 WILSHIRE BLVD #207	BEVERLY HILLS, CA 90212
GRIMALDI, GIAN	DIRECTOR	7516 WOODROW WILSON DR	LOS ANGELES, CA 90046
GRIMALDI, HUGO	DIRECTOR	220 SAN VICENTE BLVD #507	SANTA MONICA, CA 90402
GRIMALDI, MAURIZIO	FILM PRODUCER	9320 WILSHIRE BLVD #207	BEVERLY HILLS, CA 90212
GRIMES, BOB	BASEBALL TRAINER	POST OFFICE DRAWER 1207	ZEBULON, NC 27597
GRIMES, GARY	ACTOR	BDP, 10637 BURBANK BLVD	NORTH HOLLYWOOD, CA 91601
GRIMES, J WILLIAM	CABLE EXECUTIVE	ESPN PLAZA, 935 MIDDLEST	BRISTOL, CT 06010
GRIMES, MIKE	BASEBALL	POST OFFICE BOX 2437	MODESTO, CA 95351
GRIMES, TAMMY	ACTRESS-SINGER	10 E 44TH ST #700	NEW YORK, NY 10017
GRIMM, DAN	TREASURER	STATE LEGISLATIVE BUILDING	OLYMPIA, WA 98504
GRIMM, MARIA	ACTRESS	300 N SWALL DR #215	BEVERLY HILLS, CA 90211
GRIMM, RUSS	FOOTBALL	POST OFFICE BOX 17247 (DULLES)	WASHINGTON, DC 20041
GRIMME, JIMMY	TALENT AGENT	GRIMME AGENCY, 207 POWELL ST	SAN FRANCISCO, CA 94102
GRIMSBY, ROGER	BROADCAST JOURNALIST	POST OFFICE BOX 719051	SAN DIEGO, CA 92171
GRIMSLEY, JASON	BASEBALL	POST OFFICE BOX 27045	TUCSON, AZ 85726
GRIMSLEY, ROSS	BASEBALL-COACH	POST OFFICE BOX 3690, STA "B"	CALGARY, ALB T2B 4M4 CANADA
GRIMSON, STU	HOCKEY	BLACKHAWKS, 1800 W MADISON ST	CHICAGO, IL 60612
GRINER, NORMAN	DIRECTOR	720 5TH AVE	NEW YORK, NY 10019
GRINKER, CHARLES	WRITER-DIRECTOR	147 REDPOLL PATH	NORTH HILLS, NY 11577
GRINNAGE, JACK	ACTOR	1234 N HAYWORTH AVE #10	LOS ANGELES, CA 90046
GRINSTEAD, LINDA M	ACTRESS	505 S LAKE ST	BURBANK, CA 91502
GRIPPO, JOELYN A	WRITER	10915 1/2 WELLWORTH AVE	LOS ANGELES, CA 90024
GRISMAN, DAVID, QUARTET	JAZZ QUARTET	7957 NITA AVE	CANOGA PARK, CA 91304
GRISMER, RAY	COMPOSER	6520 RIVERGROVE DR	DOWNEY, CA 90240
GRISSOM, ANTONIO	BASEBALL	POLECATS, 608 N SLAPPEY BLVD	ALBANY, GA 31701
GRISSOM, MARQUIS	BASEBALL	EXPOS, 4545 DE COUBERTIN AVE	MONTREAL, QUE H1V 3P2 CANADA
GRIZZARD, GEORGE	ACTOR	400 E 54TH ST	NEW YORK, NY 10022
GRIZZARD, LEWIS	AUTHOR-COLUMNIST	POST OFFICE BOX 4689	ATLANTA, GA 30302
GROAK, EUNICE	LT GOVERNOR	STATE CAPITOL BUILDING	HARTFORD, CT 06106
GRODE, GEOFFREY THOMAS	WRITER	451 N GENESEE AVE	LOS ANGELES, CA 90036
GRODIN, CHARLES	ACTOR-WRITER	UTA, 9560 WILSHIRE BL, 5TH FL	BEVERLY HILLS, CA 90212
GRODNIK, DANIEL	FILM PRODUCER	10850 WILSHIRE BLVD #1000	LOS ANGELES, CA 90024
GROENING, MATT	CARTOONIST	15205 FRIENDS ST	PACIFIC PALISADES, CA 90272
GROFF, SCOTT	ACTOR	NBC-TV, "DAYS OF OUR LIVES"	
		3000 W ALAMEDA AVE	BURBANK, CA 91523
GROH, AL	FOOTBALL COACH	N Y GIANTS, GIANTS STADIUM	EAST RUTHERFORD, NJ 07073
GROH, DAVID	ACTOR	301 N CANON DR #305	BEVERLY HILLS, CA 90210
GROLLMAN, ELAINE	ACTRESS	64-29 231ST ST	BAYSIDE, NY 11364
GRONINGER, GERRY	BASEBALL MANAGER	POST OFFICE BOX 64939	FAYETTEVILLE, NC 28306
GRONNING, PIA	ACTRESS	6255 SUNSET BLVD #627	LOS ANGELES, CA 90028
GROOM, BUDDY	BASEBALL	POST OFFICE BOX 6212	TOLEDO, OH 43614
GROOM, SAM	ACTOR	140 RIVERSIDE DR 16-O	NEW YORK, NY 10024
GROPPUSO, MIKE	BASEBALL	POST OFFICE BOX 422229	KISSIMMEE, FL 34742
GROSBARD, ULA	FILM DIRECTOR	29 W 10TH ST	NEW YORK, NY 10011
GROSKOPF, AUBREY	FILM EXECUTIVE	12636 BEATRICE ST	LOS ANGELES, CA 90066
GROSS, CHARLES	COMPOSER	186 RIVERSIDE DR	NEW YORK, NY 10024
GROSS, DAVID P	CONDUCTOR	13490 MAHOGANY DR	RENO, NV 89511
GROSS, GREG	BASEBALL	16 RABBIT RUN RD	MALVERN, PA 19355
GROSS, JACK, JR	TV WRITER	132 S PALM DR	BEVERLY HILLS, CA 90212
GROSS, JOHN	BASEBALL	300 STADIUM WY	DAVENPORT, FL 33837

GROSS, KENNETH H	LITERARY AGENT	R/W/G, 8428 MELROSE PL #C	LOS ANGELES, CA 90069
GROSS, KEVIN	BASEBALL	1000 ELYSIAN PARK DR	LOS ANGELES, CA 90012
GROSS, KIP	BASEBALL	POST OFFICE BOX 26267	ALBUQUERQUE, NM 87125
GROSS, LARRY	SCREENWRITER	CAA, 9830 WILSHIRE BLVD	BEVERLY HILLS, CA 90212
GROSS, LLOYD	DIRECTOR	55 PALMER RD	SOUTHBURY, CT 06488
GROSS, MICHAEL	ACTOR	151 S EL CAMINO DR	BEVERLY HILLS, CA 90212
GROSS, MICHAEL	SWIMMER	PAUL EHRLICH STR 6	D-6000 FRANKFURT 70 GERMANY
GROSS, ROBERT	TV DIRECTOR-PRODUCER	301 E 10TH ST	NEW YORK, NY 10009
GROSS, SHELLY	THEATER PRODUCER	MUSIC FAIR ENTERPRISES	
		555 CITY LINE AVE	BALA CYNWOOD, PA 19004
GROSS, TOM	BASEBALL SCOUT	POST OFFICE BOX 2000	ANAHEIM, CA 92803
GROSSAN, MARK STEVEN	WRITER-PRODUCER	508 N CANON DR	BEVERLY HILLS, CA 90210
GROSSBACH, ROBERT	SCREENWRITER	LEIBOWITZ, 858 STEWART	GARDEN CITY, NY 11530
GROSSBERG, JACK	DIRECTOR-PRODUCER	20950 OXNARD ST #63	WOODLAND HILLS, CA 91367
GROSSELFINGER, FREDERICK BURT	ACTOR	84 BOURNDALE RD S	MANHASSET, NY 11030
GROSSFELD, NORMAN J	TV DIRECTOR-PRODUCER	110 LA SALLE DR	YONKERS, NY 10710
GROSSFELD, SIDNEY	DIRECTOR	6152 KENWATER AVE	WOODLAND HILLS, CA 91364
GROSSLIGHT, PETER	TALENT AGENT	10100 SANTA MONICA BLVD #1600	LOS ANGELES, CA 90067
GROSSMAN, BURT	FOOTBALL	POST OFFICE BOX 609609	SAN DIEGO, CA 92160
GROSSMAN, DAVID	TV DIRECTOR	11200 SUNSHINE TERR	STUDIO CITY, CA 91604
GROSSMAN, DIXIE BROWN	WRITER	6948 LENA AVE	CANOGA PARK, CA 91307
GROSSMAN, DOUGLAS A	SCREENWRITER	8955 BEVERLY BLVD	WEST HOLLYWOOD, CA 90048
GROSSMAN, GARY	ACTOR	12456 VENTURA BLVD #1	STUDIO CITY, CA 91604
GROSSMAN, GARY H	TV PRODUCER	9000 SUNSET BLVD #1200	LOS ANGELES, CA 90069
GROSSMAN, KENNETH	FILM EXECUTIVE	10728 WELLWORTH AVE	LOS ANGELES, CA 90024
GROSSMAN, LAWRENCE K	TV EXECUTIVE	PBS, 475 L'ENFANT PLAZA, NW	WASHINGTON, DC 20024
GROSSMAN, STEFAN	SINGER-GUITARIST	FOLKLORE, 1671 APPIAN WY	SANTA MONICA, CA 90401
GROSSO, SONNY	TV WRITER-PRODUCER	GROSSO JACOBSON, 767 3RD AVE	NEW YORK, NY 10017
GROSZ, GREGORY MICHAEL	WRITER-PRODUCER	1219 ORANGE GROVE AVE	GLENDALE, CA 91205
GROTEWOLD, JEFF	BASEBALL	POST OFFICE BOX 3449	SCRANTON, PA 18505
GROTH, MICHAEL	TV HOST	SAINT MARYS, PERIVALE LN	
		GREENFORD	MIDDLESEX ENGLAND
GROTT, MATT	BASEBALL	POST OFFICE BOX 11002	CHATTANOOGA, TN 37401
GROUND, ROBERT	WRI-DIR-PROD	4412 N 53RD LN #3	PHOENIX, AZ 85031
GROUP, MITCHELL	ACTOR-WRITER	7935 BLACKBURN AVE	LOS ANGELES, CA 90048
GROUSE, MIKE	BASEBALL SCOUT	POST OFFICE BOX 90111	ARLINGTON, TX 76004
GROUT, JAMES	ACTOR	CROUCH, 59 FIRTH ST	LONDON W1V 5TA ENGLAND
GROVE, DAVID	ARTIST	382 UNION ST	SAN FRANCISCO, CA 94133
GROVE, GEORGE W, JR	MUSIC ARRANGER	POST OFFICE BOX 241	BLOWING ROCK, NC 28605
GROVE, SCOTT	BASEBALL	POST OFFICE BOX 957	DUNEDIN, FL 34697
GROVER, EDWARD	ACTOR-WRITER	17 SYCAMORE LN	ROLLING HILLS, CA 90274
GROVES, CAROLYN	ACTRESS	SOGLIO, 423 MADISON AVE	NEW YORK, NY 10017
GROVES, CHARLES	CONDUCTOR	SEE - GROVE, SIR CHARLES	
GROVES, HERMAN	TV WRITER	4657 ARRIBA DR	TARZANA, CA 91356
GROVES, JOHN PATRICK	TV WRITER	2912 PACIFIC AVE	MANHATTAN BEACH, CA 90266
GROWE, JOAN ANDERSON	SECRETARY OF STATE	STATE CAPTOL BLDG, AURORA AVE	SAINT PAUL, MN 55155
GROZA, ALEX	BASKETBALL	6418 CAMINO CORTO	SAN DIEGO, CA 92120
GROZA, LOU "THE TOE"	FOOTBALL	5287 PARKWAY DR	BEREA, OH 44017
GRUBB, JOHNNY	BASEBALL COACH	POST OFFICE BOX 6667	RICHMOND, VA 23230
GRUBBS, GARY	ACTOR	10100 SANTA MONICA BLVD #700	LOS ANGELES, CA 90067
GRUBBS, KRIS	BASEBALL EXECUTIVE	POST OFFICE BOX 1143	BURLINGTON, NC 27216
GRUBER, KELLY	BASEBALL	SKYDOME, 300 BREMMER BL #3200	TORONTO, ONT M5V 3B3 CANADA
GRUBER, NANCY	TV PRODUCER	WPIX-TV, 220 E 42ND ST	NEW YORK, NY 10017
GRUBER, PAUL	FOOTBALL	BUCCANEERS, 1 BUCCANEER PL	TAMPA, FL 33607
GRUBERT, CARL	CARTOONIST	918 WOODLAWN ST	DES PLAINES, IL 60016
GRUDZIELANEK, MARK	BASEBALL	POST OFFICE BOX 6748	ROCKFORD, IL 61125
GRUEN, GABBY	ACTOR	936 21ST ST #F	SANTA MONICA, CA 90403
GRUENBERG, AXEL	DIRECTOR	621 SAN VICENTE BLVD	SANTA MONICA, CA 90402
GRUENER, ALLAN	ACTOR	1080 S 10TH AVE	ARCADIA, CA 91006
GRUMMAN, FRANCIS	DIRECTOR	1200 OLIVE DR	LOS ANGELES, CA 90069
GRUNDFEST, WILLIAM	TV HOST	708 GREENWICH ST #3-E	NEW YORK, NY 10014
GRUNDT, KEN	BASEBALL	POST OFFICE BOX 1295	CLINTON, IA 52733
GRUNDY, REG	TV PRODUCER	THE GRUNDY ORGANISATION	
		GRUNDY HOUSE, 448 PACIFIC HWY	
		ARTARMON	SYDNEY AUSTRALIA
GRUNEISEN, SAM	FOOTBALL COACH	RAIDERS, 332 CENTER ST	EL SEGUNDO, CA 90245
GRUNER, ANTHONY	FILM-TV EXECUTIVE	TALBOT-TV, 7 C/D BAYHAM ST	LONDON NW1 OEY ENGLAND
GRUNFELD, GABRIEL	ACTOR-WRITER	750 S SPAULDING AVE #20	LOS ANGELES, CA 90036
GRUNFIELD, ERNIE	BASKETBALL COACH	KNICKS, 4 PENNYLVANIA PLAZA	NEW YORK, NY 10019
GRUNHARD, DAN	BASEBALL	POST OFFICE BOX 11087	TACOMA, WA 98411
GRUNHARD, TIM	FOOTBALL	CHIEFS, 1 ARROWHEAD DR	KANSAS CITY, MO 64129
GRUSIN, DAVE	COMPOSER	4011 HOPEVALE DR	SHERMAN OAKS, CA 91405
GRUSIN, LARRY M	WRITER	8380 WARING AVE #102	LOS ANGELES, CA 90069
GRUWELL, DEAN	BASEBALL SCOUT	POST OFFICE BOX 2000	ANAHEIM, CA 92803
GRUWELL, SHELLEY	BODYBUILDER	BODY SHOP, 5058 N WEST AVE	FRESNO, CA 93711
GRUWELL, STEVE	BASEBALL SCOUT	POST OFFICE BOX 2000	ANAHEIM, CA 92803
GRYMES, STEPHEN	TV DIRECTOR	561 BABBLING BROOK LN	VALLEY COTTAGE, NY 10989
GRYMKOWSKI, PETE	BODYBUILDER	GOLD'S GYM, 360 HAMPTON DR	VENICE, CA 90291
GUADALCANAL DIARY	ROCK & ROLL GROUP	RUSSELL CARTER ARTIST MGMT	
		755 FIRST NATIONAL BANK BLDG	DECATUR, GA 30030
GUANTE, CECILIO	BASEBALL	JALISCO 67 SIMON BOLIVAR	SANTO DOMINGO DOM REP
GUARD, BARRIE	COMPOSER	OLAV WYPER LTD, BUNIE BUNLE CT W	
		OTTERDEN, FAVERSHAM	KENT ME13 OBY ENGLAND
GUARD, CHRISTOPHER	ACTOR	2 GERALDINE RD	LONDON W4 ENGLAND
GUARDADO, EDDIE	BASEBALL	POST OFFICE BOX 661	KENOSHA, WI 53141

Name	Occupation	Address	City/State	Zip
GUARDINO, CHARLES	ACTOR	7300 FRANKLIN AVE #649	LOS ANGELES, CA	90046
GUARDINO, HARRY	ACTOR	9738 ARBY DR	BEVERLY HILLS, CA	90210
GUARE, JOHN	SCREENWRITER	WM MORRIS, 1350 AVE OF AMERICAS	NEW YORK, NY	10019
GUARINI, FRANK	U S CONGRESSMAN	15 PATH PLAZA	JERSEY CITY, NJ	07306
GUARNACCIA, STEVEN	ARTIST	89 BLEECKER ST #6-B	NEW YORK, NY	10012
GUBANICH, CREIGHTON	BASEBALL	POST OFFICE BOX 882	MADISON, WI	53701
GUBER, LEE	THEATER PRODUCER	32 E 57TH ST	NEW YORK, NY	10022
GUBER, PETER	FILM PRODUCER	760 LAUSANNE RD	LOS ANGELES, CA	90077
GUBICZA, MARK	BASEBALL	POST OFFICE BOX 419969	KANSAS CITY, MO	64141
GUCCIONE, BOB	PUBLISHER	PENTHOUSE, 1965 BROADWAY	NEW YORK, NY	10023
GUEDEL, JOHN	WRITER-PRODUCER	8455 FOUNTAIN AVE #408	LOS ANGELES, CA	90069
GUEFEN, ANTHONY	COMPOSER-CONDUCTOR	1042 VISTA ST #3	LOS ANGELES, CA	90046
GUENETTE, ROBERT	WRITER-PRODUCER	2130 TRENTLY LN	BEVERLY HILLS, CA	90210
GUERCIO, JAMES WILLIAM	DIRECTOR-PRODUCER	CARIBOU RANCH	NEDERLAND, CO	80466
GUERRA, ESMILI	BASEBALL	1524 W NEBRASKA AVE	PEORIA, IL	61604
GUERRA, MANUEL	BASEBALL SCOUT	250 STADIUM PLAZA	ST LOUIS, MO	63102
GUERRERO, DANIEL	COMPOSER	747 S KINGSLEY DR #7	LOS ANGELES, CA	90005
GUERRERO, EPY	BASEBALL SCOUT	SKYDOME, 300 BREMMER BL #3200	TORONTO, ONT M5V 3B3	CANADA
GUERRERO, EVELYN	ACTRESS	12456 VENTURA BLVD #1	STUDIO CITY, CA	91604
GUERRERO, JUAN	BASEBALL	POST OFFICE BOX 288	HOUSTON, TX	77001
GUERRERO, MIKE	BASEBALL	POST OFFICE DRAWER 4797	EL PASO, TX	79914
GUERRERO, PEDRO	BASEBALL	250 STADIUM PLAZA	ST LOUIS, MO	63102
GUERRERO, SANDY	BASEBALL	POST OFFICE DRAWER 4797	EL PASO, TX	79914
GUEST, AL	FILM-TV PRODUCER	12039 PACOIMA CT	STUDIO CITY, CA	91604
GUEST, CORNELIA	ACTRESS	2411 BRIARCREST RD	BEVERLY HILLS, CA	90210
GUEST, DON	FILM WRITER-PRODUCER	8955 BEVERLY BLVD	WEST HOLLYWOOD, CA	90048
GUEST, ELLISA HADEN	SCREENWRITER	555 W 57TH ST #1230	NEW YORK, NY	10019
GUEST, LANCE	ACTOR	2269 LA GRANADA DR	LOS ANGELES, CA	90068
GUEST, NICHOLAS	ACTOR	POST OFFICE BOX 5617	BEVERLY HILLS, CA	90213
GUEST, PAMELA	ACTRESS	280 S BEVERLY DR #400	BEVERLY HILLS, CA	90212
GUEST, VAL	WRITER-PRODUCER	ICM, 388-396 OXFORD ST	LONDON W1	ENGLAND
GUETTEL, HENRY	THEATER PRODUCER	115 CENTRAL PARK W	NEW YORK, NY	10023
GUETTERMAN, LEE	BASEBALL	N Y YANKEES, YANKEE STADIUM	BRONX, NY	10451
GUGLIOTTA, GUY	NEWS REPORTER-AUTHOR	MIAMI HERALD, 1 HERALD PLAZA	MIAMI, FL	33101
GUIDA, THOMAS WILLIAM	DIRECTOR	1681 BLOOMFIELD PL #539	BLOOMFIELD HILLS, MI	48013
GUIDER, ELIZABETH	COLUMNIST	5700 WILSHIRE BLVD #120	LOS ANGELES, CA	90036
GUIDO, MICHAEL	ACTOR	ABC-TV, "ALL MY CHILDREN"		
		320 W 66TH ST	NEW YORK, NY	10023
GUILAROFF, SYDNEY	HAIRDRESSER	POST OFFICE BOX 253	BEVERLY HILLS, CA	90213
GUILBERT, ANN MORGAN	ACTRESS	5750 WILSHIRE BLVD #512	LOS ANGELES, CA	90036
GUILD, S ROLLINS	DIRECTOR	124 SW 8 TERR	BOCA RATON, FL	33432
GUILFOYLE, MIKE	BASEBALL	POST OFFICE BOX 2785	LAKELAND, FL	33806
GUILFOYLE, PAUL	ACTOR	129 E 29TH ST	NEW YORK, NY	10016
GUILLAUME, ROBERT	ACTOR	3853 LONGRIDGE AVE	SHERMAN OAKS, CA	91423
GUILLEN, OZZIE	BASEBALL	333 W 35TH ST	CHICAGO, IL	60616
GUILLERMIN, JOHN	FILM DIRECTOR	309 S ROCKINGHAM AVE	LOS ANGELES, CA	90049
GUINAN, ROBERT	ACTOR	1356 E 58TH ST	BROOKLYN, NY	11234
GUINN, BRIAN	BASEBALL	CUBS, 2ND & RIVERSIDE DR	DES MOINES, IA	50309
GUINN, JAMES	BASEBALL SCOUT	ATHLETICS'S, OAKLAND COLISEUM	OAKLAND, CA	94621
GUINNESS, SIR ALEC	ACTOR-DIRECTOR	KETTLE BROOK MEADOWS		
		STEEP MARSH, PETERSFORD	HAMPSHIRE	ENGLAND
GUIZAR, TITO	ACTOR-GUITARIST	THE SIERRA MADRE		
		640 LOMAS DE CHAPULTEPEC	MEXICO CITY 10 09999	MEXICO
GUIZON, FRENCHIA	ACTOR	1697 LONGWOOD AVE	LOS ANGELES, CA	90019
GULAGER, CLU	ACTOR	2118 S ATLANTA PL	TULSA, OK	74114
GULLEDGE, HUGH	BASEBALL	POST OFFICE BOX 11363	RENO, NV	89510
GULLETT, DON	BASEBALL-COACH	POST OFFICE BOX 23290	NASHVILLE, TN	37202
GULLICKSON, BILL	BASEBALL	TIGERS, TIGER STADIUM	DETROIT, MI	48216
GULLIVER, DOROTHY	ACTRESS	28792 LAJOS LN	VALLEY CENTER, CA	92082
GULLY, SCOTT	BASEBALL	POST OFFICE BOX 22093	GREENSBORO, NC	27420
GUMBEL, BRYANT	BROADCASTER	30 ROCKEFELLER PLAZA #1508	NEW YORK, NY	10112
GUMBEL, GREG	SPORTSCASTER	ESPN PLAZA, 935 MIDDLEST	BRISTOL, CT	06010
GUMP, SCOTT	GOLFER	POST OFFICE BOX 109601	PALM BCH GARDENS, FL	33418
GUMPF, JOHN	BASEBALL	14100 SIX MILE CYPRESS PKWY	FORT MYERS, FL	33912
GUND, GEORGE, III	BASKETBALL EXECUTIVE	POST OFFICE BOX 5000	RICHFIELD, OH	44286
GUND, GORDON	BASKETBALL EXECUTIVE	POST OFFICE BOX 5000	RICHFIELD, OH	44286
GUNDEN, TAMI	SINGER	POST OFFICE BOX 229	VOORHEES, NJ	08043
GUNDERSON, ERIC	BASEBALL	5999 E VAN BUREN ST	PHOENIX, AZ	85008
GUNDERSON, STEVE	U S CONGRESSMAN	POST OFFICE BOX 247	BLACK RIVER FALLS, WI	54615
GUNDLACH, ROBERT	ART DIRECTOR	RFD #1, BOX 264, CLOSTER RD	PALISADES, NY	10964
GUNN, HARTFORD N, JR	CABLE EXECUTIVE	1301 PENNSYLVANIA AVE, N	WASHINGTON, DC	20004
GUNN, JANET	ACTRESS	9300 WILSHIRE BLVD #410	BEVERLY HILLS, CA	90212
GUNN, JOSEPH A	TV WRITER	10351 SANTA MONICA BLVD #211	LOS ANGELES, CA	90025
GUNN, MARK	FOOTBALL	N Y JETS, 1000 FULTON AVE	HEMPSTEAD, NY	11550
GUNN, MOSES	ACTOR	395 NUT PLAINS RD	GUILFORD, CT	06437
GUNNER, RODERICK	FILM-TV EXECUTIVE	HIBERNIAN HOUSE, 2/14 SHORTLANDS	LONDON W6	ENGLAND
GUNNING, CHRISTOPHER	COMPOSER	THE OLD RECTORY, MILL LN		
		MONKS RISBOROUGH	BUCKS HP17 9LG	ENGLAND
GUNS N' ROSES	ROCK & ROLL GROUP	1830 S ROBERTSON BLVD #201	LOS ANGELES, CA	90035
GUNTER, CORNELL & THE COASTERS	VOCAL GROUP	8145 E CAMELBACK RD #216	SCOTTSDALE, AZ	85251
GUNTHER, C RONALD	DIRECTOR	7631 ORIOLE DR	NILES, IL	60648
GUNTHER, DIANA	ACTRESS	GARRETT, 6525 SUNSET BL, 5TH FL	LOS ANGELES, CA	90028
GUNTZELMAN, DANIEL J	TV WRITER-DIRECTOR	15069 RAYNETA DR	SHERMAN OAKS, CA	91403
GUNZENHAUSER, NORM	TV PRODUCER	8383 WILSHIRE BLVD #923	BEVERLY HILLS, CA	90211
GUOKAS, MATT	BASKETBALL COACH	POST OFFICE BOX 76	ORLANDO, FL	32802

GURDINE, JAMES G	WRITER	12726 VANOWEN ST	NORTH HOLLYWOOD, CA	91605
GURMAN, RICHARD	TV WRITER	6440 COLGATE AVE	LOS ANGELES, CA	90048
GURNEE, HAL	TV DIRECTOR	DUNBAR RD	SHARON, CT	06069
GURNER, GARY S	TV WRITER	853 16TH ST #6	SANTA MONICA, CA	90403
GURNEY, A R, JR	PLAYWRIGHT	120 W 70TH ST	NEW YORK, NY	10023
GURNEY, DAN	AUTO RACER	2334 S BROADWAY	SANTA ANA, CA	92707
GURTLER, RITA M	TV WRITER	946 POST RD	RYE, NY	10580
GUSAROV, ALEXEI	HOCKEY	NORDIQUES, 2205 AVE DU COLISEE	QUEBEC, QUE G1L 4W7	CANADA
GUSKE, TODD	BASEBALL EXECUTIVE	CUBS, 2ND & RIVERSIDE DR	DES MOINES, IA	50309
GUSS, JACK R	TV WRITER	10500 MARS LN	LOS ANGELES, CA	90077
GUSS, LOUIS	ACTOR	6310 SAN VICENTE BLVD #407	LOS ANGELES, CA	90048
GUSSOW, MEL	FILM CRITIC	N Y TIMES, 229 W 43RD ST	NEW YORK, NY	10036
GUST, DON	BASEBALL SCOUT	REDS, 100 RIVERFRONT STADIUM	CINCINNATI, OH	45202
GUSTAFSON, CHARLES	CONDUCTOR	1750 NORFOLK AVE #3	SAINT PAUL, MN	55116
GUSTAFSON, ED	BASEBALL	POST OFFICE BOX 5645	ORLANDO, FL	32855
GUTCHEON, BETH R	SCREENWRITER	CAA, 9830 WILSHIRE BLVD	BEVERLY HILLS, CA	90212
GUTERMAN, SHERYL L	TV WRITER	1335 9TH ST #4	SANTA MONICA, CA	90401
GUTFARB, WILLIAM	BASEBALL EXECUTIVE	FENWAY PARK, 4 YAWKEY WY	BOSTON, MA	02215
GUTHMAN, EDWARD	FILM CRITIC	SAN FRANCISCO CHRONICLE		
		901 MISSION ST	SAN FRANCISCO, CA	94119
GUTHRIE, ARLO	SINGER-SONGWRITER	THE FARM	WASHINGTON, MA	01223
GUTHRIE, LYNN	DIRECTOR	23238 CANZONET ST	WOODLAND HILLS, CA	91367
GUTHRIE, MARK	BASEBALL	TWINS, 501 CHICAGO AVE S	MINNEAPOLIS, MN	55415
GUTHRIE, RICHARD	ACTOR	3271 1/2 ROWENA AVE	LOS ANGELES, CA	90027
GUTHRIE, TED	BASEBALL EXECUTIVE	POST OFFICE BOX 3609	PORT CHARLOTTE, FL	33949
GUTIERREZ, ANTHONY	BASEBALL	POST OFFICE BOX 422229	KISSIMMEE, FL	34742
GUTIERREZ, GERALD	TV DIRECTOR	ROBERTS, 157 W 57TH ST	NEW YORK, NY	10019
GUTIERREZ, JACKIE	BASEBALL	AMBRES 3ER CALLEJON #29-35	CARTAGENA	COLOMBIA
GUTIERREZ, JIM	BASEBALL	POST OFFICE BOX 4756	JACKSONVILLE, FL	32201
GUTIERREZ, ORLANDO	BASEBALL UMPIRE	POST OFFICE BOX 25010	LITTLE ROCK, AZ	72221
GUTIERREZ, RAFAEL	BASEBALL	POST OFFICE BOX 2887	VERO BEACH, FL	32961
GUTIERREZ, RICKY	BASEBALL	500 NORTON ST	ROCHESTER, NY	14621
GUTIERREZ, VICENTE	SCREENWRITER	R/W/G, 8428 MELROSE PL #C	LOS ANGELES, CA	90069
GUTIERREZ, VINCE R	TV WRITER	9100 SUNSET BLVD #340	LOS ANGELES, CA	90069
GUTIERRREZ, MANUEL	CINEMATOGRAPHER	CAMERA GROUP, 25-20 30TH RD	ASTORIA, NY	11102
GUTMAN, STEVE	FOOTBALL EXECUTIVE	N Y JETS, 1000 FULTON AVE	HEMPSTEAD, NY	11550
GUTOWSKI, ROBERT M	TV EXECUTIVE	ESPN PLAZA, 935 MIDDLEST	BRISTOL, CT	06010
GUTTENBERG, STEVE	ACTOR	15237 SUNSET BLVD #48	PACIFIC PALISADES, CA	90272
GUTTERIDGE, LUCY	ACTRESS	CONWAY, 18-21 JERMYN ST	LONDON SW1	ENGLAND
GUTTERIDGE, TOM	TV DIRECTOR-PRODUCER	MENTORNS, 138-140 WARDOUR ST	LONDON W1V 3AN	ENGLAND
GUTTFREUND, ANDRE RUBEN	DIRECTOR	DGA, 7920 SUNSET BLVD, 6TH FL	LOS ANGELES, CA	90046
GUTWILLIG, ROBERT ALAN	WRITER	2237 NICHOLS CANYON RD	LOS ANGELES, CA	90046
GUY, JASMINE	ACTRESS	21243 VENTURA BLVD #101	WOODLAND HILLS, CA	91364
GUY, KEVIN	HOCKEY	POST OFFICE BOX 1540, STA "M"	CALGARY, ALTA T2P 3B8	CANADA
GUYER, CYNTHIA	ACTRESS	11712 MOORPARK ST #204	STUDIO CITY, CA	91604
GUYLAS, ELLEN M	TV WRITER	7432 CERVANTES PL	LOS ANGELES, CA	90046
GUYTON, MYRON	FOOTBALL	N Y GIANTS, GIANTS STADIUM	EAST RUTHERFORD, NJ	07073
GUZA, ROBERT O	WRITER	2423 RONDA VISTA DR	LOS ANGELES, CA	90027
GUZDAR, DARIUS	TV PRODUCER	MAZIN-WYCKOFF, 36 E 12TH ST	NEW YORK, NY	10003
GUZIK, ROB, JR	BASEBALL (PITCHER)	POST OFFICE BOX 7845	COLUMBIA, SC	29202
GUZIK, ROB, SR	BASEBALL (SCOUT)	METS, 126TH ST & ROOSEVELT AVE	FLUSHING, NY	11368
GUZMAN, JOHNNY	BASEBALL	POST OFFICE BOX 2769	HUNTSVILLE, AL	35804
GUZMAN, JOSE	BASEBALL	POST OFFICE BOX 90111	ARLINGTON, TX	76004
GUZMAN, JUAN	BASEBALL	SKYDOME, 300 BREMMER BL #3200	TORONTO, ONT M5V 3B3	CANADA
GUZZI, GEORGE	ARTIST	11 RANDLETT PARK	WEST NEWTON, MA	02165
GWILYN, MIKE	ACTOR	MARKHAM AND FROGGATT, LTD		
		JULIAN HOUSE, 4 WINDMILL ST	LONDON W1P 1HF	ENGLAND
GWYNN, CHRIS	BASEBALL	POST OFFICE BOX 419969	KANSAS CITY, MO	64141
GWYNN, TONY	BASEBALL	POST OFFICE BOX 2000	SAN DIEGO, CA	92112
GWYNNE, ANNE	ACTRESS	4350 COLFAX AVE	NORTH HOLLYWOOD, CA	91604
GWYNNE, FRED	ACTOR	10100 SANTA MONICA BLVD #1600	LOS ANGELES, CA	90067
GYLLENHAAL, STEPHEN	WRITER-PRODUCER	226 S NORTON AVE	LOS ANGELES, CA	90004
GYPSY	MUSICAL GROUP	POST OFFICE BOX 437	EXCELSIOR, MN	55331
GYSIN, FRANCIS	TV PRODUCER	NCB FILMS, DUNELM, ARKLEY	HERTS	ENGLAND

HAAGENSEN, ROBERT	DIRECTOR	3198 LYON RD, R D #3	CAZENOVIA, NY	13035
HAAK, HOWIE	BASEBALL SCOUT	POST OFFICE BOX 288	HOUSTON, TX	77001
HAAKE, JAMES "GYPSY"	ACTOR	1256 N FLORES ST #1	LOS ANGELES, CA	90069
HAAS, BELINDA	SCREENWRITER	131 S RODEO DR #300	BEVERLY HILLS, CA	90212
HAAS, CHARLES	SCREENWRITER	CAA, 9830 WILSHIRE BLVD	BEVERLY HILLS, CA	90212
HAAS, CHARLES F	FILM-TV DIRECTOR	12626 HORTENSE ST	STUDIO CITY, CA	91604
HAAS, DAVID	BASEBALL	POST OFFICE BOX 6212	TOLEDO, OH	43614
HAAS, DOLLY	ACTRESS	HIRSCHFIELD, 122 E 95TH ST	NEW YORK, NY	10028
HAAS, EDDIE	BASEBALL-SCOUT	6850 LAWRENCE RD	LANTANA, FL	33462
HAAS, HAROLD	FILM EXECUTIVE	303 S ALMONT DR	LOS ANGELES, CA	90048
HAAS, JAY	GOLFER	POST OFFICE BOX 109601	PALM BCH GARDENS, FL	33418
HAAS, JOANNE	COSTUME DESIGNER	13949 VENTURA BLVD #309	SHERMAN OAKS, CA	91423

HAAS, LUKAS	ACTOR	335 N MAPLE DR #250	BEVERLY HILLS, CA 90210
HAAS, PAUL	TALENT AGENT	11726 SAN VICENTE BLVD #300	LOS ANGELES, CA 90049
HAAS, PHILIP	SCREENWRITER	131 S RODEO DR #300	BEVERLY HILLS, CA 90212
HAAS, WALTER A	BASEBALL EXECUTIVE	ATHLETICS'S, OAKLAND COLISEUM	OAKLAND, CA 94621
HAAS, WALTER J	BASEBALL EXECUTIVE	ATHLETICS'S, OAKLAND COLISEUM	OAKLAND, CA 94621
HAASE, DEAN	BASEBALL	1090 N EUCLID AVE	SARASOTA, FL 34237
HAASE, HEATHER	ACTRESS	3500 W OLIVE AVE #1400	BURBANK, CA 91505
HAASE, ROD	ACTOR	9040 HARRATT ST #5	LOS ANGELES, CA 90069
HABER, BERNARD	WRI-DIR-PROD	71 BEVERLY RD	GREAT NECK, NY 11021
HABER, JOYCE	WRITER-COLUMNIST	1005 N REXFORD DR	LOS ANGELES, CA 90210
HABER, LES	TV PRODUCER	350 E 52ND ST #6-D	NEW YORK, NY 10022
HABERLE, JOAN	SECRETARY OF STATE	STATE HOUSE BLDG, 125 W STATE ST	TRENTON, NJ 08625
HABIB, BRIAN	FOOTBALL	VIKINGS, 9520 VIKING DR	EDEN PRAIRIE, MN 55344
HABIB, GEORGE	TV DIRECTOR	5165 CALATRAMA DR	WOODLAND HILLS, CA 91364
HABSCHEID, MARC	HOCKEY	RED WINGS, 600 CIVIC CENTER DR	DETROIT, MI 48226
HABYAN, JOHN	BASEBALL	N Y YANKEES, YANKEE STADIUM	BRONX, NY 10451
HACK, RICHARD	ACTOR	131 N WETHERLY DR #304	LOS ANGELES, CA 90048
HACK, RICHARD	TV CRITIC	6715 SUNSET BLVD	HOLLYWOOD, CA 90028
HACK, SHELLEY	ACTRESS-MODEL	1208 GEORGINA AVE	SANTA MONICA, CA 90402
HACKEL, DAVID M	TV WRITER	4221 COLFAX AVE #1	STUDIO CITY, CA 91604
HACKER, JOSEPH	ACTOR	144 S BEVERLY DR #405	BEVERLY HILLS, CA 90212
HACKER, PATRICIA	TALENT AGENT	SMITH, 121 N SAN VICENTE BLVD	BEVERLY HILLS, CA 90211
HACKER, RICH	BASEBALL COACH	SKYDOME, 300 BREMMER BL #3200	TORONTO, ONT M5V 3B3 CANADA
HACKES, PETER QUINN	NEWS CORRESPONDENT	NBC NEWS, 4001 NEBRASKA AV, SW	WASHINGTON, DC 20016
HACKETT, BARBARA BRINTON	COSTUME DESIGNER	13949 VENTURA BLVD #309	SHERMAN OAKS, CA 91423
HACKETT, BUDDY	COMEDIAN-ACTOR	800 N WHITTIER DR	BEVERLY HILLS, CA 90210
HACKETT, DINO	FOOTBALL	CHIEFS, 1 ARROWHEAD DR	KANSAS CITY, MO 64129
HACKETT, F ARTHUR	DIRECTOR	20808 E GLEN HAVEN	NORTHVILLE, MI 48167
HACKETT, GEORGE	CONDUCTOR	3651 CRESTMONT AVE	LOS ANGELES, CA 90026
HACKETT, RICHARD	DIRECTOR-PRODUCER	CHESS VALLEY FILMS, LTD	
		FILM HOUSE, LITTLE CHALFONT	BUCKS ENGLAND
HACKETT, STEVE	SINGER-SONGWRITER	200 W 57TH ST #1403	NEW YORK, NY 10019
HACKFORD, TAYLOR	WRITER-PRODUCER	2003 LA BREA TERR	LOS ANGELES, CA 90046
HACKIN, DENNIS E	SCREENWRITER	10000 SANTA MONICA BLVD #305	LOS ANGELES, CA 90067
HACKMAN, GENE	ACTOR	8500 WILSHIRE BLVD #801	BEVERLY HILLS, CA 90211
HADDAD, AVA	ACTRESS	BLOOM, 233 PARK AVE S, 10TH FL	NEW YORK, NY 10017
HADDIX, HARVEY	BASEBALL	2105 CHEVIOT HILLS DR	SPRINGFIELD, OH 45505
HADDIX, WAYNE	FOOTBALL	BUCCANEERS, 1 BUCCANEER PL	TAMPA, FL 33607
HADEN, BEN	CLERYMAN	POST OFFICE BOX 100	CHATTANOOGA, TN 37401
HADLEY, BRETT	ACTOR	STONE MANNERS, 9113 SUNSET BL	LOS ANGELES, CA 90069
HADLOCK, CHANNING	WRITER-PRODUCER	60 GRAMERCY PARK N	NEW YORK, NY 10010
HAEGER, GREG	BASEBALL	POST OFFICE BOX 64939	FAYETTEVILLE, NC 28306
HAFER, BARBARA	AUDITOR GENERAL	STATE CAPITOL BUILDING	HARRISBURG, PA 17120
HAFFNER, CRAIG ALLEN	TV WRITER	4200 TEESDALE AVE	STUDIO CITY, CA 91604
HAFTEL, LINDA	TV DIRECTOR	200 W 16TH ST #7-D	NEW YORK, NY 10011
HAGAN, MOLLY	ACTRESS	210 S ARNAZ DR #3	BEVERLY HILLS, CA 90211
HAGAR, SAMMY	SINGER-GUITARIST	31740 BROAD BEACH RD	MALIBU, CA 90265
HAGARD, J HARVEY	WRITER	5275 SEPULVEDA AVE	SAN BERNARDINO, CA 92404
HAGEN, BILL	FILM CRITIC	POST OFFICE BOX 191	SAN DIEGO, CA 92112
HAGEN, E DEANE	COMPOSER	7900 SALE AVE	CANOGA PARK, CA 91304
HAGEN, EARLE	COMPOSER	2121 AVE OF THE STARS #990	LOS ANGELES, CA 90067
HAGEN, KEVIN	ACTOR	1539 SAWTELLE BLVD #10	LOS ANGELES, CA 90025
HAGEN, NINA	SINGER	FBI, 1776 BROADWAY	NEW YORK, NY 10019
HAGEN, UTA	ACTRESS	KROLL, 390 W END AVE	NEW YORK, NY 10024
HAGER, BRITT	FOOTBALL	EAGLES, BROAD ST & PATTISON AVE	PHILADELPHIA, PA 19148
HAGER, DICK	BASEBALL SCOUT	POST OFFICE BOX 288	HOUSTON, TX 77001
HAGER, JIM	SINGER-ACTOR	2057 LAUREL CANYON BLVD	LOS ANGELES, CA 90046
HAGER, JOAN BELL	SINGER	429 DAVIDSON RD	NASHVILLE, TN 37205
HAGER, JON	SINGER-ACTOR	8661 HOLLYWOOD BLVD	LOS ANGELES, CA 90069
HAGERMAN, PAUL S	COMEDY WRITER	400 W 43RD ST #36-R	NEW YORK, NY 10036
HAGERS, THE	C & W DUO	CAMPBELL, 814 19TH AVE S	NASHVILLE, TN 37203
HAGGARD, MARTY	SINGER-SONGWRITER	17530 VENTURA BLVD #108	ENCINO, CA 91316
HAGGARD, MERLE	SINGER	POST OFFICE BOX 536	PALO CEDRO, CA 96073
HAGGARD, NATHAN	TV DIRECTOR	22255 NEEDLES ST	CHATSWORTH, CA 91311
HAGGARD, PIERS	TV DIRECTOR	DIRECTORS GUILD OF GREAT BRITAIN	
		125 TOTTENHAM COURT RD	LONDON W1P 9HN ENGLAND
HAGGARD, STEVE	SINGER	4 PARK AVE #7-N	NEW YORK, NY 10016
HAGGERTY, DAN	ACTOR	11520 DECENTE DR	STUDIO CITY, CA 91604
HAGGERTY, PAT	FOOTBALL REFEREE	NFL, 410 PARK AVE	NEW YORK, NY 10022
HAGGIS, PAUL	TV WRITER	12804 HATTERAS ST	NORTH HOLLYWOOD, CA 91607
HAGIN, WAYNE	SPORTSCASTER	333 W 35TH ST	CHICAGO, IL 60616
HAGIO, KUNIO	ARTIST	6151 N SAUGANASH AVE	CHICAGO, IL 60646
HAGLUND, CECILIA	ACTRESS	204 W 14TH ST #5-A	NEW YORK, NY 10011
HAGMAN, HEIDI	ACTRESS	23730 MALIBU COLONY RD	MALIBU, CA 90265
HAGMAN, LARRY	ACTOR-DIRECTOR	23730 MALIBU COLONY RD	MALIBU, CA 90265
HAGMANN, STUART	FILM DIRECTOR	150 S WOODBURN DR	LOS ANGELES, CA 90049
HAGON, GARRICK	ACTOR	CONWAY, 18-21 JERMYN ST	LONDON SW1 ENGLAND
HAGUE, ALBERT	ACTOR-COMPOSER	4346 REDWOOD AVE #304-A	MARINA DEL REY, CA 90292
HAHN, DAVID	DIRECTOR	33 RIVERSIDE DR	NEW YORK, NY 10023
HAHN, DIETER	TV DIRECTOR	201 E 15TH ST #6-G	NEW YORK, NY 10003
HAHN, DOUG	BASEBALL EXECUTIVE	POST OFFICE BOX 464	APPLETON, WI 54912
HAHN, JESSICA	MODEL	999 N DOHENY DR #601	LOS ANGELES, CA 90069
HAHN, PAUL	ACTOR	3316 ROWENA AVE #3	LOS ANGELES, CA 90027
HAHN, PHIL H	TV WRITER	11845 KLING ST	NORTH HOLLYWOOD, CA 91607
HAID, CHARLES	ACT-DIR-PROD	4376 FORMAN AVE	NORTH HOLLYWOOD, CA 91602

HAIG, ALEXANDER, JR	GENERAL	1155 15TH ST #800, NW	WASHINGTON, DC	20005
HAIGHT, GORDON	ACTOR	1022 GALLOWAY ST	PACIFIC PALISADES, CA	90272
HAILBURTON, RONNIE	FOOTBALL	BRONCOS, 13655 BRONCOS PKWY	ENGLEWOOD, CO	80112
HAILEY, ARTHUR	WRITER	BOX N-7776, LYFOND CAY	NASSAU	BAHAMAS
HAILEY, ELIZABETH F	WRITER	11747 CANTON PL	STUDIO CITY, CA	91604
HAILEY, OLIVER	SCREENWRITER	11747 CANTON PL	STUDIO CITY, CA	91604
HAIM, COREY	ACTOR	3960 LAUREL CANYON BLVD #384	STUDIO CITY, CA	91604
HAINES, CHARLES	MUSIC ARRANGER	ROUTE #3, BOX 369, MIRES RD	MOUNT JULIET, TN	37122
HAINES, CONNIE	SINGER	1870 CAMINTO DEL CIELO	GLENDALE, CA	91208
HAINES, F L "ROY"	COMPOSER-CONDUCTOR	7726 JAMIESON AVE	RESEDA, CA	91335
HAINES, LARRY	ACTOR	1 HIDDEN MEADOW RD	WESTON, CT	06883
HAINES, RANDA	TV DIRECTOR	1429 AVON PARK TERR	LOS ANGELES, CA	90026
HAINES-STILES, GEOFFREY	TV DIRECTOR	41 ROWAN RD	SUMMIT, NJ	07901
HAINING, MARK	ACTOR	2491 N GOWER ST	LOS ANGELES, CA	90068
HAIRSTON, CURTIS	SINGER	130 W 57TH ST #8-B	NEW YORK, NY	10019
HAIRSTON, HAROLD "HAPPY"	ACTOR-BASKETBALL	13222 ADMIRAL AVE #G	MARINA DEL REY, CA	90292
HAIRSTON, JESTER	ACTOR	5047 VALLEY RIDGE AVE	LOS ANGELES, CA	90043
HAJAK, RON	ACTOR	17420 VENTURA BLVD #4	ENCINO, CA	91316
HAJE, KHRYSTYNE	ACTRESS	POST OFFICE BOX 8750	UNIVERSAL CITY, CA	91608
HAJEK, DAVID	BASEBALL	POST OFFICE BOX 422229	KISSIMMEE, FL	34742
HAKE, ARDELL	COMPOSER	5306 LA FOREST DR	LA CANADA, CA	91011
HAKES, DON	FOOTBALL REFEREE	NFL, 410 PARK AVE	NEW YORK, NY	10022
HAKOBIAN, ALEX	SCREENWRITER	4528 VISTA DEL MONTE #6	SHERMAN OAKS, CA	91403
HAKU	WRESTLER	POST OFFICE BOX 3859	STAMFORD, CT	06905
HALABI, JESUS "CHU"	BASEBALL SCOUT	ORIOLE PARK, 333 W CAMDEN ST	BALTIMORE, MD	21201
HALAS, JOHN	FILM PRODUCER	HALAS AND BATCHELOR FILMS		
		3-7 KEAN ST	LONDON WC2	ENGLAND
HALASZ, GEORGE	WRITER	332 BONHILL RD	LOS ANGELES, CA	90049
HALASZ, LASZLO	CONDUCTOR	3 LEEDS DR	PORT WASHINGTON, NY	11050
HALDEMAN, TIM	ACTOR	4257 LINCOLN AVE	CULVER CITY, CA	90230
HALE, BARBARA	ACTRESS	POST OFFICE BOX 1980	NORTH HOLLYWOOD, CA	91604
HALE, BERNADETTE	ACTRESS	1327 N VISTA ST	LOS ANGELES, CA	90046
HALE, BILLY	TV DIRECTOR	ICM, 8899 BEVERLY BLVD	LOS ANGELES, CA	90048
HALE, BIRDIE	ACTRESS	POST OFFICE BOX 160, CATH STA	NEW YORK, NY	10025
HALE, CHERYL	SINGER	POST OFFICE BOX 282	HARTSELLE, AL	35640
HALE, CHIP	BASEBALL	POST OFFICE BOX 1659	PORTLAND, OR	97207
HALE, DE MARLO	BASEBALL COACH	POST OFFICE BOX 1718	NEW BRITAIN, CT	06050
HALE, DIANA	ACTRESS	1327 N VISTA ST	LOS ANGELES, CA	90046
HALE, GEORGIA	ACTRESS	1762 N LA BREA AVE	LOS ANGELES, CA	90028
HALE, GEORGINA	ACTRESS	74-A SAINT JOHNS		
		WOOD HIGH ST	LONDON NW8	ENGLAND
HALE, HELEN	ACTRESS	166 W 75TH ST	NEW YORK, NY	10023
HALE, JEAN	ACTRESS	715 NAPOLI DR	PACIFIC PALISADES, CA	90272
HALE, SCOTT	ACTOR-WRITER	8955 BEVERLY BLVD	WEST HOLLYWOOD, CA	90048
HALEY, CHARLES	FOOTBALL	S F 49ERS, 4949 CENTENNIAL BL	SANTA CLARA, CA	95054
HALEY, JACK	BASKETBALL	N J NETS, MEADOWLANDS ARENA	EAST RUTHERFORD, NJ	07073
HALEY, JACK, JR	WRITER-PRODUCER	1443 DEVLIN DR	LOS ANGELES, CA	90069
HALEY, JACKIE EARLE	ACTOR	843 N SYCAMORE AVE	LOS ANGELES, CA	90038
HALEY, MARK	BASEBALL COACH	POST OFFICE BOX 4218	SOUTH BEND, IN	46634
HALEY'S, BILL, COMETS	ROCK & ROLL GROUP	2011 FERRY AVE #U-19	CAMDEN, NJ	08104
HALFORD, BRUCE	DIRECTOR	2549 N CATALINA ST	LOS ANGELES, CA	90027
HALIBURTON, RONNIE	FOOTBALL	BRONCOS, 13655 BRONCOS PKWY	ENGLEWOOD, CO	80112
HALICKI, H B	FILM PRODUCER	18511 S MARIPOSA AVE	GARDENA, CA	90248
HALIDORSON, DAN	GOLFER	POST OFFICE BOX 109601	PALM BCH GARDENS, FL	33418
HALKIDIS, BOB	HOCKEY	POST OFFICE BOX 17013	INGLEWOOD, CA	90308
HALL, ADRIAN	DIRECTOR	201 WASHINGTON ST	PROVIDENCE, RI	02903
HALL, ALAN	CINEMATOGRAPHER	22 GREENFIELDS CLOSE, HORSHAM	WEST SUSSEX	ENGLAND
HALL, ALBERT	ACTOR	11726 SAN VICENTE BLVD #300	LOS ANGELES, CA	90049
HALL, ALBERT	BASEBALL	1628 SPAULDING RD	BIRMINGHAM, AL	35211
HALL, ANTHONY MICHAEL	ACTOR	65 ROOSEVELT AVE	VALLEY STREAM, NY	11581
HALL, ARSENIO	COMED-ACT-TV HOST	"THE ARSENIO HALL SHOW"		
		FOX TELEVISION CENTER		
		5746 SUNSET BLVD	HOLLYWOOD, CA	90028
HALL, BILLY	BASEBALL	12000 STADIUM RD	ADELANTO, CA	92301
HALL, BRIAN	ACTOR-WRITER	43-A PRINCESS RD, REGENTS PK	LONDON NW1 8JS	ENGLAND
HALL, BRUCE	ACTOR	CRESCENT DR	HOPEWELL JUNCTION, NY	12533
HALL, BRUCE	NEWS CORRESPONDENT	CBS NEWS, 524 W 57TH ST	NEW YORK, NY	10019
HALL, CARL A	SOUND EFFECTS	194 LINCOLN RD	BROOKLYN, NY	11225
HALL, CARLA RIGGS	SINGER-SONGWRITER	SEE - RIGGS-HALL, CARLA		
HALL, CONRAD L	CINEMATOGRAPHER	1310 N SWEETZER AVE #60	LOS ANGELES, CA	90069
HALL, COURTNEY	FOOTBALL	POST OFFICE BOX 609609	SAN DIEGO, CA	92160
HALL, DARREN	BASEBALL	CHIEFS, MAC ARTHUR STADIUM	SYRACUSE, NY	13208
HALL, DARYL	SINGER-SONGWRITER	130 W 57TH ST #2-A	NEW YORK, NY	10019
HALL, DEAN	CINEMATOGRAPHER	7715 SUNSET BLVD #1150	LOS ANGELES, CA	90046
HALL, DEIDRE	ACTRESS	9023 NORMA PL	LOS ANGELES, CA	90069
HALL, DWIGHT	BASEBALL EXECUTIVE	4385 TUTT BLVD	COLORADO SPRINGS, CO	80922
HALL, FAWN	SECRETARY-MODEL	8339 CHAPEL LAKE CT	ANNADALE, VA	22003
HALL, GARY L	DIRECTOR	7562 W 82ND ST	PLAYA DEL REY, CA	90293
HALL, GENEIEVE B	ACTRESS	215 W 92ND ST #11-1	NEW YORK, NY	10025
HALL, HUNTZ	ACTOR	12512 CHANDLER BLVD #307	NORTH HOLLYWOOD, CA	91607
HALL, JAMES	GUITARIST-SONGWRITER	49 W 12TH ST	NEW YORK, NY	10011
HALL, JAMES ANDREW	TV WRITER	49 RICHMOND PARK AVE		
		BOURNEMOUTH	DORSET	ENGLAND
HALL, JAMES LEWES	MUSIC ARRANGER	8106 WIKLE RD	BRENTWOOD, TN	37027
HALL, JERRY	MODEL	2 MUNRO TERR	LONDON SW10 ODL	ENGLAND

Christensen's

ADDRESS UPDATES

● Up-To-The-Minute Information ●
● New Addresses ● Voids ● Corrections ●
● Deletions ● Refusals ● Necrology ●
● Response Reports ●

For Complete Details Write:

ADDRESS UPDATES
CARDIFF-BY-THE-SEA PUBLISHING CO.
POST OFFICE BOX 900189 ● SAN DIEGO, CA 92190

HALL, JOAN	ARTIST	155 BANK ST #H-954	NEW YORK, NY	10014
HALL, JOE	BASEBALL	CANADIANS, 4601 ONTARIO ST	VANCOUVER, BC V5V 3H4	CANADA
HALL, JOHNNY	SINGER	6750 W 75TH ST, BLDG #2-A	OVERLAND PARK, KS	66204
HALL, JOSEPH L	DIRECTOR-PRODUCER	80 THUNDER RD	HOLBROOK, NY	11741
HALL, KAREN	TV WRITER	9242 BEVERLY DR #200	BEVERLY HILLS, CA	90210
HALL, LANI	SINGER-SONGWRITER	SEE - HALL ALPERT, LANI		
HALL, LOIS	ACTRESS	KJAR, 10653 RIVERSIDE DR	TOLUCA LAKE, CA	91602
HALL, LORI	ACTRESS	1717 N HIGHLAND AVE #701	LOS ANGELES, CA	90028
HALL, MEL	BASEBALL	N Y YANKEES, YANKEE STADIUM	BRONX, NY	10451
HALL, MONTY	TV HOST	519 N ARDEN DR	BEVERLY HILLS, CA	90210
HALL, NORMAN	TV DIRECTOR	11 AMHERST RD	GREAT NECK, NY	11021
HALL, PARNELL	SCREENWRITER	555 W 57TH ST #1230	NEW YORK, NY	10019
HALL, PETER	FILM DIRECTOR	WALL HOUSE, MONGEWELL PARK		
		WALLINGFORD	BERKS	ENGLAND
HALL, PHILIP BAKER	ACTOR	5160 1/2 CLINTON ST	LOS ANGELES, CA	90004
HALL, RALPH M	U S CONGRESSMAN	104 N SAN JACINTO ST	ROCKWALL, TX	75087
HALL, RANDY	SINGER	CAA, 9830 WILSHIRE BLVD	BEVERLY HILLS, CA	90212
HALL, RHETT	FOOTBALL	BUCCANEERS, 1 BUCCANEER PL	TAMPA, FL	33607
HALL, RICH	ACT-COMED-WRI	141 S EL CAMINO DR #205	BEVERLY HILLS, CA	90212
HALL, RICHARD D	WRI-DIR-PROD	1065 PARK AVE #19-C	NEW YORK, NY	10128
HALL, ROBERT	TV DIRECTOR	3591 WINCROSS DR	MEMPHIS, TN	38119
HALL, RON	FOOTBALL	BUCCANEERS, 1 BUCCANEER PL	TAMPA, FL	33607
HALL, RUTH	ACTRESS	422 ALANDALE AVE	LOS ANGELES, CA	90036
HALL, SAM	TV WRITER	BLUMENTHAL, 488 MADISON AVE	NEW YORK, NY	10022
HALL, SANDS	ACTOR	3739 MULTIVIEW DR	LOS ANGELES, CA	90068
HALL, SUSAN	FILM PRODUCER	200 W 58TH ST	NEW YORK, NY	10019
HALL, TIM	BASEBALL	POST OFFICE BOX 20849	CHARLESTON, SC	29413
HALL, TOM T	SINGER-SONGWRITER	POST OFFICE BOX 2757	NASHVILLE, TN	37219
HALL, TONY P	U S CONGRESSMAN	501 FEDERAL BUILDING		
		200 W 2ND ST	DAYTON, OH	45402
HALL, VICTOR	CONDUCTOR	13921 BESSEMER ST #20	VAN NUYS, CA	91401
HALL, WILLIS	PLAYWRIGHT	LONDON MGT, 235-241 REGENT ST	LONDON W1R 4PH	ENGLAND
HALL & OATES	ROCK & ROCK DUO	130 W 57TH ST #2-A	NEW YORK, NY	10019
HALL ALPERT, LANI	SINGER-SONGWRITER	31930 PACIFIC COAST HWY	MALIBU, CA	90265
HALLAHAN, CHARLES	ACTOR	1975 W SILVERLAKE DR	LOS ANGELES, CA	90039
HALLAM, JOHN	ACTOR	51 LANSDOWNE GARDENS	LONDON SW8 2EL	ENGLAND
HALLBERG, GARY	GOLFER	POST OFFICE BOX 109601	PALM BCH GARDENS, FL	33418
HALLER, BILL	BASEBALL SCOUT	N Y YANKEES, YANKEE STADIUM	BRONX, NY	10451
HALLER, DANIEL	TV DIRECTOR	5364 JED SMITH RD	HIDDEN HILLS, CA	91302
HALLER, JIM	BASEBALL	5301 NW 12TH AVE	FORT LAUDERDALE, FL	33309
HALLER, KEVIN	HOCKEY	SABRES, MEMORIAL AUDITORIUM	BUFFALO, NY	14202
HALLET, JIM	GOLFER	POST OFFICE BOX 109601	PALM BCH GARDENS, FL	33418
HALLGREN, TIM	BASEBALL SCOUT	POST OFFICE BOX 90111	ARLINGTON, TX	76004
HALLICK, TOM	ACTOR	13900 TAHITI WY	MARINA DEL REY, CA	90292
HALLIER, LORI	ACTRESS	CASSELL, 843 N SYCAMORE AVE	LOS ANGELES, CA	90038
HALLIGAN, RICHARD	COMPOSER	2509 ROSCOMARE RD	LOS ANGELES, CA	90024
HALLION, TOM	BASEBALL UMPIRE	246 SAINT MATTHEWS AVE	LOUISVILLE, KY	40207
HALLORAN, JIM	BASEBALL EXECUTIVE	POST OFFICE BOX 3169	FREDERICK, MD	21701
HALLS, LEE	MAKE-UP ARTIST	786 PALMER RD #1-D	BRONXVILLE, NY	10708
HALLSTROM, HOLLY	MODEL	5750 WILSHIRE BLVD #475-W	LOS ANGELES, CA	90036
HALLSTROM, RON	FOOTBALL	PACKERS, 1265 LOMBARDI AVE	GREEN BAY, WI	54307
HALLYDAY, JOHNNY	SINGER	19 RUE VIGNON	F-75008 PARIS	FRANCE
HALMI, ROBERT, JR	TV PRODUCER-DIRECTOR	720 5TH AVE, 9TH FLOOR	NEW YORK, NY	10019
HALPER, ROBERT M	TV DIRECTOR	250 W 94TH ST	NEW YORK, NY	10025
HALPERIN, MICHAEL H	TV WRITER	3610 STONE CANYON AVE	SHERMAN OAKS, CA	91403
HALPERN, DR HOWARD	COLUMNIST	NY TIMES SYN, 130 5TH AVE	NEW YORK, NY	10011
HALSEY, BRETT	ACTOR	141 N GRAND AVE	PASADENA, CA	91103
HALSEY, JAMES	TALENT AGENT	3225 S NORWOOD AVE	TULSA, OK	74135
HALSEY, SHERMAN	TALENT AGENT	POST OFFICE BOX 4003	BEVERLY HILLS, CA	90213
HALSTEAD, BILL	BASEBALL EXECUTIVE	157 CARSON LN	BRISTOL, VA	24201
HALSTED, DANA	ACTRESS	7080 HOLLYWOOD BLVD #704	HOLLYWOOD, CA	90028
HALTER, SHANE	BASEBALL	POST OFFICE BOX 464	APPLETON, WI	54912
HALTON, PETER	ACTOR	560 GLENWOOD RD #205	GLENDALE, CA	91202
HALTON, TONY	DIRECTOR	JENNIE, 127 W 79TH ST	NEW YORK, NY	10024
HALUCHAK, MIKE	FOOTBALL COACH	POST OFFICE BOX 609609	SAN DIEGO, CA	92160
HALVORSON, GARY	TV DIRECTOR	136 LAWRENCE ST	BROOKLYN, NY	11201
HAMAGUCHI, TED TETSUO	ACTOR	5152 MARATHON ST	LOS ANGELES, CA	90038
HAMALAIN, IRENE	HAIR STYLIST	144-14 69TH RD	FLUSHING, NY	11367
HAMANN, PAUL	PRODUCER-EDITOR	BBC, KENSINGTON HOUSE		
		RICHMOND WY	LONDON W14	ENGLAND
HAMATY, EMILE	ACTOR	1914 N ALEXANDRIA AVE	LOS ANGELES, CA	90027
HAMBLEN, FRANK	BASKETBALL COACH	BRADLEY CENTER, 1001 N 4TH ST	MILWAUKEE, WI	53203
HAMBLEN, SUZY	SINGER	POST OFFICE BOX 8085	UNIVERSAL CITY, CA	91608
HAMBLETON, T EDWARD	THEATER PRODUCER	1640 BROADWAY	NEW YORK, NY	10019
HAMBLING, GERALD	FILM EDITOR	ACE, 1041 N FORMOSA AVE	WEST HOLLYWOOD, CA	90046
HAMBURG, HARRY	DIRECTOR	535 CORDOVA #122	SANTE FE, CA	87501
HAMBURGER STEW	GUITARIST	SEE - HAMMOND, HAMBURGER STEW		
HAMEL, ALAN	TV PERSONALITY	10342 MISSISSIPPI AVE	LOS ANGELES, CA	90025
HAMEL, VERONICA	ACTRESS	2121 AVE OF THE STARS #900	LOS ANGELES, CA	90067
HAMELIN, BOB	BASEBALL	POST OFFICE BOX 3665	OMAHA, NE	68103
HAMELINE, GERARD	DIRECTOR	101 5TH AVE	NEW YORK, NY	10003
HAMER, DALE	FOOTBALL REFEREE	NFL, 410 PARK AVE	NEW YORK, NY	10022
HAMERMESH, MIRA	TV WRITER-DIRECTOR	SERED FILMS, 19 HAMILTON GARDENS	LONDON NW8	ENGLAND
HAMILL, DOROTHY	SKATER	2331 CENTURY HILL	LOS ANGELES, CA	90067
HAMILL, MARK	ACTOR	POST OFFICE BOX 124	MALIBU, CA	90265

Name	Occupation	Address	City/State	Zip
HAMILTON, ALANA	ACTRESS	391 N CAROLWOOD DR	LOS ANGELES, CA	90077
HAMILTON, ALEXA	ACTRESS	STONE MANNERS, 9113 SUNSET BL	LOS ANGELES, CA	90069
HAMILTON, ANN LEWIS	TV WRITER	PLESCHETTE, 2700 N BEACHWOOD DR	LOS ANGELES, CA	90068
HAMILTON, BERNIE	ACTOR	1272 WEST BLVD	LOS ANGELES, CA	90019
HAMILTON, CARRIE	ACTRESS	2114 RIDGEMONT DR	LOS ANGELES, CA	90046
HAMILTON, CHICO, QUINTET	JAZZ QUINTET	SHAFMAN, 723 7TH AVE, 7TH FL	NEW YORK, NY	10019
HAMILTON, COLIN	ACTOR	1717 N HIGHLAND AVE #414	LOS ANGELES, CA	90028
HAMILTON, DARRELL	FOOTBALL	BRONCOS, 13655 BRONCOS PKWY	ENGLEWOOD, CO	80112
HAMILTON, DARRYL	BASEBALL	BREWERS, 201 S 46TH ST	MILWAUKEE, WI	53214
HAMILTON, DAVE	FOOTBALL REFEREE	NFL, 410 PARK AVE	NEW YORK, NY	10022
HAMILTON, DEAN	ACTOR	1100 N ALTA LOMA RD #707	LOS ANGELES, CA	90069
HAMILTON, ERIN	ACTRESS	BURNETT, 10240 CENTURY WOODS WY	LOS ANGELES, CA	90067
HAMILTON, GEORGE	ACTOR	9141 BURTON WY #3	BEVERLY HILLS, CA	90210
HAMILTON, GEORGE, IV	SINGER	POST OFFICE BOX 283	FRANKLIN, TN	37065
HAMILTON, GREG	BASEBALL	BREWERS, 201 S 46TH ST	MILWAUKEE, WI	53214
HAMILTON, GUY	FILM DIRECTOR	THE SIMKINS PARTNERSHIP		
		45-51 WHITFIELD ST	LONDON W1P 5RJ	ENGLAND
HAMILTON, HARRY	FOOTBALL	BUCCANEERS, 1 BUCCANEER PL	TAMPA, FL	33607
HAMILTON, IAIN	COMPOSER	40 PARK AVE	NEW YORK, NY	10016
HAMILTON, JAMES	SCREENWRITER	8955 BEVERLY BLVD	WEST HOLLYWOOD, CA	90048
HAMILTON, JAMIE	BASEBALL-INSTRUCTOR	BREWERS, 201 S 46TH ST	MILWAUKEE, WI	53214
HAMILTON, JEFF	BASEBALL	POST OFFICE BOX 26267	ALBUQUERQUE, NM	87125
HAMILTON, JOEY	BASEBALL	POST OFFICE BOX 20849	CHARLESTON, SC	29413
HAMILTON, JOHN A	TV PRODUCER	POST OFFICE BOX 7996	MC LEAN, VA	22106
HAMILTON, KEN	ARTIST	4511 KENNEDY BLVD	NORTH BERGEN, NJ	07047
HAMILTON, KEN	BASEBALL	POST OFFICE BOX 2887	VERO BEACH, FL	32961
HAMILTON, KIM	ACTRESS	1229 N HORN AVE	LOS ANGELES, CA	90069
HAMILTON, LEE H	U S CONGRESSMAN	1201 E 10TH ST #107	JEFFERSONVILLE, IN	47130
HAMILTON, LEIGH	ACTRESS	200 N ROBERTSON BLVD #219	BEVERLY HILLS, CA	90211
HAMILTON, LINDA	ACTRESS	8957 NORMA PL	LOS ANGELES, CA	90069
HAMILTON, LOIS	ACTRESS-MODEL	10000 RIVERSIDE DR #6	TOLUCA LAKE, CA	91602
HAMILTON, LYNN	ACTRESS	BREWIS, 12429 LAUREL TERRACE	STUDIO CITY, CA	91604
HAMILTON, MARCUS	ARTIST	12225 RANBURNE RD	CHARLOTTE, NC	28212
HAMILTON, MICHAEL	DIRECTOR	5115 FULTON AVE	SHERMAN OAKS, CA	91423
HAMILTON, MILO	SPORTSCASTER	POST OFFICE BOX 288	HOUSTON, TX	77001
HAMILTON, RICHARD, JR	COMPOSER	412 S MC CADDEN PL	LOS ANGELES, CA	90020
HAMILTON, SUZANNA	ACTRESS	MARKHAM AND FROGGATT, LTD		
		JULIAN HOUSE, 4 WINDMILL ST	LONDON W1P 1HF	ENGLAND
HAMILTON, TOM	SINGER	10 THE LEDGES RD	NEWTON, MA	02158
HAMILTON, TOM	SPORTSCASTER	INDIANS, CLEVELAND STADIUM	CLEVELAND, OH	44114
HAMILTON, TONY	ACTOR	MTA, 9320 WILSHIRE BL, 3RD FL	BEVERLY HILLS, CA	90212
HAMILTON, WILLIAM	CARTOONIST	400 W 43RD ST	NEW YORK, NY	10036
HAMLIN, BARBARA	ARTIST	3316 CALLE LA VETA	SAN CLEMENTE, CA	32672
HAMLIN, EDITH	TV PRODUCER	99-60 63RD RD	FOREST HILLS, NY	11374
HAMLIN, HARRY	ACTOR	POST OFFICE BOX 25578	LOS ANGELES, CA	90025
HAMLIN, JOANNE	ACTRESS	TALENT REPS, 20 E 53RD ST	NEW YORK, NY	10022
HAMLIN, JOHN	TV EXECUTIVE	ABC ENTERTAINMENT CENTER		
		2040 AVE OF THE STARS	LOS ANGELES, CA	90067
HAMLIN, JONAS	BASEBALL	POST OFFICE BOX 3783	SAVANNAH, GA	31414
HAMLIN, MARY JO	ARTIST	8059 HENRY CLAY BLVD	LIVERPOOL, NY	13090
HAMLISCH, MARVIN	COMPOSER-PIANIST	970 PARK AVE #65	NEW YORK, NY	10028
HAMLYN, MICHAEL	TV PRODUCER	MIDNIGHT FILMS COMPANY		
		1-2 RAMILLIES ST, 4TH FLOOR	LONDON W1V 1DF	ENGLAND
HAMM, SAM	SCREENWRITER	SMITH, 121 N SAN VICENTE BLVD	BEVERLY HILLS, CA	90211
HAMM, STACEY	BASEBALL	POST OFFICE BOX 20849	CHARLESTON, SC	29413
HAMMAKER, ATLEE	BASEBALL	2739 STUBB BLUFF RD	KNOXVILLE, TN	37932
HAMMARGREN, ROY "TUCKER"	BASEBALL	POST OFFICE BOX 4669	CHARLESTON, WV	25304
HAMMEL, PENNY	GOLFER	2750 VOLUSA AVE #B	DAYTON BEACH, FL	32114
HAMMER	RAPPER-RAPWRITER	80 SWAN WY #130	OAKLAND, CA	94621
HAMMER, ALVIN	ACTOR	8514 LOOKOUT MOUNTAIN AVE	LOS ANGELES, CA	90046
HAMMER, BEN	ACTOR	12456 VENTURA BLVD #1	STUDIO CITY, CA	91604
HAMMER, CHARLES JAY	ACTOR	311 W 83RD ST #5-A	NEW YORK, NY	10024
HAMMER, DENNIS	FILM-TV PRODUCER	DOUGLAS S CRAMER COMPANY		
		5700 WILSHIRE BLVD, 5TH FLOOR	LOS ANGELES, CA	90036
HAMMER, JAN	SINGER-SONGWRITER	120 W 44TH ST #303	NEW YORK, NY	10036
HAMMER, JAY	ACTOR	247 S BEVERLY DR #102	BEVERLY HILLS, CA	90210
HAMMER, MC	RAPPER-RAPWRITER	SEE - HAMMER		
HAMMERSCHMIDT, JOHN PAUL	U S CONGRESSMAN	POST OFFICE BOX 1624	FORT SMITH, AR	72701
HAMMETT, MIKE	ACTOR	10982 ROEBLING AVE #308	LOS ANGELES, CA	90024
HAMMIL, JOEL	WRITER	2743 ELLISON DR	BEVERLY HILLS, CA	90210
HAMMILL, COURTNEY	ACTRESS	132 S LASKY DR #B	BEVERLY HILLS, CA	90212
HAMMILL, PETER	SINGER-GUITARIST	1841 BROADWAY #411	NEW YORK, NY	10023
HAMMOND, ALBERT	SINGER-SONGWRITER	9200 SUNSET BLVD #1215	LOS ANGELES, CA	90069
HAMMOND, ALLAN	BASEBALL	POST OFFICE BOX 3783	SAVANNAH, GA	31414
HAMMOND, BILLY	ACTOR	471-C RIVERSIDE DR	BURBANK, CA	91505
HAMMOND, BOBBY	FOOTBALL COACH	POST OFFICE BOX 888	PHOENIX, AZ	85001
HAMMOND, BRUCE	CARTOONIST	UPS, 4900 MAIN ST, 9TH FLOOR	KANSAS CITY, MO	64112
HAMMOND, CHRIS	BASEBALL	REDS, 100 RIVERFRONT STADIUM	CINCINNATI, OH	45202
HAMMOND, GREG	BASEBALL	POST OFFICE BOX 4669	CHARLESTON, WV	25304
HAMMOND, HAMBURGER STEW	GUITARIST	2547 MURFREESBORO RD	NASHVILLE, TN	37217
HAMMOND, JOHN	BASKETBALL COACH	CLIPPERS, 3939 S FIGUEROA ST	LOS ANGELES, CA	90037
HAMMOND, JOHN	SINGER-GUITARIST	POST OFFICE BOX 210103	SAN FRANCISCO, CA	94121
HAMMOND, MARK	ACTOR	1253 N HAVENHURST DR #204	LOS ANGELES, CA	90046
HAMMOND, NICHOLAS	ACTOR	16413 AKRON ST	PACIFIC PALISADES, CA	90272
HAMMOND, PETER	WRITER-PRODUCER	CHATTO AND LINNIT, LTD		

Name	Occupation	Address	City/State	ZIP/Country
		PRINCE OF WALES THEATRE		
		COVENTRY ST	LONDON W1V 7FE	ENGLAND
HAMMONDS, TOM	BASKETBALL	BULLETS, 1 HARRY S TRUMAN DR	LANDOVER, MD	20785
HAMMONS, PAUL A	WRITER-PRODUCER	45 W 60TH ST #23-F	NEW YORK, NY	10023
HAMNER, EARL	TV WRITER-PRODUCER	11575 AMANDA DR	STUDIO CITY, CA	91604
HAMNER, J GARY	TV WRITER	167 1/2 S SYCAMORE AVE	LOS ANGELES, CA	90036
HAMNER, LINDA ELIN	TV WRITER	167 1/2 S SYCAMORE AVE	LOS ANGELES, CA	90036
HAMNER, ROBERT	WRITER-PRODUCER	268 S LASKY DR #304	BEVERLY HILLS, CA	90212
HAMNER, SCOTT M	TV WRITER	132 S LASKY DR #B	BEVERLY HILLS, CA	90212
HAMPSHIRE, SUSAN	ACTRESS	BILLING RD	LONDON SW10	ENGLAND
HAMPTON, ALONZO	FOOTBALL	BUCCANEERS, 1 BUCCANEER PL	TAMPA, FL	33607
HAMPTON, CHRISTOPHER	SCREENWRITER	WM MORRIS, 31-32 SOHO SQ	LONDON W1V 5DG	ENGLAND
HAMPTON, DONNIE	FOOTBALL REFEREE	NFL, 410 PARK AVE	NEW YORK, NY	10022
HAMPTON, JAMES	ACTOR-WRITER	10552 DEERING AVE	CHATSWORTH, CA	91311
HAMPTON, LIONEL	MUSICIAN	20 W 64TH ST #28-K	NEW YORK, NY	10023
HAMPTON, MARK	BASEBALL	POST OFFICE BOX 309	GASTONA, NC	28053
HAMPTON, MIKE	BASEBALL	POST OFFICE BOX 30160	SAN BERNARDINO, CA	92413
HAMPTON, ORVILLE	SCREENWRITER	1033 6TH ST #302	SANTA MONICA, CA	90403
HAMPTON, RODNEY	FOOTBALL	N Y GIANTS, GIANTS STADIUM	EAST RUTHERFORD, NJ	07073
HAMPTON, ROGER	ACTOR	321 CAMERON PL #5	GLENDALE, CA	91207
HAMPTON-CAIN, BRENDA	STORY EDITOR	R/W/G, 8428 MELROSE PL #C	LOS ANGELES, CA	90069
HAMRICK, RONNIE	ARTIST	ROUTE #3, BOX 212	SMITHS, AL	36877
HAN, MAGGIE	ACTRESS	9200 SUNSET BLVD #710	LOS ANGELES, CA	90069
HANAUER, TERRI	ACTRESS	11726 SAN VICENTE BLVD #300	LOS ANGELES, CA	90049
HANCE, WILEY F	TV PRODUCER	WNED-TV, 184 BARTON ST	BUFFALO, NY	14213
HANCER, KEVIN	SCI-FI BOOKSELLER	5813 YORK AVE S	EDINA, MN	55410
HANCOCK, ANDY	BASEBALL SCOUT	POST OFFICE BOX 2000	SAN DIEGO, CA	92112
HANCOCK, BUTCH	SINGER	ATS MGMT, 3300 HOLLYWOOD AVE	AUSTIN, TX	78722
HANCOCK, CHRIS	BASEBALL	POST OFFICE BOX 21727	SAN FRANCISCO, CA	95151
HANCOCK, HERBIE	PIANIST-COMPOSER	1250 N DOHENY DR	LOS ANGELES, CA	90069
HANCOCK, JOHN	FILM WRITER-DIRECTOR	21531 DEERPATH LN	MALIBU, CA	90265
HANCOCK, LEE	BASEBALL	POST OFFICE DRAWER 1218	ZEBULON, NC	27597
HANCOCK, LOU	ACTRESS	LIGHT, 901 BRINGHAM AVE	LOS ANGELES, CA	90049
HANCOCK, MEL	U S CONGRESSMAN	2840 E CHESTNUT EXPRESSWAY	SPRINGFIELD, MO	65802
HANCOCK, MIKE	BASEBALL	POST OFFICE BOX 8550	STOCKTON, CA	95208
HANCOCK, PRENTIS	ACTOR	JEFFREY, 118 ST JULIANS FARM RD	LONDON SE27 ORR	ENGLAND
HAND, JON	FOOTBALL	POST OFFICE BOX 535000	INDIANPOLIS, IN	46253
HANDEL, LEO	DIRECTOR	8730 SUNSET BLVD	LOS ANGELES, CA	90069
HANDEL, LYNN	TV PRODUCER	230 E 44TH ST	NEW YORK, NY	10017
HANDELMAN, DAVID	FILM EXECUTIVE	600 BONHILL RD	LOS ANGELES, CA	90049
HANDELMAN, STANLEY MYRON	ACT-WRI-COMED	5922 WOODMAN AVE #10	VAN NUYS, CA	91401
HANDEY, JACK W	TV WRITER	8314 MARMONT LN	LOS ANGELES, CA	90069
HANDLER, DAVID	DIRECTOR	15 W 84TH ST	NEW YORK, NY	10024
HANDLER, RUBY	ACTRESS	CASSELL, 843 N SYCAMORE AVE	LOS ANGELES, CA	90038
HANDLEY, DREW	DIRECTOR	6732 AMBER CT	ALTA LOMA, CA	91701
HANDLEY, GENE	BASEBALL SCOUT	1060 W ADDISON ST	CHICAGO, IL	60613
HANDLEY, RAY	FOOTBALL COACH	N Y GIANTS, GIANTS STADIUM	EAST RUTHERFORD, NJ	07073
HANDY, JAMES	ACTOR	110 W 40TH ST #2401	NEW YORK, NY	10018
HANEL, MARCUS	BASEBALL	POST OFFICE BOX 842	SALEM, VA	24153
HANEY, CHRIS	BASEBALL	EXPOS, 4545 DE COUBERTIN AVE	MONTREAL, QUE H1V 3P2	CANADA
HANEY, LARRY	BASEBALL-COACH	BREWERS, 201 S 46TH ST	MILWAUKEE, WI	53214
HANEY, LEE	BODYBUILDER	POST OFFICE BOX 491263	ATLANTA, GA	30349
HANEY, LYNN	SINGER	RUSTRON, 200 WESTMORELAND AVE	WHITE PLAINS, NY	10606
HANEY, ROGER	BASEBALL	POST OFFICE BOX 507	DURHAM, NC	27702
HANEY, SONJA	ACTRESS	10915 HESBY ST	NORTH HOLLYWOOD, CA	91601
HANEY, TODD	BASEBALL	1501 W 16TH ST	INDIANAPOLIS, IN	46202
HANICK, JACK	TV DIRECTOR	170 BROADWAY #201	NEW YORK, NY	10038
HANICK, LINDA	TV PRODUCER	170 BROADWAY #201	NEW YORK, NY	10038
HANIFAN, JIM	FOOTBALL COACH	POST OFFICE BOX 17247 (DULLES)	WASHINGTON, DC	20041
HANISCH, RON	BASEBALL TRAINER	POST OFFICE BOX 1556	ASHEVILLE, NC	28802
HANKAL, BOB	TV DIRECTOR	420 CENTRAL PARK W #5-K	NEW YORK, NY	10025
HANKIN, LARRY	ACTOR	1046 N SPAULDING AVE #8	LOS ANGELES, CA	90046
HANKINS, JAY	BASEBALL-SCOUT	POST OFFICE BOX 7575	PHILADELPHIA, PA	19101
HANKINS, MICHAEL	BASEBALL SCOUT	1000 ELYSIAN PARK DR	LOS ANGELES, CA	90012
HANKINS, MIKE	BASEBALL	POST OFFICE BOX 2148	WOODBRIDGE, VA	22193
HANKINSON, STEPHANIE	ACTRESS	14358 MAGNOLIA BLVD #130	SHERMAN OAKS, CA	91423
HANKOFF, PETER	WRITER	1316 1/2 N FORMOSA AVE	LOS ANGELES, CA	90046
HANKS, MERTON	FOOTBALL	S F 49ERS, 4949 CENTENNIAL BL	SANTA CLARA, CA	95054
HANKS, MICHAEL	CASTING DIRECTOR	11047 WESTWOOD BLVD	CULVER CITY, CA	90230
HANKS, PAUL	SINGER	MORGAN, 21 FLEETWOOD	JACKSON, OH	45640
HANKS, TOM	ACTOR	500 S BUENA VISTA ST	BURBANK, CA	91521
HANLEY, BRIDGET	ACTRESS	16671 OAK VIEW DR	ENCINO, CA	91436
HANLEY, ROBERT	ACTOR	POST OFFICE BOX 6611	BURBANK, CA	91510
HANLEY, THOMAS F, JR	WRITER	10317 MISSISSIPPI AVE	LOS ANGELES, CA	90025
HANLEY, WILLIAM	TV WRITER	WM MORRIS, 1350 AVE OF AMERICAS	NEW YORK, NY	10019
HANLON, DICK	BASEBALL SCOUT	1000 ELYSIAN PARK DR	LOS ANGELES, CA	90012
HANMER, DON	ACTOR	7414 W 85TH ST	LOS ANGELES, CA	90045
HANN, JUDITH	TV HOST	BBC-TV, 56 WOOD LN	LONDON W12 7RJ	ENGLAND
HANNA, WILLIAM	TV PRODUCER	3400 CAHUENGA BLVD	HOLLYWOOD, CA	90068
HANNAH, DARRYL	ACTRESS	COLUMBIA PLZ, PROD BLDG #8-153	BURBANK, CA	91505
HANNAH, HERMAN	BASEBALL SCOUT	S F GIANTS, CANDLESTICK PARK	SAN FRANICSCO, CA	94124
HANNAH, PAGE	ACTRESS	POST OFFICE BOX 5617	BEVERLY HILLS, CA	90213
HANNAHS, MITCH	BASEBALL	2850 W 20TH AVE	DENVER, CO	80211
HANNAM, KEN	FILM DIRECTOR	3-A MINFORD GARDENS	LONDON W14	ENGLAND
HANNAN, DAVE	HOCKEY	MAPLE LEAFS, 60 CARLTON ST	TORONTO, ONT M5B 1L1	CANADA

Name	Occupation	Address	City / Zip
HANNAWAY, DORIAN R	TV WRITER	1276 N HAYWORTH AVE	LOS ANGELES, CA 90046
HANNING, GERALDINE	ACTRESS-SINGER	11 RIVERSIDE DR #15-FW	NEW YORK, NY 10023
HANNON, PHIL	BASEBALL-INSTRUCTOR	1060 W ADDISON ST	CHICAGO, IL 60613
HANSARD, WILLIAM	DIRECTOR	2 HAVEN ST	BOSTON, MA 02118
HANSELL, GREG	BASEBALL	POST OFFICE BOX 28268	SAN ANTONIO, TX 78228
HANSELMAN, CARL	BASEBALL	POST OFFICE BOX 21727	SAN FRANCISCO, CA 95151
HANSEN, BOBBY	BASKETBALL	KINGS, 1 SPORTS PARKWAY	SACRAMENTO, CA 95834
HANSEN, BRIAN	FOOTBALL	BROWNS, 80 1ST ST	BEREA, OH 44017
HANSEN, CORI ANNE	ACTRESS	CBS-TV, "AS THE WORLD TURNS"	
		524 W 57TH ST #5330	NEW YORK, NY 10019
HANSEN, DAVE	BASEBALL	1000 ELYSIAN PARK DR	LOS ANGELES, CA 90012
HANSEN, EDWARD A	ANIMATOR	500 S BUENA VISTA ST	BURBANK, CA 91521
HANSEN, ELSTON	BASEBALL	5301 NW 12TH AVE	FORT LAUDERDALE, FL 33309
HANSEN, GUY	BASEBALL COACH	POST OFFICE BOX 419969	KANSAS CITY, MO 64141
HANSEN, JAMES V	U S CONGRESSMAN	435 E TABERNACLE	SAINT GEORGE, UT 84770
HANSEN, NINA	ACTRESS	350 W 24TH ST	NEW YORK, NY 10011
HANSEN, PETER	ACTOR	ATKINS, 303 S CRESCENT HEIGHTS	LOS ANGELES, CA 90048
HANSEN, PHIL	FOOTBALL	BILLS, 1 BILLS DR	ORCHARD PARK, NJ 14127
HANSEN, RICKIE	COSTUME DESIGNER	13949 VENTURA BLVD #309	SHERMAN OAKS, CA 91423
HANSEN, ROGER	BASEBALL-INSTRUCTOR	POST OFFICE BOX 4100	SEATTLE, WA 98104
HANSEN, RON	BASEBALL-SCOUT	N Y YANKEES, YANKEE STADIUM	BRONX, NY 10451
HANSEN, RUTH	TALENT AGENT	3500 W OLIVE AVE #1400	BURBANK, CA 91505
HANSEN, SONNY	TV DIRECTOR	POST OFFICE BOX 84	AUGUSTA, NJ 07822
HANSEN, TERREL	BASEBALL	POST OFFICE BOX 1211	NORFOLK, VA 23502
HANSON, CONNIE	SINGER	POST OFFICE BOX 4340	HOUSTON, TX 77210
HANSON, CRAIG	BASEBALL	POST OFFICE BOX 20849	CHARLESTON, SC 29413
HANSON, CURTIS LEE	WRITER-PRODUCER	21 EASTWIND ST	VENICE, CA 90291
HANSON, ERIK	BASEBALL	POST OFFICE BOX 4100	SEATTLE, WA 98104
HANSON, HOWARD	COMPOSER-CONDUCTOR	326 OAKDALE DR	ROCHESTER, NY 14618
HANSON, JAMES	DIRECTOR	SEE - HANSON, SIR JAMES	
HANSON, KRISTINE	MODEL-NEWS REPORTER	KCRA-TV, 310 10TH ST	SACRAMENTO, CA 95814
HANSON, MARCY	ACTRESS-MODEL	6605 HOLLYWOOD BLVD #220	HOLLYWOOD, CA 90028
HANSON, PRESTON	ACTOR	9328 CAYUGA AVE	SUN VALLEY, CA 91352
HANSON, ROBERT	TREASURER	STATE CAPITOL, 600 E BOULEVARD	BISMARCK, ND 58505
HANSON, SIR JAMES	DIRECTOR	180 BROMPTON RD	LONDON SW3 1HF ENGLAND
HANSON, TERRY	TV PRODUCER	4606 EBERLINE CT	STONE MOUNTAIN, GA 30083
HANSSEN, DEIRDRE	WRITER	853 N LARRABEE ST	LOS ANGELES, CA 90069
HANTAK, DICK	FOOTBALL REFEREE	NFL, 410 PARK AVE	NEW YORK, NY 10022
HANWRIGHT, JOSEPH C	FILM DIRECTOR	POST OFFICE BOX 478	KETCHUM, ID 83340
HANZLIK, BILL	BASKETBALL	POST OFFICE BOX 4658	DENVER, CO 80204
HAPPEL, ADRIAN P	TV DIRECTOR	86 HURON RD	BELLEROSE VILLAGE, NY 11001
HAPPENINGS, THE	VOCAL GROUP	BROTHERS, 141 DUNBAR AVE	FORDS, NJ 08863
HAPPER, TOM	ACTOR	1333 N STANLEY AVE #23	LOS ANGELES, CA 90046
HARA, HIDETUMI	BASEBALL	POST OFFICE BOX 4370	SALINAS, CA 93912
HARA, MARTIN	ANIMATOR	WCBS-TV, 524 W 57TH ST	NEW YORK, NY 10019
HARADA, ERNEST	ACTOR	13952 MOORPARK ST #1	SHERMAN OAKS, CA 91423
HARAZIN, ALAN	BASEBALL EXECUTIVE	METS, 126TH ST & ROOSEVELT AVE	FLUSHING, NY 11368
HARBACH, OTTO	LYRICIST	876 PARK AVE #7-N	NEW YORK, NY 10021
HARBACH, WILLIAM O	TV DIRECTOR-PRODUCER	876 PARK AVE #7-N	NEW YORK, NY 10021
HARBARTH, TED	ACTOR	6006 LA PRADA ST	LOS ANGELES, CA 90042
HARBAUGH, JIM	FOOTBALL	BEARS, 250 N WASHINGTON RD	LAKE FOREST, IL 60045
HARBERT, TED	TV EXECUTIVE	ABC-TV, 2040 AVE OF THE STARS	LOS ANGELES, CA 90067
HARBURG, EDGAR	LYRICIST	262 CENTRAL PARK W	NEW YORK, NY 10024
HARCOURT, JACK	COMPOSER	120 CARLTON AVE #48	LOS GATOS, CA 95030
HARDAWAY, TIM	BASKETBALL	GOLDEN STATE WARRIORS	
		OAKLAND COLISEUM ARENA	
		NIMITZ FWY & HEGENBERGER RD	OAKLAND, CA 94621
HARDCASTLE, PAUL	SINGER-COMPOSER	19 MANAGEMENT, LTD	
		9 DISRAELI RD	LONDON SW ENGLAND
HARDEN, BOBBY	FOOTBALL	DOLPHINS, 2269 NW 199TH ST	MIAMI, FL 33056
HARDEN, ERNEST, JR	ACTOR	1801 AVE OF THE STARS #1250	LOS ANGELES, CA 90067
HARDEN, HOWARD, JR	TV DIRECTOR	1710 MONTEREY DR	SAN BRUNO, CA 94066
HARDEN, MARCIA GAY	ACTRESS	BLOOM, 233 PARK AVE S, 10TH FL	NEW YORK, NY 10017
HARDER, JAMES	ACTOR	531 E 72ND ST	NEW YORK, NY 10021
HARDER, WILLIAM	DIRECTOR	5629 N MILWAUKEE AVE	CHICAGO, IL 60646
HARDGE, MIKE	BASEBALL	POST OFFICE BOX 6748	ROCKFORD, IL 61125
HARDIN, GUS	SINGER	CORNERSTONE MANAGMENT	
		2 BRENTWOOD COMMONS #150	
		750 OLD HICKORY BLVD	BRENTWOOD, TN 37027
HARDIN, JERRY	ACTOR	3033 VISTA CREST DR	LOS ANGELES, CA 90068
HARDIN, MELORA	ACTRESS	11726 SAN VICENTE BLVD #300	LOS ANGELES, CA 90049
HARDING, DEBORAH	TV PRODUCER	118 E 60TH ST	NEW YORK, NY 10022
HARDING, G HOMER	TREASURER	STATE CAPITOL BUILDING	PIERRE, SD 57501
HARDING, JEFF	ACTOR	MALONE, 288 MUNSTER RD	LONDON SW6 6BQ ENGLAND
HARDING, TERRY	TV DIRECTOR-PRODUCER	WOODFIELD HOUSE, TEMPLE CLOUD	AVON BS18 5BZ ENGLAND
HARDISON, KADEEM	ACTRESS	324 N BRIGHTON ST	BURBANK, CA 91506
HARDMAN, RIC	SCREENWRITER	8733 SUNSET BLVD #102	LOS ANGELES, CA 90069
HARDTKE, JASON	BASEBALL	POST OFFICE BOX 3452	KINSTON, NC 28502
HARDWICK, DICK	ACTOR	10351 SANTA MONICA BLVD #211	LOS ANGELES, CA 90025
HARDWICK, MARY	TV DIRECTOR	13745 1/2 MULHOLLAND DR	BEVERLY HILLS, CA 90210
HARDY, JEFFREY	ACTOR	CHATTO AND LINNIT, LTD	
		PRINCE OF WALES THEATRE	
		COVENTRY ST	LONDON W1V 7FE ENGLAND
HARDY, JOHN	BASEBALL	9713 N NEW RIVER CANAL RD	PLANTATION, FL 33324
HARDY, JOHN	FILM PROD-EXEC	ENTERPRISE, 113 WARDOUR ST	LONDON W1V 3TD ENGLAND

HARDY, JOHN	FOOTBALL	BEARS, 250 N WASHINGTON RD	LAKE FOREST, IL	60045
HARDY, JOSEPH	ACTOR	129 W 147TH ST	NEW YORK, NY	10039
HARDY, JOSEPH	TV DIRECTOR	CAA, 9830 WILSHIRE BLVD	BEVERLY HILLS, CA	90212
HARDY, LARRY	BASEBALL COACH	5999 E VAN BUREN ST	PHOENIX, AZ	85008
HARDY, LUCILLE	ACTRESS	PRICE, 4055 TUJUNGA BLVD	NORTH HOLLYWOOD, CA	91602
HARDY, MARK	HOCKEY	POST OFFICE BOX 90111	ARLINGTON, TX	76004
HARDY, N E	BASEBALL EXECUTIVE	SKYDOME, 300 BREMMER BL #3200	TORONTO, ONT M5V 3B3	CANADA
HARDY, PAUL	LT GOVERNOR	POST OFFICE BOX 94004	BATON ROUGE, LA	70804
HARDY, ROBERT	ACTOR	CHATTO AND LINNIT, LTD		
		PRINCE OF WALES THEATRE		
		COVENTRY ST	LONDON W1V 7FE	ENGLAND
HARDY, ROBERT	FOOTBALL	BUCCANEERS, 1 BUCCANEER PL	TAMPA, FL	33607
HARDY, SARAH	ACTRESS	9009 WONDERLAND AVE	LOS ANGELES, CA	90046
HARDY, SCOTT	TALENT AGENT	9777 WILSHIRE BLVD #707	BEVERLY HILLS, CA	90212
HARE, DAVID	WRITER-PRODUCER	RAMSAY, 14-A GOODWINS CT		
		SAINT MARTINS LN	LONDON WC2N 4LL	ENGLAND
HARE, SHAWN	BASEBALL	POST OFFICE BOX 6212	TOLEDO, OH	43614
HAREN, DENNIS	BASEBALL SCOUT	1000 ELYSIAN PARK DR	LOS ANGELES, CA	90012
HAREWOOD, DORIAN	ACTRESS	1865 HILL DR	LOS ANGELES, CA	90041
HARFORD, BILL	BASEBALL EXECUTIVE	1060 W ADDISON ST	CHICAGO, IL	60613
HARFORD, STEVE	BASEBALL-ANNOUNCER	1060 W ADDISON ST	CHICAGO, IL	60613
HARGATE, BILL	COSTUME DESIGNER	1111 N FORMOSA AVE	LOS ANGELES, CA	90046
HARGESHEIMER, AL	BASEBALL SCOUT	POST OFFICE BOX 2000	SAN DIEGO, CA	92112
HARGITAY, MARISKA	ACTRESS	9274 WARBLER WY	LOS ANGELES, CA	90069
HARGITAY, MICKEY	ACTOR	1255 N SYCAMORE AVE	LOS ANGELES, CA	90038
HARGREAVES, ALLAN	TV-RADIO PRODUCER	LONDON MGT, 235-241 REGENT ST	LONDON W1R 4PH	ENGLAND
HARGREAVES, GLENN	ARTIST	414 CORNWALL AVE	WATERLOO, IA	50702
HARGREAVES, JOHN LAWRENCE	FILM EXECUTIVE	FIDDLERS GREEN, WOOD LN	IVER HEATH, BUCKS	ENGLAND
HARGROVE, DEAN	TV WRITER-PRODUCER	705 CALLE MIRAMAR	REDONDO BEACH, CA	90277
HARGROVE, LINDA	SINGER-SONGWRITER	809 18TH AVE S	NASHVILLE, TN	37203
HARGROVE, MARION	TV WRITER	244 SHELDON AVE	SANTA CRUZ, CA	95060
HARGROVE, MAURICE DEAN	WRITER	474 HALVERN DR	LOS ANGELES, CA	90049
HARGROVE, MIKE	BASEBALL-MANAGER	INDIANS, CLEVELAND STADIUM	CLEVELAND, OH	44114
HARGROVE, PARNENEH	WRITER	1014 MANNING AVE	LOS ANGELES, CA	90024
HARIMOTO, DALE	ACTRESS	10000 RIVERSIDE DR #6	TOLUCA LAKE, CA	91602
HARING, KEITH	ARTIST	TONY SHAFRAZI GALLERY		
		163 MERCER ST	NEW YORK, NY	10012
HARKER, STEPHENIE J	ACTRESS	1139 N VISTA ST	LOS ANGELES, CA	90046
HARKER, SUSANNAH	ACTRESS	55 ASHBURNHAM GROVE, GREENWICH	LONDON SE10 8UJ	ENGLAND
HARKEY, MIKE	BASEBALL	1060 W ADDISON ST	CHICAGO, IL	60613
HARKEY, SAHRON LEE	TV DIRECTOR-PRODUCER	491 9TH ST	BROOKLYN, NY	11215
HARKIN, TOM	U S SENATOR	880 LOCUST ST #125	DUBUQUE, IA	52001
HARKINS, MICHAEL E	SECRETARY OF STATE	LEGISLATIVE HALL	DOVER, DE	19901
HARKREADER, FIDDLIN SID	FIDDLER	525 SHELBY AVE #801	NASHVILLE, TN	37206
HARLAN, BOB	FOOTBALL EXECUTIVE	PACKERS, 1265 LOMBARDI AVE	GREEN BAY, WI	54307
HARLAN, SUSAN	CARTOONIST	POST OFFICE BOX 500	WASHINGTON, DC	20044
HARLEQUIN	ROCK & ROLL GROUP	1505 W 2ND AVE #200	VANCOUVER, BC V6H 3Y4	CANADA
HARLEY, AL	BASEBALL	POST OFFICE BOX 824	BURLINGTON, IA	52601
HARLIB, MATTHEW E	DIRECTOR	ADFILM, 300 E 40TH ST	NEW YORK, NY	10016
HARLIN, RENNY	FILM DIRECTOR	8919 SUNSET BLVD	LOS ANGELES, CA	90069
HARLOW, PAT	FOOTBALL	PATRIOTS, FOXBORO STADIUM, RT #1	FOXBORO, MA	02035
HARMAN, BARRY	SCREENWRITER	11726 SAN VICENTE BLVD #300	LOS ANGELES, CA	90049
HARMES, KRIS	BASEBALL	POST OFFICE BOX 957	DUNEDIN, FL	34697
HARMETZ, ALJEAN	TV WRITER	2065 KERWOOD AVE	LOS ANGELES, CA	90025
HARMON, ANDY	FOOTBALL	EAGLES, BROAD ST & PATTISON AVE	PHILADELPHIA, PA	19148
HARMON, BRUCE	TV WRITER-NEWS CORRES	1523 N STAFFORD ST	ARLINGTON, VA	22207
HARMON, DEBORAH	ACTRESS	13243 VALLEY HEART	SHERMAN OAKS, CA	91423
HARMON, JAMES, JR	AUTHOR-PUBLISHER	POST OFFICE BOX 25	BANKS, OR	97106
HARMON, LARRY "BOZO"	FILM EXEC-CONDUCTOR	650 N BRONSON AVE	HOLLYWOOD, CA	90004
HARMON, LUCIE	ESPERANTO EXPERT	578 GRAND AVE	OAKLAND, CA	94610
HARMON, MANNY	CONDUCTOR	8350 SANTA MONICA BLVD	LOS ANGELES, CA	90069
HARMON, MARK	ACTOR	2236 ENCINITAS BLVD #A	ENCINITAS, CA	92024
HARMON, RONNIE	FOOTBALL	POST OFFICE BOX 609609	SAN DIEGO, CA	92160
HARMON, SANDRA	TV WRITER	675 CAMELOT WY #21	LOS ANGELES, CA	90002
HARMON, TOM	SPORTSCASTER	320 N GUNSTON DR	LOS ANGELES, CA	90049
HARMON, WILLIAM	ESPERANTO EXPERT	578 GRAND AVE	OAKLAND, CA	94610
HARMONICA RASCALS, THE	MUSICAL GROUP	CLOUSHER, 193 KONHAUS RD	MECHANICSBURG, PA	17055
HARMS, CARL	ACTOR	230 W END AVE	NEW YORK, NY	10023
HARNACK, JOHN	TV DIRECTOR-PRODUCER	1049 21ST ST #4	SANTA MONICA, CA	90403
HARNAGEL, JOHN	ACTOR	1595 KENSINGTON RD	SAN MARINO, CA	91108
HARNED, ALFRED	COMPOSER	3480 2ND AVE	LOS ANGELES, CA	90018
HARNELL, JOE	COMPOSER	4146 WESLIN AVE	SHERMAN OAKS, CA	91423
HARNEY, GREGORY	DIRECTOR	POST OFFICE BOX 34	LINCOLN, MA	01773
HARNISCH, PETE	BASEBALL	2 CORNFIELD LN	COMMACK, NY	11725
HARNOS, CHRISTINE	ACTRESS	ICM, 8899 BEVERLY BLVD	LOS ANGELES, CA	90048
HARNOY, OFRA	CELLIST	DOREMI, 212 E 47TH ST #30-G	NEW YORK, NY	10017
HAROUT, MAGDA	ACTRESS	13452 VOSE ST	VAN NUYS, CA	91405
HARPAZ, UDI EHUD	COMPOSER-CONDUCTOR	5541 LAUREL CANYON BLVD #11	NORTH HOLLYWOOD, CA	91607
HARPER, ALVIN	FOOTBALL	COWBOYS, 1 COWBOYS PARKWAY	IRVING, TX	75063
HARPER, BARRY	BASEBALL EXECUTIVE	N Y YANKEES, YANKEE STADIUM	BRONX, NY	10451
HARPER, BILL	BASEBALL SCOUT	POST OFFICE BOX 7575	PHILADELPHIA, PA	19101
HARPER, BRIAN	BASEBALL	TWINS, 501 CHICAGO AVE S	MINNEAPOLIS, MN	55415
HARPER, DEREK	BASKETBALL	REUNION ARENA, 777 SPORTS ST	DALLAS, TX	75207
HARPER, DIANNE	ACTRESS	7915 VAN NOORD AVE	NORTH HOLLYWOOD, CA	91605
HARPER, DWAYNE	FOOTBALL	SEAHAWKS, 11220 NE 53RD ST	KIRKLAND, WA	98033

HARPER, GERALD	ACTOR	DALZELL, 17 BROAD CT #12	LONDON WC2B 5QN	ENGLAND
HARPER, HENRY	SCREENWRITER	8955 BEVERLY BLVD	WEST HOLLYWOOD, CA	90048
HARPER, JANET	ACTRESS-MODEL	346 E 63RD ST #4-A	NEW YORK, NY	10021
HARPER, JESSICA	ACTRESS	151 S EL CAMINO DR	BEVERLY HILLS, CA	90212
HARPER, KEN	THEATER PRODUCER	165 W 46TH ST	NEW YORK, NY	10036
HARPER, LENI	ACTRESS	O'REILLY, 8 PARK PARADE	LONDON W3 9BD	ENGLAND
HARPER, NEILL S	TV DIRECTOR	4458 CARPENTER ST	STUDIO CITY, CA	91604
HARPER, RON	ACTOR	3800 BARHAM BLVD #303	LOS ANGELES, CA	90068
HARPER, RON	BASKETBALL	CLIPPERS, 3939 S FIGUEROA ST	LOS ANGELES, CA	90037
HARPER, SCOTT E	COMPOSER	717 1/2 HAYWORTH AVE	LOS ANGELES, CA	90046
HARPER, TERRY	BASEBALL-COACH	POST OFFICE BOX 16683	GREENVILLE, SC	29606
HARPER, TESS	ACTRESS	2271 BETTY LN	BEVERLY HILLS, CA	90210
HARPER, TOMMY	BASEBALL-COACH	EXPOS, 4545 DE COUBERTIN AVE	MONTREAL, QUE H1V 3P2	CANADA
HARPER, VALERIE	ACTRESS	616 N MAPLE DR	BEVERLY HILLS, CA	90210
HARPTONES, THE	VOCAL GROUP	55 W 119TH ST	NEW YORK, NY	10026
HARRAH, DOUG	BASEBALL	POST OFFICE BOX 842	SALEM, VA	24153
HARRAH, TOBY	BASEBALL-COACH	POST OFFICE BOX 90111	ARLINGTON, TX	76004
HARREL, GREG	BASEBALL TRAINER	POST OFFICE BOX 4448	TULSA, OK	74159
HARRELL, BILL & THE VIRGINIANS	BLUEGRASS GROUP	POST OFFICE BOX 186	RIVA, MD	21140
HARRELL, CINDY	ACTRESS-MODEL	3500 W OLIVE AVE #1400	BURBANK, CA	91505
HARRELL, FLYNN	BASEBALL EXECUTIVE	POST OFFICE BOX 4209	JACKSON, MS	39296
HARRELL, JANET	TV PRODUCER	30 ROCKEFELLER PLAZA #827	NEW YORK, NY	10112
HARRELL, MICHELE	ACTRESS	427 W 51ST ST	NEW YORK, NY	10019
HARRELSON, BUD	BASEBALL-MANAGER	25 FALCON DR	HAUPPAUGE, NY	11787
HARRELSON, KEN	SPORTSCASTER	333 W 35TH ST	CHICAGO, IL	60616
HARRELSON, WOODY	ACTOR	PARAMOUNT, 5555 MELROSE AVE	LOS ANGELES, CA	90038
HARRER-BUTLER, MARTHA	ACTRESS	4239 SHADYGLADE AVE #4	STUDIO CITY, CA	91604
HARRES, HOLLIE	ACTRESS	5030 TUJUNGA AVE	NORTH HOLLYWOOD, CA	91601
HARRESCHOU, MICHAEL	SCREENWRITER	8033 LOYOLA BLVD	LOS ANGELES, CA	90045
HARRIES, ANDREW	TV DIRECTOR-PRODUCER	52 BUTE GARDENS	LONDON W6 7DX	ENGLAND
HARRIES, DAVYD	ACTOR	PLANTATION COLLEGE		
		MIDDLE WINTERSLOW		
		NEAR SALISBURY	WILTS	ENGLAND
HARRIGAN-CHARLES, ELLEN	BASEBALL EXECUTIVE	POST OFFICE BOX 1088	ST CATH, ONT L2R 3BO	CANADA
HARRIMAN, FAWNE	ACTRESS	200 N ROBERTSON BLVD #219	BEVERLY HILLS, CA	90211
HARRINGER, DENNY	BASEBALL	525 NW PEACOCK BLVD	PORT SAINT LUCIE, FL	34986
HARRINGTON, CURTIS	DIRECTOR	6286 VINE WY	LOS ANGELES, CA	90028
HARRINGTON, GLENN	ARTIST	193 6TH AVE	BROOKLYN, NY	11217
HARRINGTON, JOHN	BASEBALL EXECUTIVE	FENWAY PARK, 4 YAWKEY WY	BOSTON, MA	02215
HARRINGTON, LAURA	ACTRESS	POST OFFICE BOX 5617	BEVERLY HILLS, CA	90213
HARRINGTON, PAT, JR	ACTOR-WRITER	730 MARZELLA AVE	LOS ANGELES, CA	90049
HARRIS, ALBERT	COMPOSER-CONDUCTOR	5622 ALLOTT AVE	VAN NUYS, CA	91401
HARRIS, ALFRED	TV WRITER	16633 VENTURA BLVD #1421	ENCINO, CA	91436
HARRIS, ARNIE	PRODUCER	26011 REDBLUFF ST	CALABASAS, CA	91302
HARRIS, ART	REPORTER	WASHINGTON POST NEWSPAPER		
		1150 15TH ST, NW	WASHINGTON, DC	20071
HARRIS, BARBARA	BISHOP	138 TREMONT ST	BOSTON, MA	02111
HARRIS, BILL	TV HOST-FILM CRITIC	201 N ROBERTSON BLVD #A	BEVERLY HILLS, CA	90211
HARRIS, BROOKE	WRITER	1501 PEARL ST #3	SANTA MONICA, CA	90405
HARRIS, BURTT	FILM PRODUCER	LUMET/ALLEN, 156 W 56TH ST	NEW YORK, NY	10019
HARRIS, CASSANDRA	ACTRESS	POST OFFICE BOX 9851	GLENDALE, CA	91206
HARRIS, CHARLES	TV DIRECTOR	BLAKE, 37-41 GOWER ST	LONDON WC1E 6HH	ENGLAND
HARRIS, CHICK	FOOTBALL COACH	SEAHAWKS, 11220 NE 53RD ST	KIRKLAND, WA	98033
HARRIS, CLAUDE	U S CONGRESSMAN	FEDERAL BLDG, ROOM 204	TUSCALOOSA, AL	35401
HARRIS, CRAIG W	COMPOSER-CONDUCTOR	POST OFFICE BOX 36-A-45	LOS ANGELES, CA	90036
HARRIS, DANIELLE	ACTRESS	1154 S BARRINGTON AVE #314	LOS ANGELES, CA	90049
HARRIS, DEL	BASKETBALL COACH	BRADLEY CENTER, 1001 N 4TH ST	MILWAUKEE, WI	53203
HARRIS, DENNY	FILM DIRECTOR	12152 OLYMPIC BLVD	LOS ANGELES, CA	90064
HARRIS, DONALD	BASEBALL	POST OFFICE BOX 4448	TULSA, OK	74159
HARRIS, DOUG	BASEBALL	300 STADIUM WY	DAVENPORT, FL	33837
HARRIS, ED	ACTOR	1427 N POINSETTIA PL #303	LOS ANGELES, CA	90046
HARRIS, EDDIE	SAXOPHONIST	DE LEON, 4031 PANAMA CT	PIEDMONT, CA	94611
HARRIS, ELLEN	ARTIST	352 E 85TH ST #1-D	NEW YORK, NY	10028
HARRIS, EMMYLOU	SINGER-SONGWRITER	POST OFFICE BOX 1384	BRENTWOOD, TN	37027
HARRIS, ENID	COSTUME DESIGNER	13949 VENTURA BLVD #309	SHERMAN OAKS, CA	91423
HARRIS, FRANCO	FOOTBALL	400 W NORTH AVE	OLD ALLEGHENY, PA	15212
HARRIS, GAIL	ACTRESS	6305 YUCCA ST #214	HOLLYWOOD, CA	90028
HARRIS, GENE	BASEBALL	POST OFFICE BOX 4100	SEATTLE, WA	98104
HARRIS, GLENN WALKER, JR	ACTOR	ABC-TV, "GENERAL HOSPITAL"		
		4151 PROSPECT AVE	BURBANK, CA	91523
HARRIS, GREG A	BASEBALL (RED SOX)	FENWAY PARK, 4 YAWKEY WY	BOSTON, MA	02215
HARRIS, GREG W	BASEBALL (PADRES)	RURAL ROUTE 2, BOX 290	PITTSBORO, NC	27312
HARRIS, HAROLD A	FILM EDITOR	3525 S OCEAN BLVD #401	SOUTH PALM BEACH, FL	33480
HARRIS, HARRY	TV DIRECTOR	10999 RIVERSIDE DR	NORTH HOLLYWOOD, CA	91602
HARRIS, HERB	INSTRUMENTALIST	22 W 95TH ST	NEW YORK, NY	10025
HARRIS, JACKIE	FOOTBALL	PACKERS, 1265 LOMBARDI AVE	GREEN BAY, WI	54307
HARRIS, JAMES	BASEBALL	525 NW PEACOCK BLVD	PORT SAINT LUCIE, FL	34986
HARRIS, JAMES	DIRECTOR	RINGER, 248 1/2 S LASKY DR	BEVERLY HILLS, CA	90212
HARRIS, JAY	CARTOONIST	KING FEATURES, 216 E 45TH ST	NEW YORK, NY	10017
HARRIS, JEFF	TV WRITER-DIRECTOR	R/W/G, 8428 MELROSE PL #C	LOS ANGELES, CA	90069
HARRIS, JEFFREY	COMPOSER	3955 COLDWATER CANYON AVE	STUDIO CITY, CA	91604
HARRIS, JIMMY	ARTIST	HARRIS STUDIOS, 2310 E 101ST ST	NEW YORK, NY	10029
HARRIS, JIMMY JAM	SONGWRITER-PRODUCER	FLYTE TYME PRODUCTIONS		
		4330 NICOLLET AVE	MINNEAPOLIS, MN	55409
HARRIS, JOHN S L	COMPOSER-CONDUCTOR	5428 PARADISE VALLEY RD	CALABASAS, CA	91302

Name	Occupation	Address	City	Zip/Country
HARRIS, JONATHAN	ACTOR	16830 MARMADUKE PL	ENCINO, CA	91436
HARRIS, JOSEPH	THEATER PRODUCER	15 E 48TH ST	NEW YORK, NY	10017
HARRIS, JULIE	ACTRESS	132 BARN HILL RD	WEST CHATHAM, MA	02669
HARRIS, JULIE	FASHION DESIGNER	13 PHILLIMORE GARDENS	LONDON W8	ENGLAND
HARRIS, JULIUS	ACTOR	1947 7TH AVE	NEW YORK, NY	10026
HARRIS, KIM & REGGIE	FOLK-ROCK DUO	360 CENTRAL PARK W #16-G	NEW YORK, NY	10025
HARRIS, LARA	ACTRESS	ICM, 40 W 57TH ST	NEW YORK, NY	10019
HARRIS, LENNY	BASEBALL	1000 ELYSIAN PARK DR	LOS ANGELES, CA	90012
HARRIS, LEONARD	FOOTBALL	OILERS, 6910 FANNIN ST	HOUSTON, TX	77070
HARRIS, LEONARD R	NEWSPAPER EXECUTIVE	N Y TIMES, 229 W 43RD ST	NEW YORK, NY	10036
HARRIS, LOUIS	DIRECTOR	1914 FAIRBURN AVE	LOS ANGELES, CA	90025
HARRIS, LOWELL	ACTOR	FELBER, 2126 N CAHUENGA BLVD	LOS ANGELES, CA	90068
HARRIS, MARJORIE	ACTRESS	POST OFFICE BOX 5617	BEVERLY HILLS, CA	90213
HARRIS, MARK J	SCREENWRITER	1043 POINT VIEW ST	LOS ANGELES, CA	90035
HARRIS, MEL	ACTRESS	14755 VENTURA BLVD #1-901	SHERMAN OAKS, CA	91403
HARRIS, MIKE	BASEBALL	POST OFFICE BOX 855	BELOIT, WI	53511
HARRIS, MRS JEAN	AUTHORESS	BEDFORD HILLS CORR FACILITY		
		WESTCHESTER COUNTY	BEDFORD HILLS, NY	10507
HARRIS, NEIL PATRICK	ACTOR	11350 VENTURA BLVD #206	STUDIO CITY, CA	91604
HARRIS, ODIE	FOOTBALL	BROWNS, 80 1ST ST	BEREA, OH	44017
HARRIS, PAUL	COLUMNIST	5700 WILSHIRE BLVD #120	LOS ANGELES, CA	90036
HARRIS, PETER	ACTOR	115 W 71ST ST	NEW YORK, NY	10023
HARRIS, PHIL	ORCHESTRA LEADER	49400 J F KENNEDY TRAIL	PALM DESERT, CA	92260
HARRIS, REGGIE	BASEBALL	POST OFFICE BOX 11087	TACOMA, WA	98411
HARRIS, RICHARD	ACTOR	502 PARK AVE	NEW YORK, NY	10022
HARRIS, RICHARD	TV WRITER	MLR, 200 FULHAM RD	LONDON SW10 9PN	ENGLAND
HARRIS, ROBERT	BASEBALL	POST OFFICE BOX 360007	BIRMINGHAM, AL	35236
HARRIS, ROD	FOOTBALL	EAGLES, BROAD ST & PATTISON AVE	PHILADELPHIA, PA	19148
HARRIS, RON	WRESTLER	8725 N CHAUTAUQUA BLVD	PORTLAND, OR	97217
HARRIS, ROSS	ACTOR	6542 FULCHER AVE	NORTH HOLLYWOOD, CA	91606
HARRIS, RUSTY	BASEBALL	POST OFFICE BOX 4209	JACKSON, MS	39296
HARRIS, SAM	SINGER	1253 S HAUSER BLVD	LOS ANGELES, CA	90019
HARRIS, SID	SCREENWRITER	5146 COLDWATER CANYON AVE	SHERMAN OAKS, CA	91403
HARRIS, STAN	DIRECTOR	9200 SUNSET BLVD #428	LOS ANGELES, CA	90069
HARRIS, SUSAN	ACTRESS	LYNN, 10525 STRATHMORE DR	LOS ANGELES, CA	90024
HARRIS, SUSAN	TV WRITER-PRODUCER	WITT, 846 N CAHUENGA BLVD	LOS ANGELES, CA	90038
HARRIS, TIMOTHY H	SCREENWRITER	9000 SUNSET BLVD #1200	LOS ANGELES, CA	90069
HARRIS, TRACY	ACTOR	6227 MORSE AVE #202	NORTH HOLLYWOOD, CA	91606
HARRIS, VINCE	BASEBALL	POST OFFICE BOX 1420	WICHITA, KS	67201
HARRISON, BOB	BASEBALL SCOUT	POST OFFICE BOX 2000	ANAHEIM, CA	92803
HARRISON, CATHRYN	ACTRESS	BELFRAGE, 68 SAINT JAMES'S ST	LONDON SW1A 1LE	ENGLAND
HARRISON, CLAY	TV DIRECTOR	6229 AGNES AVE	NORTH HOLLYWOOD, CA	91606
HARRISON, DIXIE	SINGER	POST OFFICE BOX 171132	NASHVILLE, TN	37217
HARRISON, GEORGE	SINGER-SONGWRITER	FRIAR PARK RD	HENLEY-ON-THAMES	ENGLAND
HARRISON, GREGORY	ACTOR-PRODUCER	3500 W OLIVE AVE #500	BURBANK, CA	91505
HARRISON, JEANNE	TV DIRECTOR-PRODUCER	200 E 50TH ST	NEW YORK, NY	10016
HARRISON, JENILEE	ACTRESS-MODEL	3800 BARHAM BLVD #303	LOS ANGELES, CA	90068
HARRISON, KEN	COMPOSER	4146 LANKERSHIM BLVD #300	NORTH HOLLYWOOD, CA	91602
HARRISON, KENNETH R	COMPOSER	6420 WILSHIRE BLVD #425	LOS ANGELES, CA	90048
HARRISON, LINDA	ACTRESS	211 N MAIN ST #A	BERLIN, MD	21811
HARRISON, LINDSAY	SCREENWRITER	151 S EL CAMINO DR	BEVERLY HILLS, CA	90212
HARRISON, MARK	ACTOR	CBS-TV, "YOUNG & THE RESTLESS"		
		7800 BEVERLY BLVD #3305	LOS ANGELES, CA	90036
HARRISON, MICHAEL	MUSICIAN	POST OFFICE BOX 9388	STANFORD, CA	94305
HARRISON, MIKE	BASEBALL	POST OFFICE BOX 4669	CHARLESTON, WV	25304
HARRISON, NOEL	ACTOR-SINGER	10100 SANTA MONICA BLVD #700	LOS ANGELES, CA	90067
HARRISON, NOLAN	FOOTBALL	RAIDERS, 332 CENTER ST	EL SEGUNDO, CA	90245
HARRISON, PAUL	TV DIRECTOR	GARDNER, 15 KENSINGTON HIGH ST	LONDON W8 5NP	ENGLAND
HARRISON, RONALD G	DIRECTOR	1201 QUEEN VICTORIA AVE	MISSISSA, ONT L5H 3H2	CANADA
HARRISON, SALLY	ACTRESS	SEE - MC LAREN, SALLY		
HARRISON, SCHAE	ACTRESS	CBS-TV, "THE BOLD & BEAUTIFUL"		
		7800 BEVERLY BLVD #3371	LOS ANGELES, CA	90036
HARRISON, TONY	TV DIRECTOR-PRODUCER	GREYSTROKE, CAVENDISH RD		
		BOWDEN, ALTRINCHAM	CHESHIRE	ENGLAND
HARRISON, WES	COMEDIAN	32500 CONCORD DR #252	MADISON HEIGHTS, MI	48071
HARRISON, WILLIAM N	SCREENWRITER	151 S EL CAMINO DR	BEVERLY HILLS, CA	90212
HARROLD, KATHRYN	ACTRESS	10390 SANTA MONICA BLVD #300	LOS ANGELES, CA	90025
HARRON, DONALD	TV HOST	POST OFFICE BOX 4700	VANCOUVER, BC V6B 4A3	CANADA
HARROW, KATHRYN	ACTRESS	155 W 68TH ST #420	NEW YORK, NY	10023
HARROW, LISA	ACTRESS	MLR, 200 FULHAM RD	LONDON SW10 9PN	ENGLAND
HARRY, DEBORAH "BLONDIE"	SINGER-ACTRESS	425 W 21ST ST	NEW YORK, NY	10011
HARRY, EMILE	FOOTBALL	CHIEFS, 1 ARROWHEAD DR	KANSAS CITY, MO	64129
HARRY, JACKEE	ACTRESS	8649 METZ PL	LOS ANGELES, CA	90069
HARRYHAUSEN, HARRY	ACTOR	2 ILLCHESTER PL		
		WEST KENSINGTON	LONDON	ENGLAND
HARSHBARGER, L SCOTT	ATTORNEY GENERAL	STATE HOUSE BUILDING	BOSTON, MA	02133
HART, AVERY	PLAYWRIGHT	MANTELL, 675 HUDSON ST	NEW YORK, NY	10014
HART, BOBBY	SINGER-SONGWRITER	1422 LA MAR AVE #614	MEMPHIS, TN	38104
HART, BRET "HIT MAN"	WRESTLER	POST OFFICE BOX 3859	STAMFORD, CT	06905
HART, BRUCE	TV WRITER-DIRECTOR	200 W 86TH ST	NEW YORK, NY	10024
HART, CAROLE	TV WRITER	ICM, 40 W 57TH ST	NEW YORK, NY	10019
HART, CECILIA	ACTRESS	5750 WILSHIRE BLVD #512	LOS ANGELES, CA	90036
HART, CHRIS	BASEBALL	POST OFFICE BOX 2437	MODESTO, CA	95351
HART, CHRISTINA	ACTRESS	DOUBLEDAY, 5061 ELMWOOD AVE	LOS ANGELES, CA	90004
HART, CHRISTOPHER	FILM WRITER-DIRECTOR	10351 SANTA MONICA BLVD #211	LOS ANGELES, CA	90025

HART, COLONEL JIMMY	WRESTLING MANAGER ..	POST OFFICE BOX 3859	STAMFORD, CT 06905
HART, COREY	SINGER-SONGWRITER ...	81 HYMUS BLVD	MONTREAL, PQ H9R 1E2 ...... CANADA
HART, DAVID	ACTOR	9255 SUNSET BLVD #515	LOS ANGELES, CA 90069
HART, DOLORES (MOTHER DOLORES)	ACTRESS	REGINA LAUDIS CONVENT	BETHLEHEM, CT 06751
HART, DON ERWIN	MUSIC ARRANGER	117 VALLEY WY DR	ANTIOCH, TN 37013
HART, DOUGLAS C	CINEMATOGRAPHER	39-21 45TH ST	SUNNYSIDE, NY 11104
HART, DUDLEY	GOLFER	POST OFFICE BOX 109601	PALM BCH GARDENS, FL 33418
HART, FREDDIE	SINGER-SONGWRITER ...	POST OFFICE BOX 11276	KANSAS CITY, MO 64119
HART, GARY	POLITICIAN	370 17TH ST, BOX 185	DENVER, CO 80201
HART, GARY	WRESTLING MANAGER ...	POST OFFICE BOX 105366	ATLANTA, GA 31348
HART, GREGORY	ACTOR-PSYCHOTHERAPIST	6 JAY ST	SPRING VALLEY, NY 10977
HART, HARVEY	DIRECTOR	5 SULTAN ST	TORONTO, ONT M5S IL6 ...... CANADA
HART, JAMES L "COLE"	CONDUCTOR	13841 COHASSET ST	VAN NUYS, CA 91405
HART, JEFFREY	COMMENTATOR	KING FEATURES, 216 E 45TH ST	NEW YORK, NY 10017
HART, JERRY "CAJUN"	SINGER	POST OFFICE BOX 532	MALIBU, CA 90265
HART, JIMMY	WRESTLING MANAGER ...	SEE - HART, COLONEL JIMMY	....
HART, JOHN	ACTOR	35109 HIGHWAY 79 #134	WARNER SPRINGS, CA 92086
HART, JOHN	BASEBALL	4395 VALLEY FORGE DR	FAIRVIEW PARK, OH 44120
HART, JOHN	BASEBALL EXECUTIVE ..	INDIANS, CLEVELAND STADIUM	CLEVELAND, OH 44114
HART, JOHN	NEWS CORRESPONDENT ..	ICM, 40 W 57TH ST	NEW YORK, NY 10019
HART, LINDA	ACTRESS (90'S)	9255 SUNSET BLVD #515	LOS ANGELES, CA 90069
HART, MARY	TV HOST	150 S EL CAMINO DR #303	BEVERLY HILLS, CA 90212
HART, MICHELE	ACTRESS	1332 N CURSON AVE	LOS ANGELES, CA 90046
HART, MIKE	BASEBALL MANAGER	POST OFFICE BOX 2148	WOODBRIDGE, VA 22193
HART, OWEN "THE ROCKET"	WRESTLER	POST OFFICE BOX 3859	STAMFORD, CT 06905
HART, RALPH	WRITER	1614 S BEVERLY GLEN BLVD	LOS ANGELES, CA 90024
HART, SHELBY	BASEBALL	POST OFFICE BOX 1295	CLINTON, IA 52733
HART, TOMMY	FOOTBALL COACH	S F 49ERS, 4949 CENTENNIAL BL ...	SANTA CLARA, CA 95054
HART, WARREN	DIRECTOR	4345 SAMOSET RD	ROYAL OAK, MI 48072
HART FOUNDATION, THE	WRESTLING TAG TEAM ..	POST OFFICE BOX 3859	STAMFORD, CT 06905
HART-WILDEN, PAUL	FILM WRITER-DIRECTOR	EAA, 84 WARDOUR ST, 1ST FLOOR ...	LONDON W1V 3LF .... ENGLAND
HARTENSTEIN, CHUCK	BASEBALL-SCOUT	6815 DE PAUL COVE	AUSTIN, TX 78723
HARTFORD, JOHN	SINGER-SONGWRITER ...	POST OFFICE BOX 40989	NASHVILLE, TN 37204
HARTGRAVES, DEAN	BASEBALL	POST OFFICE BOX 27045	TUCSON, AZ 85726
HARTL, JOHN	FILM CRITIC	POST OFFICE BOX 70	SEATTLE, WA 98111
HARTLEY, MARIETTE	ACTRESS	9744 WILSHIRE BLVD #305	BEVERLY HILLS, CA 90212
HARTLEY, MIKE	BASEBALL	1415 CASCADE PL	EL CAJON, CA 92021
HARTLEY, RICHARD	FILM-MUSIC EDITOR ...	4146 LANKERSHIM BLVD #300	NORTH HOLLYWOOD, CA 91602
HARTMAN, DAN	SINGER-SONGWRITER ...	3 E 54TH ST #1400	NEW YORK, NY 10022
HARTMAN, MIKE	HOCKEY	SABRES, MEMORIAL AUDITORIUM	BUFFALO, NY 14202
HARTMAN, PHIL	ACTOR-SCREENWRITER ..	151 S EL CAMINO DR	BEVERLY HILLS, CA 90212
HARTMAN-BLACK, LISA	ACT-SING-MOD	8037 SUNSET BLVD #2641	LOS ANGELES, CA 90046
HARTMANN, EDMUND L	TV WRITER-PRODUCER ..	1223 S ROXBURY DR #104	LOS ANGELES, CA 90035
HARTMANN, ERICH	PHOTOGRAPHER	117 W 78TH ST	NEW YORK, NY 10024
HARTOG, KATHERINE R	TV-FILM WRITER	ANGELIKA FILMS, 1974 BROADWAY ...	NEW YORK, NY 10023
HARTOS, NICO	FILM DIRECTOR	16 WICHITA AVE	ROCKWAY, NJ 07866
HARTSELL, KATHY	ACTRESS	7080 HOLLYWOOD BLVD #704	HOLLYWOOD, CA 90028
HARTSFIELD, BOB	BASEBALL-MANAGER	POST OFFICE BOX 4756	JACKSONVILLE, FL 32201
HARTSOCK, JEFF	BASEBALL	CUBS, 2ND & RIVERSIDE DR	DES MOINES, IA 50309
HARTUNG, ANDY	BASEBALL	POST OFFICE BOX 4488	WINSTON-SALEM, NC 27115
HAPTUNG, RAYMOND C	WRITER	338 N CITRUS AVE	LOS ANGELES, CA 90036
HARTZ, JIM	TV HOST	PBS, 475 L'ENFANT PLAZA	WASHINGTON, DC 20024
HARVAT, MARTY	BASEBALL SCOUT	METS, 126TH ST & ROOSEVELT AVE ..	FLUSHING, NY 11368
HARVE, HUMBLE	RADIO PERSONALITY ...	SEE - HUMBLE HARVE	....
HARVEST, RAINBOW	ACTRESS	9200 SUNSET BLVD #710	LOS ANGELES, CA 90069
HARVEY, ANTHONY	FILM DIRECTOR	REDWAY (AIM), 5 DENMARK ST	LONDON WC2H 8LP .... ENGLAND
HARVEY, BRYAN	BASEBALL	POST OFFICE BOX 2000	ANAHEIM, CA 92803
HARVEY, DOUG	BASEBALL UMPIRE	10231 VERA CRUZ CT	SAN DIEGO, CA 92124
HARVEY, GREG	BASEBALL	300 STADIUM WY	DAVENPORT, FL 33837
HARVEY, JAN	ACTRESS	169 QUEENSGATE #8-A	LONDON SW7 5EH .... ENGLAND
HARVEY, KEN	FOOTBALL	POST OFFICE BOX 888	PHOENIX, AZ 85001
HARVEY, MICHAEL	THEATER PRODUCER	1501 BROADWAY	NEW YORK, NY 10036
HARVEY, NANCY	GOLFER	2750 VOLUSA AVE #B	DAYTON BEACH, FL 32114
HARVEY, PAUL	NEWS ANALYST	1034 PARK AVE	RIVER FOREST, IL 60305
HARVEY, RAYMOND	BASEBALL	POST OFFICE BOX 3452	KINSTON, NC 28502
HARVEY, RICHARD	FOOTBALL	PATRIOTS, FOXBORO STADIUM, RT #1	FOXBORO, MA 02035
HARVEY, RODNEY	ACTOR	9057 NEMO ST #A	WEST HOLLYWOOD, CA 90069
HARVEY, SUSAN SEAMANS	COMPOSER	6258 ATOLL AVE	VAN NUYS, CA 91401
HARVIN, TEMOTHI	ACTOR	961 EASTERN PARKWAY	BROOKLYN, NY 11213
HARWELL, ERNIE	SPORTSCASTER	TIGERS, TIGER STADIUM	DETROIT, MI 48216
HARWOOD, GWEN	ACTRESS	19758 WELLS DR	WOODLAND HILLS, CA 91364
HARWOOD, JAMES	ACTOR	3 WEEHAWKEN ST	NEW YORK, NY 10014
HARWOOD, RICHARD	TV DIRECTOR	16737 KNOLLWOOD DR	GRANADA HILLS, CA 91344
HARWOOD, RONALD	TV WRITER	BERRYGROVE HOUSE, WEST LISS	HAMPSHIRE GU33 6JY .... ENGLAND
HASBURGH, PATRICK BURKE	WRITER-PRODUCER	3884 SHERWOOD PL	SHERMAN OAKS, CA 91423
HASELMAN, BILL	BASEBALL	POST OFFICE BOX 90111	ARLINGTON, TX 76004
HASELRIG, CARLTON	FOOTBALL	STEELERS, 300 STADIUM CIR	PITTSBURGH, PA 15212
HASEN, IRWIN	CARTOONIST	68 E 79TH ST	NEW YORK, NY 10021
HASKELL, DAVID	ACTOR	3500 W OLIVE AVE #1400	BURBANK, CA 91505
HASKELL, GIL	FOOTBALL COACH	RAMS, 2327 W LINCOLN BLVD	ANAHEIM, CA 92801
HASKELL, JIMMIE	COMPOSER-CONDUCTOR ..	11800 LAUGHTON WY	NORTHRIDGE, CA 91326
HASKELL, MOLLY	FILM CRITIC	VOGUE MAGAZINE, INC	....
	....	350 MADISON AVE	NEW YORK, NY 10017
HASKELL, PETER	ACTOR	19924 ACRE ST	NORTHRIDGE, CA 91324
HASKELL, SUSAN	ACTRESS	ABC-TV, "ONE LIFE TO LIVE"	....

Name	Occupation	Address	City	Zip/Country
		56 W 66TH ST	NEW YORK, NY	10023
HASLER, CURT	BASEBALL	CANADIANS, 4601 ONTARIO ST	VANCOUVER, BC V5V 3H4	CANADA
HASLEY, WILLIAM	ACTRESS-WRITER	1523 N MARTEL AVE	HOLLYWOOD, CA	90046
HASSELHOFF, DAVID	ACTOR	151 S EL CAMINO DR	BEVERLY HILLS, CA	90212
HASSETT, MARILYN	ACTRESS	8485 BRIER DR	LOS ANGELES, CA	90046
HASSEY, RON	BASEBALL	EXPOS, 4545 DE COUBERTIN AVE	MONTREAL, QUE H1V 3P2	CANADA
HASSINGER, BRAD	BASEBALL	POST OFFICE BOX 1721	SPARTANBURG, SC	29304
HASSINGER, SARA	TV DIRECTOR	328 FISHER RD	GROSSE POINTE, MI	48230
HASSO, SIGNE	ACTRESS	582 S ORANGE AVE	LOS ANGELES, CA	90036
HASTERT, J DENNIS	U S CONGRESSMAN	515 CANNON HOUSE OFFICE BLDG	WASHINGTON, DC	20515
HASTINGS, BOB	ACTOR	10000 RIVERSIDE DR #6	TOLUCA LAKE, CA	91602
HASTINGS, SCOTT	BASKETBALL	THE PALACE OF AUBURN HILLS		
		2 CHAMPIONSHIP DR	AUBURN HILLS, MI	48326
HASTY, JAMES	FOOTBALL	N Y JETS, 1000 FULTON AVE	HEMPSTEAD, NY	11550
HATCH, CHRISTOPHER	PHOTOGRAPHER	53 COOLRIDGE RD	MILFORD, CT	06460
HATCH, ORRIN G	U S SENATOR	8402 FEDERAL BUILDING	SALT LAKE CITY, UT	84138
HATCH, RICHARD	ACTOR	1930 CENTURY PARK W #403	LOS ANGELES, CA	90067
HATCHER, BILLY	BASEBALL	REDS, 100 RIVERFRONT STADIUM	CINCINNATI, OH	45202
HATCHER, CHARLES	U S CONGRESSMAN	225 PINE AVE #201	ALBANY, GA	31702
HATCHER, CHARLES CHANDLER	DIRECTOR	2187 QUAETHEM DR	CHESTERFIELD, MO	63005
HATCHER, CHRIS	BASEBALL	POST OFFICE BOX 422229	KISSIMMEE, FL	34742
HATCHER, DALE	FOOTBALL	RAMS, 2327 W LINCOLN BLVD	ANAHEIM, CA	92801
HATCHER, JEFFREY	TV EXECUTIVE	USA NETWORK, 6 W 48TH ST	NEW YORK, NY	10036
HATCHER, KEVIN	HOCKEY	JETS, 15-1430 MAROONS RD	WINNIPEG, MAN R3G OL5	CANADA
HATCHER, MICKEY	BASEBALL-COACH	720 S DOBSON RD #59	MESA, AZ	85202
HATCHER, SHIRLEY J	ACTRESS	1407 LINDEN BLVD	BROOKLYN, NY	11212
HATCHER, TERI	ACTRESS	1999 AVE OF THE STARS #2850	LOS ANGELES, CA	90067
HATFIELD, BOBBY	SINGER	1824 PORT WHEELER DR	NEWPORT BEACH, CA	92660
HATFIELD, DR FRED	BODYBUILDER	POST OFFICE BOX 222	CANOGA PARK, CA	91305
HATFIELD, FRED	BASEBALL-SCOUT	POST OFFICE BOX 2000	ANAHEIM, CA	92803
HATFIELD, HURD	ACTOR	BALLINTERRY HOUSE, RATHCORMAC	COUNTY CORK	IRELAND
HATFIELD, MARK O	U S SENATOR-AUTHOR	PIONEER COURTHOUSE, ROOM 114		
		555 SW YAMHILL	PORTLAND, OR	97201
HATHAWAY, HILLY	BASEBALL	POST OFFICE BOX 3496	DAVENPORT, IA	52808
HATOS, STEFAN	TV WRITER	1555 ALEXIS PL	BEVERLY HILLS, CA	90210
HATTEBERG, SCOTT	BASEBALL	POST OFFICE BOX 1718	NEW BRITAIN, CT	06050
HATTEN, TOM	ACTOR	1759 SUNSET PLAZA DR	LOS ANGELES, CA	90069
HATTMAN, STEPHEN	TV WRITER-PRODUCER	11660 PICTURESQUE DR	STUDIO CITY, CA	91604
HATTON, GRADY	BASEBALL-SCOUT	S F GIANTS, CANDLESTICK PARK	SAN FRANICSCO, CA	94124
HAUCK, CHARLES R	TV WRITER	4412 ELENDA ST	CULVER CITY, CA	90230
HAUCK, GREG	BASEBALL TRAINER	POST OFFICE BOX 1457	MEDFORD, OR	97501
HAUCK, TIM	FOOTBALL	PACKERS, 1265 LOMBARDI AVE	GREEN BAY, WI	54307
HAUER, RUTGER	ACTOR	151 S EL CAMINO DR	BEVERLY HILLS, CA	90212
HAUFRECT, ALAN	ACTOR-WRITER	3525 COLDWATER CANYON AVE	STUDIO CITY, CA	91604
HAUGHIAN, KEVIN	BASEBALL EXECUTIVE	POST OFFICE BOX 4370	SALINAS, CA	93912
HAUPT, DALE	FOOTBALL COACH	EAGLES, BROAD ST & PATTISON AVE	PHILADELPHIA, PA	19148
HAUSER, FAY	ACTRESS	1999 AVE OF THE STARS #2850	LOS ANGELES, CA	90067
HAUSER, RICK	WRITER-PRODUCER	6906 PACIFIC VIEW DR	LOS ANGELES, CA	90068
HAUSER, WINGS	ACTOR-DIRECTOR	279 S BEVERLY DR #708	BEVERLY HILLS, CA	90212
HAUSMAN, ROB	BASEBALL EXECUTIVE	POST OFFICE BOX 21727	SAN FRANCISCO, CA	95151
HAUSNER, JERRY	ACTOR	10100 SANTA MONICA BLVD #700	LOS ANGELES, CA	90067
HAVEL, VACLAV	PLAYWRIGHT	UDEJVICKEHO RYBNICKU 4	CS-160 00 PRAGUE 6	CZECH
HAVENS, BRAD	BASEBALL	1304 MONTROSE AVE	ROYAL OAK, MI	48073
HAVENS, RICHIE	SINGER-GUITARIST	123 W 44TH ST #11-A	NEW YORK, NY	10036
HAVENS, TOM	BASEBALL	POST OFFICE BOX 882	MADISON, WI	53701
HAVER, JUNE	ACTRESS	MAC MURRAY, 485 HALVERN DR	LOS ANGELES, CA	90049
HAVER, SALLY	COMPOSER	PARSONS SCHOOL, 66 5TH AVE	NEW YORK, NY	10011
HAVERDINK, KEVIN	FOOTBALL	SAINTS, 1500 POYDRAS ST	NEW ORLEANS, LA	90112
HAVERS, NIGEL	ACTOR	WHITEHALL, 125 GLOUCESTER RD	LONDON SW7 4TE	ENGLAND
HAVINGA, NICHOLAS, JR	TV DIRECTOR	1250 CORNING ST	LOS ANGELES, CA	90035
HAVOC, JUNE	ACTRESS	405 OLD LONG RIDGE RD	STAMFORD, CT	06903
HAWBLITZEL, RYAN	BASEBALL	POST OFFICE DRAWER 1207	ZEBULON, NC	27597
HAWERCHUK, DALE	HOCKEY	SABRES, MEMORIAL AUDITORIUM	BUFFALO, NY	14202
HAWES, TONY	WRITER-COMEDIAN	5329 TAMPA AVE	TARZANA, CA	91356
HAWK, DAVE	BODYBUILDER	POST OFFICE BOX 97007	PITTSBIRGH, PA	15229
HAWKE, ETHAN	ACTOR	CAA, 9830 WILSHIRE BLVD	BEVERLY HILLS, CA	90212
HAWKE, SIMON	SCI-FI AUTHOR	571 EMERSON ST	DENVER, CO	80218
HAWKES, CHESNEY	SINGER	CHRYSALIS, 645 MADISON AVE	NEW YORK, NY	10022
HAWKESWORTH, JOHN	TV WRITER-PRODUCER	24 COTTERSMORE GARDENS, FLAT 2	LONDON W8	ENGLAND
HAWKINS, ANDY	BASEBALL	POST OFFICE BOX 3690, STA "B"	CALGARY, ALB T2B 4M4	CANADA
HAWKINS, BILL	FOOTBALL	RAMS, 2327 W LINCOLN BLVD	ANAHEIM, CA	92801
HAWKINS, CRAWFORD	DIRECTOR	1947 FULTON AVE	VANCOUVER, BC V7V 1T2	CANADA
HAWKINS, FRED	GOLFER	PGA SENIORS, 112 T P C BLVD	PONTE VEDRA BEACH, FL	32082
HAWKINS, HERSEY	BASKETBALL	POST OFFICE BOX 25040	PHILADELPHIA, PA	19147
HAWKINS, JAY	SINGER-SONGWRITER	SEE - HAWKINS, SCREAMIN' JAY		
HAWKINS, JOE	BASEBALL TRAINER	525 NW PEACOCK BLVD	PORT SAINT LUCIE, FL	34986
HAWKINS, PETER	ACTOR	7 HARROWBY CT, HARROWBY ST	LONDON W1H 5FA	ENGLAND
HAWKINS, RICHARD R	TV WRITER	4238 RIVERTON AVE	NORTH HOLLYWOOD, CA	91602
HAWKINS, SCREAMIN' JAY	SINGER-SONGWRITER	DORN, 165 SEAMAN AVE	NEW YORK, NY	10034
HAWKINS, TIMOTHY J	TV DIRECTOR-PRODUCER	318 W 106TH ST #20RE	NEW YORK, NY	10025
HAWKINS, TOMMY	SPORTSCASTER	2445 BANYON DR	LOS ANGELES, CA	90036
HAWKINS, TRAMAINE	SINGER-ACTRESS	POST OFFICE BOX 532	MALIBU, CA	90265
HAWKINS-MILLER, SUSAN J	WRITER	6716 CLYBOURN AVE #247	NORTH HOLLYWOOD, CA	91606
HAWKS, LARRY	BASEBALL	POST OFFICE BOX 611	WATERLOO, IA	50704
HAWN, GOLDIE	ACTRESS	CAA, 9830 WILSHIRE BLVD	BEVERLY HILLS, CA	90210

Name	Occupation	Address	City	Zip/Country
HAWORTH, BARRY	DIRECTOR	355 N MAPLE ST #119	BURBANK, CA	91505
HAWORTH, EDWARD S	WRITER-PRODUCER	1500 STONE CANYON RD	LOS ANGELES, CA	90077
HAWORTH, JILL	ACTRESS	ACTORS GROUP, 157 W 57TH ST	NEW YORK, NY	10019
HAWTHORNE, NIGEL	ACTOR	5 STUD COTTAGES, BURNT FARM RD		
		CREWES HILL, ENFIELD	MIDDLESEX	ENGLAND
HAWTHORNE, TIMOTHY R	WRITER-PRODUCER	13183-A GWYNETH DR	TUSTIN, CA	92680
HAXALL, E LEE	SCREENWRITER	1940 6TH ST #B	SANTA MONICA, CA	90405
HAY, COLIN JAMES	SINGER-SONGWRITER	575 MADISON AVE #600	NEW YORK, NY	10022
HAYDEN, DAVID	BASEBALL	POST OFFICE BOX 1721	SPARTANBURG, SC	29304
HAYDEN, JEFFREY	TV DIRECTOR	10590 WILSHIRE BLVD #408	LOS ANGELES, CA	90024
HAYDEN, LINDA	ACTRESS	5 KINGS CT, HAMMERSMITH	LONDON W6	ENGLAND
HAYDEN, MELISSA	ACTRESS	CBS-TV, "THE GUIDING LIGHT"		
		222 E 44TH ST	NEW YORK, NY	10017
HAYDEN, NORA	ACTRESS	156 E 61ST ST	NEW YORK, NY	10021
HAYDEN, TOM	ASSEMBLYMAN	1337 SANTA MONICA MALL	SANTA MONICA, CA	90401
HAYDON, CHRISTOPHER	TV WRITER-DIRECTOR	10 DENMAN RD	LONDON SE15 5NP	ENGLAND
HAYDON, ETHEL L	WRITER	14277 SUNSET BLVD	PACIFIC PALISADES, CA	90272
HAYDON, TOM	WRITER-PRODUCER	POST OFFICE BOX 1608	NORTH SYDNEY NSW 2060	AUSTRALIA
HAYEK, JULIE	ACTRESS-MODEL	5645 BURNING TREE DR	LA CANADA, CA	91011
HAYERS, SIDNEY	TV DIRECTOR-PRODUCER	10451 WYTON DR	LOS ANGELES, CA	90024
HAYES, BERNADETTE	ACTRESS	7112 1/2 LA TIJERA BLVD	LOS ANGELES, CA	90045
HAYES, BILL	ACTOR	4528 BECK AVE	NORTH HOLLYWOOD, CA	91602
HAYES, BILL	BASEBALL MANAGER	POST OFFICE BOX 4488	WINSTON-SALEM, NC	27115
HAYES, BILLIE	ACTRESS	8022 SELMA AVE	LOS ANGELES, CA	90046
HAYES, BLAIR K	TV DIRECTOR	51 CLINTON AVE	RIDGEWOOD, NJ	07450
HAYES, BRIAN	TV-RADIO HOST	CHANNEL 4, 60 CHARLOTTE ST	LONDON W1	ENGLAND
HAYES, BRIAN CAMERON	WRITER	18540 PLUMMER ST #221	NORTHRIDGE, CA	91324
HAYES, BRUCE	ACTOR	7942 NAGLE AVE	NORTH HOLLYWOOD, CA	91605
HAYES, CHARLES A	U S CONGRESSMAN	8704 S CONSTANCE	CHICAGO, IL	60617
HAYES, CHARLIE	BASEBALL	N Y YANKEES, YANKEE STADIUM	BRONX, NY	10451
HAYES, DOUG, JR	WRITER-DIRECTOR	THE HAYES COMPANY		
		1227 COLDWATER CANYON DR	BEVERLY HILLS, CA	90210
HAYES, ERIC	FOOTBALL	SEAHAWKS, 11220 NE 53RD ST	KIRKLAND, WA	98033
HAYES, FRED	BASEBALL SCOUT	REDS, 100 RIVERFRONT STADIUM	CINCINNATI, OH	45202
HAYES, GLORIA	ACTRESS	145 S FAIRFAX AVE #310	LOS ANGELES, CA	90036
HAYES, HELEN	ACTRESS	235 N BROADWAY	NYACK, NY	10960
HAYES, ISAAC	SINGER-SONGWRITER	1962 SPECTRUM CIR #700	MARIETTA, GA	30067
HAYES, JACK J	COMPOSER	8111 ZITOLA TERR	MARINA DEL REY, CA	90292
HAYES, JAMES A	U S CONGRESSMAN	103 E VERMILION	LAFAYETTE, LA	70501
HAYES, JOHN MICHAEL	SCREENWRITER	503 N ALPINE DR	BEVERLY HILLS, CA	90210
HAYES, JOHNNY	RADIO PERSONALITY	KRLA, 1401 S OAK KNOLL AVE	PASADENA, CA	91109
HAYES, JONATHAN	FOOTBALL	CHIEFS, 1 ARROWHEAD DR	KANSAS CITY, MO	64129
HAYES, JONATHAN	TV EXECUTIVE	POST OFFICE BOX 10210	STAMFORD, CT	06904
HAYES, LINDA	ACTRESS	CROSBY, 670 BUSCH GARDE	PASADENA, CA	91105
HAYES, LORD ALFRED	WRESTLING ANNOUNCER	POST OFFICE BOX 3859	STAMFORD, CT	06905
HAYES, MICHAEL	FILM WRITER-DIRECTOR	5 PROPSECT TERRACE, THE ROW		ENGLAND
HAYES, MICHAEL "P S"	WRESTLER	POST OFFICE BOX 105366	ATLANTA, GA	31348
		ELHAM, CANTERBURY	KENT CT4 6UL	ENGLAND
HAYES, OTIS R, JR	COMPOSER	1731 W 84TH ST	LOS ANGELES, CA	90047
HAYES, PATRICIA	ACTRESS	20 WEST HILL RD	LONDON SW18	ENGLAND
HAYES, PETER LIND	ACTOR-COMEDIAN	3538 PUEBLO WY	LAS VEGAS, NV	89109
HAYES, SHIRLEY	ACTRESS	50 E 10TH ST	NEW YORK, NY	10003
HAYES, SUSAN SEAFORTH	ACTRESS	4528 BECK AVE	NORTH HOLLYWOOD, CA	91602
HAYES, TED	GOLFER	PGA SENIORS, 112 T P C BLVD	PONTE VEDRA BEACH, FL	32082
HAYES, TIMOTHY	TV DIRECTOR	322 E 39TH ST	NEW YORK, NY	10016
HAYES, TROAS	ACTRESS	145 S FAIRFAX AVE #310	LOS ANGELES, CA	90036
HAYES, VON	BASEBALL	POST OFFICE BOX 2000	ANAHEIM, CA	92803
HAYESON, JIMMY	ACTOR	2289 5TH AVE #12-C	NEW YORK, NY	10037
HAYGARTH, TONY	ACTOR	2 NIGHTINGALE COTTAGE		
		MARTIN'S LN, EAST PECKHAM	KENT	ENGLAND
HAYLE, FLORENCE	ACTRESS	425 E 63RD ST #E ID-44	NEW YORK, NY	10022
HAYMAN, RICHARD	COMPOSER-CONDUCTOR	1020 PARK AVE	NEW YORK, NY	10028
HAYMER, SUSAN	TV WRITER-DIRECTOR	2883 NICHOLS CANYON RD	LOS ANGELES, CA	90046
HAYMES, DICK, JR	SINGER-ACTOR	180 CENTRAL PARK S	NEW YORK, NY	10019
HAYNES, BILLY JACK	WRESTLER	POST OFFICE BOX 3859	STAMFORD, CT	06905
HAYNES, HEATH	BASEBALL	POST OFFICE BOX 6748	ROCKFORD, IL	61125
HAYNES, JIMMY	BASEBALL	POST OFFICE BOX 418	SAINT CHARLES, IL	60174
HAYNES, JOE	FOOTBALL REFEREE	NFL, 410 PARK AVE	NEW YORK, NY	10022
HAYNES, MICHAEL	FOOTBALL	FALCONS, SUWANEE RD AT I-85	SUWANEE, GA	30174
HAYNES, TIGER	ACTOR	313 W 14TH ST	NEW YORK, NY	10014
HAYNIE, HUGH	CARTOONIST	LOUISVILLE COURIER-JOURNAL		
		525 W BROADWAY	LOUISVILLE, KY	40202
HAYNIE, JIM	ACTOR	9301 WILSHIRE BLVD #312	BEVERLY HILLS, CA	90210
HAYS, BILL	TV DIRECTOR	1 CHALLONERER CRESCENT	LONDON W14	ENGLAND
HAYS, CHANTEL	SINGER	POST OFFICE BOX 171132	NASHVILLE, TN	37217
HAYS, DAVID	THEATER PRODUCER	305 GREAT NECK RD	WATERFORD, CT	06385
HAYS, JACK	BASEBALL SCOUT	TIGERS, TIGER STADIUM	DETROIT, MI	48216
HAYS, KATHRYN	ACTRESS	211 E 70TH ST #28-A	NEW YORK, NY	10021
HAYS, LEE	WRITER-PRODUCER	113 WAVERLY PL	NEW YORK, NY	10011
HAYS, ROBERT	ACTOR	9350 WILSHIRE BLVD #324	BEVERLY HILLS, CA	90212
HAYS, WILL H, JR	SCREENWRITER	208 UNION FEDERAL BUILDING	CRAWFORDSVILLE, IN	47933
HAYSBERT, DENNIS	ACTOR	3624 CANYON CREST RD	ALTADENA, CA	91001
HAYWARD, ANN STEWART	WRITER-PRODUCER	3838 S GIBRALTER AVE	LOS ANGELES, CA	90008
HAYWARD, CHRISTOPHER	TV WRITER-PRODUCER	12546 THE VISTA	LOS ANGELES, CA	90049
HAYWARD, CHUCK	DIRECTOR	9030 WHEATLAND AVE	SUN VALLEY, CA	91352

Name	Occupation	Address	City
HAYWARD, DAVID	ACTOR	301 N CANON DR #305	BEVERLY HILLS, CA 90210
HAYWARD, DAVID W	MUSICIAN	2813 S TOPANGA CANYON BLVD	MALIBU, CA 90265
HAYWARD, HENRY	ACTOR	MMG ENTS, 250 W 57TH ST	NEW YORK, NY 10107
HAYWARD, MICHAEL	DIRECTOR	3308 TICA DR	LOS ANGELES, CA 90027
HAYWARD, WILLIAM L	WRITER	8855 SAINT IVES DR	LOS ANGELES, CA 90069
HAYWIRE	ROCK & ROLL GROUP	41 BRITAIN ST #200	TORONTO, ONT M5A 1R7 CANADA
HAYWORTH, JEAN OWENS	ACTRESS	4645 ETHEL AVE	VAN NUYS, CA 91423
HAYWORTH, TRACY	FOOTBALL	LIONS, 1200 FEATHERSTONE RD	PONTIAC, MI 48432
HAZARD, RICHARD	COMPOSER	657 PERUGIA WY	LOS ANGELES, CA 90077
HAZARD, ROBERT	SINGER	ICM, 40 W 57TH ST	NEW YORK, NY 10019
HAZELTINE, JOYCE	SECRETARY OF STATE	STATE CAPITOL BUILDING	PIERRE, SD 57501
HAZLETT, STEVE	BASEBALL	POST OFFICE BOX 661	KENOSHA, WI 53141
HEABERLIN, LARRY	SINGER	POST OFFICE BOX 405-A	EDON, MO 65026
HEAD, GARY	ARTIST	3432 GILLHAM RD #13	KANSAS CITY, MO 64111
HEAD, MARSHALL	DIRECTOR	1763 CULVER LN	GLENVIEW, IL 60025
HEAD, MURRAY	SINGER	167-170 WARDOUR ST	LONDON W1 ENGLAND
HEAD, ROY	SINGER-SONGWRITER	HUGH DANCY, 3095 HWY 301 N	LAKE CORNORANT, MS 38641
HEAD EAST	ROCK & ROLL GROUP	10350 SANTA MONICA BLVD #210	LOS ANGELES, CA 90025
HEADLEY, GLENNE	ACTRESS	7929 HOLLYWOOD BLVD	LOS ANGELES, CA 90046
HEADLEY, SHARI	ACTRESS	ABC-TV, "ALL MY CHILDREN"	
		320 W 66TH ST	NEW YORK, NY 10023
HEADLY, GLENNE	ACTRESS	ICM, 8899 BEVERLY BLVD	LOS ANGELES, CA 90048
HEADY, ROBERT K	COLUMNIST	TRIBUNE, 64 E CONCORD ST	ORLANDO, FL 32801
HEAFNER, CAROLYN	SOPRANO	1199 PARK AVE #1-E	NEW YORK, NY 10028
HEALEY, JAMES R	COLUMNIST	POST OFFICE BOX 500	WASHINGTON, DC 20044
HEALEY, MARY	ACTRESS	PETERS, FRASER & DUNLOP, LTD	
		5TH FLOOR, THE CHAMBERS	
		CHELSEA HARBOUR, LOT RD	LONDON SW10 OXF ENGLAND
HEALEY, MIKE	TV WRITER-DIRECTOR	25 KNUTSFORD RD, WILMSLOW	CHESHIRE ENGLAND
HEALEY, MYRON D	ACTOR-WRITER	1461 2ND ST	SISNA, CA 93065
HEALIS, SUSAN	ACTRESS	12007 BURGESS AVE	WHITTIER, CA 90604
HEALY, CHRISTINE	ACTRESS	192 LEXINGTON AVE #1204	NEW YORK, NY 10016
HEALY, DEBORAH	ARTIST	72 WATCHUNG AVE	UPPER MONTCLAIR, NJ 07043
HEALY, FRAN	SPORTSCASTER	METS, 126TH ST & ROOSEVELT AVE	FLUSHING, NY 11368
HEALY, MARY	SINGER-ACTRESS	3538 PUEBLO WY	LAS VEGAS, NV 89109
HEALY, PATTY	ACTRESS	POST OFFICE BOX 69590	LOS ANGELES, CA 90069
HEALY, REV TIMOTHY S	EDUCATOR-AUTHOR	GEORGETOWN UNIVERSITY	
		DEPARTMENT OF ENGLISH	
		37TH & "O" STS, NW	WASHINGTON, DC 20008
HEALY, TIM	ACTOR	BROWNE, 13 SAINT MARTINS RD	LONDON SW9 OSP ENGLAND
HEARD, GAR	BASKETBALL COACH	REUNION ARENA, 777 SPORTS ST	DALLAS, TX 75207
HEARD, JOHN	ACTOR	347 W 84TH ST #5	NEW YORK, NY 10024
HEARD, KATHERINE	ACTRESS	9057 NEMO ST #A	WEST HOLLYWOOD, CA 90069
HEARN, CHICK	SPORTSCASTER	POST OFFICE BOX 10	INGLEWOOD, CA 90306
HEARN, ED	BASEBALL	12458 CRAIG	OVERLAND PARK, KS 66213
HEARNS, TOMMY	BOXER	19785 W 12 MILE RD	SOUTHFIELD, MI 48076
HEARSHEN, IRA P	COMPOSER-CONDUCTOR	8723 1/2 CEDROS AVE	PANORAMA CITY, CA 91402
HEARST, KEVIN	ACTOR	9715 HENSAL RD	BEVERLY HILLS, CA 90210
HEARST, RICK	ACTOR	CBS-TV, "THE GUIDING LIGHT"	
		222 E 44TH ST	NEW YORK, NY 10017
HEARST, STEPHEN	TV WRITER-DIRECTOR	78 ELM PARK, STANMORE	MIDDLESEX ENGLAND
HEARST SHAW, PATRICIA	AUTHORESS-ACTRESS	110 5TH ST	SAN FRANCISCO, CA 94103
HEART	ROCK & ROLL GROUP	6300 S CENTER BLVD #200	SEATTLE, WA 98188
HEARTFIXERS, THE	BLUES BAND	450 14TH ST #201, NW	ATLANTA, GA 30318
HEASLEY, MARLA	ACTRESS	8730 SUNSET BLVD #220-W	LOS ANGELES, CA 90069
HEASTON, TRACY MATTHEW	COMPOSER-CONDUCTOR	POST OFFICE BOX 3316	ONTARIO, CA 91761
HEATERS, THE	ROCK & ROLL GROUP	K P PRODS, 132 N DOHENY DR	LOS ANGELES, CA 90048
HEATH, JIMMY	SAXOPHONIST	112-19 34TH AVE	CORONA, NY 11368
HEATH, JIMMY, QUARTET	JAZZ QUARTET	KURLAND, 173 BRIGHTON AVE	BOSTON, MA 02134
HEATH, KELLY	BASEBALL COACH	POST OFFICE BOX 15050	READING, PA 19612
HEATH, LEE	BASEBALL	POST OFFICE BOX 507	DURHAM, NC 27702
HEATH, LEONARD LAWRENCE	TV WRITER	151 TIGERTAIL RD	LOS ANGELES, CA 90049
HEATH, MIKE	BASEBALL	12137 FRUITLAND DR	RIVERVIEW, FL 33569
HEATH, PETER GRAEME	DIRECTOR	DGA, 110 W 57TH ST	NEW YORK, NY 10019
HEATH, ROBERT	WRITER-PRODUCER	POST OFFICE BOX 5373	NORTH HOLLYWOOD, CA 91616
HEATON, NEAL	BASEBALL	POST OFFICE BOX 419969	KANSAS CITY, MO 64141
HEATTER, MERRILL	TV WRITER-PRODUCER	1011 N ROXBURY DR	BEVERLY HILLS, CA 90210
HEATWOLE, LUTHER	MUSIC ARRANGER	2000 TYNE BLVD	NASHVILLE, TN 37215
HEAVEN, SIMON	DIRECTOR-PRODUCER	COMPASS FILM PRODUCTIONS	
		18-19 WARWICK ST, 3RD FLOOR	LONDON W1R 5RB ENGLAND
HEBERLEIN, JULIE	ACTRESS	NORMAN REICH, 65 W 55TH ST	NEW YORK, NY 10019
HEBERT, BOBBY	FOOTBALL	SAINTS, 1500 POYDRAS ST	NEW ORLEANS, LA 90112
HEBERT, GLENN	SINGER	312 W LEE ETTA	GALLATIN, TN 37066
HEBERT, PAUL	COMPOSER	13860 MAGNOLIA BLVD	SHERMAN OAKS, CA 91423
HEBERT, RICH	ACTOR	315 W 14TH ST #1-B	NEW YORK, NY 10014
HEBLE, KURT	BASEBALL	POST OFFICE BOX 1110	MYRTLE BEACH, SC 29578
HEBNER, RICHIE	BASEBALL-COACH	FENWAY PARK, 4 YAWKEY WY	BOSTON, MA 02215
HECHLER, KEN	SECRETARY OF STATE	STATE CAPITOL BUILDING	CHARLESTON, WV 25305
HECHT, ALBERT D	TV DIRECTOR-PRODUCER	24 HUTTON AVE	WEST ORANGE, NJ 07052
HECHT, DANIEL	GUIATRIST	POST OFFICE BOX 9388	STANFORD, CA 94305
HECHT, GINA	ACTRESS	5930 FOOTHILL DR	LOS ANGELES, CA 90068
HECHT, KEN	TV PRODUCER	EMBASSY-TV, 1438 N GOWER ST	LOS ANGELES, CA 90028
HECHT, PAUL	ACTOR	192 LEXINGTON AVE #1204	NEW YORK, NY 10016
HECHT, STEVE	BASEBALL	POST OFFICE BOX 15757	HARRISBURG, PA 17105
HECK, ANDY	FOOTBALL	SEAHAWKS, 11220 NE 53RD ST	KIRKLAND, WA 98033

HECKART, EILEEN	ACTRESS	135 COMSTOCK HILL RD	NEW CANAAN, CT	06840
HECKER, BARRY	BASKETBALL	CLIPPERS, 3939 S FIGUEROA ST	LOS ANGELES, CA	90037
HECKER, JULIE M	NEWS CORRESPONDENT	ABC NEWS, 1717 DE SALES ST, NW	WASHINGTON, DC	20036
HECKER, ROBERT L	TV WRITER	14697 DEERVALE PL	SHERMAN OAKS, CA	91403
HECKERLING, AMY	FILM WRITER-DIRECTOR	1330 SCHUYLER RD	BEVERLY HILLS, CA	90210
HECKMAN, DONALD J	WRITER	210 N PASS AVE #206	BURBANK, CA	91505
HECTOR, JOHNNY	FOOTBALL	N Y JETS, 1000 FULTON AVE	HEMPSTEAD, NY	11550
HEDAYA, DAN	ACTOR	2101 N BEACHWOOD DR	HOLLYWOOD, CA	90068
HEDDEN, ROBERT	WRI-DIR-PROD	9200 SUNSET BLVD #402	LOS ANGELES, CA	90069
HEDGECOCK, ROGER	RADIO PERSONALITY	KSDO-AM, 3180 UNIVERSITY AVE	SAN DIEGO, CA	92104
HEDGES, MICHAEL	GUITARIST	POST OFFICE BOX 9388	STANFORD, CA	94305
HEDISON, DAVID	ACTOR	2940 TRUDY DR	BEVERLY HILLS, CA	90210
HEDLEY, JACK	ACTOR	HAMPER, 4 GREAT QUEEN ST	LONDON WC2B 5DG	ENGLAND
HEDLEY, THOMAS JOHN	SCREENWRITER	NANAS, 9454 WILSHIRE BLVD	BEVERLY HILLS, CA	90212
HEDREN, TIPPI	ACTRESS	1006 FALLEN LEAF RRD	ARCADIA, CA	91006
HEELEY, DAVID E	TV DIRECTOR	31 W 31ST ST	NEW YORK, NY	10001
HEELS, DAVE	WRI-DIR-PROD	40 HAINAULT AVE, GIFFARD PARK	MILTON KEYNES MK14 5PA	ENGLAND
HEENAN, BOBBY "THE BRAIN"	WRESTLING MANAGER	POST OFFICE BOX 3859	STAMFORD, CT	06905
HEEP, DANNY	BASEBALL	327 TEAKWOOD LN	SAN ANTONIO, TX	78216
HEFFER, RICHARD ELLIOTT	ACTOR	CDA, 45-47 COURTFIELD RD #20	LONDON SW7	ENGLAND
HEFFERMAN, BERT	BASEBALL	POST OFFICE BOX 3690, STA "B"	CALGARY, ALB T2B 4M4	CANADA
HEFFERNAN, GREGORY	WRITER	5210 CALLE DE ARBOLES	TORRANCE, CA	90505
HEFFLEY, ROY	NEWS CORRESPONDENT	ABC NEWS, 1717 DE SALES ST, NW	WASHINGTON, DC	20036
HEFFLEY, WAYNE	ACTOR	245 N GRAMERCY PL	LOS ANGELES, CA	90004
HEFFNER, KYLE T	ACTOR	LIGHT, 901 BRINGHAM AVE	LOS ANGELES, CA	90049
HEFFNER, RICHARD D	TV HOST-PRODUCER	90 RIVERSIDE DR	NEW YORK, NY	10024
HEFFRON, RICHARD	FILM DIRECTOR	31712 BROAD BEACH RD	MALIBU, CA	90265
HEFLEY, JOEL	U S CONGRESSMAN	2190-A VICKERS DR	COLORADO SPRINGS, CO	80907
HEFLIN, FRANCES	ACTRESS	10 E 44TH ST #700	NEW YORK, NY	10017
HEFLIN, HOWELL	U S SENATOR	POST OFFICE BOX 228	TUSCUMBIA, AL	35674
HEFLIN, MARTA	ACTRESS	340 W 55TH ST #1-A	NEW YORK, NY	10019
HEFNER, CHRISTIE	PUBLISHING EXECUTIVE	10236 CHARING CROSS RD	LOS ANGELES, CA	90024
HEFNER, HUGH	PUBLISHING EXECUTIVE	10236 CHARING CROSS RD	LOS ANGELES, CA	90024
HEFNER, W G "BILL"	U S CONGRESSMAN	POST OFFICE BOX 385	CONCORD, NC	28026
HEFTER, SAM	WRITER	341 N ALTA VISTA BLVD	LOS ANGELES, CA	90036
HEFTI, NEAL	COMPOSER	9454 WILSHIRE BLVD #405	BEVERLY HILLS, CA	90212
HEGAN, MIKE	BASEBALL-ANNOUNCER	INDIANS, CLEVELAND STADIUM	CLEVELAND, OH	44114
HEGARTY, SUSAN	ACTRESS	BREWIS, 12429 LAUREL TERRACE	STUDIO CITY, CA	91604
HEGIRA, ANNE	ACTRESS	20 COMMERCE ST	NEW YORK, NY	10014
HEGMAN, BOB	BASEBALL SCOUT	POST OFFICE BOX 419969	KANSAS CITY, MO	64141
HEGYES, ROBERT	ACTOR-DIRECTOR	1930 CENTURY PARK W #403	LOS ANGELES, CA	90067
HEHORN, LANNY	ACTOR	5848 ROLLING RD	WOODLAND HILLS, CA	91367
HEIDEN, BETH	SKATER	3505 BLACKHAWK DR	MADISON, WI	53705
HEIDEN, ERIC	SKATER	3505 BLACKHAWK DR	MADISON, WI	53705
HEIDEN-DRYER, JANICE	ACTRESS	16140 MOORPARK ST	ENCINO, CA	91436
HEIDER, LAWRENCE	CINEMATOGRAPHER	7715 SUNSET BLVD #150	LOS ANGELES, CA	90046
HEIFFERON, MIKE	BASEBALL TRAINER	1155 W MOUND ST	COLUMBUS, OH	43223
HEIGH, HELENE	ACTRESS	1836 1/2 N EDGEMONT ST	HOLLYWOOD, CA	90027
HEIGHLEY, BRUCE	ACTOR	18646 COLLINS ST #3	TARZANA, CA	91356
HEIKIN, NANCY	ACTRESS	91 CHRISTOPHER ST	NEW YORK, NY	10014
HEILBRON, LORNA	ACTRESS	LADKIN, 11 SOUTHWICK MEWS	LONDON W2 1JG	ENGLAND
HEILBUT, FRANCIS	PIANIST-CONDUCTOR	GRIGGS, 685 W END AVE	NEW YORK, NY	10025
HEILIG, MORTON L	WRITER-PRODUCER	855 GALLOWAY ST	PACIFIC PALISADES, CA	90272
HEILMAN, PETE	BASEBALL EXECUTIVE	POST OFFICE BOX 418	SAINT CHARLES, IL	60174
HEILMAN, RON	COSTUME DESIGNER	13949 VENTURA BLVD #309	SHERMAN OAKS, CA	91423
HEIM, PAULA M	ACTRESS	15870 SILVER STAR LN	CANYON CITY, CA	91351
HEIMAN, JUDITH	SCREENWRITER	ABACAB, 123 W 44TH ST	NEW YORK, NY	10036
HEIMANN, BETSY	COSTUME DESIGNER	13949 VENTURA BLVD #309	SHERMAN OAKS, CA	91423
HEIMANN, RICHARD G	DIRECTOR	3 E 63RD ST	NEW YORK, NY	10021
HEIMER, GREGORY W	DIRECTOR	10510 SEABURY LN	LOS ANGELES, CA	90077
HEIMUELLER, GORMAN	BASEBALL-COACH	POST OFFICE BOX 1659	PORTLAND, OR	97207
HEINDEL, ROBERT	ARTIST	140 BANKS RD	EASTON, CT	06612
HEINDORF, MICHAEL	COMPOSER	2111 N CAHUENGA BLVD #9	LOS ANGELES, CA	90068
HEINE, GEORGETTE	CASTING DIRECTOR	245 E 72ND ST #11-E	NEW YORK, NY	10021
HEINEMAN, LAURIE	ACTRESS	180 RIVERSIDE DR #14-B	NEW YORK, NY	10024
HEINEMANN, ARTHUR	TV WRITER	3606 MANDEVILLE CANYON RD	LOS ANGELES, CA	90049
HEINEMANN, GEORGE A	TV DIRECTOR-PRODUCER	SHOWMAKERS, 454 W 46TH ST	NEW YORK, NY	10036
HEINEY, PAUL	TV-RADIO HOST	GURNETT, 2 NEW KINGS RD	LONDON SW6 4SA	ENGLAND
HEINKEL, DON	BASEBALL	1012 SHERATON DR	RACINE, WI	53402
HEINSOHN, TOMMY	BASKETBALL	WFXT-TV, 100 2ND AVE	NEEDHAM, MA	02194
HEINZ, CHARLES D	TV DIRECTOR	21 BRYAN DR	MONTVALE, NJ	07645
HEINZ, JUDITH	ACTRESS	8831 SUNSET BLVD #402	LOS ANGELES, CA	90069
HEINZ, JUDY	ACTRESS	525 S ARDMORE AVE #310	LOS ANGELES, CA	90020
HEISLER, HAROLD J	DIRECTOR	2044 HOLMBY AVE	LOS ANGELES, CA	90025
HEIST, AL	BASEBALL-SCOUT	S F GIANTS, CANDLESTICK PARK	SAN FRANICSCO, CA	94124
HEJBAL, FRANK	COMPOSER	POST OFFICE BOX 61-1521	NORTH MIAMI, FL	33161
HELBERG, SANDY	ACTOR-WRITER	8412 CARLTON WY	LOS ANGELES, CA	90069
HELBURN, WILLIAM D	DIRECTOR	161 E 35TH ST	NEW YORK, NY	10016
HELD, CARL	ACTOR	1817 HILLCREST RD #51	HOLLYWOOD, CA	90068
HELFAND, ERIC	BASEBALL	POST OFFICE BOX 2437	MODESTO, CA	95351
HELFER, BRITT	ACTRESS	OSCARD, 24 W 40TH ST, 17TH FL	NEW YORK, NY	10011
HELFER, RALPH D	WRITER-PRODUCER	15840 CEDARFORT DR	SAUGUS, CA	91350
HELFGOTT, DANIEL	WRITER-PRODUCER	12151 LA MAIDA ST	NORTH HOLLYWOOD, CA	91607
HELGENBERGER, MARG	ACTRESS	POST OFFICE BOX 5617	BEVERLY HILLS, CA	90213
HELIOS CREED	ROCK & ROLL GROUP	SUBTERRANEAN RECORDS		

		577 VALENCIA ST	SAN FRANCISCO, CA 94110
HELIX	ROCK & ROLL GROUP	POST OFFICE BOX 577	WATERLOO, ONT N2J 4B8 CANADA
HELLENTHAL, ALBERT W	WRITER-PRODUCER	1256 EL SUR WY	SACRAMENTO, CA 95825
HELLER, ART	TV PRODUCER	SUNBOW, 130 5TH AVE, 3RD FL	NEW YORK, NY 10011
HELLER, BARBARA	TV WRITER	1541 N VINE ST	HOLLYWOOD, CA 90028
HELLER, DANIEL	TALENT AGENT	8235 SANTA MONICA BLVD #302	LOS ANGELES, CA 90046
HELLER, FRANKLIN M	TV DIRECTOR	1364 ROCKRIMMON RD	STAMFORD, CT 06903
HELLER, JOEL	TV DIRECTOR-PRODUCER	CBS-TV, 524 W 57TH ST	NEW YORK, NY 10019
HELLER, JOHN M	TV DIRECTOR	DESIGN TV, 225 W 44TH ST, 3RD FL	NEW YORK, NY 10036
HELLER, KEN	COMPOSER-CONDUCTOR	8993 WONDERLAND AVE	LOS ANGELES, CA 90046
HELLER, LEON	SCREENWRITER	8955 BEVERLY BLVD	WEST HOLLYWOOD, CA 90048
HELLER, PAUL	DIRECTOR-PRODUCER	1666 N BEVERLY DR	BEVERLY HILLS, CA 90210
HELLER, RANDEE	ACTRESS	606 N LARCHMONT BLVD #309	LOS ANGELES, CA 90004
HELLER, ROB	TALENT AGENT	ICM, 8899 BEVERLY BLVD	LOS ANGELES, CA 90048
HELLER, RON	FOOTBALL	EAGLES, BROAD ST & PATTISON AVE	PHILADELPHIA, PA 19148
HELLERMAN, FRED	SINGER	83 GOODHILL RD	WESTON, CT 06880
HELLESTRAE, DALE	FOOTBALL	COWBOYS, 1 COWBOYS PARKWAY	IRVING, TX 75063
HELLHAMMER	ROCK & ROLL GROUP	POST OFFICE BOX 2896	TORRANCE, CA 90509
HELLINGS, SARAH	DIRECTOR	PETERS, FRASER & DUNLOP, LTD	
		5TH FLOOR, THE CHAMBERS	
		CHELSEA HARBOUR, LOT RD	LONDON SW10 OXF ENGLAND
HELLMAN, JEROME R	DIRECTOR-PRODUCER	68 MALIBU COLONY DR	MALIBU, CA 90265
HELLMAN, MONTE	WRITER-PRODUCER	8588 APPIAN WY	LOS ANGELES, CA 90046
HELLOWEEN	ROCK & ROLL GROUP	IRD, 149-03 GUY R BREWER BLVD	JAMAICA, NY 11434
HELLSTROM, GUNNAR	TV DIRECTOR	10816 3/4 LINDBROOK DR	LOS ANGELES, CA 90024
HELLWIG, JIM	WRESTLER	SEE - ULTIMATE WARRIOR, THE	
HELM, DICK	BASKETBALL COACH	POST OFFICE BOX 5000	RICHFIELD, OH 44286
HELM, FRANCES	ACTRESS	55 CENTRAL PARK W	NEW YORK, NY 10023
HELM, LEVON	ACTOR	192 LEXINGTON AVE #1204	NEW YORK, NY 10016
HELM, LEVON & THE ALL STARS	ROCK & ROLL GROUP	AMERICAN FAMOUS TALENT CORP	
		816 W EVERGREEN AVE	CHICAGO, IL 60622
HELM, PETER J	ACTOR	5424 COLFAX AVE	NORTH HOLLYWOOD, CA 91601
HELMAN, GEOFFREY	TV PRODUCER	9-D LOGAN PL, KENSINGTON	LONDON W8 6QN ENGLAND
HELMICK, PAUL A	DIRECTOR	10333 ODESSA AVE	GRANADA HILLS, CA 91344
HELMINIAK, MARK	BASEBALL EXECUTIVE	POST OFFICE BOX 1659	PORTLAND, OR 97207
HELMOND, KATHERINE	ACTRESS-DIRECTOR	2035 DAVIES WY	LOS ANGELES, CA 90046
HELMS, BOBBY	SINGER	POST OFFICE BOX 4357	MARIETTA, GA 30065
HELMS, JESSE	U S SENATOR	1513 CASWELL ST	RALEIGH, NC 27608
HELMS, TOMMY, JR	BASEBALL (MINORS)	POST OFFICE BOX 4370	SALINAS, CA 93912
HELMSLEY, HARRY & LEONA	HOTEL OWNERS	PARK LANE, 36 CENTRAL PARK S	NEW YORK, NY 10019
HELNWEIN, GOTTFRIED	ARTIST	SCHLOSS BURT BROHL	
		AUS DER BURG	BURT BROHL D-5475 GERMANY
HELOISE	CONSUMER ADVISER	KING FEATURES, 216 E 45TH ST	NEW YORK, NY 10017
HELSING, RALLI	ACTOR	310 W 93RD ST	NEW YORK, NY 10025
HELSTAR	ROCK & ROLL GROUP	POST OFFICE BOX 9217	HOUSTON, TX 77261
HELTON, KEITH	BASEBALL	POST OFFICE BOX 4756	JACKSONVILLE, FL 32201
HELTON, KIM	FOOTBALL COACH	RAIDERS, 332 CENTER ST	EL SEGUNDO, CA 90245
HELVIN, MARIE	ACTRESS-MODEL	IMG, 23 EYOT GARDENS	LONDON W6 9TN ENGLAND
HEMINGWAY, MARGAUX	ACTRESS-MODEL	9454 WILSHIRE BLVD #PH	BEVERLY HILLS, CA 90212
HEMINGWAY, MARIEL	ACTRESS-PRODUCER	POST OFFICE BOX 2249	KETCHUM, ID 83340
HEMION, MAC	DIRECTOR	POST OFFICE BOX 703	MANTOLOKING, NJ 08738
HEMMINGS, DAVID	ACTOR-DIRECTOR	STONE MANNERS, 9113 SUNSET BL	LOS ANGELES, CA 90069
HEMOND, ROLAND	BASEBALL EXECUTIVE	ORIOLE PARK, 333 W CAMDEN ST	BALTIMORE, MD 21201
HEMOND, SCOTT	BASEBALL	ATHLETICS'S, OAKLAND COLISEUM	OAKLAND, CA 94621
HEMPEL, ANOUSKA	ACTRESS	THE BLAKES HOTEL	
		3 ROLAND GARDENS	LONDON SW7 ENGLAND
HEMPHILL, SHIRLEY	ACTRESS	539 TRONA AVE	WEST COVINA, CA 91790
HEMSLEY, SHERMAN	ACTOR-COMEDIAN	8033 SUNSET BLVD #193	LOS ANGELES, CA 90046
HENCE, SAM	BASEBALL	POST OFFICE BOX 1886	COLUMBUS, GA 31902
HENDERSON, ALBERT	ACTOR	247 S BEVERLY DR #102	BEVERLY HILLS, CA 90210
HENDERSON, BRICE	SINGER-GUITARIST	417-A SARVER AVE	MADISON, TN 37115
HENDERSON, DARYL	BASEBALL	POST OFFICE BOX 309	GASTONA, NC 28053
HENDERSON, DAVE	BASEBALL (MAJORS)	ATHLETICS'S, OAKLAND COLISEUM	OAKLAND, CA 94621
HENDERSON, DEREK	BASEBALL	633 JESSAMINE ST	KNOXVILLE, TN 37917
HENDERSON, DON	DIRECTOR	1079 E OLIVE AVE	BURBANK, CA 91501
HENDERSON, DUNCAN	FILM DIRECTOR	518 1/2 VETERAN AVE	LOS ANGELES, CA 90024
HENDERSON, FLORENCE	SINGER-ACTRESS	POST OFFICE BOX 11295	MARINA DEL REY, CA 90295
HENDERSON, JAMES J, JR	DIRECTOR	15-1 GRANADA CRESCENT	WHITE PLAINS, NY 10603
HENDERSON, JEROME	FOOTBALL	PATRIOTS, FOXBORO STADIUM, RT #1	FOXBORO, MA 02035
HENDERSON, JIM	COLUMNIST	POST OFFICE BOX 500	WASHINGTON, DC 20044
HENDERSON, JOE	BASEBALL SCOUT	POST OFFICE BOX 4100	SEATTLE, WA 98104
HENDERSON, JUDY	CASTING DIRECTOR	330 W 89TH ST	NEW YORK, NY 10024
HENDERSON, KEITH	FOOTBALL	S F 49ERS, 4949 CENTENNIAL BL	SANTA CLARA, CA 95054
HENDERSON, LEE	BASEBALL	12000 STADIUM RD	ADELANTO, CA 92301
HENDERSON, LUTHER L, III	COMPOSER-CONDUCTOR	POST OFFICE BOX 3602	CULVER CITY, CA 90230
HENDERSON, MAGGIE	TALENT AGENT	247 S BEVERLY DR #102	BEVERLY HILLS, CA 90210
HENDERSON, MICHAEL	SINGER	4856 LAUREL CANYON BLVD	NORTH HOLLYWOOD, CA 91607
HENDERSON, PEDRO	BASEBALL	POST OFFICE BOX 802	WATERTOWN, NY 13601
HENDERSON, RAMON	BASEBALL COACH	POST OFFICE BOX 10336	CLEARWATER, FL 34617
HENDERSON, RICKEY	BASEBALL	ATHLETICS'S, OAKLAND COLISEUM	OAKLAND, CA 94621
HENDERSON, SKITCH	COMPOSER-CONDUCTOR	HUNT HILL FARM, UPLAND RD	
		RURAL FARM DELIVERY #3	NEW MILFORD, CT 06776
HENDERSON, STEVE	BASEBALL-INSTRUCTOR	5003 BEEKMAN CT	TAMPA, FL 33624
HENDERSON, THOMAS "HOLLYWOOD"	FOOTBALL	7 SEAFIELD LN	WESTHAMPTON BEACH, NY 11978
HENDERSON, WYMON	FOOTBALL	BRONCOS, 13655 BRONCOS PKWY	ENGLEWOOD, CO 80112

HENDLER, LAURI	ACTRESS	4034 STONE CANYON AVE	SHERMAN OAKS, CA	91403
HENDLEY, BRETT	BASEBALL	POST OFFICE BOX 2437	MODESTO, CA	95351
HENDRICKS, ELROD	BASEBALL-COACH	ORIOLE PARK, 333 W CAMDEN ST	BALTIMORE, MD	21201
HENDRICKS, JON	SINGER	WILLARD ALEXANDER, INC		
		660 MADISON AVE	NEW YORK, NY	10021
HENDRICKS, SKITCH	CASTING DIRECTOR	1438 N GOWER ST	LOS ANGELES, CA	90028
HENDRICKSON, BENJAMIN	ACTOR	LAZAROW & CO, 119 W 57TH ST	NEW YORK, NY	10019
HENDRICKSON, CALISTA	COSTUME DESIGNER	280 RIVERSIDE DR	NEW YORK, NY	10025
HENDRICKSON, DICK	GOLFER	PGA SENIORS, 112 T P C BLVD	PONTE VEDRA BEACH, FL	32082
HENDRICKSON, STEVE	FOOTBALL	POST OFFICE BOX 609609	SAN DIEGO, CA	92160
HENDRIX, LEAH AYRES	ACTRESS	16 FLEET ST #8	MARINA DEL REY, CA	90292
HENDRIX, MANNY	FOOTBALL	COWBOYS, 1 COWBOYS PARKWAY	IRVING, TX	75063
HENDRIX SINGERS, JAMES	VOCAL GROUP	POST OFFICE BOX 90639	NASHVILLE, TN	37209
HENDRY, TED	BASEBALL UMPIRE	2709 E SHAW BUTTE DR	PHOENIX, AZ	85028
HENDRYX, SHIRL	SCREENWRITER	12310 DOROTHY ST	LOS ANGELES, CA	90049
HENERSON, JAMES S	TV WRITER-PRODUCER	15300 KINGSWOOD LN	SHERMAN OAKS, CA	91403
HENGEL, DAVE	BASEBALL	5999 E VAN BUREN ST	PHOENIX, AZ	85008
HENINBURG, GUSTAV	TV HOST	WNBC-TV, 30 ROCKEFELLER PLZ	NEW YORK, NY	10112
HENKE, DENNIS	BASEBALL EXECUTIVE	10233 96TH AVE	EDMONTON, ALB TK5 0A5	CANADA
HENKE, NOLAN	GOLFER	POST OFFICE BOX 109601	PALM BCH GARDENS, FL	33418
HENKE, TOM	BASEBALL	SKYDOME, 300 BREMMER BL #3200	TORONTO, ONT M5V 3B3	CANADA
HENKIN, HILARY	SCREENWRITER	8955 BEVERLY BLVD	WEST HOLLYWOOD, CA	90048
HENKIN, HOWARD	WRITER-PRODUCER	150 E 77TH ST	NEW YORK, NY	10021
HENLEY, ARTHUR	AUTHOR-EDITOR	73-37 AUSTIN ST	FOREST HILLS, NY	11375
HENLEY, BETH	WRITER-ACTRESS	WM MORRIS, 1350 AVE OF AMERICAS	NEW YORK, NY	10019
HENLEY, DAN	BASEBALL	CANADIANS, 4601 ONTARIO ST	VANCOUVER, BC V5V 3H4	CANADA
HENLEY, DARRYL	FOOTBALL	RAMS, 2327 W LINCOLN BLVD	ANAHEIM, CA	92801
HENLEY, DON	SINGER-SONGWRITER	345 N MAPLE ST #235	BEVERLY HILLS, CA	90210
HENLEY, GAIL	BASEBALL SCOUT	1000 ELYSIAN PARK DR	LOS ANGELES, CA	90012
HENMAN, PAUL J	DIRECTOR	DGA, 7920 SUNSET BLVD, 6TH FL	LOS ANGELES, CA	90046
HENN, RICHARD A	COMPOSER-CONDUCTOR	28908 GRAYFOX ST	MALIBU, CA	90265
HENNEMAN, MIKE	BASEBALL	TIGERS, TIGER STADIUM	DETROIT, MI	48216
HENNER, MARILU	ACTRESS	151 S EL CAMINO DR	BEVERLY HILLS, CA	90212
HENNESSEY-SMITH, DONNA L	TV DIRECTOR	11 MEADOWBROOK RD	DOVER, MA	02030
HENNESSY, JOHN	FILM PRODUCER	540 TAMARAC RD	PASADENA, CA	91105
HENNING, CURT "MR PERFECT"	WRESTLER	POST OFFICE BOX 3859	STAMFORD, CT	06905
HENNING, DAN	FOOTBALL COACH	POST OFFICE BOX 609609	SAN DIEGO, CA	92160
HENNING, HAROLD	GOLFER	PGA SENIORS, 112 T P C BLVD	PONTE VEDRA BEACH, FL	32082
HENNING, LINDA KAYE	ACTRESS	4231 WARNER BLVD	BURBANK, CA	91505
HENNING, PAUL	TV WRITER-PRODUCER	4250 NAVAJO ST	NORTH HOLLYWOOD, CA	91602
HENNING, RICH	BASEBALL SCOUT	TIGERS, TIGER STADIUM	DETROIT, MI	48216
HENNINGER, RAI	BASEBALL EXECUTIVE	4385 TUTT BLVD	COLORADO SPRINGS, CO	80922
HENNIS, RANDY	BASEBALL	POST OFFICE BOX 422229	KISSIMMEE, FL	34742
HENRICHS, JEFF	BASEBALL UMPIRE	POST OFFICE BOX 608	GROVE CITY, OH	43123
HENRIE, CARY	ARTIST	220 E 36TH ST #G-5	NEW YORK, NY	10016
HENRIKSEN, LANCE	ACTOR	9540 DALE AVE	SUNLAND, CA	91040
HENRIKSON, DAN	BASEBALL	5999 E VAN BUREN ST	PHOENIX, AZ	85008
HENRY, BOB	TV DIRECTOR	11940 SAN VICENTE BLVD	LOS ANGELES, CA	90049
HENRY, BUCK	WRITER-PRODUCER	760 N LA CIENEGA BLVD	LOS ANGELES, CA	90069
HENRY, BUTCH	BASEBALL	POST OFFICE BOX 288	HOUSTON, TX	77001
HENRY, CHARLES	FOOTBALL	DOLPHINS, 2269 NW 199TH ST	MIAMI, FL	33056
HENRY, CLAUDETTE	TREASURER	STATE CAPITOL BUILDING	OKLAHOMA CITY, OK	73105
HENRY, DAVID LEE	SCREENWRITER	8955 BEVERLY BLVD	WEST HOLLYWOOD, CA	90048
HENRY, DEBI	SINGER	NBA, 2605 NORTHRIDGE DR	GARLAND, TX	75043
HENRY, DOUG	BASEBALL	2850 W 20TH AVE	DENVER, CO	80211
HENRY, DWAYNE	BASEBALL	REDS, 100 RIVERFRONT STADIUM	CINCINNATI, OH	45202
HENRY, GLORIA	ACTRESS	11846 VENTURA BLVD #100	STUDIO CITY, CA	91604
HENRY, GREGG	ACTOR	SMITH, 121 N SAN VICENTE BLVD	BEVERLY HILLS, CA	90211
HENRY, HAROLD	BASEBALL	POST OFFICE BOX 4218	SOUTH BEND, IN	46634
HENRY, JIMMY	BASEBALL	POST OFFICE BOX 2785	LAKELAND, FL	33806
HENRY, JON	BASEBALL	POST OFFICE BOX 5645	ORLANDO, FL	32855
HENRY, JUSTIN	ACTOR	3 CLARK LN	RYE, NY	10580
HENRY, LENNY	COMEDIAN	LUFF, 294 EARLS COURT RD	LONDON SW5 9BB	ENGLAND
HENRY, MIKE	PRODUCER	10803 BLIX ST	NORTH HOLLYWOOD, CA	91602
HENRY, PAUL B	U S CONGRESSMAN	166 FEDERAL BUILDING	GRAND RAPIDS, MI	49503
HENRY, RICHARD	CINEMATOGRAPHER	RWH FILMS, 157 CHARLES ST	NEW YORK, NY	10014
HENRY, ROBERT	ATTORNEY GENERAL	STATE CAPITOL BUILDING	OKLAHOMA CITY, OK	73105
HENRY, SCOTT	BASEBALL	POST OFFICE BOX 11363	RENO, NV	89510
HENSHAW, GEORGE	FOOTBALL COACH	BRONCOS, 13655 BRONCOS PKWY	ENGLEWOOD, CO	80112
HENSHAW, JERE	FILM EXECUTIVE	9541 CHEROKEE LN	BEVERLY HILLS, CA	90210
HENSLER, PAUL G	SCREENWRITER	11901 SUNSET BLVD #211	LOS ANGELES, CA	90049
HENSLEY, CHUCK	BASEBALL SCOUT	S F GIANTS, CANDLESTICK PARK	SAN FRANICSCO, CA	94124
HENSLEY, HAROLD	SINGER	POST OFFICE BOX 4234	PANORAMA CITY, CA	91412
HENSLEY, J MIYOKO	TV WRITER	16633 VENTURA BLVD #1421	ENCINO, CA	91436
HENSLEY, JANELLE	ACTRESS	1680 N VINE ST #1003	HOLLYWOOD, CA	90028
HENSLEY, JON	ACTOR	CBS-TV, "AS THE WORLD TURNS"		
		524 W 57TH ST #5330	NEW YORK, NY	10019
HENSLEY, STEVE	TV WRITER	BLOOM, 800 S ROBERTSON BLVD	LOS ANGELES, CA	90035
HENSLEY, TARI	SINGER	3909 SCOTTWOOD DR	NASHVILLE, TN	37211
HENSLEY, THOMAS R	COMPOSER-CONDUCTOR	ARCHANGEL, 8715 W 3RD ST	LOS ANGELES, CA	90048
HENSON, NICKY	ACTOR	STONE, 25 WHITEHALL	LONDON SW1A 2BS	ENGLAND
HENSON, RHYS C	CONDUCTOR	POST OFFICE BOX 3948	LOS ANGELES, CA	90078
HENSON, STEVE	BASKETBALL	BRADLEY CENTER, 1001 N 4TH ST	MILWAUKEE, WI	53203
HENTGEN, PAT	BASEBALL	SKYDOME, 300 BREMMER BL #3200	TORONTO, ONT M5V 3B3	CANADA
HENZE, HANS WERNER	COMPOSER-CONDUCTOR	ICM, 40 W 57TH ST	NEW YORK, NY	10019

Name	Occupation	Address	City
HEPBURN, AUDREY	ACTRESS	CHALET RICO BISSENSTRASSE	GSTAAD SWITZERLAND
HEPBURN, DEE	ACTRESS	50 CECIL ST, HILLMEAD	GLASGOW SCOTLAND
HEPBURN, KATHARINE	ACTRESS	244 E 49TH ST	NEW YORK, NY 10017
HEPCAT, HARRY & THE BOOGIE	ROCK & ROLL GROUP	MUSKRAT, 44 N CENTRAL AVE	ELMSFORD, NY 10523
HEPTON, BERNARD	ACTOR-DIRECTOR	MARMONT MANAGEMENT, LTD	
		LANGHAM HOUSE, 308 REGENT ST	LONDON W1R 5AL ENGLAND
HERAL, WILLIAM	DIRECTOR	KGO-TV, 277 GOLDEN GATE AVE	SAN FRANCISCO, CA 94102
HERALD, JOHN, BAND	C & W GROUP	380 LEXINGTON AVE #1119	NEW YORK, NY 10017
HERALD, STEPHEN	FILM CRITIC	BOSTON HERALD, 1 HERALD SQ	BOSTON, MA 02106
HERB, ALICE H	WRITER-PRODUCER	DGA, 110 W 57TH ST	NEW YORK, NY 10019
HERB'S HEARD	ROCK & ROLL GROUP	25 HUNTINGTON AVE #420	BOSTON, MA 02116
HERBERT, HENRY	TV DIRECTOR	CATHCART HOUSE, CATHCART RD	LONDON SW10 ENGLAND
HERBERT, LEON	ACTOR	AIM, 5 DENMARK ST	LONDON WC2H 8LP ENGLAND
HERBIG, GUNTHER	CONDUCTOR	ICM, 40 W 57TH ST	NEW YORK, NY 10019
HERCULES	WRESTLER	SEE - HERNANDEZ, HERCULES	
HERD, RICHARD	ACTOR	4610 WORSTEN AVE	SHERMAN OAKS, CA 91423
HEREDIA, GIL	BASEBALL	S F GIANTS, CANDLESTICK PARK	SAN FRANICSCO, CA 94124
HEREDIA, JULIAN	BASEBALL	POST OFFICE BOX 3496	DAVENPORT, IA 52808
HEREDIA, WILSON	BASEBALL	POST OFFICE BOX 309	GASTONA, NC 28053
HEREFORD, KATHRYN	ACTRESS-PRODUCER	914 N ROXBURY DR	BEVERLY HILLS, CA 90210
HEREK, STEPHEN	ARTIST	UTA, 9560 WILSHIRE BL, 5TH FL	BEVERLY HILLS, CA 90212
HERFEL, CHRISTIAN R, JR	DIRECTOR	TRINITY PASS	POUND RIDGE, NY 10576
HERGER, WALLY	U S CONGRESSMAN	951 LIVE OAK BLVD #10	YUBA CITY, CA 95991
HERLAN, RICHARD	TV WRITER	2319 14TH ST #13	SANTA MONICA, CA 90405
HERLIE, EILEEN	ACTRESS	ABC-TV, "ALL MY CHILDREN"	
		320 W 66TH ST	NEW YORK, NY 10023
HERLIHY, JAMES	PLAYWRIGHT	J GARON, 415 CENTRAL PARK W	NEW YORK, NY 10025
HERMAN, BILLY	BASEBALL	3111 E GARDEN #33	PALM BCH GARDENS, FL 33410
HERMAN, FRANK G	DIRECTOR	43 W 93RD ST	NEW YORK, NY 10025
HERMAN, GARY B	TV DIRECTOR-PRODUCER	ENTERTAINMENT TONIGHT	
		PARAMOUNT TELEVISION	
		5555 MELROSE AVE	LOS ANGELES, CA 90038
HERMAN, GERALD	WRITER-PRODUCER	STARSHOLMA	280 72 KILLEBERG SWEDEN
HERMAN, HARVEY	TV DIRECTOR	19 E 88TH ST	NEW YORK, NY 10028
HERMAN, HOWARD B	COMPOSER	6527 RIVERTON AVE	NORTH HOLLYWOOD, CA 91606
HERMAN, KENNETH R, JR	TV DIRECTOR	5050 HOOKTREE RD	LA CANADA, CA 91011
HERMAN, KERRY	TV DIRECTOR-PRODUCER	240 8TH ST #3-S	BROOKLYN, NY 11215
HERMAN, MAXINE	TV WRITER	999 N DOHENY DR #403	LOS ANGELES, CA 90069
HERMAN, NADINE	SINGER	POST OFFICE BOX 256577	CHICAGO, IL 60625
HERMAN, NORMAN	WRITER-PRODUCER	3350 FRYMAN RD	STUDIO CITY, CA 91604
HERMAN, PEE WEE	ACTOR-COMEDIAN	12725 VENTURA BLVD #H	STUDIO CITY, CA 91604
HERMAN, RANDY	ACTOR	2628 WASHINGTON AVE	SANTA MONICA, CA 90403
HERMAN, T NORMAN	WRITER-PRODUCER	3350 FRYMAN RD	STUDIO CITY, CA 91604
HERMAN'S HERMITS	ROCK & ROLL GROUP	BOX 81, BRIGHTON, OLDHAM	MANCHESTER OLD 5DG ENGLAND
HERMANNS, CARL B	CONDUCTOR	5120 NOBLE AVE	SHERMAN OAKS, CA 91403
HERNAIZ, JESUS	BASEBALL COACH	2908 ASHLEY ST	KINGSPORT, TN 37664
HERNANDEZ, ANGEL	BASEBALL UMPIRE	POST OFFICE BOX 608	GROVE CITY, OH 43123
HERNANDEZ, CARLOS	BASEBALL (MAJORS)	1000 ELYSIAN PARK DR	LOS ANGELES, CA 90012
HERNANDEZ, CHUCK	BASEBALL-INSTRUCTOR	POST OFFICE BOX 2000	ANAHEIM, CA 92803
HERNANDEZ, FERNANDO	BASEBALL	POST OFFICE BOX 1886	COLUMBUS, GA 31902
HERNANDEZ, HERCULES	WRESTLER	POST OFFICE BOX 3859	STAMFORD, CT 06905
HERNANDEZ, JEREMY	BASEBALL	POST OFFICE BOX 2000	SAN DIEGO, CA 92112
HERNANDEZ, JOSE	BASEBALL	2501 ALLEN AVE, SE	CANTON, OH 44707
HERNANDEZ, KEITH	BASEBALL	255 E 49TH ST #28-D	NEW YORK, NY 10017
HERNANDEZ, KIKI	BASEBALL	5301 NW 12TH AVE	FORT LAUDERDALE, FL 33309
HERNANDEZ, RAMON	BASEBALL (MINORS)	POST OFFICE BOX 1553	BILLINGS, MT 59103
HERNANDEZ, ROBERTO	BASEBALL	333 W 35TH ST	CHICAGO, IL 60616
HERNANDEZ, RUDY	BASEBALL SCOUT	ORIOLE PARK, 333 W CAMDEN ST	BALTIMORE, MD 21201
HERNANDEZ, WILLIE	BASEBALL	BO ESPINA CALLE C BOX 125	AGUADA, PR 00602
HERNANDEZ, XAVIER	BASEBALL	3549 LAY AVE	GROVES, TX 77619
HERNDON, LARRY	BASEBALL-COACH	TIGERS, TIGER STADIUM	DETROIT, MI 48216
HERNDON, VENABLE	SCREENWRITER	8955 BEVERLY BLVD	WEST HOLLYWOOD, CA 90048
HERNDON, WALTER SCOTT	WRITER-PRODUCER	1080 ARMADA DR	PASADENA, CA 91103
HEROCK, KEN	FOOTBALL EXECUTIVE	FALCONS, SUWANEE RD AT I-85	SUWANEE, GA 30174
HEROLD, BOB	BASEBALL COACH	POST OFFICE BOX 3665	OMAHA, NE 68103
HEROLD, PATRICIA	TV DIRECTOR-PRODUCER	589 7TH ST	BROOKLYN, NY 11215
HEROUX, CLAUDE	FILM PRODUCER	3515 RUE BEAUSEJOUR	MONTREAL, QUE H4K 1W5 CANADA
HERR, MICHAEL	SCREENWRITER	555 W 57TH ST #1230	NEW YORK, NY 10019
HERR, TOM	BASEBALL	METS, 126TH ST & ROOSEVELT AVE	FLUSHING, NY 11368
HERRERA, DAVE	BASEBALL SCOUT	POST OFFICE BOX 419969	KANSAS CITY, MO 64141
HERRERA, EZEQUIEL	BASEBALL	POST OFFICE BOX 12557	ST PETERSBURG, FL 33733
HERRERA, SUZANNE M	TV WRITER	11846 VENTURA BLVD #100	STUDIO CITY, CA 91604
HERRICK, F HERRICK	DIRECTOR	3633 MACK RD	SAGINAW, MI 48601
HERRING, LAURA M	ACTRESS-MODEL	132 S LASKY DR #B	BEVERLY HILLS, CA 90212
HERRING, LYNN	ACTRESS	3500 W OLIVE AVE #1400	BURBANK, CA 91505
HERRING, PEMBROKE	FILM EDITOR	22625 GILMORE ST	CANOGA PARK, CA 91307
HERRING, VINCE	BASEBALL	POST OFFICE BOX 21727	SAN FRANCISCO, CA 95151
HERRINGTON, ROWDY	SCREENWRITER	10100 SANTA MONICA BLVD #1600	LOS ANGELES, CA 90067
HERRIOTT, PAUL	DIRECTOR	425 E 58TH ST #5-B	NEW YORK, NY 10022
HERRMANN, EDWARD	ACTOR	151 S EL CAMINO DR	BEVERLY HILLS, CA 90212
HERRMANN, FRED	BASEBALL EXECUTIVE	POST OFFICE BOX 1457	MEDFORD, OR 97501
HERRMANN, MARK	FOOTBALL	POST OFFICE BOX 535000	INDIANPOLIS, IN 46253
HERROD, JEFF	FOOTBALL	POST OFFICE BOX 535000	INDIANPOLIS, IN 46253
HERRON, CINDY	ACTRESS	8230 SUNSET BLVD #23	LOS ANGELES, CA 90048
HERRON, J BARRY	DIRECTOR	324 W CAMINO REAL	ARCADIA, CA 91006

HERSH, ROBERT D	TV DIRECTOR	RURAL ROUTE #2, BOX 351-B	SOUTH SALEM, NY	10590
HERSH, RONALD S	TV DIRECTOR	70 W 38TH ST	NEW YORK, NY	10018
HERSH, STUART A	WRITER-PRODUCER	41-34 243RD ST	DOUGLASTOWN, NY	11363
HERSHEY, BARBARA	ACTRESS	CAA, 9830 WILSHIRE BLVD	BEVERLY HILLS, CA	90212
HERSHISER, OREL	BASEBALL	1000 ELYSIAN PARK DR	LOS ANGELES, CA	90012
HERSKOVITZ, MARSHALL S	TV WRITER-PRODUCER	905 CENTINELA AVE	SANTA MONICA, CA	90403
HERST, JERRY P	COMPOSER	5735 CLOVER DR	OAKLAND, CA	94618
HERSTON, KELSO	GUITARIST	1202 16TH AVE S	NASHVILLE, TN	37212
HERTEL, DENNIS	U S CONGRESSMAN	18927 KELLY RD	DETROIT, MI	48224
HERTZBERG, MICHAEL	FILM WRITER-PRODUCER	DGA, 7920 SUNSET BLVD, 6TH FL	LOS ANGELES, CA	90046
HERTZOG, LARRY	TV PRODUCER	CANNELL, 7083 HOLLYWOOD BLVD	LOS ANGELES, CA	90028
HERVEY, JASON	ACTOR	9200 SUNSET BLVD #625	LOS ANGELES, CA	90069
HERVEY, WINIFRED	TV WRITER	MTA, 9320 WILSHIRE BL, 3RD FL	BEVERLY HILLS, CA	90212
HERZBERG, JACK	DIRECTOR-PRODUCER	4314 KLING ST	BURBANK, CA	91505
HERZBERG, PAUL	ACTOR	HEATH, PARAMOUNT HOUSE		
		162-170 WARDOUR ST	LONDON W1V 3AT	ENGLAND
HERZBERG, TOM	ARTIST	4128 W EDDY ST	CHICAGO, IL	60641
HERZOG, WHITEY	BASEBALL	3613 S FOREST	INDEPENDENCE, MO	64052
HESKETH, JOE	BASEBALL	FENWAY PARK, 4 YAWKEY WY	BOSTON, MA	02215
HESS, BENNIE	SINGER-GUITARIST	14119 CHRISMAN RD	HOUSTON, TX	77039
HESS, JOHN D	TV WRITER	RD #1, BOX 112	NEW HOPE, PA	18938
HESS, LEON	FOOTBALL EXECUTIVE	N Y JETS, 1000 FULTON AVE	HEMPSTEAD, NY	11550
HESS, RICHARD	ARTIST	SOUTHOVER FARMS, ROUTE #67	ROXBURY, CT	06783
HESS, TROY	SINGER	14119 CHRISMAN RD	HOUSTON, TX	77039
HESSE, LOUIS	FILM EDITOR	23388 MULHOLLAND HIGHWAY	WOODLAND HILLS, CA	91364
HESSEMAN, HOWARD	ACTOR-WRITER	7146 LA PESA DR	HOLLYWOOD, CA	90068
HESSLER, GORDON	DIRECTOR	8910 HOLLY PL	LOS ANGELES, CA	90046
HESTER, JESSIE	FOOTBALL	POST OFFICE BOX 535000	INDIANPOLIS, IN	46253
HESTON, CHARLTON	ACTOR-DIRECTOR	2859 COLDWATER CANYON DR	BEVERLY HILLS, CA	90210
HESTON, FRASER	FILM WRITER-PRODUCER	2859 COLDWATER CANYON DR	BEVERLY HILLS, CA	90210
HESTON, JOSEPH WERNER	DIRECTOR	DGA, 110 W 57TH ST	NEW YORK, NY	10019
HETRICK, JENNIFER	ACTRESS	STONE MANNERS, 9113 SUNSET BL	LOS ANGELES, CA	90069
HETZEL, ERIC	BASEBALL	POST OFFICE BOX 2365	PAWTUCKET, RI	02861
HEUS, RICHARD	TV PRODUCER	151 S EL CAMINO DR	BEVERLY HILLS, CA	90212
HEWETT, CHRISTOPHER	ACTOR	1422 N SWEETZER #110	LOS ANGELES, CA	90069
HEWITT, CHARLES	ACTOR	5647 CARTWRIGHT AVE #47	NORTH HOLLYWOOD, CA	91601
HEWITT, DON	WRITER-PRODUCER	CBS-TV, 524 W 57TH ST	NEW YORK, NY	10019
HEWITT, FRANKIE	THEATER PRODUCER	FORD'S THEATRE		
		511 10TH ST, NW	WASHINGTON, DC	20005
HEWITT, HEATHER	ACTRESS	6324 TAHOE DR	LOS ANGELES, CA	90068
HEWITT, MARTIN	ACTOR	ICM, 8899 BEVERLY BLVD	LOS ANGELES, CA	90048
HEWITT, STEVEN W	TV EXECUTIVE	CBS-TV, 6121 SUNSET BLVD	LOS ANGELES, CA	90028
HEWLETT, ARTHUR	ACTOR	10 HEATH DR	LONDON NW3	ENGLAND
HEWLETT, DONALD	ACTOR	OLD KING'S HEAD, WHITSTABLE	KENT	ENGLAND
HEYCK, THEODORE DALY	ACTOR	11135 CALVERT ST	NORTH HOLLYWOOD, CA	91606
HEYCOCK, DAVID	TV PRODUCER	67 GIRDWOOD RD	LONDON SW18	ENGLAND
HEYDEN, PAUL VANDER	BASEBALL EXECUTIVE	POST OFFICE BOX 464	APPLETON, WI	54912
HEYDEN, YVETTE	ACTRESS	6515 WILSHIRE BLVD #205	HOLLYWOOD, CA	90028
HEYDORN, NANCY S	DIRECTOR	15443 HUSTON ST	SHERMAN OAKS, CA	91403
HEYES, DOUG, JR	TV WRITER	1900 AVE OF THE STARS #2535	LOS ANGELES, CA	90067
HEYES, DOUGLAS H	WRITER-PRODUCER	1227 COLDWATER CANYON DR	BEVERLY HILLS, CA	90210
HEYLAND, ROB	ACTOR	THE MANOR, MIDDLE LYTTLETON	WORCESTERSHIRE	ENGLAND
HEYMAN, MILLARD	CONDUCTOR	314 CLAYTON ST	WAUKEGAN, IL	60085
HEYMAN, NORMA	FILM PRODUCER	NFH PRODS, 31 SOHO SQ	LONDON W1	ENGLAND
HEYMAN, RICHARD X	SINGER-GUITARIST	51 1ST ST #1	NEW YORK, NY	10003
HEYWARD, LOUIS	WRITER-PRODUCER	6819 SEPULVEDA BLVD	VAN NUYS, CA	91405
HEYWARD, LOUIS M	TV WRITER	10717 WILSHIRE BLVD #1003	LOS ANGELES, CA	90024
HEYWOOD, ANNE	ACTRESS	9966 LIEBE DR	BEVERLY HILLS, CA	90210
HEYWOOD, CRAIG	FOOTBALL	SAINTS, 1500 POYDRAS ST	NEW ORLEANS, LA	90112
HEYWOOD, PAT	ACTRESS	13 MARLBOROUGH HILL, KINGSDOWN	BRISTOL BS2 8EZ	ENGLAND
HEYWORTH, JIM	CABLE EXECUTIVE	HBO, 1100 6TH AVE	NEW YORK, NY	10036
HEYWORTH, MALCOLM B	FILM PRODUCER	CHATSWORTH FILMS DISTRIBUTORS		
		97-99 DEAN ST	LONDON W1	ENGLAND
HI, MAE	ACTRESS	WHITAKER, 12725 VENTURA BLVD	STUDIO CITY, CA	91604
HIATT, JACK	BASEBALL-SCOUT	S F GIANTS, CANDLESTICK PARK	SAN FRANICSCO, CA	94124
HIATT, JOHN	SINGER-SONGWRITER	1016 17TH AVE #3	NASHVILLE, TN	37212
HIATT, KEVIN L	COMPOSER	1218 LODI PL #216	LOS ANGELES, CA	90038
HIATT, MICHAEL	DIRECTOR	DGA, 7920 SUNSET BLVD, 6TH FL	LOS ANGELES, CA	90046
HIATT, PHIL	BASEBALL	800 HOME RUN LN	MEMPHIS, TN	38104
HIBBARD, GREG	BASEBALL	333 W 35TH ST	CHICAGO, IL	60616
HIBLER, CHRISTOPHER	DIRECTOR	1927 MELWOOD DR	GLENDALE, CA	91207
HICKEL, WALTER J	GOVERNOR	POST OFFICE BOX A	JUNEAU, AK	99811
HICKERSON, BRYAN	BASEBALL	S F GIANTS, CANDLESTICK PARK	SAN FRANICSCO, CA	94124
HICKEY, JIM	BASEBALL COACH	POST OFFICE BOX 1556	ASHEVILLE, NC	28802
HICKEY, KEVIN	BASEBALL	ORIOLE PARK, 333 W CAMDEN ST	BALTIMORE, MD	21201
HICKEY, MARGUERITE	ACTRESS	144 S BEVERLY DR #405	BEVERLY HILLS, CA	90212
HICKEY, MARILYN	EVANGELIST	POST OFFICE BOX 17350	DENVER, CO	80217
HICKEY, PAMELA	TV WRITER-STORY ED	WARDEN, 8444 WILSHIRE BL, 4TH FL	BEVERLY HILLS, CA	90211
HICKEY, WILLIAM	ACTOR	69 W 12TH ST	NEW YORK, NY	10011
HICKLAND, CATHERINE	ACTRESS	34 23RD AVE	VENICE, CA	90291
HICKMAN, DWAYNE	ACTOR-DIRECTOR	812 16TH ST #1	SANTA MONICA, CA	90403
HICKMAN, JIM	BASEBALL-INSTRUCTOR	REDS, 100 RIVERFRONT STADIUM	CINCINNATI, OH	45202
HICKMAN, LARRY & RED HOT RIDERS	C & W GROUP	JOYCE, 2028 CHESTNUT ST	PHILADELPHIA, PA	19103
HICKMAN, WILLIAM W	FILM DIRECTOR	82-317 LANCASTER WY	INDIO, CA	92201
HICKOX, ED	BASEBALL UMPIRE	POST OFFICE BOX 608	GROVE CITY, OH	43123

Name	Occupation	Address	City
HICKOX, S BRYAN	TV EXECUTIVE	WARNER BROTHERS, INC	
		4000 WARNER BLVD	
		PRODUCER'S BLDG #4, ROOM 16	BURBANK, CA 91522
HICKS, CATHERINE	ACTRESS	2801 N KEYSTONE ST	BURBANK, CA 91504
HICKS, CHRISTOPHER	FILM CRITIC	POST OFFICE BOX 1257	SALT LAKE CITY, UT 84110
HICKS, CHUCK	ACTOR	POST OFFICE BOX 24-A-56	LOS ANGELES, CA 90024
HICKS, CLIFFORD	FOOTBALL	BILLS, 1 BILLS DR	ORCHARD PARK, NJ 14127
HICKS, DAN	SINGER-SONGWRITER	SAVOY MUSIC, 1111 KEARNEY ST	SAN FRANCISCO, CA 94133
HICKS, JOHN	SINGER	PENNY, 30 GUINAN ST	WALTHAM, MA 02154
HICKS, JOHN P	COMPOSER	3834 TRACY ST	LOS ANGELES, CA 90027
HICKS, NEIL D	SCREENWRITER	8955 BEVERLY BLVD	WEST HOLLYWOOD, CA 90048
HICKS, WOODY	BASEBALL EXECUTIVE	POST OFFICE BOX 2785	LAKELAND, FL 33806
HICZEWSKI, MARTA	BASEBALL EXECUTIVE	POST OFFICE BOX 450	BUFFALO, NY 14205
HIDY, LANCE	ARTIST	POST OFFICE BOX 806	NEWBURYPORT, MA 01950
HIERONYMUS, RICHARD E	COMPOSER	1161 N HIGHLAND AVE	LOS ANGELES, CA 90038
HIGGINS, ANTHONY	ACTOR	WM MORRIS, 31-32 SOHO SQ	LONDON W1V 5DG ENGLAND
HIGGINS, BERTIE	SINGER-SONGWRITER	5775 PEACHTREE DUNWOODY	ATLANTA, GA 30342
HIGGINS, JACK	WRITER	"SEPTEMBERTIDE"	
		MONT DE LA ROCQUE	
		SAINT AUBIN	JERSEY CHANNEL ISLS
HIGGINS, JOE	ACTOR	10823 CAMARILLO ST	NORTH HOLLYWOOD, CA 91602
HIGGINS, JOEL	ACTOR	246 16TH ST	SANTA MONICA, CA 90402
HIGGINS, JOETTE	ACTRESS	POST OFFICE BOX 5617	BEVERLY HILLS, CA 90213
HIGGINS, JOHN C	WRITER	10371 MISSISSIPPI AVE	LOS ANGELES, CA 90025
HIGGINS, KEVIN	BASEBALL	STARS, 850 LAS VEGAS BLVD N	LAS VEGAS, NV 89101
HIGGINS, MICHAEL	ACTOR	822 S ROBERTSON BLVD #200	LOS ANGELES, CA 90035
HIGGINS, SEAN	BASKETBALL	600 E MARKET ST #102	SAN ANTONIO, TX 78205
HIGGINS, THOM BEAU	DIRECTOR	DGA, 110 W 57TH ST	NEW YORK, NY 10019
HIGGS, LARRY Y	TV DIRECTOR-PRODUCER	4660 CERRILLOS DR	WOODLAND HILLS, CA 91364
HIGGS, MARK	FOOTBALL	DOLPHINS, 2269 NW 199TH ST	MIAMI, FL 33056
HIGH INERGY	ROCK & ROLL GROUP	MOTOWN, 6255 SUNSET BL, 17TH FL	LOS ANGELES, CA 90028
HIGHER GROUND	GOSPEL GROUP	6750 W 75TH ST, BLDG #2-A	OVERLAND PARK, KS 66204
HIGHER GROUND BLUEGRASS BAND	BLUEGRASS G	POST OFFICE BOX 942	RAPID CITY, SD 57709
HIGHSMITH, ALONZO	FOOTBALL	COWBOYS, 1 COWBOYS PARKWAY	IRVING, TX 75063
HIGHWAY 101	C & W GROUP	33 MUSIC SQUARE W #106-B	NASHVILLE, TN 37203
HIGHWAY CHILE	ROCK & ROLL GROUP	MELKLAAN 35-A	VELSON NOORD
HIGUERA, TED	BASEBALL	BREWERS, 201 S 46TH ST	MILWAUKEE, WI 53214
HIKEN, GERALD	ACTOR	2133 1/2 HOLLY DR #A	LOS ANGELES, CA 90068
HILARY, JENNIFER	ACTRESS	LONDON MGT, 235-241 REGENT ST	LONDON W1R 4PH ENGLAND
HILBURN, ROBERT	MUSIC CRITIC	LA TIMES, TIMES MIRROR SQ	LOS ANGELES, CA 90053
HILDEGARDE	SINGER	230 E 48TH ST	NEW YORK, NY 10017
HILGENBERG, JAY	FOOTBALL	BEARS, 250 N WASHINGTON RD	LAKE FOREST, IL 60045
HILGENBERG, JOEL	FOOTBALL	SAINTS, 1500 POYDRAS ST	NEW ORLEANS, LA 90112
HILGENSTUHLER, TED	AUTHOR-COLUMNIST	POST OFFICE BOX 4721	NORTH HOLLYWOOD, CA 91607
HILIARD, BOB	BASEBALL EXECUTIVE	80 OTTAWA ST N	HAMILTON, ONT L8H 3Z1 CANADA
HILKA, TRISHA	ACTRESS	217 S LINCOLN ST	BURBANK, CA 91506
HILL, ANDREW	TV EXECUTIVE	COLUMBIA PICTURES TV	
		COLUMBIA PLAZA	BURBANK, CA 91505
HILL, ARTHUR	ACTOR	1515 CLUB VIEW DR	LOS ANGELES, CA 90024
HILL, BARRY	TV WRITER	4 HURSTHEAD RD, CHEADLE HULME	CHESHIRE SK8 7JR ENGLAND
HILL, BENJAMIN T, JR	TV DIRECTOR	6842 RANCHITO AVE	VAN NUYS, CA 91405
HILL, BERNARD	ACTOR	WM MORRIS, 31-32 SOHO SQ	LONDON W1V 5DG ENGLAND
HILL, BOB	ACTOR	5723 LA MIRADA AVE #1	LOS ANGELES, CA 90038
HILL, BOB	BASKETBALL COACH	PACERS, 300 E MARKET ST	INDIANAPOLIS, IN 46204
HILL, BRUCE	FOOTBALL	BUCCANEERS, 1 BUCCANEER PL	TAMPA, FL 33607
HILL, CATHY	FANTASY ARTIST	374 N GROVE ST	SIERRA MADRE, CA 91024
HILL, CHRIS	BASEBALL	POST OFFICE BOX 422229	KISSIMMEE, FL 34742
HILL, DANA	ACTRESS	848 LINCOLN BLVD #D	SANTA MONICA, CA 90403
HILL, DAVE	GOLFER	PGA SENIORS, 112 T P C BLVD	PONTE VEDRA BEACH, FL 32082
HILL, DEBRA	FILM PRODUCER	PARAMOUNT PICTURES CORP	
		5555 MELROSE AVE	LOS ANGELES, CA 90038
HILL, DEBRA G	SCREENWRITER	8955 BEVERLY BLVD	WEST HOLLYWOOD, CA 90048
HILL, DONALD H	CONDUCTOR	4257 S NORTON AVE	LOS ANGELES, CA 90008
HILL, DONNIE	BASEBALL	TWINS, 501 CHICAGO AVE S	MINNEAPOLIS, MN 55415
HILL, DREW	FOOTBALL	OILERS, 6910 FANNIN ST	HOUSTON, TX 77070
HILL, ELMORE	BASEBALL SCOUT	1060 W ADDISON ST	CHICAGO, IL 60613
HILL, ERIC	BASEBALL	POST OFFICE BOX 10336	CLEARWATER, FL 34617
HILL, ERIC	FOOTBALL	POST OFFICE BOX 888	PHOENIX, AZ 85001
HILL, GEORGE	FOOTBALL COACH	DOLPHINS, 2269 NW 199TH ST	MIAMI, FL 33056
HILL, GEORGE ROY	FILM WRITER-DIRECTOR	75 ROCKEFELLER PLAZA #700	NEW YORK, NY 10019
HILL, GLENALLEN	BASEBALL	INDIANS, CLEVELAND STADIUM	CLEVELAND, OH 44114
HILL, GREG	TV DIRECTOR	631 BAY ST #6	SANTA MONICA, CA 90405
HILL, HARLAN	FOOTBALL	ROUTE #2	KILLEN, AL 35645
HILL, HEATHER H	TV DIRECTOR	83 KELLOGG ST	BROOKFIELD, CT 06804
HILL, JACK	SCREENWRITER	8955 BEVERLY BLVD	WEST HOLLYWOOD, CA 90048
HILL, JACK	TV DIRECTOR	22014 DE LA OSA ST	WOODLAND HILLS, CA 91364
HILL, JAMES	TV DIRECTOR	1 ABDALE RD	LONDON W12 ENGLAND
HILL, JIM	TV WRITER-PRODUCER	BROWN, 162-168 REGENT ST	LONDON W1R 5TB ENGLAND
HILL, JOHN	SCREENWRITER	9046 SUNSET BLVD #202	LOS ANGELES, CA 90069
HILL, JOHN D	MUSIC ARRANGER	2885 LYNCREST DR	NASHVILLE, TN 37214
HILL, KEN	BASEBALL	EXPOS, 4545 DE COUBERTIN AVE	MONTREAL, QUE H1V 3P2 CANADA
HILL, LANGDON	COLUMNIST	UPS, 4900 MAIN ST, 9TH FLOOR	KANSAS CITY, MO 64112
HILL, LAURYN	ACTRESS	CBS-TV, "AS THE WORLD TURNS"	
		524 W 57TH ST #5330	NEW YORK, NY 10019
HILL, LEONARD	TV PRODUCER	MCA/UNIVERSAL STUDIOS, INC	

	....	100 UNIVERSAL CITY PLAZA	UNIVERSAL CITY, CA 91608
HILL, LEONARD F	TV EXECUTIVE	2519 PERDIDO LN	LOS ANGELES, CA 90077
HILL, LESLIE B	WRITER-PRODUCER	715 PIER AVE	SANTA MONICA, CA 90405
HILL, LEW	BASEBALL	POST OFFICE BOX 22093	GREENSBORO, NC 27420
HILL, LYNNE REGGIARDO	WRITER-PRODUCER	1748 FRANKLIN ST	SANTA MONICA, CA 90404
HILL, MARC	BASEBALL-MANAGER	POST OFFICE BOX 9194	HAMPTON, VA 23670
HILL, MAURICE J	ACTOR-WRITER	8573 APPIAN WY	LOS ANGELES, CA 90046
HILL, MIKE	GOLFER	PGA SENIORS, 112 T P C BLVD	PONTE VEDRA BEACH, FL 32082
HILL, MILT	BASEBALL	REDS, 100 RIVERFRONT STADIUM	CINCINNATI, OH 45202
HILL, ORSINO	BASEBALL	POST OFFICE BOX 11087	TACOMA, WA 98411
HILL, PAMELA	TV DIRECTOR-PRODUCER	169 E 80TH ST	NEW YORK, NY 10021
HILL, PERRY	BASEBALL-INSTRUCTOR .	POST OFFICE BOX 90111	ARLINGTON, TX 76004
HILL, PHILL	TV DIRECTOR	LONDON MGT, 235-241 REGENT ST ...	LONDON W1R 4PH .... ENGLAND
HILL, RANDAL	FOOTBALL	DOLPHINS, 2269 NW 199TH ST	MIAMI, FL 33056
HILL, RICK	ACTOR	280 S BEVERLY DR #400	BEVERLY HILLS, CA 90212
HILL, SETH	TV WRITER-DIRECTOR ..	17130 PALISADES CIR	PACIFIC PALISADES, CA 90272
HILL, STEPHEN	SINGER-GUITARIST	2510 STINSON RD	NASHVILLE, TN 37211
HILL, STEVEN	ACTOR	18 JILL LN	MONSEY, NY 10952
HILL, TERENCE	ACTOR	POST OFFICE BOX 818	STOCKBRIDGE, MA 01262
HILL, TYRONE	BASEBALL	POST OFFICE BOX 855	BELOIT, WI 53511
HILL, TYRONE	BASKETBALL	GOLDEN STATE WARRIORS	....
	....	OAKLAND COLISEUM ARENA	....
	....	NIMITZ FWY & HEGENBERGER RD	OAKLAND, CA 94621
HILL, WALTER	WRITER-PRODUCER	31368 BROAD BEACH RD	MALIBU, CA 90265
HILL, WILLIAM	TV PRODUCER	DUKES KILN, GERARDS CROSS	BUCKS SL9 7HD .... ENGLAND
HILL CITY	C & W GROUP	102 E EXCHANGE AVE #300	FORT WORTH, TX 76106
HILLARY, SIR EDMUND	MOUNTAINEER	228-A REMUERA RD	AUCKLAND SE2 .... NEW ZEALAND
HILLBILLY JIM	WRESTLER	POST OFFICE BOX 3859	STAMFORD, CT 06905
HILLEGAS, SHAWN	BASEBALL	RURAL ROUTE 1, BOX 39-A	SOUTH FORK, PA 15956
HILLEMANN, CHARLIE	BASEBALL	POST OFFICE DRAWER 4797	EL PASO, TX 79914
HILLER, ARTHUR	FILM DIRECTOR	1218 BENEDICT CANYON DR	BEVERLY HILLS, CA 90210
HILLER, CHUCK	BASEBALL-EXECUTIVE ..	METS, 126TH ST & ROOSEVELT AVE ..	FLUSHING, NY 11368
HILLER, DAME WENDY	ACTRESS	STRATTON RD, BEACONSFIELD	BUCKS .... ENGLAND
HILLER, WALLY	TALENT AGENT	5750 WILSHIRE BLVD #512	LOS ANGELES, CA 90036
HILLERICH, JOHN	BASEBALL EXECUTIVE ..	POST OFFICE BOX 36407	LOUISVILLE, KY 40233
HILLERMAN, JOHN	ACTOR	7102 LA PRESA DR	LOS ANGELES, CA 90068
HILLIARD, DALTON	FOOTBALL	SAINTS, 1500 POYDRAS ST	NEW ORLEANS, LA 90112
HILLIARD, RANDY	FOOTBALL	BROWNS, 80 1ST ST	BEREA, OH 44017
HILLIER, BILL	TV PRODUCER	15303 VENTURA BLVD, 11TH FLOOR ..	SHERMAN OAKS, CA 91403
HILLIER, DAVID G	DIRECTOR-PRODUCER ...	6 AVENUE RD, BRENTFORD	MIDDLESEX TW8 9MS .... ENGLAND
HILLIER, RANDY	HOCKEY	PENGUINS, CIVIC ARENA, CENTRE AV	PITTSBURGH, PA 15219
HILLKIRK, JOHN	COLUMNIST	POST OFFICE BOX 500	WASHINGTON, DC 20044
HILLMAN, CHRIS	SINGER-SONGWRITER ...	1377 HANOVER LN	VENTURA, CA 93003
HILLMAN, ERIC	BASEBALL	POST OFFICE BOX 1211	NORFOLK, VA 23502
HILLMAN, RONALD E	COMPOSER	POST OFFICE BOX 5452	BEVERLY HILLS, CA 90210
HILLMAN, TREY	BASEBALL MANAGER	POST OFFICE BOX 22093	GREENSBORO, NC 27420
HILLMAN, WILLIAM B	WRITER-PRODUCER	18251 FRIAR ST	RESEDA, CA 91335
HILLS, ANNE	SINGER	5109 OAK HAVEN LN	TAMPA, FL 33617
HILLS, ANNE	SINGER-GUITARIST	HOGEYE MUSIC, 1920 CENTRAL ST ...	EVANSTON, IL 60201
HILLS, DICK	TV WRITER	9 ADDINGTON RD, WEST WICKHAM	KENT .... ENGLAND
HILLS, R WARREN	TV DIRECTOR	3800 HOOPER AVE	BALTIMORE, MD 21211
HILMER, DAVID	CINEMATOGRAPHER	7715 SUNSET BLVD #150	LOS ANGELES, CA 90046
HILMER, DAVID	TV DIRECTOR	12011 ADDISON ST	NORTH HOLLYWOOD, CA 91607
HILTON, HOWARD	BASEBALL	3139 SOUTH "N" ST	OXNARD, CA 93030
HILTON, STAN	BASEBALL-COACH	POST OFFICE BOX 1143	BURLINGTON, NC 27216
HIMELFARB, MARVIN	WRITER	10351 SANTA MONICA BLVD #211	LOS ANGELES, CA 90025
HIMES, CAROL	TV PRODUCER	PARAMOUNT TELEVISION	....
	....	5555 MELROSE AVE	LOS ANGELES, CA 90038
HIMES, ERIC L	DIRECTOR	342 W 71ST ST	NEW YORK, NY 10023
HIMMELMAN, PETER	SINGER-SONGWRITER ...	POST OFFICE BOX 95	RIDGEWOOD, NJ 07541
HINCKLEY, ALFRED	ACTOR	THE MANHATTAN PLAZA	....
	....	400 W 43RD ST	NEW YORK, NY 10036
HINCKLEY, DAVID	FILM CRITIC	N Y DAILY NEWS, 220 E 42ND ST ...	NEW YORK, NY 10017
HINCKLEY, JOHN, JR	PATIENT	SAINT ELIZABETH'S HOSPITAL	....
	....	2700 MARTIN LUTHER KING AVE	WASHINGTON, DC 20005
HINDLE, ART	ACTOR	3005 MAIN ST	SANTA MONICA, CA 90405
HINDS, BILL	CARTOONIST	UPS, 4900 MAIN ST, 9TH FLOOR	KANSAS CITY, MO 64112
HINES, BARRY	TV WRITER	LEMON, 24 POTTERY, HOLLAND PK ...	LONDON W11 4LZ .... ENGLAND
HINES, BEN	BASEBALL COACH	1000 ELYSIAN PARK DR	LOS ANGELES, CA 90012
HINES, BRUCE	BASEBALL COACH	POST OFFICE BOX 2000	ANAHEIM, CA 92803
HINES, GREGORY	ACTOR	9350 WILSHIRE BLVD #324	BEVERLY HILLS, CA 90212
HINES, MAURICE	DANCER-CHOREOGRAPHER	259 W 10TH ST	NEW YORK, NY 10014
HINES, MIMI	ACTRESS	1605 S 11TH ST	LAS VEGAS, NV 89109
HINES, RICHARD	BASEBALL	POST OFFICE BOX 2148	WOODBRIDGE, VA 22193
HINES, RONALD	ACTOR	HOWES, 66 BERKELEY HO, HAY HILL .	LONDON W1X 7LH .... ENGLAND
HINGLE, PAT	ACTOR	41 VIOLA RD	SUFFERN, NY 10901
HINKLE, BRYAN	FOOTBALL	STEELERS, 300 STADIUM CIR	PITTSBURGH, PA 15212
HINKLE, GEORGE	FOOTBALL	POST OFFICE BOX 609609	SAN DIEGO, CA 92160
HINKLE, MIKE	BASEBALL	POST OFFICE BOX 36407	LOUISVILLE, KY 40233
HINKLE, TOM	BASEBALL SCOUT	SKYDOME, 300 BREMMER BL #3200 ...	TORONTO, ONT M5V 3B3 ...... CANADA
HINKLEY, DEL	ACTOR	2513 2ND ST #6	SANTA MONICA, CA 90405
HINRICHS, JAY	BASEBALL EXECUTIVE ..	POST OFFICE BOX 419969	KANSAS CITY, MO 64141
HINSON, JAMES H "JAY"	COMPOSER-CONDUCTOR ..	421 S LAFAYETTE PARK PL	LOS ANGELES, CA 90057
HINSON, ROY	BASKETBALL	N J NETS, MEADOWLANDS ARENA	EAST RUTHERFORD, NJ 07073
HINTON, CHRIS	FOOTBALL	FALCONS, SUWANEE RD AT I-85	SUWANEE, GA 30174

Name	Occupation	Address	City / Zip
HINTON, DARBY	ACTOR	1234 BEL AIR RD	LOS ANGELES, CA 90024
HINTON, JAMES DAVID	ACTOR	2808 OAK POINT DR	LOS ANGELES, CA 90068
HINTON, S E	SCREENWRITER	8955 BEVERLY BLVD	WEST HOLLYWOOD, CA 90048
HINTON, SAM	SINGER-GUITARIST	9420 LA JOLLA SHORES DR	LA JOLLA, CA 92037
HINTON, STEVE	BASEBALL	POST OFFICE BOX 464	APPLETON, WI 54912
HIPPAUF, HERB	BASEBALL SCOUT	6850 LAWRENCE RD	LANTANA, FL 33462
HIRAX	ROCK & ROLL GROUP	POST OFFICE BOX 2428	EL SEGUNDO, CA 90245
HIRD, BOB	TV DIRECTOR-PRODUCER	LONDON MGT, 235-241 REGENT ST	LONDON W1R 4PH ENGLAND
HIRD, THORA	ACTRESS	OLD LOFT, 21 LEINSTER MEWS	
		LANCASTER GATE	LONDON W2 3EY ENGLAND
HIRE, LOIS	WRITER	17161 OAK VIEW DR	ENCINO, CA 91316
HIRO	DIRECTOR	50 CENTRAL PARK W	NEW YORK, NY 10023
HIROOKA, TATSURO	BASEBALL EXECUTIVE	POST OFFICE BOX 48	VISALIA, CA 93279
HIROSHIMA	JAZZ GROUP	6404 WILSHIRE BLVD #800	LOS ANGELES, CA 90048
HIRSCH, CHARLES S	WRITER	209 E 23RD ST	NEW YORK, NY 10010
HIRSCH, DAVID	ACTOR-TV HOST	6255 SUNSET BLVD #627	LOS ANGELES, CA 90028
HIRSCH, ELROY "CRAZY LEGS"	ACTOR	1440 MONROE ST	MADISON, WI 53711
HIRSCH, GLENN	COMEDIAN	ICM, 8899 BEVERLY BLVD	LOS ANGELES, CA 90048
HIRSCH, JAMES GORDON	TV WRITER	1075 CASIANO RD	LOS ANGELES, CA 90049
HIRSCH, JUDD	ACTOR	POST OFFICE BOX 25909	LOS ANGELES, CA 90025
HIRSCH, TIBOR	TV DIRECTOR	32 W 53RD ST	NEW YORK, NY 10019
HIRSCHBECK, JOHN	BASEBALL UMPIRE	3135 OLD WINTER TRAIL	POLAND, OH 44514
HIRSCHFELD, GERALD	CINEMATOGRAPHER	904 HIGH VIEW DR	ARROYO GRANDE, CA 93420
HIRSCHFELD, JIM	TV DIRECTOR-PRODUCER	285 CENTRAL PARK W #2-S	NEW YORK, NY 10024
HIRSCHFIELD, AL	CARICATURIST	122 E 95TH ST	NEW YORK, NY 10028
HIRSCHFIELD, ALAN J	FILM EXECUTIVE	10201 W PICO BLVD	LOS ANGELES, CA 90064
HIRSCHFIELD, LEONARD	DIRECTOR-PRODUCER	9 E 40TH ST	NEW YORK, NY 10016
HIRSCHHORN, LINDA	SINGER-PRODUCER	POST OFFICE BOX 3929	BERKELEY, CA 94703
HIRSEN, STEVEN	TV DIRECTOR	6174 GLEN OAK WALK	LOS ANGELES, CA 90068
HIRSHAN, LEN	TALENT AGENT	151 S EL CAMINO DR	BEVERLY HILLS, CA 90212
HIRSHBECK, MARK	BASEBALL UMPIRE	497 WOODLAWN AVE	STRATFORD, CT 06497
HIRT, AL	TRUMPETER	1440 MONROE ST	MADISON, WI 53711
HIRT, CHARLES C	CONDUCTOR	1318 CORDOVA AVE	GLENDALE, CA 91207
HIRT, CHRISTIANNE	ACTRESS	11726 SAN VICENTE BLVD #300	LOS ANGELES, CA 90049
HIRTENSTEINER, RICK	BASEBALL	POST OFFICE BOX 15757	HARRISBURG, PA 17105
HISEY, JASON	BASEBALL	POST OFFICE BOX 3783	SAVANNAH, GA 31414
HISKEY, BABE	GOLFER	PGA SENIORS, 112 T P C BLVD	PONTE VEDRA BEACH, FL 32082
HISLE, LARRY	BASEBALL-INSTRUCTOR	SKYDOME, 300 BREMMER BL #3200	TORONTO, ONT M5V 3B3 CANADA
HISS, ALGER	MILITARY	LAWRENCE BUTTERWISER OFFICES	
		575 MADISON AVE	NEW YORK, NY 10022
HIT MAN, THE	WRESTLER	SEE - HART, BRET "HIT MAN"	
HITCHCOCK, STERLING	BASEBALL	ALBANY YANKEES, HERITAGE PARK	ALBANY, NY 12211
HITCHCOCK, WILLIAM G	CONDUCTOR	3640 BERRY DR	STUDIO CITY, CA 91604
HITE, SHERE	AUTHORESS	POST OFFICE BOX 5282 (FDR)	NEW YORK, NY 10022
HITE, WARREN	WRITER-PRODUCER	731 N ROSE ST	BURBANK, CA 91505
HITTLEMAN, CARL K	WRITER-PRODUCER	8365 W 1ST ST	LOS ANGELES, CA 90048
HITZ	ROCK & ROLL GROUP	3717 W 50TH ST #L-2	MINNEAPOLIS, MN 55410
HITZEMAN, SHIRLEY	SINGER	PROCESS, 439 WILEY AVE	FRANKLIN, PA 16323
HITZIG, RUPPERT	WRITER-PRODUCER	34 GRAMMERCY PARK E	NEW YORK, NY 10003
HLINKA, WERNER	DIRECTOR	200 WINSTON, TWR #1815	CLIFFSIDE PARK, NJ 07010
HMIELEWSKI, CHRIS	BASEBALL	POLECATS, 608 N SLAPPEY BLVD	ALBANY, GA 31701
HNATYSCHAK, JOHN	BODYBUILDER	POST OFFICE BOX 4045	BAYTONE, NJ 07002
HO, A KITMAN	FILM PRODUCER	CAA, 9830 WILSHIRE BLVD	BEVERLY HILLS, CA 90212
HO, DON	SINGER-SONGWRITER	277 LEWERS ST	HONOLULU, HI 96815
HO, QUANG	ARTIST	1743 S CLARKSON ST	DENVER, CO 80210
HOADE, MARTIN	WRI-DIR-PROD	370 1ST AVE	NEW YORK, NY 10010
HOAG, MITZI	ACTRESS	3800 BARHAM BLVD #303	LOS ANGELES, CA 90068
HOAGE, TERRY	FOOTBALL	POST OFFICE BOX 17247 (DULLES)	WASHINGTON, DC 20041
HOAGLAND, PETER	U S CONGRESSMAN	8424 ZORINSKY FEDERAL BLDG	OMAHA, NE 68102
HOAGLIN, FRED	FOOTBALL COACH	N Y GIANTS, GIANTS STADIUM	EAST RUTHERFORD, NJ 07073
HOARD, LEROY	FOOTBALL	BROWNS, 80 1ST ST	BEREA, OH 44017
HOARE, KEN	TV WRITER	38 CHEVERTON RD	LONDON N19 3AZ ENGLAND
HOARE, TONY	PLAYWRIGHT	WGGB, 430 EDGWARE RD	LONDON W2 1EH ENGLAND
HOBAN, GORDON	ACTOR-WRITER	1722 REDCLIFF ST	LOS ANGELES, CA 90026
HOBAN, ROBERT	WRITER	1722 REDCLIFF ST	LOS ANGELES, CA 90026
HOBARD, RICK	THEATER PRODUCER	234 W 44TH ST	NEW YORK, NY 10036
HOBART, FENTON, JR	SCREENWRITER	8955 BEVERLY BLVD	WEST HOLLYWOOD, CA 90048
HOBART, ROSE	ACTRESS	23388 MULHOLLAND HIGHWAY	WOODLAND HILLS, CA 91364
HOBBS, BECKY	SINGER	TAYLOR, 2401 12TH AVE S	NASHVILLE, TN 37204
HOBBS, LYNDALL GEORGINA	DIRECTOR	DGA, 7920 SUNSET BLVD, 6TH FL	LOS ANGELES, CA 90046
HOBBS, STEPHEN	FOOTBALL	POST OFFICE BOX 17247 (DULLES)	WASHINGTON, DC 20041
HOBBY, MARION	FOOTBALL	PATRIOTS, FOXBORO STADIUM, RT #1	FOXBORO, MA 02035
HOBDAY, SIMON	GOLFER	PGA SENIORS, 112 T P C BLVD	PONTE VEDRA BEACH, FL 32082
HOBERG, RICK	ARTIST	1351 OCEAN PARK WALK #106	SANTA MONICA, CA 90405
HOBERMAN, ARTHUR	CONDUCTOR	13625 BASSETT ST	VAN NUYS, CA 91405
HOBIN, BILL	DIRECTOR-PRODUCER	DGA, 110 W 57TH ST	NEW YORK, NY 10019
HOBLIT, GREGORY	TV WRITER-DIRECTOR	328 S WESTGATE AVE	LOS ANGELES, CA 90049
HOBSON, BUTCH	BASEBALL MANAGER	FENWAY PARK, 4 YAWKEY WY	BOSTON, MA 02215
HOBSON, DAVID L	U S CONGRESSMAN	POST OFFICE BUILDING, ROOM 220	
		150 N LIMESTONE ST	SPRINGFIELD, OH 45501
HOBSON, JAMES	DIRECTOR-PRODUCER	984 BEL AIR RD	LOS ANGELES, CA 90077
HOBSON, TODD	BASEBALL	POST OFFICE BOX 1556	ASHEVILLE, NC 28802
HOCH, SCOTT	GOLFER	POST OFFICE BOX 109601	PALM BCH GARDENS, FL 33418
HOCHBERG, VICTORIA	FILM WRITER-DIRECTOR	6825 ALTA LOMA TERR	HOLLYWOOD, CA 90068
HOCHBRUECKNER, GEORGE	U S CONGRESSMAN	3771 NESCONET HWY #213	CENTEREACH, NY 11720

HOCHULI, ED	FOOTBALL REFEREE	NFL, 410 PARK AVE	NEW YORK, NY	10022
HOCK, ALLISON	TV WRITER	132 S LASKY DR #B	BEVERLY HILLS, CA	90212
HOCK, PETER	ACTOR-STUNTMAN	30 WARWICK LN	BASKING RIDGE, NJ	07920
HOCKETT, DON	COMPOSER-CONDUCTOR	1504 VIA MONTEMAR	PALOS VERDES, CA	90274
HOCKING, DENNY	BASEBALL	POST OFFICE BOX 48	VISALIA, CA	93279
HOCKS, GERRARD	ACTOR	10 AVENUE CT, RIVERDALE PK		
		RANMOOR	SHEFFIELD S10 3DR	ENGLAND
HODEL, CHRIS	BASEBALL UMPIRE	2101 E BROADWAY #35	TEMPE, AZ	85282
HODER, MARK J	COMPOSER	POST OFFICE BOX 71082	LOS ANGELES, CA	90071
HODGE, DOUGLAS	ACTOR	MEGAN WILLIS AND GARRICKS		
		7 GARRICK ST, COUNT GARDEN	LONDON WC2	ENGLAND
HODGE, GOMER	BASEBALL COACH	1501 W 16TH ST	INDIANAPOLIS, IN	46202
HODGE, KEN	HOCKEY	BRUINS, 150 CAUSEWAY ST	BOSTON, MA	02114
HODGE, MAX EUGENE	TV WRITER	4034 VENTURA CANYON AVE	SHERMAN OAKS, CA	91423
HODGE, PATRICIA	ACTRESS	ICM, 388-396 OXFORD ST	LONDON W1	ENGLAND
HODGE, ROBERT W	TV-COMEDY WRITER	350 W 55TH ST	NEW YORK, NY	10019
HODGE, ROY	BASEBALL	POST OFFICE BOX 418	SAINT CHARLES, IL	60174
HODGE, TIM	BASEBALL	POST OFFICE BOX 957	DUNEDIN, FL	34697
HODGES, CRAIG	BASKETBALL	980 N MICHIGAN AVE #1600	CHICAGO, IL	60611
HODGES, DARREN	BASEBALL	ALBANY YANKEES, HERITAGE PARK	ALBANY, NY	12211
HODGES, GEORGE ROBERT	TV WRITER	1236 N LARRABEE ST	LOS ANGELES, CA	90069
HODGES, JOY	ACTRESS	BOX 254	KATONAH, NY	10536
HODGES, KEN	CINEMATOGRAPHER	21 SOUTH DR, FERRING		
		WORTHING	SUSSEX	ENGLAND
HODGES, MICHAEL	FILM WRITER-DIRECTOR	HATTON, 29 ROEHAMPTON GATE	LONDON SW15 5JR	ENGLAND
HODGES, MIKE	ARTIST	1018 W SHAW ST	FORT WORTH, TX	76110
HODGES, PATRICIA	ACTRESS	165 W 46TH ST #1109	NEW YORK, NY	10036
HODGINS, DICK	CARTOONIST	KING FEATURES, 216 E 45TH ST	NEW YORK, NY	10017
HODGSON, DAVIS	BASEBALL SCOUT	POST OFFICE BOX 2000	ANAHEIM, CA	92803
HODSHIRE, ALLEN Z	DIRECTOR	1333 N SWEETZER AVE #3-A	LOS ANGELES, CA	90069
HODSON, CHRISTOPHER	FILM-TV DIRECTOR	5 HILLSIDE, WIMBLEDON COMMON	LONDON SW19	ENGLAND
HODSON, DONAL	ACTOR	FERNANDO PIAZZA AGENCY		
		VIA EMILIO MOROSINI 18	ROME 00153	ITALY
HOEFLING, GUS	BASEBALL EXECUTIVE	POST OFFICE BOX 7575	PHILADELPHIA, PA	19101
HOEGSTROM, JON M	DIRECTOR-PRODUCER	POST OFFICE BOX 1410	TAMPA, FL	33601
HOELTZ, EDWARD R	COMPOSER	1340 N PARKSIDE AVE	CHICAGO, IL	60651
HOEME, STEVE	BASEBALL	POST OFFICE BOX 611	WATERLOO, IA	50704
HOENIG, MICHAEL	COMPOSER	1308 FACTORY PL #12	LOS ANGELES, CA	90004
HOEST, BILL	CARTOONIST	PARADE, 750 3RD AVE	NEW YORK, NY	10017
HOESTEN, RAYMOND J	DIRECTOR	72 ELMSTREE LN	JERICHO, LI, NY	11753
HOEY, MICHAEL A	WRITER-PRODUCER	12364 EMELITA ST	NORTH HOLLYWOOD, CA	91607
HOFF, JIM	BASEBALL-INSTRUCTOR	SKYDOME, 300 BREMMER BL #3200	TORONTO, ONT M5V 3B3	CANADA
HOFF, SYD	CARTOONIST	POST OFFICE BOX 2463	MIAMI BEACH, FL	33140
HOFFBERG, SY	CINEMATOGRAPHER	POST OFFICE BOX 2230	HOLLYWOOD, CA	90078
HOFFENBERG, KARL A	WRITER-PRODUCER	234 S BUCKHOUT ST	IRVINGTON, NY	10533
HOFFITT, JOHN CRAIG	DIRECTOR-PRODUCER	13233 STONERIDGE PL	SHERMAN OAKS, CA	91423
HOFFMAN, ALEXANDRA VON	ACTRESS	150 W 75TH ST #8	NEW YORK, NY	10023
HOFFMAN, ALICE	SCREENWRITER	555 W 57TH ST #1230	NEW YORK, NY	10019
HOFFMAN, BERNARD	DIRECTOR	895 GREEN PL	WOODMERE, NY	11598
HOFFMAN, BOBBY	CASTING DIRECTOR	1438 N GOWER ST	LOS ANGELES, CA	90028
HOFFMAN, DOUGLAS	WRITER	TIME INC, 1271 6TH AVE	NEW YORK, NY	10020
HOFFMAN, DUSTIN	ACTOR	75 ROCKEFELLER PLAZA #1104	NEW YORK, NY	10019
HOFFMAN, EUGENE	ARTIST	827 ELM ST #3	FORT COLLINS, CO	80521
HOFFMAN, GARY M	DIRECTOR	4650 FORMAN AVE	TOLUCA LAKE, CA	91602
HOFFMAN, GLENN	BASEBALL-MANAGER	POST OFFICE BOX 2887	VERO BEACH, FL	32961
HOFFMAN, JOSEPH	WRITER-PRODUCER	1318 WARNER AVE	LOS ANGELES, CA	90024
HOFFMAN, MILT	DIRECTOR	4231 CANOGA AVE	WOODLAND HILLS, CA	91364
HOFFMAN, SHAUNA	ACTRESS	WHITAKER, 12725 VENTURA BLVD	STUDIO CITY, CA	91604
HOFFMAN, SHERRELL	TV DIRECTOR	243 E 71ST ST	NEW YORK, NY	10021
HOFFMAN, STEVE	FOOTBALL COACH	COWBOYS, 1 COWBOYS PARKWAY	IRVING, TX	75063
HOFFMAN, TREVOR	BASEBALL	POST OFFICE BOX 11002	CHATTANOOGA, TN	37401
HOFFMAN, WILLIAM	PLAYWRIGHT	199 PRINCE ST	NEW YORK, NY	10012
HOFFMANN, BETTYE K	TV EXECUTIVE	NBC-TV, 30 ROCKEFELLER PLAZA	NEW YORK, NY	10112
HOFFNER, JAMIE	BASEBALL	POST OFFICE BOX 598	BINGHAMTON, NY	13902
HOFFS, SUSANNA	ACTRESS-SINGER	9720 WILSHIRE BLVD #400	BEVERLY HILLS, CA	90212
HOFFS, TAMAR SIMON	WRITER-PRODUCER	1106 MARINE ST	SANTA MONICA, CA	90405
HOFSISS, JACK	FILM DIRECTOR	DGA, 110 W 57TH ST	NEW YORK, NY	10019
HOGAN, BEN	GOLFER	2911 W PAFFORD	FORT WORTH, TX	76110
HOGAN, GERALD	CABLE EXECUTIVE	1050 TECHWOOD DR, NW	ATLANTA, GA	30318
HOGAN, HULK	WRESTLER-ACTOR	POST OFFICE BOX 3859	STAMFORD, CT	06905
HOGAN, JERRY	TALENT AGENT	247 S BEVERLY DR #102	BEVERLY HILLS, CA	90210
HOGAN, LINDA	TV PRODUCER	WNYW-TV, 205 E 67TH ST	NEW YORK, NY	10021
HOGAN, PAUL	ACTOR	1900 AVE OF THE STARS #2270	LOS ANGELES, CA	90067
HOGAN, ROBERT	ACTOR	344 W 89TH ST #1-B	NEW YORK, NY	10024
HOGAN, ROGER E	COMPOSER	13150 PHILLIPPI	SYLMAR, CA	91342
HOGAN, WILLIAM H	WRITER-PRODUCER	1311 MORNINGSIDE DR	BURBANK, CA	91506
HOGARTH, FREDDIE	ACTOR	69 SAINT QUINTIN AVE, FLAT 1	LONDON W10	ENGLAND
HOGE, MERRIL	FOOTBALL	STEELERS, 300 STADIUM CIR	PITTSBURGH, PA	15212
HOGESTYN, DRAKE	ACTOR	9255 SUNSET BLVD #515	LOS ANGELES, CA	90069
HOGG, IAN	ACTOR	OXGANGS HOUSE, NETTLETON TOP	LINCOLN LN7 6S7	ENGLAND
HOGGAN, MICHAEL B	FILM EDITOR	ACE, 1041 N FORMOSA AVE	WEST HOLLYWOOD, CA	90046
HOGSETT, JOSEPH H	SECRETARY OF STATE	STATE HOUSE BUILDING	INDIANAPOLIS, IN	46204
HOGUE, ALEXANDER	PAINTER	4052 E 23RD ST	TULSA, OK	74114
HOGUE, BENOIT	HOCKEY	SABRES, MEMORIAL AUDITORIUM	BUFFALO, NY	14202
HOHMAN, ROBERT	TALENT AGENT	9220 SUNSET BLVD #311	LOS ANGELES, CA	90069

HOHN, BILL	BASEBALL UMPIRE	NATIONAL LEAGUE, 350 PARK AVE	NEW YORK, NY 10022
HOILES, CHRIS	BASEBALL	ORIOLE PARK, 333 W CAMDEN ST	BALTIMORE, MD 21201
HOIT, MICHAEL	ACTOR-PRODUCER	2166 RIDGEMONT DR	LOS ANGELES, CA 90046
HOKUF, KEN	BASEBALL	POST OFFICE BOX 2437	MODESTO, CA 95351
HOLBA, HEINZ	TALENT AGENT	L A MODELS, 8335 SUNSET BLVD	HOLLYWOOD, CA 90069
HOLBERT, RAY	BASEBALL	POST OFFICE BOX 1420	WICHITA, KS 67201
HOLBROOK, BILL	CARTOONIST	KING FEATURES, 216 E 45TH ST	NEW YORK, NY 10017
HOLBROOK, HAL	ACTOR-DIRECTOR	15301 VENTURA BLVD #345	SHERMAN OAKS, CA 91403
HOLCH, ARTHUR	WRITER-PRODUCER	49 SUMNER RD	GREENWICH, CT 06830
HOLCOMB, ROD	TV DIRECTOR	1337 BOSTON ST	ALTADENA, CA 91001
HOLCOMB, SCOTT	BASEBALL	ALBANY YANKEES, HERITAGE PARK	ALBANY, NY 12211
HOLCOMBE, WENDY	SINGER	POST OFFICE BOX 607	ALABASTER, AL 35007
HOLDEN, DAVID A	DIRECTOR	POST OFFICE BOX 392	LOS ALAMOS, CA 93440
HOLDEN, JIM	BASEBALL SCOUT	6850 LAWRENCE RD	LANTANA, FL 33462
HOLDEN, LAWRENCE	WRITER	4954 HAZELTINE AVE #4	SHERMAN OAKS, CA 91423
HOLDEN, MARJEAN	ACTRESS	6683 SUNSET BLVD #2	HOLLYWOOD, CA 90028
HOLDEN, REBECCA	ACTRESS-SINGER	1105 16TH ST S #C	NASHVILLE, TN 37212
HOLDER, RAY	COND-ARR-CHOREO	WEYBREAD HOUSE, WEYBREAD	SUFFOLK ENGLAND
HOLDERNESS, BEAR & HOT BEAR	C & W GROUP	HOT BEAR, 420 W PLATTE AVE	COLORADO SPRINGS, CO 80905
HOLDERNESS, SUE	ACTRESS	10 RECTORY CLOSE, WINDSOR	BERKS SL4 5ER ENGLAND
HOLDRIDGE, DAVID	BASEBALL	POST OFFICE BOX 1742	PALM SPRINGS, CA 92263
HOLDRIDGE, LEE	COMPOSER-CONDUCTOR	1060 SHADOW HILL WY	BEVERLY HILLS, CA 90210
HOLDSWORTH, ALLAN	SINGER-GUITARIST	17609 VENTURA BLVD #212	ENCINO, CA 91316
HOLE, JONATHAN	ACTOR	5024 BALBOA BLVD	ENCINO, CA 91316
HOLE, JUDITH F	TV PRODUCER	CBS NEWS, 524 W 57TH ST	NEW YORK, NY 10019
HOLEFELDER, SUSAN	ARTIST	POST OFFICE BOX 1666	SCOTTSDALE, AZ 85252
HOLENDER, ADAM	DIRECTOR	136 E 64TH ST	NEW YORK, NY 10021
HOLIDAY, DOC & SOUL SURVIVORS	ROCK & ROLL GROUP	J BIRD, 4905 S ATLANTIC AVE	DAYTONA BEACH, FL 32019
HOLIDAY, HOPE	ACTRESS	8538 EASTWOOD RD	LOS ANGELES, CA 90046
HOLIDAY, MARVIN "DOC"	SINGER	PROCESS, 439 WILEY AVE	FRANKLIN, PA 16323
HOLIFIELD, RICKEY	BASEBALL	POST OFFICE BOX 1110	MYRTLE BEACH, SC 29578
HOLIK, BOBBY	HOCKEY	WHALERS, 1 CIVIC CENTER PLAZA	HARTFORD, CT 06103
HOLIMAN, BOB	SINGER	AM CREAT ENT, 536 E ST	LAS VEGAS, NV 89104
HOLLAND	ROCK & ROLL GROUP	3 E 54TH ST #1400	NEW YORK, NY 10022
HOLLAND, AMY	SINGER	9044 MELROSE AVE #306	LOS ANGELES, CA 90069
HOLLAND, BETH	ACTRESS	146 CENTRAL PARK W #12-F	NEW YORK, NY 10023
HOLLAND, BRAD	ARTIST	96 GREENE ST	NEW YORK, NY 10012
HOLLAND, JAMIE	FOOTBALL	RAIDERS, 332 CENTER ST	EL SEGUNDO, CA 90245
HOLLAND, JEFFREY	ACTOR	GRIFFITHS, 185 OXFORD ST	LONDON W1R 1TA ENGLAND
HOLLAND, JOHNNY	FOOTBALL	PACKERS, 1265 LOMBARDI AVE	GREEN BAY, WI 54307
HOLLAND, RANDY	BASEBALL TRAINER	CHIEFS, MAC ARTHUR STADIUM	SYRACUSE, NY 13208
HOLLAND, SID	BASEBALL	POST OFFICE BOX 3609	PORT CHARLOTTE, FL 33949
HOLLAND, TIM	BASEBALL	POST OFFICE BOX 230	HAGERSTOWN, MD 21740
HOLLAND, TOM	WRITER-PRODUCER	10351 SANTA MONICA BLVD #211	LOS ANGELES, CA 90025
HOLLANDER, XAXIERA	AUTHORESS	410 PARK AVE, 10TH FLOOR	NEW YORK, NY 10022
HOLLANDSWORTH, TODD	BASEBALL	POST OFFICE BOX 10031	BAKERSFIELD, CA 93389
HOLLAS, DONALD	FOOTBALL	BENGALS, 200 RIVERFRONT STADIUM	CINCINNATI, OH 45202
HOLLEB, ALAN	FILM WRITER-DIRECTOR	1653 MALCOLM AVE	LOS ANGELES, CA 90024
HOLLENBACK, DAVE	BASEBALL TRAINER	POST OFFICE BOX 2437	MODESTO, CA 95351
HOLLENBAUGH, GAYLE	FILM PRODUCER	ASTA PRODS, 126 S ORLANDO AVE	LOS ANGELES, CA 90048
HOLLERITH, CHARLES, JR	THEATER PRODUCER	18 W 55TH ST	NEW YORK, NY 10019
HOLLEY, BERNARD	ACTOR	361 SANDYCOMBE RD, RICHMOND	SURREY TW9 3PR ENGLAND
HOLLEY, BOBBY	BASEBALL	POST OFFICE BOX 4756	JACKSONVILLE, FL 32201
HOLLEY, LEE	CARTOONIST	KING FEATURES, 216 E 45TH ST	NEW YORK, NY 10017
HOLLIDAY, BRIAN	BASEBALL	POST OFFICE BOX 824	BURLINGTON, IA 52601
HOLLIDAY, DAVE	BASEBALL SCOUT	POST OFFICE BOX 7000	PITTSBURGH, PA 15212
HOLLIDAY, JENNIFER	SINGER-ACTRESS	9255 SUNSET BLVD #1115	LOS ANGELES, CA 90069
HOLLIDAY, KENE	ACTOR	4659 MORSE AVE	SHERMAN OAKS, CA 91423
HOLLIDAY, POLLY	ACTRESS	LANTZ, 888 7TH AVE, 25TH FLOOR	NEW YORK, NY 10106
HOLLIMAN, EARL	ACTOR	POST OFFICE BOX 1969	STUDIO CITY, CA 91604
HOLLIMAN, JOHN	NEWS CORRESPONDENT	1050 TECHWOOD DR, NW	ATLANTA, GA 30318
HOLLINGER, HY	COLUMNIST	5700 WILSHIRE BLVD #120	LOS ANGELES, CA 90036
HOLLINGS, ERNEST F	U S SENATOR	200 E BAY ST #112	CHARLESTON, SC 29401
HOLLINGSWORTH, JIMMIE EARL	DIRECTOR	KAMINSKY, 521 MADISON AVE	NEW YORK, NY 10022
HOLLINS, DAVE	BASEBALL	POST OFFICE BOX 7575	PHILADELPHIA, PA 19101
HOLLINS, JESSE	BASEBALL	POST OFFICE DRAWER 1207	ZEBULON, NC 27597
HOLLINS, LIONEL	BASKETBALL COACH	SUNS, 2910 N CENTRAL AVE	PHOENIX, AZ 85012
HOLLOMAN, BRIDGET	ACTRESS	11846 VENTURA BLVD #100	STUDIO CITY, CA 91604
HOLLOWAY, CLYDE	U S CONGRESSMAN	POST OFFICE BOX 410	ALEXANDRIA, LA 71309
HOLLOWAY, CORNELL	FOOTBALL	POST OFFICE BOX 535000	INDIANPOLIS, IN 46253
HOLLOWAY, STERLING	ACTOR	POST OFFCIE BOX 11365	LOS ANGELES, CA 90011
HOLLY, DOYLE	SINGER-GUITARIST	POST OFFICE BOX 148	HENDERSONVILLE, TN 37075
HOLLYMAN, THOMAS B	DIRECTOR	300 E 40TH ST	NEW YORK, NY 10016
HOLLYWOOD SAXONS, THE	VOCAL GROUP	POST OFFICE BOX 01473	LOS ANGELES, CA 90001
HOLLYWOODS, THE	ROCK & ROLL GROUP	41 BRITAIN ST #200	TORONTO, ONT M5A 1R7 CANADA
HOLM, CELESTE	ACTRESS-SINGER	88 CENTRAL PARK W	NEW YORK, NY 10023
HOLM, IAN	ACTOR	80 IVERA CT	LONDON W8 ENGLAND
HOLM, JOHNNY	SINGER	3717 W 50TH ST #L-2	MINNEAPOLIS, MN 55437
HOLMAN, BRAD	BASEBALL	POST OFFICE BOX 9194	HAMPTON, VA 23670
HOLMAN, BRIAN	BASEBALL	POST OFFICE BOX 4100	SEATTLE, WA 98104
HOLMAN, RODNEY	FOOTBALL	BENGALS, 200 RIVERFRONT STADIUM	CINCINNATI, OH 45202
HOLMAN, SHAWN	BASEBALL	ROUTE 3, EDGEWOOD RD	SEWICKLEY, PA 15143
HOLMAN, W L	COMPOSER	2236 SAN MARCO DR	LOS ANGELES, CA 90068
HOLMBERG, DENNIS	BASEBALL MANAGER	POST OFFICE BOX 957	DUNEDIN, FL 34697
HOLMES, CLINT	SINGER	11122 LANDALE ST	NORTH HOLLYWOOD, CA 91602

Name	Occupation	Address	City	Zip/Country
HOLMES, DARREN	BASEBALL	2850 W 20TH AVE	DENVER, CO	80211
HOLMES, DARREN	BASEBALL	BREWERS, 201 S 46TH ST	MILWAUKEE, WI	53214
HOLMES, ELIZABETH	ACTRESS	8019 1/2 MELROSE AVE #3	LOS ANGELES, CA	90046
HOLMES, JAMES R	DIRECTOR-PRODUCER	1033 S DELPHIA ST	PARK RIDGE, IL	60068
HOLMES, JENNIFER	ACTRESS	5329 SUNNYSLOPE AVE	VAN NUYS, CA	91401
HOLMES, JERRY	FOOTBALL	PACKERS, 1265 LOMBARDI AVE	GREEN BAY, WI	54307
HOLMES, LARRY	BOXER	413 NORTHAMPTON ST	EASTON, PA	18042
HOLMES, MIKE	BASEBALL EXECUTIVE	POST OFFICE BOX 4756	JACKSONVILLE, FL	32201
HOLMES, ROBERT, JR	MUSIC ARRANGER	2509 BUCHANAN ST	NASHVILLE, TN	37208
HOLMES, RON	FOOTBALL	BRONCOS, 13655 BRONCOS PKWY	ENGLEWOOD, CO	80112
HOLMES, RUPERT	SINGER-SONGWRITER	SPOLITE ENTERPRISES, LTD		
		221 W 57TH ST, 9TH FLOOR	NEW YORK, NY	10019
HOLMES, SCOTT	ACTOR	CBS-TV, "AS THE WORLD TURNS"		
		524 W 57TH ST #5330	NEW YORK, NY	10019
HOLOHAN, PETE	FOOTBALL	CHIEFS, 1 ARROWHEAD DR	KANSAS CITY, MO	64129
HOLOVAK, MIKE	FOOTBALL EXECUTIVE	OILERS, 6910 FANNIN ST	HOUSTON, TX	77070
HOLOWCHAK, EUGENE	TV DIRECTOR	8701 METROPOLITAN	WARREN, MI	48093
HOLT, BERT	BASEBALL SCOUT	6850 LAWRENCE RD	LANTANA, FL	33462
HOLT, CHARLENE	ACTRESS	SEE - HOLT-HIARA, CHARLENE		
HOLT, DAVE	BASEBALL MANAGER	POST OFFICE BOX 238	ELMIRA, NY	14902
HOLT, DENIS	FILM PRODUCER	161 RIDGE LANGLEY, SANDERSTEAD	SURREY	ENGLAND
HOLT, FRITZ	THEATER PRODUCER	250 W 52ND ST	NEW YORK, NY	10019
HOLT, GEORGIA	ACTRESS	12341 HESBY ST	NORTH HOLLYWOOD, CA	91602
HOLT, HALEEN K	COSTUME DESIGNER	24001 GILMORE ST	WEST HILLS, CA	91307
HOLT, JENNIFER	ACTRESS	MRS BROOKE MARSH CADWALLADER		90069
		APARTADO POSTAL 170, CUERNAVACA	MORELES 62000	MEXICO
HOLT, LE ROY	FOOTBALL	DOLPHINS, 2269 NW 199TH ST	MIAMI, FL	33056
HOLT, PIERCE	FOOTBALL	S F 49ERS, 4949 CENTENNIAL BL	SANTA CLARA, CA	95054
HOLT, ROBERT I	TV WRITER	2900 VIA LA SELVA	PALOS VERDES, CA	90274
HOLT-HIARA, CHARLENE	ACTRESS	151 S EL CAMINO DR	BEVERLY HILLS, CA	90212
HOLTHOUSE, RICHARD	FILM DIRECTOR	140 FAIRBRIDGE RD	LONDON N19	ENGLAND
HOLTON, BRIAN	BASEBALL	33 WHITE PINE CT	HUNT VALLEY, MD	21030
HOLTZ, ED	BASEBALL EXECUTIVE	POST OFFICE BOX 4525	MACON, GA	31208
HOLTZ, MARK	SPORTSCASTER	POST OFFICE BOX 90111	ARLINGTON, TX	76004
HOLTZMAN, DONALD	SET DECORATOR	436 3 69TH ST	NEW YORK, NY	10021
HOLTZMAN, HENRY	DIRECTOR	33 RIVERSIDE DR	NEW YORK, NY	10023
HOLTZMAN, KEN	BASEBALL	933 PROVIDENCE	BUFFALO GROVE, IL	60089
HOLTZMAN, RICHARD	BASEBALL EXECUTIVE	POST OFFICE BOX 27045	TUCSON, AZ	85726
HOLYFIELD, EVANDER	BOXER	310 MADISON AVE #804	NEW YORK, NY	10017
HOLZEMER, MARK	BASEBALL	POST OFFICE BOX 1742	PALM SPRINGS, CA	92263
HOLZER, HANS	SCREENWRITER	555 W 57TH ST #1230	NEW YORK, NY	10019
HOM, JOHN	ARTIST	1645 AMBERWOOD DR #16	SOUTH PASADENA, CA	91030
HOME AND GARDEN	ROCK & ROLL GROUP	AFTER HOURS RECORDS		
		300 PROSPECT AVE	CLEVELAND, OH	44115
HOMEIER, SKIPPY	TV WRITER	261 S ROBERTSON BLVD	BEVERLY HILLS, CA	90211
HOMER, RAYMOND	DIRECTOR-PRODUCER	165 W 66TH ST	NEW YORK, NY	10023
HOMES, HERBERT	DIRECTOR	21 FORSTER PARKWAY	MOUNT VERNON, NY	10552
HOMGREN, MIKE	FOOTBALL COACH	S F 49ERS, 4949 CENTENNIAL BL	SANTA CLARA, CA	95054
HONEYCOMBE, GORDON	TV WRITER	ROSEMAN, 103 CHARING CROSS RD	LONDON WC2	ENGLAND
HONEYCUTT, RICK	BASEBALL	ATHLETICS'S, OAKLAND COLISEUM	OAKLAND, CA	94621
HONEYMOON SUITE	ROCK & ROLL GROUP	BOX 70, STA "C", QUEENS ST W	TORONTO, ON M6J 3M7	CANADA
HONIGBERG, GAIL R	COMEDY WRITER	2220 AVE OF THE STARS #1906	LOS ANGELES, CA	90067
HONKY TONK HEROES	C & W GROUP	POST OFFICE BOX O	EXCELSIOR, MN	55331
HONKY TONK MAN, THE	WRESTLER	POST OFFICE BOX 3859	STAMFORD, CT	06905
HOOD, CHUCK L	DIRECTOR	1015 E PROVIDENCIA AVE	BURBANK, CA	91501
HOOD, DENNIS	BASEBALL	POST OFFICE BOX 3690, STA "B"	CALGARY, ALB T2B 4M4	CANADA
HOOD, MORAG	ACTRESS	MARMONT MANAGEMENT, LTD		
		LANGHAM HOUSE, 308 REGENT ST	LONDON W1R 5AL	ENGLAND
HOOD, RANDY	BASEBALL	1090 N EUCLID AVE	SARASOTA, FL	34237
HOODOO GURUS	ROCK & ROLL GROUP	HARBOUR AGENCY PTY, LTD		
		63 WILLIAM ST, 3RD FLOOR	SYDNEY NSW 2000	AUSTRALIA
HOOGSTRATTEN, LOUISE	ACTRESS	212 COPA DE ORO RD	LOS ANGELES, CA	90024
HOOK, CHRIS	BASEBALL	POST OFFICE BOX 2001	CEDAR RAPIDS, IA	52406
HOOK, MIKE	BASEBALL	POST OFFICE BOX 230	HAGERSTOWN, MD	21740
HOOKER	ROCK & ROLL GROUP	POST OFFICE BOX 448	RADFORD, VA	24141
HOOKER, BUDDY JOE	FILM DIRECTOR	3518 W CAHUENGA BLVD #100	LOS ANGELES, CA	90068
HOOKS, BENJAMIN	NAACP PRESIDENT	260 5TH AVE	NEW YORK, NY	10001
HOOKS, CALLY	ACTRESS	2510 LYRIC AVE	LOS ANGELES, CA	90027
HOOKS, ED	ACTOR	2510 LYRIC AVE	LOS ANGELES, CA	90027
HOOKS, KEVIN	ACTOR-DIRECTOR	401 S ARDMORE ST #119	LOS ANGELES, CA	90020
HOOKS, ROBERT	ACTOR	145 N VALLEY ST	BURBANK, CA	91505
HOOKS, WILLIAM G	CABLE EXECUTIVE	HBO, 1100 6TH AVE	NEW YORK, NY	10036
HOOL, LANCE	ACTOR	13747 ROMANY DR	PACIFIC PALISADES, CA	90272
HOOPEL, MONTY	BASEBALL EXECUTIVE	POST OFFICE BOX 12	MIDLAND, TX	79702
HOOPER, BRANDON	ACTOR	ABC-TV, "GENERAL HOSPITAL"		
		4151 PROSPECT AVE	BURBANK, CA	91523
HOOPER, BUDDY	RECORD EXECUTIVE	POST OFFICE BOX 84	HERMITAGE, TN	37076
HOOPER, LESTER J, III	COMPOSER	4432 SEVENOAKS CT	WESTLAKE VILLAGE, CA	91361
HOOPER, TOBE	FILM DIRECTOR	DGA, 7920 SUNSET BLVD, 6TH FL	LOS ANGELES, CA	90046
HOOTEN, BURT	BASEBALL-COACH	POST OFFICE BOX 28268	SAN ANTONIO, TX	78228
HOOTERS, THE	ROCK & ROLL GROUP	POST OFFICE BOX 205	ARDMORE, PA	19003
HOOTKINS, WILLIAM	ACTOR	REDWAY (AIM), 5 DENMARK ST	LONDON WC2H 8LP	ENGLAND
HOOVER, CHARLES A	CONDUCTOR	12757 VENICE BLVD #3	LOS ANGELES, CA	90066
HOOVER, HOUSTON	FOOTBALL	FALCONS, SUWANEE RD AT I-85	SUWANEE, GA	30174
HOOVER, JOHN	BASEBALL	3145-B HEATHSTEAD PL	CHARLOTTE, NC	28210

Name	Occupation	Address	City	Zip
HOOYMAN, BARBARA	ACTRESS	ABC-TV, "ALL MY CHILDREN"		
		320 W 66TH ST	NEW YORK, NY	10023
HOPE, BOB	ACTOR-COMEDIAN	10346 MOORPARK ST	NORTH HOLLYWOOD, CA	91602
HOPE, JOHN	BASEBALL	POST OFFICE BOX 842	SALEM, VA	24153
HOPE, LESLIE	ACTRESS	151 S EL CAMINO DR	BEVERLY HILLS, CA	90212
HOPE, LINDA	ACTRESS	10400 MOORPARK ST	NORTH HOLLYWOOD, CA	91602
HOPKINS, ANTHONY	ACTOR	7 HIGH PARK RD, KEW, SURREY	RICHMOND TW9 3BL	ENGLAND
HOPKINS, BIG MIKE	SINGER	POST OFFICE BOX 448	RADFORD, VA	24141
HOPKINS, BO	ACTOR	12456 VENTURA BLVD #1	STUDIO CITY, CA	91604
HOPKINS, GERALD	ACTOR	ABC-TV, "GENERAL HOSPITAL"		
		4151 PROSPECT AVE	BURBANK, CA	91523
HOPKINS, JOHN	BASEBALL EXECUTIVE	POST OFFICE BOX 9503	GREENSBORO, NC	27429
HOPKINS, JOHN R	SCREENWRITER	151 S EL CAMINO DR	BEVERLY HILLS, CA	90212
HOPKINS, KAITLIN	ACTRESS	NBC-TV, "ANOTHER WORLD"		
		1268 E 14TH ST	BROOKLYN, NY	11230
HOPKINS, KAREN LEIGH	ACTRESS	131 S RODEO DR #300	BEVERLY HILLS, CA	90212
HOPKINS, LARRY J	U S CONGRESSMAN	333 W VINE ST, VINE CENTER #207	LEXINGTON, KY	40507
HOPKINS, LINDA	SINGER	2055 N IVAR ST #PH	LOS ANGELES, CA	90068
HOPKINS, NICKY	MUSICIAN	19912 ARCHWOOD ST	CANOGA PARK, CA	91306
HOPKINS, RON	BASEBALL SCOUT	POST OFFICE BOX 4100	SEATTLE, WA	98104
HOPKINS, SHIRLEY KNIGHT	ACTRESS	24 MAILMANS WY, BECKENHAM	KENT	ENGLAND
HOPKINS, TELMA	ACTRESS-SINGER	1999 AVE OF THE STARS #2850	LOS ANGELES, CA	90067
HOPKINS, WES	FOOTBALL	EAGLES, BROAD ST & PATTISON AVE	PHILADELPHIA, PA	19148
HOPMAN, GERALD	WRITER	2764 WOODWARDIA DR	LOS ANGELES, CA	90077
HOPPE, ARTHUR	POLITICIAL SATIRIST	CHRONICLE FEATURES		
		870 MARKET ST	SAN FRANCISCO, CA	94102
HOPPE, DENNIS	BASEBALL	14100 SIX MILE CYPRESS PKWY	FORT MYERS, FL	33912
HOPPEN, DAVE	BASKETBALL	310 N KINGS DR	CHARLOTTE, NC	28204
HOPPER, DENNIS	ACTOR-DIRECTOR	330 INDIANA AVE	VENICE, CA	90291
HOPPER, HAROLD H	DIRECTOR	815 AVENIDA SALVADOR	SAN CLEMENTE, CA	92672
HOPPER, PEGGE	ARTIST	O'GRADY ADVERTISING ARTS		
		3166 ALIKA AVE	HONOLULU, HI	96817
HOPPER, RICHARD	COSTUME DESIGNER	13949 VENTURA BLVD #309	SHERMAN OAKS, CA	91423
HOPSON, DENNIS	BASKETBALL	980 N MICHIGAN AVE #1600	CHICAGO, IL	60611
HORACEK, TONY	HOCKEY	FLYERS, SPECTRUM, PATTISON PL	PHILADELPHIA, PA	19148
HORAN, BARBRA	ACTRESS	928 N ALFRED ST #204	LOS ANGELES, CA	90069
HORAN, DON	DIRECTOR	248 CROWN RD	BOONTON, NJ	07005
HORAN, MAURYNE	ACTRESS	32-65TH ST	ASTORIA, NY	11103
HORAN, MIKE	FOOTBALL	BRONCOS, 13655 BRONCOS PKWY	ENGLEWOOD, CO	80112
HORAVA, MILOSLAV	HOCKEY	POST OFFICE BOX 90111	ARLINGTON, TX	76004
HORDERN, MICHAEL	ACTOR	FLAT 7, RECTORY CHAMBERS		
		OLD CHURCH ST	LONDON SW3	ENGLAND
HORGAN, PATRICK	ACTOR	201 E 89TH ST	NEW YORK, NY	10028
HORGER, EMORY	DIRECTOR	10721 ADDISON ST	NORTH HOLLYWOOD, CA	91601
HORKY, JAMES E	TV DIRECTOR	212 N VALLEY ST #14	BURBANK, CA	91505
HORLEN, JOEL	BASEBALL-COACH	POST OFFICE BOX 3665	OMAHA, NE	68103
HORN, ALAN	TV PRODUCER	1901 AVE OF THE STARS	LOS ANGELES, CA	90067
HORN, CAMILLA	ACTRESS	STEIN DLGASSE 2	8036 HERRCHING	GERMANY
HORN, JOAN KELLY	U S CONGRESSWOMAN	9666 OLIVE BLVD	SAINT LOUIS, MO	63132
HORN, LISA	TV PRODUCER	543 FOOTHILL RD	BRIDGEWATER, NJ	08807
HORN, ROBIN F	COMPOSER	2219 BEN LOMOND DR	LOS ANGELES, CA	90027
HORN, SAM	BASEBALL	ORIOLE PARK, 333 W CAMDEN ST	BALTIMORE, MD	21201
HORN, STEVE	DIRECTOR	DGA, 7920 SUNSET BLVD, 6TH FL	LOS ANGELES, CA	90046
HORN, WALT	BASEBALL TRAINER	POST OFFICE BOX 11087	TACOMA, WA	98411
HORNACEK, JEFF	BASKETBALL	SUNS, 2910 N CENTRAL AVE	PHOENIX, AZ	85012
HORNADAY, JEFFREY	CHOREOGRAPHER	132 S SPALDING DR #101	BEVERLY HILLS, CA	90212
HORNE, LENA	SINGER	23 E 74TH ST	NEW YORK, NY	10021
HORNE, SUZI	ACTRESS	3800 BARHAM BLVD #303	LOS ANGELES, CA	90068
HORNE, TYRONE	BASEBALL	POST OFFICE BOX 6748	ROCKFORD, IL	61125
HORNE, VICTORIA	ACTRESS	OAKIE, 18650 DEVONSHIRE ST	NORTHRIDGE, CA	91324
HORNER, BOB	BASEBALL	209 STEEPLECHASE DR	IRVING, TX	75062
HORNER, HARRY	FILM DIRECTOR	728 BROOKTREE RD	PACIFIC PALISADES, CA	90272
HORNER, JAMES	COMPOSER	728 BROOKTREE RD	PACIFIC PALISADES, CA	90272
HORNER, RICHARD	THEATER PRODUCER	65 W 55TH ST	NEW YORK, NY	10019
HORNSBY, BRUCE & THE RANGE	ROCK & ROLL GROUP	POST OFFICE BOX 3545	WILLIAMSBURG, VA	23187
HORNUNG, RICHARD	COSTUME DESIGNER	13949 VENTURA BLVD #309	SHERMAN OAKS, CA	91423
HOROVITCH, DAVID	ACTOR	37 CHURCH LN, TEDDINGTON	MIDDLESEX TW11 8PA	ENGLAND
HOROVITZ, ISRAEL	PLAYWRIGHT	SAFIER, 667 MADISON AVE	NEW YORK, NY	10021
HOROVITZ, LOUIS J	TV DIRECTOR	8944 CRESCENT DR	LOS ANGELES, CA	90046
HOROWICZ, MICHAEL A	NEWS WRITER	WABC-TV, 7 LINCOLN SQ	NEW YORK, NY	10023
HOROWITZ, ANTHONY	COMPOSER	13843 OXNARD ST #38	VAN NUYS, CA	91401
HOROWITZ, DAVID	TV HOST	POST OFFICE BOX 49915	LOS ANGELES, CA	90049
HOROWITZ, ED	BASEBALL	POST OFFICE BOX 230	HAGERSTOWN, MD	21740
HOROWITZ, ROBERT	BASEBALL TRAINER	POST OFFICE BOX 3496	DAVENPORT, IA	52808
HORSBRUGH, OLIVER	FILM DIRECTOR	126 HAMPTON RD, TWICKEHAM	MIDDLESEX	ENGLAND
HORSEY, DAVID	CARTOONIST	TRIBUNE, 64 E CONCORD ST	ORLANDO, FL	32801
HORSFORD, ANNA MARIA	ACTRESS	POST OFFICE BOX 29765	LOS ANGELES, CA	90029
HORSLEY, LEE	ACTOR	1941 CUMMINGS DR	LOS ANGELES, CA	90027
HORSMAN, VINCE	BASEBALL	ATHLETICS'S, OAKLAND COLISEUM	OAKLAND, CA	94621
HORTON, ETHAN	FOOTBALL	RAIDERS, 332 CENTER ST	EL SEGUNDO, CA	90245
HORTON, FRANK	U S CONGRESSMAN	314 K B KEATING FEDERAL BLDG	ROCHESTER, NY	14614
HORTON, JOHN J	DIRECTOR	17 SURREYHILL PL	HUNTINGTON, NY	11743
HORTON, NEAL	BASEBALL	250 STADIUM PLAZA	SAINT LOUIS, MO	63102
HORTON, PETER	ACTOR	222 ADELAIDE DR	SANTA MONICA, CA	90402
HORTON, RAY	FOOTBALL	COWBOYS, 1 COWBOYS PARKWAY	IRVING, TX	75063

HORTON, RICKEY	BASEBALL	4385 TUTT BLVD	COLORADO SPRINGS, CO	80922
HORTON, RICKY	BASEBALL-COACH	POST OFFICE BOX 3452	KINSTON, NC	28502
HORTON, ROBERT	ACTOR	5317 ANDASOL AVE	ENCINO, CA	91316
HORTON, WILLIE	BASEBALL	19312 STEEL ST	DETROIT, MI	48235
HORVATH, IMRE	TV DIRECTOR-PRODUCER	RAINBOW, 600 W END AVE	NEW YORK, NY	10024
HORVATH, JOHN	DIRECTOR	145 E 52ND ST	NEW YORK, NY	10022
HORVITZ, LOUIS J	TV DIRECTOR	8944 CRESCENT DR	LOS ANGELES, CA	90046
HORWICH, FRANCES	ACTRESS-TV HOST	WMAQ TEELEVISION STATION		
		MERCHANDISE MART PLAZA	CHICAGO, IL	60654
HORWITZ, ALLAN	MAGAZINE PUBLISHER	TV NEWS MAGAZINE, 80 8TH AVE	NEW YORK, NY	10011
HORWITZ, MICHAEL F	DIRECTOR	DGA, 7920 SUNSET BLVD, 6TH FL	LOS ANGELES, CA	90046
HORWITZ, MURRAY	TV DIRECTOR-PRODUCER	2836 ADDENDALE PL, NW	WASHINGTON, DC	20008
HOSEY, DWAYNE	BASEBALL	POST OFFICE BOX 1420	WICHITA, KS	67201
HOSEY, STEVE	BASEBALL	5999 E VAN BUREN ST	PHOENIX, AZ	85008
HOSKINS, BOB	ACTOR	40 BELMONT RD	EXETER, DEVEN	ENGLAND
HOSSACK, ALLISON	ACTRESS	NBC-TV, "ANOTHER WORLD"		
		1268 E 14TH ST	BROOKLYN, NY	11230
HOSSEIN, ROBERT	ACTOR	33 RUE GALILEE	75116 PARIS	FRANCE
HOSTETLER, JEFF	FOOTBALL	N Y GIANTS, GIANTS STADIUM	EAST RUTHERFORD, NJ	07073
HOSTETLER, MICHAEL	BASEBALL	POST OFFICE BOX 507	DURHAM, NC	27702
HOT ICE	RHYTHM & BLUES GROUP	POST OFFICE BOX 2095	PHILADELPHIA, PA	19103
HOT RIZE	BLUEGRASS GROUP	CASE, 1016 16TH AVE S	NASHVILLE, TN	37212
HOT SHOT	ROCK & ROLL GROUP	BROTHERS, 141 DUNBAR AVE	FORDS, NJ	08863
HOT TUNA	ROCK & ROLL GROUP	POST OFFICE BOX 5801	ATHENS, OH	45701
HOTCHKIS, JOAN	ACTRESS	201 OCEAN AVE #509-P	SANTA MONICA, CA	90402
HOTCHKISS, TOM	BASEBALL	POST OFFICE BOX 957	DUNEDIN, FL	34697
HOTEL	ROCK & ROLL GROUP	POST OFFICE BOX 24570	NASHVILLE, TN	37202
HOTROD, CHEVY KEVY & THE FLASHB	ROCK & ROLL GROUP	3717 W 50TH ST #L-2	MINNEAPOLIS, MN	55410
HOTTELET, RICHARD C	NEWS CORRESPONDENT	CBS NEWS, 524 W 57TH ST	NEW YORK, NY	10019
HOUCK, HUDSON	FOOTBALL COACH	RAMS, 2327 W LINCOLN BLVD	ANAHEIM, CA	92801
HOUCK, JOY N, JR	SCREENWRITER	8955 BEVERLY BLVD	WEST HOLLYWOOD, CA	90048
HOUDA, DOUG	HOCKEY	WHALERS, 1 CIVIC CENTER PLAZA	HARTFORD, CT	06103
HOUGH, CHARLIE	BASEBALL	333 W 35TH ST	CHICAGO, IL	60616
HOUGH, JOHN	FILM DIRECTOR	LORD GRADE FILM PRODUCTIONS		
		8 QUEEN ST	LONDON W1X 7PH	ENGLAND
HOUGH, MIKE	HOCKEY	NORDIQUES, 2205 AVE DU COLISEE	QUEBEC, QUE G1L 4W7	CANADA
HOUGH, STAN	BASEBALL COACH	POST OFFICE BOX 75089	OKLAHOMA CITY, OK	73147
HOUGH, STANLEY	TV DIRECTOR	CBS-TV, 4024 N RADFORD AVE	STUDIO CITY, CA	91604
HOUGHTON, A E, JR	WRITER	8544 WALNUT DR	LOS ANGELES, CA	90046
HOUGHTON, AMO	U S CONGRESSMAN	32 DENISON PARKWAY W	CORNING, NY	14830
HOUGHTON, DON	TV WRITER-PRODUCER	MBA, 45 FITZROY ST	LONDON W1P 5HR,	ENGLAND
HOUGHTON, JAMES	ACTOR-WRITER	8585 WALNUT DR	LOS ANGELES, CA	90046
HOUGHTON, KATHARINE	ACTRESS	134 STEELE RD	WEST HARTFORD, CT	06119
HOUGHTON, MONA	TV WRITER	8544 WALNUT DR	LOS ANGELES, CA	90046
HOUGHTON, WANDA	WRITER	1591 SUNSET PLAZA DR	LOS ANGELES, CA	90069
HOUK, TOM	BASEBALL	POST OFFICE BOX 48	VISALIA, CA	93279
HOULDEY, MICHAEL	DIRECTOR-PRODUCER	14 LOWTHER RD, BARNES	LONDON SW13 9ND	ENGLAND
HOULE, LISA	ACTRESS	9200 SUNSET BLVD #710	LOS ANGELES, CA	90069
HOUNDS, THE	ROCK & ROLL GROUP	505 N LAKE SHORE DR #65	CHICAGO, IL	60611
HOUP, KEN	BASEBALL SCOUT	METS, 126TH ST & ROOSEVELT AVE	FLUSHING, NY	11368
HOUSE, ANDERSON G	SCREENWRITER	1922 WESTHOLME AVE	LOS ANGELES, CA	90025
HOUSE, BUDDY	MUSIC ARRANGER	1000 MC MAHON DR	NASHVILLE, TN	37216
HOUSE, DANA	ACTRESS-MODEL	3349 W CAHUENGA BLVD #2-B	LOS ANGELES, CA	90068
HOUSE, HOWARD	BASEBALL	POST OFFICE BOX 855	BELOIT, WI	53511
HOUSE, JAMES	SINGER	ICM, 40 W 57TH ST	NEW YORK, NY	10019
HOUSE, TOM	BASEBALL-COACH	POST OFFICE BOX 90111	ARLINGTON, TX	76004
HOUSER, CHRISTIE M	ACTRESS	3236 BENDA ST	LOS ANGELES, CA	90068
HOUSER, HUELL	ACTOR-TV HOST	450 N ROSSMORE AVE #602	LOS ANGELES, CA	90004
HOUSER, JERRY	ACTOR	3236 BENDA ST	LOS ANGELES, CA	90068
HOUSER, LES	BASEBALL SCOUT	REDS, 100 RIVERFRONT STADIUM	CINCINNATI, OH	45202
HOUSER, PATRICK	ACTOR	POST OFFICE BOX 5617	BEVERLY HILLS, CA	90213
HOUSEROCKERS, THE	ROCK & ROLL GROUP	AWOL ENTERTAINMENT		
		157 W 57TH ST	NEW YORK, NY	10019
HOUSEY, JOE	BASEBALL COACH-SCOUT	POST OFFICE BOX 402	GENEVA, NY	14456
HOUSEY, JOE	BASEBALL SCOUT	1060 W ADDISON ST	CHICAGO, IL	60613
HOUSIE, WAYNE	BASEBALL	POST OFFICE BOX 2365	PAWTUCKET, RI	02861
HOUSLEY, PHIL	HOCKEY	JETS, 15-1430 MAROONS RD	WINNIPEG, MAN R3G 0L5	CANADA
HOUSLEY, STERLING	BASEBALL SCOUT	POST OFFICE BOX 288	HOUSTON, TX	77001
HOUSTON, ALEX	VENTRILIQUIST	POST OFFICE BOX 82	GREENBRIER, TN	37073
HOUSTON, BOBBY	FOOTBALL	N Y JETS, 1000 FULTON AVE	HEMPSTEAD, NY	11550
HOUSTON, C P	CARTOONIST	THE HOUSTON CHRONICLE		
		801 TEXAS AVE	HOUSTON, TX	77002
HOUSTON, CISSY	SINGER	2160 N CENTRAL RD	FORT LEE, NJ	07024
HOUSTON, DAVID	SINGER-GUITARIST	TFE, 324 JOHNSON BUILDING	SHREVEPORT, LA	71101
HOUSTON, FITZHUGH G	ACTOR	614 S WALNUT ST #4	INGLEWOOD, CA	90301
HOUSTON, GLYN	ACTOR	5 KINGSWOOD CLOSE, WEYBRIDGE	SURREY	ENGLAND
HOUSTON, JAMES W	TV WRITER	9255 SUNSET BLVD #1122	LOS ANGELES, CA	90069
HOUSTON, JEANNE W	TV WRITER	9255 SUNSET BLVD #1122	LOS ANGELES, CA	90069
HOUSTON, ROBERT	SCREENWRITER	8955 BEVERLY BLVD	WEST HOLLYWOOD, CA	90048
HOUSTON, SAM	WRESTLER	POST OFFICE BOX 3859	STAMFORD, CT	06905
HOUSTON, THELMA	SINGER	4296 MOUNT VERNON DR	LOS ANGELES, CA	90008
HOUSTON, TYLER	BASEBALL	POST OFFICE BOX 507	DURHAM, NC	27702
HOUSTON, WHITNEY	SINGER	2160 N CENTRAL RD	FORT LEE, NJ	07024
HOVANNISIAN, JOHN	ACTOR	11606 TERRY HILL PL	LOS ANGELES, CA	90049
HOVE, ANDERS	ACTOR	ABC-TV, "GENERAL HOSPITAL"		

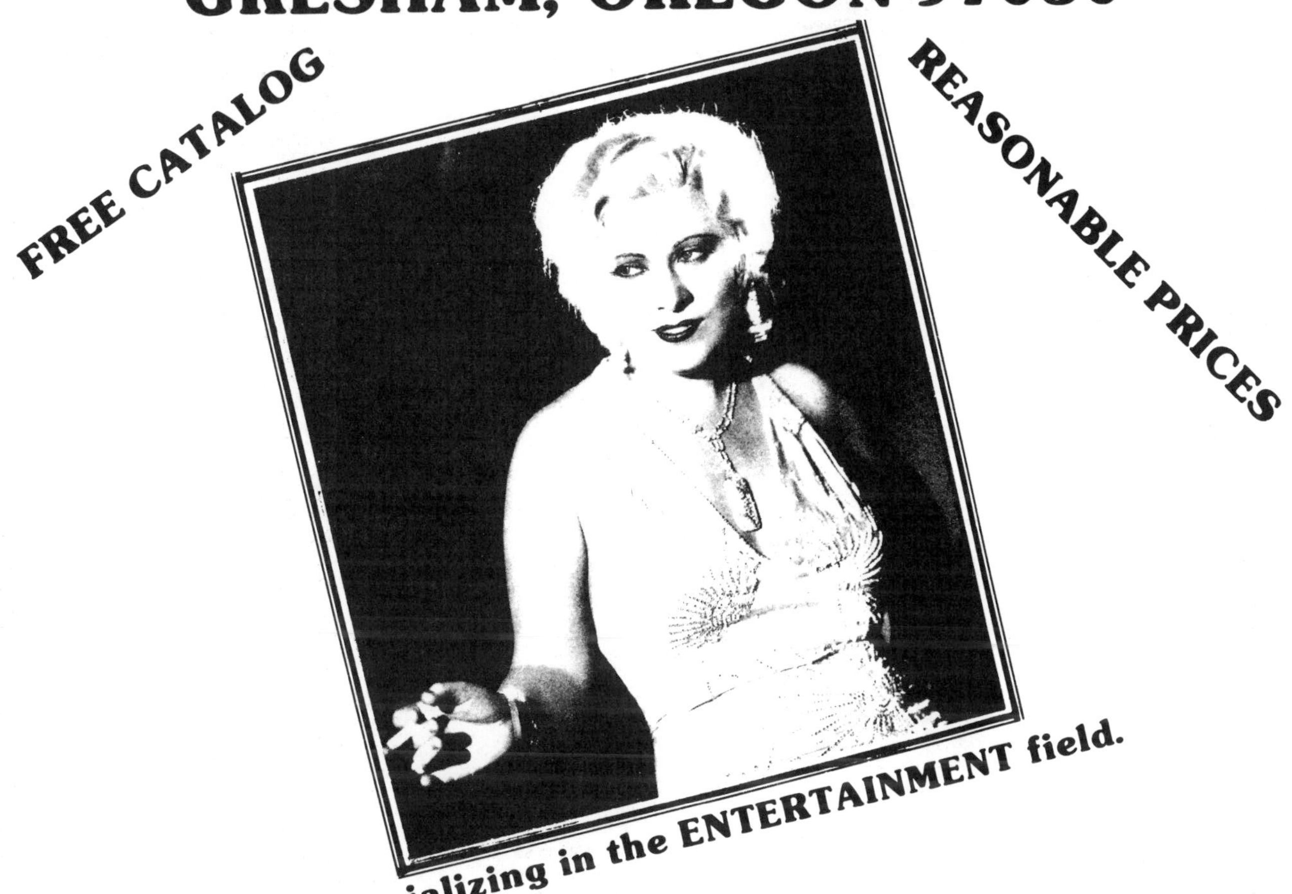
LIGHTS! CAMERA! ACTION!
GEORGIA TERRY AUTOGRAPHS
We work actively from your WANT lists.
840 N.E. COCHRAN AVENUE
GRESHAM, OREGON 97030
FREE CATALOG
REASONABLE PRICES
Specializing in the ENTERTAINMENT field.
FAST, FRIENDLY SERVICE
Member U.A.C.C.
Collector since 1952
Dealer since 1978
LIGHTS! CAMERA! ACTION!
(503) 667-0950
LIGHTS! CAMERA! ACTION!

Name	Occupation	Address	City	Zip/Country
		4151 PROSPECT AVE	BURBANK, CA	91523
HOVEN, LOUISE	ACTRESS	1211 N POINSETTIA DR #F	LOS ANGELES, CA	90046
HOVHANESS, ALAN	COMPOSER	17259 138TH AVE, SE	RENTON, WA	98055
HOVLAND, JULIE	ACTRESS	30 UNIVERSAL CITY PLAZA #251	UNIVERSAL CITY, CA	91608
HOW, JANE	ACTRESS	9 WISETON RD	LONDON SW17 7EE	ENGLAND
HOWAR, BARBARA	TV CORRES-COLUMNIST	POST OFFICE BOX 459	CHELSEA, MI	48118
HOWARD, ALAN	ACTOR	1714 N IVAR AVE #1116	HOLLYWOOD, CA	90028
HOWARD, ANNE	ACTRESS	144 S BEVERLY DR #405	BEVERLY HILLS, CA	90212
HOWARD, ANTHONY	DIRECTOR-PRODUCER	TVS STUDIOS	SOUTHAMPTON SO9 5HZ	ENGLAND
HOWARD, ARLISS	ACTOR	ICM, 8899 BEVERLY BLVD	LOS ANGELES, CA	90048
HOWARD, CHRIS	BASEBALL (CALGARY)	POST OFFICE BOX 3690, STA "B"	CALGARY, ALB T2B 4M4	CANADA
HOWARD, CHRIS	BASEBALL (VANCOUVER)	CANADIANS, 4601 ONTARIO ST	VANCOUVER, BC V5V 3H4	CANADA
HOWARD, CLARK	AUTHOR	8955 BEVERLY BLVD	WEST HOLLYWOOD, CA	90048
HOWARD, CLARK	TV WRITER	JACKINSON, 156 5TH AVE	NEW YORK, NY	10010
HOWARD, CLIFF	ACTOR-SINGER	4489 BROADWAY #2-F	NEW YORK, NY	10040
HOWARD, CLINT	ACTOR	4286 CLYBOURNE AVE	BURBANK, CA	91505
HOWARD, CY	WRITER-PRODUCER	10230 SUNSET BLVD	LOS ANGELES, CA	90024
HOWARD, CYRIL	FILM EXECUTIVE	PINEWOOD STUDIOS, IVER HEATH	IVER, BUCKS SLO ONH	ENGLAND
HOWARD, D D	ACTRESS	1999 AVE OF THE STARS #2850	LOS ANGELES, CA	90067
HOWARD, DAN	BODYBUILDER	HOWARD'S GYM, 17435 NEWHOPE	FOUNTAIN VALLEY, CA	92708
HOWARD, DAVID	BASEBALL	POST OFFICE BOX 419969	KANSAS CITY, MO	64141
HOWARD, DAVID	FOOTBALL	PATRIOTS, FOXBORO STADIUM, RT #1	FOXBORO, MA	02035
HOWARD, DENNIS	ACTOR	280 S BEVERLY DR #400	BEVERLY HILLS, CA	90212
HOWARD, DICK	BASEBALL EXECUTIVE	300 STADIUM WY	DAVENPORT, FL	33837
HOWARD, ERIK	FOOTBALL	N Y GIANTS, GIANTS STADIUM	EAST RUTHERFORD, NJ	07073
HOWARD, FRANK	BASEBALL-COACH	N Y YANKEES, YANKEE STADIUM	BRONX, NY	10451
HOWARD, GAIL	TV WRITER	875 PARK AVE	NEW YORK, NY	10021
HOWARD, GEORGE	SAXOPHONIST	10960 WILSHIRE BLVD #938	LOS ANGELES, CA	90024
HOWARD, HARLIN	GUITARIST-SONGWRITER	1625 OTTER CREEK RD	NASHVILLE, TN	37215
HOWARD, HARRY	FILM DIRECTOR	DGA, 7920 SUNSET BLVD, 6TH FL	LOS ANGELES, CA	90046
HOWARD, JAMES NEWTON	COMPOSER	3815 W OLIVE AVE #201	BRUBANK, CA	91505
HOWARD, JAN	SINGER	TESSIER, 505 CANTON PASS	MADISON, TN	37115
HOWARD, JASON	ACTOR	60 SAINT MARKS PL	NEW YORK, NY	10003
HOWARD, JERRY	DIRECTOR	DGA, 7920 SUNSET BLVD, 6TH FL	LOS ANGELES, CA	90046
HOWARD, JIM	BASEBALL SCOUT	ORIOLE PARK, 333 W CAMDEN ST	BALTIMORE, MD	21201
HOWARD, JOHN	ACTOR	14155 MAGNOLIA BLVD #303	SHERMAN OAKS, CA	91423
HOWARD, JOHN H	ARTIST	JOAN SIGMAN, 336 E 54TH ST	NEW YORK, NY	10022
HOWARD, JOSH	TV PRODUCER	CBS INC, 524 W 57TH ST	NEW YORK, NY	10019
HOWARD, KARIN	FILM DIRECTOR	3541 LANDA ST	LOS ANGELES, CA	90039
HOWARD, KEN	ACTOR	59 E 54TH ST	NEW YORK, NY	10022
HOWARD, LINDA	DIRECTOR	18306 DELANO	RESEDA, CA	91335
HOWARD, LISA	ACTRESS	9255 SUNSET BLVD #515	LOS ANGELES, CA	90069
HOWARD, MARJORIE	ACTRESS	THE WHITBY, 325 W 45TH ST	NEW YORK, NY	10036
HOWARD, MATT	BASEBALL	POST OFFICE BOX 28268	SAN ANTONIO, TX	78228
HOWARD, NANCY K	DIRECTOR	POST OFFICE BOX 323	ALPINE, NJ	07620
HOWARD, PIERRE	LT GOVERNOR	STATE CAPITOL BUIDLING	ATLANTA, GA	30334
HOWARD, RANCE	ACTOR-WRITER	4286 CLYBOURN AVE	BURBANK, CA	91505
HOWARD, RON	BASEBALL	POST OFFICE BOX 2785	LAKELAND, FL	33806
HOWARD, RON	FILM DIRECTOR-ACTOR	IMAGINE FILMS ENTERTAINMENT		
		1925 CENTURY PARK E	LOS ANGELES, CA	90067
HOWARD, SANDY	FILM DIR-PROD	8755 SHOREHAM DR #403	LOS ANGELES, CA	90060
HOWARD, STEPHEN G	DIRECTOR	DGA, 110 W 57TH ST	NEW YORK, NY	10019
HOWARD, STEVE	BASEBALL	4712 SHETLAND AVE	OAKLAND, CA	94605
HOWARD, SUSAN	ACTRESS-EVANGELIST	10632 MELVIN AVE	NORTHRIDGE, CA	91325
HOWARD, TERRY	TV WRITER	875 PARK AVE	NEW YORK, NY	10021
HOWARD, TERRY H	SINGER	2408 DALEBROOK CT #A	NASHVILLE, TN	37206
HOWARD, THOMAS	BASEBALL	INDIANS, CLEVELAND STADIUM	CLEVELAND, OH	44114
HOWARD, THOMAS K	DIRECTOR	3552 CARRIAGE HILL CIR	RANDALLSTOWN, MD	21133
HOWARD, VOLNEY, III	PRODUCER	DON-EL, 5746 SUNSET BLVD	LOS ANGELES	90028
HOWARD & TIM'S PAID VACATION	ROCK & ROLL GROUP	POST OFFICE BOX 390		
		OLD CHELSEA STATION	NEW YORK, NY	10113
HOWARTH, JERRY	SPORTSCASTER	SKYDOME, 300 BREMMER BL #3200	TORONTO, ONT M5V 3B3	CANADA
HOWE, ART	BASEBALL-MANAGER	POST OFFICE BOX 288	HOUSTON, TX	77001
HOWE, GORDIE	HOCKEY	141 NEW LONDON TURNPIKE	GLASTONBURY, CT	06033
HOWE, MARK	HOCKEY	FLYERS, SPECTRUM, PATTISON PL	PHILADELPHIA, PA	19148
HOWE, MICHAEL	ACTOR-SINGER-DANCER	TARLO, 7 FLORAL ST	LONDON WC2	ENGLAND
HOWE, STEVE	BASEBALL	N Y YANKEES, YANKEE STADIUM	BRONX, NY	10451
HOWELL, BILL	DIRECTOR	DGA, 7920 SUNSET BLVD, 6TH FL	LOS ANGELES, CA	90046
HOWELL, C THOMAS	ACTOR	926 N LA JOLLA AVE	LOS ANGELES, CA	90046
HOWELL, DAVE	BASEBALL	POST OFFICE BOX 12557	ST PETERSBURG, FL	33733
HOWELL, HOKE	ACTOR-WRITER	330 S LAMER ST	BURBANK, CA	91506
HOWELL, JACK	BASEBALL	822 S LEHIGH DR	TUCSON, AZ	85710
HOWELL, JAY	BASEBALL	1000 ELYSIAN PARK DR	LOS ANGELES, CA	90012
HOWELL, KEN	BASEBALL	POST OFFICE BOX 7575	PHILADELPHIA, PA	19101
HOWELL, KENNETH E	COMPOSER	1545 COLUMBIA DR	GLENDALE, CA	91205
HOWELL, PAT	BASEBALL	POST OFFICE BOX 1211	NORFOLK, VA	23502
HOWELL, TONEY	BASEBALL SCOUT	1060 W ADDISON ST	CHICAGO, IL	60613
HOWELLS, R TIM	BASKETBALL EXECUTIVE	5 TRIAD CENTER #500	SALT LAKE CITY, UT	84180
HOWERD, FRANKIE	COMEDIAN	LE BARS, 18 QUEEN ANNE ST	LONDON W1M 9LB	ENGLAND
HOWFIELD, IAN	FOOTBALL	OILERS, 6910 FANNIN ST	HOUSTON, TX	77070
HOWITT, DANN	BASEBALL	POST OFFICE BOX 11087	TACOMA, WA	98411
HOWLAND, BETH	ACTRESS	255 AMALFI DR	SANTA MONICA, CA	90402
		ROCKEFELLER CENTER	NEW YORK, NY	10020
HOWMAN, KARL	ACTOR	HAMMOND, GOLDEN HOUSE		
		29 GREAT PULTENEY ST	LONDON W1R 3DD	ENGLAND

Name	Occupation	Address	City / Code
HOWSON, RICHARD	WRI-DIR-PROD	EARP, 77 DEAN ST	LONDON W1V 5HA ENGLAND
HOXIE, AL	WRITER	916 N ROXBURY DR	BEVERLY HILLS, CA 90210
HOY, MARIE	FILM EXECUTIVE	19 ALBERMARLE ST	LONDON W1 ENGLAND
HOY, PETER	BASEBALL	FENWAY PARK, 4 YAWKEY WY	BOSTON, MA 02215
HOYER, DONN F	DIRECTOR	25728 WHISPERING TREES	VALENCIA, CA 91355
HOYER, STENY	U S CONGRESSMAN	4351 GARDEN CITY DR #645	LANDOVER, MD 20785
HRABOSKY, AL	BASEBALL-ANNOUNCER	250 STADIUM PLAZA	ST LOUIS, MO 63102
HRBEK, KENT	BASEBALL	TWINS, 501 CHICAGO AVE S	MINNEAPOLIS, MN 55415
HRDINA, JIRI	HOCKEY	PENGUINS, CIVIC ARENA, CENTRE AV	PITTSBURGH, PA 15219
HRICKO, ANDREA M	WRITER	2506 21ST ST	SANTA MONICA, CA 90405
HRINIAK, WALT	BASEBALL-COACH	333 W 35TH ST	CHICAGO, IL 60616
HRKAC, TONY	HOCKEY	NORDIQUES, 2205 AVE DU COLISEE	QUEBEC, QUE G1L 4W7 CANADA
HRUSOVSKY, JOHN	BASEBALL	POST OFFICE BOX 4669	CHARLESTON, WV 25304
HSU, VICTOR	DIRECTOR	DGA, 7920 SUNSET BLVD, 6TH FL	LOS ANGELES, CA 90046
HUBBARD, BRUCE	SINGER	320 E 42ND ST	NEW YORK, NY 10017
HUBBARD, CARROLL, JR	U S CONGRESSMAN	PARK SQUARE OFFICES #1	MAYFIELD, KY 42066
HUBBARD, GLENN	BASEBALL-COACH	POST OFFICE BOX 4525	MACON, GA 31208
HUBBARD, JACK	BASEBALL SCOUT	N Y YANKEES, YANKEE STADIUM	BRONX, NY 10451
HUBBARD, JEFF	BASEBALL COACH	POST OFFICE BOX 4448	TULSA, OK 74159
HUBBARD, JERRY REED	SINGER-ACTOR	SEE - REED, JERRY	
HUBBARD, JOE	BASEBALL TRAINER	136 S SYCAMORE	ELIZABETHTON, TN 37643
HUBBARD, MARK	BASEBALL	POST OFFICE BOX 22093	GREENSBORO, NC 27420
HUBBARD, RAY WYLIE	SINGER	ATS MGMT, 3300 HOLLYWOOD AVE	AUSTIN, TX 78722
HUBBARD, TRENT	BASEBALL	POST OFFICE BOX 27045	TUCSON, AZ 85726
HUBBARD, WENT	BASEBALL EXECUTIVE	POST OFFICE BOX 4448	TULSA, OK 74159
HUBCAPS, THE	ROCK & ROLL GROUP	POST OFFICE BOX 1388	DOVER, DE 19903
HUBER, JEFF	BASEBALL	POST OFFICE BOX 20849	CHARLESTON, SC 29413
HUBER, MICHAEL	BASEBALL UMPIRE	235 MAIN ST #103	TRUSSVILLE, AL 35173
HUBER, ROBERT	ARTIST	107 CRESCENT RD	SAN ANSELMO, CA 94960
HUBERT, DICK	TV PRODUCER	GATEWAY PRODS, 304 E 45TH ST	NEW YORK, NY 10017
HUBERT, JANET	ACTRESS	8730 SUNSET BLVD #220-W	LOS ANGELES, CA 90069
HUBLEY, SEASON	ACTRESS	2645 OUTPOST DR	LOS ANGELES, CA 90068
HUBLEY, WHIP	ACTOR	ICM, 8899 BEVERLY BLVD	LOS ANGELES, CA 90048
HUCK, BILLY	ACTOR	2160 S BEVERLY GLEN BLVD	LOS ANGELES, CA 90025
HUCKABEE, COOPER	ACTOR	1800 EL CERRITO PL #34	HOLLYWOOD, CA 90068
HUCKABY, JERRY	U S CONGRESSMAN	POST OFFICE BOX 34	NATCHITOCHES, LA 71457
HUCKABY, KEN	BASEBALL	POST OFFICE BOX 2887	VERO BEACH, FL 32961
HUDD, ROY	ACTOR	AZA, 652 FINCHLEY RD	LONDON NW11 7NT ENGLAND
HUDDLESTON, DAVID	ACTOR	10100 SANTA MONICA BLVD #1600	LOS ANGELES, CA 90067
HUDDLESTON, GARY	BODYBUILDER	WEST HWY 54, BOX 207	CAMDENTON, MO 65020
HUDDLESTON, GENE	SINGER	PROCESS, 439 WILEY AVE	FRANKLIN, PA 16323
HUDDY, CHARLIE	HOCKEY	OILERS, NORTHLANDS COLISEUM	EDMONTON, ALTA T5B 4M9 CANADA
HUDEK, JOHN	BASEBALL	POST OFFICE BOX 360007	BIRMINGHAM, AL 35236
HUDGENS, DAVID	BASEBALL-INSTRUCTOR	POST OFFICE BOX 288	HOUSTON, TX 77001
HUDIS, NORMAN I	TV WRITER	10100 SANTA MONICA BLVD #1600	LOS ANGELES, CA 90067
HUDLER, REX	BASEBALL	250 STADIUM PLAZA	ST LOUIS, MO 63102
HUDSON, BETTY	TV EXECUTIVE	NBC-TV, 30 ROCKEFELLER PLAZA	NEW YORK, NY 10112
HUDSON, BILL	SINGER-ACTOR	2808 WESTBROOK AVE	LOS ANGELES, CA 90046
HUDSON, CHARLES L	BASEBALL	2124 HEATHER GLEN	DALLAS, TX 75232
HUDSON, ERNIE	ACTOR	3800 BARHAM BLVD #303	LOS ANGELES, CA 90068
HUDSON, HUGH	FILM DIRECTOR	11 QUEEN'S GATE PLACE MEWS	LONDON SW7 ENGLAND
HUDSON, JOHN	FOOTBALL	EAGLES, BROAD ST & PATTISON AVE	PHILADELPHIA, PA 19148
HUDSON, KEVIN	BASEBALL TRAINER	POST OFFICE BOX 1553	BILLINGS, MT 59103
HUDSON, MIKE	HOCKEY	BLACKHAWKS, 1800 W MADISON ST	CHICAGO, IL 60612
HUDSON, TONI	ACTRESS	8721 SANTA MONICA BLVD #21	WEST HOLLYWOOD, CA 90069
HUDSON, WILLIAM R	DIRECTOR	30 W 26TH ST	NEW YORK, NY 10010
HUDSON BROTHERS, THE	VOCAL TRIO	10100 SANTA MONICA BLVD #1600	LOS ANGELES, CA 90067
HUDZ, ANTHONY	TV WRITER	6323 WILBUR AVE	RESEDA, CA 91335
HUERTA, ARMANDO M	TV DIRECTOR	4552 COLLEGE VIEW AVE	LOS ANGELES, CA 90041
HUERTA, STEVEN	TV DIRECTOR	25692 LUPITA DR	VALENCIA, CA 90028
HUFF, BRENT	ACTOR	2203 RIDGEMONT DR	LOS ANGELES, CA 90046
HUFF, CLARA	ACTOR-PRODUCER	7501 ASMAN AVE	CANOGA PARK, CA 91307
HUFF, JOHN N	TV WRITER	11611 MONTANA AVE #6	LOS ANGELES, CA 90049
HUFF, LEON	SONGWRITER-PRODUCER	309 S BROAD ST	PHILADELPHIA, PA 19107
HUFF, MICHAEL	BASEBALL	1029 PONTIAC	WILMETTE, IL 60091
HUFF, MIKE	BASEBALL	333 W 35TH ST	CHICAGO, IL 60616
HUFF, RONALD	MUSIC ARRANGER	ROUTE #4, OLD HARDING RD	FRANKLIN, TN 37064
HUFFMAN, ROD	BASEBALL	POST OFFICE BOX 21727	SAN FRANCISCO, CA 95151
HUFFMAN, ROSANNA	ACTRESS	215 S CLIFFWOOD AVE	LOS ANGELES, CA 90049
HUFFORD, ROGER E	COMPOSER	1058 ELRADO ST	NAPLES, FL 33940
HUFSEY, BILLY	ACTOR	201 N ROBERTSON BLVD #A	BEVERLY HILLS, CA 90211
HUGGINS, ROY	TV WRITER-PRODUCER	1928 MANDEVILLE CANYON RD	LOS ANGELES, CA 90049
HUGH-KELLY, DANIEL	ACTOR	130 W 42ND ST #2400	NEW YORK, NY 10036
HUGHES, BARNARD	ACTOR	250 W 94TH ST	NEW YORK, NY 10025
HUGHES, BRENDAN	ACTOR	1801 CENTURY PARK E #1415	LOS ANGELES, CA 90067
HUGHES, DEL	DIRECTOR	30 NORMAN AVE	AMITYVILLE, NY 11701
HUGHES, DEWEY WILFRED	DIRECTOR	5325 MAC ARTHUR BLVD, NW	WASHINGTON, DC 20016
HUGHES, ELINOR	DRAMA CRITIC	24 ACADEMY LN	BELLPORT, NY 11713
HUGHES, ERIC	SCREENWRITER	8955 BEVERLY BLVD	WEST HOLLYWOOD, CA 90048
HUGHES, ERNEST	COMPOSER	131 DE LA RONDO	OCEANSIDE, CA 92056
HUGHES, FINOLA	ACTRESS	4334 BELAIR DR	FLINTRIDGE, CA 91011
HUGHES, GARETH	TV PRODUCER	17108 BURBANK BLVD	ENCINO, CA 91316
HUGHES, GARY	BASEBALL SCOUT	6850 LAWRENCE RD	LANTANA, FL 33462
HUGHES, GEOFFREY	ACTOR	STONE, 25 WHITEHALL	LONDON SW1A 2BS ENGLAND
HUGHES, GERALD W	DIRECTOR	POST OFFICE BOX 9223	PITTSBURGH, PA 15224

HUGHES, HOLLIE	SINGER	3784 REALTY	ADDISON, TX	70551
HUGHES, JIM	BASEBALL SCOUT	SKYDOME, 300 BREMMER BL #3200	TORONTO, ONT M5V 3B3	CANADA
HUGHES, JOEL	SINGER	POST OFFICE BOX 500	ROBINSON CREEK, KY	41650
HUGHES, JOHN W	WRITER-PRODUCER	MCA/UNIVERSAL STUDIOS, INC		
		100 UNIVERSAL CITY PLAZA #507		
		EAST PENTHOUSE	UNIVERSAL CITY, CA	91608
HUGHES, KATHLEEN	ACTRESS	8818 RISING GLEN PL	LOS ANGELES, CA	90069
HUGHES, KEITH	BASEBALL	POST OFFICE BOX 1659	PORTLAND, OR	97207
HUGHES, KEN	FILM WRITER-DIRECTOR	2218 N BEACHWOOD DR #301	LOS ANGELES, CA	90068
HUGHES, MARK	BASKETBALL	THE PALACE OF AUBURN HILLS		
		2 CHAMPIONSHIP DR	AUBURN HILLS, MI	48326
HUGHES, MARK STEPHEN	SINGER-GUITARIST	234 E MORTON AVE	NASHVILLE, TN	37211
HUGHES, MARVIN H	MUSIC ARRANGER	2513 LINCOYA CT	NASHVILLE, TN	37214
HUGHES, NERYS	ACTRESS	BURNETT, 42-43 GRAFTON HOUSE		
		2-3 GOLDEN SQ	LONDON W1R 3AD	ENGLAND
HUGHES, PAT	SPORTSCASTER	BREWERS, 201 S 46TH ST	MILWAUKEE, WI	53214
HUGHES, PETER	ACTOR	EPSTEIN, 62 COMPAYNE GARDENS	LONDON NW6 3RY	ENGLAND
HUGHES, PRINCE A, JR	ACTOR	12189 CLARETTA ST	LAKE VIEW, CA	91342
HUGHES, RICHARD K	DIRECTOR	OCTOBER, 122 E ARRELLAGA ST	SANTA BARBARA, CA	93101
HUGHES, ROBERT E	COMPOSER-CONDUCTOR	10344 OSO AVE	CHATSWORTH, CA	91311
HUGHES, ROBERT E	FILM DIRECTOR	210 E 36TH ST #12-A	NEW YORK, NY	10016
HUGHES, TERRY	THEATER DIRECTOR	WM MORRIS, 1350 AVE OF AMERICAS	NEW YORK, NY	10019
HUGHES, TROY	BASEBALL	POST OFFICE BOX 507	DURHAM, NC	27702
HUGHES, WENDY	ACTRESS	345 N MAPLE DR #183	BEVERLY HILLS, CA	90210
HUGHES, WILLIAM J	U S CONGRESSMAN	POST OFFICE BOX 248	PENNSVILLE, NJ	08070
HUGHSON, JIM	SPORTSCASTER	SKYDOME, 300 BREMMER BL #3200	TORONTO, ONT M5V 3B3	CANADA
HUIE, WILLIAM BRADFORD	SCREENWRITER	N BROWN, 407 N MAPLE DR	BEVERLY HILLS, CA	90210
HUISMAN, RICH	BASEBALL	POST OFFICE BOX 3448	SHREVEPORT, LA	71133
HUISMANN, MARK	BASEBALL	POST OFFICE BOX 3665	OMAHA, NE	68103
HULBERT, MIKE	GOLFER	POST OFFICE BOX 109601	PALM BCH GARDENS, FL	33418
HULCE, TOM	ACTOR	2305 STANLEY HILLS	LOS ANGELES, CA	90046
HULETT, TIM	BASEBALL	ORIOLE PARK, 333 W CAMDEN ST	BALTIMORE, MD	21201
HULL, BOBBY	HOCKEY	15-1430 MAROONS RD	WINNIPEG, MAN R3G OL5	CANADA
HULL, BRETT	HOCKEY	BLUES, 5700 OAKLAND AVE	SAINT LOUIS, MO	63110
HULL, DIANNE	ACTRESS	132 S LASKY DR #B	BEVERLY HILLS, CA	90212
HULL, JODY	HOCKEY	POST OFFICE BOX 90111	ARLINGTON, TX	76004
HULL, KENT	FOOTBALL	BILLS, 1 BILLS DR	ORCHARD PARK, NJ	14127
HULME, ROBERT D	DIRECTOR	PENTANGLE, 801 WESTMOUNT DR	LOS ANGELES, CA	90069
HULMES, HARRY	FOOTBALL EXECUTIVE	N Y GIANTS, GIANTS STADIUM	EAST RUTHERFORD, NJ	07073
HULSE, DAVID	BASEBALL	POST OFFICE BOX 4448	TULSA, OK	74159
HULTZAPPLE, KEN	BASEBALL SCOUT	POST OFFICE BOX 7575	PHILADELPHIA, PA	19101
HUMAN LEAGUE, THE	ROCK & ROLL GROUP	TUNENOISE, 3-A COATES PL	EDINBURGH	SCOTLAND
HUMBARD, REV REX	EVANGELIST	CATHEDRAL OF TOMORROW		
		2700 STATE RD	CUYAHOGA FALLS, OH	44421
HUMBLE, GWEN	ACTRESS	999 N DOHENY DR #PH-12	LOS ANGELES, CA	90069
HUMBLE HARVE	RADIO PERSONALITY	KRLA, 1401 S OAK KNOLL AVE	PASADENA, CA	91109
HUMBLE PIE	ROCK & ROLL GROUP	MATZORKIS, 5000 EUCLID AVE	CLEVELAND, OH	44103
HUME, DOUGLAS	ACTOR	8383 WILSHIRE BLVD #650	BEVERLY HILLS, CA	90211
HUME, EDWARD	TV WRITER	10100 SANTA MONICA BLVD #1600	LOS ANGELES, CA	90067
HUME, PAUL	MUSIC EDITOR	3625 TILDEN ST, NW	WASHINGTON, DC	20008
HUMECKE, TONY D	COMPOSER-CONDUCTOR	1721 N KINGSLEY DR	LOS ANGELES, CA	90027
HUMENUIK, ROD	FOOTBALL COACH	PATRIOTS, FOXBORO STADIUM, RT #1	FOXBORO, MA	02035
HUMES, MARY-MARGARET	ACTRESS-MODEL	LIGHT, 901 BRINGHAM AVE	LOS ANGELES, CA	90049
HUMM, MICHAEL ALAN	WRITER	4244 VIA MARINA #466	MARINA DEL REY, CA	90291
HUMMEL, HOMER R	CONDUCTOR	3526 HOLBORO DR	LOS ANGELES, CA	90027
HUMMEL, JIM	CARTOONIST	POST OFFICE BOX 5533	SAN JOSE, CA	95190
HUMPERDINCK, ENGELBERT	SINGER	10100 SUNSET BLVD	LOS ANGELES, CA	90077
HUMPHREY, HUBERT H, III	ATTORNEY GENERAL	STATE CAPTOL BLDG, AURORA AVE	SAINT PAUL, MN	55155
HUMPHREYS, BOB	BASEBALL-INSTRUCTOR	BREWERS, 201 S 46TH ST	MILWAUKEE, WI	53214
HUMPHREYS, MIKE	BASEBALL	1155 W MOUND ST	COLUMBUS, OH	43223
HUMPHRIES, BARRY	ACTOR-COMEDIAN	REID, 32 GALENA RD	LONDON W6 OLT	ENGLAND
HUMPHRIES, DAVE	TV DIRECTOR	SEIFERT, 18 LADBROKE TERR	LONDON W11 3PG	ENGLAND
HUMPHRIES, JAY	BASKETBALL	BRADLEY CENTER, 1001 N 4TH ST	MILWAUKEE, WI	53203
HUMPHRIES, MITCH	MUSIC ARRANGER	ROUTE #8, BOX 202-A	COLUMBIA, TN	38401
HUMPHRIES, STAN	FOOTBALL	POST OFFICE BOX 17247 (DULLES)	WASHINGTON, DC	20041
HUNDLEY, CRAIG L	CONDUCTOR	POST OFFICE BOX 6327	BEVERLY HILLS, CA	90212
HUNDLEY, HOT ROD	BASKETBALL	5 TRIAD CENTER #500	SALT LAKE CITY, UT	84180
HUNDLEY, TODD	BASEBALL	METS, 126TH ST & ROOSEVELT AVE	FLUSHING, NY	11368
HUNGATE, WILLIAM DAVID	MUSIC ARRANGER	ROUTE #5, BOX 99-A	GOODLETTSVILLE, TN	37072
HUNGRY FOR WHAT	ROCK & ROLL GROUP	POST OFFICE BOX 67-A-64	LOS ANGELES, CA	90067
HUNLEY, CON	SINGER	POST OFFICE BOX 121321	NASHVILLE, TN	37212
HUNLEY, LEANN	ACTRESS-MODEL	1888 N CRESCENT HEIGHTS BLVD	LOS ANGELES, CA	90069
HUNNICUTT, GAYLE	ACTRESS	SMITH, 121 N SAN VICENTE BLVD	BEVERLY HILLS, CA	90211
HUNNIFORD, GLORIA	TV-RADIO HOST	GURNETT, 2 NEW KINGS RD	LONDON SW6 4SA	ENGLAND
HUNSICKER, GERRY	BASEBALL EXECUTIVE	METS, 126TH ST & ROOSEVELT AVE	FLUSHING, NY	11368
HUNT, ANNETTE	ACTRESS-SINGER	400 W 43RD ST #29-N	NEW YORK, NY	10036
HUNT, BOB	SCREENWRITER	8955 BEVERLY BLVD	WEST HOLLYWOOD, CA	90048
HUNT, CHRISTOPHER	TV DIRECTOR	IAMBIC PRODS, PRODUCTION HOUSE		
		147-A SAINT MICHAELS HILL	BRISTOL BS2 8DB	ENGLAND
HUNT, E HOWARD	AUTHOR	1245 N 85TH ST	MIAMI, FL	33138
HUNT, FINLEY C, JR	WRITER-PRODUCER	154-A "G" ST, SW	WASHINGTON, DC	20024
HUNT, GARTH	ACTOR	ICM, 388-396 OXFORD ST	LONDON W1	ENGLAND
HUNT, GRADY	COSTUME DESIGNER	13949 VENTURA BLVD #309	SHERMAN OAKS, CA	91423
HUNT, HAROLD GUY	GOVERNOR	ALA STATE HOUSE, 11 S UNION ST	MONTGOMERY, AL	36130
HUNT, HELEN	ACTRESS	9350 WILSHIRE BLVD #324	BEVERLY HILLS, CA	90212

HUNT, JAMES	BASEBALL EXECUTIVE	S F GIANTS, CANDLESTICK PARK	SAN FRANICSCO, CA	94124
HUNT, LAMAR	FOOTBALL EXECUTIVE	160 ELM #2800	DALLAS, TX	75021
HUNT, LESLIE	ACTRESS	SEE - HUNTLEY, LESLIE		
HUNT, LINDA	ACTRESS	454 W 57TH ST	NEW YORK, NY	10019
HUNT, LINDA	GOLFER	2750 VOLUSA AVE #B	DAYTON BEACH, FL	32114
HUNT, MARSHA	ACTRESS	13131 MAGNOLIA BLVD	VAN NUYS, CA	91403
HUNT, PAUL	AUTHOR-PUBLISHER	POST OFFICE BOX 10907	BURBANK, CA	91510
HUNT, PETER H	WRITER-PRODUCER	CAA, 9830 WILSHIRE BLVD	BEVERLY HILLS, CA	90212
HUNT, PETER ROGER	FILM DIRECTOR	2229 ROSCOMARE RD	LOS ANGELES, CA	90077
HUNT, SHANNON	BASEBALL COACH	POST OFFICE BOX 11363	RENO, NV	89510
HUNTER, BERT	BASEBALL	POST OFFICE BOX 598	BINGHAMTON, NY	13902
HUNTER, BLAKE	WRITER-PRODUCER	2327 ALTO OAK DR	LOS ANGELES, CA	90068
HUNTER, BOBBY	BASEBALL	POST OFFICE BOX 842	SALEM, VA	24153
HUNTER, BRIAN	BASEBALL (MINORS)	POST OFFICE BOX 422229	KISSIMMEE, FL	34742
HUNTER, BRIAN "BIG GAME"	BASEBALL (ATLANTA)	POST OFFICE BOX 4064	ATLANTA, GA	30302
HUNTER, DALE	HOCKEY	JETS, 15-1430 MAROONS RD	WINNIPEG, MAN R3G 0L5	CANADA
HUNTER, DAVIS Z	TV PRODUCER	163 E 81ST ST	NEW YORK, NY	10028
HUNTER, DUNCAN	U S CONGRESSMAN	133 CANNON HOUSE OFFICE BLDG	WASHINGTON, DC	20515
HUNTER, FRANK T	COMPOSER-CONDUCTOR	EAGLE RD #2, BOX 6	NEWTOWN, PA	18940
HUNTER, FREDERIC	TV WRITER	1900 AVE OF THE STARS #2535	LOS ANGELES, CA	90067
HUNTER, GRAHAM	CARTOONIST	42 CLONAVOR RD, SILVER	WEST ORANGE, NJ	07052
HUNTER, GREG	BASEBALL	POST OFFICE BOX 9194	HAMPTON, VA	23670
HUNTER, HOLLY	ACTRESS	41 SUTTER ST #1649	SAN FRANCISCO, CACA	94104
HUNTER, IAN	SINGER-SONGWRITER	ATI, 888 7TH AVE, 21ST FLOOR	NEW YORK, NY	10106
HUNTER, IVY JOE	FOOTBALL	PATRIOTS, FOXBORO STADIUM, RT #1	FOXBORO, MA	02035
HUNTER, JAMES D	DIRECTOR	75 CRESCI BLVD	HAZLET, NJ	07730
HUNTER, JEFF	FOOTBALL	LIONS, 1200 FEATHERSTONE RD	PONTIAC, MI	48432
HUNTER, JIM	BASEBALL (EL PASO)	POST OFFICE DRAWER 4797	EL PASO, TX	79914
HUNTER, JIM "CATFISH"	BASEBALL (ATHLETICS)	RURAL ROUTE #1, BOX 895	HERTSFORD, NC	27944
HUNTER, JOHN	FOOTBALL	FALCONS, SUWANEE RD AT I-85	SUWANEE, GA	30174
HUNTER, JOHN R "JAC"	CONDUCTOR	700 S LAKE AVE #317	PASADENA, CA	91106
HUNTER, KIM	ACTRESS	42 COMMERCE ST	NEW YORK, NY	10014
HUNTER, LEW R	TV WRITER	9301 WILSHIRE BLVD #312	BEVERLY HILLS, CA	90210
HUNTER, MARK	HOCKEY	WHALERS, 1 CIVIC CENTER PLAZA	HARTFORD, CT	06103
HUNTER, PATRICK	FOOTBALL	SEAHAWKS, 11220 NE 53RD ST	KIRKLAND, WA	98033
HUNTER, RACHEL	MODEL	391 N CAROLWOOD DR	LOS ANGELES, CA	90077
HUNTER, ROBERT	SINGER	POST OFFICE BOX 92	BROOKLYN, NY	11229
HUNTER, ROSS	FILM PRODUCER	370 TROUSDALE PL	BEVERLY HILLS, CA	90210
HUNTER, STEPHEN	FILM CRITIC	POST OFFICE BOX 1377	BALTIMORE, MD	21278
HUNTER, TAB	ACTOR	BOX 1048, LA TIERRA NUEVA	SANTA FE, NM	87501
HUNTER, TIM	HOCKEY	POST OFFICE BOX 1540, STA "M"	CALGARY, ALTA T2P 3BP	CANADA
HUNTER, TIM	WRITER-PRODUCER	CAA, 9830 WILSHIRE BLVD	BEVERLY HILLS, CA	90212
HUNTER, TOMMY	SINGER	2806 OPRYLAND DR	NASHVILLE, TN	37214
HUNTERS & COLLECTORS	ROCK & ROLL GROUP	POST OFFICE BOX 216		
		ALBERT PARK	VICTORIA 3206	AUSTRALIA
HUNTINGTON, DR ANN	COLUMNIST	TRIBUNE, 64 E CONCORD ST	ORLANDO, FL	32801
HUNTLEY, JOHN	AUTHOR	22 ISLINGTON GREEN	LONDON N1 8DU	ENGLAND
HUNTLEY, LESLIE	ACTRESS	8484 WILSHIRE BLVD #530	BEVERLY HILLS, CA	90211
HUPPERT, DAVE	BASEBALL MANAGER	POST OFFICE DRAWER 4797	EL PASO, TX	79914
HUPPERT, ISABELLE	ACTRESS	ARTMEDIA, 10 AVE GEORGE V	75008 PARIS	FRANCE
HURD, GALE ANN	ACTRESS	270 N CANON DR #1195	BEVERLY HILLS, CA	90210
HURD, GEORGE S	TV DIRECTOR	616 N RUSH ST	CHICAGO, IL	60611
HURD, MARC F	TV DIRECTOR	11520 YOLANDA AVE	NORTHRIDGE, CA	91326
HURDLE, CLINT	BASEBALL-MANAGER	POST OFFICE BOX 1211	NORFOLK, VA	23502
HURKOS, PETER	ACTOR-PSYCHIC	12214 VIEWCREST RD	STUDIO CITY, CA	91604
HURLBURT, JAMES R	COMPOSER	11669 VALERIO ST #241	NORTH HOLLYWOOD, CA	91605
HURLBURT, ROGER	FILM CRITIC	POST OFFICE BOX 14430	FORT LAUDERDALE, FL	33302
HURLBURT, SID	WRITER-EDITOR	POST OFFICE BOX 500	WASHINGTON, DC	20044
HURLBUT, LAURA	GOLFER	2750 VOLUSA AVE #B	DAYTON BEACH, FL	32114
HURLEY, ELIZABETH	ACTRESS	HEATH, PARAMOUNT HOUSE		
		162-170 WARDOUR ST	LONDON W1V 3AT	ENGLAND
HURLEY, GLEN	COMEDIAN	POST OFFICE BOX 99	AMBOY, IL	61310
HURLEY, GRAHAM	TV DIRECTOR-PRODUCER	40 PLAYFAIR RD, SOUTHSEA	HANTS	ENGLAND
HURLL, MICHAEL	TV PRODUCER	INTERNATIONAL ARTISTES LTD		
		MEZZANINE FL, 235 REGENT ST	LONDON W1R 8AX	ENGLAND
HURRICANE	ROCK & ROLL GROUP	GREENWALD, 20445 GRAMERCY PL	TORRANCE, CA	90501
HURST, ALBERTA	COMPOSER	POST OFFICE BOX 6189	LOS OSOS, CA	93402
HURST, BILL	BASEBALL	POST OFFICE BOX 5599	LITTLE ROCK, AR	72215
HURST, BRUCE	BASEBALL	POST OFFICE BOX 2000	SAN DIEGO, CA	92112
HURST, CHARLES	BASEBALL	POST OFFICE BOX 1721	SPARTANBURG, SC	29304
HURST, JAMES	BASEBALL	POST OFFICE BOX 3609	PORT CHARLOTTE, FL	33949
HURST, JONATHAN	BASEBALL	1501 W 16TH ST	INDIANAPOLIS, IN	46202
HURST, MAURICE	FOOTBALL	PATRIOTS, FOXBORO STADIUM, RT #1	FOXBORO, MA	02035
HURST, RICK	ACTOR	9255 SUNSET BLVD #515	LOS ANGELES, CA	90069
HURT, CINDY	SINGER	CBC, 2135 STERLING RD	DEERFIELD, IL	60015
HURT, JOHN	ACTOR	BELFRAGE, 68 SAINT JAMES'S ST	LONDON SW1A 1LE	ENGLAND
HURT, MARY BETH	ACTRESS	1619 BROADWAY #900	NEW YORK, NY	10019
HURT, WILLIAM	ACTOR	RD #1, BOX 251-A	PALISADES, NY	10964
HURTA, BOB	BASEBALL	POST OFFICE BOX 4209	JACKSON, MS	39296
HURTE, LEROY E	CONDUCTOR	7826 CRENSHAW BLVD	LOS ANGELES, CA	90043
HURTES, HETTIE LYNN	ACTRESS	8607 HOLLYWOOD BLVD	LOS ANGELES, CA	90069
HURWITZ, DAVID	TV WRITER	151 S EL CAMINO DR	BEVERLY HILLS, CA	90212
HURWITZ, HARRY	WRITER-PRODUCER	2049 CENTURY PARK E #1320	LOS ANGELES, CA	90067
HURWITZ, MARTIN	TALENT AGENT	UTA, 9560 WILSHIRE BL, 5TH FL	BEVERLY HILLS, CA	90212
HURWITZ, MITCHELL	TV WRITER	UTA, 9560 WILSHIRE BL, 5TH FL	BEVERLY HILLS, CA	90212

HURWITZ, RICHARD D	COMPOSER	2168 ALCCYONA DR	LOS ANGELES, CA	90068
HURWITZ, VICTOR	TV DIRECTOR-PRODUCER	27505 BERKSHIRE DR	SOUTHFIELD, MI	48076
HUSH, Q T	SOUL GROUP	SEE - Q T HUSH		
HUSKEY, BUTCH	BASEBALL	525 NW PEACOCK BLVD	PORT SAINT LUCIE, FL	34986
HUSKY, FERLIN	SINGER-SONGWRITER	ACE PRODS, 3407 GREEN RIDGE DR	NASHVILLE, TN	37214
HUSKY, RICK	ACT-WRI-PROD	13565 LUCCA DR	PACIFIC PALISADES, CA	90272
HUSMANN, RON	ACTOR	11550 DILLING ST	STUDIO CITY, CA	91604
HUSON, JEFF	BASEBALL	POST OFFICE BOX 90111	ARLINGTON, TX	76004
HUSON, PAUL	WRITER	6691 WHITLEY TERR	LOS ANGELES, CA	90068
HUSS, MICHAEL	DIRECTOR	12 W 96TH ST	NEW YORK, NY	10025
HUSSEIN, KING	JORDANIAN KING	BOX 1055	AMMAN	JORDAN
HUSSEIN, SADDAM	IRAQI LEADER	AL-SIJOUD PALACE	BAGHDAD	IRAQ
HUSSEIN, WARIS	FILM-TV DIRECTOR	PETERS, FRASER & DUNLOP, LTD		
		5TH FLOOR, THE CHAMBERS		
		CHELSEA HARBOUR, LOT RD	LONDON SW10 OXF	ENGLAND
HUSSEY, OLIVIA	ACTRESS	12097 SUMMIT CIR	BEVERLY HILLS, CA	90210
HUSSEY, RUTH	ACTRESS	3361 DON PABLO DR	CARLSBAD, CA	92008
HUST, GARY	BASEBALL	POST OFFICE BOX 882	MADISON, WI	53701
HUSTE, ANNEMARIE	TV HOST	104 E 30TH AVE	NEW YORK, NY	10016
HUSTON, ANJELICA	ACTRESS-DIRECTOR	2771 HUTTON DR	BEVERLY HILLS, CA	90210
HUSTON, CRAIG W	FILM DIRECTOR	256 S ROBERTSON BLVD	BEVERLY HILLS, CA	90211
HUSTON, DAN	BASEBALL SCOUT	POST OFFICE BOX 288	HOUSTON, TX	77001
HUSTON, DANNY	WRI-DIR-PROD	DGA, 7920 SUNSET BLVD, 6TH FL	LOS ANGELES, CA	90046
HUSTON, JIMMY	SCREENWRITER	8955 BEVERLY BLVD	WEST HOLLYWOOD, CA	90048
HUSTON, JOHN	GOLFER	POST OFFICE BOX 109601	PALM BCH GARDENS, FL	33418
HUSZAR, JOHN L	DIRECTOR-PRODUCER	420 E 55TH ST	NEW YORK, NY	10022
HUTCHERSON, BOBBY	VIBRAPHONIST	POST OFFICE BOX 1058	MONTARA, CA	94037
HUTCHESON, JON T	COMPOSER-LYRICIST	TECHNI-MUSE ASSOCIATES		
		471 W 144TH ST	NEW YORK, NY	10031
HUTCHINGS, PHILIP J	DIRECTOR	520 N MICHIGAN AVE #1026	CHICAGO, IL	60611
HUTCHINS, J W	SINGER	ROUTE #8, 425 OREBANK RD	KINGSPORT, TN	37664
HUTCHINS, KEN	BODYBUILDER	POST OFFICE BOX 180154	CASSELBERRY, FL	32718
HUTCHINS, WILL	ACTOR	3461 WAVERLY DR #108	LOS ANGELES, CA	90027
HUTCHINSON, JOSEPHINE	ACTRESS	360 E 55TH ST	NEW YORK, NY	10022
HUTCHINSON, KAY BAILEY	TREASURER	POST OFFICE BOX 12428	AUSTIN, TX	78711
HUTCHISON, BARBARA BAILEY	SINGER	POST OFFICE BOX 1556	GAINESVILLE, FL	32602
HUTSHING, JOE	FILM EDITOR	8369 YUCCA TRAIL	LOS ANGELES, CA	90046
HUTTO, EARL	U S CONGRESSMAN	POST OFFICE BOX 459	PANAMA CITY, FL	32402
HUTTO, MAX A	FILM DIRECTOR	560 CERRO ST	ENCINITAS, CA	92024
HUTTON, BETTY	ACTRESS	HARRISON AVE	NEWPORT, RI	02840
HUTTON, BRIAN G	FILM DIRECTOR	8848 LOOKOUT MOUNTAIN AVE	LOS ANGELES, CA	90046
HUTTON, DANNY	SINGER-SONGWRITER	2437 HORSESHOE CANYON RD	LOS ANGELES, CA	90046
HUTTON, LAUREN	ACTRESS-MODEL	124 WAVERLY PL	NEW YORK, NY	10011
HUTTON, MARK	BASEBALL	ALBANY YANKEES, HERITAGE PARK	ALBANY, NY	12211
HUTTON, RICHARD E	TV DIRECTOR-PRODUCER	310 W 106TH ST #5-B	NEW YORK, NY	10025
HUTTON, THOMAS J	COMPOSER	3461 OAK GLEN DR	LOS ANGELES, CA	90068
HUTTON, TIMOTHY	ACTOR	10100 SANTA MONICA BLVD #1600	LOS ANGELES, CA	90067
HUXLEY, CRAIG	COMPOSER	BARSKIN, 120 S VICTORY BL #104	BURBANK, CA	91502
HUYCK, GLORIA KATZ	FILM WRITER-DIRECTOR	39 OAKMONT DR	LOS ANGELES, CA	90049
HUYCK, WILLARD M, JR	FILM WRITER-DIRECTOR	39 OAKMONT DR	LOS ANGELES, CA	90049
HUYSSEN, ROGER	ARTIST	45 CORBIN DR	DARIEN, CT	06820
HWANG, DAVID HENRY	PLAYWRIGHT	19 W 44TH ST #1000	NEW YORK, NY	10036
HWANG, DEBORAH	WRITER-PRODUCER	1402 N HAVENHURST DR	LOS ANGELES, CA	90046
HWONG, LUCIA	COMPOSER	H ORENSTEIN, 157 W 57TH ST	NEW YORK, NY	10019
HYAMS, ALAN	COMPOSER-CONDUCTOR	23425 CANDLEWOOD WY	CANOGA PARK, CA	91304
HYAMS, JOSEPH I, JR	WRITER	540 N BEVERLY GLEN BLVD	LOS ANGELES, CA	90077
HYAMS, NESSA	FILM DIRECTOR	1015 GAYLEY AVE #300	LOS ANGELES, CA	90024
HYAMS, PETER	WRITER-PRODUCER	932 HILTS AVE	LOS ANGELES, CA	90024
HYATT, DONALD B	TV DIRECTOR	109 LINDEN AVE	BRANDFORD, CT	06405
HYATT, MISSY	WRESTLING ANNOUNCER	POST OFFICE BOX 105366	ATLANTA, GA	31348
HYATT, ROBERT J	WRITER-PRODUCER	6725 SUNSET BLVD #506	HOLLYWOOD, CA	90028
HYCHE, STEVE	FOOTBALL	POST OFFICE BOX 888	PHOENIX, AZ	85001
HYDE, HENRY J	U S CONGRESSMAN	50 E OAK ST #200	ADDISON, IL	60101
HYDE, JACQUELYN	ACTRESS	KJAR, 10653 RIVERSIDE DR	TOLUCA LAKE, CA	91602
HYDE, JOHN	FILM PRODUCER	PSO, 10100 SANTA MONICA BLVD	LOS ANGELES, CA	90067
HYDE, MATT	BASEBALL COACH	POST OFFICE BOX 3496	DAVENPORT, IA	52808
HYDE, MICKEY	BASEBALL	POST OFFICE BOX 10336	CLEARWATER, FL	34617
HYDE, RICH	BASEBALL	POST OFFICE BOX 1295	CLINTON, IA	52733
HYDE-WHITE, ALEX	ACTOR	8271 MELROSE AVE #110	LOS ANGELES, CA	90046
HYER WALLIS, MARTHA	ACTRESS-WRITER	4100 W ALAMEDA AVE #204	TOLUCA LAKE, CA	91602
HYERS, TIM	BASEBALL	POST OFFICE BOX 957	DUNEDIN, FL	34697
HYLANDS, SCOTT	ACTOR	10000 SANTA MONICA BLVD #305	LOS ANGELES, CA	90067
HYLEN, STEVE LENNART	DIRECTOR	DGA, 7920 SUNSET BLVD, 6TH FL	LOS ANGELES, CA	90046
HYLER, JOY	ACTRESS	1001 HAMMOND ST #9	LOS ANGELES, CA	90069
HYMAN, DICK	PIANIST-COMPOSER	4146 LANKERSHIM BLVD #300	NORTH HOLLYWOOD, CA	91602
HYMAN, DOROTHY	ACTRESS	7 NORMAN CLOSE, MONK BRETON		
		BARNSLEY	SOUTH YORKS	ENGLAND
HYMAN, KENNETH	FILM EXECUTIVE	SHERWOOD HOUSE, TILEHOUSE LN		
		DENHAM	BUCKS	ENGLAND
HYMEL, GARY	BASEBALL	POLECATS, 608 N SLAPPEY BLVD	ALBANY, GA	31701
HYMOWITZ, CAROL	COLUMNIST	THE WALL STREET JOURNAL		
		200 LIBERTY ST	NEW YORK, NY	10281
HYNES, ROBERT	ARTIST	5215 MUNCASTER MILL RD	ROCKVILLE, MD	20853
HYSER, JOYCE	ACTRESS	MTA, 9320 WILSHIRE BL, 3RD FL	BEVERLY HILLS, CA	90212
HYSON, COLE	BASEBALL	POST OFFICE BOX 611	WATERLOO, IA	50704

HYZDU, ADAM	BASEBALL	POST OFFICE BOX 21727	SAN FRANCISCO, CA	95151

I R S	WRESTLER	POST OFFICE BOX 3859	STAMFORD, CT	06905
I-TAL	ROCK & ROLL GROUP	POST OFFICE BOX 8125	ANN ARBOR, MI	48107
IACOCCA, LEE	AUTO EXEC-AUTHOR	30 SCENIC OAKS	BLOOMFIELD HILLS, MI	48304
IAN, JANIS	SINGER-SONGWRITER	629 S LUCERNE BLVD	LOS ANGELES, CA	90020
IANN, FRANCES	ACTRESS	ABC-TV, "ALL MY CHILDREN"		
		320 W 66TH ST	NEW YORK, NY	10023
IANNUCCI, SALVATORE J	TV EXECUTIVE	1901 AVE OF THE STARS #666	LOS ANGELES, CA	90067
IAQUANIELLO, MIKE	FOOTBALL	DOLPHINS, 2269 NW 199TH ST	MIAMI, FL	33056
IBARRA, MIGUEL	BASEBALL SCOUT	333 W 35TH ST	CHICAGO, IL	60616
IBBETSON, ARTHUR	CINEMATOGRAPHER	TANGLEWOOD, CHALFONT LN		
		CHORLEY WOOD	HERTS	ENGLAND
ICE, JUST	RAPPER-RAPWRITER	SEE - JUST ICE		
ICE CUBE	RAPPER-RAPWRITER	6809 VICTORIA AVE	LOS ANGELES, CA	90043
ICE-T	RAPPER-RAPWRITER	1738 CANYON DR #238	HOLLYWOOD, CA	90028
ICEHOUSE	ROCK & ROLL GROUP	VILLAGE CENTRE #27-A	KINGS CROSS, SYDNEY	AUSTRALIA
ICKO, MARSHA	FILM DIRECTOR	FILM TREE, 8554 MELROSE AVE	LOS ANGELES, CA	90069
ICON	ROCK & ROLL GROUP	MORTICELLI, 3300 MONROE AVE	ROCHESTER, NY	14618
IDAKITIS, JOHN	ACTOR	SCHWARTZ, 935 N CROFT AVE	LOS ANGELES, CA	90069
IDELS, ROBERT B	DIRECTOR-PRODUCER	4301 SUNNYSLOPE AVE	SHERMAN OAKS, CA	91423
IDELSON, WILLIAM	WRITER-PRODUCER	710 BROOKTREE RD	PACIFIC PALISADES, CA	90272
IDEN, MINDI	ACTRESS	1717 N HIGHLAND AVE #414	LOS ANGELES, CA	90028
IDLE, ERIC	ACTOR-DIRECTOR	MAYDAY, 68-A DELANCEY ST	LONDON N1 8JU	ENGLAND
IDLE EYES	ROCK & ROLL GROUP	41 BRITAIN ST #200	TORONTO, ONT M5A 1R7	CANADA
IDLE TEARS	ROCK & ROLL GROUP	MCA RECORDS COMPANY		
		70 UNIVERSAL CITY PLAZA	UNIVERSAL CITY, CA	91608
IDOL, BILLY	SINGER-SONGWRITER	8209 MELROSE AVE	LOS ANGELES, CA	90046
IEMOLA, EUGENE	FILM DIRECTOR	1870 W 10TH ST	BROOKLYN, NY	11223
IGLAVER, BRUCE	MUSICIAN	POST OFFICE BOX 60234	CHICAGO, IL	60660
IGLEHEART, WALKER	GUITARIST	4224 1/2 MC CONNELL BLVD	LOS ANGELES, CA	90066
IGLESIAS, JULIO	SINGER	5 INDIAN CREEK DR	MIAMI, FL	33514
IGLESIAS, LEE	DIRECTOR	471 AVE OF THE AMERICAS	NEW YORK, NY	10011
IGNASIAK, MIKE	BASEBALL	2850 W 20TH AVE	DENVER, CO	80211
IISLEY, BLAISE	BASEBALL	POST OFFICE BOX 36407	LOUISVILLE, KY	40233
IKE, REVERAND	EVANGELIST	4140 BROADWAY	NEW YORK, NY	10004
ILAND, TOBY	ACTOR	101 S SWEETZER AVE #103	LOS ANGELES, CA	90048
ILKIN, TUNCH	FOOTBALL	STEELERS, 300 STADIUM CIR	PITTSBURGH, PA	15212
ILLES, ROBERT	TV WRITER-PRODUCER	3735 SCADLOCK LN	SHERMAN OAKS, CA	91403
ILLMAN, ARNOLD, MD	BODYBUILDER	4180 SUNRISE HWY	MASSAPEQUA, NY	11758
ILOTT, PAMELA	TV EXEC-WRI-PROD	CBS-TV, 524 W 57TH ST	NEW YORK, NY	10019
ILSON, SAUL	TV WRITER-PRODUCER	4522 LOUISE AVE	ENCINO, CA	91316
IMAGES IN VOGUE	ROCK & ROLL GROUP	41 BRITAIN ST #200	TORONTO, ONT M5A 1R7	CANADA
IMAGINATION	ROCK & ROLL GROUP	1 LINCOLN ROAD BLDG #204	MIAMI BEACH, FL	33139
IMAN	MODEL	345 N MAPLE DR #183	BEVERLY HILLS, CA	90210
IMENEZ, MIGUEL	BASEBALL	POST OFFICE BOX 882	MADISON, WI	53701
IMHOFF, GARY	ACTOR	8019 1/2 MELROSE AVE #3	LOS ANGELES, CA	90046
IMI, TONY	CINEMATOGRAPHER	RICHARDS, 42 HAZLEBURY RD	LONDON SW6 2ND	ENGLAND
IMLACH, BRENT	BASEBALL EXECUTIVE	CANADIANS, 4601 ONTARIO ST	VANCOUVER, BC V5V 3H4	CANADA
IMMEL, JERROLD	COMPOSER-CONDUCTOR	13532 CONTOUR DR	SHERMAN OAKS, CA	91423
IMMERMAN, WILLIAM J	FILM EXECUTIVE	16524 PARK LN CIR	LOS ANGELES, CA	90049
IMPALA'S, THE	ROCK & ROLL GROUP	MARS, 168 ORCHID DR	PEARL RIVER, NY	10965
IMPASTATO, DAVID	DIRECTOR	325 S GRAND AVE	PASADENA, CA	91105
IMPERATO, CARLO	ACTOR	6120 CARTWRIGHT AVE	NORTH HOLLYWOOD, CA	91606
IMPERIAL, JASON	BASEBALL	POST OFFICE BOX 855	BELOIT, WI	53511
IMPERIALS, THE	VOCAL GROUP	POST OFFICE BOX 34397	SAN DIEGO, CA	92103
IMPRESSIONS, THE	VOCAL GROUP	50 MUSIC SQUARE W #804	NASHVILLE, TN	37203
IMPULSE	ROCK & ROLL GROUP	POST OFFICE BOX 448	RADFORD, VA	24141
IMUS, DONALD	RADIO PERSONALITY	555 W 57TH ST #1230	NEW YORK, NY	10019
IN PURSUIT	ROCK & ROLL TRIO	POST OFFICE BOX 121347	NASHVILLE, TN	37212
INCAVIGLIA, PETE	BASEBALL	POST OFFICE BOX 288	HOUSTON, TX	77001
INCE, DANE M	ACTOR	3342 ROWENA AVE #B	LOS ANGELES, CA	90027
INCE, KASEY	SCREENWRITER	3342 ROWENA AVE #B	LOS ANGELES, CA	90027
INCH, KEVIN	TV DIRECTOR-PRODUCER	1559 PALISADES DR	PACIFIC PALISADES, CA	90272
INDELLI, JOSEPH D	TV EXECUTIVE	COLUMBIA PICTURES TV		
		COLUMBIA PLAZA	BURBANK, CA	91505
INDICTOR, LLOYD	CONDUCTOR	936 TUFTS AVE	BURBANK, CA	91504
INDIG, MARK	DIRECTOR	140 W 87TH ST #B	NEW YORK, NY	10024
INDRIAGO, JUAN	BASEBALL	POST OFFICE BOX 464	APPLETON, WI	54912
INFANTE, LINDY	FOOTBALL COACH	PACKERS, 1265 LOMBARDI AVE	GREEN BAY, WI	54307
INFORMATION SOCIETY	ROCK & ROLL GROUP	FAA, 1700 BROADWAY, 5TH FLOOR	NEW YORK, NY	10019
INFUSINO, DIVINA	MUSIC CRITIC	POST OFFICE BOX 191	SAN DIEGO, CA	92112
INGALLS, DON	TV WRITER-PRODUCER	2049 CENTURY PARK E #1320	LOS ANGELES, CA	90067
INGALLS, RICK	BASEBALL SCOUT	POST OFFICE BOX 2000	ANAHEIM, CA	92803
INGBER, MANDY	ACTRESS	MTA, 9320 WILSHIRE BL, 3RD FL	BEVERLY HILLS, CA	90212
INGELS, MARTY	ACTOR	701 N OAKHURST DR	BEVERLY HILLS, CA	90210
INGELS-CLARK, JEAN	ACTRESS	11514 VENTURA BLVD #A-170	STUDIO CITY, CA	91604

Name	Occupation	Address	City	Zip/Country
INGERSOLL, JAMES	ACTOR	12509 MILBANK ST	STUDIO CITY, CA	91604
INGLE, RANDY	BASEBALL COACH	POST OFFICE BOX 16683	GREENVILLE, SC	29606
INGLE, RANDY	BASEBALL MANAGER	POST OFFICE BOX 814	PULASKI, VA	24301
INGLESSIS, ELIZABETH	TALENT AGENT	134 W 32ND ST #602	NEW YORK, NY	10001
INGMAN, NICK	COMPOSER-ARRANGER	10 THE GARDENS, EAST DULWICH	LONDON SE22 9QD	ENGLAND
INGRAFFIA, JOSEPH	DIRECTOR	13411 CONTOUR DR	SHERMAN OAKS, CA	91423
INGRAM, DAN	TV EXECUTIVE	HOW & FOREVER, 347 W 57TH ST	NEW YORK, NY	10019
INGRAM, DARRYL	FOOTBALL	BROWNS, 80 1ST ST	BEREA, OH	44017
INGRAM, GAREY	BASEBALL	POST OFFICE BOX 28268	SAN ANTONIO, TX	78228
INGRAM, JAMES	SINGER	867 MUIRFIELD RD	LOS ANGELES, CA	90005
INGRAM, LINTY	BASEBALL	12000 STADIUM RD	ADELANTO, CA	92301
INGRAM, MARK	FOOTBALL	N Y GIANTS, GIANTS STADIUM	EAST RUTHERFORD, NJ	07073
INGRAM, RICARDO	BASEBALL	POST OFFICE BOX 6212	TOLEDO, OH	43614
INGRAM, TODD	BASEBALL	POST OFFICE BOX 11363	RENO, NV	89510
INGRAMS, JONATHAN	FILM WRITER-DIRECTOR	STANMORE LODGE, HERONSGATE	HERTS WD3 5DN	ENGLAND
INHOFE, JAMES M	U S CONGRESSMAN	201 W 5TH ST #305	TULSA, OK	74103
INK SPOTS, THE	VOCAL GROUP	1001 W CYPRESS RD #314	FORT LAUDERDALE, FL	33309
INKELES, MARY ANN	ACTRESS-SINGER	101 W 12TH ST #17-P	NEW YORK, NY	10011
INMAN, BERT	BASEBALL	POST OFFICE BOX 22093	GREENSBORO, NC	27420
INMAN, JIM	TV WRITER	5878 GRACIOSA DR	LOS ANGELES, CA	90068
INMAN, JOHN	ACTOR	W & J THEATRICAL ENTS		
		51-A OAKWOOD RD	LONDON NW11 6RJ	ENGLAND
INMAN, ROGER	TV DIRECTOR	30729 LAKEFRONT DR	AGOURA, CA	91301
INNES, GEORGE	ACTOR	CONWAY, 18-21 JERMYN ST	LONDON SW1	ENGLAND
INNES, LAURA	ACTRESS	10100 SANTA MONICA BLVD #1600	LOS ANGELES, CA	90067
INNIS, JEFF	BASEBALL	METS, 126TH ST & ROOSEVELT AVE	FLUSHING, NY	11368
INNIS, ROY	CIVIL RIGHTS	800 RIVERSIDE DR #6-E	NEW YORK, NY	10032
INNOCENT, HAROLD	ACTOR	ANGEL, 12 D'ARBLAY ST, 1ST FL	LONDON W1V 3FP	ENGLAND
INNOCENT MISCHIEF	ROCK & ROLL GROUP	POST OFFICE BOX 942	RAPID CITY, SD	57709
INNOCENTI, ROBERTO	ARTIST	VIA DEGLI ARTIST 6	FLORENCE 50132	ITALY
INNOVATION	RHYTHM & BLUES GROUP	KINGSLAND, 108 SHARON DR	WEST MONROE, LA	71291
INOUYE, DANIEL	U S SENATOR	469 ENA RD	HONOLULU, HI	96814
INOUYE, JULIE	ACTRESS	POST OFFICE BOX 69590	LOS ANGELES, CA	90069
INPALER	ROCK & ROLL GROUP	1131 E HAWTHORNE AVE	SAINT PAUL, MN	55106
INSKIP, MARNIE	BROADCAST JOURNALIST	240 CENTRAL PARK S	NEW YORK, NY	10019
INSULL, SIGRID	COSTUME DESIGNER	13949 VENTURA BLVD #309	SHERMAN OAKS, CA	91423
INTERCHANGE	MUSICAL GROUP	CENTRAL, 7027 TWIN HILL	DALLAS, TX	75231
INVISIBLE MAN'S BAND, THE	ROCK & ROLL GROUP	ISLAND RECORDS COMPANY		
		444 MADISON AVE	NEW YORK, NY	10022
INVISIBLECHAINS	ROCK & ROLL GROUP	POST OFFICE BOX 21	SAN PEDRO, CA	90733
INWOOD, STEVE	ACTOR	10000 SANTA MONICA BLVD #305	LOS ANGELES, CA	90067
INXS	ROCK & ROLL GROUP	145 BROUGHAM ST, KINGS CROSS	SYDNEY 2011 NSW	AUSTRALIA
IONE	ACTRESS	AIMEE, 13743 VICTORY BLVD	VAN NUYS, CA	91401
IONESCO, EUGENE	PLAYWRIGHT	96 BLVD DU MONTPARNASSE	F-75014 PARIS	FRANCE
IORG, GARTH	BASEBALL-MANAGER	633 JESSAMINE ST	KNOXVILLE, TN	37917
IRELAND, ANDY	U S CONGRESSMAN	POST OFFICE BOX 9447	WINTER HAVEN, FL	33880
IRELAND, KATHY	MODEL-ACTRESS	9000 SUNSET BLVD #1200	LOS ANGELES, CA	90069
IRELAND, TIM	BASEBALL MANAGER	POST OFFICE BOX 8550	STOCKTON, CA	95208
IRIS, DONNIE	SINGER	ATI, 888 7TH AVE, 21ST FLOOR	NEW YORK, NY	10106
IRISH ROVERS, THE	VOCAL GROUP	FRONT ROW, 747 CARDERO ST	VANCOUVER, BC V6E 2E3	CANADA
IRIZARRY, VINCENT	ACTOR	9000 SUNSET BLVD #1200	LOS ANGELES, CA	90069
IRON BUTTERFLY	ROCK & ROLL GROUP	POST OFFICE BOX 1658	FONTANA, CA	92335
IRON MAIDEN	ROCK & ROLL GROUP	POST OFFICE BOX 391	LONDON W4 1LZ	ENGLAND
IRON SHEIK, THE	WRESTLER	POST OFFICE BOX 3859	STAMFORD, CT	06905
IRONS, JEREMY	ACTOR	194 OLD BROMPTON ST	LONDON SW5	ENGLAND
IRONSIDE, MICHAEL	ACTOR	10100 SANTA MONICA BLVD #1600	LOS ANGELES, CA	90067
IRRERA, DOM	COMEDIAN	MTA, 9320 WILSHIRE BL, 3RD FL	BEVERLY HILLS, CA	90212
IRSAY, JAMES	FOOTBALL EXECUTIVE	POST OFFICE BOX 535000	INDIANPOLIS, IN	46253
IRSAY, ROBERT	FOOTBALL EXECUTIVE	POST OFFICE BOX 535000	INDIANPOLIS, IN	46253
IRVIN, BYRON	BASKETBALL	BULLETS, 1 HARRY S TRUMAN DR	LANDOVER, MD	20785
IRVIN, JARRELL L	CONDUCTOR	3823 18TH ST #1	SAN FRANCISCO, CA	94114
IRVIN, MONTE	BASEBALL	11 DOUGLAS COURT S	HOMOSASSA, FL	32646
IRVIN, SAM	DIRECTOR	151 S EL CAMINO DR	BEVERLY HILLS, CA	90212
IRVINE, DARYL	BASEBALL	POST OFFICE BOX 2365	PAWTUCKET, RI	02861
IRVINE, GEORGE	BASKETBALL EXECUTIVE	PACERS, 300 E MARKET ST	INDIANAPOLIS, IN	46204
IRVINE, PAULA	ACTRESS	NBC-TV, "SANTA BARBARA"		
		3000 W ALAMEDA AVE	BURBANK, CA	91523
IRVING, AMY	ACTRESS	11693 SAN VICENTE BLVD #335	LOS ANGELES, CA	90049
IRVING, CLIFFORD	AUTHOR	APTDO 225, SAN MIGUEL	ALLENDE	MEXICO
IRVING, ROBERT	CONDUCTOR-PIANIST	160 W END AVE	NEW YORK, NY	10023
IRWIN, HALE	GOLFER	POST OFFICE BOX 109601	PALM BCH GARDENS, FL	33418
IRWIN, JAMES B	ASTRONAUT	POST OFFICE BOX 1387	COLORADO SPRINGS, CO	80901
IRWIN, TIM	FOOTBALL	VIKINGS, 9520 VIKING DR	EDEN PRAIRIE, MN	55344
IRWIN, TOM	ACTOR	9350 WILSHIRE BLVD #324	BEVERLY HILLS, CA	90212
ISAAC, BILL	BODYBUILDER	THE BIG ISLAND GYM		
		74-5605 ALAPA ST	KAILUA KONA, HI	96740
ISAAC, LUIS	BASEBALL COACH	4385 TUTT BLVD	COLORADO SPRINGS, CO	80922
ISAACKSEN, PETER	ACTOR	4835 PLACIDIA AVE	NORTH HOLLYWOOD, CA	91602
ISAACS, ANTONY	TV DIRECTOR-PRODUCER	KENSINGTON HOUSE, RICHMOND WY	LONDON W14 0AX	ENGLAND
ISAACS, CAROL	TV EXECUTIVE	CBS-TV, 7800 BEVERLY BLVD	LOS ANGELES, CA	90036
ISAACS, CHARLES	TV WRITER	344 DALEHURST AVE	LOS ANGELES, CA	90024
ISAACS, DAVID	TV WRITER-PRODUCER	9046 SUNSET BLVD #202	LOS ANGELES, CA	90069
ISAACS, JEREMY	TV PRODUCER	ROYAL OPERA HOUSE, COVENT GARDEN	LONDON WC2	ENGLAND
ISAACS, NAOMI	TV PRODUCER	17 CANNON PL	LONDON NW3	ENGLAND
ISAACS, PHIL	FILM EXECUTIVE	1742 S BENTLEY AVE	LOS ANGELES, CA	90025

ISAACS, SUSAN	SCREENWRITER	555 W 57TH ST #1230	NEW YORK, NY 10019
ISAACSON, MICHAEL N	COMPOSER-CONDUCTOR	4841 ALONZO AVE	ENCINO, CA 91316
ISAAK, CHRIS	SINGER-SONGWRITER	POST OFFICE BOX 547	LARKSPUR, CA 94939
ISACKSEN, PETER	ACTOR	STONE MANNERS, 9113 SUNSET BL	LOS ANGELES, CA 90069
ISCOVE, ROBERT	DIRECTOR-CHOREO	8496 HOLLYWOOD BLVD	LOS ANGELES, CA 90069
ISELIN, JOHN JAY	TV EXECUTIVE	356 W 58TH ST	NEW YORK, NY 10019
ISENBERG, GERALD I	TV DIRECTOR-PRODUCER	2208 STRADELLA RD	LOS ANGELES, CA 90077
ISHIBASHI, HERBERT, MD	BODYBUILDER	29 SHIPMAN ST #104	HILO, HI 96720
ISHIDA, JAMES	ACTOR	871 N VAIL AVE	MONTEBELLO, CA 90640
ISLAM, YUSUF	SINGER-SONGWRITER	ARIOLA STEINHAUSER STR 3	8000 MUNCIH 80 GERMANY
ISLEY BROTHERS, THE	R & B GROUP	446 LIBERTY RD	INGLEWOOD, NJ 07631
ISLEY-JASPER-ISLEY	VOCAL TRIO	ICM, 40 W 57TH ST	NEW YORK, NY 10019
ISMAIL, RAGIB	FOOTBALL	EXHIBITION STADIUM & PALACE	TORONTO, ONT N6K 3C3 CANADA
ISRAEL, AL	ACTOR	12001 VENTURA PL #335	STUDIO CITY, CA 91604
ISRAEL, CHARLES E	WRITER	5922 PENFIELD AVE	WOODLAND HILLS, CA 91367
ISRAEL, NEIL C	WRITER-PRODUCER	8511 BRIER DR	LOS ANGELES, CA 90046
ISREALSON, PETER	DIRECTOR	115 E 87TH ST	NEW YORK, NY 10028
ITALS, THE	ROCK & ROLL GROUP	CONCERTED, 312 SALEM ST	MEDFORD, MA 02155
ITO, JILL	ACTRESS	6310 SAN VICENTE BLVD #407	LOS ANGELES, CA 90048
ITO, ROBERT	ACTOR	3918 S SYCAMORE AVE	LOS ANGELES, CA 90008
ITZKOWITZ, HOWARD	ACTOR-WRITER	1017 10TH ST #14	SANTA MONICA, CA 90403
IVANEK, ZELJKO	ACTOR	145 W 45TH ST #1204	NEW YORK, NY 10036
IVAR, STAN	ACTOR	8271 MELROSE AVE #110	LOS ANGELES, CA 90046
IVENS, TERRI	ACTRESS	11350 VENTURA BLVD #206	STUDIO CITY, CA 91604
IVERSON, TOM	BASEBALL TRAINER	POST OFFICE BOX 5646	PRINCETON, WV 24740
IVES, BURL	ACTOR-SINGER	2804 OAKES AVE	ANACORTES, WA 98221
IVEY, DANA	ACTRESS	9301 WILSHIRE BLVD #312	BEVERLY HILLS, CA 90210
IVEY, JUDITH	ACTRESS	325 W 75TH ST #3	NEW YORK, NY 10023
IVEY, LELA	ACTRESS	9744 WILSHIRE BLVD #308	BEVERLY HILLS, CA 90212
IVIE, RYAN	BASEBALL	POST OFFICE BOX 611	WATERLOO, IA 50704
IVINGS, STEVE	COMEDIAN	4680 ELK LAKE DR #304	VICTORIA, BC CANADA
IVORY, JAMES	FILM DIRECTOR	MERCHANT-IVORY PRODUCTIONS	
		46 LEXINGTON ST	LONDON W1 ENGLAND
IVORY, JULIE & SNAPSHOT	ROCK & ROLL GROUP	COVER, 1425 N STAR RD	COLUMBUS, OH 43212

J J FAD	RAP GROUP-RAPWRITERS	FAA, 1700 BROADWAY, 5TH FLOOR	NEW YORK, NY 10019
J T & THE T-BIRDS	ROCK & ROLL GROUP	LCS, 1627 16TH AVE S	NASHVILLE, TN 37212
JACAS, DAVE	BASEBALL	POST OFFICE BOX 2769	HUNTSVILLE, AL 35804
JACK, MAX	SCREENWRITER	8955 BEVERLY BLVD	WEST HOLLYWOOD, CA 90048
JACK, WOLFMAN	RADIO-TV PERSONALITY	6310 SAN VICENTE BLVD #407	LOS ANGELES, CA 90048
JACKE, CHRIS	FOOTBALL	PACKERS, 1265 LOMBARDI AVE	GREEN BAY, WI 54307
JACKEE	ACTRESS	SEE - HARRY, JACKEE	
JACKMAN, FRED H	TV DIRECTOR	16730 OCTAVIA PL	ENCINO, CA 91436
JACKMAN, LAWRENCE E	TV DIRECTOR	312 W 23RD ST #3-H	NEW YORK, NY 10011
JACKMAN, MICHELE MATIS	TV DIRECTOR	736 N SYCAMORE AVE	LOS ANGELES, CA 90038
JACKMAN, TOM	ACTOR	625 N SYCAMORE AVE #117	LOS ANGELES, CA 90036
JACKSON, AL	BASEBALL-COACH	ORIOLE PARK, 333 W CAMDEN ST	BALTIMORE, MD 21201
JACKSON, ALAN	SINGER-SONGWRITER	TEN TEN MUSIC, 1010 16TH AVE S	NASHVILLE, TN 37212
JACKSON, ANDREW	ACTOR	ABC-TV, "ALL MY CHILDREN"	
		320 W 66TH ST	NEW YORK, NY 10023
JACKSON, ANNE	ACTRESS	90 RIVERSIDE DR	NEW YORK, NY 10024
JACKSON, BARRY	ACTOR	29 RATHCOOLE AVE	LONDON N8 9LY ENGLAND
JACKSON, BEVERLY A	TV DIRECTOR	5425 SPRING ST	PHILADELPHIA, PA 19139
JACKSON, BO	BASEBALL-FOOTBALL	333 W 35TH ST	CHICAGO, IL 60616
JACKSON, BOBBY	FOOTBALL COACH	POST OFFICE BOX 609609	SAN DIEGO, CA 92160
JACKSON, CEDRIC	FOOTBALL	LIONS, 1200 FEATHERSTONE RD	PONTIAC, MI 48432
JACKSON, CHRIS	BASKETBALL	POST OFFICE BOX 4658	DENVER, CO 80204
JACKSON, CHUCK	BASEBALL	POST OFFICE BOX 75089	OKLAHOMA CITY, OK 73147
JACKSON, DANNY	BASEBALL	POST OFFICE BOX 7000	PITTSBURGH, PA 15212
JACKSON, DARRIN	BASEBALL	POST OFFICE BOX 2000	SAN DIEGO, CA 92112
JACKSON, DOUGLAS	TV PRODUCER	9220 SUNSET BLVD #311	LOS ANGELES, CA 90069
JACKSON, EDWARD D M, JR	MAKE-UP ARTIST	POST OFFICE BOX 5008	PARSIPPANY, NJ 07054
JACKSON, ELMA V	ACTRESS	4526 DON MIGUEL DR	LOS ANGELES, CA 90008
JACKSON, FELIX	WRITER-PRODUCER	4149 MURIETTA AVE	SHERMAN OAKS, CA 91423
JACKSON, FREDDIE	SINGER-SONGWRITER	HUSH PRODS, 231 W 58TH ST	NEW YORK, NY 10019
JACKSON, GERALD	NEWS CORRESPONDENT	NBC NEWS, 4001 NEBRASKA AV, SW	WASHINGTON, DC 20016
JACKSON, GLENDA	ACTRESS	51 HARVEY RD, BLACKHEATH	LONDON SE3 ENGLAND
JACKSON, GRANT	BASEBALL-COACH	CUBS, 2ND & RIVERSIDE DR	DES MOINES, IA 50309
JACKSON, GREG	FOOTBALL	N Y GIANTS, GIANTS STADIUM	EAST RUTHERFORD, NJ 07073
JACKSON, J J	RADIO PERSONALITY	KMPC-FM, 5858 SUNSET BLBD	LOS ANGELES, CA 90078
JACKSON, JAMES W	DIRECTOR-PRODUCER	223 E 61ST ST	NEW YORK, NY 10021
JACKSON, JAMIE SMITH	ACTRESS	941 FERNWOOD DR	TOPANGA, CA 90290
JACKSON, JANET	ACTRESS-SINGER	345 N MAPLE ST #235	BEVERLY HILLS, CA 90210
JACKSON, JEFF	BASEBALL	POST OFFICE BOX 10336	CLEARWATER, FL 34617
JACKSON, JERMAINE	SINGER-COMPOSER	4641 HAYVENHURST DR	ENCINO, CA 91436
JACKSON, JESSE L	EVANGELIST	733 15TH ST, NW	WASHINGTON, DC 20005
JACKSON, JOE	SINGER-SONGWRITER	BASEMENT MUSIC, 6 PEMBRIDGE RD	

		TRINITY HOUSE, 2ND FLOOR	LONDON W11 ... ENGLAND
JACKSON, JOHN	BASEBALL	POST OFFICE BOX 12	MIDLAND, TX ... 79702
JACKSON, JOHN	FOOTBALL	STEELERS, 300 STADIUM CIR	PITTSBURGH, PA ... 15212
JACKSON, JOHNNIE	FOOTBALL	S F 49ERS, 4949 CENTENNIAL BL	SANTA CLARA, CA ... 95054
JACKSON, JUDY	DIRECTOR	52 ALMA ST	LONDON NW5 3DH ... ENGLAND
JACKSON, JUMP & HIS BLUES BAND	BLUES GROUP	R & B, 8959 S OGLESBY AVE	CHICAGO, IL ... 60617
JACKSON, KATE	ACTRESS	1628 MARLAY DR	LOS ANGELES, CA ... 90069
JACKSON, KEITH	FOOTBALL	EAGLES, BROAD ST & PATTISON AVE	PHILADELPHIA, PA ... 19148
JACKSON, KEITH	SINGER-SONGWRITER	SEE - ONE LAST CHANCE BAND	
JACKSON, KEITH	SPORTSCASTER	ABC SPORTS, 1330 AVE OF AMERICAS	NEW YORK, NY ... 10019
JACKSON, KENNETH, GROUP	JAZZ GROUP	POST OFFICE BOX 12752	MEMPHIS, TN ... 38182
JACKSON, KENNY	BASEBALL	2850 W 20TH AVE	DENVER, CO ... 80211
JACKSON, KENNY	FOOTBALL	EAGLES, BROAD ST & PATTISON AVE	PHILADELPHIA, PA ... 19148
JACKSON, KIRBY	FOOTBALL	BILLS, 1 BILLS DR	ORCHARD PARK, NJ ... 14127
JACKSON, LATOYA	SINGER	301 PARK AVE #1970	NEW YORK, NY ... 10022
JACKSON, LEONARD	ACTOR	60 E 42ND ST	NEW YORK, NY ... 10165
JACKSON, LEONARD	ACTOR	4 PARK AVE	NEW YORK, NY ... 10016
JACKSON, MAGGIE	ACTRESS	300 W 49TH ST	NEW YORK, NY ... 10019
JACKSON, MARK	BASKETBALL	KNICKS, 4 PENNYLVANIA PLAZA	NEW YORK, NY ... 10019
JACKSON, MARK	FOOTBALL	BRONCOS, 13655 BRONCOS PKWY	ENGLEWOOD, CO ... 80112
JACKSON, MARLON	SINGER-ACTOR	15445 VENTURA BLVD #10-246	SHERMAN OAKS, CA ... 91403
JACKSON, MARY ANN	ACTRESS	1242 ALESSANDRO DR	NEWBURY PARK, CA ... 91320
JACKSON, MAYNARD	MAYOR	68 MITCHELL	ATLANTA, GA ... 30303
JACKSON, MELODY	ACTRESS	6269 SELMA AVE #15	LOS ANGELES, CA ... 90028
JACKSON, MICHAEL	FOOTBALL	BROWNS, 80 1ST ST	BEREA, OH ... 44017
JACKSON, MICHAEL	RADIO PERSONALITY	KABC RADIO, 3321 S LA CIENEGA BL	LOS ANGELES, CA ... 90016
JACKSON, MICHAEL	SINGER-SONGWRITER	POST OFFICE BOX 933017	LOS ANGELES, CA ... 90093
JACKSON, MICHAEL GREGORY	SINGER	ARISTA RECORDS, 6 W 57TH ST	NEW YORK, NY ... 10019
JACKSON, MIKE	BASEBALL (MAJORS)	S F GIANTS, CANDLESTICK PARK	SAN FRANICSCO, CA ... 94124
JACKSON, MILLIE	SINGER	KEISHVAL ENTS, 1650 BROADWAY	NEW YORK, NY ... 10019
JACKSON, MILT	FOOTBALL COACH	POST OFFICE BOX 535000	INDIANPOLIS, IN ... 46253
JACKSON, PAUL	TV DIRECTOR-PRODUCER	ZAHL, 57 GREAT CUMBERLAND PL	LONDON W1H 7LJ ... ENGLAND
JACKSON, PAUL, JR	GUITARIST-SONGWRITER	POST OFFICE BOX 5292	NORTH HOLLYWOOD, CA ... 91616
JACKSON, PHIL	BASKETBALL COACH	980 N MICHIGAN AVE #1600	CHICAGO, IL ... 60611
JACKSON, PHILIP	ACTOR	MARKHAM AND FROGGATT, LTD	
		JULIAN HOUSE, 4 WINDMILL ST	LONDON W1P 1HF ... ENGLAND
JACKSON, RAY	BASEBALL	POST OFFICE BOX 1295	CLINTON, IA ... 52733
JACKSON, REBBIE	SINGER-SONGWRITER	4641 HAYVENHURST AVE	ENCINO, CA ... 91436
JACKSON, REGGIE	BASEBALL-ANNOUNCER	4067 WATTS	EMERYVILLE, CA ... 94608
JACKSON, REGINALD	BASEBALL SCOUT	METS, 126TH ST & ROOSEVELT AVE	FLUSHING, NY ... 11368
JACKSON, RICHARD	THEATER PRODUCER	59 KNIGHTSBRIDGE	LONDON SW1X 7RA ... ENGLAND
JACKSON, RICKEY	FOOTBALL	SAINTS, 1500 POYDRAS ST	NEW ORLEANS, LA ... 90112
JACKSON, RON	BASEBALL-INSTRUCTOR	BREWERS, 201 S 46TH ST	MILWAUKEE, WI ... 53214
JACKSON, SAMMY	ACTOR-RADIO PERS	SEE - JACKSON, SAMMY M	
JACKSON, SAMMY M	ACTOR-RADIO PERS	KMPC RADIO, 5858 SUNSET BLVD	HOLLYWOOD, CA ... 90028
JACKSON, SHERRY	ACTRESS	4933 ENCINO AVE	ENCINO, CA ... 91316
JACKSON, SONNY	BASEBALL COACH	POST OFFICE BOX 6667	RICHMOND, VA ... 23230
JACKSON, STEVE	FOOTBALL	OILERS, 6910 FANNIN ST	HOUSTON, TX ... 77070
JACKSON, STONEWALL, SR	SINGER-SONGWRITER	6007 CLOVERLAND DR	BRENTWOOD, TN ... 37027
JACKSON, STONEWALL, JR	SINGER-SONGWRITER	6007 CLOVERLAND DR	BRENTWOOD, TN ... 37027
JACKSON, STONEY	ACTOR	1602 N FULLER AVE #102	LOS ANGELES, CA ... 90046
JACKSON, TITO	SINGER	15255 DEL GADO DR	SHERMAN OAKS, CA ... 91403
JACKSON, TRAVIS	BASEBALL	101 S OLIVE ST	WALDO, AR ... 71770
JACKSON, VESTEE	FOOTBALL	DOLPHINS, 2269 NW 199TH ST	MIAMI, FL ... 33056
JACKSON, VICTORIA	ACTRESS	8330 LOOKOUT MOUNTAIN AVE	LOS ANGELES, CA ... 90046
JACKSON, WANDA	SINGER	POST OFFICE BOX 7007	OKLAHOMA CITY, OK ... 73153
JACKSON, WILFRED P	CONDUCTOR	POST OFFICE BOX 73234	LOS ANGELES, CA ... 90003
JACKSONS, THE	VOCAL GROUP	4641 HAVENHURST AVE	ENCINO, CA ... 91436
JACO, CHARLES D	NEWS CORRESPONDENT	1050 TECHWOOD DR, NW	ATLANTA, GA ... 30318
JACOBI, DEREK	ACTOR	22 CHELSHAM RD	LONDON SW4 ... ENGLAND
JACOBI, LOU	ACTOR	240 CENTRAL PARK S	NEW YORK, NY ... 10019
JACOBS, ADAM K	WRI-DIR-PROD	PARAGON CABLE, 5120 BROADWAY	NEW YORK, NY ... 10034
JACOBS, ANDREW, JR	U S CONGRESSMAN	46 E OHIO ST #441-A	INDIANAPOLIS, IN ... 46204
JACOBS, AVIVA	TV DIRECTOR	4202 RAINTREE CIR	CULVER CITY, CA ... 90230
JACOBS, BERNARD	THEATER PRODUCER	225 W 44TH ST	NEW YORK, NY ... 10036
JACOBS, CARL	ACTOR	326 E 69TH ST	NEW YORK, NY ... 10021
JACOBS, DAVID	BASEBALL EXECUTIVE	INDIANS, CLEVELAND STADIUM	CLEVELAND, OH ... 44114
JACOBS, DAVID	TV-RADIO PERS	BBC, BROADCASTING HOUSE	LONDON W1A 1AA ... ENGLAND
JACOBS, DAVID MICHAEL	TV WRITER	PLESHETTE, 2700 N BEACHWOOD DR	HOLLYWOOD, CA ... 90028
JACOBS, DEBBIE	SINGER	1680 N VINE ST #214	HOLLYWOOD, CA ... 90028
JACOBS, EMMA	ACTRESS	WM MORRIS, 31-32 SOHO SQ	LONDON W1V 5DG ... ENGLAND
JACOBS, FRANK	BASEBALL	525 NW PEACOCK BLVD	PORT SAINT LUCIE, FL ... 34986
JACOBS, GARY	TV WRITER	211 S FULLER AVE #8	LOS ANGELES, CA ... 90036
JACOBS, JAMES F	DIRECTOR-PRODUCER	18625 CASSANDRA ST	TARZANA, CA ... 91356
JACOBS, JIM	PLAYWRIGHT	ICM, 40 W 57TH ST	NEW YORK, NY ... 10019
JACOBS, JOHN	TV DIRECTOR-PRODUCER	9 TEDWORTH SQ	LONDON SW3 4DU ... ENGLAND
JACOBS, LEONARD S	DIRECTOR	3 BLUE FERN LN	RANDOLPH, NJ ... 07869
JACOBS, MARILYN	TV DIRECTOR	250 E 39TH ST	NEW YORK, NY ... 10016
JACOBS, MARTIN P	COMPOSER	6207 LUBAO AVE	WOODLAND HILLS, CA ... 91364
JACOBS, MICHAEL	PRODUCER	MCA/UNIVERSAL STUDIOS, INC	
		100 UNIVERSAL CITY PLAZA #507	UNIVERSAL CITY, CA ... 91608
JACOBS, RICHARD	BASEBALL EXECUTIVE	INDIANS, CLEVELAND STADIUM	CLEVELAND, OH ... 44114
JACOBS, RICK	TV EXECUTIVE	CBS-TV, 6121 SUNSET BLVD	LOS ANGELES, CA ... 90028
JACOBS, RONALD N	DIRECTOR-PRODUCER	11920 LAUREL HILLS RD	STUDIO CITY, CA ... 91604
JACOBS, RONALD S	DIRECTOR	JAGUAR PRODUCTIONS, INC	

		285 E 34TH ST	NEW YORK, NY	10010
JACOBS, SEAMAN B	TV WRITER	1702 CLEAR VIEW DR	BEVERLY HILLS, CA	90210
JACOBSON, ARTHUR	FILM DIRECTOR	6050 CANTERBURY DR, FOX HILLS	CULVER CITY, CA	90230
JACOBSON, DAVID	DIRECTOR	149 DUDLEY RD	WILTON, CT	06897
JACOBSON, DON "JAKE"	COMEDY WRITER	LBS COMM, 875 3RD AVE, 9TH FL	NEW YORK, NY	10022
JACOBSON, JOHN A	TV DIRECTOR	3352 LOS OLIVOS LN	LA CRESCENTA, CA	91214
JACOBSON, LARRY	TV WRITER	CAA, 9830 WILSHIRE BLVD	BEVERLY HILLS, CA	90212
JACOBSON, LAWRENCE S	TV PRODUCER	GROSSO-JACOBSON, 767 3RD AVE	NEW YORK, NY	10017
JACOBSON, PETER	GOLFER	POST OFFICE BOX 109601	PALM BCH GARDENS, FL	33418
JACOBSON, STANLEY	TV WRITER-DIRECTOR	73 CRISWELL CRESCENT	WILLOW, ONT M2N 6G2	CANADA
JACOBSON, STUART	WRI-DIR-PROD	1119 FOSTER AVE	BROOKLYN, NY	11230
JACOBSON, WILLIAM JAN	COMPOSER	POST OFFICE BOX 1504	OJAI, CA	93023
JACOBY, BOBBY	ACTOR	POST OFFICE BOX 46324	LOS ANGELES, CA	90046
JACOBY, BROOK	BASEBALL	INDIANS, CLEVELAND STADIUM	CLEVELAND, OH	44114
JACOBY, COLEMAN	TV WRITER	350 E 84TH ST	NEW YORK, NY	10018
JACOBY, FRANK D	WRI-DIR-PROD	JACOBY/STORM, 22 CRESCENT RD	WESTPORT, CT	06880
JACOBY, JOE	FOOTBALL	POST OFFICE BOX 17247 (DULLES)	WASHINGTON, DC	20041
JACOBY, SCOTT	ACTOR	3500 W OLIVE AVE #1400	BURBANK, CA	91505
JACOME, JASON	BASEBALL	POST OFFICE BOX 7845	COLUMBIA, SC	29202
JACQUET, JEAN	MUSICIAN	112-44 179TH ST	SAINT ALBANS, NY	11412
JAECKEL, RICHARD	ACTOR	POST OFFICE BOX 1818	SANTA MONICA, CA	90406
JAEGER, FREDERICK	ACTOR	LITTLE BRIARS, 289-A PETERSHAM RD		
		PETERSHAM	SURREY TW10 7DA	ENGLAND
JAEGER, JEFF	FOOTBALL	RAIDERS, 332 CENTER ST	EL SEGUNDO, CA	90245
JAFFE, ANITA L	TV WRITER	PAINE WEBBER, INC		
		1285 AVE OF THE AMERICAS	NEW YORK, NY	10019
JAFFE, DIANA	ACTRESS	3324 DURAND DR	HOLLYWOOD, CA	90068
JAFFE, HENRY	TV DIRECTOR-PRODUCER	7920 SUNSET BLVD #400	LOS ANGELES, CA	90046
JAFFE, HERB	FILM PRODUCER	LAIRD, 9336 W WASHINGTON BLVD	CULVER CITY, CA	90230
JAFFE, LEO	FILM EXECUTIVE	425 E 58TH ST	NEW YORK, NY	10022
JAFFE, ROBERT J	SCREENWRITER	8955 BEVERLY BLVD	WEST HOLLYWOOD, CA	90048
JAFFE, STANLEY R	DIRECTOR-PRODUCER	JAFFE/LANSING, 660 MADISON AVE	NEW YORK, NY	10021
JAFFE, STEVE	DIRECTOR-PRODUCER	7302 MULHOLLAND DR	LOS ANGELES, CA	90046
JAFFE, STEVEN CHARLES	WRI-DIR-PROD	1037 16TH ST #6	SANTA MONICA, CA	90403
JAFFEE, AL	CARTOONIST	MAD MAGAZINE, 485 MADISON AVE	NEW YORK, NY	10022
JAFFEY, HERBERT	TV WRITER	400 E 59TH ST	NEW YORK, NY	10022
JAFFREY, MADHUR	ACTRESS	CONWAY, 18-21 JERMYN ST	LONDON SW1	ENGLAND
JAFFREY, SAEED	ACTOR	AIM, 5 DENMARK ST	LONDON WC2H 8LP	ENGLAND
JAGGER, BIANCA	ACTRESS-MODEL	MORGANS, 237 MADISON AVE	NEW YORK, NY	10016
JAGGER, MICK	SINGER-ACTOR-WRITER	2 MUNRO TERR	LONDON SW10	ENGLAND
JAGLOM, HENRY D	WRITER-PRODUCER	8235 MONTEEL RD	LOS ANGELES, CA	90069
JAGLOM, MICHAEL	FILM DIRECTOR	8235 MONTEEL RD	LOS ANGELES, CA	90069
JAGR, JAROMIR	HOCKEY	PENGUINS, CIVIC ARENA, CENTRE AV	PITTSBURGH, PA	15219
JAHA, JOHN	BASEBALL	2850 W 20TH AVE	DENVER, CO	80211
JAHAN, MARINE	ACTRESS	6255 SUNSET BLVD #627	LOS ANGELES, CA	90028
JAHN, NORMA JEAN	SINGER-ACTRESS	8665 WILSHIRE BLVD #208	BEVERLY HILLS, CA	90211
JAICKS, AGAR	TV DIRECTOR	KGO-TV, 277 GOLDEN GATE AVE	SAN FRANCISCO, CA	94102
JAID, ILDIKO	ACTRESS	3960 LAUREL CANYON BLVD	STUDIO CITY, CA	91604
JAK	SINGER	POST OFFICE BOX 691565	LOS ANGELES, CA	90069
JAKOBY, DON	SCREENWRITER	8955 BEVERLY BLVD	WEST HOLLYWOOD, CA	90048
JALOMA, RAMIRO	TV DIRECTOR	POST OFFICE BOX 6679	GLENDALE, CA	91205
JAM, JIMMY	SONGWRITER-PRODUCER	SEE - HARRIS, JIMMY JAM		
JAM, THE	SOUL GROUP	POST OFFICE BOX 2105	DAYTON, OH	45401
JAMARILLO, RUDY	BASEBALL COACH	POST OFFICE BOX 288	HOUSTON, TX	77001
JAMERSON, DAVE	BASKETBALL	POST OFFICE BOX 272349	HOUSTON, TX	77277
JAMES, ANTHONY	ACTOR	1801 AVE OF THE STARS #1250	LOS ANGELES, CA	90067
JAMES, CHARITY	ACTRESS	205 S ARNAZ DR #4	BEVERLY HILLS, CA	90211
JAMES, CHRIS	BASEBALL	S F GIANTS, CANDLESTICK PARK	SAN FRANICSCO, CA	94124
JAMES, CLIFTON	ACTOR	95 BUTTONWOOD DR	DIX HILLS, LI, NY	11726
JAMES, CRAIG T	U S CONGRESSMAN	101 N WOODLAND BLVD #201	DE LAND, FL	32720
JAMES, DAVID	CINEMATOGRAPHER	21400 BURBANK BLVD #109	WOODLAND HILLS, CA	91367
JAMES, DENNIS	TV HOST	3681 CARIBETH DR	ENCINO, CA	91436
JAMES, DION	BASEBALL	N Y YANKEES, YANKEE STADIUM	BRONX, NY	10451
JAMES, DON	COMPOSER	2106 MOUNT OLYMPUS DR	LOS ANGELES, CA	90046
JAMES, FRANCESCA	TV DIRECTOR	ABC-TV, 101 W 67TH ST	NEW YORK, NY	10023
JAMES, FREDERICK	SCREENWRITER	8955 BEVERLY BLVD	WEST HOLLYWOOD, CA	90048
JAMES, GABRIELLE A	WRITER-PRODUCER	20654 BASSETT ST	CANOGA PARK, CA	91306
JAMES, GEORGE	SINGER	POST OFFICE BOX 5563	ROCKFORD, IL	61125
JAMES, GERALDINE	ACTRESS	BELFRAGE, 68 SAINT JAMES'S ST	LONDON SW1A 1LE	ENGLAND
JAMES, GODFREY	ACTOR	THE SHACK, WESTERN RD		
		PEVENSEY BAY	EAST SUSSEX	ENGLAND
JAMES, HOWARD	BASEBALL EXECUTIVE	POST OFFICE BOX 2001	CEDAR RAPIDS, IA	52406
JAMES, ISAIAH, JR	DIRECTOR	215 E 24TH ST	NEW YORK, NY	10010
JAMES, J C	SINGER	SEE - WARNER, CHERYL K		
JAMES, JOHN	ACTOR	POST OFFICE BOX 3248 (HTS)	HILTON HEAD ISLAND, SC	29928
JAMES, JOHN ELVIS	SINGER	38 MUSIC SQUARE E #216	NASHVILLE, TN	37203
JAMES, JOHN THOMAS	TV WRITER-PRODUCER	SEE - HUGGINS, ROY		
JAMES, JOSEPH	ACTOR	53-A DARTMOUTH RD	LONDON NW2	ENGLAND
JAMES, KING	SINGER	POST OFFICE BOX 11321		
		FLAGLER STATION	MIAMI, FL	33101
JAMES, LARRY	SINGER	WOOD, 2901 EPPERLY DR	DEL CITY, OK	73115
JAMES, LEONE	ACTRESS	8666 HOLLYWOOD BLVD	LOS ANGELES, CA	90069
JAMES, LISA	DIRECTOR	9000 SUNSET BLVD #1200	LOS ANGELES, CA	90069
JAMES, LUTHER	TV WRITER-DIRECTOR	556 W AVE 46	LOS ANGELES, CA	90065
JAMES, LYNN	FOOTBALL	BENGALS, 200 RIVERFRONT STADIUM	CINCINNATI, OH	45202

Name	Occupation	Address	City
JAMES, MIKE	BASEBALL	POST OFFICE BOX 26267	ALBUQUERQUE, NM 87125
JAMES, PAUL	SINGER	41 BRITAIN ST #200	TORONTO, ONT M5A 1R7 CANADA
JAMES, PEDR	TV DIRECTOR	DAISH, 83 EASTBOURNE MEWS	LONDON W2 6LQ ENGLAND
JAMES, REGINA	SINGER	POST OFFICE BOX 11321	
		FLAGLER STATION	MIAMI, FL 33101
JAMES, RICHARD B	DIRECTOR	23870 MADISON ST	TORRANCE, CA 90505
JAMES, RICK	SINGER-SONGWRITER	8116 MULHOLLAND TERR	LOS ANGELES, CA 90046
JAMES, SIDNEY	COMPOSER	3726 BRILLIANT DR	LOS ANGELES, CA 90065
JAMES, SONNY	SINGER-SONGWRITER	MC FADEN, 48 MUSIC SQUARE E	NASHVILLE, TN 37203
JAMES, TERRY T	COMPOSER-CONDUCTOR	1317 N SWEETZER AVE #8	LOS ANGELES, CA 90069
JAMES, TODD	BASEBALL	10233 96TH AVE	EDMONTON, ALB TK5 0A5 CANADA
JAMES, TOMMY & THE SHONDELLS	ROCK & ROLL GROUP	200 W 57TH ST #907	NEW YORK, NY 10019
JAMES, WOODROW C	COMPOSER-CONDUCTOR	6501 KESTER AVE #4	VAN NUYS, CA 91411
JAMES-REESE, CYNDI	ACTRESS	1706 S CRESCENT HGTS BLVD	LOS ANGELES, CA 90035
JAMESON, JERRY	FILM WRITER-DIRECTOR	10436 KLING ST	NORTH HOLLYWOOD, CA 91602
JAMESON, LOUISE	ACTRESS	CONWAY, 18-21 JERMYN ST	LONDON SW1 ENGLAND
JAMESON, PAULINE	ACTRESS	7 WARRINGTON GARDENS	LONDON W9 ENGLAND
JAMISON, BON	SPORTSCASTER	POST OFFICE BOX 710	LOS ANGELES, CA 90028
JAMISON, MARSHALL	TV DIRECTOR	POST OFFICE BOX 83111	LINCOLN, NB 68501
JAMISON, MILO F, JR	COMPOSER	1231 TENNYSON ST	MANHATTAN BEACH, CA 90266
JAMISON-TANCHUCK, FRANCINE	COSTUME DESIGNER	13949 VENTURA BLVD #309	SHERMAN OAKS, CA 91423
JAMMIE ANN	SINGER	POST OFFICE BOX 3525	YORK, PA 17402
JAMPEL, BARBARA	TV WRITER	830 N FORD ST	BURBANK, CA 91505
JAN & DEAN	VOCAL DUO	CLARK PRODS, 3003 W OLIVE AVE	BURBANK, CA 91510
JANA, FREDDY	BASEBALL EXECUTIVE	BANCO DEL PROGRESSO, AVE JF KENNE	SANTO DOMINGO DOM REP
		AVE JOHN F KENNEDY	SANTO DOMINGO DOM REP
JANA JAE	SINGER	4815 S HARVARD AVE #250	TULSA, OK 74135
JANAVER, RICHARD	WRITER	3920 WESLIN AVE	SHERMAN OAKS, CA 91423
JANCSO, MIKLOS	DIRECTOR	ROZSA FERENC-UTCA 71 #H	BUDAPEST VI HUNGARY
JANE'S ADDICTION	ROCK & ROLL GROUP	8800 SUNSET BLVD #401	LOS ANGELES, CA 90069
JANES, ROBERT	TV WRITER	662 ELKINS RD	LOS ANGELES, CA 90049
JANEWAY, ELIOT	ECONOMIST	15 E 80TH ST	NEW YORK, NY 10021
JANI, ROBERT	THEATER PRODUCER	1260 AVE OF THE AMERICAS	NEW YORK, NY 10020
JANIS, CONRAD	ACTOR	300 N SWALL DR #251	BEVERLY HILLS, CA 90211
JANIS, NORMA	ACTRESS	16808 MARILLA ST	SEPULVEDA, CA 91343
JANKEL, CHAZ	SINGER	ANDREW HEATH, 5 POLAND ST	LONDON W1 ENGLAND
JANKEY, LES	ACTOR	5455 WILSHIRE BLVD #1406	LOS ANGELES, CA 90036
JANKOWSKI, GENE F	TV EXECUTIVE	CBS-TV, 51 W 52ND ST	NEW YORK, NY 10019
JANNETTY, MARTY	WRESTLER	POST OFFICE BOX 3859	STAMFORD, CT 06905
JANNEY, CRAIG	HOCKEY	BRUINS, 150 CAUSEWAY ST	BOSTON, MA 02114
JANNOTTA, TONI	ACTRESS	4316 LAUREL CANYON BLVD	STUDIO CITY, CA 91604
JANOFF, CRAIG ALAN	TV DIRECTOR	46 CHESTNUT HILL, NORTH HILLS	ROSLYN, NY 11576
JANOVER, MICHAEL	SCREENWRITER	950 HARTZELL ST	PACIFIC PALISADES, CA 90272
JANSSEN, DANI	PERSONALITY	2220 AVE OF THE STARS #2803	LOS ANGELES, CA 90067
JANSSENS, MARK	HOCKEY	POST OFFICE BOX 90111	ARLINGTON, TX 76004
JANUARY, DON	GOLFER	PGA SENIORS, 112 T P C BLVD	PONTE VEDRA BEACH, FL 32082
JANUARY, LOIS	ACTRESS	225 N CRESCENT DR #103	BEVERLY HILLS, CA 90210
JANZ, PAUL	SINGER	41 BRITAIN ST #200	TORONTO, ONT M5A 1R7 CANADA
JANZEN, LEE	GOLFER	POST OFFICE BOX 109601	PALM BCH GARDENS, FL 33418
JAPP, DAVID	TV DIRECTOR-PRODUCER	IRON BRIDGE HOUSE	
		3 BRIDGE APPROACH, CHALK FARM	LONDON NW1 8BD ENGLAND
JAQUE, CHRISTIAN	FILM DIRECTOR	42 BIS RUE DE PARIS	BOULOGNE 92100 FRANCE
JAQUES, ERIC	BASEBALL	POST OFFICE DRAWER 1207	ZEBULON, NC 27597
JARAMILLO, RUDY	BASEBALL COACH	POST OFFICE BOX 288	HOUSTON, TX 77001
JARCHOW, BRUCE	ACTOR	9255 SUNSET BLVD #515	LOS ANGELES, CA 90069
JARESS, JILL	ACTRESS-WRITER	7935 BLACKBURN AVE	LOS ANGELES, CA 90048
JARKEY, HARRY	COMEDIAN	32500 CONCORD DR #252	MADISON HEIGHTS, MI 48071
JARMAN, CLAUDE, JR	ACTOR	11 DOS ENCINAS	ORINDA, CA 94563
JARMAN, DEREK	DIRECTOR-DESIGNER	SKYLINE, 24 SCALA ST	LONDON W1 ENGLAND
JAROS, JOE JAN	RECORD EXECUTIVE	AMERICATONE RECORDS CO	
		1817 LOCH LOMAND WY	LAS VEGAS, NV 89102
JARRE, MAURICE	COMPOSER	27011 SEA VISTA DR	MALIBU, CA 90265
JARREAU, AL	SINGER-SONGWRITER	9034 SUNSET BLVD #250	LOS ANGELES, CA 90069
JARRELL, BARBARA	ACTRESS	3316 ALABAMA ST	LA CRESCENTA, CA 91214
JARRET, GABE	ACTOR	9255 SUNSET BLVD #515	LOS ANGELES, CA 90069
JARRICO, PAUL	TV WRITER-PRODUCER	2017 CALIFORNIA AVE	SANTA MONICA, CA 90403
JARROTT, CHARLES	DIRECTOR-ACTOR	LONDON MGT, 235-241 REGENT ST	LONDON W1R 4PH ENGLAND
JARROTT, CHARLES B	DIRECTOR	6420 WILSHIRE BLVD #1900	LOS ANGELES, CA 90048
JARUZELSKI, WOJCIEH	GENERAL	MIN OBRONY NAROVOWEJ UL KLONOWA	1 WARSAW POLAND
JARVIK, DR ROBERT	SURGEON	825 N 300 WEST ST	SALT LAKE CITY, UT 84103
JARVIS, DAVID	ARTIST	275 INDIGO DR #310	DAYTONA BEACH, FL 32014
JARVIS, GRAHAM	ACTOR	15351 VIA DE LAS OLAS #531	PACIFIC PALISADES, CA 90272
JARVIS, JEFF	FILM CRITIC	PEOPLE/TIME & LIFE BLDG	
		ROCKEFELLER CENTER	NEW YORK, NY 10020
JARVIS, JOHN	PIANIST-COMPOSER	3101 HADDON RD	LOUISVILLE, KY 40222
JARVIS, KEVIN	BASEBALL	POST OFFICE BOX 2001	CEDAR RAPIDS, IA 52406
JARVIS, LUCY	TV EXEC-DIR-PROD	171 W 57TH ST	NEW YORK, NY 10019
JARVIS, MARTIN	ACTOR	WHITEHALL, 125 GLOUCESTER RD	LONDON SW7 4TE ENGLAND
JARVIS, SCOTT	ACTOR	210 W 16TH ST #4-F	NEW YORK, NY 10011
JASON, DAVID	ACTOR	STONE, 25 WHITEHALL	LONDON SW1A 2BS ENGLAND
JASON, GEORGE A	TV DIRECTOR	346 CALVERT RD	MERION STATION, PA 19066
JASON, HARVEY	WRITER	1280 SUNSET PLAZA DR	LOS ANGELES, CA 90069
JASON, KARYN	ACTRESS	5455 WILSHIRE BLVD #1406	LOS ANGELES, CA 90036
JASON, MELINDA	TALENT AGENT	MTA, 9320 WILSHIRE BL, 3RD FL	BEVERLY HILLS, CA 90212
JASON, MITCHELL	ACTOR	43 W 93RD ST	NEW YORK, NY 10025

JASON, PETER	ACTOR	9301 WILSHIRE BLVD #312	BEVERLY HILLS, CA	90210
JASON & THE SCORCHERS	ROCK & ROLL GROUP	POST OFFICE BOX 120235	NASHVILLE, TN	37204
JASON DRAKE, SYBIL	ACTRESS	POST OFFICE BOX 1083	BEVERLY HILLS, CA	90213
JASTER, LARRY	BASEBALL-COACH	POST OFFICE BOX 4525	MACON, GA	31208
JASTER, SCOTT	BASEBALL	POST OFFICE BOX 360007	BIRMINGHAM, AL	35236
JASTROW, TERRY	DIRECTOR-PRODUCER	13201 OLD OAK LN	LOS ANGELES, CA	90049
JAURON, DICK	FOOTBALL COACH	PACKERS, 1265 LOMBARDI AVE	GREEN BAY, WI	54307
JAUSS, DAVE	BASEBALL MANAGER	POST OFFICE BOX 3566	WEST PALM BEACH, FL	33402
JAVIER, JULIAN	BASEBALL	B #12 URB PINA, SAN FRANCISCO	DE MACORIS	DOM REP
JAVIER, STAN	BASEBALL	1000 ELYSIAN PARK DR	LOS ANGELES, CA	90012
JAVORSKY, HENRY V	CINEMATOGRAPHER	87-76 197TH ST	HOLLISWOOD, NY	11423
JAWORSKI, MATTHEW	FOOTBALL	POST OFFICE BOX 535000	INDIANPOLIS, IN	46253
JAX, GARTH	FOOTBALL	POST OFFICE BOX 888	PHOENIX, AZ	85001
JAY, ANTONY RUPERT	FILM WRITER-PRODUCER	VIDEO ARTS, 68 OXFORD ST	LONDON W1	ENGLAND
JAY, EUGENE STEPHEN	COMPOSER	2616 HOLLYRIDGE DR	LOS ANGELES, CA	90068
JAY, JODIE	SINGER	MBA, 8914 GEORGIAN DR	AUSTIN, TX	78753
JAY, JOHN	PHOTOGRAPHER	9 ARDFERN AVE, NOBURY	LONDON SW16 4RB	ENGLAND
JAY, VALERIE	SINGER	45 TUDOR CITY PL #911	NEW YORK, NY	10017
JAY & THE AMERICANS	ROCK & ROLL GROUP	WILLIAM REZEY MANAGEMENT CO		
		1775 BROADWAY, 7TH FLOOR	NEW YORK, NY	10019
JAYANT	ACTOR	15 E 11TH ST #9-C	NEW YORK, NY	10003
JAYMES, CATHERINE	TALENT AGENT	327 N LAUREL AVE	LOS ANGELES, CA	90048
JEAKINS, DOROTHY	COSTUME DESIGNER	2926 TORITO RD	SANTA BARBARA, CA	93108
JEAN, ALFRED	TV WRITER-PRODUCER	UTA, 9560 WILSHIRE BL, 5TH FL	BEVERLY HILLS, CA	90212
JEAN, DOMINGO	BASEBALL	5301 NW 12TH AVE	FORT LAUDERDALE, FL	33309
JEAN, GLORIA	ACTRESS	20309 LEADWELL ST	CANOGA PARK, CA	91303
JEAN, NORMA	SINGER	SEE - JAHN, NORMA JEAN		
JEANMAIRE, ZIZI	ACTRESS	22 RUE DE LA PAIX	75002 PARIS	FRANCE
JEANS, CHRISTOPHER	DIRECTOR	40 BEDFORD ST	NEW YORK, NY	10014
JEANS, LUKE	FILM-TV DIRECTOR	109 DOLLIS PARK	LONDON N3	ENGLAND
JEAVONS, COLIN	ACTOR	LONDON MGT, 235-241 REGENT ST	LONDON W1R 4PH	ENGLAND
JEFFCOAT, JIM	FOOTBALL	COWBOYS, 1 COWBOYS PARKWAY	IRVING, TX	75063
JEFFCOAT, MIKE	BASEBALL	POST OFFICE BOX 75089	OKLAHOMA CITY, OK	73147
JEFFERIES, GREGG	BASEBALL	POST OFFICE BOX 419969	KANSAS CITY, MO	64141
JEFFERIES, PETER	TV DIRECTOR	PICTURE BASE INTERNATIONAL		
		13-14 GOLDEN SQ	LONDON W1A 3AG	ENGLAND
JEFFERS, KATHY	ARTIST	106 E 19TH ST	NEW YORK, NY	10003
JEFFERS, SUZANNE	ACTRESS	993 PARK AVE #8-B	NEW YORK, NY	10028
JEFFERSON, B J	ACTRESS	250 W 57TH ST #2223	NEW YORK, NY	10019
JEFFERSON, EDDIE & RICHIE COLE	JAZZ DUO	2490 CHANNING WY #418	BERKELEY, CA	94704
JEFFERSON, JAMES	FOOTBALL	SEAHAWKS, 11220 NE 53RD ST	KIRKLAND, WA	98033
JEFFERSON, REGGIE	BASEBALL	INDIANS, CLEVELAND STADIUM	CLEVELAND, OH	44114
JEFFERSON, SHAWN	FOOTBALL	POST OFFICE BOX 609609	SAN DIEGO, CA	92160
JEFFERSON, WILLIAM J	U S CONGRESSMAN	506 CANNON HOUSE OFFICE BLDG	WASHINGTON, DC	20515
JEFFERSON STARSHIP, THE	ROCK & ROLL GROUP	SEE - STARSHIP, THE		
JEFFERY, WILLIAM	COMPOSER	5143 VILLAGE GREEN ST	LOS ANGELES, CA	90016
JEFFORDS, JAMES M	U S SENATOR	POST OFFICE BOX 676	MONTPELIER, VT	05602
JEFFORY, DAWN	ACTRESS	SEE - JEFFORY-NELSON, DAWN		
JEFFORY-NELSON, DAWN	ACTRESS	1308 N MARTEL AVE	LOS ANGELES, CA	90046
JEFFREY, PETER	ACTOR	LONDON MGT, 235-241 REGENT ST	LONDON W1R 4PH	ENGLAND
JEFFREY, TOM M	TV DIRECTOR-PRODUCER	SAMSON, 119 PYRMONT ST	PYRMONT NSW 2009	AUSTRALIA
JEFFREYS, ANNE	ACTRESS	STERLING, 121 S BENTLEY AVE	LOS ANGELES, CA	90049
JEFFREYS, GARLAND	SINGER	ICM, 40 W 57TH ST	NEW YORK, NY	10019
JEFFREYS, RONALD	MUSIC ARRANGER	121 APOLLO CT W	ANTIOCH, TN	37013
JEFFRIES, GEORGIA	SCREENWRITER-TV PROD	20750 DUMONT ST	WOODLAND HILLS, CA	91364
JEFFRIES, HAYWOOD	FOOTBALL	OILERS, 6910 FANNIN ST	HOUSTON, TX	77070
JEFFRIES, HERB	SINGER	CASSIDY, 417 MARAWOOD DR	WOODSTOCK, IL	60098
JEFFRIES, LIONEL	ACTOR-DIRECTOR	ICM, 388-396 OXFORD ST	LONDON W1	ENGLAND
JEFFRIES, NANCY	RECORD EXECUTIVE	A & M RECORDS COMPANY		
		595 MADISON AVE	NEW YORK, NY	10022
JEKEL, AUGUST A	DIRECTOR	4222 TROOST AVE #26	STUDIO CITY, CA	91604
JEKOT, DR WALTER	BODYBUILDER	8635 W 3RD ST	LOS ANGELES, CA	90048
JELIC, CHRIS	BASEBALL	POST OFFICE BOX 1420	WICHITA, KS	67201
JELLICK, HERB	TV EXECUTIVE	ABC-TV, 4151 PROSPECT AVE	LOS ANGELES, CA	90027
JENIOUS, CRYSTAL	ACTRESS	2441 EXPOSITION PL #1	LOS ANGELES, CA	90018
JENKINS, ANDREW	DIRECTOR	DGA, 110 W 57TH ST	NEW YORK, NY	10019
JENKINS, BRETT	BASEBALL	POST OFFICE BOX 3566	WEST PALM BEACH, FL	33402
JENKINS, CAROL MAYO	ACTRESS	606 N LARCHMONT BLVD #309	LOS ANGELES, CA	90004
JENKINS, ED	U S CONGRESSMAN	POST OFFICE BOX 70	JASPER, GA	30143
JENKINS, FERGUSON	BASEBALL	POST OFFICE BOX 1202	GUTHRIE, OK	73044
JENKINS, HOWARD P	TV DIRECTOR	17097 MAGNOLIA PARKWAY	SOUTHFIELD, MI	48075
JENKINS, IZEL	FOOTBALL	EAGLES, BROAD ST & PATTISON AVE	PHILADELPHIA, PA	19148
JENKINS, JACKIE "BUTCH"	ACTOR	G/5 NW PLAZA, BOX 72	ASHEVILLE, NC	28801
JENKINS, JOHN W R	DIRECTOR	20 145 S FAIRFAX AVE #310 PL S	LOS ANGELES, CA	90036
JENKINS, JONATHAN	BASEBALL	POST OFFICE BOX 4218	SOUTH BEND, IN	46634
JENKINS, MACK	BASEBALL COACH	POST OFFICE BOX 2001	CEDAR RAPIDS, IA	52406
JENKINS, MELVIN	FOOTBALL	LIONS, 1200 FEATHERSTONE RD	PONTIAC, MI	48432
JENKINS, RICHARD	ACTOR	853 7TH AVE #9-A	NEW YORK, NY	10019
JENKINS, ROBERT	FOOTBALL	RAMS, 2327 W LINCOLN BLVD	ANAHEIM, CA	92801
JENKINS, ROGER	TV-FILM DIRECTOR	MLR, 200 FULHAM RD	LONDON SW10 9PN	ENGLAND
JENKINS, SUSAN ANN	DIRECTOR-PRODUCER	5250 STROHM AVE	NORTH HOLLYWOOD, CA	91601
JENKINS, T CLIFFORD	CONDUCTOR	8811 CANOGA AVE #302	CANOGA PARK, CA	91304
JENKINS, TERYN	ACTRESS	29500 HEATHERCLIFF RD #155	MALIBU, CA	90265
JENNER, BRUCE	ACTOR-ATHLETE	POST OFFICE BOX 665	MALIBU, CA	90265
JENNER, LINDA THOMPSON	ACTRESS	6342 SYCAMORE MEADOWS DR	MALIBU, CA	90265

JENNERJAHN, MARY LOU	TV EXECUTIVE	CBS-TV, 51 W 52ND ST	NEW YORK, NY	10019
JENNETT, JAMES B	TV DIRECTOR	106 MAGNOLIA DR	DOBBS FERRY, NY	10522
JENNEY, LUCINDA	ACTRESS	131 S RODEO DR #300	BEVERLY HILLS, CA	90212
JENNINGS, BRENT	ACTOR	SMITH, 121 N SAN VICENTE BLVD	BEVERLY HILLS, CA	90211
JENNINGS, DAN	BASEBALL SCOUT	POST OFFICE BOX 4100	SEATTLE, WA	98104
JENNINGS, DOUG	BASEBALL	500 NORTON ST	ROCHESTER, NY	14621
JENNINGS, GRANT	HOCKEY	PENGUINS, CIVIC ARENA, CENTRE AV	PITTSBURGH, PA	15219
JENNINGS, JOHN ELVIS	SINGER	38 MUSIC SQUARE E	NASHVILLE, TN	37203
JENNINGS, JON	BASKETBALL COACH	151 MERRIMAC ST	BOSTON, MA	02114
JENNINGS, JULIA	ACTRESS	10000 RIVERSIDE DR #6	TOLUCA LAKE, CA	91602
JENNINGS, LANCE	BASEBALL	300 STADIUM WY	DAVENPORT, FL	33837
JENNINGS, PETER	BROADCAST JOURNALIST	211 CENTRAL PARK W	NEW YORK, NY	10024
JENNINGS, SANDRA	TV WRITER	64 JANE ST #A	NEW YORK, NY	10014
JENNINGS, TOMMY	SINGER-SONGWRITER	ROUTE #3, BOX 396	MOUNT JULIET, TN	37122
JENNINGS, WAYLON	SINGER-SONGWRITER	1114 17TH AVE S #104	NASHVILLE, TN	37212
JENNINGS, WILLIAM	FILM PRODUCER	POST OFFICE BOX D	TRINIDAD, CA	95570
JENRETTE, RITA	ACTRESS-MODEL	250 W 57TH ST #2530	NEW YORK, NY	10107
JENS, SALOME	ACTRESS	9400 READCREST DR	BEVERLY HILLS, CA	90210
JENSEN, DICK	SINGER	6399 WILSHIRE BLVD #506	LOS ANGELES, CA	90048
JENSEN, GORDON	SINGER	6750 W 75TH ST, BLDG #2-A	OVERLAND PARK, KS	66204
JENSEN, JIM	FOOTBALL	DOLPHINS, 2269 NW 199TH ST	MIAMI, FL	33056
JENSEN, JOHN	BASEBALL	POST OFFICE DRAWER 1207	ZEBULON, NC	27597
JENSEN, MAREN	ACTRESS	8033 SUNSET BLVD #1420	LOS ANGELES, CA	90046
JENSEN, RANDEE LYNNE	ACTRESS	3113 RIVERSIDE DR	BURBANK, CA	91505
JENSEN, SHELLEY	DIR-PROD-ED	150 S BARRINGTON AVE #1	LOS ANGELES, CA	90049
JENSEN, SHELLY	TV DIRECTOR	1426 THOMPSON AVE	GLENDALE, CA	91201
JENSSEN, ELOIS	COSTUME DESIGNER	9330 BEVERLYCREST DR	BEVERLY HILLS, CA	90210
JEPHCOTT, DOMINIC	ACTOR	MARKHAM AND FROGGATT, LTD JULIAN HOUSE, 4 WINDMILL ST	LONDON W1P 1HF	ENGLAND
JEPSEN, LES	BASKETBALL	GOLDEN STATE WARRIORS OAKLAND COLISEUM ARENA NIMITZ FWY & HEGENBERGER RD	OAKLAND, CA	94621
JERGENS, ADELE	ACTRESS	LANGAN, 32108 VILLAGE 32	CAMARILLO, CA	93010
JERGENSON, DALE R	COMPOSER	15035 WYANDOTTE ST	VAN NUYS, CA	91406
JERNIGAN, CLARENCE F	COMPOSER	920 KINGS RD #214	LOS ANGELES, CA	90069
JEROME, BETTE	ACTRESS	10250 SILVER LAKE DR	BOCA RATON, FL	33428
JERSEY, WILLIAM C	DIRECTOR	5915 HOLLIS ST	EMERYVILLE, CA	94608
JESPERSON, BOB	BASEBALL	POST OFFICE BOX 4669	CHARLESTON, WV	25304
JESSEL, RAYMOND	TV WRITER	8225 HOLLYWOOD BLVD	LOS ANGELES, CA	90069
JESSELL, IAN	TV EXECUTIVE	5700 WILSHIRE BLVD #575	LOS ANGELES, CA	90036
JESSOP, PETER	CINEMATOGRAPHER	GARDNERS COTTAGE, LITTLEWICK PL LITTLEWICK GREEN	MAIDENHEAD SL6 8RA	ENGLAND
JESSUP, JACK E	TV PRODUCER	15120 MAGNOLIA BLVD #106	SHERMAN OAKS, CA	91403
JESSYE, EVA	SINGER	102 E MADISON ST	PITTSBURG, KS	66762
JESTERS OF DESTINY	ROCK & ROLL GROUP	POST OFFICE BOX 2428	EL SEGUNDO, CA	90245
JET BLACK BERRIES	ROCK & ROLL GROUP	POST OFFICE BOX 2428	EL SEGUNDO, CA	90245
JETER, MICHAEL	ACTOR	11726 SAN VICENTE BLVD #300	LOS ANGELES, CA	90049
JETER, SHAWN	BASEBALL	CANADIANS, 4601 ONTARIO ST	VANCOUVER, BC V5V 3H4	CANADA
JETHRO TULL	ROCK & ROLL GROUP	WOOLLEY, MAISON ROUGE 2 WANSDOWN PL, FULHAM	LONDON SW6	ENGLAND
JETS, THE	VOCAL GROUP	708 N 1ST ST #135	MINNEAPOLIS, MN	55401
JETT	ARTIST	16 WAYNE PL	COMMACK, NY	11725
JETT, JOAN	SINGER	250 W 57TH ST #613	NEW YORK, NY	10107
JETTER, FRANCES	ARTIST	390 W END AVE	NEW YORK, NY	10024
JETTON, PAUL	FOOTBALL	BENGALS, 200 RIVERFRONT STADIUM	CINCINNATI, OH	45202
JEWETT, TRENT	BASEBALL COACH	POST OFFICE DRAWER 1218	ZEBULON, NC	27597
JEWISON, NORMAN	DIRECTOR-PRODUCER	23752 MALIBU RD	MALIBU, CA	90265
JHABVALA	SCREENWRITER	CAA, 9830 WILSHIRE BLVD	BEVERLY HILLS, CA	90212
JILLETTE, PENN	COMEDIAN-WRITER	142 W 49TH ST #1214	NEW YORK, NY	10019
JILLIAN, ANN	ACTRESS-SINGER	MURCIA, 4141 WOODCLIFF RD	SHERMAN OAKS, CA	91403
JILLSON, JOYCE	ACTRESS-ASTROLOGER	TRIBUNE, 64 E CONCORD ST	ORLANDO, FL	32801
JIM, HILLBILLY	WRESTLER	SEE - HILLBILLY JIM		
JIM & JESSE & THE VIRGINIA BOY	C & W GROUP	POST OFFICE BOX 27	GALLATIN, TN	37066
JIMENEZ, ALEX	BASEBALL	POST OFFICE BOX 1211	NORFOLK, VA	23502
JIMENEZ, ELVIO	BASEBALL-SCOUT	S F GIANTS, CANDLESTICK PARK	SAN FRANICSCO, CA	94124
JIMENEZ, JOE	GOLFER	PGA SENIORS, 112 T P C BLVD	PONTE VEDRA BEACH, FL	32082
JIMENEZ, MANNY	BASEBALL (MINORS)	POST OFFICE BOX 4525	MACON, GA	31208
JIMENEZ, NEAL	FILM WRITER-DIRECTOR	9220 SUNSET BLVD #311	LOS ANGELES, CA	90069
JIMENEZ, RAMON	BASEBALL	POST OFFICE BOX 2148	WOODBRIDGE, VA	22193
JIMERSON, ART	FOOTBALL	RAIDERS, 332 CENTER ST	EL SEGUNDO, CA	90245
JIMMY, BOBBY & THE CRITTERS	RAP GROUP	6354 VAN NUYS BLVD #174	VAN NUYS, CA	91401
JIMMY JAM	SONGWRITER-PRODUCER	SEE - HARRIS, JIMMY JAM		
JIRSCHELE, MIKE	BASEBALL COACH	POST OFFICE BOX 464	APPLETON, WI	54912
JIVE BUNNY	ROCK & ROLL GROUP	5-7 6TH WILLIAM ST PARTGATE, ROTHERMAN	SOUTH YORKS S62 6EP	ENGLAND
JIVE FIVE, THE	VOCAL GROUP	POST OFFICE BOX 499	QUEENS, NY	11365
JLYNE	SINGER	PTA, 208 ST COACHMAN DR	LAWTON, OK	73501
JOACHIM, BRIGITTA	TV WRITER	60 W 66TH ST #20-E	NEW YORK, NY	10023
JOBE, BILL	COSTUME DESIGNER	13949 VENTURA BLVD #309	SHERMAN OAKS, CA	91423
JOBELMANN, HERMAN F	CONDUCTOR	POST OFFICE BOX 8185	PORTLAND, OR	97207
JOBIM, ANTONIO CARLOS	GUITARIST-SONGWRITER	HOFFER, 233 1/2 E 48TH ST	NEW YORK, NY	10017
JOBOXERS, THE	ROCK & ROLL GROUP	BOXERCARE, IAN MULLARD 21 WIGMORE ST	LONDON W1	ENGLAND
JOBS, STEVE P	COMPUTERS	3475 DEER CREEK RD	PALO ALTO, CA	94304
JOCKETTY, WALT	BASEBALL EXECUTIVE	ATHLETICS'S, OAKLAND COLISEUM	OAKLAND, CA	94621

JOEL, BILLY	SINGER-SONGWRITER	334 E 59TH ST	NEW YORK, NY	10022
JOELSON, BEN	TV WRITER	908 N BEVERLY DR	BEVERLY HILLS, CA	90210
JOESKI LOVE	RAPPER-RAPWRITER	SEE - LOVE, JOESKI		
JOFFE, CHARLES H	FILM PRODUCER	860 BIRCHWOOD DR	LOS ANGELES, CA	90024
JOFFE, EDWARD	DIRECTOR-PRODUCER	5 CHURCHILL CT, STAION RD		
		NORTH HARROW	MIDDLESEX HA2 7SA	ENGLAND
JOFFE, ROLAND	FILM DIRECTOR	DAISH, 83 EASTBOURNE MEWS	LONDON W2 6LQ	ENGLAND
JOHANN, ZITA	ACTRESS	POST OFFICE BOX 302	WEST NYACK, NY	10994
JOHANNES, VICTOR L	FILM DIRECTOR	415 E 85TH ST	NEW YORK, NY	10028
JOHANSEN, DAVID	SINGER	9000 SUNSET BLVD #1200	LOS ANGELES, CA	90069
JOHANSSON, CALLE	HOCKEY	JETS, 15-1430 MAROONS RD	WINNIPEG, MAN R3G 0L5	CANADA
JOHANSSON, INGEMAR	BOXER	SVEN EKSTROM		
		RAKEGATON 9 S-41320	GOTEBORG	SWEDEN
JOHANSSON, ROGER	HOCKEY	POST OFFICE BOX 1540, STA "M"	CALGARY, ALTA T2P 3BP	CANADA
JOHARI, AZIZI	ACTRESS-MODEL	SHERRELL, 1354 LAS ROBLES DR	PALM SPRINGS, CA	92262
JOHN, DR	SINGER-SONGWRITER	SEE - DR JOHN		
JOHN, ELTON	SINGER-SONGWRITER	REID, 32 GALENA RD	LONDON W6 0LT	ENGLAND
JOHN, MICHAEL	SINGER	DTP, 5060 RANCHWOOD DR	COCOA, FL	32926
JOHN, ROBERT	SINGER	6430 SUNSET BLVD #1516	LOS ANGELES, CA	90028
JOHN, TOMMY	BASEBALL	32 ADAMS ST	CRESSKILL, NJ	07626
JOHN PAUL II, POPE	POPE	PALAZZO APOSTOLICO VATCANO	VATICAN CITY	ITALY
JOHNATHON, MICHAEL	SINGER	360 CENTRAL PARK W #16-G	NEW YORK, NY	10025
JOHNES, MILTON	ACTOR	78 TEMPLE SHEEN RD	LONDON SW14 7RR	ENGLAND
JOHNNY & THE DISTRACTIONS	ROCK & ROLL GROUP	3 E 54TH ST #1400	NEW YORK, NY	10022
JOHNNY & THE KNUCKLEHEADS	ROCK & ROLL GROUP	POST OFFICE BOX 52241	TULSA, OK	74152
JOHNS, DOUG	BASEBALL	POST OFFICE BOX 11363	RENO, NV	89510
JOHNS, GLYNIS	ACTRESS	DAN GROHN, 215 W 49TH ST	NEW YORK, NY	10019
JOHNS, STRATFORD	ACTOR	29 MOSTYN RD, MERTON PARK	LONDON SW19	ENGLAND
JOHNS, VICTORIA	TV WRITER-PRODUCER	BLOOM, 800 S ROBERTSON BLVD	LOS ANGELES, CA	90035
JOHNSON, JIMMY	BASEBALL-INSTRUCTOR	POST OFFICE BOX 288	HOUSTON, TX	77001
JOHNSON, A J	BASEBALL	POST OFFICE BOX 661	KENOSHA, WI	53141
JOHNSON, ALAN	BASEBALL-COACH	ORIOLE PARK, 333 W CAMDEN ST	BALTIMORE, MD	21201
JOHNSON, ALAN S	FILM DIRECTOR	J LENNY, 9701 WILSHIRE BLVD	BEVERLY HILLS, CA	90212
JOHNSON, ALEX	FOOTBALL	OILERS, 6910 FANNIN ST	HOUSTON, TX	77070
JOHNSON, ALEXANDRA	ACTRESS	301 N CANON DR #305	BEVERLY HILLS, CA	90210
JOHNSON, ANNE-MARIE	ACTRESS	11712 MOORPARK ST #204	STUDIO CITY, CA	91604
JOHNSON, ANTHONY	FOOTBALL	POST OFFICE BOX 535000	INDIANPOLIS, IN	46253
JOHNSON, ARCH	ACTOR	1501 BROADWAY #301-A	NEW YORK, NY	10036
JOHNSON, ARTE	ACTOR-COMEDIAN	3500 W OLIVE AVE #1400	BURBANK, CA	91505
JOHNSON, AVERY	BASKETBALL	POST OFFICE BOX 4658	DENVER, CO	80204
JOHNSON, BARRY	BASEBALL	POST OFFICE BOX 4218	SOUTH BEND, IN	46634
JOHNSON, BART	BASEBALL SCOUT	333 W 35TH ST	CHICAGO, IL	60616
JOHNSON, BEN	ACTOR	2466 LEISURE WORLD	MESA, AZ	85206
JOHNSON, BEN	RUNNER	62 BLACKTOFT	SCARBOROUGH, ON M1B 2N	CANADA
JOHNSON, BERNARD	COSTUME DESIGNER	13949 VENTURA BLVD #309	SHERMAN OAKS, CA	91423
JOHNSON, BETSY	ACTRESS	300 8TH AVE	BROOKLYN, NY	11215
JOHNSON, BILL	FOOTBALL COACH	BENGALS, 200 RIVERFRONT STADIUM	CINCINNATI, OH	45202
JOHNSON, BILLY	BASEBALL	POST OFFICE BOX 611	WATERLOO, IA	50704
JOHNSON, BOB	BASEBALL SCOUT	6850 LAWRENCE RD	LANTANA, FL	33462
JOHNSON, BOB	ILLUSTRATOR	1346 4TH ST	SAN RAFAEL, CA	94901
JOHNSON, BRAD	ACTOR	CAA, 9830 WILSHIRE BLVD	BEVERLY HILLS, CA	90212
JOHNSON, BRIAN	BASEBALL	POST OFFICE BOX 1420	WICHITA, KS	67201
JOHNSON, BRIAN	BASEBALL	4385 TUTT BLVD	COLORADO SPRINGS, CO	80922
JOHNSON, BRUCE	PRODUCER	5555 MELROSE AVE	LOS ANGELES, CA	90038
JOHNSON, BRUCE	PRODUCER	PARAMOUNT PICTURES CORP		
		1221 AVE OF THE AMERICAS	NEW YORK, NY	10036
JOHNSON, BUCK	BASKETBALL	POST OFFICE BOX 272349	HOUSTON, TX	77277
JOHNSON, CARL	BASEBALL	POST OFFICE BOX 3452	KINSTON, NC	28502
JOHNSON, CARL J	ACTOR	335 S COCHRAN AVE #104	LOS ANGELES, CA	90036
JOHNSON, CAROL BASS	SINGER	131 FRANCES ST	GALLATIN, TN	37066
JOHNSON, CHARLES	PRODUCER	MCA/UNIVERSAL STUDIOS, INC		
		100 UNIVERSAL CITY PLAZA	UNIVERSAL CITY, CA	91608
JOHNSON, CHARLES E	TV WRITER	SHAPIRO, 8827 BEVERLY BLVD	LOS ANGELES, CA	90048
JOHNSON, CHARLES FLOYD	TV WRITER-PRODUCER	JPM, 760 N LA CIENEGA BL, #200	LOS ANGELES, CA	90069
JOHNSON, CHRIS	BASEBALL	POST OFFICE BOX 15757	HARRISBURG, PA	17105
JOHNSON, COSLOUGH	TV WRITER	ICM, 8899 BEVERLY BLVD	LOS ANGELES, CA	90048
JOHNSON, DAMONE	FOOTBALL	RAMS, 2327 W LINCOLN BLVD	ANAHEIM, CA	92801
JOHNSON, DANIEL	TV WRITER-PRODUCER	DWJ ASSOCIATES, 1 ROBINSON LN	RIDGEWOOD, NJ	07450
JOHNSON, DAVE	BASEBALL	10233 96TH AVE	EDMONTON, ALB TK5 0A5	CANADA
JOHNSON, DAVEY	BASEBALL-MANAGER	1064 HOWELL BEACH RD	WINTER PARK, FL	32789
JOHNSON, DAVID	FOOTBALL	STEELERS, 300 STADIUM CIR	PITTSBURGH, PA	15212
JOHNSON, DEBORAH LIV	SINGER-GUITARIST	POST OFFICE BOX 8516	SAN DIEGO, CA	92101
JOHNSON, DENIS	PRODUCER	9 FOUNTAINE RD	LONDON SW2 3TS	ENGLAND
JOHNSON, DIANE L	SCREENWRITER	8955 BEVERLY BLVD	WEST HOLLYWOOD, CA	90048
JOHNSON, DOM	BASEBALL	POST OFFICE BOX 1742	PALM SPRINGS, CA	92263
JOHNSON, DON	ACT-SING-DIR	9555 HEATHER RD	BEVERLY HILLS, CA	90210
JOHNSON, DOTTS	ACTOR	420 W 130TH ST #64	NEW YORK, NY	10027
JOHNSON, DOUG	ARTIST	45 E 19TH ST	NEW YORK, NY	10003
JOHNSON, DREW	BASEBALL	POST OFFICE BOX 418	SAINT CHARLES, IL	60174
JOHNSON, EARNIE	BASEBALL	1090 N EUCLID AVE	SARASOTA, FL	34237
JOHNSON, EARVIN "MAGIC"	BASKETBALL	POST OFFICE BOX 10	INGLEWOOD, CA	90306
JOHNSON, EDDIE	BASKETBALL	SUNS, 2910 N CENTRAL AVE	PHOENIX, AZ	85012
JOHNSON, ELAINE D	ACTRESS	13950 NW PASSAGE #210	MARINA DEL REY, CA	90292
JOHNSON, ERIC	BASKETBALL	5 TRIAD CENTER #500	SALT LAKE CITY, UT	84180
JOHNSON, ERIK	BASEBALL	5999 E VAN BUREN ST	PHOENIX, AZ	85008

JOHNSON, ERNEST J	TV DIRECTOR	POST OFFICE BOX 35602	LOS ANGELES, CA	90035
JOHNSON, EZRA	FOOTBALL	OILERS, 6910 FANNIN ST	HOUSTON, TX	77070
JOHNSON, FERD	CARTOONIST	TRIBUNE, 64 E CONCORD ST	ORLANDO, FL	32801
JOHNSON, FRANK	CARTOONIST	KING FEATURES, 216 E 45TH ST	NEW YORK, NY	10017
JOHNSON, GARY	BASEBALL SCOUT	POST OFFICE BOX 419969	KANSAS CITY, MO	64141
JOHNSON, GEORGANN	ACTRESS	218 N GLENROY PL	LOS ANGELES, CA	90049
JOHNSON, GEORGE CLAYTON	SCREENWRITER	8955 BEVERLY BLVD	WEST HOLLYWOOD, CA	90048
JOHNSON, GRAY R	FILM DIRECTOR	POST OFFICE BOX 1447	BURBANK, CA	91507
JOHNSON, GREG	BASEBALL (3RD BASE)	POST OFFICE BOX 661	KENOSHA, WI	53141
JOHNSON, GREG	BASEBALL (PITCHER)	POST OFFICE BOX 1659	PORTLAND, OR	97207
JOHNSON, HARRIET C	COLUMNIST	POST OFFICE BOX 500	WASHINGTON, DC	20044
JOHNSON, HELEN	ACTRESS	SEE - WOOD, JUDITH		
JOHNSON, HOWARD	SINGER	180 W END AVE #1-E	NEW YORK, NY	10023
JOHNSON, HOWARD "HOJO"	BASEBALL	METS, 126TH ST & ROOSEVELT AVE	FLUSHING, NY	11368
JOHNSON, HOWARD L	WRITER	12752 MULHOLLAND DR	BEVERLY HILLS, CA	90210
JOHNSON, HOWIE	GOLFER	PGA SENIORS, 112 T P C BLVD	PONTE VEDRA BEACH, FL	32082
JOHNSON, J J	TROMBONIST-COMPOSER	4001 MURIETTA AVE	SHERMAN OAKS, CA	91423
JOHNSON, JACK	BASEBALL	POST OFFICE BOX 10031	BAKERSFIELD, CA	93389
JOHNSON, JACK	FOOTBALL REFEREE	NFL, 410 PARK AVE	NEW YORK, NY	10022
JOHNSON, JAMES A, JR	SINGER-SONGWRITER	SEE - JAMES, RICK		
JOHNSON, JAMES D	TV DIRECTOR	4840 MAMMOTH AVE	SHERMAN OAKS, CA	91423
JOHNSON, JANET	ACTRESS	SEE - JULIEN, JANET		
JOHNSON, JAY W	PIANIST	BEAR MOUNTAIN VILLAGE		
		RURAL ROUTE #2	HARRISON, ME	04040
JOHNSON, JEFF	BASEBALL	N Y YANKEES, YANKEE STADIUM	BRONX, NY	10451
JOHNSON, JESSE	SINGER-SONGWRITER	AMERICAN ARTISTS, INC		
		312 WASHINGTON AVE N	MINNEAPOLIS, MN	55401
JOHNSON, JILL	ACTRESS	43 MATHESON RD	LONDON W14	ENGLAND
JOHNSON, JIM	FOOTBALL COACH	POST OFFICE BOX 888	PHOENIX, AZ	85001
JOHNSON, JIM	HOCKEY	NORTH STARS, 7901 CEDAR AVE S	BLOOMINGTON, MN	55425
JOHNSON, JIMMIE	FOOTBALL	POST OFFICE BOX 17247 (DULLES)	WASHINGTON, DC	20041
JOHNSON, JIMMY	FOOTBALL COACH	COWBOYS, 1 COWBOYS PARKWAY	IRVING, TX	75063
JOHNSON, JOANNA	ACTRESS	CBS-TV, "THE BOLD & BEAUTIFUL"		
		7800 BEVERLY BLVD #3371	LOS ANGELES, CA	90036
JOHNSON, JODI	ACTRESS	11846 VENTURA BLVD #100	STUDIO CITY, CA	91604
JOHNSON, JOE	ACTOR	357 S REXFORD DR #203	BEVERLY HILLS, CA	90212
JOHNSON, JOE	FOOTBALL	POST OFFICE BOX 17247 (DULLES)	WASHINGTON, DC	20041
JOHNSON, JOE	SINGER	STAR, 1311 CANDLELIGHT AVE	DALLAS, TX	75216
JOHNSON, JOHN	FOOTBALL	S F 49ERS, 4949 CENTENNIAL BL	SANTA CLARA, CA	95054
JOHNSON, JOHN E, JR	TV DIRECTOR	10 W 66TH ST #15-E	NEW YORK, NY	10023
JOHNSON, JOHN H	PUBLISHING EXECUTIVE	JET MAGAZINE, 820 S MICHIGAN AVE	CHICAGO, IL	60605
JOHNSON, JOHNNIE	SINGER-GUITARIST	1880 BOGEY HILLS PLAZA #11	SAINT CHARLES, MO	63302
JOHNSON, JOHNNY	FOOTBALL	POST OFFICE BOX 888	PHOENIX, AZ	85001
JOHNSON, JUDD	BASEBALL	POST OFFICE BOX 16683	GREENVILLE, SC	29606
JOHNSON, KATHIE LEE	SINGER-TV HOST	SEE - JOHNSON-GIFFORD, KATHIE LEE		
JOHNSON, KEITH	TV EXECUTIVE	GROSSO-JACOBSON, 767 3RD AVE	NEW YORK, NY	10017
JOHNSON, KENNETH C	WRITER-PRODUCER	4319 HAYVENHURST AVE	ENCINO, CA	91436
JOHNSON, KENNY	ACTOR	NBC-TV, "SANTA BARBARA"		
		3000 W ALAMEDA AVE	BURBANK, CA	91523
JOHNSON, KENT	FOOTBALL COACH	BUCCANEERS, 1 BUCCANEER PL	TAMPA, FL	33607
JOHNSON, KEVIN	BASKETBALL	SUNS, 2910 N CENTRAL AVE	PHOENIX, AZ	85012
JOHNSON, LADY BIRD	FIRST LADY-AUTHORESS	LBJ RANCH	STONEWALL, TX	78671
JOHNSON, LAMAR	BASEBALL-COACH	2850 W 20TH AVE	DENVER, CO	80211
JOHNSON, LANCE	BASEBALL	333 W 35TH ST	CHICAGO, IL	60616
JOHNSON, LARRY	SPORTS WRITER	UPS, 4900 MAIN ST, 9TH FLOOR	KANSAS CITY, MO	64112
JOHNSON, LARRY H	SCREENWRITER	10960 WILSHIRE BLVD #922	LOS ANGELES, CA	90024
JOHNSON, LAURA	ACTRESS	1917 WEEPAH WY	LOS ANGELES, CA	90046
JOHNSON, LAURIE	COMPOSER	PRIORY HOUSE, CLAMP HILL		
		STANMORE	MIDDLESEX	ENGLAND
JOHNSON, LEE	FOOTBALL	BENGALS, 200 RIVERFRONT STADIUM	CINCINNATI, OH	45202
JOHNSON, LEZLIE BROOKS	FILM DIRECTOR	1290 OAKWOOD DR	TOPANGA CANYON, CA	90290
JOHNSON, LINDA	BASEBALL EXECUTIVE	POST OFFICE BOX 3448	SHREVEPORT, LA	71133
JOHNSON, LOIS	SINGER	POST OFFICE BOX 50	GOODLETSVILLE, TN	37072
JOHNSON, LOIS W	CONDUCTOR	5015 KESTER AVE #5	SHERMAN OAKS, CA	91423
JOHNSON, LONNI SUE	ARTIST	2109 BROADWAY #13-159	NEW YORK, NY	10023
JOHNSON, LYNN-HOLLY	ACTRESS	335 N MAPLE DR #250	BEVERLY HILLS, CA	90210
JOHNSON, MARK	BASEBALL (APPLETON)	POST OFFICE BOX 464	APPLETON, WI	54912
JOHNSON, MARK	BASEBALL (CAROLINA)	POST OFFICE DRAWER 1218	ZEBULON, NC	27597
JOHNSON, MARK	BASEBALL (UMPIRE)	666 PROSPECT RD	HONOLULU, HI	96813
JOHNSON, MARK	FILM PRODUCER	CAA, 9830 WILSHIRE BLVD	BEVERLY HILLS, CA	90212
JOHNSON, MARK M	DIRECTOR-PRODUCER	1290 OAKWOOD DR	TOPANGA CANYON, CA	90290
JOHNSON, MARY JANE	SINGER	1710 S POLK ST	AMARILLO, TX	79102
JOHNSON, MARY LEA	THEATER PRODUCER	PRODUCERS CIRCLE COMPANY		
		1350 AVE OF THE AMERICAS	NEW YORK, NY	10019
JOHNSON, MICHAEL	SINGER-GUITARIST	POST OFFICE BOX 40661	NASHVILLE, TN	37204
JOHNSON, MICHELLE	ACTRESS	10351 SANTA MONICA BLVD #211	LOS ANGELES, CA	90025
JOHNSON, MIKE	FOOTBALL	BROWNS, 80 1ST ST	BEREA, OH	44017
JOHNSON, MONICA MC GOWAN	SCREENWRITER	8955 BEVERLY BLVD	WEST HOLLYWOOD, CA	90048
JOHNSON, MOOSE	BASEBALL SCOUT	SKYDOME, 300 BREMMER BL #3200	TORONTO, ONT M5V 3B3	CANADA
JOHNSON, NANCY L	U S CONGRESSMAN	480 MYRTLE ST #200	NEW BRITAIN, CT	06053
JOHNSON, NOEL	ACTOR	218 SAINT MARGARET'S RD		
		SAINT MARGARET'S-ON-THE-THAMES		
		TWICKENHAM	MIDDLESEX	ENGLAND
JOHNSON, NORMAN E	VIOLINIST	1525 POINT VIEW ST	LOS ANGELES, CA	90035
JOHNSON, NORTH	BASEBALL EXECUTIVE	POST OFFICE BOX 3452	KINSTON, NC	28502

JOHNSON, PAGE	ACTOR	49 GROVE ST	NEW YORK, NY	10014
JOHNSON, PAT E	SCREENWRITER	8955 BEVERLY BLVD	WEST HOLLYWOOD, CA	90048
JOHNSON, PEPPER	FOOTBALL	N Y GIANTS, GIANTS STADIUM	EAST RUTHERFORD, NJ	07073
JOHNSON, PETE	AUDITOR	POST OFFICE BOX 2000	JACKSON, MS	39215
JOHNSON, PETER	COLUMNIST	POST OFFICE BOX 500	WASHINGTON, DC	20044
JOHNSON, PETER C	SINGER	225 W 57TH ST #301	NEW YORK, NY	10019
JOHNSON, PHIL	BASKETBALL COACH	5 TRIAD CENTER #500	SALT LAKE CITY, UT	84180
JOHNSON, R TOWNLEY	MUSIC ARRANGER	ROUTE #7, HILLAKE DR	LEBANON, TN	37087
JOHNSON, R VERLE	DIRECTOR	4918 SCHUYLER DR	ANNANDALE, VA	22003
JOHNSON, RAFER	ACTOR-RUNNER	4217 WOODCLIFF RD	SHERMAN OAKS, CA	91403
JOHNSON, RANDY	BASEBALL SCOUT	POST OFFICE BOX 2000	SAN DIEGO, CA	92112
JOHNSON, RANDY DAVID	BASEBALL	POST OFFICE BOX 4100	SEATTLE, WA	98104
JOHNSON, REGGIE	ACTOR	10000 SANTA MONICA BLVD #305	LOS ANGELES, CA	90067
JOHNSON, RHETA GRIMSLEY	COLUMNIST-AUTHORESS	MEMPHIS COMMERCIAL APPEAL		
		495 UNION AVE	MEMPHIS, TN	38103
JOHNSON, RICHARD	ACTOR-PRODUCER	ICM, 388-396 OXFORD ST	LONDON W1	ENGLAND
JOHNSON, RICHARD	FOOTBALL	OILERS, 6910 FANNIN ST	HOUSTON, TX	77070
JOHNSON, RICHARD D	AUDITOR	STATE CAPITOL BUILDING	DES MOINES, IA	50319
JOHNSON, ROBERT L	TV EXECUTIVE	BLACK ENTERTAINMENT TV		
		1050 31ST ST, NW	WASHINGTON, DC	20007
JOHNSON, ROGER, JR	DIRECTOR	4240 TEESDALE AVE	STUDIO CITY, CA	91604
JOHNSON, ROLAND	BASEBALL SCOUT	METS, 126TH ST & ROOSEVELT AVE	FLUSHING, NY	11368
JOHNSON, ROME	SINGER	POST OFFICE BOX 4234	PANORAMA CITY, CA	91412
JOHNSON, RON	BASEBALL MANAGER	300 STADIUM WY	DAVENPORT, FL	33837
JOHNSON, ROY, JR	MUSICIAN	3912 ARLINGTON SQ DR #5	HOUSTON, TX	77034
JOHNSON, RUSSELL	ACTOR	6310 SAN VICENTE BLVD #407	LOS ANGELES, CA	90048
JOHNSON, SANDY	BASEBALL EXEC-SCOUT	POST OFFICE BOX 90111	ARLINGTON, TX	76004
JOHNSON, SCOTT	BASEBALL TRAINER	POST OFFICE BOX 4218	SOUTH BEND, IN	46634
JOHNSON, SCOTT	GUITARIST	NEW MUSIC, 500 BROADWAY	NEW YORK	10012
JOHNSON, SCOTT	SCREENWRITER	8955 BEVERLY BLVD	WEST HOLLYWOOD, CA	90048
JOHNSON, SHARON	DIRECTOR	4201 VIA MARINA #162	MARINA DEL REY, CA	90292
JOHNSON, STANLEY R	DIRECTOR	1922 LAKE ALDEN DR	APOPKA, FL	32703
JOHNSON, STERLING	TV DIRECTOR	1315 S OAKLAND AVE	PASADENA, CA	91106
JOHNSON, STEVE	BASEBALL	POST OFFICE BOX 3783	SAVANNAH, GA	31414
JOHNSON, STEVE	BASKETBALL	GOLDEN STATE WARRIORS		
		OAKLAND COLISEUM ARENA		
		NIMITZ FWY & HEGENBERGER RD	OAKLAND, CA	94621
JOHNSON, SYDNEY	FOOTBALL	POST OFFICE BOX 17247 (DULLES)	WASHINGTON, DC	20041
JOHNSON, TIM	BASEBALL SCOUT	6850 LAWRENCE RD	LANTANA, FL	33462
JOHNSON, TIM	FOOTBALL	POST OFFICE BOX 17247 (DULLES)	WASHINGTON, DC	20041
JOHNSON, TIM	U S CONGRESSMAN	615 S MAIN	ABERDEEN, SD	57401
JOHNSON, TOM	CARTOONIST	TRIBUNE, 64 E CONCORD ST	ORLANDO, FL	32801
JOHNSON, TOM	FOOTBALL REFEREE	NFL, 410 PARK AVE	NEW YORK, NY	10022
JOHNSON, TRACY	FOOTBALL	FALCONS, SUWANEE RD AT I-85	SUWANEE, GA	30174
JOHNSON, TRAVIS	WRITER-PRODUCER	POST OFFICE BOX 2093	DENTON, TX	76201
JOHNSON, TROY	FOOTBALL	N Y JETS, 1000 FULTON AVE	HEMPSTEAD, NY	11550
JOHNSON, TROY	SINGER	6433 TOPANGA CANYON BLVD #154	CANOGA PARK, CA	91303
JOHNSON, VAN	ACTOR	STUDIO ARTISTS, 305 W 52ND ST	NEW YORK, NY	10019
JOHNSON, VAUGHAN	FOOTBALL	SAINTS, 1500 POYDRAS ST	NEW ORLEANS, LA	90112
JOHNSON, VINNIE	BASKETBALL	THE PALACE OF AUBURN HILLS		
		2 CHAMPIONSHIP DR	AUBURN HILLS, MI	48326
JOHNSON, W THOMAS	TV EXECUTIVE	1050 TECHWOOD DR, NW	ATLANTA, GA	30318
JOHNSON, WALLY	BASEBALL	2512 ADAMS ST	GARY, IN	46407
JOHNSON, WAYMER L	DIRECTOR	1101 3RD ST #816, SW	WASHINGTON, DC	20024
JOHNSON, WILLY	BASEBALL TRAINER	POST OFFICE BOX 507	DURHAM, NC	27702
JOHNSON MOUNTAIN BOYS, THE	C & W GROUP	10235 LEWIS DR	DAMASCUS, MD	20872
JOHNSON-ALDRETE, LORI	DIRECTOR	3015 CATALINA DR	DAVIS, CA	95616
JOHNSONS, THE	ROCK & ROLL GROUP	POST OFFICE BOX 53588	PHILADELPHIA, PA	19105
JOHNSTON, BECKY	COMPOSER	ICM, 8899 BEVERLY BLVD	LOS ANGELES, CA	90048
JOHNSTON, CATHY	GOLFER	2750 VOLUSA AVE #B	DAYTON BEACH, FL	32114
JOHNSTON, DAN	BASEBALL	5301 NW 12TH AVE	FORT LAUDERDALE, FL	33309
JOHNSTON, DARYL	FOOTBALL	COWBOYS, 1 COWBOYS PARKWAY	IRVING, TX	75063
JOHNSTON, ERNESTINE M	ACTRESS	40 W 135TH ST #11-R	NEW YORK, NY	10037
JOHNSTON, FRANK B	PHOTOGRAPHER	THE LORCOM TOWERS		
		4300 OLD DOMINION DR	ARLINGTON, VA	22207
JOHNSTON, FREDERICK E, JR	DIRECTOR	POST OFFICE BOX 4060	PRINCETON, NJ	08540
JOHNSTON, HARRY	U S CONGRESSMAN	1501 CORPORATE DR #250	BOYNTON BEACH, FL	33426
JOHNSTON, J BENNETT	U S SENATOR	500 FANNIN ST #7-A-12	SHREVEPORT, LA	71101
JOHNSTON, JAMES R	DIRECTOR	140 E 39TH ST	NEW YORK, NY	10016
JOHNSTON, JIM	BASEBALL SCOUT	250 STADIUM PLAZA	ST LOUIS, MO	63102
JOHNSTON, JOANNA	COSTUME DESIGNER	13949 VENTURA BLVD #309	SHERMAN OAKS, CA	91423
JOHNSTON, JOE	DIRECTOR	CAA, 9830 WILSHIRE BLVD	BEVERLY HILLS, CA	90212
JOHNSTON, JOEL	BASEBALL	POST OFFICE BOX 419969	KANSAS CITY, MO	64141
JOHNSTON, JUSTINE ALICE	ACTRESS	35-48 75TH ST	JACKSON HEIGHTS, NY	11372
JOHNSTON, KEN B	TALENT AGENT	6290 HOLLYWOOD BLVD #403	HOLLYWOOD, CA	90028
JOHNSTON, LEN	BASEBALL COACH	POST OFFICE BOX 356	BLUEFIELD, WV	24701
JOHNSTON, LENNY	BASEBALL EXECUTIVE	ORIOLE PARK, 333 W CAMDEN ST	BALTIMORE, MD	21201
JOHNSTON, LYNN	CARTOONIST	UPS, 4900 MAIN ST, 9TH FLOOR	KANSAS CITY, MO	64112
JOHNSTON, RICHARD O	COMPOSER	7900 SALE AVE	CANOGA PARK, CA	91304
JOHNSTON, TRACE	SCREENWRITER	8955 BEVERLY BLVD	WEST HOLLYWOOD, CA	90048
JOHNSTONE, ANNA HILL	COSTUME DESIGNER	13949 VENTURA BLVD #309	SHERMAN OAKS, CA	91423
JOHNSTONE, DAVEY	SINGER	9595 WILSHIRE BLVD #505	BEVERLY HILLS, CA	90212
JOHNSTONE, IAIN	DIRECTOR-PRODUCER	16 TOURNAY RD	LONDON SW6	ENGLAND
JOHNSTONE, JAY	BASEBALL-AUTHOR	853 CHAPERAL	PASADENA, CA	91107
JOINER, CHARLIE	FOOTBALL-COACH	12929 ANGOSTO WY	SAN DIEGO, CA	92128

Name	Occupation	Address	City, State	Zip
JOLAS, BETSY	COMPOSER	YALE SCHOOL OF MUSIC		
		96 WALL ST	NEW HAVEN, CT	06511
JOLGUERA, JOSE G	TV DIRECTOR	12297 SW 204 TERR	MIAMI, FL	33177
JONAS, SHIRLEY	WRI-DIR-PROD	720 GREENWICH ST #2-N	NEW YORK, NY	10014
JONES, A BERNEY	DIRECTOR	142 W END AVE #12-L	NEW YORK, NY	10023
JONES, AARON	FOOTBALL	STEELERS, 300 STADIUM CIR	PITTSBURGH, PA	15212
JONES, ALLAN	ACTOR-SINGER	10 W 66TH ST	NEW YORK, NY	10023
JONES, ANGIE	COSTUME DESIGNER	13949 VENTURA BLVD #309	SHERMAN OAKS, CA	91423
JONES, ANTHONY R	COMPOSER-CONDUCTOR	1016 S CRESCENT HGTS BLVD	LOS ANGELES, CA	90035
JONES, AYVONNE	SINGER-GUITARIST	201 E HOYT	LONG VIEW, TX	75601
JONES, BAIRD	CONDUCTOR	509 35TH ST SW	OKLAHOMA CITY, OK	73109
JONES, BARRY	BASEBALL (MAJORS)	POST OFFICE BOX 7575	PHILADELPHIA, PA	19101
JONES, BEN	SINGER	5 BLVD, SE	ATLANTA, GA	30312
JONES, BEN	U S CONGRESSMAN	1124 CLARK ST	COVINGTON, GA	30209
JONES, BERETON C	LT GOVERNOR	STATE CAPITOL BUILDING	FRANKFORT, KY	40601
JONES, BETSY	COSTUME DESIGNER	13949 VENTURA BLVD #309	SHERMAN OAKS, CA	91423
JONES, BILL	FILM CRITIC	POST OFFICE BOX 1950	PHOENIX, AZ	85001
JONES, BILL	FOOTBALL	CHIEFS, 1 ARROWHEAD DR	KANSAS CITY, MO	64129
JONES, BOBBY	BASEBALL (BINGHAMTON)	POST OFFICE BOX 598	BINGHAMTON, NY	13902
JONES, BOBBY	BASEBALL (MIDLAND)	POST OFFICE BOX 12	MIDLAND, TX	79702
JONES, BOBBY	BASEBALL MANAGER	POST OFFICE BOX 4448	TULSA, OK	74159
JONES, BOBBY & NEW LIFE	GOSPEL GROUP	6750 W 75TH ST, BLDG #2-A	OVERLAND PARK, KS	66204
JONES, BRAD	HOCKEY	POST OFFICE BOX 17013	INGLEWOOD, CA	90308
JONES, BRENT	FOOTBALL	S F 49ERS, 4949 CENTENNIAL BL	SANTA CLARA, CA	95054
JONES, CALVIN	BASEBALL	POST OFFICE BOX 4100	SEATTLE, WA	98104
JONES, CHARLES	BASKETBALL	BULLETS, 1 HARRY S TRUMAN DR	LANDOVER, MD	20785
JONES, CHARLES O	TV DIRECTOR	17800 WHITE'S FERRY RD	POOLESVILLE, MD	20837
JONES, CHARLIE	SPORTSCASTER	NBC SPORTS, 3000 W ALAMEDA AVE	BURBANK, CA	91523
JONES, CHARLOTTE	ACTRESS	205 W 57TH ST	NEW YORK, NY	10019
JONES, CHIPPER	BASEBALL	POST OFFICE BOX 507	DURHAM, NC	27702
JONES, CHRIS	BASEBALL	POST OFFICE BOX 36407	LOUISVILLE, KY	40233
JONES, CHRIS	BASEBALL	POST OFFICE BOX 288	HOUSTON, TX	77001
JONES, CHRISTINE	ACTRESS	10 E 44TH ST #700	NEW YORK, NY	10017
JONES, CHRISTINE Y	SINGER	HONEYBEE PRODS, 145 E 74TH ST	NEW YORK, NY	10021
JONES, CHUCK	CARTOONIST	POST OFFICE BOX 2319	COSTA MESA, CA	92628
JONES, CLARENCE	BASEBALL-COACH	POST OFFICE BOX 4064	ATLANTA, GA	30302
JONES, CLARENCE	FOOTBALL	N Y GIANTS, GIANTS STADIUM	EAST RUTHERFORD, NJ	07073
JONES, CLARK R	TV DIRECTOR	337 W 70TH ST	NEW YORK, NY	10023
JONES, CLAUDE EARL	ACTOR	8489 W 3RD ST #1105	LOS ANGELES, CA	90048
JONES, CRIS	BASEBALL UMPIRE	POST OFFICE BOX 25010	LITTLE ROCK, AZ	72221
JONES, DAN	BASEBALL	POST OFFICE BOX 842	SALEM, VA	24153
JONES, DANTE	FOOTBALL	BEARS, 250 N WASHINGTON RD	LAKE FOREST, IL	60045
JONES, DAVE	FILM DIRECTOR	POST OFFICE BOX 55025	SHERMAN OAKS, CA	91403
JONES, DAVEY	SINGER-ACTOR	21 ELMS RD, FAREHAM	HANTS	ENGLAND
JONES, DAVID	FILM DIR-PROD	26 FITZJOHNS AVE	LONDON NW3	ENGLAND
JONES, DAX	BASEBALL	POST OFFICE BOX 1295	CLINTON, IA	52733
JONES, DEACON	BASEBALL-INSTRUCTOR	ORIOLE PARK, 333 W CAMDEN ST	BALTIMORE, MD	21201
JONES, DEAN	ACTOR	5055 CASA DR	TARZANA, CA	91356
JONES, DEBORAH	SCREENWRITER	8955 BEVERLY BLVD	WEST HOLLYWOOD, CA	90048
JONES, DOUG	BASEBALL	POST OFFICE BOX 288	HOUSTON, TX	77001
JONES, EAMONN	ACTOR	32 EXETER RD	LONDON NW2	ENGLAND
JONES, EDDIE J	FOOTBALL EXECUTIVE	DOLPHINS, 2269 NW 199TH ST	MIAMI, FL	33056
JONES, EDWARD	TV WRITER-PRODUCER	37 E SHORE DR	BABYLON, NY	11702
JONES, ELVIN	DRUMMER	KEIKO JONES MANAGEMENT		
		415 CENTRAL PARK W	NEW YORK, NY	10025
JONES, ERIC P	DIRECTOR	3521 DAHLIA AVE	LOS ANGELES, CA	90026
JONES, ERNIE	FOOTBALL	POST OFFICE BOX 888	PHOENIX, AZ	85001
JONES, EUGENE	DIRECTOR-PRODUCER	190 E 72ND ST	NEW YORK, NY	10021
JONES, EUGENE S	FILM WRITER-DIRECTOR	461 BELLAGIO TERR	LOS ANGELES, CA	90049
JONES, EVAN	TV WRITER	MIDDLE TWINHOE, MIDFORD, BATH	AVON BA2 9QA	ENGLAND
JONES, FRED	FOOTBALL	CHIEFS, 1 ARROWHEAD DR	KANSAS CITY, MO	64129
JONES, FREDDIE	ACTOR	ICM, 388-396 OXFORD ST	LONDON W1	ENGLAND
JONES, GARY	BASEBALL MANAGER	POST OFFICE BOX 11363	RENO, NV	89510
JONES, GARY	COSTUME DESIGNER	43 JANE ST	NEW YORK, NY	10014
JONES, GEMMA	ACTOR	3 GOODWINS CT	LONDON WC2	ENGLAND
JONES, GEORGE	SINGER-COMPOSER	38 MUSIC SQUARE E #300	NASHVILLE, TN	37203
JONES, GLENN	SINGER	LOUISE C WEST MANAGEMENT		
		1775 BROADWAY, 7TH FLOOR	NEW YORK, NY	10019
JONES, GRACE	ACTRESS-SINGER-MODEL	166 BANK ST	NEW YORK, NY	10014
JONES, GRANDPA	SINGER-GUITARIST	POST OFFICE BOX 57	MOUNTAIN VIEW, AR	72560
JONES, HANK	BASEBALL SCOUT	1000 ELYSIAN PARK DR	LOS ANGELES, CA	90012
JONES, HASSAN	FOOTBALL	VIKINGS, 9520 VIKING DR	EDEN PRAIRIE, MN	55344
JONES, HENRY	ACTOR	12221 TWEED LN	LOS ANGELES, CA	90049
JONES, HENRY	FOOTBALL	BILLS, 1 BILLS DR	ORCHARD PARK, NJ	14127
JONES, HOWARD	SINGER-SONGWRITER	POST OFFICE BOX 185, HIGH WYCOM	BUCKS HP11 2E2	ENGLAND
JONES, JACK	SINGER-ACTOR	3965 DEERVALE DR	SHERMAN OAKS, CA	91403
JONES, JAMES	FOOTBALL (BROWNS)	BROWNS, 80 1ST ST	BEREA, OH	44017
JONES, JAMES	FOOTBALL (SEAHAWKS)	SEAHAWKS, 11220 NE 53RD ST	KIRKLAND, WA	98033
JONES, JAMES CELLAN	TV DIRECTOR	19 CUMBERLAND RD, KEW	SURREY	ENGLAND
JONES, JAMES EARL	ACTOR	POST OFFICE BOX 55337	SHERMAN OAKS, CA	91413
JONES, JANET	ACTRESS	SEE - JONES, JANET MARIE		
JONES, JANET MARIE	ACTRESS	14135 BERESFORD DR	BEVERLY HILLS, CA	90210
JONES, JEFF	BASEBALL COACH	TIGERS, 89 WHARNCLIFFE RD N	LONDON, ONT N6H 2A7	CANADA
JONES, JEFFREY	ACTOR	9200 SUNSET BLVD #710	LOS ANGELES, CA	90069
JONES, JEFFREY M	COMPOSER	6456 BLUCHER ST	VAN NUYS, CA	91406

Name	Occupation	Address	City	Zip/Country
JONES, JEFFREY M	DIRECTOR	520 N MICHIGAN AVE #1026	CHICAGO, IL	60611
JONES, JENNY	TV HOST	POST OFFICE BOX 3333	CHICAGO, IL	60654
JONES, JERRY	FOOTBALL EXECUTIVE	COWBOYS, 1 COWBOYS PARKWAY	IRVING, TX	75063
JONES, JIMMIE	FOOTBALL	COWBOYS, 1 COWBOYS PARKWAY	IRVING, TX	75063
JONES, JIMMY	BASEBALL	3054 NEWCASTLE DR	DALLAS, TX	75220
JONES, JOCELYN	ACTRESS	11846 VENTURA BLVD #100	STUDIO CITY, CA	91604
JONES, JOCK	FOOTBALL	BROWNS, 80 1ST ST	BEREA, OH	44017
JONES, JOE	BASEBALL-COACH	POST OFFICE BOX 419969	KANSAS CITY, MO	64141
JONES, JOE	CONDUCTOR	10556 ARNWOOD RD	LAKE VIEW TERRACE, CA	91342
JONES, JULIA HUGHES	AUDITOR	STATE CAPITOL BUILDING	LITTLE ROCK, AR	72201
JONES, JUNE	FOOTBALL COACH	LIONS, 1200 FEATHERSTONE RD	PONTIAC, MI	48432
JONES, K C	BASKETBALL COACH	POST OFFICE BOX C-900911	SEATTLE, WA	98109
JONES, KEITH	BASEBALL	POST OFFICE BOX 3004	SPRINGFIELD, IL	62708
JONES, KELLY	ACTRESS	12456 VENTURA BLVD #1	STUDIO CITY, CA	91604
JONES, KEN	ACTOR	23 LAURIER RD	LONDON NW5	ENGLAND
JONES, KENNETH VICTOR	COMPOSER-CONDUCTOR	CLEAVERS, BISHOPSTONE VILLAGE		
		SEAFORD	EAST SUSSEX BN25 2UD	ENGLAND
JONES, KIKI	BASEBALL	POST OFFICE BOX 2887	VERO BEACH, FL	32961
JONES, L DEAN, JR	FILM DIRECTOR	440 PANORAMIC HWY	MILL VALLEY, CA	94941
JONES, L Q	ACTOR-DIRECTOR	11938 COLLINS ST	NORTH HOLLYWOOD, CA	91607
JONES, LAURIS L	CONDUCTOR	POST OFFICE BOX 1126	SPRING VALLEY, CA	92077
JONES, LELAND S	WRITER-PRODUCER	124 HARRINGTON AVE	WESTWOOD, CA	07675
JONES, LYNN	BASEBALL COACH	POST OFFICE BOX 419969	KANSAS CITY, MO	64141
JONES, MARCIA MAE	ACTRESS	4541 HAZELTINE AVE #4	SHERMAN OAKS, CA	91423
JONES, MICHAEL R	TV DIRECTOR	POST OFFICE BOX 49348	LOS ANGELES, CA	90049
JONES, MICK	SINGER-SONGWRITER	145 CENTRAL PARK W	NEW YORK, NY	10023
JONES, MICKEY	ACTOR	12456 VENTURA BLVD #1	STUDIO CITY, CA	91604
JONES, MIKE	BASEBALL	POST OFFICE BOX 2001	CEDAR RAPIDS, IA	52406
JONES, MIKE	BASEBALL (SCOUT)	ATHLETICS'S, OAKLAND COLISEUM	OAKLAND, CA	94621
JONES, MIKE	FOOTBALL (CARDINALS)	POST OFFICE BOX 888	PHOENIX, AZ	85001
JONES, MIKE	FOOTBALL (RAIDERS)	RAIDERS, 332 CENTER ST	EL SEGUNDO, CA	90245
JONES, MIKE	FOOTBALL (VIKINGS)	VIKINGS, 9520 VIKING DR	EDEN PRAIRIE, MN	55344
JONES, MOTORBOAT	BASEBALL	POST OFFICE BOX 4669	CHARLESTON, WV	25304
JONES, NATALIE	FILM PRODUCER	190 E 72ND ST	NEW YORK, NY	10021
JONES, NATHAN	FOOTBALL REFEREE	NFL, 410 PARK AVE	NEW YORK, NY	10022
JONES, NORMAN	ACTOR	HOWES, 66 BERKELEY HO, HAY HILL	LONDON W1X 7LH	ENGLAND
JONES, PARNELLI	AUTO RACER	20550 EARL ST	TORRANCE, CA	90503
JONES, PAUL	ACTOR	CHATTO AND LINNIT, LTD		
		PRINCE OF WALES THEATRE		
		COVENTRY ST	LONDON W1V 7FE	ENGLAND
JONES, PETER	ACTOR-WRITER	STONE, 25 WHITEHALL	LONDON SW1A 2BS	ENGLAND
JONES, PHILIP	TV PRODUCER	26 TROWLOCK AVE, TEDDINGTON	MIDDLESEX	ENGLAND
JONES, QUINCY	COMP-ARR-PROD	POST OFFICE BOX 11509	BURBANK, CA	91510
JONES, REESA KAY	SINGER	OPERATION MUSIC ENTERPRISES		
		233 W WOODLAND AVE	OTTUMWA, IA	52501
JONES, REGGIE	FOOTBALL	SAINTS, 1500 POYDRAS ST	NEW ORLEANS, LA	90112
JONES, RICK V	COMPOSER	1016 S CRESCENT HGTS BLVD	LOS ANGELES, CA	90035
JONES, RICKIE LEE	SINGER-SONGWRITER	476 BROOME ST #6-A	NEW YORK, NY	10013
JONES, ROBERT EARL	ACTOR	THE MANHATTAN PLAZA		
JONES, ROBERT M	DIRECTOR	18617 W SOLEDAD CANYON	CANYON CITY, CA	91351
		400 W 43RD ST	NEW YORK, NY	10036
JONES, ROD	FOOTBALL	BENGALS, 200 RIVERFRONT STADIUM	CINCINNATI, OH	45202
JONES, RON	BASEBALL	2316 CHAPMAN	SEQUIN, TX	78155
JONES, RONALD	TV DIRECTOR-PRODUCER	21 HOLLAND PARK AVE	LONDON W11	ENGLAND
JONES, RONALD N	COMPOSER	11840 RIVERSIDE DR	NORTH HOLLYWOOD, CA	91607
JONES, RONNIE	FOOTBALL COACH	EAGLES, BROAD ST & PATTISON AVE	PHILADELPHIA, PA	19148
JONES, RUPPERT	BASEBALL	POST OFFICE BOX 1149	POWAY, CA	92064
JONES, RUSTY	FOOTBALL COACH	BILLS, 1 BILLS DR	ORCHARD PARK, NJ	14127
JONES, S D	WRESTLER	POST OFFICE BOX 3859	STAMFORD, CT	06905
JONES, SABRA	ACTRESS	2160 OLIVE AVE	LONG BEACH, CA	90806
JONES, SAM J	ACTOR	10100 SANTA MONICA BLVD #1600	LOS ANGELES, CA	90067
JONES, SAMUEL	CONDUCTOR	2235 SOUTHGATE BLVD	HOUSTON, TX	77030
JONES, SCOTT	FOOTBALL	PACKERS, 1265 LOMBARDI AVE	GREEN BAY, WI	54307
JONES, SHIRLEY	ACTRESS	701 N OAKHURST DR	BEVERLY HILLS, CA	90210
JONES, SHIRLEY	SINGER	CAPITOL RECORDS COMPANY		
		1750 N VINE ST	HOLLYWOOD, CA	90028
JONES, SIMON	ACTOR	HEATH, PARAMOUNT HOUSE		
		162-170 WARDOUR ST	LONDON W1V 3AT	ENGLAND
JONES, STAN	FOOTBALL COACH	BROWNS, 80 1ST ST	BEREA, OH	44017
JONES, STEPHEN	TV DIRECTOR	130 PARK VIEW	WEMBLEY HA9 6JU	ENGLAND
JONES, STEVE	GOLFER	POST OFFICE BOX 109601	PALM BCH GARDENS, FL	33418
JONES, TERRY	ACT-WRI-DIR	25 NEWMAN ST	LONDON W1	ENGLAND
JONES, TIM	BASEBALL	250 STADIUM PLAZA	ST LOUIS, MO	63102
JONES, TODD	BASEBALL	POST OFFICE BOX 4209	JACKSON, MS	39296
JONES, TOM	SINGER	363 COPA DE ORA RD	LOS ANGELES, CA	90077
JONES, TOMMY	BASEBALL MANAGER	POST OFFICE BOX 30160	SAN BERNARDINO, CA	92413
JONES, TOMMY LEE	ACTOR	POST OFFICE BOX 966	SAN SABA, TX	76877
JONES, TONY	FOOTBALL (BROWNS)	BROWNS, 80 1ST ST	BEREA, OH	44017
JONES, TONY	FOOTBALL (OILERS)	OILERS, 6910 FANNIN ST	HOUSTON, TX	77070
JONES, TRACY	BASEBALL	CANADIANS, 4601 ONTARIO ST	VANCOUVER, BC V5V 3H4	CANADA
JONES, TRENT	TV WRITER	230 W 55TH ST #29-D	NEW YORK, NY	10012
JONES, TREVOR	COMPOSER	CONTEMPORARY MEDIA MUSIC PRODS		
		46 AVENUE RD, HIGHGATE	LONDON N6 5DR	ENGLAND
JONES, WALI	BASKETBALL	MIAMI HEAT, THE MIAMI ARENA	MIAMI, FL	33136
JONES, WALTER B	U S CONGRESSMAN	108 E WILSON ST	FARMVILLE, NC	27828

JONES, WALTER L	WRITER-PRODUCER	DGA, 110 W 57TH ST	NEW YORK, NY	10019
JONES GIRLS, THE	VOCAL GROUP	POST OFFICE BOX 6010-761	SHERMAN OAKS, CA	91413
JONES SIMON, JENNIFER	ACTRESS	POST OFFICE BOX 93666	PASADENA, CA	91109
JONES-FAISON, VIOLETTE	COSTUME DESIGNER	13949 VENTURA BLVD #309	SHERMAN OAKS, CA	91423
JONESES, THE	ROCK & ROLL GROUP	DR DREAM RECORDS COMPANY		
		833 W COLLINS AVE	ORANGE, CA	92667
JONG, ERICA	AUTHORESS	121 DAVIS HILL RD	WESTON, CT	06883
JONGEWAARD, ROGER	BASEBALL SCOUT	POST OFFICE BOX 4100	SEATTLE, WA	98104
JONKE, GARY JOHN	TV WRITER	2624 MANNING AVE	LOS ANGELES, CA	90064
JONKER, J DEET	TV EXECUTIVE	ABC-TV, 7 W 66TH ST	NEW YORK, NY	10023
JONSON, KEVIN JOE	DIRECTOR	3201 LANDOVER ST #1621	ALEXANDRIA, VA	22305
JONTZ, JIM	U S CONGRESSMAN	104 W WALNUT	KOKOMO, IN	46901
JONZUN, MICHAEL	SINGER-GUITARIST	BOSTON INTL MUSIC CO		
		545 BOSTON ST	BOSTON, MA	02116
JORDAN, ARCHIE P	MUSIC ARRANGER	ROUTE #7, SPENCER CREEK RD	FRANKLIN, TN	37064
JORDAN, BARBARA	U S REPRESENTATIVE	LYNDON B JOHNSON SCHOOL		
		UNIVERSITY OF TEXAS	AUSTIN, TX	78705
JORDAN, BRIAN	BASEBALL	POST OFFICE BOX 36407	LOUISVILLE, KY	40233
JORDAN, BRIAN	FOOTBALL	FALCONS, SUWANEE RD AT I-85	SUWANEE, GA	30174
JORDAN, BUFORD	FOOTBALL	SAINTS, 1500 POYDRAS ST	NEW ORLEANS, LA	90112
JORDAN, DARIN	FOOTBALL	S F 49ERS, 4949 CENTENNIAL BL	SANTA CLARA, CA	95054
JORDAN, DIANE	SINGER	152 SHAWNEE RD	MADISON, TN	37115
JORDAN, GLENN	DIRECTOR-PRODUCER	CAA, 9830 WILSHIRE BLVD	BEVERLY HILLS, CA	90212
JORDAN, GLENN A	COMPOSER	11334 CALIFA ST	NORTH HOLLYWOOD, CA	91601
JORDAN, JAMES CARROLL	ACTOR	8333 LOOKOUT MOUNTAIN AVE	LOS ANGELES, CA	90046
JORDAN, JAMES J	DIRECTOR	COAST, 1001 N POINSETTIA PL	HOLLYWOOD, CA	90046
JORDAN, JERRY	BASEBALL SCOUT	POST OFFICE BOX 7575	PHILADELPHIA, PA	19101
JORDAN, JOEY	CHAINSAW JUGGLER	POST OFFICE BOX 60122		
		TERMINAL ANNEX	LOS ANGELES, CA	90060
JORDAN, JON	BODYBUILDER	1651 MARMONT AVE	LOS ANGELES, CA	90069
JORDAN, KEVIN	BASEBALL	POST OFFICE BOX 2148	WOODBRIDGE, VA	22193
JORDAN, LARRY K	DIRECTOR-PRODUCER	65 MAIN ST	FRAMINGHAM, MA	01701
JORDAN, MICHAEL	BASKETBALL	980 N MICHIGAN AVE #1600	CHICAGO, IL	60611
JORDAN, MICHAEL J	DIRECTOR	164 W 79TH ST	NEW YORK, NY	10024
JORDAN, MURRAY B	TV DIRECTOR	1605 1/2 S WOOSTER ST	LOS ANGELES, CA	90035
JORDAN, RICARDO	BASEBALL	POST OFFICE BOX 957	DUNEDIN, FL	34697
JORDAN, RICHARD	ACTOR	9350 WILSHIRE BLVD #324	BEVERLY HILLS, CA	90212
JORDAN, RICKY	BASEBALL	POST OFFICE BOX 7575	PHILADELPHIA, PA	19101
JORDAN, ROBERT	WRITER	SCHNEE, 11602 COLLETT AVE	GRANADA HILLS, CA	91344
JORDAN, S MARC	ACTOR	6255 SUNSET BLVD #627	LOS ANGELES, CA	90028
JORDAN, SCOTT	BASEBALL	21 NETTLE CT	COLUMBUS, GA	31909
JORDAN, STANLEY	GUITARIST-COMPOSER	C MARTIN, 242 W 30TH ST	NEW YORK, NY	10001
JORDAN, STEVE	FOOTBALL	VIKINGS, 9520 VIKING DR	EDEN PRAIRIE, MN	55344
JORDAN, TONY	FOOTBALL	OILERS, 6910 FANNIN ST	HOUSTON, TX	77070
JORDAN, WILL	COMEDIAN	435 W 57TH ST #10-F	NEW YORK, NY	10019
JORDAN, WILLIAM	ACTOR	10806 LINDBROOK DR #4	LOS ANGELES, CA	90024
JORDANAIRES, THE	VOCAL GROUP	ACE ANDERSON PRODUCTIONS		
		7656 WATER OAK POINT RD	PASADENA, MD	21122
JORDEN, TIM	FOOTBALL	POST OFFICE BOX 888	PHOENIX, AZ	85001
JORDON, EASON	TV EXECUTIVE	1050 TECHWOOD DR, NW	ATLANTA, GA	30318
JORENSEN, JOHN "SPIDER"	BASEBALL-SCOUT	1060 W ADDISON ST	CHICAGO, IL	60613
JORGENSEN, DICK	FOOTBALL REFEREE	NFL, 410 PARK AVE	NEW YORK, NY	10022
JORGENSEN, MIKE	BASEBALL-INSTRUCTOR	250 STADIUM PLAZA	ST LOUIS, MO	63102
JORGENSEN, REBEKAH L	DIRECTOR	KARLIN, 1025 CHAUTAUQUA BLVD	PACIFIC PALISADES, CA	90272
JORGENSEN, TERRY	BASEBALL	POST OFFICE BOX 1659	PORTLAND, OR	97207
JORGENSEN, TIM	FOOTBALL COACH	FALCONS, SUWANEE RD AT I-85	SUWANEE, GA	30174
JORN, DAVE	BASEBALL COACH	ALBANY YANKEES, HERITAGE PARK	ALBANY, NY	12211
JORY, TERRILL	CONDUCTOR	111 W 57TH ST #1203	NEW YORK, NY	10019
JOSE, FELIX	BASEBALL	250 STADIUM PLAZA	ST LOUIS, MO	63102
JOSELOFF, MICHAEL H	TV WRITER-PRODUCER	MAC NEIL/LEHRER, 356 W 58TH ST	NEW YORK, NY	10019
JOSEPH, ADRIAN H	TV WRITER-PRODUCER	201 LA VEREDA RD	PASADENA, CA	91105
JOSEPH, BRYAN K	TV WRITER	2615 CANYON DR	LOS ANGELES, CA	90068
JOSEPH, CHRIS	HOCKEY	OILERS, NORTHLANDS COLISEUM	EDMONTON, ALTA T5B 4M9	CANADA
JOSEPH, JACKIE	ACTRESS-WRITER	111 N VALLEY ST	BURBANK, CA	91505
JOSEPH, JAMES	COLUMNIST	UPS, 4900 MAIN ST, 9TH FLOOR	KANSAS CITY, MO	64112
JOSEPH, JEFFREY	ACTOR	SMITH, 121 N SAN VICENTE BLVD	BEVERLY HILLS, CA	90211
JOSEPH, KATHY S	TV WRITER	11108 OPHIR DR	LOS ANGELES, CA	90024
JOSEPH, KIM	ACTRESS	1350 N HIGHLAND AVE #24	LOS ANGELES, CA	90028
JOSEPH, NEAL	MUSIC ARRANGER	3301 TIMBER TRAIL	ANTIOCH, TN	37013
JOSEPH, PAUL	ACTOR	3294 RAMBLA PACIFICIO	MALIBU, CA	90265
JOSEPH, ROBERT L	TV WRITER	CAA, 9830 WILSHIRE BLVD	BEVERLY HILLS, CA	90212
JOSEPH, RONALD	ACTOR	280 S BEVERLY DR #400	BEVERLY HILLS, CA	90212
JOSEPHINA, MIKE	BASEBALL	POST OFFICE BOX 4525	MACON, GA	31208
JOSEPHS, WILFRED	COMPOSER	LONDON MGT, 235-241 REGENT ST	LONDON W1R 4PH	ENGLAND
JOSEPHSON, MARVIN	TALENT AGENT	ICM, 40 W 57TH ST	NEW YORK, NY	10019
JOSHUA, VON	BASEBALL-COACH	POST OFFICE BOX 26267	ALBUQUERQUE, NM	87125
JOURARD, JEFF	ACTOR	2721 2ND ST #112	SANTA MONICA, CA	90402
JOURDAN, LOUIS	ACTOR	1139 MAYBROOK DR	BEVERLY HILLS, CA	90210
JOURNEY	ROCK & ROLL GROUP	POST OFFICE BOX 5952	SAN FRANCISCO, CA	94101
JOVAN, SLAVITZA	ACTRESS	12377 LEWIS ST #101	GARDEN GROVE, CA	92640
JOY, CHRISTOPHER	ACTOR-PRODUCER	1034 S OGDEN DR #6	LOS ANGELES, CA	90019
JOY, RON	TV DIRECTOR	333 N PALM DR	BEVERLY HILLS, CA	90210
JOYCE, ADRIEN	SCREENWRITER	SEE - EASTMAN, CAROL		
JOYCE, ED	TV EXECUTIVE	CBS-TV, 524 W 57TH ST	NEW YORK, NY	10019
JOYCE, ELAINE	ACTRESS	724 N ROXBURY DR	BEVERLY HILLS, CA	90210

JOYCE, JIM	BASEBALL UMPIRE	7440 SW HART PL	BEAVERTON, OR	97005
JOYCE, MIKE	GOLFER	PGA SENIORS, 112 T P C BLVD	PONTE VEDRA BEACH, FL	32082
JOYCE, MIKE	SINGER	POST OFFICE BOX 120492	NASHVILLE, TN	37212
JOYCE, PATRICIA	SCREENWRITER	8955 BEVERLY BLVD	WEST HOLLYWOOD, CA	90048
JOYCE, PATRICK	SINGER	722 TYLER ST	LYNDHURST, NJ	07071
JOYCE, PAUL	TV DIRECTOR	5 TOWNLEY RD, DULWICH	LONDON SE22 8SW	ENGLAND
JOYCE, TOM	GOLFER	PGA SENIORS, 112 T P C BLVD	PONTE VEDRA BEACH, FL	32082
JOYCE, WILLIAM	ACTOR	4628 ENCINO AVE	ENCINO, CA	91316
JOYEUX, ODETTE	WRITER	1 RUE SEGUIER	75006 PARIS	FRANCE
JOYNER, MICHELLE	ACTRESS	8730 SUNSET BLVD #480	LOS ANGELES, CA	90069
JOYNER, SETH	FOOTBALL	EAGLES, BROAD ST & PATTISON AVE	PHILADELPHIA, PA	19148
JOYNER, WALLY	BASEBALL	POST OFFICE BOX 419969	KANSAS CITY, MO	64141
JOYNER-KERSEE, JACKIE	RUNNER	20214 LEADWELL ST	CANOGA PARK, CA	91304
JR CADILLAC	VOCAL GROUP	FAR WEST, 110 BOYLSTON AVE E	SEATTLE, WA	98102
JUBILEE	C & W GROUP	SCAHILL, 32 BIRCH CRESCENT	ROCHESTER, NY	14607
JUDAY, RICH	BASEBALL	POST OFFICE BOX 4488	WINSTON-SALEM, NC	27115
JUDDS, THE	C & W DUO	POST OFFICE BOX 17325	NASHVILLE, TN	37217
JUDELSON, ROBERT A	BASKETBALL EXECUTIVE	980 N MICHIGAN AVE #1600	CHICAGO, IL	60611
JUDEN, JEFF	BASEBALL	POST OFFICE BOX 27045	TUCSON, AZ	85726
JUDY'S TINY HEAD	ROCK & ROLL GROUP	25 HUNTINGTON AVE #420	BOSTON, MA	02116
JUELSGAARD, JAROD	BASEBALL	POST OFFICE BOX 1295	CLINTON, IA	52733
JUGGERNAUT	ROCK & ROLL GROUP	POST OFFICE BOX 2428	EL SEGUNDO, CA	90245
JUHASZ, VICTOR	ARTIST	576 WESTMINISTER AVE	ELIZABETH, NJ	07208
JUHL, JERRY R	SCREENWRITER	1113 W JAY ST	TORRANCE, CA	90502
JUKEBOX ROMANCE	ROCK & ROLL GROUP	POST OFFICE BOX 634	LAWRENCE, KS	66044
JULIA, RAUL	ACTOR	200 W 54TH ST #7-G	NEW YORK, NY	10019
JULIAN, ARTHUR	TV WRITER	443 BELLAGIO TERR	LOS ANGELES, CA	90049
JULIAN, JANET	ACTRESS-MODEL	MTA, 9320 WILSHIRE BL, 3RD FL	BEVERLY HILLS, CA	90212
JULIEN, JAY	TALENT AGENT	1501 BROADWAY #2600	NEW YORK, NY	10036
JULIUS, MAXINE	FILM EDITOR	LAZER, 86-88 WARDOUR ST	LONDON W1N 3LF	ENGLAND
JULUKA	RHYTHM & BLUES GROUP	10100 SANTA MONICA BLVD #1600	LOS ANGELES, CA	90067
JUMP, GORDON	ACTOR-DIRECTOR	1631 HILLCREST AVE	GLENDALE, CA	91202
JUN, ROSE MARIE	ACTRESS-SINGER	25 CENTRAL PARK W #12-Y	NEW YORK, NY	10023
JUNG, CALVIN	ACTOR	280 S BEVERLY DR #400	BEVERLY HILLS, CA	90212
JUNGLE BROTHERS, THE	RAP DUO-RAPWRITERS	FAA, 1700 BROADWAY, 5TH FLOOR	NEW YORK, NY	10019
JUNIE LOU	SINGER	PROCESS, 439 WILEY AVE	FRANKLIN, PA	16323
JUNIOR	SINGER	FAA, 1700 BROADWAY, 5TH FLOOR	NEW YORK, NY	10019
JUNIOR, E J	FOOTBALL	DOLPHINS, 2269 NW 199TH ST	MIAMI, FL	33056
JUNKIN, JOHN	ACTOR-WRITER	LONDON MGT, 235-241 REGENT ST	LONDON W1R 4PH	ENGLAND
JUNKIN, TREY	FOOTBALL	SEAHAWKS, 11220 NE 53RD ST	KIRKLAND, WA	98033
JUNKYARD DOG, THE	WRESTLER	POST OFFICE BOX 105366	ATLANTA, GA	31348
JUNOR, PENNY	TV HOST-JOURNALIST	BROWN, 162-168 REGENT ST	LONDON W1R 5TB	ENGLAND
JURAN, NATHAN	WRITER-PRODUCER	623 VIA HORQUILLA	PALOS VERDES, CA	90274
JURGELLA, JEFF	BASEBALL EXECUTIVE	POST OFFICE BOX 882	MADISON, WI	53701
JURGENSEN, SONNY	FOOTBALL	POST OFFICE BOX 53	MOUNT VERNON, VA	22121
JURGENSEN, W KEITH	CINEMATOGRAPHER	11232 DONA LOLA DR	STUDIO CITY, CA	91604
JURGENSON, ALBERT	FILM EDITOR	178 QUAI, LOUIS BLERIOT	PARIS 75016	FRANCE
JURIST, ED	TV WRITER	2720 BOTTLEBRUSH DR	LOS ANGELES, CA	90077
JUROW, MARTIN	FILM PRODUCER	3505 RANKIN ST	DALLAS, TX	75205
JURY, AL	FOOTBALL REFEREE	NFL, 410 PARK AVE	NEW YORK, NY	10022
JURZYKOWSKI, CHRISTINE	FILM PRODUCER	CINETUDES FILM PRODS		
		295 W 4TH ST	NEW YORK, NY	10014
JUST-ICE	RAPPER-RAPWRITER	FAA, 1700 BROADWAY, 5TH FLOOR	NEW YORK, NY	10019
JUSTER, EVIE	ACTRESS	875 5TH AVE	NEW YORK, NY	10021
JUSTICE, DAVE	BASEBALL	POST OFFICE BOX 4064	ATLANTA, GA	30302
JUSTICE, KATHERINE	ACTRESS	BREWIS, 12429 LAUREL TERRACE	STUDIO CITY, CA	91604
JUSTICE, SID	WRESTLER	POST OFFICE BOX 3859	STAMFORD, CT	06905
JYD	WRESTLER	SEE - JUNKYARD DOG, THE		

K B C BAND	ROCK & ROLL GROUP	ARISTA RECORDS, 6 W 57TH ST	NEW YORK, NY	10019
KAAT, JIM	BASEBALL-ANNOUNCER	100 SE 5TH AVE #509	BOCA RATON, FL	33432
KABIBBLE, ISH	ACTOR	MR MERVYN BOGUE		
		POST OFFICE BOX 536	INDIO, CA	92201
KACIN, JAY	DIRECTOR	POST OFFICE BOX 55042	VALENCIA, CA	91355
KACZENDER, GEORGE	DIRECTOR	1550 DR PENFIELD DRIVE	MONTREAL, QUE H3E 1C2	CANADA
KACZENSKI, HEIDI M	COSTUME DESIGNER	13949 VENTURA BLVD #309	SHERMAN OAKS, CA	91423
KADAFI, COL MOAMMAR	COLONEL	BAB EL AZIZIYA	TRIPOLI	LIBYA
KADIEV, PETRO	ARTIST	1351 OCEAN PARK WALK #106	SANTA MONICA, CA	90405
KADISON, ELLIS	DIRECTOR	31754 FOXFIELD DR	WESTLAKE VILLAGE, CA	91361
KADLEC, DANIEL	COLUMNIST	POST OFFICE BOX 500	WASHINGTON, DC	20044
KAEL, PAULINE	FILM CRITIC-AUTHORESS	2 BERKSHIRE HEIGHTS RD	GREAT BARRINGTON, MA	01230
KAEMMER, GARY	ARTIST	1724 OGDEN ST	DENVER, CO	80218
KAFUN, PAUL A	COMPOSER	8141 AGNES AVE	NORTH HOLLYWOOD, CA	91605
KAGAN, JEREMY PAUL	WRITER-PRODUCER	2024 N CURSON AVE	LOS ANGELES, CA	90046
KAGAN, MICHAEL	FILM PRODUCER	152 CAMPDEN HILL RD	LONDON W8 7AS	ENGLAND
KAGAN, MICHAEL H	TV WRITER-DIRECTOR	1650 WESTWOOD BLVD #201	LOS ANGELES, CA	90024
KAGEN, DAVID	ACTOR	5750 WILSHIRE BLVD #512	LOS ANGELES, CA	90036

Christensen's

ADDRESS UPDATES

• Up-To-The-Minute Information •
• New Addresses • Voids • Corrections •
• Deletions • Refusals • Necrology •
• Response Reports •

For Complete Details Write:

ADDRESS UPDATES
CARDIFF-BY-THE-SEA PUBLISHING CO.
POST OFFICE BOX 900189 • SAN DIEGO, CA 92190

KAHAN, JUDITH	ACTRESS	SMITH, 121 N SAN VICENTE BLVD	BEVERLY HILLS, CA	90211
KAHANE, KAREN	TALENT AGENT	3500 W OLIVE AVE #1400	BURBANK, CA	91505
KAHANE, ROBERT	TALENT AGENT	10100 SANTA MONICA BLVD #1600	LOS ANGELES, CA	90067
KAHLERT, JIM	TV WRITER	12121 SHETLAND LN	LOS ANGELES, CA	90069
KAHMANN, JIM	BASEBALL TRAINER	POST OFFICE BOX 1659	PORTLAND, OR	97207
KAHN, BERNARD M	SCREENWRITER	838 N ORLANDO AVE	LOS ANGELES, CA	90069
KAHN, BRIAN A	TV EXECUTIVE	HBO, 1100 6TH AVE	NEW YORK, NY	10036
KAHN, DANIEL	TV PRODUCER	SEAGULL PRODS, 42 W 12TH ST	NEW YORK, NY	10011
KAHN, DAVE	COMPOSER	4629 FULTON AVE #313	SHERMAN OAKS, CA	91423
KAHN, DONALD	CONDUCTOR	G KAHN, 6223 SELMA AVE	LOS ANGELES, CA	90028
KAHN, EDGAR C	DIRECTOR	J W THOMPSON, 466 LEXINGTON AVE	NEW YORK, NY	10028
KAHN, IRVING	TV EXECUTIVE	375 PARK AVE #3701	NEW YORK, NY	10152
KAHN, JEFF	BASEBALL SCOUT	1060 W ADDISON ST	CHICAGO, IL	60613
KAHN, LINDA M	TV EXECUTIVE	NICKELODEON, 1775 BROADWAY	NEW YORK, NY	10019
KAHN, MADELINE	ACTRESS	975 PARK AVE #9-A	NEW YORK, NY	10028
KAHN, MICHAEL	FILM EDITOR	ACE, 1041 N FORMOSA AVE	WEST HOLLYWOOD, CA	90046
KAHN, RAHLA	ACTRESS-COMEDIENNE	11846 VENTURA BLVD #100	STUDIO CITY, CA	91604
KAHN, RICHARD	FILM EXECUTIVE	1080 WALLACE RIDGE	BEVERLY HILLS, CA	90210
KAHN, SHELDON	FILM EDITOR	ACE, 1041 N FORMOSA AVE	WEST HOLLYWOOD, CA	90046
KAIKKO, PETER E	TV WRITER	19957 RAMBLING RD	COVINA, CA	91724
KAIN, JUDY	ACTRESS	12456 VENTURA BLVD #1	STUDIO CITY, CA	91604
KAISER, JEFF	BASEBALL	POST OFFICE BOX 6212	TOLEDO, OH	43614
KAISER, KEN	BASEBALL UMPIRE	56 HOLLY SUE LN	ROCHESTER, NY	14626
KAISER, RUSSEL	TV DIRECTOR-PRODUCER	235 E 53RD ST	NEW YORK, NY	10022
KAITAN, ELIZABETH	ACTRESS	8271 MELROSE AVE #110	LOS ANGELES, CA	90046
KAITZ, TAMMY	ACTRESS	10651 OTSEGO ST	NORTH HOLLYWOOD, CA	91601
KALAJIAN, JERRY	TALENT AGENT	1015 GAYLEY AVE #300	LOS ANGELES, CA	90024
KALAS, HARRY	SPORTSCASTER	POST OFFICE BOX 7575	PHILADELPHIA, PA	19101
KALASH, CARL	CONDUCTOR	3378 SENECA DR	LAS VEGAS, NV	89109
KALB, BERNARD	NEWS CORRESPONDENT	NBC NEWS, 4001 NEBRASKA AV, SW	WASHINGTON, DC	20016
KALB, MARVIN	NEWS CORRESPONDENT	NBC NEWS, 4001 NEBRASKA AV, SW	WASHINGTON, DC	20016
KALBACK, JERRY A	ARTIST	5881 SUNSET DR	HUDSON, OH	44236
KALCHEIM, LEE H	TV WRITER	555 W 57TH ST #1230	NEW YORK, NY	10019
KALDWELL, KENDAL	ACTRESS	8019 1/2 MELROSE AVE #3	LOS ANGELES, CA	90046
KALEM, TONI	ACTRESS	9301 WILSHIRE BLVD #312	BEVERLY HILLS, CA	90210
KALEMBER, PATRICIA	ACTRESS	POST OFFICE BOX 5617	BEVERLY HILLS, CA	90213
KALER, DORIS J	WRITER	1857 FOX HILLS DR	LOS ANGELES, CA	90025
KALFUS, JORDAN	DIRECTOR	2456 ASTRAL DR	LOS ANGELES, CA	90046
KALINE, AL	BASEBALL-ANNOUNCER	945 TIMBERLAKE DR	BLOOMFIELD HILLS, MI	48013
KALININA, MASHA	MISS MOSCOW	151 S EL CAMINO DR	BEVERLY HILLS, CA	90212
KALINS, MARJORIE A	TV PRODUCER	TELECOM, 909 3RD AVE	NEW YORK, NY	10022
KALIS, M B	ACTRESS	6269 SELMA AVE #15	HOLLYWOOD, CA	90028
KALIS, TODD	FOOTBALL	VIKINGS, 9520 VIKING DR	EDEN PRAIRIE, MN	55344
KALISH, AUSTIN	TV WRITER	5339 LINDLEY AVE #103	TARZANA, CA	91356
KALISH, BRUCE E	TV WRITER-PRODUCER	5339 LINDLEY AVE #103	TARZANA, CA	91356
KALISH, IRMA	TV WRITER	3831 BOWSPRIT CIR	WESTLAKE VILLAGE, CA	91361
KALISH, KAREN S	WRITER	260 W 35TH ST #702	NEW YORK, NY	10018
KALLET, BARBARA	ACTRESS	POST OFFICE BOX 338	BRIDGEPORT, NY	13030
KALLIANIOTES, HELENA	ACT-WRI-DAN	12850 MULHOLLAND DR	BEVERLY HILLS, CA	90210
KALLIS, DANNY	TV WRITER	742 RADCLIFFE AVE	PACIFIC PALISADES, CA	90272
KALLIS, STANLEY	WRITER-PRODUCER	12345 DEERBROOK LN	LOS ANGELES, CA	90049
KALMANOFF, MARTIN	COMPOSER	392 CENTRAL PARK W	NEW YORK, NY	10025
KALSER, KONSTANTIN	DIRECTOR-PRODUCER	MARATHON, 211 E 51ST ST PRODUCTIO	NEW YORK, NY	10020
KALTER, SUZY	TV WRITER	283 W RADCLIFFE DR	CLAREMONT, CA	91711
KAMEISHA, JOHN	BASEBALL	POST OFFICE BOX 1718	NEW BRITAIN, CT	06050
KAMEL, P J	SINGER	STAR, 1311 CANDLELIGHT AVE	DALLAS, TX	75216
KAMEL, STANLEY	ACTOR	9300 WILSHIRE BLVD #410	BEVERLY HILLS, CA	90212
KAMEN, MICHAEL	COMPOSER	3815 W OLIVE AVE #201	BRUBANK, CA	91505
KAMEN, ROBERT MARK	SCREENWRITER	8955 BEVERLY BLVD	WEST HOLLYWOOD, CA	90048
KAMENIR, DAVID L	COMPOSER	1224 CASIANO RD	LOS ANGELES, CA	90049
KAMIENECKI, SCOTT	BASEBALL	N Y YANKEES, YANKEE STADIUM	BRONX, NY	10451
KAMIENIECKI, SCOTT	BASEBALL	N Y YANKEES, YANKEE STADIUM	BRONX, NY	10451
KAMINSKI, DANA	ACTRESS	POST OFFICE BOX 5617	BEVERLY HILLS, CA	90213
KAMINSKY, MELVIN	ACT-WRI-DIR	SEE - BROOKS, MEL		
KAMM, LARRY	TV DIRECTOR-PRODUCER	420 E 51ST ST #7-F	NEW YORK, NY	10022
KAMMERMAN, ROY	TV WRITER	9875 RIMMELE DR	BEVERLY HILLS, CA	90210
KAMP, LOUIS	SCREENWRITER	207 S HIGHLAND AVE	LOS ANGELES, CA	90036
KAMPMANN, JUDITH K	WRITER-PRODUCER	812 JACON WY	PACIFIC PALISADES, CA	90272
KAMPMANN, STEVEN	ACTOR-WRITER	812 JACON WY	PACIFIC PALISADES, CA	90272
KAMZIC, NICK	BASEBALL SCOUT	POST OFFICE BOX 2000	ANAHEIM, CA	92803
KANAKAREDES, MELINA	ACTRESS	CBS-TV, "THE GUIDING LIGHT"		
		222 E 44TH ST	NEW YORK, NY	10017
KANALY, STEVE	ACTOR-DIRECTOR	3611 LONGRIDGE AVE	SHERMAN OAKS, CA	91423
KANANACK, ARTHUR	TV EXECUTIVE	VIACOM INTERNATIONAL, INC		
		1211 AVE OF THE AMERICAS	NEW YORK, NY	10036
KANARECK, MAURICE	TV WRITER-DIRECTOR	3 MEADWAY CT, MEADWAY	LONDON NW11	ENGLAND
KANDEL, STEPHEN	TV WRITER	214 S BEDFORD DR	BEVERLY HILLS, CA	90212
KANDER, JOHN H, II	WRITER	12203 OCTAGON ST	LOS ANGELES, CA	90049
KANE, ARNOLD	TV WRITER-PRODUCER	8381 HOLLYWOOD BLVD	LOS ANGELES, CA	90069
KANE, ART	DIRECTOR	36 GRAMERCY PARK E	NEW YORK, NY	10003
KANE, ARTIE M	CONDUCTOR	10900 WILSHIRE BLVD #900	LOS ANGELES, CA	90024
KANE, BIANCA	ACTRESS	500 E 77TH ST #228-EW	NEW YORK, NY	10021
KANE, BIG DADDY	RAPPER-RAPWRITER	FAA, 1700 BROADWAY, 5TH FLOOR	NEW YORK, NY	10019
KANE, BOB	CARTOONIST	POST OFFICE BOX 1099	FORESTVILLE, CA	95436
KANE, BRAD	ACTOR-SINGER-DANCER	500 E 77TH ST #405	NEW YORK, NY	10021

KANE, BRUCE	TV WRITER	9300 WILSHIRE BLVD #410	BEVERLY HILLS, CA	90212
KANE, BYRON	DIRECTOR	2231 BENEDICT CANYON DR	BEVERLY HILLS, CA	90210
KANE, CAROL	ACTRESS	1416 N HAVENHURST DR #1-C	LOS ANGELES, CA	90046
KANE, IRVING M	MUSIC ARRANGER	2001 BLAIR BLVD #B	NASHVILLE, TN	37212
KANE, JOHN	ACTOR-WRITER	HEATH, PARAMOUNT HOUSE		
		162-170 WARDOUR ST	LONDON W1V 3AT	ENGLAND
KANE, JOSH	TV EXECUTIVE	CBS-TV, 51 W 52ND ST	NEW YORK, NY	10020
KANE, KIERAN	SINGER	POST OFFICE BOX 121089	NASHVILLE, TN	37212
KANE, MADLEEN	SINGER	1330 SCHUYLER RD	BEVERLY HILLS, CA	90210
KANE, MICHAEL	SCREENWRITER	8955 BEVERLY BLVD	WEST HOLLYWOOD, CA	90048
KANE, MICHAEL J	TV DIRECTOR	4565 HAZELTINE AVE #6	SHERMAN OAKS, CA	91423
KANE, PETER	TV EXECUTIVE	CBS-TV, 7800 BEVERLY BLVD	LOS ANGELES, CA	90036
KANE, ROBERT G	SCREENWRITER	1427 GREENFIELD AVE	LOS ANGELES, CA	90025
KANE, SCOTT H	DIRECTOR	1621 WILMOT LN	DEERFIELD, IL	60015
KANE, TOMMY	FOOTBALL	SEAHAWKS, 11220 NE 53RD ST	KIRKLAND, WA	98033
KANER, TESSA	ACTRESS	400 W 43RD ST #28-F	NEW YORK, NY	10036
KANEW, JEFFREY	FILM DIRECTOR	51 W 83RD ST	NEW YORK, NY	10024
KANIN, FAY	FILM WRITER-PRODUCER	653 OCEAN FRONT WALK	SANTA MONICA, CA	90402
KANIN, GARSON	WRITER-PRODUCER	210 CENTRAL PARK S	NEW YORK, NY	10019
KANIN, MICHAEL	WRITER	653 OCEAN FRONT WALK	SANTA MONICA, CA	90402
KANJORSKI, PAUL	U S CONGRESSMAN	10 E SOUTH ST	WILKES-BARRE, PA	18701
KANON, JOSEPH	COMPOSER-CONDUCTOR	4236 COLFAX AVE	STUDIO CITY, CA	91604
KANSAS	ROCK & ROLL GROUP	POST OFFICE BOX 7308	CARMEL, CA	93923
KANTER, DONNA	WRITER-PRODUCER	ICM, 8899 BEVERLY BLVD	LOS ANGELES, CA	90048
KANTER, HAL	WRITER-PRODUCER	15941 WOODVALE RD	ENCINO, CA	91316
KANTER, JAY	FILM EXECUTIVE	726 N ROXBURY DR	BEVERLY HILLS, CA	90210
KANTNER-BALIN-CASADY BAND	ROCK & ROLL GROUP	POST OFFICE BOX 15-584	SAN FRANCISCO, CA	94115
KANTOR, IGO	COMPOSER	11501 DUQUE DR	STUDIO CITY, CA	91604
KANTOR, RONALD	DIRECTOR-PRODUCER	524 N CAHUENGA BLVD	LOS ANGELES, CA	90004
KAPANO, COREY	BASEBALL	POST OFFICE BOX 12	MIDLAND, TX	79702
KAPLAN, ALAN I	DIRECTOR	DGA, 110 W 57TH ST	NEW YORK, NY	10019
KAPLAN, DAVID	TV DIRECTOR	1228 HAZEL AVE	PLAINFIELD, NJ	07060
KAPLAN, EDWIN FRANCIS	TV WRITER	1223 SUNSET PLAZA DR #A	LOS ANGELES, CA	90069
KAPLAN, ELLIOT	COMPOSER	4520 SALTILLO ST	WOODLAND HILLS, CA	91364
KAPLAN, GABRIEL	COMEDIAN-ACTOR	9551 HIDDEN VALLEY RD	BEVERLY HILLS, CA	90210
KAPLAN, HENRY	DIRECTOR	DGA, 110 W 57TH ST	NEW YORK, NY	10019
KAPLAN, JANE	TV WRITER	ENTERTAINMENT TONIGHT		
		PARAMOUNT TELEVISION		
		5555 MELROSE AVE	LOS ANGELES, CA	90038
KAPLAN, JONATHAN H	DIRECTOR	CHARLEVILLE PRODUCTIONS		
		715 N LA JOLLA AVE	LOS ANGELES, CA	90046
KAPLAN, JONATHAN S	WRITER-PRODUCER	8275 KIRKWOOD DR	LOS ANGELES, CA	90046
KAPLAN, MARCY	ACTRESS	10000 SANTA MONICA BLVD #305	LOS ANGELES, CA	90067
KAPLAN, MARVIN	ACTOR	1418 N HIGHLAND AVE #102	LOS ANGELES, CA	90028
KAPLAN, MICHAEL	COSTUME DESIGNER	13949 VENTURA BLVD #309	SHERMAN OAKS, CA	91423
KAPLAN, MITCH	TALENT AGENT	8383 WILSHIRE BLVD #923	BEVERLY HILLS, CA	90211
KAPLAN, NANCY	TV DIRECTOR-PRODUCER	1393 BLUE SPRUCE LN	WANTAGH, NY	11793
KAPLAN, PATTI	DIRECTOR	DGA, 110 W 57TH ST	NEW YORK, NY	10019
KAPLAN, RICHARD N "RICK"	TV DIRECTOR-PRODUCER	ABC-TV, 7 W 66TH ST	NEW YORK, NY	10023
KAPLAN, ROBERT O	FILM PRODUCER	1112 N SHERBOURNE DR	LOS ANGELES, CA	90069
KAPLAN, SHELDON L	DIRECTOR	29818 KATHERINE ST	MAGNOLIA, TX	77355
KAPLAN, WENDY	ACTRESS	8370 WILSHIRE BLVD #310	BEVERLY HILLS, CA	90211
KAPLAN, WILLIAM	FILM DIRECTOR	233 LOS PINOS DR	PALM SPRINGS, CA	92264
KAPLEN, LAWRENCE J	WRITER-NEWS CORRES	ABC NEWS, 1717 DE SALES ST, NW	WASHINGTON, DC	20036
KAPLOW, HERBERT E	NEWS CORRESPONDENT	ABC NEWS, 1717 DE SALES ST, NW	WASHINGTON, DC	20036
KAPNER, TRUDY	COSTUME DESIGNER	2121 PASEO DEL MAR	PALOS VERDES ESTATES,	90274
KAPPESSER, BOB	BASEBALL	POST OFFICE DRAWER 4797	EL PASO, TX	79914
KAPROFF, DANA	CONDUCTOR	1120 EL MEDIO AVE	PACIFIC PALISADES, CA	90272
KAPTUR, MARCY	U S CONGRESSWOMAN	FEDERAL BUILDING, ROOM 719		
		234 SUMMIT ST	TOLEDO, OH	43604
KAPTUR, RUNE	TALENT AGENT	8484 WILSHIRE BLVD #530	BEVERLY HILLS, CA	90211
KAPTURE, MITZI	ACTRESS	15301 VENTURA BLVD #345	SHERMAN OAKS, CA	91403
KARAFF, DAVE	BASEBALL SCOUT	POST OFFICE BOX 4100	SEATTLE, WA	98104
KARAGIANIS, DAVID S	COMPOSER	435 1/2 N SIERRA BONITA AVE	LOS ANGELES, CA	90036
KARAJAN, HERBERT VON	CONDUCTOR	FESTSPIELHAUS	SALZBURG	AUSTRIA
KARAM, EDWARD M	COMPOSER-CONDUCTOR	6175 PASEO CANYON DR	MALIBU, CA	90265
KARAM, JANN	ACTRESS	10390 SANTA MONICA BLVD #300	LOS ANGELES, CA	90025
KARASEK, VALERIE	ACTRESS	6310 SAN VICENTE BLVD #407	LOS ANGELES, CA	90048
KARCHER, RICK	BASEBALL	POST OFFICE BOX 507	DURHAM, NC	27702
KARCHIN, STEVE	ARTIST	240 E 27TH ST	NEW YORK, NY	10016
KARCHNER, MATT	BASEBALL	800 HOME RUN LN	MEMPHIS, TN	38104
KARCY, BOB	TV EXECUTIVE	34 E 23RD ST	NEW YORK, NY	10010
KARDAMIS, MIKE	BASEBALL EXECUTIVE	POST OFFICE BOX 2960	SUMTER, SC	29151
KAREL, RUSS	FILM WRITER-PRODUCER	DAVID HIGHAM ASSOCIATES		
		5-8 LOWER JOHN STM GOLDEN SQ	LONDON W1R 4HA	ENGLAND
KARELLA, CLARENCE O	CONDUCTOR	POST OFFICE BOX 1132	PALM SPRINGS, CA	92263
KAREN, JAMES	ACTOR	4455 LOS FELIZ BLVD #807	LOS ANGELES, CA	90027
KAREN, ZARA	ACTRESS	5330 LANKERSHIM BLVD #210	NORTH HOLLYWOOD, CA	91601
KARIN, RITA	ACTRESS	484 W 43RD ST #11-D	NEW YORK, NY	10036
KARKOVICE, RON	BASEBALL	333 W 35TH ST	CHICAGO, IL	60616
KARL, LIZ	VIDEO EDITOR	ENTERTAINMENT TONIGHT		
		PARAMOUNT TELEVISION		
		5555 MELROSE AVE	LOS ANGELES, CA	90038
KARLEN, BETTY	ACTRESS	9165 SUNSET BLVD #202	LOS ANGELES, CA	90069
KARLEN, JOHN	ACTOR	428 E LORRAINE ST	GLENDALE, CA	91207

Name	Occupation	Address	City
KARLIN, FRED	COMPOSER-CONDUCTOR	6404 WILSHIRE BLVD #1230	LOS ANGELES, CA 90048
KARLIN, MIRIAM	ACTRESS	MC REDDIE, 91 REGENT ST	LONDON W1R 7TB ENGLAND
KARLSON, PHIL	FILM DIRECTOR	3094 PATRICIA AVE	LOS ANGELES, CA 90064
KAROFF, JEFF	PRODUCER	KEVIN BILES, 358 HAMPTON DR	VENICE, CA 90291
KARP, DAVID	TV WRITER	1116 CORSICA DR	PACIFIC PALISADES, CA 90272
KARPAN, KATHY	SECRETARY OF STATE	STATE CAPITOL BUILDING	CHEYENNE, WY 82002
KARR, PHILIP	TALENT AGENT	8383 WILSHIRE BLVD #650	BEVERLY HILLS, CA 90211
KARRAS, ALEX	ACTOR	7943 WOODROW WILSON DR	LOS ANGELES, CA 90046
KARROS, ERIC	BASEBALL	1000 ELYSIAN PARK DR	LOS ANGELES, CA 90012
KARSAY, STEVE	BASEBALL	POST OFFICE BOX 957	DUNEDIN, FL 34697
KARSH, YOUSUF	PHOTOGRAPHER	CHATEAU LAURIER	OTTAWA, ONT K1N 8S7 CANADA
KARSON, ERIC	WRITER-PRODUCER	15027 SHERMAN WY #C	VAN NUYS, CA 91405
KARSON, LEE	TV WRITER	7706 W NORTON AVE #6	LOS ANGELES, CA 90046
KARTOZIAN, THOMAS GEORGE	TV WRITER	8953 KEITH AVE	LOS ANGELES, CA 90069
KARTUN, ALLAN	DIRECTOR	12501 VALLEY SPRING LN	STUDIO CITY, CA 91604
KARTZ, KEITH	FOOTBALL	BRONCOS, 13655 BRONCOS PKWY	ENGLEWOOD, CO 80112
KARVELAS, ROBERT	ACTOR	855 LEVERING AVE #401	LOS ANGELES, CA 90024
KARVELLAS, JIM	SPORTSCASTER	WFAN-AM, 34-12 36TH ST	LONG ISLAND CITY, NY 11106
KASANDER, PAUL	TV DIRECTOR	100 RIVERSIDE DR	NEW YORK, NY 10024
KASATONOV, ALEXEI	HOCKEY	POST OFFICE BOX 504	EAST RUTHERFORD, NJ 07073
KASAY, JOHN	FOOTBALL	SEAHAWKS, 11220 NE 53RD ST	KIRKLAND, WA 98033
KASDAN, LAWRENCE	FILM WRITER-PRODUCER	UTA, 9560 WILSHIRE BL, 5TH FL	BEVERLY HILLS, CA 90212
KASDAN, MEG	FILM WRITER-PRODUCER	UTA, 9560 WILSHIRE BL, 5TH FL	BEVERLY HILLS, CA 90212
KASDORF, LENORE	ACTRESS	10000 SANTA MONICA BLVD #305	LOS ANGELES, CA 90067
KASEFF, GARY	BASEBALL EXECUTIVE	POST OFFICE BOX 4100	SEATTLE, WA 98104
KASEM, CASEY	RADIO PERS-TV HOST	138 N MAPLETON DR	LOS ANGELES, CA 90077
KASEM, JEAN	ACTRESS	138 N MAPLETON DR	LOS ANGELES, CA 90077
KASHA, AL	COMPOSER	337 S EL CAMINO DR	BEVERLY HILLS, CA 90212
KASHA, PHYLLIS	CASTING DIRECTOR	275 CENTRAL PARK W #2-C	NEW YORK, NY 10024
KASHIF	SINGER	FAA, 1700 BROADWAY, 5TH FLOOR	NEW YORK, NY 10019
KASHKASHIAN, KIM	VIOLIST-VIOLINIST	808 W END AVE #1204	NEW YORK, NY 10025
KASICH, JOHN R	U S CONGRESSMAN	200 N HIGH ST #400	COLUMBUS, OH 43215
KASKO, EDDIE	BASEBALL-SCOUT	FENWAY PARK, 4 YAWKEY WY	BOSTON, MA 02215
KASNOT, KEITH	ARTIST	VAS COMMUNICATIONS	
		4800 N 22ND ST	PHOENIX, AZ 85016
KASOFF, LAWRENCE	TV DIRECTOR	68-36 108TH ST	FOREST HILLS, NY 11375
KASPER, EDWIN T	DIRECTOR	301 W 53RD ST #10-A	NEW YORK, NY 10019
KASPER, GARY F	ACTOR	4731 LAUREL CANYON BLVD #5	NORTH HOLLYWOOD, CA 91607
KASPER, KEVIN	BASEBALL	POST OFFICE BOX 3448	SHREVEPORT, LA 71133
KASPER, STEVE	HOCKEY	POST OFFICE BOX 17013	INGLEWOOD, CA 90308
KASS, JEROME A	SCREENWRITER	141 S EL CAMINO DR #110	BEVERLY HILLS, CA 90212
KASSEBAUM, NANCY	U S SENATOR	302 RUSSELL SENATE BLDG	WASHINGTON, DC 20510
KASSEL, VIRGINIA W	WRITER	PRIMETIME ENTERTAINMENT	
		444 MADISON AVE	NEW YORK, NY 10022
KASSENBAUM, NANCY LANDON	U S SENATOR	911 N MAIN	GARDEN CITY, KS 67846
KASSORLA, DR IRENE	PSYCHOLOGIST-AUTHOR	10231 CHARING CROSS RD	LOS ANGELES, CA 90024
KASSUL, ART	ACTOR	10901 BLIX ST #1	NORTH HOLLYWOOD, CA 91602
KASTELIC, ED	HOCKEY	WHALERS, 1 CIVIC CENTER PLAZA	HARTFORD, CT 06103
KASTEN, ROBERT W, JR	U S SENATOR	517 E WISCONSIN AVE	MILWAUKEE, WI 53202
KASTEN, STAN	BB-BKBB EXECUTIVE	1 CNN CENTER #405, SOUTH TOWER	ATLANTA, GA 30303
KASTNER, ELLIOTT	FILM PRODUCER	WINKAST, PINEWOOD STUDIOS	
		IVER HEATH	BUCKS ENGLAND
KASTNER, PETER BERNARD	ACTOR-WRITER	29 PARK AVE	VENICE, CA 90291
KATE, MARY	ACTRESS	ABC-TV, 2040 AVE OF THE STARS	LOS ANGELES, CA 90067
KATES, ANNE	COLUMNIST	POST OFFICE BOX 500	WASHINGTON, DC 20044
KATES, ARTHUR L	CONDUCTOR	41055 VILLAGE 41	CAMARILLO, CA 93010
KATES, KIMBERLY	ACTRESS	5750 WILSHIRE BLVD #580	LOS ANGELES, CA 90037
KATH, CAMELIA	ACTRESS	565 S MAPLETON DR	LOS ANGELES, CA 90024
KATKOV, NORMAN	TV WRITER	166 N CYN VIEW DR	LOS ANGELES, CA 90049
KATLEMAN, HARRIS	WRITER-PRODUCER	1250 SHADOW HILL WY	BEVERLY HILLS, CA 90210
KATO, HIDEKI	BASEBALL	POST OFFICE BOX 4370	SALINAS, CA 93912
KATRINA & THE WAVES	ROCK & ROLL GROUP	28 ADDISON CLOSE	
		FELTWELL RR, THETFORD	NORFOLK 1P2 64DJ ENGLAND
KATSELAS, MILTON	FILM DIRECTOR	2559 N CATALINA AVE	LOS ANGELES, CA 90027
KATT, WILLIAM	ACTOR	15301 VENTURA BLVD #345	SHERMAN OAKS, CA 91403
KATTEN, STEVEN	TV DIRECTOR	6201 MULHOLLAND HWY	LOS ANGELES, CA 90068
KATTUS, ERIC	FOOTBALL	BENGALS, 200 RIVERFRONT STADIUM	CINCINNATI, OH 45202
KATZ, ALLAN	TV WRITER-PRODUCER	1168 N DOHENY DR	LOS ANGELES, CA 90069
KATZ, ARTHUR JOEL	WRITER-PRODUCER	703 N PALM DR	BEVERLY HILLS, CA 90210
KATZ, BERNARD	CONDUCTOR	2788 34TH AVE	SAN FRANCISCO, CA 94116
KATZ, EDWARD E	DIRECTOR	234 MEADOWBROOK AVE	NORTHBROOK, IL 60062
KATZ, GLORIA	FILM WRITER-PRODUCER	39 OAKMONT DR	LOS ANGELES, CA 90049
KATZ, HAROLD	BASKETBALL EXECUTIVE	POST OFFICE BOX 25040	PHILADELPHIA, PA 19147
KATZ, KAREN S	TV DIRECTOR-PRODUCER	LIFETIME, 1211 AVE OF THE AMERICA	NEW YORK, NY 10036
KATZ, MAX J	DIRECTOR	315 E 65TH ST	NEW YORK, NY 10021
KATZ, MIKE	BODYBUILDER	THE WORLD GYM EAST	
		295 TREADWELL ST	HAMDEN, CT 06514
KATZ, MORRIS	ARTIST	247 W 29TH ST	NEW YORK, NY 10001
KATZ, NORMAN B	FILM EXECUTIVE	1123 VISTA GRANDE DR	PACIFIC PALISADES, CA 90272
KATZ, OMRI	ACTOR	NBC-TV, 3000 W ALAMEDA AVE	BURBANK, CA 91523
KATZ, PETER	TV EXECUTIVE	11601 WILSHIRE BLVD #2480	LOS ANGELES, CA 90025
KATZ, RICHARD J	TV EXECUTIVE	CBS-TV, 6121 SUNSET BLVD	LOS ANGELES, CA 90028
KATZ, ROBERT I	TV DIRECTOR	3700 S SEPULVEDA BLVD #248	LOS ANGELES, CA 90034
KATZ, RUTH	NEWSCASTER	2109 BROADWAY #10-112	NEW YORK, NY 10023
KATZ, SAUL	BASEBALL EXECUTIVE	METS, 126TH ST & ROOSEVELT AVE	FLUSHING, NY 11368

KATZ, SHELLEY	TV WRITER	2186 BROADVIEW TERR	LOS ANGELES, CA	90068
KATZ, STEPHEN	SCREENWRITER	8955 BEVERLY BLVD	WEST HOLLYWOOD, CA	90048
KATZAROFF, ROBBIE	BASEBALL	POST OFFICE BOX 598	BINGHAMTON, NY	13902
KATZIN, LEE	FILM DIRECTOR	13425 JAVA DR	BEVERLY HILLS, CA	90210
KATZMAN, LEONARD	WRITER-PRODUCER	16117 ROYAL OAK RD	ENCINO, CA	91436
KAUAHI, KANI	FOOTBALL	POST OFFICE BOX 888	PHOENIX, AZ	85001
KAUFER, JERRY	TV EXECUTIVE	VIACOM INTERNATIONAL, INC		
		1211 AVE OF THE AMERICAS	NEW YORK, NY	10036
KAUFER, JONATHAN	WRITER-PRODUCER	8358 RIDPATH DR	LOS ANGELES, CA	90046
KAUFFMAN, EWING	BASEBALL EXECUTIVE	POST OFFICE BOX 419969	KANSAS CITY, MO	64141
KAUFFMAN, KURK	WRESTLER	POST OFFICE BOX 3859	STAMFORD, CT	06905
KAUFMAN, ANNA BELLE	COSTUME DESIGNER	13949 VENTURA BLVD #309	SHERMAN OAKS, CA	91423
KAUFMAN, ARVIN	TV EXECUTIVE	11970 MONTANA AVE	LOS ANGELES, CA	90049
KAUFMAN, BARRY N	TV WRITER	145-A UNDERMOUNTAIN RD	SALISBURY, CT	06068
KAUFMAN, CURTIS	TV PRODUCER	215 W 88TH ST	NEW YORK, NY	10024
KAUFMAN, DAVE	COLUMNIST	5700 WILSHIRE BLVD #120	LOS ANGELES, CA	90036
KAUFMAN, HAROLD	DIRECTOR	1324 BENEDICT CANYON DR	BEVERLY HILLS, CA	90210
KAUFMAN, HOWARD	TALENT AGENCT	345 N MAPLE ST #235	BEVERLY HILLS, CA	90210
KAUFMAN, JACK	WRITER-PRODUCER	3835 FAIRWAY AVE	STUDIO CITY, CA	91604
KAUFMAN, JEFF H	TALENT AGENT	4146 LANKERSHIM BLVD #300	NORTH HOLLYWOOD, CA	91602
KAUFMAN, KEN	SCREENWRITER	9200 SUNSET BLVD #402	LOS ANGELES, CA	90069
KAUFMAN, KENNETH	TV PRODUCER	TELECOM ENT, 909 3RD AVE	NEW YORK, NY	10022
KAUFMAN, LEONARD B	WRITER-PRODUCER	9026 ELEVADO AVE	LOS ANGELES, CA	90069
KAUFMAN, LLOYD, JR	DIRECTOR-PRODUCER	TROMA INC, 733 9TH AVE	NEW YORK, NY	10019
KAUFMAN, MILLARD	WRITER-PRODUCER	3574 MULTIVIEW DR	LOS ANGELES, CA	90068
KAUFMAN, PHILIP	WRITER-PRODUCER	CAA, 9830 WILSHIRE BLVD	BEVERLY HILLS, CA	90212
KAUFMAN, RICHARD	CONDUCTOR	4237 BEEMAN AVE	STUDIO CITY, CA	91604
KAUFMAN, RODGER D	SINGER-GUITARIST	ROUTE #3, BOX 109	APOLLO, PA	15613
KAUFMAN, ROSE L	SCREENWRITER	8955 BEVERLY BLVD	WEST HOLLYWOOD, CA	90048
KAUFMAN, SID	TV EXECUTIVE	CBS-TV, 51 W 52ND ST	NEW YORK, NY	10019
KAUFMANN, JEROME S	DIRECTOR	225 E 46TH ST	NEW YORK, NY	10017
KAUFMANN, MRS EWING	BASEBALL EXECUTIVE	POST OFFICE BOX 419969	KANSAS CITY, MO	64141
KAUKONEN, JORMA	SINGER-GUITARIST	BOWMAN, 2400 FULTON ST	SAN FRANCISCO, CA	94118
KAUL, DONALD	COMMENTATOR	TRIBUNE, 64 E CONCORD ST	ORLANDO, FL	32801
KAVESH, LAURA	COLUMNIST	TRIBUNE, 64 E CONCORD ST	ORLANDO, FL	32801
KAVNER, JULIE	ACTRESS	25154 MALIBU RD #2	MALIBU, CA	90265
KAVNER, STEVEN	ACTOR	430 S CLOVERDALE AVE #22	LOS ANGELES, CA	90036
KAWADRI, ANWAR	FILM DIRECTOR	115 WENDELL RD	LONDON W12 9SD	ENGLAND
KAWAK, EDWARD	BODYBUILDER	AN DER SCHMIEDE LA		
		D-5024 PULHEIM	SINNERSDORF	GERMANY
KAWASAKI, KIKUO	DIRECTOR	DGA, 7920 SUNSET BLVD, 6TH FL	LOS ANGELES, CA	90046
KAY, ALLEN STEVEN	DIRECTOR	DGA, 110 W 57TH ST	NEW YORK, NY	10019
KAY, BERNARD	ACTOR	MARTIN, 6-A DANBURY ST	LONDON N1 8JU	ENGLAND
KAY, CHARLES	ACTOR	18 EPPLE RD	LONDON SW6	ENGLAND
KAY, CLARENCE	FOOTBALL	BRONCOS, 13655 BRONCOS PKWY	ENGLEWOOD, CO	80112
KAY, DIANNE	ACTRESS	1559 PALISADES DR	PACIFIC PALISADES, CA	90272
KAY, JOHN	FILM DIRECTOR	VICARIOUS PRODUCTIONS LIMITED		
		212 BATTERSEA BRIDGE RD	LONDON SW11 3AE	ENGLAND
KAY, JOHN & STEPPENWOLF	ROCK & ROLL GROUP	9454 WILSHIRE BLVD #206	BEVERLY HILLS, CA	90212
KAY, MARY	COSMETIC EXECUTIVE	SEE - ASH, MARY KAY		
KAY, PAMELA GAIL	ACTRESS	152 W 58TH ST #9-D	NEW YORK, NY	10019
KAY-GEES	VOCAL GROUP	200 W 57TH ST #1101	NEW YORK, NY	10019
KAYAK	MUSICAL GROUP	NELSON, 1701 QUEENS RD	LOS ANGELES, CA	90069
KAYAN, CYNTHIA S	TV PROD-CASTING DIR	ENTERTAINMENT TONIGHT		
		PARAMOUNT TV PRODUCTIONS		
		1 GULF & WESTERN PLAZA	NEW YORK, NY	10023
KAYDEN, MILDRED	COMPOSER-LYRICIST	160 E 48TH ST #8-L	NEW YORK, NY	10017
KAYDEN, TONY	TV WRITER	2243 CHEREMOYA AVE	HOLLYWOOD, CA	90068
KAYDEN, WILLIAM	TV WRITER-PRODUCER	999 N DOHENY DR	LOS ANGELES, CA	90069
KAYE, CAREN	ACTRESS	12700 VENTURA BLVD #350	STUDIO CITY, CA	91604
KAYE, CELIA	ACTRESS	888 LINDA FLORA DR	LOS ANGELES, CA	90049
KAYE, CHARLES F	NEWS WRITER	CBS NEWS, 524 W 57TH ST	NEW YORK, NY	10019
KAYE, DARWOOD "WALDO"	ACTOR	9318 SCOTMONT DR	TUJUNGA, CA	91042
KAYE, EVELYN PATRICIA	AUTHOR-JOURNALIST	223 TENEFLY RD	ENGLEWOOD, NJ	07631
KAYE, JOHN	SCREENWRITER	9200 SUNSET BLVD #402	LOS ANGELES, CA	90069
KAYE, JOYCE	ACTRESS	330 MAYFAIR DR N	BROOKLYN, NY	11234
KAYE, LILA	ACTRESS	DAWSON, 47 COURTFIELD RD #9	LONDON SW7 4DB	ENGLAND
KAYE, MELVENA	SINGER	P FITZ, 1421 N LINCOLN ST	BURBANK, CA	91506
KAYE, SANDRA	SINGER	POST OFFICE BOX 344	NOLENSVILLE, TN	37135
KAYE, SHEILA	ACTRESS	424 E 57TH ST	NEW YORK, NY	10022
KAYLOR, ROBERT	FILM DIRECTOR	121 S HARPER AVE	LOS ANGELES, CA	90048
KAYSER, ALLAN	ACTOR	1100 N ALTA LOMA RD #707	LOS ANGELES, CA	90069
KAZAN, CHRIS	SCREENWRITER	LASKY, 551 5TH AVE	NEW YORK, NY	10176
KAZAN, ELIA	DIRECTOR-PRODUCER	174 E 95TH ST	NEW YORK, NY	10128
KAZAN, LAINIE	SINGER-ACTRESS	9903 SANTA MONICA BLVD #283	BEVERLY HILLS, CA	90212
KAZAN, NICHOLAS	SCREENWRITER	3014 3RD ST	SANTA MONICA, CA	90405
KAZANAS, JOHN	BASEBALL SCOUT	ATHLETICS'S, OAKLAND COLISEUM	OAKLAND, CA	94621
KAZANJIAN, HOWARD G	FILM PRODUCER	1385 OLD MILL RD	SAN MARINO, CA	91108
KAZER, BEAU	ACTOR	CBS-TV, "YOUNG & THE RESTLESS"		
		7800 BEVERLY BLVD #3305	LOS ANGELES, CA	90036
KAZIN, ALFRED	WRITER	CITY UNIVERSITY OF NEW YORK		
		ENGLISH DEPARTMENT		
		33 W 42ND ST	NEW YORK, NY	10036
KAZOR, STEVE	FOOTBALL COACH	BEARS, 250 N WASHINGTON RD	LAKE FOREST, IL	60045
KEACH, JAMES	ACTOR	9229 SUNSET BLVD #311	LOS ANGELES, CA	90069

Name	Occupation	Address	City/State	Zip
KEACH, STACY, JR	ACTOR-DIRECTOR	27425 WINDING WY	MALIBU, CA	90265
KEACH, STACY, SR	ACTOR	3969 LONGRIDGE AVE	SHERMAN OAKS, CA	91423
KEAGGY, PHIL	SINGER	4701 COLLEGE BLVD #106	LEAWOOD, KS	66211
KEALY, JANET	TV DIRECTOR-PRODUCER	201 E 30TH ST #25	NEW YORK, NY	10016
KEAN, E ARTHUR	WRITER-PRODUCER	24235 VALLEY ST	NEWHALL, CA	91321
KEAN, JANE	ACTRESS	4332 COLDWATER CANYON	STUDIO CITY, CA	91604
KEAN, LAUREL	GOLFER	2750 VOLUSA AVE #B	DAYTON BEACH, FL	32114
KEAN, NORMAN	THEATER PRODUCER	280 RIVERSIDE DR	NEW YORK, NY	10026
KEAN, SHERRY	SINGER	41 BRITAIN ST #200	TORONTO, ONT M5A 1R7	CANADA
KEANAN, STACI	ACTRESS	ABC-TV, 2040 AVE OF THE STARS	LOS ANGELES, CA	90067
KEANE, BIL	CARTOONIST	5815 E JOSHUA TREE LN	PARADISE VALLEY, AZ	85253
KEANE, BOB M	TV WRITER	1510 SCREENLAND DR	BURBANK, CA	91505
KEANE, CHRISTOPHER L	SCREENWRITER	8955 BEVERLY BLVD	WEST HOLLYWOOD, CA	90048
KEANE, DIANE	ACTRESS	23 PRIMROSE HILL		
		CHARLETON MACKRELL, NR SOMETON	SUMMERSET	ENGLAND
KEANE, KERRIE	ACTRESS	9744 WILSHIRE BLVD #308	BEVERLY HILLS, CA	90212
KEANE, MIKE	HOCKEY	CANADIENS, 2313 ST CATHERINE ST	MONTREAL, QUE H3H 1N2	CANADA
KEARNEY, JIM	FOOTBALL REFEREE	NFL, 410 PARK AVE	NEW YORK, NY	10022
KEARNEY, ROBERT	BASEBALL EXECUTIVE	POST OFFICE BOX 9194	HAMPTON, VA	23670
KEARNS, BILL	BASEBALL SCOUT	POST OFFICE BOX 4100	SEATTLE, WA	98104
KEATHLEY, GEORGE	DIRECTOR	DGA, 7920 SUNSET BLVD, 6TH FL	LOS ANGELES, CA	90046
KEATING, PAUL	BASEBALL EXECUTIVE	ALBANY YANKEES, HERITAGE PARK	ALBANY, NY	12211
KEATON, DIANE	ACTRESS-DIRECTOR	2255 VERDE OAK DR	LOS ANGELES, CA	90068
KEATON, MICHAEL	ACTOR	826 NAPOLI DR	PACIFIC PALISADES, CA	90272
KEATS, ROBERT A	TV WRITER	1326 CENTINELA AVE #2	LOS ANGELES, CA	90025
KEATS, STEVEN	ACTOR	9200 SUNSET BLVD #625	LOS ANGELES, CA	90069
KECK, JOHN	FOOTBALL REFEREE	NFL, 410 PARK AVE	NEW YORK, NY	10022
KEDROVA, LILA	ACTRESS	50 FOREST MANOR RD #3	WILLOWDALE, ONT M2J 1M	CANADA
KEE, BOB B	COMPOSER	6824 CHIMINEAS AVE	RESEDA, CA	91335
KEE, PAUL	MUSIC ARRANGER	3838 PRIEST LAKE DR	NASHVILLE, TN	37217
KEE, ROBERT	TV DIRECTOR	82 CAMBERWELL GROVE	LONDON SE5 8RP	ENGLAND
KEEFE, MIKE	CARTOONIST	POST OFFICE BOX 1709	DENVER, CO	80201
KEEFER, DON	ACTOR	4146 ALLOTT AVE	VAN NUYS, CA	91403
KEEGAN, BARBARA	ACTRESS	11846 VENTURA BLVD #100	STUDIO CITY, CA	91604
KEEGAN, DONNA	ACTRESS	1124 W ANGELENO AVE #M	BURBANK, CA	91506
KEEL	ROCK & ROLL GROUP	14755 VENTURA BLVD #1-170	SHERMAN OAKS, CA	91423
KEEL, HOWARD	ACTOR-SINGER	15353 LONGBOW DR	SHERMAN OAKS, CA	91403
KEELE, BETH	WRITER	1042 N CRESCENT HEIGHTS BLVD	LOS ANGELES, CA	90046
KEELER, RUBY	ACTRESS	LOWE, 71029 EARLY TIMES RD	RANCHO MIRAGE, CA	92270
KEELINE, JASON	BASEBALL	POST OFFICE BOX 4525	MACON, GA	31208
KEEN, DIANE	ACTRESS	MARSHALL, 44 PERRYN RD	LONDON W3 7NA	ENGLAND
KEEN, STANLEY N	CONDUCTOR	6553 39TH ST, NE	SEATTLE, WA	98115
KEENA, THOMAS	ACTOR	37 W 72ND ST #12-A	NEW YORK, NY	10023
KEENAN, JOHN	BASEBALL SCOUT	1000 ELYSIAN PARK DR	LOS ANGELES, CA	90012
KEENAN, MIKE	BASEBALL SCOUT	S F GIANTS, CANDLESTICK PARK	SAN FRANICSCO, CA	94124
KEENE, ANDRE	BASEBALL	POST OFFICE BOX 1295	CLINTON, IA	52733
KEENE, ELODIE	TV PRODUCER	8383 WILSHIRE BLVD #923	BEVERLY HILLS, CA	90211
KEENE, TOMMY	SINGER-GUITARIST	GEFFEN RECORDS COMPANY		
		9130 SUNSET BLVD	LOS ANGELES, CA	90069
KEESHAN, BOB	TV HOST	ICM, 40 W 57TH ST #1600	NEW YORK, NY	10019
KEETER, LONNIE	BASEBALL COACH	12000 STADIUM RD	ADELANTO, CA	92301
KEETON, RICK	BASEBALL COACH	POST OFFICE BOX 842	SALEM, VA	24153
KEHOE, JACK	ACTOR	19 W 44TH ST #1000	NEW YORK, NY	10036
KEHR, DAVE	FILM CRITIC	THE CHICAGO TRIBUNE		
		TRIBUNE TOWER		
		435 N MICHIGAN AVE	CHICAGO, IL	60611
KEIDEL, A DALE	DIRECTOR	382 CENTRAL PARK W	NEW YORK, NY	10025
KEIGHLEY, STEVE	BASEBALL	POST OFFICE BOX 3566	WEST PALM BEACH, FL	33402
KEILL, IAN	TV PRODUCER	4 BOYN HILL CLOSE, MAIDENHEAD	BERKSHIRE SL6 4JD	ENGLAND
KEILLOR, GARRISON	HUMORIST-RADIO PERS	300 CENTRAL PARK W	NEW YORK, NY	10024
KEIM, BETTY LOU	ACTRESS	BERLINGER, 10642 ARNEL PL	CHATSWORTH, CA	91311
KEIM, LARRY	FOOTBALL	RAMS, 2327 W LINCOLN BLVD	ANAHEIM, CA	92801
KEIN, SYBIL	SINGER	2528-A W JEROME AVE	CHICAGO, IL	60645
KEIR, ANDREW	ACTOR	MAYER MGMT, GRAFTON HOUSE #44		
		2-3 GOLDEN SQ	LONDON W1R 3AD	ENGLAND
KEISLING, PHIL	SECRETARY OF STATE	STATE CAPITOL BUILDING	SALEM, OR	97310
KEITEL, HARVEY	ACTOR	POST OFFICE BOX 49	PALISADES, NY	10964
KEITH, BRIAN	ACTOR	23449 MALIBU COLONY RD	MALIBU, CA	90265
KEITH, DAVID	ACTOR	ICM, 8899 BEVERLY BLVD	LOS ANGELES, CA	90048
KEITH, DAVID	CONDUCTOR	10238 WHITEGATE AVE	SUNLAND, CA	91040
KEITH, GERREN F	TV DIRECTOR	3332 BLAIR DR	LOS ANGELES, CA	90068
KEITH, JEFFREY ALLEN	TV WRITER	225 N ROSE ST #404	BURBANK, CA	91505
KEITH, LAWRENCE	ACTOR	SHEA & GOULD, 330 MADISON AVE	NEW YORK, NY	10017
KEITH, PENELOPE	ACTRESS	LONDON MGT, 235-241 REGENT ST	LONDON W1R 4PH	ENGLAND
KEITH, SHEILA	ACTRESS	WHITE, 2 ORMOND RD, RICHMOND	SURREY TW10 6TH	ENGLAND
KEITH, SUSAN	ACTRESS	ABC-TV, "LOVING"		
		320 W 66TH ST, STUDIO 23	NEW YORK, NY	10023
KELADA, ASAAD	TV DIRECTOR	4139 MAMMOTH AVE	SHERMAN OAKS, CA	91423
KELING, KOREY	BASEBALL	POST OFFICE BOX 1742	PALM SPRINGS, CA	92263
KELINGOS, JOHN A	VIOLINIST	VANDERBILT UNIVERSITY		
		BOX 6196, STATION B	NASHVILLE, TN	37235
KELL, GEORGE	BASEBALL-ANNOUNCER	TIGERS, TIGER STADIUM	DETROIT, MI	48216
KELLAHIN, JAMES	WRITER-PRODUCER	19869 GREENBRIAR DR	TARZANA, CA	91356
KELLARD, BILL	COSTUME DESIGNER	EUE/SCREEN GEMS, 222 E 44TH ST	NEW YORK, NY	10017
KELLARD, GRACE	ACTRESS	1156 MONUMENT ST	PACIFIC PALISADES, CA	90272

KELLARD, PHILLIP	TV WRITER	1156 MONUMENT ST	PACIFIC PALISADES, CA	90272
KELLARD, RICHARD J	TV WRITER	12634 KLING ST	STUDIO CITY, CA	91604
KELLAWAY, ROGER W	COMPOSER	HABER, 16255 VENTURA BLVD	ENCINO, CA	91436
KELLEHER, ED	FILM CRITIC	FILM JOURNAL, 244 W 49TH ST	NEW YORK, NY	10019
KELLEHER, MICK	BASEBALL-INSTRUCTOR	1060 W ADDISON ST	CHICAGO, IL	60613
KELLER, BUZZY	BASEBALL SCOUT	INDIANS, CLEVELAND STADIUM	CLEVELAND, OH	44114
KELLER, CASEY	TV WRITER	1900 AVE OF THE STARS #1530	LOS ANGELES, CA	90067
KELLER, CELENE	ACTRESS-SINGER	640 W END AVE #12-C	NEW YORK, NY	10024
KELLER, CLYDE	BASEBALL	525 NW PEACOCK BLVD	PORT SAINT LUCIE, FL	34986
KELLER, DAVE	BASEBALL COACH	POST OFFICE BOX 3452	KINSTON, NC	28502
KELLER, DONALD	DIRECTOR	117 WALWORTH AVE	SCARSDALE, NY	10583
KELLER, EYTAN	TV WRITER-PRODUCER	9307 KIRKSIDE RD	LOS ANGELES, CA	90035
KELLER, JULIA	TV CRITIC	POST OFFICE BOX 1350	COLUMBUS, OH	43216
KELLER, LARRY	BASEBALL SCOUT	BREWERS, 201 S 46TH ST	MILWAUKEE, WI	53214
KELLER, MARTHE	ACTRESS	LAMONSTRASSE 9	8 MUNICH 80	GERMANY
KELLER, MARY PAGE	ACTRESS	5303 DOON WY	ANACORTES, WA	98221
KELLER, MAX	FILM PRODUCER	AMERICAN FIRST RUN STUDIOS		
		14225 VENTURA BLVD	SHERMAN OAKS, CA	91423
KELLER, MICHELINE	FILM PRODUCER	AMERICAN FIRST RUN STUDIOS		
		14225 VENTURA BLVD	SHERMAN OAKS, CA	91423
KELLER, SHELDON	WRITER-PRODUCER	2501 ASTRAL DR	LOS ANGELES, CA	90046
KELLER, THOMAS B	TV EXECUTIVE	PBS, 475 L'ENFANT PLAZA, SW	WASHINGTON, DC	20024
KELLERMAN, SALLY	ACTRESS	9000 SUNSET BLVD #1200	LOS ANGELES, CA	90069
KELLERMANN, BARBARA	ACTRESS	ICM, 388-396 OXFORD ST	LONDON W1	ENGLAND
KELLETT, BOB	WRI-DIR-PROD	GANNET, 88 GRESHAM RD, STAINES	MIDDLESEX TW18 2AE	ENGLAND
KELLEY, AL	GOLFER	PGA SENIORS, 112 T P C BLVD	PONTE VEDRA BEACH, FL	32082
KELLEY, ALBERT	DIRECTOR	3767 ALOMAR DR	SHERMAN OAKS, CA	91403
KELLEY, DAVID E	TV WRITER-PRODUCER	UTA, 9560 WILSHIRE BL, 5TH FL	BEVERLY HILLS, CA	90212
KELLEY, DE FOREST	ACTOR	15711 ROYAL OAK RD	ENCINO, CA	91436
KELLEY, DEAN	BASEBALL	STARS, 850 LAS VEGAS BLVD N	LAS VEGAS, NV	89101
KELLEY, FRANK J	ATTORNEY GENERAL	STATE CAPITOL BUILDING	LANSING, MI	48953
KELLEY, GARY	ARTIST	HELLMAN ASSOCIATES		
		1225 W 4TH ST	WATERLOO, IA	50702
KELLEY, KITTY	AUTHORESS	3037 DUNBARTON AVE, NW	WASHINGTON, DC	20007
KELLEY, LEE CHARLES	ACTOR	35 W 45TH ST #600	NEW YORK, NY	10036
KELLEY, PATRICK	PRODUCER	PAN-ARTS, 4000 WARNER BLVD	BURBANK, CA	91522
KELLEY, RICHARD	BASEBALL	POST OFFICE BOX 64939	FAYETTEVILLE, NC	28306
KELLEY, STEVE	CARTOONIST-COMEDIAN	POST OFFICE BOX 191	SAN DIEGO, CA	92112
KELLEY, WALTER	WRITER-PRODUCER	6459 SYCAMORE MEADOWS DR	MALIBU, CA	90265
KELLEY, WAYNE	SCREENWRITER	1626 1/2 N VISTA ST	LOS ANGELES, CA	90046
KELLEY, WILLIAM	TV EXECUTIVE	NBC-TV, 30 ROCKEFELLER PLAZA	NEW YORK, NY	10112
KELLEY, WILLIAM	TV WRITER	501 S FULLLER AVE	LOS ANGELES, CA	90036
KELLJAN, BOB	WRITER-PRODUCER	9151 WARBLER PL	LOS ANGELES, CA	90069
KELLMAN, BARNET	TV DIRECTOR	718 BROADWAY	NEW YORK, NY	10003
KELLNER, FRANK	BASEBALL	POST OFFICE BOX 4209	JACKSON, MS	39296
KELLOG, MARJORIE	SCREENWRITER	555 W 57TH ST #1230	NEW YORK, NY	10019
KELLOGG, CHRISTINE	ACTRESS	400 S BEVERLY DR #216	BEVERLY HILLS, CA	90212
KELLOGG, GEOFF	BASEBALL	12000 STADIUM RD	ADELANTO, CA	92301
KELLOGG, JEFF	BASEBALL UMPIRE	POST OFFICE BOX 608	GROVE CITY, OH	43123
KELLOGG, LYNN	ACTRESS-SINGER	10583 SCENARIO LN	LOS ANGELES, CA	90077
KELLUM, MURRY	SINGER	POST OFFICE BOX 208	GOODLETTSVILLE, TN	37072
KELLY, ANNE	GOLFER	2750 VOLUSA AVE #B	DAYTON BEACH, FL	32114
KELLY, BARBARA	ACTRESS-WRITER	STUDIO, 5 KIDDERPORE AVE	LONDON NW3 7SX	ENGLAND
KELLY, BRIDGET J	COSTUME DESIGNER	127 W 95TH ST #2	NEW YORK, NY	10025
KELLY, CALVIN REGINALD	TV WRITER	5830 W GREEN VALLEY CIR #210	CULVER CITY, CA	90230
KELLY, CHRIS	TV WRITER	BURNETT, 42-43 GRAFTON HOUSE		
		2-3 GOLDEN SQ	LONDON W1R 3AD	ENGLAND
KELLY, DAVE	BASEBALL EXECUTIVE	POST OFFICE BOX 882	MADISON, WI	53701
KELLY, DAVID E	TV WRITER	UTA, 9560 WILSHIRE BL, 5TH FL	BEVERLY HILLS, CA	90212
KELLY, ELLIOT H	CONDUCTOR	691 S IROLO ST #409	LOS ANGELES, CA	90005
KELLY, GENE	ACT-DAN-DIR	725 N RODEO DR	BEVERLY HILLS, CA	90210
KELLY, GORDON	BASEBALL SCOUT	REDS, 100 RIVERFRONT STADIUM	CINCINNATI, OH	45202
KELLY, HENRY	TV-RADIO HOST	NJ MEDIA ENTERPRISES, LTD		
		10 CLORANE GARDENS	LONDON NW3 7PR	ENGLAND
KELLY, JACKIE	CASTING DIRECTOR	THE LITTLE THEATRE BUILDING		
		240 W 44TH ST	NEW YORK, NY	10036
KELLY, JAMES PATRICK, III	DIRECTOR	410 W 60TH TERR	KANSAS CITY, MO	64113
KELLY, JEAN LOUISA	ACTRESS	9200 SUNSET BLVD #710	LOS ANGELES, CA	90069
KELLY, JERRI	SINGER	CARRERE UK, 22 QUEEN ST	LONDON	ENGLAND
KELLY, JERRY, BAND	ROCK & ROLL GROUP	SEE - DAKOTA		
KELLY, JIM	FOOTBALL	BILLS, 1 BILLS DR	ORCHARD PARK, NJ	14127
KELLY, JIM	SPORTSCASTER	CBS SPORTS, 51 W 52ND ST	NEW YORK, NY	10019
KELLY, JOE	FOOTBALL	N Y JETS, 1000 FULTON AVE	HEMPSTEAD, NY	11550
KELLY, JOHN	ACTOR	KJAR, 10653 RIVERSIDE DR	TOLUCA LAKE, CA	91602
KELLY, JOHN	BASEBALL	POST OFFICE BOX 12557	ST PETERSBURG, FL	33733
KELLY, JOHN G	DIRECTOR-PRODUCER	CBS-TV, 524 W 57TH ST	NEW YORK, NY	10019
KELLY, JOHN S	TALENT AGENT	15760 VENTURA BLVD #1730	ENCINO, CA	91436
KELLY, JOHN-CHARLES	ACTIR-SINGER	37 NAGLE AVE #3-C	NEW YORK, NY	10040
KELLY, JOSE	SINGER	VISTONE, 6331 SANTA MONICA BLVD	HOLLYWOOD, CA	90038
KELLY, JUDD	SINGER-GUITARIST	1515 RICHLAND DR	BLOOMINGTON, IN	47401
KELLY, KAREN	ACTRESS	15010 VENTURA BLVD #332	SHERMAN OAKS, CA	91403
KELLY, KATIE	FILM CRITIC	WABC-TV, 7 LINCOLN SQ	NEW YORK, NY	10023
KELLY, KEVIN B	TV DIRECTOR	13 PIERPONT PL	STATEN ISLAND, NY	10314
KELLY, MARGARET	AUDITOR	POST OFFICE BOX 720	JEFFERSON CITY, MO	65102
KELLY, MATTHEW	ACTOR	RICHARDS, 42 HAZLEBURY RD	LONDON SW6 2ND	ENGLAND

KELLY, MICHAEL C	TV DIRECTOR	80 HIGHVIEW AVE	PARK RIDGE, NJ	07656
KELLY, MIKE	BASEBALL	POST OFFICE BOX 16683	GREENVILLE, SC	29606
KELLY, MIKE	WRESTLER	POST OFFICE BOX 3859	STAMFORD, CT	06905
KELLY, PAT	BASEBALL (GREENVILLE)	POST OFFICE BOX 16683	GREENVILLE, SC	29606
KELLY, PAT	BASEBALL (MANAGER)	1501 W 16TH ST	INDIANAPOLIS, IN	46202
KELLY, PAT	BASEBALL (YANKEES)	N Y YANKEES, YANKEE STADIUM	BRONX, NY	10451
KELLY, PATRICK D	DIRECTOR	PIER 62, W 23RD STATION		
		12TH AVE	NEW YORK, NY	10011
KELLY, PAULA	ACTRESS-DANCER	1801 AVE OF THE STARS #1250	LOS ANGELES, CA	90067
KELLY, PAULA	SINGER	POST OFFICE BOX 195	ENCINO, CA	91426
KELLY, ROBERTO	BASEBALL	N Y YANKEES, YANKEE STADIUM	BRONX, NY	10451
KELLY, ROZ	ACTRESS	5614 LEMP AVE	NORTH HOLLYWOOD, CA	91601
KELLY, SANDRA	COLUMNIST	UPS, 4900 MAIN ST, 9TH FLOOR	KANSAS CITY, MO	64112
KELLY, SEAN C	TV WRITER	555 W 57TH ST #1230	NEW YORK, NY	10019
KELLY, THOMAS F	DIRECTOR	360 S BURNSIDE AVE #5-K	LOS ANGELES, CA	90036
KELLY, TIM	BASEBALL SCOUT	POST OFFICE BOX 2000	ANAHEIM, CA	92803
KELLY, TIMOTHY	BASEBALL SCOUT	N Y YANKEES, YANKEE STADIUM	BRONX, NY	10451
KELLY, TOM	BASEBALL-MANAGER	TWINS, 501 CHICAGO AVE S	MINNEAPOLIS, MN	55415
KELLY, VIVIAN	ACTRESS	451 E 14TH ST #1-D	NEW YORK, NY	10009
KELLY, WINFIELD M, JR	SECRETARY OF STATE	STATE HOUSE BUILDING	ANNAPOLIS, MD	21401
KELLY'S HEROES	MUSICAL GROUP	KTA, 108 SHARON DR	WEST MONROE, LA	71291
KELMAN, ALFRED R	TV DIRECTOR	124 E 65TH ST	NEW YORK, NY	10021
KELMAN, DEBBIE	CINEMATOGRAPHER	3 MADERO LN	WAYNE, NJ	07470
KELSEY, LINDA	ACTRESS	1999 AVE OF THE STARS #2850	LOS ANGELES, CA	90067
KELSO, BILL	BASEBALL SCOUT	POST OFFICE BOX 288	HOUSTON, TX	77001
KELSO, MARK	FOOTBALL	BILLS, 1 BILLS DR	ORCHARD PARK, NJ	14127
KELTON, KEVIN	TV WRITER	11726 SAN VICENTE BLVD #300	LOS ANGELES, CA	90049
KEMENY, JOHN	FILM PRODUCER	10450 WILSHIRE BLVD	LOS ANGELES, CA	90024
KEMMER, EDWARD	ACTOR	145 W 45TH ST #1204	NEW YORK, NY	10036
KEMMERLING, WARREN	ACTOR	10819 SHOSHONE AVE	GRANADA HILLS, CA	91344
KEMP, BARRY MICHAEL	TV WRITER	17780 RIDGEWAY RD	GRANADA HILLS, CA	91344
KEMP, BRANDIS	ACTRESS	10351 SANTA MONICA BLVD #211	LOS ANGELES, CA	90025
KEMP, DONNA TURNER	DIRECTOR	14052 VALLEYHEART DR #4	SHERMAN OAKS, CA	91423
KEMP, JACK	FOOTBALL-POLITICAN	4571 7TH AVE, SW	WASHINGTON, DC	20024
KEMP, JEFF	FOOTBALL	SEAHAWKS, 11220 NE 53RD ST	KIRKLAND, WA	98033
KEMP, JEREMY	ACTOR	MARTIN, 6-A DANBURY ST	LONDON N1 8JU	ENGLAND
KEMP, PERRY	FOOTBALL	PACKERS, 1265 LOMBARDI AVE	GREEN BAY, WI	54307
KEMP, SHAWN	BASKETBALL	POST OFFICE BOX C-900911	SEATTLE, WA	98109
KEMP, STAN	FOOTBALL REFEREE	NFL, 410 PARK AVE	NEW YORK, NY	10022
KEMP, WAYNE	SINGER	POST OFFICE BOX 390	PONTOTOC, MS	38863
KEMP-WELCH, JOAN	TV DIRECTOR-PRODUCER	11 CHILWORTH MEWS	LONDON W2	ENGLAND
KEMPEL, ARTHUR B	COMPOSER	2255 N CAHUENGA BLVD #30	LOS ANGELES, CA	90068
KEMPLE, CHRIS	BASEBALL EXECUTIVE	POST OFFICE BOX 2437	MODESTO, CA	95351
KEMPLEY, RITA	FILM CRITIC	THE WASHINGTON POST		
		1150 15TH ST, NW	WASHINGTON, DC	20071
KEMPSON, LAURI	ACTRESS	8484 WILSHIRE BLVD #530	BEVERLY HILLS, CA	90211
KEMPT, BRIGITTE	ACTRESS	4942 VINELAND AVE #200	NORTH HOLLYWOOD, CA	91601
KENDAL, FELICITY	ACTRESS	CHATTO AND LINNIT, LTD		
		PRINCE OF WALES THEATRE		
		COVENTRY ST	LONDON W1V 7FE	ENGLAND
KENDALL, BEN	COMPOSER	POST OFFICE BOX 1098	PALMA DE MALLORCA	SPAIN
KENDALL, JO	ACTRESS	MARTIN, 19 HIGHGATE WEST HILL	LONDON N6 6NP	ENGLAND
KENDALL, PHIL	BASEBALL	POST OFFICE BOX 4669	CHARLESTON, WV	25304
KENDALL, SUZY	ACTRESS	DENTHAM HOUSE #44, THE MOUNT	HAMPSTEAD NW3	ENGLAND
KENDALLS, THE	C & W GROUP	WORLD CLASS TALENT AGENCY		
		1522 DEMONBREUN ST	NASHVILLE, TN	37203
KENDRICK, DENNIS	ARTIST	99 BANK ST #3-G	NEW YORK, NY	10014
KENDRICKS, EDDIE	SINGER-SONGWRITER	STAR-VEST, 102 RYDERS LN	EAST BRUNSWICK, NJ	08816
KENION, JERRY MANN	WRITER	202 COUNTRY PARK RD	GREENSBORO, NC	27408
KENIS, STEVE	TALENT AGENT	WM MORRIS, 31-32 SOHO SQ	LONDON W1V 5DG	ENGLAND
KENN, MIKE	FOOTBALL	FALCONS, SUWANEE RD AT I-85	SUWANEE, GA	30174
KENNAN, LARRY	FOOTBALL COACH	POST OFFICE BOX 535000	INDIANPOLIS, IN	46253
KENNARD, ARTHUR	TALENT AGENT	12220 HUSTON ST	NORTH HOLLYWOOD, CA	91606
KENNARD, DAVID	DIRECTOR-PRODUCER	POST OFFICE BOX 81	PALOS VERDES, CA	90274
KENNARD, DEREK	FOOTBALL	SAINTS, 1500 POYDRAS ST	NEW ORLEANS, LA	90112
KENNEDY, ADAM	SCREENWRITER	POST OFFICE BOX 679	KENT, CT	06757
KENNEDY, ADRIENNE LITA	PLAYWRIGHT	172 W 79TH ST	NEW YORK, NY	10021
KENNEDY, ANTHONY	SUPREME COURT JUDGE	1 1ST ST, NE	WASHINGTON, DC	20543
KENNEDY, ARTHUR	ACTOR	2768 WOODWARDIA DR	LOS ANGELES, CA	90024
KENNEDY, BERNADETTE	ACTRESS	5330 LANKERSHIM BLVD #210	NORTH HOLLYWOOD, CA	91601
KENNEDY, BETTY	ACTRESS	AIMEE, 13743 VICTORY BLVD	VAN NUYS, CA	91401
KENNEDY, BILL	ACTOR	140 KINGS RD	PALM BEACH, FL	33480
KENNEDY, BO	BASEBALL	POST OFFICE BOX 360007	BIRMINGHAM, AL	35236
KENNEDY, BURT	FILM WRITER-DIRECTOR	13138 MAGNOLIA BLVD	SHERMAN OAKS, CA	91423
KENNEDY, CORTEZ	FOOTBALL	SEAHAWKS, 11220 NE 53RD ST	KIRKLAND, WA	98033
KENNEDY, DANIEL	TV WRITER-PRODUCER	157 W 79TH ST	NEW YORK, NY	10024
KENNEDY, DARRYL	BASEBALL	POST OFFICE BOX 309	GASTONA, NC	28053
KENNEDY, DEAN	HOCKEY	SABRES, MEMORIAL AUDITORIUM	BUFFALO, NY	14202
KENNEDY, DR D JAMES	EVANGELIST	POST OFFICE BOX 40	FORT LAUDERDALE, FL	33302
KENNEDY, EDWARD "TED"	U S SENATOR	636 CHAIN BRIDGE RD	MC LEAN, VA	22101
KENNEDY, ETHEL	CELEBRITY	1147 CHAIN BRIDGE RD	MC LEAN, VA	22101
KENNEDY, GENE	SINGER	2125 8TH AVE S	NASHVILLE, TN	37204
KENNEDY, GEORGE	ACTOR	10000 SANTA MONICA BLVD #700	LOS ANGELES, CA	90067
KENNEDY, JAMES	ACTOR	1680 N VINE ST #726	HOLLYWOOD, CA	90028
KENNEDY, JAYNE	ACTRESS-MODEL	SEE - KENNEDY-OVERTON, JAYNE		

KENNEDY, JOAN	CELEBRITY	SQUAW ISLAND	HYANNISPORT, MA 02647
KENNEDY, JOHN	BASEBALL SCOUT	POST OFFICE BOX 7575	PHILADELPHIA, PA 19101
KENNEDY, JOHN F, JR	PERSONALITY	1040 5TH AVE	NEW YORK, NY 10028
KENNEDY, JOSEPH P, II	U S CONGRESSMAN	530 ATLANTIC AVE	BOSTON, MA 02108
KENNEDY, JOYCE LAIN	COLUMNIST	7720 EL CAMINO REAL #2-C	RANCHO LA COSTA, CA 92008
KENNEDY, KATHLEEN	FILM PRODUCER	MCA/UNIVERSAL STUDIOS, INC	
		100 UNIVERSAL CITY PLAZA	
		BUNGALOW #477	UNIVERSAL CITY, CA 91608
KENNEDY, KEN	DIRECTOR	1302 E BECKER LN	PHOENIX, AZ 85020
KENNEDY, KEVIN	BASEBALL MANAGER	POST OFFICE BOX 26267	ALBUQUERQUE, NM 87125
KENNEDY, LEON ISAAC	ACTOR-PRODUCER	POST OFFICE BOX 361039	LOS ANGELES, CA 90036
KENNEDY, MALLORY	CASTING DIRECTOR	6815 WILLOUGHBY AVE	LOS ANGELES, CA 90038
KENNEDY, MIMI	ACTRESS	10100 SANTA MONICA BLVD #1600	LOS ANGELES, CA 90067
KENNEDY, NANCY G	TV DIRECTOR-PRODUCER	320 W 84TH ST #6-C	NEW YORK, NY 10024
KENNEDY, RAY	SINGER-SONGWRITER	HARDIN, 818 19TH AVE S	NASHVILLE, TN 37203
KENNEDY, ROBERT F, JR	PERSONALITY	78 N BROADWAY	WHITE PLAINS, NY 10603
KENNEDY, ROSE	AUTHORESSS-JFK'S MOM	THE COMPOUND	HYANNIS, MA 02647
KENNEDY, SARAH	TV-RADIO HOST	THAMES TV, 306-316 EUSTON RD	LONDON NW1 3BB ENGLAND
KENNEDY, TED, JR	CELEBRITY	636 CHAIN BRIDGE RD	MC LEAN, VA 22101
KENNEDY, TERRY	BASEBALL	2411-1 ADIRONDACK ROW	SAN DIEGO, CA 92139
KENNEDY, WILLIAM J	SCREENWRITER	WRITERS INSTITUTE (SUNY)	
		WASHINGTON AVE	ALBANY, NY 12222
KENNEDY SCHLOSSBERG, CAROLINE	CELEBRITY	888 PARK AVE	NEW YORK, NY 10021
KENNEDY-MARTIN, IAN	WRITER-EDITOR	4 CASTELLAIN RD	LONDON W9 ENGLAND
KENNEDY-MARTIN, TROY	SCREENWRITER	STEEL, 110 GLOUCESTER AVE	LONDON NW1 8JL ENGLAND
KENNEDY-OVERTON, JAYNE	ACTRESS-MODEL	9255 SUNSET BLVD #706	LOS ANGELES, CA 90069
KENNELL, KARI	ACTRESS-MODEL	SEE - WHITMAN, KARI KENNELL	
KENNELLY, BARBARA B	U S CONGRESSWOMAN	1 CORPORATE CENTER	HARTFORD, CT 06103
KENNEY, EDWARD F	BASEBALL EXECUTIVE	FENWAY PARK, 4 YAWKEY WY	BOSTON, MA 02215
KENNEY, EDWARD P	BASEBALL EXECUTIVE	FENWAY PARK, 4 YAWKEY WY	BOSTON, MA 02215
KENNEY, H WESLEY	TV WRITER-PRODUCER	12996 GALEWOOD ST	STUDIO CITY, CA 91604
KENNEY, LONA B	TV WRITER	3 PETER COOPER RD #3-F	NEW YORK, Y 10010
KENNY, BRIAN	BASEBALL	1524 W NEBRASKA AVE	PEORIA, IL 61604
KENNY, DOUGLAS J	DIRECTOR	152 W 20TH ST	NEW YORK, NY 10011
KENNY, EDWARD J	DIRECTOR	152 W SHORE DR	MARBLEHEAD, MA 01945
KENNY, JOSEPH E	FILM DIRECTOR	7250 SAN LUIS AVE	CARLSBAD, CA 92008
KENNY, WILLIAM C	TV WRITER-STORY ED	POST OFFICE BOX 241	NEW VERNON, CT 07976
KENNY G	SAXOPHONIST	21940 LAMPLIGHTER	MALIBU, CA 90265
KENRICK, TONY	SCREENWRITER	151 S EL CAMINO DR	BEVERLY HILLS, CA 90212
KENSEN, KAREN	ACTRESS	4501 VISTA DEL MONTE AVE #8	SHERMAN OAKS, CA 91403
KENSIT, PATSY	ACTRESS	50 LISSON ST #1-B	LONDON NW1 5DF ENGLAND
KENT, AL	TV DIRECTOR-PRODUCER	KENT COMMUNICATIONS COMPANY	
		244 MADISON AVE	NEW YORK, NY 10016
KENT, ALEXANDRA	ACTRESS	CARROLL, 120 S VICTORY BL #104	BURBANK, CA 91502
KENT, ALLEGRA	DANCER	NEW YORK CITY BALLET	
		LINCOLN CENTER PLAZA	NEW YORK, NY 10023
KENT, ART	TV EXECUTIVE	NBC-TV, 30 ROCKEFELLER PLAZA	NEW YORK, NY 10112
KENT, ELIZABETH	ACTRESS	10000 RIVERSIDE DR #6	TOLUCA LAKE, CA 91602
KENT, ENID	ACTRESS	1717 N HIGHLAND AVE #414	LOS ANGELES, CA 90028
KENT, GEORGE	CONDUCTOR	7125 FULTON AVE #24	NORTH HOLLYWOOD, CA 91605
KENT, JANICE	ACTRESS	10000 SANTA MONICA BLVD #305	LOS ANGELES, CA 90067
KENT, JEAN	ACTRESS	THORNGLADE, CHURCH RD	
		WEST THORPE, NEAR STOWMARKET	SUFFOLK ENGLAND
KENT, JEFF	BASEBALL	METS, 126TH ST & ROOSEVELT AVE	FLUSHING, NY 11368
KENT, LINDA	DANCER	175 W 92ND ST	NEW YORK, NY 10025
KENT, MICHAEL	CONDUCTOR	POST OFFICE BOX 1150	MOUNT SHASTA, CA 96067
KENT, PAUL	ACTOR	37219 N 52ND ST #E	PALMDALE, CA 93550
KENT, SUZANNE	ACTRESS	1999 AVE OF THE STARS #2850	LOS ANGELES, CA 90067
KENT, TROY	BASEBALL	POST OFFICE BOX 4756	JACKSONVILLE, FL 32201
KENT, WALTER	COMPOSER	4611 STARK AVE	WOODLAND HILLS, CA 91364
KENTISH, DOUGLAS	FILM PRODUCER	ILLUSTRA FILMS, 13 BATEMAN ST	LONDON W1 ENGLAND
KENTUCKY COUNTRY	C & W GROUP	3661 S MARYLAND PKWY #3 - BOX 50	LAS VEGAS, NV 89109
KENTUCKY HEADHUNTERS, THE	C & W GROUP	447 W 65TH ST #3-C	NEW YORK, NY 10021
KENWITH, HERBERT	DIRECTOR-PRODUCER	1527 SUNSET PLAZA DR	LOS ANGELES, CA 90069
KENWOOD, DIANE	TV HOST-WRITER	2 SIDMOUTH RD	LONDON NW2 5JX ENGLAND
KENWORTHY, MARY LOU	ACTRESS	NATHE, 8281 MELROSE AVE #200	LOS ANGELES, CA 90046
KENWRIGHT, BILL	FILM PRODUCER	59 SHAFTESBURY AVE	LONDON W1 ENGLAND
KENYON, CURTIS	FILM EXECUTIVE	16145 MORRISON ST	ENCINO, CA 91436
KENYON, MARION	SCREENWRITER	1801 AVE OF THE STARS #1250	LOS ANGELES, CA 90067
KENYON, SANDY	ACTOR-DIRECTOR	13530 MORRISON ST	SHERMAN OAKS, CA 91423
KEOUGH, MARTY	BASEBALL-SCOUT	250 STADIUM PLAZA	ST LOUIS, MO 63102
KEPLER, JOHN	ACTOR	808 RADCLIFFE AVE	PACIFIC PALISADES, CA 90272
KEPLER, SHELL	ACTRESS	419 N LARCHMONT BLVD #195	LOS ANGELES, CA 90004
KEPSHIRE, KURT	BASEBALL	27 OAKWOOD DR	SEYMOUR, CT 06483
KERA	MODEL	POST OFFICE BOX 9786	MARINA DEL REY, CA 90265
KERAMIDAS, GEORGE	TV EXECUTIVE	284 VOORHIS AVE	RIVER EDGE, NJ 07661
KERBAWY, HAFORD	DIRECTOR	1025 YORKSHIRE	GROSSE POINT PARK, MI 48230
KERBEY, SCOTT A	TV DIRECTOR-PRODUCER	150 W 74TH ST #4-B	NEW YORK, NY 10023
KERBY, WILLIAM C	SCREENWRITER	131 S RODEO DR #300	BEVERLY HILLS, CA 90212
KERCHEVAL, KEN	ACTOR	POST OFFICE BOX 1350	LOS ANGELES, CA 90078
KERDYK, TRACY	GOLFER	2750 VOLUSA AVE #B	DAYTON BEACH, FL 32114
KERFELD, CHARLIE	BASEBALL	1001 SONOMA ST	CARSON CITY, NV 89701
KERMAN, KEN	ACTOR	2175 HUDSON TERR	FORT LEE, NJ 07024
KERN, BILL	TV DIRECTOR-PRODUCER	9255 SUNSET BLVD #706	LOS ANGELES, CA 90069
KERN, PETER	BASEBALL EXECUTIVE	POST OFFICE BOX 1556	ASHEVILLE, NC 28802

KERN, ROBERT J, JR	FILM EDITOR	ACE, 1041 N FORMOSA AVE	WEST HOLLYWOOD, CA 90046
KERN, RONNI	SCREENWRITER	7339 PACIFIC VIEW DR	LOS ANGELES, CA 90068
KERNS, JOANNA	ACTRESS	POST OFFICE BOX 49216	LOS ANGELES, CA 90049
KERNS, SANDRA	ACTRESS	620 RESOLANO DR	PACIFIC PALISADES, CA 90272
KERR, BUDDY	BASEBALL SCOUT	METS, 126TH ST & ROOSEVELT AVE	FLUSHING, NY 11368
KERR, DEBORAH	ACTRESS	LOS MONTEROS	E-29600 MARBELLA, MALA SPAIN
KERR, ELIZABETH	ACTRESS	410 N ROSSMORE AVE	LOS ANGELES, CA 90004
KERR, GLAISTER	FILM EXECUTIVE	1875 CENTURY PARK E #300	LOS ANGELES, CA 90067
KERR, JASON	BASEBALL	POST OFFICE BOX 2887	VERO BEACH, FL 32961
KERR, JEAN	PLAYWRIGHT	1 BEACH AVE	LARCHMONT, NY 10538
KERR, JOHN	SCREENWRITER	7 MILLSIDE, BOURNE END	BUCKS ENGLAND
KERR, JUDY	ACTRESS	6827 PACIFIC VIEW DR	LOS ANGELES, CA 98068
KERR, STEVE	BASKETBALL	POST OFFICE BOX 5000	RICHFIELD, OH 44286
KERR, TIM	HOCKEY	FLYERS, SPECTRUM, PATTISON PL	PHILADELPHIA, PA 19148
KERREY, J ROBERT	U S SENATOR	7602 PACIFIC ST	OMAHA, NE 68114
KERRIDGE, LINDA	ACTRESS-MODEL	9812 W OLYMPIC BLVD	BEVERLY HILLS, CA 90212
KERRIGAN, JOE	BASEBALL COACH	EXPOS, 4545 DE COUBERTIN AVE	MONTREAL, QUE H1V 3P2 CANADA
KERRY, JOHN F	U S SENATOR	10 PARK PLAZA #3220	BOSTON, MA 02116
KERSEY, JEROME	BASKETBALL	700 NE MULTNOMAH ST #600	PORTLAND, OR 97232
KERSHAW, NIK	SINGER	FAA, 1700 BROADWAY, 5TH FLOOR	NEW YORK, NY 10019
KERSHAW, WHITNEY	ACTRESS	LIGHT, 901 BRINGHAM AVE	LOS ANGELES, CA 90049
KERSHNER, IRVIN	FILM DIRECTOR	ROUTE #7, BOX 232	KENT, CT 06757
KERWIN, BRIAN	ACTOR	10402 1/2 WHEATLAND AVE	SUNLAND, CA 91040
KERWIN, JOHN J, JR	TV DIRECTOR	3014 NESTALL RD	LAGUNA BEACH, CA 92651
KESEND, ELLEN	SCREENWRITER	2107 1/2 N HIGHLAND AVE #A	LOS ANGELES, CA 90068
KESHEN, AMY	DIRECTOR	2425 NE 194TH ST	MIAMI, FL 33180
KESLER, HENRY	DIRECTOR	459 LORING AVE	LOS ANGELES, CA 90024
KESSEL, BARNEY	COMPOSER	1125 BEDFORD DR	OKLAHOMA CITY, OK 73116
KESSINGER, KEITH	BASEBALL	POST OFFICE BOX 2001	CEDAR RAPIDS, IA 52406
KESSLER, ALEC	BASKETBALL	MIAMI HEAT, THE MIAMI ARENA	MIAMI, FL 33136
KESSLER, BRUCE	DIRECTOR	4444 VIA MARINA	MARINA DEL REY, CA 90292
KESSLER, JEROME A	CONDUCTOR	1717 N HIGHLAND AVE #305	LOS ANGELES, CA 90028
KESSLER, LYLE	ACTOR-WRITER	11846 VENTURA BLVD #100	STUDIO CITY, CA 91604
KESSLER, RALPH	COMPOSER-CONDUCTOR	14400 ADDISON ST	SHERMAN OAKS, CA 91403
KESSLER, STEPHEN	LYRICIST	ICM, 40 W 57TH ST	NEW YORK, NY 10019
KESSLER, TODD E	WRITER-PRODUCER	DGA, 110 W 57TH ST	NEW YORK, NY 10019
KESSLER, ZALE	ACTOR	1953 HILLCREST RD	LOS ANGELES, CA 90068
KESTELMAN, SARA	ACTRESS	HUTTON, 200 FULHAM RD	LONDON SW14 7AH ENGLAND
KESTNBAUM, ALBERT S	DIRECTOR	2 E LYON FARM	GREENWICH, CT 06830
KETCHAM, HANK	CARTOONIST	POST OFFICE BOX 800	PEBBLE BEACH, CA 93953
KETCHAM, JERRY	DIRECTOR	24348 HIGHLANDER RD	CANOGA PARK, CA 91307
KETCHEN, DOUG	BASEBALL	POST OFFICE BOX 422229	KISSIMMEE, FL 34742
KETCHUM, DAVID	WRITER-PRODUCER	DGA, 7920 SUNSET BLVD, 6TH FL	LOS ANGELES, CA 90046
KEUTER, GREG	BASEBALL TRAINER	POST OFFICE BOX 7005	HUNTINGTON, WV 25775
KEY, JANET	ACTRESS	BROWNE, 13 SAINT MARTINS RD	LONDON SW9 OSP ENGLAND
KEY, JIMMY	BASEBALL	SKYDOME, 300 BREMMER BL #3200	TORONTO, ONT M5V 3B3 CANADA
KEY, TED	CARTOONIST	1694 GLENHARDIE RD	WAYNE, PA 19087
KEY, WADE	BASEBALL	POST OFFICE BOX 1886	COLUMBUS, GA 31902
KEYES, CHIP	TV WRITER	ICM, 8899 BEVERLY BLVD	LOS ANGELES, CA 90048
KEYES, DANIEL F	ACTOR	43 W 93RD ST	NEW YORK, NY 10025
KEYES, DOUG	TV WRITER	ICM, 8899 BEVERLY BLVD	LOS ANGELES, CA 90048
KEYES, EVELYN	ACTRESS	999 N DOHENY DR #506	LOS ANGELES, CA 90069
KEYES, PAUL W	TV WRITER-PRODUCER	10543 VALLEY SPRING LN	NORTH HOLLYWOOD, CA 91602
KEYES, PAUL WILLIAM	TV WRITER-PRODUCER	135 SCREENLAND DR	BURBANK, CA 91505
KEYLOUN, MARK	ACTOR	3500 W OLIVE AVE #1400	BURBANK, CA 91505
KEYS, GARY	DIRECTOR	228 E 89TH ST	NEW YORK, NY 10028
KEYS, JOE	SINGER	PROCESS, 439 WILEY AVE	FRANKLIN, PA 16323
KEYS, RANDOLPH	BASKETBALL	310 N KINGS DR	CHARLOTTE, NC 28204
KEYS, VINCENT R, JR	TV DIRECTOR-PRODUCER	10132 ROVEOUT LN	COLUMBIA, MD 21046
KEYS, WILLIAM	TV WRITER	16633 VENTURA BLVD #1421	ENCINO, CA 91436
KEYSER, BRIAN	BASEBALL	POST OFFICE BOX 360007	BIRMINGHAM, AL 35236
KEYSEY, KEN	AUTHOR	ROUTE 8, BOX 477	PLEASANT HILL, OR 97401
KEZZER, PAULINE	SECRETARY OF STATE	STATE CAPITOL BUILDING	HARTFORD, CT 06106
KHALIFA, SAM	BASEBALL	8825 E 2ND PL	TUCSON, AZ 85710
KHAMBATTA, PERSIS	ACTRESS-MODEL	8019 1/2 MELROSE AVE #3	LOS ANGELES, CA 90046
KHAN, CHAKA	SINGER	POST OFFICE BOX 3125	BEVERLY HILLS, CA 90212
KHAN, PRINCESS YASMIN	PRINCESS	145 CENTRAL PARK W	NEW YORK, NY 10023
KHARIN, SERGEI	HOCKEY	JETS, 15-1430 MAROONS RD	WINNIPEG, MAN R3G 0L5 CANADA
KHMARA, ED	SCREENWRITER	1945 OVERHILL RD	AGOURA, CA 91301
KHOURI, CALLIE	SCREENWRITER	ICM, 8899 BEVERLY BLVD	LOS ANGELES, CA 90048
KHRISTICH, DIMITRI	HOCKEY	JETS, 15-1430 MAROONS RD	WINNIPEG, MAN R3G 0L5 CANADA
KIAM, VICTOR K, II	FOOTBALL EXECUTIVE	PATRIOTS, FOXBORO STADIUM, RT #1	FOXBORO, MA 02035
KIBBE, MICHAEL G	COMPOSER	11311 TIARA ST	NORTH HOLLYWOOD, CA 91601
KIBBE, TOM	ACTOR	31209 PACIFIC COAST HWY	MALIBU, CA 90265
KIBBEE, GORDON	COMPOSER	3815 VALLEY MEADOW RD	ENCINO, CA 91316
KIBERD, JAMES	ACTOR	ABC-TV, "ALL MY CHILDREN"	
		320 W 66TH ST	NEW YORK, NY 10023
KIBLER, JOHN	BASEBALL UMPIRE	3046 SONIA CT	OCEANSIDE, CA 92056
KICK AXE	ROCK & ROLL GROUP	41 BRITAIN ST #200	TORONTO, ONT M5A 1R7 CANADA
KID CREOLE & THE COCONUTS	ROCK & ROLL GROUP	42 MOLYNEAUX ST	LONDON W1 ENGLAND
KID FLASH	RAPPER-RAPWRITER	FAA, 1700 BROADWAY, 5TH FLOOR	NEW YORK, NY 10019
KID N PLAY	RAP DUO-RAPWRITERS	FAA, 1700 BROADWAY, 5TH FLOOR	NEW YORK, NY 10019
KIDD, JOHN	FOOTBALL	POST OFFICE BOX 609609	SAN DIEGO, CA 92160
KIDDER, MARGOT	ACTRESS	ROSENBERG, 8428 MELROSE PL #C	LOS ANGELES, CA 90069
KIDMAN, NICOLE	ACTRESS	12725 VENTURA BLVD #H	STUDIO CITY, CA 91604

KIDWELL, TEX	SINGER-SONGWRITER	POST OFFICE BOX 536	PALM SPRINGS, CA	92263
KIDZ, THE	ROCK & ROLL GROUP	CAPURO, 6 IMPERIAL RD	WORCESTER, MA	01604
KIECKER, DANA	BASEBALL	FENWAY PARK, 4 YAWKEY WY	BOSTON, MA	02215
KIEFER, JACK	GOLFER	PGA SENIORS, 112 T P C BLVD	PONTE VEDRA BEACH, FL	32082
KIEFER, MARK	BASEBALL	2850 W 20TH AVE	DENVER, CO	80211
KIEFER, STEVE	BASEBALL	11822 OLD FASHION	GARDEN GROVE, CA	92640
KIEL, BLAIR	FOOTBALL	PACKERS, 1265 LOMBARDI AVE	GREEN BAY, WI	54307
KIEL, RICHARD	ACTOR	500 GRAND AVE	SOUTH PASADENA, CA	91030
KIEL, SUE	ACTRESS	SHERMAN, 1516 S BEVERLY DR #304	LOS ANGELES, CA	90035
KIELY, JOHN	BASEBALL	POST OFFICE BOX 6212	TOLEDO, OH	43614
KIERLAND, JOSEPH S	WRITER	2621 CRESTON DR	LOS ANGELES, CA	90068
KIESER, ELLWOOD E	WRITER	10750 OHIO AVE	LOS ANGELES, CA	90024
KIFF, KALEENA	ACTRESS	1800 N VINE ST #120	LOS ANGELES, CA	90028
KIFFIN, MONTE	FOOTBALL COACH	N Y JETS, 1000 FULTON AVE	HEMPSTEAD, NY	11550
KIGER, ROBERT	TV DIRECTOR	8928 ELLIS AVE	LOS ANGELES, CA	90034
KIGHTLY, CLARE	ACTRESS	6525 SUNSET BLVD #303	HOLLYWOOD, CA	90028
KIKER, MITCHELL	BASEBALL UMPIRE	POST OFFICE BOX 25010	LITTLE ROCK, AZ	72221
KILBERG, RICHARD	WRI-DIR-PROD	215 W 90TH ST #9-C	NEW YORK, NY	10024
KILBOURNE, WENDY	ACTRESS	9255 SUNSET BLVD #505	LOS ANGELES, CA	90069
KILBURN, TERRY	ACTOR-TEACHER	OAKLAND UNIVERSITY		
		MEADOWBROOK THEATRE		
		WALTON BLVD & SQUIRREL RD	ROCHESTER, MI	48063
KILBY, JOHN	TV DIRECTOR-PRODUCER	3 NOEL HOUSE, THE PARK, EALING	LONDON W5	ENGLAND
KILDEE, DALE	U S CONGRESSMAN	316 W WATER ST	FLINT, MI	48503
KILE, DARRYL	BASEBALL	POST OFFICE BOX 288	HOUSTON, TX	77001
KILEY, TIMOTHY	TV DIRECTOR	1645 SUNSET PLAZA DR	LOS ANGELES, CA	90069
KILGO, RUSTY	BASEBALL	POST OFFICE BOX 6748	ROCKFORD, IL	61125
KILGORE, MERLE	SINGER-SONGWRITER	POST OFFICE BOX 850	PARIS, TN	38242
KILGUS, PAUL	BASEBALL	POST OFFICE BOX 36407	LOUISVILLE, KY	40233
KILLDOZER	ROCK & ROLL GROUP	ROADKILL MUSIC COMPANY		
		933 WILLIAMSON ST	MADISON, WI	53703
KILLEA, KRISTINE	ACTRESS	5455 WILSHIRE BLVD #1406	LOS ANGELES, CA	90036
KILLEA, LUCY	STATE SENATOR	2550 5TH AVE #152	SAN DIEGO, CA	92103
KILLEBREW, HARMON	BASEBALL	POST OFFICE BOX 626	ONTARIO, OR	97914
KILLEY, JEAN-CLAUDE	SKIER	POSTMASTER/GENERAL DELIVERY	73 VAL-D'ISERE	FRANCE
KILLIAN, PHIL	ACTOR	632 W KNOLL DR	LOS ANGELES, CA	90069
KILLILEA, JOHN	BASKETBALL	POST OFFICE BOX 272349	HOUSTON, TX	77277
KILLMOND, FRANK	ACTOR	5087 SAN FELICIANO DR	WOODLAND HILLS, CA	91364
KILMER, VAL	ACTOR	POST OFFICE BOX 362	TESUQUE, NM	87574
KILNER, KEVIN	ACTOR	1999 AVE OF THE STARS #2850	LOS ANGELES, CA	90067
KILPATRICK, JAMES L	WRITER	WHITE WALNUT HILL	WOODVILLE, VA	22749
KILPATRICK, LINCOLN	ACTOR	12834 MC LENNAN AVE	GRANADA HILLS, CA	91344
KILROY, FRANCIS J "BUCKO"	FOOTBALL EXECUTIVE	PATRIOTS, FOXBORO STADIUM, RT #1	FOXBORO, MA	02035
KILROY-SILK, ROBERT	TV HOST	BBC, LIME GROVE	LONDON W12 7RJ	ENGLAND
KIM, EVAN C	ACTOR-WRITER	3218 PECK AVE	SAN PEDRO, CA	90731
KIM, PAUL W	DIRECTOR	215 PARK ROW #19-A	NEW YORK, NY	10038
KIM, WENDELL	BASEBALL-COACH	S F GIANTS, CANDLESTICK PARK	SAN FRANICSCO, CA	94124
KIM, WILLA	COSTUME DESIGNER	13949 VENTURA BLVD #309	SHERMAN OAKS, CA	91423
KIMBALL	SINGER	CAPURSO, 6 IMPERIAL RD	WORCESTER, MA	01604
KIMBALL, BILLY C	COMEDY WRITER	8955 BEVERLY BLVD	WEST HOLLYWOOD, CA	90048
KIMBALL, DAVID A	ACTOR	132 S LASKY DR #B	BEVERLY HILLS, CA	90212
KIMBALL, JEFFREY L	CINEMATOGRAPHER	POST OFFICE BOX 2230	HOLLYWOOD, CA	90078
KIMBALL, KELLY	COSTUME DESIGNER	13949 VENTURA BLVD #309	SHERMAN OAKS, CA	91423
KIMBALL, PETER WILDER	TV DIRECTOR	2008 CLIFTON AVE, 1ST FLOOR	CHICAGO, IL	60614
KIMBALL, WARD	ANIMATION DIRECTOR	8910 ARDENDALE AVE	SAN GABRIEL, CA	91775
KIMBERLIN, KEITH	BASEBALL	TIGERS, 89 WHARNCLIFFE RD N	LONDON, ONT N6H 2A7	CANADA
KIMBLE, BO	BASKETBALL	CLIPPERS, 3939 S FIGUEROA ST	LOS ANGELES, CA	90037
KIMBLE, DARIN	HOCKEY	BLUES, 5700 OAKLAND AVE	SAINT LOUIS, MO	63110
KIMBLE, JOHN	TALENT AGENT	10100 SANTA MONICA BLVD #1600	LOS ANGELES, CA	90067
KIMBLE, ROBERT I	FILM EDITOR	ACE, 1041 N FORMOSA AVE	WEST HOLLYWOOD, CA	90046
KIMBRO, ART	ACTOR	9000 SUNSET BLVD #801	LOS ANGELES, CA	90069
KIMBROUGH, JERRY	SINGER-GUITARIST	2141 BELCOURT AVE #3	NASHVILLE, TN	37212
KIMM, BRUCE	BASEBALL-COACH	RURAL ROUTE 1, BOX 13-A	AMANA, IA	52203
KIMMEL, ALAN	ART DIRECTOR	164 W 79TH ST	NEW YORK, NY	10024
KIMMEL, BRUCE	WRITER-DIRECTOR	12230 OTSEGO ST	NORTH HOLLYWOOD, CA	91607
KIMMEL, DANA	ACTRESS	150 E OLIVE AVE #111	BURBANK, CA	91502
KIMMEL, HENRY HOWARD	DIRECTOR	17215 PALISADES CIR	PACIFIC PALISADES, CA	90272
KIMMEL, JOEL	ACTOR-WRITER	638 N KILKEA DR	LOS ANGELES, CA	90048
KIMMONS, KENNETH	ACTOR	8352 FOUNTAIN AVE #D-1	LOS ANGELES, CA	90069
KINBERG, JUD	WRITER-PRODUCER	10538 WYTON DR	LOS ANGELES, CA	90024
KINCAID, ARON	ACTOR	12307 VENTURA BLVD #C	NORTH HOLLYWOOD, CA	91601
KINCAID, J D	SINGER	OME, 233 W WOODLAND AVE	OTTUMWA, IA	52501
KINCAID, JASON	ACTOR	SAMES-ROLLNICK, 250 W 57TH ST	NEW YORK, NY	10107
KIND, ROSLYN	ACTRESS	8871 BURTON WY #303	LOS ANGELES, CA	90048
KINDLE, ANDY J	DIRECTOR	6321 NEWTOWN CIR #B-1	TAMPA, FL	33615
KINDLER, ROB	CELLIST-AUTOHARPIST	POST OFFICE BOX 2001	SONOMA, CA	95476
KINER, RALPH	BASEBALL-ANNOUNCER	METS, 126TH ST & ROOSEVELT AVE	FLUSHING, NY	11368
KINES, JOE	FOOTBALL COACH	BUCCANEERS, 1 BUCCANEER PL	TAMPA, FL	33607
KING, ALAN	COMEDIAN-ACTOR	888 7TH AVE #3800	NEW YORK, NY	10106
KING, ALANA	ACTRESS	8831 SUNSET BLVD #402	LOS ANGELES, CA	90069
KING, ALBERT	SINGER-GUITARIST	ASSOCIATED BOOKING CORP		
		1995 BROADWAY, 5TH FLOOR	NEW YORK, NY	10023
KING, ANDREA	ACTRESS	1225 SUNSET PLAZA DR #3	LOS ANGELES, CA	
KING, B B	SINGER-GUITARIST	POST OFFICE BOX 16707	MEMPHIS, TN	38131
KING, BEN E	SINGER-SONGWRITER	POST OFFICE BOX 914	NEW YORK, NY	11747

KING, BERNARD	BASKETBALL	BULLETS, 1 HARRY S TRUMAN DR	LANDOVER, MD	20785
KING, BETSY	GOLFER	2750 VOLUSA AVE #B	DAYTON BEACH, FL	32114
KING, BILL	SPORTSCASTER	ATHLETICS'S, OAKLAND COLISEUM	OAKLAND, CA	94621
KING, BILLIE JEAN	TENNIS	101 W 79TH ST	NEW YORK, NY	10024
KING, BOB	BASEBALL SCOUT	POST OFFICE BOX 288	HOUSTON, TX	77001
KING, BRETT	ACTOR	CORAL SANDS HOTEL	HARBOR ISLAND	BAHAMAS
KING, BRUCE	GOVERNOR	SATE CAPITOL BUILDING	SANTE FE, NM	87503
KING, BRUCE E	DIRECTOR	403 W 54TH ST	NEW YORK, NY	10019
KING, CAROLE	SINGER-SONGWRITER	ASHER, 644 N DOHENY DR	LOS ANGELES, CA	90069
KING, CHERYL	COMEDIENNE	POST OFFICE BOX 1556	GAINESVILLE, TN	32602
KING, CHRISTOPHER	TV DIRECTOR	7 SAINT STEPHEN'S TERR	LONDON SW8	ENGLAND
KING, CLAUDE	SINGER	HOT, 306 W CHURCH ST	HORSESHOE BEND, AR	72512
KING, CLYDE	BASEBALL SCOUT	N Y YANKEES, YANKEE STADIUM	BRONX, NY	10451
KING, CORETTA SCOTT	CIVIL RIGHTS LEADER	MARTIN LUTHER KING, JR CENTER		
		FOR NONVIOLENT SOCIAL CHANGE		
		449 AUBURN AVE, NE	ATLANTA, GA	30312
KING, CORINE	SINGER	PROCESS, 439 WILEY AVE	FRANKLIN, PA	16323
KING, DAVID W	TREASURER	SATE CAPITOL BUILDING	SANTE FE, NM	87503
KING, DENIS	COMPOSER	HANCOCK, GREENER HOUSE		
		66-68 HAYMARKET	LONDON SW1Y 4AW	ENGLAND
KING, DEREK	HOCKEY	NASSAU VETS MEMORIAL COLISEUM	UNIONDALE, NY	11553
KING, DON	BOXING PROMOTOR	968 PINEHURST DR	LAS VEGAS, NV	89109
KING, DON	SINGER	POST OFFICE BOX 121089	NASHVILLE, TN	37212
KING, DONALD	TV DIRECTOR	143 W 80TH ST	NEW YORK, NY	10024
KING, DURNFORD	DIRECTOR-PRODUCER	1423 EUCLID ST	SANTA MONICA, CA	90404
KING, ED	FOOTBALL	BROWNS, 80 1ST ST	BEREA, OH	44017
KING, ERIC	BASEBALL	TIGERS, TIGER STADIUM	DETROIT, MI	48216
KING, EVELYN "CHAMPAGNE"	SINGER	156 5TH AVE #623	NEW YORK, NY	10010
KING, FREEMAN	ACTOR	10926 BLUFFSIDE DR #15	STUDIO CITY, CA	91604
KING, GREGORY WESTON	SCREENWRITER	8955 BEVERLY BLVD	WEST HOLLYWOOD, CA	90048
KING, HANK	BASEBALL SCOUT	POST OFFICE BOX 7575	PHILADELPHIA, PA	19101
KING, JACKIE	SINGER	BRAD SIMON, 122 E 57TH ST	NEW YORK, NY	10022
KING, JAMES	SINGER	POST OFFICE BOX 11321		
		FLAGLER STATION	MIAMI, FL	33101
KING, JAMES C, JR	COMPOSER	23047 SCHOOLCRAFT ST	CANOGA PARK, CA	91307
KING, JASON	BASEBALL	525 NW PEACOCK BLVD	PORT SAINT LUCIE, FL	34986
KING, JEFF	BASEBALL	POST OFFICE BOX 7000	PITTSBURGH, PA	15212
KING, JEFF	SCREENWRITER	555 W 57TH ST #1230	NEW YORK, NY	10019
KING, JOE	FOOTBALL	BENGALS, 200 RIVERFRONT STADIUM	CINCINNATI, OH	45202
KING, JOHN	TV DIRECTOR-PRODUCER	CHURCH BARTON, HIGH LITTLETON	AVON BS18 5HQ	ENGLAND
KING, JONATHAN	SINGER-SONGWRITER	JONATHAN KING ENTERPRISES		
		1 WYNDHAM YARD, WYNDHAM PL	LONDON W1H 1AR	ENGLAND
KING, KEVIN	ACTOR	17083 PALISADES CIR	PACIFIC PALISADES, CA	90272
KING, KEVIN	BASEBALL	POST OFFICE BOX 30160	SAN BERNARDINO, CA	92413
KING, KRIS	HOCKEY	POST OFFICE BOX 90111	ARLINGTON, TX	76004
KING, LARRY	BASEBALL EXECUTIVE	POST OFFICE BOX 36407	LOUISVILLE, KY	40233
KING, LARRY	RADIO PERSONALITY	MUTUAL BROADCASTING SYSTEM		
		1755 S JEFFERSON DAVIS HWY	ARLINGTON, VA	22202
KING, LOUIS	CONDUCTOR	3790 HAZELWOOD AVE #4	LAS VEGAS, NV	89109
KING, LYNWOOD B	TV DIRECTOR	12 BEEKMAN PL	NEW YORK, NY	10022
KING, MABEL	ACTRESS	7100 TEESDALE AVE	NORTH HOLLYWOOD, CA	91605
KING, MORGANA	SINGER	1930 CENTURY PARK W #403	LOS ANGELES, CA	90067
KING, PEE WEE	MUSICIAN	240 W JEFFERSON ST	LOUISVILLE, KY	40202
KING, PEE WEE & REDD STEWART	C & W GROUP	TESSIER, 505 CANTON PASS	MADISON, TN	37115
KING, PERRY	ACTOR	3647 WRIGHTWOOD DR	STUDIO CITY, CA	91604
		2157 BRENTWOOD PL	FRAZIER PARK, CA	93225
KING, RICHARD ALAN	TV DIRECTOR	PINE MOUNTAIN CLUB		
KING, RODNEY G	MOTORIST	STEVEN LERMAN, ATTORNEY AT LAW		
		9100 WILSHIRE BLVD #250-W	BEVERLY HILLS, CA	90212
KING, RON	BASEBALL SCOUT	POST OFFICE BOX 7575	PHILADELPHIA, PA	19101
KING, STACEY	BASKETBALL	980 N MICHIGAN AVE #1600	CHICAGO, IL	60611
KING, STEPHEN	NOVELIST	49 FLORIDA AVE	BANGOR, ME	04401
KING, STEVEN M	COMPOSER	2861 PIEDMONT AVE	LA CRESCENTA, CA	91214
KING, TERESA	SINGER	414 12TH ST	SACRAMENTO, CA	95814
KING, THOMAS J	TV DIRECTOR	180 W END AVE #5-M	NEW YORK, NY	10023
KING, TIM	TV DIRECTOR	19 MERCER ST	LONDON WC2	ENGLAND
KING, TOM	TV WRITER	853 7TH AVE #9-A	NEW YORK, NY	10019
KING, TOMMY	ACTOR	80-35 246TH ST	BELLEROSE, L I, NY	11426
KING, TONY	ACTOR	1333 N SWEETZER AVE	LOS ANGELES, CA	90046
KING, VIRGINIA	ACTRESS	57-26 CATALPA AVE	RIDGEWOOD, NY	11385
KING, ZALMAN	ACTOR-WRITER	1393 ROSE AVE	VENICE, CA	90291
KING CONLON, CAMMIE	ACTRESS	511 CYPRESS	FORT BRAGG, CA	95437
KING CRIMSON	ROCK & ROLL GROUP	E G MGMT, 161 W 54TH ST	NEW YORK, NY	10019
KING KOBRA	ROCK & ROLL GROUP	FAA, 1700 BROADWAY, 5TH FLOOR	NEW YORK, NY	10019
KING TEE & MIX MASTER SPADE	RAP DUO-RAPWRITERS	FAA, 1700 BROADWAY, 5TH FLOOR	NEW YORK, NY	10019
KING'S ENGLISH	ROCK & ROLL GROUP	AMERICAN FAMOUS TALENT		
		504 W ARLINGTON PL	CHICAGO, IL	60614
KING-SORENSEN, CAROLE	SINGER-SONGWRITER	15760 VENTURA BLVD #1730	ENCINO, CA	91436
KINGERY, MIKE	BASEBALL	ATHLETICS'S, OAKLAND COLISEUM	OAKLAND, CA	94621
KINGHORN, DAVID J	TV WRITER	151 S EL CAMINO DR	BEVERLY HILLS, CA	90212
KINGS, THE	ROCK & ROLL GROUP	41 BRITAIN ST #200	TORONTO, ONT M5A 1R7	CANADA
KINGSLEY, BEN	ACTOR	NEW PENWORTH HOUSE		
		STRATFORD UPON AVON	WARWICKSHIRE OV3 7QX	ENGLAND
KINGSLEY, DANITZA	ACTRESS-MODEL	10351 SANTA MONICA BLVD #211	LOS ANGELES, CA	90025
KINGSLEY, NEIMAN	ACTOR	102-10 66TH RD #6-C	FOREST HILLS, NY	11375

KINGSLEY, SIDNEY	PLAYWRIGHT	DRAMA GUILD, 234 W 44TH ST	NEW YORK, NY	10036
KINGSLEY-SMITH, TERRENCE	WRITER	1290 1/2 DEVON AVE	LOS ANGELES, CA	90024
KINGSMEN, THE	GOSPEL GROUP	POST OFFICE BOX 22707	NASHVILLE, TN	37212
KINGSMEN, THE	ROCK & ROLL GROUP	2701 NW VAUGHN ST #766	PORTLAND, OR	97210
KINGSON, ROME C	WRITER	3414 S SEPULVEDA BLVD #7	LOS ANGELES, CA	90034
KINGSTON, MARK	ACTOR	DAWSON, 47 COURTFIELD RD #9	LONDON SW7 4DB	ENGLAND
KINGSTON, WILLIAM	FILM EXECUTIVE	39 MARIAN CLOSE, HAYES	MIDDLESEX	ENGLAND
KINGSTON TRIO, THE	VOCAL TRIO	POST OFFICE BOX 34397	SAN DIEGO, CA	92103
KINGWILL, JAY	THEATER PRODUCER	226 W 47TH ST	NEW YORK, NY	10036
KINGWOOD, TYRONE	BASEBALL	TIGERS, 89 WHARNCLIFFE RD N	LONDON, ONT N6H 2A7	CANADA
KINKEAD, MAEVE	ACTRESS	CBS-TV, "THE GUIDING LIGHT"		
		222 E 44TH ST	NEW YORK, NY	10017
KINKS, THE	ROCK & ROLL GROUP	LARRY PAGE, 29 RUSTON MEWS	LONDON W11 1RB	ENGLAND
KINMONT, KATHLEEN	ACTRESS	8551 WONDERLAND AVE	LOS ANGELES, CA	90046
KINMONTH, MARGY	FILM DIRECTOR	FOXTROT FILMS LTD, FLAT 5		
		5 KENSINGTON PARK GARDENS	LONDON W11 3HB	ENGLAND
KINNAMAN, MELANIE	ACTRESS	8721 SANTA MONICA BLVD #21	WEST HOLLYWOOD, CA	90069
KINNEAL, KEN	TALENT AGENT	POST OFFICE BOX 66558	SEATTLE, WA	98166
KINNINMONT, TOM	TV DIRECTOR-PRODUCER	INDEPENDENT, 110 EUSTON RD	LONDON NW1 2DQ	ENGLAND
KINON, RICHARD	DIRECTOR	360 S CRESCENT DR	BEVERLY HILLS, CA	90212
KINSEY, TONY	COMPOSER-ARRANGER	5 THE PENNARDS		
		SUNBURY-ON-THAMES	MIDDLESEX TU16 5JZ	ENGLAND
KINSKEY, LEONID	ACTOR	11652 HUSTON ST	NORTH HOLLYWOOD, CA	91601
KINSKI, NASTASSJA	ACTRESS-MODEL	11 W 81ST ST	NEW YORK, NY	10024
KINZEL, CAROLE	TALENT AGENT	ICM, 8899 BEVERLY BLVD	LOS ANGELES, CA	90048
KINZER, MATTHEW	BASEBALL	5899 N 400 WEST	UNIONDALE, IN	46791
KIPILA, JEFF	BASEBALL	POST OFFICE BOX 12	MIDLAND, TX	79702
KIPNESS, JOSEPH	THEATER PRODUCER	KIPPYS PRODS, 144 W 52ND ST	NEW YORK, NY	10019
KIPPER, BOB	BASEBALL	TWINS, 501 CHICAGO AVE S	MINNEAPOLIS, MN	55415
KIPPER, BOB	BASEBALL	17 HILLCREST DR	AURORA, IL	60506
KIPPYCASH, JOHN	TV DIRECTOR-PRODUCER	24 ROBERT ST	PARSIPPANY, NJ	07054
KIRBY, ALEX	TV DIRECTOR	ANCHORAGE, WOODLANDS RD		
		PORTISHEAD	BRISTOL	ENGLAND
KIRBY, BRUCE	ACTOR	629 N ORLANDO AVE #3	LOS ANGELES, CA	90048
KIRBY, BRUNO	ACTOR	MTA, 9320 WILSHIRE BL, 3RD FL	BEVERLY HILLS, CA	90212
KIRBY, DURWARD	SCREENWRITER	3714 1/2 BERRY DR	STUDIO CITY, CA	91604
KIRBY, JOHN	ACTOR	4317 AVOCADO ST	LOS ANGELES, CA	90027
KIRBY, JOHN	SINGER	102 E EXCHANGE AVE #300	FORT WORTH, TX	76106
KIRBY, WAYNE	BASEBALL	4385 TUTT BLVD	COLORADO SPRINGS, CO	80922
KIRCHENBAUER, BILL	COMEDIAN	4850 RIVERTON AVE	NORTH HOLLYWOOD, CA	91607
KIRCHER, VALERIE	WRITER-PRODUCER	1556 RIDGEWAY DR	GLENDALE, CA	91202
KIRCHNER, DAVID	SINGER-SONGWRITER	106 BUTLEIGH CT	GOODLETTSVILLE, TN	37072
KIRGO, DIANA	TV WRITER	14504 GREENLEAF ST	SHERMAN OAKS, CA	91403
KIRGO, JULIE	TV WRITER-PRODUCER	KAUFMAN, 14540 GREENLEAF ST	SHERMAN OAKS, CA	91403
KIRK, BEN	MUSIC ARRANGER	3028 VISTA VALLEY CT	NASHVILLE, TN	37218
KIRK, CHUCK	BASEBALL	POST OFFICE BOX 4488	WINSTON-SALEM, NC	27115
KIRK, JAY	COMEDIAN	CLOUSHER, 193 KONHAUS RD	MECHANICSBURG, PA	17055
KIRK, PETER	BASEBALL EXECUTIVE	POST OFFICE BOX 230	HAGERSTOWN, MD	21740
KIRK, PHYLLIS	ACTRESS	BUSH, 11687 BELLAGIO RD #3	LOS ANGELES, CA	90049
KIRK, PHYLLIS	ACTRESS	1225 SUNSET PLAZA DR #1	LOS ANGELES, CA	90069
KIRK, RANDY	FOOTBALL	BROWNS, 80 1ST ST	BEREA, OH	44017
KIRK, REBA V	COMPOSER	10059 GLEN GROVE CT	ELK GROVE, CA	95624
KIRK, TOMMY	ACTOR	833 S BEACON AVE	LOS ANGELES, CA	90017
KIRKCONNELL, CLARE	ACTRESS	515 S IRVING BLVD	LOS ANGELES, CA	90020
KIRKES, SHIRLEY	ACTRESS	11620 TEXAS AVE	LOS ANGELES, CA	90025
KIRKLAND, DENNIS	TV DIRECTOR-PRODUCER	55 SAINT JAMES'S AVE		
		HAMPTON HILL	MIDDLESEX TW12 1HL	ENGLAND
KIRKLAND, SALLY	ACTRESS	1930 OCEAN AVE #11	SANTA MONICA, CA	90405
KIRKMAN, TERRY R	WRITER	1089 S GENESEE AVE	LOS ANGELES, CA	90019
KIRKPATRICK, DAVID	SCREENWRITER	8955 BEVERLY BLVD	WEST HOLLYWOOD, CA	90048
KIRKPATRICK, JEANE	JOURNALIST	6812 GRANBY ST	BETHESDA, MD	20817
KIRKWOOD, GENE	FILM PRODUCER	1221 STONE CANYON RD	LOS ANGELES, CA	90077
KIRKWOOD, JAMES	PLAYWRIGHT	58 OYSTER SHORES RD	EAST HAMPTON, NY	11937
KIRKWOOD, JAMES	WRITER	484 W 43RD ST #45-R	NEW YORK, NY	10036
KIRSCH, PAUL	BASEBALL COACH	POST OFFICE BOX 1659	PORTLAND, OR	97207
KIRSCH, PEGGY	GOLFER	2750 VOLUSA AVE #B	DAYTON BEACH, FL	32114
KIRSCHBAUM, BRUCE	TV WRITER	1617 N ORANGE GROVE AVE	LOS ANGELES, CA	90046
KIRSCHBAUM, GLENN	TV PRODUCER	9242 BEVERLY DR #200	BEVERLY HILLS, CA	90210
KIRSCHEN, ALAN	ACTOR	3410 PAUL AVE	BRONX, NY	10468
KIRSH, JILL	ACTRESS	6100 SHADYGLADE AVE	NORTH HOLLYWOOD, CA	91606
KIRSHENBAUM, SUSAN	TV WRITER	100 W 12TH ST	NEW YORK, NY	10011
KIRSTEN, DOROTHY	SOPRANO	FRENCH, 271 TAVISTOCK AVE	LOS ANGELES, CA	90049
KIRTLAND, LOUISE	ACTRESS	ANSONIA, 73RD ST & BROADWAY		
		SUITE #1714	NEW YORK, NY	10023
KIRWAN, MARY JO	ACTRESS	PACIFIC, 515 N LA CIENEGA BLVD	LOS ANGELES, CA	90048
KISCH, ANTHONY	COMEDY WRITER	POST OFFICE BOX 114	HYDE PARK, NY	12538
KISCH, JOHN DUKE	PHOTOGRAPHER-AUTHOR	POST OFFICE BOX 114	HYDE PARK, NY	12538
KISELSTEIN, SHELLY L	WRITER	232 S LASKY DR	BEVERLY HILLS, CA	90212
KISER, GARLAND	BASEBALL	2501 ALLEN AVE, SE	CANTON, OH	44707
KISER, TERRY	ACTOR-COMEDIAN	5750 WILSHIRE BLVD #512	LOS ANGELES, CA	90036
KISER, VIRGINIA	ACTRESS	9200 SUNSET BLVD #710	LOS ANGELES, CA	90069
KISH, JIMMY	SINGER-GUITARIST	200 DEDHAM DR	NASHVILLE, TN	37214
KISH, JOE	RECORD EXECUTIVE	1508 HARLEM ST #206	MEMPHIS, TN	38174
KISHON, EPHRAIM	FILM DIRECTOR	POST OFFICE BOX 229	JERUSALEM	ISRAEL
KISIO, KELLY	HOCKEY	POST OFFICE BOX 90111	ARLINGTON, TX	76004

KISON, BRUCE	BASEBALL-COACH	POST OFFICE BOX 419969	KANSAS CITY, MO	64141
KISS	ROCK & ROLL GROUP	20 E 68TH ST #6-C	NEW YORK, NY	10021
KISSEL, HOWARD	DRAMA CRITIC	N Y DAILY NEWS, 220 E 42ND ST	NEW YORK, NY	10017
KISSELL, GEORGE	BASEBALL-EXECUTIVE	250 STADIUM PLAZA	ST LOUIS, MO	63102
KISSINGER, DR HENRY	AUTHOR	435 E 52ND ST	NEW YORK, NY	10022
KITAEN, TAWNY	ACTRESS	KOHNER, 9169 SUNSET BLVD	LOS ANGELES, CA	90069
KITAY, DAVID	COMPOSER	6525 SUNSET BLVD #402	HOLLYWOOD, CA	90028
KITCHEN, MICHAEL	ACTOR	MARKHAM AND FROGGATT, LTD		
		JULIAN HOUSE, 4 WINDMILL ST	LONDON W1P 1HF	ENGLAND
KITE, GREG	BASKETBALL	POST OFFICE BOX 76	ORLANDO, FL	32802
KITE, TOM	GOLFER	POST OFFICE BOX 109601	PALM BCH GARDENS, FL	33418
KITEI, MICHAEL	TV DIRECTOR	5526 GALBRAITH RD	CINCINNATI, OH	45236
KITSON, KEN	ACTOR	AIM, 5 DENMARK ST	LONDON WC2H 8LP	ENGLAND
KITT, EARTHA	SINGER-ACTRESS	1524 LABAIG ST	LOS ANGELES, CA	90028
KITTLE, HUB	BASEBALL-COACH	3801 RICHEY RD	YAKIMA, WA	98902
KITTLE, RON	BASEBALL	728 N OLD SUMAN RD	VALPARAISO, IN	46383
KITTLESON, JOHN R	FILM DIRECTOR	2401 JOLLY DR	BURBANK, CA	91504
KITTMAN, MARVIN	TV CRITIC	NEWSDAY, 1500 BROADWAY	NEW YORK, NY	10036
KIVEL, BARRY	ACTOR	307 E 44TH ST #1412	NEW YORK, NY	10017
KIZZIAH, DAREN	BASEBALL	633 JESSAMINE ST	KNOXVILLE, TN	37917
KJAR, JOAN	ACTRESS	10653 RIVERSIDE DR	TOLUCA LAKE, CA	91602
KJAR, TYLER	TALENT AGENT	10653 RIVERSIDE DR	TOLUCA LAKE, CA	91602
KJELLAN, ALF	ACTOR-DIRECTOR	12630 MULHOLLAND DR	BEVERLY HILLS, CA	90210
KLAGES, BILL	CINEMATOGRAPHER	7715 SUNSET BLVD #150	LOS ANGELES, CA	90046
KLANE, BOB	WRITER-PRODUCER	DGA, 7920 SUNSET BLVD, 6TH FL	LOS ANGELES, CA	90046
KLASE, IRVING E	CONDUCTOR	248 S PALM DR	BEVERLY HILLS, CA	90212
KLATMAN, CAROL	TV WRITER	2351 OCEAN AVE	VENICE, CA	90291
KLATMAN, CHRISTOPHER J	COMPOSER	2351 OCEAN AVE	MARINA DEL REY, CA	90292
KLAUBER, DONALD	TV EXECUTIVE	1290 AVE OF THE AMERICAS #430	NEW YORK, NY	10019
KLAUBER, GERTAN	ACTOR	21 YALE CT, HONEYBOURNE RD	LONDON NW6	ENGLAND
KLAUS, RICHARD	BASEBALL SCOUT	S F GIANTS, CANDLESTICK PARK	SAN FRANICSCO, CA	94124
KLAWITTER, JOHN	FILM DIRECTOR	4917 MEDINA DR	WOODLAND HILLS, CA	91364
KLECZKA, GERALD D	U S CONGRESSMAN	5032 W FOREST HOME AVE	MILWAUKEE, WI	53219
KLEFFMAN, ERVIN H	CONDUCTOR	1100 S GARFIELD AVE	ALHAMBRA, CA	91801
KLEIN, ARTHUR W	TV DIRECTOR	ABC-TV, 39 W 66TH ST	NEW YORK, NY	10023
KLEIN, BARUCH	COMPOSER	484 INVERNESS DR	PACIFICA, CA	94044
KLEIN, BILL	TV EXECUTIVE	CBS-TV, 6121 SUNSET BLVD	LOS ANGELES, CA	90028
KLEIN, CALVIN	FASHION DESIGNER	205 W 39TH ST	NEW YORK, NY	10018
KLEIN, CARRIE	ACTRESS	SELECTED, 3575 W CAHUENGA BLVD	LOS ANGELES, CA	90068
KLEIN, DENNIS	WRITER-PRODUCER	4915 SAN FELICIANO DR	WOODLAND HILLS, CA	91364
KLEIN, JAIME B	SCREENWRITER	8955 BEVERLY BLVD	WEST HOLLYWOOD, CA	90048
KLEIN, JOE	BASEBALL EXECUTIVE	POST OFFICE BOX 419969	KANSAS CITY, MO	64141
KLEIN, JORDAN N	DIRECTOR	POST OFFICE BOX 1270	BELLEVIEW, FL	32620
KLEIN, JOSEPH M	CONDUCTOR	28 W 87TH ST	NEW YORK, NY	10024
KLEIN, KENNETH R	CONDUCTOR	1 FOREST AVE	GLEN COVE, NY	11542
KLEIN, LARRY	TV WRITER-PRODUCER	3003 W OLIVE AVE	BURBANK, CA	91510
KLEIN, MARTY	TALENT AGENT	9000 SUNSET BLVD #1200	LOS ANGELES, CA	90069
KLEIN, MELISSA	TV DIRECTOR-PRODUCER	344 E 85TH ST #2-F	NEW YORK, NY	10028
KLEIN, RICHARD	COLUMNIST	5700 WILSHIRE BLVD #120	LOS ANGELES, CA	90036
KLEIN, ROBERT	COMED-ACT-WRI	EDGEHILL SLEEPY HOLLOW RD	BRIARCLIFF MANOR, NY	10510
KLEIN, VIRGINIA DOODY	COLUMNIST	7720 EL CAMINO REAL #2-C	RANCHO LA COSTA, CA	92008
KLEINE, JOE	BASKETBALL	151 MERRIMAC ST	BOSTON, MA	02114
KLEINER, HARRY	SCREENWRITER	258 S SPALDING DR	BEVERLY HILLS, CA	90212
KLEINERMAN, ISAAC	DIRECTOR-PRODUCER	11 SANDUSKY RD	NEW CITY, NY	10956
KLEINMAN, IRA S	TV DIRECTOR	10 COLUMBIA RD	ARDSLEY, NY	10502
KLEINMAN, LEONARD	BASEBALL EXECUTIVE	N Y YANKEES, YANKEE STADIUM	BRONX, NY	10451
KLEINMAN, MAGGIE	SCREENWRITER	SMITH, 121 N SAN VICENTE BLVD	BEVERLY HILLS, CA	90211
KLEINMAN, MARSHA	CASTING DIRECTOR	704 N GARDNER ST #2	LOS ANGELES, CA	90046
KLEISER, RANDAL	FILM WRITER-DIRECTOR	2233 NICHOLS CANYON RD	LOS ANGELES, CA	90046
KLEMME, BRENDA	ACTRESS	1930 CENTURY PARK W #403	LOS ANGELES, CA	90067
KLEMMER, JOHN	SAXOPHONIST	ALIVE ENTERTAINMENT AGENCY		
		1775 BROADWAY, 7TH FLOOR	NEW YORK, NY	10019
KLEMP, CARDINAL JOSEF	CARIDNAL	SEKRETARIAT PRYMASA		
		KOLSKI, UL MIODOWA 17	PL-00-583 WARSAW	POLAND
KLEMPERER, WERNER	ACTOR	44 W 62ND ST, 10TH FLOOR	NEW YORK, NY	10023
KLENCK, MARGARET L	ACTRESS	MORES, ORT & SENDER		
		1 BROADCAST PLAZA, BOX 87	MERRICK, NY	11566
KLENDER, RICHARD	SINGER	805 FOREST RIDGE DR #108	BEDFORD, TX	76022
KLESH, RAY	BASEBALL EXECUTIVE	POST OFFICE BOX 1621	GREAT FALLS, MT	59403
KLETTER, RICHARD C	SCREENWRITER	401 9TH ST	SANTA MONICA, CA	90402
KLEVEN, MAX	WRITER-PRODUCER	POST OFFICE BOX 2406	OLYMPIC VALLEY, CA	95730
KLIAFAS, STEVE	BASEBALL	POST OFFICE BOX 10031	BAKERSFIELD, CA	93389
KLICK, MICHAEL J	DIRECTOR	1711 S CREST DR	LOS ANGELES, CA	90035
KLIMA, PETR	HOCKEY	OILERS, NORTHLANDS COLISEUM	EDMONTON, ALTA T5B 4M9	CANADA
KLINCHOCK, MARY ANNE	GOLFER	2750 VOLUSA AVE #B	DAYTON BEACH, FL	32114
KLINE, ANTON D	WRITER	6064 ROD AVE	WOODLAND HILLS, CA	91367
KLINE, DOUG	BASEBALL	POST OFFICE BOX 1211	NORFOLK, VA	23502
KLINE, HERBERT	WRITER-PRODUCER	1280 N LAUREL AVE #12	HOLLYWOOD, CA	90046
KLINE, J W	SINGER	5625 "O" STREET BLDG #7	LINCOLN, NE	68510
KLINE, KEVIN	ACTOR	136 E 57TH ST #1001	NEW YORK, NY	10022
KLINE, KRIS	BASEBALL SCOUT	POST OFFICE BOX 2000	ANAHEIM, CA	92803
KLINE, LINDA B	TV WRITER	115 CENTRAL PARK W	NEW YORK, NY	10023
KLINE, RICHARD	ACTOR	14322 MULHOLLAND DR	LOS ANGELES, CA	90077
KLINE, RICHARD H	CINEMATOGRAPHER	POST OFFICE BOX 2230	HOLLYWOOD, CA	90078
KLINE, RICHARD S	DIRECTOR	DGA, 7920 SUNSET BLVD, 6TH FL	LOS ANGELES, CA	90046

KLINE, ROBERT D	PRODUCER	101 OCEAN AVE #D-3	SANTA MONICA, CA	90402
KLINE, STEVE E	TV WRITER	R/W/G, 8428 MELROSE PL #C	LOS ANGELES, CA	90069
KLINE, WAYNE	TV WRITER	7245 FRANKLIN AVE #14	LOS ANGELES, CA	90046
KLING, CAROL	FILM CRITIC	POST OFFICE BOX 70	LAS VEGAS, NV	89125
KLING, WOODY	TV WRITER	R/W/G, 8428 MELROSE PL #C	LOS ANGELES, CA	90069
KLINGBELL, CHUCK	FOOTBALL	DOLPHINS, 2269 NW 199TH ST	MIAMI, FL	33056
KLINGENSMITH, REX	SINGER	PROCESS, 439 WILEY AVE	FRANKLIN, PA	16323
KLINGER, JUDSON	SCREENWRITER	8955 BEVERLY BLVD	WEST HOLLYWOOD, CA	90048
KLINGER, TONY	WRITER-PRODUCER	19 WATFORD RD, RADLET	HERTS	ENGLAND
KLINGHOFFER, MICHAEL	TV DIRECTOR-PRODUCER	MTV, 1775 BRODWAY	NEW YORK, NY	10019
KLINK, JOE	BASEBALL	ATHLETICS'S, OAKLAND COLISEUM	OAKLAND, CA	94621
KLOESS, JOE N	CONDUCTOR	17114 SADDLEHILL RD	COLBERT, WA	99005
KLONOSKI, JASON	BASEBALL	POST OFFICE BOX 5645	ORLANDO, FL	32855
KLOPPENBURG, BOB	BASKETBALL COACH	POST OFFICE BOX C-900911	SEATTLE, WA	98109
KLOSS, CARL W	DIRECTOR	RURAL DELIVERY #5		
		ECHO VALLEY RD	NEWTOWN, CT	06470
KLOUS, PATRICIA	ACTRESS	18096 KAREN DR	ENCINO, CA	91316
KLUG, SCOTT	U S CONGRESSMAN	16 N CARROLL ST #600	MADISON, WI	53703
KLUGE, MATT	BASEBALL	POST OFFICE BOX 30160	SAN BERNARDINO, CA	92413
KLUGER, GARRY	ACTOR	11650 HAYNES AVE #4	NORTH HOLLYWOOD, CA	91606
KLUGMAN, ADAM	ACTOR	22548 W PACIFIC COAST HWY #110	MALIBU, CA	90265
KLUGMAN, DEBORAH	TV WRITER	22548 W PACIFIC COAST HWY #110	MALIBU, CA	90265
KLUGMAN, DON B	WRITER-PRODUCER	1446 N WELLS ST	CHICAGO, IL	60610
KLUGMAN, JACK	ACTOR-WRITER	22548 W PACIFIC COAST HWY #110	MALIBU, CA	90265
KLUGMAN, LYNN	DIRECTOR-PRODUCER	2624 AVE "M"	BROOKLYN, NY	11210
KLUNIS, TOM	ACTOR	145 W 45TH ST #1204	NEW YORK, NY	10036
KLVAC, DAVID	BASEBALL	POST OFFICE BOX 10213	LYNCHBURG, VA	24506
KMAK, JOE	BASEBALL	2850 W 20TH AVE	DENVER, CO	80211
KNABENSHUE, CHRIS	BASEBALL	POST OFFICE BOX 2769	HUNTSVILLE, AL	35804
KNACKERT, BRENT	BASEBALL	POST OFFICE BOX 4756	JACKSONVILLE, FL	32201
KNAPP, DAVID	ACTOR	1662 MARMONT AVE	LOS ANGELES, CA	90069
KNAPP, FRANKLIN	SINGER-GUITARIST	232 WELCH RD	NASHVILLE, TN	37211
KNAPP, GREGORY	SCREENWRITER	8955 BEVERLY BLVD	WEST HOLLYWOOD, CA	90048
KNAPP, LILO	COMPOSER	570 N ROSSMORE AVE #605	LOS ANGELES, CA	90004
KNAPP, MIKE	BASEBALL	CUBS, 2ND & RIVERSIDE DR	DES MOINES, IA	50309
KNAPTON, ROBYN	TV WRITER	10390 WILSHIRE BLVD #707	LOS ANGELES, CA	90024
KNATZ, NIKITA	FILM DIRECTOR	11241 SUNSHINE TERR	STUDIO CITY, CA	91604
KNAUP, HENRY E	DIRECTOR	145 E 16TH ST	NEW YORK, NY	10003
KNEALE, NIGEL	SCREENWRITER	8955 BEVERLY BLVD	WEST HOLLYWOOD, CA	90048
KNEE DEEP IN GRASS	C & W GROUP	POST OFFICE BOX 25371	CHARLOTTE, NC	28212
KNEF, HILDERGARD	ACTRESS-SINGER	MARIA-THERESIA-STR	8000 MUNICH-BOGENHAUSE	GERMANY
KNELL, CATALAINE	ACTRESS	1236 N FLORES ST	LOS ANGELES, CA	90069
KNEPPER, BOB	BASEBALL	2045 OAKHILL RD	ROSEBURG, OR	97470
KNEUER, CAMEO YVETTE	FITNESS EXPERT	2554 LINCOLN BLVD #640	MARINA DEL REY, CA	90291
KNIEVEL, EVIL	DAREDEVIL	9960 YORK ALPHA DR	NORTH ROYALTON, OH	44133
KNIFE, DENNIS H	DIRECTOR	41-14 247TH ST	DOUGLASTON, NY	11363
KNIFFIN, ALEX	ACTOR	ABC-TV, "LOVING"		
		320 W 66TH ST, STUDIO 23	NEW YORK, NY	10023
KNIFFIN, CHUCK	BASEBALL COACH	POST OFFICE BOX 3566	WEST PALM BEACH, FL	33402
KNIGHT, ADELINE	DIRECTOR	157-20 90TH ST	HOWARD BEACH, NY	11414
KNIGHT, BILLY	BASKETBALL	PACERS, 300 E MARKET ST	INDIANAPOLIS, IN	46204
KNIGHT, CHRISTOPHER	ACTOR	280 S BEVERLY DR #400	BEVERLY HILLS, CA	90212
KNIGHT, GENE	ACTOR	1717 N HIGHLAND AVE #701	LOS ANGELES, CA	90028
KNIGHT, GLADYS & THE PIPS	VOCAL GROUP	SIDNEY A SEIDENBERG, INC		
		1414 AVE OF THE AMERICAS	NEW YORK, NY	10019
KNIGHT, HOLLY	SINGER-SONGWRITER	1585 STONE CANYON RD	LOS ANGELES, CA	90077
KNIGHT, JEAN	SINGER	POST OFFICE BOX 19004	NEW ORLEANS, LA	70179
KNIGHT, JUNE	ACTRESS	BUEHLER, 3760 EUREKA DR	STUDIO CITY, CA	91604
KNIGHT, MICHAEL E	ACTOR	9301 WILSHIRE BLVD #312	BEVERLY HILLS, CA	90210
KNIGHT, NEGELE	BASKETBALL	SUNS, 2910 N CENTRAL AVE	PHOENIX, AZ	85012
KNIGHT, PAUL	TV PRODUCER	9 LITTLE COMMON, STANMORE	MIDDLESEX	ENGLAND
KNIGHT, RAY	BASEBALL-ANNOUNCER	2308 TARA DR	ALBANY, GA	31707
KNIGHT, ROBERT M	COMPOSER-CONDUCTOR	2417 WELLINGTON ST	DENTON, TX	76201
KNIGHT, ROBIN	ACTRESS	3575 W CAHUENGA BLVD #125	LOS ANGELES, CA	90068
KNIGHT, SHIRLEY	ACTRESS	SEE - KNIGHT-HOPKINS, SHIRLEY		
KNIGHT, TONYA	BODYBUILDER	POST OFFICE BOX 5123	SANTA MONICA, CA	90405
KNIGHT, TUESDAY	ACTRESS	11712 MOORPARK ST #204	STUDIO CITY, CA	91604
KNIGHT, VICKI	SINGER	POST OFFICE BOX 171132	NASHVILLE, TN	37217
KNIGHT, VIRGIL	FOOTBALL COACH	PACKERS, 1265 LOMBARDI AVE	GREEN BAY, WI	54307
KNIGHT, VIVA	DIRECTOR-PRODUCER	9760 CHARLEVILLE BLVD	BEVERLY HILLS, CA	90212
KNIGHT, WILLIAM	ACTOR	11846 VENTURA BLVD #100	STUDIO CITY, CA	91604
KNIGHT PULLMAN, KEISHA	ACTRESS	POST OFFICE BOX 866	TEANECK, NJ	07666
KNIGHT-HOPKINS, SHIRLEY	ACTRESS	POST OFFICE BOX 69405	LOS ANGELES, CA	90069
KNIGHTS, ROBERT	FILM-TV DIRECTOR	49 WHITEHALL PARK	LONDON N19 3TW	ENGLAND
KNITTERS, THE	ROCK & ROLL GROUP	POST OFFICE BOX 48888	LOS ANGELES, CA	90048
KNOBLAUCH, CHUCK	BASEBALL	TWINS, 501 CHICAGO AVE S	MINNEAPOLIS, MN	55415
KNOBLAUH, JAY	BASEBALL	1155 W MOUND ST	COLUMBUS, OH	43223
KNOBLOCK, FRED	SINGER	151 S EL CAMINO DR	BEVERLY HILLS, CA	90212
KNOBLOCK, KEVIN	TV DIRECTOR	ENTERTAINMENT TONIGHT		
		PARAMOUNT TELEVISION		
		5555 MELROSE AVE	LOS ANGELES, CA	90038
KNODE, CHARLES	COSTUME DESIGNER	38 WATER RD	LONDON SW15 2LJ	ENGLAND
KNOLL, CATHERINE BAKER	TREASURER	STATE CAPITOL BUILDING	HARRISBURG, PA	17120
KNOOP, BOBBY	BASEBALL-COACH	POST OFFICE BOX 2000	ANAHEIM, CA	92803
KNOP, PATRICIA LOUISIANA	SCREENWRITER	8955 BEVERLY BLVD	WEST HOLLYWOOD, CA	90048

KNOPF, CHRISTOPHER	WRITER	910 25TH ST	SANTA MONICA, CA 90403
KNOPFLER, MARK	SINGER-SONGWRITER	DAMAGE MGMT, 10 SOUTHWICK MEWS	LONDON ENGLAND
KNORR, RANDY	BASEBALL	CHIEFS, MAC ARTHUR STADIUM	SYRACUSE, NY 13208
KNOTT, JOHN W, JR	NEWS CORRESPONDENT	ABC NEWS, 1717 DE SALES ST, NW	WASHINGTON, DC 20036
KNOTT, ROBERT E	DIRECTOR-PRODUCER	133 WILLOW TURN #B	MOUNT LAUREL, NJ 08054
KNOTTS, DON	ACTOR	1854 S BEVERLY GLEN #402	LOS ANGELES, CA 90025
KNOWLES, DAROLD	BASEBALL-COACH	POST OFFICE BOX 10336	CLEARWATER, FL 34617
KNOWLES, KATHY	CASTING DIRECTOR	9044 HOLLYWOOD HILLS RD	LOS ANGELES, CA 90046
KNOWLES, PATRIC	ACTOR	6243 RANDI AVE	WOODLAND HILLS, CA 91367
KNOX, ALEXANDER	ACTOR	8 HARLEY ST	LONDON W1N 2AB ENGLAND
KNOX, BUDDY	SINGER-SONGWRITER	BOX 244, DOMINION CITY	MANITOBA ROA OHO CANADA
KNOX, CHUCK	FOOTBALL COACH	SEAHAWKS, 11220 NE 53RD ST	KIRKLAND, WA 98033
KNOX, DONALD E	DIRECTOR	1770 MEADOWLARK RD	EAGAN, MN 55122
KNOX, ELYSE	ACTRESS	HARMON, 320 N GUNSTON AVE	LOS ANGELES, CA 90049
KNOX, IAN	FILM DIRECTOR	24-C DURHAM TERR	LONDON W2 5PB ENGLAND
KNOX, KENNY	GOLFER	POST OFFICE BOX 109601	PALM BCH GARDENS, FL 33418
KNOX, RICHARD	TV DIRECTOR	226 NEWPORT AVE	TAPPAN, NY 10983
KNUCKLEHEADS, THE	ROCK & ROLL GROUP	SEE - JERRY & THE KNUCKLEHEADS	
KNUDSON, JIM	BASEBALL TRAINER	POST OFFICE BOX 11002	CHATTANOOGA, TN 37401
KNUDSON, MARK	BASEBALL	STARS, 850 LAS VEGAS BLVD N	LAS VEGAS, NV 89101
KOBA, ALEX	ACTOR	12700 VENTURA BLVD #350	STUDIO CITY, CA 91604
KOBAL, JOHN C	WRITER	184 DRUMMOND ST, 4TH FLOOR	LODNON NW1 3HP ENGLAND
KOBE, GAIL	TV PRODUCER	CBS-TV, 7800 BEVERLY BLVD	LOS ANGELES 90036
KOBER, CHARLES M	TV DIRECTOR	361 MIRA MAR AVE	LONG BEACH, CA 90803
KOBER, JEFF	ACTOR	308 N ARDEN BLVD	LOS ANGELES, CA 90004
KOBER, MARTA	ACTRESS	183 N MARTEL AVE #260	LOS ANGELES, CA 90036
KOBETITSCH, KEVIN	BASEBALL	POST OFFICE BOX 464	APPLETON, WI 54912
KOBLASA, GEORGE	DIRECTOR	POST OFFICE BOX 7116	MAMMOTH LAKES, CA 93546
KOBLENTZ, DAVE	BASEBALL SCOUT	INDIANS, CLEVELAND STADIUM	CLEVELAND, OH 44114
KOBZA, GREG	BASEBALL	POST OFFICE BOX 8550	STOCKTON, CA 95208
KOCH, EDDIE B	COMPOSER	7009 JUMILLA AVE	CANOGA PARK, CA 91306
KOCH, EDWARD	MAYOR-AUTHOR	1290 AVE OF THE AMERICAS	NEW YORK, NY 10104
KOCH, HOWARD W, SR	DIRECTOR-PRODUCER	704 N CRESCENT DR	BEVERLY HILLS, CA 90212
KOCH, HOWARD W, JR	FILM PRODUCER	1156 BEVERWILL DR	LOS ANGELES, CA 90035
KOCH, KENNETH	DIRECTOR	32100 BEACHFRONT LN	WESTLAKE VILLAGE, CA 91361
KOCH, MARKUS	FOOTBALL	POST OFFICE BOX 17247 (DULLES)	WASHINGTON, DC 20041
KOCHAN, JOHN R	DIRECTOR	300 N STATE ST	CHICAGO, IL 60610
KOCUR, JOEY	HOCKEY	POST OFFICE BOX 90111	ARLINGTON, TX 76004
KOEHLER, MAURICE T L	CONDUCTOR	140 BAYONA DR	SANTA CRUZ, CA 95060
KOELLING, BRIAN	BASEBALL	POST OFFICE BOX 2001	CEDAR RAPIDS, IA 52406
KOENEKAMP, FRED J	CINEMATOGRAPHER	9756 SHOSHINE AVE	NORTHRIDGE, CA 91324
KOENIG, LAIRD	SCREENWRITER	1429 TIGERTAIL RD	LOS ANGELES, CA 90049
KOENIG, WALTER	ACTOR-WRITER	POST OFFICE BOX 4395	NORTH HOLLYWOOD, CA 91601
KOENTOPP, KEVIN	BASEBALL EXECUTIVE	STARS, 850 LAS VEGAS BLVD N	LAS VEGAS, NV 89101
KOENTOPP, LARRY	BASEBALL EXECUTIVE	STARS, 850 LAS VEGAS BLVD N	LAS VEGAS, NV 89101
KOERNER, KENNETH	TV WRITER-DIRECTOR	4311 ENSENADA DR	WOODLAND HILLS, CA 91364
KOFOED, BART	BASKETBALL	GOLDEN STATE WARRIORS	
		OAKLAND COLISEUM ARENA	
		NIMITZ FWY & HEGENBERGER RD	OAKLAND, CA 94621
KOGA, HIDE	BASEBALL MANAGER	POST OFFICE BOX 4370	SALINAS, CA 93912
KOGAN, MILT	ACTOR	6735 FOREST LAWN DR #313	HOLLYWOOD, CA 90068
KOGAN, PATRICA	TV DIRECTOR-PRODUCER	202-B SPRING ST	NEW YORK, NY 10012
KOGEN, ARNOLD	TV WRITER	4250 BONAVITA DR	ENCINO, CA 91436
KOGEN, JAY	TV PRODUCER	UTA, 9560 WILSHIRE BL, 5TH FL	BEVERLY HILLS, CA 90212
KOHAN, ALAN BUZ	TV WRITER-LYRICIST	2095 LOMA VISTA DR	BEVERLY HILLS, CA 90210
KOHAN, SILVIA	SINGER-GUITARIST	POST OFFICE BOX 9388	STANFORD, CA 94305
KOHL, HERB	BASKETBALL EXECUTIVE	BRADLEY CENTER, 1001 N 4TH ST	MILWAUKEE, WI 53203
KOHL, HERBERT	U S SENATOR	205 E WISCONSIN AVE	MILWAUKEE, WI 53202
KOHL, JIM	BASEBALL	14100 SIX MILE CYPRESS PKWY	FORT MYERS, FL 33912
KOHLER, IRENE	PIANIST	28 CASTELNAU	LONDON SW13 9RU ENGLAND
KOHLER, PAUL	COMEDIAN	10404 GREENHAVEN PARKWAY	BRECKSVILLE, OH 44141
KOHLER, SUSAN	ACTRESS	SIEGEL, 7551 SUNSET BLVD #204	LOS ANGELES, CA 90046
KOHLRUST, ROBERT	DIRECTOR-PRODUCER	19625 SUNNYSIDE	SAINT CLAIR SHORES, MI 48080
KOHN, DANIEL F	DIRECTOR	47 HITCHING POST LN	GLEN COVE, NY 11542
KOHN, HOWARD	SCREENWRITER	8955 BEVERLY BLVD	WEST HOLLYWOOD, CA 90048
KOHN, JONATHAN	FILM EXEC-WRITER	1354 N WETHERLY DR	LOS ANGELES, CA 90069
KOHN, JOSEPH R	DIRECTOR	29 W 64TH ST	NEW YORK, NY 10023
KOHN, KARL G	COMPOSER-CONDUCTOR	674 W 10TH ST	CLAREMONT, CA 91711
KOHNER, PANCHO	FILM WRITER-PRODUCER	901 STONE CANYON RD	LOS ANGELES, CA 90077
KOHNER, PASHE	FILM PRODUCER	1527 TIGERTAIL RD	LOS ANGELES, CA 90049
KOHNER, SUSAN	ACTRESS	710 PARK AVE #14-E	NEW YORK, NY 10021
KOHNERT, MARY	ACTRESS	9200 SUNSET BLVD #710	LOS ANGELES, CA 90069
KOHNO, TAKAYUKI	BASEBALL COACH	POST OFFICE BOX 4370	SALINAS, CA 93912
KOLB, JON	FOOTBALL COACH	STEELERS, 300 STADIUM CIR	PITTSBURGH, PA 15212
KOLB, PETER	BASEBALL TRAINER	2850 W 20TH AVE	DENVER, CO 80211
KOLBE, JIM	U S CONGRESSMAN	1661 N SWAN #112	TUCSON, AZ 85711
KOLBE, WINRICH	TV DIRECTOR	23012 LEONORA DR	WOODLAND HILLS, CA 91367
KOLDE, BERT	BASKETBALL EXECUTIVE	700 NE MULTNOMAH ST #600	PORTLAND, OR 97232
KOLE, NELSON	COMPOSER	2412 VISTA COLINA ST	HENDERSON, NV 89015
KOLLAR, BILL	FOOTBALL COACH	FALCONS, SUWANEE RD AT I-85	SUWANEE, GA 30174
KOLLEK, TEDDY	MAYOR	22 JAFFA RD	JERUSALEM ISRAEL
KOLLER, FRED	SINGER-SONGWRITER	5100 NEVADA AVE	NASHVILLE, TN 37209
KOLO, EDDIE	BASEBALL SCOUT	REDS, 100 RIVERFRONT STADIUM	CINCINNATI, OH 45202
KOLSTAD, ALLEN C	LT GOVERNOR	STATE CAPITOL BUILDING	HELENA, MT 59620
KOLTER, JOE	U S CONGRESSMAN	1322 7TH AVE	BEAVR FALLS, PA 15010

KOMACK, JAMES	ACT-WRI-DIR	617 N BEVERLY DR	BEVERLY HILLS, CA	90210
KOMAROV, SHELLEY	COSTUME DESIGNER	POST OFFICE BOX 5617	BEVERLY HILLS, CA	90213
KOMMINSK, BRAD	BASEBALL	CANADIANS, 4601 ONTARIO ST	VANCOUVER, BC V5V 3H4	CANADA
KOMRADA, JOHN, JR	MUSIC ARRANGER	920 FOREST ACRES CT	NASHVILLE, TN	37220
KONCAK, JON	BASKETBALL	1 CNN CENTER #405, SOUTH TOWER	ATLANTA, GA	30303
KONE, RUSSELL J	DIRECTOR	18 LINCOLN AVE	ARDSLEY, NY	10502
KONEMANN, TROY	BASEBALL	POST OFFICE BOX 3004	SPRINGFIELD, IL	62708
KONEY, CHUCK	BASEBALL SCOUT	FENWAY PARK, 4 YAWKEY WY	BOSTON, MA	02215
KONIECZKI, DOMINIC	BASEBALL	POST OFFICE BOX 661	KENOSHA, WI	53141
KONKEY, DAVID	BASEBALL EXECUTIVE	POST OFFICE BOX 4218	SOUTH BEND, IN	46634
KONNER, JOAN	TV WRITER-DIRECTOR	SNEDENS LANDING	PALISADES, NY	10964
KONNER, LAWRENCE M	SCREENWRITER	514 PALISADES AVE	SANTA MONICA, CA	90402
KONOPKI, MARK	BASEBALL	POST OFFICE BOX 10213	LYNCHBURG, VA	24506
KONRAD, DOROTHY	ACTRESS	10650 MISSOURI AVE #2	LOS ANGELES, CA	90025
KONROYD, STEVE	HOCKEY	BLACKHAWKS, 1800 W MADISON ST	CHICAGO, IL	60612
KONVITZ, JEFFREY	SCREENWRITER	12660 MULHOLLAND DR	BEVERLY HILLS, CA	90210
KOOCK, GUICH	ACTOR	2029 CENTURY PARK E #600	LOS ANGELES, CA	90067
KOOL MOE DEE	RAPPER-RAPWRITER	FAA, 1700 BROADWAY, 5TH FLOOR	NEW YORK, NY	10019
KOON, DEAN	SINGER-GUITARIST	1101 PRESIDENT	TUPELO, MS	38801
KOONCE, CALVIN, SR	BASEBALL SCOUT	POST OFFICE BOX 90111	ARLINGTON, TX	76004
KOONTZ, DAVID	SCREENWRITER	4630 MIRADOR PL	TARZANA, CA	91356
KOONTZ, DEAN R	WRITER	POST OFFICE BOX 5686	ORANGE, CA	92613
KOONTZ, ROD	BODYBUILDER	POST OFFICE BOX 2288	WESTMINISTER, CA	92683
KOOPMANN, WERNER	DIRECTOR	220 E 23RD ST	NEW YORK, NY	10010
KOOSMAN, JERRY	BASEBALL-COACH	RURAL ROUTE 2, BOX 67-E	CHASKA, MN	55318
KOOSMAN, JERRY	BASEBALL-COACH	POST OFFICE BOX 328	PITTSFIELD, MA	01202
KOPEL, HAL	DIRECTOR	3312 N 28TH ST	MC ALLEN, TX	78501
KOPELL, BERNIE	ACTOR-WRITER	19413 OLIVOS DR	TARZANA, CA	91356
KOPETSKI, MIKE	U S CONGRESSMAN	530 CENTER ST #340, NE	SALEM, OR	97301
KOPINS, KAREN	ACTRESS	10989 BLUFFSIDE DR	STUDIO CITY, CA	91604
KOPLIK, JIM	TALENT AGENT	310 MADISON AVE #804	NEW YORK, NY	10017
KOPLIN, MERT	TV WRITER-PRODUCER	THE CORPORATION FOR		
		ENTERTAINMENT & LEARNING		
		515 MADISON AVE	NEW YORK, NY	10022
KOPP, FREDERICK E	COMPOSER-CONDUCTOR	102 N GARFIELD PL #D	MONROVIA, CA	91016
KOPPEL, NURIT	ACTRESS	2160 CENTURY PARK E	LOS ANGELES, CA	90067
KOPPEL, TED	BROADCAST JOURNALIST	ABC NEWS, 1717 DE SALES ST, NW	WASHINGTON, DC	20036
KOPPLE, BARBARA J	DIRECTOR-PRODUCER	CABIN, 58 E 11TH ST	NEW YORK, NY	10003
KOPPY, MICHAEL	DIRECTOR	138 8TH ST	SAN FRANCISCO, CA	94103
KORBIN, JOYCE	ACTRESS	24 W 69TH ST	NEW YORK, NY	10023
KORD, KAZIMIERZ	CONDUCTOR	ICM, 40 W 57TH ST	NEW YORK, NY	10019
KORDA, DAVID	FILM PRODUCER	1-11 HAY HILL, BERKELEY SQ	LONDON W1H 7LF	ENGLAND
KORDA, RONALD STEVEN	TV EXECUTIVE	NBC-TV, 30 ROCKEFELLER PLAZA	NEW YORK, NY	10112
KORDIC, JOHN	HOCKEY	JETS, 15-1430 MAROONS RD	WINNIPEG, MAN R3G OL5	CANADA
KORENEK, ANDREW	BASEBALL-SCOUT	S F GIANTS, CANDLESTICK PARK	SAN FRANICSCO, CA	94124
KORENEK, TOM	BASEBALL SCOUT	S F GIANTS, CANDLESTICK PARK	SAN FRANICSCO, CA	94124
KORF, MIA	ACTRESS	ABC-TV, "ONE LIFE TO LIVE"		
		56 W 66TH ST	NEW YORK, NY	10023
KORMAN, HARVEY	ACTOR-DIRECTOR	1136 STRADELLA RD #302	LOS ANGELES, CA	90077
KORMAN, TOM	TALENT AGENT	9000 SUNSET BLVD #1200	LOS ANGELES, CA	90069
KORN, ARTUR	SINGER	NEIDHAUDP 22	A-3W KLOSTERNEULUNG	AUSTRIA
KORN, HAL	CONDUCTOR	987 SCHUMACHER DR	LOS ANGELES, CA	90048
KORN, PETER JONA	COMPOSER	GABRIEL-MAX STRASSE 9	8000 MUNCHEN 90	GERMANY
KORN, SUSAN	ACTRESS	9200 SUNSET BLVD #625	LOS ANGELES, CA	90069
KORNET, FRANK	BASKETBALL	BRADLEY CENTER, 1001 N 4TH ST	MILWAUKEE, WI	53203
KORNFELD, CRAIG	BASEBALL SCOUT	METS, 126TH ST & ROOSEVELT AVE	FLUSHING, NY	11368
KOROT, ALLA	ACTRESS	NBC-TV, "ANOTHER WORLD"		
		1268 E 14TH ST	BROOKLYN, NY	11230
KORS, R J	FOOTBALL	N Y JETS, 1000 FULTON AVE	HEMPSTEAD, NY	11550
KORTY, JOHN	FILM DIRECTOR	200 MILLER AVE	MILL VALLEY, CA	94941
KOS, JEFREY A	TV DIRECTOR	7842 W OAKTON	NILES, IL	60648
KOSAR, BERNIE	FOOTBALL	BROWNS, 80 1ST ST	BEREA, OH	44017
KOSC, GREG	BASEBALL UMPIRE	3900 FERN RD	MEDINA, OH	44256
KOSCIAK, JOHN	BASEBALL SCOUT	POST OFFICE BOX 2000	SAN DIEGO, CA	92112
KOSCO, BRYN	BASEBALL	POST OFFICE BOX 15757	HARRISBURG, PA	17105
KOSENSKI, JOHN	BASEBALL	POST OFFICE BOX 2785	LAKELAND, FL	33806
KOSLECK, MARTIN	ACTOR	1026 N LAUREL AVE	LOS ANGELES, CA	90046
KOSLOFSKI, KEVIN	BASEBALL	POST OFFICE BOX 3665	OMAHA, NE	68103
KOSLOW, LAUREN	ACTRESS	2020 AVE OF THE STARS #500	LOS ANGELES, CA	90067
KOSLOW, RON	SCREENWRITER	8955 BEVERLY BLVD	WEST HOLLYWOOD, CA	90048
KOSLOW-SCHILLACE, ZAK	ACTOR	CBS-TV, "THE BOLD & BEAUTIFUL"		
		7800 BEVERLY BLVD #3371	LOS ANGELES, CA	90036
KOSMINSKY, PETER	TV DIRECTOR	PETERS, FRASER & DUNLOP, LTD		
		5TH FLOOR, THE CHAMBERS		
		CHELSEA HARBOUR, LOT RD	LONDON SW10 OXF	ENGLAND
KOSOFSKY, JOEL M	TV PRODUCER	JENAD PRODS, 16 MONROE DR	MARLBORO, NJ	07746
KOSOWICZ, EDWARD S	DIRECTOR	35 W DEERHAVEN RD	MAHWAH, NJ	07430
KOSS, ALAN	ACTOR	8015 VARNA AVE	VAN NUYS, CA	91402
KOSS, ALLEN	TV PRODUCER	1888 CENTURY PARK E #1100	LOS ANGELES, CA	90067
KOSSOFF, ADAM	FILM WRITER-DIRECTOR	SILVER FILMS, 28 QUERNMORE RD	LONDON N4 4QX	ENGLAND
KOSSOFF, DAVID	ACTOR-WRITER	45 ROE GREEN CLOSE		
		COLLEGE LN, HATFIELD	HERTS	ENGLAND
KOSTAL, IRWIN J	CONDUCTOR	3149 DONA SUSANA DR	STUDIO CITY, CA	91604
KOSTE, WALTER	DIRECTOR	2541 MEADE CT	ANN ARBOR, MI	48105
KOSTER, HENRY	DIRECTOR-PRODUCER	3101 VILLAGE #3	CAMARILLO, CA	93010

KOSTICH, BILL	BASEBALL	POST OFFICE BOX 9194	HAMPTON, VA	23670
KOSTMAYER, PETER H	U S CONGRESSMAN	150 S MAIN ST	DOYLESTOWN, PA	18901
KOSTROFF, LARRY	DIRECTOR	2210 3RD ST	SANTA MONICA, CA	90405
KOSTYK, DENNIS M	DIRECTOR	6636 BROOKMONT TERR	NASHVILLE, TN	37205
KOTCH, DARRIN	BASEBALL	POST OFFICE BOX 6748	ROCKFORD, IL	61125
KOTCHEFF, TED	FILM DIRECTOR	13451 FIRTH DR	BEVERLY HILLS, CA	90210
KOTCHMAN, TOM	BASEBALL MGR-SCOUT	HAWKS, 5600 N GLENWOOD	BOISE, ID	83714
KOTERBA, JEFF	CARTOONIST	K C STAR, 1729 GRAND AVE	KANSAS CITY, MO	64108
KOTERO, APOLLONIA	ACTRESS	8200 WILSHIRE BLVD #218	BEVERLY HILLS, CA	90212
KOTES, CHRISTOPHER	BASEBALL	POST OFFICE BOX 1110	MYRTLE BEACH, SC	29578
KOTITE, RICH	FOOTBALL COACH	EAGLES, BROAD ST & PATTISON AVE	PHILADELPHIA, PA	19148
KOTLISKY, MARGE	ACTRESS	GEDDES, 8457 MELROSE PL #200	LOS ANGELES, CA	90069
KOTLOWITZ, ROBERT	TV EXECUTIVE	WNET-TV, 356 W 58TH ST	NEW YORK, NY	10019
KOTTKE, LEO	SINGER-GUITARIST	POST OFFICE BOX 7308	CARMEL, CA	93923
KOTTO, YAPHET	ACTOR	1930 CENTURY PARK W #403	LOS ANGELES, CA	90067
KOTTON, STEVE A	DIRECTOR	1947 GLENDON AVE #4	LOS ANGELES, CA	90025
KOTZWINKLE, WILLIAM	AUTHOR	THE BERKELEY PRESS		
		200 MADISON AVE	NEW YORK, NY	10016
KOUF, M JAMES, JR	WRITER-PRODUCER	2161 BASIL LN	LOS ANGELES, CA	90077
KOUFAX, SANDY	BASEBALL	POST OFFICE BOX BB	CARPINTERIA, CA	93013
KOUNAS, TONY	BASEBALL	POST OFFICE BOX 30160	SAN BERNARDINO, CA	92413
KOURIS, PETER C	DIRECTOR-PRODUCER	9 IVY TRAIL	ATLANTA, GA	30342
KOURY, REX	COMPOSER-CONDUCTOR	5370 HAPPY PINES DR	FORESTHILL, CA	95631
KOUT, WENDY	TV WRITER	842 N BEVERLY GLEN BLVD	LOS ANGELES, CA	90077
KOVAC, RON	SCREENWRITER	8955 BEVERLY BLVD	WEST HOLLYWOOD, CA	90048
KOVACH, TY	BASEBALL	POST OFFICE BOX 3452	KINSTON, NC	28502
KOVACK MEHTA, NANCY	ACTRESS	SEE - METHA, NANCY KOVACK		
KOVACS, MARK G	CONDUCTOR	1364 PARK AVE	LONG BEACH, CA	90804
KOVE, MARTIN	ACTOR	8705 WONDERLAND PARK AVE	LOS ANGELES, CA	90046
KOVIC, RON	SCREENWRITER-AUTHOR	507 N LUCIA AVE	REDONDO BEACH, CA	90277
KOWALCHUK, MEL	BASEBALL EXECUTIVE	10233 96TH AVE	EDMONTON, ALB TK5 0A5	CANADA
KOWALKOWSKI, SCOTT	FOOTBALL	EAGLES, BROAD ST & PATTISON AVE	PHILADELPHIA, PA	19148
KOWALL, RONALD	ACTOR-TV WRITER	4544 LAUREL GROVE AVE	STUDIO CITY, CA	91604
KOWALSKI, FRANCIS LOUIS	WRITER-PRODUCER	7847 RANCHITO AVE	PANORAMA CITY, CA	91402
KOWALSKI, L BERNARD	TV DIRECTOR-PRODUCER	17524 COMMUNITY ST	NORTHRIDGE, CA	91324
KOWITZ, BRIAN	BASEBALL	POST OFFICE BOX 16683	GREENVILLE, SC	29606
KOZ, DAVE	SAXOPHONIST	6255 SUNSET BLVD #917	HOLLYWOOD, CA	90028
KOZAK, HARLEY JANE	ACTRESS	8730 SUNSET BLVD #480	LOS ANGELES, CA	90069
KOZAK, JIM	FILM CRITIC	BOXOFFICE, 1800 N HIGHLAND AVE	LOS ANGELES, CA	90028
KOZAK, SCOTT	FOOTBALL	OILERS, 6910 FANNIN ST	HOUSTON, TX	77070
KOZERSKI, BRUCE	FOOTBALL	BENGALS, 200 RIVERFRONT STADIUM	CINCINNATI, OH	45202
KOZLOWSKI, GLEN	FOOTBALL	BEARS, 250 N WASHINGTON RD	LAKE FOREST, IL	60045
KOZLOWSKI, LINDA	ACTRESS	1109 TOWER RD	BEVERLY HILLS, CA	90210
KOZLOWSKI, MADELINE ANN	COSTUME DESIGNER	968 SIDONIA ST	ENCINITAS, CA	92024
KOZOLL, MICHAEL	TV WRITER	1726 CRISLER WY	LOS ANGELES, CA	90069
KRABBE, JEROEN	ACTOR	107 VAN EEGHENSTAAT	1071 EZ AMSTERDAM	HOLLAND
KRACHMALNICK, SAMUEL J	CONDUCTOR	11944 BRIARVALE LN	STUDIO CITY, CA	91604
KRAEMER, JOE	BASEBALL	POST OFFICE BOX 12	MIDLAND, TX	79702
KRAFT, ANNE	ACTRESS	46 W 95TH ST	NEW YORK, NY	10025
KRAFT, GABRIELLE	AUTHORESS	POCKET BOOKS (SIMON & SCHUSTER)		
		1230 AVE OF THE AMERICAS	NEW YORK, NY	10020
KRAFT, GENE	PRODUCER	7556 WOODROW WILSON DR	LOS ANGELES, CA	90046
KRAFT, ROBERT M	COMPOSER	3432 LA SOMBRA DR	LOS ANGELES, CA	90068
KRAFT, SUZANNE STANFORD	PRODUCER	7556 WOODROW WILSON DR	LOS ANGELES, CA	90046
KRAFT, WILLIAM	COMPOSER	6957 CAMROSE DR	LOS ANGELES, CA	90068
KRAGEN, GREG	FOOTBALL	BRONCOS, 13655 BRONCOS PKWY	ENGLEWOOD, CO	80112
KRAGEN, KEN	TALENT AGENT	1112 N SHERBOURNE DR	LOS ANGELES, CA	90069
KRAHENBUHL, KEN	BASEBALL	POST OFFICE BOX 4488	WINSTON-SALEM, NC	27115
KRAININ, JULIAN	WRITER-PRODUCER	67-38 FLEET ST	FOREST HILLS, NY	11375
KRAKOW, HOWARD	DIRECTOR	3267 LEDGEWOOD DR	HOLLYWOOD, CA	90068
KRAKOWER, GARY	ACTOR	823 N GENESEE AVE	LOS ANGELES, CA	90046
KRAKOWSKI, JANE	ACTRESS	EUE/SCREEN GEMS, 222 E 44TH ST	NEW YORK, NY	10017
KRAMER, DANIEL	DIRECTOR	110 W 86TH ST	NEW YORK, NY	10024
KRAMER, DEBORAH LA GORCE	COSTUME DESIGNER	POST OFFICE BOX 1166	PACIFIC PALISADES, CA	90272
KRAMER, ERIK	FOOTBALL	LIONS, 1200 FEATHERSTONE RD	PONTIAC, MI	48432
KRAMER, ERWIN	DIRECTOR	5 N CLOVER DR	GREAT NECK, NY	11021
KRAMER, JACK	TENNIS	470 N BOWLING GREEN WY	LOS ANGELES, CA	90049
KRAMER, JAMES G	TV DIRECTOR	167 CROSBY ST	NEW YORK, NY	10012
KRAMER, KATHARINE	SINGER	12386 RIDGE CIR	LOS ANGELES, CA	90049
KRAMER, KENNETH L	WRITER-PRODUCER	8955 BEVERLY BLVD	WEST HOLLYWOOD, CA	90048
KRAMER, KIMBERLEE	ACTRESS	9105 CARMELITA AVE #1	BEVERLY HILLS, CA	90210
KRAMER, LINDA O	TV PRODUCER	THE PRODUCTION COMPANY, LTD		
		72 GUTZON BORGIUM RD	STAMFORD, CT	06903
KRAMER, LOUIS	DIRECTOR	333 CABRILLO ST #D	COSTA MESA, CA	92627
KRAMER, RANDY	BASEBALL	POST OFFICE BOX 3690, STA "B"	CALGARY, ALB T2B 4M4	CANADA
KRAMER, REMI	FILM WRITER-DIRECTOR	ROUTE #2, BOX 262-B	SANDPOINT, ID	83864
KRAMER, RICHARD	TV PRODUCER	CAA, 9830 WILSHIRE BLVD	BEVERLY HILLS, CA	90212
KRAMER, RICHARD L	SCREENWRITER	8495 FOUNTAIN AVE E #1	LOS ANGELES, CA	90069
KRAMER, RONALD H	TV DIRECTOR	103 HIGH ST	ASHLAND, OR	97520
KRAMER, SEARLE	WRITER	277 S SPALDING DR #R-4	BEVERLY HILLS, CA	90212
KRAMER, STANLEY	FILM DIRECTOR	12386 RIDGE CIR	LOS ANGELES, CA	90049
KRAMER, STEPFANIE	ACTRESS-DIRECTOR	8455 BEVERLY BLVD #505	LOS ANGELES, CA	90048
KRAMER, SUSAN J	DIRECTOR	DGA, 110 W 57TH ST	NEW YORK, NY	10019
KRAMER, TERRY ALLEN	THEATER PRODUCER	711 5TH AVE	NEW YORK, NY	10022
KRAMER, TOM	BASEBALL	4385 TUTT BLVD	COLORADO SPRINGS, CO	80922

SPECIAL SUBSCRIPTION OFFER

6 BIG ISSUES FOR JUST $19.95

- ***Eight Price Guides In One —*** *Baseball, Football, Basketball, Hockey, Other Sports, Non-Sport Cards, Premium Cards, Draft Picks & Prospects Too!*
- ***Eighteen FREE Full-Color ,*** *Super-Glossy, Foil Stamped Collectors Cards In Every Issue!*

SUBSCRIBE NOW
SAVE UP TO 41%
(Off Newsstand Price)

1-800-486-1310

Mail To:
10300 Watson Road
St. Louis, MO 63127

Allan Kaye's
SPORTS CARDS
NEWS & PRICE GUIDES

Mail To:
10300 Watson Road
St. Louis, MO 63127

"Money Back If Not Satisfied"

- ☐ 6 Months (6 Issues) $19.95
- ☐ 1 Year (12 Issues) $39.95
- ☐ 2 Years (24 Issues) $74.95
- ☐ 3 Years (36 Issues) $104.95
- ☐ Canada, Foreign (12 Issues) $79.95

Your Name ____________ Age ____
Store Name ____________
Address ____________
City ________ State ____ Zip ____
Daytime Phone No. ____________

☐ New Subscription ☐ Renewal

Payment enclosed via: ☐ Check or Money Order ☐ VISA/Mastercard

Card # ☐☐☐☐-☐☐☐☐-☐☐☐☐-☐☐☐☐

Signature ____________ Exp. ______

Name	Occupation	Address	City, State	ZIP
KRANE, JONATHAN	FILM PRODUCER	1888 CENTURY PARK E #1616	LOS ANGELES, CA	90067
KRANITZ, IAN D	COMPOSER	6400 FRANKLIN AVE #115	LOS ANGELES, CA	90028
KRANITZ, RICK	BASEBALL COACH	CUBS, 2ND & RIVERSIDE DR	DES MOINES, IA	50309
KRASIK, ROY	BASEBALL EXECUTIVE	ORIOLE PARK, 333 W CAMDEN ST	BALTIMORE, MD	21201
KRASNER, JEFFREY	DIRECTOR	55 HICKS ST #22	BROOKLYN, NY	11201
KRASNY, PAUL	TV DIRECTOR	3620 GOODLAND DR	STUDIO CITY, CA	91604
KRATCH, BOB	FOOTBALL	N Y GIANTS, GIANTS STADIUM	EAST RUTHERFORD, NJ	07073
KRATOCHVIL, FRANK	DIRECTOR	15935 BENT TREE FOREST CIR	DALLAS, TX	75248
KRAUS, JOE	PUBLISHER-EDITOR	POST OFFICE BOX 55328	STOCKTON, CA	95205
KRAUSE, CHARLES	BASEBALL EXECUTIVE	BREWERS, 201 S 46TH ST	MILWAUKEE, WI	53214
KRAUSE, JERRY	BASKETBALL EXECUTIVE	980 N MICHIGAN AVE #1600	CHICAGO, IL	60611
KRAUSE, KENNETH	MUSIC ARRANGER	8209 BRENTVIEW CT	BRENTWOOD, TN	37027
KRAUSE, RON	BASEBALL	POST OFFICE BOX 3566	WEST PALM BEACH, FL	33402
KRAUSS, MARVIN A	THEATER PRODUCER	250 W 52ND ST	NEW YORK, NY	10019
KRAUSS, PERRY	DIRECTOR-PRODUCER	22460 KEARNY ST	WOODLAND HILLS, CA	91364
KRAVEC, KEN	BASEBALL SCOUT	POST OFFICE BOX 419969	KANSAS CITY, MO	64141
KRAVETZ, WALTER	DIRECTOR	DGA, 110 W 57TH ST	NEW YORK, NY	10019
KRAVITZ, LENNY	SINGER-SONGWRITER	450 BROOM ST	NEW YORK, NY	10013
KRAVITZ, SY	ACTOR	4061 S CLOVERDALE AVE	LOS ANGELES, CA	90008
KRAWITZ, HERMAN E	TV PRODUCER	333 E 57TH ST	NEW YORK, NY	10022
KRAY, WALTER	ACTOR	1528 ENSLEY AVE	LOS ANGELES, CA	90024
KRAYER, JIM	WRITER-PRODUCER	12 DAILEY DR	CROTON-ON-HUDSON, NY	10520
KREBS, DAVID	THEATER PRODUCER	65 W 55TH ST #306	NEW YORK, NY	10019
KREBS, NANCY	ACTRESS	8004 LONG HILL RD	PASADENA, MD	21122
KREBS, SUSAN	ACTRESS	2709 1/2 STRONGS DR	VENICE, CA	90291
KREDENSER, PETER	PHOTOGRAPHER	2551 ANGELO DR	LOS ANGELES, CA	90077
KREINBERG, STEVE	TV WRITER	1645 COURTNEY AVE #10	LOS ANGELES, CA	90046
KREINDEL, MITCH	WRITER	1322 3/4 N LUCILE AVE	LOS ANGELES, CA	90026
KREISMAN, STUART GLENN	TV WRITER	672 KELTON AVE #4	LOS ANGELES, CA	90024
KREITSEK, HOWARD B	TV WRITER	6740 HILLPARK DR #203	LOS ANGELES, CA	90068
KREKEL, TIM & THE SLUGGERS	ROCK & ROLL GROUP	2308 21ST AVE S #9	NASHVILLE, TN	37212
KREMENLIEV, BORIS A	COMPOSER-CONDUCTOR	10507 TROON AVE	LOS ANGELES, CA	90064
KREMER, JOE	BASEBALL EXECUTIVE	POST OFFICE DRAWER 1218	ZEBULON, NC	27597
KREMERS, JIMMY	BASEBALL	1501 W 16TH ST	INDIANAPOLIS, IN	46202
KREMPEL, PETER W	DIRECTOR	18865 RIVERSIDE DR	BIRMINGHAM, MI	48009
KRENCHICKI, WAYNE	BASEBALL MANAGER	POST OFFICE BOX 855	BELOIT, WI	53511
KREPPEL, KATE WRIGHT	ACTRESS-DANCER	15300 KILLION ST	VAN NUYS, CA	91401
KREPPEL, PAUL	ACTOR	14300 KILLION ST	VAN NUYS, CA	91401
KREPS, WILLIAM H	DIRECTOR	4200 LAND GREEN ST	ROCKVILLE, MD	20853
KRESH, PAUL	WRITER	225 PARK AVE S	NEW YORK, NY	10003
KRESKIN	PSYCHIC	201 N ROBERTSON BLVD #A	BEVERLY HILLS, CA	90211
KRESKY, CAROLYN	WRITER-PRODUCER	207 W 106TH ST	NEW YORK, NY	10025
KRETCHMER, JOHN TED	DIRECTOR	4833 WILLOWCREST AVE	NORTH HOLLYWOOD, CA	91601
KRETZ, STEVE	BASEBALL EXECUTIVE	POST OFFICE BOX 855	BELOIT, WI	53511
KREUTER, CHAD	BASEBALL	TIGERS, TIGER STADIUM	DETROIT, MI	48216
KREUZER, TERESE LOEB	WRI-DIR-PROD	EDGEWARE ASSOC, 150 9TH AVE	NEW YORK, NY	10011
KREVOKUCH, JIM	BASEBALL	POST OFFICE BOX 3746, HILL STA	AUGUSTA, GA	30904
KRICHEFSKI, BERNARD	TV PRODUCER	PETERS, FRASER & DUNLOP, LTD		
		5TH FLOOR, THE CHAMBERS		
		CHELSEA HARBOUR, LOT RD	LONDON SW10 OXF	ENGLAND
KRIEG, DAVE	FOOTBALL	SEAHAWKS, 11220 NE 53RD ST	KIRKLAND, WA	98033
KRIEGER, HAROLD	FILM DIRECTOR	1090 FIREPLACE RD	EAST HAMPTON, NY	11937
KRIEGER, ROBBY	GUITARIST-SONGWRITER	2548 HUTTON DR	BEVERLY HILLS, CA	90210
KRIEGER, ROBIN	ACTRESS	1717 N HIGHLAND AVE #701	LOS ANGELES, CA	90028
KRIEGER, STU	SCREENWRITER	3650 MEIER ST	LOS ANGELES, CA	90066
KRIEGLER, PHILIP	TV EXECUTIVE	ABC-TV, 4151 PROSPECT AVE	LOS ANGELES, CA	90027
KRIEGSMAN, MICHAEL	DIRECTOR	ABACAB, 123 W 44TH ST	NEW YORK, NY	10036
KRIGE, ALICE	ACTRESS	CAA, 9830 WILSHIRE BLVD	BEVERLY HILLS, CA	90212
KRIKES, PETER	WRITER	736 SANCHEZ ST	MONTEBELLO, CA	90640
KRIKHAM, WILLARD E	DIRECTOR	3549 N KNOLL DR	HOLLYWOOD, CA	90068
KRIM, ARTHUR B	FILM EXECUTIVE	1875 CENTURY PARK E #300	LOS ANGELES, CA	90067
KRIMMER, WORTHAM	ACTOR	ABC-TV, "ONE LIFE TO LIVE"		
		56 W 66TH ST	NEW YORK, NY	10023
KRING, STEVE	BASEBALL SCOUT	REDS, 100 RIVERFRONT STADIUM	CINCINNATI, OH	45202
KRINSKI, SANFORD	TV WRITER	674 VIA SANTA YNEZ	PACIFIC PALISADES, CA	90272
KRIS KROSS	RAP DUO	7436 SW 117TH AVE #209	MIAMI, FL	33183
KRISH, JOHN	FILM WRITER-DIRECTOR	ICM, 388-396 OXFORD ST	LONDON W1	ENGLAND
KRISTAL, SYLVIA	ACTRESS	8955 NORMA PL	LOS ANGELES, CA	90069
KRISTEN, ILENE	ACTRESS	1650 BROADWAY #302	NEW YORK, NY	10019
KRISTEN, MARTA	ACTRESS	3800 BARHAM BLVD #303	LOS ANGELES, CA	90068
KRISTOFFERSON, KRIS	SINGER-ACTOR-WRITER	3179 SUMACK RIDGE DR	MALIBU, CA	90265
KRISTON, MICHAEL	HAIR STYLIST	NBC-TV, 30 ROCKEFELLER PLAZA	NEW YORK, NY	10112
KRISTYL	C & W GROUP	POST OFFICE BOX 113	HAYS, KS	67601
KRIVDA, RICK	BASEBALL	POST OFFICE BOX 418	SAINT CHARLES, IL	60174
KRIVEN, ALBERT	TV EXECUTIVE	METROMEDIA, 205 E 67TH ST	NEW YORK, NY	10021
KRIVSKY, WAYNE	BASEBALL EXECUTIVE	POST OFFICE BOX 90111	ARLINGTON, TX	76004
KROC, JOAN	BASEBALL EXECUTIVE	8939 VILLA LA JOLLA DR #201	LA JOLLA, CA	92037
KROCH, CARL	BASEBALL EXECUTIVE	REDS, 100 RIVERFRONT STADIUM	CINCINNATI, OH	45202
KROFFT, MARTY	PUPPETEER-PRODUCER	700 GREENTREE RD	PACIFIC PALISADES, CA	90272
KROFFT, SID	PUPPETEER-PRODUCER	7710 WOODROW WILSON DR	LOS ANGELES, CA	90046
KROFINA, SHARON L	COMPOSER	10342 LINDLEY AVE #331	NORTHRIDGE, CA	91326
KROFT, STEVE	NEWS CORRESPONDENT	CBS-TV, 524 W 57TH ST	NEW YORK, NY	10019
KROIS, JULIE	MODEL	8949 SUNSET BLVD #203	LOS ANGELES, CA	90069
KROKUS	ROCK & ROLL GROUP	THE PRESS OFFICE, LTD		
		83 RIVERSIDE DR	NEW YORK, NY	10024

Name	Occupation	Address	City/Zip
KROL, JACK	BASEBALL-MANAGER	POST OFFICE BOX 36407	LOUISVILLE, KY 40233
KROLL, JACK	FILM CRITIC	NEWSWEEK, 444 MADISON AVE	NEW YORK, NY 10022
KROLL, NATHAN	DIRECTOR-PRODUCER	201 E 77TH ST	NEW YORK, NY 10021
KRON, ROBERT	HOCKEY	CANUCKS, 100 N RENFREW ST	VANCOUVER, BC V5K 3N7 CANADA
KRONE, HELMUT	DIRECTOR	1 E 62ND ST	NEW YORK, NY 10021
KRONEMEYER, SANDRA	ACTRESS	9744 WILSHIRE BLVD #308	BEVERLY HILLS, CA 90212
KRONICK, WILLIAM	WRITER-PRODUCER	950 N KINGS RD #115	LOS ANGELES, CA 90069
KRONSBERG, JEREMY JOE	WRITER-PRODUCER	POST OFFICE BOX 683	MALIBU, CA 90265
KROPP, ARTHUR J	ACTIVIST	2000 "M" ST #400, NW	WASHINGTON, DC 20036
KROST, BARRY	FILM PRODUCER	9076 SAINT IVES DR	LOS ANGELES, CA 90069
KROUSE, IAN	COMPOSER	328 N WOODS AVE	FULLERTON, CA 92632
KROUSE, WALLY	BASEBALL EXECUTIVE	POST OFFICE BOX 2001	CEDAR RAPIDS, IA 52406
KROWN, RICHARD	DIRECTOR-PRODUCER	3906 BON HOMME RD	WOODLAND HILLS, CA 91364
KRUEGER, BILL	BASEBALL	EXPOS, 4545 DE COUBERTIN AVE	MONTREAL, QUE H1V 3P2 CANADA
KRUG, FRED	DIRECTOR-PRODUCER	5911 MC DONIE AVE	WOODLAND HILLS, CA 91367
KRUGER, HARDY	ACTOR	POST OFFICE BOX 726	CRESTLINE, CA 92325
KRUGER, JEFFREY S	ENTERTAINMENT EXEC	POST OFFICE BOX 130, HOVE	EAST SUSSEX BN3 6QU ENGLAND
KRUGMAN, LOU	ACTOR	2444 N PARISH PL	BURBANK, CA 91504
KRUK, JOHN	BASEBALL	POST OFFICE BOX 7575	PHILADELPHIA, PA 19101
KRUKOW, MIKE	BASEBALL	317 W FAIRVIEW AVE	SAN GABRIEL, CA 91776
KRUM, DORRIE	ACTRESS	5455 WILSHIRE BLVD #1406	LOS ANGELES, CA 90036
KRUM, SANDY	BASEBALL TRAINER	POST OFFICE BOX 842	SALEM, VA 24153
KRUMHOLZ, CHESTER	TV WRITER	3953 BON HOMME RD	WOODLAND HILLS, CA 91364
KRUMRIE, TIM	FOOTBALL	BENGALS, 200 RIVERFRONT STADIUM	CINCINNATI, OH 45202
KRUPNICK, JERRY	TV CRITIC	THE NEWARK STAR-LEDGER	
		STAR LEDGER PLAZA	NEWARK, NJ 07101
KRUPP, UWE	HOCKEY	SABRES, MEMORIAL AUDITORIUM	BUFFALO, NY 14202
KRUSHELNYSKI, MIKE	HOCKEY	MAPLE LEAFS, 60 CARLTON ST	TORONTO, ONT M5B 1L1 CANADA
KRUSINSKI, CARL	BASEBALL EXECUTIVE	1524 W NEBRASKA AVE	PEORIA, IL 61604
KRUZE	ROCK & ROLL GROUP	POST OFFICE BOX 11283	RICHMOND, VA 23230
KRYGIER, TODD	HOCKEY	WHALERS, 1 CIVIC CENTER PLAZA	HARTFORD, CT 06103
KRYSLUR, JULIE	TALENT AGENT	118 RIVERWAY ST #7	BOSTON, MA 02215
KRYSTKOWIAK, LARRY	BASKETBALL	BRADLEY CENTER, 1001 N 4TH ST	MILWAUKEE, WI 53203
KRYSTOL	RHYTHM & BLUES GROUP	FAA, 1700 BROADWAY, 5TH FLOOR	NEW YORK, NY 10019
KU, OK-HEE	GOLFER	2750 VOLUSA AVE #B	DAYTON BEACH, FL 32114
KUBALE, BERNARD	BASEBALL EXECUTIVE	BREWERS, 201 S 46TH ST	MILWAUKEE, WI 53214
KUBEK, TONY	BASEBALL-ANNOUNCER	8323 NORTH SHORE RD	MENASHA, WI 54252
KUBIAK, GARY	FOOTBALL	BRONCOS, 13655 BRONCOS PKWY	ENGLEWOOD, CO 80112
KUBIAK, TED	BASEBALL-MANAGER	POST OFFICE BOX 2437	MODESTO, CA 95351
KUBICKI, MARC	BASEBALL	POST OFFICE BOX 4370	SALINAS, CA 93912
KUBIK, ALEX	ACTOR-WRITER	2305 LORENZO DR	LOS ANGELES, CA 90068
KUBIK, LAWRENCE	FILM WRITER-PRODUCER	1722 FERRAI DR	BEVERLY HILLS, CA 90210
KUBRICK, STANLEY	FILM WRITER-DIRECTOR	BOX 123, BOREHAMWOOD	HERTS ENGLAND
KUBSKI, AL	BASEBALL SCOUT	POST OFFICE BOX 419969	KANSAS CITY, MO 64141
KUBSKI, GIL	BASEBALL SCOUT	1060 W ADDISON ST	CHICAGO, IL 60613
KUBY, BERNIE	ACTOR	10445 EASTBORNE AVE #107	LOS ANGELES, CA 90024
KUCHARO, J MICHAEL	DIRECTOR	5848 N 44TH ST	PHOENIX, AZ 85018
KUDELSKI, BOB	HOCKEY	POST OFFICE BOX 17013	INGLEWOOD, CA 90308
KUDO, GUY	ARTIST	THE GLASS GARDEN	
		510 AVE OF THE AMERICAS	NEW YORK, NY 10001
KUEHL, JOAN S	TV PRODUCER	47 PERRY ST	NEW YORK, NY 10014
KUEHL, JOHN	BASEBALL	12000 STADIUM RD	ADELANTO, CA 92301
KUEHL, KARL	BASEBALL-EXECUTIVE	ATHLETICS'S, OAKLAND COLISEUM	OAKLAND, CA 94621
KUEHN, ANDREW J, JR	DIRECTOR	8003 HOLLYWOOD BLVD	HOLLYWOOD, CA 90046
KUEHN, BILL	BASEBALL EXECUTIVE	POST OFFICE BOX 7845	COLUMBIA, SC 29202
KUEHN, JOHN	DIRECTOR	2 PEMBROOK DR	STONY BROOK, NY 11790
KUEHNERT, MARTY	BASEBALL EXECUTIVE	POST OFFICE BOX 360007	BIRMINGHAM, AL 35236
KUFF, LINKOLN	SINGER	POST OFFICE BOX 308	BURKEVILLE, VA 23922
KUGEL, CARL	TV DIRECTOR	658 HAVERFORD AVE	PACIFIC PALISADES, CA 90272
KUHARICH, BILL	FOOTBALL EXECUTIVE	SAINTS, 1500 POYDRAS ST	NEW ORLEANS, LA 90112
KUHLMAN, RON	ACTOR	5738 WILLIS AVE	VAN NUYS, CA 91411
KUHLMANN, FRED	BASEBALL EXECUTIVE	250 STADIUM PLAZA	ST LOUIS, MO 63102
KUHN, BOWIE	BASEBALL EXECUTIVE	350 PARK AVE, 17TH FLOOR	NEW YORK, NY 10022
KUHN, CHAD	BASEBALL	POST OFFICE BOX 2769	HUNTSVILLE, AL 35804
KUHN, GRANT M	ARTIST	402 W 45TH ST #3-C	NEW YORK, NY 10036
KUHN, RICHARD	DIRECTOR	1155 BROADWAY	NEW YORK, NY 10001
KUIPER, DUANE	BASEBALL-ANNOUNCER	S F GIANTS, CANDLESTICK PARK	SAN FRANICSCO, CA 94124
KUKAR, BERNIE	FOOTBALL REFEREE	NFL, 410 PARK AVE	NEW YORK, NY 10022
KUKOFF, BERNIE	WRITER-PRODUCER	1428 WARNER AVE	LOS ANGELES, CA 90024
KULBERDA, LEN	ARTIST	131 PRENTICE AVE	SOUTH RIVER, NJ 08882
KULCSAR, MIKE	ACTOR	17160 NORDHOFF ST	NORTHRIDGE, CA 91325
KULD, PETE	BASEBALL	POST OFFICE BOX 4448	TULSA, OK 74159
KULIK, BUZZ	DIRECTOR-PRODUCER	10425 CHARING CROSS RD	LOS ANGELES, CA 90024
KULOK, SCOTT	DIRECTOR	DGA, 110 W 57TH ST	NEW YORK, NY 10019
KUMAGAI, DENICE	ACTRESS	KELMAN, 7813 SUNSET BLVD	LOS ANGELES, CA 90046
KUMIN, FRANCES E	CASTING DIRECTOR	1600 BROADWAY #609	NEW YORK, NY 10019
KUMPEL, MARK	HOCKEY	JETS, 15-1430 MAROONS RD	WINNIPEG, MAN R3G OL5 CANADA
KUNDERA, MILAN	NOVELIST	RUE SEBASTIEN BOTIN	PARIS FRANCE
KUNEY, JACK	DIRECTOR	79 W 12TH ST	NEW YORK, NY 10011
KUNHARDT, PETER W	TV PRODUCER	ABC NEWS, 7 W 66TH ST	NEW YORK, NY 10023
KUNKEL, JEFF	BASEBALL	2850 W 20TH AVE	DENVER, CO 80211
KUNKEL, SHERMAN	CINEMATOGRAPHER	7715 SUNSET BLVD #150	LOS ANGELES, CA 90046
KUNTZ, KEN	BASEBALL TRAINER	2501 ALLEN AVE, SE	CANTON, OH 44707
KUNTZ, RUSTY	BASEBALL COACH	POST OFFICE BOX 4100	SEATTLE, WA 98104
KUNZ, ANITA	ARTIST	230 ONTARION ST	ONTARIO M5A 2V5 CANADA

Name	Occupation	Address	City/State	Zip/Country
KUNZ, DEVIN	BASEBALL	POST OFFICE BOX 309	GASTONA, NC	28053
KUPCHAK, MITCH	BASKETBALL-EXECUTIVE	POST OFFICE BOX 10	INGLEWOOD, CA	90306
KUPCINET, JERRY	TV DIRECTOR	16631 NANBERRY RD	ENCINO, CA	91436
KUPERMAN, ROBERT	DIRECTOR	2032 BALMER DR	LOS ANGELES, CA	90039
KUPFER, MARVIN	WRITER-PRODUCER	1037 5TH ST #6	SANTA MONICA, CA	90403
KUPP, CRAIG	FOOTBALL	POST OFFICE BOX 888	PHOENIX, AZ	85001
KUPSEY, JOHN	BASEBALL	POST OFFICE BOX 1721	SPARTANBURG, SC	29304
KURALT, CHARLES	NEWS CORRESPONDENT	CBS NEWS, 524 W 57TH ST	NEW YORK, NY	10019
KUREISHI, HANIF	SCREENWRITER	10000 SANTA MONICA BLVD #305	LOS ANGELES, CA	90067
KURETSKI, PHILIP	WRITER	1419 MAPLE ST #A	SANTA MONICA, CA	90405
KURI, JOHN ANTHONY	DIRECTOR-PRODUCER	9300 WILSHIRE BLVD #410	BEVERLY HILLS, CA	90212
KURIGAMI, KAZUMI	FILM DIRECTOR	CAMEL, INC, VILLA SERENA 302		
		2-33-18 JINGUMARE SHIBUYA-KU	TOKOYO	JAPAN
KURLAND, NORMAN	TALENT AGENT	9242 BEVERLY DR #200	BEVERLY HILLS, CA	90210
KURNIT, SCOTT P	TV EXECUTIVE	VIEWER'S CHOICE, 1633 BROADWAY	NEW YORK, NY	10019
KUROSAWA, AKIRA	FILM DIRECTOR	SEIGO 2-21-6, SETAGAJA-KU	TOKYO 157	JAPAN
KURTH, JULIETTE	ACTRESS	COLEMAN-ROSENBERG, 210 E 58TH ST	NEW YORK, NY	10022
KURTH, WALLACE	ACTOR	ABC-TV, "GENERAL HOSPITAL"		
		4151 PROSPECT AVE	BURBANK, CA	91523
KURTH, WALLY	ACTOR	3401 OAK GLEN DR	LOS ANGELES, CA	90068
KURTIS BLOW	RAPPER-RAPWRITER	SEE - BLOW, KURTIS		
KURTZ, BOB	SPORTSCASTER	CNN, 10 COLUMBUS CIR	NEW YORK, NY	10019
KURTZ, DAVID M	COMPOSER-CONDUCTOR	1500 N BEVERLY DR	BEVERLY HILLS, CA	90210
KURTZ, GARY	FILM PRODUCER	EMI STUDIOS, BOREHAMWOOD	HERTS	ENGLAND
KURTZ, JENNIFER BURTON	TV WRITER	8383 WILSHIRE BLVD #923	BEVERLY HILLS, CA	90211
KURTZ, MARCIA JEAN	ACTRESS	STE, 888 7TH AVE, 18TH FLOOR	NEW YORK, NY	10106
KURTZ, SWOOZIE	ACTRESS	1900 AVE OF THE STARS #739	LOS ANGELES, CA	90067
KURTZMAN, HARVEY	CARTOONIST	133 DOUGLAS PL	MOUNT VERNON, NY	10552
KURVERS, TOM	HOCKEY	CANUCKS, 100 N RENFREW ST	VANCOUVER, BC V5K 3N7	CANADA
KURZ, RON	SCREENWRITER	BERNSTEIN, 119 W 57TH ST	NEW YORK, NY	10019
KURZMAN, MICHAEL	BASEBALL EXECUTIVE	S F GIANTS, CANDLESTICK PARK	SAN FRANICSCO, CA	94124
KUSCHE, HERBERT	BASEBALL EXECUTIVE	POST OFFICE BOX 450	BUFFALO, NY	14205
KUSHNER, DALE	HOCKEY	FLYERS, SPECTRUM, PATTISON PL	PHILADELPHIA, PA	19148
KUSHNER, DONALD	TV PRODUCER	1119 N MC CADDEN PL	HOLLYWOOD, CA	90038
KUSLER, JIM	SECRETARY OF STATE	STATE CAPITOL, 600 E BOULEVARD	BISMARCK, ND	58505
KUSLEY, MICHAEL	DIRECTOR	11825 MAGNOLIA BLVD #112	NORTH HOLLYWOOD, CA	91607
KUSNICK, JANET	ARTIST	1351 OCEAN PARK WALK #106	SANTA MONICA, CA	90405
KUSNYER, ART	BASEBALL-COACH	ATHLETICS'S, OAKLAND COLISEUM	OAKLAND, CA	94621
KUSSACK, ELAINE	TV WRITER	10 E 44TH ST #700	NEW YORK, NY	10017
KUSTERA, CHRISTOPHER	TV-NEWS WRITER	154 VAN REIPEN AVE	JERSEY CITY, NJ	07306
KUSTRA, BOB	LT GOVERNOR	STATE HOUSE BUILDING	SPRINGFIELD, IL	62706
KUTASH, JEFF	SINGER	1901 AVE OF THE STARS #1240	LOS ANGELES, CA	90067
KUTCHER, RANDY	BASEBALL	35918 42ND ST E	PALMDALE, CA	93550
KUTRZEBA, JOSEPH S	DIRECTOR-PRODUCER	229 E 79TH ST	NEW YORK, NY	10021
KUTZLER, JERRY	BASEBALL	CANADIANS, 4601 ONTARIO ST	VANCOUVER, BC V5V 3H4	CANADA
KUYPER, MARCIA	DIRECTOR	DGA, 110 W 57TH ST	NEW YORK, NY	10019
KUZELL, CHRISTOPHER	COMPOSER-CONDUCTOR	907 E EL CAMINO	SANTA MARIA, CA	93454
KUZYK, MIMI	ACTRESS	9200 SUNSET BLVD #710	LOS ANGELES, CA	90069
KVASNICKA, JAY	BASEBALL	POST OFFICE BOX 1659	PORTLAND, OR	97207
KWAN, NANCY	ACTRESS	4154 WOODMAN AVE	SHERMAN OAKS, CA	91403
KWAPIS, KENNETH	TV DIRECTOR	2307 1/2 ECHO PARK AVE	LOS ANGELES, CA	90026
KWASMAN, SAM	ACTOR	4331 VENTURA CANYON AVE #1	SHERMAN OAKS, CA	91423
KWESKIN, JIM	SINGER-MUSICIAN	THE MOUNTAIN RAILROAD		
		3602 ATWOOD AVE	MADISON, WI	53714
KWONG, JOSEPH C	SCREENWRITER	9100 SUNSET BLVD #360	LOS ANGELES, CA	90069
KWOUK, BURT	ACTOR	LONDON MGT, 235-241 REGENT ST	LONDON W1R 4PH	ENGLAND
KY, NOYEN CAO	GENERAL	15701 SUNBURST LN	HUNTINGTON BEACH, CA	92647
KYDD, JONATHAN	ACTOR-WRITER	NARROW ROAD, 21-22 POLAND ST	LONDON W1	ENGLAND
KYL, JON	U S CONGRESSMAN	4250 E CAMELBACK RD #140-K	PHOENIX, AZ	85018
KYLE, JOE	ACTOR	1612 SUNSET PLAZA DR	LOS ANGELES, CA	90069
KYLE, ROBERT G	TV DIRECTOR	POST OFFICE BOX 18052	DENVER, CO	80218
KYLES, SIRRON V	TALENT AGENT	POST OFFICE BOX 8305	HOUSTON, TX	77288
KYLIAN, JIRI	CHOREOGRAPHER	KONINGSSTRAAT 118	THE HAGUE	NETHERLANDS
KYNE, TERRY	TV DIRECTOR	950 WILSON ST	LAGUNA BEACH, CA	92651
KYPREOS, NICK	HOCKEY	JETS, 15-1430 MAROONS RD	WINNIPEG, MAN R3G 0L5	CANADA
KYRIAKIS, WILLIAM C	DIRECTOR	FILMSMITH CO, 122 E 42ND ST	NEW YORK, NY	10017
KYTE, JIM	HOCKEY	POST OFFICE BOX 1540, STA "M"	CALGARY, ALTA T2P 3BP	CANADA

Name	Occupation	Address	City/State	Zip/Country
L A DREAM TEAM	SOUL GROUP	3610 W 6TH ST #536	LOS ANGELES, CA	90020
L A GUNS	ROCK & ROLL GROUP	LEFT BANK, 6255 SUNSET BLVD	HOLLYWOOD, CA	90028
LA BEEF, SLEEPY	SINGER	PENNY, 30 GUINAN ST	WALTHAM, MA	02154
LA BELLA, VINCENZO	WRITER-PRODUCER	521 SWARTHMORE AVE	PACIFIC PALISADES, CA	90272
LA BELLE, PATTI	SINGER-ACTRESS	8730 SUNSET BLVD #PH-W	LOS ANGELES, CA	90069
LA BOUNTY, BILL	SINGER	9454 WILSHIRE BLVD #309	BEVERLY HILLS, CA	90212
LA CAVA, WILLIAM	DIRECTOR	313 CENTRAL PARKWAY	MOUNT VERON, NY	10552
LA CIVITA, RICHARD P	DIRECTOR	INTERNATIONAL VISION, INC		
		9 W 57TH ST, 49TH FLOOR	NEW YORK, NY	10128

Name	Occupation	Address	City
LA CROIX, LEONARD A	CONDUCTOR	25445 VIA ESCOVAR	VALENCIA, CA 91355
LA FALCE, JOHN J	U S CONGRESSMAN	FEDERAL BLDG, 100 STATE ST	ROCHESTER, NY 14614
LA FLEUR, ART	ACTOR	3500 W OLIVE AVE #1400	BURBANK, CA 91505
LA FLEUR, GUY	HOCKEY	2313 SAINT CATHERINE ST	W MONTREAL, PQ H3H 1N2 CANADA
LA FOLLETTE, DOUGLAS	SECRETARY OF STATE	STATE CAPITOL BUILDING	MADISON, WI 53702
LA FOND, BERNADETTE	TV DIRECTOR	155 E 37TH ST	NEW YORK, NY 10016
LA FONTAINE, CHRISTOPHER	TV DIRECTOR	BBC-TV, KENSINGTON HOUSE	
		RICHMOND WY	LONDON W14 ENGLAND
LA FONTAINE, PAT	HOCKEY	NASSAU VETS MEMORIAL COLISEUM	UNIONDALE, NY 11553
LA FRANCOIS, ROGER	BASEBALL COACH	CANADIANS, 4601 ONTARIO ST	VANCOUVER, BC V5V 3H4 CANADA
LA FRENIERE, CELINE M	SCREENWRITER	2317 KIMRIDGE RD	BEVERLY HILLS, CA 90210
LA GRAVENESE, RICHARD	SCREENWRITER	UTA, 9560 WILSHIRE BL, 5TH FL	BEVERLY HILLS, CA 90212
LA HENDRO, ROBERT	TV DIRECTOR	15446 SHERMAN WY	VAN NUYS, CA 91406
LA LANNE, JACK	EXERCISE INSTRUCTOR	POST OFFICE BOX 1249	BURBANK, CA 91507
LA MACCHIA, AL	BASEBALL EXECUTIVE	SKYDOME, 300 BREMMER BL #3200	TORONTO, ONT M5V 3B3 CANADA
LA MAR, DANNY	BASEBALL SCOUT	POST OFFICE BOX 7000	PITTSBURGH, PA 15212
LA MARCA	ROCK & ROLL GROUP	SCOTTI BROS, 2128 PICO BLVD	SANTA MONICA, CA 90405
LA MARR, CINNIMIN	SINGER	POST OFFICE BOX 11321	
		FLAGLER STATION	MIAMI, FL 33101
LA MOND, BILL	TV WRITER	8237 ROXBURY RD	LOS ANGELES, CA 90069
LA MOND, JO	TV WRITER	8237 ROXBURY RD	LOS ANGELES, CA 90069
LA MOTTA, JAKE	BOXER	400 E 57TH ST	NEW YORK, NY 10022
LA MOTTA, VIKKI	MODEL-COSMETICS	VICKI LA MOTTA COSMETICS, LTD	
		360 LEXINGTON AVE	NEW YORK, NY 10017
LA MOTTE, RICHARD E	COSTUME DESIGNER	13949 VENTURA BLVD #309	SHERMAN OAKS, CA 91423
LA MURA, MARK	ACTOR	9301 WILSHIRE BLVD #312	BEVERLY HILLS, CA 90210
LA PAGLIA, ANTHONY	ACTOR	9200 SUNSET BLVD #710	LOS ANGELES, CA 90069
LA PENTA, JERRY	BASEBALL SCOUT	INDIANS, CLEVELAND STADIUM	CLEVELAND, OH 44114
LA PIERE, GEORGANNE	ACTRESS	22801 TRIGGER	CHATSWORTH, CA 91311
LA PLACA, ALISON	ACTRESS	8380 MELROSE AVE #207	LOS ANGELES, CA 90069
LA PLANTE, LAURA	ACTRESS	23388 MULHOLLAND DR	WOODLAND HILLS, CA 91364
LA POINT, DAVE	BASEBALL	1336 VILLAGE LN	PLACERVILLE, CA 95667
LA POINTE, GUY	HOCKEY	2313 W SAINT CATHERINE ST	MONTREAL, PQ H3H 1N2 CANADA
LA ROCCO, LARRY	U S CONGRESSMAN	304 N 8TH ST #136	BOISE, ID 83702
LA ROCHE, DAVE	BASEBALL-COACH	METS, 126TH ST & ROOSEVELT AVE	FLUSHING, NY 11368
LA ROCQUE, GARY	BASEBALL SCOUT	1000 ELYSIAN PARK DR	LOS ANGELES, CA 90012
LA ROSA, JULIUS	ACTOR-SINGER	67 SYCAMORE LN	IRVINGTON, NY 10533
LA ROSE, STEVE	BASEBALL	POST OFFICE BOX 4209	JACKSON, MS 39296
LA RUE, D C	SINGER	111 W 57TH ST #1204	NEW YORK, NY 10019
LA RUE, DANNY	ACTOR	ZAHL, 57 GREAT CUMBERLAND PL	LONDON W1H 7LJ ENGLAND
LA RUE, EVA	ACTRESS-TV HOST	846 1/4 N FORMOSA AVE	LOS ANGELES, CA 90046
LA RUE, FLORENCE	SINGER	4300 LOUISE AVE	ENCINO, CA 91316
LA RUE, JIM	FOOTBALL COACH	BEARS, 250 N WASHINGTON RD	LAKE FOREST, IL 60045
LA RUE, LASH	ACTOR	9145 HINSON DR	MATTHEWS, NC 28105
LA RUSCH, SUZANNE	ACTRESS	13455 VENTURA BLVD #210	SHERMAN OAKS, CA 91423
LA RUSSA, TONY	BASEBALL	ATHLETICS'S, OAKLAND COLISEUM	OAKLAND, CA 94621
LA SALLE, DENISE	SINGER	POST OFFICE BOX 4603	MACON, GA 31208
LA SALLE, JOHN	COMPOSER	11049 KLING ST	NORTH HOLLYWOOD, CA 91602
LA SALLE, RICHARD	COMPOSER	POST OFFICE BOX 4679	CARMEL, CA 93921
LA SALLE, RON	SINGER	41 BRITAIN ST #200	TORONTO, ONT M5A 1R7 CANADA
LA SALLE, RON & TWIN BULLET	ROCK & ROLL GROUP	POST OFFICE BOX 4087	MISSOULA, MT 59806
LA TOURNEAUX, ROBERT	ACTOR	1155 3RD AVE	NEW YORK, NY 10021
LA VALLEY, DOUG	SINGER	ACE, 3407 GREEN RIDGE DR	NASHVILLE, TN 37214
LA VALLIERE, MIKE	BASEBALL	POST OFFICE BOX 7000	PITTSBURGH, PA 15212
LA VETTE, MAUREEN	ACTRESS	10587 CUSHDON AVE	LOS ANGELES, CA 90064
LA VOI, GREG	COSTUME DESIGNER	13949 VENTURA BLVD #309	SHERMAN OAKS, CA 91423
LA ZELLE, JAMES	ACTOR	7120 VARNA AVE	NORTH HOLLYWOOD, CA 91605
LAAZ ROCKET	ROCK & ROLL GROUP	POST OFFICE BOX 1616	NOVATO, CA 94948
LABADIE, DAVID	PHOTOJOURNALIST	POST OFFICE BOX 86080	SAN DIEGO, CA 92138
LABAN	ROCK & ROCK DUO	MEGA RECORDS SCANDINAVIA	
		FREDERIKSBORGGARDE 31	DK-1360 COPENHAGEN DENMARK
LABINE, CLAIRE	WRITER	199 BERKELEY PL	BROOKLYN, NY 11217
LABINE, MATTHEW A	TV PRODUCER	199 BERKELEY PL	BROOKLYN, NY 11217
LABORTEAUX, MATTHEW	ACTOR	15301 VENTURA BLVD #345	SHERMAN OAKS, CA 91403
LABORTEAUX, PATRICK	ACTOR	9000 SUNSET BLVD #801	LOS ANGELES, CA 90069
LABOSSIERE, LEO	BASEBALL SCOUT	ORIOLE PARK, 333 W CAMDEN ST	BALTIMORE, MD 21201
LABOY, CARLOS	BASEBALL	POST OFFICE BOX 4370	SALINAS, CA 93912
LABRADA, LEE	BODYBUILDER	POST OFFICE BOX 690971	HOUSTON, TX 77269
LACAVA, TONY	BASEBALL SCOUT	POST OFFICE BOX 2000	ANAHEIM, CA 92803
LACEY, DEBORAH	ACTRESS	247 S BEVERLY DR #102	BEVERLY HILLS, CA 90210
LACHEMAN, BRET	BASEBALL	POST OFFICE BOX 3496	DAVENPORT, IA 52808
LACHEMANN, BILL, JR	BASEBALL SCOUT	POST OFFICE BOX 2000	ANAHEIM, CA 92803
LACHEMANN, MARCEL	BASEBALL-COACH	POST OFFICE BOX 2000	ANAHEIM, CA 92803
LACHEMANN, RENE	BASEBALL-COACH	ATHLETICS'S, OAKLAND COLISEUM	OAKLAND, CA 94621
LACHER, JAMES	FOOTBALL EXECUTIVE	POST OFFICE BOX 17247 (DULLES)	WASHINGTON, DC 20041
LACHEY, JIM	FOOTBALL	POST OFFICE BOX 17247 (DULLES)	WASHINGTON, DC 20041
LACHMAN, BRAD	TV WRITER	7721 FLYNN RANCH RD	LOS ANGELES, CA 90046
LACHMAN, CLIFFORD NEIL	DIRECTOR	2652 N BEACHWOOD DR	LOS ANGELES, CA 90068
LACHMAN, MORT	TV WRITER-PRODUCER	4115-B WARNER BLVD	BURBANK, CA 91505
LACK, ANDREW	TV WRITER-PRODUCER	CBS-TV, 524 W 57TH ST	NEW YORK, NY 10019
LACOMBE, NORMAND	HOCKEY	FLYERS, SPECTRUM, PATTISON PL	PHILADELPHIA, PA 19148
LACY, CAROLYNE	WRITER	3476 TROY DR	LOS ANGELES, CA 90068
LACY, CLAY	DIRECTOR	DGA, 7920 SUNSET BLVD, 6TH FL	LOS ANGELES, CA 90046
LACY, DON & COUNTRY SPECIAL	C & W GROUP	POST OFFICE BOX 82	GREENBRIER, TN 37073
LACY, JERRY	ACT-WRI-DIR	4736 CORBIN DR	TARZANA, CA 91356

Name	Occupation	Address	City	Zip
LACY, KERRY	BASEBALL	POST OFFICE BOX 309	GASTONA, NC	28053
LACY, LEE	BASEBALL	29025 CATHERWOOD CT	AGOURA HILLS, CA	91301
LACY, N LEE	DIRECTOR	8446 MELROSE PL	LOS ANGELES, CA	90069
LACY, WILLIAM	DIRECTOR	819 N BEVERLY BLVD	LOS ANGELES, CA	90077
LADD, ALAN, JR	FILM EXECUTIVE	1010 N CRESCENT DR	BEVERLY HILLS, CA	90210
LADD, CHERYL	ACTRESS-SINGER	2485 JANIN WY	SOLVANG, CA	93463
LADD, DAVID	ACTOR	9212 HAZEN DR	BEVERLY HILLS, CA	90210
LADD, DIANE	ACTRESS	12214 VIEWCREST RD	STUDIO CITY, CA	91604
LADD, MARGARET	ACTRESS	444 21ST ST	SANTA MONICA, CA	90402
LADERMAN, EZRA	COMPOSER	POST OFFICE BOX 689	TEANECK, NJ	07666
LADMAN, CATHY	ACTRESS	8665 WILSHIRE BLVD #208	BEVERLY HILLS, CA	90211
LADOUCEUR, RANDY	HOCKEY	WHALERS, 1 CIVIC CENTER PLAZA	HARTFORD, CT	06103
LADY BROWN SUGAR BELL	C & W GROUP	PROCESS, 439 WILEY AVE	FRANKLIN, PA	16323
LAFFERTY, JERRY	BASEBALL SCOUT	POST OFFICE BOX 7575	PHILADELPHIA, PA	19101
LAFFERTY, MARCY	ACTRESS	GOLAN, 651 N KILKEA DR	LOS ANGELES, CA	90048
LAFFERTY, MARTIN C	TV PRODUCER	219 PERIMETER CENTER PARKWAY	ATLANTA, GA	30346
LAFFERTY, PERRY	TV EXECUTIVE	335 S BRISTOL AVE	LOS ANGELES, CA	90049
LAFFONT, JEAN-PIERRE	PHOTOGRAPHER	322 W 72ND ST	NEW YORK, NY	10023
LAFLEUR, GUY	HOCKEY	NORDIQUES, 2205 AVE DU COLISEE	QUEBEC, QUE G1L 4W7	CANADA
LAFRATE, AL	HOCKEY	JETS, 15-1430 MAROONS RD	WINNIPEG, MAN R3G 0L5	CANADA
LAGEMAN, JEFF	FOOTBALL	N Y JETS, 1000 FULTON AVE	HEMPSTEAD, NY	11550
LAGG, FREDERICK S	WRITER	2112 PERRY AVE	REDONDO BEACH, CA	90278
LAGLER, RENE	ART DIRECTOR	4125 PARVA AVE	LOS ANGELES, CA	90027
LAGOMARSINO, ROBERT J	U S CONGRESSMAN	5740 RALSTON ST #101	VENTURA, CA	93003
LAGOMARSINO, RON	TV DIRECTOR	36 W 84TH ST	NEW YORK, NY	10024
LAH, MICHAEL R	DIRECTOR-PRODUCER	12211 HUSTON ST	NORTH HOLLYWOOD, CA	91607
LAHTI, CHRISTINE	ACTRESS	10 W 86TH ST	NEW YORK, NY	10024
LAHTI, GARY	ACTOR	132 S LASKY DR #B	BEVERLY HILLS, CA	90212
LAID BACK	ROCK & ROLL GROUP	POST OFFICE BOX 1074	DK-1008 COPENHAGEN	DENMARK
LAIDMAN, HARVEY	TV DIRECTOR	4923 ENCINO TERR	ENCINO, CA	91316
LAIFFER, DONALD M	WRITER	7250 FRANKLIN AVE #A-215	LOS ANGELES, CA	90046
LAIMBEER, BILL	BASKETBALL	THE PALACE OF AUBURN HILLS		
		2 CHAMPIONSHIP DR	AUBURN HILLS, MI	48326
LAIN, JEWELL	ACTRESS	6255 SUNSET BLVD #627	LOS ANGELES, CA	90028
LAINE, CLEO	SINGER	THE OLD RECTORY, WAVENDON	MILTON KEYNES MK17 8LT	ENGLAND
LAINE, FRANKIE	SINGER-ACTOR	352 SAN GORGONIO ST	SAN DIEGO, CA	92106
LAIRD, BOB	CARTOONIST	POST OFFICE BOX 500	WASHINGTON, DC	20044
LAIRD, JACK	WRITER-PRODUCER	MCA/UNIVERSAL STUDIOS, INC		
		100 UNIVERSAL CITY PLAZA #422	UNIVERSAL CITY, CA	91608
LAIRD, JOYCE ANNE	ACTRESS	13207 WENTWORTH ST	ARLETA, CA	91331
LAIRD, MARLENA	TV DIRECTOR	2729 WESTSHIRE DR	HOLLYWOOD, CA	90068
LAJOIE, ROGER	ACTOR	125 N AVON ST #C	BURBANK, CA	91505
LAKE, CARNELL	FOOTBALL	STEELERS, 300 STADIUM CIR	PITTSBURGH, PA	15212
LAKE, GREG	SINGER-GUITARIST	ATI, 888 7TH AVE, 21ST FLOOR	NEW YORK, NY	10106
LAKE, OLIVER & JUMP UP	JAZZ GROUP	FAST LANE PRODUCTIONS		
		4590 MAC ARTHUR BLVD, NW	WASHINGTON, DC	20007
LAKE, PETER A	WRITER-EXECUTIVE	2554 LINCOLN BLVD	MARINA DEL REY, CA	90291
LAKE, RICKI	ACTRESS	6644 ALLOTT AVE	VAN NUYS, CA	91401
LAKE, ROY	BASEBALL EXECUTIVE	POST OFFICE BOX 10336	CLEARWATER, FL	34617
LAKE, STEVE	BASEBALL	POST OFFICE BOX 7575	PHILADELPHIA, PA	19101
LAKELAND, CHRISTINE	SINGER-GUITARIST	POST OFFICE BOX 8882	UNIVERSAL CITY, CA	91608
LAKER, TIM	BASEBALL	POST OFFICE BOX 15757	HARRISBURG, PA	17105
LAKESIDE	RHYTHM & BLUES GROUP	THE GRIFF COMPANY		
		1635 N CAHUENGA BLVD	LOS ANGELES, CA	90028
LAKEY, DAVID	BASEBALL SCOUT	POST OFFICE BOX 288	HOUSTON, TX	77001
LAKEY, GORDON	BASEBALL SCOUT	SKYDOME, 300 BREMMER BL #3200	TORONTO, ONT M5V 3B3	CANADA
LAKIN, CHRISTINE	ACTRESS	ABC-TV, 2040 AVE OF THE STARS	LOS ANGELES, CA	90067
LAKIN, HOWARD	TV WRITER-STORY ED	5658 JED SMITH RD	HIDDEN HILLS, CA	91302
LAKIN, RITA	WRITER	2744 BOTTLEBRUSH DR	LOS ANGELES, CA	90077
LAKSO, EDWARD	TV WRITER	2075 BENEDICT CANYON RD	BEVERLY HILLS, CA	90210
LALA	ACTRESS	ICM, 40 W 57TH ST	NEW YORK, NY	10019
LALLY, ROBERT J	TV DIRECTOR	4224 BLUEBELL AVE	BURBANK, CA	91505
LALLYKE, KEVIN	FILM CRITIC	FILM JOURNAL, 244 W 49TH ST	NEW YORK, NY	10019
LALOR, MIKE	HOCKEY	JETS, 15-1430 MAROONS RD	WINNIPEG, MAN R3G 0L5	CANADA
LAM, PAPILLON-SOO	ACTRESS	YEOH MGMT, 34 DERWENT GARDENS		
		REDBRIDGE	ESSEX	ENGLAND
LAM, RICKY	ARTIST	45-20 40TH ST #2-F	SUNNYSIDE, NY	11104
LAMABE, JACK	BASEBALL-COACH	POST OFFICE BOX 20849	CHARLESTON, SC	29413
LAMARR, HEDY	ACTRESS	568 ORANGE DR #47	ALTMONTE SPRINGS, FL	32701
LAMAS, LORENZO	ACTOR	641 S MARIPOSA DR	BURBANK, CA	91506
LAMB, ANNABEL	SINGER	BARRY DICKINS, ITB HAMMERHOUSE	LONDON W1	ENGLAND
LAMB, DEBRA	ACTRESS	WEBB, 7500 DEVISTA DR	LOS ANGELES, CA	90046
LAMB, LARRY	ACTOR	HEATH, PARAMOUNT HOUSE		
		162-170 WARDOUR ST	LONDON W1V 3AT	ENGLAND
LAMB, MARGARET	TALENT AGENT	6605 HOLLYWOOD BLVD #220	HOLLYWOOD, CA	90028
LAMB, MARK	HOCKEY	OILERS, NORTHLANDS COLISEUM	EDMONTON, ALTA T5B 4M9	CANADA
LAMBE, BRYAN	BASEBALL SCOUT	POST OFFICE BOX 90111	ARLINGTON, TX	76004
LAMBERT, ANN	COSTUME DESIGNER	6161 BAY SHORE WALK	BELMONT SHORES, CA	90803
LAMBERT, CHRISTOPHER	ACTOR	9220 SUNSET BLVD #201	LOS ANGELES, CA	90069
LAMBERT, DENNIS	MUSICIAN	4433 PETIT AVE	ENCINO, CA	91436
LAMBERT, EDWARD	RECORD EXECUTIVE	23445 LOS ENCINOS WY	WOODLAND HILLS, CA	91367
LAMBERT, GAVIN	SCREENWRITER	8955 BEVERLY BLVD	WEST HOLLYWOOD, CA	90048
LAMBERT, JACK	FOOTBALL	222 HIGHLAND DR	CARMEL, CA	93921
LAMBERT, JERRY	SINGER	POST OFFICE BOX 25371	CHARLOTTE, NC	28212
LAMBERT, L W & BLUE RIVER BOYS	C & W GROUP	ROUTE #1	OLIN, NC	28860

Name	Occupation	Address	City	Zip
LAMBERT, LAYNE	BASEBALL	POST OFFICE BOX 824	BURLINGTON, IA	52601
LAMBERT, MARK ROBERT	DIRECTOR	DGA, 7920 SUNSET BLVD, 6TH FL	LOS ANGELES, CA	90046
LAMBERT, PAUL	ACTOR	2806 BARRY AVE	LOS ANGELES, CA	90064
LAMBERT, REESE	BASEBALL	POST OFFICE BOX 3665	OMAHA, NE	68103
LAMBERT, ROBERT	DIRECTOR	16941 BOLLINGER ST	SEPULVEDA, CA	91343
LAMBERT, VERITY	TV PRODUCER	CINEMA VERITY LTD, THE OLD MILL		
		MILLERS WY	LONDON W6	ENGLAND
LAMBL, CHRIS	ARTIST	27-17 38TH AVE	LONG ISLAND CITY, NY	11101
LAMBRINOS, VASSILI	ACTOR	OSCARD, 24 W 40TH ST, 17TH FL	NEW YORK, NY	10011
LAMBRO, PHILLIP	COMPOSER-CONDUCTOR	1888 CENTURY PARK E #10	LOS ANGELES, CA	90067
LAMENSDORF, LEONARD R	SCREENWRITER	8955 BEVERLY BLVD	WEST HOLLYWOOD, CA	90048
LAMEY, TOMMY K	ACTOR	6125 GLEN OAK ST #5	LOS ANGELES, CA	90068
LAMKIN, KEN	DIRECTOR-PRODUCER	6876 ANGLEBUFF CIR	DALLAS, TX	75248
LAMM, KAREN	ACTRESS	9300 WILSHIRE BLVD #410	BEVERLY HILLS, CA	90212
LAMM, ROBERT	MUSICIAN-SONGWRITER	1113 SUTTON WY	BEVERLY HILLS, CA	90210
LAMNECK, JOSEPH D	DIRECTOR	DGA, 110 W 57TH ST	NEW YORK, NY	10019
LAMONT, ELAINE	SOUND EDITOR	208-06 89TH AVE	BELLAIRE, NY	11427
LAMONT, GENE	BASEBALL-MANAGER	333 W 35TH ST	CHICAGO, IL	60616
LAMONT, LISA	ACTRESS	POST OFFICE BOX 69590	LOS ANGELES, CA	90069
LAMONT, PEGGY	TV EXECUTIVE	TOMORROW ENTERTAINMENT		
		405 LEXINGTON AVE	NEW YORK, NY	10174
LAMOREAUX, E S, III "BUD"	TV PRODUCER	CBS-TV, 524 W 57TH ST	NEW YORK, NY	10019
LAMOTTE, GREG	NEWS CORRESPONDENT	1050 TECHWOOD DR, NW	ATLANTA, GA	30318
LAMOUR, DOROTHY	ACTRESS	5309 GOODLAND AVE	NORTH HOLLYWOOD, CA	91607
LAMP, DENNIS	BASEBALL	POST OFFICE BOX 450	BUFFALO, NY	14205
LAMPARSKI, RICHARD	AUTHOR	924 GARDEN ST #D	SANTA BARBARA, CA	93101
LAMPELL, MILLARD	TV WRITER	ICM, 8899 BEVERLY BLVD	LOS ANGELES, CA	90048
LAMPERT, ZOHRA	ACTRESS	ICM, 40 W 57TH ST	NEW YORK, NY	10019
LAMPKIN, TOM	BASEBALL	STARS, 850 LAS VEGAS BLVD N	LAS VEGAS, NV	89101
LAMPL, HANS	CONDUCTOR	12631 ROMAINE WY	GARDEN GROVE, CA	92645
LAMPLEY, JIM	SPORTSCASTER	3347 TARECO DR	LOS ANGELES, CA	90068
LANCASTER, BURT	ACTOR-DIRECTOR	POST OFFICE BOX 67-B-38	LOS ANGELES, CA	90067
LANCASTER, H MARTIN	U S CONGRESSMAN	FEDERAL BUILDING, ROOM 103		
		134 N JOHN ST	GOLDSBORO, NC	27530
LANCASTER, JOAN	ACTRESS	CED, 261 S ROBERTSON BLVD	BEVERLY HILLS, CA	90211
LANCASTER, JOANNA	FILM PRODUCER	POST OFFICE BOX 67-B-38	LOS ANGELES, CA	90067
LANCASTER, LES	BASEBALL	TIGERS, TIGER STADIUM	DETROIT, MI	48216
LANCASTER, LUCIE	ACTRESS	30 W 60TH ST	NEW YORK, NY	10023
LANCASTER, NEAL	GOLFER	POST OFFICE BOX 109601	PALM BCH GARDENS, FL	33418
LANCASTER, STUART	ACTOR	3096 LAKE HOLLYWOOD DR	LOS ANGELES, CA	90068
LANCE, BURT	POLITICIAN	POST OFFICE BOX 637	CALHOUN, GA	30701
LANCE, GARY	BASEBALL COACH	POLECATS, 608 N SLAPPEY BLVD	ALBANY, GA	31701
LANCE, MAJOR	SINGER	FONTANA, 161 W 54TH ST	NEW YORK, NY	10019
LANCE, PETER	COMPOSER	5302 LAUREL CANYON BLVD	NORTH HOLLYWOOD, CA	91607
LANCE, TEMPERANCE "THE TIGER"	ACTRESS-ACTIVIST	CASTLE, 1101 S ORLANDO AVE	LOS ANGELES, CA	90035
LANCELLOTTI, RICK	BASEBALL	POST OFFICE BOX 2365	PAWTUCKET, RI	02861
LANCHBERY, JOHN	CONDUCTOR	ICM, 40 W 57TH ST	NEW YORK, NY	10019
LANCIT, LAURENCE A	TV DIRECTOR-PRODUCER	601 W 50TH ST #PH	NEW YORK, NY	10019
LAND, CYNTHIA	TALENT AGENT	9255 SUNSET BLVD #505	LOS ANGELES, CA	90069
LAND, DAN	FOOTBALL	RAIDERS, 332 CENTER ST	EL SEGUNDO, CA	90245
LAND, DAVID	FILM PROD-EXEC	STIGWOOD, 118-120 WARDOUR ST	LONDON W1	ENGLAND
LAND, EDWARD W	WRITER-DIRECTOR	11645 KIOWA AVE #4	LOS ANGELES, CA	90049
LAND, PETER W	CONDUCTOR	26 VIA MEDIA	TUSTIN, CA	92680
LANDA, DENNIS G	WRITER	4701 BALBOA AVE	ENCINO, CA	91316
LANDAKER, GREGG	SOUND ENGINEER	7131 DEVERON RIDGE RD	CANOGA PARK, CA	91307
LANDAU, BEVERLY	TALENT AGENT	301 E 47TH ST #4-K	NEW YORK, NY	10017
LANDAU, EDIE	FILM PRODUCER	8863 ALCOTT ST #1	LOS ANGELES, CA	90035
LANDAU, ELY	FILM PRODUCER	8863 ALCOTT ST #1	LOS ANGELES, CA	90035
LANDAU, LUCY	ACTRESS	83-80 118TH ST	KEW GARDENS, NY	11415
LANDAU, MARTIN	ACTOR	7455 PALO VISTA DR	LOS ANGELES, CA	90046
LANDAU, RICHARD	SCREENWRITER	10377 W OLYMPIC BLVD	LOS ANGELES, CA	90064
LANDAU, SIEGFRIED	CONDUCTOR	26 OGDEN RD	SCARSDALE, NY	10583
LANDAU, TERRY	TV WRITER	8462 WYNDHAM RD	LOS ANGELES, CA	90046
LANDAU, VIVIEN	ACTRESS	MOUNT HOLLY RD E	KATONAH, NY	10536
LANDE, ART	PIANIST	2490 CHANNING WY #418	BERKELEY, CA	94704
LANDE, NATHANIEL	WRITER-DIRECTOR	25 CENTRAL PARK W	NEW YORK, NY	10023
LANDECK, PHILIP C	DIRECTOR-PRODUCER	420 LEXINGTON AVE	NEW YORK, NY	10017
LANDEN, DINSDALE	ACTOR	WHITEHALL, 125 GLOUCESTER RD	LONDON SW7 4TE	ENGLAND
LANDER, DAVID L	ACTOR-WRITER	7009 W SENALDA RD	LOS ANGELES, CA	90068
LANDER, DIANE	ACTRESS	11645 WOODBRIDGE ST	STUDIO CITY, CA	91604
LANDER SIMON, DIANE	ACTRESS	10745 CHALON RD	LOS ANGELES, CA	90077
LANDERS, ANN	COLUMNIST	THE CHICAGO TRIBUNE		
		TRIBUNE TOWER		
		435 N MICHIGAN AVE	CHCIAGO, IL	60611
LANDERS, AUDREY	ACTRESS-SINGER	3112 NICKA DR	LOS ANGELES, CA	90077
LANDERS, HARRY	ACTOR	11846 VENTURA BLVD #100	STUDIO CITY, CA	91604
LANDERS, JUDY	ACTRESS-MODEL	NIEDENFUER, 9849 DENBIGH DR	BEVERLY HILLS, CA	90210
LANDERS, LEE	BASEBALL EXECUTIVE	POST OFFICE BOX 3004	SPRINGFIELD, IL	62708
LANDERS, ROBERT	DIRECTOR	7240 ESTRELLA DE MAR	CARLSBAD, CA	92008
LANDESBERG, STEVE	COMEDIAN-ACTOR	BERNSTEIN, 355 N GENESEE AVE	LOS ANGELES, CA	90036
LANDESTOY, RAFAEL	BASEBALL-COACH	EXPOS, 4545 DE COUBERTIN AVE	MONTREAL, QUE H1V 3P2	CANADA
LANDI, JOHN JOSEPH	CINEMATOGRAPHER	ABC-TV, 125 W END AVE	NEW YORK, NY	10023
LANDIS, JOHN	FILM WRITER-DIRECTOR	DGA, 7920 SUNSET BLVD, 6TH FL	LOS ANGELES, CA	90046
LANDON, HAL, JR	ACTOR	8383 WILSHIRE BLVD #650	BEVERLY HILLS, CA	90211
LANDON, JOSEPH S	TV WRITER	PLESHETTE, 2700 N BEACHWOOD DR	HOLLYWOOD, CA	90028

Name	Occupation	Address	City/State	Zip/Country
LANDON, LAURENE	ACTRESS	8831 SUNSET BLVD #402	LOS ANGELES, CA	90069
LANDON, MICHAEL, JR	ACTOR	10930 ASHTON AVE #408	LOS ANGELES, CA	90024
LANDOR, ROSALYN	ACTRESS	9744 WILSHIRE BLVD #305	BEVERLY HILLS, CA	90212
LANDREAUX, KENNY	BASEBALL	608 N LEONARD ST	MONTEBELLO, CA	90640
LANDRES, MORRIS	FILM EXECUTIVE	10501 WILSHIRE BLVD #2111	LOS ANGELES, CA	90024
LANDRES, PAUL	TV DIRECTOR	5343 AMESTOY AVE	ENCINO, CA	91316
LANDRESS, ROGER	BASEBALL	POST OFFICE BOX 464	APPLETON, WI	54912
LANDRIEU, MARY	TREASURER	POST OFFICE BOX 94004	BATON ROUGE, LA	70804
LANDRUM, BILL	BASEBALL	EXPOS, 4545 DE COUBERTIN AVE	MONTREAL, QUE H1V 3P2	CANADA
LANDRUM, CED	BASEBALL	CUBS, 2ND & RIVERSIDE DR	DES MOINES, IA	50309
LANDRUM, CEDRIC	BASEBALL	CUBS, 2ND & RIVERSIDE DR	DES MOINES, IA	50309
LANDRUM, TITO	BASEBALL (MAJORS)	1121 KENTUCKY SE	ALBUQUERQUE, NM	87108
LANDRY, GAIL	ACTRESS	14017 SYLVAN ST	VAN NUYS, CA	91401
LANDRY, GREG	FOOTBALL COACH	BEARS, 250 N WASHINGTON RD	LAKE FOREST, IL	60045
LANDRY, RON L	RADIO PERSONALITY	28980 CLIFFSIDE DR	MALIBU, CA	90265
LANDSBERG, DAVID	ACTOR-WRITER	25809 VIA CANDICE	VALENCIA, CA	91355
LANDSBERGIS, VYTATIS	POLITICIAN	PARLIMENT HOUSE	VILNIUS	LITHUANIA
LANDSBURG, ALAN	WRITER-PRODUCER	22432 PACIFIC COAST HWY	MALIBU, CA	90265
LANDSBURG, VALERIE	ACTRESS	22745 CHAMERA LN	TOPANGA CANYON, CA	90290
LANDY, DR EUGENE	THERAPIST-TALENT AGT	19710 PACIFIC COAST HIGHWAY	MALIBU, CA	90265
LANDZATT, ANDRE	ACTOR	BDP, 10637 BURBANK BLVD	NORTH HOLLYWOOD, CA	91601
LANE, ABBE	SINGER-ACTRESS	LEFF, 444 N FARING RD	LOS ANGELES, CA	90077
LANE, ANDREW	FILM PRODUCER	9220 SUNSET BLVD #311	LOS ANGELES, CA	90069
LANE, ANDREW J	SCREENWRITER	8955 BEVERLY BLVD	WEST HOLLYWOOD, CA	90048
LANE, BRIAN	BASEBALL	POST OFFICE BOX 11002	CHATTANOOGA, TN	37401
LANE, CHARLES	ACTOR	321 GRETNA GREEN WY	LOS ANGELES, CA	90049
LANE, CRISTY	SINGER	1225 APACHE LN	MADISON, TN	37115
LANE, DIANE	ACTRESS	151 S EL CAMINO DR	BEVERLY HILLS, CA	90212
LANE, DICK "NIGHT TRAIN"	FOOTBALL	18100 MEYERS	DETROIT, MI	48235
LANE, EDWARD	ACTOR	POST OFFICE BOX 163	BRONX, NY	10471
LANE, FRANCIS	ACTOR-WRITER	STAMPA ESTERA		
		55 VIA DELLA MERCEDE	ROME	ITALY
LANE, GARY	FOOTBALL REFEREE	NFL, 410 PARK AVE	NEW YORK, NY	10022
LANE, GILA	ACTRESS	BERNSTEIN, 355 N GENESEE AVE	LOS ANGELES, CA	90036
LANE, IVA	ACTRESS	1752 FEDERAL AVE #5	LOS ANGELES, CA	90025
LANE, IVAN	COMPOSER	1085 CAROLYN WY	BEVERLY HILLS, CA	90210
LANE, JEFFREY S	TV WRITER	888 7TH AVE #1602	NEW YORK, NY	10019
LANE, JEROME	BASKETBALL	POST OFFICE BOX 4658	DENVER, CO	80204
LANE, KEVIN	BASEBALL	POST OFFICE BOX 422229	KISSIMMEE, FL	34742
LANE, LAUREN	ACTRESS	CANNELL, 7083 HOLLYWOOD BLVD	HOLLYWOOD, CA	90028
LANE, LENITA	ACTRESS	WILBUR, 4279 CLYBOURN AVE	NORTH HOLLYWOOD, CA	91602
LANE, LINDA	SCREENWRITER	8955 BEVERLY BLVD	WEST HOLLYWOOD, CA	90048
LANE, MARIE	ACTRESS	CAVANAU, 101-41 132ND ST	RICHMOND HILL, NY	11419
LANE, MC GUFFY	SINGER	ENTERTAINMENT ARTS, INC		
		819 18TH AVE S	NASHVILLE, TN	37203
LANE, MIKE	CARTOONIST	POST OFFICE BOX 1377	BALTIMORE, MD	21278
LANE, NICHOLAS J	COMPOSER	3659 EDENHURST AVE	LOS ANGELES, CA	90039
LANE, NOLAN	BASEBALL	2501 ALLEN AVE, SE	CANTON, OH	44707
LANE, PAULA MARTIN	COSTUME DESIGNER	5584 BONNEVILLE RD	HIDDEN HILLS, CA	91302
LANE, PRISCILLA	ACTRESS	RURAL ROUTE #1, NORTH SHORE RD	DERRY, NH	03038
LANE, REESE	ACTOR	2334 CLEMENT AVE	VENICE, CA	90291
LANE, ROBERT C	ACTOR	CBS-TV, 51 W 52ND ST	NEW YORK, NY	10019
LANE, ROBIN	SINGER	25 HUNTINGTON AVE #420	BOSTON, MA	02116
LANE, SCOTT	BASEBALL EXECUTIVE	POST OFFICE BOX 418	SAINT CHARLES, IL	60174
LANE, SCOTT EDWARD	ACTOR	727 ASHLAND AVE #8	SANTA MONICA, CA	90405
LANE, WILLIAM	DIRECTOR	10427 VARIEL AVE	CHATSWORTH, CA	91311
LANEUVILLE, ERIC	ACTOR	5138 W SLAUSEN AVE	LOS ANGELES, CA	90056
LANFRANCO, RAPHAEL	BASEBALL	POST OFFICE BOX 824	BURLINGTON, IA	52601
LANG, ANDREW	BASKETBALL	SUNS, 2910 N CENTRAL AVE	PHOENIX, AZ	85012
LANG, BELINDA	ACTRESS	MC REDDIE, 91 REGENT ST	LONDON W1R 7TB	ENGLAND
LANG, CHARLES	BASEBALL EXECUTIVE	POST OFFICE BOX 9194	HAMPTON, VA	23670
LANG, CHARLEY	ACTOR	NBC-TV, "DAYS OF OUR LIVES"		
		3000 W ALAMEDA AVE	BURBANK, CA	91523
LANG, CHARLEY	FILM DIRECTOR	9300 WILSHIRE BLVD #410	BEVERLY HILLS, CA	90212
LANG, DAVID	FOOTBALL	RAMS, 2327 W LINCOLN BLVD	ANAHEIM, CA	92801
LANG, GLENNA	ARTIST	43 STEARNS ST	CAMBRIDGE, MA	02138
LANG, JENNINGS	FILM PRODUCER	MCA/UNIVERSAL STUDIOS, INC		
		100 UNIVERSAL CITY PLAZA	UNIVERSAL CITY, CA	91608
LANG, JOAN	ARTIST	6 JANE ST	NEW YORK, NY	10014
LANG, JUNE	ACTRESS	MORGAN, 12756 KAHLENBERG LN	NORTH HOLLYWOOD, CA	91607
LANG, K D	SINGER	1616 W 3RD AVE	VANCOUVER, BC V6J 1K2	CANADA
LANG, KATHERINE KELLY	ACTRESS	9229 SUNSET BLVD #311	LOS ANGELES, CA	90069
LANG, KELLY	SINGER	POST OFFICE BOX 121089	NASHVILLE, TN	37212
LANG, LE-LO	FOOTBALL	BRONCOS, 13655 BRONCOS PKWY	ENGLEWOOD, CO	80112
LANG, MIKE	SINGER	3012 STONEHENGE LN	CARROLLTON, TX	75006
LANG, MIREK	DIRECTOR-PRODUCER	GARDEN FLAT, 56 ARGYLE RD	LONDON W13 8AA	ENGLAND
LANG, OTTO	FILM DIRECTOR	15454 S MOUNTAIN RD	SANTA PAULA, CA	93060
LANG, PETER	ANIMATOR-WRITER	60 HOLSWORTHY SQ, ELM ST	LONDON WC1	ENGLAND
LANG, RICHARD	TV DIRECTOR	1015 GAYLEY AVE #300	LOS ANGELES, CA	90024
LANG, ROBERT	ACTOR	BELFRAGE, 68 SAINT JAMES'S ST	LONDON SW1A 1LE	ENGLAND
LANG, ROCKY	FILM DIRECTOR	606 MOUNTAIN DR	BEVERLY HILLS, CA	90210
LANG, STAN	DIRECTOR	250 GEORGE RD #21-J	CLIFFSIDE PARK, NJ	07010
LANG, TIM	BASEBALL-INSTRUCTOR	333 W 35TH ST	CHICAGO, IL	60616
LANG, W RICHARD, JR	DIRECTOR	1015 GAYLEY AVE #300	LOS ANGELES, CA	90024
LANGAN, TOM	TV PRODUCER	CBS-TV, 7800 BEVERLY BLVD	LOS ANGELES, CA	90036

Name	Occupation	Address	City	Zip
LANGBEHN, GREGG	BASEBALL	POST OFFICE BOX 598	BINGHAMTON, NY	13902
LANGDON, HARRY	PHOTOGRAPHER	181 N MC CADDEN PL	LOS ANGELES, CA	90004
LANGDON, SUE ANN	ACTRESS	3800 BARHAM BLVD #303	LOS ANGELES, CA	90068
LANGE, HENRY J, JR	DIRECTOR	2276 BOWMONT DR	BEVERLY HILLS, CA	90210
LANGE, HOPE	ACTRESS	803 BRAMBLE WY	LOS ANGELES, CA	90049
LANGE, JESSICA	ACTRESS	CAA, 9830 WILSHIRE BLVD	BEVERLY HILLS, CA	90212
LANGE, JIM	RADIO-TV PERSONALITY	KMPC, 5858 SUNSET BLVD	LOS ANGELES, CA	90028
LANGE, MICHAEL R	TV DIRECTOR	14021 MARQUESAS WY	MARINA DEL REY, CA	90292
LANGE, ROBERT	WRI-DIR-PROD	CBS NEWS, 524 W 57TH ST	NEW YORK, NY	10019
LANGE, TED	ACT-WRI-DIR	19305 REDWING ST	TARZANA, CA	91356
LANGELLA, FRANK	ACTOR	1999 AVE OF THE STARS #2850	LOS ANGELES, CA	90067
LANGENKAMP, HEATHER	ACTRESS	1999 AVE OF THE STARS #2850	LOS ANGELES, CA	90067
LANGER, BERNHARD	GOLFER	POST OFFICE BOX 109601	PALM BCH GARDENS, FL	33418
LANGER, CHRISTINE	ACTRESS	CBS-TV, "THE GUIDING LIGHT"		
		222 E 44TH ST	NEW YORK, NY	10017
LANGFORD, BONNIE	ACTRESS-SINGER	MARSH, 19 DENMARK ST	LONDON WC2H 8NA	ENGLAND
LANGFORD, FRANCES	SINGER	POST OFFICE BOX 96	JENSEN BEACH, FL	33457
LANGFORD, RICH	BASEBALL	POST OFFICE BOX 4669	CHARLESTON, WV	25304
LANGFORD, ROBIN	ACTOR	501 W 123RD ST #10-G	NEW YORK, NY	10027
LANGHORNE, REGGIE	FOOTBALL	BROWNS, 80 1ST ST	BEREA, OH	44017
LANGLEY, DAVID	DIRECTOR	536 W 50TH ST	NEW YORK, NY	10019
LANGLEY, LEE	BASEBALL	POST OFFICE BOX 10336	CLEARWATER, FL	34617
LANGLOIS, LISA	ACTRESS	5750 WILSHIRE BLVD #512	LOS ANGELES, CA	90036
LANGLOIS, LORRAINE	FASHION DESIGNER	85 MOWAT AVE	TORONTO, ONT M6K 3E3	CANADA
LANGNER, PHILIP	THEATER PRODUCER	THEATRE GUILD PRODS		
		226 W 47TH ST	NEW YORK, NY	10036
LANGSTON, MARK	BASEBALL	POST OFFICE BOX 2000	ANAHEIM, CA	92803
LANGSTON, MURRAY	COMEDIAN-ACTOR	3701 WILOWCREST AVE	STUDIO CITY, CA	91604
LANGTON, BASIL	ACTOR-DIRECTOR	41 W 69TH ST	NEW YORK, NY	10023
LANGTON, SIMON	TV DIRECTOR	BROWN, 162-168 REGENT ST	LONDON W1R 5TB	ENGLAND
LANGWAY, ROD	HOCKEY	JETS, 15-1430 MAROONS RD	WINNIPEG, MAN R3G 0L5	CANADA
LANHAM, PAUL	FOOTBALL COACH	BROWNS, 80 1ST ST	BEREA, OH	44017
LANIER, HAL	BASEBALL-COACH	11250 SW RIO VISTA	DUNELLON, FL	32630
LANIER, KEN	FOOTBALL	BRONCOS, 13655 BRONCOS PKWY	ENGLEWOOD, CO	80112
LANKFORD, KIM	ACTRESS	905 2ND ST #15	SANTA MONICA, CA	90403
LANKFORD, PAUL	FOOTBALL	DOLPHINS, 2269 NW 199TH ST	MIAMI, FL	33056
LANKFORD, RAY	BASEBALL	250 STADIUM PLAZA	ST LOUIS, MO	63102
LANKOVA, BISTRA	WRITER-PRODUCER	165 W 46TH ST #409	NEW YORK, NY	10036
LANNOM, LES	ACTOR	11512 EMELITA ST	NORTH HOLLYWOOD, CA	91601
LANSBURGH, LARRY	WRITER-PRODUCER	POST OFFICE BOX 559	EAGLE POINT, OR	97524
LANSBURY, ANGELA	ACTRESS	635 N BONHILL RD	LOS ANGELES, CA	90049
LANSBURY, EDGAR	THEATER PRODUCER	450 W 42ND ST	NEW YORK, NY	10036
LANSBURY, WILLIAM	WRITER	10847 VICENZA WY	LOS ANGELES, CA	90077
LANSFORD, CARNEY	BASEBALL	ATHLETICS'S, OAKLAND COLISEUM	OAKLAND, CA	94621
LANSFORD, WILLIAM	TV WRITER	6953 TROLLEY WY	PLAYA DEL REY, CA	90291
LANSING, MIKE	BASEBALL	POST OFFICE BOX 15757	HARRISBURG, PA	17105
LANSING, ROBERT	ACTOR-DIRECTOR	10 E 44TH ST #700	NEW YORK, NY	10017
LANSING, SHERRY	FILM EXECUTIVE	1500 SAN YSIDRO DR	BEVERLY HILLS, CA	90210
LANSKY, KAREN	WRITER	3940 SAPPHIRE DR	ENCINO, CA	91436
LANTEAU, WILLIAM	ACTOR	2294 ALCYONA DR	LOS ANGELES, CA	90068
LANTOS, TOM	U S CONGRESSMAN	400 EL CAMINO REAL #820	SAN MATEO, CA	94402
LANTRIP, RICK	BASEBALL	POST OFFICE BOX 22093	GREENSBORO, NC	27420
LANTZ, ROBERT	TALENT-LITERARY AGT	LANTZ, 888 7TH AVE, 25TH FLOOR	NEW YORK, NY	10106
LANTZ, STU	BASKETBALL	POST OFFICE BOX 10	INGLEWOOD, CA	90306
LANTZ, WALTER	CARTOONIST	444 LAKESIDE DR #310	BURBANK, CA	91505
LANZARONE, BENJAMIN A	COMPOSER-CONDUCTOR	11455 SUNSHINE TERR	STUDIO CITY, CA	91604
LANZILLO, PAT	BODYBUILDER	CHAMPIONS TRAINING COMPLEX		
		22 4TH ST	TROY, NY	12180
LAORETTI, LARRY	GOLFER	PGA SENIORS, 112 T P C BLVD	PONTE VEDRA BEACH, FL	32082
LAPENIEKS, VILIS M	CINEMATOGRAPHER	POST OFFICE BOX 2230	HOLLYWOOD, CA	90078
LAPIDESE, JONATHAN E	WRITER	11745 LANDALE ST	NORTH HOLLYWOOD, CA	91607
LAPOTAIRE, JANE	ACTRESS	ICM, 388-396 OXFORD ST	LONDON W1	ENGLAND
LAPOTEN, GARY	FILM DIRECTOR	POST OFFICE BOX 2222	BEVERLY HILLS, CA	90213
LAPPIN-THEMELIS, MARCIA	DIRECTOR	114 W 70TH ST	NEW YORK, NY	10023
LARABEE, LOUISE	ACTRESS	HOTEL MANHATTAN PLAZA		
		400 W 43RD ST	NEW YORK, NY	10036
LARBEY, BOB	TV-COMEDY WRITER	LEMON, 24 POTTERY, HOLLAND PK	LONDON W11 4LZ	ENGLAND
LARCH, JOHN	ACTOR	4506 VARNA AVE	SHERMAN OAKS, CA	91423
LARDNER, RING, JR	WRITER	55 CENTRAL PARK W	NEW YORK, NY	10023
LARGE, EDDIE	IMPRESSIONIST	PETER PRITCHARD, MEZZANINE FL		
		235 REGENT HOUSE	LONDON W1R 8AX	ENGLAND
LARICK, DWIGHT	ACTOR	3041 W AVE 35 #1	LOS ANGELES, CA	90065
LARIONOV, IGOR	HOCKEY	CANUCKS, 100 N RENFREW ST	VANCOUVER, BC V5K 3N7	CANADA
LARKEN, JOHN DAVID	DIRECTOR	16 E 72ND ST	NEW YORK, NY	10021
LARKEN, SHEILA	ACTRESS	9229 SUNSET BLVD #311	LOS ANGELES, CA	90069
LARKIN, BARRY	BASEBALL	REDS, 100 RIVERFRONT STADIUM	CINCINNATI, OH	45202
LARKIN, BILL	TV WRITER	6725 SUNSET BLVD #506	HOLLYWOOD, CA	90028
LARKIN, GENE	BASEBALL	TWINS, 501 CHICAGO AVE S	MINNEAPOLIS, MN	55415
LARKIN, SHEILA	ACTRESS	1626 N ORANGE GROVE AVE	LOS ANGELES, CA	90046
LARKIN, TRISHA	ARTIST	843 S ELMWOOD	CHICAGO, IL	60304
LARMER, STEVE	HOCKEY	BLACKHAWKS, 1800 W MADISON ST	CHICAGO, IL	60612
LARNELLE	SINGER	POST OFFICE BOX 1776	LONGWOOD, FL	32750
LARNER, JEREMY	SCREENWRITER	8955 BEVERLY BLVD	WEST HOLLYWOOD, CA	90048
LARNER, STEVAN	CINEMATOGRAPHER	POST OFFICE BOX 1116	PACIFIC PALISADES, CA	90272
LARON, ELAINE	WRITER	7367 HOLLYWOOD BLVD #206	HOLLYWOOD, CA	90046

LAROSA, MARK	BASEBALL	POLECATS, 608 N SLAPPEY BLVD	ALBANY, GA 31701
LARRATT, IRIS	SINGER	4680 ELK LAKE DR #304	VICTORIA, BC V8Z 5M1 CANADA
LARREGUI, ED	BASEBALL	1524 W NEBRASKA AVE	PEORIA, IL 61604
LARROQUETTE, JOHN	ACTOR	POST OFFICE BOX 6303	MALIBU, CA 90265
LARRY, SHELDON	FILM DIRECTOR	143 W 21ST ST	NEW YORK, NY 10011
LARSEN, BILL	BASEBALL EXECUTIVE	POST OFFICE BOX 418	SAINT CHARLES, IL 60174
LARSEN, MILT	TV WRITER	8955 BEVERLY BLVD	WEST HOLLYWOOD, CA 90048
LARSON, DARRELL	ACTOR	2101 6TH ST	SANTA MONICA, CA 90405
LARSON, DON	BASEBALL	17090 COPPER HILL DR	MORGAN HILL, CA 95037
LARSON, DUANE	BASEBALL SCOUT	SKYDOME, 300 BREMMER BL #3200	TORONTO, ONT M5V 3B3 CANADA
LARSON, ED	BASEBALL EXECUTIVE	POST OFFICE BOX 936	BELOIT, WI 53511
LARSON, GARY	CARTOONIST	UPS, 4900 MAIN ST, 9TH FLOOR	KANSAS CITY, MO 64112
LARSON, GLEN	TV WRITER-PRODUCER	351 DELFERN DR	LOS ANGELES, CA 90077
LARSON, JACK	ACTOR	449 SKYEWIAY RD N	LOS ANGELES, CA 90049
LARSON, JILL	ACTRESS	ABC-TV, "ALL MY CHILDREN"	
		320 W 66TH ST	NEW YORK, NY 10023
LARSON, KURT	FOOTBALL	PACKERS, 1265 LOMBARDI AVE	GREEN BAY, WI 54307
LARSON, LISBY	ACTOR	ABC-TV, "LOVING"	
		320 W 66TH ST, STUDIO 23	NEW YORK, NY 10023
LARSON, LISSER FORST	BODYBUILDER	SEE - FORST-LARSON, LISSER	
LARSON, NICOLETTE	SINGER-SONGWRITER	POST OFFICE BOX 150973	NASHVILLE, TN 37215
LARSON, PAUL	ACTOR	1125 6TH ST #9	SANTA MONICA, CA 90403
LARSON, ROBERT E	DIRECTOR-PRODUCER	26544 SAND CYN RD	CANYON COUNTRY, CA 915351
LARSON, VERNON L	AUDITOR	STATE CAPITOL BUILDING	PIERRE, SD 57501
LARY, FRANK	BASEBALL	RURAL ROUTE #8, BOX 142	NORTHPORT, AL 35476
LASCHEN, TERRY	BASEBALL SCOUT	BREWERS, 201 S 46TH ST	MILWAUKEE, WI 53214
LASER BOY	ROCK & ROLL GROUP	POST OFFICE BOX 1909	MILL VALLEY, CA 94942
LASHER, MARY ANN	ARTIST	1105 LAKEPOINTE	GROSS POINTE PARK, MI 48230
LASKA, RAY	ACTOR	763 S BURLINGAME AVE	LOS ANGELES, CA 90049
LASKER, ALEX	SCREENWRITER	7 FLEET ST #105	MARINA DEL REY, CA 90292
LASKER, DEEDEE	GOLFER	2750 VOLUSA AVE #B	DAYTON BEACH, FL 32114
LASKER, JAY	RECORD EXECUTIVE	MOTOWN, 6255 SUNSET BLVD	HOLLYWOOD, CA 90028
LASKER, LAWRENCE	SCREENWRITER	ICM, 8899 BEVERLY BLVD	LOS ANGELES, CA 90048
LASKEY, DAVID	SINGER	POST OFFICE BOX 5880	SHERMAN OAKS, CA 91413
LASKO, GENE	DIRECTOR-PRODUCER	12 E 86TH ST	NEW YORK, NY 10028
LASKOS, ANDREW	SCREENWRITER	ICM, 8899 BEVERLY BLVD	LOS ANGELES, CA 90048
LASKUS, JACEK	CINEMATOGRAPHER	POST OFFICE BOX 1166	PACIFIC PALISADES, CA 90272
LASKY, GILBERT	SCREENWRITER	10969 WELLWORTH AVE #325	LOS ANGELES, CA 90024
LASKY, JESSE L	SCREENWRITER	MANN, 1 OLD COMPTON ST	LONDON W1 ENGLAND
LASKY, LARRY	BASEBALL TRAINER	POST OFFICE BOX 27045	TUCSON, AZ 85726
LASKY, PAT SILVER	SCREENWRITER	MANN, 1 OLD COMPTON ST	LONDON W1V 5PH ENGLAND
LASKY, ROBERT	ACTOR	15951 VINCENNES ST	SEPULVEDA, CA 91343
LASORDA, TOMMY	BASEBALL-MANAGER	1000 ELYSIAN PARK DR	LOS ANGELES, CA 90012
LASSALLY, PETER	TV PROCUDER	1121 LOMA VISTA DR	BEVERLY HILLS, CA 90210
LASSALLY, WALTER	LIGHTING DIRECTOR	THE ABBEY, EYE	SUFFOLK ENGLAND
LASSWELL, FRED	CARTOONIST	1111 N WESTSHORE BLVD	TAMPA, FL 33607
LAST, RUTH	ACTRESS	440 W END AVE	NEW YORK, NY 10024
LAST DRIVE, THE	ROCK & ROLL GROUP	HITCH-HYKE RECORDS	
		5 KOSMA BALANOU	ATHENS 116-36 GREECE
LASTER, OWEN	TALENT AGENT	151 S EL CAMINO DR	BEVERLY HILLS, CA 90212
LASTING, RICHARD	ACTOR	3245 PRIMERA AVE	LOS ANGELES, CA 90068
LASZLO, ANDREW	CINEMATOGRAPHER	2766 CARMAR DR	LOS ANGELES, CA 90046
LATAL, JIRI	HOCKEY	FLYERS, SPECTRUM, PATTISON PL	PHILADELPHIA, PA 19148
LATE NITE	ROCK & ROLL GROUP	BROTHERS, 141 DUNBAR AVE	FORDS, NJ 08863
LATEEF, AHMED	TV DIRECTOR	4163 MURIETTA AVE	SHERMAN OAKS, CA 91423
LATELLA, DENISE	ACTRESS	1999 N SYCAMORE AVE #15	LOS ANGELES, CA 90068
LATER, TERRY	ACTOR	259 25TH ST	SANTA MONICA, CA 90402
LATHAM, AARON	SCREENWRITER	8955 BEVERLY BLVD	WEST HOLLYWOOD, CA 90048
LATHAM, BILL	BASEBALL COACH	525 NW PEACOCK BLVD	PORT SAINT LUCIE, FL 34986
LATHAM, KENNETH D	COMPOSER	1801 LONGHILL DR	MONTEREY PARK, CA 91754
LATHAM, LOUISE	ACTRESS	2125 PIEDRAS DR	SANTA BARBARA, CA 93108
LATHAM, LYNN M	TV WRITER	PLESHETTE, 2700 N BEACHWOOD DR	LOS ANGELES, CA 90068
LATHAM, MICHAEL	TV PRODUCER	12 DEALTRY RD	LONDON SW15 ENGLAND
LATHAM, PHILIP	ACTOR	BRYAN DREW, MEZANNINE FLOOR	
		QUADRANT HOUSE, 80-82 REGENT ST	LONDON W1R 6AU ENGLAND
LATHAN, STAN	TV DIRECTOR	9200 SUNSET BLVD #423	LOS ANGELES, CA 90069
LATHON, LAMAR	FOOTBALL	OILERS, 6910 FANNIN ST	HOUSTON, TX 77070
LATHROP, PHILIP	CINEMATOGRAPHER	POST OFFICE BOX 1166	PACIFIC PALISADES, CA 90272
LATIMER, MICHAEL	TV WRITER-DIRECTOR	35 HESTERCOMBE AVE	LONDON SW6 5LL ENGLAND
LATIN QUARTER	ROCK & ROLL GROUP	TONY MEILANDT MANAGEMENT	
		1312 N LA BREA AVE	LOS ANGELES, CA 90028
LATTA, GREG	BASEBALL TRAINER	CANADIANS, 4601 ONTARIO ST	VANCOUVER, BC V5V 3H4 CANADA
LATTANZI, MATT	ACTOR-RECORD PROD	POST OFFICE BOX 2710	MALIBU, CA 90265
LATTER, DAVE	BASEBALL	POST OFFICE BOX 2769	HUNTSVILLE, AL 35804
LATTISAW, STACY	SINGER	65 W 55TH ST #6-C	NEW YORK, NY 10019
LATU, LESINI	BODYGUARD	2801 MEADOW LARK DR	SAN DIEGO, CA 92123
LAU, CHARLIE, JR	BASEBALL COACH	POST OFFICE BOX 751	UTICA, NY 13503
LAU, CHERYL	SECRETARY OF STATE	STATE CAPITOL BUILDING	CARSON CITY, NV 89710
LAUBER, KEN M	COMPOSER	244 N BOWLING GREEN WY	LOS ANGELES, CA 90049
LAUDER, ESTEE	COSMETIC EXECUTIVE	767 5TH AVE	NEW YORK, NY 10153
LAUDNER, TIM	BASEBALL	6505 VALLEY VIEW RD	CORCORAN, MN 55340
LAUER, BRAD	HOCKEY	NASSAU VETS MEMORIAL COLISEUM	UNIONDALE, NY 11553
LAUGHING DOGS, THE	ROCK & ROLL GROUP	3 E 54TH ST #1400	NEW YORK, NY 10022
LAUGHLIN, FRANK	DIRECTOR	12953 MARLBORO ST	LOS ANGELES, CA 90049
LAUGHLIN, GREG	U S CONGRESSMAN	312 S MAIN ST	VICTORIA, TX 77901

LAUGHLIN, JOHN	ACTOR	11815 MAGNOLIA BLVD #2	NORTH HOLLYWOOD, CA 91607
LAUGHLIN, TOM	ACTOR-FILM PRODUCER	20933 BIG ROCK DR	MALIBU, CA 90265
LAUGHREN, RICHARD A	SCREENWRITER	23 E 10TH ST	NEW YORK, NY 10003
LAUGHTON, ROGER	TV EXECUTIVE	WOODLANDS, 80 WOOD LN	LONDON W12 OTT ENGLAND
LAUMAN, DOUG	BASEBALL SCOUT	333 W 35TH ST	CHICAGO, IL 60616
LAUNDRA, LINDA	TV DIRECTOR-PRODUCER	400 W 43RD ST #29-L	NEW YORK, NY 10036
LAUNER, S JOHN	ACTOR	4415 ROMERO DR	TARZANA, CA 91356
LAUPER, CYNDI	SINGER-SONGWRITER	853 7TH AVE #9-D	NEW YORK, NY 10019
LAURANCE, MATTHEW	ACTOR	1951 HILLCREST RD	LOS ANGELES, CA 90068
LAURANCE, MITCHELL	ACTOR	2039 N IVAR AVE #3	LOS ANGELES, CA 90068
LAURELS, THE	VOCAL GROUP	RUDY KARDOS, 1107 ADA DR	NORTH HUNTINGTON, PA 15642
LAUREN, ELIZABETH	ACTRESS	9744 WILSHIRE BLVD #312	BEVERLY HILLS, CA 90212
LAUREN, RALPH	FASHION DESIGNER	550 7TH AVE	NEW YORK, NY 10018
LAUREN, TAMMY	ACTOR	151 S EL CAMINO DR	BEVERLY HILLS, CA 90212
LAURENCE, ASHLEY	ACTRESS	190 S CANON DR #201	BEVERLY HILLS, CA 90210
LAURENCE, MICHAEL J	TV WRITER	7 DAVIS RD	PORT WASHINGTON, NY 11050
LAURENCE, ROBERT P	TV CRITIC	POST OFFICE BOX 191	SAN DIEGO, CA 92112
LAURENSON, JAMES	ACTOR	EDWARDS, 275 KENNINGTON RD	LONDON SE1 6BY ENGLAND
LAURIE, JIM	TV EXECUTIVE	ABC NEWS, 7 W 66TH ST	NEW YORK, NY 10023
LAURIE, PIPER	ACTRESS	907 12TH ST	SANTA MONICA, CA 90403
LAURIN, MARIA	ACTRESS	CASTLE, 1101 S ORLANDO AVE	LOS ANGELES, CA 90035
LAUTENBERG, FRANK	U S SENATOR	1 GATEWAY CENTER #1001	NEWARK, NJ 07102
LAUTER, ED	ACTOR	10100 SANTA MONICA BLVD #1600	LOS ANGELES, CA 90067
LAUZERIQUE, GEORGE	BASEBALL SCOUT	INDIANS, CLEVELAND STADIUM	CLEVELAND, OH 44114
LAVAGETTO, HARRY "COOKIE"	BASEBALL	46 TARA RD	ORINDA, CA 94563
LAVALEE, ROBERT	BASEBALL SCOUT	POST OFFICE BOX 90111	ARLINGTON, TX 76004
LAVALLIERE, MIKE	BASEBALL	12 SCOTT AVE	HOCKSETT, NH 03106
LAVAN, AL	FOOTBALL COACH	S F 49ERS, 4949 CENTENNIAL BL	SANTA CLARA, CA 95054
LAVDANSKI, RICHARD M	CONDUCTOR	BOX 72, PINE ST	MOUNTAINHOME, PA 18342
LAVELLE, BILL	BASEBALL EXECUTIVE	POST OFFICE DRAWER 1207	ZEBULON, NC 27597
LAVEN, ARNOLD	DIRECTOR-PRODUCER	15954 VALLEY VISTA BLVD	ENCINO, CA 91436
LAVER, ROD	TENNIS	POST OFFICE BOX 4798	HILTON HEAD ISLAND, SC 29928
LAVI, DALIAH	ACTRESS-MODEL	POSTFACH 300 348	5000 KOLN 30 GERMANY
LAVIANO, FRANK	BASEBALL	POST OFFICE BOX 22093	GREENSBORO, NC 27420
LAVIN, CHERYL	COLUMNIST-CRITIC	TRIBUNE, 64 E CONCORD ST	ORLANDO, FL 32801
LAVIN, CHRISTINE	SINGER-GUITARIST	ROUNDER RECORDS, 1 CAMP ST	CAMBRIDGE, MA 02140
LAVIN, LINDA	ACTRESS-DIRECTOR	20781 BIG ROCK RD	MALIBU, CA 90265
LAW, ALEX	COMPOSER-CONDUCTOR	3105 S HUGHES AVE	FRESNO, CA 93706
LAW, CHRISTOPHER	ACTOR	326 N AVON ST	BURBANK, CA 91505
LAW, JOHN PHILLIP	ACTOR	1339 MILLER DR	LOS ANGELES, CA 90069
LAW, LINDSAY E	TV EXECUTIVE	356 W 58TH ST	NEW YORK, NY 10019
LAW, VANCE	BASEBALL	ATHLETICS'S, OAKLAND COLISEUM	OAKLAND, CA 94621
LAW, VERNON	BASEBALL	1748 N COBBLESTONE DR	PROVO, UT 84604
LAWLER, RALPH	BASKETBALL ANNOUNCER	KCOP-TV, 915 N LA BREA AVE	LOS ANGELES, CA 90038
LAWLER, WILLIAM	TV DIRECTOR	OREGON RD #96	ASHLAND, MA 01721
LAWLES, JACK	SINGER	ROUTE #1, BOX 327	NASHVILLE, IN 47448
LAWLESS, LOUIE	WRITER-PRODUCER	634 E WALNUT AVE	BURBANK, CA 91501
LAWLESS, TOM	BASEBALL	1736 W 25TH ST	ERIE, PA 16502
LAWLOR, BILL	BASEBALL	INDIANS, CLEVELAND STADIUM	CLEVELAND, OH 44114
LAWLOR, DICK	BASEBALL SCOUT	POST OFFICE BOX 7575	PHILADELPHIA, PA 19101
LAWLOR, JOHN H	ACTOR	433 N CAMDEN DR #400	BEVERLY HILLS, CA 90210
LAWNDALE	ROCK & ROLL GROUP	POST OFFICE BOX 1	LAWNDALE, CA 90260
LAWNER, MORDECAI	ACTOR	309 E 76TH ST	NEW YORK, NY 10021
LAWRENCE, ALAN	DIRECTOR-PRODUCER	TALCO, 279 E 44TH ST	NEW YORK, NY 10017
LAWRENCE, ANTHONY	WRITER-PRODUCER	10100 SANTA MONICA BLVD #1600	LOS ANGELES, CA 90067
LAWRENCE, CAROL	ACTRESS-SINGER	12337 RIDGE CIR	LOS ANGELES, CA 90049
LAWRENCE, DAVID	TV WRITER-PRODUCER	13331 MOORPARK ST #330	SHERMAN OAKS, CA 91423
LAWRENCE, DIARMUID	TV DIRECTOR	DAISH, 83 EASTBOURNE MEWS	LONDON W2 6LQ ENGLAND
LAWRENCE, DON	FOOTBALL COACH	BILLS, 1 BILLS DR	ORCHARD PARK, NJ 14127
LAWRENCE, DONALD L	DIRECTOR-PRODUCER	12250 N 64TH ST	SCOTTSDALE, AZ 85254
LAWRENCE, ELIZABETH	ACTRESS	145 W 45TH ST #1204	NEW YORK, NY 10036
LAWRENCE, ELLIOT	CONDUCTOR	NW AYER, 1345 AVE OF THE AMERICAS	NEW YORK, NY 10105
LAWRENCE, HENRY	COMEDIAN	EAI, 2211 INDUSTRIAL BLVD	SARASOTA, FL 33580
LAWRENCE, JAMES	TV WRITER	ROBERTS CO, 427 N CANON DR	BEVERLY HILLS, CA 90210
LAWRENCE, JEROME	SCREENWRITER	21056 LAS FLORES MESA DR	MALIBU, CA 90265
LAWRENCE, JOEY	ACTOR	9200 SUNSET BLVD #710	LOS ANGELES, CA 90069
LAWRENCE, KEVIN	BODYBUILDER	POST OFFICE BOX 3671	NEWPORT BEACH, CA 92663
LAWRENCE, KIVA	ACTRESS	109 1/2 S CLARK DR	LOS ANGELES, CA 90048
LAWRENCE, LEE	ACTOR	7461 BEVERLY BLVD #400	LOS ANGELES, CA 90036
LAWRENCE, MARC	ACTOR-DIRECTOR	14016 BORA BORA WY #19	MARINA DEL REY, CA 90292
LAWRENCE, MARJIE	ACTRESS	13 GLENHURST AVE	LONDON NW5 ENGLAND
LAWRENCE, MARTIN	COMEDIAN-ACTOR	6310 SAN VICENTE BLVD #407	LOS ANGELES, CA 90048
LAWRENCE, PATRICIA	ACTRESS	33 SAINT LUKE'S ST	LONDON SW3 ENGLAND
LAWRENCE, ROBERT	CONDUCTOR	140 E 28TH ST	NEW YORK, NY 10016
LAWRENCE, ROBERT L	DIRECTOR	DGA, 110 W 57TH ST	NEW YORK, NY 10019
LAWRENCE, STEVE	SINGER-ACTOR-WRITER	820 GREENWAY DR	BEVERLY HILLS, CA 90210
LAWRENCE, STEVEN ALAN	MAKE-UP ARTIST	NBC-TV, 1268 E 14TH ST	BROOKLYN, NY 11230
LAWRENCE, VERNON	TV DIRECTOR-PRODUCER	HANCOCK, GREENER HOUSE 66-68 HAYMARKET	LONDON SW1Y 4AW ENGLAND
LAWRENCE-SCHULTZ, VICKI	ACTRESS-SINGER	6000 LIDO AVE	LONG BEACH, CA 90803
LAWS, ELOISE	ACTRESS	POST OFFICE BOX 691736	LOS ANGELES, CA 90069
LAWS, HUBERT	FLUTIST	CASSIDY, 417 MARAWOOD DR	WOODSTOCK, IL 60098
LAWS, RONNIE	SAXOPHONIST	7461 BEVERLY BLVD #303	LOS ANGELES, CA 90036
LAWSON, DAVE	COMPOSER	OTTERDEN, FAVERSHAM	KENT ME13 OBY ENGLAND
LAWSON, DENIS	ACTOR	SHARKEY, 15 GOLDEN SQ #315	LONDON W1R 3AG ENGLAND

Name	Occupation	Address	City/State	Zip/Country
LAWSON, LEE	ACTRESS	145 E 92ND ST	NEW YORK, NY	10128
LAWSON, LEIGH	ACTOR	HEATH, PARAMOUNT HOUSE		
		162-170 WARDOUR ST	LONDON W1V 3AT	ENGLAND
LAWSON, RICHARD	ACTOR	3728 BROADLAWN DR	LOS ANGELES, CA	90068
LAWSON, STEVE	TV WRITER	ROSENSTONE, 3 E 48TH ST	NEW YORK, NY	10017
LAWSON, TERRY	FILM CRITIC	POST OFFICE BOX 1061	DAYTON, OH	45401
LAWSON, TWIGGY	MODEL-ACTRESS-DANCER	BELFRAGE, 68 SAINT JAMES'S ST	LONDON SW1A 1LE	ENGLAND
LAWTON, JONATHAN F	SCREENWRITER	864 S ROBERTSON BLVD #304	LOS ANGELES, CA	90035
LAWTON, MARCUS	BASEBALL	800 HOME RUN LN	MEMPHIS, TN	38104
LAX, BERNARD	TALENT AGENT	9105 CARMELITA AVE #1	BEVERLY HILLS, CA	90210
LAX, SUZANNE	TALENT AGENT	9105 CARMELITA AVE #1	BEVERLY HILLS, CA	90210
LAY, RODNEY & THE WILD WEST	C & W GROUP	POST OFFICE BOX 107	COFFEYVILLE, KS	67337
LAYANA, TIM	BASEBALL	11012 RHODA WY	CULVER CITY, CA	90230
LAYBOURNE, GERALDINE B	TV EXECUTIVE	MTV NETWORKS, 1775 BROADWAY	NEW YORK, NY	10019
LAYDEN, FRANK	BASKETBALL EXECUTIVE	5 TRIAD CENTER #500	SALT LAKE CITY, UT	84180
LAYDEN, SCOTT	BASKETBALL EXECUTIVE	5 TRIAD CENTER #500	SALT LAKE CITY, UT	84180
LAYNE, JERRY	ACTOR	9538 WYSTONE AVE	NORTHRIDGE, CA	91324
LAYNE, JERRY	BASEBALL UMPIRE	308 5TH ST SE	WINTER HAVEN, FL	33880
LAYNE, JOSEPH	MUSIC ARRANGER	101 BEAR TRACK	NASHVILLE, TN	37221
LAYNG, LISSA	ACTRESS	NATHE, 8281 MELROSE AVE #200	LOS ANGELES, CA	90046
LAYTON, BILLY	COMPOSER	4 JOHN'S RD	SETAUKET, NY	11733
LAYTON, GEORGE	ACTOR-WRITER	GREEN, 2 CONDUIT ST	LONDON W1R 9TG	ENGLAND
LAYTON, JOE	DIRECTOR	DGA, 7920 SUNSET BLVD, 6TH FL	LOS ANGELES, CA	90046
LAZAR, AVA	ACTRESS	2566 OVERLAND AVE #550	LOS ANGELES, CA	90064
LAZAR, IMRE, JR	TV DIRECTOR-PRODUCER	CBS-TV, 524 W 57TH ST	NEW YORK, NY	10019
LAZAR, IRVING "SWIFTY"	TALENT AGENT	1840 CARLA RIDGE	BEVERLY HILLS, CA	90210
LAZAR, LINDA	MAKE-UP ARTIST	75 BOWER CT	STATEN ISLAND, NY	10309
LAZAR, MARK	ACTOR	26110 ALIZIA CANYON DR #C	CALABASAS, CA	91302
LAZARD, JUSTIN	ACTOR	9350 WILSHIRE BLVD #324	BEVERLY HILLS, CA	90212
LAZARO, JEFF	HOCKEY	BRUINS, 150 CAUSEWAY ST	BOSTON, MA	02114
LAZAROU, MICHAEL	TV WRITER	UTA, 9560 WILSHIRE BL, 5TH FL	BEVERLY HILLS, CA	90212
LAZARUS, JERRY	SCREENWRITER	555 W 57TH ST #1230	NEW YORK, NY	10019
LAZENBY, GEORGE	ACTOR	1127 21ST ST	SANTA MONICA, CA	90403
LAZER, DAVID	TV PRODUCER	HENSON ASSOC, 117 E 69TH ST	NEW YORK, NY	10021
LAZO, JOY	ACTRESS	3460 CARDIFF AVE #115	LOS ANGELES, CA	90034
LAZY COWGIRLS, THE	ROCK & ROLL GROUP	POST OFFICE BOX 1116	CULVER CITY, CA	90232
LAZY RACER	ROCK & ROLL GROUP	5 W 86TH ST #156	NEW YORK, NY	10024
LAZZARO, SAM	BASEBALL EXECUTIVE	POST OFFICE BOX 842	SALEM, VA	24153
LE BARON, EDDIE	FOOTBALL	6330 RIVER CHASE CIR	ATLANTA, GA	30328
LE BEAU, BECKY	ACTRESS-MODEL	505 B BEVERLY DR #973	BEVERLY HILLS, CA	90212
LE BEAU, DICK	FOOTBALL COACH	BENGALS, 200 RIVERFRONT STADIUM	CINCINNATI, OH	45202
LE BEL, HARPER	FOOTBALL	FALCONS, SUWANEE RD AT I-85	SUWANEE, GA	30174
LE BLANC, CHRISTIAN	ACTOR	CBS-TV, "YOUNG & THE RESTLESS"		
		7800 BEVERLY BLVD #3305	LOS ANGELES, CA	90036
LE BLANC, LENNY	SINGER	HEARTLAND, 660 DOUGLAS AVE	ALTAMONTE SPRINGS, FL	32714
LE BLANC, ROLAND	BASEBALL SCOUT	BREWERS, 201 S 46TH ST	MILWAUKEE, WI	53214
LE BLANC, WHITNEY J	DIRECTOR	9255 SUNSET BLVD #515	LOS ANGELES, CA	90069
LE BOEUF, AL	BASEBALL COACH	POST OFFICE BOX 15050	READING, PA	19612
LE BON, SIMON	SINGER-SONGWRITER	25 TEWKESBURY AVE	PINNER, MIDDLESEX	ENGLAND
LE BROCK, KELLY	ACTRESS-MODEL	POST OFFICE BOX 727	LOS OLIVAS, CA	93441
LE BRON, JOSE	BASEBALL	12000 STADIUM RD	ADELANTO, CA	92301
LE BRON, LARRY J	WRITER	1800 MONTANA AVE	SANTA MONICA, CA	90403
LE CARRE, JOHN	WRITER	TREGIFFIAN, SAINT BURYAN		
		PEMZANCE	CORNWALL	ENGLAND
LE CLAIR, JOHN	HOCKEY	CANADIENS, 2313 ST CATHERINE ST	MONTREAL, QUE H3H 1N2	CANADA
LE CLAIR, MICHAEL	ACTOR	12517 PARAMOUNT BLVD	DOWNEY, CA	90242
LE CLERC, JEAN	ACTOR	14 E 60TH ST #904	NEW YORK, NY	10022
LE COMPTE, JOHN	BASEBALL EXECUTIVE	POST OFFICE BOX 1457	MEDFORD, OR	97501
LE COVER, LISA	ACTRESS	115 N DOHENY DR #316	LOS ANGELES, CA	90046
LE JOHN, DON	BASEBALL SCOUT	1000 ELYSIAN PARK DR	LOS ANGELES, CA	90012
LE MASTERS, KIM	TV EXECUTIVE	CBS-TV, 7800 BEVERLY BLVD	LOS ANGELES, CA	90036
LE MAT, PAUL	ACTOR	1100 N ALTA LOMA RD #805	LOS ANGELES, CA	90069
LE NOIRE, ROSETTA	ACTRESS	AMAS REPERTORY THEATRE		
		1 E 104TH ST	NEW YORK, NY	10029
LE PREVOST, NICHOLAS	ACTOR	43-A PRINCESS RD, REGENTS PK	LONDON NW1 8JS	ENGLAND
LE ROI BROTHERS, THE	ROCK & ROLL GROUP	RICE, 6908 CHERRY MEADOW DR	AUSTIN, TX	78745
LE ROY, GLORIA	ACTRESS	3500 W OLIVE AVE #1400	BURBANK, CA	91505
LE VANGIE, DANA	BASEBALL	RED SOX, CHAIN O'LAKES PARK	WINTER HAVEN, FL	33880
LE VEQUE, JOHN FRANCIS	SCREENWRITER	9027 GIBSON ST	LOS ANGELES, CA	90034
LE WINTER, JACQUELINE	TALENT AGENT	4051 RADFORD AVE #A	STUDIO CITY, CA	91604
LEACH, JALAL	BASEBALL	POST OFFICE BOX 2148	WOODBRIDGE, VA	22193
LEACH, JIM	U S CONGRESSMAN	209 W 4TH ST	DAVENPORT, IA	52801
LEACH, RICK	BASEBALL	4033 WEST CT	FLINT, MI	48504
LEACH, ROBIN	TV HOST	875 3RD AVE #1800	NEW YORK, NY	10022
LEACH, ROSEMARY	ACTRESS	WM MORRIS, 31-32 SOHO SQ	LONDON W1V 5DG	ENGLAND
LEACH, STEPHEN	HOCKEY	JETS, 15-1430 MAROONS RD	WINNIPEG, MAN R3G OL5	CANADA
LEACH, TERRY	BASEBALL	333 W 35TH ST	CHICAGO, IL	60616
LEACHMAN, CLORIS	ACTRESS	13127 BOCA DE CANON LN	LOS ANGELES, CA	90049
LEACHMAN, LAMAR	FOOTBALL COACH	LIONS, 1200 FEATHERSTONE RD	PONTIAC, MI	48432
LEADER, TONY	TV DIRECTOR	112 S LA JOLLA AVE	LOS ANGELES, CA	90048
LEADON, BERNIE	SINGER	POST OFFICE BOX 1340	TOPANGA CANYON, CA	90290
LEAF, PAUL	WRI-DRI-PROD	2800 NEILSON WY #408	SANTA MONICA, CA	90405
LEAHY, PAT	FOOTBALL	N Y JETS, 1000 FULTON AVE	HEMPSTEAD, NY	11550
LEAHY, PATRICK J	U S SENATOR	31 GREEN ACRES DR	BURLINGTON, VT	05402
LEAHY, THOMAS	BASEBALL	POST OFFICE BOX 507	DURHAM, NC	27702

Name	Occupation	Address	City	Zip
LEAHY, THOMAS F	TV EXECUTIVE	CBS-TV, 51 W 52ND ST	NEW YORK, NY	10019
LEAKE, CRAIG	WRITER-PRODUCER	CBS-TV, 524 W 57TH ST	NEW YORK, NY	10019
LEAKE-GLENN, CYNTHIA	ACTRESS	7461 BEVERLY BLVD #400	LOS ANGELES, CA	90036
LEAPING LANNY	WRESTLER	SEE - POFFO, LEAPING LANNY		
LEAR, AMANDA	SINGER-ACTRESS	POSTFACH 800149	D-8000 MUNICH 80	GERMANY
LEAR, NORMAN	TV WRITER-PRODUCER	1999 AVE OF THE STARS #500	LOS ANGELES, CA	90067
LEARMAN, RICHARD	DIRECTOR	11920 SIERRA LN	NORTHRIDGE, CA	91326
LEARNED, MICHAEL	ACTRESS	145 CENTRAL PARK W	NEW YORK, NY	10023
LEARY, BRIANNE	ACTRESS	9229 SUNSET BLVD #311	LOS ANGELES, CA	90069
LEARY, DR TIMOTHY	AUTHOR-LECTURER	3828 WILLAT AVE	CULVER CITY, CA	90230
LEARY, ROB	BASEBALL	POST OFFICE BOX 882	MADISON, WI	53701
LEARY, ROB	BASEBALL MANAGER	POST OFFICE BOX 6748	ROCKFORD, IL	61125
LEARY, TIM	BASEBALL	N Y YANKEES, YANKEE STADIUM	BRONX, NY	10451
LEARY, TIMOTHY	AUTHOR	10601 SUNBROOK DR	BEVERLY HILLS, CA	90210
LEASURE, JAN	COLUMNIST	UPS, 4900 MAIN ST, 9TH FLOOR	KANSAS CITY, MO	64112
LEATHERMAN, JEFF	BASEBALL	POST OFFICE BOX 3746, HILL STA	AUGUSTA, GA	30904
LEATHERWOLF	ROCK & ROLL GROUP	POST OFFICE BOX 9555	MARINA DEL REY, CA	90295
LEAVER, DON	TV DIRECTOR	BROWN, 162-168 REGENT ST	LONDON W1R 5TB	ENGLAND
LEAVITT, RON	TV WRITER	UTA, 9560 WILSHIRE BL, 5TH FL	BEVERLY HILLS, CA	90212
LEAVITT, SHARYN	ACTRESS	UTA, 9560 WILSHIRE BL, 5TH FL	BEVERLY HILLS, CA	90212
LEBAK, DAVID	BASEBALL	POST OFFICE BOX 20849	CHARLESTON, SC	29413
LEBEAU, STEPHAN	HOCKEY	CANADIENS, 2313 ST CATHERINE ST	MONTREAL, QUE H3H 1N2	CANADA
LEBENSON, RICHARD	ARTIST	253 WASHINGTON AVE	BROOKLYN, NY	11205
LEBENZON, MAYA	ACTRESS	335 N MAPLE DR #250	BEVERLY HILLS, CA	90210
LEBOEUF, AL	BASEBALL COACH	POST OFFICE BOX 3449	SCRANTON, PA	18505
LEBOVITZ, AMY	RECORD EXECUTIVE	AIM RECORDS, 6733 GLEEN	WHITTIER, CA	90601
LEBOW, MARTEE	SINGER	RAW MGMT, 48 W 37TH ST	NEW YORK, NY	10018
LEBOW, SYLVAN	TV PRODUCER	360 E 72ND ST #C-2200	NEW YORK, NY	10021
LEBOWITZ, LEO	CINEMATOGRAPHER	POST OFFICE BOX 10	DENVER, CO	12421
LEBOWITZ, MURRAY	ACTOR	10845 LINDBROOK DR #3	LOS ANGELES, CA	90024
LEBOWITZ, NEIL	TV WRITER	211 S BEVERLY DR #206	BEVERLY HILLS, CA	90212
LEBSOCK, JACK	SINGER-GUITARIST	103 DANA DR	HENDERSONVILLE, TN	37075
LECHMAN, DON	FILM CRITIC	THE DAILY BREEZE		
		5215 TORRANCE BLVD	TORRANCE, CA	90509
LECHOWICK, BERNARD	WRITER-PRODUCER	PLESHETTE, 2700 N BEACHWOOD DR	LOS ANGELES, CA	90068
LECKEY, ANDREW	COLUMNIST	TRIBUNE, 64 E CONCORD ST	ORLANDO, FL	32801
LECKNER, ERIC	BASKETBALL	KINGS, 1 SPORTS PARKWAY	SACRAMENTO, CA	95834
LEDDING, EDWARD	DIRECTOR-PRODUCER	6384 LA PUHTA DR	LOS ANGELES, CA	90068
LEDER, HERBERT JAY	WRITER-PRODUCER	90 RIVERSIDE DR	NEW YORK, NY	10024
LEDER, MIMI	TV DIRECTOR	131 S RODEO DR #300	BEVERLY HILLS, CA	90212
LEDER, REUBEN A	TV WRITER-PRODUCER	13400 CHANDLER BLVD	VAN NUYS, CA	91401
LEDERER, FRANCIS	ACTOR-DIRECTOR	POST OFFICE BOX 32	CANOGA PARK, CA	91305
LEDERER, RICHARD	FILM EXECUTIVE	17026 AVE SANTA YNEZ	PACIFIC PALISADES, CA	90272
LEDERER, SUZANNE	ACTRESS	13400 CHANDLER BLVD	VAN NUYS, CA	91401
LEDERGERBER, SONJA	ACTRESS	600 WILLIAMS LN	BEVERLY HILLS, CA	90210
LEDESMA, AARON	BASEBALL	525 NW PEACOCK BLVD	PORT SAINT LUCIE, FL	34986
LEDEZMA, CARLOS	BASEBALL TRAINER	POST OFFICE BOX 450	BUFFALO, NY	14205
LEDFORD, HERB	BASEBALL EXECUTIVE	POST OFFICE BOX 1535	JOHNSON CITY, TN	37605
LEDFORD, JUDITH	ACTRESS	1443 N HAYWORTH AVE	LOS ANGELES, CA	90046
LEDNA, MIKE	BASEBALL SCOUT	ORIOLE PARK, 333 W CAMDEN ST	BALTIMORE, MD	21201
LEDOUX, CHRIS	SINGER-GUITARIST	POST OFFICE BOX 253	SUMNER, IA	50674
LEDYARD, GRANT	HOCKEY	SABRES, MEMORIAL AUDITORIUM	BUFFALO, NY	14202
LEE, ALAN S	WRITER-PRODUCER	5334 DONNA AVE	TARZANA, CA	91356
LEE, ALBERT	SINGER-GUITARIST	6399 WILSHIRE BLVD #PH	LOS ANGELES, CA	90048
LEE, ANDREW L	TV DIRECTOR	310 S HAMEL RD	LOS ANGELES, CA	90048
LEE, ANNA	ACTRESS	NATHAN, 1240 N DOHENY DR	LOS ANGELES, CA	90069
LEE, ANTHONY	BASEBALL	POST OFFICE BOX 464	APPLETON, WI	54912
LEE, BARBARA	SINGER	POST OFFICE BOX 171132	NASHVILLE, TN	37217
LEE, BERTRAM M	BASKETBALL EXECUTIVE	POST OFFICE BOX 4658	DENVER, CO	80204
LEE, BETH E	COMPOSER	20533 ARCHWOOD ST	CANOGA PARK, CA	91306
LEE, BOB	BASEBALL EXECUTIVE	POST OFFICE BOX 661	KENOSHA, WI	53141
LEE, BRANDON	ACTOR	2005 LA BREA TERR	LOS ANGELES, CA	90046
LEE, BRENDA	SINGER	2174 CARSON ST	NASHVILLE, TN	38210
LEE, CARL	FOOTBALL	VIKINGS, 9520 VIKING DR	EDEN PRAIRIE, MN	55344
LEE, CECILIA	SINGER	RITA HEBREW, 8659 PINE CT	YPSILANTI, MI	48197
LEE, CHINA	ACTRESS-MODEL	SAHL, 2325 SAN YSIDRO DR	BEVERLY HILLS, CA	90210
LEE, CHRISTOPHER	ACTOR	5 SANDOWN HSE, WHEATFIELD TERR	LONDON W4	ENGLAND
LEE, DANA	ACTOR	8721 SANTA MONICA BLVD #21	WEST HOLLYWOOD, CA	90069
LEE, DAVID	TV WRITER	1650 WESTWOOD BLVD #201	LOS ANGELES, CA	90024
LEE, DEREK	BASEBALL	CANADIANS, 4601 ONTARIO ST	VANCOUVER, BC V5V 3H4	CANADA
LEE, GARY	TV WRITER	JEOPARDY, 1541 N VINE ST	HOLLYWOOD, CA	90028
LEE, GINGER	ACTRESS	PAT LYNN, 10525 STRATHMORE DR	LOS ANGELES, CA	90024
LEE, GORDON "PORKY"	ACTOR	950 W 103RD PL #202-D	DENVER, CO	80221
LEE, HYAPATIA	ACTRESS-MODEL	POST OFFICE BOX 1924	INDIANAPOLIS, IN	46206
LEE, JACK	BASEBALL SCOUT	FENWAY PARK, 4 YAWKEY WY	BOSTON, MA	02215
LEE, JAY	SCREENWRITER	POST OFFICE BOX 626	BEVERLY HILLS, CA	90213
LEE, JEAN	ACTRESS	406 W 57TH ST #3-D	NEW YORK, NY	10019
LEE, JIM	DIRECTOR	DGA, 110 W 57TH ST	NEW YORK, NY	10019
LEE, JOANA	WRI-DIR-PROD	135 S CARMELINA AVE	LOS ANGELES, CA	90049
LEE, JOHNNY	SINGER-SONGWRITER	1018 17TH AVE #11	NASHVILLE, TN	37212
LEE, JONATHAN	BASEBALL EXECUTIVE	POST OFFICE BOX 186	BUTTE, MT	59703
LEE, JONNA	ACTRESS	9229 SUNSET BLVD #311	LOS ANGELES, CA	90069
LEE, KAIULANI	ACTRESS	1650 BROADWAY #1005	NEW YORK, NY	10019
LEE, KURK	BASKETBALL	N J NETS, MEADOWLANDS ARENA	EAST RUTHERFORD, NJ	07073
LEE, LUAINE	FILM CRITIC	PASADENA STAR NEWS		

Name	Occupation	Address	City
		525 E COLORADO BLVD	PASADENA, CA 91109
LEE, LUANN L	MODEL-SINGER-TV HOST	THE KUSHNER-LOCKE COMPANY	
		11601 WILSHIRE BLVD, 21ST FL	LOS ANGELES, CA 90025
LEE, MANNY	BASEBALL	SKYDOME, 300 BREMMER BL #3200	TORONTO, ONT M5V 3B3 CANADA
LEE, MARK	BASEBALL (DENVER)	2850 W 20TH AVE	DENVER, CO 80211
LEE, MICHELE	ACT-SING-DIR	830 BIRCHWOOD	LOS ANGELES, CA 90024
LEE, MYRNA	SINGER	POST OFFICE BOX 171132	NASHVILLE, TN 37217
LEE, NELLE HARPER	AUTHOR	MC INTOSH, 18 E 41ST ST	NEW YORK, NY 10017
LEE, PAT	TV PRODUCER	1438 N GOWER ST #250	LOS ANGELES, CA 90028
LEE, PEGGY	SINGER-ACTRESS	2331 CENTURY HILL	LOS ANGELES, CA 90067
LEE, PINKY	ACTOR	27676 EMERALD	MISSION VIEJO, CA 92691
LEE, RANDY	SINGER	CUDE, 519 N HALIFAX AVE	DAYTONA BEACH, FL 32018
LEE, REBEL	SINGER-SONGWRITER	KAREN STANFORD	
		ROUTE #1, BOX 114-A	BINGER, OK 73009
LEE, ROBERT E	PLAYWRIGHT	15725 ROYAL OAK RD	ENCINO, CA 91316
LEE, ROBIN	COMPOSER	1111 E RAMON RD #10	PALM SPRINGS, CA 92262
LEE, ROBIN	SINGER	TAYLOR, 2401 12TH AVE S	NASHVILLE, TN 37204
LEE, RONNIE	FOOTBALL	SEAHAWKS, 11220 NE 53RD ST	KIRKLAND, WA 98033
LEE, RONNIE	SINGER	BARBARUS, 110 BOYLSTON AVE N	SEATTLE, WA 98102
LEE, ROSA	SINGER-SONGWRITER	SEE - MARTIN, ROSA LEE	
LEE, RUTA	ACTRESS	SHERRELL, 1354 LAS ROBLES DR	PALM SPRINGS, CA 92262
LEE, SCOOTER	SINGER	311 CHURCH ST #300	NASHVILLE, TN 37201
LEE, SCOTTY	SINGER	38 MUSIC SQUARE E #216	NASHVILLE, TN 37203
LEE, SHAWN	FOOTBALL	DOLPHINS, 2269 NW 199TH ST	MIAMI, FL 33056
LEE, SHERYL	ACTRESS	SANDERS, 1275 N HARPER	LOS ANGELES, CA 90046
LEE, SPIKE	FILM DIR-PLAYWRIGHT	124 DEKALB AVE #2	BROOKLYN, NY 11217
LEE, STAN	CARTOONIST	THE COWLES SYNDICATE	
		715 LOCUST ST	DES MOINES, IA 50304
LEE, TERRI	SINGER-GUITARIST	VILLA-ADRIAN, 2955 FRANKLIN RD	NASHVILLE, TN 37215
LEE, TERRY	BASEBALL	4385 TUTT BLVD	COLORADO SPRINGS, CO 80922
LEE, TOMMY	DRUMMER	4970 SUMMIT VIEW DR	WESTLAKE VILLAGE, CA 91362
LEE, VELMA	SINGER	POST OFFICE BOX 25371	CHARLOTTLE, NC 28212
LEE, VINECE	ACTRESS	1141 19TH ST #125	SANTA MONICA, CA 90403
LEE, WANDA	SINGER	POST OFFICE BOX 6025	NEWPORT NEWS, IA 23606
LEE, WILLIAM	TV WRITER	792 COLUMBUS AVE #1-R	NEW YORK, NY 10025
LEE, ZONA	COMPOSER	16154 GILMORE ST	VAN NUYS, CA 91406
LEECH, BEVERLY	ACTRESS	301 N CANON DR #305	BEVERLY HILLS, CA 90210
LEECH, ELIZABETH J	MUSIC ARRANGER	4501 ALCOTT DR	NASHVILLE, TN 37215
LEECH, IAN M	DIRECTOR	DGA, 7920 SUNSET BLVD, 6TH FL	LOS ANGELES, CA 90046
LEECH, MICHAEL A	MUSIC ARRANGER	4501 ALCOTT DR	NASHVILLE, TN 37215
LEECH, RICHARD	ACTOR	27 CLAYLANDS RD	LONDON SW8 1NX ENGLAND
LEEDS, PETER	ACTOR	626 N SCREENLAND DR	BURBANK, CA 91505
LEEDS, PHIL	ACTOR	1422 N SWEETZER AVE #309	WEST HOLLYWOOD, CA 90069
LEEDS, ROBERT	TV DIRECTOR	DGA, 7920 SUNSET BLVD, 6TH FL	LOS ANGELES, CA 90046
LEEK, TIIU	TV HOST	ZADEH, 11759 IOWA AVE	LOS ANGELES, CA 90025
LEEKLEY, JOHN	TV WRITER-PRODUCER	CAA, 9830 WILSHIRE BLVD	BEVERLY HILLS, CA 90212
LEEMAN, GARY	HOCKEY	MAPLE LEAFS, 60 CARLTON ST	TORONTO, ONT M5B 1L1 CANADA
LEEMING, JAN	ACTRESS-AUTHORESS	ARLINGTON, 1-3 CHARLOTTE ST	LONDON W1P 1HD ENGLAND
LEEN, JEFF	NEWS REPORTER-AUTHOR	MIAMI HERALD, 1 HERALD PLAZA	MIAMI, FL 33101
LEEN, TAMMY & JOHN & LEEN TWO	C & W GROUP	WOOD, 2901 EPPERLY DR	DEL CITY, OK 73115
LEES, BENJAMIN	COMPOSER	28 CAMBRIDGE RD	GREAT NECK, NY 11023
LEES, MICHAEL	ACTOR	908 CHELSEA CLOISTERS	
		SLOANE AVE	LONDON SW3 ENGLAND
LEES, ROBERT	WRITER	1600 COURTNEY AVE	LOS ANGELES, CA 90046
LEESON, MICHAEL J	FILM-TV WRITER	3725 ALOMAR DR	SHERMAN OAKS, CA 91405
LEETCH, BRIAN	HOCKEY	POST OFFICE BOX 90111	ARLINGTON, TX 76004
LEETCH, THOMAS	WRITER-PRODUCER	14593 DEERVALE PL	SHERMAN OAKS, CA 91403
LEEWOOD, JACK	DIRECTOR-PRODUCER	6220 OWENSMOUTH AVE #310	WOODLAND HILLS, CA 91367
LEFCOURT, PETER	TV WRITER-PRODUCER	999 N DOHENY DR #906	LOS ANGELES, CA 90069
LEFEBVRE, JIM	BASEBALL-MANAGER	1060 W ADDISON ST	CHICAGO, IL 60613
LEFEBVRE, JOE	BASEBALL-INSTRUCTOR	N Y YANKEES, YANKEE STADIUM	BRONX, NY 10451
LEFEBVRE, LEFTY	BASEBALL SCOUT	FENWAY PARK, 4 YAWKEY WY	BOSTON, MA 02215
LEFEBVRE, SYLVAIN	HOCKEY	CANADIENS, 2313 ST CATHERINE ST	MONTREAL, QUE H3H 1N2 CANADA
LEFFERTS, CRAIG "LEFTY"	BASEBALL	ORIOLE PARK, 333 W CAMDEN ST	BALTIMORE, MD 21201
LEFFERTS, GEORGE	TV WRITER-PRODUCER	ROBBINS REST	FIRE ISLAND, NY 11776
LEFKOWITZ, STEVE	ACTOR	13100 MAXELLA AVE #2	MARINA DEL REY, CA 90292
LEFT, THE	ROCK & ROLL GROUP	POST OFFICE BOX 185	RED LION, PA 17356
LEFTIN, CHARLES	BASEBALL SCOUT	REDS, 100 RIVERFRONT STADIUM	CINCINNATI, OH 45202
LEFTWICH, ED H	DIRECTOR	DGA, 110 W 57TH ST	NEW YORK, NY 10019
LEFTWICH, PHIL	BASEBALL	POST OFFICE BOX 12	MIDLAND, TX 79702
LEGACY	ROCK & ROLL GROUP	POST OFFICE BOX 25654	RICHMOND, VA 23260
LEGAL WEAPON	ROCK & ROLL GROUP	1626 N WILCOX ST #722	HOLLYWOOD, CA 90078
LEGARD, JOHN B	FILM EDITOR	75 HOLLAND PARK	LONDON W11 3SL ENGLAND
LEGEND	ROCK & ROLL GROUP	POST OFFICE BOX 1909	MILL VALLEY, CA 94942
LEGENDARY GOLDEN VAMPIRES, THE	ROCK & ROLL GROUP	LINTRUPER STR 39	1000 BERLIN 49 GERMANY
LEGENDARY STARDUST COWBOY	SINGER	POST OFFICE BOX 26265	FORT WORTH, CA 76116
LEGG, GREG	BASEBALL	POST OFFICE BOX 3449	SCRANTON, PA 18505
LEGGETT, BRAD	FOOTBALL	SAINTS, 1500 POYDRAS ST	NEW ORLEANS, LA 90112
LEGGETT, EARL	FOOTBALL COACH	BRONCOS, 13655 BRONCOS PKWY	ENGLEWOOD, CO 80112
LEGGETT, LAVRIAN	WRITER	8195 HOLLYWOOD BLVD	LOS ANGELES, CA 90069
LEGGETT, SUZANNE LEE	ACTRESS	BDP, 10637 BURBANK BLVD	NORTH HOLLYWOOD, CA 91601
LEGION OF DOOM	WRESTLING TAG TEAM	POST OFFICE BOX 3859	STAMFORD, CT 06905
LEGRAND, MICHEL	PIANIST-COMPOSER	LE GRAND MOULIN	ROVRES 28 FRANCE
LEGS DIAMOND	VOCAL GROUP	POST OFFICE BOX 1816	BURBANK, CA 91507
LEH, ROBERT	ACTOR	410 N ROSSMORE AVE #302	LOS ANGELES, CA 90004

Name	Occupation	Address	City	Zip
LEHANE, GREGORY	DIRECTOR	334 W 87TH ST #9-C	NEW YORK, NY	10024
LEHMAN, ALFRED E	COSTUME DESIGNER	5526 RHODES AVE	NORTH HOLLYWOOD, CA	91607
LEHMAN, DENNIS	BASEBALL EXECUTIVE	INDIANS, CLEVELAND STADIUM	CLEVELAND, OH	44114
LEHMAN, ERNEST	FILM WRITER-PRODUCER	11759 CHENAULT ST	LOS ANGELES, CA	90049
LEHMAN, LILLIAN	ACTRESS	14850 PARTHENIA ST #3	PANORAMA CITY, CA	91402
LEHMAN, MIKE	BASEBALL	500 NORTON ST	ROCHESTER, NY	14621
LEHMAN, ORIN	THEATER PRODUCER	67 E 82ND ST	NEW YORK, NY	10028
LEHMAN, RICHARD	U S CONGRESSMAN	2115 KERN ST #210	FRESNO, CA	93721
LEHMAN, ROBERT	DIRECTOR	14401 HARTSOOK ST	SHERMAN OAKS, CA	91403
LEHMAN, WILLIAM	U S CONGRESSMAN	2020 NE 163RD ST	NORTH MIAMI BEACH, FL	33162
LEHMANN, MICHAEL	FILM DIRECTOR	DGA, 7920 SUNSET BLVD, 6TH FL	LOS ANGELES, CA	90046
LEHMANN, TED	ACTOR	1617 GRIFFITH PARK BLVD	LOS ANGELES, CA	90026
LEHR, GEORGE	TV DIRECTOR-PRODUCER	3134 VETERAN AVE	LOS ANGELES, CA	90034
LEHR, KENETTE	TV WRITER	10901 WHIPPLE ST #27	NORTH HOLLYWOOD, CA	91602
LEHR, ZELLA	SINGER	38 MUSIC SQUARE E #300	NASHVILLE, TN	37203
LEHRMAN, PHILLIP A	CONDUCTOR	4417 77TH ST	LUBBOCK, TX	79424
LEHRMAN, STEVEN	WRITER-PRODUCER	107-40 QUEENS BLVD	FOREST HILLS, NY	11375
LEI, LYDIA	ACTRESS	8235 SANTA MONICA BLVD #202	LOS ANGELES, CA	90046
LEIB, GIL	CONDUCTOR	9725 CHARNOCK AVE #2	LOS ANGELES, CA	90034
LEIB, GREG	BASEBALL TRAINER	80 OTTAWA ST N	HAMILTON, ONT L8H 3Z1	CANADA
LEIBERT, PHYLLIS R	TV EXECUTIVE	NBC-TV, 30 ROCKEFELLER PLAZA	NEW YORK, NY	10112
LEIBLE, RAY	BASEBALL UMPIRE	2101 E BROADWAY #35	TEMPE, AZ	85282
LEIBMAN, RON	ACTOR-WRITER	10530 STRATHMORE DR	LOS ANGELES, CA	90024
LEIBMAN, SUE	TALENT AGENT	19 W 44TH ST #1000	NEW YORK, NY	10036
LEIBNER, RICHARD A	TALENT AGENT	10 COLUMBUS CIR #2310	NEW YORK, NY	10019
LEIBOW, RUTH I	COMPOSER	11105 ROSE AVE #209	LOS ANGELES, CA	90034
LEIBRANDT, CHARLIE	BASEBALL	POST OFFICE BOX 4064	ATLANTA, GA	30302
LEIBU, DOLLEE	COMPOSER	1247 N SWEETZER AVE #2	LOS ANGELES, CA	90069
LEICHT, ALLAN	TV WRITER-PRODUCER	CAA, 9830 WILSHIRE BLVD	BEVERLY HILLS, CA	90212
LEIDER, GERRY	BASEBALL EXECUTIVE	POST OFFICE BOX 594	WELLAND, ONT L3B 5R3	CANADA
LEIDER, JERRY	BASEBALL EXECUTIVE	POST OFFICE BOX 11363	RENO, NV	89510
LEIDER, JERRY	FILM PRODUCER	222 N CARMELINA AVE	LOS ANGELES, CA	90049
LEIF, RONNIE	TALENT AGENT	132 S LASKY DR #B	BEVERLY HILLS, CA	90212
LEIFER, CAROL	ACTRESS	151 S EL CAMINO DR	BEVERLY HILLS, CA	90212
LEIFF, PHILIP	TV DIRECTOR-PRODUCER	702 FORDHAM RD	BALA-CYNWYD, PA	19004
LEIGH, A NORMAN	DIRECTOR	19 NIRVANA AVE	GREAT NECK, NY	11023
LEIGH, JANET	ACTRESS	1625 SUMMITRIDGE DR	BEVERLY HILLS, CA	90210
LEIGH, JENNIFER JASON	ACTRESS	335 N MAPLE DR #254	BEVERLY HILLS, CA	90210
LEIGH, MIKE	FILM WRITER-DIRECTOR	8 EARLHAM GROVE	LONDON N22	ENGLAND
LEIGH, NORMAN	DIRECTOR	19 NIRVANA AVE	GREAT NECK, NY	11023
LEIGH-HUNT, BARBARA	ACTRESS	WHITEHALL, 125 GLOUCESTER RD	LONDON SW7 4TE	ENGLAND
LEIGH-HUNT, RONALD	ACTOR	INTERNATIONAL ARTISTES LTD		
		MEZZANINE FL, 235 REGENT ST	LONDON W1R 8AX	ENGLAND
LEIGHTON, DYAN	TV WRITER	6725 SUNSET BLVD #506	HOLLYWOOD, CA	90028
LEIGHTON, HARVEY	BASEBALL EXECUTIVE	N Y YANKEES, YANKEE STADIUM	BRONX, NY	10451
LEIGHTON, ROBERTA	ACTRESS	NBC-TV, "DAYS OF OUR LIVES"		
		3000 W ALAMEDA AVE	BURBANK, CA	91523
LEIN, CHRIS	BASEBALL COACH	POST OFFICE BOX 356	BLUEFIELD, WV	24701
LEINEN, PAT	BASEBALL	500 NORTON ST	ROCHESTER, NY	14621
LEINSDORF, ERICH	CONDUCTOR	209 E 56TH ST	NEW YORK, NY	10022
LEIP, TOM	BASEBALL EXECUTIVE	POST OFFICE BOX 4758	SPOKANE, WA	99202
LEIPER, DAVE	BASEBALL	10233 96TH AVE	EDMONTON, ALB TK5 0A5	CANADA
LEIPER, TIM	BASEBALL	POST OFFICE BOX 1211	NORFOLK, VA	23502
LEISER, ERNEST	TV PRODUCER	CBS-TV, 51 W 52ND ST	NEW YORK, NY	10019
LEISER, SCOTT C	DIRECTOR	4489 HARVARD RD	DETROIT, MI	48224
LEISURE, DAVID	ACTOR	1999 AVE OF THE STARS #2850	LOS ANGELES, CA	90067
LEITCH, CHRISTOPHER L	WRITER	3444 WONDER VIEW DR	LOS ANGELES, CA	90068
LEITCH, DONOVAN	ACTOR	1949 N WILTON PL	LOS ANGELES, CA	90068
LEITER, AL	BASEBALL	CHIEFS, MAC ARTHUR STADIUM	SYRACUSE, NY	13208
LEITER, MARK	BASEBALL	TIGERS, TIGER STADIUM	DETROIT, MI	48216
LEITER, MARK	BASEBALL	37 BROWN AVE	PINE BRANCH, NJ	08741
LEITERMAN, DOUGLAS	PRODUCER-EXECUTIVE	MOTION PICTURE GUARANTORS		
		43 BRITAIN ST	TORONTO, ONT M5A 1R7	CANADA
LEITH, VIRGINIA	ACTRESS	POST OFFICE BOX 691661	LOS ANGELES, CA	90069
LEITNER, TED	SPORTSCASTER	KFMB-TV, 7677 ENGINEER RD	SAN DIEGO, CA	92111
LEITNER, TED	SPORTSCASTER	POST OFFICE BOX 2000	SAN DIEGO, CA	92112
LEIUS, SCOTT	BASEBALL	TWINS, 501 CHICAGO AVE S	MINNEAPOLIS, MN	55415
LEKAS, TED	BASEBALL SCOUT	SKYDOME, 300 BREMMER BL #3200	TORONTO, ONT M5V 3B3	CANADA
LEKAS, TED T	WRITER	4512 ALLA RD #3	LOS ANGELES, CA	90066
LELAND, DAVID	FILM WRITER-DIRECTOR	6-5 GATCOMBE RD	LONDON N19 9PT	ENGLAND
LELAND, ROBERT	DIRECTOR-PRODUCER	3706 E 15TH ST	LONG BEACH, CA	90804
LELOUCH, CLAUDE	FILM DIRECTOR	15 AVENUE HOCHE	PARIS 75008	FRANCE
LEM, CAROL	TV EXECUTIVE	10720 OHIO AVE #4	LOS ANGELES, CA	90024
LEMACK, TONY	FOOTBALL	POST OFFICE BOX 888	PHOENIX, AZ	85001
LEMAY, BOB	BASEBALL	POST OFFICE BOX 64939	FAYETTEVILLE, NC	28306
LEMBECK, HELAINE	ACTRESS	1251 N CRESCENT HGTS BLVD #B	WEST HOLLYWOOD, CA	90046
LEMBECK, MICHAEL	ACTOR-DIRECTOR	9350 WILSHIRE BLVD #324	BEVERLY HILLS, CA	90212
LEMIEUX, CLAUDE	HOCKEY	POST OFFICE BOX 504	EAST RUTHERFORD, NJ	07073
LEMIEUX, JOCELYN	HOCKEY	BLACKHAWKS, 1800 W MADISON ST	CHICAGO, IL	60612
LEMIEUX, MARIO	HOCKEY	PENGUINS, CIVIC ARENA, CENTRE AV	PITTSBURGH, PA	15219
LEMKE, MARK	BASEBALL	POST OFFICE BOX 4064	ATLANTA, GA	30302
LEMMO, JOAN	ACTRESS	11752 MAGNOLIA BLVD	NORTH HOLLYWOOD, CA	91607
LEMMON, CHRIS	ACTOR	7887 HILLSIDE AVE	LOS ANGELES, CA	90046
LEMMON, JACK	ACTOR-DIRECTOR	141 S EL CAMINO DR #201	BEVERLY HILLS, CA	90212
LEMMONS, KAZI	ACTRESS	888 7TH AVE #602	NEW YORK, NY	10106

LEMOINE, JACQUES	DIRECTOR	THE SUN GROUP COMPANY	
		505 5TH AVE, 11TH FLOOR	NEW YORK, NY 10017
LEMON, ARTHUR E	PHOTOGRAPHER	CROWN COTTAGE, HIGH ST	
		EAST MARKHAM, NEWARK	NOTTS NG22 OQL ENGLAND
LEMON, BOB	BASEBALL-SCOUT	1141 CLAIBORNE DR	LONG BEACH, CA 90807
LEMON, CHET	BASEBALL	4805 HIGHLANDS PLACE DR	LAKELAND, FL 33813
LEMON, JIM	BASEBALL-COACH	136 S SYCAMORE	ELIZABETHTON, TN 37643
LEMON, MEADOWLARK	ACTOR-BASKETBALL	POST OFFICE BOX 398	SIERRA VISTA, AZ 85635
LEMON, MICHAEL	ACTOR	POST OFFICE BOX 241609	LOS ANGELES, CA 90024
LEMON DROPS, THE	ROCK & ROLL GROUP	POST OFFICE BOX 791551	DALLAS, TX 75379
LEMOND, GREG	BICYCLIST	1101 WILSON AVE #1800	ARLINGTON, VA 22209
LEMONRANDE, RUSTY	SCREENWRITER	8955 BEVERLY BLVD	WEST HOLLYWOOD, CA 90048
LEMP, CHRIS	BASEBALL	POST OFFICE BOX 418	SAINT CHARLES, IL 60174
LEMPERT, PETER	ACTOR	8951 KEITH AVE	WEST HOLLYWOOD, CA 90069
LEMPERT, SELMA CLAUDIA	ACTRESS	4141 N BRAESWOOD BLVD #6	HOUSTON, TX 77025
LEMS, KRISTIN	SINGER-PIANIST	FLYING FISH RECORDS	
		1304 W CHUBERT AVE	CHICAHO, IL 60614
LENA, VINCENT	DIRECTOR	910 ALMOND HILL CT	MANCHESTER, MO 63033
LENARD, ELISSA	DIRECTOR	6056 BEEMAN AVE	NORTH HOLLYWOOD, CA 91606
LENARD, KATHRYN	TV EXECUTIVE	NBC-TV, 30 ROCKEFELLER PLAZA	NEW YORK, NY 10112
LENDL, IVAN	TENNIS	800 NORTH ST	GREENWICH, CT 06830
LENDROTH, SHERRIE	ACTRESS	1234 N HAYWORTH AVE #A	WEST HOLLYWOOD, CA 90046
LENHARDT, DON	BASEBALL-SCOUT	FENWAY PARK, 4 YAWKEY WY	BOSTON, MA 02215
LENNIE, ANGUS	ACTOR	COLIN, STEWART, BERET ASSOCIATES	
		THE OLD CLUB HOUSE	
		CAMBRIDGE PARK	TWICKENHAM ENGLAND
LENNON, JANET	SINGER	14234 DICKENS ST #1	SHERMAN OAKS, CA 91423
LENNON, JULIAN	SINGER-COMPOSER	7319 WOODROW WILSON DR	LOS ANGELES, CA 90046
LENNON, KIPP	ACTOR	944 HARDING AVE	VENICE, CA 90291
LENNON, PATRICK	BASEBALL	POST OFFICE BOX 4100	SEATTLE, WA 98104
LENNON, PAUL	COMEDIAN	32500 CONCORD DR #252	MADISON HEIGHTS, MI 48071
LENNON, SEAN	CELEBRITY	THE DAKOTA, 1 W 72ND ST	NEW YORK, NY 10023
LENNON SISTERS, THE	VOCAL GROUP	944 HARDING AVE	VENICE, CA 90291
LENNOX, ANNIE	SINGER	POST OFFICE BOX 245	LONDON N89 QG ENGLAND
LENNY, JACK	THEATER PRODUCER	140 W 58TH ST	NEW YORK, NY 10019
LENO, JAY	COMEDIAN-ACTOR	1151 TOWER RD	BEVERLY HILLS, CA 90210
LENOX, JOHN THOMAS	DIRECTOR-PRODUCER	6603 MAMMOTH AVE	VAN NUYS, CA 91405
LENS, TERENCE	FILM PRODUCER	ROSE COTTAGE, FULMER RD	FULMER, BUCKS ENGLAND
LENSKA, RULA	ACTRESS-MODEL	306-16 EUSTON RD	LONDON NW13 ENGLAND
LENSKI, ROBERT W	TV WRITER	222 N GLENROY AVE	LOS ANGELES, CA 90049
LENT, NORMAN	U S CONGRESSMAN	2280 GRAND AVE #300	BALDWIN, NY 11510
LENTINE, JIM	BASEBALL-SCOUT	POST OFFICE BOX 90111	ARLINGTON, TX 76004
LENTZ, PAT	ACTRESS	13740 RUNNYMEDE ST	VAN NUYS, CA 91405
LENYOUN, LORELEI	DIRECTOR	19303 WEXFORD ST	DETROIT, MI 48234
LENZ, KAY	ACTRESS	9255 SUNSET BLVD #515	LOS ANGELES, CA 90069
LENZ, RICK	ACTOR	POST OFFICE BOX 69590	LOS ANGELES, CA 90069
LENZER, NORMAN	WRITER-PRODUCER	14637 HILLTREE RD	SANTA MONICA, CA 90402
LEO, MALCOLM	WRITER-PRODUCER	10048 CIELO DR	BEVERLY HILLS, CA 90210
LEODAS, GUS	DIRECTOR	LEODAS, 333 E 49TH ST	NEW YORK, NY 10017
LEOGRAND, BARBARA	SINGER	POST OFFICE BOX 171132	NASHVILLE, TN 37217
LEOKUM, ARKADY	WRITER-COLUMNIST	UPS, 4900 MAIN ST, 9TH FLOOR	KANSAS CITY, MO 64112
LEOKUM, LEONARD	DIRECTOR	DGA, 110 W 57TH ST	NEW YORK, NY 10019
LEON, DANILO	BASEBALL	POST OFFICE BOX 3609	PORT CHARLOTTE, FL 33949
LEON, FRED	BASEBALL SCOUT	REDS, 100 RIVERFRONT STADIUM	CINCINNATI, OH 45202
LEON, MICHAEL	ACTOR	POST OFFICE BOX 241609	LOS ANGELES, CA 90024
LEON, MIKE	BASEBALL TRAINER	800 HOME RUN LN	MEMPHIS, TN 38104
LEON, RUTH L	TV DIRECTOR-PRODUCER	155 W 68TH ST #26-E	NEW YORK, NY 10023
LEON, STEPHEN	ACTOR	2800 PELHAM PL	LOS ANGELES, CA 90068
LEONARD, ADA	CONDUCTOR	BERNSTEIN, 11408 BERWICK ST	LOS ANGELES, CA 90049
LEONARD, BILL	TV PRODUCER	CBS-TV, 524 W 57TH ST	NEW YORK, NY 10019
LEONARD, BUCK	BASEBALL	605 ATLANTIC AVE	ROCKY MOUNT, NC 27801
LEONARD, DENNIS	BASEBALL	4102 EVERGREEN LN	BLUE SPRINGS, MO 64015
LEONARD, DONALD M	WRITER	2549 THAMES ST	LOS ANGELES, CA 90046
LEONARD, GARY	BODYBUILDER	POST OFFICE BOX 1459	CLOVIS, CA 93613
LEONARD, GLENN	SINGER	PERLE, 4475 VINELAND AVE	STUDIO CITY, CA 91602
LEONARD, HERBERT	DIRECTOR-PRODUCER	5300 FULTON AVE	VAN NUYS, CA 91401
LEONARD, HUGH	PLAYWRIGHT	THEROS, COLIEMORE RD, DALKEY	DUBLIN IRELAND
LEONARD, JEFF	BASEBALL	1626 N FELTON ST	PHILADELPHIA, PA 19151
LEONARD, JOHN	TV CRITIC	NY MAGAZINE, 755 2ND AVE	NEW YORK, NY 10017
LEONARD, LU	ACTRESS	12245 CHANDLER BLVD #302	NORTH HOLLYWOOD, CA 91607
LEONARD, MARK	BASEBALL	S F GIANTS, CANDLESTICK PARK	SAN FRANICSCO, CA 94124
LEONARD, MARY	ACTRESS	CBS-TV, "THE GUIDING LIGHT"	
		222 E 44TH ST	NEW YORK, NY 10017
LEONARD, SHELDON	ACTOR-DIRECTOR	1141 LOMA VISTA DR	BEVERLY HILLS, CA 90210
LEONARD, SUGAR RAY	BOXER-ACTOR	1505 BRADY CT	MITCHELLVILLE, MD 20716
LEONARD, TERRY JAMES	DIRECTOR	11074 OSO	CHATSWORTH, CA 91011
LEONE, JOHN J	WRITER-PRODUCER	DGA, 7920 SUNSET BLVD, 6TH FL	LOS ANGELES, CA 90046
LEONE, SERGIO	FILM DIRECTOR	MINISTRY OF TOURISM	
		VIA DELLA FERRA TELLA	ROME ITALY
LEONETTI, MATTHEW R	CINEMATOGRAPHER	POST OFFICE BOX 2230	HOLLYWOOD, CA 90078
LEONG, EUGENE	TV DIRECTOR	1947 N HARDING AVE	ALTADENA, CA 91001
LEONHARDT, DAVE	BASEBALL	POST OFFICE BOX 64939	FAYETTEVILLE, NC 28306
LEONI, TEA	ACTRESS	335 N MAPLE DR #250	BEVERLY HILLS, CA 90210
LEONTI, CINCY	SINGER	PROCESS, 439 WILEY AVE	FRANKLIN, PA 16323
LEONTOVICH, EUGENIE	ACTRESS	45 W 81ST ST #609	NEW YORK, NY 10024

LEOPOLD, GLENN I	SCREENWRITER	8955 BEVERLY BLVD	WEST HOLLYWOOD, CA 90048
LEPARD, JEREMY	CINEMATOGRAPHER	3975 WITZEL DR	SHERMAN OAKS, CA 91423
LEPEL, JOEL	BASEBALL MANAGER	POST OFFICE BOX 661	KENOSHA, WI 53141
LEPPERT, DON	BASEBALL-EXECUTIVE	TWINS, 501 CHICAGO AVE S	MINNEAPOLIS, MN 55415
LERER, GAYLE	WRITER	242 S REXFORD DR	BEVERLY HILLS, CA 90212
LERMAN, APRIL	ACTRESS	10351 SANTA MONICA BLVD #211	LOS ANGELES, CA 90025
LERNER, ALBERT	COMPOSER	4223 VANTAGE AVE	STUDIO CITY, CA 91604
LERNER, DAVID	TV WRITER	1021 HILL ST #4	SANTA MONICA, CA 90405
LERNER, FRED	TV DIRECTOR	14639 BLEDSOE ST	SYLMAR, CA 91342
LERNER, JOSEPH	DIRECTOR	2502 ANTIGUA TERR #M-4	CONONUT CREEK, FL 33066
LERNER, KAREN G	TV WRITER-PRODUCER	ABC-TV, 7 W 66TH ST	NEW YORK, NY 10023
LERNER, LARRY	DIRECTOR	328 W 11TH ST #1-B	NEW YORK, NY 10014
LERNER, MICHAEL	ACTOR	POST OFFICE BOX 5617	BEVERLY HILLS, CA 90213
LERNER, MURRAY	WRITER-PRODUCER	630 9TH AVE	NEW YORK, NY 10036
LEROY, MERVYN	DIRECTOR-PRODUCER	615 N CAMDEN DR	BEVERLY HILLS, CA 90210
LERSKY, LESTER	FILM PRODUCER	485 MADISON AVE	NEW YORK, NY 10022
LESCHIN, DEBORAH	TV WRITER	13002 DICKENS ST	NORTH HOLLYWOOD, CA 91604
LESCHIN, LUISA	ACTRESS	536 N ORANGE DR	LOS ANGELES, CA 90036
LESCO, KENNETH R	DIRECTOR	2555 N LINCOLN ST	BURBANK, CA 91504
LESEMANN, FREDERICK	COMPOSER	216 S OCCIDENTAL BLVD #203	LOS ANGELES, CA 90057
LESH, DAVID	ARTIST	5693 N MERIDIAN ST	INDIANPOLIS, IN 46208
LESHAY, JERRY	TV DIRECTOR	4149 FARMDALE AVE	STUDIO CITY, CA 91604
LESHNER, MARTIN	TV WRITER	840 N LARRABEE ST #4-217	LOS ANGELES, CA 90069
LESKANIC, CURTIS	BASEBALL	POST OFFICE BOX 5645	ORLANDO, FL 32855
LESLIE, ALEEN	WRITER	1700 LEXINGTON RD	BEVERLY HILLS, CA 90210
LESLIE, BETHEL	ACTRESS-WRITER	113 N SAN VICENTE BLVD #202	BEVERLY HILLS, CA 90211
LESLIE, JOAN	ACTRESS	CALDWELL, 2228 N CATALINA ST	LOS ANGELES, CA 90027
LESSAC, MICHAEL	TV DIRECTOR	1742 NICHOLS CANYON RD	LOS ANGELES, CA 90046
LESSER, ELANA	TV WRITER	8955 BEVERLY BLVD	WEST HOLLYWOOD, CA 90048
LESSER, LEN	ACTOR	934 N EVERGREEN ST	BURBANK, CA 91505
LESSING, NORMAN	TV WRITER	663 HIGHTREE RD	SANTA MONICA, CA 90402
LESTER, CHUCK	FOOTBALL COACH	BILLS, 1 BILLS DR	ORCHARD PARK, NJ 14127
LESTER, DON	TV PRODUCER	363 E 76TH ST #15-C	NEW YORK, NY 10021
LESTER, GENE	DIRECTOR-PRODUCER	4918 ALCOVE AVE	NORTH HOLLYWOOD, CA 91607
LESTER, JIMMY	BASEBALL COACH	POST OFFICE BOX 611	WATERLOO, IA 50704
LESTER, KETTY	ACTRESS	5931 COMEY AVE	LOS ANGELES, CA 90034
LESTER, LARRY	DIRECTOR	24837 PARCHMAN AVE	NEWHALL, CA 91321
LESTER, MARK	DIRECTOR-PRODUCER	17628 CAMINO YATASTO	PACIFIC PALISADES, CA 90272
LESTER, RICHARD	FILM DIR-COMP	RIVER LN, PETERSHAM	SURREY ENGLAND
LESTER, RONNIE	BASKETBALL	POST OFFICE BOX 10	INGLEWOOD, CA 90306
LESTER, SEELEG	WRITER-PRODUCER	6228 RIVIERA CIR	LONG BEACH, CA 90815
LESTER, SUSAN C	DIRECTOR	14 HORATIO ST	NEW YORK, NY 10014
LESTER, TOM	ACTOR	POST OFFICE BOX 1854	BEVERLY HILLS, CA 90213
LET'S ACTIVE	ROCK & ROLL GROUP	37 LEE ST	WATERBURY, CT 06708
LETELLIER, JACQUES	DIRECTOR	1160 5TH AVE	NEW YORK, NY 10029
LETENDRE, MARK	BASEBALL TRAINER	S F GIANTS, CANDLESTICK PARK	SAN FRANICSCO, CA 94124
LETHIN, LORI	ACTRESS	4342 GENTRY AVE #3	STUDIO CITY, CA 91604
LETT, JIM	BASEBALL COACH	POST OFFICE BOX 23290	NASHVILLE, TN 37202
LETTERIO, SHANE	BASEBALL	POST OFFICE BOX 4756	JACKSONVILLE, FL 32201
LETTERMAN, DAVID	COMEDIAN-TV HOST	30 ROCKEFELLER PLAZA #1410-W	NEW YORK, NY 10112
LETTERMEN, THE	VOCAL TRIO	LETTERMEN PRODUCTIONS	
		4318 BEN AVE	STUDIO CITY, CA 91604
LETTS, BARRY	TV DIRECTOR-PRODUCER	2 QUEENS AVE	LONDON N20 OJE ENGLAND
LEUGER, JOHN	ACTOR	200 E 68TH ST	LONG BEACH, CA 90805
LEVANE, FUZZY	BASKETBALL	KNICKS, 4 PENNYLVANIA PLAZA	NEW YORK, NY 10019
LEVANT, BRIAN	TV WRITER-DIRECTOR	9528 DALEGROVE DR	BEVERLY HILLS, CA 90210
LEVATO, TONY	BASEBALL SCOUT	POST OFFICE BOX 419969	KANSAS CITY, MO 64141
LEVEL 42	JAZZ GROUP	OUTLAW MGMT, 145 OXFORD ST	LONDON W1 ENGLAND
LEVEN, MELVILLE A	COMPOSER-CONDUCTOR	11577 DILLING ST	STUDIO CITY, CA 91604
LEVENSON, JEFFREY	CELLIST	SAN DIEGO STATE UNIVERSITY	
		MUSIC DEPARTMENT	
		5402 COLLEGE AVE	SAN DIEGO, CA 92082
LEVENSON, ROBERT	DIRECTOR	125 OAK ST	TENAFLY, NJ 07670
LEVENTON, ANNABEL	ACTRESS	HATTON, 29 ROEHAMPTON GATE	LONDON SW15 5JR ENGLAND
LEVEQUE, JOHN FRANCIS	SCREENWRITER	9027 GIBSON ST	LOS ANGELES, CA 90034
LEVER, FAT	BASKETBALL	REUNION ARENA, 777 SPORTS ST	DALLAS, TX 75207
LEVER, JUDY	TV DIRECTOR-PRODUCER	52 WESTBOURNE PARK RD	LONDON W2 5HI ENGLAND
LEVERINGTON, SHELBY	ACTRESS	11325 MORRISON ST #211	NORTH HOLLYWOOD, CA 91601
LEVEY, DAVID	COSTUME DESIGNER	13949 VENTURA BLVD #309	SHERMAN OAKS, CA 91423
LEVEY, ED	ACTOR	921 SUPERBA AVE	VENICE, CA 90291
LEVEY, WILLIAM A	FILM WRITER-DIRECTOR	2001 S BARRINGTON AVE #210	LOS ANGELES, CA 90025
LEVI, ALAN J	WRITER-PRODUCER	3951 LONGRIDGE AVE	SHERMAN OAKS, CA 91423
LEVI, PAUL ALAN	COMPOSER	105 W 73RD ST	NEW YORK, NY 10023
LEVI, VICKI GOLD	ACTRESS	211 CENTRAL PARK W	NEW YORK, NY 10024
LEVI, WAYNE	GOLFER	POST OFFICE BOX 109601	PALM BCH GARDENS, FL 33418
LEVIEN, PHILIP	ACTOR	1202 N POINSETTIA DR	WEST HOLLYWOOD, CA 90046
LEVIEV, MILCHO I	COMPOSER	12027 CALIFA ST	NORTH HOLLYWOOD, CA 91607
LEVIN, ALAN	TV EXECUTIVE	235 21ST ST	SANTA MONICA, CA 90402
LEVIN, ALAN .. (MODESTO)	BASEBALL EXECUTIVE	POST OFFICE BOX 2437	MODESTO, CA 95351
LEVIN, ALAN .. (SOUTH BEND)	BASEBALL EXECUTIVE	POST OFFICE BOX 4218	SOUTH BEND, IN 46634
LEVIN, ALAN .. (WELLAND)	BASEBALL EXECUTIVE	POST OFFICE BOX 594	WELLAND, ONT L3B 5R3 CANADA
LEVIN, ALAN M	WRITER-PRODUCER	88 CLAREMONT AVE	MAPLEWOOD, NJ 07040
LEVIN, ALVIN IRVING	COMPOSER-CONDUCTOR	8612 JELLICO AVE	NORTHRIDGE, CA 91325
LEVIN, AUDREY DAVIS	TV WRITER	2751 MOTOR AVE	LOS ANGELES, CA 90064
LEVIN, CARL M	U S SENATOR	477 MICHIGAN AVE #1860	DETROIT, MI 48226

Name	Occupation	Address	City	Zip
LEVIN, CHARLES	ACTOR	1357 3/4 N ALTA VISTA BLVD	LOS ANGELES, CA	90046
LEVIN, DEBORAH	ACTRESS	1800 N VINE ST #120	LOS ANGELES, CA	90028
LEVIN, HERMAN	THEATER PRODUCER	424 MADISON AVE	NEW YORK, NY	10019
LEVIN, IRA	AUTHOR-WRITER	HAROLD OBER, 40 E 49TH ST	NEW YORK, NY	10017
LEVIN, IRVING H	FILM PRODUCER	805 N ROXBURY DR	BEVERLY HILLS, CA	90210
LEVIN, LEAR	WRITER-PRODUCER	16 W 88TH ST	NEW YORK, NY	10024
LEVIN, LEONARD T	DIRECTOR	114 W 25TH ST	BALTIMORE, MD	21218
LEVIN, LISSA	TV WRITER	ICM, 8899 BEVERLY BLVD	LOS ANGELES, CA	90048
LEVIN, MICHAEL	ACTOR	CBS-TV, "AS THE WORLD TURNS"		
		524 W 57TH ST #5330	NEW YORK, NY	10019
LEVIN, MICHAEL	WRI-DIR-PROD	421 W BROADWAY, 2ND FLOOR	NEW YORK, NY	10012
LEVIN, MOSHE	CINEMATOGRAPHER	3224 DURAND DR	LOS ANGELES, CA	90068
LEVIN, PETER	TV DIRECTOR	TIVOLI, 10313 W PICO BLVD	LOS ANGELES, CA	90064
LEVIN, SANDER M	U S CONGRESSMAN	17117 W NINE MILE RD #1120	SOUTHFIELD, MI	48075
LEVIN, SIDNEY	FILM DIRECTOR	POST OFFICE BOX 1166	PACIFIC PALISADES, CA	90272
LEVIN, STEWART	COMPOSER	280 S BEVERLY DR #411	BEVERLY HILLS, CA	90212
LEVINE, ALEXANDRA	ACTRESS	1930 CENTURY PARK W #403	LOS ANGELES, CA	90067
LEVINE, ARNOLD	DIRECTOR	420 MARION ST	OCEANSIDE, NY	11572
LEVINE, EMILY	TV WRITER	6547 CAHUENGA TERR	LOS ANGELES, CA	90068
LEVINE, FLOYD	ACTOR	280 S BEVERLY DR #400	BEVERLY HILLS, CA	90212
LEVINE, GILBERT	CONDUCTOR	ICM, 40 W 57TH ST	NEW YORK, NY	10019
LEVINE, HANK	MUSIC ARRANGER	POST OFFICE BOX 532	HENDERSONVILLE, TN	37075
LEVINE, JOSEPH E	FILM PRODUCER	277 PARK AVE	NEW YORK, NY	10017
LEVINE, KEN	SPORTSCASTER	WBAL RADIO, 3800 HOOPER AVE	BALTIMORE, MD	21211
LEVINE, KEN NEIL	WRITER-PRODUCER	829 THAYER AVE	LOS ANGELES, CA	90024
LEVINE, LAURA	TV WRITER	1756 MIDVALE AVE	LOS ANGELES, CA	90024
LEVINE, LOUIS P	DIRECTOR	2677 HIGH RIDGE RD	STANFORD, CT	06903
LEVINE, MARIAN	ARTIST	ABC NEWS, 47 W 66TH ST	NEW YORK, NY	10023
LEVINE, MEL	U S CONGRESSMAN	5250 W CENTURY BLVD #447	LOS ANGELES, CA	90045
LEVINE, MICHAEL	AUTHOR-PUBLICIST	8730 SUNSET BLVD, 6TH FLOOR	LOS ANGELES, CA	90069
LEVINE, MICHAEL A	TV EXECUTIVE	NBC-TV, 3000 W ALAMEDA AVE	BURBANK, CA	91523
LEVINE, NED	ARTIST	301 FRANKEL BLVD	MERRICK, NY	11566
LEVINE, RICHARD DAVID	DIRECTOR	DGA, 110 W 57TH ST	NEW YORK, NY	10019
LEVINE, RICK	FILM DIRECTOR	DGA, 7920 SUNSET BLVD, 6TH FL	LOS ANGELES, CA	90046
LEVINE, SAM	MUSIC ARRANGER	5013 MANUEL DR	NASHVILLE, TN	37211
LEVINE, SCOTT	CINEMATOGRAPHER	401 E 74TH ST #18-E	NEW YORK, NY	10021
LEVINE, SID	BASEBALL EXECUTIVE	95 RIVER ST	ONEONTA, NY	13820
LEVINE, STANLEY M	COMPOSER	13508 DEBELL ST	PACOIMA, CA	91331
LEVINE, TED	ACTOR	10390 SANTA MONICA BLVD #300	LOS ANGELES, CA	90025
LEVINGSTON, CLIFF	BASKETBALL	980 N MICHIGAN AVE #1600	CHICAGO, IL	60611
LEVINSKY, WALTER	CONDUCTOR-CONDUCTOR	379 BOGERT RD	RIVERDGE, NJ	07661
LEVINSON, AMY	DIRECTOR	1338 PRINCETON ST #E	SANTA MONICA, CA	90404
LEVINSON, BARRY	FILM WRITER-DIRECTOR	CAA, 9830 WILSHIRE BLVD	BEVERLY HILLS, CA	90212
LEVINSON, DAVID	TV WRITER	3115 DEEP CANYON DR	BEVERLY HILLS, CA	90210
LEVINSON, FRED F	DIRECTOR	12 1/2 E 82ND ST	NEW YORK, NY	10028
LEVINSON, MARK	FILM PRODUCER	151 S EL CAMINO DR	BEVERLY HILLS, CA	90212
LEVINSON, ROBERT S	PRODUCER	650 N BRONSON AVE #250	LOS ANGELES, CA	90004
LEVINSON, WILLIAM G	TV-COMEDY WRITER	241 CENTRAL PARK W	NEW YORK, NY	10024
LEVISOHN, DAVID	CINEMATOGRAPHER	7715 SUNSET BLVD #150	LOS ANGELES, CA	90046
LEVITCH, LEON	COMPOSER	13107 KELOWNA ST	PACOIMA, CA	91331
LEVITT, ALFRED L	WRITER	4124 STANSBURY AVE	SHERMAN OAKS, CA	91423
LEVITT, GENE	TV WRITER-DIRECTOR	9200 SUNSET BLVD #PH-25	LOS ANGELES, CA	90069
LEVITT, HELEN SLOTE	WRITER	4124 STANSBURY AVE	SHERMAN OAKS, CA	91423
LEVITT, STEPHEN I	DIRECTOR	330 8TH AVE	NEW YORK, NY	10001
LEVRA, JIM	FOOTBALL COACH	BEARS, 250 N WASHINGTON RD	LAKE FOREST, IL	60045
LEVY, ALAN	CABLE EXECUTIVE	HBO, 1100 6TH AVE	NEW YORK, NY	10036
LEVY, BRUCE	SONGWRITER	17071 GRESHAM ST	NORTHRIDGE, CA	91325
LEVY, DAVE	FOOTBALL COACH	LIONS, 1200 FEATHERSTONE RD	PONTIAC, MI	48432
LEVY, DAVID	NOVELIST	16633 VENTURA BLVD #1421	ENCINO, CA	91436
LEVY, EDMOND	TV WRITER-DIRECTOR	135 CENTRAL PARK W	NEW YORK, NY	10023
LEVY, EUGENE	ACT-WRI-COMED	9000 SUNSET BLVD #1200	LOS ANGELES, CA	90069
LEVY, FRANKLIN R	TV-FILM PRODUCER	3500 W OLIVE AVE #500	BURBANK, CA	91505
LEVY, GARY	ACTOR-DIRECTOR	4429 MAMMOTH AVE	SHERMAN OAKS, CA	91423
LEVY, JEFERY L	SCREENWRITER	8955 BEVERLY BLVD	WEST HOLLYWOOD, CA	90048
LEVY, JULES	WRITER-PRODUCER	10128 EMPYREAN WY	LOS ANGELES, CA	90067
LEVY, LAWRENCE	DIRECTOR	DGA, 7920 SUNSET BLVD, 6TH FL	LOS ANGELES, CA	90046
LEVY, LAWRENCE H	TV WRITER	11746 THUNDERBIRD AVE	NORTHRIDGE, CA	91326
LEVY, LEW	TV WRITER	R/W/G, 8428 MELROSE PL #C	LOS ANGELES, CA	90069
LEVY, MARV	FOOTBALL COACH	BILLS, 1 BILLS DR	ORCHARD PARK, NJ	14127
LEVY, MRS ROCHELLE	BASEBALL EXECUTIVE	POST OFFICE BOX 7575	PHILADELPHIA, PA	19101
LEVY, NORMAN B	FILM EXECUTIVE	4965 QUEEN FLORENCE LN	WOODLAND HILLS, CA	91364
LEVY, PETER J	TV DIRECTOR-PRODUCER	CORNICHE PRODS, 120 BOERUM PL	BROOKLYN, NY	11021
LEVY, RALPH L	WRITER-PRODUCER	206 MC KENZIE ST	SANTE FE, NM	87501
LEVY, ROBERT J	DIRECTOR	DGA, 110 W 57TH ST	NEW YORK, NY	10019
LEVY, ROBERT L	FILM WRITER-PRODUCER	9573 LANIA LN	BEVERLY HILLS, CA	90210
LEVY, THOMAS P	FILM PRODUCER	11680 LAURELWOOD DR	STUDIO CITY, CA	91604
LEW, JOYCELYNE	ACTRESS	WEBB, 7500 DEVISTA DR	LOS ANGELES, CA	90046
LEWALLYN, DENNIS	BASEBALL-COACH	POST OFFICE BOX 2887	VERO BEACH, FL	32961
LEWENSTEIN, ABRAHAM M	WRITER	232 N CLARK DR #8	BEVERLY HILLS, CA	90211
LEWENSTEIN, BRAM	TALENT AGENT	6310 SAN VICENTE BLVD #407	LOS ANGELES, CA	90048
LEWIN, ALBERT E	TV WRITER	4104 STANSBURY AVE	SHERMAN OAKS, CA	91423
LEWIN, BEN	TV DIRECTOR	ACTT, 111 WARDOUR ST	LONDON W1	ENGLAND
LEWIN, NICHOLAS SPENCER	DIRECTOR	JENNIE, 127 W 79TH ST	NEW YORK, NY	10024
LEWIN, NICK	COMEDIAN	13906 VENTURA BLVD #156	SHERMAN OAKS, CA	91423
LEWIN, ROBERT C	WRITER	918 9TH ST #D	SANTA MONICA, CA	90403

LEWIN, TERESA	WRI-DIR-PROD	200 E 36TH ST #2-G	NEW YORK, NY	10016
LEWINE, ROBERT F	TV PRODUCER	9360 READCREST DR	BEVERLY HILLS, CA	90210
LEWIS, AL	ACTOR	420 MADISON AVE #1400	NEW YORK, NY	10017
LEWIS, ALAN	BASEBALL	POST OFFICE BOX 10031	BAKERSFIELD, CA	93389
LEWIS, ALBERT	FOOTBALL	CHIEFS, 1 ARROWHEAD DR	KANSAS CITY, MO	64129
LEWIS, ALLAN	BASEBALL-SCOUT	INDIANS, CLEVELAND STADIUM	CLEVELAND, OH	44114
LEWIS, ANDREW	TV PRODUCER	TONACHEL & LEWIS, 186 5TH AVE	NEW YORK, NY	10010
LEWIS, ANTHONY	BASEBALL	POST OFFICE BOX 12557	ST PETERSBURG, FL	33733
LEWIS, ARTHUR BERNARD	TV WRITER	4112 WESLIN AVE	SHERMAN OAKS, CA	91423
LEWIS, BILL	FOOTBALL	POST OFFICE BOX 888	PHOENIX, AZ	85001
LEWIS, BOB	FOOTBALL REFEREE	NFL, 410 PARK AVE	NEW YORK, NY	10022
LEWIS, BOBBY	SINGER-SONGWRITER	324 MAIN AVE #323	NORWALK, CT	06851
LEWIS, BUD	ARTIST	1351 OCEAN PARK WALK #106	SANTA MONICA, CA	90405
LEWIS, CARL	TRACK & FIELD	1801 OCEAN PARK BLVD #112	SANTA MONICA, CA	90405
LEWIS, CHARLOTTE	ACTRESS	UTA, 9560 WILSHIRE BL, 5TH FL	BEVERLY HILLS, CA	90212
LEWIS, CHRISTOPHER A	SEC OF COMMONWEALTH	STATE CAPITOL BUILDING	HARRISBURG, PA	17120
LEWIS, DAN	BASEBALL	5999 E VAN BUREN ST	PHOENIX, AZ	85008
LEWIS, DANIEL DAY	ACTOR	65 CONNAUGHT ST	LONDON W2	ENGLAND
LEWIS, DARREN	BASEBALL	S F GIANTS, CANDLESTICK PARK	SAN FRANICSCO, CA	94124
LEWIS, DARREN	FOOTBALL	BEARS, 250 N WASHINGTON RD	LAKE FOREST, IL	60045
LEWIS, DARRYL	FOOTBALL	OILERS, 6910 FANNIN ST	HOUSTON, TX	77070
LEWIS, DAVID	ACTOR	9165 SUNSET BLVD #202	LOS ANGELES, CA	90069
LEWIS, DAWNN	ACTRESS	9229 SUNSET BLVD #311	LOS ANGELES, CA	90069
LEWIS, DIANA	ACTRESS (30'S)	POWELL, 383 W VERDE NORTE	PALM SPRINGS, CA	92262
LEWIS, DIANA	ACTRESS (80'S)	8019 1/2 MELROSE AVE #3	LOS ANGELES, CA	90046
LEWIS, EDWARD	FILM-TV PRODUCER	400 S BEVERLY DR #211	BEVERLY HILLS, CA	90212
LEWIS, ELIZABETH	CASTING DIRECTOR	CLAIRE/CASTING, 333 PARK AVE S	NEW YORK, NY	10010
LEWIS, ELLIOTT B	TV WRITER-DIRECTOR	R/W/G, 8428 MELROSE PL #C	LOS ANGELES, CA	90069
LEWIS, GARRY	FOOTBALL	RAIDERS, 332 CENTER ST	EL SEGUNDO, CA	90245
LEWIS, GARY & THE PLAYBOYS	ROCK & ROLL GROUP	POST OFFICE BOX 53664	INDIANAPOLIS, IN	46253
LEWIS, GEOFFREY	ACTOR	19756 COLLIER ST	WOODLAND HILLS, CA	91364
LEWIS, GERALD	COMPTROLLER	STATE CAPITOL BUILDING	TALLAHASSEE, FL	32399
LEWIS, GREG	FOOTBALL	BRONCOS, 13655 BRONCOS PKWY	ENGLEWOOD, CO	80112
LEWIS, HARRY	ACTOR	THE HAMBURGER HAMLET		
		44 E WALTON ST	CHICAGO, IL	60611
LEWIS, HUEY & THE NEWS	ROCK & ROLL GROUP	POST OFFICE BOX 818	MILL VALLEY, CA	94942
LEWIS, IAN	FILM EXECUTIVE	LITTLE ORCHARD, DEVENISH LN		
		SUNNINGDALE, ASCOT	BERKS SL5 9QU	ENGLAND
LEWIS, JERRY	COMED-ACT-DIR	1701 WALDMAN AVE	LAS VEGAS, NV	89102
LEWIS, JERRY	U S CONGRESSMAN	1826 ORANGE TREE LN #104	REDLANDS, CA	92373
LEWIS, JERRY D	WRITER	15757 SUNSET BLVD	PACIFIC PALISADES, CA	90272
LEWIS, JERRY LEE	SINGER-COMPOSER	LEWIS FARMS	NESBIT, MS	38651
LEWIS, JIM	BASEBALL (MAJORS)	500 NORTON ST	ROCHESTER, NY	14621
LEWIS, JIM	BASEBALL (MINORS)	POST OFFICE BOX 422229	KISSIMMEE, FL	34742
LEWIS, JOE	BASEBALL SCOUT	TIGERS, TIGER STADIUM	DETROIT, MI	48216
LEWIS, JOHN	U S CONGRESSMAN	100 PEACHTREE ST #750, SW	ATLANTA, GA	30303
LEWIS, JOHNNY	BASEBALL-INSTRUCTOR	250 STADIUM PLAZA	ST LOUIS, MO	63102
LEWIS, JONATHAN	FILM WRITER-DIRECTOR	GREAT WESTERN FILMS		
		6 LYMINGTON MANSIONS		
		LYMINGTON RD	LONDON NW6	ENGLAND
LEWIS, JOSEPH	DIRECTOR	13900 PALAWAN WY	MARINA DEL REY, CA	90292
LEWIS, JULIETTE	ACTRESS	5750 WILSHIRE BLVD #580	LOS ANGELES, CA	90037
LEWIS, KENNETH	GUITARIST	ROUTE #3, BOX 210		
		BAYVIEW DR	GALLATIN, TN	37066
LEWIS, KEVIN	FOOTBALL	S F 49ERS, 4949 CENTENNIAL BL	SANTA CLARA, CA	95054
LEWIS, LEO	FOOTBALL	VIKINGS, 9520 VIKING DR	EDEN PRAIRIE, MN	55344
LEWIS, LEONARD	TV WRITER-DIRECTOR	40 CROSS DEEP, TWICKENHAM	MIDDLESEX TW1 4RA	ENGLAND
LEWIS, LIANE	BASEBALL EXECUTIVE	POST OFFICE BOX 10213	LYNCHBURG, VA	24506
LEWIS, MARK	BASEBALL	INDIANS, CLEVELAND STADIUM	CLEVELAND, OH	44114
LEWIS, MICA	BASEBALL	POST OFFICE BOX 5645	ORLANDO, FL	32855
LEWIS, MIKE	BASEBALL	POST OFFICE BOX 48	VISALIA, CA	93279
LEWIS, MIKE	MUSIC ARRANGER	908 HOLLY FOREST	NASHVILLE, TN	37221
LEWIS, MILDRED	PRODUCER	MCA/UNIVERSAL STUDIOS, INC		
		100 UNIVERSAL CITY PLAZA #507	UNIVERSAL CITY, CA	91608
LEWIS, MO	FOOTBALL	N Y JETS, 1000 FULTON AVE	HEMPSTEAD, NY	11550
LEWIS, MORTON	DIRECTOR-PRODUCER	39 STREATHAM HILL	LONDON SW2 4TP	ENGLAND
LEWIS, MYRON	FILM DIRECTOR	5228 FERNWOOD AVE #6	LOS ANGELES, CA	90028
LEWIS, NATE	FOOTBALL	POST OFFICE BOX 609609	SAN DIEGO, CA	92160
LEWIS, PHILIP	DIRECTOR	13 HUBBARD DR	WHITE PLAINS, NY	10605
LEWIS, RANDY	MUSIC CRITIC	LA TIMES, TIMES MIRROR SQ	LOS ANGELES, CA	90053
LEWIS, REGGIE	BASEBALL SCOUT	333 W 35TH ST	CHICAGO, IL	60616
LEWIS, REGGIE	BASKETBALL	151 MERRIMAC ST	BOSTON, MA	02114
LEWIS, RICHARD	COMEDIAN-ACTOR	8001 HEMET PL	LOS ANGELES, CA	90046
LEWIS, RICHARD P	TV WRITER	2160 CENTURY PARK E #2105	LOS ANGELES, CA	90067
LEWIS, RICHIE	BASEBALL	500 NORTON ST	ROCHESTER, NY	14621
LEWIS, ROBERT MICHAEL	TV DIRECTOR	DGA, 7920 SUNSET BLVD, 6TH FL	LOS ANGELES, CA	90046
LEWIS, RON	FOOTBALL	S F 49ERS, 4949 CENTENNIAL BL	SANTA CLARA, CA	95054
LEWIS, SCOTT	BASEBALL	POST OFFICE BOX 2000	ANAHEIM, CA	92803
LEWIS, SHARI	VENTRILOQUIST	603 N ALTA DR	BEVERLY HILLS, CA	90210
LEWIS, SHERMAN	FOOTBALL COACH	S F 49ERS, 4949 CENTENNIAL BL	SANTA CLARA, CA	95054
LEWIS, STEPHEN L	DIRECTOR-PRODUCER	11328 BRILL DR	STUDIO CITY, CA	91604
LEWIS, SUSAN	ACTRESS	362 VALLEY RD	WAYNE, NJ	07470
LEWIS, T R "TROY"	BASEBALL	POST OFFICE BOX 418	SAINT CHARLES, IL	60174
LEWIS, TERRY	SONGWRITER-PRODUCER	FLYTE TYME PRODUCTIONS		
		4330 NICOLLET AVE	MINNEAPOLIS, MN	55409

LEWIS, TOM	U S CONGRESSMAN	27000 PGA BLVD #1	PALM BCH GARDENS, FL	33410
LEWIS FAMILY, THE	C & W GROUP	POST OFFICE BOX 120376	NASHVILLE, TN	37212
LEWIS/SHAFFER BAND	ROCK & ROLL GROUP	POST OFFICE BOX 18368	DENVER, CO	80218
LEWISTON, DENIS	FILM DIRECTOR	SUN CHARIOT FILM/TV, LTD		
		61 TATTENHAM CRESCENT, EPSOM	SURREY	ENGLAND
LEWTHWAITE, BILL	WRITER-PRODUCER	17 BESBURY PARK, MINCHINHAMPTON	GLOUCESTERSHIRE GL6 9E	ENGLAND
LEYLAND, JIM	BASEBALL-MANAGER	POST OFFICE BOX 7000	PITTSBURGH, PA	15212
LEYLAND, RICHARD	TV DIRECTOR-PRODUCER	460 KINGS RD	LONDON SW10	ENGLAND
LEYNA, NICK	BASEBALL MANAGER	CHIEFS, MAC ARTHUR STADIUM	SYRACUSE, NY	13208
LEYRITZ, JIM	BASEBALL	N Y YANKEES, YANKEE STADIUM	BRONX, NY	10451
LEYTON, SAUL	DIRECTOR-PRODUCER	150 E 52ND ST	NEW YORK, NY	10022
LEYVA, NICK	BASEBALL MANAGER	2 ALGONQUIN CT	WAYNE, PA	19087
LEZCANO, CARLOS	BASEBALL-COACH	POST OFFICE BOX 9194	HAMPTON, VA	23670
LI BRETTO, JOHN C	TV DIRECTOR-PRODUCER	30 ROCKEFELLER PLAZA #508	NEW YORK, NY	10112
LIAO, SHARMEN CHENG-YU	ARTIST	504 LINDARAXA PARK	ALAHAMBRA, CA	91801
LIAPIS, PETER	ACTOR	9300 WILSHIRE BLVD #410	BEVERLY HILLS, CA	90212
LIBAEK, SVEN E	COMPOSER-CONDUCTOR	12513 MARTHA ST	NORTH HOLLYWOOD, CA	91607
LIBERATORE, ED	BASEBALL SCOUT	ORIOLE PARK, 333 W CAMDEN ST	BALTIMORE, MD	21201
LIBERTI, JOHN A	TV DIRECTOR	4301 COLFAX AVE #214	STUDIO CITY, CA	91604
LIBERTI-BERGMANN, GAIL	DIRECTOR	14040 SUNSET BLVD	PACIFIC PALISADES, CA	90272
LIBERTY, MARCUS	BASKETBALL	POST OFFICE BOX 4658	DENVER, CO	80204
LIBERTY SILVER	ROCK & ROLL GROUP	41 BRITAIN ST #200	TORONTO, ONT M5A 1R7	CANADA
LIBIN, PAUL	THEATER PRODUCER	CIRCLE IN THE SQUARE		
		1633 BROADWAY	NEW YORK, NY	10019
LIBOV, MORTON	DIRECTOR	8787 SHOREHAM DR #1209	WEST HOLLYWOOD, CA	90069
LIBRETTO, JOHN C	TV DIRECTOR	20 W 64TH ST	NEW YORK, NY	10023
LICATA, KENNETH	DIRECTOR	331 ROBERTS LN	SCOTCH PLAINS, NJ	07076
LICHT, ANDY	FILM PRODUCER	4000 WARNER BLVD	BURBANK, CA	91522
LICHT, JEREMY	ACTOR	2659 S BARRINGTON AVE #202	LOS ANGELES, CA	90064
LICHTENSTEIN, JUNE M	TV PRODUCER	5670 RIVERDALE	RIVERDALE, NY	10471
LICHTI, TODD	BASKETBALL	POST OFFICE BOX 4658	DENVER, CO	80204
LICHTMAN, JAMES	DIRECTOR	4444 WOODMAN AVE #28	SHERMAN OAKS, CA	91423
LICHTMAN, MYLA R	SCREENWRITER	8955 BEVERLY BLVD	WEST HOLLYWOOD, CA	90048
LICHTMAN, PAUL	ACT-WRI-PROD	4001 VAN NOORD AVE	STUDIO CITY, CA	91604
LICINI, CHUCK	ACTOR	4358 MAMMOTH AVE #4	SHERMAN OAKS, CA	91423
LICU, MARIO	ACTOR	1818 1/2 WEBSTER AVE	LOS ANGELES, CA	90026
LIDBACK, JENNY	GOLFER	2750 VOLUSA AVE #B	DAYTON BEACH, FL	32114
LIDDELL, DAVE	BASEBALL	2850 W 20TH AVE	DENVER, CO	80211
LIDDLE, DWIGHT H	FILM DIRECTOR	999 N DOHENY DR #403	LOS ANGELES, CA	90069
LIDDLE, STEVE	BASEBALL MANAGER	POST OFFICE BOX 48	VISALIA, CA	93279
LIDDY, G GORDON	AUTHOR	STONE MANNERS, 9113 SUNSET BL	LOS ANGELES, CA	90069
LIDEKS, MARA	TV WRITER	22443 WELBY WY	CANOGA PARK, CA	91307
LIDSTER, DOUG	HOCKEY	CANUCKS, 100 N RENFREW ST	VANCOUVER, BC V5K 3N7	CANADA
LIEB, ROBERT P	ACTOR	4428 WORSTER AVE	NORTH HOLLYWOOD, CA	91604
LIEBER, ERIC	WRITER-PRODUCER	1200 N DOHENY DR	LOS ANGELES, CA	90069
LIEBER, MIMI	ACTRESS	301 N CANON DR #305	BEVERLY HILLS, CA	90210
LIEBER, PAUL	ACTOR	STONE MANNERS, 9113 SUNSET BL	LOS ANGELES, CA	90069
LIEBERMAN, JACK H	WRITER-PRODUCER	3995 PROSPECT AVE	LOS ANGELES, CA	90027
LIEBERMAN, JANE	COLUMNIST	5700 WILSHIRE BLVD #120	LOS ANGELES, CA	90036
LIEBERMAN, JEFF	DIRECTOR	51 WARREN ST	HASTINGS-ON-HUDSON, NY	10706
LIEBERMAN, JOSEPH I	U S SENATOR	1 COMMERCIAL PLAZA	HARTFORD, CT	06103
LIEBERMAN, LORI	SINGER-SONGWRITER	J LENNER, 3 W 57TH ST	NEW YORK, NY	10019
LIEBERMAN, MARTIN R	DIRECTOR	488 WILLITS ST	BIRMINGHAM, MI	48009
LIEBERMAN, RICK	ACTOR	7471 MELROSE AVE #14	LOS ANGELES, CA	90046
LIEBERSON, SANFORD	FILM PRODUCER	PATHE, 76 HAMMERSMITH RD	LONDON W14 8YR	ENGLAND
LIEBERT, ALAN	BASEBALL	POST OFFICE BOX 360007	BIRMINGHAM, AL	35236
LIEBERTHAL, DENNIS	BASEBALL SCOUT	TIGERS, TIGER STADIUM	DETROIT, MI	48216
LIEBERTHAL, GARY B	TV EXECUTIVE	1901 AVE OF THE STARS #666	LOS ANGELES, CA	90067
LIEBERTHAL, MIKE	BASEBALL	POST OFFICE BOX 15050	READING, PA	19612
LIEBHART, VINCE	CASTING DIRECTOR	275 CENTRAL PARK W #2-C	NEW YORK, NY	10024
LIEBY, BRENT	BASEBALL TRAINER	POST OFFICE BOX 1721	SPARTANBURG, SC	29304
LIEGH, RONNIE & ALLIANCE	ROCK & ROLL GROUP	DMR, 117 HIGHBRIDGE ST	FAYETTEVILLE, NY	13066
LIEN, JENNIFER	ACTRESS	NBC-TV, "ANOTHER WORLD"		
		1268 E 14TH ST	BROOKLYN, NY	11230
LIENHARD, STEVE	BASEBALL	POST OFFICE DRAWER 4797	EL PASO, TX	79914
LIEPKE, MALCOLM T	ARTIST	30 W 72ND ST	NEW YORK, NY	10023
LIEPPMAN, KEITH	BASEBALL-INSTRUCTOR	ATHLETICS'S, OAKLAND COLISEUM	OAKLAND, CA	94621
LIETZKE, BRUCE	GOLFER	POST OFFICE BOX 109601	PALM BCH GARDENS, FL	33418
LIFE	MUSICAL GROUP	CLOUSHER, 193 KONHAUS RD	MECHANICSBURG, PA	17055
LIFEBOAT	ROCK & ROLL GROUP	POST OFFICE BOX 326	BOSTON, MA	02101
LIFFORD, TINA	ACTRESS	301 N CANON DR #305	BEVERLY HILLS, CA	90210
LIFGREN, KELLY	BASEBALL	12000 STADIUM RD	ADELANTO, CA	92301
LIGERMAN, NATHAN	WRITER	5235 SUNNYSLOPE AVE	VAN NUYS, CA	91401
LIGHT, GEORGE A	DIRECTOR	4305 JOPLIN DR	ROCKVILLE, MD	20853
LIGHT, JUDITH	ACTRESS	3690 LAUREL CANYON BLVD #280	STUDIO CITY, CA	91604
LIGHT, KARL	ACTOR	11 ALEXANDER ST	PRINCETON, NJ	08540
LIGHT, RONNY	MUSIC ARRANGER	POST OFFICE BOX 121145	NASHVILLE, TN	37212
LIGHTFOOT, GORDON	SINGER-SONGWRITER	1365 YONGE ST #207	TORONTO, ONT M4T 2P7	CANADA
LIGHTFOOT, JIM	U S CONGRESSMAN	POST OFFICE BOX 1984	SHENANDOAH, IA	51601
LIGHTFOOT, LEONARD	ACTOR	1615 W ALAMEDA AVE #222	BURBANK, CA	91506
LIGHTFOOT, TERRY	JAZZ MUSICIAN	THE THREE HORSESHOES, HARPENDEN	HERTS	ENGLAND
LIGHTFOOT-EILAND, LINDA	ACTRESS	6706 LEMP AVE	NORTH HOLLYWOOD, CA	91606
LIGHTHILL, BRIAN	FILM DIRECTOR	FRENCH'S, 52 HOLLAND PARK MEWS	LONDON W11	ENGLAND
LIGHTMAN, HERB	DIRECTOR	POST OFFICE BOX 8272	UNIVERSAL CITY, CA	91608
LIGHTMAN, JULES	DIRECTOR	1825 SHELL AVE	VENICE, CA	90291

Name	Occupation	Address	City	Code
LIGHTSTONE, MARILYN	ACTRESS	8380 MELROSE AVE #207	LOS ANGELES, CA	90069
LIGHTSTONE, PETER	TV WRITER	390 W END AVE	NEW YORK, NY	10024
		1211 AVE OF THE AMERICAS	NEW YORK, NY	10036
LIGON, TOM	ACTOR	227 WAVERLY PL	NEW YORK, NY	10014
LILE, FORD	ACTOR	1750 CAMINO PALMERO #439	LOS ANGELES, CA	90046
LILLIQUIST, DEREK	BASEBALL	INDIANS, CLEVELAND STADIUM	CLEVELAND, OH	44114
LILLIS, BOB	BASEBALL-COACH	S F GIANTS, CANDLESTICK PARK	SAN FRANICSCO, CA	94124
LILLO, MARIE	ACTRESS	840 N LARRABEE ST #2-102	WEST HOLLYWOOD, CA	90069
LILLY, BRENDA	ACTRESS	5306 HERMITAGE AVE #64	NORTH HOLLYWOOD, CA	91607
LILLY, EVERETT	SINGER	ROUTE #1, BOX 161-E	BECKLEY, WV	25801
LILLY, LOU	DIRECTOR	2528 MANDEVILLE CANYON RD	LOS ANGELES, CA	90049
LILLY, SAMMY	FOOTBALL	RAMS, 2327 W LINCOLN BLVD	ANAHEIM, CA	92801
LILLY, SARAH	ACTRESS	5455 WILSHIRE BLVD #1406	LOS ANGELES, CA	90036
LIM, PIK-SEN	ACTRESS	OCA, 34 GRAFTON TERR	LONDON NW5 4HY	ENGLAND
LIM, STEPHEN	DIRECTOR	842 N STANLEY AVE	HOLLYWOOD, CA	90046
LIMA, JOSE	BASEBALL	POST OFFICE BOX 2785	LAKELAND, FL	33806
LIMAN, ARTHUR L	ATTORNEY	1285 AVE OF THE AMERICAS	NEW YORK, NY	10019
LIMBACH, CHRIS	BASEBALL	POST OFFICE BOX 15050	READING, PA	19612
LIMBAUGH, RUSH	RADIO-TV PERS	EXCELLENCE IN BROADCASTING		
		EIB BUILDING, 17TH FLOOR		
		2 PENNSYLVANIA PLAZA	NEW YORK, NY	10121
LIMELITERS, THE	VOCAL GROUP	17530 VENTURA BLVD #108	ENCINO, CA	91316
LIMITED WARRANTY	ROCK & ROLL GROUP	POST OFFICE BOX 437	EXCELSIOR, MN	55331
LINARES, JULIO	BASEBALL SCOUT	POST OFFICE BOX 288	HOUSTON, TX	77001
LINARES, MARIO	BASEBALL	POST OFFICE BOX 1556	ASHEVILLE, NC	28802
LINARES, RONALD	ACTOR	13840 WYANDOTTE ST	VAN NUYS, CA	91405
LINCOLN, FRAN	COMPOSER	5827 ERNEST ST	LOS ANGELES, CA	90034
LINCOLN, LAR PARK	ACTRESS	10390 SANTA MONICA BLVD #300	LOS ANGELES, CA	90025
LINCOLN COUNTY	C & W GROUP	SCA, 46 E HERBERT AVE	SALT LAKE CITY, UT	84111
LIND, GRETCHEN	ACTRESS	10845 LINDBROOK DR #3	LOS ANGELES, CA	90024
LIND, JACK	BASEBALL EXECUTIVE	POST OFFICE BOX 7000	PITTSBURGH, PA	15212
LIND, JOSE	BASEBALL	POST OFFICE BOX 7000	PITTSBURGH, PA	15212
LIND, ORLANDO	BASEBALL	POST OFFICE BOX 1659	PORTLAND, OR	97207
LIND, TRACI	ACTRESS	CAA, 9830 WILSHIRE BLVD	BEVERLY HILLS, CA	90212
LINDAHL, HAL	WRITER	1468 FOREST GLEN DR #20	HACIENDA HEIGHTS, CA	91745
LINDAUER, JERRY D	CABLE EXECUTIVE	T M CABLE TELEVISION		
		2381 MORSE AVE	IRVINE, CA	92714
LINDBERG, LAWRENCE	TV DIRECTOR	91 CENTRAL PARK W	NEW YORK, NY	10023
LINDBERGH, ANN MORROW	AVIATRIX-AUTHORESS	SCOTT'S COVE	DARIEN, CT	06820
LINDBLAD, PAUL	BASEBALL-COACH	POST OFFICE BOX 9194	HAMPTON, VA	23670
LINDEBERG, DON	BASEBALL SCOUT	N Y YANKEES, YANKEE STADIUM	BRONX, NY	10451
LINDEMAN, BARD	COLUMNIST	TRIBUNE, 64 E CONCORD ST	ORLANDO, FL	32801
LINDEMAN, JIM	BASEBALL	POST OFFICE BOX 7575	PHILADELPHIA, PA	19101
LINDEMANN, CARL, JR	TV EXECUTIVE	CBS-TV, 51 W 52ND ST	NEW YORK, NY	10019
LINDEMUTH, THOMAS	BASEBALL EXECUTIVE	POST OFFICE BOX 488	ERIE, PA	16512
LINDEN, HAL	ACTOR-DIRECTOR	9200 SUNSET BLVD #PH-20	LOS ANGELES, CA	90069
LINDEN, JENNIE	ACTRESS	JOELLE MARTIN, BRITANNIA HOUSE		
		1-11 GLENTHORNE RD	LONDON W6 OLI	ENGLAND
LINDEN, TREVOR	HOCKEY	CANUCKS, 100 N RENFREW ST	VANCOUVER, BC V5K 3N7	CANADA
LINDEN, V CAESAR	CONDUCTOR	POST OFFICE BOX 2645	LOS ANGELES, CA	90028
LINDEN, WILLIAM E, JR	TV DIRECTOR	2716 FOX MILL RD	HERNDON, VA	22071
LINDER, CARL	BASEBALL EXECUTIVE	REDS, 100 RIVERFRONT STADIUM	CINCINNATI, OH	45202
LINDER, KATE	ACTRESS	1801 AVE OF THE STARS #1250	LOS ANGELES, CA	90067
LINDER, STU	FILM EDITOR	ACE, 1041 N FORMOSA AVE	WEST HOLLYWOOD, CA	90046
LINDFORS, VIVECA	ACTRESS	172 E 95TH ST	NEW YORK, NY	10028
LINDHEIM, RICHARD	TV WRITER	166 N CARSON RD	BEVERLY HILLS, CA	90211
LINDLEY, AUDRA	ACTRESS	145 S CANON DR #301	BEVERLY HILLS, CA	90212
LINDLEY, LAURIE	ACTRESS	495 MAR VISTA DR	MONTEREY, CA	93940
LINDNER, SUSAN JANE	TV WRITER	10780 1/2 WILKINS AVE	LOS ANGELES, CA	90024
LINDROTH, LLOYD	HARPIST-COMPOSER	POST OFFICE BOX 148270	NASHVILLE, TN	37214
LINDSAY, CYNTHIA	WRITER	24932 MALIBU RD	MALIBU, CA	90265
LINDSAY, DARIAN	BASEBALL	POST OFFICE BOX 7845	COLUMBIA, SC	29202
LINDSAY, DIANE	SINGER	POST OFFICE BOX 4114	SYLMAR, CA	91342
LINDSAY, ROBERT	ACTOR	FELIX DE WOLFE, 1 ROBERT ST		
		ADELPHI	LONDON WC2N 6BH	ENGLAND
LINDSAY, TIM	BASEBALL	POST OFFICE BOX 1110	MYRTLE BEACH, SC	29578
LINDSEY, DALE	FOOTBALL COACH	PATRIOTS, FOXBORO STADIUM, RT #1	FOXBORO, MA	02035
LINDSEY, DARRELL	BASEBALL	POST OFFICE BOX 10336	CLEARWATER, FL	34617
LINDSEY, DOUG	BASEBALL	POST OFFICE BOX 3449	SCRANTON, PA	18505
LINDSEY, ELIZABETH	ACTRESS	LIGHT, 901 BRINGHAM AVE	LOS ANGELES, CA	90049
LINDSEY, GEORGE	ACT-SING-COMED	10000 SANTA MONICA BLVD #305	LOS ANGELES, CA	90067
LINDSEY, GEORGE T	WRITER-PRODUCER	13535 VALERIO ST #223	VAN NUYS, CA	91405
LINDSEY, KEITH	ACTOR	7247 BALBOA BLVD #C	VAN NUYS, CA	91406
LINDSEY, MINNIE S	ACTRESS	334 VERNON AVE	VENICE, CA	90291
LINDSEY, MORT	COMPOSER-CONDUCTOR	6970 FERNHILL DR	MALIBU, CA	90265
LINDSLEY, CLARKE	ACTOR	CASSELL, 843 N SYCAMORE AVE	LOS ANGELES, CA	90038
LINDSLEY, WILLIAM C	DIRECTOR	28362 FORESTBROOK ST	FARMINGTON HILLS, MI	48018
LINDSTROM, PIA	FILM CRITIC	30 ROCKEFELLER PLAZA #700	NEW YORK, NY	10112
LINEBACK, RICHARD	ACTOR	2525 LYRIC AVE	LOS ANGELES, CA	90027
LINEBERGER, JAMES L	SCREENWRITER	555 W 57TH ST #1230	NEW YORK, NY	10019
LINEHAN, JOYCE	TALENT AGENT	POST OFFICE BOX 817	JAMAICA PLAIN, MA	02130
LING, EUGENE F	WRITER	808 ADELAIDE PL	SANTA MONICA, CA	90402
LING, PETER	TV WRITER	13 HIGH WICKHAM	HASTINGS	ENGLAND
LING, SYDNEY	ACTOR-DIRECTOR	BROUWERSGRACHT, 68-1013 GX	AMSTERDAM	NETEHERLANDS
LINGNER, ADAM	FOOTBALL	BILLS, 1 BILLS DR	ORCHARD PARK, NJ	14127

LINK, ROBERT L	DIRECTOR	600 N MC CLURG CT	CHICAGO, IL	60611
LINK, WILLIAM	TV WRITER-PRODUCER	1501 SKYLARK LN	LOS ANGELES, CA	90069
LINKE, BETTINA BRENNA	ACTRESS	4373 CLYBOURN AVE	NORTH HOLLYWOOD, CA	91602
LINKE, PAUL	ACTOR	3925 MICHAEL AVE	LOS ANGELES, CA	90066
LINKE, RICHARD O	TV PROD-TALENT AGT	4445 CARTWRIGHT AVE #305	NORTH HOLLYWOOD, CA	91602
LINKLETTER, ART	TV PERSONALITY	1100 BEL AIR RD	LOS ANGELES, CA	90077
LINKLETTER, JACK	TV PERSONALITY	765 BAKER ST	COSTA MESA, CA	92626
LINN, DENNIS R	DIRECTOR	BIG ORANGE PRODUCTIONS		
		2791 BIRD AVE	MIAMI, FL	33133
LINN, RAY L, JR	COMPOSER	POST OFFICE BOX 475	HOMEWOOD, CA	95718
LINN, ROBERT T	COMPOSER	3275 DE WITT DR	LOS ANGELES, CA	90068
LINN, ROBERTA	SINGER	HEINECKE'S, 8961 SUNSET BLVD	LOS ANGELES, CA	90069
LINN, TERI ANN	ACTRESS	4267 MARINA CITY DR #312	MARINA DEL REY, CA	90292
LINN-BAKER, MARK	ACTOR	1033 GAYLEY AVE #201	LOS ANGELES, CA	90024
LINNETTE, SHERI	SINGER	POST OFFICE BOX 171132	NASHVILLE, TN	37217
LINSAY, GEORGE T	WRITER-DIRECTOR	13535 VALERIO ST #223	VAN NUYS, CA	91405
LINSEMAN, KEN	HOCKEY	OILERS, NORTHLANDS COLISEUM	EDMONTON, ALTA T5B 4M9	CANADA
LINSKEY, MIKE	BASEBALL	POST OFFICE BOX 1420	WICHITA, KS	67201
LINSON, ART	DIRECTOR-PRODUCER	DGA, 110 W 57TH ST	NEW YORK, NY	10019
LINSON, DONNA	COSTUME DESIGNER	9648 YOAKUM DR	BEVERLY HILLS, CA	90210
LINTERMANS, GLORIA	COLUMNIST	UPS, 4900 MAIN ST, 9TH FLOOR	KANSAS CITY, MO	64112
LINTON, DOUG	BASEBALL	CHIEFS, MAC ARTHUR STADIUM	SYRACUSE, NY	13208
LINTON, SHERWIN	SINGER	POST OFFICE BOX 33100	MINNEAPOLIS, MN	55433
LINVILLE, ALBERT	ACTOR	7 W 81ST ST	NEW YORK, NY	10024
LINVILLE, JOANNE	ACTRESS	3148 FRYMAN RD	STUDIO CITY, CA	91604
LINVILLE, LARRY	ACTOR	9454 WILSHIRE BLVD #M-3	BEVERLY HILLS, CA	90211
LIONNI, LEO	ARTIST	35 E 85TH ST #10-D	NEW YORK, NY	10028
LIOTTA, BEN	BASEBALL EXECUTIVE	80 OTTAWA ST N	HAMILTON, ONT L8H 3Z1	CANADA
LIOTTA, CHARLES	TV DIRECTOR	2492 WELLESLEY AVE	LOS ANGELES, CA	90064
LIOTTA, JERRY I	DIRECTOR	11 GAYLORD DR	WILTON, CT	06897
LIOTTA, RAY	ACTOR	CAA, 9830 WILSHIRE BLVD	BEVERLY HILLS, CA	90212
LIPACK, MICHAEL	PHOTOGRAPHER	253-26 61ST AVE	LITTLE NECK, NY	11362
LIPARI, JOANNA	ACTRESS	7471 MELROSE AVE #14	LOS ANGELES, CA	90046
LIPINSKI, WILLIAM	U S CONGRESSMAN	5832 S ARCHER AVE	CHICAGO, IL	60638
LIPKIN, SEYMOUR	PIANIST-CONDUCTOR	420 W END AVE	NEW YORK, NY	10024
LIPMAN, DANIEL	TV WRITER	620 VIA DE LA PAZ	PACIFIC PALISADES, CA	90272
LIPMAN, HAROLD	DIRECTOR	35 E 35TH ST	NEW YORK, NY	10016
LIPMAN, MAUREEN	ACTRESS	HUTTON, 200 FULHAM RD	LONDON SW14 7AH	ENGLAND
LIPNICK, EDWARD	WRITER	20608 PACIFIC COAST HWY	MALIBU, CA	90265
LIPON, JOHN	BASEBALL-MANAGER	POST OFFICE BOX 2785	LAKELAND, FL	33806
		NORTHSIDE STATION	ATLANTA, GA	30355
LIPPERT, NORMAN E	DIRECTOR	15640 W TIMBER LN	LIBERTYVILLE, IL	60048
LIPPETT, RONNIE	FOOTBALL	PATRIOTS, FOXBORO STADIUM, RT #1	FOXBORO, MA	02035
LIPPMAN, JOHN	COLUMNIST	VARIETY, 475 PARK AVE S	NEW YORK, NY	10016
LIPPS, LOUIS	FOOTBALL	STEELERS, 300 STADIUM CIR	PITTSBURGH, PA	15212
LIPPS, INC	VOCAL GROUP	FAA, 1700 BROADWAY, 5TH FLOOR	NEW YORK, NY	10019
LIPSCOMB, DENNIS	ACTOR	1999 AVE OF THE STARS #2850	LOS ANGELES, CA	90067
LIPSCOMB, JAMES C	TV WRITER	31 E 31ST ST	NEW YORK, NY	10016
LIPSCOMB, THOMAS H	TV PRODUCER	CARAVELLE, 145 E 74TH ST	NEW YORK, NY	10021
LIPSEY, JOHN	BASEBALL UMPIRE	2101 E BROADWAY #35	TEMPE, AZ	85282
LIPSON, G ROBERT	DIRECTOR	1565 OLD CHATHAM DR	BLOOMFIELD HILLS, MI	48013
LIPSON, MARK	BASEBALL	14100 SIX MILE CYPRESS PKWY	FORT MYERS, FL	33912
LIPSTONE, HOWARD	TV WRITER-EXECUTIVE	111 S ROCKINGHAM AVE	LOS ANGELES, CA	90049
LIPSTONE, JANE	TV EXECUTIVE	111 S ROCKINGHAM AVE	LOS ANGELES, CA	90049
LIPSYTE, ROBERT M	NEWS CORRES-WRITER	CBS NEWS, 524 W 57TH ST	NEW YORK, NY	10019
LIPTON, CELIA	SINGER	POST OFFICE BOX 15011	PLANTATION, FL	33318
LIPTON, DANIEL	CONDUCTOR	225 W 34TH ST #1012	NEW YORK, NY	10001
LIPTON, E TRINA	PHOTOGRAPHER	60 E 8TH ST #310	NEW YORK, NY	10003
LIPTON, JAMES	THEATER WRI-PROD	159 E 80TH ST	NEW YORK, NY	10021
LIPTON, LARRY	FILM DIRECTOR	3006 BELLEVUE AVE	LOS ANGELES, CA	90026
LIPTON, LEONARD	TV DIRECTOR	ABC-TV, 7 W 66TH ST	NEW YORK, NY	10023
LIPTON, PEGGY	ACTRESS	15250 VENTURA BLVD #900	SHERMAN OAKS, CA	91403
LIPTON, ROBERT	ACTOR	11300 W OLYMPIC BLVD #870	LOS ANGELES, CA	90064
LIPTON, SANDY	ACTRESS	145 S FAIRFAX AVE #310	LOS ANGELES, CA	90036
LIRA, FELIPE	BASEBALL	POST OFFICE BOX 2785	LAKELAND, FL	33806
LIRIANO, NELSON	BASEBALL	4385 TUTT BLVD	COLORADO SPRINGS, CO	80922
LIS, JOE	BASEBALL	POST OFFICE BOX 1110	MYRTLE BEACH, SC	29578
LISA LISA	ROCK & ROLL DUO	747 10TH AVE	NEW YORK, NY	10019
LISAK, STEVE	ACTOR	6048 OLIVE AVE	LONG BEACH, CA	90805
LISANTI, MICHELLE P	TV WRITER	4730 BEN AVE #23	NORTH HOLLYWOOD, CA	91607
LISBERGER, STEVEN	WRITER-PRODUCER	431 7TH ST	SANTA MONICA, CA	90402
LISHAWA, CHESTER	TV DIRECTOR	90 SURREY LN	TENAFLY, NJ	07670
LISI, GAETANO	DIRECTOR	225 E 88TH ST	NEW YORK, NY	10028
LISI, VIRNA	ACTRESS	VIA DI FILOMARINO 4	ROME	ITALY
LISS, STEPHANIE A	WRITER	4941 WHITSETT AVE	NORTH HOLLYWOOD, CA	91607
LISSON, MARK	WRITER	1961 HOLMBY AVE	LOS ANGELES, CA	90025
LIST, PAUL	BASEBALL	POST OFFICE DRAWER 1218	ZEBULON, NC	27597
LIST, SHELLEY P	TV WRITER	2919 GRAND CANAL	VENICE, CA	90291
LISTACH, PAT	BASEBALL	2850 W 20TH AVE	DENVER, CO	80211
LISTER, ALTON	BASKETBALL	GOLDEN STATE WARRIORS		
		OAKLAND COLISEUM ARENA		
		NIMITZ FWY & HEGENBERGER RD	OAKLAND, CA	94621
LISTER, DEREK	TV WRITER-DIRECTOR	14 KENWYN RD, WIMBLEDON	LONDON SW20 8TR	ENGLAND
LISTER, WALTER	WRITER	39 WENDT AVE	LARCHMONT, NY	10538
LISTON, IAN	ACTOR	HISS & BOO, 24 W GROVE		

		WALTON ON THAMES	SURREY KT12 5NX	ENGLAND
LITHGOW, JOHN	ACTOR	1319 WARNALL AVE	LOS ANGELES, CA	90024
LITT, LARRY	COMEDIAN	POST OFFICE BOX 3574	MIAMI BEACH, FL	33152
LITTELL, MARK	BASEBALL-COACH	POST OFFICE BOX 8550	STOCKTON, CA	95208
LITTELL, ROBERT	SCREENWRITER	8955 BEVERLY BLVD	WEST HOLLYWOOD, CA	90048
LITTLE, BIG TINY	SINGER-SONGWRITER	FROST, W 3985 TAFT DR	SPOKANE, WA	99208
LITTLE, BRYAN	BASEBALL MANAGER	12000 STADIUM RD	ADELANTO, CA	92301
LITTLE, CLEAVON	ACTOR	SMITH, 121 N SAN VICENTE BLVD	BEVERLY HILLS, CA	90211
LITTLE, DAVID	FOOTBALL	STEELERS, 300 STADIUM CIR	PITTSBURGH, PA	15212
LITTLE, DICK	BASEBALL COACH	POST OFFICE BOX 4370	SALINAS, CA	93912
LITTLE, DWIGHT	FILM DIRECTOR	1680 N VINE ST #517	HOLLYWOOD, CA	90028
LITTLE, GRADY	BASEBALL MANAGER	POST OFFICE BOX 16683	GREENVILLE, SC	29606
LITTLE, JOYCE	ACTRESS	LIGHT, 901 BRINGHAM AVE	LOS ANGELES, CA	90049
LITTLE, MICHELLE	ACTRESS	662 N VAN NESS AVE #305	LOS ANGELES, CA	90004
LITTLE, MIKE	BASEBALL	POST OFFICE BOX 4488	WINSTON-SALEM, NC	27115
LITTLE, RICH	ACTOR-COMEDIAN	24800 PACIFIC COAST HWY	MALIBU, CA	90265
LITTLE, ROD	ILLUSTRATOR	POST OFFICE BOX 500	WASHINGTON, DC	20044
LITTLE, SCOTT	BASEBALL-MANAGER	POST OFFICE BOX 3746, HILL STA	AUGUSTA, GA	30904
LITTLE, SYD	IMPRESSIONIST	PETER PRITCHARD, MEZZANINE FL		
		235 REGENT HOUSE	LONDON W1R 8AX	ENGLAND
LITTLE, TAWNY	TV HOST	KCAL-TV, 5515 MELROSE AVE	LOS ANGELES, CA	90038
LITTLE ANTHONY	SINGER	SEE - GOURDINE, LITTLE ANTHONY		
LITTLE RICHARD	SINGER-SONGWRITER	151 S EL CAMINO DR	BEVERLY HILLS, CA	90212
LITTLE RIVER BAND	ROCK & ROLL GROUP	87-91 PALMERSTIN CRESCENT		
		ALBERT PARK	MELBOURNE U1C 3206	AUSTRALIA
LITTLE STEVEN & DISCIPLES OF S	ROCK & ROLL GROUP	9200 SUNSET BLVD #915	LOS ANGELES, CA	90069
LITTLE TOYOKO	WRESTLER	POST OFFICE BOX 3859	STAMFORD, CT	06905
LITTLEFIELD, DAVE	BASEBALL SCOUT	TIGERS, TIGER STADIUM	DETROIT, MI	48216
LITTLEFIELD, NANCY	WRI-DIR-PROD	41-61 KISSENA BLVD #2077	FLUSHING, NY	11355
LITTLEFIELD, WARREN	TV EXECUTIVE	409 N BUNDY DR	LOS ANGELES, CA	90049
LITTLER, CRAIG	ACTOR	11675 DARLINGTON AVE #302	LOS ANGELES, CA	90049
LITTLER, GENE	GOLFER	POST OFFICE BOX 1949	RANCHO SANTE FE, CA	92067
LITTLES, GENE	BASKETBALL COACH	310 N KINGS DR	CHARLOTTE, NC	28204
LITTLETON, CAROL	FILM EDITOR	UTA, 9560 WILSHIRE BL, 5TH FL	BEVERLY HILLS, CA	90212
LITTLETON, TWYLA SUE	ACTRESS	9200 SUNSET BLVD #625	LOS ANGELES, CA	90069
LITTMAN, GREGG	ACTOR	1140 N DETROIT ST	WEST HOLLYWOOD, CA	90046
LITTMAN, LYNNE	TV DIRECTOR-PRODUCER	6620 CAHUENGA TERR	LOS ANGELES, CA	90068
LITTO, GEORGE	FILM PRODUCER	215 S BEVERLY BLVD #202	BEVERLY HILLS, CA	90212
LITTON, GREG	BASEBALL	5999 E VAN BUREN ST	PHOENIX, AZ	85008
LITVACK, IRWIN	ACTOR	40 BRIGHTON FIRST RD	BROOKLYN, NY	11235
LITVACK, JOHN ALAN	TV DIR-EXEC	1741 PIER AVE	SANTA MONICA, CA	90405
LITVACK, NEAL	CABLE EXECUTIVE	HBO, 1100 6TH AVE	NEW YORK, NY	10036
LITVAK, ILENE	WRI-DIR-PROD	240-22 69TH AVE	DOUGLASTON, NY	11362
LIU, CAROLINE	ACTRESS	9229 SUNSET BLVD #208	LOS ANGELES, CA	90069
LIVE	RHYTHM & BLUES GROUP	PERLE, 4475 VINELAND AVE	STUDIO CITY, CA	91602
LIVELY, LORI LYNN	ACTRESS	9200 SUNSET BLVD #625	LOS ANGELES, CA	90069
LIVELY, ROBYN	ACTRESS	9200 SUNSET BLVD #625	LOS ANGELES, CA	90069
LIVESEY, BILL	BASEBALL SCOUT	N Y YANKEES, YANKEE STADIUM	BRONX, NY	10451
LIVESEY, JEFF	BASEBALL	1155 W MOUND ST	COLUMBUS, OH	43223
LIVESEY, STEVE	BASEBALL	POST OFFICE BOX 2148	WOODBRIDGE, VA	22193
LIVING COLOUR	ROCK & ROLL GROUP	150 W 51ST ST #1027	NEW YORK, NY	10019
LIVINGSTON, ALAN W	WRITER-PRODUCER	945 N ALPINE DR	BEVERLY HILLS, CA	90210
LIVINGSTON, BOB	U S CONGRESSMAN	111 VETERANS BLVD	METAIRIE, LA	70005
LIVINGSTON, DAVID W	MUSIC ARRANGER	2325 BELLEVUE DR	BOWLING GREEN, KY	42101
LIVINGSTON, HAROLD	SCREENWRITER	8955 BEVERLY BLVD	WEST HOLLYWOOD, CA	90048
LIVINGSTON, JANE	TV PRODUCER	WNYW-TV, 205 E 67TH ST	NEW YORK, NY	10021
LIVINGSTON, JAY	COMPOSER-LYRICIST	ASCAP, 1 LINCOLN PLAZA	NEW YORK, NY	10023
LIVINGSTON, ROBERT C	DIRECTOR	46 LARIAT RD	PALM SPRINGS, CA	92262
LIVINGSTON, ROBERT H	TV DIRECTOR	347 W 39TH ST	NEW YORK, NY	10018
LIVINGSTON, ULYSSES G	COMPOSER	27027 WHITESTONE RD	ROLLING HILLS, CA	90274
LIVINGSTONE, DOUGLAS	TV WRITER-DIRECTOR	LEMON, 24 POTTERY, HOLLAND PK	LONDON W11 4LZ	ENGLAND
LIVINGSTONE, SCOTT	BASEBALL	TIGERS, TIGER STADIUM	DETROIT, MI	48216
LIVINGTON, FRANCIS	ARTIST	1844 CHURCH ST	SAN FRANCISCO, CA	94131
LIVNEH, SAMUEL	ACTOR	14948 MOORPARK ST #103	SHERMAN OAKS, CA	91403
LIZER, KARI	ACTRESS	8643 WALNUT DR	LOS ANGELES, CA	90046
LIZZI, JOAN	ACTOR	13040 DRONFIELD AVE #26	SYLMAR, CA	91342
LIZZY BORDEN	ROCK & ROLL GROUP	POST OFFICE BOX 2428	EL SEGUNDO, CA	90245
LL COOL J	RAPPER-RAPWRITER	298 ELIZABETH ST #1	NEW YORK, NY	10012
LLE, LOUIS	FILM DIRECTOR	LE COUEL, 46260 LIMOGNE	EN QUERCY	FRANCE
LLEN, CAZ	SINGER	CUDE, 519 N HALIFAX AVE	DAYTONA BEACH, FL	32118
LLENAS, WINSTON	BASEBALL-SCOUT	INDIANS, CLEVELAND STADIUM	CLEVELAND, OH	44114
LLEWELYN, DOUG	ACTOR-TV HOST	8075 W 3RD ST #303	LOS ANGELES, CA	90048
LLEWELYN-DAVIES, MELISSA	TV DIRECTOR	3 RICHMOND CRESCENT	LONDON N1	ENGLAND
LLOYD, CHARLES F	COMPOSER	ROUTE #1, BOX 63	BIG SUR, CA	93920
LLOYD, CHRISTOPHER	ACTOR-PRODUCER	POST OFFICE BOX 491246	LOS ANGELES, CA	90049
LLOYD, EMILY ANN	ACTRESS	1800 N VINE ST #120	LOS ANGELES, CA	90028
LLOYD, EUAN	FILM PRODUCER	PINEWOOD STUDIOS, IVER HEATH	IVER, BUCKS SLO ONH	ENGLAND
LLOYD, GRAEME	BASEBALL	633 JESSAMINE ST	KNOXVILLE, TN	37917
LLOYD, GREG	FOOTBALL	STEELERS, 300 STADIUM CIR	PITTSBURGH, PA	15212
LLOYD, IAN	SINGER	1790 BROADWAY #PH	NEW YORK, NY	10019
LLOYD, INNES	TV PRODUCER	89 QUEEN'S RD, RICHMOND	SURREY	ENGLAND
LLOYD, JAN R	FILM DIRECTOR	15 QUARTERDECK ST	MARINA DEL REY, CA	90292
LLOYD, JOHN	TV PRODUCER	LONDON MGT, 235-241 REGENT ST	LONDON W1R 4PH	ENGLAND
LLOYD, KATHLEEN	ACTRESS	10100 SANTA MONICA BLVD #700	LOS ANGELES, CA	90067
LLOYD, KEVIN	ACTOR	STOCKBROOK HOUSE, 8 KING ST		

Name	Occupation	Address	City	Zip/Country
		DUFFIELD	DERBY	ENGLAND
LLOYD, LAUREN	FILM PRODUCER	5254 MELROSE AVE #405-D	LOS ANGELES, CA	90038
LLOYD, LELAND	SINGER-GUITARIST	654 HARDING PL	NASHVILLE, TN	37211
LLOYD, LINDA BEATSON	ACTRESS	2708 ANGELO DR	LOS ANGELES, CA	90077
LLOYD, MARILYN	U S CONGRESSWOMAN	253 JAY SOLOMON FEDERAL		
		OFFICE BUILDING	CHATTANOOGA, TN	37401
LLOYD, MIKE	TV DIRECTOR-PRODUCER	EXPERIENCE COUNTS COMPANY		
		5-7 CARNABY ST	LONDON W1V 1PG	ENGLAND
LLOYD, NORMAN	ACT-DIR-PROD	1813 OLD RANCH RD	LOS ANGELES, CA	90049
LLOYD, TED	TV PRODUCER	CROFT HAM, KEWFERRY DR		
		NORTHWOOD	MIDDLESEX	ENGLAND
LLOYD, YOLANDA	ACTRESS	BDP, 10637 BURBANK BLVD	NORTH HOLLYWOOD, CA	91601
LLYNNE, BOBBE	SINGER	TERRY, 909 PARKVIEW AVE	LODI, CA	95240
LO BIANCO, TONY	ACT-WRI-DIR	888 7TH AVE #602	NEW YORK, NY	10106
LO CASALE, AL	FOOTBALL EXECUTIVE	RAIDERS, 332 CENTER ST	EL SEGUNDO, CA	90245
LO CICERO, THOMAS V	DIRECTOR	13730 HART	OAK PARK, MI	48237
LOACH, KENNETH	TV DIRECTOR	DAISH, 83 EASTBOURNE MEWS	LONDON W2 6LQ	ENGLAND
LOAIZA, STEVE	BASEBALL	POST OFFICE BOX 3746, HILL STA	AUGUSTA, GA	30904
LOBELL, MIKE	FILM PRODUCER	826 HAMPTON DR	VENICE, CA	90291
LOBER, LIONEL	WRITER	2700 E CAHUENGA BLVD #4211	LOS ANGELES, CA	90068
LOBL, VICTOR	TV DIRECTOR	1726 CRISLER WY	LOS ANGELES, CA	90069
LOBO	SINGER-SONGWRITER	DENIS VAUGHAN MANAGEMENT		
		HEATHCOAT HOUSE		
		19-20 SAVILE RD	LONDON W1	ENGLAND
LOBUE, J D	DIRECTOR	2960 BRIAR KNOLL DR	LOS ANGELES, CA	90046
LOCANE, AMY	ACTRESS	10100 SANTA MONICA BLVD #1600	LOS ANGELES, CA	90067
LOCANTE, SAM G	ACTOR	235 W END AVE	NEW YORK, NY	10023
LOCATELL, CAROL	ACTRESS	4153 WOODMAN AVE	SHERMAN OAKS, CA	91423
LOCHER, DICK	CARTOONIST	THE CHICAGO TRIBUNE		
		TRIBUNE TOWER		
		435 N MICHIGAN AVE	CHICAGO, IL	60611
LOCHHEAD, LEE	DIRECTOR	4039 CAMELLIA AVE	STUDIO CITY, CA	91604
LOCHNER, C DAVID	FILM DIR-PROD-ED	18 NEW RD, SHENLEY, RADLETT	HERTS WD7 9EA	ENGLAND
LOCHTE, RICHARD S	SCREENWRITER-NOVELIST	2700 NEILSON WY	SANTA MONICA, CA	90405
LOCKE, PETER	TV PRODUCER	1119 N MC CADDEN PL	HOLLYWOOD, CA	90038
LOCKE, RICHARD B	TV DIRECTOR	2940 COTTONWOOD CT	NEWBURY PARK, CA	91320
LOCKE, RICHARD E	TV DIRECTOR	948 WINFIELD ST	NEWBURY PARK, CA	91320
LOCKE, SAM D	TV WRITER	3043 NICHOLS CANYON RD	HOLLYWOOD, CA	90046
LOCKE, SONDRA	ACTRESS-DIRECTOR	111 STONE CANYON RD	LOS ANGELES, CA	90077
LOCKER, KENNETH A	FILM WRITER-DIRECTOR	1607 N VISTA ST	LOS ANGELES, CA	90046
LOCKERMAN, BRAD	ACTOR	10870 ASHTON AVE #209	LOS ANGELES, CA	90024
LOCKETT, RON	BASEBALL	POST OFFICE BOX 10336	CLEARWATER, FL	34617
LOCKHART, ANNE	ACTRESS	28245 DRIVER AVE	AGOURA HILLS, CA	91301
LOCKHART, EUGENE	FOOTBALL	PATRIOTS, FOXBORO STADIUM, RT #1	FOXBORO, MA	02035
LOCKHART, IAN	BASKETBALL	SUNS, 2910 N CENTRAL AVE	PHOENIX, AZ	85012
LOCKHART, JUNE	ACTRESS	404 SAN VICENTE BLVD #208	SANTA MONICA, CA	90402
LOCKHART, KEITH	BASEBALL	POST OFFICE BOX 11087	TACOMA, WA	98411
LOCKHART, LAUREL	ACTRESS	DON SCHWARTZ, 8749 SUNSET BLVD	LOS ANGELES, CA	90069
LOCKHART, RAY	DIRECTOR	DGA, 110 W 57TH ST	NEW YORK, NY	10019
LOCKLEAR, DEAN	BASEBALL	1090 N EUCLID AVE	SARASOTA, FL	34237
LOCKLEAR, HEATHER	ACTRESS-MODEL	10350 WILSHIRE BLVD #502	LOS ANGELES, CA	90024
LOCKLIN, HANK	SINGER-SONGWRITER	ROUTE 1, BOX 123	MILTON, FL	32570
LOCKLIN, LORYN	ACTRESS	ICM, 8899 BEVERLY BLVD	LOS ANGELES, CA	90048
LOCKMAN, WHITNEY	BASEBALL-EXEC-SCOUT	EXPOS, 4545 DE COUBERTIN AVE	MONTREAL, QUE H1V 3P2	CANADA
LOCKWOOD, E GREY	DIRECTOR	DGA, 7920 SUNSET BLVD, 6TH FL	LOS ANGELES, CA	90046
LOCKWOOD, GARY	ACTOR	3083 1/2 RAMBLA PACIFICA	MALIBU, CA	90265
LOCKWOOD, JULIA	ACTRESS	112 CASTLENAN	LONDON SW13	ENGLAND
LOCKWOOD, LESTER	THEATER PRODUCER	325 W END AVE	NEW YORK, NY	10023
LOCKWOOD, VERA	ACTRESS	325 W END AVE	NEW YORK, NY	10023
LOCONTO, FRANK X	SINGER	7766 NW 44TH ST	SUNRISE, FL	33321
LODDING, RICHARD	BASEBALL	POST OFFICE BOX 30160	SAN BERNARDINO, CA	92413
LODGE, DAVID	ACTOR	8 SYDNEY RD, RICHMOND	SURREY	ENGLAND
LODGE, J C	SINGER	POST OFFICE BOX 42517	WASHINGTON, DC	20015
LODGE, LINDA	ACTRESS	1429 N HAVENHURST DR #2	WEST HOLLYWOOD, CA	90046
LODGIC	ROCK & ROLL GROUP	7250 BEVERLY BLVD #102	LOS ANGELES, CA	90036
LODISH, MIKE	FOOTBALL	BILLS, 1 BILLS DR	ORCHARD PARK, NJ	14127
LOE, EDWARD A, JR	COMPOSER-CONDUCTOR	6245 GOODLAND PL	NORTH HOLLYWOOD, CA	91606
LOE, JUDY	ACTRESS	PETERS, FRASER & DUNLOP, LTD		
		5TH FLOOR, THE CHAMBERS		
		CHELSEA HARBOUR, LOT RD	LONDON SW10 OXF	ENGLAND
LOEB, JOSEPH, III	SCREENWRITER	CAA, 9830 WILSHIRE BLVD	BEVERLY HILLS, CA	90212
LOEB, MARC	BASEBALL	POST OFFICE BOX 1110	MYRTLE BEACH, SC	29578
LOEB, MARSHA	TALENT AGENT	3575 CAHUENGA BLVD #450	LOS ANGELES, CA	90068
LOEW, RICHARD	DIRECTOR	217 E 49TH ST	NEW YORK, NY	10017
LOEWENSTINE, CARL	BASEBALL SCOUT	1000 ELYSIAN PARK DR	LOS ANGELES, CA	90012
LOFARO, STEPHEN	TV DIRECTOR	3081 TOWNSHIP AVE	SIMI VALLEY, CA	93063
LOFARO, THOMAS	DIRECTOR	913 EUCLID ST #3	SANTA MONICA, CA	90403
LOFGREN, DENNIS	DIRECTOR	2600 10TH ST	BERKELEY, CA	94710
LOFGREN, NILS	SINGER-GUITARIST	1801 CENTURY PARK E #1132	LOS ANGELES, CA	90067
LOFLAND, DANA	GOLFER	2750 VOLUSA AVE #B	DAYTON BEACH, FL	32114
LOFTIN, BO	BASEBALL	POST OFFICE BOX 2001	CEDAR RAPIDS, IA	52406
LOFTIN, WILLIAM	FILM DIRECTOR	22041 JONESPORT LN	HUNTINGTON BEACH, CA	92646
LOFTON, CHRIS	WRITER	13537 HAYNES ST	VAN NUYS, CA	91401
LOFTON, JAMES	FOOTBALL	BILLS, 1 BILLS DR	ORCHARD PARK, NJ	14127
LOFTON, KENNY	BASEBALL	INDIANS, CLEVELAND STADIUM	CLEVELAND, OH	44114

LOFTON, ROD	BASEBALL	POST OFFICE BOX 230	HAGERSTOWN, MD 21740
LOFTON, STEVE	FOOTBALL	POST OFFICE BOX 888	PHOENIX, AZ 85001
LOGAN, ANGELA	ACTRESS	21 E 22ND ST #71	NEW YORK, NY 10010
LOGAN, BRUCE	DIRECTOR	9601 WILSHIRE BLVD #506	BEVERLY HILLS, CA 90210
LOGAN, DON	BASEBALL EXECUTIVE	STARS, 850 LAS VEGAS BLVD N	LAS VEGAS, NV 89101
LOGAN, ERNIE	FOOTBALL	BROWNS, 80 1ST ST	BEREA, OH 44017
LOGAN, MARC	FOOTBALL	DOLPHINS, 2269 NW 199TH ST	MIAMI, FL 33056
LOGAN, PHYLLIS	ACTRESS	DAWSON, 47 COURTFIELD RD #9	LONDON SW7 4DB ENGLAND
LOGAN, ROBERT	ACTOR	BDP, 10637 BURBANK BLVD	NORTH HOLLYWOOD, CA 91601
LOGAN, ROBERT T	COMPOSER	11825 SNELLING ST	SUN VALLEY, CA 91352
LOGAN, TERRY	BASEBALL SCOUT	POST OFFICE BOX 7575	PHILADELPHIA, PA 19101
LOGAN, TODD	BASEBALL	POST OFFICE BOX 48	VISALIA, CA 93279
LOGE, MARC	ACTOR	2067 N ARYGYLE AVE #3	LOS ANGELES, CA 90068
LOGGIA, KRISTINA	ACTRESS	5750 WILSHIRE BLVD #512	LOS ANGELES, CA 90036
LOGGIA, ROBERT	ACTOR-DIRECTOR	1718 ANGELO DR	BEVERLY HILLS, CA 90210
LOGGINS, DAVE	SINGER	CALHOUN, 1609 CUMBERLAND ST	LITTLE ROCK, AK 72206
LOGGINS, DAVID	SINGER-SONGWRITER	POST OFFICE BOX 120475	NASHVILLE, TN 37212
LOGGINS, KENNY	SINGER-SONGWRITER	985 HOT SPRINGS RD	SANTA BARBARA, CA 93108
LOHAUS, BRAD	BASKETBALL	BRADLEY CENTER, 1001 N 4TH ST	MILWAUKEE, WI 53203
LOHMILLER, CHIP	FOOTBALL	POST OFFICE BOX 17247 (DULLES)	WASHINGTON, DC 20041
LOHR, BILL	BASEBALL SCOUT	TWINS, 501 CHICAGO AVE S	MINNEAPOLIS, MN 55415
LOHR, BOB	GOLFER	POST OFFICE BOX 109601	PALM BCH GARDENS, FL 33418
LOIEDERMAN, ROBERTO C	WRITER	6471 LANGDON AVE	VAN NUYS, CA 91406
LOISELLE, CLAUDE	HOCKEY	MAPLE LEAFS, 60 CARLTON ST	TORONTO, ONT M5B 1L1 CANADA
LOISELLE, RICHARD	BASEBALL	POST OFFICE BOX 20849	CHARLESTON, SC 29413
LOJESKI, EDWARD, JR	CONDUCTOR	24905 EL DORADO MEADOW RD	CALABASAS, CA 91302
LOKEY, BEN	ACTOR	4019 ROGEN DR	ENCINO, CA 91436
LOLICH, MICKEY	BASEBALL	6252 ROBINHILL	WASHINGTON, MI 48094
LOLLOBRIGIDA, GINA	ACTRESS-PHOTOGRAPHER	VIA APPIA ANTICA 223	ROME 1-00178 ITALY
LOLLOS, JOHN S	TV DIRECTOR-PRODUCER	KING FEATURES, 216 E 45TH ST	NEW YORK, NY 10017
LOM, HERBERT	ACTOR	HEATH, PARAMOUNT HOUSE 162-170 WARDOUR ST	LONDON W1V 3AT ENGLAND
LOMAN, MICHAEL	TV WRITER-PRODUCER	12034 OTSEGO ST	NORTH HOLLYWOOD, CA 91607
LOMBARD, RON	ACTOR	18350 HATTERAS ST #218	TARZANA, CA 91356
LOMBARDI, ROSE	ACTRESS	114-09 ROCKAWAY BLVD	OZONE PARK, NY 11420
LOMBARDI, STEVE	WRESTLER	POST OFFICE BOX 3859	STAMFORD, CT 06905
LOMBARDO, LOUIS J	FILM DIRECTOR	5455 LONGRIDGE AVE	VAN NUYS, CA 91401
LOMBARDO, PHILIP J	DIRECTOR	24 MASTERTON RD	BRONXVILLE, NY 10708
LOMBARDO, TIM	BASEBALL UMPIRE	POST OFFICE BOX 716	PLAINVILLE, CT 06062
LOMBARDOZZI, STEVE	BASEBALL	RURAL ROUTE 2, BOX 211	AUBURN, NY 13021
LOMON, KEVIN	BASEBALL	POST OFFICE BOX 507	DURHAM, NC 27702
LOMOND, BRITT	DIRECTOR	4155 BELLAIRE AVE	STUDIO CITY, CA 91604
LOMPALL & THE CHASER BROTHERS	C & W GROUP	POST OFFICE BOX 40484	NASHVILLE, TN 37212
LONCRAINE, RICHARD	FILM DIRECTOR	SEIFERT, 18 LADBROKE TERR	LONDON W11 3PG ENGLAND
LONDON, BOBBY	CARTOONIST	KING FEATURES, 216 E 45TH ST	NEW YORK, NY 10017
LONDON, CHARLES S	DIRECTOR	641 LEXINGTON AVE	NEW YORK, NY 10022
LONDON, DAMIAN	ACTOR	659 1/4 N HUNTLEY DR	WEST HOLLYWOOD, CA 90069
LONDON, DARREN	TRAINER	5301 NW 12TH AVE	FORT LAUDERDALE, FL 33309
LONDON, JERRY	WRI-DIR-PROD	CAA, 9830 WILSHIRE BLVD	BEVERLY HILLS, CA 90212
LONDON, JULIE	ACTRESS-SINGER	16074 ROYAL OAK RD	ENCINO, CA 91316
LONDON, LISA	ACTRESS-MODEL	1680 N VINE ST #203	HOLLYWOOD, CA 90028
LONDON, MEL	DIRECTOR	170 2ND AVE	NEW YORK, NY 10003
LONDON, PAMELA	ACTRESS	151 S EL CAMINO DR	BEVERLY HILLS, CA 90212
LONDON, ROY	WRITER-ACTOR	308 N SYCAMORE AVE #506	LOS ANGELES, CA 90036
LONDONER, CARROLL	CONDUCTOR	3751 NELLIS BLVD #404	LAS VEGAS, NV 89121
LONE, JOHN	ACTOR	1341 OCEAN AVE #104	SANTA MONICA, CA 90401
LONE JUSTICE	ROCK & ROLL GROUP	ARTISTES & THEATRICAL SERVICES LTD, LEEDS	YORKSHIRE LS1 6LS ENGLAND
LONESOME STRANGERS, THE	C & W GROUP	6520 SELMA AVE #443	LOS ANGELES, CA 90028
LONEY, TROY	HOCKEY	PENGUINS, CIVIC ARENA, CENTRE AV	PITTSBURGH, PA 15219
LONG, BILL	BASEBALL	7699 DIMMICK RD	CINCINNATI, OH 45241
LONG, BOB	BASEBALL UMPIRE	POST OFFICE BOX 608	GROVE CITY, OH 43123
LONG, DON	BASEBALL MANAGER	POST OFFICE BOX 12	MIDLAND, TX 79702
LONG, DON, SR	BASEBALL SCOUT	POST OFFICE BOX 2000	ANAHEIM, CA 92803
LONG, GENE	DIRECTOR	316-B STEVENSON LN	BALTIMORE, MD 21204
LONG, GRANT	BASKETBALL	MIAMI HEAT, THE MIAMI ARENA	MIAMI, FL 33136
LONG, HOWIE	FOOTBALL	26 STRAWBERRY LN	ROLLING HILLS, CA 90274
LONG, JILL	U S CONGRESSWOMAN	1300 S HARRISON #3105	FORT WAYNE, IN 46805
LONG, JIM	MUSIC ARRANGER	751 HARPETH BEND DR	NASHVILLE, TN 37221
LONG, JON	BASEBALL EXECUTIVE	POST OFFICE BOX 3448	SHREVEPORT, LA 71133
LONG, KEVIN	BASEBALL	POST OFFICE BOX 3665	OMAHA, NE 68103
LONG, LORETTA M	ACTRESS	6040 BOULEVARD EAST	WEST NEW YORK, NJ 07093
LONG, NATE	TV DIRECTOR	5580 VILLAGE GREEN ST	LOS ANGELES, CA 90016
LONG, NIA	ACTRESS	CBS-TV, "THE GUIDING LIGHT" 222 E 44TH ST	NEW YORK, NY 10017
LONG, SHELLEY	ACTRESS	CAA, 9830 WILSHIRE BLVD	BEVERLY HILLS, CA 90212
LONG, STANLEY	DIRECTOR-PRODUCER	SALON PRODS, 13-14 ARCHER ST	LONDON W1 ENGLAND
LONG, STEVE	BASEBALL	POST OFFICE BOX 3566	WEST PALM BEACH, FL 33402
LONG, SUMNER A	TV WRITER	1268 S CAMDEN DR	LOS ANGELES, CA 90035
LONG, TERRY	FOOTBALL	STEELERS, 300 STADIUM CIR	PITTSBURGH, PA 15212
LONG, TONY	BASEBALL	300 STADIUM WY	DAVENPORT, FL 33837
LONG, WINONA M	CONDUCTOR	1292 S CITRUS AVE	LOS ANGELES, CA 90019
LONG RYDERS, THE	ROCK & ROLL GROUP	7523 HOLLYWOOD BLVD #313	HOLLYWOOD, CA 90046
LONGDEN, JOHNNY	ACTOR	BAR BJ RANCH, 247 W LEMON AVE	ARCADIA, CA 91006
LONGENECKER, JOHN O	FILM EXECUTIVE	13610 S GRAMERCY PL	GARDENA, CA 90249

LONGENECKER, JOHN W	FILM DIRECTOR	124 S ELM DR #3	BEVERLY HILLS, CA	90212
LONGFORD-WILLIAMS, BERNADETTE	DANCER	7 W 87TH ST #5-H	NEW YORK, NY	10024
LONGLEY, MITCH	ACTOR	NBC-TV, "ANOTHER WORLD"		
		1268 E 14TH ST	BROOKLYN, NY	11230
LONGMIRE, TONY	BASEBALL	POST OFFICE BOX 7575	PHILADELPHIA, PA	19101
LONGO, DICK	DIRECTOR	11636 PALA MESA DR	NORTHRIDGE, CA	91326
LONGO, TONY	ACTOR	24 WESTWIND ST	MARINA DEL REY, CA	90292
LONGOBARDO, VINCENT	TV PRODUCER	MTV: MUSIC TV, 1775 BROADWAY	NEW YORK, NY	10019
LONGSTREET, HARRY S	WRITER	5330 YARMOUTH AVE #309	ENCINO, CA	91316
LONGSTREET, RENEE	WRITER	5330 YARMOUTH AVE #309	ENCINI, CA	91316
LONGSTREET, STEPHEN	SCREENWRITER	1133 MIRADERO RD	BEVERLY HILLS, CA	90210
LONGSTRETH, EMILY	ACTRESS	9301 WILSHIRE BLVD #312	BEVERLY HILLS, CA	90210
LONGTIN, VICTOR	TV DIRECTOR-PRODUCER	110-07 73RD RD	FOREST HILLS, NY	11375
LONNEN, RAY	ACTOR	EVANS, 221 NEW KINGS RD	LONDON SW6 4XE	ENGLAND
LONNETT, JOE	BASEBALL-INSTRUCTOR	POST OFFICE BOX 7000	PITTSBURGH, PA	15212
LONOW, CLAUDIA	ACTRESS	9300 WILSHIRE BLVD #410	BEVERLY HILLS, CA	90212
LONOW, MARK M	WRITER	6107 MULHOLLAND HWY	LOS ANGELES, CA	90068
LONSDALE, PAMELA	TV PRODUCER	LONDON MGT, 235-241 REGENT ST	LONDON W1R 4PH	ENGLAND
LONZO & WORLD CLASS WRECKING	RAP DUO-RAPWRITERS	FAA, 1700 BROADWAY, 5TH FLOOR	NEW YORK, NY	10019
LOOK, DEAN	FOOTBALL REFEREE	NFL, 410 PARK AVE	NEW YORK, NY	10022
LOOK, THE	ROCK & ROLL GROUP	ICM, 40 W 57TH ST	NEW YORK, NY	10019
LOOK ONE LOOK	ROCK & ROLL GROUP	25 HUNTINGTON AVE #420	BOSTON, MA	02116
LOOK UP	ROCK & ROLL GROUP	2055 MOUNT PARAN RD, NW	ATLANTA, GA	30327
LOOKABILL, TOM	ACTOR	12339 SATICOY ST	NORTH HOLLYWOOD, CA	91605
LOOMIS, ROD	ACTOR	12600 MIRADA ST	NORTH HOLLYWOOD, CA	91607
LOOMIS, STEPHEN	COSTUME DESIGNER	13949 VENTURA BLVD #309	SHERMAN OAKS, CA	91423
LOONEY, BRIAN	BASEBALL	POST OFFICE BOX 6748	ROCKFORD, IL	61125
LOOPER, BENNY	BASEBALL SCOUT	POST OFFICE BOX 4100	SEATTLE, WA	98104
LOOS, MARY	WRITER	335 AMALFI DR	SANTA MONICA, CA	90402
LOOSE, WILLIAM G	COMPOSER	POST OFFICE BOX 53	BALBOA ISLAND, CA	92662
LOOSE ENDS	ROCK & ROLL GROUP	MANNA MANAGEMENT AGENCY		
		9 CARNABY ST, 4TH FLOOR	LONDON W1	ENGLAND
LOPER, GEORGE	DIRECTOR	151 N CARONDELET ST	LOS ANGELES, CA	90026
LOPER, JAMES L	COMMUNICATIONS CONSUL	735 HOLLADAY RD	PASADENA, CA	91106
LOPERT, TANYA	ACTRESS	ARTMEDIA, 10 AVE GEORGE V	PARIS 75008	FRANCE
LOPES, DAVEY	BASEBALL-COACH	ORIOLE PARK, 333 W CAMDEN ST	BALTIMORE, MD	21201
LOPEZ, AL	BASEBALL	3601 BEACH DR	TAMPA, FL	33609
LOPEZ, ALBIE	BASEBALL	POST OFFICE BOX 1886	COLUMBUS, GA	31902
LOPEZ, FRANK	ART DIRECTOR	154 W 73RD ST	NEW YORK, NY	10023
LOPEZ, JAVY	BASEBALL	POST OFFICE BOX 16683	GREENVILLE, SC	29606
LOPEZ, JUAN	BASEBALL MGR-SCOUT	POST OFFICE BOX 1434	BRISTOL, VA	24203
LOPEZ, LISA	SINGER	ALAMO TALENT, 217 ARDEN GROVE	SAN ANTONIO, TX	78215
LOPEZ, LUIS	BASEBALL	STARS, 850 LAS VEGAS BLVD N	LAS VEGAS, NV	89101
LOPEZ, MARIO	ACTOR	11350 VENTURA BLVD #206	STUDIO CITY, CA	91604
LOPEZ, MICHAEL	TV DIRECTOR	301 E 73RD ST #2-A	NEW YORK, NY	10021
LOPEZ, NANCY	GOLFER	3203 COUNTRY CLUB RD	STAFFORD, TX	77477
LOPEZ, PAUL	COSTUME DESIGNER	4406 PRICE ST	LOS ANGELES, CA	90027
LOPEZ, PAUL R	COMPOSER	12115 MAGNOLIA BLVD #143	NORTH HOLLYWOOD, CA	91607
LOPEZ, PEDRO	BASEBALL	POST OFFICE BOX 1420	WICHITA, KS	67201
LOPEZ, PERRY	ACTOR	8520 SHERWOOD DR	LOS ANGELES, CA	90069
LOPEZ, ROBERT	DIRECTOR-PRODUCER	222 BEACH 97TH ST	ROCKAWAY BEACH, NY	11693
LOPEZ, TRINI	SINGER-ACTOR	1139 ABRIGO RD	PALM SPRINGS, CA	92262
LOPEZ-CEPERO	TV DIRECTOR	131 W PARK AVE	LINDENWOOD, NJ	08021
LOPEZ-COBOS, JESUS	CONDUCTOR	ICM, 40 W 57TH ST	NEW YORK, NY	10019
LOPINTO, DORIAN	ACTRESS	144 S BEVERLY DR #405	BEVERLY HILLS, CA	90212
LORBER, JEFF	MUSICIAN	LEFT BANK MANAGEMENT		
		2519 CARMEN CREST DR	LOS ANGELES, CA	90068
LORD, ALBERT	ACTOR	1327 1/2 N KINGSLEY DR	LOS ANGELES, CA	90027
LORD, ARTHUR A	TV WRITER-PRODUCER	4911 CALVIN AVE	TARZANA, CA	91356
LORD, DON	SINGER	POST OFFICE BOX 11276	ROCHESTER, NY	14611
LORD, MARJORIE	ACTRESS	VOLK, 1110 MAYTOR PL	BEVERLY HILLS, CA	90210
LORD, ROSEMARY	ACTRESS	TASMOR, 12001 VENTURA PL, 3RD FL	STUDIO CITY, CA	91604
LORD, WILLIAM E	TV EXECUTIVE	ABC-TV, 7 W 66TH ST	NEW YORK, NY	10023
LORDS, TRACI	ACTRESS-MODEL-SINGER	3349 W CAHUENGA BLVD #2-B	LOS ANGELES, CA	90068
LORDS OF THE NEW CHURCH	ROCK & ROLL GROUP	MONOPOLY, 5040 W HARVARD	CLARKSTON, MI	48016
LOREA, TONY	ACTOR	4421 KLING ST #15	BURBANK, CA	91505
LOREDO, ARMANDO	COMPOSER	2117 VESTAL AVE	LOS ANGELES, CA	90026
LOREN, SOPHIA	ACTRESS	1151 HIDDEN VALLEY RD	THOUSAND OAKS, CA	91360
LORENTZEN, ROBERT	DIRECTOR-PRODUCER	1508 82ND ST, NW	BRADENTON, FL	33529
LORENZ, MIKE & JUMP STREET	C & W GROUP	TGI, 1957 KILBURN DR	ATLANTA, GA	30324
LORENZO, LEONORA D	NEWS CORRESPONDENT	340 NATIONAL PRESS BLDG		
		529 14TH ST, NW	WASHINGTON, DC	20045
LORESCH, GARY	BODYBUILDER	THE GROVE GYM		
		5008 FAIRVIEW AVE	DOWNERS GROVE, IL	60515
LORIA, JEFFREY	BASEBALL EXECUTIVE	POST OFFICE BOX 75089	OKLAHOMA CITY, OK	73147
LORIMER, JIM	BODYBUILDER	425 LONGFELLOW AVE	WORTHINGTON, OH	43085
LORIMORE, ALEC	WRITER	8955 BEVERLY BLVD	WEST HOLLYWOOD, CA	90048
LORIN, WILL	TV WRITER	10701 WILSHIRE BLVD #1801	LOS ANGELES, CA	90024
LORING, ANN	ACTRESS	303 W 66TH ST #18 H-E	NEW YORK, NY	10023
LORING, GLORIA	SINGER-ACTRESS	1930 CENTURY PARK W #403	LOS ANGELES, CA	90067
LORING, LISA	ACTRESS	MARX, 11130 HUSTON ST #6	NORTH HOLLYWOOD, CA	91601
LORING, LYNN	ACTRESS-TV PRODUCER	506 N CAMDEN DR	BEVERLY HILLS, CA	90210
LORIO, LISA	BODYBUILDER	POST OFFICE BOX 23596	SAN DIEGO, CA	92193
LORMS, JOHN	BASEBALL	POST OFFICE BOX 3452	KINSTON, NC	28502
LORRING, JOAN	ACTRESS	345 E 68TH ST	NEW YORK, NY	10021

Name	Occupation	Address	City	Zip/Country
LORRY, RED & YELLOW	ROCK & ROCK DUO	THE COACH HOUSE, FETTER LN	YORKSKIRE	ENGLAND
LOS ILLEGALS	ROCK & ROLL GROUP	ICM, 40 W 57TH ST	NEW YORK, NY	10019
LOS LOBOS	ROCK & ROLL GROUP	POST OFFICE BOX 1304	BURBANK, CA	91507
LOSAK, STANLEY	TV DIRECTOR-PRODUCER	11 W 81ST ST	NEW YORK, NY	10024
LOSHIN, MICHAEL S	WRITER	478 DANIELS DR	BEVERLY HILLS, CA	90212
LOSSO, ERNEST A	DIRECTOR	DGA, 110 W 57TH ST	NEW YORK, NY	10019
LOTAS, JOHN	THEATER PRODUCER	355 LEXINGTON AVE	NEW YORK, NY	10017
LOTT, BILLY	BASEBALL	POST OFFICE BOX 2887	VERO BEACH, FL	32961
LOTT, RONNIE	FOOTBALL	VIKINGS, 9520 VIKING DR	EDEN PRAIRIE, MN	55344
LOTT, TRENT	U S SENATOR	3100 S PASCAGOULA ST	PASCAGOULA, MS	39567
LOTTERBY, SYDNEY	TV WRITER-DIRECTOR	63 BLACK LION LN, HAMMERSMITH	LONDON W6 9BG	ENGLAND
LOTTIMER, EB	ACTOR	345 N MAPLE DR #183	BEVERLY HILLS, CA	90210
LOTTMAN, EVAN	FILM EDITOR	ACE, 1041 N FORMOSA AVE	WEST HOLLYWOOD, CA	90046
LOUDEN, VERNON R	DIRECTOR	400 CANAL ST #329	SAN RAFAEL, CA	94901
LOUDERMILK, JOHN D	SINGER-SONGWRITER	3000 HILLSBORO RD #66	NASHVILLE, TN	37215
LOUDIN, ROBERT	DIRECTOR	2260 CAHUENGA BLVD #307	LOS ANGELES, CA	90069
LOUDON, DOROTHY	ACTRESS	101 CENTRAL PARK W	NEW YORK, NY	10023
LOUGANIS, GREG	DIVER	POST OFFICE BOX 4068	MALIBU, CA	90265
LOUGHERY, DAVID	SCREENWRITER	8955 BEVERLY BLVD	WEST HOLLYWOOD, CA	90048
LOUGHERY, KEVIN	BASKETBALL COACH	1 CNN CENTER #405, SOUTH TOWER	ATLANTA, GA	30303
LOUGHLIN, LORI	ACTRESS-SINGER	151 S EL CAMINO DR	BEVERLY HILLS, CA	90212
LOUGHLIN, MARK	BASEBALL	POST OFFICE BOX 1556	ASHEVILLE, NC	28802
LOUGHLIN, WARNER	ACTRESS	8075 W 3RD ST #303	LOS ANGELES, CA	90048
LOUIE, BEBE	ACTRESS	FELBER, 2126 N CAHUENGA BLVD	LOS ANGELES, CA	90068
LOUIE, DIANE M	CONDUCTOR	8633 W KNOLL DR #306	LOS ANGELES, CA	90069
LOUIS-DREYFUS, JULIA	ACTRESS	131 S RODEO DR #300	BEVERLY HILLS, CA	90212
LOUISE, FHIONA	ACTRESS-DIRECTOR	EAA, 84 WARDOUR ST, 1ST FLOOR	LONDON W1V 3LF	ENGLAND
LOUISE, TANYA	ACTRESS	8484 WILSHIRE BLVD #530	BEVERLY HILLS, CA	90211
LOUISE, TINA	ACTRESS	310 E 46TH ST #18-T	NEW YORK, NY	10017
LOUISIANA	RHYTHM & BLUES GROUP	KINGSLAND, 108 SHARON DR	WEST MONROE, LA	71291
LOUISIANA HOT SAUCE	C & W GROUP	POST OFFICE BOX 9104	SHREVEPORT, LA	71139
LOUISIANA PURCHASE	RHYTHM & BLUES GROUP	POST OFFICE BOX 19066	NEW ORLEANS, LA	70179
LOUNGE LIZARDS, THE	ROCK & ROLL GROUP	ISLAND RECORDS COMPANY		
		75 ROCKEFELLER PLAZA	NEW YORK, NY	10019
LOUNSBERY, DANIEL	ACTOR	83 WASHINGTON PL	NEW YROK, NY	10011
LOUVIN, CHARLIE	SINGER	102 JACKSTAFF DR	HENDERSONVILLE, TN	37075
LOUVIN, CHARLIE, JR	SINGER	120 ANDERSON LN	HENDERSONVILLE, TN	37075
LOVAT, TOM	FOOTBALL COACH	POST OFFICE BOX 888	PHOENIX, AZ	85001
LOVE, DAVIS, III	GOLFER	POST OFFICE BOX 109601	PALM BCH GARDENS, FL	33418
LOVE, DUVAL	FOOTBALL	RAMS, 2327 W LINCOLN BLVD	ANAHEIM, CA	92801
LOVE, GEOFF	BANDLEADER-COMPOSER	GAY, 24 DENMARK ST	LONDON WC2H 8HJ	ENGLAND
LOVE, JOESKI	RAPPER-RAPWRITER	FAA, 1700 BROADWAY, 5TH FLOOR	NEW YORK, NY	10019
LOVE, LEJUAN	RAPPER-RAPWRITER	FAA, 1700 BROADWAY, 5TH FLOOR	NEW YORK, NY	10019
LOVE, MIKE	SINGER-SONGWRITER	101 MESA LN	SANTA BARBARA, CA	91309
LOVE, PETER	ACTOR	5955 TUJUNGA AVE	NORTH HOLLYWOOD, CA	91601
LOVE, ROBERT	TV PRODUCER	SCOTTISH TV, COWCADDENS	GLASGOW G2 3PR	SCOTLAND
LOVE, SANDI	COSTUME DESIGNER	6515 WILSHIRE BLVD #205	HOLLYWOOD, CA	90028
LOVE, WILL	BASEBALL	POST OFFICE BOX 11363	RENO, NV	89510
LOVE & MONEY	ROCK & ROLL GROUP	POLYGRAM RECORDS CO		
		810 7TH AVE	NEW YORK, NY	10019
LOVE & ROCKETS	ROCK & ROLL GROUP	5, THE LAKES, BUSHEY	HERFORDSHIRE WD2 1HS	ENGLAND
LOVE RELATION	MUSICAL GROUP	5625 "O" STREET BLDG #7	LINCOLN, NE	68510
LOVE TRACTOR	ROCK & ROLL GROUP	BIG TIME RECORDS COMPANY		
		6777 HOLLYWOOD BLVD	HOLLYWOOD, CA	90028
LOVE/HATE	ROCK & ROLL GROUP	8436 W 3RD ST #730	LOS ANGELES, CA	90048
LOVEDAY, DENISE	ACTRESS	1801 AVE OF THE STARS #1250	LOS ANGELES, CA	90067
LOVELACE, VANCE	BASEBALL	POST OFFICE BOX 6212	TOLEDO, OH	43614
LOVELADY, JOHN	PUPPETEER	160 W 97TH ST #8-J	NEW YORK, NY	10025
LOVELESS, DAVID R	COSTUME DESIGNER	11 RIVERSIDE DR	NEW YORK, NY	10023
LOVELESS, PATTY	SINGER-SONGWRITER	POST OFFICE BOX 363	GROVEPORT, OH	43125
LOVELL, DYSON	FILM PRODUCER	1585 SUNSET PLAZA DR	LOS ANGELES, CA	90069
LOVELL, GLENN	FILM CRITIC	POST OFFICE BOX 5533	SAN JOSE, CA	95190
LOVELL, JAMES	ASTRONAUT	5725 E RIVER RD	CHICAGO, IL	60611
LOVELL, JIM	BASEBALL TRAINER	POST OFFICE BOX 16683	GREENVILLE, SC	29606
LOVELL, RICK	ARTIST	2860 LAKEWIND CT	ALPHARETTA, GA	30201
LOVELL, ROSEMARY	ACTRESS	5830 MORELLA AVE	NORTH HOLLYWOOD, CA	91607
LOVENHEIM, ROBERT	WRITER	1123 CEDAR ST	SANTA MONICA, CA	90405
LOVER, ANTHONY	TV DIRECTOR-PRODUCER	LIBERTY STUDIOS, 238 E 26TH ST	NEW YORK, NY	10010
LOVERBOY	ROCK & ROLL GROUP	406-68 WATER ST #406	VANCOUVER, BC V6B 1A4	CANADA
LOVESIN, JOHNNY	SINGER	41 BRITAIN ST #200	TORONTO, ONT M5A 1R7	CANADA
LOVETT, BILL	FOOTBALL REFEREE	NFL, 410 PARK AVE	NEW YORK, NY	10022
LOVETT, JOSEPH F	TV PRODUCER	ABC-TV, "20/20," 11 5TH AVE	NEW YORK, NY	10003
LOVETT, LYLE	SINGER-SONGWRITER	4155 E JEWELL AVE #412	DENVER, CO	80222
LOVICH, LENE	SINGER	ATI, 888 7TH AVE, 21ST FLOOR	NEW YORK, NY	10106
LOVIGLIO, JAY	BASEBALL-MANAGER	POST OFFICE DRAWER 1207	ZEBULON, NC	27597
LOVILLE, DEREK	FOOTBALL	SEAHAWKS, 11220 NE 53RD ST	KIRKLAND, WA	98033
LOVING, LISA	ACTRESS	2175 HUDSON TERR #P-2	FORT LEE, NJ	07024
LOVINGER, ALLAN	BASEBALL TRAINER	POST OFFICE BOX 9194	HAMPTON, VA	23670
LOVINGER, JEFFREY	DIRECTOR	DGA, 110 W 57TH ST	NEW YORK, NY	10019
LOVULLO, SAM	TV PRODUCER	POST OFFICE BOX 140400	NASHVILLE, TN	37214
LOVULLO, TOREY	BASEBALL	1155 W MOUND ST	COLUMBUS, OH	43223
LOW, CYNTHIA	TV WRITER	POST OFFICE BOX 470	CRESSKILL, NJ	07626
LOW, RICHARD H	TV PRODUCER	MANTICORE PRODS, 1025 5TH AVE	NEW YORK, NY	10028
LOWDER, AARON	SINGER	POST OFFICE BOX 25371	CHARLOTTE, NC	28212
LOWDERMILK, KIRK	FOOTBALL	VIKINGS, 9520 VIKING DR	EDEN PRAIRIE, MN	55344

LOWE, BARRY	ACTOR	31 S AUDLEY ST	LONDON W1	ENGLAND
LOWE, CHAD	ACTOR	WOOD/FOLEY, 975 HANCOCK AVE	LOS ANGELES, CA	90069
LOWE, CHAN	CARTOONIST	POST OFFICE BOX 14430	FORT LAUDERDALE, FL	33302
LOWE, DAVID, JR	DIRECTOR-PRODUCER	151 S EL CAMINO DR	BEVERLY HILLS, CA	90212
LOWE, DION	BASEBALL SCOUT	REDS, 100 RIVERFRONT STADIUM	CINCINNATI, OH	45202
LOWE, EDWIN S	THEATER PRODUCER	375 PARK AVE	NEW YORK, NY	10152
LOWE, GWEN HILLIER	ACTRESS	250 S SAN FERNANDO BLVD #225	BURBANK, CA	91502
LOWE, JOHN H, III	ACTOR	250 S SAN FERNANDO BLVD #225	BURBANK, CA	91502
LOWE, KEVIN	HOCKEY	OILERS, NORTHLANDS COLISEUM	EDMONTON, ALTA T5B 4M9	CANADA
LOWE, LONNIE	BASEBALL EXECUTIVE	POST OFFICE BOX 1535	JOHNSON CITY, TN	37605
LOWE, MICHAEL A	TV PRODUCER	TAKE TWO COMM, 6050 BOULEVARD EAS	WEST NEW YORK, NJ	07093
LOWE, NICK	SINGER	ICM, 40 W 57TH ST	NEW YORK, NY	10019
LOWE, Q V	BASEBALL COACH	POST OFFICE BOX 338	JAMESTOWN, NY	14702
LOWE, ROB	ACTOR	WOOD/FOLEY, 975 HANCOCK AVE	LOS ANGELES, CA	90069
LOWE, RUDY	ACTOR	1617 N POINSETTIA PL #305	LOS ANGELES, CA	90046
LOWELL, BOBBY	SINGER-SONGWRITER	IRON PONY RECORDS		
		3345 "R" ST	LINCOLN, IL	68503
LOWELL, CAREY	ACTRESS	DUNNE, 40 W 12TH ST	NEW YORK, NY	10011
LOWELL, ROSS	DIRECTOR	421 W 54TH ST	NEW YORK, NY	10019
LOWELL, SHELLEY	ARTIST	1449 BATES CT, NE	ATLANTA, GA	30319
LOWELL, WILLIAM F	DIRECTOR	201 GLEN ST	SOUTH NATICK, MA	01760
LOWENS, CURT	ACTOR	6381 W 6TH ST	LOS ANGELES, CA	90048
LOWENSTEIN, AL	TV PRODUCER	EMBASSY TV, 1438 N GOWER ST	LOS ANGELES, CA	90028
LOWERY, BILL	U S CONGRESSMAN	880 FRONT ST	SAN DIEGO, CA	92188
LOWERY, DAVID	BASEBALL	POST OFFICE BOX 3609	PORT CHARLOTTE, FL	33949
LOWERY, NICK	FOOTBALL	CHIEFS, 1 ARROWHEAD DR	KANSAS CITY, MO	64129
LOWERY, NITA	U S CONGRESSWOMAN	235 MAMARONECK AVE #105	WHITE PLAINS, NY	10605
LOWRIE, MARGARET	NEWS CORRESPONDENT	1050 TECHWOOD DR, NW	ATLANTA, GA	30318
LOWRY, ALAN	FOOTBALL COACH	COWBOYS, 1 COWBOYS PARKWAY	IRVING, TX	75063
LOWRY, BRIAN	COLUMNIST	5700 WILSHIRE BLVD #120	LOS ANGELES, CA	90036
LOWRY, DAVE	HOCKEY	BLUES, 5700 OAKLAND AVE	SAINT LOUIS, MO	63110
LOWRY, DICK	TV DIRECTOR	704 N GARDNER ST #5	LOS ANGELES, CA	90046
LOWRY, DWIGHT	BASEBALL COACH	POST OFFICE BOX 64939	FAYETTEVILLE, NC	28306
LOWRY, GARY	GUITARIST	613 HILLSBORO RD		
		EXECUTIVE HOUSE #A-27	FRANKLIN, TN	37064
LOWRY, LYNN	ACTRESS	8360 MELROSE AVE #203	LOS ANGELES, CA	90069
LOWRY, SYLVIA	SINGER	125 MILLWOOD DR	NASHVILLE, TN	37217
LOXTON, DAVID R	TV DIRECTOR	935 PARK AVE	NEW YORK, NY	10028
LOY, MYRNA	ACTRESS	425 E 63RD ST	NEW YORK, NY	10021
LOYND, MIKE	BASEBALL	POST OFFICE BOX 36407	LOUISVILLE, KY	40233
LOYOLA, JUAN	BASEBALL SCOUT	REDS, 100 RIVERFRONT STADIUM	CINCINNATI, OH	45202
LOZ NETTO	ROCK & ROLL GROUP	POST OFFICE BOX 1318	BEVERLY HILLS, CA	90213
LU, LISA	ACTRESS	1737 N ORANGE GROVE AVE	LOS ANGELES, CA	90046
LU PONE, PATTI	ACTRESS	130 W 42ND ST #2400	NEW YORK, NY	10036
LUBA	ROCK & ROLL GROUP	POST OFFICE BOX 641		
		STATION ABUNTSIC	MONTREAL H3L 3P2	CANADA
LUBER, KEN	WRITER-PRODUCER	1052 KAGAWA ST	PACIFIC PALISADES, CA	90272
LUBIN, ARTHUR	FILM DIRECTOR	2881 SEATTLE DR	HOLLYWOOD, CA	90046
LUBIN, LOIS PHYLLIS	WRITER	11744 DARLINGTON AVE #103	LOS ANGELES, CA	90049
LUBOFF, NORMAN	COMPOSER-CONDUCTOR	35 WEST SHORE DR	PORT WASHINGTON, NY	11050
LUBOV, SHERRI	ACTRESS	1032 S HAYWORTH AVE	LOS ANGELES, CA	90035
LUBRATICH, STEVE	BASEBALL	10380 MAYA LINDA RD #C-219	SAN DIEGO, CA	92126
LUBRATICH, STEVE	BASEBALL MANAGER	POST OFFICE BOX 1420	WICHITA, KS	67201
LUCAS, A GAR	DIRECTOR	DGA, 110 W 57TH ST	NEW YORK, NY	10019
LUCAS, CARRIE	SINGER	FAA, 1700 BROADWAY, 5TH FLOOR	NEW YORK, NY	10019
LUCAS, GARY	BASEBALL-COACH	POST OFFICE BOX 1295	CLINTON, IA	52733
LUCAS, GEORGE	WRI-DIR-PROD	POST OFFICE BOX 2009	SAN RAFAEL, CA	94912
LUCAS, GUS	TV EXECUTIVE	ABC-TV, 4151 PROSPECT AVE	LOS ANGELES, CA	90027
LUCAS, J FRANK	ACTOR	400 W 43RD ST #40-G	NEW YORK, NY	10036
LUCAS, JOHN MEREDYTH	WRITER-PRODUCER	BLOOM, 800 S ROBERTSON BLVD	LOS ANGELES, CA	90036
LUCAS, JONATHAN	TV DIRECTOR	8690 FRANKLIN AVE	LOS ANGELES, CA	90069
LUCAS, MARK H	DIRECTOR	337 E 50TH ST #2-A	NEW YORK, NY	10022
LUCAS, MATT	SINGER	POST OFFICE BOX 1830	GRETNA, LA	70053
LUCAS, TIM	FOOTBALL	BRONCOS, 13655 BRONCOS PKWY	ENGLEWOOD, CO	80112
LUCATORTO, TONY	ACTOR	14355 HUSTON ST #255	SHERMAN OAKS, CA	91423
LUCCHESI, VINCENT	ACTOR	21900 MARYLEE ST	WOODLAND HILLS, CA	91367
LUCCHINO, LARRY	BASEBALL EXECUTIVE	ORIOLE PARK, 333 W CAMDEN ST	BALTIMORE, MD	21201
LUCCI, SUSAN	ACTRESS	16 CARTERET PL	GARDEN CITY, NY	11530
LUCE, JANICE	COMPOSER	23124 JONATHAN ST	CANOGA PARK, CA	91304
LUCE, ROGER	BASEBALL	POST OFFICE BOX 3609	PORT CHARLOTTE, FL	33949
LUCERO, KEVIN	BASEBALL	POST OFFICE BOX 3783	SAVANNAH, GA	31414
LUCEY, PAUL EDWARD	WRITER	415 MARGUERITA AVE	SANTA MONICA, CA	90402
LUCHENBILL, GLORIA	ACTRESS	415 S SHIRLEY PL	BEVERLY HILLS, CA	90212
LUCHETTI, LARRY	BASEBALL	POST OFFICE BOX 3783	SAVANNAH, GA	31414
LUCIANO, MICHAEL	FILM EDITOR	ACE, 1041 N FORMOSA AVE	WEST HOLLYWOOD, CA	90046
LUCKA, KLAUS	DIRECTOR	DGA, 110 W 57TH ST	NEW YORK, NY	10019
LUCKHAM, KEN	BASEBALL	POST OFFICE BOX 4209	JACKSON, MS	39296
LUCKINBILL, LAURENCE	ACTOR-WRITER	470-K MAIN ST	RIDGEFIELD, CT	06877
LUCKING, WILLIAM	ACTOR	10100 SANTA MONICA BLVD #700	LOS ANGELES, CA	90067
LUCKMAN, SID	FOOTBALL	5303 SAINT CHARLES RD	BELLWOOD, IL	60104
LUCKY LOOK	C & W GROUP	POST OFFICE BOX 156	ROSELLE, NJ	07203
LUCRAFT, HOWARD	COMPOSER-CONDUCTOR	POST OFFICE BOX 91	LOS ANGELES, CA	90078
LUDDY, TOM	FILM PRODUCER	ZOETROPE, 916 KEARNY ST	SAN FRANCISCO, CA	94133
LUDEL, WILLIAM	DIRECTOR	170 W 74TH ST	NEW YORK, NY	10023
LUDLUM, ROBERT	AUTHOR	H MORRISON, 58 W 10TH ST	NEW YORK, NY	10011

LUDWIG, CRAIG	HOCKEY	NASSAU VETS MEMORIAL COLISEUM	UNIONDALE, NY 11553
LUDWIG, FORREST	TV EXECUTIVE	3001 EDMONTON RD	GLENDALE, CA 91206
LUDWIG, JERROLD L	FILM EDITOR	10860 KLING ST	NORTH HOLLYWOOD, CA 91602
LUDWIG, JERRY	TV WRITER-PRODUCER	11262 HOMEDALE ST	LOS ANGELES, CA 90049
LUDWIG, PAMELA	ACTRESS	6732 VARNA AVE	VAN NUYS, CA 91401
LUDWIG, SALEM	ACTOR	80 LA SALLE ST	NEW YORK, NY 10027
LUDWIN, RICHARD A	WRITER-PRODUCER	616 VETERAN AVE #117	LOS ANGELES, CA 90024
LUEBBER, STEVE	BASEBALL COACH	500 NORTON ST	ROCHESTER, NY 14621
LUEBBERS, LARRY	BASEBALL	POST OFFICE BOX 2001	CEDAR RAPIDS, IA 52406
LUECKEN, RICK	BASEBALL	2739 SHAWOWDALE	HOUSTON, TX 77043
LUEDTKE, KURT M	SCREENWRITER	DISKANT, 1033 GAYLEY AVE	LOS ANGELES, CA 90024
LUENEBURG, CAL	BODYBUILDER	THE ACE PROMOTER	
		24531 O'LINDA TRAIL N	SCANDIA, MN 55073
LUENING, OTTO	COMPOSER-CONDUCTOR	460 RIVERSIDE DR	NEW YORK, NY 10027
LUESCHER, CHRISTINA	SCREENWRITER	8955 BEVERLY BLVD	WEST HOLLYWOOD, CA 90048
LUFRANO, JOAN M	TV PRODUCER	CHILDREN'S TV WORKSHOP	
		1 LINCOLN PLAZA	NEW YORK, NY 10023
LUFT, HERBERT	FILM PRODUCER	POST OFFICE BOX 6148	BEVERLY HILLS, CA 90212
LUFTIG, DON L	TV WRITER-PRODUCER	119 MILLBURN AVE	MILLBURN, NJ 07041
LUGAR, RICHARD G	U S SENATOR	10 W MARKET ST #1180	INDIANAPOLIS, IN 46204
LUGER, LEX	WRESTLER	POST OFFICE BOX 105366	ATLANTA, GA 31348
LUGINBUHL, TIM	BASEBALL SCOUT	ORIOLE PARK, 333 W CAMDEN ST	BALTIMORE, MD 21201
LUGO, JOSE	BASEBALL SCOUT	ORIOLE PARK, 333 W CAMDEN ST	BALTIMORE, MD 21201
LUGO, URBANO	BASEBALL	ROOSEVELT RES TIUNA ENT BPH 444	ROSALES, CARACAS VENEZUELA
LUHRS, JANET	TV PRODUCER	990 AVE OF THE AMERICAS #21-E	NEW YORK, NY 10018
LUIESE	SINGER	SKEPNER, 7 MUSIC SQUARE N	NASHVILLE, TN 37203
LUIKEN, CAROL A	COSTUME DESIGNER	ABC-TV, 101 W 67TH ST	NEW YORK, NY 10023
LUIS, JOE	BASEBALL	RED SOX, CHAIN O'LAKES PARK	WINTER HAVEN, FL 33880
LUISI, ED	TV DIRECTOR	21-24 CRESCENT ST	ASTORIA, NY 11105
LUISI, JAMES	ACTOR	14315 RIVERSIDE DR #111	SHERMAN OAKS, CA 91423
LUJACK, JOHNNY	FOOTBALL	3700 HARRISON ST	DAVENPORT, IA 52806
LUJAN, JESSE	BODYBUILDER	6514 LAKE ASHMERE CT	SAN DIEGO, CA 92119
LUKACHYK, ROB	BASEBALL	POST OFFICE BOX 8550	STOCKTON, CA 95208
LUKAS, CHRISTOPHER W	DIRECTOR-PRODUCER	159 RIVER RD	GRANDVIEW, NY 10960
LUKAS, ERNEST A	DIRECTOR	2833 SHERIDAN PL	EVANSTON, IL 60201
LUKATHER, PAUL	ACTOR	14185 SKYLINE DR	HACIENDA HEIGHTS, CA 91745
LUKE, COLIN	TV DIRECTOR	18 REGENTS PARK RD	LONDON NW1 ENGLAND
LUKEMAN, ROBERT M	NEWS CORRES-WRITER	ABC NEWS, 1717 DE SALES ST, NW	WASHINGTON, DC 20036
LUKEN, CHARLES	U S CONGRESSMAN	602 MAIN ST #1300	CINCINNATI, OH 45202
LUKENBILL, FRANK	BASKETBALL EXECUTIVE	KINGS, 1 SPORTS PARKWAY	SACRAMENTO, CA 95834
LUKENBILL, GREGG	BASKETBALL EXECUTIVE	KINGS, 1 SPORTS PARKWAY	SACRAMENTO, CA 95834
LUKER, DALE	BASEBALL UMPIRE	2101 E BROADWAY #35	TEMPE, AZ 85282
LUKETICH, STAN	BASEBALL COACH	1201 HYDE PARK BLVD	NIAGARA FALLS, NY 14301
LUKEVICS, MITCH	BASEBALL EXECUTIVE	N Y YANKEES, YANKEE STADIUM	BRONX, NY 10451
LULU	SINGER-ACTRESS	ANGEL, 12 D'ARBLAY ST, 1ST FL	LONDON W1V 3FP ENGLAND
LUM, MIKE	BASEBALL-INSTRUCTOR	333 W 35TH ST	CHICAGO, IL 60616
LUMBLY, CARL	ACTOR	9744 WILSHIRE BLVD #308	BEVERLY HILLS, CA 90212
LUMET, BARUCH	ACTOR	7969 W NORTON AVE #A-8	WEST HOLLYWOOD, CA 90046
LUMET, SIDNEY	FILM WRITER-DIRECTOR	1380 LEXINGTON AVE	NEW YORK, NY 10028
LUMLEY, JOANNA	ACTRESS	RENTON, 23 CRESCENT LN	LONDON SW4 9PT ENGLAND
LUMLEY, MIKE	BASEBALL	TIGERS, 89 WHARNCLIFFE RD N	LONDON, ONT N6H 2A7 CANADA
LUMME, JYRKI	HOCKEY	CANUCKS, 100 N RENFREW ST	VANCOUVER, BC V5K 3N7 CANADA
LUNA, CASEY	LT GOVERNOR	SATE CAPITOL BUILDING	SANTE FE, NM 87503
LUND, ART	ACTOR	15216 SUTTON ST	SHERMAN OAKS, CA 91403
LUND, BILL	ACTOR	14 IVY BANK LN, HAWORTH	
		NEAR KEIGHLEY	WEST YORKSHIRE ENGLAND
LUND, DEANNA	ACTRESS	545 HOWARD DR	SALEM, VA 24153
LUND, JOHN	ACTOR	2777 COLDWATER CANYON	BEVERLY HILLS, CA 90210
LUND, LICILLE	ACTRESS	HIGGINS, 3424 SHORE HGTS DR	MALIBU, CA 90265
LUND, MARTIN C	COMPOSER	3891 CLAYTON AVE	LOS ANGELES, CA 90027
LUNDBERG, DAN	WRITER	3347 BONNIE HILL DR	LOS ANGELES, CA 90068
LUNDE, CHRISTINE	ACTRESS	3349 W CAHUENGA BLVD #2-B	LOS ANGELES, CA 90068
LUNDEN, JOAN	TV HOST	1965 BROADWAY #500	NEW YORK, NY 10023
LUNDGREN, DOLF	BODYBUILDER-ACTOR	29055 CLIFFSIDE DR	MALIBU, CA 90265
LUNDINE, STANLEY N	LT GOVERNOR	STATE CAPITOL BUILDING	ALBANY, NY 12224
LUNDSTROM, LINDA	FASHION DESIGNER	462 WELLINGTON ST W	TORONTO, ONT M5V 1E3 CANADA
LUNDY, CARMEN	SINGER	BRIDGE, 106 FORT GREENE PL	BROOKLYN, NY 11217
LUNDY, JESSICA	ACTRESS	280 S BEVERLY DR #400	BEVERLY HILLS, CA 90212
LUNDY, ROGER J	WRITER-PRODUCER	142 ASHLAND AVE	RIVER FOREST, IL 60305
LUNETTA, DAN	BASEBALL EXECUTIVE	500 NORTON ST	ROCHESTER, NY 14621
LUNGHI, CHERIE	ACTRESS	ICM, 388-396 OXFORD ST	LONDON W1 ENGLAND
LUNGREN, DAN	ATTORNEY GENERAL	STATE CAPITOL BUILDING	SACRAMENTO, CA 95814
LUNHAM, LLOYD R	COMPOSER-CONDUCTOR	6423 WILBUR AVE	RESEDA, CA 91335
LUNSFORD, ALICE N	WRITER	KLAUSNER, 71 PARK AVE	NEW YORK, NY 10016
LUPANO, KENNETH L	TV DIRECTOR-PRODUCER	151 W 25TH ST, 11TH FLOOR	NEW YORK, NY 10001
LUPINO, RICHARD	ACTOR	OSCARD, 24 W 40TH ST, 17TH FL	NEW YORK, NY 10011
LUPINO-DUFF, IDA	ACTRESS-WRITER	11665 WEDDINGTON ST	NORTH HOLLYWOOD, CA 91601
LUPINSKI, ED	ACTOR	568 1/2 E VERDUGO AVE	BURBANK, CA 91501
LUPO, FRANK	TV WRITER-PRODUCER	CANNELL, 7083 HOLLYWOOD BLVD	LOS ANGELES, CA 90028
LUPONE, PATTI	SINGER	ICM, 8899 BEVERLY BLVD	LOS ANGELES, CA 90048
LUPTON, JOHN	ACTOR	2528 TILDEN AVE	LOS ANGELES, CA 90064
LUPTON, KEITH	BASEBALL EXECUTIVE	POST OFFICE BOX 3169	FREDERICK, MD 21701
LUPUS, PETER	ACTOR	11375 DONA LISA DR	STUDIO CITY, CA 91604
LURIE, BOB	BASEBALL EXECUTIVE	S F GIANTS, CANDLESTICK PARK	SAN FRANICSCO, CA 94124
LURIE, CONNIE	BASEBALL EXECUTIVE	S F GIANTS, CANDLESTICK PARK	SAN FRANICSCO, CA 94124

LURIE, GEORGIE	COLUMNIST	POST OFFICE BOX 500	WASHINGTON, DC	20044
LURIE, RANAN	CARTOONIST	UPS, 4900 MAIN ST, 9TH FLOOR	KANSAS CITY, MO	64112
LUSARDI, LINDA	ACTRESS	YELLOW BALLOON PRODUCTIONS		
		21 FAIRMILE AVE, COBHAM	SURREY KT11 2JA	ENGLAND
LUSH, JANE	TV PRODUCER	BBC, KENSINGTON HOUSE		
		RICHMOND WY	LONDON W14	ENGLAND
LUSHUS DAIM & THE PRETTY VAIN	SOUL GROUP	CONCEITED/MOTOWN RECORDS		
		6255 SUNSET BLVD	HOLLYWOOD, CA	90028
LUSK, RON	ARTIST	2914 MERIDA AVE	FORT WORTH, TX	76109
LUSSIER, ROBERT	ACTOR	2126 SUNSET CREST DR	LOS ANGELES, CA	90046
LUSTIG, JO	FILM PROD-TAL AGT	POST OFFICE BOX 472	LONDON SW7 4NL	ENGLAND
LUSTIG, MILTON	COMPOSER	6708 MAMMOTH AVE	VAN NUYS, CA	91405
LUSTIG, WILLIAM	FILM EXECUTIVE	9301 WILSHIRE BLVD #602	BEVERLY HILLS, CA	90210
LUSTMAN, NADIA	ACTRESS	LIGHT, 901 BRINGHAM AVE	LOS ANGELES, CA	90049
LUTOSLAWSKI, WITOLD	COMPOSER	81-523 WARSZAWA		
		UL SMIALA NR 39	WARSAW	POLAND
LUTTRELL, MARTHA	TALENT AGENT	ICM, 8899 BEVERLY BLVD	LOS ANGELES, CA	90048
LUTZ, BRENT	BASEBALL	POST OFFICE BOX 1110	MYRTLE BEACH, SC	29578
LUTZ, DAVID	FOOTBALL	CHIEFS, 1 ARROWHEAD DR	KANSAS CITY, MO	64129
LUTZ, JOLEEN	ACTRESS	8019 1/2 MELROSE AVE #3	LOS ANGELES, CA	90046
LUZ, FRANC	ACTOR	606 N LARCHMONT BLVD #309	LOS ANGELES, CA	90004
LUZAK, DENNIS	ARTIST	81 PINETREE RD	REDDING RIDGE, CT	06876
LUZINSKI, GREG	BASEBALL	320 JACKSON RD	MEDFORD, NJ	08055
LYALL, MAX	PIANIST	GOLDEN GATE BAPTIST SEMINARY		
		STRAWBERRY POINT	MILL VALLEY, CA	94941
LYDEN, MITCH	BASEBALL	POST OFFICE BOX 1211	NORFOLK, VA	23502
LYDIARD, ROBERT	ACTOR	341 W 47TH ST #3-F	NEW YORK, NY	10036
LYDON, JIMMY	ACTOR-DIRECTOR	1317 LOS ARBOLES AVE, NW	ALBUQUERQUE, NM	87107
LYDY, SCOTT	BASEBALL	POST OFFICE BOX 11363	RENO, NV	89510
LYE, MARK	GOLFER	POST OFFICE BOX 109601	PALM BCH GARDENS, FL	33418
LYGHT, TODD	FOOTBALL	RAMS, 2327 W LINCOLN BLVD	ANAHEIM, CA	92801
LYLES, A C	WRITER-PRODUCER	2115 LINDA FLORA DR	LOS ANGELES, CA	90077
LYLES, FRED	PRODUCER	MCA/UNIVERSAL STUDIOS, INC		
		100 UNIVERSAL CITY PLAZA #69	UNIVERSAL CITY, CA	91608
LYLES, ROBERT	FOOTBALL	FALCONS, SUWANEE RD AT I-85	SUWANEE, GA	30174
LYMAN, JIM	BASKETBALL COACH	POST OFFICE BOX 25040	PHILADELPHIA, PA	19147
LYN, DAVID	ACTOR-DIRECTOR	9 PAGET TERR, PENARTH	SOUTH GLAM CF6 1DR	ENGLAND
LYNCH, ALFRED	ACTOR-DIRECTOR	HEATH, PARAMOUNT HOUSE		
		162-170 WARDOUR ST	LONDON W1V 3AT	ENGLAND
LYNCH, DAVID	BASEBALL	POST OFFICE BOX 11002	CHATTANOOGA, TN	37401
LYNCH, DAVID KEITH	FILM WRITER-DIRECTOR	POST OFFICE BOX 93624	LOS ANGELES, CA	90093
LYNCH, ED	BASEBALL EXECUTIVE	POST OFFICE BOX 2000	SAN DIEGO, CA	92112
LYNCH, KELLY	ACTRESS-MODEL	804 WOODACRES RD	SANTA MONICA, CA	90402
LYNCH, LORENZO	FOOTBALL	POST OFFICE BOX 888	PHOENIX, AZ	85001
LYNCH, MICHAEL	ACTOR	ABC-TV, "GENERAL HOSPITAL"		
		4151 PROSPECT AVE	BURBANK, CA	91523
LYNCH, PATRICIA	TV PRODUCER	NBC-TV, 30 ROCKEFELLER PLAZA	NEW YORK, NY	10112
LYNCH, PAUL	FILM DIRECTOR	33 HARBOUR SQ #3223	TORONTO, ONTARIO	CANADA
LYNCH, RICHARD	ACTOR	9300 WILSHIRE BLVD #410	BEVERLY HILLS, CA	90212
LYNCH, ROBERT	ARTIST	8408 BLAKISTON LN	ALEXANDRIA, VA	22308
LYNCH, RONDA J	TV PRODUCER	ERNST-VAN PRAAG, 135 E 55TH ST	NEW YORK, NY	10022
LYND, EVA	ACTRESS	335 N MAPLE DR #360	BEVERLY HILLS, CA	90210
LYNDE, JANICE	ACTRESS	7211 MULHOLLAND DR	LOS ANGELES, CA	90068
LYNDHURST, NICHOLAS	ACTOR	CHATTO AND LINNIT, LTD		
		PRINCE OF WALES THEATRE		
		COVENTRY ST	LONDON W1V 7FE	ENGLAND
LYNDON, AMY	ACTRESS	KAE, 4100 ARCH DR #30	STUDIO CITY, CA	91604
LYNE, ADRIAN	FILM DIRECTOR	DGA, 7920 SUNSET BLVD, 6TH FL	LOS ANGELES, CA	90046
LYNGSTAD, FRIDA	SINGER-SONGWRITER	POST OFFICE BOX 26072		
		S-100 41	STOCKHOLM	SWEDEN
LYNLEY, CAROL	ACTRESS	POST OFFICE BOX 2190	MALIBU, CA	90265
LYNN, ANN	ACTRESS	SARABAND, 265 LIVERPOOL RD	LONDON N1 1LX	ENGLAND
LYNN, BETSY	SINGER	830 GLASTONBURY RD #614	NASHVILLE, TN	37217
LYNN, BETTY	ACTRESS	10424 TENNESSEE AVE	LOS ANGELES, CA	90064
LYNN, CHERYL	ACTRESS-SINGER	POST OFFICE BOX 667	SMITHTOWN, NY	11787
LYNN, DAME VERA	ACTRESS	4 SANDHURST AVE, BISPHAM		
		BLACKPOOL	LANCASHIRE FY2 9AV	ENGLAND
LYNN, DIANNA & THE CALICO BAND	C & W GROUP	PENNY, 30 GUINAN ST	WALTHAM, MA	02154
LYNN, ERIC	COLUMNIST	TRIBUNE, 64 E CONCORD ST	ORLANDO, FL	32801
LYNN, FRED	BASEBALL	801 INVERNESS DR	RANCHO MIRAGE, CA	92270
LYNN, GINGER	ACTRESS-MODEL	SEE - ALLEN, GINGER LYNN		
LYNN, GREG	BASEBALL TRAINER	S F GIANTS, CANDLESTICK PARK	SAN FRANICSCO, CA	94124
LYNN, JANET	ICE SKATER	1716 GRANDVIEW	ROCHESTER HILLS, MI	48064
LYNN, JEFFREY	ACTOR	11600 ACAMA ST	STUDIO CITY, CA	91604
LYNN, JONATHAN	ACTOR-WRITER-DIRECTOR	1383 MILLER PL	LOS ANGELES, CA	90069
LYNN, LORETTA	SINGER-SONGWRITER	POST OFFICE BOX 120369	NASHVILLE, TN	37212
LYNN, RON	FOOTBALL COACH	POST OFFICE BOX 609609	SAN DIEGO, CA	92160
LYNN, SHERRY	ACTRESS	POST OFFICE BOX 360	BEVERLY HILLS, CA	90213
LYNNE, AMY	ACTRESS	8271 MELROSE AVE #110	LOS ANGELES, CA	90046
LYNNE, GILLIAN	CHOREO-DIR	SIMPSON, 52 SHAFTESBURY AVE	LONDON W1V 7DE	ENGLAND
LYNNE, JEFF	SINGER-SONGWRITER	2621 DEEP CANYON DR	BEVERLY HILLS, CA	90210
LYNNE, MIKE	FOOTBALL EXECUTIVE	VIKINGS, 9520 VIKING DR	EDEN PRAIRIE, MN	55344
LYNYRD SKYNYRD	ROCK & ROLL GROUP	3 E 54TH ST #1400	NEW YORK, NY	10022
LYON, FRANCIS D	DIRECTOR	312 PLACITA ELEGANCIA	GREEN VALLEY, AZ	85614
LYON, LARA	ACTRESS	8271 MELROSE AVE #110	LOS ANGELES, CA	90046

Name	Occupation	Address	City	Code
LYON, LISA	BODYBUILDER-MODEL	POST OFFICE BOX 585	SANTA MONICA, CA	90406
LYON, RONALD	WRI-DIR-PROD	ABC-TV, 2040 AVE OF THE STARS	LOS ANGELES, CA	90067
LYONS, BARRY	BASEBALL	POST OFFICE BOX 27045	TUCSON, AZ	85726
LYONS, EDDIE	BASEBALL-SCOUT	1060 W ADDISON ST	CHICAGO, IL	60613
LYONS, JACK	WRITER	569 N ROSSMORE AVE #104	LOS ANGELES, CA	90004
LYONS, JEFFREY	FILM CRITIC	WPIX-TV, 11 WPIX PLAZA	NEW YORK, NY	10017
LYONS, PHYLLIS	ACTRESS	ABC-TV, "ALL MY CHILDREN"		
		320 W 66TH ST	NEW YORK, NY	10023
LYONS, ROBERT F	ACTOR	1801 AVE OF THE STARS #1250	LOS ANGELES, CA	90067
LYONS, STEVE	BASEBALL	POST OFFICE BOX 4064	ATLANTA, GA	30302
LYONS, STEVEN	ARTIST	160-C FILLMORE ST	SAN FRANCISCO, CA	94117
LYONS, STUART	FILM PRODUCER	OUR MAN IN LONDON, LTD		
		PINEWOOD STUDIOS, IVER HEATH	BUCKS	ENGLAND
LYONS, TED	BASEBALL	1401 LOREE ST	VINTON, LA	70668
LYRAS, DEAN S	FILM DIRECTOR	4518 KRAFT AVE	NORTH HOLLYWOOD, CA	91602
LYRES, THE	ROCK & ROLL GROUP	611 BROADWAY #526	NEW YORK, NY	10012
LYTHGOE, NIGEL	CHOREO-PROD	BLATT, THE COACH HOUSE		
		1-A LARPENT AVE	LONDON SW15 6UP	ENGLAND
LYTLE, ALEV N	SCREENWRITER	8955 BEVERLY BLVD	WEST HOLLYWOOD, CA	90048
LYTTHANS, JAMES D	CONDUCTOR	302 VISTA DEL CANON	ANAHEIM, CA	92807
LYTTON, DEBBIE	ACTRESS	905 N BEVERLY DR	BEVERLY HILLS, CA	90210
LYX	ROCK & ROLL GROUP	5625 "O" STREET BLDG #7	LINCOLN, NE	68510

Name	Occupation	Address	City	Code
M & M	ROCK & ROLL GROUP	41 BRITAIN ST #200	TORONTO, ONT M5A 1R7	CANADA
M C 5	MUSICAL GROUP	POST OFFICE BOX 82	GREAT NECK, NY	11021
M F Q	FOLK QUARTET	POST OFFICE BOX 2050	MALIBU, CA	90265
MA, YO-YO	CELLIST	ICM, 40 W 57TH ST	NEW YORK, NY	10019
MAAS, BILL	FOOTBALL	CHIEFS, 1 ARROWHEAD DR	KANSAS CITY, MO	64129
MAAS, KEVIN	BASEBALL	N Y YANKEES, YANKEE STADIUM	BRONX, NY	10451
MAAS, PETER	AUTHOR	SIMON & SCHUSTER, INC		
		1230 AVE OF THE AMERICAS	NEW YORK, NY	10020
MABRY, JOHN	BASEBALL	POST OFFICE BOX 3004	SPRINGFIELD, IL	62708
MABRY, JOHN	FOOTBALL	FALCONS, SUWANEE RD AT I-85	SUWANEE, GA	30174
MABRY, MOSS	COSTUME DESIGNER	13949 VENTURA BLVD #309	SHERMAN OAKS, CA	91423
MABUS, RAY	GOVERNOR	POST OFFICE BOX 2000	JACKSON, MS	39215
MAC, BOBBY & THE BREAKWAY	C & W GROUP	POST OFFICE BOX 8305	HOUSTON, TX	77004
MAC ALLEN, JAMES	DIRECTOR	246 E 46TH ST	NEW YORK, NY	10019
MAC ANDREW, GAIL	TV PRODUCER	21 W 58TH ST #8-A	NEW YORK, NY	10019
MAC ARTHUR, MARK	BASEBALL	POST OFFICE BOX 48	VISALIA, CA	93279
MAC BIRD, BONNIE	SCREENWRITER	CE & H, 9465 WILSHIRE BLVD	BEVERLY HILLS, CA	90212
MAC CABE, COLIN	FILM EXECUTIVE	BFI, 21 STEPHEN ST	LONDON W1P 1PL	ENGLAND
MAC COLL, CATRIONA	ACTRESS	MANSON, 288 MUNSTER RD	LONDON SW6 6BQ	ENGLAND
MAC CORKINDALE, SIMON	ACTOR	1221 N KINGS RD #104	LOS ANGELES, CA	90069
MAC DERMIND, PAUL	HOCKEY	JETS, 15-1430 MAROONS RD	WINNIPEG, MAN R3G 0L5	CANADA
MAC DERMOT, GALT	COMPOSER	ASCAP, 1 LINCOLN PLAZA	NEW YORK, NY	10020
MAC DONALD, ALEIDA	COSTUME DESIGNER	13949 VENTURA BLVD #309	SHERMAN OAKS, CA	91423
MAC DONALD, BOB	BASEBALL <RELEASED>	SKYDOME, 300 BREMMER BL #3200	TORONTO, ONT M5V 3B3	CANADA
MAC DONALD, BRUCE-BRIGHT	COMPOSER	3230 ROWENA AVE	LOS ANGELES, CA	90027
MAC DONALD, GUS	TV WRITER-PRODUCER	SCOTTISH TV, COWCADDENS	GLASGOW	SCOTLAND
MAC DONALD, JOHN N	COMPOSER	400-A AVE "F"	REDONDO BEACH, CA	90277
MAC DONALD, MARCY	ACTRESS	521 S REESE PL	BURBANK, CA	91506
MAC DONALD, ROB	BASEBALL	SKYDOME, 300 BREMMER BL #3200	TORONTO, ONT M5V 3B3	CANADA
MAC DONALD, RYAN	ACTOR	968 N SAN VICENTE BLVD	WEST HOLLYWOOD, CA	90069
MAC DONNEIL, DENNIS	TALENT AGENT	POST OFFICE BOX 1616	NOVATO, CA	94948
MAC DONNELL, RAY	ACTOR	ABC-TV, "ALL MY CHILDREN"		
		320 W 66TH ST	NEW YORK, NY	10023
MAC DOWELL, ANDIE	ACTRESS-MODEL	ICM, 388-396 OXFORD ST	LONDON W1	ENGLAND
MAC FARLANE, MIKE	BASEBALL	POST OFFICE BOX 419969	KANSAS CITY, MO	64141
MAC GILLIVRAY, GREG A	DIRECTOR	POST OFFICE BOX 205	SOUTH LAGUNA, CA	92677
MAC GRAW, ALI	ACTRESS-MODEL	1679 ALTA MURA RD	PACIFIC PALISADES, CA	90272
MAC GREGOR, DOUG	CARTOONIST	POST OFFICE BOX 10	FORT MYERS, FL	33902
MAC GREGOR, JEFF	ACTOR-GAME SHOW HOST	151 S EL CAMINO DR	BEVERLY HILLS, CA	90212
MAC GREGOR, MARY	SINGER	151 S EL CAMINO DR	BEVERLY HILLS, CA	90212
MAC INTOSH, JAY W	ACTRESS	POST OFFICE BOX 605	PACIFIC PALISADES, CA	90272
MAC INTYRE, HAROLD	SINGER	2464 BRASILIA CIR	MISSISS, ONT L5N 2G1	CANADA
MAC KAY, BILL	BASEBALL EXECUTIVE	RED SOX, CHAIN O'LAKES PARK	WINTER HAVEN, FL	33880
MAC KAY, KAREN	SINGER	POST OFFICE BOX 3174		
MAC KAY, KENNETH H "BUDDY"	LT GOVERNOR	STATE CAPITOL BUILDING	TALLAHASSEE, FL	32399
MAC KENZIE, BILL	BASEBALL SCOUT	6850 LAWRENCE RD	LANTANA, FL	33462
MAC KENZIE, GISELE	ACTRESS-SINGER	11014 BLIX AVE	NORTH HOLLYWOOD, CA	91604
MAC KENZIE, GORDIE	BASEBALL-SCOUT	INDIANS, CLEVELAND STADIUM	CLEVELAND, OH	44114
MAC KENZIE, JOHN	FILM-TV DIRECTOR	PETERS, FRASER & DUNLOP, LTD		
		5TH FLOOR, THE CHAMBERS		
		CHELSEA HARBOUR, LOT RD	LONDON SW10 0XF	ENGLAND
MAC KENZIE, KEITH	TV DIRECTOR	10 LEGH RD, PRESTBURY, MACCLES	CHESHIRE SK10 4HX	ENGLAND
MAC KENZIE, MARY BETH	ACTRESS	644 N ORCHARD DR	BURBANK, CA	91506
MAC KENZIE, MURDO	DIRECTOR-PRODUCER	POST OFFICE BOX 6767	BEND, OR	97701

Name	Occupation	Address	City/State	Zip
MAC KENZIE, PATCH	ACTRESS	8322 BEVERLY BLVD #200	LOS ANGELES, CA	90048
MAC KENZIE, PHILIP CHARLES	ACTOR	2712 GLENDOWER AVE	LOS ANGELES, CA	90027
MAC KENZIE, ROBERT	TV PERS-WRITER	KTVU-TV, 2 JACK LONDON SQ	OAKLAND, CA	94607
MAC KENZIE, WILL	ACTOR-TV DIRECTOR	3955 ALOMAR ST	SHERMAN OAKS, CA	91423
MAC KEY, BOBBY	SINGER	SEIFERT, 1407 KENOVA AVE	CINCINNATI, OH	45237
MAC LACHLAN, JANET	ACTRESS	1919 N TAFT AVE	LOS ANGELES, CA	90068
MAC LACHLAN, KYLE	ACTOR	760 N LA CIENEGA BLVD	LOS ANGELES, CA	90069
MAC LAINE, SHIRLEY	ACTRESS	PARKER, 25200 OLD MALIBU RD	MALIBU, CA	90265
MAC LAREN, FAWNA	MODEL	MODELS & PROMOTION AGENCY		
MAC LAREN, JIM	ACTOR	NBC-TV, "ANOTHER WORLD"		
		1268 E 14TH ST	BROOKLYN, NY	11230
MAC LEAN, JEAN	DIRECTOR	240 E 76TH ST	NEW YORK, NY	10021
MAC LEAN, JOHN	HOCKEY	POST OFFICE BOX 504	EAST RUTHERFORD, NJ	07073
MAC LEAN, PETER	ACTOR	742 PORTOLA TERR	LOS ANGELES, CA	90042
MAC LEAN, ROBERT	FILM EXECUTIVE	8439 SUNSET BLVD #404	LOS ANGELES, CA	90069
MAC LEAN & MAC LEAN	ROCK & ROLL GROUP	41 BRITAIN ST #200	TORONTO, ONT M5A 1R7	CANADA
MAC LEARN, R D	SINGER	4680 ELK LAKE DR #304	VICTORIA, BC V8Z 5M1	CANADA
MAC LELLAN, BRIAN	HOCKEY	POST OFFICE BOX 1540, STA "M"	CALGARY, ALTA T2P 3BP	CANADA
MAC LEOD, ANNE	TV PRODUCER	CHILDREN'S TV WORKSHOP		
		1 LINCOLN PLAZA	NEW YORK, NY	10023
MAC LEOD, GAVIN	ACTOR	14680 VALLEY VISTA	SHERMAN OAKS, CA	91403
MAC LEOD, JOHN	BASKETBALL COACH	KNICKS, 4 PENNYLVANIA PLAZA	NEW YORK, NY	10019
MAC LEOD, MURRAY	ACTOR	533 18TH ST	SANTA MONICA, CA	90402
MAC MAHON, DAVID	TV DIRECTOR	17 BARNET GATE LN, ARKLEY	HERTS EN5 2AA	ENGLAND
MAC MILLAN, KEITH	DIRECTOR	1961 N VAN NESS AVE	HOLLYWOOD, CA	90068
MAC MILLAN, KENNETH	CINEMATOGRAPHER	11 SHERBORNE GARDENS	LONDON W13 8AS	ENGLAND
MAC MILLAN, STEPHANIE K	DIRECTOR	DGA, 7920 SUNSET BLVD, 6TH FL	LOS ANGELES, CA	90046
MAC MURRAY, KATHERINE	ACTRESS	485 HALVERN DR	LOS ANGELES, CA	90049
MAC NAIR, SUSAN	THEATER PRODUCER	QUAD PRODS, 890 BROADWAY	NEW YORK, NY	10003
MAC NAUGHTAN, ALAN	ACTOR	19 ARUNDEL CT, ARUNDEL GARDENS	LONDON W11 2LP	ENGLAND
MAC NAUGHTON, IAN	TV DIRECTOR	PERCHAER WEG 3	8137 BERG 1	GERMANY
MAC NAUGHTON, ROBERT	ACTOR	ICM, 8899 BEVERLY BLVD	LOS ANGELES, CA	90048
MAC NEAL, CATHERINE	ACTRESS	8831 SUNSET BLVD #304	LOS ANGELES, CA	90069
MAC NEE, PATRICK	ACTOR	39 GUILDFORD PARK RD, GUILDFORD	SURREY GUZ 5NA	ENGLAND
MAC NEIL	TV JOURNALIST	WM MORRIS, 1350 AVE OF AMERICAS	NEW YORK, NY	10019
MAC NEIL, DOUG	BASEBALL	RED SOX, CHAIN O'LAKES PARK	WINTER HAVEN, FL	33880
MAC NELLY, JEFFREY	CARTOONIST	333 E GRACE ST	RICHMOND, VA	23219
MAC PHAIL, ANDY	BASEBALL EXECUTIVE	TWINS, 501 CHICAGO AVE S	MINNEAPOLIS, MN	55415
MAC PHERSON, ELLE	MODEL	40 E 61ST ST	NEW YORK, NY	10021
MAC RAE, CARMEN	SINGER	2200 SUMMITRIDGE DR	BEVERLY HILLS, CA	90210
MAC RAE, ELIZABETH	ACTRESS	TALENT REPS, 20 E 53RD ST	NEW YORK, NY	10022
MAC RAE, MEREDITH	ACTRESS	13659 VICTORY BLVD #588	VAN NUYS, CA	91401
MAC TAVISH, CRAIG	HOCKEY	OILERS, NORTHLANDS COLISEUM	EDMONTON, ALTA T5B 4M9	CANADA
MACAL, ZDENEK	CONDUCTOR	ICM, 40 W 57TH ST	NEW YORK, NY	10019
MACAULAY, MORENIKE	TV PRODUCER	LICATA INT'L, 31 W 21ST ST	NEW YORK, NY	10010
MACCHIO, RALPH	ACTOR	972 NICHOLS RD	DEER PARK, NY	11729
MACE, RAY	COMPOSER-CONDUCTOR	1306 WARNER AVE	LOS ANGELES, CA	90024
MACHA, KEN	BASEBALL-COACH	EXPOS, 4545 DE COUBERTIN AVE	MONTREAL, QUE H1V 3P2	CANADA
MACHADO, JULIO	BASEBALL	BREWERS, 201 S 46TH ST	MILWAUKEE, WI	53214
MACHADO, MARIO J	ACTOR	5750 BRIARCLIFF RD	LOS ANGELES, CA	90068
MACHADO, MIGUEL	BASEBALL SCOUT	ORIOLE PARK, 333 W CAMDEN ST	BALTIMORE, MD	21201
MACHEMER, DAVE	BASEBALL-INSTRUCTOR	BREWERS, 201 S 46TH ST	MILWAUKEE, WI	53214
MACHT, STEPHEN	ACTOR	248 S RODEO DR	BEVERLY HILLS, CA	90212
MACHTLEY, RONALD	U S CONGRESSMAN	320 THAMES ST #267	NEWPORT, RI	02840
MACINNIS, AL	HOCKEY	POST OFFICE BOX 1540, STA "M"	CALGARY, ALTA T2P 3BP	CANADA
MACIVER, NORM	HOCKEY	OILERS, NORTHLANDS COLISEUM	EDMONTON, ALTA T5B 4M9	CANADA
MACK, BERNARD BURNELL	TV WRITER	3214 HIGHLAND AVE #A	SANTA MONICA, CA	90405
MACK, BRICE H	FILM DIRECTOR	10841 WRIGHTWOOD LN	STUDIO CITY, CA	91604
MACK, BRICE HARVEY	CINEMATOGRAPHER	10941 1/2 BLOOMFIELD ST	NORTH HOLLYWOOD, CA	91602
MACK, CEDRIC	FOOTBALL	POST OFFICE BOX 609609	SAN DIEGO, CA	92160
MACK, CONNIE	U S SEANTOR	517 HART SENATE OFFICE BLDG	WASHINGTON, DC	20510
MACK, JIMMIE	SINGER	TWM MGMT, 641 LEXINGTON AVE	NEW YORK, NY	10022
MACK, JOE	FOOTBALL	POST OFFICE BOX 17247 (DULLES)	WASHINGTON, DC	20041
MACK, KEVIN	FOOTBALL	BROWNS, 80 1ST ST	BEREA, OH	44017
MACK, LONNIE	SINGER-GUITARIST	POST OFFICE BOX 20043		
		COLUMBUS CIRCLE STATION	NEW YORK, NY	10023
MACK, MILTON	FOOTBALL	SAINTS, 1500 POYDRAS ST	NEW ORLEANS, LA	90112
MACK, QUINN	BASEBALL	1501 W 16TH ST	INDIANAPOLIS, IN	46202
MACK, RAY	BASEBALL	POST OFFICE BOX 507	DURHAM, NC	27702
MACK, ROY	CONDUCTOR	7506 HESPERIA AVE	RESEDA, CA	91335
MACK, SCOTT	ARTIST	4403 HOLLY ST	KANSAS CITY, MO	64111
MACK, SHANE	BASEBALL	TWINS, 501 CHICAGO AVE S	MINNEAPOLIS, MN	55415
MACK, WARNER	SINGER-GUITARIST	1136 SUNNY MEADE DR	NASHVILLE, TN	37216
MACK & JAMIE	COMEDY DUO	151 S EL CAMINO DR	BEVERLY HILLS, CA	90212
MACKALL, MICHELLE	GOLFER	2750 VOLUSA AVE #B	DAYTON BEACH, FL	32114
MACKANIN, PETE	BASEBALL MANAGER	POST OFFICE BOX 23290	NASHVILLE, TN	37202
MACKER, JOHN J	WRITER-PRODUCER	DGA, 7920 SUNSET BLVD, 6TH FL	LOS ANGELES, CA	90046
MACKEY, MARTIN	DIRECTOR-PRODUCER	11038 LANDALE ST	NORTH HOLLYWOOD, CA	91602
MACKIE, BOB	COSTUME DESIGNER	8636 MELROSE AVE	LOS ANGELES, CA	90069
MACKRIDES, GREG	FOOTBALL COACH	N Y JETS, 1000 FULTON AVE	HEMPSTEAD, NY	11550
MACLIN, LONNIE	BASEBALL	POST OFFICE BOX 36407	LOUISVILLE, KY	40233
MACONSAW	ROCK & ROLL GROUP	POST OFFICE BOX 448	RADFORD, VA	24141
MACOUN, JAMIE	HOCKEY	POST OFFICE BOX 1540, STA "M"	CALGARY, ALTA T2P 3BP	CANADA
MACRAEG, JEFF	SINGER-SONGWRITER	PUTI TAI NOBIO #6	BARRIGADA HEIGHTS, GU	96911
MACY, BILL	ACTOR	10130 ANGELO CIR	BEVERLY HILLS, CA	90210

MAD DADDY'S, THE	ROCK & ROLL GROUP	JEM RECORDS, 3619 KENNEDY RD	SOUTH PLAINFIELD, NJ	07080
MAD LADS, THE	RHYTHM & BLUES GROUP	UPS, 781 EUGENE RD	MEMPHIS, TN	38116
MAD MAX	ROCK & ROLL GROUP	POST OFFICE BOX 2896	TORRANCE, CA	90509
MADDALENA, JULIE	ACTRESS	12115 HOFFMAN ST	STUDIO CITY, CA	91604
MADDEN, BETTY PECHA	COSTUME DESIGNER	13949 VENTURA BLVD #309	SHERMAN OAKS, CA	91423
MADDEN, DAVE	ACTOR	1800 N VINE ST #120	LOS ANGELES, CA	90028
MADDEN, JERRY	TV DIRECTOR-PRODUCER	SHERRELL, 1354 LAS ROBLES DR	PALM SPRINGS, CA	92262
MADDEN, JOE	FOOTBALL COACH	POST OFFICE BOX 609609	SAN DIEGO, CA	92160
MADDEN, JOHN	SPORTSCASTER	1 W 72ND ST	NEW YORK, NY	10023
MADDEN, JOHN PHILIP	DIRECTOR	DGA, 110 W 57TH ST	NEW YORK, NY	10019
MADDEN, LEE	DIRECTOR	16918 MARQUEZ AVE	PACIFIC PALISADES, CA	90272
MADDEN, WILLIAM JAMES	ACTOR	4218 SAINT CLAIR AVE	STUDIO CITY, CA	91604
MADDON, JOE	BASEBALL-INSTRUCTOR	POST OFFICE BOX 2000	ANAHEIM, CA	92803
MADDOW, BEN	WRITER	2781 WESTSHIRE DR	LOS ANGELES, CA	90068
MADDOX, DIANA	FILM WRITER-DIRECTOR	521 N ELM DR	BEVERLY HILLS, CA	90210
MADDOX, GARRY	BASEBALL-ANNOUNCER	POST OFFICE BOX 7575	PHILADELPHIA, PA	19101
MADDOX, GREG	BASEBALL	1060 W ADDISON ST	CHICAGO, IL	60613
MADDOX, JERRY	BASEBALL	5539 BAYWOOD	RIVERSIDE, CA	92504
MADDOX, LELAND	BASEBALL SCOUT	POST OFFICE BOX 7000	PITTSBURGH, PA	15212
MADDUX, GREG	BASEBALL	1060 W ADDISON ST	CHICAGO, IL	60613
MADDUX, MIKE	BASEBALL	POST OFFICE BOX 2000	SAN DIEGO, CA	92112
MADDUX, R LEE	TV WRITER	2402 4TH ST #15	SANTA MONICA, CA	90405
MADEJA, KEN	BASEBALL SCOUT	POST OFFICE BOX 4100	SEATTLE, WA	98104
MADERO, RITA	COMEDIENNE	400 CENTRAL PARK W #10-C	NEW YORK, NY	10025
MADERSKI, GEORGE	CHOREOGRAPHER	8343 118TH ST	KEW GARDENS, NY	11415
MADERSKI, RUTH	CHOREOGRAPHER	8343 118TH ST	KEW GARDENS, NY	11415
MADIGAN, AMY	ACTRESS	662 N VAN NESS AVE #305	LOS ANGELES, CA	90004
MADISON, GUY	ACTOR	35022 1/2 AVE "H"	YUCAIPA, CA	92399
MADISON, JOEL	COMEDIAN	POST OFFICE BOX 9532	MADISON, WI	53715
MADLOCK, BILL	BASEBALL	453 E DECATUR ST	DECATUR, IL	62251
MADNESS	ROCK & ROLL GROUP	STERLING ARTISTES MGMT		
		167 CALEDONIAN RD	LONDON N1 OSL	ENGLAND
MADOC, PHILIP	ACTOR	WATERSIDE HOUSE, LONDON COLONY	HERTS	ENGLAND
MADOC, RUTH	ACTRESS	BRAMBLE COTTAGE, GAWTRY	CAMBS	ENGLAND
MADONNA	SINGER-ACTRESS	8461 SUNSET BLVD #485	WEST HOLLYWOOD, CA	90069
MADRID, ALEX	BASEBALL	1626 W 5TH ST	MESA, AZ	85201
MADRIL, AL	WRESTLER	8725 N CHAUTAUQUA BLVD	PORTLAND, OR	97217
MADRIL, BILL	BASEBALL	RED SOX, CHAIN O'LAKES PARK	WINTER HAVEN, FL	33880
MADSEN, KENNETH KORT	DIRECTOR	DGA, 110 W 57TH ST	NEW YORK, NY	10019
MADSEN, LANCE	BASEBALL	POST OFFICE BOX 4209	JACKSON, MS	39296
MADSEN, MICHAEL	ACTOR	400 S BEVERLY DR #216	BEVERLY HILLS, CA	90212
MADSEN, VIRGINIA	ACTRESS	8730 SANTA MONICA BLVD #I	LOS ANGELES, CA	90069
MADURGA, GONZALO	ACTOR	807 RIVERSIDE DR #5-G	NEW YORK, NY	10032
MADUSA	WRESTLING MANAGER	POST OFFICE BOX 105366	ATLANTA, GA	31348
MAESTRO, JOHNNY & BROOKLYN BRID	ROCK & ROLL GROUP	KNIGHT, 185 CLINTON AVE	STATEN ISLAND, NY	10301
MAFFETT, DEBRA SUE	ACTRESS-MODEL	2969 PASSMORE DR	LOS ANGELES, CA	90068
MAFFIA, DANIEL	ARTIST	44 N DEAN ST	ENGLEWOOD, NJ	07631
MAGADAN, DAVE	BASEBALL	METS, 126TH ST & ROOSEVELT AVE	FLUSHING, NY	11368
MAGALLANES, BOBBY	BASEBALL	POST OFFICE BOX 9194	HAMPTON, VA	23670
MAGALLANES, EVER	BASEBALL	CANADIANS, 4601 ONTARIO ST	VANCOUVER, BC V5V 3H4	CANADA
MAGALLANES, WILLIE	BASEBALL	POST OFFICE BOX 36407	LOUISVILLE, KY	40233
MAGEE, ANDREW	GOLFER	POST OFFICE BOX 109601	PALM BCH GARDENS, FL	33418
MAGEE, BO	BASEBALL	POST OFFICE BOX 309	GASTONA, NC	28053
MAGEE, KEN	ACTOR	12244 CALIFA ST	NORTH HOLLYWOOD, CA	91607
MAGGART, BRANDON	ACTOR	9200 SUNSET BLVD #710	LOS ANGELES, CA	90069
MAGGART, MIKE	BASEBALL SCOUT	POST OFFICE BOX 288	HOUSTON, TX	77001
MAGGERT, JEFF	GOLFER	POST OFFICE BOX 109601	PALM BCH GARDENS, FL	33418
MAGGI, BARBARA	MAKE-UP ARTIST	646 PARK AVE	PATERSON, NJ	07504
MAGGI, MARIA	ACTRESS	57 WARWICK RD	GREAT NECK, NY	11023
MAGGS, DON	FOOTBALL	OILERS, 6910 FANNIN ST	HOUSTON, TX	77070
MAGID, ANN LISA	TV DIRECTOR	NBC-TV, 30 ROCKEFELLER PLAZA	NEW YORK, NY	10112
MAGID, RON	PLAYWRIGHT	1313 OCEAN FRONT WK	SANTA MONICA, CA	90401
MAGINNIS, MOLLY	COSTUME DESIGNER	933 17TH ST #14	SANTA MONICA, CA	90403
MAGISTRETTI, PAUL	WRITER	10535 WYTON DR	LOS ANGELES, CA	90024
MAGIT, DEBRA	ACTRESS	730 N BEVERLY GLEN BLVD	LOS ANGELES, CA	90077
MAGLIE, SAL	BASEBALL	77 MORNINGSIDE DR	GRAND ISLAND, NY	14072
MAGNANTE, MIKE	BASEBALL	POST OFFICE BOX 419969	KANSAS CITY, MO	64141
MAGNE, MICHEL	COMPOSER	20 RUE MOUFFELTARD	PARIS 75005	FRANCE
MAGNER, MARTIN	TV DIRECTOR	1282 S BURNSIDE AVE	LOS ANGELES, CA	90019
MAGNESS, CLIFF	WRITER-PRODUCER	12110 GREENOCK LN	LOS ANGELES, CA	90049
MAGNOLI, ALBERT	FILM DIRECTOR	3970 OVERLAND AVE #148	CULVER CITY, CA	90322
MAGNUSON, ANN	ACTRESS	MORRA, 801 WESTMOUNT DR	LOS ANGELES, CA	90069
MAGOWAN, PETER	BASEBALL EXECUTIVE	S F GIANTS, CANDLESTICK PARK	SAN FRANICSCO, CA	94124
MAGRANE, JOE	BASEBALL	250 STADIUM PLAZA	ST LOUIS, MO	63102
MAGRUDER, REV JEB STUART	CLERYMAN-WATERGATE	720 W MONUMENT ST	COLORADO SPRINGS, CO	80901
MAGUIRE, JEFFREY P	SCREENWRITER	8955 BEVERLY BLVD	WEST HOLLYWOOD, CA	90048
MAGUIRE, KEVIN	BASEBALL	POST OFFICE BOX 3746, HILL STA	AUGUSTA, GA	30904
MAGUIRE, KEVIN	HOCKEY	MAPLE LEAFS, 60 CARLTON ST	TORONTO, ONT M5B 1L1	CANADA
MAGUIRE, THOMAS P	FILM DIRECTOR	342 CULVER BLVD #4	PLAYA DEL REY, CA	90293
MAGUIRE, TOBEY	ACTOR	9171 WILSHIRE BLVD #300	BEVERLY HILLS, CA	90210
MAGWOOD, HOWARD	DIRECTOR-PRODUCER	23852 CASSANDRA BAY	LAGUNA NIGUEL, CA	92677
MAGWOOD, PAUL	FILM DIRECTOR	27176 GARZA DR	SAUGUS, CA	91350
MAGYAR, DEZSO D	DIRECTOR	1539 CALMAR CT	LOS ANGELES, CA	90024
MAHAFFEY, VALERIE	ACTRESS	SMITH, 121 N SAN VICENTE BLVD	BEVERLY HILLS, CA	90211
MAHAN, JOEL	ACTOR-SINGER	273 BERGEN AVE	JERSEY CITY, NJ	07305

JEANNE HOYT

Autographs

Buy, sell and trade in all areas, specializing in entertainers of the past and present

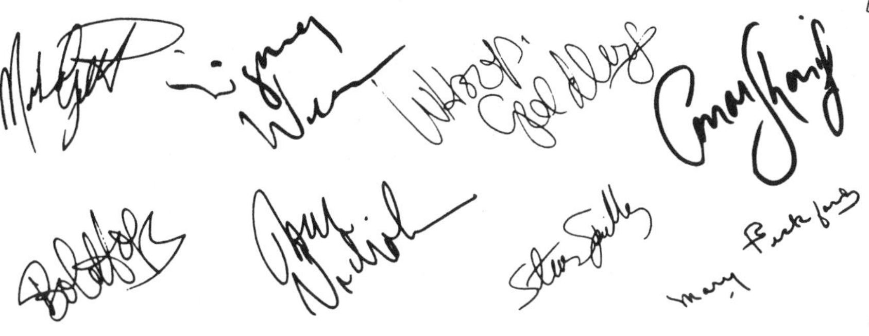

ALL MATERIAL GUARANTEED FOR THE LIFE OF THE AUTOGRAPH

Actively looking for in-person signatures only of participants of "WE ARE THE WORLD" — top prices paid!

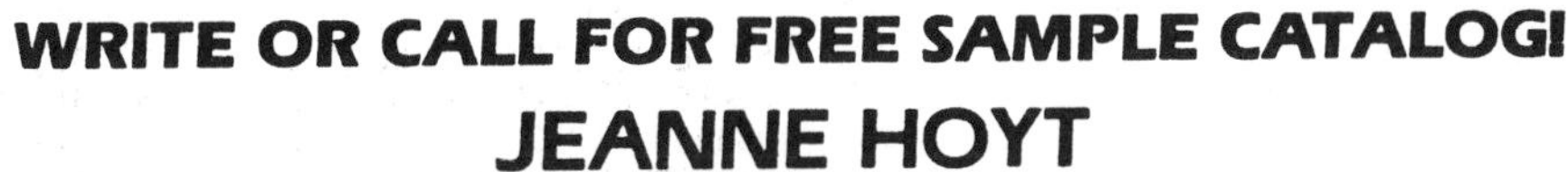

WRITE OR CALL FOR FREE SAMPLE CATALOG!

JEANNE HOYT
P.O. Box 1517 • Rohnert Park, CA 94927-1517
707/584-4077

MAHAR, TED	FILM CRITIC	OREGONIAN, 1320 SW BROADWAY	PORTLAND, OR 97201
MAHARIS, GEORGE	ACTOR	13150 MULHOLLAND DR	BEVERLY HILLS, CA 90210
MAHAY, RON	BASEBALL	RED SOX, CHAIN O'LAKES PARK	WINTER HAVEN, FL 33880
MAHER, BILL	ACTOR	9200 SUNSET BLVD #428	LOS ANGELES, CA 90069
MAHER, PATRICIA	ACTRESS-PRODUCER	205 WASHINGTON AVE #9	SANTA MONICA, CA 90403
MAHLBERG, GREG	BASEBALL-MANAGER	POST OFFICE BOX 402	GENEVA, NY 14456
MAHLER, RICK	BASEBALL	7911 QUIRT DR	SAN ANTONIO, TX 78227
MAHN, ANTONY L	TV PRODUCER	MAC NEIL/LEHRER, 356 W 58TH ST	NEW YORK, NY 10019
MAHOGANY RUSH	ROCK & ROLL GROUP	65 W 55TH ST #306	NEW YORK, NY 10019
MAHOMES, PAT	BASEBALL	TWINS, 501 CHICAGO AVE S	MINNEAPOLIS, MN 55415
MAHONEY, BOB	FILM DIRECTOR	EDEN FILMS, 28 YOEMAN'S ROW	LONDON SW3 2AH ENGLAND
MAHONEY, JAMES A	DIRECTOR	DGA, 110 W 57TH ST	NEW YORK, NY 10019
MAHONEY, KATHERINE	ARTIST	60 HURD RD	BELMONT, MA 02178
MAHONEY, RICHARD	SECRETARY OF STATE	STATE CAPITOL, 1700 W WASHINGTON	PHOENIX, AZ 85007
MAHONY, JOHN	FILM EXECUTIVE	NATIONAL SCREEN SERVICE, LTD	
		15 WADSWORTH RD, PERIVALE	
		GREENFORD	MIDDLESEX ENGLAND
MAHORN, RICK	BASKETBALL	POST OFFICE BOX 25040	PHILADELPHIA, PA 19147
MAHURIN, MATT	ARTIST-CARTOONIST	L A TIMES, TIMES SQ MIRROR	LOS ANGELES, CA 90053
MAIBAUM, PAUL	WRITER	1557 N STANLEY AVE	LOS ANGELES, CA 90046
MAIER, FRANCIS X	WRITER	5700 ETIWANDA AVE	TARZANA, CA 91356
MAIER, MARTY	BASEBALL SCOUT	250 STADIUM PLAZA	ST LOUIS, MO 63102
MAIER, MAYLOU	ACTRESS	723 CARNELIAN ST	REDONDO BEACH, CA 90277
MAIER, STEVEN PERRY	TV EXECUTIVE	ABC-TV, 4151 PROSPECT AVE	LOS ANGELES, CA 90027
MAIETTA, TONY	ACTOR	12377 LEWIS ST #101	GARDEN GROVE, CA 92640
MAILER, LEV	ACTOR	12249 1/2 CANTURA ST	STUDIO CITY, CA 91604
MAILER, NORMAN	AUTHOR	142 COLUMBIA HEIGHTS PL	BROOKLYN, NY 11201
MAILHOUSE, ROBERT	ACTOR	NBC-TV, "DAYS OF OUR LIVES"	
		3000 W ALAMEDA AVE	BURBANK, CA 91523
MAILLAN, JACQUELINE	ACTRESS	M BRU, 33 CHAMPS-ELYSEES	PARIS 75008 FRANCE
MAIN, DAVID	TV WRITER-PRODUCER	QUADRANT, 950 TONGE ST	TORONTO, ONTARIO CANADA
MAIN ATTRACTION, THE	ROCK & ROLL GROUP	2600 NONCONNAH BLVD #390	MEMPHIS, TN 38132
MAINIERI, DEMIE	BASEBALL SCOUT	BREWERS, 201 S 46TH ST	MILWAUKEE, WI 53214
MAINSTREET	MUSICAL GROUP	32500 CONCORD DR #252	MADISON HEIGHTS, MI 48071
MAIR, AL	RECORD EXECUTIVE	ATTIC, 624 KING ST W	TORONTO, ONT M5V 1M7 CANADA
MAISEL, SALLY J	WRITER	7454 TYRONE AVE	VAN NUYS, CA 91405
MAISONETTE, HECTOR	ACTOR	7250 FRANKLIN AVE #709	LOS ANGELES, CA 90046
MAITLAND, BETH	ACTRESS	STONE MANNERS, 9113 SUNSET BL	LOS ANGELES, CA 90069
MAITLAND, SCOTT R	CINEMATOGRAPHER	622 E PALM AVE #A	BURBANK, CA 91501
MAITZ, DON	ARTIST	50 MAPLE ST	PLAINVILLE, CT 06062
MAJAL, TAJ	MUSICIAN	1671 APPIAN WY	SANTA MONICA, CA 90401
MAJER, STEFFEN	BASEBALL	POST OFFICE BOX 5599	LITTLE ROCK, AR 72215
MAJERLE, DAN	BASKETBALL	SUNS, 2910 N CENTRAL AVE	PHOENIX, AZ 85012
MAJKOWSKI, DON	FOOTBALL	PACKERS, 1265 LOMBARDI AVE	GREEN BAY, WI 54307
MAJOR, ANN SOMERS	COSTUME DESIGNER	1024 CHAUTAUQUA BLVD	PACIFIC PALISADES, CA 90272
MAJOR, NORMAN S	COMPOSER	2009 N GREENLEAF ST	SANTA ANA, CA 92706
MAJORS, LEE	ACTOR-DIRECTOR	411 ISLE OF CAPRI DR	FORT LAUDERDALE, FL 33301
MAJORS, LEE, II	ACTOR	22852 PACIFIC COAST HWY #E	MALIBU, CA 90265
MAJORS, STEVE	ACTOR-DIRECTOR	THE STUNTMAN'S FEDERATION	
		96 NORLAND HOUSE	
		QUEENSDALE CRESCENT	LONDON W11 ENGLAND
MAJTYKA, ROY	BASEBALL MANAGER	POST OFFICE BOX 1721	SPARTANBURG, SC 29304
MAK, KAM	ARTIST	45 HENRY ST #17	NEW YORK, NY 10002
MAKAREWICZ, SCOTT	BASEBALL	POST OFFICE BOX 4209	JACKSON, MS 39296
MAKAROV, SERGEI	HOCKEY	POST OFFICE BOX 1540, STA "M"	CALGARY, ALTA T2P 3BP CANADA
MAKELA, MIKKO	HOCKEY	SABRES, MEMORIAL AUDITORIUM	BUFFALO, NY 14202
MAKEPEACE, CHRIS	ACTOR	15 CLEVELAND ST	TORONTO, ONT CANADA
MAKIN' TIME	ROCK & ROLL GROUP	34-38 PROVOST ST	LONDON N1 ENGLAND
MAKO	ACTOR	6310 SAN VICENTE BLVD #407	LOS ANGELES, CA 90048
MAKOUL, RUDY	WRITER	3435 VINTON AVE #6	LOS ANGELES, CA 90034
MAKOVSKY, JUDIANNA	COSTUME DESIGNER	345 S END AVE #3-M	NEW YORK, NY 10280
MAKSUDIAN, MIKE	BASEBALL	CHIEFS, MAC ARTHUR STADIUM	SYRACUSE, NY 13208
MALAHIDE, PATRICK	ACTOR	43-A PRINCESS RD, REGENTS PK	LONDON NW1 8JS ENGLAND
MALANDRO, KRISTINA	ACTRESS	10647 WILKINS AVE #307	LOS ANGELES, CA 90024
MALARA, ANTHONY C	TV EXECUTIVE	CBS-TV, 51 W 52ND ST	NEW YORK, NY 10019
MALAVASI, RAY	FOOTBALL COACH	10131 THESUS DR	HUNTINGTON BEACH, CA 92646
MALAVE, OMAR	BASEBALL COACH	POST OFFICE BOX 465	MED HAT, ALB T1A 7G2 CANADA
MALCOLM, ANDREW H	AUTHOR	TIMES BOOKS, 201 E 50TH ST	NEW YORK, NY 10022
MALCOLM, WILLIAM J	TV DIRECTOR	NBC-TV, 30 ROCKEFELLER PLAZA	NEW YORK, NY 10112
MALDEN, KARL	ACTOR	1845 MANDEVILLE CANYON RD	LOS ANGELES, CA 90049
MALDONADO, ALBERT	BASEBALL	POST OFFICE BOX 10031	BAKERSFIELD, CA 93389
MALDONADO, CANDY	BASEBALL	BREWERS, 201 S 46TH ST	MILWAUKEE, WI 53214
MALDONADO, CARLOS	BASEBALL	POST OFFICE BOX 3665	OMAHA, NE 68103
MALDONADO, FELIX	BASEBALL MANAGER	RED SOX, CHAIN O'LAKES PARK	WINTER HAVEN, FL 33880
MALEK, LEONARD	FILM EDITOR	3650 S BENTLEY AVE	LOS ANGELES, CA 90034
MALEK-YONAN, ROSIE	ACTRESS-WRITER	3411 COUNTRY CLUB DR	GLENDALE, CA 91208
MALENA, DON	SINGER	POST OFFICE BOX 1104	HARVEY, LA 70059
MALERSTEIN, SUSAN	ACTRESS	3543 MEIER ST	LOS ANGELES, CA 90066
MALES, WILLIAM J	COSTUME DESIGNER	7095 HOLLYWOOD BLVD #734	HOLLYWOOD, CA 90028
MALET, ARTHUR	ACTOR-PRODUCER	419 HILL ST #2	SANTA MONICA, CA 90405
MALEY, DAVID	HOCKEY	POST OFFICE BOX 504	EAST RUTHERFORD, NJ 07073
MALEY, JERRY	BASEBALL EXECUTIVE	POST OFFICE BOX 802	BATAVIA, NY 14021
MALHAM, CHRIS	COMEDY WRITER	210 WHISPERWOOD LN	MARIETTA, GA 30064
MALICK, TERRENCE	WRITER-PRODUCER	2265 NICHOLS CANYON RD	LOS ANGELES, CA 90046
MALIKYAN, KEVORK	ACTOR	42 WILTON RD, MUSWELL HILL	LONDON N10 1LS ENGLAND

MALIN, KYM	ACTRESS-MODEL	9229 SUNSET BLVD #208	LOS ANGELES, CA	90069
MALIN, MARY	COSTUME DESIGNER	2410 HORSESHOE CANYON RD	LOS ANGELES, CA	90046
MALINDA, JIM	ACTOR	1930 TAMARIND AVE #3	LOS ANGELES, CA	90068
MALINDA, RAY	ACTOR	3917 RIVERSIDE DR	BURBANK, CA	91505
MALINOSKI, CHRIS	BASEBALL	POST OFFICE BOX 3566	WEST PALM BEACH, FL	33402
MALIS, CLAIRE	ACTRESS	6525 SUNSET BLVD #600	LOS ANGELES, CA	90038
MALIS, MARK	CASTING DIRECTOR	MCA/UNIVERSAL STUDIOS, INC		
		100 UNIVERSAL CITY PLAZA #463	UNIVERSAL CITY, CA	91608
MALKIN, RACHEL	ACTRESS	120 N VISTA ST	LOS ANGELES, CA	90036
MALKMUS, BOBBY	BASEBALL-SCOUT	POST OFFICE BOX 2000	SAN DIEGO, CA	92112
MALKOVICH, JOHN	ACTOR	346 S LUCERNE BLVD	LOS ANGELES, CA	90020
MALLARD, STEVE	SINGER	581-D OLD HICKORY BLVD	JACKSON, TN	38301
MALLE, LOUIS	FILM DIRECTOR	222 CENTRAL PARK S	NEW YORK, NY	10019
MALLEE, JOHN	BASEBALL	POST OFFICE BOX 1721	SPARTANBURG, SC	29304
MALLER, JONATHAN	DIRECTOR	3 EDGEWOOD AVE	GLEN HEAD, NY	11545
MALLETTE, PAT	FOOTBALL REFEREE	NFL, 410 PARK AVE	NEW YORK, NY	10022
MALLETTE, TROY	HOCKEY	POST OFFICE BOX 90111	ARLINGTON, TX	76004
MALLEY, HOWARD G	DIRECTOR	11523 DUQUE DR	STUDIO CITY, CA	91604
MALLICOAT, ROB	BASEBALL	POST OFFICE BOX 27045	TUCSON, AZ	85726
MALLIE, JOANNE P	TV WRITER-PRODUCER	CBS-TV, 524 W 57TH ST	NEW YORK, NY	10019
MALLIK, UMESH	SCREENWRITER	MOLLIKO, 16-18 NEW BRIDGE ST	LONDON EC4	ENGLAND
MALLON, MEG	GOLFER	2750 VOLUSA AVE #B	DAYTON BEACH, FL	32114
MALLORY, BARBARA	ACTRESS	SCHWARTZ, 12800 MILBANK ST	STUDIO CITY, CA	91604
MALLORY, CAROLE W	MODEL-AUTHORESS	POSEIDON PRESS/POCKET BOOKS		
		SIMON & SCHUSTER, INC		
		1230 AVE OF THE AMERICAS	NEW YORK, NY	10020
MALLORY, DRUE	ACTRESS	HEINZ, 43 HAY'S MEWS, BERKELEY SQ	LONDON W1X 7RU	ENGLAND
MALLORY, EDWARD	TV DIRECTOR	3158 OAKSHIRE DR	HOLLYWOOD, CA	90068
MALLORY, TREVOR	BASEBALL	POST OFFICE BOX 1110	MYRTLE BEACH, SC	29578
MALLORY, VICTORIA	ACTRESS	10351 SANTA MONICA BLVD #211	LOS ANGELES, CA	90025
MALLOW, THOMAS W	THEATER PRODUCER	AMERICAN THEATER PRODUCTIONS		
		1500 BROADWAY	NEW YORK, NY	10036
MALLOY, LARKIN	ACTOR	ABC-TV, "LOVING"		
		320 W 66TH ST, STUDIO 23	NEW YORK, NY	10023
MALMSTEEN, YNGWIE & RISING FORC	ROCK & ROLL GROUP	24514 CALVERT ST #210	WOODLAND HILLS, CA	91367
MALMUTH, BRUCE	ACT-WRI-DIR	9981 ROBBINS DR	BEVERLY HILLS, CA	90212
MALOCHE, LESLIE	CONDUCTOR	1838 ALDER DR	LOS ANGELES, CA	90065
MALONE, BRENDAN	BASKETBALL COACH	THE PALACE OF AUBURN HILLS		
		2 CHAMPIONSHIP DR	AUBURN HILLS, MI	48326
MALONE, CHUCK	BASEBALL	POST OFFICE BOX 10336	CLEARWATER, FL	34617
MALONE, H ADRIAN	WRITER-PRODUCER	1901 AVE OF THE STARS	LOS ANGELES, CA	90067
MALONE, J C	ACTRESS	2133 LOUELLA AVE	VENICE, CA	90291
MALONE, JO JO	ACTRESS	10850 RIVERSIDE DR #505	NORTH HOLLYWOOD, CA	91602
MALONE, JOEL	WRITER-PRODUCER	4455 ETHEL AVE	NORTH HOLLYWOOD, CA	91604
MALONE, JOSEPH D	TREASURER	STATE HOUSE BUILDING	BOSTON, MA	02133
MALONE, KARL	BASKETBALL	5 TRIAD CENTER #500	SALT LAKE CITY, UT	84180
MALONE, KEVIN	BASEBALL SCOUT	TWINS, 501 CHICAGO AVE S	MINNEAPOLIS, MN	55415
MALONE, KITTY	ACTRESS	2586 N BEACHWOOD DR	LOS ANGELES, CA	90068
MALONE, MATTHEW	BASEBALL UMPIRE	235 MAIN ST #103	TRUSSVILLE, AL	35173
MALONE, MOSES	BASKETBALL	1 CNN CENTER #405, SOUTH TOWER	ATLANTA, GA	30303
MALONE, NANCY	ACTRESS-DIRECTOR	LILAC PRODS, 4507 AUCKLAND AVE	NORTH HOLLYWOOD, CA	91602
MALONE, TODD	BASEBALL	POST OFFICE BOX 2148	WOODBRIDGE, VA	22193
MALONEY, CHRIS	BASEBALL MANAGER	POST OFFICE BOX 1535	JOHNSON CITY, TN	37605
MALONEY, COLEEN	ACTRESS	280 S BEVERLY DR #400	BEVERLY HILLS, CA	90212
MALONEY, J CON	BASEBALL EXECUTIVE	POST OFFICE BOX 4209	JACKSON, MS	39296
MALONEY, RYAN	BASEBALL	RED SOX, CHAIN O'LAKES PARK	WINTER HAVEN, FL	33880
MALONEY, TOM	BASEBALL EXECUTIVE	2850 W 20TH AVE	DENVER, CO	80211
MALOOF, JACK	BASEBALL COACH	POST OFFICE BOX 1420	WICHITA, KS	67201
MALOOLY, MAGGIE	ACTRESS	POST OFFICE BOX 583	BURBANK, CA	91502
MALTIN, LEONARD	FILM CRITIC-CORRES	3553 WILLOWCREST	STUDIO CITY, CA	91604
MALVIN, ARTHUR	TV PRODUCER	622 N LINDEN DR	BEVERLY HILLS, CA	90210
MALZONE, FRANK	BASEBALL-SCOUT	FENWAY PARK, 4 YAWKEY WY	BOSTON, MA	02215
MALZONE, JOHN	BASEBALL	POST OFFICE BOX 10213	LYNCHBURG, VA	24506
MAMAKOS, PETER	ACTOR-WRITER	POST OFFICE BOX 43	ENCINO, CA	91316
MAMAS & THE PAPAS, THE	ROCK & ROLL GROUP	35 W 57TH ST #500	NEW YORK, NY	10019
MAMAS BOYS	ROCK & ROLL GROUP	ICM, 40 W 57TH ST	NEW YORK, NY	10019
MAMET, DAVID	SCREENWRITER	555 W 57TH ST #1230	NEW YORK, NY	10019
MAMEY, NORMAN	COMPOSER-CONDUCTOR	716 BALBOA AVE	GLENDALE, CA	91206
MAMMOLA, MARK	BASEBALL	POST OFFICE BOX 3496	DAVENPORT, IA	52808
MANAGHAM, ERIC	BASEBALL	POST OFFICE BOX 6212	TOLEDO, OH	43614
MANAHAN, ANTHONY	BASEBALL	POST OFFICE DRAWER 1218	ZEBULON, NC	27597
MANARD, BIFF	ACTOR-WRITER	433 N CAMDEN DR #400	BEVERLY HILLS, CA	90210
MANASSE, GEORGE	DIRECTOR	200 W 10TH ST	NEW YORK, NY	10014
MANBER, DAVID	SCREENWRITER	315 E 86TH ST	NEW YORK, NY	10028
MANBY, C ROBERT	FILM EXECUTIVE	RKO-NEDERLANDER		
		1440 BROADWAY	NEW YORK, NY	10018
MANCHESTER, MELISSA	SINGER-SONGWRITER	15822 HIGH KNOLL RD	ENCINO, CA	91436
MANCHESTER, WILLIAM	AUTHOR	POST OFFICE BOX 329	MIDDLETON, CT	06457
MANCINI, ANTOINETTA	COMPOSER	1999 SANTA ANA AVE	COSTA MESA, CA	92627
MANCINI, HENRY	PIANIST-COMPOSER	261 BARODA DR	LOS ANGELES, CA	90077
MANCINI, RAY "BOOM BOOM"	BOXER	848 LINCOLN BLVD #G	SANTA MONICA, CA	90403
MANCINI, RIC	ACTOR	1246 53RD ST	BROOKLYN, NY	11219
MANCINI, THOMAS E	COMPOSER	1999 SANTA ANA AVE	COSTA MESA, CA	92627
MANCUSO, JAMES	TV DIRECTOR	KINGSTON CANYON	AUSTIN, NV	89310
MANCUSO, NICK	ACTOR	7160 GRASSWOOD AVE	MALIBU, CA	90265

Name	Occupation	Address	City/State	Zip
MANDAN, ROBERT	ACTOR	10351 SANTA MONICA BLVD #211	LOS ANGELES, CA	90025
MANDARICH, TONY	FOOTBALL	PACKERS, 1265 LOMBARDI AVE	GREEN BAY, WI	54307
MANDEL, ALAN R	SCREENWRITER	13257 VALLEYHEART DR	SHERMAN OAKS, CA	91423
MANDEL, BABALOO	SCREENWRITER	CAA, 9830 WILSHIRE BLVD	BEVERLY HILLS, CA	90212
MANDEL, DENIS	ACTOR	866 WESTMOUNT DR #306	LOS ANGELES, CA	90069
MANDEL, ELIZABETH	DIRECTOR	1268 CLAYTON ST	SAN FRANCISCO, CA	94114
MANDEL, HOWIE	ACTOR-COMEDIAN	208 N CANON DR	BEVERLY HILLS, CA	90210
MANDEL, JOHNNY	COMPOSER-CONDUCTOR	28946 CLIFFSIDE DR	MALIBU, CA	90265
MANDEL, LORING	SCREENWRITER	ROSENSTONE/WENDER, 3 E 48TH ST	NEW YORK, NY	11743
MANDEL, MARC	WRITER	20625 KINGSBORO WY	WOODLAND HILLS, CA	91364
MANDEL, MIKE	SINGER	41 BRITAIN ST #200	TORONTO, ONT M5A 1R7	CANADA
MANDEL, ROBERT	DIRECTOR	12129 TRAVIS ST	LOS ANGELES, CA	90049
MANDEL, SAUL	ARTIST	163 MAYTIME DR	JERICHO, NY	11753
MANDELBAUM, LEONARD	DIRECTOR	165 W END AVE	NEW YORK, NY	10023
MANDELBERG, CYNTHIA	TV WRITER	2580 ROSCOMARE RD	LOS ANGELES, CA	90077
MANDELL, HANS E	DIRECTOR	3900 GREYSTONE AVE	RIVERDALE, NY	10463
MANDELL, JAMES E	COMPOSER	1839 N MARIPOSA AVE	LOS ANGELES, CA	90027
MANDLIN, HARVEY	DIRECTOR	250 W 99TH ST	NEW YORK, NY	10025
MANDRELL, BARBARA	SINGER-MUSICIAN	128 RIVER RD	HENDERSONVILLE, TN	37075
MANDRELL, ERLINE	ACTRESS-DRUMMER	128 RIVER RD	HENDERSONVILLE, TN	37075
MANDRELL, LOUISE	SINGER-MUSICIAN	128 RIVER RD	HENDERSONVILLE, TN	37075
MANDUKE, JOSEPH	DIRECTOR	236 S CLARK DR	BEVERLY HILLS, CA	90211
MANDYLOR, COSTAS	ACTOR	151 S EL CAMINO DR	BEVERLY HILLS, CA	90212
MANES, FRITZ	FILM PRODUCER	MALPASO, 4000 WARNER BLVD	BURBANK, CA	91522
MANETTI, LARRY	ACTOR	4615 WINNETKA AVE	WOODLAND HILLS, CA	91364
MANFRED, JIM	BASEBALL	POST OFFICE BOX 7845	COLUMBIA, SC	29202
MANFREDINI, HARRY	COMPOSER	LIVE MUSIC PUBLISHING		
		793 BINGHAM RD	RIDGEWOOD, NJ	07450
MANGANO, MICHAEL	DIRECTOR	400 E 54TH ST	NEW YORK, NY	10022
MANGIONE, CHUCK	FLUEGELHORNIST	DI MARIA, GATES MUSIC		
		1845 CLINTON AVE N	ROCHESTER, NY	14621
MANGRAVITE, TOM	DIRECTOR	DGA, 110 W 57TH ST	NEW YORK, NY	10019
MANGRUM, DAWN	ACTRESS	3627 VALLEY MEADOW RD	SHERMAN OAKS, CA	91403
MANGUM, JOHN	FOOTBALL	BEARS, 250 N WASHINGTON RD	LAKE FOREST, IL	60045
MANGURIAN, PETE	FOOTBALL COACH	BRONCOS, 13655 BRONCOS PKWY	ENGLEWOOD, CO	80112
MANHATTAN TRANSFER, THE	VOCAL GROUP	3575 CAHUENGA BLVD #450	LOS ANGELES, CA	90068
MANHATTANS, THE	VOCAL GROUP	WORLDWIDE ENTERTAINMENT COMPLEX		
		641 LEXINGTON AVE	NEW YORK, NY	10022
MANHEIM, CHRISTOPHER W	WRITER	2134 BEACHWOOD TERR	LOS ANGELES, CA	90068
MANHEIM, MICHAEL	WRITER-PRODUCER	8100 GOULD AVE	LOS ANGELES, CA	90046
MANHEIM, RICHARD	ACTOR	2134 BEACHWOOD TERR	LOS ANGELES, CA	90068
MANICCHIA, BRYAN	BASEBALL	POST OFFICE BOX 1721	SPARTANBURG, SC	29304
MANICHELLO, RICHARD	DIRECTOR	142 E 16TH ST	NEW YORK, NY	10003
MANILOW, BARRY	SINGER-COMPOSER	POST OFFICE BOX 933017	LOS ANGELES, CA	90093
MANILOW, EDNA	ACTRESS-SINGER	145 E 27TH ST	NEW YORK, NY	10023
MANINGS, ALAN	TV PRODUCER	CBS-TV, 7800 BEVERLY BLVD	LOS ANGELES, CA	90036
MANINGS, ALLAN S	WRITER	30918 BROAD BEACH RD	MALIBU, CA	90265
MANKIEWICZ, DON	TV WRITER	3944 EL LADO DR	LA CRESCENTA, CA	91214
MANKIEWICZ, JOSEPH L	WRITER-PRODUCER	RFD #2, BOX 82	BEDFORD, NY	10506
MANKIEWICZ, THOMAS F	WRITER-PRODUCER	1609 MAGNETIC TERR	LOS ANGELES, CA	90069
MANKOFSKY, ISIDORE	CINEMATOGRAPHER	1734 N ORANGE GROVE AVE	LOS ANGELES, CA	90046
MANLEY, CYNTHIA	SINGER	9000 SUNSET BLVD #611	LOS ANGELES, CA	90069
MANLEY, STEPHEN	ACTOR	9000 SUNSET BLVD #801	LOS ANGELES, CA	90069
MANN, ABBY	WRITER-PRODUCER	1240 LA COLLINA RD	BEVERLY HILLS, CA	90210
MANN, ALLAN	DIRECTOR	DGA, 7920 SUNSET BLVD, 6TH FL	LOS ANGELES, CA	90046
MANN, ANDREA	ACTRESS	9165 SUNSET BLVD #202	LOS ANGELES, CA	90069
MANN, BARRY	SINGER-SONGWRITER	1010 LAUREL WY	BEVERLY HILLS, CA	90210
MANN, BERNARD	BASKETBALL EXECUTIVE	N J NETS, MEADOWLANDS ARENA	EAST RUTHERFORD, NJ	07073
MANN, CHARLES	FOOTBALL	POST OFFICE BOX 17247 (DULLES)	WASHINGTON, DC	20041
MANN, DANIEL GERARD	DIRECTOR	6328 FRONDOSA DR	MALIBU, CA	90265
MANN, DANNY	WRITER-PRODUCER	DGA, 7920 SUNSET BLVD, 6TH FL	LOS ANGELES, CA	90046
MANN, DELBERT	DIRECTOR-PRODUCER	6613 S ARLINGTON AVE	LOS ANGELES, CA	90043
MANN, DOLORES	ACTRESS	10000 RIVERSIDE DR #6	TOLUCA LAKE, CA	91602
MANN, EARL F	DIRECTOR	4105 SAUGUS AVE	SHERMAN OAKS, CA	91403
MANN, EDWARD	DIRECTOR	DGA, 7920 SUNSET BLVD, 6TH FL	LOS ANGELES, CA	90046
MANN, HUMMIE	COMPOSER-CONDUCTOR	3341 FAY AVE	CULVER CITY, CA	90230
MANN, JODIE	ACTRESS	5455 WILSHIRE BLVD #1406	LOS ANGELES, CA	90036
MANN, JOHNNY	COMPOSER-CONDUCTOR	19764 CORBIN DR	CHATSWORTH, CA	91311
MANN, KELLY	BASEBALL	POST OFFICE BOX 6667	RICHMOND, VA	23230
MANN, MICHAEL	WRITER-PRODUCER	13746 SUNSET BLVD	PACIFIC PALISADES, CA	90272
MANN, RALPH S	TALENT AGENT	ICM, 40 W 57TH ST	NEW YORK, NY	10019
MANN, RICHARD	FOOTBALL COACH	BROWNS, 80 1ST ST	BEREA, OH	44017
MANN, SHARON	FILM DIRECTOR	644 1/2 WOODLAWN AVE	VENICE, CA	90291
MANN, STANLEY	FILM WRITER-PRODUCER	1431 N STANLEY AVE	LOS ANGELES, CA	90046
MANN, TED	DIRECTOR-PRODUCER	9255 DOHENY RD #2906	LOS ANGELES, CA	90069
MANN, THOMAS LEW	ACTOR	1667 BIANCA ST	LA VERNE, CA	91750
MANN'S, MANFRED, EARTH BAND	ROCK & ROLL GROUP	LLOYD SEGAL, 1116 N CORY AVE	LOS ANGELES, CA	90069
MANNA, CONSTANCE	ARTIST	32 STEPHENS DR	TARRYTOWN, NY	10591
MANNERS, DAVID	ACTOR	3011 FOOTHILL RD	SANTA BARBARA, CA	93105
MANNERS, KIM I	DIRECTOR	9000 SUNSET BLVD #1200	LOS ANGELES, CA	90069
MANNERS, MICKEY	COMEDIAN	POST OFFICE BOX 69590	LOS ANGELES, CA	90069
MANNERS, MISSY	ACTRESS	SEE - MISSY		
MANNERS, SAM B	DIRECTOR	4201 VANALDEN AVE	TARZANA, CA	91356
MANNERS, SCOTT	ACTOR	1623 BRUCE CT	LOS ANGELES, CA	90026
MANNES, ELENA S	WRITER-PRODUCER	DGA, 110 W 57TH ST	NEW YORK, NY	10019

MANNES, MICHAEL LAWRENCE	DIRECTOR	10 E 13TH ST #PH-D	NEW YORK, NY	10003
MANNHEIM STEAMROLLER	NEW AGE GROUP	10100 SANTA MONICA BLVD #1600	LOS ANGELES, CA	90067
MANNING, DANNY	BASKETBALL	CLIPPERS, 3939 S FIGUEROA ST	LOS ANGELES, CA	90037
MANNING, ED	BASKETBALL	600 E MARKET ST #102	SAN ANTONIO, TX	78205
MANNING, HENRY	BASEBALL	POST OFFICE BOX 4218	SOUTH BEND, IN	46634
MANNING, HUGH	ACTOR	PLUNKETT, 4 OVINGTON GARDENS	LONDON SW3 1LS	ENGLAND
MANNING, IRENE	ACTRESS	3165 LA MESA DR	SAN CARLOS, CA	94070
MANNING, JACK	ACTOR	26815 BASSWOOD AVE	PALOS VERDES, CA	90274
MANNING, MONROE	WRITER	9161 HILLSBORO DR	LOS ANGELES, CA	90034
MANNING, RICK	BASEBALL-ANNOUNCER	INDIANS, CLEVELAND STADIUM	CLEVELAND, OH	44114
MANNING, RUTH	ACTRESS	1250 N LAUREL AVE #A	WEST HOLLYWOOD, CA	90046
MANNIX, BOBBIE	COSTUME DESIGNER	1111 TAMARIND AVE	HOLLYWOOD, CA	90038
MANNO, BRUCE	BASEBALL EXECUTIVE	BREWERS, 201 S 46TH ST	MILWAUKEE, WI	53214
MANNO, CHARLES	DIRECTOR-PRODUCER	342 E 67TH ST	NEW YORK, NY	10021
MANNWEILER, DAVID	FILM CRITIC	POST OFFICE BOX 145	INDIANAPOLIS, IN	46206
MANOFF, DINAH	ACTRESS	POST OFFICE BOX 5617	BEVERLY HILLS, CA	90213
MANOUCHEHRY, FARHAD	WRITER-PRODUCER	1330 N CRESCENT HGTS BLVD #14	LOS ANGELES, CA	90046
MANRIQUE, FRED	BASEBALL	CARRERA 6 #21 SANTE FE	CIUDAD, BOLIVAR	VENEZUELA
MANRIQUE, ROBERT	COMPOSER	130 CATAMARAN #4	MARINA DEL REY, CA	90292
MANSBACH, ROBERT H	WRITER-PRODUCER	DGA, 110 W 57TH ST	NEW YORK, NY	10019
MANSBRIDGE, JOHN	ART DIRECTOR	POST OFFICE BOX 1166	PACIFIC PALISADES, CA	90272
MANSFIELD, MIKE	TV DIRECTOR	5-7 CARNABY ST, 2ND FLOOR	LONDON W1V 1AG	ENGLAND
MANSFIELD, PETER	DIRECTOR	DGA, 110 W 57TH ST	NEW YORK, NY	10019
MANSKER, ERIC	ACTOR	10604 LOUISE AVE	GRANADA HILLS, CA	91344
MANSOLINO, DOUG	BASEBALL-COACH	333 W 35TH ST	CHICAGO, IL	60616
MANSON, DAVE	HOCKEY	BLACKHAWKS, 1800 W MADISON ST	CHICAGO, IL	60612
MANSON, EDDY	COMPOSER-CONDUCTOR	7245 HILLSIDE AVE #216	LOS ANGELES, CA	90046
MANSON, MAURICE	ACTOR	8811 CANOGA AVE #361	CANOGA PARK, CA	91304
MANSPERGER, DICK	FOOTBALL EXECUTIVE	COWBOYS, 1 COWBOYS PARKWAY	IRVING, TX	75063
MANSUR, JEFF	BASEBALL	POST OFFICE BOX 661	KENOSHA, WI	53141
MANTEE, PAUL	ACTOR	3709 LAS FLORES CANYON RD #4	MALIBU, CA	90265
MANTEGNA, JOE	ACTOR	11271 VALLEY SPRING LN	STUDIO CITY, CA	91602
MANTEL, RICHARD	ARTIST	99 LEXINGTON AVE	NEW YORK, NY	10016
MANTELL, JAMES	ACTOR	2054 PARAMOUNT DR	HOLLYWOOD, CA	90068
MANTELL, JOE	ACTOR	4919 ENCINO AVE	ENCINO, CA	91316
MANTHA, MOE	HOCKEY	JETS, 15-1430 MAROONS RD	WINNIPEG, MAN R3G 0L5	CANADA
MANTLE, MICKEY	BASEBALL	42 CENTRAL PARK S	NEW YORK, NY	10019
MANTLEY, JOHN	SCREENWRITER	4121 LONGRIDGE AVE	SHERMAN OAKS, CA	91423
MANTO, JEFF	BASEBALL	802 3RD AVE	BRISTOL, PA	19007
MANTON, JOCK	TV DIRECTOR	42 W 67TH ST	NEW YORK, NY	10023
MANTON, THOMAS	U S CONGRESSMAN	46-12 QUEENS BLVD	SUNNYSIDE, NY	11104
MANTOOTH, RANDOLPH	ACTOR	5750 WILSHIRE BLVD #512	LOS ANGELES, CA	90036
MANUEL, BARRY	BASEBALL	POST OFFICE BOX 75089	OKLAHOMA CITY, OK	73147
MANUEL, CHARLIE	BASEBALL-MANAGER	4930 BOWER RD, SW	ROANOKE, VA	24018
MANUEL, JERRY	BASEBALL-COACH	EXPOS, 4545 DE COUBERTIN AVE	MONTREAL, QUE H1V 3P2	CANADA
MANUEL, SAMUEL	COLUMNIST	POST OFFICE BOX 500	WASHINGTON, DC	20044
MANULI, JOANNE A	TV PRODUCER	345 E 80TH ST #29-F	NEW YORK, NY	10021
MANULIS, MARTIN	TV PRODUCER	1520 S BEVERLY GLEN BLVD	LOS ANGELES, CA	90024
MANUS, WILLARD	TV WRITER	248 S LASKY DR	BEVERLY HILLS, CA	90212
MANUSKY, GREG	FOOTBALL	VIKINGS, 9520 VIKING DR	EDEN PRAIRIE, MN	55344
MANVELL, ROGER	AUTHOR	BOSTON UNIVERSITY		
		COMMUNICATIONS DEPARTMENT		
		640 COMMONWEALTH AVE	BOSTON, MA	02215
MANWARING, KIRT	BASEBALL	S F GIANTS, CANDLESTICK PARK	SAN FRANICSCO, CA	94124
MANZA, RALPH	ACTOR	550 HYGEIA AVE	LEUCADIA, CA	92024
MANZANERA, PHIL	SINGER	E G RECORDS, 242 E 62ND ST	NEW YORK, NY	10021
MANZANILLO, JOSIAS	BASEBALL	POST OFFICE BOX 2365	PAWTUCKET, RI	02861
MANZANILLO, RAVELO	BASEBALL	CHIEFS, MAC ARTHUR STADIUM	SYRACUSE, NY	13208
MANZAREK, RAY	KEYBOARDIST	232 S RODEO DR	BEVERLY HILLS, CA	90212
MANZATT, RUSSELL V	SCREENWRITER	19904 SUMMIT DR	TOPANGA, CA	90290
MAPLES, MARLA	ACTRESS-MODEL	420 MADISON AVE #1400	NEW YORK, NY	10017
MAPSON, DOUG	BASEBALL SCOUT	1060 W ADDISON ST	CHICAGO, IL	60613
MAR, JEFFREY K	CONDUCTOR	12304 MARSHALL ST	CULVER CITY, CA	90230
MAR & THE HOWLERS	ROCK & ROLL GROUP	905 28 1/2 ST	AUSTIN, TX	78705
MARA, TIMOTHY J	FOOTBALL EXECUTIVE	N Y GIANTS, GIANTS STADIUM	EAST RUTHERFORD, NJ	07073
MARA, WELLINGTON T	FOOTBALL EXECUTIVE	N Y GIANTS, GIANTS STADIUM	EAST RUTHERFORD, NJ	07073
MARA HUGGINS, ADELE	ACTRESS	1928 MANDEVILLE CANYON RD	LOS ANGELES, CA	90049
MARAK, PAUL	BASEBALL	POST OFFICE BOX 6667	RICHMOND, VA	23230
MARANNE, ANDRE	ACTOR	SIMONS, 9-15 NEAL ST	LONDON WC2H 9PU	ENGLAND
MARASCO, VICKI	ACTRESS	8336 FAUST AVE	CANOGA PARK, CA	90211
MARBLE, ALICE	TENNIS	77300 INDIANA	PALM DESERT, CA	92260
MARCEAU, MARCEL	PANTOMINIST	15 AVE MONTAIGNE	F-75008 PARIS	FRANCE
MARCEL, TERRY	WRITER-PRODUCER	LONDON MGT, 235-241 REGENT ST	LONDON W1R 4PH	ENGLAND
MARCELINO, MARIO	ACTOR-WRITER	1418 N HIGHLAND AVE #102	LOS ANGELES, CA	90028
MARCELLINO, FRED	ARTIST	432 PARK AVE S	NEW YORK, NY	10016
MARCELLINO, MUZZY	COMPOSER	14633 ROUND VALLEY DR	SHERMAN OAKS, CA	91403
MARCH, ALEX	DIRECTOR-PRODUCER	DGA, 7920 SUNSET BLVD, 6TH FL	LOS ANGELES, CA	90046
MARCH, LORI	ACTRESS	OSCARD, 24 W 40TH ST, 17TH FL	NEW YORK, NY	10011
MARCHAN, JOSE	BASEBALL	POST OFFICE BOX 64939	FAYETTEVILLE, NC	28306
MARCHAND, CORINE	ACTRESS	ARTMEDIA, 10 AVE GEORGE V	PARIS 75008	FRANCE
MARCHAND, GUY	ACTOR	11 RUE EUGENE LABICHE	75016 PARIS	FRANCE
MARCHAND, NANCY	ACTRESS	205 W 89TH ST	NEW YORK, NY	10024
MARCHAND-DOMAINE, GUY	ACTOR	DE CLAIRE CT, LA TRUCHE	GROSROUVRE 78125	FRANCE
MARCHESE, JOE	BASEBALL COACH	RED SOX, CHAIN O'LAKES PARK	WINTER HAVEN, FL	33880
MARCHESE, JOSEPH V	DIRECTOR	45-15 170TH ST	FLUSHING, NY	11358

MARCHESE, SUSAN M	COMPOSER	28242 REY DE COPAS LN	MALIBU, CA	90265
MARCHETTA, CAMILLE	TV WRITER	3600 STONE CANYON AVE	SHERMAN OAKS, CA	91403
MARCHIANO, SAL	SPORTSCASTER	ESPN PLAZA, 935 MIDDLEST	BRISTOL, CT	06010
MARCHIBRODA, TED	FOOTBALL-COACH	BILLS, 1 BILLS DR	ORCHARD PARK, NJ	14127
MARCHMENT, BRYAN	HOCKEY	JETS, 15-1430 MAROONS RD	WINNIPEG, MAN R3G 0L5	CANADA
MARCHOK, CHRIS	BASEBALL	POST OFFICE BOX 15757	HARRISBURG, PA	17105
MARCIANO, JOE	FOOTBALL COACH	SAINTS, 1500 POYDRAS ST	NEW ORLEANS, LA	90112
MARCIL, ALLAN J	TV PRODUCER	ICM, 8899 BEVERLY BLVD	LOS ANGELES, CA	90048
MARCIONA, GENE	TV WRITER-PRODUCER	1 MEDIA CROSSWAYS	WOODBURY, NY	11797
MARCIONE, GENE	TV WRITER-DIRECTOR	7993 SANGAMON AVE	SUN VALLEY, CA	91352
MARCIONE, JAMES	DIRECTOR	19805 NEEDLES ST	CHATSWORTH, CA	91311
MARCIULIONIS, SARUNAS	BASKETBALL	GOLDEN STATE WARRIORS		
		OAKLAND COLISEUM ARENA		
		NIMITZ FWY & HEGENBERGER RD	OAKLAND, CA	94621
MARCOS, IMELDA	PERSONALITY	2439 MAKIKI DR	HONOLULU, HI	96822
MARCOTT, MIGUEL	ACTOR	1717 N HIGHLAND AVE #701	LOS ANGELES, CA	90028
MARCOVICCI, ANDREA	ACTRESS-SINGER	8273 W NORTON AVE	LOS ANGELES, CA	90046
MARCUS, ANN	TV WRITER	9000 SUNSET BLVD #1200	LOS ANGELES, CA	90069
MARCUS, CHESTER L, JR	COMPOSER	TRYON PARK RECORDS		
		201 IRVINGTON RD	TEANECK, NJ	07666
MARCUS, ELLIS	WRITER-PRODUCER	15660 WOODFIELD PL	SHERMAN OAKS, CA	91403
MARCUS, JERRY	CARTOONIST	KING FEATURES, 216 E 45TH ST	NEW YORK, NY	10017
MARCUS, KEN	PHOTOGRAPHER	6916 MELROSE AVE	LOS ANGELES, CA	90038
MARCUS, LAWRENCE B	TV WRITER	ICM, 8899 BEVERLY BLVD	LOS ANGELES, CA	90048
MARCUS, LYDIA	COMPOSER	2019 STANLEY HILLS DR	LOS ANGELES, CA	90046
MARCUS, MIKE	TALENT AGENT	CAA, 9830 WILSHIRE BLVD	BEVERLY HILLS, CA	90212
MARCUS, RICHARD	ACTOR	10000 SANTA MONICA BLVD #305	LOS ANGELES, CA	90067
MARDEN, MICHAEL	TV EXECUTIVE	CBS-TV, 7800 BEVERLY BLVD	LOS ANGELES, CA	90036
MARDER, JEFF	COMEDIAN	EAI, 2211 INDUSTRIAL BLVD	SARASOTA, FL	33580
MARDONES, BENNY	SINGER	PANACEA, 132 NASSAU ST	NEW YORK, NY	10038
MAREK'S, LOU SQUEEZE PLAY	MUSICAL GROUP	3928 SHRINE PARK	LEAVENWORTH, KS	66048
MARESCA, JAMES P	COMPOSER	167 BLEECKER ST	NEW YORK, NY	10012
MAREVIL, PHILLIPPE	ACTOR	28 RUE DES SABLONS	PARIS 75116	FRANCE
MARFIELD, DWIGHT H	ACTOR	45 W 74TH ST	NEW YORK, NY	10023
MARGARET, HRH THE PRINCESS	PRINCESS	KESINGTON PALACE	LONDON N5	ENGLAND
MARGENAU, ERIC	BASEBALL EXECUTIVE	POST OFFICE BOX 9194	HAMPTON, VA	23670
MARGHEIM, GREG	BASEBALL	POST OFFICE BOX 2001	CEDAR RAPIDS, IA	52406
MARGINAL MAN	ROCK & ROLL GROUP	POST OFFICE BOX 2428	EL SEGUNDO, CA	90245
MARGO, LARRY	ACTOR	14526 1/2 DICKENS ST	SHERMAN OAKS, CA	91403
MARGO, PHILIP F	FILM-TV WRITER	140 S ALMONT DR	BEVERLY HILLS, CA	90211
MARGOLIN, ARNOLD	WRI-DIR-PROD	727 CAVANAGH RD	GLENDALE, CA	91207
MARGOLIN, JANET	ACTRESS	7667 SEATTLE PL	LOS ANGELES, CA	90046
MARGOLIN, STUART	ACTOR-DIRECTOR	9401 WILSHIRE BLVD #700	BEVERLY HILLS, CA	90212
MARGOLIS, HERB	PRODUCER	MCA/UNIVERSAL STUDIOS, INC		
		100 UNIVERSAL CITY PLAZA #473	UNIVERSAL CITY, CA	91608
MARGOLIS, HERBERT F	STORY EDITOR	5409 KATHERINE AVE	VAN NUYS, CA	91401
MARGOLIS, JACK S	WRITER	POST OFFICE BOX 69447	LOS ANGELES, CA	90069
MARGOLIS, JEFF	TV DIRECTOR	1339 SCHUYLER RD	BEVERLY HILLS, CA	90210
MARGOLYES, MIRIAM	ACTRESS	43-A PRINCESS RD, REGENTS PK	LONDON NW1 8JS	ENGLAND
MARGULIES, FRED	TV DIRECTOR-PRODUCER	315 W END AVE #2-C	NEW YORK, NY	10023
MARGULIES, JIMMY	CARTOONIST	THE RECORD, 150 RIVER ST	HACKENSACK, NJ	07601
MARGULIES, LEE	NEWS WRITER	L A TIMES, TIMES MIRROR SQUARE	LOS ANGELES, CA	90053
MARGULIES, MICHAEL	CINEMATOGRAPHER	POST OFFICE BOX 2230	HOLLYWOOD, CA	90078
MARGULIES, STAN	TV PRODUCER	16965 STRAWBERRY DR	ENCINO, CA	91316
MARHENAU, ERIC	BASEBALL EXECUTIVE	POST OFFICE BOX 7845	COLUMBIA, SC	29202
MARIANO, BOB	BASEBALL COACH	5301 NW 12TH AVE	FORT LAUDERDALE, FL	33309
MARIANO, JOHN	ACTOR	1539 SAWTELLE BLVD #10	LOS ANGELES, CA	90025
MARICHAL, JUAN	BASEBALL	3178 NW 19TH ST	MIAMI, FL	33125
MARIE, ANNE	SINGER	SEE - ANNE MARIE		
MARIE, DENISE	SINGER	SEE - DENISE MARIE		
MARIE, ROSE	ACTRESS	6916 CHISOLM AVE	VAN NUYS, CA	91406
MARIE, TEENA	SINGER	FAA, 1700 BROADWAY, 5TH FLOOR	NEW YORK, NY	10019
MARIELL, JEANE-PIERRE	ACTOR	FRANCE DEGAND AGENCE		
		94 RUE LAURISTON	PARIS 95116	FRANCE
MARIENTHAL, ERIC	SAXOPHONIST	RON MOSS, 2635 GRIFFITH PARK BL	LOS ANGELES, CA	90039
MARIK, JERRY	BASEBALL SCOUT	POST OFFICE BOX 4100	SEATTLE, WA	98104
MARILLION	ROCK & ROLL GROUP	THE STATION AGENCY		
		132 LIVERPOOL RD	LONDON N1 1LA	ENGLAND
MARILYN	SINGER	33-34 CLEVELAND ST	LONDON W1	ENGLAND
MARIN, ANDREW PETER	SCREENWRITER	808 TARCUTO WY	LOS ANGELES, CA	90077
MARIN, JOSE	BASEBALL	POST OFFICE BOX 10213	LYNCHBURG, VA	24506
MARIN, RICHARD	TV CRITIC	TIMES, 3600 NEW YORK AVE, NW	WASHINGTON, DC	20002
MARIN, RICHARD "CHEECH"	ACTOR-COMEDIAN	32020 PACIFIC COAST HIGHWAY	MALIBU, CA	92065
MARIN, RIKKI	ACTRESS	32020 PACIFIC COAST HIGHWAY	MALIBU, CA	90265
MARINARO, ED	ACTOR-FOOTBALL	1466 N DOHENY DR	LOS ANGELES, CA	90069
MARINELLI, JOE	ACTOR	2029 CENTURY PARK E #3250	LOS ANGELES, CA	90067
MARINI, MARC	BASEBALL	POST OFFICE BOX 1886	COLUMBUS, GA	31902
MARINO, AMERIGO	COMPOSER	POST OFFICE BOX 2125	BIRMINGHAM, AL	35201
MARINO, DAN	FOOTBALL	DOLPHINS, 2269 NW 199TH ST	MIAMI, FL	33056
MARINO, FRANK	SINGER	POST OFFICE BOX 836	NYACK, NY	10960
MARINOVICH, TODD	FOOTBALL	RAIDERS, 332 CENTER ST	EL SEGUNDO, CA	90245
MARINUS, DEREK	ACTOR-DIRECTOR	16 GRANTHAM RD	LONDON W4 2RS	ENGLAND
MARION, FRED	FOOTBALL	PATRIOTS, FOXBORO STADIUM, RT #1	FOXBORO, MA	02035
MARION, RICHARD	ACTOR	149 N GRAMERCY PL	LOS ANGELES, CA	90004
MARIS, ADA	ACTRESS	639 N LARCHMONT BLVD #207	LOS ANGELES, CA	90004

Name	Occupation	Address	City/State	Zip
MARIUCCI, JOHN	TV DIRECTOR	DOYLE DANE BERNBACH		
		437 MADISON AVE	NEW YORK, NY	10022
MARK, DANIEL J	COMPOSER	POST OFFICE BOX 1206	STUDIO CITY, CA	91604
MARK, PETER A	CONDUCTOR	OPERA, 261 W BUTE ST	NORFOLK, VA	23510
MARKBREIT, JERRY	FOOTBALL REFEREE	NFL, 410 PARK AVE	NEW YORK, NY	10022
MARKELL, DAVID	ACTOR	225 N CORDOVA ST #A	BURBANK, CA	91505
MARKELL, ROBERT	TV EXECUTIVE	CBS-TV, 6121 SUNSET BLVD	LOS ANGELES, CA	90028
MARKELL, ROBERT	TV PRODUCER	28 SIDNEY PL	BROOKLYN, NY	11201
MARKES, LARRY W, JR	TV WRITER	3860 BERRY CT	STUDIO CITY, CA	91604
MARKEY, EDWARD	U S CONGRESSMAN	JOHN F KENNEDY BLDG #1508	BOSTON, MA	02203
MARKHAM, MONTE	ACTOR	26328 INGLESIDE WY	MALIBU, CA	90265
MARKI, CSILLA	COSTUME DESIGNER	13949 VENTURA BLVD #309	SHERMAN OAKS, CA	91423
MARKIE, BIZ	RAP DUO-RAPWRITERS	SEE - BIZ MARKIE		
MARKIEWICZ, BRANDON	BASEBALL	POST OFFICE BOX 3496	DAVENPORT, IA	52808
MARKLIN, PETER	ACTOR	100 W 9TH ST	NEW YORK, NY	10011
MARKOE, MERRILL	TV WRITER	ICM, 40 W 57TH ST	NEW YORK, NY	10019
MARKOV, MARGARET	ACTRESS	2781 BENEDICT CANYON DR	BEVERLY HILLS, CA	90210
MARKOWITZ, BRAD B	TV WRITER	2016 EUCLID ST #11	SANTA MONICA, CA	90405
MARKOWITZ, GARY L	FILM WRITER-DIRECTOR	110 S WESTGATE AVE	LOS ANGELES, CA	90049
MARKOWITZ, MITCHELL	SCREENWRITER	501 EL MEDIO AVE	PACIFIC PALISADES, CA	90272
MARKOWITZ, RICHARD	COMPOSER-CONDUCTOR	POST OFFICE BOX 24309	LOS ANGELES, CA	90024
MARKOWITZ, ROBERT L	WRITER-PRODUCER	11521 AMANDA DR	STUDIO CITY, CA	91604
MARKS, ARTHUR	WRITER-PRODUCER	20010 WELLS DR	WOODLAND HILLS, CA	91364
MARKS, BEAU E	FILM DIRECTOR	5439 AMIGO AVE	TARZANA, CA	91356
MARKS, BRAD	TALENT AGENCT	1888 CENTURY PARK E #1040	LOS ANGELES, CA	90067
MARKS, DAVE	TV DIRECTOR	1470 S BEVERLY DR	LOS ANGELES, CA	90035
MARKS, GERTRUDE ROSS	WRITER	10538 EASTBORNE AVE #106	LOS ANGELES, CA	90024
MARKS, HOWARD L	TV PRODUCER	655 MADISON AVE	NEW YORK, NY	10021
MARKS, LANCE	BASEBALL	POST OFFICE BOX 4525	MACON, GA	31208
MARKS, LARRY B	TV DIRECTOR	248 N HEWLETT AVE	MERRICK, NY	11566
MARKS, LAURENCE	WRITER	240 S MANSFIELD AVE	LOS ANGELES, CA	90036
MARKS, LOUIS	TV WRITER-PRODUCER	PETERS, FRASER & DUNLOP, LTD		
		5TH FLOOR, THE CHAMBERS		
		CHELSEA HARBOUR, LOT RD	LONDON SW10 OXF	ENGLAND
MARKS, MARIANNE	ACTRESS-MODEL	POST OFFICE BOX 15101	LAS VEGAS, NV	89114
MARKS, RICHARD	FILM EDITOR	648 ASHLAND AVE	SANTA MONICA, CA	90405
MARKS, WALTER	TV WRITER	130 W 57TH ST	NEW YORK, NY	10019
MARKUS, DANIEL S	TALENT AGENT	ALIVE ENTERTAINMENT AGENCY		
		1775 BROADWAY, 7TH FLOOR	NEW YORK, NY	10019
MARKUS, JERRY	TV DIRECTOR-PRODUCER	12969 GREENLEAF ST	STUDIO CITY, CA	91604
MARKUS, JOHN A	TV WRITER-PRODUCER	400 E 70TH ST #2305	NEW YORK, NY	10021
MARKUS, LEAH	TV WRITER	131 S RODEO DR #300	BEVERLY HILLS, CA	90212
MARKUS, MARK J	COMPOSER	12969 GREENLEAF ST	STUDIO CITY, CA	91604
MARKWART, NEVIN	HOCKEY	BRUINS, 150 CAUSEWAY ST	BOSTON, MA	02114
MARKY MARK & FUNKY BUNCH	RAP GROUP	POST OFFICE BOX 207	QUINCY, MA	02269
MARLAND, DOUGLAS	TV WRITER-DIRECTOR	STROUD MGMT, 119 W 57TH ST	NEW YORK, NY	10019
MARLAS, DENNIS C	DIRECTOR	447 SUNSET RD	WINNETKA, IL	60093
MARLENEE, RON	U S CONGRESSMAN	103 N BROADWAY	BILLINGS, MT	59101
MARLENS, NEAL	TV WRITER-PRODUCER	373 MILDAS DR	MALIBU, CA	90265
MARLES, BILL	COMPOSER	14748 MAGNOLIA BLVD #C	SHERMAN OAKS, CA	91403
MARLETTE, DOUG	CARTOONIST	POST OFFICE BOX 32188	CHARLOTTE, NC	28232
MARLIN-JONES, DAVEY	DIRECTOR	DGA, 110 W 57TH ST	NEW YORK, NY	10019
MARLOW, EUGENE	TV DIRECTOR-PRODUCER	175 5TH AVE #700	NEW YORK, NY	10010
MARLOW, JEAN	ACTRESS	32 EXETER RD	LONDON NW2	ENGLAND
MARLOW, JESS	BROADCAST JOURNALIST	KABC-TV, 4151 PROSPECT AVE	LOS ANGELES, CA	90027
MARLOW, LORRI	ACTRESS	8418 BLACKBURN AVE #1	LOS ANGELES, CA	90048
MARLOWE, LINDA	ACTRESS	17 KILLYON RD	LONDON SW8 2XS	ENGLAND
MARLOWE, PAT	ACTRESS	3130 ELLINGTON DR	LOS ANGELES, CA	90068
MARLOWE, SCOTT	ACTOR	11032 MOORPARK ST #12	NORTH HOLLYWOOD, CA	91602
MARMELSTEIN, LINDA	TV WRITER-PRODUCER	DANIEL WILSON PROD, 300 W 55TH ST	NEW YORK, NY	10019
MARMOR, HELEN	TV PRODUCER	POST OFFICE BOX 938		
		MURRAY HILL STATION	NEW YORK, NY	10156
MARMOREK, EILEEN	ACTRESS	21731 SATICOY ST #49	CANOGA PARK, CA	91304
MARMORSTEIN, MALCOLM	WRITER	2350 HOLLYRIDGE DR	LOS ANGELES, CA	90068
MARNER, EUGENE	WRITER-PRODUCER	141 BERGEN ST	BROOKLYN, NY	11217
MAROCCO, FRANK	COMPOSER	7063 WHITAKER AVE	VAN NUYS, CA	91406
MAROIS, DANIEL	HOCKEY	MAPLE LEAFS, 60 CARLTON ST	TORONTO, ONT M5B 1L1	CANADA
MAROIS, MARIO	HOCKEY	BLUES, 5700 OAKLAND AVE	SAINT LOUIS, MO	63110
MAROLAKOS, JOHN	ACTOR	707 SANFORD AVE	NEWARK, NJ	07106
MARONEY, KELLI	ACTRESS	6255 SUNSET BLVD #627	LOS ANGELES, CA	90028
MAROONEY, JAMES J	DIRECTOR	DGA, 110 W 57TH ST	NEW YORK, NY	10019
MAROSS, JOE	ACTOR	336 S DOHENY DR #5	BEVERLY HILLS, CA	90211
MAROTTA, MONICA JUNG	WRITER	23049 LEONORA DR	WOODLAND HILLS, CA	91367
MARQUAND, SERGE	ACTOR	47 RUE VIELLE DU TEMPLE	PARIS 75004	FRANCE
MARQUARDT, CHUCK	BASEBALL TRAINER	POST OFFICE BOX 186	BUTTE, MT	59703
MARQUETTE, JACQUES	DIRECTOR	DGA, 7920 SUNSET BLVD, 6TH FL	LOS ANGELES, CA	90046
MARQUEZ, IHOSVANY	BASEBALL	POST OFFICE BOX 418	SAINT CHARLES, IL	60174
MARQUEZ, RAMON	BASEBALL SCOUT	REDS, 100 RIVERFRONT STADIUM	CINCINNATI, OH	45202
MARR, ALAN	BASEBALL SCOUT	S F GIANTS, CANDLESTICK PARK	SAN FRANICSCO, CA	94124
MARR, OCEANA	ACTRESS	1680 N VINE ST #1003	HOLLYWOOD, CA	90028
MARR, SALLY K	ACTRESS	8485 MELROSE PL #E	LOS ANGELES, CA	90069
MARRERO, FRANK	DIRECTOR-PRODUCER	236 W 52ND ST	NEW YORK, NY	10019
MARRERO, ORESTE	BASEBALL	POST OFFICE DRAWER 4797	EL PASO, TX	79914
MARRIS, WEBB R	WRITER	17841 PORTO MARINA WY	PACIFIC PALISADES, CA	90272
MARS, KENNETH	ACTOR	144 S BEVERLY DR #405	BEVERLY HILLS, CA	90212

MARSAC, MAURICE	ACTOR	3972 SUNSWEPT DR	STUDIO CITY, CA	91604
MARSALIS, BRANFORD	SAXOPHONIST	WILKINS, 3 HASTINGS SQ	CAMBRIDGE, MA	02139
MARSALIS, DELFEAYO	RECORD PRODUCER	BRAWYNN MUSIC COMPANY		
		8318 HICKORY ST	NEW ORLEANS, LA	70118
MARSALIS, ELLIS	PIANIST	POST OFFICE BOX 19004		
		MID CITY STATION	NEW ORLEANS, LA	70118
MARSALIS, WYNTON	TRUMPETER	31 FORT AVE #2	BOSTON, MA	02119
MARSDEN, ROY	ACTOR	DAWSON, 47 COURTFIELD RD #9	LONDON SW7 4DB	ENGLAND
MARSELLS, THE	ROCK & ROLL GROUP	25 HUNTINGTON AVE #420	BOSTON, MA	02116
MARSH, BRAD	HOCKEY	RED WINGS, 600 CIVIC CENTER DR	DETROIT, MI	48226
MARSH, DONALD T	MUSIC ARRANGER	526 FOX HUNT CIR	HIGHLANDS RANCH, CO	80126
MARSH, EARLE F	AUTHOR	SHOWTIME, 1633 BROADWAY	NEW YORK, NY	10019
MARSH, JEAN	ACTRESS	THE PHEASANT, CHINNOR HILL	OXFORDSHIRE OX9 4BN	ENGLAND
MARSH, JOAN	ACTRESS	1329 PLAZA DE SONADORES	MONTECITO, CA	93108
MARSH, KEITH	ACTOR	BRYAN DREW, MEZANNINE FLOOR		
		QUADRANT HOUSE, 80-82 REGENT ST	LONDON W1R 6AU	ENGLAND
MARSH, LINDA	ACTRESS	4041 ALTA MESA DR	STUDIO CITY, CA	91604
MARSH, MARIAN	ACTRESS	POST OFFICE BOX 1	PALM DESERT, CA	92260
MARSH, RANDY	BASEBALL UMPIRE	3271 MADONNA DR	COVINGTON, KY	41017
MARSH, RAY	TV DIRECTOR-PRODUCER	4721 GREENBUSH AVE	SHERMAN OAKS, CA	91423
MARSH, RONALD	TV PRODUCER	BBC-TV, 56 WOOD LN	LONDON W12 7RJ	ENGLAND
MARSH, TERENCE	SCREENWRITER	8955 BEVERLY BLVD	WEST HOLLYWOOD, CA	90048
MARSH, TOM	BASEBALL	POST OFFICE BOX 15050	READING, PA	19612
MARSHAK, DARRYL A	TALENT AGENT	280 S BEVERLY DR #400	BEVERLY HILLS, CA	90212
MARSHALL	ACTOR	11 AVE D'EYLAU	PARIS 75116	FRANCE
MARSHALL, ALAN	TV PRODUCER	11 GREAT MARBOROUGH ST	LONDON W1	ENGLAND
MARSHALL, ALEXANDER	COMEDY WRITER	SANMAR PRODS, 365 W 19TH ST	NEW YORK, NY	10011
MARSHALL, AMELIA	ACTRESS	CBS-TV, "THE GUIDING LIGHT"		
		222 E 44TH ST	NEW YORK, NY	10017
MARSHALL, BRYAN	ACTOR	MARTIN, 6-A DANBURY ST	LONDON N1 8JU	ENGLAND
MARSHALL, BURT	ACTOR	167 ARGONAUT ST	PLAYA DEL REY, CA	90293
MARSHALL, DAVID B	DIRECTOR	146 CENTRAL PARK W #22-E	NEW YORK, NY	10023
MARSHALL, E G	ACTOR	BRYAN LAKE RD & OREGON ROAD		
		RURAL FARM DELIVERY #2	MOUNT KISCO, NY	10549
MARSHALL, FRANK	FILM PRODUCER	AMBLIN ENTERPRISES		
		100 UNIVERSAL CITY PLAZA	UNIVERSAL CITY, CA	91608
MARSHALL, GARRY	WRITER-PRODUCER	10067 RIVERSIDE DR	TOLUCA LAKE, CA	91602
MARSHALL, GEORGE E	FILM DIRECTOR	554 WESTBOURNE DR	LOS ANGELES, CA	90048
MARSHALL, JAMES	ACTOR	1999 AVE OF THE STARS #2850	LOS ANGELES, CA	90067
MARSHALL, JOHN	FOOTBALL COACH	S F 49ERS, 4949 CENTENNIAL BL	SANTA CLARA, CA	95054
MARSHALL, KEN	ACTOR	9301 WILSHIRE BLVD #312	BEVERLY HILLS, CA	90210
MARSHALL, LARRY P	CONDUCTOR	4470 VENTURA CANYON AVE	SHERMAN OAKS, CA	91423
MARSHALL, LEONARD	FOOTBALL	N Y GIANTS, GIANTS STADIUM	EAST RUTHERFORD, NJ	07073
MARSHALL, MELORA	ACTRESS	POST OFFICE BOX 151	TOPANGA, CA	90290
MARSHALL, MERI DEE	ACTRESS	3800 BARHAM BLVD #303	LOS ANGELES, CA	90068
MARSHALL, MIKE	BASEBALL (1ST BASE)	13063 VENTURA BLVD	STUDIO CITY, CA	91604
MARSHALL, MIKE	BASEBALL (PITCHER)	ATHLETIC DEPARTMENT		
		HENDERSON STATE COLLEGE	ARKADELPHIA, AR	71923
MARSHALL, MIRIANNE	ACTRESS	300 E 57TH ST	NEW YORK, NY	10022
MARSHALL, NEAL WILLIAM	TV WRITER-PRODUCER	4115 WOODCLIFF RD	SHERMAN OAKS, CA	91403
MARSHALL, PAUL	BASEBALL EXECUTIVE	POST OFFICE BOX 824	BURLINGTON, IA	52601
MARSHALL, PENNY	ACTRESS-DIRECTOR	1849 SAWTELLE BLVD #500	LOS ANGELES, CA	90025
MARSHALL, PETER	ACTOR-TV HOST	16714 OAK VIEW DR	ENCINO, CA	91436
MARSHALL, PETER	MUSICIAN	3530 GRAND VIEW BLVD	LOS ANGELES, CA	90066
MARSHALL, RANDY	BASEBALL	POST OFFICE BOX 1211	NORFOLK, VA	23502
MARSHALL, ROB DOYLE	ACTOR	1 GLENWOOD RD	SCARSDALE, NY	10583
MARSHALL, ROGER	SCREENWRITER	20 MARCHMONT RD, RICHMOND	SURREY	ENGLAND
MARSHALL, SARAH	ACTRESS	11726 SAN VICENTE BLVD #300	LOS ANGELES, CA	90049
MARSHALL, STEVE	TV WRITER	10100 SANTA MONICA BLVD #348	LOS ANGELES, CA	90067
MARSHALL, THURGOOD	SUPREME COURT JUDGE	1 1ST ST, NE	WASHINGTON, DC	20543
MARSHALL, WILBER	FOOTBALL	POST OFFICE BOX 17247 (DULLES)	WASHINGTON, DC	20041
MARSHALL, WILLIAM	FILM PRODUCER	11351 DRONFIELD AVE	PACOIMA, CA	91331
MARSHALL RAFFIN, TRUDY	ACTRESS	1852 MARCHEETA PL	LOS ANGELES, CA	90069
MARSTON, JOEL	ACTOR	9424 LA TUNA CANYON RD	SUN VALLEY, CA	91352
MARSTON, MERLIN	ACTOR	6721 LEXINGTON AVE #7	LOS ANGELES, CA	90038
MARTEL, ED	BASEBALL	1155 W MOUND ST	COLUMBUS, OH	43223
MARTEL, EDMOND J	COMPOSER-CONDUCTOR	5136 TOPANGA CANYON BLVD	WOODLAND HILLS, CA	91367
MARTEL, GENE	DIRECTOR	108 LAWN TERR	MAMARONECK, NY	10543
MARTEL, LINDA	SINGER	BROWN, 3011 WOODWAY LN	COLUMBIA, SC	29206
MARTEL, RAY	ACTOR	5330 LANKERSHIM BLVD #210	NORTH HOLLYWOOD, CA	91601
MARTEL, RICK	WRESTLER	POST OFFICE BOX 3859	STAMFORD, CT	06905
MARTELL, DARRYL	COSTUME DESIGNER	13949 VENTURA BLVD #309	SHERMAN OAKS, CA	91423
MARTELL, DONNA	ACTRESS	DON SCHWARTZ, 8749 SUNSET BLVD	LOS ANGELES, CA	90069
MARTELL, LINDA	SINGER	POST OFFICE BOX 5702	COLUMBIA, SC	29206
MARTENSON, LESLIE H	TV DIRECTOR	2288 COLDWATER CANYON DR	BEVERLY HILLS, CA	90210
MARTIN, AL	BASEBALL	POST OFFICE BOX 450	BUFFALO, NY	14205
MARTIN, AMANDA	ACTRESS-WRITER	14211 DICKENS ST #14	SHERMAN OAKS, CA	91403
MARTIN, AMERICA	ACTRESS	7080 HOLLYWOOD BLVD #704	HOLLYWOOD, CA	90028
MARTIN, ANNE	BROADCAST JOURNALIST	KABC-TV, 4151 PROSPECT AVE	LOS ANGELES, CA	90027
MARTIN, ANNE-MARIE	ACTRESS	144 S BEVERLY DR #405	BEVERLY HILLS, CA	90212
MARTIN, BARNEY	ACTOR	12838 MILBANK ST	STUDIO CITY, CA	91604
MARTIN, BOB	SINGER	ZACK, 234 POTTERS AVE	WARWICK, RI	02886
MARTIN, CHARLES E	WRITER-PRODUCER	304 S ELM DR	BEVERLY HILLS, CA	90212
MARTIN, CHRIS	BASEBALL	POST OFFICE BOX 15757	HARRISBURG, PA	17105
MARTIN, CHRIS	FOOTBALL	CHIEFS, 1 ARROWHEAD DR	KANSAS CITY, MO	64129

MARTIN, DAVID O'B	U S CONGRESSMAN	E J NOBLE MEDICAL CENTER BLDG	CANTON, NY	13617
MARTIN, DEAN	ACTOR-SINGER	1900 AVE OF THE STARS #1230	LOS ANGELES, CA	90067
MARTIN, DEREK	ACTOR	GARROD MGMT, SAINT MARTINS		
		SANDHILLS MEADOWS, SHEPPERTON	MIDDLESEX	ENGLAND
MARTIN, DEWEY	ACTOR	1430 STONEWOOD CT	SAN PEDRO, CA	90732
MARTIN, DICK	ACT-WRI-DIR-COMED	11030 CHALON RD	LOS ANGELES, CA	90077
MARTIN, DICK	BASEBALL TRAINER	TWINS, 501 CHICAGO AVE S	MINNEAPOLIS, MN	55415
MARTIN, DOLLY READ	ACTRESS-MODEL	11030 CHALON RD	LOS ANGELES, CA	90077
MARTIN, DON	CARTOONIST	MAD MAGAZINE, 485 MADISON AVE	NEW YORK, NY	10022
MARTIN, EDWARD R	CINEMATOGRAPHER	7667 MULHOLLAND DR	LOS ANGELES, CA	90046
MARTIN, ELLIOT	THEATER PRODUCER	152 W 58TH ST	NEW YORK, NY	10019
MARTIN, ERIC	FOOTBALL	SAINTS, 1500 POYDRAS ST	NEW ORLEANS, LA	90112
MARTIN, ERNEST	THEATER PRODUCER	THE MARK TAPOR FORUM		
		135 N GRAND AVE	LOS ANGELES, CA	90012
MARTIN, GREGG	BASEBALL	POST OFFICE BOX 957	DUNEDIN, FL	34697
MARTIN, HELEN	ACTRESS	1440 N FAIRFAX #109	LOS ANGELES, CA	90046
MARTIN, HENRY	CARTOONIST	TRIBUNE, 64 E CONCORD ST	ORLANDO, FL	32801
MARTIN, IAN ROBERT	TV PRODUCER	THAMES TV, 306 EUSTON RD	LONDON NW1	ENGLAND
MARTIN, JACK L	MUSIC ARRANGER	1906 SOUTH ST #301	NASHVILLE, TN	37212
MARTIN, JAMES G	GOVERNOR	STATE CAPITOL BUILDING	RALEIGH, NC	27603
MARTIN, JAMES M	CONDUCTOR	1532 YALE ST	SANTA MONICA, CA	90404
MARTIN, JAMES M	TV DIRECTOR	141 SAINT MARKS PL	MASSAPEQUA, NY	11758
MARTIN, JARED	ACTOR	15060 VENTURA BLVD #350	SHERMAN OAKS, CA	91403
MARTIN, JEFF	BASKETBALL	CLIPPERS, 3939 S FIGUEROA ST	LOS ANGELES, CA	90037
MARTIN, JERRY	BASEBALL-INSTRUCTOR	POST OFFICE BOX 7575	PHILADELPHIA, PA	19101
MARTIN, JESSICA	ACTRESS-COMEDIENNE	SARABAND, 265 LIVERPOOL RD	LONDON N1 1LX	ENGLAND
MARTIN, JIMMY & SUNNY MOUNTAIN	BLUEGRASS GROUP	POST OFFICE BOX 809	GOODLETTSVILLE, TN	37072
MARTIN, JOHN	BASEBALL COACH	POST OFFICE BOX 15050	READING, PA	19612
MARTIN, JOHN J	ACTOR-WRITER	61 FULTON ST	WEEHAWKEN, NJ	07087
MARTIN, JOHN JAMES	DIRECTOR	DGA, 110 W 57TH ST	NEW YORK, NY	10019
MARTIN, JONATHAN	TV PRODUCER	ARKLE, 15 VALENTINE WY		
		CHALFONT SAINT GILES	BUCKS	ENGLAND
MARTIN, JUDY	WRESTLER	SEE - GLAMOUR GIRLS, THE		
MARTIN, KELLIE	ACTRESS	ABC-TV, 2040 AVE OF THE STARS	LOS ANGELES, CA	90067
MARTIN, KELVIN	FOOTBALL	COWBOYS, 1 COWBOYS PARKWAY	IRVING, TX	75063
MARTIN, LAUREN	ACTRESS	8383 WILSHIRE BLVD #650	BEVERLY HILLS, CA	90211
MARTIN, LUCY	ACTRESS	250 W 57TH ST #2317	NEW YORK, NY	10107
MARTIN, MARDIK	SCREENWRITER	2837 LA CASTANA DR	LOS ANGELES, CA	90046
MARTIN, MELISSA	ACTRESS	LOOK TALENT, 166 GEARY ST	SAN FRANCISCO, CA	94108
MARTIN, MICHAEL	SINGER	TMG, 14 MUSIC SQUARE E	NASHVILLE, TN	37203
MARTIN, MILLICENT	SINGER-ACTRESS	POST OFFICE BOX 101	REDDING, CT	06875
MARTIN, NAN	ACTRESS	33604 PACIFIC COAST HIGHWAY	MALIBU, CA	90265
MARTIN, NED	SPORTSCASTER	NESN, 70 BROOKLINE AVE	BOSTON, MA	02215
MARTIN, NORBERTO	BASEBALL	CANADIANS, 4601 ONTARIO ST	VANCOUVER, BC V5V 3H4	CANADA
MARTIN, PAMELA SUE	ACTRESS-PRODCUER	POST OFFICE BOX 25578	LOS ANGELES, CA	90025
MARTIN, PAUL L	CONDUCTOR	24630 PARK ST #5	TORRANCE, CA	90505
MARTIN, PETER	COMPOSER-ORCHESTRATOR	51-A CADOGAN ST	LONDON SW3 2QL	ENGLAND
MARTIN, RICCI	ACTRESS	9911 W PICO BLVD #560	LOS ANGELES, CA	90035
MARTIN, ROBERT E	TV DIRECTOR-PRODUCER	NBC-TV, 30 ROCKEFELLER PLAZA	NEW YORK, NY	10112
MARTIN, ROSA LEE	SINGER-SONGWRITER	POST OFFICE BOX 101	KIRKSVILLE, MO	63501
MARTIN, SAMMY	FOOTBALL	PATRIOTS, FOXBORO STADIUM, RT #1	FOXBORO, MA	02035
MARTIN, SCOTT V	TV DIRECTOR	888 7TH AVE #1603	NEW YORK, NY	10106
MARTIN, STEPHEN G	DIRECTOR-PRODUCER	420 E 55TH ST	NEW YORK, NY	10022
MARTIN, STEVE	ACTOR-COMEDIAN	POST OFFICE BOX 929	BEVERLY HILLS, CA	90213
MARTIN, STEVE	BASEBALL	POST OFFICE BOX 230	HAGERSTOWN, MD	21740
MARTIN, TED	CARTOONIST	UPS, 4900 MAIN ST, 9TH FLOOR	KANSAS CITY, MO	64112
MARTIN, TENILLE MARIE	ACTRESS	1450 BELFAST DR	LOS ANGELES, CA	90069
MARTIN, TIM	SINGER	216 TAYLOR RD	COLLINSVILLE, VA	24078
MARTIN, TODD	ACTOR	10391 ALMAYO AVE	LOS ANGELES, CA	90064
MARTIN, TONY	ACTOR-SINGER	10390 WILSHIRE BLVD #1507	LOS ANGELES, CA	90024
MARTIN, TONY	FOOTBALL	DOLPHINS, 2269 NW 199TH ST	MIAMI, FL	33056
MARTIN, W HUGH	TV DIRECTOR-PRODUCER	54 MAGNOLIA DR	DOBBS FERRY, NY	10522
MARTIN, WAYNE	FOOTBALL	SAINTS, 1500 POYDRAS ST	NEW ORLEANS, LA	90112
MARTIN, WILLIAM B	DIRECTOR	POST OFFICE BOX 3388	HOLLYWOOD, CA	90028
MARTINDALE, RYAN	BASEBALL	POST OFFICE BOX 3452	KINSTON, NC	28502
MARTINDALE, WINK	GAME SHOW HOST	1650 VETERAN AVE #104	LOS ANGELES, CA	90024
MARTINELLI, JOHN A	FILM EDITOR	ACE, 1041 N FORMOSA AVE	WEST HOLLYWOOD, CA	90046
MARTINEZ, A	ACTOR	6835 WILD LIFE RD	MALIBU, CA	90265
MARTINEZ, AL	TV WRITER	MTA, 9320 WILSHIRE BL, 3RD FL	BEVERLY HILLS, CA	90212
MARTINEZ, ALMA	ACTRESS	KOHNER, 9169 SUNSET BLVD	LOS ANGELES, CA	90069
MARTINEZ, BUCK	SPORTSCASTER	SKYDOME, 300 BREMMER BL #3200	TORONTO, ONT M5V 3B3	CANADA
MARTINEZ, CARLOS	BASEBALL	INDIANS, CLEVELAND STADIUM	CLEVELAND, OH	44114
MARTINEZ, CARMELO	BASEBALL	REDS, 100 RIVERFRONT STADIUM	CINCINNATI, OH	45202
MARTINEZ, CHITO	BASEBALL	ORIOLE PARK, 333 W CAMDEN ST	BALTIMORE, MD	21201
MARTINEZ, CONSTANTINO	BASEBALL	2701 KATHLEEN ST	TAMPA, FL	33607
MARTINEZ, DAVE	BASEBALL (REDS)	REDS, 100 RIVERFRONT STADIUM	CINCINNATI, OH	45202
MARTINEZ, DAVID	BASEBALL (EL PASO)	POST OFFICE DRAWER 4797	EL PASO, TX	79914
MARTINEZ, DENNIS	BASEBALL	EXPOS, 4545 DE COUBERTIN AVE	MONTREAL, QUE H1V 3P2	CANADA
MARTINEZ, DOMINGO	BASEBALL	CHIEFS, MAC ARTHUR STADIUM	SYRACUSE, NY	13208
MARTINEZ, EDGAR	BASEBALL	POST OFFICE BOX 4100	SEATTLE, WA	98104
MARTINEZ, ERIC	BASEBALL (ASHEVILLE)	POST OFFICE BOX 651	AUBURN, NY	13021
MARTINEZ, ERIC	BASEBALL (QUAD CITY)	POST OFFICE BOX 3496	DAVENPORT, IA	52808
MARTINEZ, FRANK	BASEBALL	POST OFFICE BOX 3004	SPRINGFIELD, IL	62708
MARTINEZ, HECTOR	ARTIST	1013 LEONARD PL	LOS ANGELES, CA	90022
MARTINEZ, JOE	BASEBALL	POST OFFICE BOX 2437	MODESTO, CA	95351

Name	Occupation	Address	City, State	Zip
MARTINEZ, JOSE	BASEBALL	525 NW PEACOCK BLVD	PORT SAINT LUCIE, FL	34986
MARTINEZ, JOSE	BASEBALL-COACH	1060 W ADDISON ST	CHICAGO, IL	60613
MARTINEZ, JULIAN	BASEBALL	POST OFFICE BOX 5599	LITTLE ROCK, AR	72215
MARTINEZ, LUIS .. (ALBUQUERQUE)	BASEBALL	POST OFFICE BOX 26267	ALBUQUERQUE, NM	87125
MARTINEZ, MANNY	BASEBALL	POST OFFICE BOX 2437	MODESTO, CA	95351
MARTINEZ, MARTY	BASEBALL COACH	POST OFFICE BOX 4100	SEATTLE, WA	98104
MARTINEZ, MATTHEW G, JR	U S CONGRESSMAN	400 N MONTELLO BLVD #100	MONTEBELLO, CA	90640
MARTINEZ, PABLO	BASEBALL	12000 STADIUM RD	ADELANTO, CA	92301
MARTINEZ, PEDRO	BASEBALL (ALBUQ)	POST OFFICE BOX 26267	ALBUQUERQUE, NM	87125
MARTINEZ, PEDRO	BASEBALL (WICHITA)	POST OFFICE BOX 1420	WICHITA, KS	67201
MARTINEZ, RAMON	BASEBALL (DODGERS)	1000 ELYSIAN PARK DR	LOS ANGELES, CA	90012
MARTINEZ, RAMON	BASEBALL (SALEM)	POST OFFICE BOX 842	SALEM, VA	24153
MARTINEZ, TINO	BASEBALL	POST OFFICE BOX 4100	SEATTLE, WA	98104
MARTINEZ, WILLIAM	BASEBALL	POST OFFICE BOX 6748	ROCKFORD, IL	61125
MARTINO, AL	SINGER	927 N REXFORD DR	BEVERLY HILLS, CA	90210
MARTINO, NICK	TV DIRECTOR	ENTERTAINMENT TONIGHT		
		PARAMOUNT TELEVISION		
		5555 MELROSE ST	LOS ANGELES, CA	90038
MARTINO, RUSS N	COMPOSER-CONDUCTOR	208 N TORREY PINES DR	LAS VEGAS, NV	89107
MARTINSON, LESLIE	TV DIRECTOR	2288 COLDWATER CANYON DR	BEVERLY HILLS, CA	90210
MARTON, ANDREW	DIRECTOR-PRODUCER	8856 APPIAN WY	LOS ANGELES, CA	90046
MARTS, LONNIE	FOOTBALL	CHIEFS, 1 ARROWHEAD DR	KANSAS CITY, MO	64129
MARTYN, JOHN	SINGER-SONGWRITER	ISLAND RECORDS COMPANY		
		444 MADISON AVE	NEW YORK, NY	10022
MARTZ, NEAL S	MAKE-UP ARTIST	158-10 SANFORD AVE	FLUSHING, NY	11358
MARTZKE, RUDY	SPORTS WRITER	POST OFFICE BOX 500	WASHINGTON, DC	20044
MARUCCI, MAT	COMPOSER	POST OFFICE BOX 8464	UNIVERSAL CITY, CA	91608
MARVE, EUGENE	FOOTBALL	BUCCANEERS, 1 BUCCANEER PL	TAMPA, FL	33607
MARVEL, ANDY	RECORD EXECUTIVE	ALYSSA RECORDS, 8 PASTORE LN	ROSLYN HEIGHTS, NY	11577
MARVEL, JAMES	SINGER	POST OFFICE BOX 110423	NASHVILLE, TN	37211
MARVELETTES, THE	VOCAL GROUP	BROTHERS, 141 DUNBAR AVE	FORDS, NJ	08863
MARVELLS, THE	VOCAL GROUP	POST OFFICE BOX 22707	NASHVILLE, TN	37203
MARVIN, GEORGE	DIRECTOR	5904 NW 81ST AVE	TAMARAC, FL	33321
MARVIN, IRA	WRITER-PRODUCER	33 W 67TH ST	NEW YORK, NY	10023
MARVIN, MIKE	SCREENWRITER	9300 WILSHIRE BLVD #410	BEVERLY HILLS, CA	90212
MARVIN, WILLIAM	CARTOONIST	POST OFFICE BOX 2416		
		TERMINAL ANNEX STATION	LOS ANGELES, CA	90051
MARX, ARTHUR	PLAYWRIGHT	1244 BEL AIR RD	LOS ANGELES, CA	90077
MARX, CHRISTY L	SCREENWRITER	8955 BEVERLY BLVD	WEST HOLLYWOOD, CA	90048
MARX, JOHN	TALENT AGENT	10100 SANTA MONICA BLVD #1600	LOS ANGELES, CA	90067
MARX, LLOYD	COMPOSER-CONDUCTOR	364 W 18TH ST	NEW YORK, NY	10011
MARX, MARGARET	ACTRESS	247 S BEVERLY DR #102	BEVERLY HILLS, CA	90210
MARX, MIKE	TALENT AGENT	11130 HUSTON ST #6	NORTH HOLLYWOOD, CA	91601
MARX, RICHARD	SINGER-SONGWRITER	15250 VENTURA BLVD #900	SHERMAN OAKS, CA	91403
MARX, RICHARD H	CONDUCTOR	1478 GLEN OAKS BLVD	PASADENA, CA	91105
MARX, SAMUEL	WRITER-PRODUCER	430 S BURNSIDE AVE #3-G	LOS ANGELES, CA	90036
MARYLAND, RUSSELL	FOOTBALL	COWBOYS, 1 COWBOYS PARKWAY	IRVING, TX	75063
MARZANO, JOHN	BASEBALL	FENWAY PARK, 4 YAWKEY WY	BOSTON, MA	02215
MASAK, RON	ACTOR	RAMKAY, 5440 SHIRLEY AVE	TARZANA, CA	91356
MASEKELA, HUGH	TRUMPETER	52 GROVER CT, PARADISE RD	LONDON SW4	ENGLAND
MASER, GERHARD A	DIRECTOR	POST OFFICE BOX 715	ONELO, FL	33558
MASHORE, DAMON	BASEBALL	POST OFFICE BOX 2437	MODESTO, CA	95351
MASHORE, JUSTIN	BASEBALL	POST OFFICE BOX 64939	FAYETTEVILLE, NC	28306
MASINI, ALFRED M	TV PRODUCER	TELEREP, 875 3RD AVE	NEW YORK, NY	10022
MASIUS, JOHN	TV WRITER-PRODUCER	14100 SUNSET BLVD	PACIFIC PALISADES, CA	90272
MASK, MARILYN	ACTRESS	1414 1/2 S SIERRA BONITA AVE	LOS ANGELES, CA	90019
MASLANSKY, PAUL	DIRECTOR-PRODUCER	22852 PACIFIC COAST HWY #B	MALIBU, CA	90265
MASLIN, JANET	FILM CRITIC	N Y TIMES, 229 W 43RD ST	NEW YORK, NY	10036
MASLIN, NIGEL	TV DIRECTOR-PRODUCER	3 THE COURTYARD, SUDBOURNE PK		
		ORFORD, WOODBRIDGE	SUFFOLK IP12 2AJ	ENGLAND
MASON, BARBARA	SINGER	WMOT MGMT, 1228 SPRUCE ST	PHILADELPHIA, PA	19107
MASON, BILL (ENGLISH)	FILM DIRECTOR	DELL QUAY HOUSE, DELL QUAY		
		CHICHESTER	SUSSEX PO20 7EE	ENGLAND
MASON, DARREL	BASEBALL UMPIRE	POST OFFICE BOX 25010	LITTLE ROCK, AZ	72221
MASON, DAVE	SINGER-SONGWRITER	15490 VENTURA BLVD #210	SHERMAN OAKS, CA	91403
MASON, GEOFFREY	TV PRODUCER	NBC-TV, 30 ROCKEFELLER PLAZA	NEW YORK, NY	10112
MASON, JACKIE	COMEDIAN	30 PARK AVE	NEW YORK, NY	10016
MASON, JOE	BASEBALL SCOUT	METS, 126TH ST & ROOSEVELT AVE	FLUSHING, NY	11368
MASON, LOLA	ACTRESS	913 S SPALDING AVE	LOS ANGELES, CA	90036
MASON, MADISON	ACTOR	8485 MELROSE PL #E	LOS ANGELES, CA	90069
MASON, MARGARET	ACTRESS	11846 VENTURA BLVD #100	STUDIO CITY, CA	91604
MASON, MARLYN	ACTRESS-SINGER	POST OFFICE BOX 1684	STUDIO CITY, CA	91604
MASON, MARSHA	ACTRESS	1200 TURQUESA LN	PACIFIC PALISADES, CA	90272
MASON, MARSHALL W	TV DIRECTOR	165 CHRISTOPHER ST	NEW YORK, NY	10014
MASON, MARTY	BASEBALL COACH	POST OFFICE BOX 5599	LITTLE ROCK, AR	72215
MASON, MIKE	BASEBALL COACH	POST OFFICE BOX 464	APPLETON, WI	54912
MASON, MURIEL	ACTOR	45 SUTTON	LOS ANGELES, CA	10036
MASON, PAUL	TV WRITER	13355 MULHOLLAND DR	BEVERLY HILLS, CA	90210
MASON, ROGER	BASEBALL	POST OFFICE BOX 7000	PITTSBURGH, PA	15212
MASON, TERRY "SLAM DUNK"	BASKETBALL	2801 MEADOW LARK DR	SAN DIEGO, CA	92123
MASON, TODD Q	COMPOSER-CONDUCTOR	612 E MAPLE AVE	EL SEGUNDO, CA	90245
MASON, VIVIEN	SINGER	1776 N SYCAMORE AVE #216	HOLLYWOOD, CA	90028
MASON, WILLIAM	DIRECTOR	230 RIVERSIDE DR	NEW YORK, NY	10025
MASON DIXON	C & W GROUP	POST OFFICE BOX 214	FLINT, TX	75762
MASQUERADERS, THE	MUSICAL GROUP	COOKIN MUSIC, 120 W 25TH ST	NEW YORK, NY	10001

MASS PRODUCTION	ROCK & ROLL GROUP	PEPPER PRODS, 200 W 72ND ST	NEW YORK, NY 10023
MASSARELLI, JOHN	BASEBALL	POST OFFICE BOX 4209	JACKSON, MS 39296
MASSARI, JOHN	COMPOSER-CONDUCTOR	5913 WILLOUGHBY AVE	LOS ANGELES, CA 90038
MASSARI, MARK ELLIOTT	WRITER-PRODUCER	227 S MADISON AVE	PASADENA, CA 91101
MASSE, BILLY	BASEBALL	1155 W MOUND ST	COLUMBUS, OH 43223
MASSELINK, BEN	SCREENWRITER	570 ERSKINE DR	PACIFIC PALISADES, CA 90272
MASSENBURG, TONY	BASKETBALL	600 E MARKET ST #102	SAN ANTONIO, TX 78205
MASSENGALE, DON	GOLFER	PGA SENIORS, 112 T P C BLVD	PONTE VEDRA BEACH, FL 32082
MASSET, ANDREW	ACTOR	11635 HUSTON ST	NORTH HOLLYWOOD, CA 91601
MASSEY, DANIEL	ACTOR	BELFRAGE, 68 SAINT JAMES'S ST	LONDON SW1A 1LE ENGLAND
MASSEY, GENE	WRITER-PRODUCER	550 S BARRINGTON AVE #2209	LOS ANGELES, CA 90049
MASSEY, PERRY E, JR	TV EXECUTIVE	22525 DARDENNE ST	WOODLAND HILLS, CA 91364
MASSEY, ROBERT	FOOTBALL	POST OFFICE BOX 888	PHOENIX, AZ 85001
MASSEY, WAYNE	ACTOR-SINGER	POST OFFICE BOX 2757	NASHVILLE, TN 37219
MASSEY, WAYNE	BASEBALL EXECUTIVE	1060 W ADDISON ST	CHICAGO, IL 60613
MASSIE, BRETT	BASEBALL TRAINER	POST OFFICE BOX 28268	SAN ANTONIO, TX 78228
MASSION, RIVI	ACTRESS	13722 ALBERS ST	VAN NUYS, CA 91401
MASTELLER, DAN	BASEBALL	POST OFFICE BOX 5645	ORLANDO, FL 32855
MASTER, WILLIAM J	FILM DIRECTOR	8146 BILLOW VISTA	PLAYA DEL REY, CA 90293
MASTEROFF, JOE	PLAYWRIGHT	2 HORATIO ST	NEW YORK, NY 10014
MASTERS, BEN	ACTOR	9200 SUNSET BLVD #710	LOS ANGELES, CA 90069
MASTERS, DAVE	BASEBALL	5999 E VAN BUREN ST	PHOENIX, AZ 85008
MASTERS, FRANKIE	CONDUCTOR	132 TURKEY HILL RD	CARY, IL 60013
MASTERS, MARIE	ACTRESS	15 W 75TH ST #3-B	NEW YORK, NY 10023
MASTERS, WILLIAM H, III	WRITER-PRODUCER	155 E 88TH ST #6-B	NEW YORK, NY 10028
MASTERS OF CEREMONY, THE	RAP GROUP-RAPWRITERS	FAA, 1700 BROADWAY, 5TH FLOOR	NEW YORK, NY 10019
MASTERSON, MARY STUART	ACTRESS	ICM, 40 W 57TH ST	NEW YORK, NY 10019
MASTERSON, PETER	FILM WRITER-DIRECTOR	9255 SUNSET BLVD #1122	LOS ANGELES, CA 90069
MASTORAKIS, NICO	WRITER-PRODUCER	OMEGA ENTERTAINMENT, LTD	
		8760 SHOREHAM DR	LOS ANGELES, CA 90069
MASTROGEORGE, HARRY	FILM DIRECTOR	10619 LANDALE ST	NORTH HOLLYWOOD, CA 91602
MASTROIANNI, MARCELLO	ACTOR	VIA MARIA ADELAIDE 8	ROME ITALY
MASUCCI, TONY	TV DIRECTOR	CBS-TV, 6121 SUNSET BLVD	LOS ANGELES, CA 90028
MASUOKA, MARK STEPHEN	TV WRITER	1233 KENISTON AVE	LOS ANGELES, CA 90019
MASUR, RICHARD	ACTOR-WRITER	SMITH, 121 N SAN VICENTE BLVD	BEVERLY HILLS, CA 90211
MATA, EDUARDO	CONDUCTOR	ICM, 40 W 57TH ST	NEW YORK, NY 10019
MATA, VIC	BASEBALL	AVE DE MARTIRES 131	SANTON DOMINGO DOM REP
MATACHUN, PAUL	BASEBALL	POST OFFICE BOX 309	GASTONA, NC 28053
MATALON, VIVIAN	FILM DIRECTOR	STE, 888 7TH AVE, 18TH FLOOR	NEW YORK, NY 10106
MATASEJE, VERONICA	RECORD EXECUTIVE	ACCLAIM RECORDS, 1426 LUDBROOK	MISSISS, ONT L5J 3P4 CANADA
MATER, BOB	MUSIC ARRANGER	1441 LEBANON RD #E-36	NASHVILLE, TN 37210
MATER, GENE PAUL	TV EXECUTIVE	CBS-TV, 51 W 52ND ST	NEW YORK, NY 10019
MATERIAL	MUSICAL GROUP	GEORGIAKARAKOS, 45 W 81ST ST	NEW YORK, NY 10024
MATHENY, MIKE	BASEBALL	POST OFFICE BOX 8550	STOCKTON, CA 95208
MATHER, GEORGE E	DIRECTOR	12330 HUSTON ST	NORTH HOLLYWOOD, CA 91607
MATHERS, JERRY	ACTOR	34965 VIA ARANDA	VALENCIA, CA 91355
MATHES, COLONEL DAVE	GUITARIST	POST OFFICE BOX 22653	NASHVILLE, TN 37202
MATHES, ED	BASEBALL SCOUT	BREWERS, 201 S 46TH ST	MILWAUKEE, WI 53214
MATHESON, DON	ACTOR	10275 1/2 MISSOURI AVE	LOS ANGELES, CA 90025
MATHESON, EVE	ACTRESS	COULSON, 37 BERWICK ST	LONDON W1V 3RF ENGLAND
MATHESON, MEGAN MURPHY	BALLERINA	1221 STONE CANYON RD	LOS ANGELES, CA 90077
MATHESON, MIKE	BASEBALL UMPIRE	POST OFFICE BOX 25010	LITTLE ROCK, AZ 72221
MATHESON, TIM	ACTOR-MAGAZINE EXEC	1221 STONE CANYON RD	LOS ANGELES, CA 90077
MATHEWS, CARMEN S	ACTRESS	101 MARCHANT RD	WEST REDDING, CT 06896
MATHEWS, CAROLE	ACTRESS	15300 VENTURA BLVD #207	SHERMAN OAKS, CA 91403
MATHEWS, EDDIE	BASEBALL	13744 RECUERDO DR	DEL MAR, CA 92014
MATHEWS, GREG	BASEBALL	POST OFFICE BOX 3449	SCRANTON, PA 18505
MATHEWS, JOYCE	ACTRESS	16901 VIA GRANDE	MISSION VIEJO, CA 92675
MATHEWS, ONZY D	COMPOSER	5114 EDGEWOOD PL	LOS ANGELES, CA 90019
MATHEWS, TERRY	BASEBALL	POST OFFICE BOX 90111	ARLINGTON, TX 76004
MATHIAS, ANNA	ACTRESS	1930 WEEPAH WY	LOS ANGELES, CA 90046
MATHIAS, BOB	ACTOR-ATHELETE	7469 E PINE AVE	FRESNO, CA 93727
MATHIAS, JOHNNY	SINGER	1469 STEBBINS TERR	LOS ANGELES, CA 90069
MATHIEU, MIREILLE	SINGER	12 RUE DU BOIS DE BOULOGNE	F-92200 NEUILLY FRANCE
MATHILE, MIKE	BASEBALL	POST OFFICE BOX 15757	HARRISBURG, PA 17105
MATHIS, JOHNNY	SINGER	3500 W OLIVE AVE #750	BURBANK, CA 91505
MATHIS, SAMANTHA	ACTRESS	1861 MIDVALE AVE #2	LOS ANGELES, CA 90025
MATHIS, TERANCE	FOOTBALL	N Y JETS, 1000 FULTON AVE	HEMPSTEAD, NY 11550
MATHISON, MELISSA	SCREENWRITER	655 MAC CULLOCH DR	LOS ANGELES, CA 90049
MATHOT, OLIVER	ACTOR	42 BIS RUE BOURDIGNON	SAINT MAUR 94100 FRANCE
MATICH, TREVOR	FOOTBALL	N Y JETS, 1000 FULTON AVE	HEMPSTEAD, NY 11550
MATICKA, JERRY M	DIRECTOR	404 E 66TH ST	NEW YORK, NY 10021
MATKIN, KIRK	VIDEO EDITOR	ENTERTAINMENT TONIGHT	
		PARAMOUNT TELEVISION	
		5555 MELROSE AVE	LOS ANGELES, CA 90038
MATLACK, JON	BASEBALL-COACH	STARS, 850 LAS VEGAS BLVD N	LAS VEGAS, NV 89101
MATLIN, MARLEE	ACTRESS	335 N MAPLE DR #270	BEVERLY HILLS, CA 90210
MATLOVSKY, DEBORAH	FILM EDITOR	51 W 86TH ST #1703	NEW YORK, NY 10024
MATOS, DOMINGO	BASEBALL	POST OFFICE BOX 6748	ROCKFORD, IL 61125
MATOS, FRANSISCO	BASEBALL	POST OFFICE BOX 2769	HUNTSVILLE, AL 35804
MATOS, MALVIN	BASEBALL	POST OFFICE BOX 309	GASTONA, NC 28053
MATRIX	ROCK & ROLL GROUP	8465 KEYSTONE CROSSING #204	INDIANAPOLIS, IN 46240
MATSON, DONNA M	TV DIRECTOR	4418 AVOCADO ST	LOS ANGELES, CA 90027
MATSON, JOHNNY	COMEDIAN	7221 OAK AVE, MILLER BEACH	GARY, IN 46403
MATSON, KEITH	BASEBALL EXECUTIVE	POST OFFICE BOX 2000	SAN DIEGO, CA 92112

MATSON, OLLIE	FOOTBALL	1319 N HUDSON AVE	LOS ANGELES, CA 90019
MATSUI, ROBERT	U S CONGRESSMAN	2353 RAYBURN HOUSE OFFICE BLDG	WASHINGTON, DC 20515
MATSUURA, TOSHIAKI	DIRECTOR	CREATIVE ENTERPRISE INTL	
		6630 SUNSET BLVD	HOLLYWOOD, CA 90028
MATTEA, KATHY	SINGER	POST OFFICE BOX 150245	NASHVILLE, TN 37215
MATTEAU, STEPHANE	HOCKEY	POST OFFICE BOX 1540, STA "M"	CALGARY, ALTA T2P 3BP CANADA
MATTELSON, MARVIN	ARTIST	37 CARY RD	GREAT NECK, NY 11021
MATTER, ALEX	SCREENWRITER	8955 BEVERLY BLVD	WEST HOLLYWOOD, CA 90048
MATTES, RON	FOOTBALL	BEARS, 250 N WASHINGTON RD	LAKE FOREST, IL 60045
MATTHAU, CAROL	AUTHORESS	RANDOM HOUSE, 201 E 50TH ST	NEW YORK, NY 10022
MATTHAU, CHARLES	FILM DIRECTOR	10100 SANTA MONICA BLVD #2200	LOS ANGELES, CA 90067
MATTHEWS, AL	ACTOR	9 MANATON CRES, SOUTHALL	MIDDLESEX UB1 2SY ENGLAND
MATTHEWS, ANN-SARA	ACTRESS	1650 BROADWAY #1005	NEW YORK, NY 10019
MATTHEWS, AUBREY	FOOTBALL	LIONS, 1200 FEATHERSTONE RD	PONTIAC, MI 48432
MATTHEWS, BILLIE	FOOTBALL COACH	LIONS, 1200 FEATHERSTONE RD	PONTIAC, MI 48432
MATTHEWS, BRUCE	FOOTBALL	OILERS, 6910 FANNIN ST	HOUSTON, TX 77070
MATTHEWS, CLAY	FOOTBALL	BROWNS, 80 1ST ST	BEREA, OH 44017
MATTHEWS, DENISE	SINGER-ACTRESS	SEE - VANITY	
MATTHEWS, DENNY	SPORTSCASTER	POST OFFICE BOX 419969	KANSAS CITY, MO 64141
MATTHEWS, FRANCIS	ACTOR	BURNETT, 42-43 GRAFTON HOUSE	
		2-3 GOLDEN SQ	LONDON W1R 3AD ENGLAND
MATTHEWS, HALE	THEATER PRODUCER	1088 PARK AVE	NEW YORK, NY 10028
MATTHEWS, IAN	SINGER-SONGWRITER	MAGNA ARTISTS, 9200 SUNSET BLVD	LOS ANGELES, CA 90069
MATTHEWS, KERWIN	ACTOR	67-A BUENA VISTA TERR	SAN FRANCISCO, CA 94117
MATTHEWS, LLEWELLYN E	COMPOSER	13528 CURTIS & KING RD	NORWALK, CA 90650
MATTHEWS, MARILYN	COSTUME DESIGNER	1223 WILSHIRE BLVD #513	SANTA MONICA, CA 90403
MATTHEWS, RANDY	SINGER-GUITARIST	POST OFFICE BOX 9004	CANTON, OH 44711
MATTHEWS, RICKY JAMES	SINGER-SONGWRITER	SEE - JAMES, RICK	
MATTHEWS, WALT	BASEBALL SCOUT	POST OFFICE BOX 288	HOUSTON, TX 77001
MATTHEWS, WENDY	ACTRESS	BETHEL AGENCY, 513 W 54TH ST	NEW YORK, NY 10019
MATTHEWS, WILLIAM ROBERT	DIRECTOR	DGA, 110 W 57TH ST	NEW YORK, NY 10019
MATTHIUS, GAIL	COMEDIAN	ICM, 8899 BEVERLY BLVD	LOS ANGELES, CA 90048
MATTICK, BOB	BASEBALL EXECUTIVE	SKYDOME, 300 BREMMER BL #3200	TORONTO, ONT M5V 3B3 CANADA
MATTICKS, DON	DIRECTOR	815 YORKTOWN RD	TURNERSVILLE, NJ 08012
MATTINGLY, DON	BASEBALL	N Y YANKEES, YANKEE STADIUM	BRONX, NY 10451
MATTOX, FRANK	BASEBALL EXECUTIVE	2850 W 20TH AVE	DENVER, CO 80211
MATTSON, ROBIN	ACTRESS	917 MANNING AVE	LOS ANGELES, CA 90024
MATULAVICH, PETER	DIRECTOR	1414 PASEO MANZANA	SAN DIMAS, CA 91773
MATURE, VICTOR	ACTOR	POST OFFICE BOX 706	RANCHO SANTE FE, CA 92067
MATURO, MIMI O'BRIEN	TV DIRECTOR	3480 BARHAM BLVD	LOS ANGELES, CA 90068
MATUSZEK, LEN	BASEBALL	7674 GINNALA CT	CINCINNATI, OH 45243
MATUTE, RAUL	COMPOSER	20933 TOMLEE AVE	TORRANCE, CA 90503
MATZA, JOSEPH	DIRECTOR	26729 LATIGO SHORE DR	MALIBU, CA 90265
MATZNICK, DAN	BASEBALL	1090 N EUCLID AVE	SARASOTA, FL 34237
MAUCH, BILLY	ACTOR	538-C W NORTHWEST HWY	PALATINE, IL 66067
MAUCH, GENE	BASEBALL	46 LA RONDA DR	RANCHO MIRAGE, CA 92270
MAUCLAIR, JACQUES	ACTOR	17 RUE DES ARCHIVES	PARIS 75004 FRANCE
MAUGER, PATRICIA A	TV PRODUCER	5 TUDOR CITY PL #1716	NEW YORK, NY 10017
MAUGHAN, SHARON	ACTRESS	COULSON, 37 BERWICK ST	LONDON W1V 3RF ENGLAND
MAULDIN, BILL	CARTOONIST	401 N WABASH AVE	CHICAGO, IL 60611
MAULDIN, JOE B	GUITARIST	POST OFFICE BOX 210216	NASHVILLE, TN 37221
MAULDIN, NAT	TV WRITER	7050 PACIFIC VIEW DR	LOS ANGELES, CA 90068
MAULDIN, STEVE W	MUSIC ARRANGER	1905 STRATFORD AVE	NASHVILLE, TN 37216
MAULE, BRAD	ACTOR	4136 DIXIE CANYON	SHERMAN OAKS, CA 91423
MAURER, BRUCE	FOOTBALL REFEREE	NFL, 410 PARK AVE	NEW YORK, NY 10022
MAURER, LUCILLE	TREASURER	STATE HOUSE BUILDING	ANNAPOLIS, MD 21401
MAURER, NORMAN	WRITER-PRODUCER	3100 CAVENDISH DR	LOS ANGELES, CA 90064
MAURER, ROB	BASEBALL	POST OFFICE BOX 75089	OKLAHOMA CITY, OK 73147
MAURER, RON	BASEBALL	POST OFFICE BOX 28268	SAN ANTONIO, TX 78228
MAUREY, NICOLE	ACTRESS	21 CHEMIN VAULLONS	78160 MARY-LE-ROI FRANCE
MAURIER, CLAIRE	ACTRESS	11 RUE MONTAGUE-LE-BREUIL	91360 EPIANY SUR ORGE FRANCE
MAURIN, YVES-MARIE	ACTRESS	61 RUE CAULAINCOURT	PARIS 75018 FRANCE
MAUSER, TIM	BASEBALL	POST OFFICE BOX 3449	SCRANTON, PA 18505
MAVEN, MAX	MINDREADER	1746 N ORANGE DR #1106	LOS ANGELES, CA 90028
MAVROULES, NICHOLAS	U S CONGRESSMAN	10 WELCOME ST	HAVERHILL, MA 01830
MAX, PETER	ARTIST	118 RIVERSIDE DR	NEW YORK, NY 10024
MAX CHEER	ROCK & ROLL GROUP	POST OFFICE BOX 198	COLLINSVILLE, CT 06022
MAXIE, BRETT	FOOTBALL	SAINTS, 1500 POYDRAS ST	NEW ORLEANS, LA 90112
MAXIE, LARRY	BASEBALL SCOUT	1060 W ADDISON ST	CHICAGO, IL 60613
MAXVILL, DAL	BASEBALL-EXECUTIVE	250 STADIUM PLAZA	ST LOUIS, MO 63102
MAXWELL, BILLY	GOLFER	PGA SENIORS, 112 T P C BLVD	PONTE VEDRA BEACH, FL 32082
MAXWELL, DAPHNE	ACTRESS	REID, 16540 ADLON RD	ENCINO, CA 91436
MAXWELL, JAMES	ACTOR	FRENCH'S, 52 HOLLAND PARK MEWS	LONDON W11 ENGLAND
MAXWELL, JANE	TV EXECUTIVE	1050 TECHWOOD DR, NW	ATLANTA, GA 30318
MAXWELL, JODY	ACTRESS-MODEL	POST OFFICE BOX 9786	MARINA DEL REY, CA 90265
MAXWELL, LOIS	ACTRESS	150 CARLTON ST	TORONTO, ONT CANADA
MAXWELL, MORRIS J	COMPOSER	2219 BAXTER ST	LOS ANGELES, CA 90039
MAXWELL, PAT	BASEBALL	POST OFFICE BOX 1886	COLUMBUS, GA 31902
MAXWELL, RICHARD	SCREENWRITER	555 W 57TH ST #1230	NEW YORK, NY 10019
MAXWELL, ROBERTA	ACTRESS	236 W 45TH ST	NEW YORK, NY 10036
MAXWELL, RONALD F	FILM DIRECTOR	ICM, 8899 BEVERLY BLVD	LOS ANGELES, CA 90048
MAXWELL, VERNON	BASKETBALL	POST OFFICE BOX 272349	HOUSTON, TX 77277
MAXX, THE	RHYTHM & BLUES GROUP	POST OFFICE BOX 11283	RICHMOND, VA 23230
MAY, ALAN	HOCKEY	JETS, 15-1430 MAROONS RD	WINNIPEG, MAN R3G 0L5 CANADA
MAY, ANGELA	ACTRESS	3500 W OLIVE AVE #1400	BURBANK, CA 91505

MAY, ARKIE	SINGER-GUITARIST	RURAL ROUTE #2, BOX 78-A5		
		PATES FORD RD	SMITHVILLE, TN	37166
MAY, BILLY	COMPOSER	22852 VIA CORDOVA	LAGUNA NIGUEL, CA	92677
MAY, BRIAN	COMPOSER	POST OFFICE BOX 562	BEVERLY HILLS, CA	90213
MAY, DEBORAH	ACTRESS	10000 SANTA MONICA BLVD #305	LOS ANGELES, CA	90067
MAY, DERRICK	BASEBALL	1060 W ADDISON ST	CHICAGO, IL	60613
MAY, ELAINE	ACT-WRI-DIR	146 CENTRAL PARK W #4-E	NEW YORK, NY	10023
MAY, JACK T	DIRECTOR	520 N MICHIGAN AVE #1026	CHICAGO, IL	60611
MAY, JANET	ACTRESS	10845 LINDBROOK DR #3	LOS ANGELES, CA	90024
MAY, LEE	BASEBALL (MAJORS)	POST OFFICE BOX 419969	KANSAS CITY, MO	64141
MAY, LEE	BASEBALL (MINORS)	POST OFFICE BOX 1211	NORFOLK, VA	23502
MAY, LENORA	ACTRESS	8271 MELROSE AVE #110	LOS ANGELES, CA	90046
MAY, MARK	FOOTBALL	POST OFFICE BOX 609609	SAN DIEGO, CA	92160
MAY, MILT	BASEBALL-COACH	POST OFFICE BOX 7000	PITTSBURGH, PA	15212
MAY, PHIL & THE FALLEN ANGELS	ROCK & ROLL GROUP	105 EMLYN RD	LONDON W12 9TG	ENGLAND
MAY, PHILIP	WRITER-PRODUCER	12078 MOUND VIEW PL	STUDIO CITY, CA	91604
MAY, SCOTT	BASEBALL	CUBS, 2ND & RIVERSIDE DR	DES MOINES, IA	50309
MAY, TED	TV DIRECTOR	CHILDREN'S TV WORKSHOP		
		1 LINCOLN PLAZA	NEW YORK, NY	10023
MAYALL, RIK	ACTOR-WRITER	169 QUEENSGATE #8-A	LONDON SW7 5EH	ENGLAND
MAYALL'S, JOHN, BLUESBREAKERS	RHYTHM & BLUES GROUP	POST OFFICE BOX 210103	SAN FRANCISCO, CA	94121
MAYBERRY, ROBERT	TV DIRECTOR	23957 VIA ONDA	VALENCIA, CA	91355
MAYBERRY, RUSSELL	TV DIRECTOR	DGA, 7920 SUNSET BLVD, 6TH FL	LOS ANGELES, CA	90046
MAYBERRY, TONY	FOOTBALL	BUCCANEERS, 1 BUCCANEER PL	TAMPA, FL	33607
MAYEHOFF, EDDIE	ACTOR	369 PASEO DE PLAYA #411	VENTURA, CA	93001
MAYENZET, MARIA	ACTRESS	L A TALENT, 8335 SUNSET BLVD	LOS ANGELES, CA	90069
MAYER, BILL	ARTIST	428 SYCAMORE ST	DECATUR, GA	30030
MAYER, CHIP	ACTOR	12700 VENTURA BLVD #350	STUDIO CITY, CA	91604
MAYER, CHRISTOPHER	ACTOR	329 N WETHERLY DR #205	BEVERLY HILLS, CA	90211
MAYER, DOE	FILM DIRECTOR	2510 4TH ST #C	SANTA MONICA, CA	90405
MAYER, DR JEAN	COLUMNIST	THE WASHINGTON POST		
		WRITERS GROUP		
		1150 15TH ST, NW	WASHINGTON, DC	20071
MAYER, GERALD	DIRECTOR-PRODUCER	104 S GLENROY AVE	LOS ANGELES, CA	90049
MAYER, HAROLD	DIRECTOR-PRODUCER	50 FERRISS ESTATE	NEW MILFORD, CT	06776
MAYER, HERBERT	CONDUCTOR	201 W 86TH ST	NEW YORK, NY	10024
MAYER, JERRY	ACTOR	400 W 43RD ST #33-G	NEW YORK, NY	10036
MAYER, JERRY	TV WRITER-PRODUCER	POST OFFICE BOX 732	PACIFIC PALISADES, CA	90272
MAYER, MIRIAM	COMPOSER	1500 S SHERBOURNE DR	LOS ANGELES, CA	90035
MAYER, PIETER	DIRECTOR	DGA, 7920 SUNSET BLVD, 6TH FL	LOS ANGELES, CA	90046
MAYERSBERG, PAUL	SCREENWRITER	409 N CAMDEN DR	BEVERLY HILLS, CA	90210
MAYERSON, MARC	WRITER	8955 BEVERLY BLVD	WEST HOLLYWOOD, CA	90048
MAYES, KEVIN L	ARTIST	1202 TULSA ST	WICHITA, KS	67216
MAYES, WENDELL	SCREENWRITER	1504 BEL AIR RD	LOS ANGELES, CA	90077
MAYEUR, ROBERT G	COMPOSER	838 BARRINGTON AVE #101	LOS ANGELES, CA	90049
MAYFAIR, BILLY	GOLFER	POST OFFICE BOX 109601	PALM BCH GARDENS, FL	33418
MAYFIELD, CURTIS	SINGER-SONGWRITER	WM MORRIS, 1350 AVE OF AMERICAS	NEW YORK, NY	10019
MAYHEW, MARTIN	FOOTBALL	POST OFFICE BOX 17247 (DULLES)	WASHINGTON, DC	20041
MAYHEW-SMITH, RICHARD	WRITER-DIRECTOR	21 COLESHILL RD, TEDDINGTON	MIDDLESEX TW11 OLL	ENGLAND
MAYLAM, TONY	DIRECTOR	9000 SUNSET BLVD #1200	LOS ANGELES, CA	90069
MAYNARD, EARL	BODYBUILDER	SPORTS WORLD RACQUETBALL		
		AND FITNESS CENTER		
		6666 GREEN VALLEY CIR	CULVER CITY, CA	90230
MAYNARD, JIMMY	GUITARIST	325-A HICKORY RIDGE RD		
		ROUTE #5	LEBANON, TN	37087
MAYNARD, JOYCE	COLUMNIST	N Y TIMES SYN, 130 5TH AVE	NEW YORK, NY	10011
MAYNARD, MIMI	ACTRESS	9229 SUNSET BLVD #311	LOS ANGELES, CA	90069
MAYNARD, ROBERT C	JOURNALIST-COLUMNIST	UPS, 4900 MAIN ST, 9TH FLOOR	KANSAS CITY, MO	64112
MAYNARD, TOW	BASEBALL	POST OFFICE BOX 4756	JACKSONVILLE, FL	32201
MAYNARD, VINCENT	WRITER-PRODUCER	2293 W 20TH ST	NEW YORK, NY	10018
MAYNE, BRENT	BASEBALL	POST OFFICE BOX 419969	KANSAS CITY, MO	64141
MAYNE, FERDINAND	ACTOR	100 S DOHENY DR #620	LOS ANGELES, CA	90048
MAYNES, CHARLES WILLIAM	COLUMNIST	N Y TIMES SYN, 130 5TH AVE	NEW YORK, NY	10011
MAYNOR, ASA	ACTRESS-PRODUCER	POST OFFICE BOX 1641	BEVERLY HILLS, CA	90213
MAYO, GEOFFREY M	DIRECTOR	58 W 15TH ST	NEW YORK, NY	10011
MAYO, TODD	BASEBALL	POST OFFICE BOX 15757	HARRISBURG, PA	17105
MAYO, VIRGINIA	ACTRESS	109 EAST AVE DES LAS ABOLES	THOUSAND OAKS, CA	91360
MAYO, WHITMAN	ACTOR	9000 5TH AVE	INGLEWOOD, CA	90305
MAYO-CHANDLER, KAREN	ACTRESS	L A TALENT, 8335 SUNSET BLVD	LOS ANGELES, CA	90069
MAYOH, ROYSTON	TV DIRECTOR-PRODUCER	35 PHEASANT'S WY		
		RICKMANSWORTH	HERTS	ENGLAND
MAYRON, MELANIE	ACTRESS-WRITER	1418 N OGDEN DR	LOS ANGELES, CA	90046
MAYS, ALVOID	FOOTBALL	POST OFFICE BOX 17247 (DULLES)	WASHINGTON, DC	20041
MAYS, DEBORAH	ACTRESS-MODEL	SEE - NAMATH, DEBORAH MAYS		
MAYS, TRAVIS	BASKETBALL	KINGS, 1 SPORTS PARKWAY	SACRAMENTO, CA	95834
MAYS, WILLIE	BASEBALL	51 MOUNT VERNON LN	ATHERTON, CA	94025
MAYSE, GARY	BASEBALL EXECUTIVE	POST OFFICE BOX 1295	CLINTON, IA	52733
MAYSE, STEVE	ARTIST	5317 BUENA VISTA	ROELAND PARK, KS	66205
MAYSEY, MATT	BASEBALL	1501 W 16TH ST	INDIANAPOLIS, IN	46202
MAZE	RHYTHM & BLUES GROUP	V JONES, 805 MORAGA RD	LAFAYETTE, CA	94549
MAZER, IRA	DIRECTOR	DGA, 110 W 57TH ST	NEW YORK, NY	10019
MAZEROSKI, BILL	BASEBALL	RURAL ROUTE 6, BOX 130	GREENBURG, PA	15601
MAZMAN-HAYDEN, MELONIE	ACTRESS	1717 N HIGHLAND AVE #701	LOS ANGELES, CA	90028
MAZMANIAN, MARIUS	ACTOR	2446 1/2 N GOWER ST	HOLLYWOOD, CA	90068
MAZOTTI, PASCAL	ACTOR	19 PLACE DU MARCHE SAINT HONORE	PARIS 75001	FRANCE

MAZUCA, FRED	BASEBALL SCOUT	POST OFFICE BOX 7575	PHILADELPHIA, PA	19101
MAZUER, MERRILL M	DIRECTOR	GOODMAN, 8909 OLYMPIC BLVD	BEVERLY HILLS, CA	90211
MAZUR, EDWARD	COMPTROLLER	STATE CAPITOL BUILDING	RICHMOND, VA	23219
MAZUR, JAY	HOCKEY	CANUCKS, 100 N RENFREW ST	VANCOUVER, BC V5K 3N7	CANADA
MAZURSKY, PAUL	WRITER-PRODUCER	16 E 11TH ST #3-A	NEW YORK, NY	10003
MAZZILLI, LEE	BASEBALL	12 CARPENTERS DRK RD	GREENWICH, CT	06830
MAZZOLA, REPARATA	ACTRESS	MELNICK, 15267 MULHOLLAND DR	LOS ANGELES, CA	90077
MAZZOLI, ROMANO	U S CONGRESSMAN	600 MARTIN LUTHER KING, JR PL		
		FEDERAL BUILDING, ROOM 551	LOUISVILLE, KY	40202
MAZZONE, LEO	BASEBALL COACH	POST OFFICE BOX 4064	ATLANTA, GA	30302
MAZZUCA, JOSEPH	TV DIRECTOR	22856 COVELLO ST	CANOGA PARK, CA	91307
MC ADAMS, JAMES D	TV WRITER-PRODUCER	15980 VALLEY WOOD RD	SHERMAN OAKS, CA	91403
MC ALARY, MIKE	COLUMNIST	NY DAILY NEWS, 220 E 42ND ST	NEW YORK, NY	10017
MC ALISTER, FRED	BASEBALL SCOUT	250 STADIUM PLAZA	ST LOUIS, MO	63102
MC ALLISTER, STEVE	BASEBALL SCOUT	BREWERS, 201 S 46TH ST	MILWAUKEE, WI	53214
MC ALLISTER, SUSIE	GOLFER	2750 VOLUSA AVE #B	DAYTON BEACH, FL	32114
MC ALPIN, MIKE	BASEBALL COACH-SCOUT	633 JESSAMINE ST	KNOXVILLE, TN	37917
MC ALPINE, DONALD	CINEMATOGRAPHER	POST OFFICE BOX 2230	HOLLYWOOD, CA	90078
MC ALPINE, JAMES	ACTOR	AIMEE, 13743 VICTORY BLVD	VAN NUYS, CA	91401
MC ANALLY, MAC	SINGER	POST OFFICE BOX 2831	MUSCLE SHOALS, AL	35660
MC ANDREW, JAMIE	BASEBALL	POST OFFICE BOX 26267	ALBUQUERQUE, NM	87125
MC ANDREW, MARIANNE	ACTRESS	5750 WILSHIRE BLVD #512	LOS ANGELES, CA	90036
MC ANUFF, DES	THEATER DIRECTOR	WM MORRIS, 1350 AVE OF AMERICAS	NEW YORK, NY	10019
MC ARDLE, ANDREA	ACTRESS	713 DISSTON ST	PHILADELPHIA, PA	19111
MC ARTHUR, ALEX	ACTOR	BYMEL, 723 WESTMOUNT DR	WEST HOLLYWOOD, CA	90069
MC ARTHUR, KIMBERLY ANN	ACTRESS-MODEL	145 S FAIRFAX AVE #310	LOS ANGELES, CA	90036
MC AVOY, EUGENE T	DIRECTOR	DGA, 7920 SUNSET BLVD, 6TH FL	LOS ANGELES, CA	90046
MC BEAN, WAYNE	HOCKEY	NASSAU VETS MEMORIAL COLISEUM	UNIONDALE, NY	11553
MC BEE, RIVES	GOLFER	PGA SENIORS, 112 T P C BLVD	PONTE VEDRA BEACH, FL	32082
MC BRIDE, BAKE	BASEBALL-INSTRUCTOR	250 STADIUM PLAZA	ST LOUIS, MO	63102
MC BRIDE, ELIZABETH	COSTUME DESIGNER	DOUG APATOW, 10559 BLYTHE AVE	LOS ANGELES, CA	90064
MC BRIDE, HARLEE	ACTRESS	705 WESTMOUNT DR #302	LOS ANGELES, CA	90069
MC BRIDE, JAMES M	WRI-DIR-PROD	9200 SUNSET BLVD #402	LOS ANGELES, CA	90069
MC BRIDE, JEFF	COMEDIAN	ICM, 8899 BEVERLY BLVD	LOS ANGELES, CA	90048
MC BRIDE, JOSEPH	FILM CRITIC	117 N KINGS RD	LOS ANGELES, CA	90048
MC BROOM, AMANDA	SINGER-SONGWRITER	22903 MARIANO ST	WOODLAND HILLS, CA	91367
MC BROOM, BRUCE V	ACTOR	829 1/2 N FULLER AVE	LOS ANGELES, CA	90046
MC CABE, JOHN	COMPOSER	49 BURNS AVE, SOUTHALL	MIDDLESEX	ENGLAND
MC CABE, RON	ACTOR	14570 BENEFIT ST	SHERMAN OAKS, CA	91403
MC CABE, SANDRA	ACTRESS	1228 HILLDALE AVE	LOS ANGELES, CA	90069
MC CAFFERTY, JOHN W	FILM EDITOR	3123 BARRY AVE	LOS ANGELES, CA	90066
MC CAFFERTY, SIOBHAN	ACTRESS	433 N CAMDEN DR #400	BEVERLY HILLS, CA	90210
MC CAFFERTY, SIOBHAN E	ACTRESS	346 E 63RD ST #4-A	NEW YORK, NY	10021
MC CAFFERTY, SUZANNE	FILM PRODUCER	ASTA PRODS, 126 S ORLANDO AVE	LOS ANGELES, CA	90048
MC CAFFERY, DENNIS	BASEBALL	POST OFFICE BOX 3496	DAVENPORT, IA	52808
MC CAFFREY, ED	FOOTBALL	N Y GIANTS, GIANTS STADIUM	EAST RUTHERFORD, NJ	07073
MC CAFFREY, NEIL W	CINEMATOGRAPHER	CBS-TV, 524 W 57TH ST	NEW YORK, NY	10019
MC CAIN, FRANCES LEE	ACTRESS	8075 W 3RD ST #303	LOS ANGELES, CA	90048
MC CAIN, JOHN	U S SENATOR	5353 N 16TH ST	PHOENIX, AZ	85016
MC CALL, C W	SINGER-SONGWRITER	BILL FRIES, 206 W 44TH ST	OMAHA, NE	68131
MC CALL, JADE	ACTOR	1351 N ORANGE DR #105	HOLLYWOOD, CA	90028
MC CALL, JOAN	WRITER	9022 SUNSET BLVD #531	LOS ANGELES, CA	90069
MC CALL, LARRY	BASEBALL COACH	POST OFFICE BOX 418	SAINT CHARLES, IL	60174
MC CALL, MARY ANN	ACTOR	1546 N GORDON ST	HOLLYWOOD, CA	90028
MC CALL, MITZI	ACTRESS-WRITER	3635 WRIGHTWOOD	STUDIO CITY, CA	91604
MC CALL, ROD	BASEBALL	POST OFFICE BOX 1886	COLUMBUS, GA	31902
MC CALLA, DEIDRE	SINGER	OLIVIA RECORDS COMPANY		
		4400 MARKET ST	OAKLAND, CA	94608
MC CALLA, IRISH	ACTRESS	MC INTYRE, 920 OAK TERR	PRESCOTT, AZ	86301
MC CALLISTER, BLAINE	GOLFER	POST OFFICE BOX 109601	PALM BCH GARDENS, FL	33418
MC CALLISTER, GEORGE	ACTOR	4141 WHITSETT AVE	STUDIO CITY, CA	91604
MC CALLISTER, LON	ACTOR	POST OFFICE BOX 396	LITTLE RIVER, CA	95456
MC CALLUM, DAVID	ACTOR	10 E 44TH ST #700	NEW YORK, NY	10017
MC CALLUM, RICK	TV PRODUCER	29 ROSTREVOR RD	LONDON SW6	ENGLAND
MC CALLUM, SCOTT	LT GOVERNOR	STATE CAPITOL BUILDING	MADISON, WI	53702
MC CAMBRIDGE, MERCEDES	ACTRESS	1001 GENTRY ST #8-I	LA JOLLA, CA	92037
MC CAMENT, RANDY	BASEBALL	15601 N 60TH AVE	GLENDALE, AZ	85306
MC CANDLESS, AL	U S CONGRESSMAN	74-075 EL PASEO #A-7	PALM DESERT, CA	92260
MC CANDLESS, EARL R	COMPOSER	POST OFFICE BOX 828	SOLANA BEACH, CA	92075
MC CANLIES, TIMOTHY B	SCREENWRITER	131 S RODEO DR #300	BEVERLY HILLS, CA	90212
MC CANN, BRIAN	BASEBALL TRAINER	CUBS, 2ND & RIVERSIDE DR	DES MOINES, IA	50309
MC CANN, CHUCK	ACTOR-COMEDIAN	2941 BRIAR KNOLL DR	LOS ANGELES, CA	90046
MC CANN, DANIEL	ACTOR	1411 S DETROIT ST	LOS ANGELES, CA	90046
MC CANN, DAVID DE WITT	TV DIRECTOR	POST OFFICE BOX 4325	DIAMOND BAR, CA	91765
MC CANN, ELIZABETH	THEATER PRODUCER	1501 BROADWAY	NEW YORK, NY	10036
MC CANN, JOE	BASEBALL	525 NW PEACOCK BLVD	PORT SAINT LUCIE, FL	34986
MC CANN, JULIE	ACTRESS	6255 SUNSET BLVD #627	LOS ANGELES, CA	90028
MC CANTS, KEITH	FOOTBALL	BUCCANEERS, 1 BUCCANEER PL	TAMPA, FL	33607
MC CANTS, REID	COMEDIAN	POST OFFICE BOX 82	GREAT NECK, NY	11022
MC CAREN, JOSEPH	ACTOR	400 W 43RD ST #35-F	NEW YORK, NY	10036
MC CARREN, FRED	ACTOR	364 S CLOVERDALE AVE #104	LOS ANGELES, CA	90036
MC CARROLL, THOMAS	NEWS CORRESPONDENT	TIME/TIME & LIFE BLDG		
		ROCKEFELLER CENTER	NEW YORK, NY	10020
MC CARTER, GORDON	FOOTBALL REFEREE	NFL, 410 PARK AVE	NEW YORK, NY	10022
MC CARTHY, ANDREW	ACTOR	4708 VESPER AVE	SHERMAN OAKS, CA	91403

MC CARTHY, ANN	COSTUME DESIGNER	SEE - LAMBERT, ANN		
MC CARTHY, BARNETTA	ACTRESS	18653 VENTURA BLVD #349	TARZANA, CA	91356
MC CARTHY, DANIEL	BASEBALL EXECUTIVE	N Y YANKEES, YANKEE STADIUM	BRONX, NY	10451
MC CARTHY, DENNIS	COMPOSER-CONDUCTOR	535 BIRMINGHAM RD	BURBANK, CA	91504
MC CARTHY, EUGENE	U S SENATOR	POST OFFICE BOX 22	WOODVILLE, VA	22749
MC CARTHY, FRANK	ACTOR	10351 SANTA MONICA BLVD #211	LOS ANGELES, CA	90025
MC CARTHY, GREG	BASEBALL	POST OFFICE BOX 3452	KINSTON, NC	28502
MC CARTHY, JOHN J	TV PRODUCER	400 E 59TH ST #3-D	NEW YORK, NY	10022
MC CARTHY, JULIANNA	ACTRESS	STONE MANNERS, 9113 SUNSET BL	LOS ANGELES, CA	90069
MC CARTHY, KEVIN	ACTOR	12425 SARAH ST	STUDIO CITY, CA	91604
MC CARTHY, KEVIN D	TV DIRECTOR	12425 SARAH ST	STUDIO CITY, CA	91604
MC CARTHY, KYLE S	DIRECTOR	121 W 72ND ST	NEW YORK, NY	10023
MC CARTHY, LEO T	LT GOVERNOR	STATE CAPITOL BUILDING	SACRAMENTO, CA	95814
MC CARTHY, LIN	ACTOR	233 N SWALL DR	BEVERLY HILLS, CA	90211
MC CARTHY, MATT	TV DIRECTOR	16 RAMILLIES ST	LONDON W1V 1DL	ENGLAND
MC CARTHY, MOLLIE	TALENT AGENT	19 W 44TH ST #1000	NEW YORK, NY	10018
MC CARTHY, NOBU	ACTRESS	372 N ENCINITAS	MONROVIA, CA	91016
MC CARTHY, PATRICIA E	WRI-DIR-PROD	39 E ROCKS RD	NORWALK, CT	06851
MC CARTHY, RICHARD	TV DIRECTOR	2 OSWALD ST, CREMORNE	SYDNEY NSW	AUSTRALIA
MC CARTHY, SHEILA	ACTRESS	BYMEL, 723 WESTMOUNT DR	WEST HOLLYWOOD, CA	90069
MC CARTHY, TODD	COLUMNIST	5700 WILSHIRE BLVD #120	LOS ANGELES, CA	90036
MC CARTHY, TOM	BASEBALL	POST OFFICE BOX 6667	RICHMOND, VA	23230
MC CARTNEY, LINDA	MUSICIAN-PHOTOGRAPHER	WATERFALL ESTATE, NEAR PEAMARCH		
		SAINT LEONARD-ON-THE-SEA	SUSSEX	ENGLAND
MC CARTNEY, PAUL & WINGS	ROCK & ROLL GROUP	WATERFALL ESTATE, NEAR PEAMARCH		
		SAINT LEONARD-ON-THE-SEA	SUSSEX	ENGLAND
MC CARTY, DAVID	BASEBALL	POST OFFICE BOX 5645	ORLANDO, FL	32855
MC CARTY, ROBERT	FILM WRITER-DIRECTOR	222 W 83RD ST	NEW YORK, NY	10024
MC CARTY, SCOTT	BASEBALL	POST OFFICE BOX 11363	RENO, NV	89510
MC CARVER, TIM	BASEBALL-ANNOUNCER	RURAL ROUTE #1	MILLINGTON, TN	38053
MC CARY, ROD	ACTOR	10100 SANTA MONICA BLVD #700	LOS ANGELES, CA	90067
MC CASHIN, CONSTANCE	ACTRESS	2037 DESFORD DR	BEVERLY HILLS, CA	90210
MC CASKEY, EDWARD W	FOOTBALL EXECUTIVE	BEARS, 250 N WASHINGTON RD	LAKE FOREST, IL	60045
MC CASKEY, MICHAEL B	FOOTBALL EXECUTIVE	BEARS, 250 N WASHINGTON RD	LAKE FOREST, IL	60045
MC CASKILL, KIRK	BASEBALL	333 W 35TH ST	CHICAGO, IL	60616
MC CASKILL, RODERICK C	ACTOR	7401 VARIEL AVE	CANOGA PARK, CA	91303
MC CASLIN, MARY & JIM RINGER	VOCAL DUO	1671 APPIAN WY	SANTA MONICA, CA	90401
MC CASLIN, MAYLO	ACTRESS	LIGHT, 901 BRINGHAM AVE	LOS ANGELES, CA	90049
MC CAULEY, PAUL G	COMEDY WRITER	4401 KLING ST #16	BURBANK, CA	91505
MC CAY, PEGGY	ACTRESS	8811 WONDERLAND AVE	LOS ANGELES, CA	90046
MC CLAIN, CADY	ACTRESS	ABC-TV, "ALL MY CHILDREN"		
		320 W 66TH ST	NEW YORK, NY	10023
MC CLAIN, CHARLY	SINGER	POST OFFICE BOX 2757	NASHVILLE, TN	37219
MC CLAIN, SCOTT	BASEBALL	POST OFFICE BOX 418	SAINT CHARLES, IL	60174
MC CLALLUM, NAPOLEON	FOOTBALL	RAIDERS, 332 CENTER ST	EL SEGUNDO, CA	90245
MC CLANAHAN, RUE	ACTRESS	16601 WOODVALE RD	ENCINO, CA	91436
MC CLELLAN, PAUL	BASEBALL	5999 E VAN BUREN ST	PHOENIX, AZ	85008
MC CLELLAND, TIM	BASEBALL UMPIRE	5405 WOODLAND AVE	WEST DES MOINES, IA	50265
MC CLENDON, DEBBIE	SINGER	POST OFFICE BOX 2341	PASADENA, CA	91102
MC CLENDON, LLOYD	BASEBALL	POST OFFICE BOX 7000	PITTSBURGH, PA	15212
MC CLENDON, SKIP	FOOTBALL	BENGALS, 200 RIVERFRONT STADIUM	CINCINNATI, OH	45202
MC CLINTON, DELBERT	SINGER-GUITARIST	POST OFFICE BOX 2689	DANBURY, CT	06813
MC CLINTON, O B	SINGER	TESSIER, 505 CANTON PASS	MADISON, TN	37115
MC CLINTON, TIM	BASEBALL	525 NW PEACOCK BLVD	PORT SAINT LUCIE, FL	34986
MC CLORY, SEAN	ACTOR-DIRECTOR	6612 WHITLEY TERR	LOS ANGELES, CA	90068
MC CLOSKEY, FRANK	U S CONGRESSMAN	501 S MADISON	BLOOMINGTON, IN	47403
MC CLOSKEY, JACK	BASKETBALL EXECUTIVE	THE PALACE OF AUBURN HILLS		
		2 CHAMPIONSHIP DR	AUBURN HILLS, MI	48326
MC CLOSKEY, LEIGH	ACTOR	6032 PHILIP AVE	MALIBU, CA	90265
MC CLOSKEY, PETE	U S REPRESENTATIVE	2200 GENGO RD	PALO ALTO, CA	94304
MC CLOUD, GEORGE	BASKETBALL	PACERS, 300 E MARKET ST	INDIANAPOLIS, IN	46204
MC CLOUGHAN, DAVE	FOOTBALL	POST OFFICE BOX 535000	INDIANPOLIS, IN	46253
MC CLURE, BOB	BASEBALL	250 STADIUM PLAZA	ST LOUIS, MO	63102
MC CLURE, CATHY	TV PRODUCER	185 CLAREMONT AVE #5-J	NEW YORK, NY	10027
MC CLURE, DOUG	ACTOR	14936 STONESBORO PL	SHERMAN OAKS, CA	91403
MC CLURE, HARRY	TV DIRECTOR	KMOX-TV, 1 MEMORIAL DR	SAINT LOUIS, MO	63102
MC CLURE, MARC	ACTOR	1420 BEAUDRY BLVD	GLENDALE, CA	91208
MC CLURE, MIKE	FOOTBALL EXECUTIVE	OILERS, 6910 FANNIN ST	HOUSTON, TX	77070
MC CLURE, PAULA	NEWS REPORTER	ENTERTAINMENT TONIGHT		
		PARAMOUNT TELEVISION		
		5555 MELROSE AVE	LOS ANGELES, CA	90038
MC CLURE, TANE	ACTRESS	132 S LASKY DR #B	BEVERLY HILLS, CA	90212
MC CLURE-WHITE, LINDA	ACTRESS	CASSELL, 843 N SYCAMORE AVE	LOS ANGELES, CA	90038
MC CLURG, EDIE	ACTRESS	MTA, 9320 WILSHIRE BL, 3RD FL	BEVERLY HILLS, CA	90212
MC COID, KATIE	ACTRESS	1629 RODNEY DR #2	LOS ANGELES, CA	90027
MC COLLISTER, CHARLIE	ACTOR	4442 PRESIDIO DR	SIMI VALLEY, CA	93063
MC COLLOUGH, MIKE	BASEBALL	POST OFFICE BOX 309	GASTONA, NC	28053
MC COLLOUM, BILL	U S CONGRESSMAN	1801 LEE RD #301	WINTER PARK, FL	32789
MC COMBIE, J A S	SCREENWRITER	8955 BEVERLY BLVD	WEST HOLLYWOOD, CA	90048
MC COMBS, RED	BASKETBALL EXECUTIVE	600 E MARKET ST #102	SAN ANTONIO, TX	78205
MC CONNELL, JUDITH	ACTRESS	3300 BENNETT DR	LOS ANGELES, CA	90068
MC CONNELL, MITCH	U S SENATOR	600 FEDERAL PL #136-C	LOUISVILLE, KY	40202
MC CONNELL, THOMAS	TV WRITER-DIRECTOR	8401 BROADACRE DR	SUN VALLEY, CA	91332
MC CONNELL, WALT	BASEBALL	POST OFFICE BOX 12	MIDLAND, TX	79702
MC COO, MARILYN	SINGER-ACTRESS	POST OFFICE BOX 7905	BEVERLY HILLS, CA	90212

MC COO & DAVIS	VOCAL DUO	POST OFFICE BOX 7905	BEVERLY HILLS, CA	90212
MC COOK, JOHN	ACT-SING-COND	4154 COLBATH AVE	SHERMAN OAKS, CA	91413
MC CORD, JONAS	WRI-DIR-PROD	555 W 57TH ST #1230	NEW YORK, NY	10019
MC CORD, KENT	ACTOR	1738 N ORANGE GROVE AVE	LOS ANGELES, CA	90046
MC CORMACK, DON	BASEBALL MANAGER	POST OFFICE BOX 15050	READING, PA	19612
MC CORMACK, PATTY	ACTRESS-MODEL	12731 MOORPARK #3	STUDIO CITY, CA	91604
MC CORMACK, TOM	BASEBALL SCOUT	250 STADIUM PLAZA	ST LOUIS, MO	63102
MC CORMICK, MAUREEN	ACTRESS	2812 N SHELL CREEK PL	WESTLAKE VILLAGE, CA	91361
MC CORMICK, PAT	ACT-WRI-COMED	4303 KLUMP AVE	NORTH HOLLYWOOD, CA	91602
MC CORMICK, PAT	SWIMMER	POST OFFICE BOX 250	SEAL BEACH, CA	90740
MC CORMICK, TIM	BASKETBALL	1 CNN CENTER #405, SOUTH TOWER	ATLANTA, GA	30303
MC COURT, MALACHY	ACTOR	SAPERSTEIN, 160 W 72ND ST	NEW YORK, NY	10023
MC COVEY, WILLIE	BASEBALL	POST OFFICE BOX 620342	WOODSIDE, CA	94062
MC COWAN, GEORGE	TV DIRECTOR	409 N CANON DR #202	BEVERLY HILLS, CA	90210
MC COWEN, ALEC	ACTOR	3 GOODWINS CT, SAINT MARTINS LN	LONDON WG2	ENGLAND
MC COY, AL	SPORTSCASTER	SUNS, 2910 N CENTRAL AVE	PHOENIX, AZ	85012
MC COY, BILLY W	DIRECTOR	316 DALZELL AVE	PITTSBURGH, PA	15202
MC COY, CHARLIE	SINGER-GUITARIST	2314 SPRING BRANCH DR	MADISON, TN	37115
MC COY, DENNYS	TV WRITER-STORY ED	WARDEN, 8444 WILSHIRE BL, 4TH FL	BEVERLY HILLS, CA	90211
MC COY, JAY & THE RENAGADES	ROCK & ROLL GROUP	STRICKLAND, 1407 N 14TH AVE	OMAHA, NE	68102
MC COY, LARRY	BASEBALL UMPIRE	RURAL ROUTE 1	GREENWAY, AR	72430
MC COY, MATT	ACTOR	15760 VENTURA BLVD #1730	ENCINO, CA	91436
MC COY, SID	TV DIRECTOR	1221 OCEAN AVE	SANTA MONICA, CA	90401
MC COY, TREY	BASEBALL	POST OFFICE BOX 4448	TULSA, OK	74159
MC CRACKEN, JEFF	ACTOR	15760 VENTURA BLVD #1730	ENCINO, CA	91436
MC CRAE, GEORGE	SINGER-SONGWRITER	495 SE 10TH CT	HIALEAH, FL	33010
MC CRAE, GWEN	SINGER-SONGWRITER	495 SE 10TH CT	HIALEAH, FL	33010
MC CRARY, DARIUS	ACTOR	ABC-TV, 2040 AVE OF THE STARS	LOS ANGELES, CA	90067
MC CRARY'S, THE	VOCAL GROUP	1021 N CRESCENT HGTS BLVD #302	HOLLYWOOD, CA	90046
MC CRAY, JIM	BASEBALL SCOUT	BREWERS, 201 S 46TH ST	MILWAUKEE, WI	53214
MC CRAY, KEN	PRODUCER	LANDON, 10202 W WASHINGTON BLVD	CULVER CITY, CA	90230
MC CRAY, RODNEY	BASEBALL	POST OFFICE BOX 1211	NORFOLK, VA	23502
MC CRAY, RODNEY	BASKETBALL	REUNION ARENA, 777 SPORTS ST	DALLAS, TX	75207
MC CREA, JODY	ACTOR-RANCHER	RURAL ROUTE #1	CAMARILLO, CA	93010
MC CREADY, JIM	BASEBALL	POST OFFICE BOX 7845	COLUMBIA, SC	29202
MC CREARY, BOB	BASEBALL	POST OFFICE BOX 48	VISALIA, CA	93279
MC CREARY, LEW	COMPOSER	8437 WHITE OAK BLVD	NORTHRIDGE, CA	91324
MC CREEDY, SHARON	ACTRESS	18 18TH AVE #A	VENICE, CA	90291
MC CRERY, JIM	U S CONGRESSMAN	621 EDWARDS ST	SHREVEPORT, LA	71101
MC CRIMMON, BRAD	HOCKEY	RED WINGS, 600 CIVIC CENTER DR	DETROIT, MI	48226
MC CUAIG, DONALD M	DIRECTOR	4208 FARMDALE AVE	STUDIO CITY, CA	91604
MC CUE, DERON	BASEBALL COACH	POST OFFICE BOX 1295	CLINTON, IA	52733
MC CUE, RICHARD T	DIRECTOR	57 PINE TREE LN	TAPPAN, NY	10983
MC CUEN, BILL	SECRETARY OF STATE	STATE CAPITOL BUILDING	LITTLE ROCK, AR	72201
MC CULLERS, LANCE	BASEBALL	POST OFFICE BOX 75089	OKLAHOMA CITY, OK	73147
MC CULLOUGH, ANDREW	DIRECTOR	550 S BARRINGTON AVE #2301	LOS ANGELES, CA	90049
MC CULLOUGH, BRIAN	DIRECTOR	53 PRINCETON PL	WAYNE, NJ	07470
MC CULLOUGH, HOWARD	BASEBALL SCOUT	FENWAY PARK, 4 YAWKEY WY	BOSTON, MA	02215
MC CULLOUGH, JULIE	MODEL	6515 WILSHIRE BLVD #205	HOLLYWOOD, CA	90028
MC CULLOUGH, KIMBERLY	ACTRESS	9200 SUNSET BLVD #625	LOS ANGELES, CA	90069
MC CULLOUGH, ROBERT L	TV WRITER	CAA, 9830 WILSHIRE BLVD	BEVERLY HILLS, CA	90212
MC CUMBER, MARK	GOLFER	POST OFFICE BOX 109601	PALM BCH GARDENS, FL	33418
MC CUNE, GARY	BASEBALL EXECUTIVE	800 HOME RUN LN	MEMPHIS, TN	38104
MC CURDY, DAVE	U S CONGRESSMAN	POST OFFICE BOX 1265	NORMAN, OK	73070
MC CURDY, JEAN H	TV EXECUTIVE	WARNER BROTHERS, INC		
		4000 WARNER BLVD	BURBANK, CA	91522
MC CURDY, JIM	BASEBALL EXECUTIVE	POST OFFICE BOX 186	BUTTE, MT	59703
MC CURRY, ANN	ACTRESS	5921 CANYON COVE	LOS ANGELES, CA	90068
MC CURRY, JEFF	BASEBALL	POST OFFICE BOX 3746, HILL STA	AUGUSTA, GA	30904
MC DADE, JOSEPH	U S CONGRESSMAN	514 SCRANTON LIFE BUILDING	SCRANTON, PA	18503
MC DANIEL, LE CHARLS	FOOTBALL COACH	POST OFFICE BOX 609609	SAN DIEGO, CA	92160
MC DANIEL, MEL	SINGER	191 DICKERSON BAY RD	GALLATIN, TN	37066
MC DANIEL, RANDALL	FOOTBALL	VIKINGS, 9520 VIKING DR	EDEN PRAIRIE, MN	55344
MC DANIEL, TERRY	BASEBALL	POST OFFICE BOX 1211	NORFOLK, VA	23502
MC DANIEL, TERRY	FOOTBALL	RAIDERS, 332 CENTER ST	EL SEGUNDO, CA	90245
MC DANIEL, XAVIER	BASKETBALL	POST OFFICE BOX C-900911	SEATTLE, WA	98109
MC DANIELS, GENE	SINGER	POST OFFICE BOX 82	GREAT NECK, NY	11021
MC DAVID, RAY	BASEBALL	12000 STADIUM RD	ADELANTO, CA	92301
MC DERMIT, MICKEY	SINGER	PROCESS, 439 WILEY AVE	FRANKLIN, PA	16323
MC DERMOTT, BRIAN	ACTOR-WRITER	27 UPPER BERKELEY ST	LONDON W1	ENGLAND
MC DERMOTT, DYLAN	ACTOR	CAA, 9830 WILSHIRE BLVD	BEVERLY HILLS, CA	90212
MC DERMOTT, HUGH J	TV DIRECTOR	1806 "B" ST	BELMAR, NJ	07719
MC DERMOTT, JIM	U S CONGRESSMAN	TOWER BUILDING, 1809 7TH AVE	SEATTLE, WA	98101
MC DERMOTT, THOMAS J	DIRECTOR	DGA, 7920 SUNSET BLVD, 6TH FL	LOS ANGELES, CA	90046
MC DEVITT, TOM	BASEBALL SCOUT	REDS, 100 RIVERFRONT STADIUM	CINCINNATI, OH	45202
MC DIVITT, JAMES A	ASTRONAUT	POST OFFICE BOX 3105	ANAHEIM, CA	92803
MC DONAGH, JUNE	FILM EDITOR	42 KINGFISHER DR, HAM		
		RICHMOND	SURREY	ENGLAND
MC DONALD, BARRY L	MUSIC ARRANGER	322 GREENWAY AVE	NASHVILLE, TN	37205
MC DONALD, BEN	BASEBALL	ORIOLE PARK, 333 W CAMDEN ST	BALTIMORE, MD	21201
MC DONALD, CHAD	BASEBALL	POST OFFICE BOX 15757	HARRISBURG, PA	17105
MC DONALD, CHRIS	MUSIC ARRANGER	4809 LYNN DR	NASHVILLE, TN	37211
MC DONALD, CHRISTOPHER	ACTOR	STONE MANNERS, 9113 SUNSET BL	LOS ANGELES, CA	90069
MC DONALD, GRAEME	TV DIRECTOR-PRODUCER	ANGILA TV FILMS & DRAMA, LTD		
		48 LEICESTER SQ	LONDON WC2H 7FB	ENGLAND

MC DONALD, JAMES B	COMPOSER	13907 JUDAH AVE	HAWTHORNE, CA	90250
MC DONALD, JERRY	ARTIST	180 CLIPPER ST	SAN FRANCISCO, CA	94114
MC DONALD, JOE	BASEBALL EXECUTIVE	TIGERS, TIGER STADIUM	DETROIT, MI	48216
MC DONALD, JOHN E	WRITER-PRODUCER	1548 OAK GROVE DR	LOS ANGELES, CA	90041
MC DONALD, KEVIN	BASEBALL	POST OFFICE BOX 3566	WEST PALM BEACH, FL	33402
MC DONALD, LE ROY	DIRECTOR	318 N BEVERLY DR #156	BEVERLY HILLS, CA	90210
MC DONALD, MARK	CINEMATOGRAPHER	THE LIBRARY SUITE, THE MANSION		
		OTTERSHAW PARK	SURREY	ENGLAND
MC DONALD, MAUREEN	COLUMNIST	POST OFFICE BOX 500	WASHINGTON, DC	20044
MC DONALD, MICHAEL	SINGER-SONGERWITER	345 N MAPLE ST #235	BEVERLY HILLS, CA	90210
MC DONALD, MIKE	BASEBALL	POST OFFICE BOX 4756	JACKSONVILLE, FL	32201
MC DONALD, MIKE	COMEDIAN	ECI, 29 COMMONWEATH AVE	BOSTON, MA	02116
MC DONALD, MIKE	FOOTBALL	RAMS, 2327 W LINCOLN BLVD	ANAHEIM, CA	92801
MC DONALD, QUINTUS	FOOTBALL	POST OFFICE BOX 535000	INDIANPOLIS, IN	46253
MC DONALD, ROBERT	DIRECTOR	45 GRAMERCY PARK N	NEW YORK, NY	10010
MC DONALD, TIM	FOOTBALL	POST OFFICE BOX 888	PHOENIX, AZ	85001
MC DONALD, TREVOR	TV JOURNALIST	ITN, WELL ST	LONDON W1	ENGLAND
MC DONNELL, M J	TV DIRECTOR	16 W 64TH ST	NEW YORK, NY	10023
MC DONNELL, MARY	ACTRESS	15760 VENTURA BLVD #1730	ENCINO, CA	91436
MC DONNELL, VIRGINIA B	WRITER	18 8TH ST	SHALMIAR, FL	32579
MC DONOUGH, DAN	BASEBALL EXECUTIVE	POST OFFICE BOX 64939	FAYETTEVILLE, NC	28306
MC DONOUGH, HUBIE	HOCKEY	NASSAU VETS MEMORIAL COLISEUM	UNIONDALE, NY	11553
MC DONOUGH, JOSEPH F	DIRECTOR	1000 W SADDLE RIVER RD	HO-HO-KUS, NJ	07423
MC DONOUGH, KIT	ACTRESS	9744 WILSHIRE BLVD #308	BEVERLY HILLS, CA	90212
MC DONOUGH, MARY	ACTRESS	2029 CENTURY PARK E #600	LOS ANGELES, CA	90067
MC DONOUGH, RICHARD J	DIRECTOR	9454 WILSHIRE BLVD #805	BEVERLY HILLS, CA	90212
MC DONOUGH, SEAN	SPORTSCASTER	WSBK-TV, 83 BIRMINGHAM PKWY	BOSTON, MA	02215
MC DONOUGH, WILL	COLUMNIST	THE BOSTON GLOBE		
		135 MORRISSEY BLVD	BOSTON, MA	02107
MC DORMAND, FRANCES	ACTRESS	280 RIVERSIDE DR	NEW YORK, NY	10025
MC DOUGAL, JULIUS	BASEBALL	CHIEFS, MAC ARTHUR STADIUM	SYRACUSE, NY	13208
MC DOUGALL, CALLUM	FILM DIRECTOR	3 CASTELLAIN RD, LITTLE VENICE	LONDON W9	ENGLAND
MC DOUGALL, DON	DIRECTOR	DGA, 7920 SUNSET BLVD, 6TH FL	LOS ANGELES, CA	90046
MC DOWALL, RODDY	ACTOR	3110 BROOKDALE RD	STUDIO CITY, CA	91604
MC DOWELL, BUBBA	FOOTBALL	OILERS, 6910 FANNIN ST	HOUSTON, TX	77070
MC DOWELL, JACK	BASEBALL	333 W 35TH ST	CHICAGO, IL	60616
MC DOWELL, MALCOLM	ACTOR	ICM, 388-396 OXFORD ST	LONDON W1	ENGLAND
MC DOWELL, ODDIBE	BASEBALL	10233 96TH AVE	EDMONTON, ALB TK5 0A5	CANADA
MC DOWELL, ROGER	BASEBALL	1000 ELYSIAN PARK DR	LOS ANGELES, CA	90012
MC DOWELL, RONNIE	SINGER	POST OFFICE BOX 452	PORTLAND, TN	37148
MC DUFFIE, JAMES E	COMPOSER-CONDUCTOR	1826 JEWETT DR	LOS ANGELES, CA	90046
MC DUFFIE, WAYNE	FOOTBALL COACH	FALCONS, SUWANEE RD AT I-85	SUWANEE, GA	30174
MC ELHINEY, BILL	MUSIC ARRANGER	1319 BURTON VALLEY RD	NASHVILLE, TN	37215
MC ELRATHESLICK, LORI	ARTIST	7528 TERRACE ST	KANSAS CITY, MO	64114
MC ELROY, CHUCK	BASEBALL	1060 W ADDISON ST	CHICAGO, IL	60613
MC ELROY, REGGIE	FOOTBALL	RAIDERS, 332 CENTER ST	EL SEGUNDO, CA	90245
MC ELROY, VANN	FOOTBALL	SEAHAWKS, 11220 NE 53RD ST	KIRKLAND, WA	98033
MC ELWEE, BOB	FOOTBALL REFEREE	NFL, 410 PARK AVE	NEW YORK, NY	10022
MC ENANEY, WILL	BASEBALL-COACH	POST OFFICE BOX 726	POMPANO BEACH, FL	33064
MC ENNAN, JAIME	ACTOR	KELMAN, 7813 SUNSET BLVD	LOS ANGELES, CA	90046
MC ENROE, ANNIE	ACTRESS	ROSENBERG, 8428 MELROSE PL #C	LOS ANGELES, CA	90069
MC ENROE, JOHN	TENNIS	23712 MALIBU COLONY DR	MALIBU, CA	90265
MC ENTIRE, REBA	SINGER	POST OFFICE BOX 121996	NASHVILLE, TN	37212
MC EUEN, JOHN	SINGER	9000 SUNSET BLVD #1200	LOS ANGELES, CA	90069
MC EVEETY, DERNARD	TV DIRECTOR	4420 HASKELL AVE	ENCINO, CA	91436
MC EVEETY, VINCENT	TV DIRECTOR	14561 MULHOLLAND DR	LOS ANGELES, CA	90077
MC EWAN, GERALDINE	ACTRESS	MARMONT MANAGEMENT, LTD		
		LANGHAM HOUSE, 308 REGENT ST	LONDON W1R 5AL	ENGLAND
MC EWEN, BOB	U S CONGRESSMAN	301 N HIGH ST	HILLSBORO, OH	45133
MC EWEN, CRAIG	FOOTBALL	POST OFFICE BOX 609609	SAN DIEGO, CA	92160
MC EWEN, KENNETH	TV DIRECTOR	35 SUNRISE DR	MONTVALE, NJ	07645
MC FADDEN, BARNEY	ACTOR	8730 SUNSET BLVD #480	LOS ANGELES, CA	90069
MC FADDEN, BOB	ACTOR	ALLAIRE PRODS, 360 ALLAIRE AVE	LEONIA, NJ	07605
MC FADDEN, GATES	ACTRESS	2510 CANYON DR	LOS ANGELES, CA	90068
MC FADDEN & WHITEHEAD	VOCAL DUO	FAA, 1700 BROADWAY, 5TH FLOOR	NEW YORK, NY	10019
MC FARLAND, SPANKY	ACTOR	8500 BUCKNER LN	FORT WORTH, TX	76100
MC FARLIN, JASON	BASEBALL	POST OFFICE BOX 21727	SAN FRANCISCO, CA	95151
MC FARLIN, TERRIC	BASEBALL	POST OFFICE BOX 10031	BAKERSFIELD, CA	93389
MC FERRIN, BOBBY	SINGER-SONGWRITER	600 W 58TH ST #9188	NEW YORK, NY	10019
MC GAFFIGAN, ANDY	BASEBALL	POST OFFICE BOX 419969	KANSAS CITY, MO	64141
MC GANN, DON	BASEBALL TRAINER	10233 96TH AVE	EDMONTON, ALB TK5 0A5	CANADA
MC GANN, MARK	FILM DIRECTOR	22 KING ST #19	NEW YORK, NY	10014
MC GANN, PAUL	ACTOR	7 WINDMILL ST	LONDON W1	ENGLAND
MC GARITY, JEREMY	BASEBALL	POST OFFICE BOX 12557	ST PETERSBURG, FL	33733
MC GARRIGLE, KATE & ANNA	VOCAL GROUP	611 BROADWAY #822	NEW YORK, NY	10012
MC GAVIN, DARREN	ACTOR	470 PARK AVE	NEW YORK, NY	10022
MC GAVIN, GRAEM	ACTRESS	POST OFFICE BOX 2958	BEVERLY HILLS, CA	90213
MC GEE, BRIAN	BASEBALL	1524 W NEBRASKA AVE	PEORIA, IL	61604
MC GEE, BUFORD	FOOTBALL	RAMS, 2327 W LINCOLN BLVD	ANAHEIM, CA	92801
MC GEE, HENRY	ACTOR	MAGERY ARMSTRONG MANAGEMENT		
		10 GREYCOAT GARDENS, GREYCOAT PL	LONDON SW1P 2QA	ENGLAND
MC GEE, HENRY	TV EXECUTIVE	HBO, 1100 6TH AVE	NEW YORK, NY	10036
MC GEE, JAMES R, JR	TV PRODUCER	KING FEATURES, 216 E 45TH ST	NEW YORK, NY	10017
MC GEE, JIM	NEWS REPORTER	MIAMI HERALD, 1 HERALD PLAZA	MIAMI, FL	33101
MC GEE, KIRK	SINGER	POST OFFICE BOX 626	FRANKLIN, TN	37064

MC GEE, TIM	FOOTBALL	BENGALS, 200 RIVERFRONT STADIUM	CINCINNATI, OH	45202
MC GEE, VONETTA	ACTRESS	9744 WILSHIRE BLVD #308	BEVERLY HILLS, CA	90212
MC GEE, WILLIE	BASEBALL	S F GIANTS, CANDLESTICK PARK	SAN FRANICSCO, CA	94124
MC GEHEE, KEVIN	BASEBALL	POST OFFICE BOX 3448	SHREVEPORT, LA	71133
MC GEORGE, MISSIE	GOLFER	2750 VOLUSA AVE #B	DAYTON BEACH, FL	32114
MC GHEE, JAMES W	DIRECTOR-PRODUCER	ROUTE #4, BOX 318, NICHOLS RD	LENOIR CITY, TN	37771
MC GHEE, KANAVIS	FOOTBALL	N Y GIANTS, GIANTS STADIUM	EAST RUTHERFORD, NJ	07073
MC GHEE, SCOTT	WRESTLER	POST OFFICE BOX 3859	STAMFORD, CT	06905
MC GHEE-ANDERSON, KATHLEEN	TV WRITER	9200 SUNSET BLVD #431	LOS ANGELES, CA	90069
MC GIBBON, DUNCAN SCOTT	TV WRITER	860 S WESTGATE AVE #205	LOS ANGELES, CA	90049
MC GIBBON, JOSANN	SCREENWRITER	9200 SUNSET BLVD #402	LOS ANGELES, CA	90069
MC GILL, BOB	HOCKEY	BLACKHAWKS, 1800 W MADISON ST	CHICAGO, IL	60612
MC GILL, TONY	SINGER	POST OFFICE BOX 23262	NASHVILLE, TN	37202
MC GILLIS, KELLY	ACTRESS	13428 MAXELLA AVE #513	MARINA DEL REY, CA	90292
MC GILLIVRAY, DAVID	TV WRITER	22-A BIRCHINGTON RD	LONDON NW6	ENGLAND
MC GINLEY, CHERIE J	TV DIRECTOR-PRODUCER	432 N OAKHURST DR #B	BEVERLY HILLS, CA	90210
MC GINLEY, JOHN R	FOOTBALL EXECUTIVE	STEELERS, 300 STADIUM CIR	PITTSBURGH, PA	15212
MC GINLEY, TED	ACTOR	3042 FRANKLIN CANYON DR	BEVERLY HILLS, CA	90210
MC GINN, CHRISTY	ACTRESS	ABC-TV, "ALL MY CHILDREN"		
		320 W 66TH ST	NEW YORK, NY	10023
MC GINNIS, DAVID	FOOTBALL COACH	BEARS, 250 N WASHINGTON RD	LAKE FOREST, IL	60045
MC GINNIS, ROBERT	ARTIST	13 ARCADIA RD	OLD GREENWICH, CT	06870
MC GINNIS, RUSS	BASEBALL	CUBS, 2ND & RIVERSIDE DR	DES MOINES, IA	50309
MC GINNISS, JOE	AUTHOR-NOVELIST	G P PUTNAM, 200 MADISON AVE	NEW YORK, NY	10016
MC GINTY, MICK	ARTIST	10008 ROSCOE BLVD	SUN VALLEY, CA	91352
MC GLOCKLIN, JON	BASKETBALL	BRADLEY CENTER, 1001 N 4TH ST	MILWAUKEE, WI	53203
MC GLONE, BRIAN	BASEBALL	POST OFFICE BOX 824	BURLINGTON, IA	52601
MC GLONE, WARREN	RAPPER-RAPWRITER	SEE - STEADY B		
MC GONAGLE, GEORGE	BASEBALL EXECUTIVE	POST OFFICE BOX 356	BLUEFIELD, WV	24701
MC GONNIGAL, BRETT	BASEBALL	POST OFFICE BOX 21727	SAN FRANCISCO, CA	95151
MC GONNIGAL, BRUCE	FOOTBALL	BROWNS, 80 1ST ST	BEREA, OH	44017
MC GOOHAN, PATRICK	ACT-WRI-DIR	16808 BOLLINGER DR	PACIFIC PALISADES, CA	90272
MC GOUGH, DORIN	ACTRESS	1239 N SWEETZER AVE #12	LOS ANGELES, CA	90069
MC GOUGH, GREG	BASEBALL	POST OFFICE BOX 4370	SALINAS, CA	93912
MC GOVERN, ELIZABETH	ACTRESS	17319 MAGNOLIA BLVD	ENCINO, CA	91316
MC GOVERN, GEORGE	POLITICIAN	POST OFFICE BOX 5591 (FS)	WASHINGTON, DC	20016
MC GOVERN, MAUREEN	SINGER	529 W 42ND ST #7-F	NEW YORK, NY	10036
MC GOVERN, ROB	FOOTBALL	STEELERS, 300 STADIUM CIR	PITTSBURGH, PA	15212
MC GOWAN, STUART E	TV WRITER-DIRECTOR	12133 HUSTON ST	NORTH HOLLYWOOD, CA	91607
MC GOWAN, TOM	ACTOR-WRITER	8955 BEVERLY BLVD	WEST HOLLYWOOD, CA	90048
MC GOY, NEAL	SINGER	3198 ROYAL LN #204	DALLAS, TX	75229
MC GRADY, BRYNJA	ACTRESS	1800 N HIGHLAND AVE #405	LOS ANGELES, CA	90028
MC GRADY, MIKE	FILM CRITIC	NEWSDAY, 1500 BROADWAY	NEW YORK, NY	10036
MC GRADY, PHYLLIS	DIRECTOR	649 W DEMING PL #2-W	CHICAGO, IL	60614
MC GRAIL, DAVID L	TV DIRECTOR	56 MARION RD	WESTPORT, CT	06880
MC GRATH, BOB	SINGER	GREENGRASS, 16 E 48TH ST	NEW YORK, NY	10017
MC GRATH, DEREK	ACTOR-WRITER	201 N ROBERTSON BLVD #A	BEVERLY HILLS, CA	90211
MC GRATH, JOHN	TV WRITER-DIRECTOR	FREEWAY FILMS, 67 GEORGE ST	EDINBURGH EH2 2JG	ENGLAND
MC GRATH, JOSEPH	TV WRITER-DIRECTOR	ICM, 388-396 OXFORD ST	LONDON W1	ENGLAND
MC GRATH, KERRY	ACTRESS	7461 BEVERLY BLVD #400	LOS ANGELES, CA	90036
MC GRATH, MICHAEL	TREASURER	STATE CAPTOL BLDG, AURORA AVE	SAINT PAUL, MN	55155
MC GRATH, RAYMOND	U S CONGRESSMAN	203 ROCKAWAY AVE	VALLEY STREAM, NY	11580
MC GRAW, TOM	BASEBALL (COACH)	METS, 126TH ST & ROOSEVELT AVE	FLUSHING, NY	11368
MC GRAW, TOM	BASEBALL (PITCHER)	POST OFFICE BOX 8550	STOCKTON, CA	95208
MC GRAW, TUG	BASEBALL	2318 PEROT ST	PHILADELPHIA, PA	19130
MC GREEVEY, MICHAEL S	TV WRITER	25603 ALMENDRA DR	VALENCIA, CA	91355
MC GREGOR, SCOTT	BASEBALL	STAR ROUTE 1, BOX 2800-133	TEHACHAPI, CA	93561
MC GRIFF, FRED	BASEBALL	POST OFFICE BOX 2000	SAN DIEGO, CA	92112
MC GRIFF, TERRY	BASEBALL	POST OFFICE BOX 27045	TUCSON, AZ	85726
MC GRIGGS, LAMAR	FOOTBALL	N Y GIANTS, GIANTS STADIUM	EAST RUTHERFORD, NJ	07073
MC GRORY, MARY	NEWS REPORTER	UPS, 4900 MAIN ST, 9TH FLOOR	KANSAS CITY, MO	64112
MC GRUDER, MICHAEL	FOOTBALL	DOLPHINS, 2269 NW 199TH ST	MIAMI, FL	33056
MC GUANE, THOMAS	WRITER-PRODUCER	HOFFMAN ROUTE	LIVINGSTON, MT	59047
MC GUINN, ROGER	SINGER-SONGWRITER	POST OFFICE BOX 1265	MORRO BAY, CA	93442
MC GUIRE, AL	SPORTSCASTER	NBC SPORTS, 30 ROCKEFELLER PLZ	NEW YORK, NY	10112
MC GUIRE, BARRY	SINGER-EVANGLIST	POST OFFICE BOX 320	LINDALE, TX	75771
MC GUIRE, BIFF	ACTOR	315 W 57TH ST #4-H	NEW YORK, NY	10019
MC GUIRE, BILL	BASEBALL-COACH	4668 DREXEL ST	OMAHA, NE	68117
MC GUIRE, BILL	SINGER	3125 19TH ST #217	BAKERSFIELD, CA	93301
MC GUIRE, DON	SCREENWRITER	8955 BEVERLY BLVD	WEST HOLLYWOOD, CA	90048
MC GUIRE, DOROTHY	ACTRESS	121 COPLEY PL	BEVERLY HILLS, CA	90210
MC GUIRE, MAEVE	ACTRESS	10100 SANTA MONICA BLVD #1600	LOS ANGELES, CA	90067
MC GUIRE, MICHAEL	ACTOR	9229 SUNSET BLVD #311	LOS ANGELES, CA	90069
MC GUIRE, MICKEY	DIRECTOR	7309 FRANKLIN AVE #102	LOS ANGELES, CA	90046
MC GUIRE, PATRICK D	ACTOR	10662 1/2 EASTBORNE AVE	LOS ANGELES, CA	90024
MC GUIRE, PHYLLIS	SINGER	100 RANCHO CIR	LAS VEGAS, NV	89119
MC GUIRE, SARAH	GOLFER	2750 VOLUSA AVE #B	DAYTON BEACH, FL	32114
MC GWIRE, DAN	FOOTBALL	SEAHAWKS, 11220 NE 53RD ST	KIRKLAND, WA	98033
MC GWIRE, MARK	BASEBALL	ATHLETICS'S, OAKLAND COLISEUM	OAKLAND, CA	94621
MC HAFFIE, DEBORAH	GOLFER	2750 VOLUSA AVE #B	DAYTON BEACH, FL	32114
MC HALE, JOHN	BASEBALL EXECUTIVE	CANADIANS, 4601 ONTARIO ST	VANCOUVER, BC V5V 3H4	CANADA
MC HALE, KEVIN	BASKETBALL	151 MERRIMAC ST	BOSTON, MA	02114
MC HALE, TOM	FOOTBALL	BUCCANEERS, 1 BUCCANEER PL	TAMPA, FL	33607
MC HAMMER	RAPPER-RAPWRITER	SEE - HAMMER		
MC HATTIE, STEPHEN	ACTOR	853 7TH AVE #9-A	NEW YORK, NY	10019

MC HUGH, JUDY	TALENT AGENT	8601 WILSHIRE BLVD #1000	BEVERLY HILLS, CA	90211
MC HUGH, MATTHEW F	U S CONGRESSMAN	CARRIAGE HOUSE-TERRACE HILL	ITHACA, NY	14850
MC ILVAINE, JOE	BASEBALL EXECUTIVE	POST OFFICE BOX 2000	SAN DIEGO, CA	92112
MC INDOO, HILARY	TV WRITER	52 WESTON RD	WESTPORT, CT	06880
MC INERNEY, STEVE	BASEBALL TRAINER	POST OFFICE BOX 6212	TOLEDO, OH	43614
MC INNERNY, TIM	ACTOR	HOPE, 108 LEONARD ST	LONDON EC2A 4RH	ENGLAND
MC INTIRE, THOMAS	MUSIC ARRANGER	622-A ERMAC DR	NASHVILLE, TN	37210
MC INTOSH, TIM	BASEBALL	2850 W 20TH AVE	DENVER, CO	80211
MC INTYRE, GUY	FOOTBALL	S F 49ERS, 4949 CENTENNIAL BL	SANTA CLARA, CA	95054
MC INTYRE, JOE	BASEBALL	POST OFFICE BOX 1721	SPARTANBURG, SC	29304
MC INTYRE, JOHN	ACTOR	RURAL ROUTE #1	TROY, MT	59935
MC INTYRE, JOHN	HOCKEY	POST OFFICE BOX 17013	INGLEWOOD, CA	90308
MC INTYRE, REBA	SINGER	POST OFFICE BOX 121996	NASHVILLE, TN	37212
MC JULIEN, PAUL	FOOTBALL	PACKERS, 1265 LOMBARDI AVE	GREEN BAY, WI	54307
MC KAMIE, SEAN	BASEBALL	POST OFFICE BOX 2887	VERO BEACH, FL	32961
MC KANNA, WILLIAM R	DIRECTOR	1 UNION SQUARE W	NEW YORK, NY	10003
MC KAY, CRAIG	FILM EDITOR	ACE, 1041 N FORMOSA AVE	WEST HOLLYWOOD, CA	90046
MC KAY, DAVE	BASEBALL-COACH	ATHLETICS'S, OAKLAND COLISEUM	OAKLAND, CA	94621
MC KAY, GARDNER	ACTOR	445 KAWAILOA RD #10	KAILUA, HI	96734
MC KAY, JEFF	BASEBALL SCOUT	POST OFFICE BOX 419969	KANSAS CITY, MO	64141
MC KAY, JIM	TV SPORTS HOST	47 W 66TH ST	NEW YORK, NY	10023
MC KAY, MARION	COMPOSER-CONDUCTOR	220 COLLINGWOOD AVE	DAYTON, OH	45419
MC KAY, PEGGY	ACTRESS	10351 SANTA MONICA BLVD #211	LOS ANGELES, CA	90025
MC KAY, RANDY	HOCKEY	RED WINGS, 600 CIVIC CENTER DR	DETROIT, MI	48226
MC KAY, RON	BASEBALL COACH	POST OFFICE BOX 751	UTICA, NY	13503
MC KAY, THERESA	SINGER	4680 ELK LAKE DR #304	VICTORIA, BC	CANADA
MC KEAN, JIM	BASEBALL UMPIRE	4601 DOVER ST NE	SAINT PETERSBURG, FL	33703
MC KEAN, MICHAEL	ACTOR	3570 WILLOWCREST AVE	STUDIO CITY, CA	91604
MC KEAN, MICHAEL JOHN	TV WRITER-DIRECTOR	12143 MAXWELLTON RD	STUDIO CITY, CA	91604
MC KEAN, SUE ANN	BODYBUILDER	POST OFFICE BOX 4466	MOUNTAIN VIEW, CA	94040
MC KEAND, CAROL EVAN	TV WRITER-PRODUCER	507 N ALTA DR	BEVERLY HILLS, CA	90210
MC KEAND, MARTIN	TV PRODUCER	56 FITZJOHNS AVE	LONDON NW3	ENGLAND
MC KEAND, NIGEL	TV WRITER-PRODUCER	507 N ALTA DR	BEVERLY HILLS, CA	90210
MC KEE, PAMELA	ACTRESS	616 W 7TH ST	COLUMBIA, TN	38401
MC KEE, ROBERT O	TV WRITER	9022 SUNSET BLVD #531	LOS ANGELES, CA	90069
MC KEE, RON	BASEBALL EXECUTIVE	POST OFFICE BOX 1556	ASHEVILLE, NC	28802
MC KEE, TODD	ACTOR	4514 FARMDALE AVE	NORTH HOLLYWOOD, CA	91602
MC KEE, WILLIAM (ERIE)	BASEBALL EXECUTIVE	POST OFFICE BOX 488	ERIE, PA	16512
MC KEE, WILLIAM (ROCKFORD)	BASEBALL EXECUTIVE	POST OFFICE BOX 6748	ROCKFORD, IL	61125
MC KEEFE, ELLEN	TV EXECUTIVE	NBC-TV, 30 ROCKEFELLER PLAZA	NEW YORK, NY	10112
MC KEEL, WALT	BASEBALL	POST OFFICE BOX 10213	LYNCHBURG, VA	24506
MC KEGNEY, TONY	HOCKEY	BLACKHAWKS, 1800 W MADISON ST	CHICAGO, IL	60612
MC KEITHEN, W FOX	SECRETARY OF STATE	POST OFFICE BOX 94004	BATON ROUGE, LA	70804
MC KEITHENS, THE	C & W GROUP	POST OFFICE BOX 8078	NASHVILLE, TN	37207
MC KELLAR, DANICA	ACTRESS	4151 PROSPECT AVE	HOLLYWOOD, CA	90027
MC KELLEN, IAN	ACTOR	25 EARL'S TERR	LONDON W8	ENGLAND
MC KELLER, KEITH	FOOTBALL	BILLS, 1 BILLS DR	ORCHARD PARK, NJ	14127
MC KENNA, ANDREW	BASEBALL EXECUTIVE	1060 W ADDISON ST	CHICAGO, IL	60613
MC KENNA, CHRIS	ACTOR	ABC-TV, "ONE LIFE TO LIVE"		
		56 W 66TH ST	NEW YORK, NY	10023
MC KENNA, JAMES	TV EXECUTIVE	CBS-TV, 51 W 52ND ST	NEW YORK, NY	10019
MC KENNA, THOMAS PATRICK	ACTOR	535 KINGS RD, 19 THE PLAZA #2	LODNON SW10 OSZ	ENGLAND
MC KENNA, VIRGINIA	ACTRESS	67 GLEBE PL	LONDON SW3	ENGLAND
MC KENZIE, DICK	FOOTBALL REFEREE	NFL, 410 PARK AVE	NEW YORK, NY	10022
MC KENZIE, JIM	HOCKEY	WHALERS, 1 CIVIC CENTER PLAZA	HARTFORD, CT	06103
MC KENZIE, JULIA	ACTRESS	YOUNG, 31 KINGS RD	LONDON SN3 4RP	ENGLAND
MC KENZIE, KATIE	SINGER	4540 KEARNY VILLA RD #114	SAN DIEGO, CA	92123
MC KENZIE, RALEIGH	FOOTBALL	POST OFFICE BOX 17247 (DULLES)	WASHINGTON, DC	20041
MC KENZIE WALDMAN, FAY	ACTRESS	4325 REDWOOD AVE #2	MARINA DEL REY, CA	90292
MC KEON, BRIAN	BASEBALL	12000 STADIUM RD	ADELANTO, CA	92301
MC KEON, DOUG	ACTOR	818 6TH ST #202	SANTA MONICA, CA	90403
MC KEON, JACK	BASEBALL-EXECUTIVE	9985 RUE CHANTENAR	SAN DIEGO, CA	92131
MC KEON, NANCY	ACTRESS	POST OFFICE BOX 6778	BURBANK, CA	91510
MC KEON, PHILIP	ACTOR	POST OFFICE BOX 6778	BURBANK, CA	91510
MC KERN, LEO	ACTOR	12 SUMMERHILL RD	OXFORD OX2 7JY	ENGLAND
MC KERNAN, JOHN R, JR	GOVERNOR	STATE HOUSE BUILDING	AUGUSTA, GA	04333
MC KEY, DERRICK	BASKETBALL	POST OFFICE BOX C-900911	SEATTLE, WA	98109
MC KINNEY, BILL	ACTOR-SINGER	BDP, 10637 BURBANK BLVD	NORTH HOLLYWOOD, CA	91601
MC KINNEY, BILLY	BASKETBALL EXECUTIVE	TIMBERWOLVES, 600 1ST AVE N	MINNEAPOLIS, MN	55403
MC KINNEY, PAT	SINGER	TAYLOR, 2401 12TH AVE S	NASHVILLE, TN	37204
MC KINNON, FRED	CINEMATOGRAPHER	7715 SUNSET BLVD #150	LOS ANGELES, CA	90046
MC KINNON, ROBERT	TV DIRECTOR	1365 YORK AVE #20-H	NEW YORK, NY	10021
MC KINSEY, BEVERLEE	ACTRESS	CBS-TV, "THE GUIDING LIGHT"		
		222 E 44TH ST	NEW YORK, NY	10017
MC KISSACK, PERRI ARLETTE	SINGER-SONGWRITER	SEE - PEBBLES		
MC KITTRICK, BOBB	FOOTBALL COACH	S F 49ERS, 4949 CENTENNIAL BL	SANTA CLARA, CA	95054
MC KNIGHT, DENNIS	FOOTBALL	EAGLES, BROAD ST & PATTISON AVE	PHILADELPHIA, PA	19148
MC KNIGHT, JEFF	BASEBALL	POST OFFICE BOX 1211	NORFOLK, VA	23502
MC KNIGHT, MARK	BASEBALL SCOUT	INDIANS, CLEVELAND STADIUM	CLEVELAND, OH	44114
MC KNIGHT, THOMAS	TV DIRECTOR	25547 VIA JARDIN	VALENCIA, CA	91355
MC KOY, KEITH	BASEBALL	POST OFFICE BOX 611	WATERLOO, IA	50704
MC KUEN, ROD	SINGER-POET	1155 ANGELO DR	BEVERLY HILLS, CA	90210
MC KYER, TIM	FOOTBALL	FALCONS, SUWANEE RD AT I-85	SUWANEE, GA	30174
MC LAGAN, IAN	SINGER	POST OFFICE BOX 2276	GARDEN GROVE, CA	92642
MC LAGLEN, ANDREW	FILM DIRECTOR	POST OFFICE BOX 1056	FRIDAY HARBOR, WA	98250

Name	Occupation	Address	City/State	Zip/Country
MC LAIN, CHARLES	BASEBALL	POST OFFICE BOX 4669	CHARLESTON, WV	25304
MC LAIN, DENNY	BASEBALL-KEYBOARDIST	6093 WATERVIEW CT	BLOOMFIELD, MI	48322
MC LAIN, TOMMY	SINGER	MEAUX, 566 BROCK ST	HOUSTON, TX	77023
MC LAREN, DUNCAN	CINEMATOGRAPHER	MOONBEAM COTTAGE, HIGH ST		
		BAGSHOT	SURREY GU19 5AH	ENGLAND
MC LAREN, JOHN	BASEBALL-COACH	FENWAY PARK, 4 YAWKEY WY	BOSTON, MA	02215
MC LAREN, SALLY	ACTRESS-TV HOST	GLASS, 28 BERKELEY SQ	LONDON W1X 6HD	ENGLAND
MC LAUGHLIN, BRIAN	MUSIC EXECUTIVE	BROADCAST MUSIC, 320 W 57TH ST	NEW YORK, NY	10019
MC LAUGHLIN, DICK	BASEBALL-INSTRUCTOR	1000 ELYSIAN PARK DR	LOS ANGELES, CA	90012
MC LAUGHLIN, JIM	BASEBALL SCOUT	POST OFFICE BOX 2000	ANAHEIM, CA	92803
MC LAUGHLIN, JOHN	SINGER-SONGWRITER	KURLAND, 173 BRIGHTON AVE	BOSTON, MA	02134
MC LEAN, DON	SINGER-SONGWRITER	OLD MANITOU RD	GARRISON, NY	10524
MC LEAN, MICHAEL	PRODUCER	WARNER BROTHERS, INC		
		4000 WARNER BLVD	BURBANK, CA	91522
MC LEAN, MICHAEL	TV DIRECTOR	4200 HAYVENHURST AVE	ENCINO, CA	91436
MC LEAN, WILSON	ARTIST	902 BROADWAY	NEW YORK, NY	10010
MC LEMORE, MARK	BASEBALL	ORIOLE PARK, 333 W CAMDEN ST	BALTIMORE, MD	21201
MC LEOD, BRIAN	BASEBALL	POST OFFICE BOX 21727	SAN FRANCISCO, CA	95151
MC LEOD, CATHERINE	ACTRESS	4146 ALLOTT AVE	VAN NUYS, CA	91423
MC LERIE, ALLYN ANN	ACTRESS	3344 CAMPANIL DR	SANTA BARBARA, CA	93109
MC LISH, CAL	BASEBALL-SCOUT	BREWERS, 201 S 46TH ST	MILWAUKEE, WI	53214
MC LISH, RACHEL	BODYBUILDER	3114 ABINGTON ST	BEVERLY HILLS, CA	90210
MC LLWAIN, DAVE	HOCKEY	JETS, 15-1430 MAROONS RD	WINNIPEG, MAN R3G 0L5	CANADA
MC LURE, BEN	BASEBALL SCOUT	SKYDOME, 300 BREMMER BL #3200	TORONTO, ONT M5V 3B3	CANADA
MC LYTE	RAPPER-RAPWRITER	FAA, 1700 BROADWAY, 5TH FLOOR	NEW YORK, NY	10019
MC MAHON, ED	TV HOST-ACTOR	NBC-TV, 3000 W ALAMEDA AVE	BURBANK, CA	91523
MC MAHON, FRANKLIN	ARTIST	1665 W DEVONSHIRE LN	LAKE FOREST, IL	60045
MC MAHON, JENNA	WRITER-PRODUCER	CAA, 9830 WILSHIRE BLVD	BEVERLY HILLS, CA	90212
MC MAHON, JIM	FOOTBALL	EAGLES, BROAD ST & PATTISON AVE	PHILADELPHIA, PA	19148
MC MAHON, JOHN	TV PRODUCER	CARSON, 10045 RIVERSIDE DR	TOLUCA LAKE, CA	91602
MC MAHON, LEO J	WRITER	6501 CAMELLIA AVE	NORTH HOLLYWOOD, CA	91606
MC MANUS, MARSHA	TALENT AGENT	SMITH, 121 N SAN VICENTE BLVD	BEVERLY HILLS, CA	90211
MC MANUS, MICHAEL L	ACTOR-WRITER	5127 GREENBUSH AVE	SHERMAN OAKS, CA	91423
MC MANUS, SEAN	TV EXECUTIVE	NBC SPORTS, 30 ROCKEFELLER PLZ	NEW YORK, NY	10112
MC MARTIN, JOHN	ACTOR	SAMES-ROLLNICK, 250 W 57TH ST	NEW YORK, NY	10107
MC MENAMIN, PATRIC ALAN	SCREENWRITER	7279 WOODROW WILSON DR	LOS ANGELES, CA	90068
MC MICHAEL, CHUCK	BASEBALL SCOUT	POST OFFICE BOX 419969	KANSAS CITY, MO	64141
MC MICHAEL, GREG	BASEBALL	POST OFFICE BOX 16683	GREENVILLE, SC	29606
MC MICHAEL, STEVE	FOOTBALL	BEARS, 250 N WASHINGTON RD	LAKE FOREST, IL	60045
MC MILLAN, DOUG	BASEBALL SCOUT	S F GIANTS, CANDLESTICK PARK	SAN FRANICSCO, CA	94124
MC MILLAN, ERIK	FOOTBALL	N Y JETS, 1000 FULTON AVE	HEMPSTEAD, NY	11550
MC MILLAN, J ALEX	U S CONGRESSMAN	401 TRADE ST, ROOM 222	CHARLOTTE, NC	28202
MC MILLAN, NATE	BASKETBALL	POST OFFICE BOX C-900911	SEATTLE, WA	98109
MC MILLAN, RONNIE	ACTOR	611 N HOWARD ST #107	GLENDALE, CA	91206
MC MILLAN, ROY	BASEBALL-SCOUT	6850 LAWRENCE RD	LANTANA, FL	33462
MC MILLEN, C THOMAS	U S CONGRESSMAN	6196 OXON HILL RD #370	OXON HILL, MD	20745
MC MILLEN, PAT	TV PRODUCER	"DONAHUE", 30 ROCKEFELLER PLAZA	NEW YORK, NY	10112
MC MILLIAN, AUDRAY	FOOTBALL	VIKINGS, 9520 VIKING DR	EDEN PRAIRIE, MN	55344
MC MULLAN, JAMES	ARTIST	VISIBLE STUDIO, 99 LEXINGTON AVE	NEW YORK, NY	10016
MC MULLAN, JIM	ACTOR	515 MOUNT HOLYOKE AVE	PACIFIC PALISADES, CA	90272
MC MULLEN, JAY	WRITER-PRODUCER	DGA, 110 W 57TH ST	NEW YORK, NY	10019
MC MULLEN, JIM	ACTOR	515 MOUNT HOLYOKE AVE	PACIFIC PALISADES, CA	90272
MC MULLEN, JOHN	BASEBALL EXECUTIVE	POST OFFICE BOX 288	HOUSTON, TX	77001
MC MURRAY, BROCK	BASEBALL	POST OFFICE BOX 10031	BAKERSFIELD, CA	93389
MC MURRAY, MARY	FILM DIRECTOR	CONWAY, 18-21 JERMYN ST	LONDON SW1	ENGLAND
MC MURRY, MURRY	ACTOR	922 N CORDOVA ST	BURBANK, CA	91505
MC MURTREY, JOAN	ACTRESS	SMITH, 121 N SAN VICENTE BLVD	BEVERLY HILLS, CA	90211
MC MURTRY, CRAIG	BASEBALL	55 ROSE DR	TROY, TX	76579
MC MURTRY, LARRY	SCREENWRITER	POST OFFICE BOX 552	ARCHER CITY, TX	76351
MC MURTY, CRAIG	BASEBALL	5999 E VAN BUREN ST	PHOENIX, AZ	85008
MC MYLER, PAMELA	ACTRESS	1680 N VINE ST #203	HOLLYWOOD, CA	90028
MC NABB, BUCK	BASEBALL	POST OFFICE BOX 824	BURLINGTON, IA	52601
MC NAIR, BARBARA	ACTRESS-SINGER	8721 SUNSET BLVD #PH-7	LOS ANGELES, CA	90069
MC NALLY, JIM	FOOTBALL COACH	BENGALS, 200 RIVERFRONT STADIUM	CINCINNATI, OH	45202
MC NALLY, KEVIN	ACTOR-WRITER	162-A LADBROOKE GROVE	LONDON W10	ENGLAND
MC NALLY, STEPHEN	ACTOR	624 N HILLCREST RD	BEVERLY HILLS, CA	90210
MC NALLY, TERRENCE	ACTOR-PLAYWRIGHT	218 W 10TH ST	NEW YORK, NY	10014
MC NAMARA, DENNY	BASEBALL	POST OFFICE BOX 2785	LAKELAND, FL	33806
MC NAMARA, DERMOT	ACTOR	556 MAIN ST	ROOSEVELT ISLAND, NY	10044
MC NAMARA, JIM	BASEBALL	S F GIANTS, CANDLESTICK PARK	SAN FRANICSCO, CA	94124
MC NAMARA, JOHN	BASEBALL MANAGER	1008 WILSON PIKE	BRENTWOOD, TN	37021
MC NAMARA, JULIANNE	ACTRESS	3500 W OLIVE AVE #1400	BURBANK, CA	91505
MC NAMARA, MARK	BASKETBALL	POST OFFICE BOX 76	ORLANDO, FL	32802
MC NAMARA, PATRICK	ACTOR	27350 ESCONDIDO BEACH RD #114	MALIBU, CA	90265
MC NAMARA, ROBERT	POLITICIAN	2412 TRACY PL, NW	WASHINGTON, DC	20008
MC NAMARA, WILLIAM	ACTOR	1124 W ANGELENO AVE #M	BURBANK, CA	91506
MC NEAL, TRAVIS	FOOTBALL	SEAHAWKS, 11220 NE 53RD ST	KIRKLAND, WA	98033
MC NEEL, RICHARD	ARTIST	222 WILLOW AVE #5	HOBOKEN, NJ	07012
MC NEELY, BIG JAY	SAXOPHONIST	843 S MARIPOSA AVE #5	LOS ANGELES, CA	90005
MC NEELY, JEFF	BASEBALL	POST OFFICE BOX 1718	NEW BRITAIN, CT	06050
MC NEELY, JERRY	WRITER-PRODUCER	4240 GAYLE DR	TARZANA, CA	91356
MC NEELY, LARRY	BANJOIST	17530 VENTURA BLVD #108	ENCINO, CA	91316
MC NEICE, IAN	ACTOR	MARKHAM AND FROGGATT, LTD		
		JULIAN HOUSE, 4 WINDMILL ST	LONDON W1P 1HF	ENGLAND
MC NEIL, FREEMAN	FOOTBALL	N Y JETS, 1000 FULTON AVE	HEMPSTEAD, NY	11550

MC NEIL, KATE	ACTRESS	3248 OAKSHIRE DR	LOS ANGELES, CA	90068
MC NEIL, LESLIE	DIRECTOR	299 RIVERSIDE DR	NEW YORK, NY	10024
MC NEILL, DON	TV-RADIO HOST	110 DE WINDT	WINNETKA, IL	60093
MC NEILL, HARRY	TV DIRECTOR	107 S HIGHLAND AVE	SOUTH NYACK, NY	10960
MC NEILL, HARRY J	ACTOR	8446 LANGDON AVE #4	SEPULVEDA, CA	91343
MC NEILL, MIKE	HOCKEY	NORDIQUES, 2205 AVE DU COLISEE	QUEBEC, QUE G1L 4W7	CANADA
MC NEW, JULIE	BODYBUILDER	POST OFFICE BOX 86	SANTA MONICA, CA	90406
MC NICHOL, JIMMY	ACTOR-SINGER	POST OFFICE BOX 5813	SHERMAN OAKS, CA	91413
MC NICHOL, KRISTY	ACTRESS	POST OFFICE BOX 5813	SHERMAN OAKS, CA	91413
MC NICHOL, TOMMY	ACTOR-SINGER	1717 N HIGHLAND AVE #414	LOS ANGELES, CA	90028
MC NKIGHT, JEFF	BASEBALL	500 NORTON ST	ROCHESTER, NY	14621
MC NULTY, FRANK	PUBLISHING EXECUTIVE	PARADE, 750 3RD AVE	NEW YORK, NY	10017
MC NULTY, MICHAEL R	U S CONGRESSMAN	33 2NS ST	TROY, NY	12180
MC NURTY, GREG	FOOTBALL	PATRIOTS, FOXBORO STADIUM, RT #1	FOXBORO, MA	02035
MC PEAKE BROTHERS, THE	C & W GROUP	1215 W NORTH ST	WYTHEVILLE, VA	24382
MC PHAIL, DAVID	ARTIST	E P DUTTON/CHILDREN'S BOOKS		
		2 PARK AVE	NEW YORK, NY	10016
MC PHAIL, MARLIN	BASEBALL COACH	POST OFFICE BOX 7845	COLUMBIA, SC	29202
MC PHARLIN, J JAMES	TV DIRECTOR	ABC-TV, 190 N STATE ST	CHICAGO, IL	60601
MC PHEE, JOHN	WRITER	475 DRAKE'S CORNER RD	PRINCETON, NJ	08540
MC PHEE, MIKE	HOCKEY	CANADIENS, 2313 ST CATHERINE ST	MONTREAL, QUE H3H 1N2	CANADA
MC PHERSON, BILL	FOOTBALL COACH	S F 49ERS, 4949 CENTENNIAL BL	SANTA CLARA, CA	95054
MC PHERSON, CRAIG	ARTIST	112 E 19TH ST #3-F	NEW YORK, NY	10003
MC PHERSON, DON	DIRECTOR	EGGERS, 6345 FOUNTAIN AVE	HOLLYWOOD, CA	90028
MC PHERSON, JOHN A	FILM DIRECTOR	445 S BEVERLY DR #310	BEVERLY HILLS, CA	90212
MC PHERSON, PATRICIA	ACTRESS	145 S FAIRFAX AVE #310	LOS ANGELES, CA	90036
MC PHERSON, STEPHEN F	TV WRITER-DIRECTOR	8225 LINCOLN TERR	LOS ANGELES, CA	90069
MC PHILLIPS, HUGH	TV DIRECTOR	4256 CAHUENGA BLVD	NORTH HOLLYWOOD, CA	91602
MC QUAKER, LYNNE	ACTRESS	430 S CLOVERDALE AVE #22	LOS ANGELES, CA	90036
MC QUEEN, BUTTERFLY	ACTRESS	3060-A DENT ST, TERRANCE MANOR	AUGUSTA, GA	30906
MC QUEEN, CHAD	ACTOR	8306 WILSHIRE BLVD #438	BEVERLY HILLS, CA	90211
MC QUEEN, DAVE	BASEBALL TRAINER	136 S SYCAMORE	ELIZABETHTON, TN	37643
MC QUEEN, MAX	FILM CRITIC	POST OFFICE BOX 1547	MESA, AZ	85201
MC QUEEN, NEILE	ACTRESS	TOFFEL, 2323 BOWMONT DR	BEVERLY HILLS, CA	90210
MC QUEEN, STACY TOTTEN	MODEL	POST OFFICE BOX 6867	MALIBU, CA	90265
MC QUIRE, BILL	SINGER	3125 19TH ST #217	BAKERSFIELD, CA	93301
MC RAE, BASIL	HOCKEY	NORTH STARS, 7901 CEDAR AVE S	BLOOMINGTON, MN	55425
MC RAE, BRIAN	BASEBALL	POST OFFICE BOX 419969	KANSAS CITY, MO	64141
MC RAE, CARMEN	SINGER-ACTRESS	2200 SUMMITRIDGE DR	BEVERLY HILLS, CA	90210
MC RAE, CHARLES	FOOTBALL	BUCCANEERS, 1 BUCCANEER PL	TAMPA, FL	33607
MC RAE, HAL	BASEBALL-MANAGER	POST OFFICE BOX 419969	KANSAS CITY, MO	64141
MC RAE, PAUL ANTHONY	CONDUCTOR	POST OFFICE BOX 160	HIGHLAND PARK, IL	60035
MC RANEY, GERALD	ACTOR-DIRECTOR	329 N WETHERLY DR #101	BEVERLY HILLS, CA	90211
MC REYNOLDS, DALE	BASEBALL SCOUT	1000 ELYSIAN PARK DR	LOS ANGELES, CA	90012
MC REYNOLDS, JAMES	SINGER-GUITARIST	POST OFFICE BOX 304	GALLATIN, TN	37066
MC REYNOLDS, JESSE	SINGER-GUITARIST	POST OFFICE BOX 304	GALLATIN, TN	37066
MC REYNOLDS, JESSE KEITH	SINGER-GUITARIST	ROUTE #2, BOX 60-D	GALLATIN, TN	37066
MC REYNOLDS, JIM & JESSE	VOCAL DUO	POST OFFICE BOX BOX 304	GALLATIN, TN	37066
MC REYNOLDS, KEVIN	BASEBALL	POST OFFICE BOX 419969	KANSAS CITY, MO	64141
MC ROBERTS, BRIONY	ACTRESS	BURNETT, 42-43 GRAFTON HOUSE		
		2-3 GOLDEN SQ	LONDON W1R 3AD	ENGLAND
MC SERCH	RAPPER-RAPWRITER	POST OFFICE BOX 4455	NEW YORK, NY	10101
MC SHAN	RAPPER-RAPWRITER	FAA, 1700 BROADWAY, 5TH FLOOR	NEW YORK, NY	10019
MC SHANE, IAN	ACTOR	999 N DOHENY DR #PH	LOS ANGELES, CA	90069
MC SHANE, JOE	BASEBALL EXECUTIVE	525 NW PEACOCK BLVD	PORT SAINT LUCIE, FL	34986
MC SHANE, JOHN D	DIRECTOR	15 CHRISTOPHER ST	NEW YORK, NY	10014
MC SHERRY, JOHN	BASEBALL UMPIRE	31 OGDEN PL W	DOBBS FERRY, NY	10522
MC SHY D	RAPPER-RAPWRITERS	FAA, 1700 BROADWAY, 5TH FLOOR	NEW YORK, NY	10019
MC SORLEY, MARTY	HOCKEY	POST OFFICE BOX 17013	INGLEWOOD, CA	90308
MC TIERNAN, JOHN	FILM WRITER-DIRECTOR	151 S EL CAMINO DR	BEVERLY HILLS, CA	90212
MC VAY, JOHN	FOOTBALL EXECUTIVE	S F 49ERS, 4949 CENTENNIAL BL	SANTA CLARA, CA	95054
MC VAY, LEWIS	SINGER	HEARTLAND, 660 DOUGLAS AVE	ALTAMONTE SPRINGS, FL	32714
MC VICAR, DANIEL	ACTOR	CBS-TV, "THE BOLD & BEAUTIFUL"		
		7800 BEVERLY BLVD #3371	LOS ANGELES, CA	90036
MC VIE, CHRISTINE	SINGER-SONGWRITER	9744 LLOYDCREST DR	BEVERLY HILLS, CA	90210
MC VIE, JOHN	SINGER-SONGWRITER	12304 ADDISON ST	NORTH HOLLYWOOD, CA	91607
MC WANE, RICK	BASEBALL TRAINER	POST OFFICE BOX 5645	ORLANDO, FL	32855
MC WETHY, JOHN F	NEWS CORRESPONDENT	ABC NEWS, 1717 DE SALES ST, NW	WASHINGTON, DC	20036
MC WHERTER, NED	GOVERNOR	STATE CAPITOL BUILDING	NASHVILLE, TN	37243
MC WILLIAM, TIM	BASEBALL	POST OFFICE BOX 1420	WICHITA, KS	67201
MC WILLIAMS, CAROLINE	ACTRESS	2195 MANDEVILLE CANYON	LOS ANGELES, CA	90049
MC WILLIAMS, FLEMING	SINGER	POST OFFICE BOX 211	EAST PRAIRIE, MO	63845
MC WILLIAMS, KEN & THE SOUTHERN	C & W GROUP	POST OFFICE BOX 4234	PANORAMA CITY, CA	91412
MC WILLIAMS, LARRY	BASEBALL	736 HENSON DR	HURST, TX	76053
MC WILLIAMS, PETE	TV PRODUCER	209 E 25TH ST #4-A	NEW YORK, NY	10010
MEACHAM, RUSTY	BASEBALL	POST OFFICE BOX 3665	OMAHA, NE	68103
MEAD, ROBERT	TREASURER	STATE CAPITOL BUILDING	FRANKFORT, KY	40601
MEAD, TERRY M	MUSIC ARRANGER	704 HERITAGE SQ DR	MADISON, TN	37115
MEADE, JULIA	ACTRESS	1010 5TH AVE	NEW YORK, NY	10028
MEADE, PAUL	BASEBALL	POST OFFICE BOX 1886	COLUMBUS, GA	31902
MEADOW, BARRY	TV WRITER	9000 SUNSET BLVD #1200	LOS ANGELES, CA	90069
MEADOWS, AUDREY	ACTRESS	350 TROUSDALE PL	BEVERLY HILLS, CA	90210
MEADOWS, JAYNE	ACTRESS	16185 WOODVALE RD	ENCINO, CA	91436
MEADOWS, JOYCE	ACTRESS	9250 WILSHIRE BLVD #208	BEVERLY HILLS, CA	90212
MEADOWS, KRISTEN	ACTRESS	15301 VENTURA BLVD #345	SHERMAN OAKS, CA	91403

MEADOWS, LOUIE	BASEBALL	POST OFFICE BOX 3449	SCRANTON, PA 18505
MEADOWS, SCOTT	BASEBALL	500 NORTON ST	ROCHESTER, NY 14621
MEADS, DON	BASEBALL	BOX 70, FEDERAL RD	ENGLISHTOWN, NJ 07726
MEADS, JOHNNY	FOOTBALL	OILERS, 6910 FANNIN ST	HOUSTON, TX 77070
MEAGHER, KEVIN M	WRITER-PRODUCER	110 WORTH ST #3	NEW YORK, NY 10013
MEAGHER, RICK	HOCKEY	BLUES, 5700 OAKLAND AVE	SAINT LOUIS, MO 63110
MEALING, PENNY	SINGER	9200 SUNSET BLVD #621	LOS ANGELES, CA 90069
MEALS, JERRY	BASEBALL UMPIRE	POST OFFICE BOX 608	GROVE CITY, OH 43123
MEALY, BARBARA	ACTRESS	1605 N CAHUENGA BLVD #202	LOS ANGELES, CA 90028
MEANS, HOWARD	COMMENTATOR	KING FEATURES, 216 E 45TH ST	NEW YORK, NY 10017
MEANS, JOHN A	TV DIRECTOR	4707 LA VILLA MARINA #H	MARINA DEL REY, CA 90292
MEANS, MARIANNE	COMMENTATOR	KING FEATURES, 216 E 45TH ST	NEW YORK, NY 10017
MEARA, ANNE	COMEDIENNE-ACTRESS	118 RIVERSIDE DR #5-A	NEW YORK, NY 10024
MEARES, PAT	BASEBALL	POST OFFICE BOX 5645	ORLANDO, FL 32855
MEAT PUPPETS, THE	ROCK & ROLL GROUP	POST OFFICE BOX 110	TEMPE, AZ 85281
MEATLOAF	SINGER-SONGWRITER	BOX 68, STOCKPORT	CHESHIRE SK3 OJY ENGLAND
MECHSNER, SUSAN	ACTRESS-MODEL	S M TALENT, 1408 S PALM AVE	SAN GABRIEL, CA 91776
MECIR, JIM	BASEBALL	POST OFFICE BOX 30160	SAN BERNARDINO, CA 92413
MECKLENBURG, KARL	FOOTBALL	BRONCOS, 13655 BRONCOS PKWY	ENGLEWOOD, CO 80112
MECO	MUSICAL GROUP	RANDALL, 9340 DAVANA RD	SHERMAN OAKS, CA 91403
MEDAK, KAREN	ACTRESS	301 N CANON DR #305	BEVERLY HILLS, CA 90210
MEDAK, PETER	FILM DIRECTOR	1712 STANLEY AVE	LOS ANGELES, CA 90046
MEDAVOY, MIKE	FILM EXECUTIVE	9262 OAKMERE RD	LOS ANGELES, CA 90035
MEDDICK, JIM	CARTOONIST	UNITED FEATURE, 200 PARK AVE	NEW YORK, NY 10166
MEDFORD, DON	FILM DIRECTOR	1 DRIFTWOOD ST #6	MARINA DEL REY, CA 90292
MEDFORD, LISA	DIRECTOR	4240 VIA MARINA #33	MARINA DEL REY, CA 90292
MEDFORD, LYNN PARKER	ACTRESS	9300 WILSHIRE BLVD #410	BEVERLY HILLS, CA 90212
MEDIATE, ROCCO	GOLFER	POST OFFICE BOX 109601	PALM BCH GARDENS, FL 33418
MEDIAVILLA, RICK	BASEBALL	POST OFFICE BOX 3783	SAVANNAH, GA 31414
MEDIEVAL STEEL	ROCK & ROLL GROUP	1254 LAMAR AVE #312	MEMPHIS, TN 38114
MEDINA, LUIS	BASEBALL	POST OFFICE BOX 3665	OMAHA, NE 68103
MEDINA, PATRICIA	ACTRESS	10000 SANTA MONICA BLVD #305	LOS ANGELES, CA 90067
MEDLEY, BILL	SINGER-SONGWRITER	THE HOP, 18774 BROOKHURST ST	FOUNTAIN VALLEY, CA 92708
MEDLIN, JAMES E	SCREENWRITER	8955 BEVERLY BLVD	WEST HOLLYWOOD, CA 90048
MEDLINSKY, HARVEY	DIRECTOR	9555 W OLYMPIC BLVD	BEVERLY HILLS, CA 90212
MEDLOCK, T TRAVIS	ATTORNEY GENERAL	POST OFFICE BOX 11369	COLUMBIA, SC 29211
MEDOWAY, CARY C	WRITER-PRODUCER	859 N FULLER AVE	LOS ANGELES, CA 90046
MEDUSA	MUSICAL GROUP	50 MUSIC SQUARE W #102	NASHVILLE, TN 37203
MEDVED, DOUG	FANTASY ARTIST	5654 N 19TH AVE	PHOENIX, AZ 85015
MEDVED, MICHAEL	WRITER-FILM CRITIC	1224 ASHLAND AVE	SANTA MONICA, CA 90405
MEDVIN, SCOTT	BASEBALL	4712 MICHAEL AVE	NORTH OLMSTEAD, OH 44070
MEDWIN, MICHAEL	ACT-WRI-PROD	COULSON, 37 BERWICK ST	LONDON W1V 3RF ENGLAND
MEEGAN, GENE	BASEBALL EXECUTIVE	POST OFFICE BOX 4606	HELENA, MT 59604
MEEHAN, JOHN	CHOREOGRAPHER	AMERICAN BALLET, 888 7TH AVE	NEW YORK, NY 10019
MEEHAN, THOMAS E	SCREENWRITER	555 W 57TH ST #1230	NEW YORK, NY 10019
MEEK, STAN	BASEBALL SCOUT	TIGERS, TIGER STADIUM	DETROIT, MI 48216
MEEKER, TONY	TREASURER	STATE CAPITOL BUILDING	SALEM, OR 97310
MEEKS, TIM	BASEBALL	POST OFFICE BOX 450	BUFFALO, NY 14205
MEENTS, SCOTT	BASKETBALL	POST OFFICE BOX C-900911	SEATTLE, WA 98109
MEETINGS, THE	ROCK & ROLL GROUP	ROCKFEVER, 535 BROADWAY	LAWRENCE, MA 01841
MEGADETH	ROCK & ROLL GROUP	888 7TH AVE #1602	NEW YORK, NY 10019
MEGAHEY, LESLIE	TV WRITER-DIRECTOR	3 HOLLY VILLAS, WELLESLEY AVE	LONDON W6 ENGLAND
MEGAHY, FRANCIS	WRITER-PRODUCER	BEDFORD PRODS, 6 VIGO ST	LONDON W1X 1AH ENGLAND
MEGGETT, DAVID	FOOTBALL	N Y GIANTS, GIANTS STADIUM	EAST RUTHERFORD, NJ 07073
MEGGS, BROWN	SCREENWRITER	1450 EL MIRADOR DR	PASADENA, CA 91103
MEGNOT, ROYA	ACTRESS	9229 SUNSET BLVD #311	LOS ANGELES, CA 90069
MEHLER, EDWARD	ACTOR	8831 SUNSET BLVD #402	LOS ANGELES, CA 90069
MEHTA, MEHLI	CONDUCTOR	321 TILDEN AVE	LOS ANGELES, CA 90049
MEIER, DON	WRITER-PRODUCER	320 LOCUST RD, BOX 279	WINNETKA, IL 60093
MEILANDT, TONY	TALENT AGENT	1680 N VINE ST #1101	HOLLYWOOD, CA 90028
MEISEL, ANN	ARTIST	270 PARK AVE S #10-C	NEW YORK, NY 10010
MEISNER, GUNTER	ACTOR	SCHILDHORNSTR 74	D-1000 BERLIN 41 GERMANY
MEISNER, RANDY	SINGER-SONGWRITER	2565 ZORADA DR	LOS ANGELES, CA 90046
MEISSNER, JOE	COMPOSER	5015 BILOXI AVE	NORTH HOLLYWOOD, CA 91601
MEISSNER, SCOTT	BASEBALL TRAINER	POST OFFICE BOX 8550	STOCKTON, CA 95208
MEISSNER, STAN	SINGER	41 BRITAIN ST #200	TORONTO, ONT M5A 1R7 CANADA
MEISTER, DAVID L	CABLE EXECUTIVE	INFOTECH, 600 MADISON AVE	NEW YORK, NY 10022
MEJIA, DELFINO	BASEBALL	POST OFFICE BOX 11363	RENO, NV 89510
MEJIA, ROBERT	BASEBALL	POST OFFICE BOX 2887	VERO BEACH, FL 32961
MEJIAS, SAM	BASEBALL-MANAGER	POST OFFICE BOX 5646	PRINCETON, WV 24740
MEKLER, OSCAR	CONDUCTOR	386 HUNTLEY DR	LOS ANGELES, CA 90048
MEKONS, THE	ROCK & ROLL GROUP	6 CLIFTON MANSIONS	
		COLDHARBOR LN, BRIXTON	LONDON SW9 8LL ENGLAND
MELANDER, JON	FOOTBALL	PATRIOTS, FOXBORO STADIUM, RT #1	FOXBORO, MA 02035
MELANIE	SINGER	DENIS VAUGHAN MANAGEMENT	
		HEATHCOAT HOUSE	
		18-20 SAVILE RD	LONDON W1 ENGLAND
MELCHIOR, IB J	WRITER-PRODUCER	8228 MARMONT LN	LOS ANGELES, CA 90069
MELE, ARTHUR	DIRECTOR	3387 N KNOLL DR	LOS ANGELES, CA 90068
MELE, GARY	ARTIST	1029 PARK AVE	HOBOKEN, NJ 07030
MELE, SAM	BASEBALL-MANAGER	FENWAY PARK, 4 YAWKEY WY	BOSTON, MA 02215
MELENDEZ, JOSE	BASEBALL	POST OFFICE BOX 2000	SAN DIEGO, CA 92112
MELENDEZ, LUIS	BASEBALL-INSTRUCTOR	250 STADIUM PLAZA	ST LOUIS, MO 63102
MELENDEZ, STEVE	BASEBALL TRAINER	POST OFFICE BOX 4488	WINSTON-SALEM, NC 27115
MELESKI, MARK	BASEBALL COACH	POST OFFICE BOX 2365	PAWTUCKET, RI 02861

Name	Occupation	Address	City	Zip/Country
MELGAR, FABIAN	ARTIST	381 PARK AVE S	NEW YORK, NY	10016
MELLANBY, SCOTT	HOCKEY	FLYERS, SPECTRUM, PATTISON PL	PHILADELPHIA, PA	19148
MELLE, GIL	COMPOSER	6404 WILSHIRE BLVD #900	LOS ANGELES, CA	90048
MELLENCAMP, JOHN COUGAR	SINGER-SONGWRITER	ROUTE #1, BOX 361	NASHVILLE, IN	47448
MELLINGER, LEONIE	ACTRESS	535 KINGS RD, 19 THE PLAZA #2	LODNON SW10 OSZ	ENGLAND
MELLINGER, MICHAEL	ACTOR	L'EPINE SMITH, 10 WYNDHAM PL	LONDON W1H 1AS	ENGLAND
MELLNER, SHIRLEY	TV PRODUCER	10000 SANTA MONICA BLVD #310	LOS ANGELES, CA	90067
MELLOR, TOM	BASEBALL UMPIRE	2101 E BROADWAY #35	TEMPE, AZ	85282
MELLOW, DICK	MUSIC ARRANGER	921 KIRKWOOD AVE	NASHVILLE, TN	37204
MELMAN, JEFFREY	DIRECTOR-PRODUCER	3694 BUENA PARK DR	STUDIO CITY, CA	91604
MELMAN, LARRY "BUD"	ACTOR-COMEDIAN	30 ROCKEFELLER PLAZA #1410-W	NEW YORK, NY	10112
MELMED, JERRY	DIRECTOR	45 5TH AVE	NEW YORK, NY	10003
MELNICK, DANIEL	FILM PRODUCER	1123 SUNSET HILLS DR	LOS ANGELES, CA	90069
MELNICK, MARK	FILM EDITOR	ACE, 1041 N FORMOSA AVE	WEST HOLLYWOOD, CA	90046
MELO, JUAN	BASEBALL SCOUT	250 STADIUM PLAZA	ST LOUIS, MO	63102
MELO, NIELS	DIRECTOR-PRODUCER	POST OFFICE BOX 1116	BELMONT, CA	94002
MELONAS, EMILIE	ACTRESS	1241 1/2 N JUNE ST	LOS ANGELES, CA	90038
MELTON, BARRY "THE FISH"	SINGER-SONGWRITER	17337 VENTURA BLVD #300-C	ENCINO, CA	91316
MELTON, FRANKLIN	TV DIRECTOR	13950 NW PASSAGE	MARINA DEL REY, CA	90292
MELTON, SID	ACTOR	5347 CEDROS AVE	VAN NUYS, CA	91410
MELTZER, MARTHA	TV WRITER	17525 LORNE ST	NORTHRIDGE, CA	91325
MELTZER, NEWTON	WRITER-PRODUCER	67 YALE ST	ROSLYN HEIGHTS, NY	11577
MELVILLE, LOUIS	ACTOR	22-A CYGNET HOUSE, 188 KINGS RD	LONDON SW3	ENGLAND
MELVIN, ALLAN	ACTOR	271 N BOWLING GREEN WY	LOS ANGELES, CA	90049
MELVIN, BILL	BASEBALL	POST OFFICE DRAWER 1207	ZEBULON, NC	27597
MELVIN, BOB	BASEBALL	POST OFFICE BOX 419969	KANSAS CITY, MO	64141
MELVIN, DONNIE	SINGER	45 OVERLOOK TERR	NEW YORK, NY	10033
MELVIN, DOUG	BASEBALL EXECUTIVE	ORIOLE PARK, 333 W CAMDEN ST	BALTIMORE, MD	21201
MELVIN, HAROLD & THE BLUE NOTES	VOCAL GROUP	PLAZA 1000, SUITE 622	VOORHEES, NJ	08043
MELVIN, MURRAY	ACTOR	535 KINGS RD, 19 THE PLAZA #2	LODNON SW10 OSZ	ENGLAND
MELVIN, VIRGIL	BASEBALL SCOUT	250 STADIUM PLAZA	ST LOUIS, MO	63102
MELVOIN, JEFF	TV WRITER	153 GRETA GREEN WY	LOS ANGELES, CA	90049
MELVOIN, MICHAEL	COMPOSER	5638 CARLTON WY	LOS ANGELES, CA	90028
MEMMOTT, MARK	COLUMNIST	POST OFFICE BOX 500	WASHINGTON, DC	20044
MEN WITHOUT HATS	ROCK & ROLL GROUP	41 BRITAIN ST #200	TORONTO, ONT M5A 1R7	CANADA
MENCHEL, DONALD	TV EXECUTIVE	445 PARK AVE	NEW YORK, NY	10022
MENCHER, HY	ACTOR	325 W 86TH ST	NEW YORK, NY	10024
MENDELSOHN, ALFRED	DIRECTOR	129 E 82ND ST	NEW YORK, NY	10028
MENDELSOHN, JACK	TV WRITER	14066 ROBLAR RD	SHERMAN OAKS, CA	91423
MENDELSON, LEE	WRITER-PRODUCER	1408 CHAPIN AVE	BURLINGAME, CA	94010
MENDELUK, GEORGE	DIRECTOR-PRODUCER	6263 TOPIA DR	MALIBU, CA	90265
MENDENHALL, KIRT	BASEBALL	TIGERS, 89 WHARNCLIFFE RD N	LONDON, ONT N6H 2A7	CANADA
MENDENHALL, MATT	BODYBUILDER	POST OFFICE BOX 934	SANTA MONICA, CA	90406
MENDEZ, JESUS	BASEBALL	POST OFFICE BOX 5599	LITTLE ROCK, AR	72215
MENDEZ, RICARDO	BASEBALL	POST OFFICE BOX 882	MADISON, WI	53701
MENDILLO, STEPHEN	ACTOR	BOB WATERS, 1501 BROADWAY	NEW YORK, NY	10036
MENDLESON, ANTHONY	COSTUME DESIGNER	37 CROMWELL RD	LONDON SW7	ENGLAND
MENDOZA, MARIO	BASEBALL-MANAGER	POST OFFICE BOX 1742	PALM SPRINGS, CA	92263
MENDOZA, MINNIE	BASEBALL EXECUTIVE	INDIANS, CLEVELAND STADIUM	CLEVELAND, OH	44114
MENDOZA, NICOLAS OLIVEROS	DIRECTOR	DGA, 7920 SUNSET BLVD, 6TH FL	LOS ANGELES, CA	90046
MENDOZA, VINCENT J	COMPOSER	12300 PACIFIC AVE	LOS ANGELES, CA	90066
MENEDEZ, JESUS	BASEBALL	POST OFFICE BOX 36407	LOUISVILLE, KY	40233
MENEES, TIM	CARTOONIST	UPS, 4900 MAIN ST, 9TH FLOOR	KANSAS CITY, MO	64112
MENEFEE, PETE	COSTUME DESIGNER	13949 VENTURA BLVD #309	SHERMAN OAKS, CA	91423
MENENDEZ, DANNY	BASEBALL SCOUT	BREWERS, 201 S 46TH ST	MILWAUKEE, WI	53214
MENENDEZ, RAMON	FILM DIRECTOR	DGA, 7920 SUNSET BLVD, 6TH FL	LOS ANGELES, CA	90046
MENENDEZ, TONY	BASEBALL	POST OFFICE BOX 23290	NASHVILLE, TN	37202
MENGEL, BRAD	BASEBALL	633 JESSAMINE ST	KNOXVILLE, TN	37917
MENGER, WILLIAM H	WRITER	1862 S NEWELL RD	MALIBU, CA	90265
MENGES, CHRIS	FILM DIRECTOR	7 WESLEYAN PL	LONDON NW5 1LG	ENGLAND
MENHART, PAUL	BASEBALL	633 JESSAMINE ST	KNOXVILLE, TN	37917
MENKE, DENIS	BASEBALL-COACH	POST OFFICE BOX 7575	PHILADELPHIA, PA	19101
MENKEN, ALAN	RECORD PRODUCER	3432 LA SOMBRA DR	LOS ANGELES, CA	90068
MENKEN, SHEPARD	ACTOR	3401 S COAST VIEW DR	MALIBU, CA	90265
MENKIN, LAWRENCE	WRITER-PRODUCER	SAN FRANCISCO LITERARY AGENCY		
		899 E FRANCISCO BLVD	SAN RAFAEL, CA	94901
MENNIN, PETER	COMPOSER	JUILLIARD SCHOOL OF MUSIC		
		LINCOLN CENTER	NEW YORK, NY	10023
MENOTTI, GARY	TV DIRECTOR	1503 1/2 W 10TH ST	AUSTIN, TX	78703
MENOTTI, GIAN CARLO	COMPOSER	GILFORD HADDINGTON	E LOTHIAN EH41 4JF	SCOTLAND
MENSY, TIM	SINGER-SONGWRITER	MORESS, 1209 16TH AVE S	NASHVILLE, TN	37212
MENTAL AS ANYTHING	ROCK & ROLL GROUP	OLD SOUTH HEAD RD #17-79	BONDI JUNCTION NSW	AUSTRALIA
MENTEER, DAVID	TV DIRECTOR	4104 MAGNA CARTA RD	WOODLAND HILLS, CA	91364
MENTEER, GARY	WRITER-PRODUCER	1907 N CURSON AVE	LOS ANGELES, CA	90046
MENTION, MICHEL H	COMPOSER	21747 CANON DR	TOPANGA, CA	90290
MENTORS, THE	ROCK & ROLL GROUP	POST OFFICE BOX 2428	EL SEGUNDO, CA	90245
MENUDO	ROCK & ROLL GROUP	PADOSA HATO REY		
		157 PONCE DE LEON	SAN JUAN	PUERTO RICO
MENUHIN, YEHUDI	VIOLINIST	BUHLSTR	CH-3730 GSTAAD-NEURET	SWITZERLAND
MENVILLE, CHARLES	TV WRITER	31833 BROAD BEACH RD	MALIBU, CA	90265
MENZA, DONALD J	COMPOSER	12328 MAGNOLIA BLVD	NORTH HOLLYWOOD, CA	91607
MENZHUBER, CHUCK	BASEBALL SCOUT	250 STADIUM PLAZA	ST LOUIS, MO	63102
MENZIES, HEATHER	ACTRESS	15930 WOODVALE RD	ENCINO, CA	91436
MENZIES, JAMES C	TV WRITER	15925 KITTRIDGE ST	VAN NUYS, CA	91406
MEPHITIS, PAT	SCREENWRITER	555 W 57TH ST #1230	NEW YORK, NY	10019

Name	Occupation	Address	City	Zip/Country
MERCADIER, MARTHE	ACTRESS	1 RUE PAUL DELAROCHE	PARIS 75016	FRANCE
MERCADO, BUDDY	BASEBALL SCOUT	INDIANS, CLEVELAND STADIUM	CLEVELAND, OH	44114
MERCADO, ORLANDO	BASEBALL	POST OFFICE BOX 1211	NORFOLK, VA	23502
MERCADO, RAFAEL	BASEBALL	POST OFFICE BOX 11363	RENO, NV	89510
MERCED, ORLANDO	BASEBALL	POST OFFICE BOX 7000	PITTSBURGH, PA	15212
MERCEDES, FELICIANO	BASEBALL	POST OFFICE BOX 418	SAINT CHARLES, IL	60174
MERCEDES, HENRY	BASEBALL	POST OFFICE BOX 11087	TACOMA, WA	98411
MERCEDES, JUAN	BASEBALL	POST OFFICE BOX 418	SAINT CHARLES, IL	60174
MERCEDES, LUIS	BASEBALL	500 NORTON ST	ROCHESTER, NY	14621
MERCER, JANE	WRITER	27 WESTCROFT SQ	LONDON W6 OTD	ENGLAND
MERCER, MARIAN	ACTRESS	25901 PIUMA	CALABASAS, CA	91302
MERCER, ROBERT PIERCE	TALENT AGENT	POST OFFICE BOX 2458	TOLUCA LAKE, CA	91602
MERCEY BROTHERS, THE	C & W GROUP	4680 ELK LAKE DR #304	VICTORIA, BC V8Z 5M1	CANADA
MERCHAN, RICHARD	ARTIST	27-09 24TH AVE	ASTORIA, NY	11102
MERCHANT, ISMAIL	FILM PRODUCER	46 LEXINGTON ST	LONDON W1	ENGLAND
MERCHANT, MARK	BASEBALL	POST OFFICE BOX 4756	JACKSONVILLE, FL	32201
MERCKER, KENT	BASEBALL	POST OFFICE BOX 4064	ATLANTA, GA	30302
MERCOURI, MELINA	ACTRESS	ANAGNOSTROPOULON 25	ATHENS	GREECE
MERCURIO, MICOLE	ACTRESS	1999 AVE OF THE STARS #2850	LOS ANGELES, CA	90067
MERCY RIVER BOYS, THE	C & W GROUP	6750 W 75TH ST, BLDG #2-A	OVERLAND PARK, KS	66204
MERCYFUL FATE	ROCK & ROLL GROUP	328 HVIDOREVEJ	3TV 2650 HVIDOVRE	DENMARK
MERDIN, JONATHAN L	DIRECTOR	DGA, 110 W 57TH ST	NEW YORK, NY	10019
MEREDITH, BURGESS	ACT-WRI-DIR	POST OFFICE BOX 757	MALIBU, CA	90265
MEREDITH, DON	ACTOR	POST OFFICE BOX 597	SANTE FE, NM	87504
MEREDITH, JO ANNE	ACTRESS	SHERRELL, 1354 LAS ROBLES DR	PALM SPRINGS, CA	92262
MEREDITH, LEE	ACTRESS	STRATFORD, 221 W 57TH ST	NEW YORK, NY	10019
MEREDITH, SUSAN, AARON RUSSELL	C & W GROUP	TESSIER, 505 CANTON PASS	MADISON, TN	37115
MERIGLIANO, FRANK	BASEBALL	POST OFFICE BOX 360007	BIRMINGHAM, AL	35236
MERIL, MACHA	ACTRESS	AG ALPHA ARTISTS AGENCE		
		27 RUE DE LA POMPE	PARIS 75016	FRANCE
MERIWETHER, CHUCK	BASEBALL UMPIRE	POST OFFICE BOX 608	GROVE CITY, OH	43123
MERIWETHER, LEE	ACTRESS	POST OFFICE BOX 260402	ENCINO, CA	91326
MERKEL, BILLY	BASEBALL SCOUT	ATHLETICS'S, OAKLAND COLISEUM	OAKLAND, CA	94621
MERKLE, JAY J	TV EXECUTIVE	33 BEDFORD CENTER RD	BEDFORD HILLS, NY	10507
MERLIN, BARBARA	WRITER	3044 MOTOR AVE	LOS ANGELES, CA	90064
MERLIN, JAN	ACTOR-WRITER	9016 WONDERLAND AVE	LOS ANGELES, CA	90046
MERLIS, GEORGE	TV PRODUCER	PARAMOUNT TELEVISION		
		ENTERTAINMENT TONIGHT		
		5555 MELROSE AVE	LOS ANGELES, CA	90038
MERRELL, MURIEL L	COMPOSER	823 LAUREL AVE	LOS ANGELES, CA	90046
MERRELL, RICHARD	ACTOR	300 E 46TH ST	NEW YORK, NY	10017
MERRICK, DAVID	THEATER PRODUCER	246 W 44TH ST	NEW YORK, NY	10036
MERRICK, DAWN	ACTRESS	9000 SUNSET BLVD #1200	LOS ANGELES, CA	90069
MERRICK, MIKE	THEATER PRODUCER	9000 SUNSET BLVD	LOS ANGELES, CA	90069
MERRIFIELD, DOUG	BASEBALL TRAINER	633 JESSAMINE ST	KNOXVILLE, TN	37917
MERRIFIELD, ED	FOOTBALL REFEREE	NFL, 410 PARK AVE	NEW YORK, NY	10022
MERRILL, BOB	COMPOSER	ASCAP, 1 LINCOLN PLAZA	NEW YORK, NY	10023
MERRILL, CAROL	MODEL	29800 W CUTHBERT RD	MALIBU, CA	90265
MERRILL, DINA	ACTRESS	POST OFFICE BOX 67-B-69	LOS ANGELES, CA	90067
MERRILL, DURWOOD	BASEBALL UMPIRE	POST OFFICE BOX 115	HOOKS, TX	75561
MERRILL, GARY	ACTOR	THORNHURST RD	FALMOUTH FORESIDE, MA	04105
MERRILL, HOWARD	TV WRITER	136 S PALM DR	BEVERLY HILLS, CA	90212
MERRILL, KIETH	WRITER-PRODUCER	11930 RHUS RIDGE RD	LOS ALTOS, CA	94022
MERRILL, ROBERT	BARITONE	79 OXFORD DR	NEW ROCHELLE, NY	10801
MERRILL, SI	DIRECTOR	DGA, 110 W 57TH ST	NEW YORK, NY	10019
MERRILL, STUMP	BASEBALL-MANAGER	18 MERRYMEETING RD	TOPSHAM, ME	04086
MERRIMAN, BRETT	BASEBALL	POST OFFICE BOX 12	MIDLAND, TX	79702
MERRIMAN, CATHY	ACTRESS	850 7TH AVE #1003	NEW YORK, NY	10019
MERRITT, JERRY	SINGER	STUDIO ONE, 4009 E 18TH ST	VANCOUVER, WA	98661
MERRITT, STANLEY S	WRITER-PRODUCER	DGA, 110 W 57TH ST	NEW YORK, NY	10019
MERRITT, STEVE	CHOREOGRAPHER	8235 SANTA MONICA BLVD #302	LOS ANGELES, CA	90046
MERRITT, TERESA	ACTRESS	192-06 110TH RD	SAINT ALBANS, NY	11412
MERRIWEATHER, JAMES	BASEBALL	POST OFFICE BOX 64939	FAYETTEVILLE, NC	28306
MERRIWEATHER, MIKE	FOOTBALL	VIKINGS, 9520 VIKING DR	EDEN PRAIRIE, MN	55344
MERSEREAU, SCOTT	FOOTBALL	N Y JETS, 1000 FULTON AVE	HEMPSTEAD, NY	11550
MERTEN, LAURI	GOLFER	2750 VOLUSA AVE #B	DAYTON BEACH, FL	32114
MERTENS, PATRICIA	ACTRESS	315 E 70TH ST #1-H	NEW YORK, NY	10021
MERULLO, MATT	BASEBALL	333 W 35TH ST	CHICAGO, IL	60616
MERWALD, FRANK	TV DIRECTOR-PRODUCER	3734 CLARINGTON AVE #5	LOS ANGELES, CA	90034
MERY-CLARK, LAURENCE	FILM EDITOR	34 KENSINGTON SQ	LONDON W8 5HH	ENGLAND
MES, DE DE	SINGER	MICK LLOYD, 817 18TH AVE S	NASHVILLE, TN	37203
MES, ERICA	BODYBUILDER	BETTER BODIES MODEL &		
		SPORTS MANAGEMENT COMPANY		
		12 W 21ST ST	NEW YORK, NY	10010
MESA, JOSE	BASEBALL	ORIOLE PARK, 333 W CAMDEN ST	BALTIMORE, MD	21201
MESE, JOHN	BODYBUILDER	NPC, 170 NE 99TH ST	MIAMI SHORES, FL	33138
MESSECAR, CAROL ANN	TV-COMEDY WRITER	215 ANDREW ST	MAMARONECK, NY	10543
MESSENGER SERVICE	ROCK & ROLL GROUP	FPM, 1256 JAMAICA PLAIN STATION	BOSTON, MA	02130
MESSICK, DALE	CARTOONIST	TRIBUNE, 64 E CONCORD ST	ORLANDO, FL	32801
MESSICK, DON	ACTOR-VOICE OVERS	POST OFFICE BOX 5426	SANTA BARBARA, CA	93108
MESSICK, KATHY	ACTRESS	8075 W 3RD ST #550	LOS ANGELES, CA	90048
MESSIER, MARK	HOCKEY	OILERS, NORTHLANDS COLISEUM	EDMONTON, ALTA T5B 4M9	CANADA
MESSINA, DIANNE	TV WRITER	14413 COLLINS ST	VAN NUYS, CA	91401
MESSINA, JIM	SINGER-SONGWRITER	2110 E VALLEY RD	SANTA BARBARA, CA	93108
MESSINA, PHILLIP	FILM WRITER-DIRECTOR	358 S CITRUS AVE	LOS ANGELES, CA	90036

MESSING, HAROLD	DIRECTOR	61 W 62ND ST	NEW YORK, NY	10023
MESSINGER, DOMINIC A	COMPOSER-CONDUCTOR	12000 RHODE ISLAND AVE #4	LOS ANGELES, CA	90025
MESSMORE, FRANCIS B	ART DIRECTOR	530 W 28TH ST	NEW YORK, NY	10001
MESSURI, ANTHONY C	DIRECTOR	16 FAIRVIEW AVE	TARRYTOWN, NY	10591
MESTER, JORGE	CONDUCTOR	ICM, 40 W 57TH ST	NEW YORK, NY	10019
METAL MC	ROCK & ROLL GROUP	FAA, 1700 BROADWAY, 5TH FLOOR	NEW YORK, NY	10019
METCALF, ERIC	FOOTBALL	BROWNS, 80 1ST ST	BEREA, OH	44017
METCALF, LAURIE	ACTRESS	6755 TYRONE AVE	VAN NUYS, CA	91406
METCALFE, BURT	TV WRITER-DIRECTOR	11800 BROOKDALE LN	STUDIO CITY, CA	91604
METCALFE, GORDON	ACTOR	2523 IVAN HILL TERR	LOS ANGELES, CA	90039
METH, MYRNA	CASTING DIRECTOR	4421 1/2 N OGDEN DR	LOS ANGELES, CA	90036
METHA, NANCY KOVACK	ACTRESS	240 E 72ND ST	NEW YORK, NY	10021
METHA, ZUBIN	COMPOSER-CONDUCTOR	240 E 72ND ST	NEW YORK, NY	10021
METRAL, SOPHIE	ACTRESS	20 RUE SAUFFREY	75017 PARIS	FRANCE
METRANO, ART	ACTOR	1330 N DOHENY DR	LOS ANGELES, CA	90069
METRINKO, MARSHA	ACTRESS	249 E 48TH ST	NEW YORK, NY	10017
METROS, THE	ROCK & ROLL GROUP	MTM RECORDS, 21 MUSIC SQUARE E	NASHVILLE, TN	37203
METTER, ALAN	FILM WRITER-DIRECTOR	8315 MARMONT LN	LOS ANGELES, CA	90069
METZ, BELINDA	SINGER	41 BRITAIN ST #200	TORONTO, ONT M5A 1R7	CANADA
METZELAARS, PETE	FOOTBALL	BILLS, 1 BILLS DR	ORCHARD PARK, NJ	14127
METZENBAUM, HOWARD	U S SENATOR	140 RUSSELL SENATE OFFICE BLDG	WASHINGTON, DC	20515
METZENBAUM, HOWARD M	U S SENATOR	1240 E 9TH ST #2915	CLEVELAND, OH	44199
METZGER, DOUGLAS	TV DIRECTOR	718 RANCHO RD	THOUSAND OAKS, CA	91362
METZLER, ROBERT F	WRITER-PRODUCER	10971 SAVONA RD	LOS ANGELES, CA	90077
METZNER, JEFFREY	DIRECTOR	295 5TH AVE	NEW YORK, NY	10016
MEULENS, HENSLEY	BASEBALL	NY YANKEES, YANKEE STADIUM	BRONX, NY	10451
MEURISSE, PAUL	ACTOR	4 BLVD JEAN MERMOZ	92 NEUILLY-S-SEINE	FRANCE
MEURY, BILLY	BASEBALL	POST OFFICE BOX 611	WATERLOO, IA	50704
MEVORACH, LINDA	DIRECTOR	DGA, 110 W 57TH ST	NEW YORK, NY	10019
MEWS, MARVIN	DIRECTOR	1209 PARLIAMENT CT	LIBERTYVILLE, IL	60048
MEYER, BARRY M	TV EXECUTIVE	WARNER BROTHERS TV		
		4000 WARNER BLVD	BURBANK, CA	91522
MEYER, BERN	TV DIRECTOR	170 AVE "C"	NEW YORK, NY	10009
MEYER, BESS	ACTRESS	UTA, 9560 WILSHIRE BL, 5TH FL	BEVERLY HILLS, CA	90212
MEYER, BILL	BASEBALL SCOUT	ATHLETICS'S, OAKLAND COLISEUM	OAKLAND, CA	94621
MEYER, BRIAN	BASEBALL	205 S LAKESIDE DR	MEDFRORD, NJ	08055
MEYER, ELLEN	CASTING DIRECTOR	POST OFFICE BOX 2147	MALIBU, CA	90265
MEYER, GEORGE	TV PRODUCER	UTA, 9560 WILSHIRE BL, 5TH FL	BEVERLY HILLS, CA	90212
MEYER, JAY	BASEBALL	1524 W NEBRASKA AVE	PEORIA, IL	61604
MEYER, JOEY	BASEBALL	POST OFFICE BOX 450	BUFFALO, NY	14205
MEYER, JOSEPH B	ATTORNEY GENERAL	STATE CAPITOL BUILDING	CHEYENNE, WY	82002
MEYER, KEN	FOOTBALL COACH	SEAHAWKS, 11220 NE 53RD ST	KIRKLAND, WA	98033
MEYER, MARCIA	SINGER-GUITARIST	POST OFFICE BOX 86183	NORTH VANCOUVER, BC	CANADA
MEYER, NATALIE	SECRETARY OF STATE	STATE CAPITOL BUILDING	DENVER, CO	80203
MEYER, NICHOLAS	WRITER-PRODUCER	2109 STANLEY HILLS DR	LOS ANGELES, CA	90046
MEYER, RICK	BASEBALL	POST OFFICE BOX 10336	CLEARWATER, FL	34617
MEYER, RON	FOOTBALL COACH	POST OFFICE BOX 535000	INDIANPOLIS, IN	46253
MEYER, RUSS	BASEBALL-COACH	N Y YANKEES, YANKEE STADIUM	BRONX, NY	10451
MEYER, RUSS	FILM WRITER-PRODUCER	POST OFFICE BOX 3748	HOLLYWOOD, CA	90078
MEYER, TOM	CARTOONIST	S F CHRONICLE, 901 MISSION ST	SAN FRANCISCO, CA	94119
MEYERING, RALPH, JR	ACTOR	13455 VENTURA BLVD #210	SHERMAN OAKS, CA	91423
MEYERS, ALFRED	DIRECTOR	253 EVERETT PL	ENGLEWOOD, NJ	07631
MEYERS, ARI	ACTRESS	301 N CANON DR #203	BEVERLY HILLS, CA	90210
MEYERS, DON	BASEBALL	POST OFFICE BOX 10031	BAKERSFIELD, CA	93389
MEYERS, HOWARD	TV WRITER	8383 WILSHIRE BLVD #923	BEVERLY HILLS, CA	90211
MEYERS, JAN	U S CONGRESSWOMAN	7133 W 95TH ST #217	OVERLAND PARK, KS	66212
MEYERS, JOHN F	WRITER-PRODUCER	1221 OCEAN AVE #PH-4	SANTA MONICA, CA	90401
MEYERS, NANCY	FILM WRITER-PRODUCER	8955 BEVERLY BLVD	WEST HOLLYWOOD, CA	90048
MEYERS, RON	TV PRODUCER	1438 N GOWER ST	LOS ANGELES, CA	90028
MEYERS, WARREN B	CONDUCTOR	8440 FOUNTAIN AVE #108	LOS ANGELES, CA	90069
MEYERS, WILLIAM K	COMPOSER	5677 SPREADING OAK DR	LOS ANGELES, CA	90068
MEYERSON, PETER A	WRITER-PRODUCER	8778 WONDERLAND AVE	LOS ANGELES, CA	90046
MEYJES, MENNO	SCREENWRITER	8955 BEVERLY BLVD	WEST HOLLYWOOD, CA	90048
MEZA, LORENZO	BASEBALL	POST OFFICE BOX 3004	SPRINGFIELD, IL	62708
MFUME, KWEISI	U S CONGRESSMAN	3000 DRUID PARK DR	BALTIMORE, MD	21215
MIADES, JAMES	TV DIRECTOR	106 COLBERG AVE	ROSLINDALE, MA	02131
MIAMI SOUND MACHINE, THE	ROCK & ROLL GROUP	SEE - ESTEFAN, GLORIA &		
		MIAMI SOUND MACHINE		
MICALE, PAUL J	ACTOR	6614 COSTELLO AVE	VAN NUYS, CA	91405
MICELI, DANNY	BASEBALL	POST OFFICE BOX 464	APPLETON, WI	54912
MICHAEL, ALIKI	ACTRESS	106 WILSDEN AVE, LUTON	BEDS LU1 5HR	ENGLAND
MICHAEL, BOB	U S CONGRESSMAN	1029 N GLENWOOD ST	PEORIA, IL	61606
MICHAEL, GENE	BASEBALL-EXECUTIVE	N Y YANKEES, YANKEE STADIUM	BRONX, NY	10451
MICHAEL, GEORGE	SINGER-COMPOSER	1149 CALLE VISTA	BEVERLY HILLS, CA	90210
MICHAEL, HRH PRINCESS	PRINCESS	KENSINGTON PALACE	LONDON N5	ENGLAND
MICHAEL, RALPH	ACTOR	KRUGER, 121 GLOUCESTER PL	LONDON W1H 3PL	ENGLAND
MICHAEL, STEPHEN	FILM EDITOR	4355 MC CONNELL BLVD	LOS ANGELES, CA	90066
MICHAEL, WERNER	TV EXECUTIVE	MGM-TV, 10202 W WASHINGTON BL	CULVER CITY, CA	90230
MICHAELIAN, KATHRYN	TV WRITER	22500 MAC FARLANE DR	WOODLAND HILLS, CA	91364
MICHAELIAN, MICHAEL	SCREENWRITER	11421 CANTON DR	STUDIO CITY, CA	91604
MICHAELS, AL	SPORTSCASTER	ABC SPORTS, 524 W 57TH ST	NEW YORK, NY	10019
MICHAELS, BOB	BASEBALL EXECUTIVE	POST OFFICE BOX 238	ELMIRA, NY	14902
MICHAELS, DAVID	DIRECTOR	DGA, 110 W 57TH ST	NEW YORK, NY	10019
MICHAELS, DIANA MADDOX	WRITER	1614 THAYER AVE	LOS ANGELES, CA	90024
MICHAELS, JEANNA	ACTRESS	SIPOLE, 29604 TROTWOOD AVE	SAN PEDRO, CA	90732

Name	Occupation	Address	City	Zip/Country
MICHAELS, JOSEPH E	DIRECTOR	334 E 49TH ST #2-B	NEW YORK, NY	10017
MICHAELS, JULIE	ACTRESS-MODEL	8485 MELROSE PL #E	LOS ANGELES, CA	90069
MICHAELS, LORNE	TV WRITER-PRODUCER	88 CENTRAL PARK W	NEW YORK, NY	10023
MICHAELS, MARGARET	ACTRESS	9105 CARMELITA AVE #1	BEVERLY HILLS, CA	90210
MICHAELS, MARILYN	COMEDIENNE	185 W END AVE	NEW YORK, NY	10023
MICHAELS, MARK	DIRECTOR	DGA, 7920 SUNSET BLVD, 6TH FL	LOS ANGELES, CA	90046
MICHAELS, RICHARD	FILM DIRECTOR	1934 WESTRIDGE RD	LOS ANGELES, CA	90049
MICHAELS, ROBERT, BAND	ROCK & ROLL GROUP	BISHOP, 2505 PLAINVIEW AVE	PITTSBURGH, PA	15226
MICHAELS, ROXANNA	ACTRESS	7461 BEVERLY BLVD #400	LOS ANGELES, CA	90036
MICHAELS, SAL	TALENT AGENT	FAA, 1700 BROADWAY, 5TH FLOOR	NEW YORK, NY	10019
MICHAELS, SHAWN	WRESTLER	POST OFFICE BOX 3859	STAMFORD, CT	06905
MICHAELS, TIMOTHY	SINGER	5625 "O" STREET BLDG #7	LINCOLN, NE	68510
MICHAELS, TOMMY	ACTOR	ABC-TV, "ALL MY CHILDREN"		
		320 W 66TH ST	NEW YORK, NY	10023
MICHAELSEN, KARI	ACTRESS	1930 CENTURY PARK W #403	LOS ANGELES, CA	90067
MICHALAK, TONY	BASEBALL SCOUT	S F GIANTS, CANDLESTICK PARK	SAN FRANICSCO, CA	94124
MICHAUD, DAN	CONDUCTOR	20165 SEAGULL WY	SARATOGA, CA	95070
MICHAUD, GEORGE	TALENT AGENT	10113 RIVERSIDE DR	TOLUCA LAKE, CA	91602
MICHEL, ODILE	ACTRESS	14 RUE LOUIS BRAILLE	MAIS-ALF 94700	FRANCE
MICHEL, PATRICIA SCOTT	ACTRESS	5657 WILSHIRE BLVD #290	LOS ANGELES, CA	90036
MICHEL, ROBERT H	U S CONGRESSMAN	100 MONROE ST #107, NE	PEORIA, IL	61602
MICHELE, MICHAEL	ACTRESS-MODEL	424 W END AVE #17-B	NEW YORK, NY	10023
MICHELE & DAVID	VOCAL DUO	5625 "O" STREET BLDG #7	LINCOLN, NE	68510
MICHELET, MICHEL	COMPOSER	1624 N COURTNEY AVE	LOS ANGELES, CA	90046
MICHELIS, JAY	TV EXECUTIVE	NBC-TV, 3000 W ALAMEDA AVE	BURBANK, CA	91523
MICHELL, KEITH	ACTOR	LARNER, 130 W 57TH ST	NEW YORK, NY	10019
MICHELLE, VICKI	ACTRESS	FOSTER, 33 ABBEY LODGE, PARK RD	LONDON NW8 7RJ	ENGLAND
MICHELMORE, CLIFF	TV HOST	WHITE HOUSE, REIGATE	SURREY	ENGLAND
MICHELMORE, GUY	TV HOST	72 GOLDSMITH AVE	LONDON W3 6HN	ENGLAND
MICHELS, GLORIA	TV PRODUCER	AMERICAN TV PRODS, 521 5TH AVE	NEW YORK, NY	10017
MICHELS, JEANNE	ACTRESS	BARTLETT ASSOC, 155 SPRING ST	NEW YORK, NY	10012
MICHELS, JOHN	FOOTBALL COACH	VIKINGS, 9520 VIKING DR	EDEN PRAIRIE, MN	55344
MICHELSON, AMY	ACTRESS	8730 SUNSET BLVD #220-W	LOS ANGELES, CA	90069
MICHELSON, GEORGE S	GOVERNOR	STATE CAPITOL BUILDING	PIERRE, SD	57501
MICHI, WEGLYN	NEWS WRITER	957 PARK AVE	NEW YORK, NY	10028
MICHU, CLEMENT	ACTOR	4 RUE GASTON COUTE	PARIS 75018	FRANCE
MICKEY MOUSE CLUB	FAN CLUB	POST OFFICE BOX 10200	LAKE BUENA VISTA, FL	32830
MICRODISNEY	ROCK & ROLL GROUP	TIGER WARD MANAGEMENT		
		40 WHITTINGTON CT		
		AYLMER RD	LONDON N2 OBT	ENGLAND
MIDDENDORF, TRACY	ACTRESS	NBC-TV, "DAYS OF OUR LIVES"		
		3000 W ALAMEDA AVE	BURBANK, CA	91523
MIDDLE OF THE ROAD	ROCK & ROLL GROUP	18 IRVINE DR, LINWOOD	REFREWSHIRE	ENGLAND
MIDDLEBROOKS, HARRY	ACTOR	19013 COMMUNITY ST	NORTHRIDGE, CA	91324
MIDDLETON, GREGORY E	COMPOSER	406 W MARIPOSA AVE	ALTADENA, CA	91001
MIDDLETON, RON	FOOTBALL	POST OFFICE BOX 17247 (DULLES)	WASHINGTON, DC	20041
MIDGLEY, LESLIE	TV PRODUCER	14 OLD FARM LN	HARTSDALE, NY	10530
MIDKIFF, DALE	ACTOR	6369 LA PUNTA DR	LOS ANGELES, CA	90068
MIDLER, BETTE	SING-ACT-COMED	POST OFFICE BOX 46039	HOLLYWOOD, CA	90046
MIDNIGHT STAR	RHYTHM & BLUES GROUP	POST OFFICE BOX 9481	COLUMBUS, OH	43209
MIELKE, GARY	BASEBALL-CAOCH	POST OFFICE BOX 309	GASTONA, NC	28053
MIESKE, MATT	BASEBALL	2850 W 20TH AVE	DENVER, CO	80211
MIETZELFELD, MARY	ARTIST	140 WAVERLY PL	NEW YORK, NY	10014
MIFELOW, ALVIN R	DIRECTOR	ALMIF, 853 7TH AVE	NEW YORK, NY	10019
MIGHTY CLOUDS OF JOY, THE	GOSPEL GROUP	19301 VENTURA BLVD #205	TARZA, CA	91356
MIGHTY DIAMONDS, THE	REGGAE GROUP	POST OFFICE BOX 42517	WASHINGTON, DC	20015
MIGHTY FIRE	ROCK & ROLL GROUP	222 S FIGUEROA ST #921	LOS ANGELES, CA	90012
MIGHTY FLYERS, THE	ROCK & ROLL GROUP	POST OFFICE BOX 2458	TOLUCA LAKE, CA	91602
MIGHTY LEMON DROPS, THE	ROCK & ROLL GROUP	SIRE RECORDS COMPANY		
		75 ROCKEFELLER PLAZA	NEW YORK, NY	10019
MIGHTY MOFOS, THE	ROCK & ROLL GROUP	POST OFFICE BOX 18481	MINNEAPOLIS, MN	55418
MIHAESCO, EUGENE	ARTIST	160 E 38TH ST #34-C	NEW YORK, NY	10016
MIHALKA, GEORGE	FILM DIRECTOR	2030 CLOSSE #4	MONTREAL, QUE H3H 1Z9	CANADA
MIHO	ACTRESS	400 W 43RD ST #30-R	NEW YORK, NY	10036
MIHOCES, GARY	SPORTS WRITER	POST OFFICE BOX 500	WASHINGTON, DC	20044
MIKE & THE MECHANICS	ROCK & ROLL GROUP	POST OFFICE BOX 107	LONDON N65 ARU	ENGLAND
MIKELL, GEORGE	ACTOR	23 SHUTTLEWORTH RD	LONDON SW11	ENGLAND
MIKKELSEN, DWIGHT B	COMPOSER	2208 W PEYTON AVE	BURBANK, CA	91504
MIKKELSEN, LINC	BASEBALL	POST OFFICE BOX 8550	STOCKTON, CA	95208
MIKULEWICZ, BILL	ART DIRECTOR	245 W 107TH ST #11-D	NEW YORK, NY	10025
MIKULIK, JOE	BASEBALL	POST OFFICE BOX 27045	TUCSON, AZ	85726
MIKULSKI, BARBARA	U S SENATOR	320 HART SENATE OFFICE BLDG	WASHINGTON, DC	20510
MILACKI, BOB	BASEBALL	ORIOLE PARK, 333 W CAMDEN ST	BALTIMORE, MD	21201
MILAN, TED	DIRECTOR	315 E 68TH ST	NEW YORK, NY	10021
MILAN, TOMAS	ACTOR	VIA VIRGILO ORSINI 27	ROME	ITALY
MILANDER, STAN	TALENT AGENT	4146 LANKERSHIM BLVD #300	NORTH HOLLYWOOD, CA	91602
MILANO, ALYSSA	ACTRESS	POST OFFICE BOX 3684	LOS ANGELES, CA	90078
MILAVSKY, J RONALD	TV EXECUTIVE	NBC-TV, 30 ROCKEFELLER PLAZA	NEW YORK, NY	10112
MILBOURNE, LARRY	BASEBALL-MANAGER	POST OFFICE BOX 3783	SAVANNAH, GA	31414
MILBURN, SUE	TV WRITER	3811 SUNSHINE CT	STUDIO CITY, CA	91604
MILCH, DAVID	TV WRITER-PRODUCER	ICM, 8899 BEVERLY BLVD	LOS ANGELES, CA	90048
MILCHAN, ARNON	FILM PRODUCER	9808 WILSHIRE BLVD #201	BEVERLY HILLS, CA	90212
MILCHIN, MIKE	BASEBALL	POST OFFICE BOX 36407	LOUISVILLE, KY	40233
MILDREN, JACK	LT GOVERNOR	STATE CAPITOL BUILDING	OKLAHOMA CITY, OK	73105
MILES, CHRISTOPHER	FILM WRITER-DIRECTOR	10 SELWOOD PL	LONDON SW7	ENGLAND

Name	Occupation	Address	City / Zip
MILES, DARYL R	ARTIST	DALLAS TIMES-HERALD	
		1101 PACIFIC AVE	DALLAS, TX 75202
MILES, DOUGLAS K	WRITER-PRODUCER	27 SOMMER AVE	GLEN RIDGE, NJ 07028
MILES, JIM	SECRETARY OF STATE	POST OFFICE BOX 11369	COLUMBIA, SC 29211
MILES, JOANNA	ACTRESS	2062 N VINE ST	LOS ANGELES, CA 90028
MILES, KELLY	ACTRESS	10624 BLOOMFIELD ST	NORTH HOLLYWOOD, CA 91602
MILES, LEO	FOOTBALL REFEREE	NFL, 410 PARK AVE	NEW YORK, NY 10022
MILES, PETER	ACTOR-AUTHOR	268 N BOWLING GREEN WY	LOS ANGELES, CA 90049
MILES, SARAH	ACTRESS	MARTIN, 6-A DANBURY ST	LONDON N1 8JU ENGLAND
MILES, SYLVIA	ACTRESS	240 CENTRAL PARK S	NEW YORK, NY 10024
MILES, VERA	ACTRESS	POST OFFICE BOX 1704	BIG BEAR LAKE, CA 92315
MILEY, DAVE	BASEBALL MANAGER	POST OFFICE BOX 11002	CHATTANOOGA, TN 37401
MILFORD, JOHN	ACTOR	SAVAGE, 6212 BANNER AVE	LOS ANGELES, CA 90038
MILFORD, PENELOPE	ACTRESS	219 MARKET ST	VENICE, CA 90291
MILICEVIC, DJORDJE	SCREENWRITER	8955 BEVERLY BLVD	WEST HOLLYWOOD, CA 90048
MILINICHIK, JOE	FOOTBALL	RAMS, 2327 W LINCOLN BLVD	ANAHEIM, CA 92801
MILITELLO, SAM	BASEBALL	1155 W MOUND ST	COLUMBUS, OH 43223
MILITO, SEBASTIAN	TV WRITER	6619 MATILIJA AVE	VAN NUYS, CA 91405
MILIUS, JOHN	WRITER-PRODUCER	9336 W WASHINGTON, THE MANSION	CULVER CITY, CA 90232
MILKEE, HARRY	COMEDIAN	2211 INDUSTRIAL BLVD	SARASOTA, FL 33580
MILLAN, BERNIE	BASEBALL	525 NW PEACOCK BLVD	PORT SAINT LUCIE, FL 34986
MILLAN, FELEX	BASEBALL-EXECUTIVE	METS, 126TH ST & ROOSEVELT AVE	FLUSHING, NY 11368
MILLAR, GAVIN	TV WRITER-DIRECTOR	HEATH, PARAMOUNT HOUSE	
		162-170 WARDOUR ST	LONDON W1V 3AT ENGLAND
MILLAR, JEFF	CARTOONIST	UPS, 4900 MAIN ST, 9TH FLOOR	KANSAS CITY, MO 64112
MILLAR, STUART	WRITER-PRODUCER	300 CENTRAL PARK W #15-G	NEW YORK, NY 10024
MILLARD, DAVID	TV DIRECTOR-PRODUCER	LITTLE SPLINTERS	
		YEW TREE GARDENS	
		PANNAL ASH, HARROGATE	YORKS ENGLAND
MILLARD, WILLIAM J, III	DIRECTOR	30 RIVERSIDE PLAZA	NEW YORK, NY 10010
MILLARES, JOSE	BASEBALL	POST OFFICE BOX 3169	FREDERICK, MD 21701
MILLAY, DIANA	ACTRESS	RICHARD ASTOR, 1697 BROADWAY	NEW YORK, NY 10019
MILLEN, HUGH	FOOTBALL	PATRIOTS, FOXBORO STADIUM, RT #1	FOXBORO, MA 02035
MILLEN, MATT	FOOTBALL	POST OFFICE BOX 17247 (DULLES)	WASHINGTON, DC 20041
MILLER, AL	FOOTBALL COACH	BRONCOS, 13655 BRONCOS PKWY	ENGLEWOOD, CO 80112
MILLER, AL	SINGER	POST OFFICE BOX 5701	LINCOLN, NE 68505
MILLER, ALDEN	WRITER-PRODUCER	13272 CHELTENHAM DR	SHERMAN OAKS, CA 91423
MILLER, ALICE	GOLFER	2750 VOLUSA AVE #B	DAYTON BEACH, FL 32114
MILLER, ALLAN	ACTOR	13340 VALLEY VISTA BLVD	SHERMAN OAKS, CA 91423
MILLER, ALLAN	FILM DIRECTOR	194 RIVERSIDE DR	NEW YORK, NY 10025
MILLER, ANN	ACTRESS-DANCER	618 N ALTA DR	BEVERLY HILLS, CA 90210
MILLER, ANTHONY	FOOTBALL	POST OFFICE BOX 609609	SAN DIEGO, CA 92160
MILLER, ARTHUR	AUTHOR-PLAYWRIGHT	BOX 320, RR #1, TOPHET RD	ROXBURY, CT 06783
MILLER, BARRY	ACTOR	SMITH, 121 N SAN VICENTE BLVD	BEVERLY HILLS, CA 90211
MILLER, BARRY	BASEBALL	POST OFFICE BOX 21727	SAN FRANCISCO, CA 95151
MILLER, BILL	BASEBALL EXECUTIVE	POST OFFICE BOX 507	DURHAM, NC 27702
MILLER, BOB	BASEBALL EXECUTIVE	POST OFFICE BOX 230	HAGERSTOWN, MD 21740
MILLER, BOB	BASEBALL SCOUT	S F GIANTS, CANDLESTICK PARK	SAN FRANICSCO, CA 94124
MILLER, BOB	COSTUME DESIGNER	5534 ENCINO AVE #208	ENCINO, CA 91316
MILLER, BOB	GOVERNOR	STATE CAPITOL BUILDING	CARSON CITY, NV 89710
MILLER, BRENT	BASEBALL	POST OFFICE BOX 230	HAGERSTOWN, MD 21740
MILLER, BRETT	FOOTBALL	N Y JETS, 1000 FULTON AVE	HEMPSTEAD, NY 11550
MILLER, BRUCE PHILLIP	ACTOR	13233 HESBY ST	SHERMAN OAKS, CA 91423
MILLER, BRUCE R	FILM CRITIC	POST OFFICE BOX 118	SIOUX CITY, IA 51102
MILLER, BRUCE W	COMPOSER-CONDUCTOR	21136 TULSA ST	CHATSWORTH, CA 91311
MILLER, BUZZ	ACTOR	8 W 9TH ST	NEW YORK, NY 10011
MILLER, CHARLOTTE RUTH	TV WRITER	9000 SUNSET BLVD #1200	LOS ANGELES, CA 90069
MILLER, CHERYL	ACTRESS	6767 FOREST LAWN DR #115	LOS ANGELES, CA 90068
MILLER, CHRIS	FOOTBALL	FALCONS, SUWANEE RD AT I-85	SUWANEE, GA 30174
MILLER, CHRISTOPHER D	DIRECTOR	424 ASHLAND AVE	SANTA MONICA, CA 90405
MILLER, CLARENCE E	U S CONGRESSMAN	212 S BROAD ST	LANCASTER, OH 43130
MILLER, CLAY	ACTOR	10845 LINDBROOK DR #3	LOS ANGELES, CA 90024
MILLER, COREY	FOOTBALL	N Y GIANTS, GIANTS STADIUM	EAST RUTHERFORD, NJ 07073
MILLER, DAMIAN	BASEBALL	POST OFFICE BOX 661	KENOSHA, WI 53141
MILLER, DANIEL W	RECORD EXECUTIVE	POST OFFICE BOX 8604	MADISON, WI 53708
MILLER, DARRELL	BASEBALL	6246 PROMONTORY LN	RIVERSIDE, CA 92506
MILLER, DAVE	BASEBALL EXECUTIVE	TIGERS, TIGER STADIUM	DETROIT, MI 48216
MILLER, DAVID	BASEBALL	POST OFFICE BOX 230	HAGERSTOWN, MD 21740
MILLER, DAVID	FILM DIRECTOR	1843 THAYER AVE #1	LOS ANGELES, CA 90025
MILLER, DAVID W	NEWS-SPORTS WRITER	30 ROCKEFELLER PLAZA #1426	NEW YORK, NY 10112
MILLER, DEBORAH A	DIRECTOR	6636 VESPER AVE	VAN NUYS, CA 91405
MILLER, DENISE	ACTRESS	8730 SUNSET BLVD #480	LOS ANGELES, CA 90069
MILLER, DENNIS	ACTOR-COMEDIAN	POST OFFICE BOX 4150	LOS ANGELES, CA 90078
MILLER, DENNY	ACTOR	1104 FOOTHILL RD	OJAI, CA 93023
MILLER, DOUGLAS	SINGER	10100 SANTA MONICA BLVD #1600	LOS ANGELES, CA 90067
MILLER, DYAR	BASEBALL-COACH	4385 TUTT BLVD	COLORADO SPRINGS, CO 80922
MILLER, ED	DIRECTOR	145 S FAIRFAX AVE #310	LOS ANGELES, CA 90036
MILLER, FRANK R	TV DIRECTOR	80-396 PEBBLE BEACH	LA QUINA, CA 92253
MILLER, FRANK, DVM	COLUMNIST	THE CHRONICLE FEATURES	
		870 MARKET ST	SAN FRANCISCO, CA 94102
MILLER, FREEMAN	TV PRODUCER	BURSON, 230 PARK AVE S	NEW YORK, NY 10003
MILLER, GAIL	TV WRITER-PRODUCER	50 E 89TH ST #5-E	NEW YORK, NY 10028
MILLER, GEORGE	FILM DIRECTOR	30 ORWELL ST, KINGS CROSS	SYDNEY 2011 AUSTRALIA
MILLER, GEORGE	FILM EXECUTIVE	21 ALBION ST	LONDON W2 ENGLAND
MILLER, GEORGE	U S CONGRESSMAN	3220 BLUME DR #281	RICHMOND, CA 94806

MILLER, GEORGE TRUMBALL	TV DIRECTOR	3 REED ST, ALBERT PARK	VICTORIA 3206 ... AUSTRALIA
MILLER, HARVEY	SCREENWRITER	8955 BEVERLY BLVD	WEST HOLLYWOOD, CA ... 90048
MILLER, HARVEY	TV DIRECTOR	151 S EL CAMINO DR	BEVERLY HILLS, CA ... 90212
MILLER, HENRY R	DIRECTOR	35-10 168TH ST	FLUSHING, NY ... 11358
MILLER, HOWARD W	TV WRITER	9000 SUNSET BLVD #1200	LOS ANGELES, CA ... 90069
MILLER, IRA	SCREENWRITER	8955 BEVERLY BLVD	WEST HOLLYWOOD, CA ... 90048
MILLER, IRVING	COMPOSER	7259 HILLSIDE AVE #101	LOS ANGELES, CA ... 90046
MILLER, J PHILIP	TV DIRECTOR-PRODUCER	11 EXETER ST	BOSTON, MA ... 02116
MILLER, JAMES M	WRITER-PRODUCER	9300 WILSHIRE BLVD #410	BEVERLY HILLS, CA ... 90212
MILLER, JASON	ACT-WRI-DIR	10000 SANTA MONICA BLVD #305	LOS ANGELES, CA ... 90067
MILLER, JAY	HOCKEY	POST OFFICE BOX 17013	INGLEWOOD, CA ... 90308
MILLER, JEFF	BASEBALL	POST OFFICE BOX 824	BURLINGTON, IA ... 52601
MILLER, JIM	BASEBALL SCOUT	POST OFFICE BOX 2000	SAN DIEGO, CA ... 92112
MILLER, JIM	FOOTBALL EXECUTIVE	SAINTS, 1500 POYDRAS ST	NEW ORLEANS, LA ... 90112
MILLER, JODY	SINGER	HALSEY, 3225 S NORWOOD AVE	TULSA, OK ... 74135
MILLER, JOHN	U S CONGRESSMAN	145 S 3RD AVE #201	EDMONDS, WA ... 98020
MILLER, JOHNNY	GOLFER	POST OFFICE BOX 2260	NAPA, CA ... 94558
MILLER, JON	SPORTSCASTER	WMAR-TV, 6400 YORK RD	BALTIMORE, MD ... 21212
MILLER, JONATHAN WRIGHT	FILM DIRECTOR	83 BERMUDA RD	LONDON W4 5AJ ... ENGLAND
MILLER, JOSEPH E	COSTUME DESIGNER	ABC-TV, 320 W 66TH ST	NEW YORK, NY ... 10023
MILLER, JULIE	ACTRESS-SINGER	8075 W 3RD ST #303	LOS ANGELES, CA ... 90048
MILLER, KARYL	TV WRITER	14455 DUNBAR PL	SHERMAN OAKS, CA ... 91423
MILLER, KEITH	BASEBALL (MAJORS)	POST OFFICE BOX 419969	KANSAS CITY, MO ... 64141
MILLER, KEITH	BASEBALL (MINORS)	POST OFFICE BOX 450	BUFFALO, NY ... 14205
MILLER, KELLY	HOCKEY	JETS, 15-1430 MAROONS RD	WINNIPEG, MAN R3G 0L5 ... CANADA
MILLER, KEVIN	BASEBALL	POST OFFICE BOX 64939	FAYETTEVILLE, NC ... 28306
MILLER, KEVIN	HOCKEY	RED WINGS, 600 CIVIC CENTER DR	DETROIT, MI ... 48226
MILLER, KURT	BASEBALL	POST OFFICE BOX 3609	PORT CHARLOTTE, FL ... 33949
MILLER, LARRY	ACTOR-WRITER	12424 WILSHIRE BLVD #840	LOS ANGELES, CA ... 90025
MILLER, LARRY H	BASKETBALL EXECUTIVE	5 TRIAD CENTER #500	SALT LAKE CITY, UT ... 84180
MILLER, LEE	TV DIRECTOR-PRODUCER	137 N CARMELINA AVE	LOS ANGELES, CA ... 90049
MILLER, LES	FOOTBALL	SAINTS, 1500 POYDRAS ST	NEW ORLEANS, LA ... 90112
MILLER, MARC	DIRECTOR-PRODUCER	FINELINE, 22 CLEVELAND SQ	LONDON W2 6DG ... ENGLAND
MILLER, MARK C	TV WRITER	8383 WILSHIRE BLVD #923	BEVERLY HILLS, CA ... 90211
MILLER, MARTY	BASEBALL SCOUT	ATHLETICS'S, OAKLAND COLISEUM	OAKLAND, CA ... 94621
MILLER, MAX	WRITER-PRODUCER	3130 DONA MARIA DR	STUDIO CITY, CA ... 91604
MILLER, MELISAA	SCREENWRITER	8955 BEVERLY BLVD	WEST HOLLYWOOD, CA ... 90048
MILLER, MICHAEL J	TV DIRECTOR	433 COCHRAN AVE #201	LOS ANGELES, CA ... 90038
MILLER, MICHAEL L	WRITER-PRODUCER	9100 WILSHIRE BLVD #517	BEVERLY HILLS, CA ... 90210
MILLER, MIKE	WRESTLER	8725 N CHAUTAUQUA BLVD	PORTLAND, OR ... 97217
MILLER, MITCH	MUSICIAN-CONDUCTOR	345 W 58TH ST	NEW YORK, NY ... 10019
MILLER, MULGREW	PIANIST	LANDMARK RECORDS COMPANY	...
	...	10TH & PARKER STS	BERKELEY, CA ... 94710
MILLER, NEAL	BASEBALL	RURAL ROUTE 1, BOX 860	KAUFMAN, TX ... 75142
MILLER, NOLAN	COSTUME DESIGNER	241 S ROBERTSON BLVD	BEVERLY HILLS, CA ... 90211
MILLER, ORLANDO	BASEBALL	POST OFFICE BOX 4209	JACKSON, MS ... 39296
MILLER, PAT	BASEBALL	POST OFFICE BOX 8550	STOCKTON, CA ... 95208
MILLER, PATSY RUTH	ACTRESS	425 SIERRA MADRE N	PALM DESERT, CA ... 92260
MILLER, PAUL	BASEBALL	POST OFFICE BOX 7000	PITTSBURGH, PA ... 15212
MILLER, PAUL D	TV DIRECTOR	4249 WOODCLIFF RD	SHERMAN OAKS, CA ... 91403
MILLER, PENELOPE ANN	ACTRESS	KINCAID, 36 NANCY ST #2	VENICE, CA ... 90291
MILLER, PETE	BODYBUILDER	913 BROWN AVE	EVANSTON, IL ... 60202
MILLER, RAY	BASEBALL-COACH	POST OFFICE BOX 7000	PITTSBURGH, PA ... 15212
MILLER, REGGIE	BASKETBALL	PACERS, 300 E MARKET ST	INDIANAPOLIS, IN ... 46204
MILLER, RICH	BASEBALL-INSTRUCTOR	METS, 126TH ST & ROOSEVELT AVE	FLUSHING, NY ... 11368
MILLER, RICHARD "DICK"	ACTOR	8852 WONDERLAND AVE	LOS ANGELES, CA ... 90046
MILLER, RICHARD M	DIRECTOR	333 PARK AVE	NEW YORK, NY ... 10010
MILLER, RICK	BASEBALL COACH	POST OFFICE BOX 21727	SAN FRANCISCO, CA ... 95151
MILLER, ROBERT ELLIS	FILM-TV DIRECTOR	1901 AVE OF THE STARS #1040	LOS ANGELES, CA ... 90067
MILLER, ROBERT J	WRITER-NEWS CORRES	ABC NEWS, 1717 DE SALES ST, NW	WASHINGTON, DC ... 20036
MILLER, ROBERT JOHN	TV PRODUCER	TVS, TELEVISION CENTRE	SOUTHHAMPTON SO9 5HZ ... ENGLAND
MILLER, ROGER	BASEBALL	POST OFFICE BOX 21727	SAN FRANCISCO, CA ... 95151
MILLER, ROGER	SINGER-SONGWRITER	MORESS, 1209 16TH AVE S	NASHVILLE, TN ... 37212
MILLER, ROGER L	TV DIRECTOR	520 N MICHIGAN AVE #1026	CHICAGO, IL ... 60611
MILLER, RUSS	BASEBALL TRAINER	TIGERS, TIGER STADIUM	DETROIT, MI ... 48216
MILLER, SANDI	SINGER	POST OFFICE BOX 17472	NASHVILLE, TN ... 37217
MILLER, SCOTT	BASEBALL	POST OFFICE BOX 957	DUNEDIN, FL ... 34697
MILLER, SCOTT	FOOTBALL	DOLPHINS, 2269 NW 199TH ST	MIAMI, FL ... 33056
MILLER, SHARRON	FILM DIRECTOR	15301 VENTURA BLVD #345	SHERMAN OAKS, CA ... 91403
MILLER, SIDNEY	ACTOR-DIRECTOR	2724 BOTTLEBRUSH DR	LOS ANGELES, CA ... 90077
MILLER, SKEDGE	ACTOR	326 E 74TH ST	NEW YORK, NY ... 10021
MILLER, STAN	ARTIST	3138 17TH AVE E	SPOKANE, WA ... 99203
MILLER, STANLEY	FILM-TV WRITER	THE DEAL CUTTER COMPANY	...
	...	171 BEACH ST, DEAL	KENT ... ENGLAND
MILLER, STEPHEN A	TV WRITER	9300 WILSHIRE BLVD #410	BEVERLY HILLS, CA ... 90212
MILLER, STEVE	SINGER-SONGWRITER	POST OFFICE BOX 4127	BELLEVUE, WA ... 98004
MILLER, STEVE	TV DIRECTOR	5530 COLBATH AVE	VAN NUYS, CA ... 91401
MILLER, SUNNIE	LYRICIST	316 W 79TH ST	NEW YORK, NY ... 10024
MILLER, TERRY	TV DIRECTOR-PRODUCER	7 WAPPING RD	...
	...	MERCHANTS LANDING	BRISTOL BS1 4RH ... ENGLAND
MILLER, TERRY, BAND	C & W GROUP	POST OFFICE BOX O	EXCELSIOR, MN ... 55331
MILLER, THOMAS	PRODUCER	3970 OVERLAND AVE	CULVER CITY, CA ... 90230
MILLER, TODD	BASEBALL	RED SOX, CHAIN O'LAKES PARK	WINTER HAVEN, FL ... 33880
MILLER, TY	ACTOR	12767 JOLETTE AVE	GRANADA HILLS, CA ... 91344
MILLER, VICTOR B	SCREENWRITER	555 W 57TH ST #1230	NEW YORK, NY ... 10019

Name	Occupation	Address	City	Zip
MILLER, WALTER C	WRITER-PRODUCER	2401 CREST VIEW DR	LOS ANGELES, CA	90046
MILLER, WALTER D	LT GOVERNOR	STATE CAPITOL BUILDING	PIERRE, SD	57501
MILLER, WARREN	ACTOR	1241 1/2 N HAVENHURST DR	LOS ANGELES, CA	90046
MILLER, WINSTON	WRITER-PRODUCER	727 N RODEO DR	BEVERLY HILLS, CA	90210
MILLER, ZELL BRYAN	GOVERNOR	STATE CAPITOL BUIDLING	ATLANTA, GA	30334
MILLERICK, KERRY	DIRECTOR	7300 FRANKLIN AVE	LOS ANGELES, CA	90046
MILLETAIRE, CARL	ACTOR	1025 N FAIRFAX AVE #117	LOS ANGELES, CA	90046
MILLETTE, JOE	BASEBALL	POST OFFICE BOX 3449	SCRANTON, PA	18505
MILLIAN, ANDRA	ACTRESS	280 S BEVERLY DR #400	BEVERLY HILLS, CA	90212
MILLIARD, BRYAN	FOOTBALL	SEAHAWKS, 11220 NE 53RD ST	KIRKLAND, WA	98033
MILLIGAN, RANDY	BASEBALL	ORIOLE PARK, 333 W CAMDEN ST	BALTIMORE, MD	21201
MILLIGAN, SPIKE	ACTOR-DIRECTOR	9 ORME CT	LONDON W2	ENGLAND
MILLIKEN, BOB	BASEBALL-INSTRUCTOR	250 STADIUM PLAZA	ST LOUIS, MO	63102
MILLIKEN, MARTHA	ACTRESS	8380 MELROSE AVE #207	LOS ANGELES, CA	90069
MILLIKEN, SUE	FILM PRODUCER	119 PYRMONT ST	PYRMONT NSW 2009	AUSTRALIA
MILLIN, DAVID	CINEMATOGRAPHER	POST OFFICE BOX 2230	HOLLYWOOD, CA	90078
MILLING, JAMES	FOOTBALL	N Y GIANTS, GIANTS STADIUM	EAST RUTHERFORD, NJ	07073
MILLION DOLLAR MAN, THE	WRESTLER	SEE - DI BIASE, TED		
MILLOT, CHARLES	ACTOR	18 RUE DE FG SAINT HONORE	PARIS 75008	FRANCE
MILLS, ALAN	BASEBALL	500 NORTON ST	ROCHESTER, NY	14621
MILLS, ALLEN	TALENT AGENT	POST OFFICE BOX K-350	TARZANA, CA	91356
MILLS, ALLEY	ACTRESS	15301 VENTURA BLVD #345	SHERMAN OAKS, CA	91403
MILLS, ALVIN M	COMPOSER-CONDUCTOR	2916 SAINT GEORGE ST #110	LOS ANGELES, CA	90027
MILLS, ANDREW	WRITER-EDITOR	TV GUIDE, 100 MATSONFORD RD	RADNOR, PA	19088
MILLS, ARNOLD	TALENT AGENT	8721 SUNSET BLVD	LOS ANGELES, CA	90069
MILLS, ARTHUR R	THEATER PRODUCER	47 W 68TH ST	NEW YORK, NY	10023
MILLS, BRAD	BASEBALL MANAGER	CUBS, 2ND & RIVERSIDE DR	DES MOINES, IA	50309
MILLS, BUNNIE	SINGER	POST OFFICE BOX 8074	BOSSIER CITY, LA	71113
MILLS, CASSANDRA	TALENT AGENT	17337 VENTURA BLVD #100	ENCINO, CA	91316
MILLS, DONN LAURENCE	COMPOSER-CONDUCTOR	4213 CALLE ABRIL	SAN CLEMENTE, CA	92672
MILLS, DONNA	ACTRESS-MODEL	2660 BENEDICT CANYON DR	BEVERLY HILLS, CA	90210
MILLS, ERNIE	FOOTBALL	STEELERS, 300 STADIUM CIR	PITTSBURGH, PA	15212
MILLS, FRANK	PIANIST	4881 YONGE ST #412	TORONTO, ONTARIO	CANADA
MILLS, HAYLEY	ACTRESS	81 HIGH ST, HAMPTON	MIDDLESEX	ENGLAND
MILLS, JEFF	FOOTBALL	BRONCOS, 13655 BRONCOS PKWY	ENGLEWOOD, CO	80112
MILLS, JOHN & DONALD	VOCAL DUO	9255 SUNSET BLVD #411	LOS ANGELES, CA	90069
MILLS, JUDSON	ACTOR	CBS-TV, "AS THE WORLD TURNS"		
		524 W 57TH ST #5330	NEW YORK, NY	10019
MILLS, JULIET	ACTRESS	4036 FOOTHILL RD	CARPINTERIA, CA	93013
MILLS, LEEANN	ACTRESS	12023 VENTURA BLVD	STUDIO CITY, CA	91604
MILLS, ROBERT L	TV WRITER	4241 BECK AVE	STUDIO CITY, CA	91604
MILLS, ROGER	DIRECTOR-PRODUCER	2 ABDALE RD	LONDON W12 7ET	ENGLAND
MILLS, ROYCE	ACTOR	STONE, 25 WHITEHALL	LONDON SW1A 2BS	ENGLAND
MILLS, SAM	FOOTBALL	SAINTS, 1500 POYDRAS ST	NEW ORLEANS, LA	90112
MILLS, SIR JOHN	ACTOR	HILL HOUSE, DENHAM VILLAGE	BUCKINGHAMSHIRE	ENGLAND
MILLS, STEPHANIE	SINGER	LEFT BANK, 6255 SUNSET BLVD	HOLLYWOOD, CA	90028
MILLS, STEVE	TV DIRECTOR-PRODUCER	CBS-TV, 4024 RADFORD ST	STUDIO CITY, CA	91604
MILLS, TIM	FOOTBALL REFEREE	NFL, 410 PARK AVE	NEW YORK, NY	10022
MILLS, WILBUR	U S CONGRESSMAN	SHEA & GOULD LAW OFFICES		
		1627 "K" ST, NW	WASHINGTON, DC	20006
MILLS BROTHERS, THE	VOCAL GROUP	9255 SUNSET BLVD #200	LOS ANGELES, CA	90069
MILLSAPS, BRYANT	SECRETARY OF STATE	STATE CAPITOL BUILDING	NASHVILLE, TN	37243
MILNER, BRIAN	BASEBALL COACH	POST OFFICE BOX 22093	GREENSBORO, NC	27420
MILNER, MARTIN	ACTOR-RADIO PERS	9000 SUNSET BLVD #1200	LOS ANGELES, CA	90069
MILNES, RICHARD	FILM EXECUTIVE	WEINTRAUB HOUSE		
		167-169 WARDOUR ST	LONDON W1V 3TA	ENGLAND
MILO, CANDI	ACTRESS	280 S BEVERLY DR #400	BEVERLY HILLS, CA	90212
MILO, JANA	ACTRESS	13549 HAYNES ST	VAN NUYS, CA	91401
MILRAD, ABRAHAM	WRITER-PRODUCER	10833 MASSACHUSETTS AVE	LOS ANGELES, CA	90024
MILSAP, RONNIE	SINGER-SONGWRITER	12 MUSIC CIRCLE S	NASHVILLE, TN	37203
MILSTEIN, NATHAN	VIOLINIST	17 CHESTER SQ	LONDON SW1	ENGLAND
MILSTEIN, SIDNEY	DIRECTOR	6 WINDROSE WY	GREENWICH, CT	06830
MILSTIEN, DAVID	BASEBALL	POST OFFICE BOX 2365	PAWTUCKET, RI	02861
MILT, VICTOR	DIRECTOR	300 LAKE FRONT RD	PUTNAM VALLEY, NY	10579
MILTON, CHARLES H	TV PRODUCER	CBS-TV, 51 W 52ND ST	NEW YORK, NY	10019
MILTON, CHERILYN	ACTRESS	10845 LINDBROOK DR #3	LOS ANGELES, CA	90024
MILTON, DAVID SCOTT	TV WRITER	1235 24TH ST #1	SANTA MONICA, CA	90404
MILTON, RICHARD	WRITER-PRODUCER	1137 S SHENANDOAH ST	LOS ANGELES, CA	90035
MIMBS, MARK	BASEBALL	POST OFFICE BOX 26267	ALBUQUERQUE, NM	87125
MIMBS, MIKE	BASEBALL	POST OFFICE BOX 28268	SAN ANTONIO, TX	78228
MIMIEUX, YVETTE	ACTRESS-WRITER	500 PERUGIA WY	LOS ANGELES, CA	90077
MINARD, TOMMIE	ACTRESS	10000 RIVERSIDE DR #6	TOLUCA LAKE, CA	91602
MINAYA, OMAR	BASEBALL SCOUT	POST OFFICE BOX 90111	ARLINGTON, TX	76004
MINCHEY, NATE	BASEBALL	POST OFFICE BOX 16683	GREENVILLE, SC	29606
MINCHIN, STEPHEN	TV DIRECTOR-PRODUCER	THAMES TV, 149 TOTTENHAM CT RD	LONDON W1	ENGLAND
MINCY, CHARLES	FOOTBALL	CHIEFS, 1 ARROWHEAD DR	KANSAS CITY, MO	64129
MINDWARP, ZODIAC/LOVE REACTION	ROCK & ROLL GROUP	145 OXFORD ST	LONDON W1	ENGLAND
MINEO, SAMUEL H	COMPOSER	4348 SEPULVEDA BLVD	SHERMAN OAKS, CA	91403
MINER, ALLEN	WRITER-PRODUCER	644 TUALLITAN RD	LOS ANGELES, CA	90049
MINER, JAN	ACTRESS	300 E 46TH ST #9-J	NEW YORK, NY	10017
MINER, RACHEL	ACTRESS	CBS-TV, "THE GUIDING LIGHT"		
		222 E 44TH ST	NEW YORK, NY	10017
MINER, STEVE	FILM DIRECTOR	1137 2ND ST #103	SANTA MONICA, CA	90403
MINER, TONY	THEATER-TV EXECUTIVE	145 W 58TH ST #12-J	NEW YORK, NY	10019
MINER, W PETER	TV DIRECTOR	315 W 106TH ST	NEW YORK, NY	10025

MINETA, NORMAN Y	U S CONGRESSMAN	1245 S WINCHESTER BLVD #310	SAN JOSE, CA	95128
MINGORI, STEVE	BASEBALL-COACH	633 JESSAMINE ST	KNOXVILLE, TN	37917
MINIMAL MAN	ROCK & ROLL GROUP	49R ELLIS ST #1842	SAN FRANCISCO, CA	94102
MINK, PATSY	U S CONGRESSMAN	POST OFFICE BOX 50144	HONOLULU, HI	96850
MINK DEVILLE	ROCK & ROLL GROUP	STEVENS ENTERPRISES		
		240 CENTRAL PARK S	NEW YORK, NY	10019
MINKUS, BARBARA	ACTRESS	2029 CENTURY PARK E #600	LOS ANGELES, CA	90067
MINN, HAUNANI	ACTRESS	8831 SUNSET BLVD #304	LOS ANGELES, CA	90069
MINNELLI, LIZA	ACTRESS-SINGER	BLACK, 150 E 69TH ST #21-G	NEW YORK, NY	10021
MINNESOTA FATS	BILLARDS	HERMITAGE PARK HOTEL		
		231 6TH AVE N	NASHVILLE, TN	37219
MINNICK, DANI	ACTRESS	280 S BEVERLY DR #400	BEVERLY HILLS, CA	90212
MINNIFIELD, FRANK	FOOTBALL	BROWNS, 80 1ST ST	BEREA, OH	44017
MINNIS, BILLY	BASEBALL	POST OFFICE BOX 3496	DAVENPORT, IA	52808
MINNIX, BRUCE M	WRITER-DIRECTOR	20 JACKSON ST	CAPE MAY, NJ	08204
MINOFF, MARVIN	WRITER	15745 ROYAL OAK RD	ENCINO, CA	91436
MINOGUE, KYLIE	SINGER	POST OFFICE BOX 292, WATFORD	HERTSFORDSHIRE	ENGLAND
MINOR, BLAS	BASEBALL	POST OFFICE BOX 450	BUFFALO, NY	14205
MINOR, BOB	ACTOR-DIRECTOR	10401 7TH AVE	INGLEWOOD, CA	90303
MINOR, BOB	BASEBALL SCOUT	METS, 126TH ST & ROOSEVELT AVE	FLUSHING, NY	11368
MINOR, HARRY	BASEBALL SCOUT	METS, 126TH ST & ROOSEVELT AVE	FLUSHING, NY	11368
MINOR, RITA	ACTRESS	10401 7TH AVE	INGELWOOD, CA	90303
MINOR, STEVE	BASEBALL SCOUT	BREWERS, 201 S 46TH ST	MILWAUKEE, WI	53214
MINOR, WENDELL	ARTIST	227 W 4TH ST	NEW YORK, NY	10014
MINOSO, MINNIE	BASEBALL	4250 MARIN DR	CHICAGO, IL	60613
MINOT, ANNA S	ACTRESS	226 W 10TH ST	NEW YORK, NY	10014
MINOW, NEWTON N	AUTHOR	375 PALOS RD	GLENCOE, IL	60022
MINS, PETER	ACTOR	917 N LARRABEE ST #18	LOS ANGELES, CA	90069
MINSKOFF, JEROME	THEATER PRODUCER	1350 AVE OF THE AMERICAS	NEW YORK, NY	10019
MINSKY, DIANA	SINGER	1031 GRAND AVE	SOUTH SAN FRANCISCO, C	94080
MINTER, GORDON	DIRECTOR	181 MONTCLAIR DR	SANTA CRUZ, CA	95060
MINTER, KELLY	ACTRESS	280 S BEVERLY DR #400	BEVERLY HILLS, CA	90212
MINTER, NIKI MOORE	DIRECTOR	7330 PYRAMID DR	LOS ANGELES, CA	90046
MINTON, FAITH	ACTRESS	5455 WILSHIRE BLVD #1406	LOS ANGELES, CA	90036
MINTON, GREG	BASEBALL	2004 E CLIPPER LN	GILBERT, AZ	85234
MINTON, JULES	TV WRITER	JEOPARDY, 1541 N VINE ST	HOLLYWOOD, CA	90028
MINTZ, ART	PHOTOGRAPHER	245 W 99TH ST	NEW YORK, NY	10025
MINTZ, ELI	ACTOR	86-11 KINGSTON PL	JAMAICA, NY	11423
MINTZ, LARRY	WRITER-PRODUCER	1323 S BENTLEY AVE #C	LOS ANGELES, CA	90025
MINTZ, MURRAY	FILM DIRECTOR	717 HAMPSHIRE ST	SAN FRANCISCO, CA	94110
MINTZ, ROBERT	TV WRITER-PRODUCER	2777 GLENDOWER AVE	LOS ANGELES, CA	90027
MINTZ, STEVE	BASEBALL	POST OFFICE BOX 2887	VERO BEACH, FL	32961
MINUTELLI, GINO	BASEBALL	POST OFFICE BOX 23290	NASHVILLE, TN	37202
MINUTEMEN	ROCK & ROLL GROUP	POST OFFICE BOX 1	LAWNDALE, CA	90260
MIR	C & W GROUP	POST OFFICE BOX 25371	CHARLOTTE, NC	28212
MIRABELLI, JOHN	BASEBALL SCOUT	TIGERS, TIGER STADIUM	DETROIT, MI	48216
MIRACLE, IRENE	ACTRESS	280 S BEVERLY DR #400	BEVERLY HILLS, CA	90212
MIRANADA, NOEL	TV DIRECTOR	POST OFFICE BOX 55294	VALENCIA, CA	91355
MIRANDA, A J, III	DIRECTOR	853 N LARRABEE ST #4	LOS ANGELES, CA	90069
MIRANDA, ANGEL	BASEBALL	2850 W 20TH AVE	DENVER, CO	80211
MIRANDA, BILLY	SINGER	POST OFFICE BOX 11321		
		FLAGLER STATION	MIAMI, FL	33101
MIRANDA, GEOVANY	BASEBALL	300 STADIUM WY	DAVENPORT, FL	33837
MIRANDA, VICTOR	TV DIRECTOR-PRODUCER	RURAL ROUTE #3, BOX 775	MONTGOMERY, NY	12549
MIRISCH, ANDREW	TV WRITER-PRODUCER	MCA/UNIVERSAL STUDIOS, INC		
		100 UNIVERSAL CITY PLAZA #507	UNIVERSAL CITY, CA	91608
MIRISCH, MARVIN	FILM PRODUCER	723 N CRESCENT DR	BEVERLY HILLS, CA	90210
MIRISCH, WALTER	FILM EXEC-PROD	647 WARNER AVE	LOS ANGELES, CA	90024
MIRKIN, DR GENE	COLUMNIST-AUTHOR	N Y TIMES SYN, 130 5TH AVE	NEW YORK, NY	10011
MIRMAN, EDIE	ACTRESS	9744 WILSHIRE BLVD #308	BEVERLY HILLS, CA	90212
MIROJNICK, ELLEN	COSTUME DESIGNER	POST OFFICE BOX 1166	PACIFIC PALISADES, CA	90272
MIRREN, HELEN	ACTRESS	AL PARKER, 55 PARK LN	LONDON W1Y 3DD	ENGLAND
MIRSKY, ZIPPORAH	TV PRODUCER	ABC-TV, "GOOD MORNING AMERICA"		
		1965 BROADWAY	NEW YORK, NY	10023
MIRZA, FRED	COMPOSER	13506 HARTLAND ST	VAN NUYS, CA	91405
MIRZOEFF, EDWARD	TV PRODUCER	BBC, KENSINGTON HOUSE		
		RICHMOND WY	LONDON W14	ENGLAND
MISCH, DAVID A	COMEDY WRITER	175 RIVERSIDE DR #4-G	NEW YORK, NY	10024
MISCHER, DON	TV DIRECTOR-PRODUCER	14951 ALVA RD	PACIFIC PALISADES, CA	90272
MISCIK, BOBBY	BASEBALL MANAGER	POST OFFICE BOX 3169	FREDERICK, MD	21701
MISHKIN, MEYER	TALENT AGENT	2355 BENEDICT CANYON DR	BEVERLY HILLS, CA	90210
MISHKIN, PHILIP	TV WRITER	3844 RIDGEMOOR DR	STUDIO CITY, CA	91604
MISIOROWSKI, ROBERT A	TV WRITER-FILM DIR	1885 VETERAN AVE #206	LOS ANGELES, CA	90025
MISKE, BOB	BASEBALL SCOUT	1000 ELYSIAN PARK DR	LOS ANGELES, CA	90012
MISKO, ERNEST	COSTUME DESIGNER	14821 SEPTO ST	MISSION HILLS, CA	91345
MISLOVE, MICHAEL	SCREENWRITER	1302 N SWEETZER AVE #601	LOS ANGELES, CA	90069
MISON, GEORGE	FOOTBALL	LIONS, 1200 FEATHERSTONE RD	PONTIAC, MI	48432
MISRAKI, PAIL	COMPOSER	35 AVE BUGEAUD	PARIS 75018	FRANCE
MISS ELIZABETH	WRESTLING MANAGER	POST OFFICE BOX 3859	STAMFORD, CT	06905
MISSING PERSONS	ROCK & ROLL GROUP	9903 SANTA MONICA BLVD #129	BEVERLY HILLS, CA	90212
MISSION	ROCK & ROLL GROUP	FRANTIC RECORDS COMPANY		
		2105 MARYLAND AVE	BALTIMORE, MD	21218
MISSISSIPPI BAND	C & W GROUP	OBA, 5601 ODANA RD	MADISON, WI	53719
MISTAL, KAREN	ACTRESS	10351 SANTA MONICA BLVD #211	LOS ANGELES, CA	90025
MISURACA, MIKE	BASEBALL	14100 SIX MILE CYPRESS PKWY	FORT MYERS, FL	33912

Name	Occupation	Address	City
MITACEK, MICHAEL	COMPOSER	178-H CASUDA CANYON DR	MONTEREY PARK, CA 91754
MITCHELL, ALEX	WRI-DIR-PROD	425 45TH ST	BROOKLYN, NY 11220
MITCHELL, ANITA VELEZ	WRI-DIR-CHOREO	171 W 57TH ST	NEW YORK, NY 10019
MITCHELL, ANN	ACTRESS	CBS-TV, "AS THE WORLD TURNS"	
		524 W 57TH ST #5330	NEW YORK, NY 10019
MITCHELL, ANTONIO	BASEBALL	POST OFFICE BOX 3746, HILL STA	AUGUSTA, GA 30904
MITCHELL, BETSY FAITH	SINGER	2409 LEOM ST #304	AUSTIN, TX 78705
MITCHELL, BOBBY	FOOTBALL EXECUTIVE	POST OFFICE BOX 17247 (DULLES)	WASHINGTON, DC 20041
MITCHELL, BRIAN	ACTOR	14980 VALLEY VISTA BLVD	SHERMAN OAKS, CA 91403
MITCHELL, BRIAN	FOOTBALL	POST OFFICE BOX 17247 (DULLES)	WASHINGTON, DC 20041
MITCHELL, CAMERON	ACTOR	9744 WILSHIRE BLVD #308	BEVERLY HILLS, CA 90212
MITCHELL, CHARLIE	BASEBALL	POST OFFICE BOX 23290	NASHVILLE, TN 37202
MITCHELL, COLEMAN "CHICK"	WRITER-PRODUCER	151 S EL CAMINO DR	BEVERLY HILLS, CA 90212
MITCHELL, CORY M	TV EXECUTIVE	ORION PICTURES, 711 5TH AVE	NEW YORK, NY 10022
MITCHELL, DON	ACTOR	1930 S MARVIN AVE	LOS ANGELES, CA 90016
MITCHELL, DON	BASEBALL SCOUT	POST OFFICE BOX 7000	PITTSBURGH, PA 15212
MITCHELL, DONNA	ACTRESS	SMITH, 121 N SAN VICENTE BLVD	BEVERLY HILLS, CA 90211
MITCHELL, EDGAR	ASTRONAUT	POST OFFICE BOX 3163	PALM BEACH, FL 33480
MITCHELL, ESTHER O	TV WRITER	4770 BREWSTER DR	TARZANA, CA 91356
MITCHELL, GEORGE J	U S SENATOR	POST OFFICE BOX 8300	PORTLAND, ME 04104
MITCHELL, GLORIA CARBONE	TV WRITER	10303 VALLEY SPRING LN	NORTH HOLLYWOOD, CA 91602
MITCHELL, GORDON B	TV WRITER	19525 BRAEWOOD DR	TARZANA, CA 91356
MITCHELL, GWENDOLYN	ACTRESS	6605 HOLLYWOOD BLVD #220	HOLLYWOOD, CA 90028
MITCHELL, JAMES	ACTOR	330 W 72ND ST #12-C	NEW YORK, NY 10023
MITCHELL, JOHN	BASEBALL	POST OFFICE BOX 3690, STA "B"	CALGARY, ALB T2B 4M4 CANADA
MITCHELL, JOHN H	TV EXECUTIVE	1801 AVE OF THE STARS #312	LOS ANGELES, CA 90067
MITCHELL, JOHN W	TV WRITER-DIRECTOR	9926 WOODLEY AVE	SEPULVEDA, CA 91343
MITCHELL, JONI	SINGER-SONGWRITER	10960 WILSHIRE BLVD #938	LOS ANGELES, CA 90024
MITCHELL, KATIE	ACTRESS	8322 BEVERLY BLVD #200	LOS ANGELES, CA 90048
MITCHELL, KEITH	BASEBALL	POST OFFICE BOX 6667	RICHMOND, VA 23230
MITCHELL, KEVIN	BASEBALL	POST OFFICE BOX 4100	SEATTLE, WA 98104
MITCHELL, KIM	SINGER-GUITARIST	POST OFFICE BOX 9, STA "J"	TORONTO, ONT M4L 4Y8 CANADA
MITCHELL, LAUREN	ACTRESS	606 N LARCHMONT BLVD #309	LOS ANGELES, CA 90004
MITCHELL, LAWRENCE E	DIRECTOR	11524 LAURELCREST DR	STUDIO CITY, CA 91604
MITCHELL, LOFTEN	PLAYWRIGHT	ANN ELMO, 60 E 42ND ST	NEW YORK, NY 10017
MITCHELL, MARCUS J	MUSIC ARRANGER	4501 PACKARD DR #E-3	NASHVILLE, TN 37211
MITCHELL, NORMAN	ACTOR-TV WRITER	KINGFISHER COTTAGE	
		29 SUMMER GARDENS, EAST MOLESEY	SURREY KT8 9LT ENGLAND
MITCHELL, PETER	COSTUME DESIGNER	13949 VENTURA BLVD #309	SHERMAN OAKS, CA 91423
MITCHELL, ROBERT JAMES	DIRECTOR	6611 SANTA MONICA BLVD	HOLLYWOOD, CA 90038
MITCHELL, ROBIN	RECORD EXECUTIVE	SCOTTI BROS, 2128 W PICO BLVD	SANTA MONICA, CA 90405
MITCHELL, ROLAND	FOOTBALL	PACKERS, 1265 LOMBARDI AVE	GREEN BAY, WI 54307
MITCHELL, RUTH	THEATER PRODUCER	1270 AVE OF THE AMERICAS	NEW YORK, NY 10020
MITCHELL, SAM	BASKETBALL	TIMBERWOLVES, 600 1ST AVE N	MINNEAPOLIS, MN 55403
MITCHELL, SASHA	ACTRESS	9057 NEMO ST #A	WEST HOLLYWOOD, CA 90069
MITCHELL, SCOEY	COMEDIAN-ACTOR	664 W BROADWAY #A	GLENDALE, CA 91204
MITCHELL, SCOTT	FOOTBALL	DOLPHINS, 2269 NW 199TH ST	MIAMI, FL 33056
MITCHELL, SHIRLEY	ACTRESS	133 S OAKHURST DR	BEVERLY HILLS, CA 90212
MITCHELL, WARREN	ACTOR	28 SHELDON AVE	LONDON N6 ENGLAND
MITCHELSON, MARK	BASEBALL	RED SOX, CHAIN O'LAKES PARK	WINTER HAVEN, FL 33880
MITCHELSON, MARVIN	TALENT AGENT	1801 CENTURY PARK E #1900	LOS ANGELES, CA 90067
MITCHUM, CARRIE	ACTRESS	822 S ROBERTSON BLVD #200	LOS ANGELES, CA 90035
MITCHUM, CHRISTOPHER	ACTOR	860 SAN YSIDRO RD	SANTA BARBARA, CA 93108
MITCHUM, ROBERT	ACTOR	860 SAN YSIDRO RD	SANTA BARBARA, CA 93108
MITTA, ALEXANDER	FILM DIRECTOR	190 S CANON DR #201	BEVERLY HILLS, CA 90210
MITTELMAN, STEVE	COMEDIAN	ICM, 8899 BEVERLY BLVD	LOS ANGELES, CA 90048
MITTERRAND, FRANCOIS	PRESIDENT	55 ET RUE DE FAUBOURG	
		SAINT HONORE	F-75008 PARIS FRANCE
MITTLEMAN, MINA	COSTUME DESIGNER	4128 VANTAGE AVE	STUDIO CITY, CA 91604
MITTLEMAN, RICHARD "RICK"	TV WRITER	3945 VALLEY MEADOW RD	ENCINO, CA 91436
MITTLEMAN, STEVE	ACTOR	8821 BEVERLY BLVD	LOS ANGELES, CA 90048
MITTY, NOMI	ACTRESS	5455 WILSHIRE BLVD #1406	LOS ANGELES, CA 90036
MITWELL, JILL B	TV DIRECTOR	221 W 26TH ST #51	NEW YORK, NY 10001
MITZ, ALONZO	FOOTBALL	BENGALS, 200 RIVERFRONT STADIUM	CINCINNATI, OH 45202
MITZMAN, NEWT	WRITER-PRODUCER	663 N BROADWAY	HASTINGS-ON-HUDSON, NY 10706
MIVAL, ERIC	FILM-VIDEO DIRECTOR	30 LONGPARK, CHESHAM BOIS	
		AMERSHAM	BUCKS HP6 5LA ENGLAND
MIX, STEVE	BASKETBALL	WPHL-TV, 5001 WYNNEFIELD AVE	PHILADELPHIA, PA 19131
MIXON, TOMMY	BASEBALL SCOUT	1000 ELYSIAN PARK DR	LOS ANGELES, CA 90012
MIYORI, KIM	ACTRESS	8033 SUNSET BLVD #770	LOS ANGELES, CA 90046
MIZE, JOHNNY	BASEBALL	POST OFFICE BOX 112	DEMOREST, GA 30535
MIZE, LARRY	GOLFER	POST OFFICE BOX 109601	PALM BCH GARDENS, FL 33418
MIZEROCK, JOHN	BASEBALL	POST OFFICE BOX 580	PUNZSUTAWNEY, PA 15767
MIZIKER, RON	TV PRODUCER	500 S BUENA VISTA ST	BURBANK, CA 91521
MLICKI, DAVE	BASEBALL	2501 ALLEN AVE, SE	CANTON, OH 44707
MMAHAT, KEVIN	BASEBALL	3268 CASTLE DR	KENNER, LA 70065
MOAKLEY, JOE	U S CONGRESSMAN	WORLD TRADE CENTER #220	BOSTON, MA 02110
MOAR, ANDREA	ACTRESS	6255 SUNSET BLVD #627	LOS ANGELES, CA 90028
MOBLEY, MARY ANN	ACTRESS	2751 HUTTON DR	BEVERLY HILLS, CA 90210
MOBY GRAPE	ROCK & ROLL GROUP	MATTHEW KATZ PRODS	
		555 POST ST	SAN FRANCISCO, CA 94102
MOCCIO, FRANK	FILM DIRECTOR	321 E 69TH ST #5-C	NEW YORK, NY 10021
MOCHRIE, DOTTIE	GOLFER	2750 VOLUSA AVE #B	DAYTON BEACH, FL 32114
MOCK, CECIL	BASEBALL UMPIRE	235 MAIN ST #103	TRUSSVILLE, AL 35173
MOCK, JULIAN	BASEBALL SCOUT	REDS, 100 RIVERFRONT STADIUM	CINCINNATI, OH 45202

MOCK, PAT	CASTING DIRECTOR	MCA/UNIVERSAL STUDIOS, INC		
		100 UNIVERSAL CITY PLAZA #473	UNIVERSAL CITY, CA	91608
MODANO, MIKE	HOCKEY	NORTH STARS, 7901 CEDAR AVE S	BLOOMINGTON, MN	55425
MODEAN, JAYNE	ACTRESS-MODEL	2021 GLENCOE WY	LOS ANGELES, CA	90067
MODELL, ARTHUR B	FOOTBALL EXECUTIVE	BROWNS, 80 1ST ST	BEREA, OH	44017
MODELS, THE	ROCK & ROLL GROUP	GEFFEN RECORDS COMPANY		
		9130 SUNSET BLVD	LOS ANGELES, CA	90069
MODER, DICK	DIRECTOR	22435 PAUL REVERE DR	WOODLAND HILLS, CA	91364
MODERN ROMANCE	ROCK & ROLL GROUP	TOPLAND LIMITED		
		30 GREAT PORTLAND ST	LONDON W1	ENGLAND
MODERN TALKING	ROCK & ROLL GROUP	HALLERSTR 40	2000 HAMBURG 13	GERMANY
MODERNAIRES, THE	VOCAL GROUP	POST OFFICE BOX 195	ENCINO, CA	91426
MODES, SONIA	SINGER	COVER, 1425 N STAR RD	COLUMBUS, OH	43212
MODINE, MATTHEW	ACTOR	1632 N BEVERLY DR	BEVERLY HILLS, CA	90210
MOECK, WALTER F	CONDUCTOR	14209 CHANDLER BLVD	VAN NUYS, CA	91401
MOEGLE, DICKIE	FOOTBALL	4047 ABERDEEN WY	HOUSTON, TX	77025
MOELLER, DENNIS	BASEBALL	POST OFFICE BOX 3665	OMAHA, NE	68103
MOELLER, RICHARD	TV DIRECTOR	345 W 55TH ST	NEW YORK, NY	10019
MOER, PAUL E	COMPOSER	9323 KESTER AVE	PANORAMA CITY, CA	91402
MOESCHE, CARL	BASEBALL SCOUT	N Y YANKEES, YANKEE STADIUM	BRONX, NY	10451
MOESSINGER, DAVID	WRITER-PRODUCER	3861 KINGSWOOD RD	SHERMAN OAKS, CA	91405
MOFFAT, KATHERINE "KITTY"	ACTRESS	9300 WILSHIRE BLVD #410	BEVERLY HILLS, CA	90212
MOFFATT, JOHN	ACTOR	59-A WARRINGTON ST	LONDON W9	ENGLAND
MOFFATT, KATY	SINGER-GUITARIST	3122 SALE ST	DALLAS, TX	75219
MOFFATT, PETER	TV DIRECTOR	BROWN, 162-168 REGENT ST	LONDON W1R 5TB	ENGLAND
MOFFET, JORDAN H	TV WRITER	157 S MARTEL AVE	LOS ANGELES, CA	90036
MOFFETT, D W	ACTOR	10390 SANTA MONICA BLVD #300	LOS ANGELES, CA	90025
MOFFITT, JOHN	PRODUCER	1438 N GOWER ST #250	LOS ANGELES, CA	90028
MOFFITT, WILLIAM	DIRECTOR-PRODUCER	785 NEW YORK DR	ALTADENA, CA	91001
MOFOS, THE	ROCK & ROLL GROUP	SEE - MIGHTY MOFOS, THE		
MOGER, STANLEY	TV PRODUCER	SFM MEDIA CORP, 1180 6TH AVE	NEW YORK, NY	10036
MOGILNY, ALEXANDER	HOCKEY	SABRES, MEMORIAL AUDITORIUM	BUFFALO, NY	14202
MOGULL, ARTHUR	RECORD EXECUTIVE	2720 BENEDICT CANYON DR	BEVERLY HILLS, CA	90210
MOHLER, MIKE	BASEBALL	POST OFFICE BOX 2769	HUNTSVILLE, AL	35804
MOHORCIC, DALE	BASEBALL	15501 ROCKSIDE RD	MAPLE HEIGHTS, OH	44137
MOHR, CHRIS	FILM PRODUCER	BBC, ELSTREE TV CENTRE	BOREHAMWOOD, HERTS,	ENGLAND
MOHR, CHRIS	FOOTBALL	BILLS, 1 BILLS DR	ORCHARD PARK, NJ	14127
MOHR, MAJ GEN HENRY	COLUMNIST-ARMY GEN	SAINT LOUIS GLOBE-DEMOCRAT		
		710 N TUCKER BLVD	SAINT LOUIS, MO	63101
MOHR, MARGIT	COMPOSER	5067 TOPANGA CANYON BLVD	WOODLAND HILLS, CA	91364
MOIO, JOHN	TV DIRECTOR	11708 CANTON PL	STUDIO CITY, CA	91604
MOIR, JAMES	TV PRODUCER	BBC-TV, 56 WOOD LN	LONDON W12 7RJ	ENGLAND
MOIR, MICHAEL	DIRECTOR	DGA, 110 W 57TH ST	NEW YORK, NY	10019
MOJAVE	C & W GROUP	VP, 2779 MIRADA RD	HIGHLAND, CA	92346
MOJO	RHYTHM & BLUES GROUP	3401 S ONEIDA WY #D	DENVER, CO	80224
MOJSLEJENKO, RALF	FOOTBALL	S F 49ERS, 4949 CENTENNIAL BL	SANTA CLARA, CA	95054
MOLDEN, PRENTISS	ACTOR	24105 WILLOW CREEK RD	DIAMOND BAR, CA	91765
MOLE, RALPH	DIRECTOR-PRODUCER	156 MYRTLE ST	HAWORTH, NJ	07641
MOLER, RON	FILM PRODUCER	3393 BENNETT DR	LOS ANGELES, CA	90068
MOLIN, BUD	TV DIRECTOR	557 E VERDUGO AVE	BURBANK, CA	91501
MOLINA, ALFRED	ACTOR	COULSON, 37 BERWICK ST	LONDON W1V 3RF	ENGLAND
MOLINA, ISLAY	BASEBALL	POST OFFICE BOX 11363	RENO, NV	89510
MOLINARI, SUSAN	U S CONGRESSWOMAN	14 NEW DROP LN	STATEN ISLAND, NY	10306
MOLINARO, AL	ACTOR	POST OFFICE BOX 9218	GLENDALE, CA	91226
MOLINARO, BOBBY	BASEBALL-MANAGER	POST OFFICE BOX 3609	PORT CHARLOTTE, FL	33949
MOLITOR, PAUL	BASEBALL	BREWERS, 201 S 46TH ST	MILWAUKEE, WI	53214
MOLKENTHINE, JOANN	COSTUME DESIGNER	339 E 58TH ST	NEW YORK, NY	10022
MOLL, RICHARD	ACTOR	7561 W 82ND ST	PLAYA DEL REY, CA	90293
MOLLER, RANDY	HOCKEY	POST OFFICE BOX 90111	ARLINGTON, TX	76004
MOLLICA, MAE	BODYBUILDER	1106 2ND ST #116	ENCINITAS, CA	92024
MOLLIN, LARRY	TV WRITER	10960 WILSHIRE BLVD #922	LOS ANGELES, CA	90024
MOLLO, DICK	SINGER	POST OFFICE BOX 171132	NASHVILLE, TN	37217
MOLLOHAN, ALAN	U S CONGRESSMAN	CITY-COUNTY COMPLEX, ROOM 102	FAIRMONT, WV	26554
MOLLOT, LAWRENCE	DIRECTOR	MRC FILMS, 71 W 23RD ST	NEW YORK, NY	10010
MOLLOY, JACK A	ARTIST	1645 HENNEPIN AVE S #201	MINNEAPOLIS, MN	55403
MOLLOY, JOSEPH	BASEBALL EXECUTIVE	N Y YANKEES, YANKEE STADIUM	BRONX, NY	10451
MOLLY HATCHET	ROCK & ROLL GROUP	POST OFFICE BOX 6600	MACON, GA	51215
MOLPUS, DICK	SECRETARY OF STATE	POST OFFICE BOX 2000	JACKSON, MS	39215
MOLTER, KATHY	ACTRESS	10350 WILSHIRE BLVD #502	LOS ANGELES, CA	90024
MOMENT OF TRUTH	VOCAL GROUP	BERGEN, 159 W 53RD ST	NEW YORK, NY	10019
MOMENTS, THE	VOCAL GROUP	POST OFFICE BOX 82	GREAT NECK, NY	11021
MOMESSO, SERGIO	HOCKEY	CANUCKS, 100 N RENFREW ST	VANCOUVER, BC V5K 3N7	CANADA
MOMPRES, DANILO	BASEBALL	POST OFFICE BOX 7845	COLUMBIA, SC	29202
MONACELLA, ALFRED	TV WRITER	615 N CANON DR	BEVERLY HILLS, CA	90210
MONAGHAN, THOMAS	BASEBALL EXECUTIVE	TIGERS, TIGER STADIUM	DETROIT, MI	48216
MONAHAN, MARK	BASEBALL SCOUT	TIGERS, TIGER STADIUM	DETROIT, MI	48216
MONASH, PAUL	WRITER-PRODUCER	9121 ALTO CEDRO DR	BEVERLY HILLS, CA	90210
MONASTER, NATE	TV WRITER	826 N KINGS RD	LOS ANGELES, CA	90069
MONBOUQUETTE, BILL	BASEBALL-COACH	POST OFFICE BOX 957	DUNEDIN, FL	34697
MONCRIEF, SIDNEY	BASKETBALL	1 CNN CENTER #405, SOUTH TOWER	ATLANTA, GA	30303
MONCRIEFF, KAREN	ACTRESS	1848 BAGLEY AVE	LOS ANGELES, CA	90035
MONDALE, ELEANOR	NEWS REPORTER	WCCO-TV, 90 S 11TH ST	MINNEAPOLIS, MN	55403
MONDALE, WALTER F	VICE-PRESIDENT	2200 1ST BANK PL E	MINNEAPOLIS, MN	55402
MONDAY, RICK	BASEBALL-ANNOUNCER	POST OFFICE BOX 2000	SAN DIEGO, CA	92112
MONDE, ARTHUR	ACTOR	358 W ALAMEDA AVE	BURBANK, CA	91506

Name	Occupation	Address	City	Zip
MONDEAUX, JOEL	DIRECTOR	2033 CHEREMOYA AVE	HOLLYWOOD, CA	90068
MONDESI, RAUL	BASEBALL	POST OFFICE BOX 26267	ALBUQUERQUE, NM	87125
MONDOR, BEN	BASEBALL EXECUTIVE	POST OFFICE BOX 2365	PAWTUCKET, RI	02861
MONDY, PIERRE	ACTOR	ARTMEDIA, 10 AVE GEORGE V	PARIS 75008	FRANCE
MONET, GABY	TV PRODUCER	CONCEPTS UNLTD, 315 W 57TH ST	NEW YORK, NY	10019
MONEY, EDDIE	ROCK & ROLL GROUP	POST OFFICE BOX 1994	SAN FRANCISCO, CA	94101
MONEY & MC MARVELOUS	RAP DUO-RAPWRITERS	FAA, 1700 BROADWAY, 5TH FLOOR	NEW YORK, NY	10019
MONGE, SID	BASEBALL-COACH	POST OFFICE BOX 64939	FAYETTEVILLE, NC	28306
MONGIELLO, MIKE	BASEBALL	POST OFFICE BOX 360007	BIRMINGHAM, AL	35236
MONICA, CORBETT	COMEDIAN-ACTOR	101 W 57TH ST #11-E	NEW YORK, NY	10019
MONJONYA	ROCK & ROLL GROUP	POST OFFICE BOX 82	GREAT NECK, NY	11022
MONK, ART	FOOTBALL	POST OFFICE BOX 17247 (DULLES)	WASHINGTON, DC	20041
MONK, JULIUS	DIRECTOR-PRODUCER	VENDOME, 350 W 57TH ST	NEW YORK, NY	10019
MONK, KERMIT & HIS STONE MOUNTA	C & W GROUP	POST OFFICE BOX 316	CHUCKEY, TN	37641
MONK, MICHAEL	BASEBALL EXECUTIVE	POST OFFICE BOX 2000	SAN DIEGO, CA	92112
MONKEES, THE	ROCK & ROLL GROUP	POST OFFICE BOX 1461	NEW YORK, NY	10101
MONKEY SEE-MONKEY DO	ROCK & ROLL GROUP	BERNARD KUNZ FEURIGSTR 16	D-1000 BERLIN 62	GERMANY
MONKHOUSE, BOB	ACTOR-WRITER	118 BEAUFORT ST	LONDON SW3 6BU	ENGLAND
MONKOVICH, GEORGE J	ACTOR	442 S OAKHURST DR #6	BEVERLY HILLS, CA	90212
MONKS, JAMES	ACTOR	23 E 39TH ST	NEW YORK, NY	10016
MONKS, JOHN, JR	ACTOR-WRITER	1058 NAPOLI DR	PACIFIC PALISADES, CA	90272
MONOD, JACQUES	ACTOR	16 RUE THIBAUD	PARIS 75014	FRANCE
MONOSON, LAWRENCE	ACTOR	9300 WILSHIRE BLVD #410	BEVERLY HILLS, CA	90212
MONPERE, CAROL	WRI-DIR-PROD	104 WALNUT ST	SAN FRANCISCO, CA	94118
MONROE, BILL	SINGER-GUITARIST	3819 DICKERSON RD	NASHVILLE, TN	37207
MONROE, DEL	ACTOR	8831 SUNSET BLVD #402	LOS ANGELES, CA	90069
MONROE, EARL "THE PEARL"	BASKETBALL	113 W 88TH ST	NEW YORK, NY	10025
MONROE, JAMES & TENNESSEE THUND	C & W GROUP	TESSIER, 505 CANTON PASS	MADISON, TN	37115
MONROE, LARRY	BASEBALL EXEC-SCOUT	333 W 35TH ST	CHICAGO, IL	60616
MONROE, MICHAEL	ACTOR	1161 N DOHENY DR	LOS ANGELES, CA	90069
MONS, RENE	BASEBALL SCOUT	POST OFFICE BOX 7000	PITTSBURGH, PA	15212
MONSKY, MARK	TV EXECUTIVE	METROMEDIA TV, 205 E 67TH ST	NEW YORK, NY	10021
MONTAGNA, PETER	MAKE-UP ARTIST	30 ROCKEFELLER PLAZA #680-E	NEW YORK, NY	10020
MONTAGNON, PETER	WRI-DIR-PROD	ANTELOPE, 3 FITZROY SQ	LONDON W1P 5AH	ENGLAND
MONTAGUE, BRUCE	ACTOR-WRITER	30 ARCHIBALD RD	LONDON N7 OAL	ENGLAND
MONTAGUE, ED	BASEBALL UMPIRE	800 PULHEMUS RD #30	SAN MATEO, CA	94402
MONTAGUE, LEE	ACTOR	5 KEATS CLOSE	LONDON NW3	ENGLAND
MONTALBAN, RICARDO	ACTOR-DIRECTOR	1423 ORIOLE DR	LOS ANGELES, CA	90069
MONTALBANO, ANGELA B	CASTING DIRECTOR	WILLIAM ESTY, 100 E 42ND ST	NEW YORK, NY	10016
MONTALVO, ROB	BASEBALL	633 JESSAMINE ST	KNOXVILLE, TN	37917
MONTANA	C & W GROUP	POST OFFICE BOX O	EXCELSIOR, MN	55331
MONTANA, JOE	FOOTBALL	S F 49ERS, 4949 CENTENNIAL BL	SANTA CLARA, CA	95054
MONTANA, KARLA	ACTRESS	POST OFFICE BOX 5617	BEVERLY HILLS, CA	90213
MONTANA, MONTE	ACTOR	520 MURRAY CANYON DR #412	PALM SPRINGS, CA	92262
MONTANA SKY	C & W GROUP	POST OFFICE BOX O	EXCELSIOR, MN	55331
MONTANINO, GENNARDO	FILM WRITER-DIRECTOR	5639 SATSUMA AVE	NORTH HOLLYWOOD, CA	91601
MONTANO, FRAN	ACTOR	SCHWARTZ, 935 N CROFT AVE	LOS ANGELES, CA	90069
MONTE, TONY	ARRANGER-CONDUCTOR	345 E 81ST ST #5-B	NEW YORK, NY	10028
MONTEFIORE, GENE	TV DIRECTOR	LINCOLN TOWERS, 142 W END AVE	NEW YORK, NY	10023
MONTEL, JOAN	SINGER	KCA, 928 MOSS ST	NEW ORLEANS, LA	70119
MONTEL, MICHAEL	DIRECTOR	9000 SUNSET BLVD #1200	LOS ANGELES, CA	90069
MONTELEONE, RICH	BASEBALL	N Y YANKEES, YANKEE STADIUM	BRONX, NY	10451
MONTERO, ALBERTO	BASEBALL	POST OFFICE BOX 824	BURLINGTON, IA	52601
MONTEVECCHI, LILIANE	SINGER	ICM, 8899 BEVERLY BLVD	LOS ANGELES, CA	90048
MONTGOMERY, ALTON	FOOTBALL	BRONCOS, 13655 BRONCOS PKWY	ENGLEWOOD, CO	80112
MONTGOMERY, BELINDA	ACTRESS	15301 VENTURA BLVD #345	SHERMAN OAKS, CA	91403
MONTGOMERY, BEN	FOOTBALL REFEREE	NFL, 410 PARK AVE	NEW YORK, NY	10022
MONTGOMERY, BOB	SPORTSCASTER	WSBK-TV, 83 BIRMINGHAM PKWY	BOSTON, MA	02215
MONTGOMERY, CHET	BASEBALL EXECUTIVE	POST OFFICE BOX 7000	PITTSBURGH, PA	15212
MONTGOMERY, CHUCK	FILM EDITOR	ACE, 1041 N FORMOSA AVE	WEST HOLLYWOOD, CA	90046
MONTGOMERY, DANNY	BASEBALL SCOUT	1000 ELYSIAN PARK DR	LOS ANGELES, CA	90012
MONTGOMERY, DAVID	BASEBALL EXECUTIVE	POST OFFICE BOX 7575	PHILADELPHIA, PA	19101
MONTGOMERY, DON	BASEBALL	POST OFFICE BOX 21727	SAN FRANCISCO, CA	95151
MONTGOMERY, ELIZABETH	ACTRESS	1230 BENEDICT CANYON DR	BEVERLY HILLS, CA	90210
MONTGOMERY, G V "SONNY"	U S CONGRESSMAN	POST OFFICE BOX 5618	MERIDAN, MS	39302
MONTGOMERY, GEORGE	ACTOR	POST OFFICE BOX 69983	LOS ANGELES, CA	90069
MONTGOMERY, GLENN	FOOTBALL	OILERS, 6910 FANNIN ST	HOUSTON, TX	77070
MONTGOMERY, JEFF	BASEBALL	POST OFFICE BOX 419969	KANSAS CITY, MO	64141
MONTGOMERY, JULIA	ACTRESS	9301 WILSHIRE BLVD #312	BEVERLY HILLS, CA	90210
MONTGOMERY, KATHRYN	FILM-TV WRITER	2937 WESTBROOK AVE	LOS ANGELES, CA	90046
MONTGOMERY, MELBA	SINGER	1300 DIVISION ST #103	NASHVILLE, TN	37203
MONTGOMERY, RAY	BASEBALL	POST OFFICE BOX 4209	JACKSON, MS	39296
MONTGOMERY, RED	ACTRESS	247 S BEVERLY DR #102	BEVERLY HILLS, CA	90210
MONTGOMERY, SHERI	MODEL	WILHELMINA, 300 PARK AVE	NEW YORK, NY	10010
MONTIEL, DAVID	ARTIST	115 W 16TH ST #211	NEW YORK, NY	10011
MONTOVA, MAX	FOOTBALL	RAIDERS, 332 CENTER ST	EL SEGUNDO, CA	90245
MONTOYA, ALBERT	BASEBALL	POST OFFICE BOX 1110	MYRTLE BEACH, SC	29578
MONTOYA, CARLOS	GUITARIST	345 W 58TH ST	NEW YORK, NY	10019
MONTOYA, NORMAN	BASEBALL	POST OFFICE BOX 1742	PALM SPRINGS, CA	92263
MONTOYO, CHARLIE	BASEBALL	2850 W 20TH AVE	DENVER, CO	80211
MONTROSE, JACK	COMPOSER	2236 HACIENDA AVE	LAS VEGAS, NV	89119
MONTROSE/FROOM	ROCK & ROLL GROUP	3 E 54TH ST #1400	NEW YORK, NY	10022
MONTROSS, CHRISTOPHER	TV DIRECTOR	6310 FRANKLIN RD	BIRMINGHAM, MI	48010
MONTY, EVA	ACTRESS	7938 DRISCOLL AVE	VAN NUYS, CA	91406
MONTY, GLORIA	TV DIRECTOR-PRODUCER	16065 JEANNE LN	ENCINO, CA	91316

MONTY, JERRY	WRESTLER	POST OFFICE BOX 3859	STAMFORD, CT 06905
MONZON, DAN	BASEBALL (2ND BASE)	POST OFFICE BOX 4218	SOUTH BEND, IN 46634
MONZON, DAN	BASEBALL (SCOUT)	333 W 35TH ST	CHICAGO, IL 60616
MONZON, JOSE	BASEBALL	633 JESSAMINE ST	KNOXVILLE, TN 37917
MOO-YOUNG, IAN	ANIMATION DIRECTOR	26-27 GREAT SUTTON ST	LONDON EC1 ENGLAND
MOOD EXPRESS	C & W GROUP	POST OFFICE BOX 5563	ROCKFORD, IL 61125
MOODY, AUNT ESSIE	ACTRESS	PAT LYNN, 10525 STRATHMORE DR	LOS ANGELES, CA 90024
MOODY, JIM	U S CONGRESSMAN	135 W WELLS ST #618	MILWAUKEE, WI 53203
MOODY, JOHN W	DIRECTOR	100 KINGS POINT DR #810	NORTH MIAMI BEACH, FL 33160
MOODY, KYLE	BASEBALL	POST OFFICE BOX 611	WATERLOO, IA 50704
MOODY, LAURENCE	TV DIRECTOR	32 THE RIDGE, SURBITON	SURREY KT5 8HX ENGLAND
MOODY, LLOYD	GOLFER	PGA SENIORS, 112 T P C BLVD	PONTE VEDRA BEACH, FL 32082
MOODY, LYNNE	ACTRESS	8708 SKYLINE DR	LOS ANGELES, CA 90046
MOODY, ORVILLE	GOLFER	PGA SENIORS, 112 T P C BLVD	PONTE VEDRA BEACH, FL 32082
MOODY, PAULA	STUNTWOMAN	3518 W CAHUENGA BLVD #206-A	LOS ANGELES, CA 90068
MOODY, PHILIP T	COMPOSER	4179 HAZELTINE AVE	SHERMAN OAKS, CA 91403
MOODY, RON	ACTOR	INGLESIDE, 41 THE GREEN	
		SOUTHGATE	LONDON N14 ENGLAND
MOODY BLUES, THE	ROCK & ROLL GROUP	WEINTRAUB ENTERTAINMENT GROUP	
		11111 SANTA MONICA BL, 10TH FL	LOS ANGELES 90025
MOOMAW, DR DONN D	CLERGYMAN-FOOTBALL	3124 CORDA DR	LOS ANGELES, CA 90049
MOON, SARAH	DIRECTOR	DGA, 7920 SUNSET BLVD, 6TH FL	LOS ANGELES, CA 90046
MOON, WALLY	BASEBALL-MANAGER	POST OFFICE BOX 3169	FREDERICK, MD 21701
MOON, WARREN	FOOTBALL	OILERS, 6910 FANNIN ST	HOUSTON, TX 77070
MOONEY, TOM	BASEBALL SCOUT	POST OFFICE BOX 288	HOUSTON, TX 77001
MOONEY, TROY	BASEBALL	POST OFFICE BOX 842	SALEM, VA 24153
MOONGLOWS, THE	VOCAL GROUP	5300 POWERLINE RD #202	FORT LAUDERDALE, FL 33309
MOONJEAN, HANK	FILM PRODUCER	8374 MULHOLLAND DR	LOS ANGELES, CA 90046
MOONLIGHT DRIVE	ROCK & ROLL GROUP	41 BRITAIN ST #200	TORONTO, ONT M5A 1R7 CANADA
MOONSHINE CLOGGERS, THE	C & W GROUP	POST OFFICE BOX 418	BRENTWOOD, TN 37027
MOOR, BILL	ACTOR	9200 SUNSET BLVD #710	LOS ANGELES, CA 90069
MOORE, ALAN	MUSIC ARRANGER	4909 GRANNY WHITE PIKE	NASHVILLE, TN 37220
MOORE, ALVY	ACTOR	8546 AMESTOY AVE	NORTHRIDGE, CA 91324
MOORE, ARCHIE	BOXER	3517 EAST ST	SAN DIEGO, CA 92102
MOORE, BOB	FOOTBALL REFEREE	NFL, 410 PARK AVE	NEW YORK, NY 10022
MOORE, BOBBY	BASEBALL	POST OFFICE BOX 6667	RICHMOND, VA 23230
MOORE, BOO	BASEBALL	POST OFFICE BOX 10213	LYNCHBURG, VA 24506
MOORE, BRAD	BASEBALL	POST OFFICE BOX 1211	NORFOLK, VA 23502
MOORE, CAMILLA	ACTRESS	ABC-TV, "GENERAL HOSPITAL"	
		4151 PROSPECT AVE	BURBANK, CA 91523
MOORE, CHERI	TV PRODUCER	38 RUE DE GRENELLE	PARIS 75007 FRANCE
MOORE, CLAYTON	ACTOR	4720 PARK OLIVO	CALABASAS, CA 91302
MOORE, CONSTANCE	ACTRESS	1661 FERRARI DR	BEVERLY HILLS, CA 90210
MOORE, CRAIG & MOORE, BAND	C & W GROUP	JOYCE, 2028 CHESTNUT ST	PHILADELPHIA, PA 19103
MOORE, DAN	COSTUME DESIGNER	4416 FINLEY AVE	LOS ANGELES, CA 90027
MOORE, DARYL	BASEBALL	POST OFFICE BOX 230	HAGERSTOWN, MD 21740
MOORE, DAVE	BASEBALL EXECUTIVE	TWINS, 501 CHICAGO AVE S	MINNEAPOLIS, MN 55415
MOORE, DAVID LEON	SPORTS WRITER	POST OFFICE BOX 500	WASHINGTON, DC 20044
MOORE, DEMI	ACTRESS	CAA, 9830 WILSHIRE BLVD	BEVERLY HILLS, CA 90212
MOORE, DENA	ACTRESS	6116 FULTON AVE #315	VAN NUYS, CA 91401
MOORE, DENNIS "MICKEY"	DIRECTOR	26706 LATIGO SHORE DR	MALIBU, CA 90265
MOORE, DERICK C	NEWS CORRES-WRITER	53 "D" ST, SE	WASHINGTON, DC 20003
MOORE, DICKIE	ACTOR	165 W 46TH ST #907	NEW YORK, NY 10036
MOORE, DUDLEY	ACTOR-WRITER	5505 OCEAN FRONT WALK	MARINA DEL REY, CA 90292
MOORE, EDDIE N, JR	TREASURER	STATE CAPITOL BUILDING	RICHMOND, VA 23219
MOORE, ERIC	FOOTBALL	N Y GIANTS, GIANTS STADIUM	EAST RUTHERFORD, NJ 07073
MOORE, GARY	SINGER-SONGWRITER	PARK ROCK, 4 MONTAGU, 71 BAKER	LONDON W1H 1AB ENGLAND
MOORE, GARY	TV HOST	POST OFFICE BOX 533	NORTHEAST HARBOR, ME 04662
MOORE, H THOMAS	DIRECTOR	DGA, 7920 SUNSET BLVD, 6TH FL	LOS ANGELES, CA 90046
MOORE, HERMAN	FOOTBALL	LIONS, 1200 FEATHERSTONE RD	PONTIAC, MI 48432
MOORE, IRVING	TV DIRECTOR	5126 RANCHITO AVE	SHERMAN OAKS, CA 91423
MOORE, JACKIE	BASEBALL-COACH	REDS, 100 RIVERFRONT STADIUM	CINCINNATI, OH 45202
MOORE, JACKIE	SINGER	FAA, 1700 BROADWAY, 5TH FLOOR	NEW YORK, NY 10019
MOORE, JAMES W	DIRECTOR	38 E 19TH ST	NEW YORK, NY 10003
MOORE, JOHN F	TV DIRECTOR	984 ESPLANADE	PELHAM, NY 10803
MOORE, JOSEPH PAUL	FILM DIRECTOR	5720 OWENSMOUTH AVE #129	WOODLAND HILLS, CA 91367
MOORE, JUANITA	ACTRESS	3802-L DUNSFORD LN	INGLEWOOD, CA 90305
MOORE, KAREN	ACTRESS	3575 W CAHUENGA BLVD #254	HOLLYWOOD, CA 90028
MOORE, KATHY	BODYBUILDER	16088 GREEN VALLEY HGTS RD	RAMONA, CA 92065
MOORE, KELLY	SINGER-GUITARIST	3724 TIBBS DR	NASHVILLE, TN 37211
MOORE, KENNETH J	COMPOSER-CONDUCTOR	843 MALTMAN AVE	LOS ANGELES, CA 90026
MOORE, KERWIN	BASEBALL	300 STADIUM WY	DAVENPORT, FL 33837
MOORE, KINGMAN	TV DIRECTOR	2750 MARKET ST #202	SAN FRANCISCO, CA 94114
MOORE, LAWRENCE	TV DIRECTOR-PRODUCER	536 FULHAM PALACE RD	LONDON SW6 6JH ENGLAND
MOORE, LESLI NOBLES	TV DIRECTOR	18415 "J" COLLINS ST	TARZANA, CA 91356
MOORE, LEWIS	SINGER	POST OFFICE BOX 383	WEST POINT, GA 31833
MOORE, MARCUS	BASEBALL	633 JESSAMINE ST	KNOXVILLE, TN 37917
MOORE, MARY TYLER	ACTRESS	927 5TH AVE	NEW YORK, NY 10021
MOORE, MELBA	SINGER	200 CENTRAL PARK S #8-R	NEW YORK, NY 10019
MOORE, MICKEY	FILM DIRECTOR	26706 LATIGO SHORE DR	MALIBU, CA 90265
MOORE, MIKE	ATTORNEY GENERAL	POST OFFICE BOX 2000	JACKSON, MS 39215
MOORE, MIKE	BASEBALL (MAJORS)	ATHLETICS'S, OAKLAND COLISEUM	OAKLAND, CA 94621
MOORE, MIKE	BASEBALL (MINORS)	POST OFFICE BOX 1886	COLUMBUS, GA 31902
MOORE, MILLIE	FILM EDITOR	ACE, 1041 N FORMOSA AVE	WEST HOLLYWOOD, CA 90046
MOORE, MONTE	SPORTSCASTER	ATHLETICS'S, OAKLAND COLISEUM	OAKLAND, CA 94621

MOORE, RICHARD	CINEMATOGRAPHER	887 CHATTANOOGA AVE	PACIFIC PALISADES, CA 90272
MOORE, ROB	FOOTBALL	N Y JETS, 1000 FULTON AVE	HEMPSTEAD, NY 11550
MOORE, ROBERT MICHAEL	COSTUME DESIGNER	13949 VENTURA BLVD #309	SHERMAN OAKS. CA 91423
MOORE, ROGER	ACTOR	CHALET FENIL	GRUND BEI GSTAAD SWITZERLAND
MOORE, STEVE	CARTOONIST	TRIBUNE, 64 E CONCORD ST	ORLANDO, FL 32801
MOORE, TAYLOR	BASEBALL EXECUTIVE	POST OFFICE BOX 3448	SHREVEPORT, LA 71133
MOORE, TERRY	ACTRESS	833 OCEAN AVE #104	SANTA MONICA, CA 90403
MOORE, THOMAS	TV PRODUCER-EXECUTIVE	91 DORCHESTER RD	DARIEN, CT 06820
MOORE, THOMAS LEE	TV DIRECTOR-PRODUCER	KOLMER VISIONS, 880 CANAL ST	STAMFORD, CT 06902
MOORE, TIM	BASEBALL	POST OFFICE BOX 661	KENOSHA, WI 53141
MOORE, TIM	SINGER	POST OFFICE BOX 669	WOODSTOCK, NY 12498
MOORE, TOM	FOOTBALL COACH	VIKINGS, 9520 VIKING DR	EDEN PRAIRIE, MN 55344
MOORE, TOM	TV DIRECTOR	VINCENT ANDREWS MGMT	
		488 MADISON AVE	NEW YORK, NY 10022
MOORE, VINCE	BASEBALL	POST OFFICE BOX 4525	MACON, GA 31208
MOORE, WENDELL	SINGER	439 GAINESVILLE AVE	MEMPHIS, TN 38109
MOORES, JAMES	PRODUCER	641 CALIFORNIA AVE	VENICE, CA 90291
MOORHEAD, CARLOS	U S CONGRESSMAN	420 N BRAND BLVD	GLENDALE, CA 91203
MOOSEKIAN, VAHAN	ACTOR	1321 WELLESLEY AVE #3	LOS ANGELES, CA 90025
MORA, JIM, JR	FOOTBALL COACH	POST OFFICE BOX 609609	SAN DIEGO, CA 92160
MORA, JIM, SR	FOOTBALL-COACH	SAINTS, 1500 POYDRAS ST	NEW ORLEANS, LA 90112
MORA, PHILIPPE	FILM DIRECTOR	822 S ROBERTSON BLVD #200	LOS ANGELES, CA 90035
MORABITO, BRUCE D	CONDUCTOR	7609 HINDS AVE	NORTH HOLLYWOOD, CA 91605
MORAHAN, CHRISTOPHER	DIRECTOR-PRODUCER	WHITEHALL, 125 GLOUCESTER RD	LONDON SW7 4TE ENGLAND
MORALES, ARMANDO	BASEBALL	POST OFFICE BOX 4669	CHARLESTON, WV 25304
MORALES, DAN	ATTORNEY GENERAL	POST OFFICE BOX 12428	AUSTIN, TX 78711
MORALES, ESAI	ACTOR	1147 S WOOSTER ST	LOS ANGELES, CA 90035
MORALES, JORGE	BASEBALL	POST OFFICE BOX 9194	HAMPTON, VA 23670
MORALES, JOSE	BASEBALL-COACH	INDIANS, CLEVELAND STADIUM	CLEVELAND, OH 44114
MORALES, PEDRO	WRESTLER	POST OFFICE BOX 3859	STAMFORD, CT 06905
MORALES, RICH	BASEBALL	POST OFFICE BOX 4370	SALINAS, CA 93912
MORALES, SYLVIA	WRITER-PRODUCER	DGA, 7920 SUNSET BLVD, 6TH FL	LOS ANGELES, CA 90046
MORAN, ERIN	ACTRESS	11075 SANTA MONICA BLVD #150	LOS ANGELES, CA 90025
MORAN, GAYLE	SINGER	COREA, 2635 GRIFFITH PARK BLVD	LOS ANGELES, CA 90039
MORAN, JAMES P	U S CONGRESSMAN	5115-G FRANCONIA RD	ALEXANDRIA, VA 22302
MORAN, JIM	BASEBALL SCOUT	POST OFFICE BOX 419969	KANSAS CITY, MO 64141
MORAN, MIKE	COMPOSER	OLAV WYPER, LTD, BRUCE CT WEST	
		OTTERDEN, FAVERSHAM	KENT ME13 OBY ENGLAND
MORAN, PAUL	GOLFER	PGA SENIORS, 112 T P C BLVD	PONTE VEDRA BEACH, FL 32082
MORAN, RICH	FOOTBALL	PACKERS, 1265 LOMBARDI AVE	GREEN BAY, WI 54307
MORANDINI, MICKEY	BASEBALL	POST OFFICE BOX 7575	PHILADELPHIA, PA 19101
MORANIS, RICK	ACTOR	90 RIVERSIDE DR #14-E	NEW YORK, NY 10024
MORANVILLE, JOHN B	DIRECTOR	4624 CAHUENGA BLVD	TOLUCA LAKE, CA 91602
MORDECAI, MIKE	BASEBALL	POST OFFICE BOX 16683	GREENVILLE, SC 29606
MORDENTE, TONY	DIRECTOR	4541 COMBER AVE	ENCINO, CA 91316
MORE, ALEXANDRA	ACTRESS	5330 LANKERSHIM BLVD #210	NORTH HOLLYWOOD, CA 91601
MORE, CAMILLA	ACTRESS	6255 SUNSET BLVD #627	LOS ANGELES, CA 90028
MORE, CARMEN	ACTRESS	4051 RADFORD AVE #A	STUDIO CITY, CA 91604
MOREAU, JEANNE	ACTRESS	193 RUE DEL'UNIVERSITE	75007 PARIS FRANCE
MOREHEAD, FRANK	ACTOR	10032 COLLETT AVE	SEPULVEDA, CA 91343
MOREHOUSE, STEPHANIE KLINE	COSTUME DESIGNER	894 S BRONSON AVE	LOS ANGELES, CA 90005
MOREL, JACQUES	ACTOR	45 BLVD SAINT-JACQUES	PARIS 75014 FRANCE
MORELLA, CONSTANCE	U S CONGRESSWOMAN	11141 GEORGIA AVE #302	WHEATON, MD 20902
MORELLI, CARL J	BODYBUILDER	605 3RD AVE	NEW YORK, NY 10158
MORENO, ARMANDO	BASEBALL	POST OFFICE BOX 450	BUFFALO, NY 14205
MORENO, CARLOS	BASEBALL SCOUT	REDS, 100 RIVERFRONT STADIUM	CINCINNATI, OH 45202
MORENO, JAIME	BASEBALL COACH	POST OFFICE BOX 20849	CHARLESTON, SC 29413
MORENO, JUAN	BASEBALL	POST OFFICE BOX 7845	COLUMBIA, SC 29202
MORENO, MARK C	NEWS CORRES-WRITER	ABC NEWS, 1717 DE SALES ST, NW	WASHINGTON, DC 20036
MORENO, RITA	ACTRESS	1620 AMALFI DR	PACIFIC PALISADES, CA 90272
MORESS, STAN	TALENT AGENT	SCOTTI BROS, 2128 PICO BLVD	SANTA MONICA, CA 90405
MORETTI, MOONDOG	WRESTLER	8725 N CHAUTAUQUA BLVD	PORTLAND, OR 97217
MOREY, SEAN	COMEDIAN	2828 3RD ST #17	SANTA MONICA, CA 90405
MORFOGEN, ANN	TV EXECUTIVE	CBS-TV, 524 W 57TH ST	NEW YORK, NY 10019
MORGAN	DIRECTOR	POST OFFICE BOX 1812	BEVERLY HILLS, CA 90213
MORGAN, ALEXANDRA	ACTRESS	19710 PACIFIC COAST HWY	MALIBU, CA 90265
MORGAN, ANDRE E	FILM WRITER-PRODUCER	120 S EL CAMINO DR #204	BEVERLY HILLS, CA 90212
MORGAN, ANDREW	TV DIRECTOR	28 WYNDHAM ST	LONDON W1H 1DD ENGLAND
MORGAN, ANTHONY	FOOTBALL	BEARS, 250 N WASHINGTON RD	LAKE FOREST, IL 60045
MORGAN, BARRY	TALENT AGENT	7250 BEVERLY BLVD #102	LOS ANGELES, CA 90036
MORGAN, CHARLENE	SINGER	ROUTE #7, BOX 52-C	MURFREESBORO, TN 37130
MORGAN, CHRISTOPHER	WRITER-PRODUCER	10437 SARAH ST	NORTH HOLLYWOOD, CA 91602
MORGAN, CINDY	ACTRESS	1801 AVE OF THE STARS #1250	LOS ANGELES, CA 90067
MORGAN, DAN	GOLFER	PGA SENIORS, 112 T P C BLVD	PONTE VEDRA BEACH, FL 32082
MORGAN, DANNY	SINGER	POST OFFICE BOX 6507	CINCINNATI, OH 45206
MORGAN, DEBBI	ACTRESS	1801 AVE OF THE STARS #1250	LOS ANGELES, CA 90067
MORGAN, DENNIS	ACTOR-SINGER	POST OFFICE BOX 3036	AHWAHNEE, CA 93601
MORGAN, DONALD MAXWELL	DIRECTOR	POST OFFICE BOX 1166	PACIFIC PALISADES, CA 90272
MORGAN, ELAINE	PLAYWRIGHT	24 ABERFFRWD RD, MOUNTAIN ASH	GLAMORGAN ENGLAND
MORGAN, GIL	GOLFER	POST OFFICE BOX 109601	PALM BCH GARDENS, FL 33418
MORGAN, HARRY	ACTOR-DIRECTOR	13172 BOCA DE CANON LN	LOS ANGELES, CA 90049
MORGAN, HENRY	ACTOR-HUMORIST	350 E 84TH ST	NEW YORK, NY 10028
MORGAN, JACK	COMPOSER	6902 TEXHOMA AVE	VAN NUYS, CA 91406
MORGAN, JAN	TV EXECUTIVE	ZINK COMM, 245 W 19TH ST	NEW YORK, NY 10011
MORGAN, JANE	ACTRESS	27740 PACIFIC COAST HIGHWAY	MALIBU, CA 90265

MORGAN, JAYE P	SINGER-ACTRESS	30366 CORNELL SCHOOL RD	AGOURA HILLS, CA 91301
MORGAN, JEFFREY PAUL	ACTOR	5258 CAHUENGA BLVD	NORTH HOLLYWOOD, CA 91601
MORGAN, JOE	BASEBALL (BOSTON)	FENWAY PARK, 4 YAWKEY WY	BOSTON, MA 02215
MORGAN, JOE	BASEBALL (CINCINNATI)	ESPN PLAZA, 935 MIDDLEST	BRISTOL, CT 06010
MORGAN, JOHN W	COMPOSER	18445 COLLINS ST #113	TARZANA, CA 91356
MORGAN, JON	SINGER	5625 "O" STREET BLDG #7	LINCOLN, NE 68510
MORGAN, JUSTIN	DIRECTOR-PRODUCER	28525 TRAILRIDERS DR	PALOS VERDES, CA 90274
MORGAN, KEVIN	BASEBALL	POST OFFICE BOX 64939	FAYETTEVILLE, NC 28306
MORGAN, LORRIE	SINGER	POST OFFICE BOX 22765	NASHVILLE, TN 37202
MORGAN, LYNN MARIE	TV DIRECTOR	8333 COLUMBUS AVE #23	SEPULVEDA, CA 91343
MORGAN, MICHAEL D	CONDUCTOR	SOFFER, 130 W 56TH ST	NEW YORK, NY 10019
MORGAN, MICHAEL D	RECORD EXECUTIVE	POST OFFICE BOX 2388	PRESCOTT, AZ 86302
MORGAN, MICHELE	ACTRESS	5 RUE JACQUES DULUD	92200 NEUILLY FRANCE
MORGAN, MIKE	BASEBALL	1060 W ADDISON ST	CHICAGO, IL 60613
MORGAN, MILES	FILM DIRECTOR	129 E 74TH ST	NEW YORK, NY 10021
MORGAN, MONTY	TV PRODUCER	CREATIVE PROG, 28 E 10TH ST	NEW YORK, NY 10003
MORGAN, NANCY	ACTRESS	8380 MELROSE AVE #207	LOS ANGELES, CA 90069
MORGAN, PATRICK	DIRECTOR	DGA, 110 W 57TH ST	NEW YORK, NY 10019
MORGAN, PAUL C	DIRECTOR	2705 GLENDOWER AVE	LOS ANGELES, CA 90027
MORGAN, SCOTT	BASEBALL	2501 ALLEN AVE, SE	CANTON, OH 44707
MORGAN, SHELLEY TAYLOR	ACTRESS	9200 SUNSET BLVD #625	LOS ANGELES, CA 90069
MORGAN, TRACY	ACTRESS	BDP, 10637 BURBANK BLVD	NORTH HOLLYWOOD, CA 91601
MORGAN, WAYNE	BASEBALL SCOUT	SKYDOME, 300 BREMMER BL #3200	TORONTO, ONT M5V 3B3 CANADA
MORGANNA	KISSING BANDIT	POST OFFICE BOX 20281	COLUMBUS, OH 43220
MORGANTI, LEN	ARTIST	1351 OCEAN PARK WALK #106	SANTA MONICA, CA 90405
MORHAIM, JOSEPH	TV WRITER	2511 ANGELO DR	LOS ANGELES, CA 90077
MORHEIM, LOU	TV WRITER	2511 ANGELO DR	LOS ANGELES, CA 90077
MORI, JEANNE	ACTRESS	301 N CANON DR #305	BEVERLY HILLS, CA 90210
MORIARTY, CATHY	ACTRESS	9005 BURTON WY #601	LOS ANGELES, CA 90048
MORIARTY, MICHAEL	ACTOR	200 W 58TH ST #3-B	NEW YORK, NY 10019
MORICK, DAVE	ACTOR	4851 BEEMAN AVE	NORTH HOLLYWOOD, CA 91607
MORILLO, CEASAR	BASEBALL	300 STADIUM WY	DAVENPORT, FL 33837
MORIN, JIM	CARTOONIST	THE MIAMI HERALD	
		1 HERALD PLAZA	MIAMI, FL 33101
MORIN, STEPHANE	HOCKEY	NORDIQUES, 2205 AVE DU COLISEE	QUEBEC, QUE G1L 4W7 CANADA
MORIN-TORRE, LORRAINE	ACTRESS	165 W 46TH ST #1109	NEW YORK, NY 10036
MORING, JO	TV EXECUTIVE	NBC-TV, 30 ROCKEFELLER PLAZA	NEW YORK, NY 10112
MORISON, PATRICIA	ACTRESS-SINGER	400 S HAUSER BLVD #9-L	LOS ANGELES, CA 90036
MORITA, NORIYUKI "PAT"	ACTOR -COMEDIAN	POST OFFICE BOX 491278	LOS ANGELES, CATN 90049
MORITZ, LOUISA	ACTRESS-MODEL	SAINT MORITZ, 120 S REEVES DR	BEVERLY HILLS, CA 90212
MORLAN, JOE	BASEBALL SCOUT	250 STADIUM PLAZA	ST LOUIS, MO 63102
MORLANE, MIKE	BASEBALL	POST OFFICE BOX 1110	MYRTLE BEACH, SC 29578
MORLEY, ANGELA	COMPOSER-CONDUCTOR	23624 DEL CERRO CIR	CANOGA PARK, CA 91304
MORLEY, DONALD	ACTOR	GRIFFITH, 6 RYDE PL	E TWICKENHAM TW1 2EH ENGLAND
MORLEY, RUTH	COSTUME DESIGNER	130 W 42ND ST #1804	NEW YORK, NY 10036
MORMAN, AL	BASEBALL	POST OFFICE BOX 1556	ASHEVILLE, NC 28802
MORNING	C & W GROUP	1515 ALMEADA WY #107	SAN JOSE, CA 95126
MOROAICA, HORIA	CONDUCTOR	3332 CALIFORNIA ST	HUNTINGTON PARK, CA 90255
MORODER, GIORGIO	COMPOSER-PRODUCER	9348 CIVIC CENTER DR #101	BEVERLY HILLS, CA 90210
MORPHET, DAVID	WRITER-PRODUCER	GREENPARK, 101 HONOR OAK PARK	LONDON SE23 3LB ENGLAND
MORPHY, PAT	BASEBALL	5301 NW 12TH AVE	FORT LAUDERDALE, FL 33309
MORRELL, DAVID	AUTHOR	1805 W BENTON ST	IOWA CITY, IA 52240
MORRICONE, ENNIO	COMPOSER	3815 W OLIVE AVE #201	BRUBANK, CA 91505
MORRIS, ANITA	ACTRESS	13758 MULHOLLAND DR	BEVERLY HILLS, CA 90210
MORRIS, BOB	TV DIRECTOR-PRODUCER	322 E 84TH ST	NEW YORK, NY 10028
MORRIS, CHRIS	BASKETBALL	N J NETS, MEADOWLANDS ARENA	EAST RUTHERFORD, NJ 07073
MORRIS, CLIFFORD J	COMPOSER	CLIFFHANGER, 1620 VALLEY ST	FORT LEE, NJ 07024
MORRIS, COLIN	PLAYWRIGHT	75 HILLWAY	LONDON N6 ENGLAND
MORRIS, COLLEEN	ACTRESS	ASHER, 644 N DOHENY DR	LOS ANGELES, CA 90069
MORRIS, DUANE	ACTOR	484 W 43RD ST #30-L	NEW YORK, NY 10036
MORRIS, EARLE E, JR	COMPTROLLER GENERAL	POST OFFICE BOX 11369	COLUMBIA, SC 29211
MORRIS, GARRETT	ACTOR	3740 BARHAM BLVD #E-116	LOS ANGELES, CA 90068
MORRIS, GARY	ACTOR-SINGER	6027 CHURCH DR	SUGARLAND, TX 77478
MORRIS, GREG	ACTOR	3191 BEL AIR RD	LAX VEGAS, NV 89109
MORRIS, HAL	BASEBALL	REDS, 100 RIVERFRONT STADIUM	CINCINNATI, OH 45202
MORRIS, HOWARD	ACTOR-DIRECTOR	18457 CLIFF TOP WY	MALIBU, CA 90265
MORRIS, IONA	ACTRESS	BONNIE ALLEN, 250 W 57TH ST	NEW YORK, NY 10107
MORRIS, JEREMIAH	TV DIRECTOR	3677 MEADVILLE DR	SHERMAN OAKS, CA 91403
MORRIS, JOE	FOOTBALL	BROWNS, 80 1ST ST	BEREA, OH 44017
MORRIS, JOHN	CARTOONIST	177 E HARTSDALE AVE	HARTSDALE, NY 10530
MORRIS, JOHN D	BASEBALL	2775 KIPPS COLONY DR #105	GULFPORT, FL 33707
MORRIS, JOHN S "JACK"	BASEBALL	SKYDOME, 300 BREMMER BL #3200	TORONTO, ONT M5V 3B3 CANADA
MORRIS, JON	HOCKEY	POST OFFICE BOX 504	EAST RUTHERFORD, NJ 07073
MORRIS, JONATHAN	ACTOR	HEATH, PARAMOUNT HOUSE	
		162-170 WARDOUR ST	LONDON W1V 3AT ENGLAND
MORRIS, KENNETH J	TV WRITER-PRODUCER	1125 N CLARK ST #D	LOS ANGELES, CA 90069
MORRIS, LARRY	PHOTOGRAPHER	THE WASHINGTON POST	
		1150 15TH ST, NW	WASHINGTON, DC 20071
MORRIS, LINDA K	SONGWRITER	2920 NEILSON WY #103	SANTA MONICA, CA 90405
MORRIS, MARC	BASEBALL	POST OFFICE BOX 48	VISALIA, CA 93279
MORRIS, MARTIN	TV DIRECTOR	4256 CAMELLIA AVE	STUDIO CITY, CA 91604
MORRIS, MYRA	ACTRESS	100 W 89TH ST #2-H	NEW YORK, NY 10024
MORRIS, PHIL	ACTOR	704 THE STRAND	MANHATTAN BEACH, CA 90266
MORRIS, RICHARD	SINGER	ICM, 8899 BEVERLY BLVD	LOS ANGELES, CA 90048
MORRIS, ROBERT F	TV DIRECTOR	332 E 84TH ST	NEW YORK, NY 10028

Name	Occupation	Address	City	Zip
MORRIS, ROBERT T	COMPOSER	POST OFFICE BOX 11103	BEVERLY HILLS, CA	90213
MORRIS, ROD	BASEBALL	POST OFFICE BOX 4448	TULSA, OK	74159
MORRIS, ROY J	TV WRITER-DIRECTOR	1718 SUNSET PLAZA DR	LOS ANGELES, CA	90069
MORRISON, BUD	DIRECTOR	8383 WILSHIRE BLVD #610	BEVERLY HILLS, CA	90211
MORRISON, DAN	BASEBALL UMPIRE	9223 122ND WY N	SEMINOLE, FL	33542
MORRISON, HOBBY	DIRECTOR	DGA, 7920 SUNSET BLVD, 6TH FL	LOS ANGELES, CA	90046
MORRISON, JIM	BASEBALL (MAJORS)	11202 VERANDA CT	BRADENTON, FL	33529
MORRISON, JIM	BASEBALL (MINORS)	POST OFFICE BOX 10213	LYNCHBURG, VA	24506
MORRISON, KEITH	BASEBALL	POLECATS, 608 N SLAPPEY BLVD	ALBANY, GA	31701
MORRISON, PAUL	TV DIRECTOR	57 PARKHOLME RD	LONDON E8 3AQ	ENGLAND
MORRISON, SID	U S CONGRESSMAN	3311 W CLEARWATER #105	KENEWICK, WA	99336
MORRISON, VAN	SINGER-SONGWRITER	12304 SANTA MONICA BLVD #300	LOS ANGELES, CA	90025
MORRISS, FRANK	FILM EDITOR	10100 SANTA MONICA BLVD #1600	LOS ANGELES, CA	90067
MORRISSEY, JIM	FOOTBALL	BEARS, 250 N WASHINGTON RD	LAKE FOREST, IL	60045
MORROW, BARRY	FILM-TV WRITER	151 S EL CAMINO DR	BEVERLY HILLS, CA	90212
MORROW, CHRIS	BASEBALL	POST OFFICE BOX 28268	SAN ANTONIO, TX	78228
MORROW, COUSIN BRUCIE	RADIO PERSONALITY	SEE - COUSIN BRUCIE		
MORROW, DAN	BODYBUILDER	POST OFFICE BOX 11883	FRESNO, CA	93775
MORROW, JEFF	ACTOR	4828 BALBOA AVE #B	ENCINO, CA	91316
MORROW, KAREN	ACTRESS	4231 FAIR AVE	NORTH HOLLYWOOD, CA	91602
MORROW, LIZA	ACTRESS	POST OFFICE BOX 5617	BEVERLY HILLS, CA	90213
MORROW, MARY	ACTRESS	1801 AVE OF THE STARS #1250	LOS ANGELES, CA	90067
MORROW, PAUL DAVID	ACTOR-WRITER	7422 HAZELTINE AVE #1	VAN NUYS, CA	91405
MORROW, RED	BASEBALL UMPIRE	POST OFFICE BOX 25010	LITTLE ROCK, AZ	72221
MORROW, SCOTT D	CHOREOGRAPHER	LORRAINE, 2269 OCEAN AVE	BROOKLYN, NY	11229
MORROW, STEVE	BASEBALL TRAINER	POST OFFICE BOX 419969	KANSAS CITY, MO	64141
MORROW, TIMMIE	BASEBALL	POST OFFICE BOX 3609	PORT CHARLOTTE, FL	33949
MORROW, TODD	SINGER	XHRM-FM, 4183 M L KING WY	SAN DIEGO, CA	92102
MORSE, BOBBY	FOOTBALL	SAINTS, 1500 POYDRAS ST	NEW ORLEANS, LA	90112
MORSE, CARLETON E	WRITER	BOX 50, STAR ROUTE	REDWOOD CITY, CA	94062
MORSE, JOHN HOLLINGSWORTH	DIRECTOR	3219 OAKDELL LN	STUDIO CITY, CA	91604
MORSE, ROBERT	ACTOR	13830 DAVANA TERR	SHERMAN OAKS, CA	91403
MORSE, STEVE, BAND	ROCK & ROLL GROUP	ICM, 40 W 57TH ST	NEW YORK, NY	10019
MORSE, SUSAN E	FILM EDITOR	ACE, 1041 N FORMOSA AVE	WEST HOLLYWOOD, CA	90046
MORSER, C BRUCE	ARTIST	2566 5TH AVE N	SEATTLE, WA	98109
MORSS, ANTHONY	CONDUCTOR	1199 PARK AVE #1-E	NEW YORK, NY	10028
MORTENSEN, TONY	BASEBALL	12000 STADIUM RD	ADELANTO, CA	92301
MORTIMER, JOHN	SCREENWRITER	PETERS, FRASER & DUNLOP, LTD		
		5TH FLOOR, THE CHAMBERS		
		CHELSEA HARBOUR, LOT RD	LONDON SW10 OXF	ENGLAND
MORTIMER, JOHNNIE	TV WRITER	PETERS, FRASER & DUNLOP, LTD		
		5TH FLOOR, THE CHAMBERS		
		CHELSEA HARBOUR, LOT RD	LONDON SW10 OXF	ENGLAND
MORTON, BILL	TV PRODUCER	BBC, KENSINGTON HOUSE		
		RICHMOND WY	LONDON W14	ENGLAND
MORTON, DAVID	COMPOSER	2254 S WELLESLEY AVE	LOS ANGELES, CA	90064
MORTON, ERIGI	WRESTLER	POST OFFICE BOX 3859	STAMFORD, CT	06905
MORTON, GARY	COMEDIAN	40241 CLUBVIEW DR	RANCHO MIRAGE, CA	92270
MORTON, HOWARD	ACTOR	12311 CANTURA ST	STUDIO CITY, CA	91604
MORTON, JOE	ACTOR	606 N LARCHMONT BLVD #309	LOS ANGELES, CA	90004
MORTON, JOHN	ACTOR-WRITER	KLAUSNER, 71 PARK AVE	NEW YORK, NY	10016
MORTON, JOHN	BASKETBALL	POST OFFICE BOX 5000	RICHFIELD, OH	44286
MORTON, JOSEPH B	DIRECTOR-PRODUCER	212 N GROVE #1-N	OAK PARK, IL	60302
MORTON, JOSHUA DILL	CINEMATOGRAPHER	9 OAK KNOLL GARDEN	PASADENA, CA	91106
MORTON, KEVIN	BASEBALL	POST OFFICE BOX 2365	PAWTUCKET, RI	02861
MORTON, LAWRENCE	COMPOSER	1113 N SWEETZER AVE	LOS ANGELES, CA	90069
MORTON, LEONARD HUGH, SR	MUSIC ARRANGER	4120 W HAMILTON RD	NASHVILLE, TN	37218
MORTON, MICKEY	ACTOR	10433 WILSHIRE BLVD #120	LOS ANGELES, CA	90024
MORTON, RICKY	WRESTLER	POST OFFICE BOX 105366	ATLANTA, GA	31348
MORTON, ROB	SCREENWRITER	8955 BEVERLY BLVD	WEST HOLLYWOOD, CA	90048
MOSCONI, WILLIE	BILLARDS	1804 PROSPECT RIDGE	HIDDEN HEIGHTS, NJ	08035
MOSEBAR, DON	FOOTBALL	RAIDERS, 332 CENTER ST	EL SEGUNDO, CA	90245
MOSEBY, LLOYD	BASEBALL	3400 KINGMONT DR	LOOMIS, CA	95650
MOSEL, TAD	PLAYWRIGHT	400 E 57TH ST	NEW YORK, NY	10022
MOSELEY, DICK	FOOTBALL COACH	PACKERS, 1265 LOMBARDI AVE	GREEN BAY, WI	54307
MOSELEY, ROY	AUTHOR	152 IVOR CT, GLOUCESTER PL	LONDON NW1	ENGLAND
MOSER, JAMES	WRITER-PRODUCER	24620 MALIBU RD	MALIBU, CA	90265
MOSES, ALBERT	ACTOR	12 PICKERING CT, GRANVILLE RD	LONDON N22 4EL	ENGLAND
MOSES, BEN	DIRECTOR-PRODUCER	5750 WILSHIRE BLVD #512	LOS ANGELES, CA	90036
MOSES, BILLY R	ACTOR	405 SYCAMORE RD	SANTA MONICA, CA	90402
MOSES, DAVID	ACTOR	10528 CIMARRON ST	LOS ANGELES, CA	90047
MOSES, GILBERT	FILM DIRECTOR	449 N HIGHLAND AVE	LOS ANGELES, CA	90036
MOSES, HARRY	ACTOR	13424 GALEWOOD ST	SHERMAN OAKS, CA	91423
MOSES, HARRY	TV PRODUCER	CBS-TV, 524 W 57TH ST	NEW YORK, NY	10019
MOSES, HARRY	WRITER-PRODUCER	103 E 84TH ST	NEW YORK, NY	10028
MOSES, JOHN	BASEBALL	POST OFFICE BOX 3690, STA "B"	CALGARY, ALB T2B 4M4	CANADA
MOSES, JUDITH	TV PRODUCER-REPORTER	ABC-TV NEWS, "20-20"		
		7 W 66TH ST	NEW YORK, NY	10023
MOSES, KATHRYN	SINGER	GATES, 1845 CLINTON AVE N	ROCHESTER, NY	14621
MOSES, RICK	ACTOR-SINGER	17420 VENTURA BLVD #4	ENCINO, CA	91316
MOSIMAN, MARNIE	ACTRESS	9744 WILSHIRE BLVD #308	BEVERLY HILLS, CA	90212
MOSLEY, ROGER E	ACTOR	3756 PRESTWICK DR	LOS ANGELES, CA	90027
MOSLEY, TONY	BASEBALL	POST OFFICE BOX 1718	NEW BRITAIN, CT	06050
MOSS, ARNOLD	ACT-WRI-DIR	301 E 66TH ST	NEW YORK, NY	10021
MOSS, CHARLES	BASEBALL TRAINER	FENWAY PARK, 4 YAWKEY WY	BOSTON, MA	02215

Name	Occupation	Address	City	Zip
MOSS, FRANK	FILM WRITER-PRODUCER	12512 CHANDLER BLVD #105	NORTH HOLLYWOOD, CA	91607
MOSS, GENE	ACTOR-WRITER	3429 BONNIE HILL DR	LOS ANGELES, CA	90068
MOSS, GEOFFREY	ARTIST-CARTOONIST	315 E 68TH ST	NEW YORK, NY	10021
MOSS, IRA	RECORD EXECUTIVE	176 BEACH	NEPOSNIT QUEENS, NY	11694
MOSS, JEFFREY	TV WRITER-PRODUCER	CHILDREN'S TV WORKSHOP		
		1 LINCOLN PLAZA	NEW YORK, NY	10023
MOSS, JERRY	RECORD EXECUTIVE	A & M RECORDS, 1416 N LA BREA AVE	HOLLYWOOD, CA	90028
MOSS, JOHN	BASEBALL EXECUTIVE	POST OFFICE BOX 38	KINGS MOUNTAIN, NC	28086
MOSS, LEONARD L	COMPOSER	POST OFFICE BOX 3448	SANTA MONICA, CA	90403
MOSS, LES	BASEBALL-INSTRUCTOR	S F GIANTS, CANDLESTICK PARK	SAN FRANICSCO, CA	94124
MOSS, MARSHALL	COMPOSER-CONDUCTOR	1840 DEER HILL TRIAL	TOPANGA, CA	90290
MOSS, RONN	ACTOR	CBS-TV, "THE BOLD & BEAUTIFUL"		
		7800 BEVERLY BLVD #3371	LOS ANGELES, CA	90036
MOSS, STERLING	ACTOR	46 SHEPHERD ST, MAYFAIR	LONDON W1Y 8JN	ENGLAND
MOSS, STEWART	ACTOR	9744 WILSHIRE BLVD #308	BEVERLY HILLS, CA	90212
MOSS, WINSTON	FOOTBALL	RAIDERS, 332 CENTER ST	EL SEGUNDO, CA	90245
MOSS, WINSTON	TV WRITER	4714 RODEO LN #3	LOS ANGELES, CA	90016
MOSS, ZEFROSS	FOOTBALL	POST OFFICE BOX 535000	INDIANPOLIS, IN	46253
MOSS-TRENTON, TONI	ACTRESS	436 N ALTA VISTA BLVD	LOS ANGELES, CA	90036
MOSSLER, HELEN	TV EXECUTIVE	5555 MELROSE AVE	LOS ANGELES, CA	90038
MOSSMAN, TOM	TV DIRECTOR	24043 W AVE CRESCENTA	VALENCIA, CA	91355
MOST, ABE	COMPOSER	17030 OTSEGO ST	ENCINO, CA	91316
MOST, DONALD	ACTOR	6643 BUTTON WILLOW	AGOURA HILLS, CA	91301
MOST, MICKEY	TALENT AGENT	42-48 CHARLBEROUTE ST	LONDON NW8	ENGLAND
MOTA, ANDY	BASEBALL	POST OFFICE BOX 27045	TUCSON, AZ	85726
MOTA, CARLOS	BASEBALL	2501 ALLEN AVE, SE	CANTON, OH	44707
MOTA, DOMINGO	BASEBALL	800 HOME RUN LN	MEMPHIS, TN	38104
MOTA, GARY	BASEBALL	POST OFFICE BOX 1556	ASHEVILLE, NC	28802
MOTA, JOSE	BASEBALL	POST OFFICE BOX 3665	OMAHA, NE	68103
MOTA, MANNY	BASEBALL-COACH	3926 LOS OLIVOS LN	LA CRESCENTA, CA	91214
MOTA, WILLIE	BASEBALL	14100 SIX MILE CYPRESS PKWY	FORT MYERS, FL	33912
MOTCH, JACK	COMPOSER	3439 FOWLER AVE	SANTA CLARA, CA	95051
MOTEN, ERIC	FOOTBALL	POST OFFICE BOX 609609	SAN DIEGO, CA	92160
MOTLEY, DARRYL	BASEBALL	1324 N RESSIT	PORTLAND, OR	97201
MOTLEY CRUE	ROCK & ROLL GROUP	DOC MC GHEE MANAGEMENT		
		240 CENTRAL PARK S	NEW YORK, NY	10019
MOTORHEAD	ROCK & ROLL GROUP	GWR/PROFILE RECORDS		
		740 BROADWAY	NEW YORK, NY	10003
MOTTA, DICK	BASKETBALL COACH	KINGS, 1 SPORTS PARKWAY	SACRAMENTO, CA	95834
MOTTA, KIP	BASKETBALL COACH	POST OFFICE BOX C-900911	SEATTLE, WA	98109
MOTTA, WILLIAM A	ARTIST	ROAD & TRACK MAGAZINE		
		1499 MONROVIA AVE	NEWPORT BEACH, CA	92663
MOTTOLA, TOMMY	RECORD EXECUTIVE	SONY RECORDS, 51 W 52ND ST	NEW YORK, NY	10019
MOTTON, CURT	BASEBALL-COACH	ORIOLE PARK, 333 W CAMDEN ST	BALTIMORE, MD	21201
MOTUZAS, JEFF	BASEBALL	POST OFFICE BOX 2148	WOODBRIDGE, VA	22193
MOUL, MAXINE	LT GOVERNOR	STATE CAPITOL BUILDING	LINCOLN, NE	68509
MOULTON, DEBORAH S	TV WRITER	24 FLORENCE AVE	OYSTER BAY, NY	11771
MOULTON, LESLIE	TV DIRECTOR	11732 NE 102ND PL	KIRKLAND, WA	98033
MOUNT, PEGGY	ACTRESS	STONE, 25 WHITEHALL	LONDON SW1A 2BS	ENGLAND
MOUNTAIN	ROCK & ROLL GROUP	310 MADISON AVE #804	NEW YORK, NY	10017
MOUNTAIN, SALLY	SINGER	POST OFFICE DRAWER 160	HENDERSONVILLE, TN	37075
MOUNTIE, THE	WRESTLER	POST OFFICE BOX 3859	STAMFORD, CT	06905
MOUNTON, JAMES	BASEBALL	POST OFFICE BOX 422229	KISSIMMEE, FL	34742
MOUSHON, DAN	BASEBALL EXECUTIVE	POST OFFICE BOX 3004	SPRINGFIELD, IL	62708
MOUSKOURI, NANA	SINGER-SONGWRITER	10100 SANTA MONICA BLVD #1600	LOS ANGELES, CA	90067
MOUTON, LYLE	BASEBALL	POST OFFICE BOX 2148	WOODBRIDGE, VA	22193
MOVING TARGETS	ROCK & ROLL GROUP	195 HIGH ST	IPSWICH, MA	01938
MOVITA	ACTRESS	2766 MOTOR AVE	LOS ANGELES, CA	90064
MOVSHOVITZ, HOWIE	FILM CRITIC	POST OFFICE BOX 1709	DENVER, CO	80201
MOWATT, ZEKE	FOOTBALL	N Y GIANTS, GIANTS STADIUM	EAST RUTHERFORD, NJ	07073
MOWERY, JAMES WILLIAM	TV DIRECTOR	1517 E GARFIELD AVE #114	GLENDALE, CA	91205
MOWRY, DAVID	BASEBALL	POST OFFICE BOX 20849	CHARLESTON, SC	29413
MOWRY, LARRY	GOLFER	PGA SENIORS, 112 T P C BLVD	PONTE VEDRA BEACH, FL	32082
MOXEY, JOHN LLEWELLYN	DIRECTOR	22313 CARBON MESA RD	MALIBU, CA	90265
MOYA, FELIX	BASEBALL	POST OFFICE BOX 3566	WEST PALM BEACH, FL	33402
MOYE, MICHAEL	TV WRITER-PRODUCER	UTA, 9560 WILSHIRE BL, 5TH FL	BEVERLY HILLS, CA	90212
MOYER, JAMIE	BASEBALL	409 N 4TH ST	SOUDERTON, PA	18964
MOYER, KEN	FOOTBALL	BENGALS, 200 RIVERFRONT STADIUM	CINCINNATI, OH	45202
MOYER, PAUL	BROADCAST JOURNALIST	KABC-TV, 4151 PROSPECT AVE	LOS ANGELES, CA	90027
MOYER, PAUL	FOOTBALL COACH	SEAHAWKS, 11220 NE 53RD ST	KIRKLAND, WA	98033
MOYER, TOM	FILM PRODUCER	6464 HOLISTER AVE	GOLETA, CA	93117
MOYERS, BILL	NEWS CORRESPONDENT	CBS NEWS, 524 W 57TH ST	NEW YORK, NY	10019
MOYLE, ALLAN	WRITER-PRODUCER	49 PARK AVE	NEW YORK, NY	10016
MOYNIHAN, DANIEL PATRICK	U S SENATOR	405 LEXINGTON AVE #4101	NEW YORK, NY	10174
MOYNIHAN, GEORGE E	TV EXECUTIVE	WESTINGHOUSE, 888 7TH AVE	NEW YORK, NY	10106
MOZART ON FIFTH	JAZZ TRIO	MAINSTAGE MANAGEMENT		
		976 CAPTAIN'S WALK	ANNAPOLIS, MD	21403
MR MISTER	ROCK & ROLL GROUP	POST OFFICE BOX 69343	LOS ANGELES, CA	90069
MR PERFECT	WRESTLER	SEE - HENNING, CURT "MR PERFECT"		
MR PETE	TV HOST	KTLA-TV, 5800 SUNSET BLVD	LOS ANGELES, CA	90028
MR ROGERS	TV PERSONALITY	SEE - ROGERS, MR		
MR T	ACTOR	SEE - T, MR		
MR WIZARD	TV PERSONALITY	SEE - HERBERT, DON "MR WIZARD"		
MR WONDERFUL	WRESTLER	SEE - ORNDORFF, PAUL		
MRAZEK, ROBERT J	U S CONGRESSMAN	143 MAIN ST	HUNTINGTON, NY	11743

Name	Occupation	Address	City	Zip/Country
MUBARAK, HOSNI	PRESIDENT	ROYAL PALACE	CAIRO	EGYPT
MUCERNIO, GREG	BASEBALL	POST OFFICE BOX 20849	CHARLESTON, SC	29413
MUDD, HOWARD	FOOTBALL COACH	CHIEFS, 1 ARROWHEAD DR	KANSAS CITY, MO	64129
MUDD, JODIE	GOLFER	POST OFFICE BOX 109601	PALM BCH GARDENS, FL	33418
MUDD, ROGER	BROADCAST JOURNALIST	7167 OLD DOMINION DR	MC LEAN, VA	22101
MUELLER, JEFF	PRODUCER	LICHT, 4000 WARNER BLVD	BURBANK, CA	91522
MUELLER, LEO	CONDUCTOR	SCHWEIZERTALSTRASSE, S I 20	A-1130 VIENNA	AUSTRIA
MUELLER, PETE	CARTOONIST	THE READER, 635 STATE ST	SAN DIEGO, CA	92101
MUELLER-STAHL, ARMIN	ACTOR	GARTENWEG 31	D-2430 SIRKSDORF	GERMANY
MUELLERLEILE, MARIANNE	ACTRESS	9255 SUNSET BLVD #515	LOS ANGELES, CA	90069
MUFFETT, BILLY	BASEBALL-COACH	TIGERS, TIGER STADIUM	DETROIT, MI	48216
MUGGLI, DEBBIE	BODYBUILDER	18110 MIDWAY RD #208	DALLAS, TX	75287
MUGLESTONS, THE	ROCK & ROLL GROUP	MUGS, 10336 PARISE DR	WHITTIER, CA	90604
MUHAMMAD, BURNELL	BODYBUILDER	POST OFFICE BOX FLOOR 374	FLATS 3	BERMUDA
MUHAMMAD, MARGARET	BODYBUILDER	POST OFFICE BOX FLOOR 374	FLATS 3	BERMUDA
MUIR, ALLAN L	DIRECTOR	DGA, 7920 SUNSET BLVD, 6TH FL	LOS ANGELES, CA	90046
MUIR, BILL	FOOTBALL COACH	POST OFFICE BOX 535000	INDIANPOLIS, IN	46253
MUIR, E ROGER	TV PRODUCER	1465 E PUTNAM AVE #434	OLD GREENWICH, CT	06870
MUIR, ELLEN	ACTRESS	NY TV ACADEMY, 110 W 57TH ST	NEW YORK, NY	10019
MUIR, ESTHER	ACTRESS	587-D HERITAGE HILLS DR	SOMERS, NY	10589
MUIR, FRANK	TV EXECUTIVE	YOUNG, 31 KINGS RD	LONDON SW3 4RP	ENGLAND
MUIR, JEAN	ACTRESS	UNIVERSITY OF NEW MEXICO		
		THEATER ARTS DEPARTMENT		
		CENTRAL & UNIVERSITY	ALBUQUERQUE, NM	87131
MULA, FRANK C	TV WRITER	5043 BUFFALO AVE #3	SHERMAN OAKS, CA	91423
MULARKEY, MIKE	FOOTBALL	STEELERS, 300 STADIUM CIR	PITTSBURGH, PA	15212
MULCAHY, RUSSELL	FILM DIRECTOR	131 S RODEO DR #300	BEVERLY HILLS, CA	90212
MULDAUR, DIANA	ACTRESS	259 QUADRO VECCHIO ST	PACIFIC PALISADES, CA	90272
MULDAUR, MARIA	SINGER-SONGWRITER	POST OFFICE BOX 5535	MILL VALLEY, CA	94942
MULE DEER, GARY	COMEDIAN	POST OFFICE BOX 4003	BEVERLY HILLS, CA	90213
MULGREW, KATE	ACTRESS	11938 FOXBORO DR	LOS ANGELES, CA	90049
MULHARE, EDWARD	ACTOR	6045 SUNNYSLOPE AVE	VAN NUYS, CA	91041
MULHERN, MATT	ACTOR	9350 WILSHIRE BLVD #324	BEVERLY HILLS, CA	90212
MULHOLLAND, TERRY	BASEBALL	POST OFFICE BOX 7575	PHILADELPHIA, PA	19101
MULL, JACK	BASEBALL-MANAGER	POST OFFICE BOX 1295	CLINTON, IA	52733
MULL, MARTIN	ACT-WRI-COMED	338 CHADBORUNE AVE	LOS ANGELES, CA	90049
MULLALLY, MEGAN	ACTRESS	9100 SUNSET BLVD #300	LOS ANGELES, CA	90069
MULLALLY, MICHAEL F	DIRECTOR	11292 CANTON DR	STUDIO CITY, CA	91604
MULLAVEY, GREG	ACTOR	4640 DANZA	WOODLAND HILLS, CA	91364
MULLEN, BRIAN	HOCKEY	POST OFFICE BOX 90111	ARLINGTON, TX	76004
MULLEN, JOE	HOCKEY	PENGUINS, CIVIC ARENA, CENTRE AV	PITTSBURGH, PA	15219
MULLEN, MARJORIE	TV DIRECTOR	9203 SUMMERTIME LN	CULVER CITY, CA	90230
MULLENDORE, JOS	COMPOSER	1590 PLEASANT WY	PASADENA, CA	91105
MULLER, ALFRED	DIRECTOR	NEXUS, 10 E 40TH ST	NEW YORK, NY	10011
MULLER, FREDERICK	FILM PRODUCER	48 CRANLEY GARDENS	LONDON SW7 3DE	ENGLAND
MULLER, KIRK	HOCKEY	POST OFFICE BOX 504	EAST RUTHERFORD, NJ	07073
MULLER, ROBERT	SCREENWRITER	ROSE COTTAGE, PLUM ST, GLEMSFORD	SUFFOLK	ENGLAND
MULLIGAN, GERARD A	TV WRITER	ICM, 40 W 57TH ST	NEW YORK, NY	10019
MULLIGAN, JAMES M	TV WRITER	30507 RHONE DR	RANCHO PALISADES, CA	90274
MULLIGAN, RICHARD	ACTOR	ICM, 8899 BEVERLY BLVD	LOS ANGELES, CA	90048
MULLIGAN, ROBERT	DIRECTOR-PRODUCER	1120 STONE CANYON RD	LOS ANGELES, CA	90077
MULLIGAN, SEAN	BASEBALL	POST OFFICE BOX 20849	CHARLESTON, SC	29413
MULLIN, CHRIS	BASKETBALL	GOLDEN STATE WARRIORS		
		OAKLAND COLISEUM ARENA		
		NIMITZ FWY & HEGENBERGER RD	OAKLAND, CA	94621
MULLINGS, PETER	TV DIRECTOR-PRODUCER	11 WARWICK GARDENS	LONDON W14	ENGLAND
MULLINIKS, RANCE	BASEBALL	SKYDOME, 300 BREMMER BL #3200	TORONTO, ONT M5V 3B3	CANADA
MULLINS, CAM	MUSIC ARRANGER	1409 WINTHORNE DR	NASHVILLE, TN	37217
MULLINS, KENNY	SINGER	POST OFFICE BOX 1084	NEWARK, DE	19175
MULLINS, MARCY ECKROTH	CARTOONIST	POST OFFICE BOX 500	WASHINGTON, DC	20044
MULLINS, PETER	ART DIRECTOR	11 WARWICK GARDENS	LONDON W14	ENGLAND
MULLIS, KELLY	ACTRESS	5330 LANKERSHIM BLVD #210	NORTH HOLLYWOOD, CA	91601
MULRONEY, BRIAN	PRIME MINISTER	"STORNOWAY"	OTTAWA, ONT	CANADA
MULRONEY, DERMOT	ACTOR	15760 VENTURA BLVD #1730	ENCINO, CA	91436
MULVILLE, DUANE	BASEBALL	POST OFFICE BOX 10336	CLEARWATER, FL	34617
MUMFORD, THAD	TV WRITER	3130 OAKSHIRE DR	LOS ANGELES, CA	90068
MUMMY CALLS	ROCK & ROLL GROUP	GEFFEN RECORDS COMPANY		
		9130 SUNSET BLVD	LOS ANGELES, CA	90069
MUMPHREY, JERRY	BASEBALL	3913 SILVERWOOD	TYLER, TX	75701
MUNCHAK, MIKE	FOOTBALL	OILERS, 6910 FANNIN ST	HOUSTON, TX	77070
MUNDA, STEVEN	BASEBALL	POST OFFICE BOX 22093	GREENSBORO, NC	27420
MUNDINGER, KARIN	GOLFER	2750 VOLUSA AVE #B	DAYTON BEACH, FL	32114
MUNE, IAN	ACTOR-WRITER	8955 BEVERLY BLVD	WEST HOLLYWOOD, CA	90048
MUNI, CRAIG	HOCKEY	OILERS, NORTHLANDS COLISEUM	EDMONTON, ALTA T5B 4M9	CANADA
MUNISTERI, MARY R	TV WRITER	433 W 53RD ST	NEW YORK, NY	10019
MUNK, CHRIS	BASKETBALL	5 TRIAD CENTER #500	SALT LAKE CITY, UT	84180
MUNNOCH, PHILIP	TV WRITER	13 BARRY AVE, WINDSOR	BERSKIRE SL4 5JA	ENGLAND
MUNOZ, ANTHONY	FOOTBALL	BENGALS, 200 RIVERFRONT STADIUM	CINCINNATI, OH	45202
MUNOZ, BOBBY	BASEBALL	ALBANY YANKEES, HERITAGE PARK	ALBANY, NY	12211
MUNOZ, J J	BASEBALL	POST OFFICE BOX 10336	CLEARWATER, FL	34617
MUNOZ, JOSE	BASEBALL	POST OFFICE BOX 26267	ALBUQUERQUE, NM	87125
MUNOZ, MIKE	BASEBALL	TIGERS, TIGER STADIUM	DETROIT, MI	48216
MUNOZ, OMAR	BASEBALL	1501 W 16TH ST	INDIANAPOLIS, IN	46202
MUNOZ, ORLANDO	BASEBALL	POST OFFICE BOX 1742	PALM SPRINGS, CA	92263

Name	Occupation	Address	City	Zip/Country
MUNOZ, OSCAR	BASEBALL	POST OFFICE BOX 5645	ORLANDO, FL	32855
MUNOZ, PEDRO	BASEBALL	TWINS, 501 CHICAGO AVE S	MINNEAPOLIS, MN	55415
MUNRO, CAROLINE	ACTRESS-MODEL	22 GRAFTON ST	LONDON W1	ENGLAND
MUNRO, RALPH	SECRETARY OF STATE	STATE LEGISLATIVE BUILDING	OLYMPIA, WA	98504
MUNSEL, PATRICE	ACTRESS-SINGER	300 CENTRAL PARK W #PH-31-D	NEW YORK, NY	10024
MUNSHOWER, THOMAS PAUL	DIRECTOR	1380 E SAHARA BLVD	LAS VEGAS, NV	81904
MUNTEAN, RICK	BASEBALL EXECUTIVE	POST OFFICE BOX 3449	SCRANTON, PA	18505
MUNTNER, SIMON	TV WRITER	9200 SUNSET BLVD #431	LOS ANGELES, CA	90069
MUNVES, CHRYSTIE	TV PRODUCER	WNBC NEWS, 30 ROCKEFELLER PLZ	NEW YORK, NY	10020
MUPPETS, THE	PUPPETS	227 E 67TH ST	NEW YORK, NY	10021
MURAD, MAURICE	TV WRITER-DIRECTOR	3 TRAILSIDE CT	NEW YORK, NY	10956
MURAWSKI, ALEX	ARTIST	4900 ROWENA ST	AUSTIN, TX	78751
MURCER, BOBBY	BASEBALL-EXECUTIVE	POST OFFICE BOX 75089	OKLAHOMA CITY, OK	73147
MURCHISON, WILLIAM	COLUMNIST	POST OFFICE BOX 225237	DALLAS, TX	75265
MURDOCH, K RUPERT	PUBLISH EXECUTIVE	THE STAR, 660 WHITE PLAINS RD	TARRYTOWN, NY	10591
MURDOCH, MARY ANN	FILM CRITIC	POST OFFICE BOX 490	OCALA, FL	32678
MURDOCK, ALLAN R	DIRECTOR	26751 SIMONE	DEARBORN HEIGHTS, MI	48127
MURDOCK, GEORGE	ACTOR	5733 SUNFIELD AVE	LAKEWOOD, CA	90712
MURDOCK, LYDIA	SINGER	MALAMUD, MEDIA CONSULTANTS		
		14923 CYPRESS HILLS	DALLAS, TX	75248
MURDOCK, RUPERT	PUBLISHING EXECUTIVE	210 SOUTH ST	NEW YORK, NY	10002
MUREO, GUS	BASEBALL SCOUT	BREWERS, 201 S 46TH ST	MILWAUKEE, WI	53214
MURILLO, MARIO	EVANGELIST-AUTHOR	POST OFFICE BOX 4971	CHATSWORTH, CA	91311
MURILLO, SAL	TALENT AGENT	3661 S MARYLAND PKWY #3 - BOX 50	LAS VEGAS, NV	89109
MURKOWSKI, FRANK	U S SENATOR	109 MAIN ST	KETCHIKAN, AK	99901
MURO, CARLOS	BASEBALL SCOUT	POST OFFICE BOX 288	HOUSTON, TX	77001
MUROVICH, LUCILLE	DIRECTOR	DGA, 110 W 57TH ST	NEW YORK, NY	10019
MURPHY	C & W GROUP	TM, 1019 17TH AVE S	NASHVILLE, TN	37212
MURPHY, A D	COLUMNIST	5700 WILSHIRE BLVD #120	LOS ANGELES, CA	90036
MURPHY, AUSTIN	U S CONGRESSMAN	1801-C BRODHEAD RD	ALIQUIPPA, PA	15001
MURPHY, BEN	ACTOR	3601 VISTA PACIFICA #17	MALIBU, CA	90265
MURPHY, BETTY	ACTRESS	10850 RIVERSIDE DR #505	NORTH HOLLYWOOD, CA	91602
MURPHY, BOB	SPORTSCASTER	METS, 126TH ST & ROOSEVELT AVE	FLUSHING, NY	11368
MURPHY, BRIAN	ACTOR	35 GILDEN RD	LONDON NW5	ENGLAND
MURPHY, BRIAN	BASEBALL SCOUT	POST OFFICE BOX 419969	KANSAS CITY, MO	64141
MURPHY, BRIANNE	CINEMATOGRAPHER	POST OFFICE BOX 2230	HOLLYWOOD, CA	90078
MURPHY, CALVIN	BASKETBALL	POST OFFICE BOX 272349	HOUSTON, TX	77277
MURPHY, CHUCK	BASEBALL EXECUTIVE	POST OFFICE BOX 349	DAYTONA BEACH, FL	32115
MURPHY, CULLEN	CARTOONIST	KING FEATURES, 216 E 45TH ST	NEW YORK, NY	10017
MURPHY, DALE	BASEBALL	POST OFFICE BOX 7575	PHILADELPHIA, PA	19101
MURPHY, DWAYNE	BASEBALL	1132 "Wv AVE #H-6	LANCASTER, CA	93534
MURPHY, E DANNY	ACTOR	7080 HOLLYWOOD BLVD #704	HOLLYWOOD, CA	90028
MURPHY, EDDIE	ACT-COMED-WRI-PROD	2727 BENEDICT CANYON DR	BEVERLY HILLS, CA	90210
MURPHY, GEORGE	ACTOR-POLITICIAN	100 WORTH AVE #419	PALM BEACH, FL	33480
MURPHY, GORDON	HOCKEY	FLYERS, SPECTRUM, PATTISON PL	PHILADELPHIA, PA	19148
MURPHY, JEREMIAH	SINGER	3426 CROFFUT PL, SE	WASHINGTON, DC	20019
MURPHY, JOE	HOCKEY	OILERS, NORTHLANDS COLISEUM	EDMONTON, ALTA T5B 4M9	CANADA
MURPHY, JOHN B "JACK"	DIRECTOR	2133 NE 19TH AVE	FORT LAUDERDALE, FL	33305
MURPHY, JOHN P	TV DIRECTOR	DGA, 7920 SUNSET BLVD, 6TH FL	LOS ANGELES, CA	90046
MURPHY, JOHN W	DIRECTOR	17400 BURBANK BLVD #221	ENCINO, CA	91316
MURPHY, KEVIN	BASEBALL SCOUT	TWINS, 501 CHICAGO AVE S	MINNEAPOLIS, MN	55415
MURPHY, KEVIN	FOOTBALL	BUCCANEERS, 1 BUCCANEER PL	TAMPA, FL	33607
MURPHY, LARRY	HOCKEY	PENGUINS, CIVIC ARENA, CENTRE AV	PITTSBURGH, PA	15219
MURPHY, LYLE "SPUD"	COMPOSER-CONDUCTOR	817 N VINE ST	LOS ANGELES, CA	90038
MURPHY, MARK	FOOTBALL	PACKERS, 1265 LOMBARDI AVE	GREEN BAY, WI	54307
MURPHY, MATT "GUITAR"	SINGER-GUITARIST	CONCERTED, 312 SALEM ST	MEDFORD, MA	02155
MURPHY, MAUREEN	COMEDIENNE	6310 SAN VICENTE BLVD #407	LOS ANGELES, CA	90048
MURPHY, MICHAEL MARTIN	SINGER-SONGWRITER	POST OFFICE BOX FFF	TAOS, NM	87571
MURPHY, MIKE	BASEBALL SCOUT	6850 LAWRENCE RD	LANTANA, FL	33462
MURPHY, MIKE	FOOTBALL COACH	POST OFFICE BOX 888	PHOENIX, AZ	85001
MURPHY, PATRICK	BASEBALL	POST OFFICE BOX 824	BURLINGTON, IA	52601
MURPHY, RICHARD	BASEBALL EXECUTIVE	POST OFFICE BOX 328	PITTSFIELD, MA	01202
MURPHY, RICHARD	WRITER-PRODUCER	R/W/G, 8428 MELROSE PL #C	LOS ANGELES, CA	90069
MURPHY, ROB	BASEBALL	POST OFFICE BOX 288	HOUSTON, TX	77001
MURPHY, ROB	HOCKEY	CANUCKS, 100 N RENFREW ST	VANCOUVER, BC V5K 3N7	CANADA
MURPHY, ROBERT J	TV WRITER-DIRECTOR	ABC NEWS, 7 W 66TH ST	NEW YORK, NY	10023
MURPHY, ROSEMARY	ACTRESS	220 E 73RD ST	NEW YORK, NY	10021
MURPHY, RYAN	SINGER	POST OFFICE BOX FFF	TAOS, NM	87571
MURPHY, SHAUN	BASEBALL	POST OFFICE BOX 3566	WEST PALM BEACH, FL	33402
MURPHY, TAB	SCREENWRITER	151 S EL CAMINO DR	BEVERLY HILLS, CA	90212
MURPHY, TIM	BASEBALL EXECUTIVE	POST OFFICE BOX 3609	PORT CHARLOTTE, FL	33949
MURPHY, TOD	BASKETBALL	TIMBERWOLVES, 600 1ST AVE N	MINNEAPOLIS, MN	55403
MURRAY, ANNE	SINGER	4881 YONGE ST #412	TORONTO, ONT M2N 5X3	CANADA
MURRAY, ARTHUR	DANCE INSTRUCTOR	2877 KALAKAUA AVE	HONOLULU, HI	96815
MURRAY, BERT	WRITER	11175 HUSTON ST	NORTH HOLLYWOOD, CA	91601
MURRAY, BILL	ACTOR-FILM DIRECTOR	RFD #1, BOX 250-A		
		WASHINGTON SPRINGS RD	PALISADES, NY	10964
MURRAY, BRYAN	ACTOR	PETERS, FRASER & DUNLOP, LTD		
		5TH FLOOR, THE CHAMBERS		
		CHELSEA HARBOUR, LOT RD	LONDON SW10 OXF	ENGLAND
MURRAY, CHARLES ALAN	SCIENTIST	THE MANHATTAN INSTITUTE		
		FOR POLICY RESEARCH		
		131 SPRING ST	NEW YORK, NY	10012
MURRAY, COLLEEN	ACTRESS-MODEL	410 SANTA ROSA AVE	SANTA BARBARA, CA	93108
MURRAY, DAROLD O	DIRECTOR	DGA, 110 W 57TH ST	NEW YORK, NY	10019

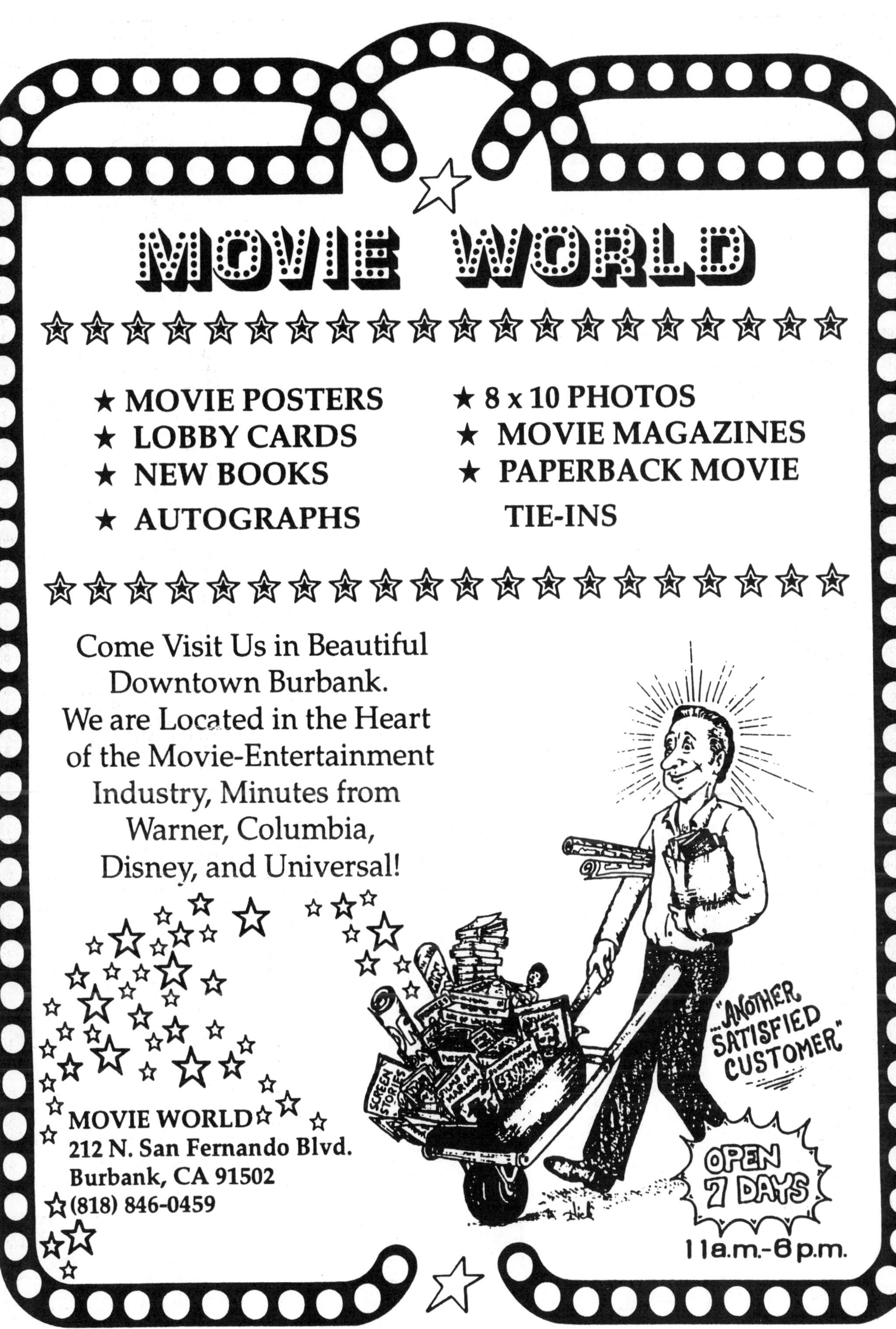
MOVIE WORLD
★ MOVIE POSTERS
★ LOBBY CARDS
★ NEW BOOKS
★ AUTOGRAPHS
★ 8 x 10 PHOTOS
★ MOVIE MAGAZINES
★ PAPERBACK MOVIE TIE-INS
Come Visit Us in Beautiful Downtown Burbank. We are Located in the Heart of the Movie-Entertainment Industry, Minutes from Warner, Columbia, Disney, and Universal!
"ANOTHER SATISFIED CUSTOMER"
SCREEN STORIES
OPEN 7 DAYS
11a.m.-6p.m.
MOVIE WORLD
212 N. San Fernando Blvd.
Burbank, CA 91502
(818) 846-0459

MURRAY, DON	ACT-WRI-DIR	15301 VENTURA BLVD #345	SHERMAN OAKS, CA	91403
MURRAY, EDDIE	BASEBALL	METS, 126TH ST & ROOSEVELT AVE	FLUSHING, NY	11368
MURRAY, EDDIE	FOOTBALL	LIONS, 1200 FEATHERSTONE RD	PONTIAC, MI	48432
MURRAY, FRANCIS W	FOOTBALL EXECUTIVE	PATRIOTS, FOXBORO STADIUM, RT #1	FOXBORO, MA	02035
MURRAY, GLENN	BASEBALL	POST OFFICE BOX 3566	WEST PALM BEACH, FL	33402
MURRAY, JAN	ACTOR-COMEDIAN	1157 CALLE VISTA DR	BEVERLY HILLS, CA	90210
MURRAY, JOE	COMEDIAN	POST OFFICE BOX 830	ALBANY, NY	12201
MURRAY, JOHN A	ACTOR	51 LEROY ST	NEW YORK, NY	10014
MURRAY, KATHERINE	DANCE INSTRUCTOR	2877 KALAKAUA AVE	HONOLULU, HI	96815
MURRAY, LU	TV DIRECTOR	ENTERTAINMENT TONIGHT		
		PARAMOUNT TELEVISION		
		5555 MELROSE AVE	LOS ANGELES, CA	90038
MURRAY, LYN	CONDUCTOR	3603 WESTFALL DR	ENCINO, CA	91436
MURRAY, MATT	BASEBALL	POST OFFICE BOX 16683	GREENVILLE, SC	29606
MURRAY, PEG	ACTRESS	41 GREENWICH AVE	NEW YORK, NY	10014
MURRAY, PHILIP W	DIRECTOR	1609 CENTRAL AVE	WILMETTE, IL	60091
MURRAY, RUBY	SINGER	10-A VICTORIA PARADE, TORQUAY	DEVON	ENGLAND
MURRAY, SEAN	COMPOSER	410 SANTA ROSA AVE	SANTA BARBARA, CA	93108
MURRAY, STEVE	BASEBALL COACH	POST OFFICE BOX 30160	SAN BERNARDINO, CA	92413
MURRAY, TROY	HOCKEY	BLACKHAWKS, 1800 W MADISON ST	CHICAGO, IL	60612
MURRAY, WARREN	WRITER-PRODUCER	GENERAL DELIVERY	DORSET, VT	05251
MURRELL, DAVID	FILM-TV EXECUTIVE	KPMG PEAT MARWICK, 1 PUDDLE DOCK		
		BLACKFAIARS	LONDON EC4V 3PD	ENGLAND
MURTAGH, KATE	ACTRESS	15146 MOORPARK ST	SHERMAN OAKS, CA	91403
MURTAUGH, MIKE	BASEBALL EXECUTIVE	POST OFFICE BOX 418	SAINT CHARLES, IL	60174
MURTHA, JOHN	U S CONGRESSMAN	POST OFFICE BOX 780	JOHNSTOWN, PA	15907
MURZYN, DANA	HOCKEY	CANUCKS, 100 N RENFREW ST	VANCOUVER, BC V5K 3N7	CANADA
MUSANTE, TONY	ACTOR-WRITER	10000 SANTA MONICA BLVD #305	LOS ANGELES, CA	90067
MUSBURGER, BRENT	SPORTSCASTER	CBS SPORTS, 51 W 52ND ST	NEW YORK, NY	10019
MUSCARELLA, STEVE	TV WRITER-DIRECTOR	830 WARREN AVE	VENICE, CA	90291
MUSE, MARGARET	ACTRESS	1418 N HIGHLAND AVE #102	LOS ANGELES, CA	90028
MUSER, TONY	BASEBALL MANAGER	2850 W 20TH AVE	DENVER, CO	80211
MUSER, WOLFGANG	ACTOR	3905 EUREKA DR	STUDIO CITY, CA	91604
MUSETTO, V A	FILM CRITIC	N Y POST, 210 SOUTH ST	NEW YORK, NY	10002
MUSIC, LORENZO	WRITER	1717 N HIGHLAND AVE #414	LOS ANGELES, CA	90028
MUSICAL YOUTH	RHYTHM & BLUES GROUP	FAA, 1700 BROADWAY, 5TH FLOOR	NEW YORK, NY	10019
MUSIL, FRANTISEK	HOCKEY	POST OFFICE BOX 1540, STA "M"	CALGARY, ALTA T2P 3BP	CANADA
MUSILLI, JOHN	DIRECTOR	CAMERA THREE PRODUCTIONS		
		555 W 57TH ST	NEW YORK, NY	10019
MUSKIE, EDMUND	U S SENATOR	1101 VERMONT AVE, NW	WASHINGTON, DC	20005
MUSOLINO, MIKE	BASEBALL	POST OFFICE BOX 1742	PALM SPRINGS, CA	92263
MUSSELMAN, BILL	BASKETBALL COACH	TIMBERWOLVES, 600 1ST AVE N	MINNEAPOLIS, MN	55403
MUSSELMAN, DAVID L	TV PRODUCER	630 9TH AVE #1410	NEW YORK, NY	10036
MUSSELMAN, JEFF	BASEBALL	POST OFFICE BOX 11087	TACOMA, WA	98411
MUSSER, ANDY	SPORTSCASTER	POST OFFICE BOX 7575	PHILADELPHIA, PA	19101
MUSSETT, JOSE	BASEBALL	POST OFFICE BOX 3496	DAVENPORT, IA	52808
MUSSETTER, JUDE	ACTRESS	3500 W OLIVE AVE #1400	BURBANK, CA	91505
MUSSINA, MIKE	BASEBALL	ORIOLE PARK, 333 W CAMDEN ST	BALTIMORE, MD	21201
MUSTAF, JERROD	BASKETBALL	KNICKS, 4 PENNYLVANIA PLAZA	NEW YORK, NY	10019
MUSTANG, SALLY	SINGER	2028 CHESTNUT ST	PHILADELPHIA, PA	19103
MUSTER, BRAD	FOOTBALL	BEARS, 250 N WASHINGTON RD	LAKE FOREST, IL	60045
MUTI, ORNELLA	ACTRESS	3 QUAI MALAQUAIS	F-75006 PARIS	FRANCE
MUTI, RICCARDO	CONDUCTOR-MUSIC DIR	1420 LOCUST ST #400	PHILADELPHIA, PA	19102
MUTIS, JEFF	BASEBALL	4385 TUTT BLVD	COLORADO SPRINGS, CO	80922
MUTRUX, CHARLES FLOYD	WRITER-PRODUCER	DGA, 7920 SUNSET BLVD, 6TH FL	LOS ANGELES, CA	90046
MUTSCHLER, HARRY R	DIRECTOR	DGA, 110 W 57TH ST	NEW YORK, NY	10019
MYATT, NANCYLEE	ACTRESS-WRITER	190 S CANON DR #201	BEVERLY HILLS, CA	90210
MYERS, BARBARA	CABLE EXECUTIVE	HBO, 1100 6TH AVE	NEW YORK, NY	10036
MYERS, BUD	TV DIRECTOR	84-09 35TH AVE #4-E	JACKSON HEIGHTS, NY	11372
MYERS, CHIP	FOOTBALL COACH	N Y JETS, 1000 FULTON AVE	HEMPSTEAD, NY	11550
MYERS, CHRIS	BASEBALL	POST OFFICE BOX 15757	HARRISBURG, PA	17105
MYERS, DAVE	BASEBALL MANAGER	1316 KING ST	BELLINGHAM, WA	98226
MYERS, GREG	BASEBALL	SKYDOME, 300 BREMMER BL #3200	TORONTO, ONT M5V 3B3	CANADA
MYERS, JIM	BASEBALL	5999 E VAN BUREN ST	PHOENIX, AZ	85008
MYERS, JOHN T	U S CONGRESSMAN	107 HALLECK FEDERAL BUILDING	LAFAYETTE, IN	47901
MYERS, LAURENCE	FILM PROD-EXEC	CAMBRIDGE THEATRE, EARLHAM ST	LONDON WC2H 9HU	ENGLAND
MYERS, LOU	ARTIST	58 LAKEVIEW AVE W	PEEKSKILL, NY	10566
MYERS, MICHAEL	FILM EXECUTIVE	69 NEW OXFORD ST	LONDON WC1A 1DG	ENGLAND
MYERS, PAULENE	ACTRESS	CONNECTIONS, 370 W 51ST ST	NEW YORK, NY	10019
MYERS, PETER	COMPOSER	4146 LANKERSHIM BLVD #300	NORTH HOLLYWOOD, CA	91602
MYERS, PETER S	FILM EXECUTIVE	1753 ALTA MURA RD	PACIFIC PALISADES, CA	90272
MYERS, RANDY	BASEBALL	POST OFFICE BOX 2000	SAN DIEGO, CA	92112
MYERS, RONALD	BASEBALL EXECUTIVE	POST OFFICE BOX 2785	LAKELAND, FL	33806
MYERS, RUSSELL	CARTOONIST	TRIBUNE, 64 E CONCORD ST	ORLANDO, FL	32801
MYERS, RUTH	COSTUME DESIGNER	13949 VENTURA BLVD #309	SHERMAN OAKS, CA	91423
MYERS, SIDNEY	DIRECTOR	2 W 45TH ST	NEW YORK, NY	10036
MYERS, STANLEY	COMPOSER	102-A BEAUFORT ST	LONDON SW3	ENGLAND
MYERS, STANLEY A	COMPOSER-CONDUCTOR	215 W 1ST ST #204	TUSTIN, CA	92680
MYERS, TOM	BASEBALL	POST OFFICE BOX 11363	RENO, NV	89510
MYERSON, BESS	COLUMNIST-ADVOCATE	2 E 71ST ST	NEW YORK, NY	10021
MYERSON, ROBERT	WRITER-PRODUCER	17 W 67TH ST	NEW YORK, NY	10023
MYHERS, JOHN	ACTOR-WRITER	8841 EVANVIEW DR	LOS ANGELES, CA	90069
MYHRUM, ROBERT	TV DIRECTOR	POST OFFICE BOX 99	PERU, VT	05152
MYLES, GODFREY	FOOTBALL	COWBOYS, 1 COWBOYS PARKWAY	IRVING, TX	75063
MYLES, JOHN M	CONDUCTOR	11458 SWINTON AVE	GRANADA HILLS, CA	91344

MYLES, MEG	ACTRESS	33 RIVERSIDE DR #11-F	NEW YORK, NY 10023
MYLES, STAN	TV EXECUTIVE	CBS-TV, 7800 BEVERLY BLVD	LOS ANGELES, CA 90036
MYRICK, BOBBY	BASEBALL-SCOUT	POST OFFICE BOX 2000	ANAHEIM, CA 92803
MYRICK, GARY & THE FIGURES	ROCK & ROLL GROUP	POST OFFICE BOX 7308	CARMEL, CA 93921
MYROW, FREDRIC E	COMPOSER-CONDUCTOR	208 S SAINT ANDREWS PL	LOS ANGELES, CA 90004
MYROW, JEFFREY B	TV WRITER-DIRECTOR	1209 TURQUESA LN	PACIFIC PALISADES, CA 90272
MYSTICS, THE	VOCAL GROUP	CONTRERA, 88 ANADOR ST	STATEN ISLAND, NY 10303

N R B O	C & W GROUP	ROUNDER RECORDS, 1 CAMP ST	CAMBRIDGE, MA 02140
N'DOUR, YOUSSOU	SINGER	VERNA GILLIS, SOUNDSCAPE	
		500 W 52ND ST	NEW YORK, NY 10019
NABBIE, JIM	SINGER	5300 POWERLINE RD #202	FORT LAUDERDALE, FL 33309
NABEL, WILLIAM J	ACTOR	39 JORDAN LN	STAMFORD, CT 06903
NABHOLZ, CHRIS	BASEBALL	EXPOS, 4545 DE COUBERTIN AVE	MONTREAL, QUE H1V 3P2 CANADA
NABORS, JIM	ACTOR-SINGER	151 S EL CAMINO DR	BEVERLY HILLS, CA 90212
NACCARATO, STAN	BASEBALL EXECUTIVE	POST OFFICE BOX 11087	TACOMA, WA 98411
NACHMAN, JERRY	TV EXECUTIVE	NBC-TV, 30 ROCKEFELLER PLAZA	NEW YORK, NY 10112
NACHTIGALL, ANDREW	ACTOR	26665 SEAGULL WY #A-104	MALIBU, CA 90265
NADEL, BRUCE	DIRECTOR	BROOK TRAIL	CROTON-ON-HUDSON, NY 10520
NADEL, ERIC	SPORTSCASTER	POST OFFICE BOX 90111	ARLINGTON, TX 76004
NADELL, EDMUND	TV DIRECTOR	RURAL ROUTE #1	
		SPRING LAKE RD	SHERMAN, CT 06784
NADER, GEORGE	ACTOR	52 S IWA PL	LAHAINA, HI 96761
NADER, JOHN	BASEBALL EXECUTIVE	95 RIVER ST	ONEONTA, NY 13820
NADER, MICHAEL	ACTOR	7565 JALMIA WY	LOS ANGELES, CA 90046
NADER, RALPH	CONSUMER ADVOCATE	POST OFFICE BOX 19367	WASHINGTON, DC 20036
NADER, SAM	BASEBALL EXECUTIVE	95 RIVER ST	ONEONTA, NY 13820
NADLER, HARVEY "BUDDY"	DIRECTOR	3770 DUNN DR #14	LOS ANGELES, CA 90034
NADOOLMAN, DEBORAH	COSTUME DESIGNER	13949 VENTURA BLVD #309	SHERMAN OAKS, CA 91423
NAEHRING, TIM	BASEBALL	FENWAY PARK, 4 YAWKEY WY	BOSTON, MA 02215
NAFIE, CAROL LEE	TV DIRECTOR	861 10TH ST	MANHATTAN BEACH, CA 90266
NAGASHIMA, KAZUSHIGA	BASEBALL	POST OFFICE BOX 2887	VERO BEACH, FL 32961
NAGATA, DAVID	DIRECTOR	56 E 66TH ST	NEW YORK, NY 10021
NAGATA, RUSSELL	COMPTROLLER	STATE CAPITOL BUILDING	HONOLULU, HI 96813
NAGEL, DON	ACTOR	14155 MAGNOLIA BLVD #110	VAN NUYS, CA 91423
NAGESH, INDIRA	DIRECTOR-PRODUCER	15758 STARE ST	SEPULVEDA, CA 91343
NAGLE, BROWNING	FOOTBALL	N Y JETS, 1000 FULTON AVE	HEMPSTEAD, NY 11550
NAGLE, DAVID	U S CONGRESSMAN	102 S CLINTON #505	IOWA CITY, IA 52240
NAGY, CHARLES	BASEBALL	INDIANS, CLEVELAND STADIUM	CLEVELAND, OH 44114
NAGY, IVAN	WRITER-PRODUCER	10128 EMPYREAN WY	CENTURY CITY, CA 90067
NAHABEDIAN, DAVE	BASEBALL SCOUT	S F GIANTS, CANDLESTICK PARK	SAN FRANICSCO, CA 94124
NAHAN, STU	SPORTSCASTER	11274 CANTON DR	STUDIO CITY, CA 91604
NAIL, JOANNE	ACTRESS	4261 TROOST AVE #2	STUDIO CITY, CA 91604
NAILL, JERRY & THE ARMADILLO EX	C & W GROUP	POST OFFICE BOX 1373	LEWISVILLE, TX 75067
NAILS, THE	ROCK & ROLL GROUP	TERRY DUNE MGMT	
		125 E 15TH ST	NEW YORK, NY 10003
NAILZ	WRESTLER	POST OFFICE BOX 3859	STAMFORD, CT 06905
NAIR, MIRA	COMPOSER-PRODUCER	ICM, 40 W 57TH ST	NEW YORK, NY 10019
NAISBITT, JOHN	COLUMNIST	UPS, 4900 MAIN ST, 9TH FLOOR	KANSAS CITY, MO 64112
NAJEE	SAXOPHONIST	HUSH PRODS, 231 W 58TH ST	NEW YORK, NY 10019
NAKANO, DESMOND	SCREENWRITER	3554 LAURELVALE DR	STUDIO CITY, CA 91604
NAKANO, GEORGE H	DIRECTOR	UNO, 119 W 22ND ST	NEW YORK, NY 10011
NAKED PREY, THE	ROCK & ROLL GROUP	POST OFFICE BOX 22	SUN VALLEY, CA 91353
NALEPINSKI, BRUCE A	DIRECTOR	5 KARLSRUHE LN	EAST HAMPTON, NY 11937
NANAS, HERB	TAL AGT-FILM PROD	SCOTTI BROS, 2128 PICO BLVD	SANTA MONICA, CA 90405
NANAS, HERB A	FILM PRODUCER	4915 TYRONE AVE #230	SHERMAN OAKS, CA 91423
NANAS, JOSEPH M	COMPOSER	306 WALDON DR	VENTNOR CITY, NJ 08406
NANCE, LARRY	BASKETBALL	POST OFFICE BOX 5000	RICHFIELD, OH 44286
NANCE, ROSCOE	SPORTS WRITER	POST OFFICE BOX 500	WASHINGTON, DC 20044
NANKANO, DESMOND L	SCREENWRITER	8955 BEVERLY BLVD	WEST HOLLYWOOD, CA 90048
NANKIN, MICHAEL	WRITER-PRODUCER	336 S COCHRAN AVE #4	LOS ANGELES, CA 90036
NANTUCKET	ROCK & ROLL GROUP	J BIRD, 250 N KEPLER RD	DE LAND, FL 32724
NAPIER, CHARLES	ACTOR	MTA, 9320 WILSHIRE BL, 3RD FL	BEVERLY HILLS, CA 90212
NAPIER, HUGO	ACTOR	2207 N BEACHWOOD DR	LOS ANGELES, CA 90068
NARDINO, FLORENCE	ACTRESS	539 COGNEWAUGH RD	COS COB, CT 06807
NARDO, PATRICIA	TV WRITER	4020 PACHECO DR	SHERMAN OAKS, CA 91403
NARIZZANO, DINO	TV DIRECTOR	465 W BROADWAY	NEW YORK, NY 10012
NARIZZANO, SILVIO	TV-FILM DIRECTOR	AL PARKER, 55 PARK LN	LONDON W1Y 3DD ENGLAND
NARRON, JERRY	BASEBALL-MANAGER	500 NORTON ST	ROCHESTER, NY 14621
NARZ, JACK	TV HOST	1905 BEVERLY PL	BEVERLY HILLS, CA 90210
NASCHEL, LARRY	ACTOR	1512 MARLAY DR	LOS ANGELES, CA 90069
NASELLA, JIM	FILM DIRECTOR	1423 WINCHESTER AVE	GLENDALE, CA 91201
NASH, FRANKLIN M	DIRECTOR	202 W 10TH ST	NEW YORK, NY 10014
NASH, GRAHAM	SINGER-SONGWRITER	10960 WILSHIRE BLVD #938	LOS ANGELES, CA 90024
NASH, JOE	FOOTBALL	SEAHAWKS, 11220 NE 53RD ST	KIRKLAND, WA 98033
NASH, JOHN	BASKETBALL EXECUTIVE	BULLETS, 1 HARRY S TRUMAN DR	LANDOVER, MD 20785
NASH, JOHNNY	SINGER-SONGWRITER	CHALET NIVAL OBERBORT	CH-3780 GSTAAD SWITZERLAND

Name	Occupation	Address	City	Zip/Country
NASH, N RICHARD	SCREENWRITER	8955 BEVERLY BLVD	WEST HOLLYWOOD, CA	90048
NASH, RICHARD	COMPOSER	19323 OXNARD ST	TARZANA, CA	91356
NASH, ROBIN	TV PRODUCER	BBC, KENSINGTON HOUSE		
		RICHMOND WY	LONDON W14	ENGLAND
NASH, SARAH	SINGER	1680 N VINE ST #214	HOLLYWOOD, CA	90028
NASH, VILL	SINGER	PAM, 815 18TH AVE S	NASHVILLE, TN	37203
NASH THE SLASH	ROCK & ROLL GROUP	41 BRITAIN ST #200	TORONTO, ONT M5A 1R7	CANADA
NASHVILLE SOUNDS OF DALLAS	C & W GROUP	SODP, 29 HUDSON ST	WATERFORD, NY	12188
NASHVILLE TEENS, THE	ROCK & ROLL GROUP	AMBER HOUSE MANAGEMENT		
		278 SEVEN SISTERS RD	LONDON	ENGLAND
NASSIF, CHRISTOPHER	TALENT AGENT	8721 SUNSET BLVD #102	LOS ANGELES, CA	90069
NASTASE, ILLE	TENNIS	15 E 69TH ST	NEW YORK, NY	10021
NAT, MARIE-JOSE	ACTRESS	10, RUE ROYALE	F-75008 PARIS	FRANCE
NATAL, ROB	BASEBALL	1501 W 16TH ST	INDIANAPOLIS, IN	46202
NATALE, VINCE	ARTIST	189 UNION AVE	NEW PROVIDENCE, NJ	07974
NATANSON, AGATHE	ACTRESS	31 AVE FELIX FAURE	PARIS 75015	FRANCE
NATCHER, WILLIAM	U S CONGRESSMAN	414 E 10TH ST	BOWLING GREEN, KY	42101
NATHAN, STEPHEN	ACTOR-WRITER	8685 CRESCENT DR	LOS ANGELES, CA	90046
NATHAN, TONY	FOOTBALL COACH	DOLPHINS, 2269 NW 199TH ST	MIAMI, FL	33056
NATHANSON, EDWARD	TV DIRECTOR-PRODUCER	POST OFFICE BOX 64	FAIRFIELD, CT	06430
NATHANSON, TED	TV DIRECTOR-PRODUCER	NBC-TV, 30 ROCKEFELLER PLAZA	NEW YORK, NY	10112
NATHKIN, RICK	SCREENWRITER	3249 CORINTH AVE	LOS ANGELES, CA	90066
NATIVADAD, KITTEN	ACTRESS-NODEL	POST OFFICE BOX 48938	LOS ANGELES, CA	90048
NATKIN, RICK	SCREENWRITER	9200 SUNSET BLVD #402	LOS ANGELES, CA	90069
NATTIEL, RICKY	FOOTBALL	BRONCOS, 13655 BRONCOS PKWY	ENGLEWOOD, CO	80112
NATTRESS, RIC	HOCKEY	POST OFFICE BOX 1540, STA "M"	CALGARY, ALTA T2P 3BP	CANADA
NATURAL DISASTERS, THE	WRESTLING TAG TEAM	POST OFFICE BOX 3859	STAMFORD, CT	06905
NATWICK, MILDRED	ACTRESS	1001 PARK AVE	NEW YORK, NY	10028
NAUD, MELINDA	ACTRESS	12330 VIEWCREST RD	STUDIO CITY, CA	91604
NAUERT, PAUL	BASEBALL UMPIRE	235 MAIN ST #103	TRUSSVILLE, AL	35173
NAUGHTON, DAVID	ACTOR-SINGER	9000 SUNSET BLVD #1200	LOS ANGELES, CA	90069
NAUGHTON, DEIRDRE	COSTUME DESIGNER	13949 VENTURA BLVD #309	SHERMAN OAKS, CA	91423
NAUGHTON, JAMES	ACTOR	ICM, 8899 BEVERLY BLVD	LOS ANGELES, CA	90048
NAVA, GREGORY JAMES	FILM WRITER-DIRECTOR	10541 BLYTHE AVE	LOS ANGELES, CA	90064
NAVA, LIPSO	BASEBALL	POST OFFICE BOX 9194	HAMPTON, VA	23670
NAVA, MARLO	BASEBALL	POST OFFICE BOX 661	KENOSHA, WI	53141
NAVARRA, JACK J	COMPOSER	5802 S ADELE AVE	WHITTIER, CA	90606
NAVARRO, JAIME	BASEBALL	BREWERS, 201 S 46TH ST	MILWAUKEE, WI	53214
NAVARRO, NELSON	TV DIRECTOR	78-08 WOODSIDE AVE	ELMHURST, NY	11373
NAVARRO, TITO	BASEBALL	POST OFFICE BOX 1211	NORFOLK, VA	23502
NAVEDA, EDGAR	BASEBALL	POST OFFICE BOX 1659	PORTLAND, OR	97207
NAVERT, RANDY	TALENT AGENT	3465 ENCINAL CANYON RD	MALIBU, CA	90265
NAYLOR, CAL	TV DIRECTOR	17606 POSETANO RD	PACIFIC PALISADES, CA	90272
NAZARETH	ROCK & ROLL GROUP	3101 E EISENHOWER HWY #3	ANN ARBOR, MI	48104
NAZARIO, JOE	BODYBUILDER	9157 RESEDA BLVD	NORTHRIDGE, CA	91324
NAZARRO, RAY	FILM DIRECTOR	10965 BLUFFSIDE DR #15	STUDIO CITY, CA	91604
NEAGLE, DENNY	BASEBALL	POST OFFICE BOX 7000	PITTSBURGH, PA	15212
NEAL, CURLY	BASKETBALL	POST OFFICE BOX 76	ORLANDO, FL	32802
NEAL, DAN	FOOTBALL COACH	EAGLES, BROAD ST & PATTISON AVE	PHILADELPHIA, PA	19148
NEAL, DAVID	BASEBALL	POST OFFICE BOX 3496	DAVENPORT, IA	52808
NEAL, PATRICIA	ACTRESS	POST OFFICE BOX 1043	EDGARTOWN, MA	02539
NEAL, RICHARD	U S CONGRESSMAN	1550 MAIN ST #309	SPRINGFIELD, MA	01103
NEAL, STEPHEN L	U S CONGRESSMAN	421 FEDERAL BUILDING	WINSTON-SALEM, NC	27101
NEALON, KEVIN	COMEDIAN	5039 1/2 ROSEWOOD AVE	LOS ANGELES, CA	90004
NEALY, ED	BASKETBALL	SUNS, 2910 N CENTRAL AVE	PHOENIX, AZ	85012
NEAME, CHRISTOPHER	ACTOR	5 BELLSIZE SQ #2	LONDON NW3	ENGLAND
NEAME, RONALD	DIRECTOR	2317 KIMRIDGE RD	BEVERLY HILLS, CA	90210
NEAPOLITANS, THE	C & W GROUP	PROCESS, 439 WILEY AVE	FRANKLIN, PA	16323
NEAR, HOLLY	ACTRESS-SINGER	ROSENBERG, 8428 MELROSE PL #C	LOS ANGELES, CA	90069
NEARY, JACK	BODYBUILDER	190 SUTHERLAND DR	TORONTO, ONT M4G 1J2	CANADA
NEARY, R PATRICK	TV WRITER	1642 MANKATO CT	CLAREMONT, CA	91711
NEBBIA, MICHAEL	TV DIRECTOR	330 E 71ST ST	NEW YORK, NY	10021
NEBBIA, THOMAS	DIRECTOR	911 9TH ST #202	SANTA MONICA, CA	90403
NEBENZAL, HAROLD	WRITER-PRODUCER	2024 COLDWATER CANYON DR	BEVERLY HILLS, CA	90210
NEBSETH, AMY	DIRECTOR	DGA, 7920 SUNSET BLVD, 6TH FL	LOS ANGELES, CA	90046
NEDERLANDER, HARRY	BASEBALL EXECUTIVE	N Y YANKEES, YANKEE STADIUM	BRONX, NY	10451
NEDERLANDER, JAMES	BASEBALL EXECUTIVE	N Y YANKEES, YANKEE STADIUM	BRONX, NY	10451
NEDERLANDER, ROBERT	BASEBALL EXECUTIVE	N Y YANKEES, YANKEE STADIUM	BRONX, NY	10451
NEDIN, TIM	BASEBALL	14100 SIX MILE CYPRESS PKWY	FORT MYERS, FL	33912
NEDVED, PETR	HOCKEY	CANUCKS, 100 N RENFREW ST	VANCOUVER, BC V5K 3N7	CANADA
NEDWELL, ROBIN	ACTOR	ICM, 388-396 OXFORD ST	LONDON W1	ENGLAND
NEEDHAM, CONNIE	ACTRESS	19721 CASTLEBAR DR	ROWLAND HEIGHTS, CA	91748
NEEDHAM, HAL	WRITER-PRODUCER	2220 AVE OF THE STARS #302	LOS ANGELES, CA	90067
NEEDHAM, TRACEY	ACTRESS	9229 SUNSET BLVD #311	LOS ANGELES, CA	90069
NEEDLE, ANDREW	DIRECTOR	1122 18TH ST #109	SANTA MONICA, CA	90403
NEEL, TROY	BASEBALL	POST OFFICE BOX 11087	TACOMA, WA	98411
NEELEY, TED	ACTOR-SINGER	12744 SARAH ST	STUDIO CITY, CA	91604
NEELY, CAM	HOCKEY	BRUINS, 150 CAUSEWAY ST	BOSTON, MA	02114
NEELY, JEFF	BASEBALL	POST OFFICE BOX 450	BUFFALO, NY	14205
NEELY, KENNETH "DOC"	BODYBUILDER	POST OFFICE BOX 490338	COLLEGE PARK, GA	30349
NEELY, PHILLIP	TV DIRECTOR	DGA, 7920 SUNSET BLVD, 6TH FL	LOS ANGELES, CA	90046
NEELY, SAM	SINGER	POST OFFICE BOX 1373	LEWISVILLE, TN	65067
NEER, JUDIE	TV WRITER	5714 TROOST AVE	NORTH HOLLYWOOD, CA	91601
NEESON, LIAM	ACTOR	1999 AVE OF THE STARS #2850	LOS ANGELES, CA	90067
NEFF, BILL	DIRECTOR	1103 N CEDARVIEW	BOZEMAN, MT	59715

NEFF, HILDEGARD	ACTRESS	KOHNER, 9169 SUNSET BLVD	LOS ANGELES, CA	90069
NEFF, MARTY	BASEBALL	POST OFFICE BOX 3746, HILL STA	AUGUSTA, GA	30904
NEFF, WILLIAM	ACTOR	17050 SUNSET BLVD	PACIFIC PALISADES, CA	90272
NEFT, ANN	TV WRITER	3620 GLENRIDGE DR	SHERMAN OAKS, CA	91423
NEGATIVE FIX	ROCK & ROLL GROUP	39 POPLAR ST	MELROSE, MA	02176
NEGRI, PATTI	ACTRESS	1717 N HIGHLAND AVE #414	LOS ANGELES, CA	90028
NEGRIN, SOL	TV DIRECTOR	873 CUSTER ST	VALLEY STREAM, NY	11580
NEGRON, TAYLOR	ACTOR-COMEDIAN	ICM, 8899 BEVERLY BLVD	LOS ANGELES, CA	90048
NEGULESCO, JEAN	DIRECTOR-PRODUCER	20508 MANDEL ST	CANOGA PARK, CA	91306
NEHLS, ALLYN R	TV DIRECTOR	ABC-TV, 190 N STATE ST	CHICAHO, IL	60601
NEIDERER, JON	BASEBALL SCOUT	POST OFFICE BOX 2000	ANAHEIM, CA	92803
NEIDHART, JIM "THE ANVIL"	WRESTLER-FOOTBALL	POST OFFICE BOX 3859	STAMFORD, CT	06905
NEIDLINGER, JIM	BASEBALL	POST OFFICE BOX 26267	ALBUQUERQUE, NM	87125
NEIERS, MIKE	CINEMATOGRAPHER	7715 SUNSET BLVD #150	LOS ANGELES, CA	90046
NEIGHBORHOODS, THE	ROCK & ROLL GROUP	25 HUNTINGTON AVE #420	BOSTON, MA	02116
NEIGHER, GEOFFREY MARK	TV WRITER	342 N MC CADDEN PL	LOS ANGELES, CA	90004
NEIGHER, STEPHEN	STORY EDITOR	147 N MARTEL AVE	LOS ANGELES, CA	90036
NEILL, MIKE	BASEBALL	POST OFFICE BOX 11363	RENO, NV	89510
NEILL, NOEL	ACTRESS	331 SAGE LN	SANTA MONICA, CA	90402
NEILL, SAM	ACTOR	ICM, 388-396 OXFORD ST	LONDON W1	ENGLAND
NEILSEN, INGA	ACTRESS	8360 MELROSE AVE #203	LOS ANGELES, CA	90069
NEILSON, JOHN	ACTOR-WRITER	4501 VISTA DEL MONTE AVE #8	SHERMAN OAKS, CA	91403
NEIMAN, LE ROY	ARTIST	1 W 67TH ST	NEW YORK, NY	10023
NEITZEL, R A	BASEBALL	POST OFFICE BOX 15050	READING, PA	19612
NELKIN, STACEY	ACTRESS	2770 HUTTON DR	BEVERLY HILLS, CA	90210
NELLES, RALPH	BASEBALL EXECUTIVE	POST OFFICE BOX 1144	BILLINGS, MT	59103
NELLIGAN, KATE	ACTRESS	3 GOODWIN'S CT	LONDON WC2	ENGLAND
NELSON	ROCK & ROLL GROUP	3907 W ALAMEDA BLVD #102	BURBANK, CA	91505
NELSON, BARRY	ACTOR	134 W 58TH ST	NEW YORK, NY	10019
NELSON, BILL	ARTIST	1402 WILMINGTON AVE	RICHMOND, VA	23227
NELSON, BOB	BASEBALL	312 ALTA VISTA AVE	SOUTH PASADENA, CA	91030
NELSON, BONNIE	SINGER	TRIANGLE TALENT, INC		
		9701 TAYLORSVILLE RD	LOUISVILLE, KY	40299
NELSON, BYRON	GOLFER	ROUTE #2, FAIRWAY RANCH	ROANOKE, TX	76262
NELSON, CARLYLE	CONDUCTOR	215 CHAPIN LN	BURLINGAME, CA	94010
NELSON, CAROL	BASEBALL EXECUTIVE	POST OFFICE BOX 1742	PALM SPRINGS, CA	92263
NELSON, CHRISTOPHER ALAN	DIRECTOR	DGA, 7920 SUNSET BLVD, 6TH FL	LOS ANGELES, CA	90046
NELSON, CRAIG R	DIRECTOR	1900 AVE OF THE STARS #2535	LOS ANGELES, CA	90067
NELSON, CRAIG T	ACT-WRI-DIR	9350 WILSHIRE BLVD #324	BEVERLY HILLS, CA	90212
NELSON, DARRIN	FOOTBALL	VIKINGS, 9520 VIKING DR	EDEN PRAIRIE, MN	55344
NELSON, DAVE	BASEBALL-COACH	INDIANS, CLEVELAND STADIUM	CLEVELAND, OH	44114
NELSON, DAVID	ACTOR-DIRECTOR	WESTERN INTERNATIONAL MEDIA		
		8732 SUNSET BLVD	LOS ANGELES, CA	90038
NELSON, DAVID P	TV DIRECTOR	321-A LARCHMONT ACRES W	LARCHMONT, NY	10538
NELSON, DAVID P	TV PRODUCER	ULICK/MAYO PRODS, 141 5TH AVE	NEW YORK, NY	10010
NELSON, DON	BASKETBALL-COACH	GOLDEN STATE WARRIORS		
		OAKLAND COLISEUM ARENA		
		NIMITZ FWY & HEGENBERGER RD	OAKLAND, CA	94621
NELSON, E BENJAMIN	GOVERNOR	STATE CAPITOL BUILDING	LINCOLN, NE	68509
NELSON, ED	ACTOR	9000 SUNSET BLVD #801	LOS ANGELES, CA	90069
NELSON, FRANK	ACTOR	8906 EVANVIEW DR	LOS ANGELES, CA	90069
NELSON, FRED	BASEBALL EXECUTIVE	POST OFFICE BOX 288	HOUSTON, TX	77001
NELSON, GARY	DIRECTOR	CAA, 9830 WILSHIRE BLVD	BEVERLY HILLS, CA	90212
NELSON, GENE	ACTOR-DIRECTOR	2 STERN LN	ATHERTON, CA	94025
NELSON, GENE	BASEBALL	ATHLETICS'S, OAKLAND COLISEUM	OAKLAND, CA	94621
NELSON, HARRIET HILLIARD	ACTRESS-SINGER	4179 VALLEY MEADOW	ENCINO, CA	91316
NELSON, HELEN V	DIRECTOR	350 E 52ND ST	NEW YORK, NY	10022
NELSON, JEFF	BASEBALL	POST OFFICE BOX 3690, STA "B"	CALGARY, ALB T2B 4M4	CANADA
NELSON, JEROME	BASEBALL	POST OFFICE BOX 3566	WEST PALM BEACH, FL	33402
NELSON, JESSICA	ACTRESS	301 N CANON DR #305	BEVERLY HILLS, CA	90210
NELSON, JOHN ALLEN	ACTOR	9000 SUNSET BLVD #1200	LOS ANGELES, CA	90069
NELSON, JUDD	ACTOR	POST OFFICE BOX 69170	LOS ANGELES, CA	90069
NELSON, LARRY	GOLFER	POST OFFICE BOX 109601	PALM BCH GARDENS, FL	33418
NELSON, LINDSEY	SPORTSCASTER	CBS SPORTS, 51 W 52ND ST	NEW YORK, NY	10019
NELSON, LORI	ACTRESS	8831 SUNSET BLVD #402	LOS ANGELES, CA	90069
NELSON, MARGERY	ACTRESS	SELECTED, 3575 W CAHUENGA BLVD	LOS ANGELES, CA	90068
NELSON, MARI	ACTRESS	11726 SAN VICENTE BLVD #300	LOS ANGELES, CA	90049
NELSON, MEL	BASEBALL SCOUT	250 STADIUM PLAZA	ST LOUIS, MO	63102
NELSON, MIKE	BASEBALL EXECUTIVE	1524 W NEBRASKA AVE	PEORIA, IL	61604
NELSON, PRINCE ROGERS	SINGER-SONGWRITER	SEE - PRINCE		
NELSON, RALPH	BASEBALL EXECUTIVE	S F GIANTS, CANDLESTICK PARK	SAN FRANICSCO, CA	94124
NELSON, RICHARD H	TV WRITER	22715 CALVERT ST	WOODLAND HILLS, CA	91367
NELSON, ROB	BASEBALL	CANADIANS, 4601 ONTARIO ST	VANCOUVER, BC V5V 3H4	CANADA
NELSON, ROBERT	COMEDIAN	POST OFFICE BOX 1556	GAINESVILLE, FL	32602
NELSON, SANDY	DRUMMER	2911 CARDIFF AVE	LOS ANGELES, CA	90034
NELSON, SCOTT	BASEBALL SCOUT	1060 W ADDISON ST	CHICAGO, IL	60613
NELSON, STEVE	FOOTBALL COACH	PATRIOTS, FOXBORO STADIUM, RT #1	FOXBORO, MA	02035
NELSON, SUSIE	SINGER	TESSIER, 505 CANTON PASS	MADISON, TN	37115
NELSON, TRACY	ACTRESS	405 SYCAMORE RD	SANTA MONICA, CA	90402
NELSON, TRACY	SINGER	POST OFFICE BOX 1343	MARIETTA, GA	30061
NELSON, WILLIE	SINGER-SONGWRITER	POST OFFICE BOX 33280	AUSTIN, TX	78764
NELSON-SEAGREN, KAM	ACTRESS	120 S THURSTON AVE	LOS ANGELES, CA	90049
NEMEC, CORIN "CORKEY"	ACTOR	9348 CIVIC CENTER DR #407	BEVERLY HILLS, CA	90210
NEMERSON, ROY E	TV-COMEDY WRITER	200 E 78TH ST	NEW YORK, NY	10021
NEMIROFF, PAUL R	DIRECTOR	152 COLD SPRING RD	SYOSSET, NY	11791

Name	Occupation	Address	City	Zip/Country
NEMITZ, DONALD J	COMPOSER	20716 LULL ST	CANOGA PARK, CA	91306
NEMMERS, LARRY	FOOTBALL REFEREE	NFL, 410 PARK AVE	NEW YORK, NY	10022
NEMO, GINA	ACTRESS	9300 WILSHIRE BLVD #410	BEVERLY HILLS, CA	90212
NEN, ROBB	BASEBALL	POST OFFICE BOX 4448	TULSA, OK	74159
NEPUS, RIA	SCREENWRITER	418 N MAPLE DR #E	BEVERLY HILLS, CA	90210
NERAT, DAN	BASEBALL	POST OFFICE BOX 2437	MODESTO, CA	95351
NERO, FRANCO	ACTOR	PAOLO PETRI-MARINA DIBERTY		
NERO, PETER	PIANIST	4114 ROYAL CREST PL	ENCINO, CA	91436
NERO, TONI	ACTRESS	145 S FAIRFAX AVE #310	LOS ANGELES, CA	90036
NERVOUS EATERS	ROCK & ROLL GROUP	POST OFFICE BOX 579		
		KENMORE STATION	BOSTON, MA	02215
NERYDA	EXOTIC DANCER	THE ACTOR'S FUND HOME		
		155 W HUDSON AVE	ENGLEWOOD, NJ	07631
NESI, THOMAS	WRITER	11621 CHENAULT ST #5	LOS ANGELES, CA	90049
NESLER, BOB	ARTIST	1351 OCEAN PARK WALK #106	SANTA MONICA, CA	90405
NESMITH, EUGENE	ACTOR	444 W 49TH ST #2-B	NEW YORK, NY	10019
NESMITH, MICHAEL	SINGER-PRODUCER	50 N LA CIENEGA BLVD 210	BEVERLY HILLS, CA	90211
NESOR, AL	ACTOR	2780 NE 183RD ST #603-C	NORTH MIAMI BEACH, FL	33160
NESSIM, BARBARA	ARTIST	240 E 15TH ST	NEW YORK, NY	10003
NESTICO, SAMUEL L	COMPOSER	12230 SINTONTE CT	SAN DIEGO, CA	92128
NETHERCOTT, GEOFFREY	DIRECTOR-PRODUCER	CINEVENTURE, 95 FRAMPTON ST	LONDON NW8	ENGLAND
NETHERY, SCOTT	BASEBALL SCOUT	POST OFFICE BOX 4100	SEATTLE, WA	98104
NETSCH, DAWN C	COMPTROLLER	STATE HOUSE BUILDING	SPRINGFIELD, IL	62706
NETTLES, GRAIG	BASEBALL-COACH	13 NORTH LN	DEL MAR, CA	92014
NETTLES, JIM	BASEBALL MANAGER	POST OFFICE BOX 4756	JACKSONVILLE, FL	32201
NETTLETON, JOHN	ACTOR	SARABAND, 265 LIVERPOOL RD	LONDON N1 1LX	ENGLAND
NETTLETON, LOIS	ACTRESS	1263 N FLORES AVE	LOS ANGELES, CA	90069
NEUBAUER, LEONARD	SCREENWRITER	340 S OAKHURST DR	BEVERLY HILLS, CA	90212
NEUDECKER, JERRY	BASEBALL UMPIRE	AMERICAN LEAGUE, 350 PARK AVE	NEW YORK, NY	10022
NEUFELD, JOHN A	WRITER	1203 N SWEETZER AVE #115	LOS ANGELES, CA	90069
NEUFELD, MACE	DIRECTOR-PRODUCER	624 N ARDEN DR	BEVERLY HILLS, CA	90210
NEUFELD, SIGMUND, JR	FILM DIRECTOR	1867 RISING GLEN RD	LOS ANGELES, CA	90069
NEUHARTH, ALLEN H	PUBLISHING EXECUTIVE	POST OFFICE BOX 500	WASHINGTON, DC	20044
NEUKUM, JOHN E	DIRECTOR	430 S FULLER AVE #2-M	LOS ANGELES, CA	90036
NEUMAN, DAVID	SCREENWRITER	8955 BEVERLY BLVD	WEST HOLLYWOOD, CA	90048
NEUMAN, E JACK	WRITER-PRODUCER	1849 RISING GLEN RD	LOS ANGELES, CA	90069
NEUMAN, MATT	TV WRITER	10100 SANTA MONICA BLVD #1600	LOS ANGELES, CA	90067
NEUMAN, SAM WILLIAM	WRITER-PRODUCER	9300 CREBS AVE	NORTHRIDGE, CA	91324
NEUMANN, DOROTHY	ACTRESS	10860 KINGSLAND ST	LOS ANGELES, CA	90034
NEUMANN, E JACK	TV WRITER	1900 AVE OF THE STARS #2535	LOS ANGELES, CA	90067
NEUMANN, JENNY	ACTRESS	145 S FAIRFAX AVE #310	LOS ANGELES, CA	90036
NEUMANN, ROGER L	COMPOSER-CONDUCTOR	4940 CAHUENGA BLVD	NORTH HOLLYWOOD, CA	91601
NEUMANN, SUSAN L	RECORD EXECUTIVE	BEE HIVE, 1130 COLFAX	EVANSTON, IL	60201
NEUMNA, ALAN	WRITER-PRODUCER	6725 SUNSET BLVD #505	LOS ANGELES, CA	90028
NEURINGER, SUSAN	TV PRODUCER	641 5TH AVE	NEW YORK, NY	10022
NEUSTEIN, JOSEPH	TV WRITER	834 PEARL ST	SANTA MONICA, CA	90405
NEUWIRTH, BEBE	ACTRESS	315 W 57TH ST #4-H	NEW YORK, NY	10019
NEVENS, PAUL	ACTOR	360 W 55TH ST	NEW YORK, NY	10019
NEVERS, TOM	BASEBALL	POST OFFICE BOX 422229	KISSIMMEE, FL	34742
NEVIL, STEVE	ACTOR	10914 NATIONAL BLVD #201	LOS ANGELES, CA	90064
NEVILLE, AARON	SINGER-SONGWRITER	POST OFFICE BOX 750187	NEW ORLEANS, LA	70130
NEVILLE, LIL	SCI-FI AUTHOR	2443 MORENO DR	LOS ANGELES, CA	90039
NEVILLE, TOM	FOOTBALL	S F 49ERS, 4949 CENTENNIAL BL	SANTA CLARA, CA	95054
NEVILLE BROTHERS, THE	RHYTHM & BLUES GROUP	POST OFFICE BOX 750187	NEW ORLEANS, LA	70130
NEVINS, CLAUDETTE	ACTRESS	3500 W OLIVE AVE #1400	BURBANK, CA	91505
NEVINSON, NANCY	ACTRESS	23 MILL CLOSE, FISHBOURNE	CHICHESTER	ENGLAND
NEW BREED, THE	ROCK & ROLL GROUP	POST OFFICE BOX 791551	DALLAS, TX	75379
NEW CHRISTY MINSTRELS, THE	VOCAL GROUP	1484 S BEVERLY DR 309	LOS ANGELES, CA	90035
NEW COUNTRY IMAGE	C & W GROUP	STM, 1311 CANDLELIGHT AVE	DALLAS, TX	75216
NEW EDITION	RHYTHM & BLUES GROUP	POST OFFICE BOX 77505	SAN FRANCISCO, CA	94107
NEW ENGLAND	ROCK & ROLL GROUP	AUCION MGMT, 645 MADISON AVE	NEW YORK, NY	10021
NEW FOUNDATION	WRESTLING TAG TEAM	POST OFFICE BOX 3859	STAMFORD, CT	06905
NEW GRASS REVIVAL	C & W GROUP	POST OFFICE BOX 128037	NASHVILLE, TN	37212
NEW KIDS ON THE BLOCK, THE	ROCK & ROLL GROUP	POST OFFICE BOX 7001	QUINCY, MA	02269
NEW MATH	ROCK & ROLL GROUP	POST OFFICE BOX 14563	SAN FRANCISCO, CA	94114
NEW MODELS, THE	ROCK & ROLL GROUP	POST OFFICE BOX 36		
		ANSONIA STATION	NEW YORK, NY	10023
NEW ORDER	ROCK & ROLL GROUP	86 PALATINE RD, DUDSBURY	MANCHESTER 20	ENGLAND
NEW PRESIDENTS, THE	ROCK & ROLL GROUP	LOST KINGDOM RECORDS		
		4729 SARATOGA AVE	SAN DIEGO, CA	92107
NEW REGIME	ROCK & ROLL GROUP	41 BRITAIN ST #200	TORONTO, ONT M5A 1R7	CANADA
NEW RELATIONS, THE	C & W GROUP	POST OFFICE BOX O	EXCELSIOR, MN	55331
NEW RIDERS OF THE PURPLE SAGE	ROCK & ROLL GROUP	150 5TH AVE #1103	NEW YORK, NY	10011
NEW VIRGINIANS, THE	VOCAL GROUP	VA TECH, 321 PATTON HALL	BLACKSBURG, VA	24061
NEWALL, GEORGE	DIRECTOR	DGA, 110 W 57TH ST	NEW YORK, NY	10019
NEWARK, DEREK	ACTOR	MAC DERMOT, 14 LEAMORE ST	LONDON W6 0JZ	ENGLAND
NEWBERRY, TOM	FOOTBALL	RAMS, 2327 W LINCOLN BLVD	ANAHEIM, CA	92801
NEWBORN, IRA	COMPOSER	3524 VERDUGO TERR	LOS ANGELES, CA	90065
NEWBROOK, PETER	CINEMATOGRAPHER	TITAN INTERNATIONAL PRODUCTIONS		
		185-A NEWMARKER RD		
		NORWICH	NORFOLK NR4 6AP	ENGLAND
NEWBURY, MICKEY	SINGER-SONGWRITER	128 RIVER RD	HENDERSONVILLE, TN	37075
NEWBY, JEFFREY	DIRECTOR	6026 WILKINSON AVE	NORTH HOLLYWOOD, CA	91606
NEWCLEUS	RHYTHM & BLUES GROUP	FAA, 1700 BROADWAY, 5TH FLOOR	NEW YORK, NY	10019
NEWCOME, JOHN	TENNIS	POST OFFICE BOX 469	NEW BRAUNFELS, TX	78130

NEWELL, GEORGE M, JR	DIRECTOR	14 INNESS PL	GLEN RIDGE, NJ	07028
NEWELL, MIKE	FILM-TV DIRECTOR	HEATH, PARAMOUNT HOUSE		
		162-170 WARDOUR ST	LONDON W1V 3AT	ENGLAND
NEWELL, NORMAN	SONGWRITER	GOLDEN HOUSE #52		
NEWFIELD, MARC	BASEBALL	POST OFFICE BOX 4756	JACKSONVILLE, FL	32201
NEWHART, BOB	ACTOR-COMEDIAN	420 AMAPOLA LN	LOS ANGELES, CA	90077
NEWHOUSE, ANDRE	BASEBALL	POST OFFICE BOX 464	APPLETON, WI	54912
NEWHOUSE, DAVID	WRITER	17616 CANTARA ST	NORTHRIDGE, CA	91325
NEWIRTH, BEBE	ACTRESS	222 S ORANGE DR	LOS ANGELES, CA	90036
NEWKIRK, CRAIG	BASEBALL	POST OFFICE BOX 3609	PORT CHARLOTTE, FL	33949
NEWLAND, JOHN	DIRECTOR-PRODUCER	1727 NICHOLS CANYON	LOS ANGELES, CA	90046
NEWLEY, ANTHONY	SING-ACT-WRI	9000 SUNSET BLVD #1200	LOS ANGELES, CA	90069
NEWLIN, JIM	BASEBALL	POST OFFICE BOX 4756	JACKSONVILLE, FL	32201
NEWMAN, AL	BASEBALL	POST OFFICE BOX 90111	ARLINGTON, TX	76004
NEWMAN, ALAN	BASEBALL	POST OFFICE BOX 5645	ORLANDO, FL	32855
NEWMAN, ALAN	COMPOSER	28904 CLIFFSIDE DR	MALIBU, CA	90265
NEWMAN, ALFRED S	FILM EXECUTIVE	2400 BROADWAY ST #100	SANTA MONICA, CA	90404
NEWMAN, ANTHONY	FOOTBALL	RAMS, 2327 W LINCOLN BLVD	ANAHEIM, CA	92801
NEWMAN, BARRY	ACTOR	425 N OAKHURST DR	BEVERLY HILLS, CA	90210
NEWMAN, CARROLL	TV PRODUCER	CARROLL NEWMAN PRODUCTIONS		
		1640 S SEPULVEDA BLVD, 4TH FL	LOS ANGELES, CA	90025
NEWMAN, CHRISTINE TUDOR	ACTRESS	ABC-TV, "LOVING"		
		320 W 66TH ST, STUDIO 23	NEW YORK, NY	10023
NEWMAN, COLIN	SINGER	POST OFFICE BOX 2428	EL SEGUNDO, CA	90245
NEWMAN, DAVID	SCREENWRITER	555 W 57TH ST #1230	NEW YORK, NY	10019
NEWMAN, FREDERICK	ACTOR	34 W 87TH ST #3	NEW YORK, NY	10024
NEWMAN, JACK	TV WRITER-PRODUCER	NBC-TV, 3000 W ALAMEDA AVE	BURBANK, CA	91523
NEWMAN, JEFF	BASEBALL-COACH	INDIANS, CLEVELAND STADIUM	CLEVELAND, OH	44114
NEWMAN, JIMMY C	SINGER-SONGWRITER	ROUTE #2	CHRISTINA, TN	37037
NEWMAN, JOHNNY	BASKETBALL	310 N KINGS DR	CHARLOTTE, NC	28204
NEWMAN, JOSEPH	FILM DIRECTOR	10900 WINNETKA AVE	CHATSWORTH, CA	91311
NEWMAN, JULIA	TV PRODUCER	WINKLER VIDEO, 248 E 48TH ST	NEW YORK, NY	10017
NEWMAN, LARAINE	ACTRESS	10480 ASHTON AVE	LOS ANGELES, CA	90024
NEWMAN, LAUNA JANE	WRITER	11945 ADDISON ST	STUDIO CITY, CA	91607
NEWMAN, LEE	COMPOSER	1400 N FAIRFAX AVE #13	LOS ANGELES, CA	90046
NEWMAN, LESLIE	SCREENWRITER	555 W 57TH ST #1230	NEW YORK, NY	10019
NEWMAN, LOIS	ACTRESS	5711 1/2 LEXINGTON AVE	LOS ANGELES, CA	90038
NEWMAN, MARK	BASEBALL EXECUTIVE	N Y YANKEES, YANKEE STADIUM	BRONX, NY	10451
NEWMAN, MICHAEL	GUITARIST	SOFFER, 130 W 56TH ST	NEW YORK, NY	10019
NEWMAN, NANETTE	ACTRESS	SEVEN PINES, WENTWORTH	SURREY GU25 4QP	ENGLAND
NEWMAN, PAMELA	ACTRESS	6310 SAN VICENTE BLVD #407	LOS ANGELES, CA	90048
NEWMAN, PAUL	ACTOR-DIRECTOR	1120 5TH AVE #1-C	NEW YORK, NY	10128
NEWMAN, PHYLLIS	ACTRESS	529 W 42ND ST #7-F	NEW YORK, NY	10036
NEWMAN, ROBERT M	TV EXECUTIVE	NBC NEWS, 30 ROCKEFELLER PLAZA	NEW YORK, NY	10112
NEWMAN, THOMAS	COMPOSER	3815 W OLIVE AVE #201	BRUBANK, CA	91505
NEWMAN, TIM D	DIRECTOR	1711 N OGDEN DR	LOS ANGELES, CA	90046
NEWMAN-MANTEE, ANNE	ACTRESS	24632 MALIBU RD	MALIBU, CA	90265
NEWMAN-MINSON, LAUNA	TV EXECUTIVE	ABC-TV, 2040 AVE OF THE STARS	LOS ANGELES, CA	90067
NEWMAR, JULIE	ACTRESS-MODEL	204 S CARMELINA AVE	LOS ANGELES, CA	90049
NEWS, P N	WRESTLER	POST OFFICE BOX 105366	ATLANTA, GA	31348
NEWSOM, TOMMY	TRUMPETER	19315 WELLS DR	TARZANA, CA	91356
NEWSOME, HARRY	FOOTBALL	VIKINGS, 9520 VIKING DR	EDEN PRAIRIE, MN	55344
NEWSOME, VINCE	FOOTBALL	BROWNS, 80 1ST ST	BEREA, OH	44017
NEWSON, MATT	BASEBALL EXECUTIVE	POST OFFICE BOX 4488	WINSTON-SALEM, NC	27115
NEWSON, WARREN	BASEBALL	333 W 35TH ST	CHICAGO, IL	60616
NEWTON, JUICE	SINGER-SONGWRITER	POST OFFICE BOX 25330	NASHVILLE, TN	37203
NEWTON, NATE	FOOTBALL	COWBOYS, 1 COWBOYS PARKWAY	IRVING, TX	75063
NEWTON, RICHARD	WRITER-PRODUCER	14637 VALLEY VISTA BLVD	SHERMAN OAKS, CA	91403
NEWTON, SANDI	ACTRESS-TV HOST	10751 WILSHIRE BLVD #505	LOS ANGELES, CA	90024
NEWTON, TIM	FOOTBALL	BUCCANEERS, 1 BUCCANEER PL	TAMPA, FL	33607
NEWTON, WAYNE	SINGER-ACTOR	6629 S PECOS RD	LAS VEGAS, NV	89120
NEWTON, WILLIAM M	DIRECTOR-PRODUCER	4340 45TH ST S	SAINT PETERSBURG, FL	33711
NEWTON-JOHN, OLIVIA	SINGER-ACTRESS	POST OFFICE BOX 2710	MALIBU, CA	90265
NEY, ERIN	ACTRESS	CARSON/ADLER, 250 W 57TH ST	NEW YORK, NY	10107
NEY, RICHARD	ACTOR	800 S SAN RAFAEL AVE	PASADENA, CA	91105
NEZELEK, ANDY	BASEBALL	POST OFFICE BOX 16683	GREENVILLE, SC	29606
NGOR, DR HAING S	ACTOR	945 N BEAUDRY AVE	LOS ANGELES, CA	90012
NGUYEN, DUSTIN	ACTOR	9301 WILSHIRE BLVD #312	BEVERLY HILLS, CA	90210
NGUYEN, FRANCINE	ACTRESS	8235 SANTA MONICA BLVD #202	LOS ANGELES, CA	90046
NICASTRO, MICHELLE	ACTRESS	10351 SANTA MONICA BLVD #211	LOS ANGELES, CA	90025
NICAUD, PHILIPPE	ACTOR	26 RUE DES PLANTES	PARIS 75014	FRANCE
NICELY, HIAWATHA	BASEBALL EXECUTIVE	POST OFFICE BOX 814	PULASKI, VA	24301
NICHLAUS, JACK	GOLFER	11760 U S HIGHWAY 1 #6	NORTH PALM BEACH, FL	33408
NICHLES, DON	U S SENATOR	601 "D" AVE #201	LAWTON, OK	73501
NICHOLAS, DENISE	ACTRESS	HILL, 932 LONGWOOD AVE	LOS ANGELES, CA	90019
NICHOLAS, JAMES D	WRITER-PRODUCER	1922 GRIFFITH PARK BLVD	LOS ANGELES, CA	90039
NICHOLAS, JOHN GEORGE	DIRECTOR	1 BROOKSIDE CIR	BRONXVILLE, TN	10708
NICHOLAS, JOHN P	DIRECTOR	431 N FULTON AVE	MOUNT VERNON, NY	10552
NICHOLAS, PAUL	ACTOR-SINGER	MARSH, 19 DENMARK ST	LONDON WC2H 8NA	ENGLAND
NICHOLLS, BERNIE	HOCKEY	POST OFFICE BOX 90111	ARLINGTON, TX	76004
NICHOLS, BOB	COMPOSER	1633 W 81ST ST	LOS ANGELES, CA	90047
NICHOLS, BOBBY	GOLFER	PGA SENIORS, 112 T P C BLVD	PONTE VEDRA BEACH, FL	32082
NICHOLS, CARL	BASEBALL	2603 BILLINGS ST	COMPTON, CA	90220
NICHOLS, CHARLES	FILM DIRECTOR	1890 EUCLID AVE	SAN MARINO, CA	91108
NICHOLS, DANA BAKER	COSTUME DESIGNER	13949 VENTURA BLVD #309	SHERMAN OAKS, CA	91423

NICHOLS, DICK	U S CONGRESSMAN	POST OFFICE BOX 1321	MC PHERSON, KS	67460
NICHOLS, GERALD	FOOTBALL	BUCCANEERS, 1 BUCCANEER PL	TAMPA, FL	33607
NICHOLS, NICHELLE	ACTRESS	23281 LEONORA DR	WOODLAND HILLS, CA	91367
NICHOLS, PAUL R	TV EXECUTIVE	HOUR MAGAZINE, 5746 SUNSET BLVD	HOLLYWOOD, CA	90028
NICHOLS, PETER	TV WRITER	STEVENS, 2 TERRETTS PL, UPPER ST	LONDON N1 1QZ	ENGLAND
NICHOLS, ROD	BASEBALL	INDIANS, CLEVELAND STADIUM	CLEVELAND, OH	44114
NICHOLS, ROGER S	COMPOSER	4105 DUNDEE DR	LOS ANGELES, CA	90027
NICHOLS, SCOTT	BASEBALL	POST OFFICE BOX 36407	LOUISVILLE, KY	40233
NICHOLS, STEPHEN	ACTOR	6287 VINE WY	LOS ANGELES, CA	90068
NICHOLS, STEVE	BASEBALL SCOUT	ATHLETICS'S, OAKLAND COLISEUM	OAKLAND, CA	94621
NICHOLSON, BRADLEY	SINGER	CUDE, 519 N HALIFAX AVE	DAYTONA BEACH, FL	32018
NICHOLSON, DANA WHEELER	ACTRESS	11726 SAN VICENTE BLVD #300	LOS ANGELES, CA	90049
NICHOLSON, ERWIN W	TV DIRECTOR	333 E 58TH ST	NEW YORK, NY	10022
NICHOLSON, JACK	ACTOR-DIRECTOR	9911 W PICO BLVD #PH-A	LOS ANGELES, CA	90035
NICHOLSON, JAMES R	FILM DIRECTOR	1248 N CRESCENT HGTS BLVD	LOS ANGELES, CA	90046
NICHOLSON, JOHN J	DIRECTOR	10000 SANTA MONICA BLVD #305	LOS ANGELES, CA	90067
NICHOLSON, ROBERT A	DIRECTOR	4120 NW 26TH TERR	LIGHTHOUSE POINT, FL	33064
NICHOPOULOS, DR GEORGE	DOCTOR	1734 MADISON AVE	MEMPHIS, TN	38014
NICHTERN, CLAIRE	THEATER PRODUCER	75 ROCKEFELLER PLAZA	NEW YORK, NY	10019
NICHTING, CHRIS	BASEBALL	POST OFFICE BOX 28268	SAN ANTONIO, TX	78228
NICITA, WALLIS	FILM PRODUCER	5254 MELROSE AVE #405-D	LOS ANGELES, CA	90038
NICKEL, AL	COSTUME DESIGNER	13949 VENTURA BLVD #309	SHERMAN OAKS, CA	91423
NICKELL, JOHN PAUL	DIRECTOR	DGA, 110 W 57TH ST	NEW YORK, NY	10019
NICKELS, GARY	BASEBALL SCOUT	ORIOLE PARK, 333 W CAMDEN ST	BALTIMORE, MD	21201
NICKENS, DARYL G	TV WRITER	132 S LASKY DR #B	BEVERLY HILLS, CA	90212
NICKERSON, HARDY	FOOTBALL	STEELERS, 300 STADIUM CIR	PITTSBURGH, PA	15212
NICKLAUS, JACK	GOLFER	POST OFFICE BOX 109601	PALM BCH GARDENS, FL	33418
NICKLOUS, MIKE	BASEBALL EXECUTIVE	800 HOME RUN LN	MEMPHIS, TN	38104
NICKOLAOU, VELLO	TV DIRECTOR	ENTERTAINMENT TONIGHT		
		PARAMOUNT TELEVISION		
		5555 MELROSE AVE	LOS ANGELES, CA	90038
NICKS, STEVIE	SINGER-SONGWRITER	345 N MAPLE ST #235	BEVERLY HILLS, CA	90210
NICKSAY, DAVID	DIRECTOR-PRODUCER	POST OFFICE BOX 7210	VENTURA, CA	93006
NICKSON-SOUL, JULIA	ACTRESS	2232 MORENO DR	LOS ANGELES, CA	90039
NICOL, ALEXANDER	ACTOR-DIRECTOR	10601 OHIO AVE	LOS ANGELES, CA	90024
NICOLAU, NICK	FOOTBALL COACH	BILLS, 1 BILLS DR	ORCHARD PARK, NJ	14127
NICOLET, DANIELLE	ACTRESS	8484 WILSHIRE BLVD #530	BEVERLY HILLS, CA	90211
NIECHNIEDOWICZ, PAUL M	DIRECTOR	DGA, 7920 SUNSET BLVD, 6TH FL	LOS ANGELES, CA	90046
NIED, DAVID	BASEBALL	POST OFFICE BOX 6667	RICHMOND, VA	23230
NIEDENFUER, TOM	BASEBALL	9849 DENBIGH DR	BEVERLY HILLS, CA	90210
NIEHAUS, DAVE	SPORTSCASTER	POST OFFICE BOX 4100	SEATTLE, WA	98104
NIEHAUS, LENNIE	COMPOSER	24201 GILMORE ST	CANOGA PARK, CA	91307
NIEKRO, JOE	BASEBALL	39 SHADOW LN	LAKELAND, FL	33813
NIEKRO, PHIL	BASEBALL-MANAGER	6382 NICHOLS RD	FLOWERY BRANCH, GA	30542
NIELSEN, BRIGITTE	ACTRESS	12400 WILSHIRE BLVD #930	LOS ANGELES, CA	90025
NIELSEN, CHRIS	SINGER	POST OFFICE BOX 8768		
		STATION L	EDMONTON, ALT T6E 0B7	CANADA
NIELSEN, JERRY	BASEBALL	ALBANY YANKEES, HERITAGE PARK	ALBANY, NY	12211
NIELSEN, JOHN WARD	DIRECTOR	DGA, 7920 SUNSET BLVD, 6TH FL	LOS ANGELES, CA	90046
NIELSEN, KEVIN	BASEBALL	POST OFFICE BOX 12557	ST PETERSBURG, FL	33733
NIELSEN, LESLIE	ACTOR	1622 VIEWMONT DR	LOS ANGELES, CA	90069
NIELSEN, SHAUN	SINGER	POST OFFICE BOX 25083	NASHVILLE, TN	37202
NIEMANN, RANDY	BASEBALL COACH	POST OFFICE BOX 598	BINGHAMTON, NY	13902
NIEMCEK, BRADLEY B	TV EXECUTIVE	NEWSLINK, 205 LEXINGTON AVE	NEW YORK, NY	10016
NIERENBERG, GEORGE T	TV DIRECTOR-PRODUCER	230 PARK AVE #460	NEW YORK, NY	10169
NIETHAMMER, DARREN	BASEBALL	POST OFFICE BOX 4448	TULSA, OK	74159
NIETO, ROY	BASEBALL	POST OFFICE BOX 1556	ASHEVILLE, NC	28802
NIETO, TOM	BASEBALL COACH	POST OFFICE BOX 11002	CHATTANOOGA, TN	37401
NIEUWENDYK, JOE	HOCKEY	POST OFFICE BOX 1540, STA "M"	CALGARY, ALTA T2P 3BP	CANADA
NIEVES, ERNIE	BASEBALL	POST OFFICE BOX 4669	CHARLESTON, WV	25304
NIEVES, MEL	BASEBALL	POST OFFICE BOX 507	DURHAM, NC	27702
NIGGEMEYER, AL	DIRECTOR	23 SCOTLAND ST	SAN FRANCISCO, CA	94133
NIGHT CROSSING	ROCK & ROLL GROUP	FASTFIRE RECORDS		
		220 E 42ND ST	NEW YORK, NY	10017
NIGHT RANGER	ROCK & ROLL GROUP	POST OFFICE BOX 1000	GLEN ELLEN, CA	95442
NIGHT RIDER	ROCK & ROLL GROUP	POST OFFICE BOX O	EXCELSIOR, MN	55331
NIGHTHAWKS, THE	RHYTHM & BLUES GROUP	POST OFFICE BOX 210103	SAN FRANCISCO, CA	94121
NIGITA, SALVATORE	DIRECTOR	DGA, 110 W 57TH ST	NEW YORK, NY	10019
NIGRO, JOE	BASEBALL SCOUT	POST OFFICE BOX 4100	SEATTLE, WA	98104
NIGRO, ROBERT	TV DIRECTOR	317 W 103RD ST	NEW YORK, NY	10025
NIGRO-CHACON, GIOVANNA	TV WRITER-DIRECTOR	1341 SINALOA DR	GLENDALE, CA	91207
NILAN, CHRIS	HOCKEY	BRUINS, 150 CAUSEWAY ST	BOSTON, MA	02114
NILE, WILLIE	SINGER	WM MORRIS, 1350 AVE OF AMERICAS	NEW YORK, NY	10019
NILES, WENDELL	ANNOUNCER-TV PERS	10357 VALLEY SPRING LN	NORTH HOLLYWOOD, CA	91602
NILSON, LOY	TV DIRECTOR	1275 15TH ST	FORT LEE, NJ	07024
NILSSON, DAVE	BASEBALL	2850 W 20TH AVE	DENVER, CO	80211
NILSSON, HARRY	SINGER-SONGWRITER	23960 LONG VALLEY RD	HIDDEN VALLEY, CA	91302
NIMESGERN, JOHN	PHILOSOPHER-COACH	2801 MEADOW LARK DR	SAN DIEGO, CA	92123
NIMMO, DEREK	ACTOR	BURNETT, 42-43 GRAFTON HOUSE		
		2-3 GOLDEN SQ	LONDON W1R 3AD	ENGLAND
NIMOY, LEONARD	ACT-WRI-DIR	ICM, 8899 BEVERLY BLVD	LOS ANGELES, CA	90048
NIP DIVERS, THE	ROCK & ROLL GROUP	22714 SUSANA CT	TORRANCE, CA	90505
NIPAR, YVETTE	ACTRESS	1999 AVE OF THE STARS #2850	LOS ANGELES, CA	90067
NIPPER, AL	BASEBALL	5105 VILLE MARIA LN	HAZELWOOD, MO	63042
NIPPERT, LOUIS	BASEBALL EXECUTIVE	REDS, 100 RIVERFRONT STADIUM	CINCINNATI, OH	45202

NIPPERT, MRS LOUIS	BASEBALL EXECUTIVE	REDS, 100 RIVERFRONT STADIUM	CINCINNATI, OH	45202
NIRVANA DEVILS, THE	ROCK & ROLL GROUP	LINTRUPER STR 39	1000 BERLIN 49	GERMANY
NISHIJIMA, TAKAYURI	BASEBALL	POST OFFICE BOX 4370	SALINAS, CA	93912
NISSALKE, TOM	BASKETBALL COACH	310 N KINGS DR	CHARLOTTE, NC	28204
NITECAPS, THE	ROCK & ROLL GROUP	3 E 54TH ST #1400	NEW YORK, NY	10022
NITTY GRITTY DIRT BAND, THE	C & W GROUP	4155 E JEWELL AVE #412	DENVER, CO	80222
NIVEN, KIP	ACTOR	20781 BIG ROCK DR	MALIBU, CA	90265
NIVEN, LARRY	WRITER	3961 VANALDEN AVE	TARZANA, CA	91356
NIVER, JAMES	TV DIRECTOR	3878 FREDONIA DR	LOS ANGELES, CA	90068
NIXON, AGNES E	TV WRITER-PRODUCER	774 CONESTOGA RD	ROSEMONT, PA	19010
NIXON, DONELL	BASEBALL	4385 TUTT BLVD	COLORADO SPRINGS, CO	80922
NIXON, JAMES	SINGER-GUITARIST	2830 BRONTE AVE	NASHVILLE, TN	37216
NIXON, NORM	BASKETBALL	607 MARHUERITA AVE	SANTA MONICA, CA	90402
NIXON, OTIS	BASEBALL	POST OFFICE BOX 23, OLD HWY 74	EVERGREEN, NC	28438
NIXON, PATRICIA	FIRST LADY-AUTHORESS	577 CHESTNUT RIDGE RD	WOODCLIFF LAKE, NJ	07675
NIXON, RICHARD	PRESIDENT-AUTHOR	577 CHESTNUT RIDGE RD	WOODCLIFF LAKE, NJ	07675
NIXON, RUSS	BASEBALL-COACH	POST OFFICE BOX 4100	SEATTLE, WA	98104
NOAH, PETER R	TV WRITER	523 PACIFIC ST	SANTA MONICA, CA	90405
NOAH, ROBERT	TV WRITER-PRODUCER	1023 BENEDICT CANYON DR	BEVERLY HILLS, CA	90210
NOBLE, BRIAN	FOOTBALL	PACKERS, 1265 LOMBARDI AVE	GREEN BAY, WI	54307
NOBLE, CHELSEA	ACTRESS	8730 SUNSET BLVD #220-W	LOS ANGELES, CA	90069
NOBLE, JAMES	ACTOR	80 BYWATER LN	BLACK ROCK, CT	06605
NOBLE, JON	FILM WRITER-DIRECTOR	RAFFLES HOTEL #185		
		1 BEACH RD	SINGAPORE 0718	CHINA
NOBLE, KARA	ACTRESS-SINGER	JAMES, 22 WESTBERE RD	LONDON NW2 3SR,	ENGLAND
NOBLE, KATINA	ACTRESS	41 BALMORAL RD, SAINT ANDREWS	BRISTOL BS7 988	ENGLAND
NOBLE, PAUL	TV PRODUCER	WNEW-TV, 205 E 67TH ST	NEW YORK, NY	10021
NOBLE, THOM	FILM EDITOR	POST OFFICE BOX 5617	BEVERLY HILLS, CA	90213
NOBLES, VERNON	FILM DIRECTOR	MTA, 9320 WILSHIRE BL, 3RD FL	BEVERLY HILLS, CA	90212
NOBOA, JUNIOR	BASEBALL	METS, 126TH ST & ROOSEVELT AVE	FLUSHING, NY	11368
NOCHIMSON, SHIRLEY	TV DIRECTOR-PRODUCER	CWT PRODS, 17 E 45TH ST	NEW YORK, NY	10017
NOCKS, ARNOLD J	DIRECTOR	RURAL DELIVERY #1, BOX 103	KINTERSVILLE, PA	18930
NOEL, CHRIS	ACTRESS	6100 HOLLYWOOD BLVD #201	HOLLYWOOD, FL	33024
NOEL, DENISE	ACTRESS	GEORGE LAMBERT AGENCE		
		13 BIS AVE LA MOTTE PIQUET	PARIS 75007	FRANCE
NOEL, MAGALI	ACTRESS	4 RUE VALENTIN HAVY	PARIS 75015	FRANCE
NOEL, RICHARD	COMPOSER	864 AMBER DR	CAMARILLO, CA	93010
NOFTE, DONAVAN MERLE	DIRECTOR	DGA, 7920 SUNSET BLVD, 6TH FL	LOS ANGELES, CA	90046
NOGA, AL	FOOTBALL	VIKINGS, 9520 VIKING DR	EDEN PRAIRIE, MN	55344
NOGA, NIKO	FOOTBALL	LIONS, 1200 FEATHERSTONE RD	PONTIAC, MI	48432
NOGULICH, NATALIA	ACTRESS	1999 AVE OF THE STARS #2850	LOS ANGELES, CA	90067
NOHUCHI, DR THOMAS	CORONER	1110 AVOCA AVE	PASADENA, CA	91105
NOKES, MATT	BASEBALL	N Y YANKEES, YANKEE STADIUM	BRONX, NY	10451
NOLAN, DARIN	BASEBALL	POST OFFICE BOX 1110	MYRTLE BEACH, SC	29578
NOLAN, DICK	FOOTBALL COACH	COWBOYS, 1 COWBOYS PARKWAY	IRVING, TX	75063
NOLAN, JEANETTE	ACTRESS	1417 SAMOA WY	LAGUNA BEACH, CA	92651
NOLAN, KATHLEEN	ACTRESS	360 E 55TH ST #PH	NEW YORK, NY	10022
NOLAN, KENNY	SINGER-SONGWRITER	BENNETT, 211 S BEVERLY DR	BEVERLY HILLS, CA	90219
NOLAN, MIKE	FOOTBALL COACH	BRONCOS, 13655 BRONCOS PKWY	ENGLEWOOD, CO	80112
NOLAN, OWEN	HOCKEY	NORDIQUES, 2205 AVE DU COLISEE	QUEBEC, QUE G1L 4W7	CANADA
NOLAN, WILLIAM F	TV WRITER	5301 JOHN DODSON DR	AGOURA HILLS, CA	91301
NOLAND, J D	BASEBALL	POST OFFICE BOX 1420	WICHITA, KS	67201
NOLIN, MICHAEL FARRELL	WRITER-PRODUCER	7890 WILLOW GLEN RD	LOS ANGELES, CA	90046
NOLL, CHUCK	FOOTBALL COACH	STEELERS, 300 STADIUM CIR	PITTSBURGH, PA	15212
NOLTE, ERIC	BASEBALL	2850 W 20TH AVE	DENVER, CO	80211
NOLTE, NICK	ACTOR	29555 RAINSFORD PL	MALIBU, CA	90265
NOMURA, DON	BASEBALL EXECUTIVE	POST OFFICE BOX 4370	SALINAS, CA	93912
NOONAN, DANNY	FOOTBALL	COWBOYS, 1 COWBOYS PARKWAY	IRVING, TX	75063
NOONAN, KERRY	ACTRESS	6565 SUNSET BLVD #300	LOS ANGELES, CA	90028
NOONE, KATHLEEN	ACTRESS	130 W 42ND ST #1804	NEW YORK, NY	10036
NOONE, PETER	SINGER-ACTOR	9265 ROBIN LN	LOS ANGELES, CA	90069
NOONOO, BOB	TV WRITER	9528 BOLTON RD	LOS ANGELES, CA	90034
NORCROSS, CLAYTON	ACTOR	951 GALLOWAY ST	PACIFIC PALISADES, CA	90272
NORD THE BARBARIAN	WRESTLER	SEE - BERZERKER, THE		
NORDEN, CHRISTER	COMPOSER	POST OFFICE BOX 4663	PANORAMA CITY, CA	91412
NORDEN, DENIS	ACTOR-WRITER	YOUNG, 31 KING'S RD	LONDON SW3 4RP	ENGLAND
NORDMARK, ROBERT	HOCKEY	CANUCKS, 100 N RENFREW ST	VANCOUVER, BC V5K 3N7	CANADA
NORELL, JAMES E	TV WRITER	151 S EL CAMINO DR	BEVERLY HILLS, CA	90212
NORELL, MICHAEL	TV WRITER	151 S EL CAMINO DR	BEVERLY HILLS, CA	90212
NORFORD, GEORGE E	TV EXECUTIVE	WESTINGHOUSE, 888 7TH AVE	NEW YORK, NY	10106
NORIEGA, GEN MANUEL	GENERAL	INMATE #38699-079		
		METROPOLITAN CORRECTIONAL CTR		
		15801 SW 137TH AVE	MIAMI, FL	33177
NORIEGA, REY	BASEBALL	ALBANY YANKEES, HERITAGE PARK	ALBANY, NY	12211
NORLAND, DEAN E	NEWS CORRESPONDENT	ABC NEWS, 1717 DE SALES ST, NW	WASHINGTON, DC	20036
NORMAN, BARRY	TV WRITER	BROWN, 162-168 REGENT ST	LONDON W1R 5TB	ENGLAND
NORMAN, BEN	DIRECTOR	1221 SUNSET PLAZA DR #11	LOS ANGELES, CA	90069
NORMAN, BRUCE	WRITER-PRODUCER	14 THE RYDE, HATFIELD	HERTS	ENGLAND
NORMAN, CAROL	ACTRESS	405 MIDLAND AVE	GARFIELD, NJ	07026
NORMAN, DAN	BASEBALL-COACH	POST OFFICE BOX 1886	COLUMBUS, GA	31902
NORMAN, DAVID J	DIRECTOR	258 BROADWAY	NEW YORK, NY	10007
NORMAN, GREG	GOLFER	POST OFFICE BOX 109601	PALM BCH GARDENS, FL	33418
NORMAN, JIM ED	MUSIC ARRANGER	22110 CLARENDON ST #101	WOODLAND HILLS, CA	91367
NORMAN, JUNIOR	SINGER	PROCESS, 439 WILEY AVE	FRANKLIN, PA	16323
NORMAN, KEN	BASKETBALL	CLIPPERS, 3939 S FIGUEROA ST	LOS ANGELES, CA	90037

Name	Occupation	Address	City	Zip
NORMAN, KENNY	BASEBALL	POST OFFICE BOX 661	KENOSHA, WI	53141
NORMAN, LES	BASEBALL	POST OFFICE BOX 464	APPLETON, WI	54912
NORMAN, MARC B	WRITER-PRODUCER	28 LATIMER RD	SANTA MONICA, CA	90402
NORMAN, NELSON	BASEBALL-INSTRUCTOR	EXPOS, 4545 DE COUBERTIN AVE	MONTREAL, QUE H1V 3P2	CANADA
NORMAN, PETER RIES	DIRECTOR	WEST HEBRON RD	SALEM, NY	12865
NORMAN, THEODORE	COMPOSER	451 WESTMOUNT DR	LOS ANGELES, CA	90048
NORMAN, ZACK	ACTOR	STONE MANNERS, 9113 SUNSET BLVD	LOS ANGELES, CA	90069
NORMINGTON, JOHN	ACTOR	BROWNE, 13 SAINT MARTINS RD	LONDON SW9 0SP	ENGLAND
NORR, CARL	DIRECTOR	DGA, 110 W 57TH ST	NEW YORK, NY	10019
NORRIS, BILL	BASEBALL	POST OFFICE BOX 1718	NEW BRITAIN, CT	06050
NORRIS, CHRISTOPHER	ACTRESS	9165 SUNSET BLVD #202	LOS ANGELES, CA	90069
NORRIS, CHUCK	ACTOR	18653 VENTURA BLVD #751	TARZANA, CA	91356
NORRIS, JOE	BASEBALL	POST OFFICE BOX 6748	ROCKFORD, IL	61125
NORRIS, MIKE	ACTOR	1930 CENTURY PARK W #403	LOS ANGELES, CA	90067
NORRIS, PATRICIA	COSTUME DESIGNER	POST OFFICE BOX 1166	PACIFIC PALISADES, CA	90272
NORTE, RUBEN	TV DIRECTOR	ENTERTAINMENT TONIGHT		
		PARAMOUNT TELEVISION		
		5555 MELROSE AVE	LOS ANGELES, CA	90038
NORTH, ALEX	COMPOSER	630 RESOLANO DR	PACIFIC PALISADES, CA	90272
NORTH, BARBARA	ACTRESS	19133 OXNARD ST	TARZANA, CA	91356
NORTH, HOPE	ACTRESS	RAPER, 159 N SHOSHONE ST	FLAGSTAFF, AZ	86001
NORTH, JAY	ACTOR	11532 CHIQUITA ST	NORTH HOLLYWOOD, CA	91604
NORTH, JAY	BASEBALL COACH	POST OFFICE BOX 12557	ST PETERSBURG, FL	33733
NORTH, KIM	ACTRESS	247 S BEVERLY DR #102	BEVERLY HILLS, CA	90210
NORTH, LAMAR	BASEBALL SCOUT	ORIOLE PARK, 333 W CAMDEN ST	BALTIMORE, MD	21201
NORTH, LT COL OLIVER	LIEUTENANT COLONEL	703 KENTLAND DR	GREAT FALLS, VA	22066
NORTH, NOELLE	ACTRESS	13335 CHANDLER BLVD	VAN NUYS, CA	91401
NORTH, SHEREE	ACTRESS	27 VILLAGE PARK WY	SANTA MONICA, CA	90405
NORTH, STEVEN	ACTOR-WRITER	19133 OXNARD ST	TARZANA, CA	91356
NORTHAM, JEREMY	ACTOR	HEATH, PARAMOUNT HOUSE		
		162-170 WARDOUR ST	LONDON W1V 3AT	ENGLAND
NORTHERN GOLD	C & W GROUP	1300 DIVISION ST #103-A	NASHVILLE, TN	37203
NORTHERN PIKES	ROCK & ROLL GROUP	41 BRITAIN ST #200	TORONTO, ONT M5A 1R7	CANADA
NORTHROP, WAYNE	ACTOR	21919 W CANON DR	TOPANGA CANYON, CA	90290
NORTHSHIELD, ROBERT	TV WRITER-PRODUCER	CBS-TV, 524 W 57TH ST	NEW YORK, NY	10019
NORTON, BILL W L	FILM WRITER-DIRECTOR	151 S EL CAMINO DR	BEVERLY HILLS, CA	90212
NORTON, CHARLES	TV DIRECTOR	2403 CRESTVIEW DR	HOLLYWOOD, CA	90046
NORTON, DON W	DIRECTOR	5332 S SHONE DR	CHICAGO, IL	60637
NORTON, DOUGLAS	AUDITOR	STATE CAPITOL, 1700 W WASHINGTON	PHOENIX, AZ	85007
NORTON, ELEANOR ELIAS	SCREENWRITER	8955 BEVERLY BLVD	WEST HOLLYWOOD, CA	90048
NORTON, ELEANOR HOLMES	U S DELEGATE	1631 LONGWORTH HOUSE OFF BLDG	WASHINGTON, DC	20515
NORTON, GAIL	ATTORNEY GENERAL	STATE CAPITOL BUILDING	DENVER, CO	80203
NORTON, JEFF	HOCKEY	NASSAU VETS MEMORIAL COLISEUM	UNIONDALE, NY	11553
NORTON, KEN	ACTOR-BOXER	16 S PECK DR	LAGUNA NIGUEL, CA	92677
NORTON, KEN	FOOTBALL	COWBOYS, 1 COWBOYS PARKWAY	IRVING, TX	75063
NORTON, ROSANNA	COSTUME DESIGNER	13949 VENTURA BLVD #309	SHERMAN OAKS, CA	91423
NORTON, ROSE MARIE	ACTRESS	245 W 75TH ST	NEW YORK, NY	10023
NORTON, WILLIAM LLOYD	FILM WRITER-DIRECTOR	2509 OCEAN FRONT WALK	VENICE, CA	90291
NORTON BUFFALO STAMPEDE	ROCK & ROLL GROUP	POST OFFICE BOX 2489	SAN RAFAEL, CA	94901
NORTON-TAYLOR, JUDY	ACTRESS-MODEL	6767 FOREST LAWN DR #115	LOS ANGELES, CA	90068
NORVET, ROBERT W	FILM EXECUTIVE	534 AVONDALE AVE	LOS ANGELES, CA	90049
NORVILLE, DEBORAH	BROADCAST JOURNALIST	829 PARK AVE #10-A	NEW YORK, NY	10021
NORWICH, CASMERA J	TV-COMEDY WRITER	601 W 163RD ST #1106	NEW YORK, NY	10032
NORWOOD, AUDRIANNE	ACTRESS	5657 WILSHIRE BLVD #290	LOS ANGELES, CA	90036
NORWOOD, LEE	HOCKEY	POST OFFICE BOX 504	EAST RUTHERFORD, NJ	07073
NORWOOD, SCOTT	FOOTBALL	BILLS, 1 BILLS DR	ORCHARD PARK, NJ	14127
NOSEK, RANDY	BASEBALL	POST OFFICE BOX 2785	LAKELAND, FL	33806
NOSSECK, NOEL	WRITER-PRODUCER	20406 SEABOARD RD	MALIBU, CA	90265
NOSSEK, JOE	BASEBALL-COACH	333 W 35TH ST	CHICAGO, IL	60616
NOTEY, JANET COLE	ACTRESS	1831 DEERHILL TRAIL	TOPANGA, CA	90290
NOTO, LORE	THEATER PRODUCER	181 SULLIVAN ST	NEW YORK, NY	10012
NOURI, MICHAEL	ACTOR	6036 HAZELHURST PL #C	NORTH HOLLYWOOD, CA	91606
NOVACEK, JAY	FOOTBALL	COWBOYS, 1 COWBOYS PARKWAY	IRVING, TX	75063
NOVACK, SHELLY	ACTRESS	390 VANCE ST	PACIFIC PALISADES, CA	90272
NOVAK, FRANK	FOOTBALL COACH	OILERS, 6910 FANNIN ST	HOUSTON, TX	77070
NOVAK, KIM	ACTRESS	POST OFFICE BOX 925	MALIBU, CA	90265
NOVAK, RALPH	WRITER-EDITOR	PEOPLE/TIME & LIFE BLDG		
		ROCKEFELLER CENTER	NEW YORK, NY	10020
NOVAK, ROBERT	NEWS REPORTER	1750 PENNSYLVANIA AVE #1312, NW	WASHINGTON, DC	20006
NOVAK, STAN	BASKETBALL	THE PALACE OF AUBURN HILLS		
		2 CHAMPIONSHIP DR	AUBURN HILLS, MI	48326
NOVAKOVICH, ALEX	ACTRESS-MODEL	2118 CALIFORNIA AVE	SANTA MONICA, CA	90403
NOVECK, FIMA	TV DIRECTOR-PRODUCER	161 E 61ST ST	NEW YORK, NY	10021
NOVELLO, DON	ACT-WRI-COMED	POST OFFICE BOX 245	FAIRFAX, CA	94930
NOVELLO, JOSEPH	TV DIRECTOR	84 MIDVALE AVE	MILLINGTON, NJ	07946
NOVIK, M S	DIRECTOR	300 W 23RD ST	NEW YORK, NY	10011
NOVOA, RAFAEL	BASEBALL	5999 E VAN BUREN ST	PHOENIX, AZ	85008
NOVOSELSKY, BRENT	FOOTBALL	VIKINGS, 9520 VIKING DR	EDEN PRAIRIE, MN	55344
NOWAK, HENRY J	U S CONGRESSMAN	U S COURTHOUSE, ROOM 212	BUFFALO, NY	14202
NOWAK, MICHAEL	CONDUCTOR	16733 BOLLINGER DR	PACIFIC PALISADES, CA	90272
NOWELL, DAVID	CINEMATOGRAPHER	7715 SUNSET BLVD #150	LOS ANGELES, CA	90046
NOWORYTA, STEVE	BASEBALL EXECUTIVE	333 W 35TH ST	CHICAGO, IL	60616
NOXON, NICOLAS L	WRITER-PRODUCER	11139 HORTENSE ST	NORTH HOLLYWOOD, CA	91602
NOYCE, PHILLIP	FILM DIRECTOR	11726 SAN VICENTE BLVD #300	LOS ANGELES, CA	90049
NRBO	C & W GROUP	SEE - N R B O		

Name	Occupation	Address	City	Zip
NRBQ & THE WHOLE WHEAT HORNS	RHYTHM & BLUES GROUP	POST OFFICE BOX 210103	SAN FRANCISCO, CA	94121
NUCKLES, WILLIAM PAUL	DIRECTOR	CONDOR CRAG STUNT RD	CALABASAS, CA	91302
NUCLEAR ASSAULT	ROCK & ROLL GROUP	POST OFFICE BOX 4164	OSBORNVILLE, NJ	08723
NUELL, DAVID	TV DIRECTOR	ENTERTAINMENT TONIGHT		
		PARAMOUNT TELEVISION		
		5555 MELROSE AVE	LOS ANGELES, CA	90038
NUGENT, BARNEY	BASEBALL TRAINER	POST OFFICE BOX 3449	SCRANTON, PA	18505
NUGENT, NELLE	THEATER PRODUCER	1501 BROADWAY	NEW YORK, NY	10036
NUGENT, TED	SINGER-GUITARIST	POST OFFICE BOX 15108	ANN ARBOR, MI	49106
NUMAN, GARY	SINGER-SONGWRITER	39-41 NORTH RD	LONDON N7 7DP	ENGLAND
NUMMINEN, TEPPO	HOCKEY	JETS, 15-1430 MAROONS RD	WINNIPEG, MAN R3G 0L5	CANADA
NUNEVILLER, TOM	BASEBALL	POST OFFICE BOX 15050	READING, PA	19612
NUNEZ, ALEX	BASEBALL	14100 SIX MILE CYPRESS PKWY	FORT MYERS, FL	33912
NUNEZ, CAMILO	BASEBALL SCOUT	ORIOLE PARK, 333 W CAMDEN ST	BALTIMORE, MD	21201
NUNEZ, EDWIN	BASEBALL	2850 W 20TH AVE	DENVER, CO	80211
NUNLEY, LOUIS	MUSIC ARRANGER	POST OFFICE BOX 2112	NASHVILLE, TN	37214
NUNLEY, LOUISE	SINGER	POST OFFICE BOX 2112	NASHVILLE, TN	37214
NUNN, ALICE	ACTRESS	976 N LARRABEE ST #228	LOS ANGELES, CA	90069
NUNN, FREDDIE JOE	FOOTBALL	POST OFFICE BOX 888	PHOENIX, AZ	85001
NUNN, SAM	U S SENATOR	915 MAIN ST	PERRY, GA	31069
NUNN, TERRI	ACTRESS	4293 VINTON AVE	CULVER CITY, CA	90230
NUNS, THE	ROCK & ROLL GROUP	JEM RECORDS COMPANY		
		3619 KENNEDY RD	SOUTH PLAINFIELD, NJ	07080
NUREYEV, RUDOLF	ACTOR-DANCER	GORLINSKY, 35 DOVER ST	LONDON W1	ENGLAND
NURMI, MAILA	ACTRESS	6569 S VERMONT AVE	LOS ANGELES, CA	90044
NURSE, KARL	DIRECTOR	294 SHAWMUT AVE	BOSTON, MA	02116
NUSSBAUM, STANLEY	COMPOSER	2051 BENTLEY AVE #104	LOS ANGELES, CA	90025
NUSSLE, JAMES ALLEN	U S CONGRESSMAN	POST OFFICE BOX 445	MARION, IA	52302
NUTTER ADAMSON, MAYF	ACTOR	POST OFFICE BOX 69590	LOS ANGELES, CA	90069
NUTZLE, FUTZIE	CARTOONIST	POST OFFICE BOX 325	AROMAS, CA	95004
NUXHALL, JOE	BASEBALL-ANNOUNCER	REDS, 100 RIVERFRONT STADIUM	CINCINNATI, OH	45202
NUYEN, FRANCE	ACTRESS	MORELL, 1800 FRANKLIN CYN TERR	BEVERLY HILLS, CA	90210
NYBY, CHRISTIAN, III	DIRECTOR	1030 GREEN LN	LA CANADA, CA	91011
NYE, ANITA	SONGWRITER	1241 CORSICA DR	PACIFIC PALISADES, CA	90272
NYE, BARRY D	TV DIRECTOR-EDITOR	11317 BLIX ST	NORTH HOLLYWOOD, CA	91602
NYE, CARRIE	ACTRESS	109 E 79TH ST	NEW YORK, NY	10019
NYE, COTTON	BASEBALL SCOUT	POST OFFICE BOX 7575	PHILADELPHIA, PA	19101
NYE, DOROTHY	WRITER-PRODUCER	POST OFFICE BOX 7141	CARMEL, CA	93921
NYE, LOUIS	ACTOR-COMEDIAN	1241 CORSICA DR	PACIFIC PALISADES, CA	90272
NYGREN, CARRIE	MODEL	ELITE MODELS, 111 E 22ND ST	NEW YORK, NY	10010
NYIRI, DANIEL	FILM DIRECTOR	PHOENIX FILMS, 6 FLITCROFT ST	LONDON WC2 8DJ	ENGLAND
NYKVIST, SVEN	CINEMATOGRAPHER	4 FLORAGATAN	STOCKHOLM 11431	SWEDEN
NYLONS, THE	ROCK & ROLL GROUP	366 ADELAIDE ST E #436	TORONTO, ONT M5A 3X9	CANADA
NYMAN, JERRY	BASEBALL-COACH	POST OFFICE BOX 594	WELLAND, ONT L3B 5R3	CANADA
NYMAN, MICHAEL	COMPOSER	STONE, HALLINAN, MC DONALD, LTD		
		100 EBUIRY ST	LONDON SW1W 9QD	ENGLAND
NYPE, RUSSELL	ACTOR	178 E 78TH ST	NEW YORK, NY	10021
NYRO, LAURA	SINGER-SONGWRITER	POST OFFICE BOX 186	SHOREHAM, NY	11786

Name	Occupation	Address	City	Zip
O, GARY	SINGER-SONGWRITER	SEE - GARY O		
O, RODNEY & JOE COOLEY	RAP DUO-RAPWRITERS	SEE - RODNEY O & JOE COOLEY		
O'BANNON, DAN	FILM WRITER-DIRECTOR	MORTON AGY, 1105 GLENDON AVE	LOS ANGELES, CA	90024
O'BANNON, FRANK L	LT GOVERNOR	STATE HOUSE BUILDING	INDIANAPOLIS, IN	46204
O'BIREN, DAN	BASEBALL SCOUT	POST OFFICE BOX 288	HOUSTON, TX	77001
O'BRIAN, HUGH	ACTOR	3195 BENEDICT CANYON DR	BEVERLY HILLS, CA	90210
O'BRIEN, CHARLIE	BASEBALL	METS, 126TH ST & ROOSEVELT AVE	FLUSHING, NY	11368
O'BRIEN, CUBBY	ACTOR	11274 DULCET AVE	NORTHRIDGE, CA	91324
O'BRIEN, DANIEL	BASEBALL EXECUTIVE	POST OFFICE BOX 2000	ANAHEIM, CA	92803
O'BRIEN, DAVID	ACTOR	370 LEXINGTON AVE #707	NEW YORK, NY	10017
O'BRIEN, JACK	DIRECTOR	POST OFFICE BOX 2171	SAN DIEGO, CA	92112
O'BRIEN, JIM	TV DIRECTOR	DAISH, 83 EASTBOURNE MEWS	LONDON W2 6LQ	ENGLAND
O'BRIEN, JOHN	BASEBALL	POST OFFICE BOX 3004	SPRINGFIELD, IL	62708
O'BRIEN, KEN	FOOTBALL	N Y JETS, 1000 FULTON AVE	HEMPSTEAD, NY	11550
O'BRIEN, LIAM	WRITER	2259 SAN YSIDRO DR	BEVERLY HILLS, CA	90210
O'BRIEN, MARGARET	ACTRESS	1250 LA PERESA DR	THOUSAND OAKS, CA	91362
O'BRIEN, MARIA	ACTRESS	1930 CENTURY PARK W #403	LOS ANGELES, CA	90067
O'BRIEN, PETE	BASEBALL	POST OFFICE BOX 4100	SEATTLE, WA	98104
O'BRIEN, PETER	FILM PRODUCER	264 SEATON ST	TORONTO, ONT M5A 2T4	CANADA
O'BRIEN, TIM	NEWS CORRESPONDENT	ABC NEWS, 1717 DE SALES ST, NW	WASHINGTON, DC	20036
O'BRIEN, TIM	SINGER	POST OFFICE BOX 6025	NEWPORT NEWS, VA	23606
O'BRYAN	SINGER-SONGWRITER	POST OFFICE BOX 48306	LOS ANGELES, CA	90048
O'BRYAN, FRAN	TALENT AGENT	9085 W 3RD ST #303	LOS ANGELES, CA	90048
O'CALLAGHAN, RICHARD	ACTOR	HEATH, PARAMOUNT HOUSE		
		162-170 WARDOUR ST	LONDON W1V 3AT	ENGLAND
O'CON, PAULINE	CASTING DIRECTOR	ABC-TV, 2040 AVE OF THE STARS	LOS ANGELES, CA	90067
O'CONNELL, ELINORE	SINGER-ACTRESS	6310 SAN VICENTE BLVD #407	LOS ANGELES, CA	90048
O'CONNELL, HELEN	SINGER	1260 S BEVERLY GLEN BLVD	LOS ANGELES, CA	90024

Name	Occupation	Address	City	Zip/Country
O'CONNELL, JERRY	ACTOR	160 PERTH AVE	TORONTO, ONT M6P 3X5	CANADA
O'CONNELL, SHAWN	BASEBALL	POST OFFICE BOX 418	SAINT CHARLES, IL	60174
O'CONNELL, TAAFFE	ACTRESS	11846 VENTURA BLVD #100	STUDIO CITY, CA	91604
O'CONNOR, CARROLL	ACT-WRI-DIR-PROD	30826 BROAD BEACH RD	MALIBU, CA	90265
O'CONNOR, DES	SINGER	235-241 REGENT ST	LONDON W1A 2JT	ENGLAND
O'CONNOR, DONALD	ACTOR-DIRECTOR	POST OFFICE BOX 4524	NORTH HOLLYWOOD, CA	91607
O'CONNOR, GLYNNIS	ACTRESS	8957 NORMA PL	LOS ANGELES, CA	90069
O'CONNOR, HUGH	ACTOR	30826 BROAD BEACH RD	MALIBU, CA	90265
O'CONNOR, JACK	BASEBALL	POST OFFICE BOX 430	YUCCA VALLEY, CA	92284
O'CONNOR, JOHN J	TV CRITIC	N Y TIMES, 229 W 43RD ST	NEW YORK, NY	10036
O'CONNOR, KEVIN	BASEBALL	POST OFFICE BOX 507	DURHAM, NC	27702
O'CONNOR, KEVIN	BASEBALL UMPIRE	POST OFFICE BOX 608	GROVE CITY, OH	43123
O'CONNOR, MARK	MUSICIAN	CASE, 1016 16TH AVE S	NASHVILLE, TN	37212
O'CONNOR, MICHAEL	ACTOR	NBC-TV, "DAYS OF OUR LIVES"		
		3000 W ALAMEDA AVE	BURBANK, CA	91523
O'CONNOR, PAT	BASEBALL EXECUTIVE	POST OFFICE BOX 422229	KISSIMMEE, FL	34742
O'CONNOR, RICHARD L	DIRECTOR	7247 WHITSETT AVE #1	STUDIO CITY, CA	91604
O'CONNOR, RICHARD L	TV PRODUCER	14937 VENTURA BLVD #201	SHERMAN OAKS, CA	91403
O'CONNOR, SANDRA DAY	SUPREME COURT JUDGE	1 1ST ST, NE	WASHINGTON, DC	20543
O'CONNOR, TIM	ACTOR	10000 SANTA MONICA BLVD #305	LOS ANGELES, CA	90067
O'DANIEL, JIM H	COSTUME DESIGNER	445 1/2 RIALTO AVE	VENICE, CA	90291
O'DAY, ALAN	SINGER	9200 SUNSET BLVD #222	LOS ANGELES, CA	90069
O'DAY, MOLLY	ACTRESS	POST OFFICE BOX 2123	AVILA BEACH, CA	93424
O'DELL, HOLLY	SINGER	1711 18TH AVE S #C-1	NASHVILLE, TN	37212
O'DELL, KENNY	SINGER-SONGWRITER	GELFAND/BRESLAUER		
		7 MUSIC CIRCLE N	NASHVILLE, TN	37203
O'DELL, PAUL	TV DIRECTOR	35 NORMANDY AVE, HIGH BARNET	HERTFORDSHIRE	ENGLAND
O'DELL, TONY	ACTOR	417 GRIFFITH PARK DR	BURBANK, CA	91506
O'DONNELL, CHRIS	ACTRESS	UTA, 9560 WILSHIRE BL, 5TH FL	BEVERLY HILLS, CA	90212
O'DONNELL, ERIK	BASEBALL	POST OFFICE BOX 9194	HAMPTON, VA	23670
O'DONNELL, NEIL	FOOTBALL	STEELERS, 300 STADIUM CIR	PITTSBURGH, PA	15212
O'DONNELL, ROBERT H	DIRECTOR	28 W 120 ROBIN LN	WEST CHICAGO, IL	60185
O'DONNELL, STEVE	BASEBALL	POST OFFICE BOX 2887	VERO BEACH, FL	32961
O'DONNELL, TIMOTHY J	TV WRITER	1620 VISTA DR	GLENDALE, CA	91201
O'DONOGHUE, JOHN	BASEBALL	POST OFFICE BOX 230	HAGERSTOWN, MD	21740
O'DONOGHUE, JOHN, SR	BASEBALL-COACH	153 KIRKCALDY DR	ELKTON, MD	21921
O'DONOGHUE, MICHAEL	TV WRITER-PRODUCER	1619 BROADWAY #402	NEW YORK, NY	10019
O'DOWD, DAN	BASEBALL EXECUTIVE	INDIANS, CLEVELAND STADIUM	CLEVELAND, OH	44114
O'DRISCOLL, MARTHA	ACTRESS	APPLETON, 22 INDIAN CIRCLE DR		
		INDIAN CREEK VILLAGE	MIAMI BEACH, FL	33154
O'FARRELL, LEO FRANCIS	TV DIRECTOR	1713 N NORTH PARK AVE #4	CHICAGO, IL	60614
O'FLAHERTY, DENNIS M	SCREENWRITER	8955 BEVERLY BLVD	WEST HOLLYWOOD, CA	90048
O'GARA, MIKE	TV PRODUCER	ENTERTAINMENT TONIGHT		
		PARAMOUNT TELEVISION		
		5555 MELROSE AVE	LOS ANGELES, CA	90038
O'GRADY, GAIL	ACTRESS	9229 SUNSET BLVD #311	LOS ANGELES, CA	90069
O'HALLAREN, WILLIAM	WRITER	30071 ANDROMEDA LN	MALIBU, CA	90265
O'HALLORAN, GREG	BASEBALL	633 JESSAMINE ST	KNOXVILLE, TN	37917
O'HARA, CATHERINE	ACTRESS-COMEDIENNE	SCTV, 110 LOMBARD ST	TORONTO, ONT M5C IM3	CANADA
O'HARA, DAN	BASEBALL EXECUTIVE	POST OFFICE BOX 751	UTICA, NY	13503
O'HARA, GERRY	FILM WRITER-DIRECTOR	51 ELM PARK GARDENS #K	LONDON SW10	ENGLAND
O'HARA, JENNY	ACTRESS	8663 WONDERLAND AVE	LOS ANGELES, CA	90046
O'HARA, KATHLEEN	ACTRESS	3349 W CAHUENGA BLVD #2-B	LOS ANGELES, CA	90068
O'HARA, MAUREEN	ACTRESS	POST OFFICE BOX 1400		
		CHRISTEANSTED	SAINT CROIX, VI	00820
O'HARA, MICHAEL	TV WRITER	4063 RADFORD AVE #203-B	STUDIO CITY, CA	91604
O'HARE, BRIAN	SINGER	5625 "O" STREET BLDG #7	LINCOLN, NE	68510
O'HEARN, PATRICK	SYNTHESIZER-COMPOSER	COLUMBIA PICTURES COMPANY		
		3400 RIVERSIDE DR		
		PRODUCERS BLDG #3-17	BURBANK, CA	91505
O'HERLIHY, DAN	ACTOR	31016 BROAD BEACH RD	MALIBU, CA	90265
O'HERLIHY, MICHAEL	DIRECTOR	1659 N KINGS RD	LOS ANGELES, CA	90069
O'HERN, JIM	GOLFER	PGA SENIORS, 112 T P C BLVD	PONTE VEDRA BEACH, FL	32082
O'HORGAN, THOMAS FOSTER	DIRECTOR	DGA, 110 W 57TH ST	NEW YORK, NY	10019
O'JAYS, THE	VOCAL TRIO	9255 SUNSET BLVD #610	LOS ANGELES, CA	90069
O'KEEFE, JAMES	MUSIC ARRANGER	1609 1/2 S BENTLEY AVE	LOS ANGELES, CA	90025
O'KEEFE, MICHAEL	ACTOR	CAA, 9830 WILSHIRE BLVD	BEVERLY HILLS, CA	90212
O'KEEFE, PAUL	ACTOR-KEYBOARDIST	18 W 86TH ST	NEW YORK, NY	10024
O'KEEFFE, MILES	ACTOR	POST OFFICE BOX 216	MALIBU, CA	90265
O'KOREN, MIKE	BASKETBALL	N J NETS, MEADOWLANDS ARENA	EAST RUTHERFORD, NJ	07073
O'LAUGHLIN, MARJORIE	TREASURER	STATE HOUSE BUILDING	INDIANAPOLIS, IN	46204
O'LEARY, DERRY	COMPOSER-CONDUCTOR	801 E KENSINGTON RD	LOS ANGELES, CA	90026
O'LEARY, JAMES "REBEL"	SINGER-SONGWRITER	POST OFFICE BOX 3525	YORK, PA	17402
O'LEARY, JOHN	ARTIST	547 N 20TH ST	PHILADELPHIA, PA	19130
O'LEARY, PAT	COLUMNIST	TRIBUNE, 64 E CONCORD ST	ORLANDO, FL	32801
O'LEARY, TROY	BASEBALL	POST OFFICE DRAWER 4797	EL PASO, TX	79914
O'LOUGHLIN, CHAD	BASEBALL	POST OFFICE BOX 855	BELOIT, WI	53511
O'LOUGHLIN, GERALD S	ACTOR-DIRECTOR	POST OFFICE BOX 832	ARLETA, CA	91331
O'LOUGHLIN, JIM	TALENT AGENT	11833 LAUREL WOOD DR #8	STUDIO CITY, CA	91604
O'MAHONEY, PRINCESS	ACTRESS	5838 BUSCH DR	MALIBU, CA	90265
O'MALLEY, DAN	SCREENWRITER	9200 SUNSET BLVD #402	LOS ANGELES, CA	90069
O'MALLEY, DARAGH	ACTOR	18 GRATTAN HALL, LOWER MOUNT ST	DUBLIN 2	IRELAND
O'MALLEY, DAVE	SCREENWRITER	11726 SAN VICENTE BLVD #300	LOS ANGELES, CA	90049
O'MALLEY, KATHY	COLUMNIST-CRITIC	TRIBUNE, 64 E CONCORD ST	ORLANDO, FL	32801
O'MALLEY, PETER	BASEBALL EXECUTIVE	326 S HUDSON AVE	LOS ANGELES, CA	90020

O'MALLEY, SUZANNE	SCREENWRITER	9000 SUNSET BLVD #1200	LOS ANGELES, CA	90069
O'MARA, DONALD	TV PRODUCER	ERNST-VAN PRAAG, 135 E 55TH ST	NEW YORK, NY	10022
O'MARA, KATE	ACTRESS	LADKIN, 11 SOUTHWICK MEWS	LONDON W2 1JG	ENGLAND
O'MEARA, MARK	GOLFER	POST OFFICE BOX 109601	PALM BCH GARDENS, FL	33418
O'NEAL, ALEXANDER	SINGER-SONGWRITER	FAA, 1700 BROADWAY, 5TH FLOOR	NEW YORK, NY	10019
O'NEAL, CHARLES E	WRITER	741 CHAPALA DR	PACIFIC PALISADES, CA	90272
O'NEAL, FREDERICK	ACTOR-DIRECTOR	41 CONVENT AVE	NEW YORK, NY	10027
O'NEAL, KELLEY	BASEBALL	POST OFFICE BOX 2785	LAKELAND, FL	33806
O'NEAL, KEVIN	SCREENWRITER	12320 BURBANK BLVD #112	NORTH HOLLYWOOD, CA	91607
O'NEAL, LESLIE	FOOTBALL	POST OFFICE BOX 609609	SAN DIEGO, CA	92160
O'NEAL, MARK	BASEBALL TRAINER	POST OFFICE BOX 3783	SAVANNAH, GA	31414
O'NEAL, PATRICK	ACTOR-DIRECTOR	ROSENBERG, 8428 MELROSE PL #C	LOS ANGELES, CA	90069
O'NEAL, RON	ACTOR-DIRECTOR	10100 SANTA MONICA BLVD #700	LOS ANGELES, CA	90067
O'NEAL, RYAN	ACTOR	21368 PACIFIC COAST HWY	MALIBU, CA	90265
O'NEAL, TATUM	ACTRESS	23712 MALIBU COLONY RD	MALIBU, CA	90265
O'NEIL, BUCK	BASEBALL-SCOUT	POST OFFICE BOX 419969	KANSAS CITY, MO	64141
O'NEIL, EMMITT-LEON	FILM DIRECTOR	1345 N HAYWORTH AVE #209	LOS ANGELES, CA	90046
O'NEIL, JAMES	ATTORNEY GENERAL	STATE CAPITOL, 320 S MAIN ST	PROVIDENCE, RI	02903
O'NEIL, ROBERT VINCENT	SCREENWRITER	8955 BEVERLY BLVD	WEST HOLLYWOOD, CA	90048
O'NEIL, SHANE	FILM EXECUTIVE	RKO-GENERAL, 1440 BROADWAY	NEW YORK, NY	10018
O'NEIL, TERRY	TV PRODUCER	CBS-TV, 51 W 52ND ST	NEW YORK, NY	10019
O'NEIL, TRICIA	ACTRESS	15301 VENTURA BLVD #345	SHERMAN OAKS, CA	91403
O'NEILL, DAN	BASEBALL	POST OFFICE BOX 2365	PAWTUCKET, RI	02861
O'NEILL, DICK	ACTOR	9200 SUNSET BLVD #PH-20	LOS ANGELES, CA	90069
O'NEILL, DOUG	BASEBALL	POST OFFICE BOX 6748	ROCKFORD, IL	61125
O'NEILL, EDWARD	ACTOR	2607 GRAND CANAL	VENICE, CA	90291
O'NEILL, EILEEN	ACTRESS	9056 SANTA MONICA BLVD #201	LOS ANGELES, CA	90069
O'NEILL, EILEEN	WRITER	9654 HIGH RIDGE DR	BEVERLY HILLS, CA	90210
O'NEILL, FREDERICK	TV DIRECTOR	492 WAYNE AVE	SPRINGFIELD, PA	19064
O'NEILL, JENNIFER	ACTRESS-MODEL	32356 MULHOLLAND HWY	MALIBU, CA	90265
O'NEILL, JIMMY	RADIO-TV PERSONALITY	KRLA, 1401 S OAK KNOLL AVE	PASADENA, CA	91109
O'NEILL, MICHAEL G	DIRECTOR	DGA, 110 W 57TH ST	NEW YORK, NY	10019
O'NEILL, PAUL	BASEBALL	REDS, 100 RIVERFRONT STADIUM	CINCINNATI, OH	45202
O'NEILL, ROBERT F	TV WRITER-PRODUCER	22855 PAUL REVERE DR	CALABASAS, CA	91302
O'NEILL, THOMAS P "TIP"	POLITICIAN	CAPE COD	HARWICH PORT, MA	02646
O'NORA, BRIAN	BASEBALL UMPIRE	POST OFFICE BOX 608	GROVE CITY, OH	43123
O'REILLY, CYRIL	ACTOR	POST OFFICE BOX 5617	BEVERLY HILLS, CA	90213
O'REILLY, JIM	BASEBALL TRAINER	1524 W NEBRASKA AVE	PEORIA, IL	61604
O'REILLY, TOM	BASEBALL EXECUTIVE	POST OFFICE BOX 338	JAMESTOWN, NY	14702
O'ROURKE, JOSEPH J	DIRECTOR	5 HOLLY DR	FAIRFIELD, NJ	07006
O'ROURKE, MIKE	TV DIRECTOR	1626 N WILCOX AVE #315	LOS ANGELES, CA	90028
O'ROURKE, P J	SCREENWRITER	555 W 57TH ST #1230	NEW YORK, NY	10019
O'SHANNON, DANIEL T	TV WRITER	151 S EL CAMINO DR	BEVERLY HILLS, CA	90212
O'SHEA, MILO	ACTOR	THE BANCROFT HOTEL		
		40 W 72ND ST #17-A	NEW YORK, NY	10023
O'SHEA, PEGGY	TV WRITER	200 CENTRAL PARK S	NEW YORK, NY	10019
O'SHEA, PHILIP	TV WRITER-DIRECTOR	45 HAZEL RD	LONDON NW10 5PU	ENGLAND
O'SHEA, TERRY	FOOTBALL	STEELERS, 300 STADIUM CIR	PITTSBURGH, PA	15212
O'STEEN, SAM	TV WRITER-DIRECTOR	190 N CANON DR #202	BEVERLY HILLS, CA	90210
O'SULLIVAN, GILBERT	SINGER	LAURIE JAY, 32 WILLESDEN LN	LONDON NW6 7ST	ENGLAND
O'SULLIVAN, KEVIN	TV EXECUTIVE	WORLDVISION, 660 MADISON AVE	NEW YORK, NY	10021
O'SULLIVAN, MAUREEN	ACTRESS	1839 UNION ST	SCHENECTATY, NY	12309
O'SULLIVAN, RICHARD	ACTOR	AMA, 5 ANGELERS LN, LENTISH TOWN	LONDON NW5 3DG	ENGLAND
O'TOOLE, ANNETTE	ACTRESS	360 MORTON ST	ASHLAND, OR	97520
O'TOOLE, PETER	ACTOR-PRODUCER	98 HEATH ST	LONDON NW3	ENGLAND
O'TOOLE, STANLEY	FILM PRODUCER	28 SAINT PATRICK'S AVE, CHARVIL	TWYFORD, BERKS	ENGLAND
OAK RIDGE BOYS, THE	C & W GROUP	329 ROCKLAND RD	HENDERSONVILLE, TN	37075
OAKAR, MARY ROSE	U S CONGRESSWOMAN	FEDERAL COUNT BUILDING #523	CLEVELAND, OH	44114
OAKES, RANDI	ACTRESS	3681 ALOMAR DR	SHERMAN OAKS, CA	91423
OAKES, RODNEY H	COMPOSER	228 EL MOLINO AVE	PASADENA, CA	91101
OAKES, TODD	BASEBALL COACH	5999 E VAN BUREN ST	PHOENIX, AZ	85008
OAKLEY, CHARLES	BASKETBALL	KNICKS, 4 PENNYLVANIA PLAZA	NEW YORK, NY	10019
OAKLEY, JOHN	FILM PRODUCER	65-67 LEDBURY RD	LONDON W11	ENGLAND
OASIS	GOSPEL GROUP	2447 W MOUND ST	COLUMBUS, OH	43204
OATES, ADAM	HOCKEY	BLUES, 5700 OAKLAND AVE	SAINT LOUIS, MO	63110
OATES, BART	FOOTBALL	N Y GIANTS, GIANTS STADIUM	EAST RUTHERFORD, NJ	07073
OATES, DIANE M	DIRECTOR	DGA, 110 W 57TH ST	NEW YORK, NY	10019
OATES, ED	DIRECTOR	137 HERITAGE VILLAGE #A	SOUTHBURY, CT	06488
OATES, JOHN	SINGER-SONGWRITER	130 W 57TH ST #12-B	NEW YORK, NY	10019
OATES, JOHNNY	BASEBALL-MANAGER	ORIOLE PARK, 333 W CAMDEN ST	BALTIMORE, MD	21201
OATES, RONG	MUSIC ARRANGER	113 BEAR TRACK	NASHVILLE, TN	37221
OBANDO, SHERMAN	BASEBALL	POST OFFICE BOX 2148	WOODBRIDGE, VA	22193
OBER, ARLON L E	COMPOSER	1253 19TH ST	SANTA MONICA, CA	90404
OBERKFELL, KEN	BASEBALL	10233 96TH AVE	EDMONTON, ALB TK5 0A5	CANADA
OBERLY, CHARLES M, III	ATTORNEY GENERAL	LEGISLATIVE HALL	DOVER, DE	19901
OBERSTAR, JAMES L	U S CONGRESSMAN	CHISHOLM CITY HALL		
		316 W LAKE ST	CHISHOLM, MN	55719
OBEY, DAVID R	U S CONGRESSMAN	FEDERAL BUILDING, 317 1ST ST	WAUSAU, WI	54401
OBOLER, ARCH	WRITER-PRODUCER	32436 W MULHOLLAND HWY	MALIBU, CA	90265
OBROW, JEFFREY	TV DIRECTOR	9000 SUNSET BLVD #1200	LOS ANGELES, CA	90069
OBSESSION	ROCK & ROLL GROUP	POST OFFICE BOX 300	SOLEBURY, PA	18963
OBST, LYNDA	FILM PRODUCER	PARAMOUNT PICTURES CORP		
		HILL/OBST PRODUCTIONS		
		5555 MELROSE AVE	LOS ANGELES, CA	90038
OCASEK, RIC	SINGER-SONGWRITER	LOOKOUT, 506 SANTA MONICA BLVD	SANTA MONICA, CA	90401

Name	Occupation	Address	City	Code
OCASEK, RIC	SINGER-SONGWRITER	RZO, 110 W 57TH ST, 7TH FLOOR	NEW YORK, NY	10019
OCEAN, BILLY	SINGER-COMPOSER	ASCOT	BERKSHIRE	ENGLAND
OCHAGAVIA, CARLOS	ARTIST	FRANK LAVATY, 50 E 50TH ST	NEW YORK, NY	10022
OCHOA, ALEX	BASEBALL	POST OFFICE BOX 418	SAINT CHARLES, IL	60174
OCHOA, BETH N	COMPOSER	866 LEE HALL	SAN ANTONIO, TX	78212
OCHOA, LEVY	BASEBALL SCOUT	6850 LAWRENCE RD	LANTANA, FL	33462
OCIEPKA, BOB	BASKETBALL COACH	PACERS, 300 E MARKET ST	INDIANAPOLIS, IN	46204
OCKER, DAVID A	COMPOSER	4313 FINLEY AVE	LOS ANGELES, CA	90027
OCKRENT, MIKE	TV DIRECTOR	SARABAND, 265 LIVERPOOL RD	LONDON N1 1LX	ENGLAND
OCNOFF, EDWARD E	COMPOSER-CONDUCTOR	505 DORADO CT	AGOURA, CA	91301
ODAM, NORMAN	SINGER	POST OFFICE BOX 26265	FORT WORTH, TX	76116
ODDIE, WILLIAM	ACTOR-WRITER	8 CHALCOT RD	LONDON NW1	ENGLAND
ODEGARD, BON BOYD	FOOTBALL	N Y JETS, 1000 FULTON AVE	HEMPSTEAD, NY	11550
ODELEIN, LYLE	HOCKEY	CANADIENS, 2313 ST CATHERINE ST	MONTREAL, QUE H3H 1N2	CANADA
ODENKIRK, BOB	TV WRITER	131 S RODEO DR #300	BEVERLY HILLS, CA	90212
ODITZ, CAROL	COSTUME DESIGNER	650 W END AVE	NEW YORK, NY	10025
ODJICK, GINO	HOCKEY	CANUCKS, 100 N RENFREW ST	VANCOUVER, BC V5K 3N7	CANADA
ODOM, BOYD	BASEBALL SCOUT	POST OFFICE BOX 7000	PITTSBURGH, PA	15212
ODOM, CLIFF	FOOTBALL	DOLPHINS, 2269 NW 199TH ST	MIAMI, FL	33056
ODOMES, NATE	FOOTBALL	BILLS, 1 BILLS DR	ORCHARD PARK, NJ	14127
ODOR, ROUGLAS	BASEBALL	2501 ALLEN AVE, SE	CANTON, OH	44707
ODYSSEY	SOUL GROUP	60 EVERGREEN PL #200	EAST ORANGE, NJ	07018
OEHLER, DALE D	COMPOSER	4298 BAKMAN AVE	NORTH HOLLYWOOD, CA	91602
OERTER, AL	TRACK & FIELD	135 W ISLIP RD	WEST ISLIP, NY	11797
OESTER, RON	BASEBALL	3780 NINEMILE RD	CINCINNATI, OH	45255
OESTREICHER, CHRISTINE	FILM PRODUCER	FLAMINGO PICS, 47 LONSDALE SQ	LONDON N1 1EW	ENGLAND
OESTREICHER, GERARD	THEATER PRODUCER	680 MADISON AVE	NEW YORK, NY	10021
OFFENDERS, THE	ROCK & ROLL GROUP	805 NORWALK LN	AUSTIN, TX	78703
OFFERDAHL, JOHN	FOOTBALL	DOLPHINS, 2269 NW 199TH ST	MIAMI, FL	33056
OFFERMAN, JOSE	BASEBALL (DODGERS)	1000 ELYSIAN PARK DR	LOS ANGELES, CA	90012
OFFERMAN, JOSE	BASEBALL (SCOUT)	POST OFFICE BOX 90111	ARLINGTON, TX	76004
OFFS, THE	ROCK & ROLL GROUP	1230 GRANT AVE #531	SAN FRANCISCO, CA	94133
OFIELD, JACK	DIRECTOR-PRODUCER	POST OFFICE BOX 12792	SAN DIEGO, CA	92112
OGANESOFF, IGOR	WRITER-PRODUCER	140 W END AVE	NEW YORK, NY	10023
OGDEN, JAMIE	BASEBALL	POST OFFICE BOX 661	KENOSHA, WI	53141
OGEA, CHAD	BASEBALL	POST OFFICE BOX 3452	KINSTON, NC	28502
OGG, ALAN	BASKETBALL	MIAMI HEAT, THE MIAMI ARENA	MIAMI, FL	33136
OGIENS, MICHAEL	TV EXECUTIVE	CBS-TV, 51 W 52ND ST	NEW YORK, NY	10019
OGILVY, IAN	ACTOR	BELFRAGE, 68 SAINT JAMES'S ST	LONDON SW1A 1LE	ENGLAND
OGLE, JIM	BASEBALL EXECUTIVE	5301 NW 12TH AVE	FORT LAUDERDALE, FL	33309
OGLESBY, ALFRED	FOOTBALL	DOLPHINS, 2269 NW 199TH ST	MIAMI, FL	33056
OGLIARUSO, MIKE	BASEBALL	633 JESSAMINE ST	KNOXVILLE, TN	37917
OGLIVIE, BEN	BASEBALL-SCOUT	BREWERS, 201 S 46TH ST	MILWAUKEE, WI	53214
OGRODNICK, JOHN	HOCKEY	POST OFFICE BOX 90111	ARLINGTON, TX	76004
OH, SOON-TECK	ACTOR	8235 SANTA MONICA BLVD #202	LOS ANGELES, CA	90046
OHER, JOSEPH	DIRECTOR	1314 W WRIGHTWOOD AVE	CHICAGO, IL	60614
OHIO EXPRESS, THE	SOUL GROUP	810 ABE LINCOLN AVE #3-B	CARTERET, NJ	07008
OHIO PLAYERS, THE	SOUL GROUP	888 8TH AVE #1-F	NEW YORK, NY	10019
OHLMEYER, DONALD W, JR	TV DIRECTOR-PRODUCER	9744 WILSHIRE BLVD, 4TH FLOOR	BEVERLY HILLS, CA	90212
OHLMS, MARK	BASEBALL	633 JESSAMINE ST	KNOXVILLE, TN	37917
OHMAN, JACK	CARTOONIST	PORTLAND OREGONIAN		
		1320 SW BROADWAY	PORTLAND, OR	97201
OILY RAGS	ROCK & ROLL GROUP	SIGNATURE RECORDS COMPANY		
		1414 AVE OF THE AMERICAS	NEW YORK, NY	10019
OINGO BOINGO	ROCK & ROLL GROUP	6363 SUNSET BLVD #716	HOLLYWOOD, CA	90028
OJAKLI, SUMYA	CARTOONIST	302 MARINE AVE	BROOKLYN, NY	11209
OJEDA, BOB	BASEBALL	1000 ELYSIAN PARK DR	LOS ANGELES, CA	90012
OKIE, RICHARD C	TV EXECUTIVE	NBC-TV, 3000 W ALAMEDA AVE	BURBANK, CA	91523
OKON, GLORIA	ACTOR-SINGER	OK TAPE, 112-23 15TH AVE	COLLEGE POINT, NY	11356
OKON, THEODORE	DIRECTOR	16 CENTER DR	MALBA, NY	11357
OKOYE, CHRISTIAN	FOOTBALL	CHIEFS, 1 ARROWHEAD DR	KANSAS CITY, MO	64129
OKUN, LILIAN	TV DIRECTOR-PRODUCER	307 E 44TH ST	NEW YORK, NY	10017
OLAJUWON, AKEEM	BASKETBALL	POST OFFICE BOX 272349	HOUSTON, TX	77277
OLANDER, JIM	BASEBALL	2850 W 20TH AVE	DENVER, CO	80211
OLAUSSON, FREDRIK	HOCKEY	JETS, 15-1430 MAROONS RD	WINNIPEG, MAN R3G 0L5	CANADA
OLAZABAL, JOSE MARIA	GOLFER	POST OFFICE BOX 109601	PALM BCH GARDENS, FL	33418
OLBINSKI, RAFAL	ARTIST	111-39 76TH RD #E-1	FOREST HILLS, NY	11375
OLCZYK, ED	HOCKEY	JETS, 15-1430 MAROONS RD	WINNIPEG, MAN R3G 0L5	CANADA
OLD MAN FROM THE MOUNTAIN BAND	C & W GROUP	POST OFFICE BOX 11276	ROCHESTER, NY	14611
OLDAK, IRVING	ACTOR	52 SOUNDVIEW DR	PORT WASHINGTON, NY	11050
OLDAKER, NANCY	COMEDY WRITER	50 W 40TH ST #217	NEW YORK, NY	10018
OLDFIELD, MIKE	MUSICIAN-COMPOSER	LITTLE HALINGS, TILEHOUSE LN	DENHAM, BUCKS	ENGLAND
OLDFIELD, SALLY	SINGER	BRONZE, 100 CHALK FARM RD	LONDON NW1	ENGLAND
OLDFIELD, W ALAN	COMPOSER-CONDUCTOR	4454 SIMPSON AVE	NORTH HOLLYWOOD, CA	91607
OLDHAM, BRUCE	CINEMATOGRAPHER	7715 SUNSET BLVD #150	LOS ANGELES, CA	90046
OLDHAM, DAVID	BASEBALL EXECUTIVE	POST OFFICE BOX 28268	SAN ANTONIO, TX	78228
OLDHAM, GARY	ACTOR	HEATH, PARAMOUNT HOUSE		
		162-170 WARDOUR ST	LONDON W1V 3AT	ENGLAND
OLDHAM, NICK	FILM EXECUTIVE-PR	LAY, 235-245 GOSWELL RD	LONDON EC1V 7JD	ENGLAND
OLDS, GERRY C	COMPOSER	POST OFFICE BOX 1033	BOLINAS, CA	94924
OLERUD, JOHN	BASEBALL	SKYDOME, 300 BREMMER BL #3200	TORONTO, ONT M5V 3B3	CANADA
OLESEN, WINSTRUP H	CONDUCTOR	8215 JAMIESON AVE	RESEDA, CA	91335
OLHAVA, JODY LEE	ACTRESS	11956 COLLINS ST	NORTH HOLLYWOOD, CA	91607
OLIANSKY, JOEL	WRITER-PRODUCER	1320 MILLER DR #11	LOS ANGELES, CA	90069
OLIGARIO, CAROLE	WRITER	1276 N HARPER AVE	LOS ANGELES, CA	90046

Name	Occupation	Address	City	Zip
OLIM, DOROTHY	THEATER PRODUCER	1540 BROADWAY	NEW YORK, NY	10036
OLIN, JIM	U S CONGRESSMAN	406 1ST ST #706	ROANOKE, VA	24011
OLIN, KEN	ACTOR	11840 CHAPARAL ST	LOS ANGELES, CA	90049
OLIN, LENA	SCREENWRITER	ICM, 8899 BEVERLY BLVD	LOS ANGELES, CA	90048
OLIN, STEVE	BASEBALL	INDIANS, CLEVELAND STADIUM	CLEVELAND, OH	44114
OLINEY, ALAN	TV DIRECTOR	6725 SHERBOURNE DR	LOS ANGELES, CA	90056
OLIPHANT, JUDI	ACTRESS-SINGER	STAR TALENT, 1050 N MAPLE ST	BURBANK, CA	91505
OLIPHANT, MIKE	FOOTBALL	BROWNS, 80 1ST ST	BEREA, OH	44017
OLIPHANT, PATRICK	CARTOONIST	UPS, 4900 MAIN ST, 9TH FLOOR	KANSAS CITY, MO	64112
OLITSKY, EVE	ARTIST	FISCHBACH GALLERY, 24 W 57TH ST	NEW YORK, NY	10019
OLITZKY, STEVEN L	COMPOSER	2301 23RD ST	SANTA MONICA, CA	90405
OLIVA, JOSE	BASEBALL	POST OFFICE BOX 4448	TULSA, OK	74159
OLIVA, SERGIO	BODYBUILDER	OLIVIA'S GYM, 7383 ROGERS AVE	CHICAGO, IL	60626
OLIVA, TONY	BASEBALL-COACH	212 SPRING VALLEY DR	BLOOMINGTON, MN	55420
OLIVADOTTI, TOM	FOOTBALL COACH	DOLPHINS, 2269 NW 199TH ST	MIAMI, FL	33056
OLIVARES, OMAR	BASEBALL	250 STADIUM PLAZA	ST LOUIS, MO	63102
OLIVAS, CONRAD, III	CINEMATOGRAPHER	7715 SUNSET BLVD #150	LOS ANGELES, CA	90046
OLIVEIRA, DONA	BODYBUILDER	POST OFFICE BOX M47	HOBOKEN, NJ	07030
OLIVEN, CONSTANCE	TV DIRECTOR	25 LEXINGTON DR	CROTON-ON-HUDSON, NY	10520
OLIVER, BRIAN	BASKETBALL	POST OFFICE BOX 25040	PHILADELPHIA, PA	19147
OLIVER, DAVE	BASEBALL COACH	POST OFFICE BOX 90111	ARLINGTON, TX	76004
OLIVER, FERGIE	SPORTSCASTER	SKYDOME, 300 BREMMER BL #3200	TORONTO, ONT M5V 3B3	CANADA
OLIVER, GEORGE V	CONDUCTOR	5845 LANCASTER DR	SAN DIEGO, CA	92120
OLIVER, GORDON	ACTOR-DIRECTOR	200 N SWALL DR #453	BEVERLY HILLS, CA	90210
OLIVER, JACK	TV DIRECTOR	4802 NORWICH AVE	SHERMAN OAKS, CA	91403
OLIVER, JOE	BASEBALL	REDS, 100 RIVERFRONT STADIUM	CINCINNATI, OH	45202
OLIVER, JOHN	COMPOSER	BOSTON SYMPHONY ORCHESTRA		
		SYMPHONY HALL	BOSTON, MA	02115
OLIVER, LOUIS	FOOTBALL	DOLPHINS, 2269 NW 199TH ST	MIAMI, FL	33056
OLIVER, MAURICE	FOOTBALL	BUCCANEERS, 1 BUCCANEER PL	TAMPA, FL	33607
OLIVER, NATE	BASEBALL-COACH	POST OFFICE BOX 12	MIDLAND, TX	79702
OLIVER, ROBIN R	DIRECTOR	22307 MAC FARLANE DR	WOODLAND HILLS, CA	91364
OLIVER, STEPHEN	COMPOSER	LEMON, 24 POTTERY, HOLLAND PK	LONDON W11 4LZ	ENGLAND
OLIVERAS, FRANCISCO	BASEBALL	5999 E VAN BUREN ST	PHOENIX, AZ	85008
OLIVERAS, MAX	BASEBALL MANAGER	10233 96TH AVE	EDMONTON, ALB TK5 0A5	CANADA
OLIVO, FRANK	TV DIRECTOR	333 E 23RD ST	NEW YORK, NY	10010
OLIVOR, JANE	SINGER	10100 SANTA MONICA BLVD #1600	LOS ANGELES, CA	90067
OLKEN, JONATHAN	TV EXECUTIVE	130 W 75TH ST	NEW YORK, NY	10023
OLLIE & JERRY	VOCAL DUO	FAA, 1700 BROADWAY, 5TH FLOOR	NEW YORK, NY	10019
OLMEDA, JOSE	BASEBALL	POST OFFICE BOX 507	DURHAM, NC	27702
OLMOS, EDWARD JAMES	ACTOR	18034 VENTURA BLVD #228]	ENCINO, CA	91316
OLSAVSKY, JERRY	FOOTBALL	STEELERS, 300 STADIUM CIR	PITTSBURGH, PA	15212
OLSEN, ASHLEY	ACTRESS	ABC-TV, 2040 AVE OF THE STARS	LOS ANGELES, CA	90067
OLSEN, DANA	SCREENWRITER	8955 BEVERLY BLVD	WEST HOLLYWOOD, CA	90048
OLSEN, DAVID N	FOOTBALL EXECUTIVE	BILLS, 1 BILLS DR	ORCHARD PARK, NJ	14127
OLSEN, LEILA HEE	ACTRESS	9229 SUNSET BLVD #311	LOS ANGELES, CA	90069
OLSEN, MERLIN	ACTOR-FOOTBALL	1080 LORAIN RD	SAN MARINO, CA	91108
OLSEN, STANLEY B	DIRECTOR	WINGS, 825 ADMORE DR	SIDNEY, BC V81 351	CANADA
OLSEN, STEVE	BASEBALL	1090 N EUCLID AVE	SARASOTA, FL	34237
OLSHWANGER, RON	PHOTOGRAPHER	970 N SPOED RD	SAINT LOUIS, MO	63146
OLSMAN, PHIL	DIRECTOR	2051 STANLEY HILLS DR	LOS ANGELES, CA	90046
OLSON, GLEN	TV WRITER	1650 WESTWOOD BLVD #201	LOS ANGELES, CA	90024
OLSON, GREG	BASEBALL (BRAVES)	POST OFFICE BOX 4064	ATLANTA, GA	30302
OLSON, GREGG	BASEBALL (ORIOLES)	ORIOLE PARK, 333 W CAMDEN ST	BALTIMORE, MD	21201
OLSON, JAMES	ACTOR	250 W 57TH ST #2223	NEW YORK, NY	10019
OLSON, NANCY	ACTRESS	945 N ALPINE DR	BEVERLY HILLS, CA	90210
OLYMPICS, THE	VOCAL GROUP	MONARCH PRODUCTIONS		
		9227 BELLFLOWER ST	BELLFLOWER, CA	90706
OMARR, SYDNEY	WRITER	201 OCEAN AVE #1706-B	SANTA MONICA, CA	90402
OMDAHL, LLOYD	LT GOVERNOR	STATE CAPITOL, 600 E BOULEVARD	BISMARCK, ND	58505
OMEGA'S PROMISE	VOCAL GROUP	5625 "O" STREET BLDG #7	LINCOLN, NE	68510
OMEN	ROCK & ROLL GROUP	POST OFFICE BOX 2428	EL SEGUNDO, CA	90245
OMENS, SHERWOOD "WOODY"	CINEMATOGRAPHER	POST OFFICE BOX 2230	HOLLYWOOD, CA	90078
ONO LENNON, YOKO	SINGER-SONGWRITER	THE DAKOTA, 1 W 72ND ST	NEW YORK, NY	10023
ONASSIS, JACQUELINE KENNEDY	FIRST LADY-AUTHOR	1040 5TH AVE	NEW YORK, NY	10028
ONCEA, JOHN	BASEBALL EXECUTIVE	POST OFFICE BOX 488	ERIE, PA	16512
ONE LAST CHANCE BAND	RHYTHM & BLUES BAND	2939 ALTA VOSTA DR #103	SAN DIEGO, CA	92139
ONE MAN GANG, THE	WRESTLER	POST OFFICE BOX 105366	ATLANTA, GA	31348
ONE TO ONE	ROCK & ROLL GROUP	41 BRITAIN ST #200	TORONTO, ONT M5A 1R7	CANADA
ONE WAY	RHYTHM & BLUES GROUP	PERK'S MUSIC COMPANY		
		1866 PENOBSCOT BLVD	DETROIT, MI	48226
ONOFRIO, MICHAEL, JR	DIRECTOR	1 CYPRESS LN	RIDGEFIELD, CT	06877
ONTIVEROS, STEVE	BASEBALL	POST OFFICE BOX 6212	TOLEDO, OH	43614
ONTKEAN, MICHAEL	ACTOR	7120 GRASSWOOD AVE	MALIBU, CA	90265
OORE, GARY	TV HOST	12 S CALIBOQUE CAY	HILTON HEAD ISLAND, SC	29928
OPATOSHU, DAN	SCREENWRITER	8201 MANNIX DR	LOS ANGELES, CA	90046
OPATOSHU, DAVID	ACTOR-WRITER	4161 DIXIE CANYON AVE	SHERMAN OAKS, CA	91423
OPENDEN, LORI	CASTING DIRECTOR	18648 STARE ST	NORTHRIDGE, CA	91324
OPHULS, MARCEL	FILM DIRECTOR	10, RUE ERNST-DELOISON	F-92200 NEUILLY	FRANCE
OPIE, WINFIELD	DIRECTOR	9426 VIA MONIQUE	BURBANK, CA	91504
OPOTOWSKY, STAN	TV EXECUTIVE-AUTHOR	ABC-TV, 7 W 66TH ST	NEW YORK, NY	10023
OPPENHEIMER, ALAN	ACTOR	6987 LOS TILOS RD	LOS ANGELES, CA	90068
OPPENHEIMER, DAMON	BASEBALL SCOUT	POST OFFICE BOX 2000	SAN DIEGO, CA	92112
OPPENHEIMER, JOEL	WRITER-POET	WESTBETH, 463 WEST ST	NEW YORK, NY	10019
OPPENHEIMER, PEER J	WRITER	3971 ROYAL OAK PL	ENCINO, CA	91436

OPPERMAN, DAN	BASEBALL	POST OFFICE BOX 26267	ALBUQUERQUE, NM	87125
OPUIYOU, LYNDELL	MAKE-UP ARTIST	281 W 11TH ST	NEW YORK, NY	10014
OPUS	ROCK & ROLL GROUP	330 W 58TH ST #5-P	NEW YORK, NY	10019
OQUENDO, JOSE	BASEBALL	250 STADIUM PLAZA	ST LOUIS, MO	63102
OQUIST, MIKE	BASEBALL	500 NORTON ST	ROCHESTER, NY	14621
ORAGGS, JULIAN	DIRECTOR	1419 DAUPHINE ST	NEW ORLEANS, LA	70116
ORAVEC, MIKE	BASEBALL EXECUTIVE	POST OFFICE BOX 230	HAGERSTOWN, MD	21740
ORBEN, ROBERT	WRITER	1200 N NASH ST #1122	ARLINGTON, VA	22209
ORCHID, ELLEN	ACTRESS	318 E 34TH ST #4-B	NEW YORK, NY	10016
ORDUNG, WYOTT	DIRECTOR	11920 CHANDLER BLVD #218	NORTH HOLLYWOOD, CA	91607
ORECK, MARY	TALENT AGENT	8271 MELROSE AVE #110	LOS ANGELES, CA	90046
OREM, DALE	FOOTBALL REFEREE	NFL, 410 PARK AVE	NEW YORK, NY	10022
ORENSTEIN, BERNARD	TV WRITER	12366 RIDGE CIR	LOS ANGELES, CA	90049
ORENSTEIN, LARRY	COMPOSER	4050 STANSBURY AVE	SHERMAN OAKS, CA	91423
ORENTREICH, BRIAN D	TV DIRECTOR-PRODUCER	249 E 48TH ST #7-E	NEW YORK, NY	10017
ORGEL, LEE	WRITER	421 S VAN NESS AVE #39	LOS ANGELES, CA	90020
ORGOLINI, ARNOLD H	WRITER-PRODUCER	12717 MARLBORO ST	LOS ANGELES, CA	90049
ORIGINAL DRIFTERS, THE	VOCAL GROUP	CAROLINA ATTRACTIONS		
		203 CULVER AVE	CHARLESTON, SC	29407
ORIGINAL EXCITERS, THE	VOCAL GROUP	JAMES EVANS, 200 W 57TH ST	NEW YORK, NY	10019
ORIGINAL FLAMINGOS, THE	VOCAL GROUP	POST OFFICE BOX 262	CARTERET, NJ	07008
ORIGINAL MIRRORS, THE	VOCAL GROUP	1790 BROADWAY #PH	NEW YORK, NY	10019
ORIGINAL RIVER ROAD BOYS, THE	VOCAL GROUP	STAR ATTRACTIONS		
		2039 ANTOINE DR	HOUSTON, TX	77055
ORIGINAL SIN	ROCK & ROLL GROUP	POST OFFICE BOX 836	NYACK, NY	10960
ORIGINALS, THE	VOCAL GROUP	ROY JAY'S, 12340 NW MARSHALL ST	PORTLAND, OR	97229
ORION	VOCAL GROUP	POST OFFICE BOX 40686	NASHVILLE, TN	37204
ORLAND, JOHN W	WRITER	2810 KELTON AVE	LOS ANGELES, CA	90064
ORLANDI, FELICE	ACTOR-WRITER	3800 REDLAW DR	NORTH HOLLYWOOD, CA	91604
ORLANDO, BO	FOOTBALL	OILERS, 6910 FANNIN ST	HOUSTON, TX	77070
ORLANDO, KAT & THE REACTIONS	ROCK & ROLL GROUP	POST OFFICE BOX 18368	DENVER, CO	80218
ORLANDO, TONY	SINGER	804 N CRESCENT DR	BEVERLY HILLS, CA	90210
ORLEANS	ROCK & ROLL GROUP	POST OFFICE BOX 120308	NASHVILLE, TN	37212
ORLIKOFF, SUSAN D	DIRECTOR	15239 RAYNETA DR	SHERMAN OAKS, CA	91403
ORLOFF, ARTHUR E	WRITER	2318 COLDWATER CANYON DR	BEVERLY HILLS, CA	90210
ORLOFF, JOHN	DIRECTOR	1193 SUMMIT DR	BEVERLY HILLS, CA	90210
ORLONS, THE	VOCAL GROUP	2011 FERRY AVE #U-19	CAMDEN, NJ	08104
ORMENY, TOM	ACTOR	12833 LANDALE ST	NORTH HOLLYWOOD, CA	91604
ORMSBY, ALAN	SCREENWRITER	8955 BEVERLY BLVD	WEST HOLLYWOOD, CA	90048
ORNADEL, CYRIL	COMPOSER-CONDUCTOR	STONE, 25 WHITEHALL	LONDON SW1A 2BS	ENGLAND
ORNSTEIN, JOE	BASEBALL EXECUTIVE	POST OFFICE BOX 464	APPLETON, WI	54912
ORNSTEIN, MICHAEL	FILM EDITOR	633 CRESTMOORE PL	VENICE, CA	90291
OROOP, JOSEPH	COMPOSER	7826 LAUREL CANYON BLVD #6	NORTH HOLLYWOOD, CA	91605
OROSCO, JESSE	BASEBALL	BREWERS, 201 S 46TH ST	MILWAUKEE, WI	53214
ORPHAN	ROCK & ROLL GROUP	POST OFFICE BOX 141		
		STATION C	WINNIPEG, MAN R3M 3S3	CANADA
ORR, BENJAMIN	SINGER-SONGWRITER	LOOKOUT, 506 SANTA MONICA BLVD	SANTA MONICA, CA	90401
ORR, BOBBY	HOCKEY	1800 W MADISON ST	CHICAGO, IL	60612
ORR, DAVID H	DIRECTOR	6214 DANBURY ST	DALLAS, TX	75214
ORR, DON	FOOTBALL REFEREE	NFL, 410 PARK AVE	NEW YORK, NY	10022
ORR, GREG	BASEBALL SCOUT	N Y YANKEES, YANKEE STADIUM	BRONX, NY	10451
ORR, RICHARD	TALENT AGENT	FELBER, 2126 N CAHUENGA BLVD	LOS ANGELES, CA	90068
ORR, SAMUEL	TV WRITER	2612 ELM AVE	MANHATTAN BEACH, CA	90266
ORR, TERRY	FOOTBALL	POST OFFICE BOX 17247 (DULLES)	WASHINGTON, DC	20041
ORR, WAYNE	CINEMATOGRAPHER	7715 SUNSET BLVD #150	LOS ANGELES, CA	90046
ORRALL, ROBERT ELLIS	SINGER	3 E 54TH ST #1400	NEW YORK, NY	10022
ORSATTI, FRANK	TV DIRECTOR	3518 W CAHUENGA BLVD #106	HOLLYWOOD, CA	90068
ORSI, GINGER	ACTRESS	GARRETT, 6525 SUNSET BL, 5TH FL	LOS ANGELES, CA	90028
ORSI, LEIGH ANN	ACTRESS	GARRETT, 6525 SUNSET BL, 5TH FL	LOS ANGELES, CA	90028
ORSULAK, JOE	BASEBALL	ORIOLE PARK, 333 W CAMDEN ST	BALTIMORE, MD	21201
ORTEGA, HECTOR	BASEBALL	POST OFFICE BOX 6748	ROCKFORD, IL	61125
ORTEGA, KENNY	COMPOSER	CAA, 9830 WILSHIRE BLVD	BEVERLY HILLS, CA	90212
ORTH, JOAN C	NEWS WRITER	401 E 65TH ST #14-J	NEW YORK, NY	10021
ORTH, PETER	TV EXECUTIVE	ABC-TV, 4151 PROSPECT AVE	LOS ANGELES, CA	90027
ORTIS, RAMON	BASEBALL SCOUT	333 W 35TH ST	CHICAGO, IL	60616
ORTIZ, ANGEL	BASEBALL	POST OFFICE BOX 1295	CLINTON, IA	52733
ORTIZ, BASILO	BASEBALL	POST OFFICE BOX 3169	FREDERICK, MD	21701
ORTIZ, HECTOR	BASEBALL	POST OFFICE BOX 10031	BAKERSFIELD, CA	93389
ORTIZ, JAVIER	BASEBALL	POST OFFICE BOX 3665	OMAHA, NE	68103
ORTIZ, JUNIOR	BASEBALL	INDIANS, CLEVELAND STADIUM	CLEVELAND, OH	44114
ORTIZ, LUIS	BASEBALL	POST OFFICE BOX 10213	LYNCHBURG, VA	24506
ORTIZ, RAMON	BASEBALL COACH	POST OFFICE BOX 3783	SAVANNAH, GA	31414
ORTIZ, RAY	BASEBALL	POST OFFICE BOX 5645	ORLANDO, FL	32855
ORTIZ, SOLOMON P	U S CONGRESSMAN	3649 LEOPARD #510	CORPUS CHRISTI, TX	78408
ORTIZ-GIL, LEON	FILM EDITOR	ACE, 1041 N FORMOSA AVE	WEST HOLLYWOOD, CA	90046
ORTMAYER, STEVE	FOOTBALL COACH	RAIDERS, 332 CENTER ST	EL SEGUNDO, CA	90245
ORTON, BILL	U S CONGRESSMAN	51 S UNIVERSITY DR #317	PROVO, UT	84606
ORTON, COWBOY BOB	WRESTLER	POST OFFICE BOX 3859	STAMFORD, CT	06905
ORTON, DAVID	FILM PRODUCER	THE RED HOUSE, 3 KING ST, POTTEN	BEDFORDSHIRE SG19 2ET	ENGLAND
ORTON, JOHN	BASEBALL	POST OFFICE BOX 2000	ANAHEIM, CA	92803
ORTON, PETER Z	SCREENWRITER	29025 MALIBU DR	AGOURA, CA	91301
ORTUSO, DOMINICK	TV DIRECTOR	893 BLUE SPRING DR	WESTLAKE VILLAGE, CA	91359
OSBORN, PAUL	PLAYWRIGHT	1165 PARK AVE	NEW YORK, NY	10028
OSBORN, RONALD E	SCREENWRITER	8955 BEVERLY BLVD	WEST HOLLYWOOD, CA	90048
OSBORN, THOMAS M	CONDUCTOR	20349 DELITA DR	WOODLAND HILLS, CA	91364

OSBORNE, ANGELA	WRI-DIR-PROD	75 E END AVE	NEW YORK, NY 10028
OSBORNE, JEFFREY	SINGER-SONGWRITER	10100 SANTA MONICA BLVD #1600	LOS ANGELES, CA 90067
OSBORNE, JOHN	PLAYWRIGHT	PETERS, FRASER & DUNLOP, LTD	
		5TH FLOOR, THE CHAMBERS	
		CHELSEA HARBOUR, LOT RD	LONDON SW10 OXF ENGLAND
OSBORNE, LAWRENCE	TV DIRECTOR	142 145 S FAIRFAX AVE #310 MANOR	LOS ANGELES, CA 90036
OSBORNE, MARIE	ACTRESS	YEATS, 110 CALLE BELLA LOMA	SAN CLEMENTE, CA 92672
OSBORNE, MARK	HOCKEY	JETS, 15-1430 MAROONS RD	WINNIPEG, MAN R3G 0L5 CANADA
OSBORNE, MAROLYN SMITH	ACTRESS	SEE - SMITH OSBORNE, MADOLYN	
OSBORNE, ROBERT	FILM CRITIC	KTTV-TV, 5746 SUNSET BLVD	LOS ANGELES, CA 90028
OSBOURNE, OZZY	SINGER-SONGWRITER	184 SUTHERLAND AVE	LONDON W9 ENGLAND
OSGOOD, CHARLES	NEWS CORRESPONDENT	CBS NEWS, 524 W 57TH ST	NEW YORK, NY 10019
OSHA, ELIZABETH A	TV PRODUCER	ABC-TV "20/20", 7 W 66TH ST	NEW YORK, NY 10023
OSHEN, JEFFREY	CASTING DIRECTOR	1438 N GOWER ST #432	LOS ANGELES, CA 90028
OSHIMA, NAGISA	DIRECTOR	2-15-7 AKASAKA, MINATO-KU	TOKYO JAPAN
OSIECKI, JOHN J	CONDUCTOR	32017 KINGSPARK CT	WESTLAKE VILLAGE, CA 91361
OSIK, KEITH	BASEBALL	POST OFFICE DRAWER 1218	ZEBULON, NC 27597
OSLIN, K T	SINGER-SONGWRITER	MORESS, 1209 16TH AVE S	NASHVILLE, TN 37212
OSMOND, ALAN	SINGER	754 E OSMOND LN	PROVO, UT 84604
OSMOND, CLIFF	ACTOR	630 BENVENIDA	PACIFIC PALISADES, CA 90272
OSMOND, CLIFF	SCREENWRITER	2049 CENTURY PARK E #1320	LOS ANGELES, CA 90067
OSMOND, DONNY	SINGER	1570 BROOKHOLLOW DR #118	SANTA ANA, CA 92705
OSMOND, JIMMY	SINGER	7106 S HIGHLAND DR	SALT LAKE CITY, UT 84121
OSMOND, KEN	ACTOR	9863 WORNOM AVE	SUNLAND, CA 91010
OSMOND, MARIE	SINGER-ACTRESS	1420 E 800 NORTH	OREM, UT 84059
OSMOND BROTHERS, THE	VOCAL GROUP	3325 N UNIVERSITY AVE #150	PROVO, UT 84604
OSOWSKI, TOM	BASEBALL SCOUT	POST OFFICE BOX 2000	ANAHEIM, CA 92803
OSTBERG, ROBERT	TV DIRECTOR	1222 SHARON RD	SANTA ANA, CA 92706
OSTEEN, CLAUDE	BASEBALL-COACH	POST OFFICE BOX 26267	ALBUQUERQUE, NM 87125
OSTEEN, DAVE	BASEBALL	POST OFFICE BOX 36407	LOUISVILLE, KY 40233
OSTEEN, GAVIN	BASEBALL	POST OFFICE BOX 11087	TACOMA, WA 98411
OSTER, DAVE	BASEBALL EXECUTIVE	POST OFFICE BOX 402	GENEVA, NY 14456
OSTERBERG, JAMES	SINGER-SONGWRITER	SEE - POP, IGGY	
OSTERHAGE, JEFF	ACTOR	210 N CORDOVA #D	BURBANK, CA 91505
OSTERMAN, LESTER	THEATER PRODUCER	1650 BROADWAY	NEW YORK, NY 10019
OSTERMEYER, BILL	BASEBALL	12000 STADIUM RD	ADELANTO, CA 92301
OSTERWALD, BIBI	ACTRESS	4219 WARNER BLVD	BURBANK, CA 91505
OSTLUND, RICHARD	ACTOR	432 S NORTON AVE #305	LOS ANGELES, CA 90020
OSTROFF, DANIEL	TALENT AGENT	9200 SUNSET BLVD #402	LOS ANGELES, CA 90069
OSTROFF, HOWARD	TV WRITER	10789 OHIO AVE #2	LOS ANGELES, CA 90024
OSTROW, ABE	COMPOSER-CONDUCTOR	13427 RIVERSIDE DR #A	SHERMAN OAKS, CA 91423
OSTROW, JOANNE	TV CRITIC	POST OFFICE BOX 1709	DENVER, CO 80201
OSTROW, STUART	THEATER PRODUCER	POST OFFICE BOX 188	POUND RIDGE, NY 10576
OSUNA, AL	BASEBALL	POST OFFICE BOX 288	HOUSTON, TX 77001
OSWALD, GERD	DIRECTOR	237 SPALDING DR #A	BEVERLY HILLS, CA 90212
OSWALD PORTER, MARINA	LEE HARVEY'S EX-WIFE	ROUTE #1, ROCKWELL COUNTY	HEATH, TX 75087
OTANEZ, WILLIS	BASEBALL	POST OFFICE BOX 2887	VERO BEACH, FL 32961
OTERO, RICKY	BASEBALL	POST OFFICE BOX 7845	COLUMBIA, SC 29202
OTHER ONES, THE	ROCK & ROLL GROUP	BOX 620-349	1000 BERLIN 62 GERMANY
OTIS, AMOS	BASEBALL-COACH	13558 FREEPORT RD	SAN DIEGO, CA 92129
OTIS, CARRIE	ACTRESS	CAA, 9830 WILSHIRE BLVD	BEVERLY HILLS, CA 90212
OTIS, DONALD G	DIRECTOR	KHJ-TV, 5515 MELROSE AVE	HOLLYWOOD, CA 90038
OTIS, JOHNNY	SINGER-GUITARIST	POST OFFICE BOX 6024	CHICAGO, IL 60660
OTNES, FRED	ARTIST	26 CHALBURN RD	WEST REDDING, CT 06896
OTRIN, JOHN	ACTOR	BDP, 10637 BURBANK BLVD	NORTH HOLLYWOOD, CA 91601
OTSUKI, TAMAYO	COMEDIENNE	8235 SANTA MONICA BLVD	LOS ANGELES, CA 90046
OTT, ED	BASEBALL-COACH	POST OFFICE BOX 288	HOUSTON, TX 77001
OTTER, C L "BUTCH"	LT GOVERNOR	STATE HOUSE BUILDING	BOISE, ID 83720
OTTO, DAVE	BASEBALL	INDIANS, CLEVELAND STADIUM	CLEVELAND, OH 44114
OTTO, GREG	COMEDIAN	3800 BARHAM BLVD #303	LOS ANGELES, CA 90068
OTTO, HENRY B	WRITER	25161 MALIBU RD	MALIBU, CA 90265
OTTO, JOEL	HOCKEY	POST OFFICE BOX 1540, STA "M"	CALGARY, ALTA T2P 3BP CANADA
OTTO, LINDA	DIRECTOR	DGA, 7920 SUNSET BLVD, 6TH FL	LOS ANGELES, CA 90046
OTTO OF AUSTRIA, KING	KING	HINDENBURGER-STR 15	8134 POCKING GERMANY
OUGHTON, TAYLOR	ARTIST	DARK HOLLOW RD	JAMISON, PA 18929
OULMANN, RENE	DIRECTOR	300 E 51ST ST	NEW YORK, NY 10022
OULTON, BRIAN	ACTOR	CLIFFORD COTTAGE	
		STRATFORD-ON-AVON	WARKS CV37 8HR ENGLAND
OUMANSKY, ANDRE	ACTOR	3 RUE ETEX	PARIS 75018 FRANCE
OUTCRY	ROCK & ROLL GROUP	6112 KELLOGG AVE	MINNEAPOLIS, MN 55424
OUTFIELD, THE	ROCK & ROLL TRIO	SCARF, UNIT E-1, BOW WORKS	
		REGENT'S PARK	LONDON E3 ENGLAND
OUTLAWS, THE	ROCK & ROLL GROUP	WOMACK, 217 SMOKE RISE CIR	MARIETTA, GA 30067
OVENSON, W VAL	LT GOVERNOR	STATE CAPITOL BUILDING	SALT LAKE CITY, UT 84114
OVERACRE, GARY	ARTIST	3802 VINEYARD TRACE	MARIETTA, GA 30062
OVERALL, PARK	ACTRESS	4904 SANCOLA AVE	NORTH HOLLYWOOD, CA 91602
OVERSHINER	C & W GROUP	POST OFFICE BOX 25371	CHARLOTTE, NC 28212
OVERSTREET, PAUL	SINGER-SONGWRITER	POST OFFICE BOX 2977	HENDERSONVILLE, TN 37077
OVERSTREET, TOMMY	SINGER-GUITARIST	POST OFFICE BOX 455	BRENTWOOD, TN 37027
OVERTON, DON	FOOTBALL	LIONS, 1200 FEATHERSTONE RD	PONTIAC, MI 48432
OVITZ, MICHAEL	TALENT AGENT	CAA, 9830 WILSHIRE BLVD	BEVERLY HILLS, CA 90212
OWEN, BILL	ACTOR	STONE, 25 WHITEHALL	LONDON SW1A 2BS ENGLAND
OWEN, DAVE	BASEBALL-SCOUT	RURAL ROUTE 5, BOX 281	CLEBURNE, TX 76031
OWEN, LARRY	BASEBALL	804 WHITE PINE ST	NEW CARLISLE, OH 45344
OWEN, LAWRENCE	DIRECTOR	323 N CALIFORNIA ST	BURBANK, CA 91505

Name	Occupation	Address	City	Zip
OWEN, SPIKE	BASEBALL	EXPOS, 4545 DE COUBERTIN AVE	MONTREAL, QUE H1V 3P2	CANADA
OWEN-THOMAS, GAVIN	TV DIRECTOR	3390 CREATWOOD TRAIL	SMYRNA, GA	30080
OWENS, ANN	SINGER	TRENDA, 18747 SHERMAN WY	RESEDA, CA	91335
OWENS, BUCK	SINGER-SONGWRITER	MC FADDEN, 818 18TH AVE S	NASHVILLE, TN	37203
OWENS, CHARLES	GOLFER	PGA SENIORS, 112 T P C BLVD	PONTE VEDRA BEACH, FL	32082
OWENS, DALE	BASEBALL EXECUTIVE	POST OFFICE BOX 36407	LOUISVILLE, KY	40233
OWENS, DAN	FOOTBALL	LIONS, 1200 FEATHERSTONE RD	PONTIAC, MI	48432
OWENS, GARY	RADIO PERSONALITY	POST OFFICE BOX 76	ORLANDO, FL	32802
OWENS, GEOFFREY	ACTOR	19 W 44TH ST #1500	NEW YORK, NY	10036
OWENS, GRANT	ACTOR	13403 CANTARA ST	VAN NUYS, CA	91402
OWENS, HARRY R	COMPOSER-ORCH LEADER	POST OFFICE BOX 5454	EUGENE, OR	97405
OWENS, JAMES L	COMPOSER-CONDUCTOR	ROUTE #2, BOX 171-J	LINDALE, TX	75771
OWENS, JAY	BASEBALL	POST OFFICE BOX 5645	ORLANDO, FL	32855
OWENS, JIM	SINGER	POST OFFICE BOX 418	BRENTWOOD, TN	37027
OWENS, LAURA	ACTRESS	8380 MELROSE AVE #207	LOS ANGELES, CA	90069
OWENS, PAUL	BASEBALL-EXECUTIVE	POST OFFICE BOX 7575	PHILADELPHIA, PA	19101
OWENS, SUSIE	MODEL-PERFUME EXEC	5521 GREENVILLE AVE #104	DALLAS, TX	75206
OWENS, WAYNE	U S CONGRESSMAN	125 S STATE ST	SALT LAKE CITY, UT	84138
OWENSBY, EARL	DIRECTOR-PRODUCER	POST OFFICE BOX 184	SHELBY, NC	28150
OWNES, MAJOR R	U S CONGRESSMAN	289 UTICA AVE	BROOKLYN, NY	11213
OXENBERG, CATHERINE	ACTRESS-MODEL	POST OFFICE BOX 25909	LOS ANGELES, CA	90025
OXFORD, VERNON	SINGER-GUITARIST	POST OFFICE BOX 50	HERMITAGE, TN	37076
OXLEY, MICHAEL G	U S CONGRESSMAN	100 E MAIN CROSS ST	FINDLAY, OH	45840
OY, JENNA VON	ACTRESS	NBC-TV, 3000 W ALAMEDA AVE	BURBANK, CA	91523
OYSTER, DAVID	DIRECTOR	4437 FINLEY AVE	LOS ANGELES, CA	90027
OYSTERS, THE	ROCK & ROLL GROUP	611 BROADWAY #526	NEW YORK, NY	10012
OZ	ROCK & ROLL GROUP	COMBAT RECORDS COMPANY		
		149-03 GUY BREWER BLVD	JAMAICA, NY	11454
OZ, FRANK	PUPPETEER	117 E 69TH ST	NEW YORK, NY	10024
OZARCHUK, JOYCE	WRITER	1112 MAPLE ST	SANTA MONICA, CA	90405
OZARK MOUNTAIN DAREDEVILS	C & W GROUP	POST OFFICE BOX 437	EXCELSIOR, MN	55331
OZIMEK, KENNETH H	SINGER-GUITARIST	300 BERKLEY DR #R-2	MADISON, TN	37115
OZNOWICZ, FRANK RICHARD	DIRECTOR	DGA, 7920 SUNSET BLVD, 6TH FL	LOS ANGELES, CA	90046
OZORIA, CLAUDIO	BASEBALL	POLECATS, 608 N SLAPPEY BLVD	ALBANY, GA	31701
OZUNA, GABBY	BASEBALL	POST OFFICE BOX 5599	LITTLE ROCK, AR	72215
OZUNA, MATEO	BASEBALL	POST OFFICE BOX 12557	ST PETERSBURG, FL	33733
OZZ KNOZZ	C & W GROUP	4615 SOUTHWEST FREEWAY #475	HOUSTON, TX	77027

Name	Occupation	Address	City	Zip
P C QUEST	RAP GROUP	POST OFFICE BOX 720423	NORMAN, OK	73007
PAAR, JACK	TV HOST	9 CHATEAU RIDGE DR	GREENWICH, CT	06830
PACE, IRENE M	TV DIRECTOR	POST OFFICE BOX 387	UNIONVILLE, NY	10988
PACE, JUDY	ACTRESS	4139 CLOVERDALE AVE	LOS ANGELES, CA	90008
PACELLI, FRANK T	TV DIRECTOR	POST OFFICE BOX 69191	LOS ANGELES, CA	90069
PACHECO, YOGI	BASEBALL	1524 W NEBRASKA AVE	PEORIA, IL	61604
PACINI, DENI	BASEBALL SCOUT	1000 ELYSIAN PARK DR	LOS ANGELES, CA	90012
PACINO, AL	ACTOR	301 W 57TH ST #16-C	NEW YORK, NY	10017
PACIOREK, TOM	SPORTSCASTER	333 W 35TH ST	CHICAGO, IL	60616
PACK, JACKIE	SINGER	RAINBOW, 124 W BALTIMORE AVE	LANSDOWNE, PA	19050
PACK, ROGER LOYD	ACTOR	56 LADY SOMERSET RD	LONDON NW5 1TU	ENGLAND
PACKARD, RON	U S CONGRESSMAN	2121 PALOMAR AIRPORT RD #105	CARLSBAD, CA	92009
PACKARD, VANCE	AUTHOR	87 MILL RD	NEW CANAAN, CT	06840
PACKWOOD, BOB	U S SENATOR	101 SW MAIN #240	PORTLAND, OR	97204
PACKWOOD, ROBERT	U S SENATOR	257 RUSSELL BUILDING	WASHINGTON, DC	20510
PACOME, MARIA	ACTRESS	2 TER RUE SAINT-SAVEUR		
		BALLAINVILLI	LONGJUMEAU 91160	FRANCE
PACULA, JOANNA	ACTRESS	POST OFFICE BOX 5617	BEVERLY HILLS, CA	90213
PADDIO, GERALD	BASKETBALL	POST OFFICE BOX 5000	RICHFIELD, OH	44286
PADGETT, CHARLES	BASEBALL EXECUTIVE	POST OFFICE BOX 64939	FAYETTEVILLE, NC	28306
PADILLA, DANNY	BODYBUILDER	WORLD GYM, 2210 MAIN ST	SANTA MONICA, CA	90405
PADILLA, MANUEL, JR	ACTOR	242 S LAMAR ST	BURBANK, CA	91506
PADLOCK	ROCK & ROLL GROUP	ISLAND TRADING COMPANY		
		14 E 4TH ST	NEW YORK, NY	10012
PADNICK, GLENN A	TV WRITER	2158 BEVERWIL DR	LOS ANGELES, CA	90034
PAFFEN, WILLIE	BASEBALL SCOUT	FENWAY PARK, 4 YAWKEY WY	BOSTON, MA	02215
PAFFGEN, CRISTA	SINGER-SONGWRITER	SEE - NICO		
PAGANO, RICHARD	ARTIST	18 CUMBERLAND ST	WEST BABYLON, NY	11704
PAGE, ANTHONY	FILM DIRECTOR	HEATH, PARAMOUNT HOUSE		
		162-170 WARDOUR ST	LONDON W1V 3AT	ENGLAND
PAGE, CHRIS	COMPOSER	1611 RIVERSIDE DR	GLENDALE, CA	91201
PAGE, DIAMOND DALLAS	WRESTLER	POST OFFICE BOX 105366	ATLANTA, GA	31348
PAGE, JIM	SINGER-GUITARIST	FLYING FISH RECORDS		
		1304 W SCHUBERT ST	CHICAGO, IL	60614
PAGE, JIMMY	SINGER-GUITARIST	PHIL CARSON, ATLANTIC RECORDS		
		75 ROCKEFELLER PLAZA	NEW YORK, NY	10019
PAGE, JUDY	TALENT AGENT	SMITH, 121 N SAN VICENTE BLVD	BEVERLY HILLS, CA	90211
PAGE, KEN	SINGER	GLOBENFELT, 1205 FRANKLIN AVE	GARDEN CITY, NY	11530
PAGE, LE WANDA	ACTRESS	5000 LANKERSHIM BLVD #7 & 9	NORTH HOLLYWOOD, CA	91601

Name	Occupation	Address	City
PAGE, MITCHELL	BASEBALL-COACH	POST OFFICE BOX 11087	TACOMA, WA 98411
PAGE, PATTI	SINGER	1412 SAN LUCAS CT	SOLONA BEACH, CA 92075
PAGE, TOMMY	SINGER-SONGWRITER	15237 SUNSET BLVD	PACIFIC PALISADES, CA 90272
PAGEL, MIKE	FOOTBALL	RAMS, 2327 W LINCOLN BLVD	ANAHEIM, CA 92801
PAGES, JAVIER	BASEBALL	POLECATS, 608 N SLAPPEY BLVD	ALBANY, GA 31701
PAGES, THE	ROCK & ROLL GROUP	CHIZ, 7031 WOODROW WILSON DR	LOS ANGELES, CA 90068
PAGET, PORTMAN	TV DIRECTOR	44 W END AVE	NEW YORK, NY 10028
PAGET, ROBERT	WRITER-PRODUCER	MANHATAN FILMS COMPANY	
		217 BROMPTON RD	LONDON SW3 ENGLAND
PAGETT, GARY	ACTOR	4051 RADFORD AVE #A	STUDIO CITY, CA 91604
PAGETT, NICOLA	ACTRESS	3 MARTINDALE RD	LONDON SW14 ENGLAND
PAGLIANI, LEANNE	BASEBALL EXECUTIVE	12000 STADIUM RD	ADELANTO, CA 92301
PAGLIARULO, MIKE "PAGS"	BASEBALL	TWINS, 501 CHICAGO AVE S	MINNEAPOLIS, MN 55415
PAGNOZZI, TOM	BASEBALL	250 STADIUM PLAZA	ST LOUIS, MO 63102
PAHLAVI, PRINCESS ASHRAF	PRINCESS	12 AVE MONTAIGNE	F-75016 PARIS FRANCE
PAI, SUE FRANCES	ACTRESS-MODEL	ICM, 40 W 57TH ST	NEW YORK, NY 10019
PAI-RITCHIE, DAVID S	WRITER	3673 BERRY DR	STUDIO CITY, CA 91604
PAICH, DAVID F	COMPOSER-CONDUCTOR	POST OFFICE BOX 6008	SHERMAN OAKS, CA 91413
PAICH, MARTIN	COMPOSER	24157 LUPIN HILL RD	CALABASAS, CA 91302
PAID VACATION	ROCK & ROLL GROUP	POST OFFICE BOX 390	
		OLD CHELSEA STATION	NEW YORK, NY 10113
PAIGE, ELAINE	ACTRESS	SHARKEY, 15 GOLDEN SQ #315	LONDON W1R 3AG ENGLAND
PAIGE, JANIS	ACTRESS	1700 RISING GLEN RD	LOS ANGELES, CA 90069
PAIGE, MICHAEL	CONDUCTOR	9876 WILSHIRE BLVD #GS-1	BEVERLY HILLS, CA 90210
PAIGE, STEPHONE	FOOTBALL	CHIEFS, 1 ARROWHEAD DR	KANSAS CITY, MO 64129
PAIGE, TONY	FOOTBALL	DOLPHINS, 2269 NW 199TH ST	MIAMI, FL 33056
PAINE, BARRY E	DIRECTOR-PRODUCER	BRAESIDE COTTAGE	
		RHODYATE BLAGDON	BRISTOL ENGLAND
PAINE, CATHEY	ACTRESS	1717 N HIGHLAND AVE #701	LOS ANGELES, CA 90028
PAINE, JEFFREY THOMAS	WRITER	1869 VERDUGO LOMA DR	GLENDALE, CA 91208
PAINE, KEN	DIRECTOR	1 WINDSOR ST	LARCHMONT, NY 10538
PAINTED WILLIE	ROCK & ROLL GROUP	10649 BURBANK BLVD	NORTH HOLLYWOOD, CA 91601
PAINTER, DWAIN	FOOTBALL COACH	STEELERS, 300 STADIUM CIR	PITTSBURGH, PA 15212
PAINTER, GARY	BASEBALL	POST OFFICE BOX 1718	NEW BRITAIN, CT 06050
PAINTER, LANCE	BASEBALL	POST OFFICE BOX 1420	WICHITA, KS 67201
PAINTERS & DOCKERS	ROCK & ROLL GROUP	POST OFFICE BOX 38	
		CARLTON SOUTH	VICTORIA 3053 AUSTRALIA
PAINTON, PEGGY	ACTRESS	4065 GLENALBYN DR	LOS ANGELES, CA 90065
PAISER, DINA	ACTRESS	119 BANK ST	NEW YORK, NY 10014
PAISLEY, BOB & SOUTHERN GRASS	C & W GROUP	POST OFFICE BOX 156	ROSELLE, NJ 07203
PAKALINI, JACKSON J	CONDUCTOR	1024 N STANLEY AVE #1	LOS ANGELES, CA 90046
PAKCHANIAN, KOURKEN	DIRECTOR	DGA, 110 W 57TH ST	NEW YORK, NY 10019
PAKULA, ALAN	WRITER-PRODUCER	330 W 58TH ST #5-H	NEW YORK, NY 10019
PALACE	ROCK & ROLL GROUP	POST OFFICE BOX 1909	MILL VALLEY, CA 94942
PALACIOS, REY	BASEBALL	359 VAN BRUNT ST	BROOKLYN, NY 11321
PALACIOS, VICENTE	BASEBALL	POST OFFICE BOX 7000	PITTSBURGH, PA 15212
PALANCE, BROOKE	ACTRESS	2451 HOLLY DR	LOS ANGELES, CA 90068
PALANCE, HOLLY	ACTRESS	2753 ROSCOMARE RD	LOS ANGELES, CA 90077
PALANCE, JACK	ACTOR-DIRECTOR	STAR ROUTE #1, BOX 805	
		CIELO RANCH	TEHACHAPI, CA 93561
PALANCE, VIRGINIA	PRODUCER	1438 N GOWER ST #31	LOS ANGELES, CA 90038
PALANCE, VIRGINIA BAKER	ACTRESS	SEE - BAKER, VIRGINIA	
PALAO, GELSA T	COMPOSER	6541 KESTER AVE #205	VAN NUYS, CA 91411
PALENCAR, JOHN JUDE	ARTIST	6763 MIDDLEBROOK BLVD	MIDDLEBURG HGTS, OH 44130
PALERMO, STEVE	BASEBALL UMPIRE	7921 W 118TH	OVERLAND PARK, KS 66210
PALEY, STANLEY	WRITER	350 S FULLER AVE #8-L	LOS ANGELES, CA 90036
PALFI-ANDOR, LOTTA	ACTRESS	123 W 93RD ST	NEW YORK, NY 10025
PALIES, CHRIS	WRESTLER-ACTOR	SEE - BUNDY, KING KONG	
PALIFOX	C & W GROUP	FIELDS, 3753 VINEYARD CT	MARIETTA, GA 30062
PALIN, MICHAEL	ACTOR-WRITER	25 NEWMAN ST	LONDON W1 ENGLAND
PALL, DONN	BASEBALL	333 W 35TH ST	CHICAGO, IL 60616
PALL, DONN	BASEBALL	11541 VIENNA	PALOS PARK, IL 60464
PALL, LAWRENCE	FILM DIRECTOR	RURAL ROUTE #2	ERIN, ONT N0B 1T0 CANADA
PALLARDY, THOMAS P	MUSIC ARRANGER	ROUTE #1, BOX 257	NOLENSVILLE, TN 37135
PALLENBERG, ROSPO	FILM WRITER-DIRECTOR	9021 BURROUGHS RD	LOS ANGELES, CA 90046
PALLONE, DAVE	BB UMPIRE-AUTHOR	VIKING PRESS, 40 W 23RD ST	NEW YORK, NY 10010
PALLONE, FRANK, JR	U S CONGRESSMAN	540 BROADWAY #119	LONG BRANCH, NJ 08753
PALMEIRO, ORLANDO	BASEBALL	POST OFFICE BOX 3496	DAVENPORT, IA 52808
PALMEIRO, RAFAEL	BASEBALL	POST OFFICE BOX 90111	ARLINGTON, TX 76004
PALMER, ARNOLD	GOLFER	POST OFFICE BOX 52	YOUNGSTOWN, PA 15696
PALMER, BETSY	ACTRESS	5657 WILSHIRE BLVD #290	LOS ANGELES, CA 90036
PALMER, BYRON	ACTOR-SINGER	7044 LOS TILOS RD	HOLLYWOOD, CA 90068
PALMER, CHRIS	FOOTBALL	OILERS, 6910 FANNIN ST	HOUSTON, TX 77070
PALMER, DEAN	BASEBALL	POST OFFICE BOX 90111	ARLINGTON, TX 76004
PALMER, DON	COMPOSER-CONDUCTOR	3048 CLOUDCREST	LA CRESCENTA, CA 91214
PALMER, ELIZABETH	COSTUME DESIGNER	6231 BUFFALO AVE	VAN NUYS, CA 91401
PALMER, GENE	DIRECTOR	MCA/UNIVERSAL STUDIOS, INC	
		100 UNIVERSAL CITY PLAZA	UNIVERSAL CITY, CA 91608
PALMER, GEOFFREY	ACTOR	MARMONT MANAGEMENT, LTD	
		LANGHAM HOUSE, 308 REGENT ST	LONDON W1R 5AL ENGLAND
PALMER, JIM	BASEBALL-ANNOUNCER	WMAR-TV, 6400 YORK RD	BALTIMORE, MD 21212
PALMER, KARL	BASKETBALL	5 TRIAD CENTER #500	SALT LAKE CITY, UT 84180
PALMER, NORMAN	FILM EDITOR	9549 ENCINO AVE	NORTHRIDGE, CA 91325
PALMER, PATRICK	FILM PRODUCER	5254 MELROSE AVE #405-D	LOS ANGELES, CA 90038
PALMER, PETER	ACTOR	12428 HESBY ST	NORTH HOLLYWOOD, CA 91607

PALMER, RENZO	ACTOR	FRANCE DEGAND AGENCE	
		94 RUE LAURISTON	PARIS 75116 ... FRANCE
PALMER, ROBERT	SINGER-SONGWRITER	2-A CHELSEA MANOR, THS, BLOOD ST	LONDON SW3 ... ENGLAND
PALMER, SANDRA	GOLFER	2750 VOLUSA AVE #B	DAYTON BEACH, FL ... 32114
PALMER, SCOTT	ACTOR	8831 SUNSET BLVD #304	LOS ANGELES, CA ... 90069
PALMER, T STEVEN	TV DIRECTOR	4336 BEEMAN AVE	STUDIO CITY, CA ... 91604
PALMER, TOM	ACTOR	CBS-TV, "YOUNG & THE RESTLESS"	
		7800 BEVERLY BLVD #3305	LOS ANGELES, CA ... 90036
PALMER, TOM	TV WRITER-PRODUCER	151 S EL CAMINO DR	BEVERLY HILLS, CA ... 90212
PALMER, TONY	WRITER-PRODUCER	4 KENSINGTON PARK GARDENS	LONDON W11 3HB ... ENGLAND
PALMERIO, ANTHONY J	TV WRITER	SCOTT MEREDITH, 845 3RD AVE	NEW YORK, NY ... 10022
PALMISANO, CONRAD	FILM DIRECTOR	13346 GLENOAKS BLVD	SYLMAR, CA ... 91342
PALTROW, BRUCE W	WRITER-PRODUCER	304 21ST ST	SANTA MONICA, CA ... 90402
PALUMBO, DENNIS	SCREENWRITER	4942 RADFORD AVE	NORTH HOLLYWOOD, CA ... 91607
PALUMBO, MARIO J	ATTORNEY GENERAL	STATE CAPITOL BUILDING	CHARLESTON, WV ... 25305
PALUMBO, THOMAS	DIRECTOR	211 SPORTSMAN AVE	FREEPORT, L I, NY ... 11520
PALYO, CATHEY	BODYBUILDER	GOLD'S GYM, 510 LEWIS RD	SANTA ROSA, CA ... 95401
PAMLANYE, JIM	BASEBALL SCOUT	ORIOLE PARK, 333 W CAMDEN ST	BALTIMORE, MD ... 21201
PANAMA, NORMAN	WRITER-PRODUCER	750 S BUNDY DR #301	LOS ANGELES, CA ... 90049
PANDEMONIUM	ROCK & ROLL GROUP	POST OFFICE BOX 2428	EL SEGUNDO, CA ... 90245
PANDORAS	ROCK & ROLL GROUP	POST OFFICE BOX 49217	LOS ANGELES, CA ... 90049
PANETTA, LEON	U S CONGRESSMAN	380 ALVARADO ST	MONTEREY, CA ... 93940
PANKIN, STUART	ACTOR	11846 VENTURA BLVD #100	STUDIO CITY, CA ... 91604
PANKOVITS, JIM	BASEBALL-MANAGER	POST OFFICE BOX 1718	NEW BRITAIN, CT ... 06050
PANKOW, JAMES	MUSICIAN-COMPOSER	9301 WILSHIRE BLVD #212	BEVERLY HILLS, CA ... 90210
PANNO, CARLO	TV WRITER	1541 N VINE ST	HOLLYWOOD, CA ... 90028
PANTHER	ROCK & ROLL GROUP	GREENWALD PRODUCTIONS	
		20445 GRAMMERCY PL	TORRANCE, CA ... 90501
PANTING, DEANNA	BODYBUILDER	POST OFFICE BOX 2669	WINNIPEG, MAN R3C 4B3 ... CANADA
PANTOLIANO, JOE	ACTOR	1514 ELECTRIC AVE #F	VENICE, CA ... 90291
PANZER, WILLIAM	FILM PRODUCER	1438 N GOWER ST #401	LOS ANGELES, CA ... 90038
PAOLUCCI, ANNE	PLAYWRIGHT	SAINT JOHN'S UNIVERSITY	
		81-10 UTOPA PARKWAY &	
		GRAND CENTRAL	JAMAICA, NY ... 11439
PAONESSA, DONALD J	SCREENWRITER	8955 BEVERLY BLVD	WEST HOLLYWOOD, CA ... 90048
PAPAI, RAY A	COMPOSER-CONDUCTOR	501 E PROVIDENCE RD	PALATINE, IL ... 60067
PAPAS, IRENE	ACTRESS	XENOKRATOUS 39	ATHENS-KOLONAKI ... GREECE
PAPAS, MICHAEL	WRI-DIR-PROD	ONYX FILM PRODUCTIONS, LTD	
		20 FITZROY SQ	LONDON W1 ... ENGLAND
PAPAZIAN, ROBERT A	WRITER-PRODUCER	500 S SEPULVEDA BLVD #600	LOS ANGELES, CA ... 90049
PAPELL, STAN	WRITER	203 MONTANA AVE #204	SANTA MONICA, CA ... 90403
PAPIN, RALPH L	DIRECTOR	DGA, 7920 SUNSET BLVD, 6TH FL	LOS ANGELES, CA ... 90046
PAPP, FRANK	TV DIRECTOR	404 E 55TH ST	NEW YORK, NY ... 10022
PAPPALARDI, FELIX	SINGER	3 E 54TH ST #1400	NEW YORK, NY ... 10022
PAPPAPORT, DAVID	ACTOR	6219 PRIMROSE AVE	LOS ANGELES, CA ... 90068
PAPPAS, DR ARTHUR M	BASEBALL EXECUTIVE	FENWAY PARK, 4 YAWKEY WY	BOSTON, MA ... 02215
PAPPAS, ERIK	BASEBALL	POST OFFICE BOX 3665	OMAHA, NE ... 68103
PAQUETTE, CRAIG	BASEBALL	POST OFFICE BOX 2769	HUNTSVILLE, AL ... 35804
PARACHUTE CLUB, THE	ROCK & ROLL GROUP	41 BRITAIN ST #200	TORONTO, ONT M5A 1R7 ... CANADA
PARADISE EXPRESS	ROCK & ROLL GROUP	8949 SUNSET BLVD #203	LOS ANGELES, CA ... 90069
PARAGON, JOHN	TV WRITER-DIRECTOR	1262 N FLORES ST	LOS ANGELES, CA ... 90069
PARANADA, BETH	SINGER-SONGWRITER	2801 MEADOW LARK DR	SAN DIEGO, CA ... 92123
PARANADA, GLORIA	ACTRESS-MODEL	2801 MEADOW LARK DR	SAN DIEGO, CA ... 92123
PARANADA, ORLANDO "STIR FRY"	CHEF	2801 MEADOW LARK DR	SAN DIEGO, CA ... 92123
PARANADA, TRINA	ACTRESS-MODEL	2801 MEADOW LARK DR	SAN DIEGO, CA ... 92123
PARCELLS, BILL	FOOTBALL COACH	N Y GIANTS, GIANTS STADIUM	EAST RUTHERFORD, NJ ... 07073
PARCHMAN, GEN	COMPOSER-PLAYWRIGHT	1502 CLOVERNOLL DR	CINCINNATI, OH ... 45231
PARDEE, JACK	FOOTBALL COACH	OILERS, 6910 FANNIN ST	HOUSTON, TX ... 77070
PARE, MICHAEL	ACTOR-SINGER	2804 PACIFIC AVE	VENICE, CA ... 90291
PAREDES, DANIEL	COSTUME DESIGNER	13949 VENTURA BLVD #309	SHERMAN OAKS, CA ... 91423
PARENT, GAIL	SCREENWRITER-TV PROD	2001 MANDEVILLE CANYON RD	LOS ANGELES, CA ... 90049
PARENT, MARK	BASEBALL	500 NORTON ST	ROCHESTER, NY ... 14621
PARETSKY, SARA	AUTHOR-NOVELIST	8428 MELROSE PL #E	LOS ANGELES, CA ... 90069
PARFITT, JUDY	ACTRESS	CONWAY, 18-21 JERMYN ST	LONDON SW1 ... ENGLAND
PARINS, ROBERT J	FOOTBALL EXECUTIVE	PACKERS, 1265 LOMBARDI AVE	GREEN BAY, WI ... 54307
PARIS	ROCK & ROLL GROUP	POST OFFICE BOX 682	LEBANON, IN ... 46052
PARIS, BOB	BODYBUILDER	8033 SUNSET BLVD #238	LOS ANGELES, CA ... 90046
PARIS, DUKE	SINGER-GUITARIST	141 EDGEWOOD DR	HENDERSONVILLE, TN ... 37075
PARIS, JEFF	SINGER-GUITARIST	2519 CARMEN CREST DR	LOS ANGELES, CA ... 90068
PARIS, JOHNNY & THE HURRICANES	ROCK & ROLL GROUP	1764 PARKWAY DR	SOUTH MAUMEE, OH ... 43537
PARIS, JUAN	BASEBALL	POST OFFICE BOX 2365	PAWTUCKET, RI ... 02861
PARIS, JULIE	ACTRESS	1930 CENTURY PARK W #403	LOS ANGELES, CA ... 90067
PARIS, WILLIAM	FOOTBALL	POST OFFICE BOX 535000	INDIANPOLIS, IN ... 46253
PARISH, ROBERT	BASKETBALL	151 MERRIMAC ST	BOSTON, MA ... 02114
PARISH SISTERS, THE	VOCAL GROUP	WOOD, 2901 EPPERLY DR	DEL CITY, OK ... 73115
PARISOT, DEAN	FILM DIRECTOR	ICM, 40 W 57TH ST	NEW YORK, NY ... 10019
PARK, THOMAS E	TV PRODUCER	ENTERTAINMENT TONIGHT	
		PARAMOUNT TELEVISION	
		5555 MELROSE AVE	LOS ANGELES, CA ... 90038
PARK, W B	CARTOONIST	UNITED FEATURE, 200 PARK AVE	NEW YORK, NY ... 10166
PARK-LINCOLN, LAR	ACTRESS	SEE - LINCOLN, LAR PARK	
PARKE, BERT	BASEBALL EXECUTIVE	POST OFFICE BOX 5599	LITTLE ROCK, AR ... 72215
PARKE, DOROTHY	ACTRESS	9200 SUNSET BLVD #625	LOS ANGELES, CA ... 90069
PARKER, ALAN	FILM WRITER-DIRECTOR	WM MORRIS, 31-32 SOHO SQ	LONDON W1V 5DG ... ENGLAND
PARKER, ALAN C	CONDUCTOR	13839 BURTON ST	PANORAMA CITY, CA ... 91402

PARKER, ANTHONY	DIRECTOR-PRODUCER	CHARLESWORTH, 60 OLD BROMPTON	LONDON SW7 3LQ	ENGLAND
PARKER, BILL	SINGER-GUITARIST	ROUTE #7, BOX 669	BROKEN ARROW, OK	74012
PARKER, BRAD	BASEBALL	POST OFFICE BOX 882	MADISON, WI	53701
PARKER, BRIAN	TV DIRECTOR	8 LILIAN RD	LONDON SW16 5HN	ENGLAND
PARKER, CECELIA	ACTRESS	5287 TETON LN	VENTURA, CA	93003
PARKER, CHARLIE & HIS ORCHESTRA	ORCHESTRA LEADER	BILL POTTS, 731 MONROE ST	ROCKVILLE, MD	20850
PARKER, CLAY	BASEBALL	POST OFFICE BOX 4100	SEATTLE, WA	98104
PARKER, COLONIAL TOM	TALENT AGENT	POST OFFICE BOX 220	MADISON, TN	37118
PARKER, DAVE	BASEBALL	7864 RIDGE RD	CINCINNATI, OH	45237
PARKER, DAVID E	RECORD EXECUTIVE	AMHERST RECORDS CO		
		1800 MAIN ST	BUFFALO, NY	14208
PARKER, DENNIS F	COMPOSER-CONDUCTOR	POST OFFICE BOX 4102	NORTH HOLLYWOOD, CA	91607
PARKER, ED	KARATE INSTRUCTOR	1705 E WALNUT ST	PASADENA, CA	91106
PARKER, ELEANOR	ACTRESS	2195 LA PAZ WY	PALM SPRINGS, CA	92262
PARKER, ELLEN	ACTRESS	CBS-TV, "THE GUIDING LIGHT"		
		222 E 44TH ST	NEW YORK, NY	10017
PARKER, FESS	ACTOR	PARKER'S RED LION RESORT HOTEL		
		633 E CABRILLO BLVD	SANTA BARBARA, CA	93103
PARKER, FRANCINE	TV DIRECTOR-PRODUCER	847 N ALEXANDRIA AVE	LOS ANGELES, CA	90029
PARKER, GALE	COSTUME DESIGNER	13949 VENTURA BLVD #309	SHERMAN OAKS, CA	91423
PARKER, GEORGE A	DIRECTOR	529 W 42ND ST	NEW YORK, NY	10036
PARKER, GLENN	FOOTBALL	BILLS, 1 BILLS DR	ORCHARD PARK, NJ	14127
PARKER, GRAHAM	SINGER-GUITARIST	ICM, 40 W 57TH ST	NEW YORK, NY	10019
PARKER, J STANFORD	TV WRITER	8271 MELROSE AVE #110	LOS ANGELES, CA	90046
PARKER, JAMESON	ACTOR	10100 SANTA MONICA BLVD #1600	LOS ANGELES, CA	90067
PARKER, JANET LEE	ACTRESS	1895 N AVE 52	LOS ANGELES, CA	90042
PARKER, JEAN	ACTRESS	617 COLUMBUS AVE #E	GLENDALE, CA	91204
PARKER, JENNIFER	ACTRESS	POST OFFICE BOX 3002	LOS ANGELES, CA	90078
PARKER, JOHN C	COMPOSER-CONDUCTOR	3036 NICHOLS CANYON RD	LOS ANGELES, CA	90046
PARKER, JOHNNY	FOOTBALL COACH	N Y GIANTS, GIANTS STADIUM	EAST RUTHERFORD, NJ	07073
PARKER, KEN	BASEBALL SCOUT	POST OFFICE BOX 7000	PITTSBURGH, PA	15212
PARKER, KIT	FILM EXECUTIVE	1245 10TH ST	MONTEREY, CA	93940
PARKER, LARA	ACTRESS	1441 BONNELL	TOPANGA, CA	90290
PARKER, LINDA R	ACTRESS	4054 WITZEL DR	SHERMAN OAKS, CA	91423
PARKER, MARION	TALENT AGENT	POST OFFICE BOX 74368	HOUSTON, TX	77274
PARKER, MIKE	U S CONGRESSMAN	245 E CAPITOL ST	JACKSON, MS	39201
PARKER, MONICA S	WRITER	427 N CANON DR #213	BEVERLY HILLS, CA	90210
PARKER, MORTEN	WRITER-PRODUCER	1457 BROADWAY #801	NEW YORK, NY	10036
PARKER, NOELLE	ACTRESS	POST OFFICE BOX 5617	BEVERLY HILLS, CA	90213
PARKER, NORMA JEAN	SINGER	POST OFFICE BOX 390	PONTOTOC, MS	38863
PARKER, NORMAN	ACTOR	KOHNER, 9169 SUNSET BLVD	LOS ANGELES, CA	90069
PARKER, RAY, JR	SINGER-GUITARIST	151 S EL CAMINO DR	BEVERLY HILLS, CA	90212
PARKER, RICHARD "RICK"	BASEBALL	POST OFFICE BOX 27045	TUCSON, AZ	85726
PARKER, ROBERT ANDREW	ARTIST	POST OFFICE BOX 114	WEST CORNWALL, CT	06796
PARKER, ROBERT B	AUTHOR-NOVELIST	555 W 57TH ST #1230	NEW YORK, NY	10019
PARKER, RON	TV PRODUCER	ABC-TV, 2040 AVE OF THE STARS	LOS ANGELES, CA	90067
PARKER, RUSS	BASEBALL EXECUTIVE	POST OFFICE BOX 3690, STA "B"	CALGARY, ALB T2B 4M4	CANADA
PARKER, SARAH JESSICA	ACTRESS-SINGER	8730 SANTA MONICA BLVD #I	LOS ANGELES, CA	90069
PARKER, SCOTT	SCREENWRITER	8955 BEVERLY BLVD	WEST HOLLYWOOD, CA	90048
PARKER, SUZY	ACTRESS	770 HOT SPRINGS RD	SANTA BARBARA, CA	93103
PARKER, TIM	BASEBALL	POST OFFICE DRAWER 1207	ZEBULON, NC	27597
PARKER, TOM	TALENT AGENT	SEE - PARKER, COLONEL TOM		
PARKER, VIVECA	ACTRESS	165 W 46TH ST #409	NEW YORK, NY	10036
PARKER, WES	BASEBALL-ACTOR	POST OFFICE BOX 550	SANTA MONICA, CA	90406
PARKER, WILLARD	ACTOR	74-580 FAIRWAY DR	INDIANA WELLS, CA	92260
PARKERS, WALTER F	SCREENWRITER	8955 BEVERLY BLVD	WEST HOLLYWOOD, CA	90048
PARKES, CLIFFORD	FILM PRODUCER	SUNNYFIELDS LODGE		
		LAWRENCE ST, MILL ST	LONDON NW7	ENGLAND
PARKES, ROGER	TV WRITER	CARTLANDS COTTAGE, KINGS LN		
		COOKHAM DEAN	BERKS SL6 9AY	ENGLAND
PARKES, WALTER F	SCREENWRITER	1619 THAYER AVE	LOS ANGELES, CA	90024
PARKHURST, MICHAEL	WRITER-PRODUCER	7753 DENSMORE AVE	VAN NUYS, CA	91406
PARKIN, JUDD	TV EXECUTIVE	NBC-TV, 3000 W ALAMEDA AVE	BURBANK, CA	91523
PARKINS, BARBARA	ACTRESS	1930 CENTURY PARK W #403	LOS ANGELES, CA	90067
PARKINSON, BOB	TV WRITER-PRODUCER	1717 N HIGHLAND AVE #814	HOLLYWOOD, CA	90028
PARKINSON, DIAN	MODEL-ACTRESS	4655 NATICK AVE #1	SHERMAN OAKS, CA	91403
PARKINSON, ERIC	BASEBALL	POST OFFICE BOX 842	SALEM, VA	24153
PARKINSON, MARIA	ACTRESS	8228 SUNSET BLVD #311	LOS ANGELES, CA	90046
PARKINSON, ROBIN	ACTOR	20 KINGSTON LN, TEDDINGTON	MIDDLESEX	ENGLAND
PARKS, ANDREW	ACTOR	1830 GRACE AVE	LOS ANGELES, CA	90028
PARKS, CATHERINE	ACTRESS	6310 SAN VICENTE BLVD #407	LOS ANGELES, CA	90048
PARKS, DEREK	BASEBALL	POST OFFICE BOX 1659	PORTLAND, OR	97207
PARKS, GORDON	FILM WRITER-DIRECTOR	860 UNITED NATIONS PLAZA	NEW YORK, NY	10017
PARKS, MICHAEL	ACTOR	1320 ARMACOST AVE #12	LOS ANGELES, CA	90025
PARKS, ROSA	CIVIL RIGHTS	231 W LAFAYETTE ST	DEARBORN, MI	48226
PARKS, TOM	COMEDIAN	CARLIN, 901 BRINGHAM AVE	LOS ANGELES, CA	90049
PARKS, VAN DYKE	COMPOSER	POST OFFICE BOX 1207	STUDIO CITY, CA	91604
PARLAN, STAN	TV PRODUCER	140 E 28TH ST	NEW YORK, NY	10016
PARLIAMENT	VOCAL GROUP	FAA, 1700 BROADWAY, 5TH FLOOR	NEW YORK, NY	10019
PARMA, LEON	BASEBALL EXECUTIVE	POST OFFICE BOX 2000	SAN DIEGO, CA	92112
PARMAN, CLIFF	MUSIC ARRANGER	POST OFFICE BOX 70	PULASKI, TN	38478
PARNELL, CHIC	COMPOSER	812 N KILKEA DR	LOS ANGELES, CA	90046
PARNELL, MARK	BASEBALL	800 HOME RUN LN	MEMPHIS, TN	38104
PARONE, EDWARD	TV DIRECTOR	1336 N HARPER AVE N	LOS ANGELES, CA	90046
PAROUTAUD, FRED C	COMPOSER	1316 BARRY AVE #9	LOS ANGELES, CA	90025

Name	Occupation	Address	City	Zip
PARR, JOHN	SINGER-SONGWRITER	DMA, 21182 EASTFARM	NORTHFIELD, MI	48167
PARR, RICK	BASEBALL EXECUTIVE	POST OFFICE DRAWER 4797	EL PASO, TX	79914
PARRA, FRANKLIN	BASEBALL	POST OFFICE BOX 309	GASTONA, NC	28053
PARRA, JOSE	BASEBALL	POST OFFICE BOX 10031	BAKERSFIELD, CA	93389
PARRACK, ART	BASEBALL SCOUT	POST OFFICE BOX 7575	PHILADELPHIA, PA	19101
PARRETT, JEFF	BASEBALL	ATHLETICS'S, OAKLAND COLISEUM	OAKLAND, CA	94621
PARRILLO, JOHN	BODYBUILDER	5143 KENNEDY AVE	CINCINNATI, OH	45213
PARRIOTT, JAMES D	WRITER-PRODUCER	2340 CANYON DR	HOLLYWOOD, CA	90068
PARRIOTT, SARA	SCREENWRITER	9200 SUNSET BLVD #402	LOS ANGELES, CA	90069
PARRIS, FRED & THE SATINS	VOCAL GROUP	MARS, 168 ORCHID DR	PEARL RIVER, NY	10965
PARRIS, GEORGE	SINGER-GUITARIST	2732 MC KEIGE ST	NASHVILLE, TN	37214
PARRIS, STEVE	BASEBALL	POST OFFICE BOX 15050	READING, PA	19612
PARRISH, DOROTHY	ACTRESS	5657 WILSHIRE BLVD #290	LOS ANGELES, CA	90036
PARRISH, JEFF "BULLDOG"	BODYBUILDER-ACTOR	2801 MEADOW LARK DR	SAN DIEGO, CA	92123
PARRISH, JULIE	ACTRESS	11640 OXNARD ST #H	NORTH HOLLYWOOD, CA	91607
PARRISH, LANCE	BASEBALL	POST OFFICE BOX 2000	ANAHEIM, CA	92803
PARRISH, LARRY	BASEBALL	4989 E STATE RD #544	HAINES CITY, FL	33844
PARROS, PETER	ACTOR	7651 CAMELLIA VAE	NORTH HOLLYWOOD, CA	91605
PARROTT, ANDREW	CONDUCTOR	WENTWORTH, 5 LOCKWOOD RD	SCARSDALE, NY	10583
PARROTT, MIKE	BASEBALL COACH	POST OFFICE BOX 15757	HARRISBURG, PA	17105
PARRY, KEN	ACTOR	PBR, 138 PUTNEY BRIDGE RD	LONDON SW15 2NQ	ENGLAND
PARSLEY, REED	TV WRITER-DIRECTOR	1701 35TH AVE	SEATTLE, WA	98122
PARSLOW, PHILIP	DIRECTOR	3535 LOADSTONE DR	SHERMAN OAKS, CA	91403
PARSONS, ALAN, PROJECT	ROCK & ROCK DUO	WOOLSONGS COMPANY		
		30 THE AVE MUSWELL HILL	LONDON N10	ENGLAND
PARSONS, CASEY	BASEBALL MANAGER	POST OFFICE BOX 2769	HUNTSVILLE, AL	35804
PARSONS, CLIVE	FILM PRODUCER	10 PEMBRIDGE PL	LONDON W2 4XB	ENGLAND
PARSONS, HARRIET	WRITER-PRODUCER	2253 COLDWATER CANYON DR	BEVERLY HILLS, CA	90210
PARSONS, JOHN	BASEBALL EXECUTIVE	POST OFFICE BOX 488	ERIE, PA	16512
PARSONS, KARYN	ACTRESS	KJAR, 10653 RIVERSIDE DR	TOLUCA LAKE, CA	91602
PARSONS, LINDSLEY, III	FILM DIRECTOR	8618 ORION AVE	SEPULVEDA, CA	91343
PARSONS, NANCY	ACTRESS	4220 CAHUENGA BLVD	NORTH HOLLYWOOD, CA	91602
PARSONS, NICHOLAS	ACTOR-COMEDIAN	MARSH, 19 DENMARK ST	LONDON WC2H 8NA	ENGLAND
PARSONS, SHELLY	ACTRESS	1736 1/4 GRIFFITH PARK BLVD	LOS ANGELES, CA	90026
PARSONS, WAYNE	TV DIRECTOR	13380 GOLDEN VALLEY LN	GRANADA HILLS, CA	91344
PART, JENNIFER JACKSON	CASTING DIRECTOR	4000 WARNER BLVD	BURBANK, CA	91505
PARTON, DOLLY	SINGER-ACTRESS	9035 NORMA PL	LOS ANGELES, CA	90069
PARTON, RANDY	SINGER-SONGWRITER	821 19TH AVE S	NASHVILLE, TN	37202
PARTON, REGIS	DIRECTOR	DGA, 7920 SUNSET BLVD, 6TH FL	LOS ANGELES, CA	90046
PARTON, STELLA	SINGER	POST OFFICE BOX 120295	NASHVILLE, TN	37212
PARTRICK, DAVE	BASEBALL	POST OFFICE BOX 3496	DAVENPORT, IA	52808
PARTRIDGE, DEREK	TALK SHOW HOST	DOWNES PRESENTERS, 96 BROADWAY		
		BEXLEY HEATH	KENT DA6 7DE	ENGLAND
PARTY, THE	ROCK & ROLL GROUP	5000 S BUENA VISTA ST	BURBANK, CA	91521
PARUCHA, ROBERT CARL	ACTOR	9200 SUNSET BLVD #630	LOS ANGELES, CA	90069
PASATIERI, THOMAS	COMPOSER	500 W END AVE	NEW YORK, NY	10024
PASCAL, FRANCOISE	ACTRESS	89 RIVERVIEW GARDENS	LONDON SW13	ENGLAND
PASCAL, GISELLE	ACTRESS	AGENCE M ETIENNE		
		78 CHAMPS-ELYSEES	PARIS 75008	FRANCE
PASCAL, JEAN-CLAUDE	ACTOR	133 BLVD EXELMANS	F-75016 PARIS	FRANCE
PASCAL, MARY ANN	ACTRESS	9744 WILSHIRE BLVD #308	BEVERLY HILLS, CA	90212
PASCALE, JOE	FOOTBALL COACH	POST OFFICE BOX 888	PHOENIX, AZ	85001
PASCHKE, JIM	SPORTSCASTER	BREWERS, 201 S 46TH ST	MILWAUKEE, WI	53214
PASCO, RICHARD	ACTOR	WHITEHALL, 125 GLOUCESTER RD	LONDON SW7 4TE	ENGLAND
PASCUAL, CAMILO	BASEBALL-SCOUT	1000 ELYSIAN PARK DR	LOS ANGELES, CA	90012
PASCUAL, CARLOS	BASEBALL-SCOUT	METS, 126TH ST & ROOSEVELT AVE	FLUSHING, NY	11368
PASCUCCI, JAMES	ACTOR	1680 N VINE ST #203	HOLLYWOOD, CA	90028
PASCUZZI, ARTHUR	ACTOR	8 ROBERT DR	CHATHAM TOWNSHIP, NJ	07928
PASDAR, ADRIAN	ACTOR	3176 LINDO ST	LOS ANGELES, CA	90068
PASEORNEK, MICHAEL	SCREENWRITER	555 W 57TH ST #1230	NEW YORK, NY	10019
PASETTA, MARTIN A, JR	TV DIRECTOR	10615 BELLAGIO RD	LOS ANGELES, CA	90077
PASETTA, MARTIN A, SR	TV DIRECTOR-PRODUCER	10615 BELLAGIO RD	LOS ANGELES, CA	90077
PASKAY, STEVE	TV WRITER	ENTERTAINMENT TONIGHT		
		PARAMOUNT TELEVISION		
		5555 MELROSE AVE	LOS ANGELES, CA	90038
PASKIEVITCH, TOM	BASEBALL	POST OFFICE BOX 611	WATERLOO, IA	50704
PASKOSKI, SUSAN	DIRECTOR	1 UNIVERSITY PL	NEW YORK, NY	10003
PASLAWSKI, GREG	HOCKEY	SABRES, MEMORIAL AUDITORIUM	BUFFALO, NY	14202
PASQUA, DAN	BASEBALL	333 W 35TH ST	CHICAGO, IL	60616
PASQUALE, LARRY	FOOTBALL COACH	POST OFFICE BOX 609609	SAN DIEGO, CA	92160
PASQUALINA, ROBERT	DIRECTOR	1900 AVE OF THE STARS #800	LOS ANGELES, CA	90067
PASQUESI, DAVID	ACTOR	9350 WILSHIRE BLVD #324	BEVERLY HILLS, CA	90212
PASQUIN, JOHN R	DIRECTOR	DGA, 110 W 57TH ST	NEW YORK, NY	10019
PASS, JOE	GUITARIST	SALLE, 451 N CANON DR	BEVERLY HILLS, CA	90210
PASSARELLA, JOSEPH	DIRECTOR-PRODUCER	88 KEMPSHALL TERR	FANWOOD, NJ	07023
PASSARIELLO, KEN	BODYBUILDER	POST OFFICE BOX 76	ORLANDO, FL	32802
PASSARO, GERARD	TV DIRECTOR-PRODUCER	SPORTSCHANNEL ASSOCIATES		
		150 CROSSWAYS PARK W	WOODBURY, NY	11797
PASSAS, PETER	DIRECTOR	44 CIRCLE DR E	RIDGEFIELD, CT	06877
PASSENGER	C & W GROUP	1209 BAYLOR ST	AUSTIN, TX	78703
PASSION STORY	ROCK & ROLL GROUP	41 BRITAIN ST #200	TORONTO, ONT M5A 1R7	CANADA
PASTOR, RENEE	TV PRODUCER	430 E 57TH ST	NEW YORK, NY	10022
PASTORE, JACK	BASEBALL SCOUT	POST OFFICE BOX 7575	PHILADELPHIA, PA	19101
PASTORELLI, ROBERT	ACTOR	2751 HOLLY RIDGE DR	LOS ANGELES, CA	90068
PASTORNICKY, CLIFF	BASEBALL SCOUT	POST OFFICE BOX 4100	SEATTLE, WA	98104

PATAKI, MICHAEL	DIRECTOR	4068 KRAFT AVE	STUDIO CITY, CA 91604
PATCHETT, TOM	WRITER-PRODUCER	1043 FRANKLIN ST	SANTA MONICA, CA 90403
PATE, MICHAEL	ACTOR	21 BUKDARRA RD	BELLVUE HILL 2023 AUSTRALIA
PATE, STEVE	GOLFER	POST OFFICE BOX 109601	PALM BCH GARDENS, FL 33418
PATEMAN, MICHAEL	DIRECTOR	155 E 35TH ST	NEW YORK, NY 10016
PATERNOSTRO, RUSSELL	FOOTBALL COACH	SAINTS, 1500 POYDRAS ST	NEW ORLEANS, LA 90112
PATERRA, HERB	FOOTBALL COACH	LIONS, 1200 FEATHERSTONE RD	PONTIAC, MI 48432
PATERSON, ALLEN	DIRECTOR-PRODUCER	422 VIEW PARK CT	MILL VALLEY, CA 94941
PATERSON, BILL	ACTOR	GARDNER, 15 KENSINGTON HIGH ST	LONDON W8 5NP ENGLAND
PATIK, VICKIE	TV WRITER	ICM, 8899 BEVERLY BLVD	LOS ANGELES, CA 90048
PATINKIN, MANDY	ACTRESS	200 W 90TH ST	NEW YORK, NY 10024
PATNODE, HAROLD	TV DIRECTOR	6294 OCCOQUAN FOREST DR	MANASSA, VA 22111
PATRIC, JASON	ACTOR	335 N MAPLE DR #250	BEVERLY HILLS, CA 90210
PATRICK, BRONSWELL	BASEBALL	POST OFFICE BOX 2769	HUNTSVILLE, AL 35804
PATRICK, BUTCH	ACTOR	POST OFFICE BOX 857	FARMINGVILLE, NY 11738
PATRICK, DENNIS	ACTOR	5750 WILSHIRE BLVD #512	LOS ANGELES, CA 90036
PATRICK, DENNIS	DIRECTOR	9744 WILSHIRE BLVD #305	BEVERLY HILLS, CA 90212
PATRICK, DICK	SPORTS WRITER	POST OFFICE BOX 500	WASHINGTON, DC 20044
PATRICK, JAMES	HOCKEY	POST OFFICE BOX 90111	ARLINGTON, TX 76004
PATRICK, JOHN	PLAYWRIGHT	FORTUNA HILL ESTATE, BOX 2386	SAINT THOMAS, VI 00801
PATRICK, LOUGENIA	TV WRITER	14955 DICKENS ST #12	SHERMAN OAKS, CA 91403
PATRICK, ROBERT	PLAYWRIGHT	LA MAMA, 74-A E 4TH ST	NEW YORK, NY 10003
PATRICK, TOM	ARTIST	4537 JEFFERSON ST #202	KANSAS CITY, MO 64111
PATRICK, VINCENT	SCREENWRITER	555 W 57TH ST #1230	NEW YORK, NY 10019
PATRIOT	C & W GROUP	POST OFFICE BOX O	EXCELSIOR, MN 55331
PATRIZI, MIKE	BASEBALL	POST OFFICE BOX 7845	COLUMBIA, SC 29202
PATRON, VIRGILIO HOMERO	CONDUCTOR	5055 UNION PACIFIC AVE	LOS ANGELES, CA 90022
PATTEN, ROBERT	ACTOR	24932 MALIBU RD	MALIBU, CA 90265
PATTERSON, BOB	BASEBALL	POST OFFICE BOX 7000	PITTSBURGH, PA 15212
PATTERSON, CRAIG	FOOTBALL	POST OFFICE BOX 888	PHOENIX, AZ 85001
PATTERSON, DANNY	BASEBALL	POST OFFICE BOX 309	GASTONA, NC 28053
PATTERSON, DAVE	BASEBALL	5999 E VAN BUREN ST	PHOENIX, AZ 85008
PATTERSON, DAVID J	FILM PRODUCER	360 PLACE ROYALE	MONTREAL, QUE H2Y 2V1 CANADA
PATTERSON, DICK	ACTOR	10525 STRATHMORE DR	LOS ANGELES, CA 90024
PATTERSON, ELIZABETH J	U S CONGRESSWOMAN	POST OFFICE BOX 1330	SPARTANBURG, SC 29304
PATTERSON, ELVIS	FOOTBALL	RAIDERS, 332 CENTER ST	EL SEGUNDO, CA 90245
PATTERSON, FLOYD	BOXER	SPRINGFIELD RD, BOX #336	NEW PALTZ, NY 12561
PATTERSON, GIL	BASEBALL COACH	POST OFFICE BOX 882	MADISON, WI 53701
PATTERSON, GRADY L, JR	TREASURER	POST OFFICE BOX 11369	COLUMBIA, SC 29211
PATTERSON, JEFF	BASEBALL	POST OFFICE BOX 10336	CLEARWATER, FL 34617
PATTERSON, JEFFREY L	CONDUCTOR	1525 AMHERST AVE #209	LOS ANGELES, CA 90025
PATTERSON, JOHN	BASEBALL	S F GIANTS, CANDLESTICK PARK	SAN FRANICSCO, CA 94124
PATTERSON, JOHN T	TV DIRECTOR	508 N GLEN TRAIL	TOPANGA, CA 90290
PATTERSON, KEN	BASEBALL	1060 W ADDISON ST	CHICAGO, IL 60613
PATTERSON, LAURA J	TV DIRECTOR	5310 CIRCLE DR #107	SHERMAN OAKS, CA 91401
PATTERSON, LORNA	ACTRESS	5028 WILLOW CREST AVE	NORTH HOLLYWOOD, CA 91601
PATTERSON, MELODY	ACTRESS	GRIFFITH, 12959 OXNARD ST #16	VAN NUYS, CA 91401
PATTERSON, MICHAEL	COMPOSER	4342 SAINT CLAIR AVE	STUDIO CITY, CA 91604
PATTERSON, NEVA	ACTRESS	2498 MANDEVILLE CANYON	LOS ANGELES, CA 90049
PATTERSON, RAY	BASKETBALL EXECUTIVE	POST OFFICE BOX 272349	HOUSTON, TX 77277
PATTERSON, RICHARD	WRITER-PRODUCER	135 MEDIO DR	LOS ANGELES, CA 90049
PATTERSON, RICHARD E	COMPOSER	2406 CAMINITO OCEAN COVE	CARDIFF BY THE SEA, CA 92007
PATTERSON, RICK	BASEBALL MANAGER	1090 N EUCLID AVE	SARASOTA, FL 34237
PATTERSON, SHAWN	FOOTBALL	PACKERS, 1265 LOMBARDI AVE	GREEN BAY, WI 54307
PATTERSON, STEVE	BASKETBALL EXECUTIVE	POST OFFICE BOX 272349	HOUSTON, TX 77277
PATTI, SANDI	SINGER	HELVERING, 530 GRAND AVE	ANDERSON, IN 46012
PATTON, DAVID W	MUSIC ARRANGER	126 GRAPEVINE RD	HENDERSONVILLE, TN 37075
PATTON, DAVID, BAND	C & W GROUP	POST OFFICE BOX 1373	LEWISVILLE, TX 75067
PATTON, DONALD	DIRECTOR	9538 JELLICO AVE	NORTHRIDGE, CA 91324
PATTON, JACK	BASEBALL EXECUTIVE	POST OFFICE BOX 11363	RENO, NV 89510
PATTON, JOHNNY	SINGER	POST OFFICE BOX 418	BRENTWOOD, TN 37027
PATTON, LOWELL	BASEBALL EXECUTIVE	POST OFFICE BOX 10031	BAKERSFIELD, CA 93389
PATTON, MARVCUS	FOOTBALL	BILLS, 1 BILLS DR	ORCHARD PARK, NJ 14127
PATTULLO, G ROBSON, III	TV DIRECTOR	308 E 79TH ST #7-A	NEW YORK, NY 10021
PAUL, ADRIAN	ACTOR	STONE MANNERS, 9113 SUNSET BL	LOS ANGELES, CA 90069
PAUL, ALEXANDRA	ACTRESS	190 S CANON DR #201	BEVERLY HILLS, CA 90210
PAUL, BYRON	ACTOR-DIRECTOR	103 S ROCKINGHAM AVE	LOS ANGELES, CA 90049
PAUL, DON MICHAEL	ACTOR	POST OFFICE BOX 5617	BEVERLY HILLS, CA 90213
PAUL, EDDIE	STUNTMAN	STUNTS, 124 NEVADA ST	EL SEGUNDO, CA 90245
PAUL, GEORGE	DIRECTOR	WM MORRIS, 1350 AVE OF AMERICAS	NEW YORK, NY 10019
PAUL, HENRY, BAND	C & W GROUP	210 25TH AVE N #N-101	NASHVILLE, TN 37203
PAUL, JIM	BASEBALL EXECUTIVE	POST OFFICE DRAWER 4797	EL PASO, TX 79914
PAUL, JODY	COMPOSER	1321 S KENISTON AVE	LOS ANGELES, CA 90019
PAUL, MARKUS	FOOTBALL	BEARS, 250 N WASHINGTON RD	LAKE FOREST, IL 60045
PAUL, MIKE	BASEBALL COACH	POST OFFICE BOX 4100	SEATTLE, WA 98104
PAUL, RICHARD	ACTOR	2029 CENTURY PARK E #600	LOS ANGELES, CA 90067
PAUL, STEVE	FILM DIRECTOR	8776 SUNSET BLVD	LOS ANGELES, CA 90069
PAUL, VAUGHN	DIRECTOR	4344 PROMENDE WY	MARINA DEL REY, CA 90292
PAULEY, JANE	TV HOST	271 CENTRAL PARK W #10-E	NEW YORK, NY 10024
PAULING, DR LINUS	CHEMIST-EDUCATOR	DEER FLAT RANCH	BIG SUR, CA 93920
PAULINO, DARIO	BASEBALL	POST OFFICE BOX 4525	MACON, GA 31208
PAULINO, ELVIN	BASEBALL	CUBS, 2ND & RIVERSIDE DR	DES MOINES, IA 50309
PAULSEN, ALBERT	ACTOR	132 S LASKY DR #B	BEVERLY HILLS, CA 90212
PAULSEN, DAVID	TV WRITER-DIRECTOR	15652 WOODFIELD PL	SHERMAN OAKS, CA 91403
PAULSEN, J J	TV WRITER	CAA, 9830 WILSHIRE BLVD	BEVERLY HILLS, CA 90212

Name	Occupation	Address	City
PAULSEN, PAT	COMEDIAN-ACTOR	37 OLD COURTHOUSE SQ #312	SANTA ROSA, CA 95404
PAULSEN, TROY	BASEBALL	POST OFFICE BOX 15050	READING, PA 19612
PAUP, BRYCE	FOOTBALL	PACKERS, 1265 LOMBARDI AVE	GREEN BAY, WI 54307
PAVAN, MARISA	ACTRESS	LORCASTER LOLA MOULOUDJI	
		27, RUE DE RICHELIEU	F-75001 PARIS FRANCE
PAVAROTTI, LUCIANO	TENOR	941 VIA GIARDINI	
		41040 SALICETA SOUTH GUILIANO	MODENA ITALY
PAVELOFF, DAVID	BASEBALL	POST OFFICE BOX 3169	FREDERICK, MD 21701
PAVIN, COREY	GOLFER	POST OFFICE BOX 109601	PALM BCH GARDENS, FL 33418
PAVLICK, GREG	BASEBALL-COACH	METS, 126TH ST & ROOSEVELT AVE	FLUSHING, NY 11368
PAVLIK, ROGER	BASEBALL	POST OFFICE BOX 75089	OKLAHOMA CITY, OK 73147
PAVLOU, GEORGE	FILM DIRECTOR	CCA, 4 COURT LODGE	
		48 SLOANE SQ	LONDON SW1W 8AT
PAVLOVA, NATASHA	ACTRESS	6255 SUNSET BLVD #627	LOS ANGELES, CA 90028
PAWLOWSKI, JOHN	BASEBALL	10233 96TH AVE	EDMONTON, ALB TK5 0A5 CANADA
PAWLOWSKI, TERESA	ACTRESS	301 E 79TH ST #30-S	NEW YORK, NY 10021
PAXMAN, JEREMY	TV HOST-AUTHOR	BBC-TV, 56 WOOD LN	LONDON W12 7RJ ENGLAND
PAXON, BILL	U S CONGRESSMAN	5500 MAIN ST	WILLIAMSVILLE, NY 14221
PAXSON, JOHN	BASKETBALL	980 N MICHIGAN AVE #1600	CHICAGO, IL 60611
PAXTON, BILL	ACTOR	7920 SUNSET BLVD #350	LOS ANGELES, CA 90046
PAXTON, DARRIN	BASEBALL	POLECATS, 608 N SLAPPEY BLVD	ALBANY, GA 31701
PAXTON, GLENN	CONDUCTOR	913 MARCO PL	MARINA DEL REY, CA 90292
PAXTON, TOM	SINGER-SONGWRITER	PRODUCERS, 5109 OAK HAVEN LN	TAMPA, FL 33617
PAYLOR, JIM	BASEBALL UMPIRE	POST OFFICE BOX 716	PLAINVILLE, CT 06062
PAYLOW, CLARK	DIRECTOR	4938 RUBIO AVE	ENCINO, CA 91436
PAYNE, BOB	BASEBALL EXECUTIVE	POST OFFICE BOX 2000	SAN DIEGO, CA 92112
PAYNE, BRUCE	ACTOR	HEATH, PARAMOUNT HOUSE	
		162-170 WARDOUR ST	LONDON W1V 3AT ENGLAND
PAYNE, C F	ARTIST	1800 LEAR ST #5	DALLAS, TX 75215
PAYNE, DEVIN	PRODUCER	3700 VENTURA CANYON AVE	SHERMAN OAKS, CA 91423
PAYNE, DONALD	U S CONGRESSMAN	970 BROAD ST	NEWARK, NJ 07102
PAYNE, FREDA	SINGER	10160 CIELO DR	BEVERLY HILLS, CA 90210
PAYNE, GARELD	COMPOSER-CONDUCTOR	1306 W 1ST ST	COFFEYVILLE, KS 67337
PAYNE, HARRIET	COMPOSER	3254-A SAN AMADEO	LAGUNA HILLS, CA 92653
PAYNE, JOHN	ACTOR	6363 DELAPLANE RD	MALIBU, CA 90265
PAYNE, JULIE	ACTRESS	SEE - PAYNE TOWNE, JULIE	
PAYNE, KENNY	BASKETBALL	POST OFFICE BOX 25040	PHILADELPHIA, PA 19147
PAYNE, LEWIS F	U S CONGRESSMAN	POST OFFICE BOX 256	NELLYSFORD, VA 22958
PAYNE, ROBERT	COMPOSER	27506 DIANE MARIE CIR	SAUGUS, CA 91350
PAYNE, SCHERRIE	SINGER	8544 EASTWOOD RD	LOS ANGELES, CA 90046
PAYNE TOWNE, JULIE	ACTRESS	9200 SUNSET BLVD #625	LOS ANGELES, CA 90069
PAYNTER, ROBERT	CINEMATOGRAPHER	55 WORTHING RD, HORSHAM	SUSSEX ENGLAND
PAYOLA$, THE	ROCK & ROLL GROUP	41 BRITAIN ST #200	TORONTO, ONT M5A 1R7 CANADA
PAYS, AMANDA	ACTRESS-MODEL	1724 LAS FLORES DR	GLENDALE, CA 91207
PAYS, HOWARD	ACTOR-AGENT	CCA, 4 COURT LODGE	
		48 SLOANE SQ	LONDON SW1W 8AT ENGLAND
PAYTON, DOUGLAS	ACTOR	730 ASHLAND AVE #A	SANTA MONICA, CA 90405
PAYTON, GARY	BASKETBALL	POST OFFICE BOX C-900911	SEATTLE, WA 98109
PAYTON, WALTER	FOOTBALL	1251 E GOLF RD	SCHAUMBURG, IL 60195
PAYTON-WRIGHT, PAMELA	ACTRESS	21 E 93RD ST	NEW YORK, NY 10028
PAZIK, MIKE	BASEBALL-INSTRUCTOR	ORIOLE PARK, 333 W CAMDEN ST	BALTIMORE, MD 21201
PEACE, LYNCH	SINGER	TRENDA, 18747 SHERMAN WY	RESEDA, CA 91335
PEACE, STEVE	FILM PRODUCER	430 DAVIDSON ST	CHULA VISTA, CA 90210
PEACE CORPSE	ROCK & ROLL GROUP	POST OFFICE BOX 242	POMONA, CA 91769
PEAKER, E J	ACTRESS	4935 DENSMORE AVE	ENCINO, CA 91436
PEALE, DR NORMAN VINCENT	EVANGELIST-AUTHOR	1025 5TH AVE	NEW YORK, NY 10028
PEARCE, CHRISTOPHER	FILM EXECUTIVE	8200 WILSHIRE BLVD	BEVERLY HILLS, CA 90211
PEARCE, JEFF	BASEBALL	POST OFFICE BOX 611	WATERLOO, IA 50704
PEARCE, RICHARD	DIRECTOR	767 PASEO MIRAMAR	PACIFIC PALISADES, CA 90271
PEARCY, STEVE	SINGER	1818 ILLION ST	SAN DIEGO, CA 92110
PEARL, BARRY	ACTOR	2029 CENTURY PARK E #600	LOS ANGELES, CA 90067
PEARL, BILL	BODYBUILDER	POST OFFICE BOX 1080	PHOENIX, OR 97535
PEARL, FREDERICK	ACTOR	18 LAFAYETTE AVE	MIDDLETON, NY 10940
PEARL, LESLIE	SINGER	1101 N KING'S HWY #107	CHERRY HILL, NJ 08034
PEARL, MINNIE	SINGER-ACTRESS	874 CURTISWOOD LN	NASHVILLE, TN 37204
PEARL, RENEE	ACTRESS	BRAMSON, 240 CENTRAL PARK S	NEW YORK, NY 10019
PEARLBERG, IRVING	WRITER	11829 SUNSHINE TERR	STUDIO CITY, CA 91604
PEARLBERG, NANCY	ACTRESS	11829 SUNSHINE TERR	STUDIO CITY, CA 91604
PEARLMAN, STEPHEN	ACTOR	5224 RIVERTON AVE	NORTH HOLLYWOOD, CA 91601
PEARLSTEIN, DAVID B	COMPOSER	2147 HOLLY DR	LOS ANGELES, CA 90068
PEARSON, ALBIE	BASEBALL	CCF, RR #1, BOX 109	LINDALE, TX 75771
PEARSON, DURK J	SCIENTIST-AUTHOR	POST OFFICE BOX 1067	HOLLYWOOD, FL 33022
PEARSON, EUAN	TV WRITER-DIRECTOR	4 BEECHES RD, FARNHAM, COMMON	BUCKS SL2 3PR ENGLAND
PEARSON, GLENN	TV DIRECTOR	15810 KENTFIELD ST	DETROIT, MI 48223
PEARSON, JAYICE	FOOTBALL	CHIEFS, 1 ARROWHEAD DR	KANSAS CITY, MO 64129
PEARSON, KEVIN	BASEBALL	POST OFFICE BOX 23290	NASHVILLE, TN 37202
PEARSON, LINLEY	ATTORNEY GENERAL	STATE HOUSE BUILDING	INDIANAPOLIS, IN 46204
PEARSON, NOEL	FILM PRODUCER	CAA, 9830 WILSHIRE BLVD	BEVERLY HILLS, CA 90212
PEARSON, PAULETTE	SINGER-ACTRESS	WASHINGTON, 4604 PLACIDIA AVE	TOLUCA LAKE, CA 91602
PEARSON, RICHARD	ACTOR	EDWARDS, 275 KENNINGTON RD	LONDON SE1 6BY ENGLAND
PEARSON, RONALD	TV DIRECTOR	41793 SYCAMORE DR	NOVI, MI 48050
PEARSON, SCOTT	HOCKEY	NORDIQUES, 2205 AVE DU COLISEE	QUEBEC, QUE G1L 4W7 CANADA
PEARSON, TONY	BODYBUILDER	POST OFFICE BOX 299	NORTHRIDGE, CA 91328
PEART, PAULINE	ACTRESS	LM AGENCY, 213 EDGWARE RD	LONDON W2 1ES ENGLAND
PEASE, DON J	U S CONGRESSMAN	JACKSON BETTS FEDERAL BLDG	MANSFIELD, OH 44092

PEASE, JOHN	FOOTBALL COACH	SAINTS, 1500 POYDRAS ST	NEW ORLEANS, LA	90112
PEASE, PATSY	ACTRESS	13538 VALLEY HEART DR	SHERMAN OAKS, CA	91403
PEATMAN, LEIGHTON	WRITER	667 LACHMAN LN	PACIFIC PALISADES, CA	90272
PEBBLES	SINGER-SONGWRITER	8730 SUNSET BLVD #PH-W	LOS ANGELES, CA	90069
PEBLEY, ED	BASEBALL SCOUT	333 W 35TH ST	CHICAGO, IL	60616
PECCATIELLO, LARRY	FOOTBALL COACH	POST OFFICE BOX 17247 (DULLES)	WASHINGTON, DC	20041
PECHIN, CHRISTOPHER	TV DIRECTOR	11565 ADDISON ST	NORTH HOLLYWOOD, CA	91601
PECK, BOB	ACTOR	MARKHAM AND FROGGATT, LTD		
		JULIAN HOUSE, 4 WINDMILL ST	LONDON W1P 1HF	ENGLAND
PECK, BRIAN	ACTOR-DIRECTOR	13201 HANEY PL	LOS ANGELES, CA	90049
PECK, CLARE	ACTRESS	703 9TH ST #3	SANTA MONICA, CA	90402
PECK, GREGORY	ACTOR	POST OFFICE BOX 837	BEVERLY HILLS, CA	90213
PECK, KIMI ZAN	SCREENWRITER	8955 BEVERLY BLVD	WEST HOLLYWOOD, CA	90048
PECK, RAY	SINGER	POST OFFICE BOX 256577	CHICAGO, IL	60625
PECK, ROBERT NEWTON	AUTHOR	500 SWEETWATER CLUB CIR	LONGWOOD, FL	32779
PECK, STEPHEN	DIRECTOR-PRODUCER	1039 MAPLE ST	SANTA MONICA, CA	90405
PECK, STEVE	BASEBALL	POST OFFICE BOX 12	MIDLAND, TX	79702
PECKHAM, PETER	BASEBALL EXECUTIVE	POST OFFICE BOX 2000	SAN DIEGO, CA	92112
PECOTA, BILL	BASEBALL	METS, 126TH ST & ROOSEVELT AVE	FLUSHING, NY	11368
PEDEN, JOHN H B	DIRECTOR	168 5TH AVE	NEW YORK, NY	10010
PEDERSEN, ALLEN	HOCKEY	BRUINS, 150 CAUSEWAY ST	BOSTON, MA	02114
PEDERSEN, JUDY	ARTIST	96 GREENE ST	NEW YORK, NY	10012
PEDERSEN, TED	TV WRITER	2620 OAKWOOD AVE	VENICE, CA	90291
PEDERSON, BARRY	HOCKEY	PENGUINS, CIVIC ARENA, CENTRE AV	PITTSBURGH, PA	15219
PEDERSON, MARK	HOCKEY	FLYERS, SPECTRUM, PATTISON PL	PHILADELPHIA, PA	19148
PEDERSON, RUFUS J, JR	TV DIRECTOR	45 CREEK RD	FAIRFAX, CA	93930
PEDERSON, STU	BASEBALL	CHIEFS, MAC ARTHUR STADIUM	SYRACUSE, NY	13208
PEDRAZA, RODNEY	BASEBALL	POLECATS, 608 N SLAPPEY BLVD	ALBANY, GA	31701
PEDRE, JORGE	BASEBALL	CUBS, 2ND & RIVERSIDE DR	DES MOINES, IA	50309
PEDRIANA, LESA ANN	MAKE-UP ARTIST-MODEL	MARCUS, 6916 MELROSE AVE	LOS ANGELES, CA	90038
PEDRIQUE, AL	BASEBALL	POST OFFICE BOX 3665	OMAHA, NE	68103
PEEBLES, ANN	SINGER	TRENDA, 18747 SHERMAN WY	RESEDA, CA	91335
PEEBLES, DANNY	FOOTBALL	BROWNS, 80 1ST ST	BEREA, OH	44017
PEEK, TIM	BASEBALL	POST OFFICE BOX 11087	TACOMA, WA	98411
PEELER, H ELMO	COMPOSER-CONDUCTOR	2646 WOODSTOCK RD	LOS ANGELES, CA	90046
PEEPLES, NIA	ACTRESS-TV HOST	3575 W CAHUENGA BLVD #520	LOS ANGELES, CA	90068
PEEPLES, SAMUEL A	WRITER-PRODUCER	11371 QUAIL CREEK RD	NORTHRIDGE, CA	91326
PEERCE, LARRY	FILM DIRECTOR	7731 FIRENZE AVE	LOS ANGELES, CA	90046
PEETE, N GARLAND	TV DIRECTOR	67 W 68TH ST	NEW YORK, NY	10023
PEETE, ROBERT L	TV WRITER	3850 CRESTWAY DR	LOS ANGELES, CA	90043
PEETE, RODNEY	FOOTBALL	LIONS, 1200 FEATHERSTONE RD	PONTIAC, MI	48432
PEETE, WILLIE	FOOTBALL COACH	PACKERS, 1265 LOMBARDI AVE	GREEN BAY, WI	54307
PEETERS, BARBARA	DIRECTOR	11600 SAN VICENTE BLVD	LOS ANGELES, CA	90049
PEGASUS	ROCK & ROLL GROUP	41 BRITAIN ST #200	TORONTO, ONT M5A 1R7	CANADA
PEGGY SUE & SONNY WRIGHT	VOCAL DUO	TAYLOR, 2401 12TH AVE S	NASHVILLE, TN	37204
PEGRAM, ERRIC	FOOTBALL	FALCONS, SUWANEE RD AT I-85	SUWANEE, GA	30174
PEGUERO, JULIO	BASEBALL	POST OFFICE BOX 3449	SCRANTON, PA	18505
PEGUES, STEVE	BASEBALL	STARS, 850 LAS VEGAS BLVD N	LAS VEGAS, NV	89101
PEGUESE, WILLIS	FOOTBALL	OILERS, 6910 FANNIN ST	HOUSTON, TX	77070
PEIRCE, NEAL	COLUMNIST	THE WASHINGTON POST		
		WRITERS GROUP		
		1150 15TH ST, NW	WASHINGTON, DC	20071
PEKKONEN, DONNA	TV WRITER	13518 CONTOUR DR	SHERMAN OAKS, CA	91423
PEL, WINSLOW PINNEY	ARTIST	HACK GREEN RD	POUND RIDGE, NY	10576
PELAVIN, DANIEL	ARTIST	46 COMMERCE ST	NEW YORK, NY	10014
PELDON, ASHLEY	ACTRESS	888 7TH AVE #602	NEW YORK, NY	10106
PELEKOUDAS, LEE	BASEBALL EXECUTIVE	POST OFFICE BOX 4100	SEATTLE, WA	98104
PELFREY, DANNY	COMPOSER	6457 HESPERIA AVE	RESDEDA, CA	91335
PELIKAN, LISA	ACTRESS	POST OFFICE BOX 57593	SHERMAN OAKS, CA	91403
PELISSIE, JEAN-MARIE	DIRECTOR	333 E 34TH ST	NEW YORK, NY	10016
PELL, CLAIBORNE	U S SENATOR	418 FEDERAL BUILDING	PROVIDENCE, RI	02903
PELLANT, GARY	BASEBALL SCOUT	333 W 35TH ST	CHICAGO, IL	60616
PELLATT, JOHN	TV-FILM EXECUTIVE	AUSTRALIAN FILM COMMISION		
		VICTORY HOUSE, 99-101 REGENT ST		
		2ND FLOOR	LONDON W1	ENGLAND
PELLEGRIN, RAYMOND	ACTOR	EUROP' ACTEURS AGENCE		
		35 RUE DE RIVOLI	PARIS 75004	FRANCE
PELLEGRINI, MARIO	FILM DIRECTOR	1601 HOLLINDALE DR	ALEXANDRA, VA	22306
PELOSI, NANCY	U S CONGRESSWOMAN	450 GOLDEN GATE AVE #13407	SAN FRANCISCO, CA	94102
PELTIER, DAN	BASEBALL	POST OFFICE BOX 75089	OKLAHOMA CITY, OK	73147
PELTZER, KURT	BASEBALL	POST OFFICE BOX 1295	CLINTON, IA	52733
PELUCE, MEENO	ACTOR	2713 N KEYSTONE ST	BURBANK, CA	91504
PELUSO, ANTHONY D	CONDUCTOR	246 ARON PL	ANAHEIM, CA	92804
PELUSO, LISA	ACTRESS	103 W 80TH ST #4-C	NEW YORK, NY	10024
PELUSO, MIKE	HOCKEY	BLACKHAWKS, 1800 W MADISON ST	CHICAGO, IL	60612
PEMBER, RON	ACTOR	DAWSON, 47 COURTFIELD RD #9	LONDON SW7 4DB	ENGLAND
PEMBERTON, RUDY	BASEBALL	POST OFFICE BOX 2785	LAKELAND, FL	33806
PEMBLETON, ARTHUR	DIRECTOR	423 "G" ST	SALT LAKE CITY, UT	84103
PENA, ALEJANDRO	BASEBALL	POST OFFICE BOX 4064	ATLANTA, GA	30302
PENA, ANTHONY	ACTOR	CBS-TV, "YOUNG & THE RESTLESS"		
		7800 BEVERLY BLVD #3305	LOS ANGELES, CA	90036
PENA, ELIZABETH	ACTRESS	9301 WILSHIRE BLVD #312	BEVERLY HILLS, CA	90210
PENA, FRANK	BASEBALL SCOUT	BREWERS, 201 S 46TH ST	MILWAUKEE, WI	53214
PENA, GERONIMO	BASEBALL	250 STADIUM PLAZA	ST LOUIS, MO	63102
PENA, JIM	BASEBALL	5999 E VAN BUREN ST	PHOENIX, AZ	85008

Name	Occupation	Address	City	Zip
PENA, ORLANDO	BASEBALL-SCOUT	333 W 35TH ST	CHICAGO, IL	60616
PENA, PEDRO	BASEBALL	5999 E VAN BUREN ST	PHOENIX, AZ	85008
PENA, RAMON	BASEBALL-SCOUT	TIGERS, TIGER STADIUM	DETROIT, MI	48216
PENA, TONY	BASEBALL	FENWAY PARK, 4 YAWKEY WY	BOSTON, MA	02215
PENARANDA, JAIRO	FOOTBALL COACH	RAMS, 2327 W LINCOLN BLVD	ANAHEIM, CA	92801
PENBERTHY, MARK	ARTIST	47 GREENE ST	NEW YORK, NY	10013
PENDER, SHAWN	BASEBALL SCOUT	POST OFFICE BOX 288	HOUSTON, TX	77001
PENDERGRASS, TEDDY	SINGER-SONGWRITER	1505 FLAT ROCK RD	NARBERTH, PA	19072
PENDLE, FRANK	ACTOR	17197 SIERRA HWY 36	CANYON COUNTRY, CA	91351
PENDLETON, AUSTIN	COMEDIAN	155 E 76TH ST	NEW YORK, NY	10021
PENDLETON, TERRY	BASEBALL	POST OFFICE BOX 4064	ATLANTA, GA	30302
PENDLETON, WYMAN	ACTOR	36 BEDFORD ST	NEW YORK, NY	10014
PENDRELL, ERNEST	DIRECTOR	POST OFFICE BOX 7218	GLENDALE, CA	91205
PENDRY, JOE	FOOTBALL COACH	CHIEFS, 1 ARROWHEAD DR	KANSAS CITY, MO	64129
PENGHLIS, THAAO	ACTOR	MTA, 9320 WILSHIRE BL, 3RD FL	BEVERLY HILLS, CA	90212
PENGUINS, THE	VOCAL GROUP	DUNCAN, 708 W 137TH ST	GARDENA, CA	90247
PENHALL, BRUCE	ACTOR	319 36TH ST #A	MANHATTAN BEACH, CA	90266
PENLAND, ROY TIMOTHY	DIRECTOR	133 VIRGINIA AVE	GLENDALE, CA	91202
PENN, ARTHUR	DIRECTOR	ICM, 40 W 57TH ST	NEW YORK, NY	10019
PENN, CHRISTOPHER	ACTOR	6728 ZUMIREZ DR	MALIBU, CA	90265
PENN, IRVING	PHOTOGRAPHER	POST OFFICE BOX 934 (FDR)	NEW YORK, NY	10150
PENN, LEO	FILM WRITER-DIRECTOR	6728 ZUMIREZ DR	MALIBU, CA	90265
PENN, MARINA	ACTRESS	1270 N HAVENHURST DR #12-B	LOS ANGELES, CA	90046
PENN, MATTHEW	ACTOR	355 W 85TH ST	NEW YORK, NY	10024
PENN, NINA	ACTRESS	1605 N CAHUENGA BLVD #202	LOS ANGELES, CA	90028
PENN, SEAN	ACTOR-DIRECTOR	POST OFFICE BOX 2630	MALIBU, CA	90265
PENN & TELLER	COMEDIANS-MAGICIANS	POST OFFICE BOX 1196	NEW YORK, NY	10185
PENNARIO, LEONARD	PIANIST-COMPOSER	1140 CALLE VISTA DR	BEVERLY HILLS, CA	90210
PENNEY, EDMUND F	WRITER-DIRECTOR	2144 ROCKLEDGE RD	LOS ANGELES, CA	90068
PENNEY, SCOTT	TALENT AGENT	MTA, 9320 WILSHIRE BL, 3RD FL	BEVERLY HILLS, CA	90212
PENNINGTON, ANN	ACTRESS-MODEL	701 N OAKHURST DR	BEVERLY HILLS, CA	90210
PENNINGTON, BILL	MUSIC ARRANGER	190 TOWNSHIP DR	HENDERSONVILLE, TN	37075
PENNINGTON, BRAD	BASEBALL	POST OFFICE BOX 3169	FREDERICK, MD	21701
PENNINGTON, JANICE	MODEL-ACTRESS	433 N CAMDEN DR #600	BEVERLY HILLS, CA	90210
PENNINGTON, MARLA	ACTRESS	3800 BARHAM BLVD #303	LOS ANGELES, CA	90068
PENNINGTON, MICHAEL	ACTOR	41 MARLBOROUGH HILL	LONDON NW8	ENGLAND
PENNINO, JOHNNY	SINGER	POST OFFICE BOX 1830	GRETNA, LA	70053
PENNOCK, CHRISTOPHER	ACTOR	25150 1/2 MALIBU RD	MALIBU, CA	90265
PENNY, JOE	ACTOR	10453 SARAH ST	NORTH HOLLYWOOD, CA	91602
PENNY, JOHN	RECORD EXEC-TAL AGENT	30 GUINAN ST	WALTHAM, MA	02154
PENNY, JOHN, BAND	C & W GROUP	30 GUINAN ST	WALTHAM, MA	02154
PENNY, SYDNEY	ACTRESS	3090 CALVERT CT	CAMARILLO, CA	93010
PENNY, TIMOTHY J	U S CONGRESSMAN	POST OFFICE BOX 3148	MANKATO, MN	56001
PENNYE, DARWIN	BASEBALL	POST OFFICE BOX 15757	HARRISBURG, PA	17105
PENNYFEATHER, WILLIAM	BASEBALL	POST OFFICE BOX 450	BUFFALO, NY	14205
PENVERN, ANDRE	ACTOR	7 RUE NEUVE NOTRE DAME	VERSAILLES 78000	FRANCE
PENYCATE, JOHN	TV DIRECTOR-PRODUCER	BBC-TV, LIME GROVE	LONDON W12 7RJ	ENGLAND
PEOPLES, DAVID	GOLFER	POST OFFICE BOX 109601	PALM BCH GARDENS, FL	33418
PEOPLES, DAVID	SCREENWRITER	SHAPIRO, 8827 BEVERLY BLVD	LOS ANGELES, CA	90048
PEOPLES, DON	ACTOR	78 W 12TH ST	NEW YORK, NY	10011
PEOPLES, MARILYN	MAKE-UP ARTIST	POST OFFICE BOX 1541	BRONX, NY	10451
PEP, WILLIE	BOXER	36 WAYLAND ST	HARTFORD, CT	06114
PEPITONE, JOE	BASEBALL	667 E 79TH ST	BROOKLYN, NY	11236
PEPLOE, MARK	FILM WRITER-DIRECTOR	WRITERS GUILD, 430 EDGWARE RD	LONDON W2 1EH	ENGLAND
PEPPARD, GEORGE	ACTOR-DIRECTOR	POST OFFICE BOX 1643	BEVERLY HILLS, CA	90213
PEPPER, BUDDY	ACTOR-COMPOSER	JAREST, 4516 LENNOX AVE	SHERMAN OAKS, CA	91423
PEPPER, MARTHA	ACTRESS	881 7TH AVE #1007	NEW YORK, NY	10019
PEPPERMAN, PAUL E	SCREENWRITER	8955 BEVERLY BLVD	WEST HOLLYWOOD, CA	90048
PEPPERMAN, RICHARD	TV DIRECTOR	215 W 75TH ST	NEW YORK, NY	10023
PEPPIATT, FRANK	TV WRITER	9579 1/2 LIME ORCHARD RD	BEVERLY HILLS, CA	90210
PERALTA, CHRISTINA	ACTRESS	7080 HOLLYWOOD BLVD #704	HOLLYWOOD, CA	90028
PERAZA, OZZIE	BASEBALL	POST OFFICE BOX 230	HAGERSTOWN, MD	21740
PERCELAY, DAVID	TV EXECUTIVE	CBS-TV, 524 W 57TH ST	NEW YORK, NY	10019
PERCEVAL, DAVID	ACTOR	10845 LINDBROOK DR #3	LOS ANGELES, CA	90024
PERCIVAL, LANCE	TV PERSONALITY	STONE, 25 WHITEHALL	LONDON SW1A 2BS	ENGLAND
PERCUDANI, DICK	BASKETBALL	SUNS, 2910 N CENTRAL AVE	PHOENIX, AZ	85012
PERDUE, WILL	BASKETBALL	980 N MICHIGAN AVE #1600	CHICAGO, IL	60611
PERE UBU	ROCK & ROLL GROUP	ROUGH TRADE RECORDS		
		61-71 COLLIER	LONDON N1	ENGLAND
PEREIRA, CORD	BASEBALL EXECUTIVE	HAWKS, 5600 N GLENWOOD	BOISE, ID	83714
PERENCHIO, ANDREW	FILM-TV EXECUTIVE	23526 MALIBU COLONY DR #77	MALIBU, CA	90265
PEREW, THOMAS JOHN	TV WRITER	1327 N LAUREL AVE #16	LOS ANGELES, CA	90046
PEREZ, BEBAN	BASEBALL	POST OFFICE BOX 3496	DAVENPORT, IA	52808
PEREZ, CARLOS	BASEBALL	POST OFFICE BOX 6748	ROCKFORD, IL	61125
PEREZ, CESAR	BASEBALL	5301 NW 12TH AVE	FORT LAUDERDALE, FL	33309
PEREZ, DARIO	BASEBALL	300 STADIUM WY	DAVENPORT, FL	33837
PEREZ, DAUD	COMPOSER	1022 S STANLEY AVE	LOS ANGELES, CA	90019
PEREZ, DAVID	BASEBALL	POST OFFICE BOX 4448	TULSA, OK	74159
PEREZ, EDDIE	BASEBALL	POST OFFICE BOX 16683	GREENVILLE, SC	29606
PEREZ, EDUARDO	BASEBALL	POST OFFICE BOX 1742	PALM SPRINGS, CA	92263
PEREZ, EUSEBIO	BASEBALL SCOUT	POST OFFICE BOX 2000	ANAHEIM, CA	92803
PEREZ, JOSE	ACTOR	10100 SANTA MONICA BLVD #1600	LOS ANGELES, CA	90067
PEREZ, LIVIA E	DIRECTOR	DGA, 110 W 57TH ST	NEW YORK, NY	10019
PEREZ, MELIDO	BASEBALL	N Y YANKEES, YANKEE STADIUM	BRONX, NY	10451
PEREZ, MICHAEL	BASEBALL	RURAL ROUTE 2, BOX 165-A	YAUCO, PR	00768

PEREZ, MIKE	BASEBALL	250 STADIUM PLAZA	ST LOUIS, MO	63102
PEREZ, PASCUAL	BASEBALL	N Y YANKEES, YANKEE STADIUM	BRONX, NY	10451
PEREZ, PEDRO	BASEBALL	POST OFFICE BOX 4488	WINSTON-SALEM, NC	27115
PEREZ, PHILIP J	DIRECTOR	408 8TH ST	MANHATTAN BEACH, CA	90266
PEREZ, ROBERT	BASEBALL	633 JESSAMINE ST	KNOXVILLE, TN	37917
PEREZ, TONY	ACTOR	1801 AVE OF THE STARS #1250	LOS ANGELES, CA	90067
PEREZ, TONY	BASEBALL-COACH	LOS FLORES #113	SANTURCE, PR	00911
PEREZ, VLADIMIR	BASEBALL	300 STADIUM WY	DAVENPORT, FL	33837
PEREZ, YORKIS	BASEBALL	POST OFFICE BOX 6667	RICHMOND, VA	23230
PEREZCHICA, TONY	BASEBALL	INDIANS, CLEVELAND STADIUM	CLEVELAND, OH	44114
PERFECT, MR	WRESTLER	SEE - HENNING, CURT "MR PERFECT"		
PERIGNY, DON	BASEBALL	1090 N EUCLID AVE	SARASOTA, FL	34237
PERINE, PARKE	WRITER-PRODUCER	13370 CONTOUR DR	SHERMAN OAKS, CA	91423
PERINI, DANIEL J	COMPOSER	5821 WHEELHOUSE LN	AGOURA, CA	91301
PERISIC, ZORAN	WRITER-PRODUCER	L'EPINE SMITH, 10 WYNDHAM PL	LONDON W1H 1AS	ENGLAND
PERITO, NICK	CONDUCTOR	5798 PENLAND RD	CALABASAS, CA	91302
PERKEL, JANE	ACTRESS	442 E 20TH ST #8-B	NEW YORK, NY	10009
PERKINS, ANTHONY	ACTOR-WRITER	2840 SEATTLE DR	LOS ANGELES, CA	90046
PERKINS, BRUCE	FOOTBALL	POST OFFICE BOX 535000	INDIANPOLIS, IN	46253
PERKINS, CARL	SINGER-SONGWRITER	459 COUNTRY CLUB LN	JACKSON, TN	38301
PERKINS, CARL C	U S CONGRESSMAN	POST OFFICE BOX 486	MOREHEAD, KY	40351
PERKINS, CHRISTOPHER	ACTOR	10845 LINDBROOK DR #3	LOS ANGELES, CA	90024
PERKINS, CURT	ACTOR	SQUIRE, 204 TINKLER ST	LA FAYETTE, IN	47901
PERKINS, ELIZABETH	ACTRESS	CAA, 9830 WILSHIRE BLVD	BEVERLY HILLS, CA	90212
PERKINS, FRANK S	COMPOSER	3057 PATRICIA AVE	LOS ANGELES, CA	90064
PERKINS, GIL	ACTOR	1841 FAIRBURN AVE	LOS ANGELES, CA	90025
PERKINS, JACK	ACTOR	19620 WELLS DR	TARZANA, CA	91356
PERKINS, JAMES N	CABLE EXECUTIVE	6 E 68TH ST	NEW YORK, NY	10021
PERKINS, MILLIE	ACTRESS	4311 ALCOVE AVE #9	STUDIO CITY, CA	91604
PERKINS, PAUL	BASEBALL	POST OFFICE BOX 30160	SAN BERNARDINO, CA	92413
PERKINS, RICHARD	DIRECTOR	729 MUSKINGUM AVE	PACIFIC PALISADES, CA	90272
PERKINS, RON	ACTOR	400 W 43RD ST #45-G	NEW YORK, NY	10036
PERKINS, ROWLAND	TALENT AGENT	CAA, 9830 WILSHIRE BLVD	BEVERLY HILLS, CA	90212
PERKINS, SAM	BASKETBALL	POST OFFICE BOX 10	INGLEWOOD, CA	90306
PERKINS, STEVE	SPORTS WRITER	UPS, 4900 MAIN ST, 9TH FLOOR	KANSAS CITY, MO	64112
PERKINS, SUZANNE	ACTRESS	853 1/2 N FULLER AVE	LOS ANGELES, CA	90046
PERKINS, TONY	ACTOR-DIRECTOR	SEE - PERKINS, ANTHONY		
PERKINS, TONY	COMEDIAN	EAI, 2211 INDUSTRIAL BLVD	SARASOTA, FL	33580
PERKINS, WALTER	CINEMATOGRAPHER	1428 TIGERTAIL RD	LOS ANGELES, CA	90049
PERLEE, CHARLES R	CONDUCTOR	463 W RIVERSIDE DR #A	BURBANK, CA	91506
PERLMAN, ITZHAK	VIOLINIST	173 RIVERSIDE DR #3-C	NEW YORK, NY	10024
PERLMAN, JON	BASEBALL	1019 FORREST LN	CARTHAGE, TX	75633
PERLMAN, RHEA	ACTRESS	31020 BROAD BEACH RD	MALIBU, CA	90265
PERLMAN, RON	ACTOR	345 N MAPLE DR #183	BEVERLY HILLS, CA	90210
PERLOVE, PAUL	TV WRITER-PRODUCER	211 S BEVERLY DR #206	BEVERLY HILLS, CA	90212
PERLOW, ROBERT	TV WRITER	447 1/2 KELTON AVE	LOS ANGELES, CA	90024
PERLOZZO, SAM	BASEBALL COACH	REDS, 100 RIVERFRONT STADIUM	CINCINNATI, OH	45202
PERNA, BOBBY	BASEBALL	POST OFFICE BOX 4669	CHARLESTON, WV	25304
PERON, ISABEL	PRESIDENT	MORETO 3, LOS JERONIMOS	MADRID	SPAIN
PERONA, JOE	BASEBALL	POST OFFICE BOX 2785	LAKELAND, FL	33806
PERONE, ANTHONY	TV DIRECTOR	4541 NW 9TH AVE	POMPANO, FL	33064
PEROPAT, GLORIA	DIRECTOR	55 MORTON ST	NEW YORK, NY	10014
PEROZO, DANNY	BASEBALL	POST OFFICE BOX 7845	COLUMBIA, SC	29202
PERRANOSKI, RON	BASEBALL-COACH	1000 ELYSIAN PARK DR	LOS ANGELES, CA	90012
PERREAU, GIGI	ACTRESS	268 N BOWLING GREEN WY	LOS ANGELES, CA	90049
PERREN, FREDERICK J	COMPOSER	4028 COLFAX AVE	STUDIO CITY, CA	91604
PERRET, GENE	TV WRITER	1485 W HAVEN RD	SAN MARINO, CA	91108
PERRIE, GREGG	ACTOR	3832 LOMINA AVE	LONG BEACH, CA	90808
PERRIMAN, BRETT	FOOTBALL	LIONS, 1200 FEATHERSTONE RD	PONTIAC, MI	48432
PERRIN, JACQUES	ACTOR	REGGANE FILMS, 38 RUE LEON	PARIS 75018	FRANCE
PERRIN, VIC	ACTOR	4218 TROOST AVE #17	STUDIO CITY, CA	91604
PERRINE, VALERIE	ACTRESS-MODEL	8271 MELROSE AVE #110	LOS ANGELES, CA	90046
PERRY, ALFRED	CONDUCTOR	13900 TAHITI WY #129	MARINA DEL REY, CA	90292
PERRY, CHRIS	GOLFER	POST OFFICE BOX 109601	PALM BCH GARDENS, FL	33418
PERRY, DRU-ANNE	ACTRESS	RITCH, 1443 N HAYWORTH AVE	LOS ANGELES, CA	90046
PERRY, ELIZABETH	ACTRESS	850 7TH AVE #1003	NEW YORK, NY	10019
PERRY, FELTON	ACTOR	540 S SAINT ANDREWS PL #5	LOS ANGELES, CA	90020
PERRY, FRANK	DIRECTOR-PRODUCER	655 PARK AVE	NEW YORK, NY	10021
PERRY, GAYLORD	BASEBALL	320 E JEFFERIES ST	GAFFNEY, SC	29342
PERRY, GERALD	BASEBALL	250 STADIUM PLAZA	ST LOUIS, MO	63102
PERRY, GERALD	FOOTBALL	RAMS, 2327 W LINCOLN BLVD	ANAHEIM, CA	92801
PERRY, GREGORY	MUSIC ARRANGER	POST OFFICE BOX 50939	NASHVILLE, TN	37205
PERRY, HERBERT	BASEBALL	POST OFFICE BOX 3452	KINSTON, NC	28502
PERRY, HERBERT O	COMPOSER-CONDUCTOR	POST OFFICE BOX 664	RANCHO SANTE FE, CA	92067
PERRY, HOWARD G	COMPOSER-CONDUCTOR	2729 E 58TH ST	HUNTINGTON PARK, CA	90255
PERRY, JIMMY	ACT-WRI-DIR	STONE, 25 WHITEHALL	LONDON SW1A 2BS	ENGLAND
PERRY, JOE	SINGER	POST OFFICE BOX 703	ALLSTON, MA	02134
PERRY, JOHN	TV PRODUCER	LORIMAR, 4024 RADFORD AVE	STUDIO CITY, CA	91604
PERRY, JOHN BENNETT	ACTOR	10100 SANTA MONICA BLVD #1600	LOS ANGELES, CA	90067
PERRY, JOYCE	TV WRITER	2250 N GOWER ST	HOLLYWOOD, CA	90068
PERRY, KENNY	GOLFER	POST OFFICE BOX 109601	PALM BCH GARDENS, FL	33418
PERRY, LEMUEL	COMPOSER	6140 CANTERBURY DR #6-202	CULVER CITY, CA	90230
PERRY, LUKE	ACTOR	5700 WILSHIRE BLVD #575	LOS ANGELES, CA	90036
PERRY, MATT	BASEBALL EXECUTIVE	POST OFFICE BOX 64939	FAYETTEVILLE, NC	28306
PERRY, MICHAEL DEAN	FOOTBALL	BROWNS, 80 1ST ST	BEREA, OH	44017

Name	Occupation	Address	City/State	Zip/Country
PERRY, MORRIS	ACTOR	SARABAND, 265 LIVERPOOL RD	LONDON N1 1LX	ENGLAND
PERRY, PAT	BASEBALL	1115 W FRANKLIN	TAYLORVILLE, IL	62568
PERRY, ROD	FOOTBALL COACH	SEAHAWKS, 11220 NE 53RD ST	KIRKLAND, WA	98033
PERRY, ROGER	ACTOR	3800 BARHAM BLVD #303	LOS ANGELES, CA	90068
PERRY, SCOTT	MUSIC EDITOR	7637 CAPISTRANO AVE	CANOGA PARK, CA	91304
PERRY, SIMON	WRITER-PRODUCER	UMBRELLA, TWICKENHAM STUDIOS		
		SAINT MARGARETS	TWICKENHAM TW1 2AW	ENGLAND
PERRY, STEVE	SINGER-COMPOSER	POST OFFICE BOX 97	LARKSPUR, CA	94939
PERRY, TIM	BASKETBALL	SUNS, 2910 N CENTRAL AVE	PHOENIX, AZ	85012
PERRY, WILLIAM "THE FRIG"	FOOTBALL	BEARS, 250 N WASHINGTON RD	LAKE FOREST, IL	60045
PERRYMAN, JOHN	ACTOR	12456 VENTURA BLVD #1	STUDIO CITY, CA	91604
PERRYMAN, MACK	CABLE EXECUTIVE	HBO, 1100 6TH AVE	NEW YORK, NY	10036
PERRYMAN, ROBERT	FOOTBALL	BRONCOS, 13655 BRONCOS PKWY	ENGLEWOOD, CO	80112
PERSCHKE, GREG	BASEBALL	CANADIANS, 4601 ONTARIO ST	VANCOUVER, BC V5V 3H4	CANADA
PERSHING, D'VAUGHN E	CONDUCTOR	19142 SYLVAN ST	RESEDA, CA	91335
PERSIAN WOLF	ROCK & ROLL GROUP	1419 8TH AVE #4-N	BROOKLYN, NY	11215
PERSICO, JOSEPH E	AUTHOR	VIKING PRESS, 40 W 23RD ST	NEW YORK, NY	10010
PERSING, TIM	BASEBALL	POST OFFICE BOX 48	VISALIA, CA	93279
PERSKY, LISA JANE	ACTRESS	POST OFFICE BOX 5617	BEVERLY HILLS, CA	90213
PERSKY, WILLIAM	WRITER-DIRECTOR	7450 PALO VISTA DR	LOS ANGELES, CA	90046
PERSOFF, NEHEMIAH	ACTOR	5847 TAMPA AVE	TARZANA, CA	91356
PERSON, CHUCK	BASKETBALL	PACERS, 300 E MARKET ST	INDIANAPOLIS, IN	46204
PERSON, ROBERT	BASEBALL	1090 N EUCLID AVE	SARASOTA, FL	34237
PERSONS, PETER	GOLFER	POST OFFICE BOX 109601	PALM BCH GARDENS, FL	33418
PERSSON, CARINA	ACTRESS-MODEL	1116 SMITH ST #220	HONOLULU, HI	96817
PERSUADERS, THE	VOCAL GROUP	1500 BROADWAY #160	NEW YORK, NY	10036
PERSUASIONS, THE	VOCAL GROUP	101 W 57TH ST #2-A	NEW YORK, NY	10019
PERTWEE, BILL	ACTOR	STONE, 25 WHITEHALL	LONDON SW1A 2BS	ENGLAND
PERTWEE, JON	ACTOR-COMEDIAN	26 SEATON CLOSE, LYNDEN GATE		
		PUTNEY HEATH	LONDON SW15 3JJ	ENGLAND
PERZIGIAN, JERRY	TV WRITER-PRODUCER	948 14TH ST #5	SANTA MONICA, CA	90403
PESCI, JOE	ACTOR	CAA, 9830 WILSHIRE BLVD	BEVERLY HILLS, CA	90212
PESCIA, LISA	ACTRESS	8485 MELROSE PL #E	LOS ANGELES, CA	90069
PESCOW, DONNA	ACTRESS	POST OFFICE BOX 93575	LOS ANGELES, CA	90093
PESETSKY, ALAN	WRITER-PRODUCER	185 W END AVE	NEW YORK, NY	10023
PESKY, JOHNNY	BASEBALL-EXECUTIVE	FENWAY PARK, 4 YAWKEY WY	BOSTON, MA	02215
PET SHOP BOYS, THE	ROCK & ROLL GROUP	101-109 LADBROKE GROVE	LONDON W11	ENGLAND
PETAGINE, ROBERTO	BASEBALL	POST OFFICE BOX 422229	KISSIMMEE, FL	34742
PETALE, ALEXANDER	ACTOR	11015 AQUA VISTA ST	NORTH HOLLYWOOD, CA	91602
PETE, LAWRENCE	FOOTBALL	LIONS, 1200 FEATHERSTONE RD	PONTIAC, MI	48432
PETER, LAURENCE J	AUTHOR-EDUCATOR	2332 VIA ANACAPA	PALOS VERDES, CA	90274
PETER, PAUL & MARY	VOCAL TRIO	7250 BEVERLY BLVD #102	LOS ANGELES, CA	90036
PETEREK, JEFF	BASEBALL	POST OFFICE BOX 5	HARBERT, MI	49115
PETERMAN, DON	CINEMATOGRAPHER	POST OFFICE BOX 2230	HOLLYWOOD, CA	90078
PETERMAN, STEVEN	ACTOR	2314 N BEACHWOOD DR	LOS ANGELES, CA	90068
PETERMAN, STEVEN	TV WRITER-PRODUCER	8383 WILSHIRE BLVD #923	BEVERLY HILLS, CA	90211
PETERMANN, FRED	DIRECTOR	2115 CASTILIAN DR	HOLLYWOOD, CA	90068
PETERS, ARLEN S	WRITER	2847 NICHOLS CANYON PL	LOS ANGELES, CA	90046
PETERS, AUDREY	ACTRESS	145 W 45TH ST #1204	NEW YORK, NY	10036
PETERS, BARBARA	TV DIRECTOR	4243 BAKMAN AVE	NORTH HOLLYWOOD, CA	91602
PETERS, BARRY	FILM EDITOR	L'EPINE SMITH, 10 WYNDHAM PL	LONDON W1H 1AS	ENGLAND
PETERS, BERNADETTE	ACTRESS-SINGER	277 W END AVE	NEW YORK, NY	10023
PETERS, BETH	ACTRESS-SINGER	POST OFFICE BOX 38641	VAN NUYS, CA	90038
PETERS, BOB	ARTIST	POST OFFICE BOX 7014	PHOENIX, AZ	85011
PETERS, BROCK	ACT-SING-WRI-PROD	POST OFFICE BOX 8156	NORTH HOLLYWOOD, CA	91608
PETERS, CHARLIE	SCREENWRITER	151 S EL CAMINO DR	BEVERLY HILLS, CA	90212
PETERS, CLARKE	ACTOR-SINGER	MARKHAM AND FROGGATT, LTD		
		JULIAN HOUSE, 4 WINDMILL ST	LONDON W1P 1HF	ENGLAND
PETERS, DAN C	DIRECTOR	201 E 60TH ST	NEW YORK, NY	10021
PETERS, DON	BASEBALL	POST OFFICE BOX 2769	HUNTSVILLE, AL	35804
PETERS, DONALD A	WRITER	12801 CHANDLER BLVD	NORTH HOLLYWOOD, CA	91607
PETERS, DOUG	BASEBALL	300 STADIUM WY	DAVENPORT, FL	33837
PETERS, FLOYD	FOOTBALL COACH	VIKINGS, 9520 VIKING DR	EDEN PRAIRIE, MN	55344
PETERS, GORDON	ACTOR	20 ELM TREE AVE, ESTER	SURREY	ENGLAND
PETERS, HANK	BASEBALL EXECUTIVE	INDIANS, CLEVELAND STADIUM	CLEVELAND, OH	44114
PETERS, HOUSE, JR	ACTOR	999 DONALD ST, OLD HARBOR	WHEDLKY ISLAND, WA	98277
PETERS, JEAN	ACTRESS	507 N PALM DR	BEVERLY HILLS, CA	90210
PETERS, JON	FILM PRODUCER	9 BEVERLY PARK	BEVERLY HILLS, CA	90210
PETERS, KATHARYN WELLS	ACTRESS	1252 1/2 S RIDGELEY DR	LOS ANGELES, CA	90019
PETERS, KELLY JEAN	ACTRESS	1717 N BEVERLY GLEN BLVD	LOS ANGELES, CA	90024
PETERS, LANCE	SCREENWRITER-NOVELIST	UNDERWORLD PRODUCTIONS, LTD		
		SANDRINGHAM, UNIT 14		
		70-78 CROOK RD, CENTENNIAL PARK	SYDNEY 2021	AUSTRALIA
PETERS, MARGIE	SINGER	PERLE, 4475 VINELAND AVE	STUDIO CITY, CA	91602
PETERS, MARJORIE	TV WRITER	1027 23RD ST	SANTA MONICA, CA	90403
PETERS, MICHAEL	DIRECTOR	DGA, 110 W 57TH ST	NEW YORK, NY	10019
PETERS, MICHAEL	DIRECTOR-CHOREO	10000 SANTA MONICA BLVD #305	LOS ANGELES, CA	90067
PETERS, MIKE	CARTOONIST	POST OFFICE BOX 1061	DAYTON, OH	45401
PETERS, REED	BASEBALL	POST OFFICE BOX 3448	SHREVEPORT, LA	71133
PETERS, RICKY	BASEBALL MANAGER	POST OFFICE BOX 651	AUBURN, NY	13021
PETERS, ROBERTA	SINGER	FIELDS, 64 GARDEN RD	SCARSDALE, NY	10583
PETERS, SUZANNA	ACTRESS	12021 WILSHIRE BLVD #230	LOS ANGELES, CA	90025
PETERS, TOM	COLUMNIST	TRIBUNE, 64 E CONCORD ST	ORLANDO, FL	32801
PETERS, WILLIAM	WRITER-PRODUCER	166 BANK ST #4-A	NEW YORK, NY	10014
PETERSEN, CHRIS	DIRECTOR	10520 LE CONTE AVE	LOS ANGELES, CA	90024

Name	Occupation	Address	City	Zip
PETERSEN, DONALD G	SCREENWRITER	8955 BEVERLY BLVD	WEST HOLLYWOOD, CA	90048
PETERSEN, JIM	BASKETBALL	GOLDEN STATE WARRIORS		
		OAKLAND COLISEUM ARENA		
		NIMITZ FWY & HEGENBERGER RD	OAKLAND, CA	94621
PETERSEN, MARK	TV DIRECTOR	8 CHOLMELEY PARK	LONDON N6	ENGLAND
PETERSEN, PAT	ACTOR	1634 VETERAN AVE	LOS ANGELES, CA	90025
PETERSEN, PAUL	ACTOR	145 S FAIRFAX AVE #310	LOS ANGELES, CA	90036
PETERSEN, WILLIAM L	ACTOR	3330 W CAHUENGA BLVD #400	LOS ANGELES, CA	90068
PETERSEN, WOLFGANG	FILM DIRECTOR	BAVARIA ATELIER		
		8022 GEISELGASTEIG	MUNICH	GERMANY
PETERSMANN, DIRK	TV DIRECTOR	2950 BELDEN DR	HOLLYWOOD, CA	90068
PETERSON, ADAM	BASEBALL	STARS, 850 LAS VEGAS BLVD N	LAS VEGAS, NV	89101
PETERSON, AMANDA	ACTRESS	11350 VENTURA BLVD #206	STUDIO CITY, CA	91604
PETERSON, BART	BASEBALL	14100 SIX MILE CYPRESS PKWY	FORT MYERS, FL	33912
PETERSON, BRIAN	BASEBALL COACH	800 HOME RUN LN	MEMPHIS, TN	38104
PETERSON, CASSANDRA "ELVIRA"	ACTRESS-PRODUCER	POST OFFICE BOX 38246	HOLLYWOOD, CA	90038
PETERSON, COLLIN	U S CONGRESSMAN	714 LAKE AVE #107	DETROIT LAKE, MN	56501
PETERSON, DIANE	ACTRESS-STUNTWOMAN	1801 AVE OF THE STARS #640	LOS ANGELES, CA	90067
PETERSON, DICK	TV DIRECTOR	2030 CASA GRANDE ST	PASADENA, CA	91104
PETERSON, DONNA J	COSTUME DESIGNER	13949 VENTURA BLVD #309	SHERMAN OAKS, CA	91423
PETERSON, FRED	BASEBALL SCOUT	ORIOLE PARK, 333 W CAMDEN ST	BALTIMORE, MD	21201
PETERSON, HARDING	BASEBALL EXECUTIVE	N Y YANKEES, YANKEE STADIUM	BRONX, NY	10451
PETERSON, HERB	ACTOR	201 CLUB DR	WOODMERE, NY	11598
PETERSON, LUCKY	SINGER-MUSICIAN	POST OFFICE BOX 60234	CHICAGO, IL	60660
PETERSON, MAURICE	SCREENWRITER	555 W 57TH ST #1230	NEW YORK, NY	10019
PETERSON, PAUL	ACTOR	145 S FAIRFAX AVE #310	LOS ANGELES, CA	90036
PETERSON, PETE	U S CONGRESSMAN	120 S CALEDONIA ST	MARIANNA, FL	32446
PETERSON, RICHARD	TV DIRECTOR	2080 CASA GRANDE ST	PASADENA, CA	91104
PETERSON, RICK	BASEBALL COACH	CANADIANS, 4601 ONTARIO ST	VANCOUVER, BC V5V 3H4	CANADA
PETERSON, ROBERT W	AUDITOR	STATE CAPITOL, 600 E BOULEVARD	BISMARCK, ND	58505
PETERSON, ROBERTA	TV DIRECTOR	252 JACKSON ST	NEWTON CENTRE, MA	02159
PETERSON, ROBYN	ACTRESS	9300 WILSHIRE BLVD #410	BEVERLY HILLS, CA	90212
PETERSON, ROD	TV PRODUCER	LORIMAR, 4024 RADFORD AVE	STUDIO CITY, CA	91604
PETERSON, RODERICK	TV WRITER	4451 BEN AVE	NORTH HOLLYWOOD, CA	91607
PETERSON, ROGER	ACTOR	225 E 74TH ST #5-P	NEW YORK, NY	10021
PETERSON, ROGER	NEWS CORRESPONDENT	ABC NEWS, 1717 DE SALES ST, NW	WASHINGTON, DC	20036
PETERSON, THEODORE R	COMPOSER	18565 ARMINTA ST	RESEDA, CA	91335
PETHERBRIDGE, EDWARD	ACTOR	HEATH, PARAMOUNT HOUSE		
		162-170 WARDOUR ST	LONDON W1V 3AT	ENGLAND
PETIT, MICHEL	HOCKEY	MAPLE LEAFS, 60 CARLTON ST	TORONTO, ONT M5B 1L1	CANADA
PETIT, PASCALE	ACTOR	ART SERVICE MANAGEMENT		
		78 CHAMPS-ELYSEES	PARIS 75008	FRANCE
PETIT, TOM	TV EXECUTIVE	NBC-TV, 30 ROCKEFELLER PLAZA	NEW YORK, NY	10112
PETITBON, RICHIE	FOOTBALL COACH	POST OFFICE BOX 17247 (DULLES)	WASHINGTON, DC	20041
PETITCLERC, DEANE B	SCREENWRITER	UTA, 9560 WILSHIRE BL, 5TH FL	BEVERLY HILLS, CA	90212
PETITTO, DAVE	TV WRITER	21919 GALVEZ ST	WOODLAND HILLS, CA	91364
PETKOVSEK, MARK	BASEBALL	POST OFFICE BOX 450	BUFFALO, NY	14205
PETRALLI, GENO	BASEBALL	POST OFFICE BOX 90111	ARLINGTON, TX	76004
PETRANTO, RUSSELL	TV DIRECTOR	R/W/G, 8428 MELROSE PL #C	LOS ANGELES, CA	90069
PETRE, CARL	TV DIRECTOR	309 BOOTHBAY CT	SAINT CHARLES, MO	63301
PETRI, THOMAS	U S CONGRESSMAN	14 WESTERN AVE	FON DE LAC, WI	54935
PETRICK, JACK	TV EXECUTIVE	PUBLIC BROADCASTING		
		1111 16TH ST, NW	WASHINGTON, DC	20036
PETRICONE, ARTHUR	FILM DIRECTOR	9 CACCAMO TRAIL	WESTPORT, CT	06880
PETRIE, ANN	WRI-DIR-PROD	77 BLEECKER ST	NEW YORK, NY	10012
PETRIE, DANIEL M	FILM-TV DIRECTOR	13201 HANEY PL	LOS ANGELES, CA	90049
PETRIE, DANIEL M, JR	FILM DIRECTOR	500 S BUENA VISTA ST #2-B-5	BURBANK, CA	91521
PETRIE, DONALD M	ACTOR-DIRECTOR	9220 SUNSET BLVD #311	LOS ANGELES, CA	90069
PETRIE, DOROTHEA G	WRITER	13201 HANEY PL	LOS ANGELES, CA	90049
PETROCELLI, RICO	BASEBALL-MANAGER	POST OFFICE BOX 2365	PAWTUCKET, RI	02861
PETROFF, PAUL	DIRECTOR	20 GUTHEIL LN	GREAT NECK, NY	11024
PETROFF, TOM	BASEBALL EXECUTIVE	TIGERS, TIGER STADIUM	DETROIT, MI	48216
PETROU, DAVID MICHAEL	WRITER-PRODUCER	2739 "O" ST, NW	WASHINGTON, DC	20007
PETROVIC, DRAZEN	BASKETBALL	700 NE MULTNOMAH ST #600	PORTLAND, OR	97232
PETROWSKI, ALLEN	CONDUCTOR	16306 BLACKHAWK ST	GRANADA HILLS, CA	91344
PETRUCELLI, ANTHONY J	DIRECTOR	103 5TH AVE	NEW YORK, NY	10003
PETRY, DAN	BASEBALL	1808 CARTLEN DR	PLACENTIA, CA	92670
PETRY, STAN	FOOTBALL	CHIEFS, 1 ARROWHEAD DR	KANSAS CITY, MO	64129
PETRYNI, MICHAEL	TV WRITER	17817 SAN FERNANDO MISS BLVD	GRANADA HILLS, CA	91344
PETTIET, CHRISTOPHER	ACTOR	10351 SANTA MONICA BLVD #211	LOS ANGELES, CA	90025
PETTIFER, JULIAN	TV DIRECTOR	9 ROLAND GARDENS	LONDON SW7 3PE	ENGLAND
PETTIFORD, VALARIE	ACTRESS	ABC-TV, "ONE LIFE TO LIVE"		
		56 W 66TH ST	NEW YORK, NY	10023
PETTINI, JOE	BASEBALL MANAGER	POST OFFICE BOX 5599	LITTLE ROCK, AR	72215
PETTIS, GARY	BASEBALL	13 MILLINGTON CT	ALAMEDA, CA	94501
PETTIT, JOANNA	ACTRESS	10100 SANTA MONICA BLVD #700	LOS ANGELES, CA	90067
PETTIT, TOM	TV CORRESPONDENT	NBC NEWS, 4001 NEBRASKA AV, SW	WASHINGTON, DC	20016
PETTITTE, STEVE	BASEBALL	POST OFFICE BOX 22093	GREENSBORO, NC	27420
PETTY, KYLE	AUTO RACER	830 W LEXINGTON RD	HIGH POINT, NC	27262
PETTY, LORI	ACTRESS	POST OFFICE BOX 5617	BEVERLY HILLS, CA	90213
PETTY, RICHARD	AUTO RACER	ROUTE #3, BOX 631	RANDLEMAN, NC	27317
PETTY, ROSS	ACTOR	24 KING ST	NEW YORK, NY	10014
PETTY, TOM & THE HEARTBREAKERS	ROCK & ROLL GROUP	LOOKOUT, 506 SANTA MONICA BLVD	SANTA MONICA, CA	90401
PEVEY, MARTY	BASEBALL	POST OFFICE BOX 6212	TOLEDO, OH	43614
PEVSNER, DONALD L	COLUMNIST	UPS, 4900 MAIN ST, 9TH FLOOR	KANSAS CITY, MO	64112

Name	Occupation	Address	City	Zip
PEVSNER, THOMAS	FILM PRODUCER	13 WILDWOOD GROVE, NORTH END	LONDON NW3	ENGLAND
PEYSER, ANTHONY L	WRITER	415 N SYCAMORE AVE	LOS ANGELES, CA	90036
PEYSER, ARNOLD	TV WRITER	141 TIGERTAIL RD	LOS ANGELES, CA	90049
PEYSER, JOHN	WRITER-PRODUCER	19721 REDWING ST	WOODLAND HILLS, CA	91364
PEYSER, LOIS	TV WRITER	141 TIGERTAIL RD	LOS ANGELES, CA	90049
PEYSER, MICHAEL	DIRECTOR	DGA, 110 W 57TH ST	NEW YORK, NY	10019
PEYSER, PENNY	ACTRESS	9200 SUNSET BLVD #710	LOS ANGELES, CA	90069
PEYSON, ROBERT	DIRECTOR	333 PEARL ST	NEW YORK, NY	10038
PEYTON, HARLEY	TV PRODUCER	CAA, 9830 WILSHIRE BLVD	BEVERLY HILLS, CA	90212
PEYTON, PHILIP	DIRECTOR	138 E 78TH ST	NEW YORK, NY	10021
PEYTON, STEVE	PRODUCER	20249 BLYTHE ST	CANOGA PARK, CA	91306
PEZZONI, RON	BASEBALL	POST OFFICE BOX 30160	SAN BERNARDINO, CA	92413
PFAFF, JASON	BASEBALL	POST OFFICE BOX 2785	LAKELAND, FL	33806
PFEIFER, HOWARD R	CONDUCTOR	911 N KINGS RD #103	LOS ANGELES, CA	90069
PFEIFFER, CONSTANCE	ACTRESS-WRITER	16124 SUNSET BLVD #B	PACIFIC PALISADES, CA	90272
PFEIFFER, DEDEE	ACTRESS	UTA, 9560 WILSHIRE BL, 5TH FL	BEVERLY HILLS, CA	90212
PFEIFFER, FRANK	DIRECTOR	1629 N 24TH AVE	MELROSE PARK, IL	60160
PFEIFFER, MICHELLE	ACTRESS	ICM, 8899 BEVERLY BLVD	LOS ANGELES, CA	90048
PFENNING, WESLEY	ACTRESS	6106 GLEN OAK	HOLLYWOOD, CA	90068
PFISTER, WALTER J, JR	TV WRITER-PRODUCER	36 W 44TH ST #1201	NEW YORK, NY	10036
PFIZER, BERYL	TV WRITER-PRODUCER	349 E 62ND ST	NEW YORK, NY	10021
PFLIEGER, JEAN	ACTRESS	1441 S SHENANDOAH ST #2	LOS ANGELES, CA	90035
PFUND, RANDY	BASKETBALL COACH	POST OFFICE BOX 10	INGLEWOOD, CA	90306
PHANTOM LIMBS, THE	ROCK & ROLL GROUP	1230 GRANT AVE #531	SAN FRANCISCO, CA	94133
PHANTOMS, THE	VOCAL GROUP	POST OFFICE BOX 830	ALBANY, NY	12201
PHANTON OPERA	ROCK & ROLL GROUP	POST OFFICE BOX 21	SAN PEDRO, CA	90733
PHARES, RON	FOOTBALL REFEREE	NFL, 410 PARK AVE	NEW YORK, NY	10022
PHELAN, ANNA HAMILTON	SCREENWRITER	CAA, 9830 WILSHIRE BLVD	BEVERLY HILLS, CA	90212
PHELAN, JOSEPH	ACTOR	10845 LINDBROOK DR #3	LOS ANGELES, CA	90024
PHELPS, ALAN	SINGER-GUITARIST	ROUTE #1, BOX 520	MOUNT VERNON, TX	75457
PHELPS, DICK	BASEBALL EXECUTIVE	POST OFFICE BOX 8550	STOCKTON, CA	95208
PHELPS, STUART	DIRECTOR	3617 CODY RD	SHERMAN OAKS, CA	91403
PHIFER, ROMAN	FOOTBALL	RAMS, 2327 W LINCOLN BLVD	ANAHEIM, CA	92801
PHILBIN, BILL	CINEMATOGRAPHER	7715 SUNSET BLVD #150	LOS ANGELES, CA	90046
PHILBIN, JACK	TV PRODUCER	19704 BOB-O-LINK DR	HIALEAH, FL	33015
PHILBIN, JOHN	ACTOR	KOHNER, 9169 SUNSET BLVD	LOS ANGELES, CA	90069
PHILBIN, MARY	ACTRESS	8788 CORAL SPRINGS CT #8202	HUNTINGTON BEACH, CA	92646
PHILBIN, REGIS	TV HOST	955 PARK AVE	NEW YORK, NY	10029
PHILCOX, TODD	FOOTBALL	BROWNS, 80 1ST ST	BEREA, OH	44017
PHILIP, HRH PRINCE	PRINCE	DUKE OF EDINBURGH KG KT OM		
		BUCKINGHAM PALACE	LONDON SW1	ENGLAND
PHILIPS, EMO	COMEDIAN	1780 BROADWAY #1201	NEW YORK, NY	10019
PHILIPS, LEE	TV DIRECTOR	11939 GORHAM AVE #104	LOS ANGELES, CA	90049
PHILIPSON, NEIL	TV DIRECTOR	52 W 87TH ST	NEW YORK, NY	10024
PHILLIPS, ANDY	COMPOSER-CONDUCTOR	2475 TIERRA DR	LOS OSOS, CA	93402
PHILLIPS, BOBBIE	MODEL	SWIMSUIT INTERNATIONAL		
		801 2ND AVE	NEW YORK, NY	10017
PHILLIPS, CHYNNA	ACTRESS-SINGER	938 2ND ST #302	SANTA MONICA, CA	90403
PHILLIPS, CLYDE B	FILM PRODUCER	13395 CONTOUR DR	SHERMAN OAKS, CA	91423
PHILLIPS, DAVE	BASEBALL UMPIRE	29 HOLLOWAY DR	LAKE SAINT LOUIS, MO	63367
PHILLIPS, DEE	BASEBALL SCOUT	TIGERS, TIGER STADIUM	DETROIT, MI	48216
PHILLIPS, DICK	BASEBALL EXECUTIVE	CANADIANS, 4601 ONTARIO ST	VANCOUVER, BC V5V 3H4	CANADA
PHILLIPS, ERICA	COSTUME DESIGNER	149 S BEDFORD DR	BEVERLY HILLS, CA	90212
PHILLIPS, GRACE	ACTRESS	ABC-TV, "ONE LIFE TO LIVE"		
		56 W 66TH ST	NEW YORK, NY	10023
PHILLIPS, J R	BASEBALL	POST OFFICE BOX 12	MIDLAND, TX	79702
PHILLIPS, JAMES C	COMPOSER	10963 WHIPPLE ST #6	NORTH HOLLYWOOD, CA	91602
PHILLIPS, JEFF	ACTOR	CBS-TV, "THE GUIDING LIGHT"		
		222 E 44TH ST	NEW YORK, NY	10017
PHILLIPS, JOE	FOOTBALL	POST OFFICE BOX 609609	SAN DIEGO, CA	92160
PHILLIPS, JOHN	ACTOR	MARMONT MANAGEMENT, LTD		
		LANGHAM HOUSE, 308 REGENT ST	LONDON W1R 5AL	ENGLAND
PHILLIPS, JOSEPH RILEY	SINGER-GUITARIST	213 S MAIN ST	CROSSVILLE, TN	38555
PHILLIPS, JULIA	FILM PRODUCER	2534 BENEDICT CANYON DR	BEVERLY HILLS, CA	90210
PHILLIPS, JULIANNE	ACTRESS-MODEL	POST OFFICE BOX 5617	BEVERLY HILLS, CA	90213
PHILLIPS, LANCE	ACTOR	953 17TH ST #E	SANTA MONICA, CA	90403
PHILLIPS, LESLIE	ACTOR-DIRECTOR	BELFRAGE, 68 SAINT JAMES'S ST	LONDON SW1A 1LE	ENGLAND
PHILLIPS, LESLIE	COLUMNIST	POST OFFICE BOX 500	WASHINGTON, DC	20044
PHILLIPS, LOU DIAMOND	ACTOR	1999 AVE OF THE STARS #2850	LOS ANGELES, CA	90067
PHILLIPS, MAC KENZIE	ACTRESS-SINGER	AIMEE, 13743 VICTORY BLVD	VAN NUYS, CA	91401
PHILLIPS, MEL	FOOTBALL COACH	DOLPHINS, 2269 NW 199TH ST	MIAMI, FL	33056
PHILLIPS, MICHAEL S	FILM PRODUCER	1501 GILCREST DR	BEVERLY HILLS, CA	90210
PHILLIPS, MICHELLE	ACTRESS-SINGER	10557 TROON AVE	LOS ANGELES, CA	90064
PHILLIPS, NIC	TV DIRECTOR	WHITE ACRE COTTAGE, WHITE LN		
		GUILFORD	SURREY GU4 8PR	ENGLAND
PHILLIPS, RALPH	TV WRITER	8383 WILSHIRE BLVD #923	BEVERLY HILLS, CA	90211
PHILLIPS, RONALD	DIRECTOR	1317 EL HITO CT	PACIFIC PALISADES, CA	90272
PHILLIPS, SAMANTHA	ACTRESS	335 N MAPLE DR #360	BEVERLY HILLS, CA	90210
PHILLIPS, SHAWN	SINGER-SONGWRITER	TWM MGMT, 641 LEXINGTON AVE	NEW YORK, NY	10022
PHILLIPS, SIAN	ACTRESS	14 PETHERTON RD	LONDON N5	ENGLAND
PHILLIPS, STEVE	BASEBALL	POST OFFICE BOX 22093	GREENSBORO, NC	27420
PHILLIPS, STU	GUITARIST	1001 FRANKLIN RD	BRENTWOOD, TN	37027
PHILLIPS, TEDDY S, SR	CONDUCTOR	6252 1/2 NITA AVE	WOODLAND HILLS, CA	91364
PHILLIPS, TONY	BASEBALL	TIGERS, TIGER STADIUM	DETROIT, MI	48216
PHILLIPS, WADE	FOOTBALL COACH	BRONCOS, 13655 BRONCOS PKWY	ENGLEWOOD, CO	80112

PHILLIPS, WENDY	ACTRESS	3231 GREENFIELD AVE	LOS ANGELES, CA 90034
PHILLIPS, WILLIAM F	WRITER-PRODUCER	8721 SANTA MONICA BLVD #21	WEST HOLLYWOOD, CA 90069
PHILLIPS, WOOLF	COMPOSER-CONDUCTOR	16319 VILLAGE 16	CAMARILLO, CA 93010
PHINNEY, DAVID G	FILM DIR-PROD	3629 CORINTH AVE	LOS ANGELES, CA 90066
PHOENIX, RIVER	ACTOR	1450 BELFAST DR	LOS ANGELES, CA 90069
PHOENIX, ROGER	TV DIRECTOR	ROUTE #1, BOX 404	STONY POINT, NY 10980
PHOENIX, STEVE	BASEBALL	POST OFFICE BOX 2769	HUNTSVILLE, AL 35804
PHOTOGLO, JIM	SINGER-SONGWRITER	1453 YALE ST #B	SANTA MONICA, CA 90404
PHYLISS, SANDRA	ACTRESS	KROLL, 390 W END AVE	NEW YORK, NY 10024
PIA	ACTRESS-MODEL	SEE - REYES, PIA	
PIANO, VINCENT C	TV PRODUCER	MIZLOU PROGRAMMING, 352 7TH AVE	NEW YORK, NY 10001
PIATNIK, MIKE	BASEBALL SCOUT	POST OFFICE BOX 90111	ARLINGTON, TX 76004
PIATT, DOUG	BASEBALL	POST OFFICE BOX 15757	HARRISBURG, PA 17105
PIATT, JEAN	ACTOR	9 PL VAUBAN	PARIS 75007 FRANCE
PIAZZA, MIKE	BASEBALL	POST OFFICE BOX 28268	SAN ANTONIO, TX 78228
PICARD, NICOLE	ACTRESS	10000 RIVERSIDE DR #6	TOLUCA LAKE, CA 91602
PICARD, PAUL	TV PRODUCER	4000 WARNER BLVD	BURBANK, CA 91522
PICARDO, ROBERT	ACTOR	4926 COMMONWEALTH AVE	LA CANADA, CA 91011
PICASSO, PALOMA	JEWELERY DESIGNER	1021 PARK AVE	NEW YORK, NY 10021
PICCIOLO, ROB	BASEBALL-COACH	POST OFFICE BOX 2000	SAN DIEGO, CA 92112
PICCIRILLO, CHARLES	DIRECTOR	18 PARSONAGE RD	GREENWICH, CT 06830
PICCOLI, MICHEL	ACTOR	11 RUE DE LIONS SAINT PAUL	PARIS 4E FRANCE
PICCOLO, JOHN D	DIRECTOR	4 E 89TH ST	NEW YORK, NY 10028
PICERNI, CHARLES F	DIRECTOR	5113 TOPEKA DR	TARZANA, CA 91356
PICERNI, PAUL	ACTOR	19119 WELLS DR	TARZANA, CA 91356
PICHARDO, HIPOLITO	BASEBALL	800 HOME RUN LN	MEMPHIS, TN 38104
PICHINSON, MARTY	TALENT AGENT	518 N LA CIENEGA BLVD	LOS ANGELES, CA 90048
PICK, CHUCK	CELEBRITY CAR PARKER	CHUCK'S PARKING COMPANY	
		13437 VENTURA BLVD #218	SHERMAN OAKS, CA 91423
PICKEL, BILL	FOOTBALL	N Y JETS, 1000 FULTON AVE	HEMPSTEAD, NY 11550
PICKENS, CHARLES	ARTIST	1351 OCEAN PARK WALK #106	SANTA MONICA, CA 90405
PICKENS, CHEROKEE WATIE RILEY	SINGER	CUDE, 519 N HALIFAX AVE	DAYTON BEACH, FL 32018
PICKENS, PIC	SINGER	CUDE, 519 N HALIFAX AVE	DAYTONA BEACH, FL 32018
PICKERING, BILL	SINGER	1522 28TH ST	LUBBOCK, TX 79405
PICKERING, DONALD	ACTOR	BACK COURT, MANOR HOUSE	
		EASTLEEACH	GLOS ENGLAND
PICKETT, BOB	BASEBALL	RED SOX, CHAIN O'LAKES PARK	WINTER HAVEN, FL 33880
PICKETT, CHARLIE	SINGER-GUITARIST	TWIN TONE RECORDS CO	
		44 NORTHWEST AVE	MIAMI, FL 33169
PICKETT, CINDY	ACTRESS	2433 GREEN VALLEY RD	LOS ANGELES, CA 90046
PICKETT, JAY	ACTOR	NBC-TV, "DAYS OF OUR LIVES"	
		3000 W ALAMEDA AVE	BURBANK, CA 91523
PICKETT, OWEN B	U S CONGRESSMAN	2710 VIRGINIA BEACH BLVD	VIRGINIA BEACH, VA 23452
PICKETT, WILSON	SINGER	200 W 57TH ST #910	NEW YORK, NY 10019
PICKETTS, BILL	BASEBALL	POST OFFICE BOX 11363	RENO, NV 89510
PICKING, KEN	SPORTS WRITER	POST OFFICE BOX 500	WASHINGTON, DC 20044
PICKLE, J J	U S CONGRESSMAN	763 FEDERAL BUILDING	AUSTIN, TX 78701
PICKLES, CAROLYN	ACTRESS	CONWAY, 18-21 JERMYN ST	LONDON SW1 ENGLAND
PICKLES, CHRISTINA	ACTRESS	137 S WESTGATE AVE	LOS ANGELES, CA 90049
PICKLES, JIM	BASEBALL EXECUTIVE	POST OFFICE BOX 1721	SPARTANBURG, SC 29304
PICKLES, VIVIAN	ACTRESS	PETERS, FRASER & DUNLOP, LTD	
		5TH FLOOR, THE CHAMBERS	
		CHELSEA HARBOUR, LOT RD	LONDON SW10 OXF ENGLAND
PICKNELL, DORSENA	BASEBALL EXECUTIVE	POST OFFICE BOX 75089	OKLAHOMA CITY, OK 73147
PICKREN, STACEY	ACTRESS	3291 TARECO DR	LOS ANGELES, CA 90068
PICKUP, RONALD	ACTOR	LONDON MGT, 235-241 REGENT ST	LONDON W1R 4PH ENGLAND
PICO, JEFF	BASEBALL	POST OFFICE BOX 11087	TACOMA, WA 98411
PICOLA, LENNY	BASEBALL	POST OFFICE BOX 36407	LOUISVILLE, KY 40233
PICON-BOREL, RAYMOND	PHOTOGRAPHER	16 RUE CASSINI	PARIS 75014 FRANCE
PICOTA, LEN	BASEBALL	POST OFFICE BOX 15757	HARRISBURG, PA 17105
PICOTA, RENE	BASEBALL SCOUT	REDS, 100 RIVERFRONT STADIUM	CINCINNATI, OH 45202
PIECES OF A DREAM	JAZZ GROUP	HARMON, 1127 E HORTTER ST	PHILADELPHIA, PA 19138
PIECH, PETER M	TV PRODUCER	2565 S OCEAN BLVD	HIGHLAND BEACH, FL 33487
PIECKA, ANDREW	ACTOR	1605 N MARTEL AVE #35	LOS ANGELES, CA 90046
PIED PIPERS, THE	VOCAL GROUP	32500 CONCORD DR #252	MADISON HEIGHTS, MI 48071
PIEDMONT, LEON	SCREENWRITER	8955 BEVERLY BLVD	WEST HOLLYWOOD, CA 90048
PIEL, MIKE	FOOTBALL	RAMS, 2327 W LINCOLN BLVD	ANAHEIM, CA 92801
PIENOVI, ANDY	BASEBALL SCOUT	SKYDOME, 300 BREMMER BL #3200	TORONTO, ONT M5V 3B3 CANADA
PIER, VIRGINIA LEE	ACTRESS-DANCER	POST OFFICE BOX 1263	NEW YORK, NY 10009
PIERAULD, GUY	ACTOR	145 RUE DU GAL LECLERC	SAINT-LEU-LA-FORET 953 FRANCE
PIERCE, BRADLEY	ACTOR	150 E OLIVE AVE #111	BURBANK, CA 91502
PIERCE, CAROLINE	GOLFER	2750 VOLUSA AVE #B	DAYTON BEACH, FL 32114
PIERCE, CHARLES	IMPERSONATOR	4445 CARTWRIGHT AVE #309	NORTH HOLLYWOOD, CA 91602
PIERCE, DEVON	ACTRESS	6310 SAN VICENTE BLVD #407	LOS ANGELES, CA 90048
PIERCE, EDDIE	BASEBALL	800 HOME RUN LN	MEMPHIS, TN 38104
PIERCE, NAT	COMPOSER	446 1/2 S WILTON PL	LOS ANGELES, CA 90020
PIERCE, RICKY	BASKETBALL	BRADLEY CENTER, 1001 N 4TH ST	MILWAUKEE, WI 53203
PIERCE, ROB	BASEBALL	POST OFFICE BOX 11363	RENO, NV 89510
PIERCE, ROGER LAWRENCE	ACTOR	4438 MURIETTA AVE #17	SHERMAN OAKS, CA 91423
PIERCE, THOMAS	COSTUME DESIGNER	13949 VENTURA BLVD #309	SHERMAN OAKS, CA 91423
PIERCE, TIANA	ACTRESS	11054 VENTURA BLVD #289	STUDIO CITY, CA 91604
PIERCY, ANDY	SINGER	3 E 54TH ST #1400	NEW YORK, NY 10022
PIEROTTI, JOHN	CARTOONIST	2004 OCEAN AVE	BRIGANTINE, NJ 08203
PIERPOINT, ERIC	ACTOR	10929 MORRISON ST #14	NORTH HOLLYWOOD, CA 91601
PIERSALL, JIMMY	BASEBALL	1105 OAKVIEW DR	WHEATON, IL 60187

Name	Occupation	Address	City	Code
PIERSON, DORI D	SCREENWRITER	8955 BEVERLY BLVD	WEST HOLLYWOOD, CA	90048
PIERSON, FRANK	FILM WRITER-DIRECTOR	1223 AMALFI DR	PACIFIC PALISADES, CA	90272
PIERSON, MARK	FILM PRODUCER	POST OFFICE BOX 38246	HOLLYWOOD, CA	90038
PIES, JUDY	ACTRESS	11687 MONTANA AVE #101	LOS ANGELES, CA	90049
PIESTRUP, DONALL J	COMPOSER	4425 CLYBOURN AVE	NORTH HOLLYWOOD, CA	91602
PIETZSCH, STEVE	ARTIST	3057 LARRY DR	DALLAS, TX	75228
PIFER, ALICE	TV PRODUCER	ABC-TV, 7 W 66TH ST	NEW YORK, NY	10023
PIGAUT, ROGER	ACTOR	ARTMEDIA, 10 AVE GEORGE V	PARIS 75008	FRANCE
PIGLIA, PAOLA	ARTIST	100 W 87TH ST #3-A	NEW YORK, NY	10024
PIGOTT-SMITH, TIM	ACTOR	WHITEHALL, 125 GLOUCESTER RD	LONDON SW7 4TE	ENGLAND
PIKE, ANDREA	ACTRESS	4225 ETHEL AVE #6	STUDIO CITY, CA	91604
PIKE, DAVE	SINGER	PENNY, 30 GUINAN ST	WALTHAM, MA	02154
PIKE, DON	FILM DIRECTOR	DGA, 7920 SUNSET BLVD, 6TH FL	LOS ANGELES, CA	90046
PIKE, GREGORY ALLEN	DIRECTOR	8787 SHOREHAM DR #101	LOS ANGELES, CA	90069
PIKE, JOHN S	TV EXECUTIVE	PARAMOUNT TELEVISION		
		5555 MELROSE AVE	LOS ANGELES, CA	90038
PIKE, MARK	FOOTBALL	BILLS, 1 BILLS DR	ORCHARD PARK, NJ	14127
PILAR, BONNIE BEN	ACTRESS	30 LINCOLN PLAZA #29-H	NEW YORK, NY	10023
PILAVIN, BARBARA	ACTRESS	ATKINS, 303 S CRESCENT HEIGHTS	LOS ANGELES, CA	90048
PILCHER, SALLY	TV DIRECTOR	1313 N RITCHIE CT #2602	CHICAGO, IL	60610
PILEDRIVER	ROCK & ROLL GROUP	POST OFFICE BOX 249		
		STATION M	TORONTO, ONT M6S 4T3	CANADA
PILEGGI, NICHOLAS	SCREENWRITER	555 W 57TH ST #1230	NEW YORK, NY	10019
PILKINTON, LEM	BASEBALL COACH	POST OFFICE BOX 30160	SAN BERNARDINO, CA	92413
PILLER, MICHAEL B	TV WRITER-PRODUCER	737 N ORANGE DR	LOS ANGELES, CA	90038
PILLMAN, BRIAN "FLYING"	WRESTLER	POST OFFICE BOX 105366	ATLANTA, GA	31348
PILLOW	BODYBUILDER	POST OFFICE BOX 1076	VENICE, CA	90294
PILLOW, DARYL	SINGER	TAYLOR, 2401 12TH AVE S	NASHVILLE, TN	37204
PILLOW, RAY	SINGER	ROUTE #4, NEW HWY 96 W	FRANKLIN, TN	37064
PILLSBURY, DREW	ACTOR	8730 SUNSET BLVD #220-W	LOS ANGELES, CA	90069
PILOF, JUDY	DIRECTOR	235 W 75TH ST	NEW YORK, NY	10023
PILSON, NEAL H	TV EXECUTIVE	CBS-TV, 51 W 52ND ST, 24TH FL	NEW YORK, NY	10019
PIMENTEL, WANDER	BASEBALL	POST OFFICE BOX 3004	SPRINGFIELD, IL	62708
PINA, MICKEY	BASEBALL	POST OFFICE BOX 2365	PAWTUCKET, RI	02861
PINCHOT, BRONSON	ACTOR-PRODUCER	9200 SUNSET BLVD #428	LOS ANGELES, CA	90069
PINCHUK, SHELDON	WRITER	4506 EL CABALLERO DR	TARZANA, CA	91356
PINCKNEY, ED	BASKETBALL	151 MERRIMAC ST	BOSTON, MA	02114
PINCKNEY, LEO	BASEBALL EXECUTIVE	POST OFFICE BOX 1313	AUBURN, NY	13021
PINE, DAVE	SINGER	PENNY, 30 GUINAN ST	WALTHAM, MA	02154
PINE, GRANVILLE	DIRECTOR	3975 VAN NOORD AVE	STUDIO CITY, CA	91604
PINE, ROBERT	ACTOR-DIRECTOR	3975 VAN NOORD AVE	STUDIO CITY, CA	91604
PINE, TINA	SCREENWRITER	8955 BEVERLY BLVD	WEST HOLLYWOOD, CA	90048
PINEDA, JOSE	BASEBALL	POST OFFICE BOX 22093	GREENSBORO, NC	27420
PINEDA, RENE	COMPOSER	309 MONTEREY RD	SOUTH PASADENA, CA	91030
PINETUCKETT	C & W GROUP	POST OFFICE BOX 25371	CHARLOTTE, NC	28212
PINIELLA, LOU	BASEBALL	103 MACINTYRE LN	ALLENDALE, NJ	07401
PINK FLOYD	ROCK & ROLL GROUP	43 PORTLAND RD	LONDON W11	ENGLAND
PINKETT, ALLEN	FOOTBALL	OILERS, 6910 FANNIN ST	HOUSTON, TX	77070
PINKHAM, SHEILA	ACTRESS	8489 W 3RD ST #1105	LOS ANGELES, CA	90048
PINKINS, TONYA	ACTRESS	ABC-TV, "ALL MY CHILDREN"		
		320 W 66TH ST	NEW YORK, NY	10023
PINKNEY, ALTON	BASEBALL	POST OFFICE BOX 2887	VERO BEACH, FL	32961
PINKNEY, JERRY	ARTIST	41 FURNACE DOCK RD	CROTON-ON-HUTSON, NY	10520
PINKY	ROCK & ROLL GROUP	ICM, 40 W 57TH ST	NEW YORK, NY	10019
PINNOCK, TREVOR	CONDUCTOR	ICM, 40 W 57TH ST	NEW YORK, NY	10019
PINOTEAU, CLAUDE	FILM DIRECTOR	21 RUE MADELEINE-MICHELIS	NEUILLY 92200	FRANCE
PINSENT, LEAH	ACTRESS	9229 SUNSET BLVD #311	LOS ANGELES, CA	90069
PINSKER, LEW	TV PRODUCER	MEDSTAR, 5920 HAMILTON BLVD	ALLENTOWN, PA	18106
PINSKER, SETH	FILM DIRECTOR	461 1/2 N SIERRA BONITA AVE	LOS ANGELES, CA	90036
PINSON, VADA	BASEBALL-COACH	TIGERS, TIGER STADIUM	DETROIT, MI	48216
PINTER, HAROLD	SCREENWRITER	ACTAC, 16 CADOGAN LN	LONDON SW1	ENGLAND
PINTER, JOHN	FLUTIST	POST OFFICE BOX 770		
		WESLEYAN STATION	MIDDLETON, CT	06457
PINTER, MARK	ACTOR	NBC-TV, "ANOTHER WORLD"		
		1268 E 14TH ST	BROOKLYN, NY	11230
PINTO, DAVID H	COMPOSER	410 S OAK AVE	PASADENA, CA	91107
PINTOFF, ERNEST	FILM DIRECTOR	1842 OUTPOST DR	LOS ANGELES, CA	90068
PIOLI, JUDY	TV WRITER	129 FLEET ST	MARINA DEL REY, CA	90292
PIOTROWICZ, BRIAN	BASEBALL	POST OFFICE BOX 2887	VERO BEACH, FL	32961
PIOTROWSKY, GENE	WRI-DIR-PROD	WETLAND PRODS, 107 MORTON ST	NEW YORK, NY	10014
PIPER, LARA	ACTRESS	9105 CARMELITA AVE #1	BEVERLY HILLS, CA	90210
PIPER, MONICA	COMEDIENNE	9000 SUNSET BLVD #1200	LOS ANGELES, CA	90069
PIPER, ROWDY RODDY	WRESTLER-ACTOR	POST OFFICE BOX 3859	STAMFORD, CT	06905
PIPER, WILLIAM	TV DIRECTOR	ABC-TV, 4151 PROSPECT AVE	HOLLYWOOD, CA	90027
PIPER ROAD SPRING BAND	BLUEGRASS GROUP	POST OFFICE BOX 138	BLACK EARTH, WI	53515
PIPPEN, SCOTTIE	BASKETBALL	980 N MICHIGAN AVE #1600	CHICAGO, IL	60611
PIPS, THE	VOCAL GROUP	SEE - KNIGHT, GLADYS & PIPS		
PIRANHA	RHYTHM & BLUES GROUP	KINGSLAND, 108 SHARON DR	WEST MONROE, LA	71291
PIRARO, DAN	CARTOONIST	CHRONICLE FEATURES		
		870 MARKET ST	SAN FRANCISCO, CA	94102
PIRATES OF THE MISSISSIPPI	C & W GROUP	POST OFFICE BOX 17087	NASHVILLE, TN	37217
PIRES, GERARD	DIRECTOR	19 RUE CLEMENT MAROT	PARIS 75008	FRANCE
PIRIE, DR LYNNE	BODYBUILDER	NORTH PHOENIX HEATH INSTITUTE		
		750 E THUNDERBIRD RD	PHOENIX, AZ	85022
PIRKL, GREG	BASEBALL	POST OFFICE BOX 4756	JACKSONVILLE, FL	32201

Name	Occupation	Address	City	Code
PIROSH, ROBERT	SCREENWRITER	133 S BEDFORD DR #C	BEVERLY HILLS, CA	90212
PISANO, AL	ARTIST	630 1ST AVE #25-N	NEW YORK, NY	10016
PISIER, MARIE-FRANCE	ACTRESS	3, QUAI MALAQUAIS	F-75006 PARIS	FRANCE
PISKOR, KIRK	BASEBALL	300 STADIUM WY	DAVENPORT, FL	33837
PISTONE, KIMBERLEY	ACTRESS	SHERMAN, 1516 S BEVERLY DR #304	LOS ANGELES, CA	90035
PITCHER, BARBARA	ACTRESS	1245 PARK AVE #19-C	NEW YORK, NY	10128
PITCHER, SCOTT	BASEBALL	POST OFFICE BOX 9194	HAMPTON, VA	23670
PITCHFORD, DEAN	LYRICIST-PRODUCER	1701 QUEENS RD	LOS ANGELES, CA	90069
PITCOCK, JOAN	GOLFER	2750 VOLUSA AVE #B	DAYTON BEACH, FL	32114
PITHEY, WENSLEY	ACTOR	10 DOWNSIDE	LONDON SW15 2AE	ENGLAND
PITLIK, DAVID	ACTOR-TV WRITER	8955 BEVERLY BLVD	WEST HOLLYWOOD, CA	90048
PITMAN, JOHN	TV PRODUCER	BBC, KENSINGTON HOUSE		
		RICHMOND WY	LONDON W14	ENGLAND
PITNEY, GENE	SINGER	8901 6 MILE RD	CALEDONIA, WI	53108
PITSIS, TED	ACTOR	6217 AFTON PL #6	LOS ANGELES, CA	90028
PITSS, JOHN	SPORTS WRITER	POST OFFICE BOX 500	WASHINGTON, DC	20044
PITT, INGRID	ACTRESS	LANGFORD ASSOC, GARDEN STUDIOS		
		11-15 BETTERTON ST	LONDON WC2	ENGLAND
PITT, PETER	FILM EDITOR	4 FAIR CLOSE, BUSHEY	HERTS	ENGLAND
PITT, STEFFANIE	ACTRESS	REDWAY (AIM), 5 DENMARK ST	LONDON WC2H 8LP	ENGLAND
PITTA, MARK	COMEDIAN	10351 SANTA MONICA BLVD #211	LOS ANGELES, CA	90025
PITTELLI, PATRICK	DIRECTOR	DGA, 110 W 57TH ST	NEW YORK, NY	10019
PITTENGER, RICHARD	TV DIRECTOR	ABC-TV, 7 W 66TH ST	NEW YORK, NY	10023
PITTMAN, BRUCE	DIRECTOR	PLESHETTE, 2700 N BEACHWOOD DR	LOS ANGELES, CA	90068
PITTMAN, JOE	BASEBALL SCOUT	POST OFFICE BOX 288	HOUSTON, TX	77001
PITTMAN, PARK	BASEBALL	POST OFFICE BOX 1659	PORTLAND, OR	97207
PITTS, ELIJAH	FOOTBALL COACH	BILLS, 1 BILLS DR	ORCHARD PARK, NJ	14127
PITTS, GAYLEN	BASEBALL-COACH	250 STADIUM PLAZA	ST LOUIS, MO	63102
PITTS, MIKE	FOOTBALL	EAGLES, BROAD ST & PATTISON AVE	PHILADELPHIA, PA	19148
PITTS, TED	ARTIST	343 N WEST ST	XENIA, OH	45385
PITTSBURG	C & W GROUP	4680 ELK LAKE DR #304	VICTORIA, BC V8Z 5M1	CANADA
PIVONKA, MICHAL	HOCKEY	JETS, 15-1430 MAROONS RD	WINNIPEG, MAN R3G 0L5	CANADA
PIZER, HOWARD	BASEBALL EXECUTIVE	333 W 35TH ST	CHICAGO, IL	60616
PIZZI, DONNA L	TV WRITER	GLORIA SAFIER MGMT		
		667 MADISON AVE	NEW YORK, NY	10021
PIZZI, RAY M	COMPOSER	POST OFFICE BOX 8137	VAN NUYS, CA	91406
PLACE, MARY KAY	ACTOR-WRITER	2739 MOTOR AVE	LOS ANGELES, CA	90064
PLACE, MIKE	BASEBALL	POST OFFICE BOX 4525	MACON, GA	31208
PLAKINGER, TINA	BODYBUILDER	21100 ERWIN ST	WOODLAND HILLS, CA	91367
PLAKSON, SUZIE	ACTRESS	1999 AVE OF THE STARS #2850	LOS ANGELES, CA	90067
PLAN 9	ROCK & ROLL GROUP	POST OFFICE BOX 817	JAMAICA PLAIN, MA	02130
PLANER, NIGEL	ACTOR	PETERS, FRASER & DUNLOP, LTD		
		5TH FLOOR, THE CHAMBERS		
		CHELSEA HARBOUR, LOT RD	LONDON SW10 OXF	ENGLAND
PLANET	ROCK & ROLL GROUP	STERLING, 10020 PIONEER BL #104	SANTA FE SPRINGS, CA	90670
PLANET 10	ROCK & ROLL GROUP	FAST LANE PRODUCTIONS		
		4590 MAC ARTHUR BLVD, NW	WASHINGTON, DC	20007
PLANET PATROL	ROCK & ROLL GROUP	FUTURE BEAT ALLIANCE		
		1747 1ST AVE	NEW YORK, NY	10128
PLANT, ROBERT	SINGER-SONGWRITER	PHIL CARSON, ATLANTIC RECORDS		
		75 ROCKEFELLER PLAZA	NEW YORK, NY	10019
PLANTE, JAMES F	TV EXECUTIVE	NBC-TV, 30 ROCKEFELLER PLAZA	NEW YORK, NY	10112
PLANTENBERG, ERIK	BASEBALL	POST OFFICE BOX 10213	LYNCHBURG, VA	24506
PLANTIER, PHIL	BASEBALL	FENWAY PARK, 4 YAWKEY WY	BOSTON, MA	02215
PLASCHKES, OTTO	FILM PRODUCER	BFTPA, 162 WARDOUR ST	LONDON W1V 3AT	ENGLAND
PLASTER, ALLEN	BASEBALL	POST OFFICE BOX 3169	FREDERICK, MD	21701
PLASTICLAND	ROCK & ROLL GROUP	POST OFFICE BOX 2896	TORRANCE, CA	90509
PLATER, ALAN	SCREENWRITER	RAMSAY, 14-A GOODWINS CT		
		SAINT MARTINS LN	LONDON WC2N 4LL	ENGLAND
PLATINUM	ROCK & ROLL GROUP	JIMMY ALLEN ARTIST MGMT		
		1548 ASHLAND AVE	SAINT PAUL, MN	55104
PLATINUM BLONDE	ROCK & ROLL GROUP	POST OFFICE BPX 1223, STA "F"	TORONTO, ONT M4Y 2T8	
PLATNICK, JONATHAN	TV WRITER	51 7TH AVE S	NEW YORK, NY	10014
PLATT, HOWARD	ACTOR	22828 PACIFIC COAST HWY #C	MALIBU, CA	90265
PLATTEN, DANIEL	HAIR STYLIST	237 LAFAYETTE ST #11-E	NEW YORK, NY	10012
PLATTERS, THE	VOCAL GROUP	SEE - FIVE PLATTERS, THE		
PLATZ, TOM	BODYBUILDER	POST OFFICE BOX 1262	SANTA MONICA, CA	90406
PLAVSIC, ADRIEN	HOCKEY	CANUCKS, 100 N RENFREW ST	VANCOUVER, BC V5K 3N7	CANADA
PLAYER, GARY	GOLFER	PGA SENIORS, 112 T P C BLVD	PONTE VEDRA BEACH, FL	32082
PLAYER, SUSAN	ACTRESS	SEE - PLAYER-JARREAU, SUSAN		
PLAYER-JARREAU, SUSAN	ACTRESS	11752 LA MAIDA ST	NORTH HOLLYWOOD, CA	91607
PLAYGROUND SLAP, THE	ROCK & ROLL GROUP	3246 VIA CALIENTE DEL SOL	JAMUL, CA	92035
PLAZA, RON	BASEBALL-COACH	ATHLETICS'S, OAKLAND COLISEUM	OAKLAND, CA	94621
PLEASANTS, EDWIN A	COMPOSER	1879 CLOVERDALE AVE	LOS ANGELES, CA	90019
PLEASENCE, DONALD	ACTOR	7 W EATON PLACE MEWS	LONDON W1	ENGLAND
PLEASURE	SOUL GROUP	POST OFFICE BOX 601	PORTRLAND, OR	97207
PLEASURE, LACY	DANCER-MODEL	POST OFFICE BOX 639	SUN VALLEY, CA	91353
PLEDGER, KINNIS	BASEBALL	POST OFFICE BOX 360007	BIRMINGHAM, AL	35236
PLEIS, BILL	BASEBALL-SCOUT	1000 ELYSIAN PARK DR	LOS ANGELES, CA	90012
PLEMEL, LEE	BASEBALL	POST OFFICE BOX 5599	LITTLE ROCK, AR	72215
PLEMMONS, RON	BASEBALL	1090 N EUCLID AVE	SARASOTA, FL	34237
PLEMMONS, SCOTT	BASEBALL	POST OFFICE BOX 2001	CEDAR RAPIDS, IA	52406
PLESAC, DAN	BASEBALL	BREWERS, 201 S 46TH ST	MILWAUKEE, WI	53214
PLESHETTE, JOHN	ACTOR-WRITER	2643 CRESTON DR	LOS ANGELES, CA	90068
PLESHETTE, LYNN	LITERARY AGENT	2643 CRESTON DR	LOS ANGELES, CA	90068

PLESHETTE, SUZANNE	ACTRESS-WRITER	POST OFFICE BOX 1492	BEVERLY HILLS, CA 90213
PLESKOW, ERIC	FILM EXECUTIVE	ORION, 1888 CENTURY PARK E	LOS ANGELES, CA 90067
PLETCHER, ELDON	CARTOONIST	331 TIFFANY ST	SLIDELL, LA 70458
PLETENIK, CRAIG	BASEBALL EXECUTIVE	5999 E VAN BUREN ST	PHOENIX, AZ 85008
PLEVEN, PATRICK A	TV EXECUTIVE	1160 5TH AVE	NEW YORK, NY 10029
PLIMPTON, GEORGE	AUTHOR	541 E 72ND ST	NEW YORK, NY 10021
PLIMPTON, MARTHA	ACTRESS	662 N VAN NESS AVE #305	LOS ANGELES, CA 90004
PLISSNER, MARTIN	NEWS CORRES-WRITER	CBS NEWS, 2020 "M" ST, NW	WASHINGTON, DC 20036
PLITT, HENRY G	TV PRODUCER	1801 CENTURY PARK E #1225	LOS ANGELES, CA 90067
PLONE, ALLEN LEE	DIRECTOR	317 N ORANGE DR	LOS ANGELES, CA 90036
PLOWDEN, JULIAN	WRITER	11660 TERRY HILL PL	LOS ANGELES, CA 90049
PLOWRIGHT, DAVID	TV EXECUTIVE	GRANADA TV CENTRE	MANCHESTER M60 9EA ENGLAND
PLOWRIGHT, JOAN	ACTRESS	ICM, 388-396 OXFORD ST	LONDON W1 ENGLAND
PLOZET, THOMAS P	NEWS CORRESPONDENT	NBC NEWS, 4001 NEBRASKA AV, SW	WASHINGTON, DC 20016
PLUMB, EVE	ACTRESS	145 S FAIRFAX AVE #310	LOS ANGELES, CA 90036
PLUMB, FLORA	ACTRESS	DIAMOND, 215 N BARRINGTON AVE	LOS ANGELES, CA 90049
PLUMB, NEELY	COMPOSER	6463 FIRMAMENT AVE	VAN NUYS, CA 91406
PLUMB, SUSAN	ACTRESS	9250 WILSHIRE BLVD #208	BEVERLY HILLS, CA 90212
PLUMB, TED	FOOTBALL COACH	POST OFFICE BOX 888	PHOENIX, AZ 85001
PLUMMER, AMANDA	ACTRESS	49 WAMPUM HILL RD	WESTON, CT 06883
PLUMMER, BILL	BASEBALL-MANAGER	POST OFFICE BOX 4100	SEATTLE, WA 98104
PLUMMER, BRIAN	SINGER	41 BRITAIN ST #200	TORONTO, ONT M5A 1R7 CANADA
PLUMMER, CHRISTOPHER	ACTOR	49 WAMPUM HILL RD	WESTON, CT 06883
PLUMMER, DALE	BASEBALL	POST OFFICE BOX 1211	NORFOLK, VA 23502
PLUMMER, GARY	FOOTBALL	POST OFFICE BOX 609609	SAN DIEGO, CA 92160
PLUMMER, SCOTTY	SINGER	TERRY, 909 PARKVIEW AVE	LODI, CA 95240
PLUNK, ERIC	BASEBALL	2501 ALLEN AVE, SE	CANTON, OH 44707
PLUNKETT, JIM	FOOTBALL	51 KILROY WY	ATHERTON, CA 94025
PLUTE, THEODORE M	CONDUCTOR	6728 HILLPARK DR #407	LOS ANGELES, CA 90068
PLYMPTON, JEFF	BASEBALL	POST OFFICE BOX 2365	PAWTUCKET, RI 02861
PLYMPTON, JEFF	BASEBALL	FENWAY PARK, 4 YAWKEY WY	BOSTON, MA 02215
PLYTAS, STEVE	ACTOR	70 LANSBURY AVE, FELTHAM	MIDDLESEX TW14 OJR ENGLAND
POCO	ROCK & ROLL GROUP	POST OFFICE BOX 24475	NASHVILLE, TN 37202
PODDANY, EUGENE	COMPOSER	2036 GRIFFITH PARK BLVD	LOS ANGELES, CA 90039
PODELL, MICHAEL	TV EXECUTIVE	ABC-TV, 7 W 66TH ST	NEW YORK, NY 10023
PODELL, RICK	ACTOR	1100 N ALTA LOMA RD #707	LOS ANGELES, CA 90069
PODEWELL, CATHY	ACTRESS	MTA, 9320 WILSHIRE BL, 3RD FL	BEVERLY HILLS, CA 90212
PODHORETZ, NORMAN	AUTHOR-EDITOR	AMERICAN JEWISH COMMUNITY	
		COMMENTARY MAGAZINE	
		165 E 56TH ST	NEW YORK, NY 10022
PODOBNIK, JEFF	BASEBALL EXECUTIVE	POST OFFICE BOX 7000	PITTSBURGH, PA 15212
PODRES, JOHNNY	BASEBALL-COACH	POST OFFICE BOX 7575	PHILADELPHIA, PA 19101
POE, CHARLES	BASEBALL	POST OFFICE BOX 4218	SOUTH BEND, IN 46634
POFFO, ELIZABETH	WRESTLING MANAGER	SEE - MISS ELIZABETH	
POFFO, LEAPING LANNY	WRESTLER	POST OFFICE BOX 3859	STAMFORD, CT 06905
POFFO, RANDY	WRESTLER	SEE - SAVAGE, RANDY	
		"MACHO MAN"	
POGUE, CHARLES E, JR	ACTOR-WRITER	8955 BEVERLY BLVD	WEST HOLLYWOOD, CA 90048
POGUES, THE	ROCK & ROLL GROUP	POST OFFICE BOX 2428	EL SEGUNDO, CA 90245
POHL, DAN	GOLFER	POST OFFICE BOX 109601	PALM BCH GARDENS, FL 33418
POHLAD, CARL	BASEBALL EXECUTIVE	TWINS, 501 CHICAGO AVE S	MINNEAPOLIS, MN 55415
POHLAD, JAMES	BASEBALL EXECUTIVE	TWINS, 501 CHICAGO AVE S	MINNEAPOLIS, MN 55415
POHLAD, ROBERT	BASEBALL EXECUTIVE	TWINS, 501 CHICAGO AVE S	MINNEAPOLIS, MN 55415
POHLAD, WILLIAM	BASEBALL EXECUTIVE	TWINS, 501 CHICAGO AVE S	MINNEAPOLIS, MN 55415
POINDEXTER, ADM JOHN	ADMIRAL	1322 MERRY RIDGE RD #400	WASHINGTON, DC 20036
POINDEXTER, BUSTER	SINGER	SEE - JOHANSEN, DAVID	
POINDEXTER, LARRY	ACTOR	3500 W OLIVE AVE #1400	BURBANK, CA 91505
POINT BLANK	ROCK & ROLL GROUP	ATI, 888 7TH AVE, 21ST FLOOR	NEW YORK, NY 10106
POINTER, AARON	FOOTBALL REFEREE	NFL, 410 PARK AVE	NEW YORK, NY 10022
POINTER, ANITA	SINGER	12060 CREST CT	BEVERLY HILLS, CA 90210
POINTER, PRISCILLA	ACTRESS	10100 SANTA MONICA BLVD #1600	LOS ANGELES, CA 90067
POINTER, RUTH	SINGER	29652 CUTHBERT RD	MALIBU, CA 90265
POINTER, SIDNEY	ACT-WRI-DIR	9350 WILSHIRE BLVD #310	BEVERLY HILLS, CA 90212
POINTER SISTERS, THE	VOCAL TRIO	8730 SUNSET BLVD #PH-W	LOS ANGELES, CA 90069
POIRE, ALAIN	FILM PRODUCER	13 RUE MADELEINE MICHELIS	NEUILLY 92200 FRANCE
POISON	ROCK & ROLL GROUP	345 N MAPLE ST #235	BEVERLY HILLS, CA 90210
POISON GIRLS	ROCK & ROLL GROUP	ALLIED AGENCY & MANAGEMENT	
		76 TOTTENHAM COURT RD	LONDON W1P 9PA ENGLAND
POITEVINT, RAY	BASEBALL EXECUTIVE	BREWERS, 201 S 46TH ST	MILWAUKEE, WI 53214
POITIER, SIDNEY	ACTOR-DIRECTOR	1007 COVE WY	BEVERLY HILLS, CA 90210
POITRENAUD, JACQUEST	FILM DIRECTOR	72 RUE SAINT DENIS	PARIS 75001 FRANCE
POLAK, RICH	BASEBALL	POST OFFICE BOX 2148	WOODBRIDGE, VA 22193
POLAKOFF, JAMES	DIRECTOR	POST OFFICE BOX 8205	NEWPORT BEACH, CA 92660
POLAN, LOIS ANNE	DIRECTOR	DGA, 7920 SUNSET BLVD, 6TH FL	LOS ANGELES, CA 90046
POLANSKI, ROMAN	ACT-WRI-DIR-PROD	ICM, 388-396 OXFORD ST	LONDON W1 ENGLAND
POLDBERG, BRIAN	BASEBALL MANAGER	800 HOME RUN LN	MEMPHIS, TN 38104
POLE, DICK	BASEBALL COACH	POST OFFICE BOX 2365	PAWTUCKET, RI 02861
POLE, FRANCIS	ACTRESS	400 W 43RD ST	NEW YORK, NY 10036
POLEDOURIS, BASIL	COMPOSER	4549 ALONZO AVE	ENCINO, CA 91316
POLEVOY, ROY	TV EXECUTIVE	ABC-TV, 4151 PROSPECT AVE	LOS ANGELES, CA 90027
POLIC, HENRY, III	ACTOR	5307 WILKERSON AVE #20	LOS ANGELES, CA 90046
POLICE, THE	ROCK & ROLL GROUP	6363 SUNSET BLVD #716	HOLLYWOOD, CA 90028
POLICH, JOHN	TV DIRECTOR	1612 RANDALL ST	GLENDALE, CA 91201
POLICY, CARMEN	FOOTBALL EXECUTIVE	S F 49ERS, 4949 CENTENNIAL BL	SANTA CLARA, CA 95054
POLIDAR, GUS	BASEBALL	LA AVE DE PRO-PATRIA BLQO 3	PATRIA B#9, CARACAS VENEZUELA

POLIDOR, GUS	BASEBALL	POST OFFICE BOX 11087	TACOMA, WA	98411
POLIER, DAN	WRITER	13926 MAGNOLIA BLVD	SHERMAN OAKS, CA	91423
POLIKOFF, GERALD	TV DIRECTOR	533 WOODMERE BLVD	WOODMERE, NY	11598
POLINSKI, JOHN J	COMPOSER-CONDUCTOR	13170 BRACKEN ST	PACOIMA, CA	91331
POLITO, GENE	CINEMATOGRAPHER	4701 ABBEYVILLE AVE	WOODLAND HILLS, CA	91364
POLK, JAMES E	CONDUCTOR	POST OFFICE BOX 19345-A	LOS ANGELES, CA	90019
POLK, LEE	WRITER-PRODUCER	150 E 69TH ST	NEW YORK, NY	10021
POLL, JULIE M	TV WRITER	200 E 78TH ST	NEW YORK, NY	10021
POLL, LEE	COSTUME DESIGNER	13949 VENTURA BLVD #309	SHERMAN OAKS, CA	91423
POLL, MARTIN	FILM PRODUCER	919 3RD AVE	NEW YORK, NY	10019
POLLACK, BERNIE	COSTUME DESIGNER	13949 VENTURA BLVD #309	SHERMAN OAKS, CA	91423
POLLACK, BRIAN	ACTOR-TV WRITER	7608 WILLOW GLEN RD	LOS ANGELES, CA	90046
POLLACK, CHRIS	BASEBALL	POST OFFICE BOX 15757	HARRISBURG, PA	17105
POLLACK, FRANK	FOOTBALL	S F 49ERS, 4949 CENTENNIAL BL	SANTA CLARA, CA	95054
POLLACK, SYDNEY	WRI-DIR-PROD	13525 LUCCA DR	PACIFIC PALISADES, CA	90272
POLLAK, CHERYL A	ACTRESS	10390 SANTA MONICA BLVD #300	LOS ANGELES, CA	90025
POLLAK, KEVIN	ACTOR	ICM, 8899 BEVERLY BLVD	LOS ANGELES, CA	90048
POLLAN, TRACY	ACTRESS	3960 LAUREL CANYON BLVD	STUDIO CITY, CA	91604
POLLARD, DAMON	BASEBALL	300 STADIUM WY	DAVENPORT, FL	33837
POLLARD, JOHN	SINGER	POST OFFICE BOX 25371	CHARLOTTE, NC	28212
POLLARD, MICHAEL J	ACTOR	520 S BURNSIDE AVE #12-A	LOS ANGELES, CA	90036
POLLARD, SU	ACTRESS-SINGER	GAY, 24 DENMARK ST	LONDON WC2H 8HJ	ENGLAND
POLLEY, DALE	BASEBALL	POST OFFICE BOX 6667	RICHMOND, VA	23230
POLLICK, TENO	ACTOR	7733 HAMPTON AVE #1	LOS ANGELES, CA	90046
POLLIN, ABE	BASKETBALL EXECUTIVE	BULLETS, 1 HARRY S TRUMAN DR	LANDOVER, MD	20785
POLLNER, MILDRED	TV DIRECTOR-PRODUCER	444 E 86TH ST #21-J	NEW YORK, NY	10028
POLLOCK, ALAN M	TV DIRECTOR	4428 SEDGWICK ST, NW	WASHINGTON, DC	20016
POLLOCK, DAVID M	TV WRITER	11019 AMERY AVE	SOUTH GATE, CA	90280
POLLOCK, JASON	TV PRODUCER	BREAKFAST TV, CENTRE		
		HAWLEY CRESCENT	LONDON NW1	ENGLAND
POLLUTRO, JODY	MAKE-UP ARTIST	145 E 16TH ST	NEW YORK, NY	10003
POLO, TERI	ACTRESS	ICM, 40 W 57TH ST	NEW YORK, NY	10019
POLONCHEK, JOHN	FOOTBALL COACH	PATRIOTS, FOXBORO STADIUM, RT #1	FOXBORO, MA	02035
POLONE, JUDY	TV PRODUCER	THE POLONE COMPANY		
		1640 S SEPULVEDA BLVD, 4TH FL	LOS ANGELES, CA	90025
POLONI, JOHN	BASEBALL COACH	CHIEFS, MAC ARTHUR STADIUM	SYRACUSE, NY	13208
POLONIA, LUIS	BASEBALL	POST OFFICE BOX 2000	ANAHEIM, CA	92803
POLONSKY, ABRAHAM	FILM WRITER-DIRECTOR	135 S MC CARTHY DR	BEVERLY HILLS, CA	90212
POLONSKY, HANK V	FILM DIRECTOR	DGA, 7920 SUNSET BLVD, 6TH FL	LOS ANGELES, CA	90046
POLSON, BETH	TV DIRECTOR-PRODUCER	10100 SANTA MONICA BLVD #310	LOS ANGELES, CA	90067
POLYNICE, OLDEN	BASKETBALL	POST OFFICE BOX C-900911	SEATTLE, WA	98109
POMERANTZ, EARL	TV WRITER	320 PACIFIC ST	SANTA MONICA, CA	90405
POMERANTZ, JEFFREY	ACTOR-WRITER	8322 BEVERLY BLVD #200	LOS ANGELES, CA	90048
POMERANTZ, MARK	COMPOSER-CONDUCTOR	14415 MAGNOLIA BLVD	SHERMAN OAKS, CA	91423
POMEROY, MARIANNE	ARTIST	5200 WESLAYAN ST #A-107	HOUSTON, TX	77005
POMEROY-STRASSER, PATRICIA	ACTRESS	8 WILSHIRE RUN	SCOTCH PLAINS, NJ	07076
POMPIAN, PAUL	TV WRITER-PRODUCER	425 N OAKHURST DR #101	BEVERLY HILLS, CA	90210
POMUS, JEROME "DOC"	SONGWRITER	253 W 72ND ST	NEW YORK, NY	10023
PONAZECKI, JOE	ACTOR	CBS-TV, "THE GUIDING LIGHT"		
		222 E 44TH ST	NEW YORK, NY	10017
PONCE, CARLOS	BASEBALL COACH	POST OFFICE BOX 2960	SUMTER, SC	29151
PONCE, DANY	ACTOR	14539 PETON DR	HACIENDA HEIGHTS, CA	91745
PONCE, LUANNE	ACTRESS	14539 PETON DR	HACIENDA HEIGHTS, CA	91745
PONCE, PONCE	ACTOR	13501 DELANO ST	VAN NUYS, CA	91405
PONCINO, LARRY	BASEBALL UMPIRE	2101 E BROADWAY #35	TEMPE, AZ	85282
POND, SHERRI	SINGER	POST OFFICE BOX 208	GOODLETTSVILLE, TN	37072
PONDER, JIMMY	SINGER	POST OFFICE BOX 82	GREAT NECK, NY	11022
PONICSAN, DARRYL	SCREENWRITER	8955 BEVERLY BLVD	WEST HOLLYWOOD, CA	90048
PONS, BEATRICE	ACTRESS	220 E 72ND ST #10-D	NEW YORK, NY	10021
PONTE, ED	BASEBALL	POST OFFICE BOX 4209	JACKSON, MS	39296
PONTI, CARLO	FILM PRODUCER	RUE CHARLES BONNET 6	GENEVA	SWITERLAND
PONTIAC BROTHERS, THE	ROCK & ROLL GROUP	POST OFFICE BOX 22	SUN VALLEY, CA	91353
PONZO, ROSEMARY	COSTUME DESIGNER	181 7TH AVE #3-B	NEW YORK, NY	10011
POOLE, BOB	BASEBALL SCOUT	POST OFFICE BOX 7575	PHILADELPHIA, PA	19101
POOLE, DUANE E	COMPOSER-WRITER	7974 WOODROW WILSON DR	LOS ANGELES, CA	90046
POOLE, GEORGE E	COMPOSER	801 W WARD #128	RIDGECREST, CA	93555
POOLE, JIM	BASEBALL	ORIOLE PARK, 333 W CAMDEN ST	BALTIMORE, MD	21201
POOLE, JIM	FOOTBALL REFEREE	NFL, 410 PARK AVE	NEW YORK, NY	10022
POOLEY, OLAF	ACTOR-WRITER	3456 ALANA DR	SHERMAN OAKS, CA	91403
POON, ANNA MARIA	ACTRESS	110 E 9TH ST #C-1005	LOS ANGELES, CA	90079
POOR, PETER	TV WRITER-PRODUCER	1150 5TH AVE	NEW YORK, NY	10028
POP, IGGY	SINGER-SONGWRITER	250 W 57TH ST #603	NEW YORK, NY	10107
POP, JULIE	ACTRESS	8228 SUNSET BLVD #311	LOS ANGELES, CA	90046
POP, THE	MUSICAL GROUP	6430 SUNSET BLVD #1516	LOS ANGELES, CA	90028
POP ART	ROCK & ROLL GROUP	STONEGARDEN RECORDS		
		12436 MARVA AVE	GRANADA HILLS, CA	91344
POP RIVETS, THE	ROCK & ROLL GROUP	JIM'S RECORDS		
		4526 LIBERTY AVE	PITTSBURGH, PA	15224
POP-O-PIES, THE	ROCK & ROLL GROUP	POST OFFICE BOX 14563	SAN FRANCISCO, CA	94114
POPADICS, JOEL	ARTIST	22 SCRIBNER PL	WAYNE, NJ	07470
POPE, CARMELITA	ACTRESS	14144 VENTURA BLVD #260	SHERMAN OAKS, CA	91423
POPE, DONNA	SINGER	POST OFFICE BOX 25371	CHARLOTTE, NC	28212
POPE, KEVIN	CARTOONIST	TRIBUNE, 64 E CONCORD ST	ORLANDO, FL	32801
POPE, MIKE	FOOTBALL COACH	N Y GIANTS, GIANTS STADIUM	EAST RUTHERFORD, NJ	07073
POPE, STEPHANIE	ACTRESS	3500 W OLIVE AVE #1400	BURBANK, CA	91505

POPE, STEVE	BASEBALL SCOUT	POST OFFICE BOX 4100	SEATTLE, WA	98104
POPE, THOMAS	SCREENWRITER	8955 BEVERLY BLVD	WEST HOLLYWOOD, CA	90048
POPEK, JOE	BASEBALL SCOUT	250 STADIUM PLAZA	ST LOUIS, MO	63102
POPKIN, LEO	DIRECTOR	9970 SUNSET BLVD	BEVERLY HILLS, CA	90210
POPOVICH, GREGG	BASKETBALL COACH	600 E MARKET ST #102	SAN ANTONIO, TX	78205
POPP, JOE	FOOTBALL COACH	BROWNS, 80 1ST ST	BEREA, OH	44017
POPP, K W	ARTIST	19 HALL AVE	LARCHMONT, NY	10538
POPPITI, ED	BASEBALL EXECUTIVE	POST OFFICE BOX 7005	HUNTINGTON, WV	25775
POPPLEWELL, TOM	BASEBALL	ALBANY YANKEES, HERITAGE PARK	ALBANY, NY	12211
POPSON, DAVE	BASKETBALL	151 MERRIMAC ST	BOSTON, MA	02114
POPSTIN, S LEE	FILM WRITER-DIRECTOR	1030 TOWER RD	BEVERLY HILLS, CA	90210
POQUETTE, TOM	BASEBALL MANAGER	POST OFFICE BOX 464	APPLETON, WI	54912
PORATH, GIDEON	CINEMATOGRAPHER	7452 WOODROW WILSON DR	LOS ANGELES, CA	90046
PORETZ, CAROL	ACTRESS	837 1/4 N ALFRED ST	LOS ANGELES, CA	90069
PORGES, PAUL PETER	ARTIST-WRITER	MAD MAGAZINE, 485 MADISON AVE	NEW YORK, NY	10022
PORGES, WALTER	TV PRODUCER	ABC-TV, 7 W 66TH ST	NEW YORK, NY	10023
PORIZKOVA, PAULINA	MODEL-ACTRESS	PADELL, 1775 BROADWAY, 7TH FL	NEW YORK, NY	10019
PORK & THE HAVANA DUCKS	C & W GROUP	POST OFFICE BOX 1771	CHAMPAIGN, IL	61820
PORT, CHRIS	FOOTBALL	SAINTS, 1500 POYDRAS ST	NEW ORLEANS, LA	90112
PORT, MIKE	BASEBALL EXECUTIVE	POST OFFICE BOX 2000	ANAHEIM, CA	92803
PORTEOUS, EMMA	COSTUME DESIGNER	CONWAY, 18-21 JERMYN ST	LONDON SW1	ENGLAND
PORTEOUS, PETER	ACTOR	GLENCOT PARKSIDE, CHEAM VILLAGE	SURREY SM3 8BS	ENGLAND
PORTER, BEN E, JR	CONDUCTOR	POST OFFICE BOX 320	MC CLOUD, CA	96057
PORTER, BETH	TV PRODUCER	PETERS, FRASER & DUNLOP, LTD		
		5TH FLOOR, THE CHAMBERS		
		CHELSEA HARBOUR, LOT RD	LONDON SW10 OXF	ENGLAND
PORTER, DARRELL	BASEBALL	19 NE DAYVIEW DR	LEES SUMMIT, MO	64063
PORTER, DON	ACTOR-DIRECTOR	1900 AVE OF THE STARS #2270	LOS ANGELES, CA	90067
PORTER, EDDIE RAY	SINGER-GUITARIST	MOD LANG MANAGEMENT		
		48 SHATTLUCK SQ #138	BERKELEY, CA	94704
PORTER, ERIC	ACTOR	HEATH, PARAMOUNT HOUSE		
		162-170 WARDOUR ST	LONDON W1V 3AT	ENGLAND
PORTER, FRED H	DIRECTOR	7 W 16TH ST #4	NEW YORK, NY	10011
PORTER, H DALE	CONDUCTOR	4432 CANDLEBERRY AVE	SEAL BEACH, CA	90740
PORTER, JAMES F	CONDUCTOR	1062 HANLEY AVE	LOS ANGELES, CA	90049
PORTER, JEAN	ACTRESS	1034 12TH ST	SANTA MONICA, CA	90403
PORTER, JOHN E	U S CONGRESSMAN	104 WILMOT RD #410	DEERFIELD, IL	60015
PORTER, KEVIN	FOOTBALL	CHIEFS, 1 ARROWHEAD DR	KANSAS CITY, MO	64129
PORTER, MADISON T	ACTOR	4918 W MARTIN L KING BLVD #4	LOS ANGELES, CA	90016
PORTER, NYREE DAWN	ACTRESS	28 BERKELEY SQ	LONDON W1X 6HD	ENGLAND
PORTER, NYREE DAWN	ACTRESS	LONDON MGT, 235-241 REGENT ST	LONDON W1R 4PH	ENGLAND
PORTER, RALPH	WRITER-PRODUCER	251 E 61ST ST	NEW YORK, NY	10021
PORTER, ROBERT	FILM PRODUCER	SAINT JAMES FILM PRODUCTIONS		
		73 SAINT JAMES ST	LONDON SW1	ENGLAND
PORTER, ROBERT G	COMPOSER-CONDUCTOR	9825 MELINDA DR	BEVERLY HILLS, CA	90210
PORTER, ROBERT M	COMPOSER	350 VASSAR AVE	BERKELEY, CA	94708
PORTER, ROSS	SPORTCASTER	1000 ELYSIAN PARK DR	LOS ANGELES, CA	90012
PORTER, RUFUS	FOOTBALL	SEAHAWKS, 11220 NE 53RD ST	KIRKLAND, WA	98033
PORTER, STEPHEN	BASEBALL EXECUTIVE	POST OFFICE BOX 12557	ST PETERSBURG, FL	33733
PORTER, STEPHEN W	DIRECTOR	DGA, 110 W 57TH ST	NEW YORK, NY	10019
PORTER, SYLVIA	COLUMNIST	UPS, 4900 MAIN ST, 9TH FLOOR	KANSAS CITY, MO	64112
PORTER, TERRY	BASKETBALL	700 NE MULTNOMAH ST #600	PORTLAND, OR	97232
PORTERFIELD, RON	BASEBALL TRAINER	POST OFFICE BOX 4209	JACKSON, MS	39296
PORTILLO, ROSE	ACTRESS	957 TULAROSA DR	LOS ANGELES, CA	90026
PORTUGAL, MARK	BASEBALL	POST OFFICE BOX 288	HOUSTON, TX	77001
PORTUGUES, GLADYS	BODYBUILDER	POST OFFICE BOX 69-A-05	HOLLYWOOD, CA	90069
PORYES, MICHAEL D	WRITER	1659 VETERAN AVE	LOS ANGELES, CA	90024
POSADA, JORGE	BASEBALL	POST OFFICE BOX 22093	GREENSBORO, NC	27420
POSADA, LEO	BASEBALL-INSTRUCTOR	1000 ELYSIAN PARK DR	LOS ANGELES, CA	90012
POSEY, PAMELA EILERSON	DIRECTOR	SEE - EILERSON POSEY, PAMELA		
POSEY, PARKER	ACTRESS	CBS-TV, "AS THE WORLD TURNS"		
		524 W 57TH ST #5330	NEW YORK, NY	10019
POSEY, SANDY	SINGER	430 OAK GROVE #110	MINNEAPOLIS, MN	55403
POSEY, STEPHEN L	CINEMATOGRAPHER	6320 TRANCAS CANYON RD	MALIBU, CA	90265
POSHARD, GLENN	U S CONGRESSMAN	110 N DIVISION	CARTERVILLE, IL	62918
POSNER, IRINA	WRITER-PRODUCER	DGA, 110 W 57TH ST	NEW YORK, NY	10019
POSNER, NEIL B	CONDUCTOR	4261 TROOST AVE #3	STUDIO CITY, CA	91604
POSSELT, LEE	TV DIRECTOR	40968 FOREST HOME BLVD	FOREST FALLS, CA	92339
POST, HOWARD	ARTIST	1236 MARGO DR	TEMPE, AZ	85281
POST, MARKIE	ACTRESS	4425 TALOFA AVE	TOLUCA LAKE, CA	91602
POST, MEREDITH	TV-COMEDY WRITER	250 W 22ND ST #2-C	NEW YORK, NY	10011
POST, MIKE	COMPOSER	10453 KLING ST	NORTH HOLLYWOOD, CA	91602
POST, TED	FILM DIRECTOR	T P FILMS, BLUMENTHAL & LEVIN		
		3250 OCEAN PARK BLVD	SANTA MONICA, CA	90405
POSTAL, JULIUS B	TV DIRECTOR	POST OFFICE BOX 46	RIDGEWOOD, NY	11385
POSTER, STEVEN	CINEMATOGRAPHER	POST OFFICE BOX 2230	HOLLYWOOD, CA	90078
POSTER, TOM	COLUMNIST-CRITIC	TRIBUNE, 64 E CONCORD ST	ORLANDO, FL	32801
POSTIER, PAUL	BASEBALL	POST OFFICE BOX 75089	OKLAHOMA CITY, OK	73147
POSTIFF, JAMES "J P"	BASEBALL	1524 W NEBRASKA AVE	PEORIA, IL	61604
POSTIL, LELAND	COMPOSER	4507 CARPENTER AVE	NORTH HOLLYWOOD, CA	91607
POSTLER, PAUL	BASEBALL	POST OFFICE BOX 75089	OKLAHOMA CITY, OK	73147
POSTLEWAIT, KATHY	GOLFER	2750 VOLUSA AVE #B	DAYTON BEACH, FL	32114
POSTON, TIFFANIE	ACTRESS	3500 W OLIVE AVE #1400	BURBANK, CA	91505
POSTON, TOM	ACTOR	2830 DEEP CANYON DR	BEVERLY HILLS, CA	90210
POTAMKIN, BUZZ	TV PRODUCER	POST OFFICE BOX 46187	LOS ANGELES, CA	90046

POTE, LOU	BASEBALL	POST OFFICE BOX 3448	SHREVEPORT, LA	71133
POTTER, ALLEN M	ACTOR-TV PRODUCER	NBC-TV, 30 ROCKEFELLER PLAZA	NEW YORK, NY	10112
POTTER, ANTHONY ROSS	WRITER-PRODUCER	DGA, 110 W 57TH ST	NEW YORK, NY	10019
POTTER, CAROL EASTMAN	ACTRESS	5700 WILSHIRE BLVD #575	LOS ANGELES, CA	90036
POTTER, CHRIS	FILM CRITIC	POST OFFICE BOX 1147	ANN ARBOR, MI	48106
POTTER, DENNIS	SCREENWRITER	8955 BEVERLY BLVD	WEST HOLLYWOOD, CA	90048
POTTER, JERRY	SPORTS WRITER	POST OFFICE BOX 500	WASHINGTON, DC	20044
POTTER, JESSICA	ACTRESS	3061 N BEACHWOOD DR	LOS ANGELES, CA	90068
POTTER, RICK, JR	DIRECTOR	910 DIABLO RD	DANVILLE, CA	94526
POTTER, SCOTT	BASEBALL UMPIRE	POST OFFICE BOX 608	GROVE CITY, OH	43123
POTTER EASTMAN, CAROL	ACTRESS	5700 WILSHIRE BLVD #575	LOS ANGELES, CA	90036
POTTS, ANNIE	ACTRESS	1601 N CAMPBELL ST	GLENDALE, CA	91207
POTTS, CLIFF	ACTOR	15301 VENTURA BLVD #345	SHERMAN OAKS, CA	91403
POTTS, MIKE	BASEBALL	POST OFFICE BOX 507	DURHAM, NC	27702
POTTS, NANCY	COSTUME DESIGNER	13949 VENTURA BLVD #309	SHERMAN OAKS, CA	91423
POUGET, ELY	ACTRESS	301 N CANON DR #305	BEVERLY HILLS, CA	90210
POUGH, CLYDE	BASEBALL	POST OFFICE BOX 3452	KINSTON, NC	28502
POULIN, DAVE	HOCKEY	BRUINS, 150 CAUSEWAY ST	BOSTON, MA	02114
POULIOT, STEPHEN	WRITER-PRODUCER	1223 CABRILLO AVE	VENICE, CA	90291
POULIS, GEORGE	BASEBALL TRAINER	POST OFFICE BOX 611	WATERLOO, IA	50704
POULSON, GERALD	FILM DIRECTOR	GPA FILMS, 14 PEMBROKE RD	DUBLIN 4,	IRELAND
POUND, LESLIE	FILM EXECUTIVE	322 W 57TH ST #44-M	NEW YORK, NY	10019
POUNDER, C C H	ACTRESS	SMITH, 121 N SAN VICENTE BLVD	BEVERLY HILLS, CA	90211
POUNDSTONE, PAULA	COMEDIENNE	1027 CHELSEA AVE	SANTA MONICA, CA	90403
POUSETTE, LENA	ACTRESS	1177 LATIGO CANYON	MALIBU, CA	90265
POUSETTE-DART BAND, THE	ROCK & ROLL GROUP	3 E 54TH ST #1400	NEW YORK, NY	10022
POVICH, MAURY	BROADCAST JOURNALIST	250 W 57TH ST #26-W	NEW YORK, NY	10019
POVILAITIS, DAVID	ARTIST	5415 N SHERIDAN RD	CHICAGO, IL	60640
POVILL, JONATHAN	TV WRITER	1503 BAINUM DR	TOPANGA, CA	90290
POWELL, ADDISON	ACTOR	334 W 86TH ST	NEW YORK, NY	10024
POWELL, ALONZO	BASEBALL	POST OFFICE BOX 3690, STA "B"	CALGARY, ALB T2B 4M4	CANADA
POWELL, ANTHONY	COSTUME DESIGNER	GLYNNE, 11 GLOUCESTER RD	LONDON SW7 4PP	ENGLAND
POWELL, BARBARA	ACTRESS	9777 WILSHIRE BLVD #707	BEVERLY HILLS, CA	90212
POWELL, BARBARA	TV DIRECTOR	12070 MOUND VIEW PL	STUDIO CITY, CA	91604
POWELL, BRADLEY R	COMPOSER	POST OFFICE BOX 8891	UNIVERSAL CITY, CA	91608
POWELL, COREY	BASEBALL	POST OFFICE BOX 3566	WEST PALM BEACH, FL	33402
POWELL, DENNIS	BASEBALL	POST OFFICE BOX 3690, STA "B"	CALGARY, ALB T2B 4M4	CANADA
POWELL, DREXEL	CARTOONIST	215 S MC DOWELL ST	RALEIGH, NC	27602
POWELL, DWANE	CARTOONIST	POST OFFICE BOX 191	RALEIGH, NC	27602
POWELL, FORREST	COMPOSER	1150 E 56TH ST	LOS ANGELES, CA	90011
POWELL, GEN COLIN L	U S GENERAL	CHAIRMAN, JOINT CHIEFS OF STAFF THE PENTAGON, ROOM 2-E-872	WASHINGTON, DC	20318
POWELL, GORDON	BASEBALL	POST OFFICE BOX 855	BELOIT, WI	53511
POWELL, HOLLY	ACTRESS	223 W 14TH ST	NEW YORK, NY	10011
POWELL, HOMER	DIRECTOR	1413 N KINGSLEY DR	LOS ANGELES, CA	90029
POWELL, HOSKEN	BASEBALL SCOUT	POST OFFICE BOX 2000	SAN DIEGO, CA	92112
POWELL, JANE	ACTRESS	230 W 55TH ST #14-B	NEW YORK, NY	10019
POWELL, JILL	ACTRESS	CBS-TV, "AS THE WORLD TURNS" 524 W 57TH ST #5330	NEW YORK, NY	10019
POWELL, JIMMY	GOLFER	PGA SENIORS, 112 T P C BLVD	PONTE VEDRA BEACH, FL	32082
POWELL, JODY	PRESS SECRETARY	1901 "L" ST, NW	WASHINGTON, DC	20036
POWELL, JOHN	BASEBALL UMPIRE	235 MAIN ST #103	TRUSSVILLE, AL	35173
POWELL, JOHN "BOOG"	BASEBALL	U S ANGLERS MARINE	KEY WEST, FL	33040
POWELL, KEN	BASEBALL	POST OFFICE BOX 309	GASTONA, NC	28053
POWELL, LARRY	DIRECTOR	17270 DEVONSHIRE ST	NORTHRIDGE, CA	91325
POWELL, LEWIS F, JR	SUPREME COURT JUDGE	1 1ST ST, NE	WASHINGTON, DC	20543
POWELL, NORMAN S	WRITER-PRODUCER	12070 MOUND VIEW PL	STUDIO CITY, CA	91604
POWELL, RANDOLPH	ACTOR	2644 HIGHLAND AVE	SANTA MONICA, CA	90405
POWELL, REGINALD G	COMPOSER	POST OFFICE BOX 1518	STUDIO CITY, CA	91604
POWELL, RICHARD M	TV WRITER	24554 MALIBU RD	MALIBU, CA	90265
POWELL, ROBERT	ACTOR	ICM, 388-396 OXFORD ST	LONDON W1	ENGLAND
POWELL, ROGER	SINGER	POST OFFICE BOX 135	BEARSVILLE, NY	12409
POWELL, ROSS	BASEBALL	POST OFFICE BOX 23290	NASHVILLE, TN	37202
POWELL, SANDI	SINGER	3198 ROYAL LN #204	DALLAS, TX	75229
POWELL, SHAWN	BASEBALL-INSTRUCTOR	N Y YANKEES, YANKEE STADIUM	BRONX, NY	10451
POWELL, SUE	SINGER	38 MUSIC SQUARE E #300	NASHVILLE, TN	37203
POWELL, SUSAN	ACTRESS	6333 BRYN MAWR DR	LOS ANGELES, CA	90068
POWELL, TERRY	SINGER	5625 "O" STREET BLDG #7	LINCOLN, NE	68510
POWELL, TOM	COMEDIAN	32500 CONCORD DR #252	MADISON HGTS, MI	48071
POWELL, TRISTRAM	TV PRODUCER	THE CASSAROTTO COMPANY 60-66 WARDOUR ST	LODNON WN3 3HP	ENGLAND
POWER, ROMINA	ACTRESS	CELLINO SAN MARCO	PROVINZ BRINDISE	ITALY
POWER, TED	BASEBALL	3490 TIFFANY RIDGE LN	CINCINNATI, OH	45241
POWER, TYRONE, JR	ACTOR	823 N GARDNER ST	LOS ANGELES, CA	90046
POWER, UDANA	ACTRESS	838 N DOHENY DR #1402	LOS ANGELES, CA	90069
POWER, VIC	BASEBALL-SCOUT	POST OFFICE BOX 2000	ANAHEIM, CA	92803
POWER PLAY	RHYTHM & BLUES GROUP	POST OFFICE BOX 11283	RICHMOND, VA	23230
POWERPLAY	ROCK & ROLL GROUP	BROTHERS, 141 DUNBAR AVE	FORDS, NJ	08863
POWERS, ALEXANDRA	ACTRESS	POST OFFICE BOX 5617	BEVERLY HILLS, CA	90213
POWERS, GEORGE A, JR	DIRECTOR	DGA, 7920 SUNSET BLVD, 6TH FL	LOS ANGELES, CA	90046
POWERS, JERRY	SINGER-SONGWRITER	POST OFFICE BOX 1058	LA MESA, CA	91944
POWERS, JIM	WRESTLER	POST OFFICE BOX 3859	STAMFORD, CT	06905
POWERS, KATHERINE	DIRECTOR	DGA, 110 W 57TH ST	NEW YORK, NY	10019
POWERS, MALA	ACTRESS	10543 VALLEY SPRING LN	NORTH HOLLYWOOD, CA	91602
POWERS, MIKE	BASEBALL SCOUT	333 W 35TH ST	CHICAGO, IL	60616

POWERS, RANDY	BASEBALL (SALINAS)	POST OFFICE BOX 4370	SALINAS, CA 93912
POWERS, RAY	ACTOR	2100 N BEACHWOOD DR #307	LOS ANGELES, CA 90068
POWERS, RON	MEDIA CRITIC	GELLER MGMT, 250 W 57TH ST	NEW YORK, NY 10019
POWERS, STEFANIE	ACTRESS	2661 HUTTON DR	BEVERLY HILLS, CA 90210
POWERS, STEVE	BASEBALL	POST OFFICE BOX 824	BURLINGTON, IA 52601
POWERS, TERRY	BASEBALL	RED SOX, CHAIN O'LAKES PARK	WINTER HAVEN, FL 33880
POWERS, UDANA	ACTRESS	3500 W OLIVE AVE #1400	BURBANK, CA 91505
POWERS, WARREN	FOOTBALL	BRONCOS, 13655 BRONCOS PKWY	ENGLEWOOD, CO 80112
POYNER, JAY	TV DIRECTOR-PRODUCER	444 E 82ND ST #28-C	NEW YORK, NY 10028
POZEN, PAT	COMPOSER	133 S CROFT AVE #9	LOS ANGELES, CA 90048
PRADY, BILL	TV WRITER	UTA, 9560 WILSHIRE BL, 5TH FL	BEVERLY HILLS, CA 90212
PRAGER, HOWARD	BASEBALL	POST OFFICE BOX 4209	JACKSON, MS 39296
PRAIRIE FIRE	C & W GROUP	OME, 233 W WOODLAND AVE	OTTUMWA, IA 52501
PRAISER, IAN R	SCREENWRITER	5020 TILDEN AVE #C	SHERMAN OAKS, CA 91423
PRANGE, LAURIE	ACTRESS	1519 SARGENT PL	LOS ANGELES, CA 90026
PRATHER, DAVID B	ACTOR	1002 N LARRABEE ST	LOS ANGELES, CA 90069
PRATHER, JOAN	ACTRESS	31647 SEA LEVEL DR	MALIBU, CA 90265
PRATT, CHARLES A, JR	FILM EXECUTIVE	15725 WOODVALE RD	ENCINO, CA 91436
PRATT, DEBORAH	ACTRESS	3301 OAKDELL RD	STUDIO CITY, CA 91604
PRATT, JUDSON	ACTOR	8745 OAK PARK AVE	NORTHRIDGE, CA 91325
PRATT, MIKE	BASKETBALL COACH	310 N KINGS DR	CHARLOTTE, NC 28204
PRATT, TODD	BASEBALL	POST OFFICE BOX 15050	READING, PA 19612
PRATT, TOM	FOOTBALL COACH	CHIEFS, 1 ARROWHEAD DR	KANSAS CITY, MO 64129
PRATTE, EVAN	BASEBALL	POST OFFICE BOX 64939	FAYETTEVILLE, NC 28306
PRAWAR, RUTH	SCREENWRITER	CAA, 9830 WILSHIRE BLVD	BEVERLY HILLS, CA 90212
PREATE, ERNEST D, JR	ATTORNEY GENERAL	STATE CAPITOL BUILDING	HARRISBURG, PA 17120
PRECHT, ROBERT	DIRECTOR	803 N LINDEN DR	BEVERLY HILLS, CA 90210
PREECE, MICHAEL	TV DIRECTOR	12233 EVERGLADE ST	LOS ANGELES, CA 90066
PREJAN, PATRICT	ACTOR	103 RUE DU MAL JOFFRE	COLOMBE 92700 FRANCE
PREJEAN, LEE	BASEBALL UMPIRE	POST OFFICE BOX 608	GROVE CITY, OH 43123
PRELL, JERRY	ACTOR	206 3RD AVE	VENICE, CA 90291
PRELUTSKY, BURT	ACTOR-WRITER	POST OFFICE BOX 5617	BEVERLY HILLS, CA 90213
PREMICE, JOSEPHINE	ACTRESS	755 W END AVE	NEW YORK, NY 10023
PREMINGER, MIKE	COMEDIAN-WRITER	11613 OTSEGO ST	NORTH HOLLYWOOD, CA 91601
PRENDERGAST, FRANK	DIRECTOR	8748 HOLLOWAY DR	LOS ANGELES, CA 90069
PRENTICE, JOHN	CARTOONIST	KING FEATURES, 216 E 45TH ST	NEW YORK, NY 10017
PRENTICE, MILES	BASEBALL EXECUTIVE	POST OFFICE BOX 12	MIDLAND, TX 79702
PRENTISS, ED	ACTOR	267 TOYOPA DR	PACIFIC PALISADES, CA 90272
PRENTISS, PAULA	ACTRESS	719 N FOOTHILL RD	BEVERLY HILLS, CA 90210
PRESCOTT, ELEANOR	TV PRODUCER	ABC-TV, "20/20", 7 W 66TH ST	NEW YORK, NY 10023
PRESEREN, JOE	BASEBALL EXECUTIVE	POST OFFICE BOX 4448	TULSA, OK 74159
PRESLE, MICHELINE	ACTRESS	6 RUE ANTOINE DUBOIS	F-75006 PARIS FRANCE
PRESLEY, JIM	BASEBALL	POST OFFICE BOX 75089	OKLAHOMA CITY, OK 73147
PRESLEY, LISA MARIE	ACTRESS	12614 PROMONTORY RD	LOS ANGELES, CA 90049
PRESLEY, PRISCILLA BEAULIEU	ACTRESS-MODEL	1167 SUMMIT DR	BEVERLY HILLS, CA 90210
PRESLEY, VESPER	ELVIS'S DAD	3764 ELVIS PRESLEY BLVD	MEMPHIS, TN 38116
PRESLEY, WAYNE	HOCKEY	BLACKHAWKS, 1800 W MADISON ST	CHICAGO, IL 60612
PRESS, LINDA	SINGER	POST OFFICE BOX 1764	LAKE ARROWHEAD, CA 92352
PRESSBURGER, FRED	DIRECTOR	SPECTRA, 140 W 57TH ST	NEW YORK, NY 10025
PRESSEY, PAUL	BASKETBALL	600 E MARKET ST #102	SAN ANTONIO, TX 78205
PRESSLER, LARRY	U S SENATOR	POST OFFICE BOX 1372	SIOUX FALLS, SD 57102
PRESSMAN, DAVID	DIRECTOR	333 CENTRAL PARK W	NEW YORK, NY 10025
PRESSMAN, EDWARD R	FILM-TV PRODUCER	4063 RADFORD AVE	STUDIO CITY, CA 91604
PRESSMAN, ELLEN	TV PRODUCER	CAA, 9830 WILSHIRE BLVD	BEVERLY HILLS, CA 90212
PRESSMAN, LAWRENCE	ACTOR	15033 ENCANTO DR	SHERMAN OAKS, CA 91403
PRESSMAN, MICHAEL	FILM WRITER-DIRECTOR	8635 LOOKOUT MOUNTAIN AVE	LOS ANGELES, CA 90046
PRESTON, BILLY	SINGER-SONGWRITER	4271 GARTHWAITE AVE	LOS ANGELES, CA 90008
PRESTON, BOB	TALENT AGENT	CED, 261 S ROBERTSON BLVD	BEVERLY HILLS, CA 90211
PRESTON, DUNCAN	ACTOR	46 HILLTOP HOUSE, HORNSEY LN	LONDON N6 ENGLAND
PRESTON, FRANCES W	COMPOSER-LYRICIST	BROADCAST MUSIC, 320 W 57TH ST	NEW YORK, NY 10019
PRESTON, KELLY	ACTRESS	MTA, 9320 WILSHIRE BL, 3RD FL	BEVERLY HILLS, CA 90212
PRESTON, MARILYN	TV CRITIC	THE CHICAGO TRIBUNE	
		TRIBUNE TOWER	
		435 N MICHIGAN AVE	CHICAGO, IL 60611
PRESTON, WAYDE	ACTOR	POST OFFICE BOX 8713	UNIVERSAL CITY, CA 91608
PRESTON, WILLIAM	ACTOR	219 E 32ND ST #3-D	NEW YORK, NY 10016
PRETENDERS, THE	ROCK & ROLL GROUP	3 E 54TH ST #1400	NEW YORK, NY 10022
PRETO, MARTIN	SINGER-GUITARIST	17634 COKE AVE	BELLFLOWER, CA 90706
PREUSS, GORDON A	TV DIRECTOR	WLS-TV, 190 N STATE ST	CHICAGO, IL 60601
PREVIEW	ROCK & ROLL GROUP	3 E 54TH ST #1400	NEW YORK, NY 10022
PREVIN, ANDRE	COMPOSER-CONDUCTOR	8 SHERWOOD LN	BEDFORD HILLS, NY 10507
PREVIN, DORY	COMPOSER-SINGER	BAKER, 2533 ZORADA DR	LOS ANGELES, CA 90046
PREVIN, STEVE	DIRECTOR	10960 WILSHIRE BLVD #922	LOS ANGELES, CA 90024
PREVIN, STEVE	FILM EXECUTIVE	487 S HAMEL RD	LOS ANGELES, CA 90048
PREVOST, FRANCOIS	ACTOR	5 RUE BREZIN	F-75014 PARIS FRANCE
PREVOST, JOSETTE	ACTRESS	9255 SUNSET BLVD #401	WEST HOLLYWOOD, CA 90069
PREWITT, MELISSA	SINGER	LIMELITERS, 50 MUSIC SQUARE W	NASHVILLE, TN 37212
PREZIA, BENITO	ACTOR	1315 N JUNE ST #205	LOS ANGELES, CA 90028
PRIAULX, ROBERT	DIRECTOR	90 E CHESTER RD	NEW ROCHELLE, NY 10801
PRICE, AL	BASEBALL TRAINER	BREWERS, 201 S 46TH ST	MILWAUKEE, WI 53214
PRICE, ALAN	SINGER-SONGWRITER	CROMWELL MANAGEMENT AGENCY	
		THE COACH HOUSE	
		9A THE BROADWAY	
		HUNTINGDON	CAMBS PE17 4BX ENGLAND
PRICE, ANNABELLA	ACTRESS	10351 SANTA MONICA BLVD #211	LOS ANGELES, CA 90025

		23 E LANCASTER AVE	ARDMORE, PA	19003
PRICE, BILLY & KEYSTONE RHYTHM	RHYTHM & BLUES GROUP	CORNERSTONE MANAGEMENT		
PRICE, BRYAN	BASEBALL COACH	POST OFFICE BOX 9194	HAMPTON, VA	23670
PRICE, DARIA	SCREENWRITER	555 W 57TH ST #1230	NEW YORK, NY	10019
PRICE, DAVID E	U S CONGRESSMAN	1777 CHAPEL HILL-DURHAM BL #202	CHAPIL HILL, NC	27514
PRICE, DENISE	SINGER	POST OFFICE BOX 17087	NASHVILLE, TN	37217
PRICE, JEFFREY L	SCREENWRITER	8955 BEVERLY BLVD	WEST HOLLYWOOD, CA	90048
PRICE, JIM	FOOTBALL	RAMS, 2327 W LINCOLN BLVD	ANAHEIM, CA	92801
PRICE, JOHN A	TV PRODUCER	201 E 15TH ST #7-C	NEW YORK, NY	10003
PRICE, JUDY	TV EXECUTIVE	CBS-TV, 7800 BEVERLY BLVD	LOS ANGELES, CA	90036
PRICE, KENNY	SINGER-SONGWRITER	19 LA CRESTA DR	FLORENCE, KY	41042
PRICE, LEONTYNE	SINGER	9 VAN DAM ST	NEW YORK, NY	10003
PRICE, LINDSAY	ACTRESS	ABC-TV, "ALL MY CHILDREN"		
		320 W 66TH ST	NEW YORK, NY	10023
PRICE, LLOYD	SINGER	MARS, 168 ORCHID DR	PEARL RIVER, NY	10965
PRICE, LORIN E	THEATER PRODUCER	1501 BROADWAY	NEW YORK, NY	10036
PRICE, MARK	ACTOR-COMEDIAN	9744 WILSHIRE BLVD #308	BEVERLY HILLS, CA	90212
PRICE, MARK	BASKETBALL	POST OFFICE BOX 5000	RICHFIELD, OH	44286
PRICE, MARY GRANT	COSTUME DESIGNER	13949 VENTURA BLVD #309	SHERMAN OAKS, CA	91423
PRICE, MIKE H	FILM CRITIC	POST OFFICE BOX 1870	FORT WORTH, TX	76101
PRICE, MITCHELL	FOOTBALL	BENGALS, 200 RIVERFRONT STADIUM	CINCINNATI, OH	45202
PRICE, NICK	GOLFER	POST OFFICE BOX 109601	PALM BCH GARDENS, FL	33418
PRICE, PENNY	BODYBUILDER	POST OFFICE BOX 1490		
		RADIO CITY STATION	NEW YORK, NY	10101
PRICE, PETER	FILM DIRECTOR	10 DOVE PARK, CHORLEYWOOD	HERTS	ENGLAND
PRICE, RAY	SINGER	POST OFFICE BOX 1986	MOUNT PLEASANT, TX	75230
PRICE, RAYMOND	JOURNALIST-COLUMNIST	N Y TIMES SYN, 130 5TH AVE	NEW YORK, NY	10011
PRICE, RICHARD J	SCREENWRITER-AUTHOR	1015 GAYLEY AVE #301	LOS ANGELES, CA	90024
PRICE, RICHARD S	FILM EXECUTIVE	SEYMOUR MEWS HOUSE		
		SEYMOUR MEWS, WIGMORE ST	LONDON W1	ENGLAND
PRICE, RICK	SINGER	JP, 600 NEVAN RD	VIRGINIA BEACH, VA	23451
PRICE, STANLEY	SCREENWRITER	17 CRANLEY GARDENS	LONDON N6	ENGLAND
PRICE, VINCENT	ACTOR	9255 SWALLOW DR	LOS ANGELES, CA	90069
PRICE, WARREN	ATTORNEY GENERAL	STATE CAPITOL BUILDING	HONOLULU, HI	96813
PRICE SISTERS, THE	VOCAL DUO	MBA, 8914 GEORGIAN DR	AUSTIN, TX	78753
PRICEMAN, GEORGE	ACTOR	6968 DUME DR	MALIBU, CA	90265
PRIDDY, NANCY	ACTRESS	200 N ROBERTSON BLVD #214	BEVERLY HILLS, CA	90211
PRIDE, CHARLEY	SINGER	3198 ROYAL LN #204	DALLAS, TX	75229
PRIDE, CURTIS	BASEBALL	POST OFFICE BOX 598	BINGHAMTON, NY	13902
PRIDEAUX, JAMES	TV WRITER	840 N LARRABEE ST #4-123	LOS ANGELES, CA	90069
PRIDESMEN, THE	C & W GROUP	3198 ROYAL LN #204	DALLAS, TX	75229
PRIEST, DAN	ACTOR-WRITER	8618 AQUEDUCT AVE	SEPULVEDA, CA	91343
PRIEST, PAT	ACTRESS	POST OFFICE BOX 1298	HATLEY, ID	83333
PRIEST, ROBERT M	DIRECTOR	5937 HILLVIEW PARK AVE	VAN NUYS, CA	91401
PRIESTLEY, JASON, JR	ACTOR	UTA, 9560 WILSHIRE BL, 5TH FL	BEVERLY HILLS, CA	90212
PRIESTLEY, JASON, SR	CINEMATOGRAPHER	POST OFFICE BOX 2230	HOLLYWOOD, CA	90078
PRIESTLEY, THOMAS A	DIRECTOR	DGA, 110 W 57TH ST	NEW YORK, NY	10019
PRIME TIME	VOCAL GROUP	TOTAL EXPERIENCE RECORDS		
		1800 N ARGYLE AVE	HOLLYWOOD, CA	90028
PRIME TYME	ROCK & ROLL GROUP	POST OFFICE BOX 448	RADFORD, VA	24141
PRIMEAU, KEITH	HOCKEY	RED WINGS, 600 CIVIC CENTER DR	DETROIT, MI	48226
PRIMES, ROBERT	CINEMATOGRAPHER	POST OFFICE BOX 2230	HOLLYWOOD, CA	90078
PRIMUS, BARRY	ACTOR-DIRECTOR	2735 CRESTON DR	LOS ANGELES, CA	90068
PRINCE	SING-SONGWRI-ACT-DIR	9401 KIOWA TRAIL	CHANHASSEN, MN	55317
PRINCE, HAROLD S	DIRECTOR-PRODUCER	1270 AVE OF THE AMERICAS	NEW YORK, NY	10020
PRINCE, JOHN H	COMPOSER-CONDUCTOR	2050 VOLK AVE	LONG BEACH, CA	90815
PRINCE, JONATHAN	ACTOR	10340 CALVIN AVE	LOS ANGELES, CA	90025
PRINCE, MICHAEL	ACTOR	5750 WILSHIRE BLVD #512	LOS ANGELES, CA	90036
PRINCE, PAM	TALENT AGENT	151 S EL CAMINO DR	BEVERLY HILLS, CA	90212
PRINCE, ROBERT H	COMPOSER-CONDUCTOR	2246 MANDEVILLE CANYON RD	LOS ANGELES, CA	90049
PRINCE, TOM	BASEBALL	POST OFFICE BOX 7000	PITTSBURGH, PA	15212
PRINCE, WILLIAM	ACTOR	750 N KINGS RD #307	LOS ANGELES, CA	90069
PRINCE, WINTHROP	CARTOONIST	THE CHRONICLE FEATURES		
		870 MARKET ST	SAN FRANCISCO, CA	94102
PRINCESS DIANA	PRINCESS	KENNSINGTON PALACE	LONDON W8	ENGLAND
PRINCESS STEPHANIE	PRINCESS	475 CASTLE PL	BEVERLY HILLS, CA	90210
PRINCI, ELAINE	ACTRESS	4906 LEDGE AVE	NORTH HOLLYWOOD, CA	91601
PRINCIPAL, VICTORIA	ACTRESS-PRODUCER	10000 SANTA MONICA BLVD #400	LOS ANGELES, CA	90067
PRINCZ, GARY	DIRECTOR	4 SPUR DR	NANUET, NY	10954
PRINDLE, KAREN	TV DIRECTOR	629 W FULLERTON PARKWAY	CHICAGO, IL	60614
PRINE, ANDREW	ACTOR	3264 LONGRIDGE AVE	SHERMAN OAKS, CA	91423
PRINE, JOHN	SINGER-SONGWRITER	4121 WILSHIRE BLVD #215	LOS ANGELES, CA	90010
PRING, ROBERT E	COMPOSER	230 W 54TH ST #511	NEW YORK, NY	10019
PRINGEL, PERCY	WRESTLING MANAGER	SEE - BEARER, PAUL		
PRINGLE, BRYAN	ACTOR	MARKHAM AND FROGGATT, LTD		
		JULIAN HOUSE, 4 WINDMILL ST	LONDON W1P 1HF	ENGLAND
PRIOR, ALLAN	NOVELIST	MLR, 200 FULHAM RD	LONDON SW10 9PN	ENGLAND
PRIOR, MIKE	FOOTBALL	POST OFFICE BOX 535000	INDIANPOLIS, IN	46253
PRISM	ROCK & ROLL GROUP	68 WATER ST #406	VANCOUVER, BC V6B 1A4	CANADA
PRISONER	MUSICAL GROUP	2130 E CRAWFORD ST #309	SALINA, KS	67401
PRISONERS, THE	ROCK & ROLL GROUP	BIG BEAT RECORDS CO		
		134 GRAFTON RD		
		KENTISH TOWN	LONDON NW5 4BA	ENGLAND
PRITCHARD, JOEL	LT GOVERNOR	STATE LEGISLATIVE BUILDING	OLYMPIA, WA	98504
PRITCHARD, KEVIN	BASKETBALL	GOLDEN STATE WARRIORS		

		OAKLAND COLISEUM ARENA	
		NIMITZ FWY & HEGENBERGER RD	OAKLAND, CA 94621
PRITCHARD, MIKE	FOOTBALL	FALCONS, SUWANEE RD AT I-85	SUWANEE, GA 30174
PRITCHETT, ANTHONY	BASEBALL	POST OFFICE BOX 4218	SOUTH BEND, IN 46634
PRITCHETT, CHRIS	BASEBALL	POST OFFICE BOX 3496	DAVENPORT, IA 52808
PRITCHETT, DAVE	BASKETBALL-COACH	TIMBERWOLVES, 600 1ST AVE N	MINNEAPOLIS, MN 55403
PRITCHETT, JAMES	ACTOR	53 W 74TH ST	NEW YORK, NY 10023
PRITCHETT, KELVIN	FOOTBALL	LIONS, 1200 FEATHERSTONE RD	PONTIAC, MI 48432
PRITCHETT, TONY	SINGER-SONGWRITER	POST OFFICE BOX 110423	NASHVILLE, TN 37211
PRITCHETT, WES	FOOTBALL	FALCONS, SUWANEE RD AT I-85	SUWANEE, GA 30174
PRITZKER, STEVEN	TV WRITER-PRODUCER	8071 WOODROW WILSON DR	LOS ANGELES, CA 90046
PRIVATE LIGHTING	ROCK & ROLL GROUP	FRED HELLER, 1756 BROADWAY	NEW YORK, NY 10019
PROBERT, BOB	HOCKEY	RED WINGS, 600 CIVIC CENTER DR	DETROIT, MI 48226
PROBOLA, DICK	BASEBALL SCOUT	POST OFFICE BOX 2000	ANAHEIM, CA 92803
PROCESS AND THE DOO RAGS	VOCAL GROUP	COLUMBIA RECORDS CO	
		51 W 52ND ST	NEW YORK, NY 10019
PROCLAIMERS, THE	ROCK & ROLL GROUP	POST OFFICE BOX 309	EDINBURGH EH9 1JE SCOTLAND
PROCTOR, DAVID	BASEBALL	525 NW PEACOCK BLVD	PORT SAINT LUCIE, FL 34986
PROCTOR, MEL	SPORTSCASTER	BULLETS, 1 HARRY S TRUMAN DR	LANDOVER, MD 20785
PROCTOR, MURPH	BASEBALL	POST OFFICE BOX 10031	BAKERSFIELD, CA 93389
PROCTOR, PHILIP	ACTOR-WRITER	9824 WANDA PARK DR	BEVERLY HILLS, CA 90210
PRODIGAL	ROCK & ROLL GROUP	POST OFFICE BOX 1254	MOUNT DORA, FL 32757
PROEHL, RICKY	FOOTBALL	POST OFFICE BOX 888	PHOENIX, AZ 85001
PROFT, PATRICK	TV WRITER	841 BIENVENEDA AVE	PACIFIC PALISADES, CA 90272
PROHASKA, TOM	BASEBALL EXECUTIVE	1201 HYDE PARK BLVD	NIAGARA FALLS, NY 14301
PROPER DOS	RAP DUO-RAPWRITERS	POST OFFICE BOX 3429	ALHAMBRA, CA 91803
PROPHET, TONY	SINGER	1227 SAXON DR	NASHVILLE, TN 37215
PROPP, BRIAN	HOCKEY	NORTH STARS, 7901 CEDAR AVE S	BLOOMINGTON, MN 55425
PROPS, RENEE	ACTRESS	CBS-TV, "AS THE WORLD TURNS"	
		524 W 57TH ST #5330	NEW YORK, NY 10019
PROSER, CHIP	SCREENWRITER	9255 SUNSET BLVD #1122	LOS ANGELES, CA 90069
PROSKY, ROBERT	ACTOR	SMITH, 121 N SAN VICENTE BLVD	BEVERLY HILLS, CA 90211
PROVAS, PAUL	BASEBALL SCOUT	1060 W ADDISON ST	CHICAGO, IL 60613
PROVENCE, DENIS	ACTOR	57 AVE PAUL DOUMER	PARIS 75016 FRANCE
PROVENZA, PAUL	ACTOR	22 NAVY ST #303	VENICE, CA 90291
PROVINE, DOROTHY	ACTRESS	DAY, 8832 FERNCLIFF NE	BAINBRIDGE ISLAND, WA 98110
PROVOST, JON	ACTOR	627 MONTCLAIR DR	SANTA ROSA, CA 95409
PROWSE, DAVE	ACTOR	7 CARLYLE RD	CROYDON CRO 7HN ENGLAND
PROWSE, JOHN	TV DIRECTOR	GLEN COTTAGE, CHALFORD	GLOS ENGLAND
PROWSE, JULIET	ACTRESS-DANCER	343 S BEVERLY GLEN BLVD	LOS ANGELES, CA 90024
PRUDHOMME, PAUL	CHEF-AUTHOR	406 CHARTES ST #2	NEW ORLEANS, LA 70130
PRUEITT, GERALD	WRITER-PRODUCER	50 E 42ND ST	NEW YORK, NY 10017
PRUETT, JEANNE	SINGER	1300 DIVISION ST #102	NASHVILLE, TN 37203
PRUETT, KEITH	ACTOR	ABC-TV, "LOVING"	
		320 W 66TH ST, STUDIO 23	NEW YORK, NY 10023
PRUITT, DILLARD	GOLFER	POST OFFICE BOX 109601	PALM BCH GARDENS, FL 33418
PRUITT, DON	BASEBALL	POST OFFICE BOX 855	BELOIT, WI 53511
PRUITT, JASON	BASEBALL	POST OFFICE BOX 464	APPLETON, WI 54912
PRUITT, MICKEY	FOOTBALL	COWBOYS, 1 COWBOYS PARKWAY	IRVING, TX 75063
PRUSAN, JODY	ACTRESS	145 S FAIRFAX AVE #310	LOS ANGELES, CA 90036
PRUTER, ROBERT	R & B EDITOR	POST OFFICE BOX 768	ELMHURST, IL 60126
PRYBYLINSKI, BRUCE	BASEBALL	POST OFFICE BOX 2148	WOODBRIDGE, VA 22193
PRYBYLINSKI, DON	BASEBALL	POST OFFICE BOX 5599	LITTLE ROCK, AR 72215
PRYCE, JONATHAN	ACTOR	BLOOM, 233 PARK AVE S, 10TH FL	NEW YORK, NY 10017
PRYOR, DAVID	U S CONGRESSMAN	3030 FEDERAL BUILDING	LITTLE ROCK, AR 72201
PRYOR, GLORIA	TV HOST	POST OFFICE BOX 15324	BEVERLY HILLS, CA 90209
PRYOR, NICHOLAS	ACTOR	8963 BURTON WY #304	LOS ANGELES, CA 90048
PRYOR, RAIN	ACTRESS	MTA, 9320 WILSHIRE BL, 3RD FL	BEVERLY HILLS, CA 90212
PRYOR, RICHARD	ACTOR-COMEDIAN	1115 MORAGA DR	LOS ANGELES, CA 90049
PRYSOCK, ARTHUR	SINGER	D PALMER, 211 W 53RD ST	NEW YORK, NY 10019
PRZEWODEK, CAMILLE	ARTIST	4029 23RD ST	SAN FRANCISCO, CA 94114
PSYCHEDELIC FURS, THE	ROCK & ROLL GROUP	AMANITA, 1 CATHEDRAL ST	LONDON SE1 ENGLAND
PUBLIC ENEMY	RAP GROUP-RAPWRITERS	FAA, 1700 BROADWAY, 5TH FLOOR	NEW YORK, NY 10019
PUBLIC IMAGE, LTD	ROCK & ROLL GROUP	FBI, 1776 BORADWAY, 6TH FLOOR	NEW YORK, NY 10019
PUCKETT, GARY	SINGER-SONGWRITER	7817 BACKER RD	SAN DIEGO, CA 92126
PUCKETT, KIRBY	BASEBALL	TWINS, 501 CHICAGO AVE S	MINNEAPOLIS, MN 55415
PUESCHNER, CRAIG	BASEBALL	POST OFFICE BOX 2001	CEDAR RAPIDS, IA 52406
PUETT, TOMMY	ACTOR-TV HOST	ABC-TV, 2040 AVE OF THE STARS	LOS ANGELES, CA 90067
PUGH, SCOTT	BASEBALL	POST OFFICE BOX 4758	SPOKANE, WA 99202
PUGH, TIM	BASEBALL	POST OFFICE BOX 23290	NASHVILLE, TN 37202
PUGH, WILLARD E	ACTOR	1999 AVE OF THE STARS #2850	LOS ANGELES, CA 90067
PUGH-TASIOS, SUSAN	TV DIRECTOR	19 ANAVITRON, 15124 AMAROUSSION	ATHENS GREECE
PUGLISI, ROBERT	ACTOR	8570 WONDERLAND AVE	LOS ANGELES, CA 90046
PUHL, TERRY	BASEBALL	POST OFFICE BOX 8	MELBILLE, SASK CANADA
PUIG, ED	BASEBALL	800 HOME RUN LN	MEMPHIS, TN 38104
PUJOLS, LUIS	BASEBALL-INSTRUCTOR	EXPOS, 4545 DE COUBERTIN AVE	MONTREAL, QUE H1V 3P2 CANADA
PULASKY, DEBORAH	BASEBALL EXECUTIVE	POST OFFICE BOX 328	PITTSFIELD, MA 01202
PULEO, CHARLES	BASEBALL	8208 CORTELAND DR	KNOXVILLE, TN 37909
PULICE, SHAR	ACTRESS	2624 LETICIA DR	HACIENDA HEIGHTS, CA 91745
PULIDO, CARLOS	BASEBALL	POST OFFICE BOX 5645	ORLANDO, FL 32855
PULITZER, ROAXNNE	AUTHORESS-CLEBERITY	VILLARD PRESS, 201 E 50TH ST	NEW YORK, NY 10022
PULITZER, ROXANNE	CELEBRITY	CHESTERFIELD HOTEL	
		363 COCOANUT ROW	PALM BEACH, FL 33480
PULLEN, DOUG	FILM CRITIC	POST OFFICE BOX 2007	KALAMAZOO, MI 49003
PULLI, FRANK	BASEBALL UMPIRE	4898 CARDINAL TRAIL	PALM HARBOR, FL 33563

PULLIAM, HARVEY	BASEBALL	POST OFFICE BOX 3665	OMAHA, NE	68103
PULTZ, ALAN	TV DIRECTOR	3583 WOODCLIFF RD	SHERMAN OAKS, CA	91403
PUMPIAN, PAUL	TV WRITER	10711 WHEATLAND AVE	SUNLAND, CA	91040
PUNCHATZ, DON IVAN	ARTIST	2605 WESTGATE DR	ARLINGTON, TX	76105
PUNSLEY, BERNARD	ACTOR	1415 GRANVIA ALTAMIRA	PALOS VERDES, CA	90274
PUOPOLO, LOUIS A	DIRECTOR	381 PARK AVE S	NEW YORK, NY	10016
PUPKEWITZ, DAVID	TV PRODUCER	FOCUS FILMS LTD, ROTUNDA STUDIOS		
		116-118 FINCHLEY RD	LONDON NW3 5HT	ENGLAND
PURCELL, EVELYN	FILM DIRECTOR	1355 MILLER PL	LOS ANGELES, CA	90069
PURCELL, JOSEPH	TV DIRECTOR	1760 HILLCREST AVE	GLENDALE, CA	91202
PURCELL, LEE	ACTRESS	3800 BARHAM BLVD #303	LOS ANGELES, CA	90068
PURCELL, SARAH	ACTRESS	6525 SUNSET BLVD #600	LOS ANGELES, CA	90038
PURDEE, NATHAN	ACTOR	1776 N SYCAMORE AVE #110	HOLLYWOOD, CA	90028
PURDIE, JOHN	ACT-WRI-DIR	WESTBOURNE, 25 WESTBOURNE GROVE	LONDON W2 4UA	ENGLAND
PURDUM, HERBERT R	TV WRITER	1301 N SPARKS ST	BURBANK, CA	91506
PURDY, SHAWN	BASEBALL	POST OFFICE BOX 1742	PALM SPRINGS, CA	92263
PURIM, FLORA	SINGER	SEE - AIRTO & FLORA PURIM		
PURL, LINDA	ACTRESS	10417 RAVENWOOD CT	LOS ANGELES, CA	90077
PURNELL, RUSS	FOOTBALL COACH	SEAHAWKS, 11220 NE 53RD ST	KIRKLAND, WA	98033
PURPLE THINGS, THE	ROCK & ROLL GROUP	36 HANWAY ST	LONDON W1	ENGLAND
PURPURA, CHARLES	FILM-TV WRITER	6 COACHMAN LN	LEVITTOWN, NY	11756
PURSE, WILLIAM E	COMPOSER-CONDUCTOR	5531 PATTILAR AVE	WOODLAND HILLS, CA	91367
PURSELL, CARL D	U S CONGRESSMAN	361 W EISENHOWER PKWY	ANN ARBOR, MI	48103
PURSELL, TERRY & SUSAN WRIGHT	VOCAL DUO	GOOD, 2500 NW 39TH ST	OKLAHOMA CITY, OK	73112
PURSELL, WILLIAM W	MUSIC ARRANGER	895 S CURTISWOOD LN	NASHVILLE, TN	37204
PURSER, DOROTHY ANN	TV WRITER	155 E 38TH ST #88	NEW YORK, NY	10016
PURTZER, TOM	GOLFER	POST OFFICE BOX 109601	PALM BCH GARDENS, FL	33418
PURVES, PETER	ACTOR	ARLINGTON, 1 CHARLOTTE ST	LONDON W1	ENGLAND
PUSH COMES TO SHOVE	ROCK & ROLL GROUP	25 HUNTINGTON AVE #420	BOSTON, MA	02116
PUSH PUSH	ROCK & ROLL GROUP	25 HUNTINGTON AVE #420	BOSTON, MA	02116
PUSSYWILLOWS, THE	ROCK & ROLL GROUP	POST OFFICE BOX 1123	HOBOKEN, NJ	07030
PUTCH, JOHN	ACTOR	8271 MELROSE AVE #110	LOS ANGELES, CA	90046
PUTNAM, GEORGE	BROADCAST JOURNALIST	2355 KIMBRIDGE RD	BEVERLY HILLS, CA	90210
PUTNAM, LORI	ACTRESS	165 W 46TH ST #1109	NEW YORK, NY	10036
PUTNAM, NORBERT	GUITARIST-PRODUCER	134 4TH AVE N	FRANKLIN, TN	37064
PUTNAM, ROSIE	BASEBALL EXECUTIVE	POST OFFICE BOX 1721	SPARTANBURG, SC	29304
PUTSKI, IVAN	WRESTLER	1315 S DAIRY ASHFORD ST #N	HOUSTON, TX	77077
PUTTKAMER, RICHARD K	DIRECTOR	6 PEACEDALE RD	NEEDHAM, MA	02192
PUTTNAM, DAVID T	FILM PRODCUER	ENIGMA PRODUCTIONS		
		15 QUEENS GATE PL, MEWS	LONDON SW7 5BG	ENGLAND
PUZO, MARIO	AUTHOR-SCREENWRITER	866 MANOR LN	BAY SHORE, NY	11706
PYE, CHRIS B	DIRECTOR	STONE MANNERS, 9113 SUNSET BL	LOS ANGELES, CA	90069
PYE, EDDIE	BASEBALL	POST OFFICE BOX 26267	ALBUQUERQUE, NM	87125
PYLE, DENVER	ACT-WRI-DIR	10614 WHIPPLE ST	NORTH HOLLYWOOD, CA	91602
PYLE, RICHARD C	TV DIRECTOR	CHEYNEY RD	CHEYNEY, PA	19319
PYNE, NATASHA	ACTRESS	43-A PRINCESS RD, REGENTS PK	LONDON NW1 8JS	ENGLAND
PYTKA, JOHN A	DIRECTOR	520 N MICHIGAN AVE #1026	CHICAGO, IL	60611
PYTKA, JOSEPH	DIRECTOR	408 BOULEVARD OF THE ALLIES	PITTSBURGH, PA	15219
PYZNARSKI, TIM	BASEBALL	10716 S AUSTIN	CHICAGO RIDGE, IL	60415

Q, STACEY	SINGER	SEE - STACEY Q		
Q T HUSH	SOUL GROUP	POST OFFICE BOX 10161	DETROIT, MI	48210
QUABIUS, FAITH	ACTRESS	9165 CORDELL DR	LOS ANGELES, CA	90069
QUADE, MIKE	BASEBALL MANAGER	POST OFFICE BOX 15757	HARRISBURG, PA	17105
QUADLING, LEW	COMPOSER-CONDUCTOR	POST OFFICE BOX 482	LAGUNA, CA	92677
QUAGLIA, JOHN D	HAIR STYLIST	144 E 36TH ST #PH-NE	NEW YORK, NY	10016
QUAID, DAVID L	DIRECTOR	POST OFFICE BOX 1617	DUXBURY, MA	02332
QUAID, DENNIS	ACTOR	2 E 86TH ST	NEW YORK, NY	10028
QUAID, DIANE	TV DIRECTOR	17 SEAMAN AVE	NEW YORK, NY	10034
QUAID, RANDY	ACTOR	15760 VENTURA BLVD #1730	ENCINO, CA	91436
QUALEN, JOHN	ACTOR	22903 NADINE CIR #A	TORRANCE, CA	90505
QUALLS, KEVIN	BASEBALL EXECUTIVE	TIGERS, TIGER STADIUM	DETROIT, MI	48216
QUANTRILL, PAUL	BASEBALL	POST OFFICE BOX 2365	PAWTUCKET, RI	02861
QUARLES, NORMA	NEWS CORRESPONDENT	NBC NEWS, 4001 NEBRASKA AV, SW	WASHINGTON, DC	20016
QUARSHIE, HUGH	ACTOR	SHARKEY, 15 GOLDEN SQ #315	LONDON W1R 3AG	ENGLAND
QUART, JULIE	PUZZLES WRITER	UPS, 4900 MAIN ST, 9TH FLOOR	KANSAS CITY, MO	64112
QUARTERFLASH	ROCK & ROLL GROUP	POST OFFICE BOX 8231	PORTLAND, OR	97207
QUASARANO, JOSEPH R	DIRECTOR	16835 BIRCHER ST	GRANADA HILLS, CA	91344
QUATEMAN, BILL	SINGER	14302 COLLINS ST	VAN NUYS, CA	91401
QUAYLE, ANNA	ACTRESS	DAWSON, 47 COURTFIELD RD #9	LONDON SW7 4DB	ENGLAND
QUAYLE, ANTHONY	ACTOR	498 ELYSTAN PL	LONDON SW3 3JY	ENGLAND
QUAYLE, DAN	VICE PRESIDENT	THE ADMIRAL HOUSE		
		34TH & MASSACHUSETTS AVE	WASHINGTON, DC	20005
QUAYLE, JOHN	ACTOR	BURNETT, 42-43 GRAFTON HOUSE		
		2-3 GOLDEN SQ	LONDON W1R 3AD	ENGLAND
QUAYLE, MARILYN	VICE PRES WIFE	THE ADMIRAL HOUSE		
		34TH & MASSACHUSETTS AVE	WASHINGTON, DC	20005

QUEEN	ROCK & ROLL GROUP ...	46 PEMBRIDGE RD	LONDON W11 3HN .... ENGLAND
QUEEN, MEL	BASEBALL-EXECUTIVE ..	SKYDOME, 300 BREMMER BL #3200 ...	TORONTO, ONT M5V 3B3 ...... CANADA
QUEEN KONG	WRESTLER-ACTRESS	4789 VINELAND AVE #100	NORTH HOLLYWOOD, CA 91602
QUEENSRYCHE	ROCK & ROLL GROUP ...	HARRIS MANAGEMENT AGENCY	....
	....	4801 BEACH DR, SW	SEATTLE, WA 98116
QUENTIN, JOHN	ACTOR	GARDNER, 15 KENSINGTON HIGH ST ..	LONDON W8 5NP .... ENGLAND
QUERY, JEFF	FOOTBALL	PACKERS, 1265 LOMBARDI AVE	GREEN BAY, WI 54307
QUESADA, PETER A	CONDUCTOR	2125 COVE AVE	LOS ANGELES, CA 90026
QUESTED, JOHN	DIRECTOR-PRODUCER ...	GOLDCREST FILMS & TELEVISION	....
	....	15 KENSINGTON HIGH ST	LONDON W8 5NA .... ENGLAND
QUESTEL, MAE	ACTRESS	27 E 65TH ST #7-C	NEW YORK, NY 10021
QUEZADA, ROBERTO A	FILM PRODUCER	15445 VENTURA BLVD #10	SHERMAN OAKS, CA 91413
QUICHE	C & W GROUP	BAR, 158 S BROADWAY	LAWRENCE, MA 01843
QUICK, DIANA	ACTRESS	HEATH, PARAMOUNT HOUSE	....
	....	162-170 WARDOUR ST	LONDON W1V 3AT .... ENGLAND
QUICK, ELDON	ACTOR	2312 CHEREMOYA AVE	LOS ANGELES, CA 90068
QUICK, JIM	BASEBALL UMPIRE	POST OFFICE BOX 6538	INCLINE VILLAGE, NV 89450
QUICK CHANCE	C & W GROUP	TESSIER, 505 CANTON PASS	MADISON, TN 37115
QUICKSILVER, ELIZABETH J	TV WRITER	9310 AIRDROME ST	LOS ANGELES, CA 90035
QUIET RIOT	ROCK & ROLL GROUP ...	5550 WILSHIRE BLVD #202	LOS ANGELES, CA 90036
QUIGLEY, JOAN	ASTROLOGER	1055 CALIFORNIA ST #14	SAN FRANCISCO, CA 94108
QUIGLEY, LINNEA	ACTRESS-MODEL	13659 VICTORY BLVD #467	VAN NUYS, CA 91401
QUIGLEY, MAY	ACTRESS	LIGHT, 901 BRINGHAM AVE	LOS ANGELES, CA 90049
QUIJADA, ED	BASEBALL	POST OFFICE BOX 824	BURLINGTON, IA 52601
QUILLEN, JAMES H "JIMMY"	U S CONGRESSMAN	FED BLDG, ROOM 157, 1ST FLOOR ...	KINGSPORT, TN 37662
QUILLEY, DENIS	ACTOR-SINGER	22 WILLOW RD	LONDON NW3 .... ENGLAND
QUILLS, KENT	BASEBALL EXECUTIVE ..	EXPOS, 4545 DE COUBERTIN AVE	MONTREAL, QUE H1V 3P2 ..... CANADA
QUINE, RICHARD	ACTOR-DIRECTOR	DGA, 7920 SUNSET BLVD, 6TH FL ...	LOS ANGELES, CA 90046
QUINETTE, RICHARD R	DIRECTOR	DGA, 110 W 57TH ST	NEW YORK, NY 10019
QUINLAN, KATHLEEN	ACTRESS	POST OFFICE BOX 2465	MALIBU, CA 90265
QUINLAN, PETER FRANCIS	SINGER	4680 ELK LAKE DR #304	VICTORIA, BC V8Z 5M1 ...... CANADA
QUINLAN, TOM	BASEBALL	CHIEFS, MAC ARTHUR STADIUM	SYRACUSE, NY 13208
QUINN, AIDAN	ACTOR	CAA, 9830 WILSHIRE BLVD	BEVERLY HILLS, CA 90212
QUINN, AILEEN	ACTRESS	400 MADISON AVE #20	NEW YORK, NY 10007
QUINN, ANTHONY	ACTOR-DIRECTOR	60 E END AVE	NEW YORK, NY 10028
QUINN, BILL	ACTOR	16302 VILLAGE #16	CAMARILLO, CA 93010
QUINN, BOB	BASEBALL EXECUTIVE ..	REDS, 100 RIVERFRONT STADIUM	CINCINNATI, OH 45202
QUINN, COLLEEN	ACTRESS	ABC-TV, "LOVING"	....
	....	320 W 66TH ST, STUDIO 23	NEW YORK, NY 10023
QUINN, DAN	HOCKEY	BLUES, 5700 OAKLAND AVE	SAINT LOUIS, MO 63110
QUINN, FRANCESCO	ACTOR	1230 N HORN AVE #730	LOS ANGELES, CA 90069
QUINN, HOWARD	TV DIRECTOR	6703 PORTSHEAD RD	MALIBU, CA 90265
QUINN, JAMES	FILM PRODUCER	108 MARINE PARADE	BRIGHTON .... ENGLAND
QUINN, JAMES	TV DIRECTOR	R/W/G, 8428 MELROSE PL #C	LOS ANGELES, CA 90069
QUINN, JANE BRYANT	COLUMNIST	NEWSWEEK, 444 MADISON AVE	NEW YORK, NY 10022
QUINN, MARTHA	VIDEO JOCKEY	3562 LAURELVALE DR	STUDIO CITY, CA 91604
QUINN, MAUREEN	ACTRESS	9255 SUNSET BLVD #515	LOS ANGELES, CA 90069
QUINN, PATRICK	TREASURER	STATE HOUSE BUILDING	SPRINGFIELD, IL 62706
QUINN, ROBERT J	TV DIRECTOR	12152 MOORPARK ST #303	STUDIO CITY, CA 91604
QUINN, ROBERT JOSEPH	TV DIRECTOR	35 WENDT AVE	LARCHMONT, NY 10538
QUINN, ROBERT L	WRITER-PRODUCER	4731 VINELAND AVE #2-A	NORTH HOLLYWOOD, CA 91602
QUINN, SALLY	JOURNALIST	1150 15TH ST, NW	WASHINGTON, DC 20005
QUINN, SCHULYER	ACTRESS	CBS-TV, "AS THE WORLD TURNS"	....
	....	524 W 57TH ST #5330	NEW YORK, NY 10019
QUINN, STANLEY J, JR	DIRECTOR	36 CHURCH ST	NOANK, CT 06340
QUINN, THOMAS	ACTOR-SINGER	1 NASSAU RD	KENDALL PARK, NJ 08824
QUINN, VIRGINIA	MUSIC PRODUCER	QUINN ASSOC, 309 W 57TH ST	NEW YORK, NY 10019
QUINNETT, BRIAN	BASKETBALL	KNICKS, 4 PENNYLVANIA PLAZA	NEW YORK, NY 10019
QUINONES, ELLIOT	BASEBALL	POST OFFICE BOX 4669	CHARLESTON, WV 25304
QUINONES, LUIS	BASEBALL	TWINS, 501 CHICAGO AVE S	MINNEAPOLIS, MN 55415
QUINONES, REY	BASEBALL	CLE RONDA 216 VILLA ANADALUCIA ..	RIO PIEDRAS, PR 00926
QUINTAL, STEPHANE	HOCKEY	BRUINS, 150 CAUSEWAY ST	BOSTON, MA 02114
QUINTANA, CARLOS	BASEBALL	FENWAY PARK, 4 YAWKEY WY	BOSTON, MA 02215
QUINTELL, JOHN	BASEBALL	ALBANY YANKEES, HERITAGE PARK ...	ALBANY, NY 12211
QUINTERO, JOSE	DIRECTOR	LANTZ, 888 7TH AVE, 25TH FLOOR ..	NEW YORK, NY 10106
QUIRK, JAMIE	BASEBALL	ATHLETICS'S, OAKLAND COLISEUM ...	OAKLAND, CA 94621
QUIRK, JIM	FOOTBALL REFEREE	NFL, 410 PARK AVE	NEW YORK, NY 10022
QUIRKE, PAULINE	ACTRESS	HAMMOND, GOLDEN HOUSE	....
	....	29 GREAT PULTENEY ST	LONDON W1R 3DD .... ENGLAND
QUISENBERRY, BYRON	DIRECTOR-PRODUCER ...	7501 ASMAN AVE	CANOGA PARK, CA 91307
QUISENBERRY, DAN	BASEBALL	12208 BUENA VISTA	LEAWOOD, KS 66209
QUIST, JACK	SINGER	50 MUSIC SQUARE W #905	NASHVILLE, TN 37203
QUIVERS, ROBIN	TV HOST	WWOR-TV, 9 BROADCAST PLAZA	SECAUCAS, NJ 07096
QUON, MIKE	ARTIST	568 BROADWAY	NEW YORK, NY 10012

R & B CADETS	RHYTHM & BLUES GROUP	611 BROADWAY #526	NEW YORK, NY 10012
R C B	ACTOR	SEE - RCB	....

R O A R	ROCK & ROLL GROUP	11833 LAUREL WOOD DR #8	STUDIO CITY, CA 91604
RAABE, BRIAN	BASEBALL	14100 SIX MILE CYPRESS PKWY	FORT MYERS, FL 33912
RABB, ELLIS	DIRECTOR	20 W 64TH ST #27-R	NEW YORK, NY 10023
RABBITT, EDDIE	SINGER-SONGWRITER	MORESS, 1209 16TH AVE S	NASHVILLE, TN 37212
RABE, DAVID	PLAYWRIGHT	440 W END AVE #16-B	NEW YORK, NY 10024
RABEL, ED	NEWS CORRESPONDENT	CBS NEWS, 524 W 57TH ST	NEW YORK, NY 10019
RABENECKER, ROB	BASEBALL EXECUTIVE	POST OFFICE BOX 3566	WEST PALM BEACH, FL 33402
RABIN, ALVIN	TV DIRECTOR-PRODUCER	4455 GAYLE DR	TARZANA, CA 91356
RABIN, ARTHUR	WRITER	401 S HARVARD BLVD #304	LOS ANGELES, CA 90020
RABIN, TREVOR	SINGER	330 W 58TH ST #7	NEW YORK, NY 10019
RABINOVITCH, DAVID	WRITER-PRODUCER	150 MADRONE AVE	LARKSPUR, CA 94939
RABINOWITZ, HARRY	COMPOSER-CONDUCTOR	HONOR MUSIC, YELLOW COTTAGE	
		WALKING BOTTOM, PEASLAKE	SURREY GU5 9RR ENGLAND
RABSON, JAN	ACTOR	5657 WILSHIRE BLVD #290	LOS ANGELES, CA 90036
RABWIN, PAUL HARTLEY	TV PRODUCER	HARTLEY'S, 5509 LA JOLLA BLVD	LA JOLLA, CA 92037
RACE, HANDSOME HARLEY	WRESTLER	POST OFFICE BOX 105366	ATLANTA, GA 31348
RACE, ROGER	TV PRODUCER	44 RITHERDOM RD	LONDON SW17 ENGLAND
RACERS, THE	ROCK & ROLL GROUP	POST OFFICE BOX 2095	PHILADELPHIA, PA 19103
RACHINS, ALAN	ACT-WRI-DIR	9000 SUNSET BLVD #1200	LOS ANGELES, CA 90069
RACIMO, VICTORIA	ACTRESS	ROSENBERG, 8428 MELROSE PL #C	LOS ANGELES, CA 90069
RACINA, THOM	AUTHOR	3449 WAVERLY DR	LOS ANGELES, CA 90027
RACINE, YVES	HOCKEY	RED WINGS, 600 CIVIC CENTER DR	DETROIT, MI 48226
RACIOT, MARC	ATTORNEY GENERAL	STATE CAPITOL BUILDING	HELENA, MT 59620
RACKMIL, GLADYS	THEATER PRODUCER	250 W 52ND ST	NEW YORK, NY 10019
RACKZA, MIKE	BASEBALL	POST OFFICE BOX 11087	TACOMA, WA 98411
RACY, ALI JIHAD	COMPOSER	3570 TILDEN AVE	LOS ANGELES, CA 90034
RADAKOVICH, DAN	FOOTBALL COACH	BROWNS, 80 1ST ST	BEREA, OH 44017
RADCLIFF, MIKE	BASEBALL SCOUT	TWINS, 501 CHICAGO AVE S	MINNEAPOLIS, MN 55415
RADCLYFFE, SARAH	FILM PRODUCER	WORKING TITLE, 10 LIVONIA ST	LONDON W1V 3PH ENGLAND
RADDATZ, JERRY	BASEBALL SCOUT	REDS, 100 RIVERFRONT STADIUM	CINCINNATI, OH 45202
RADECIC, SCOTT	FOOTBALL	POST OFFICE BOX 535000	INDIANPOLIS, IN 46253
RADEN, DON	CARTOONIST	UPS, 4900 MAIN ST, 9TH FLOOR	KANSAS CITY, MO 64112
RADER, DOUG	BASEBALL-COACH	ATHLETICS'S, OAKLAND COLISEUM	OAKLAND, CA 94621
RADER, JACK	ACTOR	20251 ARCHWOOD ST	CANOGA PARK, CA 91306
RADFORD, G W	BASEBALL EXECUTIVE	SKYDOME, 300 BREMMER BL #3200	TORONTO, ONT M5V 3B3 CANADA
RADFORD, MARSHA	BODYBUILDER	1017 STEVENS CREEK RD #208-J	AUGUSTA, GA 30907
RADFORD, MICHAEL	FILM DIRECTOR	3-B RICKERING MEWS	LONDON W2 5AD ENGLAND
RADIN, PAUL	TV PRODUCER	1606 GILCREST DR	BEVERLY HILLS, CA 90210
RADINSKY, SCOTT	BASEBALL	333 W 35TH ST	CHICAGO, IL 60616
RADISON, DAN	BASEBALL MANAGER	ALBANY YANKEES, HERITAGE PARK	ALBANY, NY 12211
RADKE, BRAD	BASEBALL	POST OFFICE BOX 661	KENOSHA, WI 53141
RADNITZ, BRAD	TV WRITER	2049 CENTURY PARK E #1320	LOS ANGELES, CA 90067
RADNITZ, ROBERT B	FILM WRITER-PRODUCER	19728 PACIFIC COAST HWY	MALIBU, CA 90265
RADWASTE	ROCK & ROLL GROUP	POST OFFICE BOX 94565	PASADENA, CA 91109
RADY, ERNEST	BASEBALL EXECUTIVE	POST OFFICE BOX 2000	SAN DIEGO, CA 92112
RADZIEWICZ, DOUG	BASEBALL	POST OFFICE BOX 3004	SPRINGFIELD, IL 62708
RADZIWILL, LEE	CELEBRITY	9255 SUNSET BLVD #901	LOS ANGELES, CA 90069
RAE, ANGELA	ACTRESS	10600 HOLMAN AVE #1	LOS ANGELES, CA 90024
RAE, CHARLOTTE	ACTRESS	POST OFFICE BOX 49991	LOS ANGELES, CA 90049
RAE, JOLENE	ACTRESS	KJAR, 10653 RIVERSIDE DR	TOLUCA LAKE, CA 91602
RAFEL, LISA	ACTRESS	151 S EL CAMINO DR	BEVERLY HILLS, CA 90212
RAFELSON, ROBERT	FILM WRITER-DIRECTOR	8222 MARMONT LN	LOS ANGELES, CA 90069
RAFFELL, DONALD H	COMPOSER	3757 WOODCLIFF RD	SHERMAN OAKS, CA 91403
RAFFERTY, GERRY	SINGER-SONGWRITER	MICHAEL GRAY MANAGEMENT	
		51 PADDINGTON ST	LONDON W1 ENGLAND
RAFFERTY BAKER, FRANCES	ACTRESS	22141 BURBANK BLVD #4	WOODLAND HILLS, CA 91367
RAFFIL, STEWART	WRITER-PRODUCER	DGA, 7920 SUNSET BLVD, 6TH FL	LOS ANGELES, CA 90046
RAFFIN, DEBORAH	ACTRESS	1750 VENTURA BLVD #202	STUDIO CITY, CA 91604
RAFFO, TOMMY	BASEBALL	POST OFFICE BOX 2001	CEDAR RAPIDS, IA 52406
RAFKIN, ALAN	TV WRITER-DIRECTOR	1008 SAINT BIMINI CIR	PALM SPRINGS, CA 92262
RAFKO, KAYE LANI RAE	MISS AMERICA-NURSE	4932 FRARY LN	MONROE, MI 48161
RAFNER, LEE	FILM DIRECTOR	13554 HAMLIN ST	VAN NUYS, CA 91401
RAFSANJANI, HASHEMI	PRESIDENT	THE MAJLIS	TEHRAN IRAN
RAFT, WALTER R	DIRECTOR	8569 RAMBLEWOOD DR	CORAL SPRINGS, FL 33065
RAGAIN, JANICE	BODYBUILDER	POST OFFICE BOX 34541	LOS ANGELES, CA 90034
RAGAN, JAMES	FILM PRODUCER	3342 OAK GLEN DR	LOS ANGELES, CA 90068
RAGGETT, HUGH	FILM DIRECTOR	THORPE PARK COTTAGE	
		THORPE-LE-SOKEN	ESSEX CO16 OHN ENGLAND
RAGGIO, LISA	ACTRESS	1680 N VINE ST #517	HOLLYWOOD, CA 90028
RAGIN, JOHN S	ACTOR	5708 BRIARCLIFF RD	LOS ANGELES, CA 90068
RAGIR, MARSHALL B	WRITER-PRODUCER	2920 11TH ST #4	SANTA MONICA, CA 90405
RAGLAND, GARY	ACTOR	1054 17TH ST	SANTA MONICA, CA 90403
RAGLAND, GREG	ARTIST	258 BROADWAY #4-E	NEW YORK, NY 10007
RAGLAND, ROBERT O	COMPOSER-PIANIST	9931 YOUNG DR #A	BEVERLY HILLS, CA 90212
RAGONESE, ANTHONY S	ACTOR	380 N SAN VICENTE BLVD	LOS ANGELES, CA 90048
RAGOTZY, JACK	DIRECTOR	2057 CASTILIAN DR	HOLLYWOOD, CA 90068
RAGSDALE, CARL VAN DYKE	DIRECTOR-PRODUCER	4725 STILL9165 SUNSET BLVD #202 D	LOS ANGELES, CA 90069
RAGSDALE, JOHN W	MUSIC ARRANGER	2805 27TH AVE S	NASHVILLE, TN 37212
RAHALL, NICK JOE, II	U S CONGRESSMAN	110 1/2 MAIN ST	BECKLEY, WV 25801
RAIDER, HONEY	TALENT AGENT	TALENT REPS, 20 E 53RD ST	NEW YORK, NY 10022
RAIDER, THE	WRESTLER	POST OFFICE BOX 3859	STAMFORD, CT 06905
RAIL	VOCAL GROUP	J BAUER, 2500 116TH AVE, NE	BELLEVUE, WA 98004
RAILSBACK, STEVE	ACTOR	POST OFFICE BOX 1308	LOS ANGELES, CA 90078
RAINBOLT, SHEREE	ACTRESS	10845 LINDBROOK DR #3	LOS ANGELES, CA 90024
RAINBOLT, WILLIAM	ACTOR-DIRECTOR	6818 CAHUENGA PARK TERR	LOS ANGELES, CA 90068

RAINBOW EXPRESS	C & W GROUP	BENNETT, 4630 DEEPDALE DR	CORPUS CHRISTI, TX 78413
RAINE, GILLIAN	ACTRESS	13 BILLING RD	LONDON SW10 ENGLAND
RAINER, LUISE	ACTRESS	KNITTEL, VICO MORCOTE	LUGANO 6911 SWITZERLAND
RAINER, PETER	WRITER-FILM CRITIC	1323 9TH ST	SANTA MONICA, CA 90401
RAINER DART, IRIS	AUTHORESS	3555 BEVERLY GLEN BLVD	SHERMAN OAKS, CA 91423
RAINES, EARL E	CONDUCTOR	2835 N HIGHVIEW	ALTADENA, CA 91001
RAINES, FRANK	FOOTBALL COACH	SEAHAWKS, 11220 NE 53RD ST	KIRKLAND, WA 98033
RAINES, TIM	BASEBALL	333 W 35TH ST	CHICAGO, IL 60616
RAINES-CROWE, CRISTINA	ACTRESS	12700 VENTURA BLVD #350	STUDIO CITY, CA 91604
RAINEY, FORD	ACTOR	3821 CARBON CANYON RD	MALIBU, CA 90265
RAINFORTH, VINCE	BASEBALL UMPIRE	235 MAIN ST #103	TRUSSVILLE, AL 35173
RAINONE, LOUIS J	TV DIRECTOR	9480 BLUEWING TERR	CINCINNATI, OH 45241
RAINS, JACK	SECRETARY OF STATE	POST OFFICE BOX 12428	AUSTIN, TX 78711
RAINWATER, GREGG	ACTOR	POST OFFICE BOX 291836	LOS ANGELES, CA 90029
RAISON, ROBERT	TALENT AGENT	1930 CENTURY PARK W #403	LOS ANGELES, CA 90067
RAITT, BONNIE	SINGER	POST OFFICE BOX 626	HOLLYWOOD, CA 90078
RAITT, JAMES	COMPOSER	340 W 55TH ST #1-A	NEW YORK, NY 10019
RAITT, JOHN	ACTOR	1164 NAPOLI DR	PACIFIC PALISADES, CA 90272
RAJKOWSKI, DAN	BASEBALL EXECUTIVE	633 JESSAMINE ST	KNOXVILLE, TN 37917
RAJSICH, DAVE	BASEBALL-COACH	POST OFFICE BOX 3746, HILL STA	AUGUSTA, GA 30904
RAKI, LAYA	ACTRESS	ATKINS, 303 S CRESCENT HEIGHTS	LOS ANGELES, CA 90048
RAKOCZY, GREGG	FOOTBALL	PATRIOTS, FOXBORO STADIUM, RT #1	FOXBORO, MA 02035
RAKOFF, ALVIN	FILM DIRECTOR	JARA, 1 THE ORCHARD	
		CHISWICK	LONDON W41 JZ ENGLAND
RAKSIN, DAVID	COMPOSER-CONDUCTOR	6519 ALDEA AVE	VAN NUYS, CA 91406
RALEY, DAN	BASEBALL COACH	POST OFFICE BOX 2785	LAKELAND, FL 33806
RALFE, DON	COMPOSER	POST OFFICE BOX 1223	STUDIO CITY, CA 91604
RALLING, ANTONY C	TV DIRECTOR-PRODUCER	THE COACH HOUSE, TANKERVILLE	
		KINGSTON HILL	SURREY ENGLAND
RALPH, CURTIS	BASEBALL	5301 NW 12TH AVE	FORT LAUDERDALE, FL 33309
RALPH, SHERYL LEE	ACTRESS-SINGER	938 S LONGWOOD AVE	LOS ANGELES, CA 90019
RALPH & JANICE	VOCAL DUO	POST OFFICE BOX C	RIVER EDGE, NJ 07661
RALSTON, ESTHER	ACTRESS	35 HEATHER WY	VENTURA, CA 93003
RALSTON, ROBERT	ORGANIST	17027 TENNYSON PL	GRANADA HILLS, CA 91344
RALSTON, TERI	ACTRESS	8228 SUNSET BLVD #212	LOS ANGELES, CA 90046
RALSTON, VERA HRUBA	ACTRESS	4121 CRESCIENTA DR	SANTA BARBARA, CA 93110
RAM'S, BUCK, PLATTERS	VOCAL GROUP	SEE - PLATTERS, THE	
RAMAGE, ROB	HOCKEY	MAPLE LEAFS, 60 CARLTON ST	TORONTO, ONT M5B 1L1 CANADA
RAMANN, LOURDES	ACTOR	300 E 57TH ST	NEW YORK, NY 10022
RAMANNE, CARA	ACTRESS	38 NEWPORT BEACH BLVD	EAST MORICHES, NY 11940
RAMATI, ALEXANDER	WRI-DIR-PROD	5000 S QUEBEC #500	DENVER, CO 80237
RAMBIS, KURT	BASKETBALL	SUNS, 2910 N CENTRAL AVE	PHOENIX, AZ 85012
RAMBO, DACK	ACTOR	RAMBO HORSE RANCH	EARLIMART, CA 93219
RAMBO, DAN	BASEBALL	POST OFFICE BOX 3448	SHREVEPORT, LA 71133
RAMBO, JOHN	WRESTLER	8725 N CHAUTAUQUA BLVD	PORTLAND, OR 97217
RAMBO, MATT	BASEBALL	POST OFFICE BOX 4209	JACKSON, MS 39296
RAMEY, JOHN	BASEBALL SCOUT	POST OFFICE BOX 4100	SEATTLE, WA 98104
RAMIN, RON	COMPOSER-CONDUCTOR	969 HILGARD AVE	LOS ANGELES, CA 90024
RAMIN, SID	COMPOSER-CONDUCTOR	799 PARK AVE	NEW YORK, NY 10021
RAMIREZ, DANNY	BASEBALL	POST OFFICE BOX 3169	FREDERICK, MD 21701
RAMIREZ, HECTOR	BASEBALL	POST OFFICE BOX 7845	COLUMBIA, SC 29202
RAMIREZ, HECTOR	CINEMATOGRAPHER	7715 SUNSET BLVD #150	LOS ANGELES, CA 90046
RAMIREZ, JANIE C & CACTUS BAND	C & W GROUP	ALAMO, 217 ARDEN GROVE	SAN ANTONIO, TX 78215
RAMIREZ, MANNY	BASEBALL	POST OFFICE BOX 3452	KINSTON, NC 28502
RAMIREZ, MIKE	CARTOONIST	POST OFFICE BOX 367	SAN CLEMENTE, CA 93912
RAMIREZ, OMAR	BASEBALL	POST OFFICE BOX 3452	KINSTON, NC 28502
RAMIREZ, RAFAEL	BASEBALL	POST OFFICE BOX 288	HOUSTON, TX 77001
RAMIREZ, RAY	BASEBALL TRAINER	POST OFFICE BOX 75089	OKLAHOMA CITY, OK 73147
RAMIREZ, ROBERTO	BASEBALL (AUGUSTA)	POST OFFICE BOX 3746, HILL STA	AUGUSTA, GA 30904
RAMIREZ, ROBERTO	BASEBALL (EVERETT)	POST OFFICE BOX 7893	EVERETT, WA 98201
RAMIS, HAROLD	ACT-WRI-DIR	14198 ALISAL LN	SANTA MONICA, CA 90402
RAMONE, KAREN	SINGER	GARY KURFIRST, OVERLAND PRODS	
		1775 BROADWAY, 7TH FLOOR	NEW YORK, NY 10019
RAMONE, PHIL	SINGER-SONGWRITER	GARY KURFIRST, OVERLAND PRODS	
		1775 BROADWAY, 7TH FLOOR	NEW YORK, NY 10019
RAMONES, THE	ROCK & ROLL GROUP	GARY KURFIRST, OVERLAND PRODS	
		1775 BROADWAY, 7TH FLOOR	NEW YORK, NY 10019
RAMOS, BOBBY	BASEBALL COACH	POST OFFICE BOX 422229	KISSIMMEE, FL 34742
RAMOS, DOMINGO	BASEBALL	CARR DUARTE KM 8 1/2 LICEY AL MED	SANTIAGO DOM REP
RAMOS, EDDY	BASEBALL	POST OFFICE BOX 1556	ASHEVILLE, NC 28802
RAMOS, JOHN	BASEBALL	1155 W MOUND ST	COLUMBUS, OH 43223
RAMOS, JOSE	BASEBALL	TIGERS, 89 WHARNCLIFFE RD N	LONDON, ONT N6H 2A7 CANADA
RAMOS, KEN	BASEBALL	2501 ALLEN AVE, SE	CANTON, OH 44707
RAMOS, RICHARD	ACTOR	265 RIVERSIDE DR	NEW YORK, NY 10025
RAMOS, RUDY	ACTOR	280 S BEVERLY DR #400	BEVERLY HILLS, CA 90212
RAMPLING, CHARLOTTE	ACTRESS	1 AVENUE EMILE-AUGIER	78290 CROISSY-SUR-SEIN FRANCE
RAMRUS, ALVIN	SCREENWRITER	15254 EARLHAM ST	PACIFIC PALISADES, CA 90272
RAMSAY, JACK	BASKETBALL	PRISM CABLE, 225 CITY LINE AVE	BALA-CYNWYD, PA 19004
RAMSAY, WES	MUSIC ARRANGER	4402 UTAH AVE	NASHVILLE, TN 37209
RAMSEY, AL	CONDUCTOR	2205 FRONTIER AVE	LAS VEGAS, NV 89106
RAMSEY, DONALD A	WRITER	2280 THE TERR	LOS ANGELES, CA 90049
RAMSEY, ELMER H	COMPOSER-CONDUCTOR	3648 MOUNTCLEF BLVD	THOUSAND OAKS, CA 91360
RAMSEY, FERNANDO	BASEBALL	CUBS, 2ND & RIVERSIDE DR	DES MOINES, IA 50309
RAMSEY, GORDON	ACTOR	90 MARION AVE	STATEN ISLAND, NY 10304
RAMSEY, JOANNE	SINGER	POST OFFICE BOX 171132	NASHVILLE, TN 37217

RAMSEY, LOGAN	ACTOR	12923 KILLION ST	VAN NUYS, CA	91401
RAMSEY, MIKE	BASEBALL MANAGER	POST OFFICE BOX 3783	SAVANNAH, GA	31414
RAMSEY, MIKE	HOCKEY	SABRES, MEMORIAL AUDITORIUM	BUFFALO, NY	14202
RAMSEY, VAN BROUGHTON	COSTUME DESIGNER	205 W 57TH ST	NEW YORK, NY	10019
RAMSTAD, JIM	U S CONGRESSMAN	8120 PENN AVE S #152	BLOOMINGTON, MN	55431
RAMUNO, PHILIP	TV DIRECTOR	26045 FARMFIELD RD	CALABASAS, CA	91302
RANBERG, CHUCK	TV PRODUCER	R/W/G, 8428 MELROSE PL #C	LOS ANGELES, CA	90069
RAND, GARY & THE STRANGERS	GOSPEL GROUP	POST OFFICE BOX 723591	ATLANTA, GA	30339
RAND, JOSEPH E	COMPOSER	1813 SCOTT RD #F	BURBANK, CA	91504
RAND, KEVIN	BASEBALL-INSTRUCTOR	N Y YANKEES, YANKEE STADIUM	BRONX, NY	10451
RAND, LINDA L	ACTRESS	4569 FINLEY AVE #1	LOS ANGELES, CA	90027
RANDA, JOE	BASEBALL	POST OFFICE BOX 464	APPLETON, WI	54912
RANDALL, ANNE	ACTRESS-MODEL	7461 BEVERLY BLVD #400	LOS ANGELES, CA	90036
RANDALL, BARTON	ACTOR-SCREENWRITER	901 LEVERING AVE #24	LOS ANGELES, CA	90024
RANDALL, BOB	SCREENWRITER	555 W 57TH ST #1230	NEW YORK, NY	10019
RANDALL, GLENN H, JR	DIRECTOR	DGA, 7920 SUNSET BLVD, 6TH FL	LOS ANGELES, CA	90046
RANDALL, HARRY	DIRECTOR	POST OFFICE BOX 220	PEQUANNOCK, NJ	07440
RANDALL, JAIME LYNNE	ACTRESS	6363 SUNSET BLVD #701	HOLLYWOOD, CA	90028
RANDALL, MARK	BASEBALL	POST OFFICE BOX 1721	SPARTANBURG, SC	29304
RANDALL, RUSS	TV DIRECTOR	704 N ARDEN DR	BEVERLY HILLS, CA	90210
RANDALL, SANDY	BODYBUILDER	POST OFFICE BOX 14363	SCOTTSDALE, AZ	85267
RANDALL, SAP	BASEBALL	711 CRANE AVE	WHISTLER, AL	36612
RANDALL, STEVE	ACTOR-WRITER	1912 COMSTOCK AVE	LOS ANGELES, CA	90025
RANDALL, TONY	ACTOR-WRITER	1 W 81ST ST #6-D	NEW YORK, NY	10024
RANDAZZO, TEDDY	SINGER	5254 OAK ISLAND RD	ORLANDO, FL	32809
RANDELL, RON	ACTOR	152 S ROXBURY DR	BEVERLY HILLS, CA	90212
RANDLE, ERVIN	FOOTBALL	CHIEFS, 1 ARROWHEAD DR	KANSAS CITY, MO	64129
RANDLE, JOHN	FOOTBALL	VIKINGS, 9520 VIKING DR	EDEN PRAIRIE, MN	55344
RANDOLPH, BOOTS	SAXOPHONIST	209 PRINTERS ALLEY	NASHVILLE, TN	37201
RANDOLPH, DONALD	ACTOR	1825 N KINGSLEY DR	LOS ANGELES, CA	90027
RANDOLPH, JENNINGS	U S SENATOR	300 3RD ST	EILKINS, WV	26241
RANDOLPH, JOHN	ACTOR	1850 WHITLEY PL	LOS ANGELES, CA	90028
RANDOLPH, JOYCE	ACTRESS	295 CENTRAL PARK W	NEW YORK, NY	10024
RANDOLPH, TY	ACTRESS	9230 OLYMPIC BLVD #201	BEVERLY HILLS, CA	90212
RANDOLPH, WILLIE	BASEBALL	648 JUNIPER PL	FRANKLIN LAKES, NJ	07417
RANDY, ANTHONY	COMPOSER	1162 S MOSCADA AVE	WALNUT, CA	91789
RANDY & THE RAINBOWS	VOCAL GROUP	POST OFFICE BOX 499	QUEENS, NY	11365
RANEY, THOMAS D	COMPOSER	3957 BRILLIANT DR	LOS ANGELES, CA	90065
RANGEL, CHARLES B	U S CONGRESSMAN	74 W 132ND ST	NEW YORK, NY	10037
RANGEL, MARIA	ACTRESS	12456 VENTURA BLVD #1	STUDIO CITY, CA	91604
RANGERS, THE	C & W GROUP	DORRIS, 110 30TH AVE N	NASHVILLE, TN	37203
RANHEIM, PAUL	HOCKEY	POST OFFICE BOX 1540, STA "M"	CALGARY, ALTA T2P 3BP	CANADA
RANIER, CROWN PRINCE, III	CROWN PRINCE	GRIMALDI PALACE	MONTE CARLO	MONACO
RANIER, THOMAS J	COMPOSER	282 LONGBRANCH CIR	BREA, CA	92621
RANIQUE, SABRINA	ACTRESS	POST OFFICE BOX 966	NEW YORK, NY	10150
RANK & FILE	C & W GROUP	611 BROADWAY #526	NEW YORK, NY	10012
RANKIN, BILLY	SINGER	3101 E EISENHOWER HWY #3	ANN ARBOR, MI	48104
RANKIN, KENNY	SINGER-SONGWRITER	8033 SUNSET BLVD #1037	LOS ANGELES, CA	90046
RANNOW, JERRY	TV WRITER	9250 WARBLER WY	LOS ANGELES, CA	90069
RANSLEY, PETER	TV WRITER	PETERS, FRASER & DUNLOP, LTD		
		5TH FLOOR, THE CHAMBERS		
		CHELSEA HARBOUR, LOT RD	LONDON SW10 OXF	ENGLAND
RANSOHOFF, MARTIN	WRITER-PRODUCER	210 N CAROLWOOD DR	LOS ANGELES, CA	90077
RANSOM, ROBERT V, JR	MUSIC ARRANGER	616 MALTA DR	NASHVILLE, TN	37207
RANSOM, RONALD SCOTT	FILM DIRECTOR	POST OFFICE BOX 1100	TELLURIDE, CO	81435
RANSON, GERALD W	DIRECTOR	171 W 79TH ST	NEW YORK, NY	10024
RANTZ, JIM	BASEBALL EXECUTIVE	TWINS, 501 CHICAGO AVE S	MINNEAPOLIS, MN	55415
RANTZEN, ESTHER	TV PRODUCER	GAY, 24 DENMARK ST	LONDON WC2H 8HJ	ENGLAND
RAPAPORT, MICHAEL	ACTOR	1801 AVE OF THE STARS #1250	LOS ANGELES, CA	90067
RAPELYE, MARY LINDA	ACTRESS	WM MORRIS, 1350 AVE OF AMERICAS	NEW YORK, NY	10019
RAPF, MATTHEW W	SCREENWRITER	120 MALIBU COLONY DR	MALIBU, CA	90265
RAPF, MAURICE	WRITER-PRODUCER	6 CONANT RD	HANOVER, NH	03755
RAPHAEL	SINGER	WM MORRIS, 1350 AVE OF AMERICAS	NEW YORK, NY	10019
RAPHAEL, FRED	FILM WRITER-DIRECTOR	POST OFFICE BOX 1950 (ATRIUM)	BRIDGEHAMPTON, NY	1193
RAPHAEL, MARILYN	ACTRESS	2058 CORNELL PL	MERRICK, NY	11566
RAPHAEL, SALLY JESSY	TV HOST	510 W 57TH ST #200	NEW YORK, NY	10019
RAPHEL, JEROME	ACTOR	53 W 83RD ST	NEW YORK, NY	10024
RAPISARDA, TONY	ACTOR	12423 STANWOOD PL	LOS ANGELES, CA	90066
RAPOPORT, I C	TV WRITER	559 MUSKINGUM AVE	PACIFIC PALISADES, CA	90272
RAPOSO, JOSEPH G	COMPOSER	JONICO MUSIC, 881 7TH AVE	NEW YORK, NY	10019
RAPP, PATRICK	BASEBALL	5999 E VAN BUREN ST	PHOENIX, AZ	85008
RAPP, PAUL	FILM WRITER-DIRECTOR	301 N ALPINE DR	BEVERLY HILLS, CA	90210
RAPP, VIC	FOOTBALL COACH	BEARS, 250 N WASHINGTON RD	LAKE FOREST, IL	60045
RAPP, WILLIAM	DIRECTOR	2203 HASTINGS DR #3	BELMONT, CA	94002
RAPPAPORT, JOHN H	TV WRITER	15946 WOODVALE RD	ENCINO, CA	91436
RAPPER, IRVING	FILM DIRECTOR	10777 WILSHIRE BLVD #16	LOS ANGELES, CA	90024
RAPPOLI, PAUL	BASEBALL	POST OFFICE BOX 10213	LYNCHBURG, VA	24506
RAPPORT, LOUISE	ACTRESS	10845 LINDBROOK DR #3	LOS ANGELES, CA	90024
RAPPY, FLOYD M	ARTIST	2074 COYLE ST	BROOKLYN, NY	11229
RAPUANO, ED	BASEBALL UMPIRE	POST OFFICE BOX 608	GROVE CITY, OH	43123
RARE EARTH	ROCK & ROLL GROUP	NORTHERN INTL TALENT		
		5224 S LOGAN ST	LANSING, MI	48910
RASCHE, DAVID	ACTOR	POST OFFICE BOX 5617	BEVERLY HILLS, CA	90213
RASCHELLA, CAROLE P	TV WRITER	8736 OAKDALE AVE	NORTHRIDGE, CA	91324
RASCOE, JUDITH E	SCREENWRITER	8955 BEVERLY BLVD	WEST HOLLYWOOD, CA	90048

RASER, BOB	DIRECTOR	4400 YORKFIELD CT	WESTLAKE VILLAGE, CA	91361
RASH, STEVE	DIRECTOR	3742 LOWER MOUNTAIN RD	FOREST GROVE, PA	18922
RASHAD, AHMAD	FOOTBALL	30 ROCKEFELLER PLAZA #1411	NEW YORK, NY	10112
RASHAD, PHYLICIA	ACTRESS	BRET ADAMS, 448 W 44TH ST	NEW YORK, NY	10036
RASHID, ROBERT	DIRECTOR	6620 STEADMAN ST	DEARBORN, MI	48126
RASKIN, CAROLYN	WRITER-PRODUCER	4112 WOODCLIFF RD	SHERMAN OAKS, CA	91403
RASKING, KAREN W	WRITER	11008 AYRES AVE	LOS ANGELES, CA	90064
RASKING, RICHARD A	WRITER	8306 WILSHIRE BLVD #429	BEVERLY HILLS, CA	90211
RASKY, HARRY	WRITER-PRODUCER	POST OFFICE BOX 500		
		STATION A	TORONTO, ONT M5W 1E6	CANADA
RASMUSSEN, BLAIR	BASKETBALL	POST OFFICE BOX 4658	DENVER, CO	80204
RASMUSSEN, DENNIS	BASEBALL	500 NORTON ST	ROCHESTER, NY	14621
RASPBERRY, LARRY	SINGER	POST OFFICE BOX 0	MINNEAPOLIS, MN	55331
RATCLIFFE, SAMUEL D	TV WRITER	ICM, 40 W 57TH ST	NEW YORK, NY	10019
RATEKIN, MARK	BASEBALL	POST OFFICE BOX 3496	DAVENPORT, IA	52808
RATH, EARL	CINEMATOGRAPHER	6063 SUNSET BLVD	LOS ANGELES, CA	90028
RATHER, DAN	NEWS CORRESPONDENT	CBS-TV, 524 W 57TH ST	NEW YORK, NY	10019
RATHMAN, TOM	FOOTBALL	S F 49ERS, 4949 CENTENNIAL BL	SANTA CLARA, CA	95054
RATIONAL YOUTH	ROCK & ROLL GROUP	41 BRITAIN ST #200	TORONTO, ONT M5A 1R7	CANADA
RATLIFF, DARYL	BASEBALL	POST OFFICE DRAWER 1218	ZEBULON, NC	27597
RATNER, HARVEY	BASKETBALL EXECUTIVE	TIMBERWOLVES, 600 1ST AVE N	MINNEAPOLIS, MN	55403
RATNER, MARC	ACTOR	18518 MAYALL ST #J	NORTHRIDGE, CA	91324
RATT	ROCK & ROLL GROUP	LEFT BANK, 6255 SUNSET BLVD	HOLLYWOOD, CA	90028
RATTLE, SIMON	CONDUCTOR	201 W 54TH ST #4-C	NEW YORK, NY	10019
RATTRAY, HEATHER	ACTRESS	CBS-TV, "AS THE WORLD TURNS"		
		524 W 57TH ST #5330	NEW YORK, NY	10019
RATZENBERGER, JOHN	ACTOR	1999 AVE OF THE STARS #2850	LOS ANGELES, CA	90067
RATZLAFF, DAVID	TV DIRECTOR	1306 S FINLEY RD #3-B	LOMBARD, IL	60148
RAU, DOUG	BASEBALL	ROUTE #1, BOX 154-A	COLUMBUS, TX	78934
RAUCH, CHRIS	BASEBALL	POST OFFICE BOX 1211	NORFOLK, VA	23502
RAUCH, EARL M	SCREENWRITER	5900 CLOVER HEIGHTS AVE	MALIBU, CA	90265
RAUCH, ELLEN	FILM DIRECTOR	333 E 79TH ST	NEW YORK, NY	10021
RAUCH, MICHAEL	TV DIRECTOR	333 E 79TH ST	NEW YORK, NY	10021
RAUCHER, HERMAN	SCREENWRITER	555 W 57TH ST #1230	NEW YORK, NY	10019
RAUNCH HANDS	ROCK & ROLL GROUP	POST OFFICE BOX 1558		
		MADISON SQUARE STATION	NEW YORK, NY	10159
RAUSCH, LEON	SINGER	1300 DIVISION ST #102	NASHVILLE, TN	37203
RAUSEO, VICTOR	WRITER-PRODUCER	2920 NEILSON WY #103	SANTA MONICA, CA	90405
RAVE	VOCAL GROUP	8831 SUNSET BLVD #200	LOS ANGELES, CA	90069
RAVE-UPS, THE	ROCK & ROLL GROUP	POST OFFICE BOX 1818	BEVERLY HILLS, CA	90213
RAVEN, EDDY	SINGER-GUITARIST	POST OFFICE BOX 1402	HENDERSONVILLE, TN	37075
RAVEN, LUIS	BASEBALL	POST OFFICE BOX 1742	PALM SPRINGS, CA	92263
RAVEN, SIMON	NOVELIST-SCREENWRITER	BROWN, 162-168 REGENT ST	LONDON W1R 5TB	ENGLAND
RAVENEL, ARTHUR, JR	U S CONGRESSMAN	POST OFFICE BOX 1538	BEAUFORT, SC	29902
RAVENSCROFT, RONALD A	COMPOSER-CONDUCTOR	1960 N VERMONT AVE	LOS ANGELES, CA	90027
RAVETCH, IRVING	SCREENWRITER	8277 SKYLINE DR	LOS ANGELES, CA	90046
RAVIER, CLAUDE	TALENT AGENT	BRB, 666 N ROBERTSON BLVD	LOS ANGELES, CA	90060
RAVIN'	ROCK & ROLL GROUP	POST OFFICE BOX 448	RADFORD, VA	24141
RAVYNS, THE	ROCK & ROLL GROUP	ATI, 888 7TH AVE, 21ST FLOOR	NEW YORK, NY	10106
RAW POWER	ROCK & ROLL GROUP	POST OFFICE BOX 242	PONOMA, CA	91769
RAWI, OUSAMA	CINEMATOGRAPHER	LONDON MGT, 235-241 REGENT ST	LONDON W1R 4PH	ENGLAND
RAWLE, JEFF	ACTOR	HAMMOND, GOLDEN HOUSE		
		29 GREAT PULTENEY ST	LONDON W1R 3DD	ENGLAND
RAWLEY, PETER	TALENT AGENT	ICM, 8899 BEVERLY BLVD	LOS ANGELES, CA	90048
RAWLINGS, RICHARD M, JR	CINEMATOGRAPHER	POST OFFICE BOX 2230	HOLLYWOOD, CA	90078
RAWLINS, DAVID	DIRECTOR	1999 N SYCAMORE AVE #19	HOLLYWOOD, CA	90068
RAWLINS, JOHN	DIRECTOR	DGA, 7920 SUNSET BLVD, 6TH FL	LOS ANGELES, CA	90046
RAWLINS, ROBERT	GOLFER	PGA SENIORS, 112 T P C BLVD	PONTE VEDRA BEACH, FL	32082
RAWLS, LOU	SINGER	109 FREMONT PL W	LOS ANGELES, CA	90005
RAY, CLIFFORD	BASKETBALL	REUNION ARENA, 777 SPORTS ST	DALLAS, TX	75207
RAY, FRED OLEN	DIRECTOR-PRODUCER	POST OFFICE BOX 3563	VAN NUYS, CA	91407
		TENNESSEE STATE PRISON	NASHVILLE, TN	37203
RAY, JAMES EARL	AUTHOR	STATION A WEST		
RAY, JOHNNY	BASEBALL (MAJORS)	RURAL ROUTE #1, BOX 64	CHOUTEAU, OK	74337
RAY, JOHNNY	BASEBALL (MINORS)	POST OFFICE BOX 11002	CHATTANOOGA, TN	37401
RAY, MALCOLM W	DIRECTOR	DGA, 7920 SUNSET BLVD, 6TH FL	LOS ANGELES, CA	90046
RAY, MARC B	WRITER	23369 OSTRONIC DR	WOODLAND HILLS, CA	91367
RAY, MARGUERITE	ACTRESS	1329 N VISTA ST #106	LOS ANGELES, CA	90046
RAY, RICK	BASEBALL TRAINER	POST OFFICE BOX 751	UTICA, NY	13503
RAY, ROB	HOCKEY	SABRES, MEMORIAL AUDITORIUM	BUFFALO, NY	14202
RAY, ROBIN	ACTOR-WRITER	WILKINSON, 115 HAZLEBURY RD	LONDON SW6 2LX	ENGLAND
RAY, SATYAJIT	DIRECTOR	1/1 BISHOP LEFROY RD #8	CALCUTTA 20	INDIA
RAY, WADE	GUITARIST	ROUTE #3	SPARTA, IL	62286
RAY, GOODMAN & BROWN	VOCAL TRIO	HUSH PRODS, 231 W 58TH ST	NEW YORK, NY	10019
RAYBOURN, HERB	BASEBALL SCOUT	N Y YANKEES, YANKEE STADIUM	BRONX, NY	10451
RAYBURN, GENE	TV HOST-ACTOR	LEE ROBINS, 245 5TH AVE	NEW YORK, NY	10016
RAYE, BOBBY	COMEDIAN	CLOUSHER, 193 KONHAUS RD	MECHANICSBURG, PA	17055
RAYE, JIMMY	FOOTBALL COACH	PATRIOTS, FOXBORO STADIUM, RT #1	FOXBORO, MA	02035
RAYE, KATHY	SINGER	POST OFFICE BOX 6025	NEWPORT NEWS, VA	23606
RAYE, MARTHA	ACT-SING-DAN-COMED	1153 ROSCOMARE RD	LOS ANGELES, CA	90077
RAYFIEL, DAVID	SCREENWRITER	555 W 57TH ST #1230	NEW YORK, NY	10019
RAYFORD, FLOYD	BASEBALL-COACH	POST OFFICE BOX 3449	SCRANTON, PA	18505
RAYMOND, CLAUDE	BASEBALL-ANNOUNCER	EXPOS, 4545 DE COUBERTIN AVE	MONTREAL, QUE H1V 3P2	CANADA

Name	Occupation	Address	City	Zip/Country
RAYMOND, FRANK	CINEMATOGRAPHER	POST OFFICE BOX 2230	HOLLYWOOD, CA	90078
RAYMOND, GENE	ACTOR	250 TRINO WY	PACIFIC PALISADES, CA	90272
RAYMOND, GUY	ACTOR	550 ERSKINE DR	PACIFIC PALISADES, CA	90272
RAYMOND, GUY MICHAEL	DIRECTOR	6 RIDENOUR CT	TOWSON, MD	21204
RAYMOND, JINNY	TALENT AGENT	606 N LARCHMONT BLVD #309	LOS ANGELES, CA	90004
RAYMOND, PAULA	ACTRESS	POST OFFICE BOX 86	BEVERLY HILLS, CA	90213
RAYMOND, ROBIN	ACTRESS	10390 WILSHIRE BLVD #302	LOS ANGELES, CA	90024
RAYMOND, ROY	ACTOR-SINGER	360 CENTRAL PARK W #11-A	NEW YORK, NY	10025
RAYMOND, SID	ACTOR	19380 COLLINS AVE #927	MIAMI BEACH, FL	33160
RAYMOND, SUSAN CULLINAN	TV DIRECTOR	VIDEO VERITE, 927 MADISON AVE	NEW YORK, NY	10021
RAYNER, GORDON	DIRECTOR	7722 VENTURA CANYON AVE	PANORAMA CITY, CA	91402
RAYNER, HANSEL M	CONDUCTOR	14711 COBALT ST	SYLMAR, CA	91342
RAYNOR, TED	PRODUCER	8480 W BEVERLY BLVD #133	LOS ANGELES, CA	90048
RAYVID, JAY	TV EXECUTIVE	WQED-TV, 4802 5TH AVE	PITTSBURGH, PA	15213
RAZNICK, DEBORAH	TV WRITER	15215 MAGNOLIA BLVD #108	SHERMAN OAKS, CA	91403
RDINE, AL	SINGER-SONGWRITER	POST OFFICE BOX 36	BIG SUR, CA	93920
REA, BEN	TV DIRECTOR-PRODUCER	TV CENTRE, 3-4 WOKING BUSINESS PK		
		ALBERT PARK, WOKING	SURREY GU21 5JY	ENGLAND
REA, DAVID C	WRITER-PRODUCER	2 HORSENDEN AVE, GREENFORD	MIDDLESEX	ENGLAND
REA, ELIZABETH W	CASTING DIRECTOR	1021 PARK AVE	NEW YORK, NY	10028
REA, PEGGY	ACTRESS	432 S CURSON AVE	LOS ANGELES, CA	90036
REA, SHAYNE	BASEBALL	POST OFFICE BOX 464	APPLETON, WI	54912
REA, STEPHEN	ACTOR	HOPE, 108 LEONARD ST	LONDON EC2A 4RH	ENGLAND
REACH, STEPHANIE	SINGER	9744 WILSHIRE BLVD #400	BEVERLY HILLS, CA	90212
REACTIONS, THE	ROCK & ROLL GROUP	POST OFFICE BOX 570	ROCKVILLE CENTRE, NY	11571
READ, ANTHONY	WRITER-PRODUCER	7 CEDAR CHASE, TAPLOW		
		MAIDENHEAD	BERKS	ENGLAND
READ, BOBBIE	COSTUME DESIGNER	8940 HOLLY PL	LOS ANGELES, CA	90046
READ, JAMES	ACTOR	ICM, 8899 BEVERLY BLVD	LOS ANGELES, CA	90048
READ, JOHN	FILM WRITER-PRODUCER	123 HAVERSTOCK HILL #9	LONDON NW3	ENGLAND
READY, RANDY	BASEBALL	ATHLETICS'S, OAKLAND COLISEUM	OAKLAND, CA	94621
READY FOR THE WORLD	RHYTHM & BLUES GROUP	FAA, 1700 BROADWAY, 5TH FLOOR	NEW YORK, NY	10019
REAGAN, MAUREEN	ACTRESS	10217 DUNLEER DR	LOS ANGELES, CA	90064
REAGAN, MICHAEL	AUTHOR-RADIO PERS	4740 ALLOTT AVE	SHERMAN OAKS, CA	91403
REAGAN, NANCY	ACTRESS-FIRST LADY	668 SAINT CLOUD RD	LOS ANGELES, CA	90077
REAGAN, ROBERT	DIRECTOR	2200 JEFFERSONIA WY	LOS ANGELES, CA	90049
REAGAN, RONALD	ACTOR-PRESIDENT	668 SAINT CLOUD RD	LOS ANGELES, CA	90077
REAGAN, RONALD, JR	DANCER	1283 DEVON AVE	LOS ANGELES, CA	90024
REAL LIFE	ROCK & ROLL GROUP	POST OFFICE BOX 214		
		ALBERT PARK	VICTORIA 3206	AUSTRALIA
REAM, BILLY	ACTOR	1296 W DISCOVERY	SAN MARCUS, CA	92069
REAM, L MICHAEL	DIRECTOR	DGA, 110 W 57TH ST	NEW YORK, NY	10019
REAMS, RONALD	BASEBALL	POST OFFICE BOX 1110	MYRTLE BEACH, SC	29578
REARDIN, J WILLIAM	TV DIRECTOR-PRODUCER	317 W 107TH ST #B	NEW YORK, NY	10025
REARDON, JEFF	BASEBALL	POST OFFICE BOX 4064	ATLANTA, GA	30302
REARDON, JOHN	TV DIRECTOR	APPLE TREE HOUSE		
		26 DOWER PARK		
		SAINT LEONARD'S HILL		
		WINDSOR	BERKS	ENGLAND
REASON, LIONEL I	CONDUCTOR	3012 NEWTON ST	BATON ROUGE, LA	70802
REASON, REX	ACTOR	20105 RHAPSODY RD	WALNUT, CA	91789
REASON, RHODES	ACTOR	409 WINCHESTER AVE	GLENDALE, CA	91201
REASONOVER, BOB	BASEBALL SCOUT	POST OFFICE BOX 7575	PHILADELPHIA, PA	19101
REASONOVER, LARRY	BASEBALL SCOUT	POST OFFICE BOX 7575	PHILADELPHIA, PA	19101
REASONS, GARY	FOOTBALL	N Y GIANTS, GIANTS STADIUM	EAST RUTHERFORD, NJ	07073
REAVES, GARY	NEWS CORRESPONDENT	CBS NEWS, 524 W 57TH ST	NEW YORK, NY	10019
REAVES, J MICHAEL	TV WRITER	841 1/2 N VENDOME ST	LOS ANGELES, CA	90026
REAVES-PHILLIPS, SANDRA	SINGER	SHAFMAN, 723 7TH AVE, 7TH FL	NEW YORK, NY	10019
REAVEY, MARGARET	WRITER	2513 RALSTON LN	REDONDO BEACH, CA	90278
REBACK, KATHERINE JAY	WRITER	1269 N FLORES ST #B-2	LOS ANGELES, CA	90069
REBELS, THE	C & W GROUP	POST OFFICE BOX 1830	GRETNA, LA	70053
REBERGER, FRANK	BASEBALL-COACH	POST OFFICE BOX 21727	SAN FRANCISCO, CA	95151
REBOULET, JEFF	BASEBALL	POST OFFICE BOX 1659	PORTLAND, OR	97207
REBOZO, CHARLES "BEBE"	CELEBRITY	490 BAY LN	KEY BISCAYNE, FL	33149
RECASNER, MARIE-ALISE	ACTRESS	9255 SUNSET BLVD #515	LOS ANGELES, CA	90069
RECCHI, MARK	HOCKEY	PENGUINS, CIVIC ARENA, CENTRE AV	PITTSBURGH, PA	15219
RECKELL, PETER	ACTOR	8033 SUNSET BLVD #4016	HOLLYWOOD, CA	90046
RECTOR, RICKY RAY	SINGER-GUITARIST	2022 20TH AVE S	NASHVILLE, TN	37212
RED, SPANISH	WRESTLER	SEE - SPANISH RED		
RED 7	ROCK & ROLL GROUP	POST OFFICE BOX 2210	NOVATO, CA	94948
RED DEMON, THE	WRESTLER	POST OFFICE BOX 3859	STAMFORD, CT	06905
RED HORSE BAND	C & W GROUP	NATIONAL BOOKING AGENCY		
		2605 NORTHRIDGE DR	GARLAND, TX	75043
RED HOT CHILI PEPPERS	ROCK & ROLL GROUP	11116 AQUA VISTA ST #39	STUDIO CITY, CA	91602
RED LETTER	ROCK & ROLL GROUP	41 BRITAIN ST #200	TORONTO, ONT M5A 1R7	CANADA
RED LOUISIANA	ROCK & ROLL GROUP	DENIS VAUGHAN MGMT		
		HEATHCOAT HOUSE		
		19-20 SAVILE ROW	LONDON W1	ENGLAND
RED RIDER	ROCK & ROLL GROUP	41 BRITAIN ST #200	TORONTO, ONT M5A 1R7	CANADA
RED ROCKERS, THE	ROCK & ROLL GROUP	ICM, 40 W 57TH ST	NEW YORK, NY	10019
RED STAR, KEVIN	ARTIST	340 READ ST	SANTA FE, NM	87501
REDA, LOUIS J	AUTHOR-PRODUCER	44 N 2ND ST	EASTON, PA	18042
REDACK, JAY	TV WRITER	1991 STRADELLA RD	LOS ANGELES, CA	90077
REDBONE	ROCK & ROLL GROUP	FAR OUT MGMT, 7417 SUNSET BLVD	LOS ANGELES, CA	90046
REDBONE, LEON	SINGER-GUITARIST	HANDLER, 179 AQUETONG RD	NEW HOPE, PA	18938

REDD, MARY-ROBIN	ACTRESS	515 N SIERRA DR	BEVERLY HILLS, CA	90210
REDD-FORREST, VERONICA	ACTRESS	10351 SANTA MONICA BLVD #211	LOS ANGELES, CA	90025
REDDING, DAVE	FOOTBALL COACH	CHIEFS, 1 ARROWHEAD DR	KANSAS CITY, MO	64129
REDDING, JULI	ACTRESS	115 N CAROLWOOD DR	LOS ANGELES, CA	90077
REDDING, REGGIE	FOOTBALL	FALCONS, SUWANEE RD AT I-85	SUWANEE, GA	30174
REDDING HUTNER, JULI	ACTRESS	115 N CAROLWOOD DR	LOS ANGELES, CA	90024
REDDY, HELEN	SINGER	820 STANFORD ST	SANTA MONICA, CA	90403
REDEKER, BILL	NEWS CORRESPONDENT	ABC NEWS, 7 W 66TH ST	NEW YORK, NY	10023
REDEKER, QUINN	ACTOR-WRITER	17931 WELBY WY	RESEDA, CA	91335
REDENBACHER, ORVILLE	POPCORN ENTREPRENEUR	1780 AVE DEL MUNDO #704	CORONADO, CA	92118
REDFIELD, DENNIS	ACTOR	3500 W OLIVE AVE #1400	BURBANK, CA	91505
REDFIELD, JOE	BASEBALL	31273 GANADO DR	RANCHO PALOS VRDS, CA	90274
REDFORD, J A C	COMPOSER	11318 MAYBROOK AVE	WHITTIER, CA	90603
REDFORD, JEFF	ACTOR	3912 WILLOW CREST AVE	NORTH HOLLYWOOD, CA	91604
REDFORD, ROBERT	ACTOR-DIRECTOR	1223 WILSHIRE BLVD #412	SANTA MONICA, CA	90403
REDGRAVE, LYNN	ACTRESS	21342 COLINA DR	TOPANGA CANYON, CA	90290
REDGRAVE, VANESSA	ACTRESS	31-32 SOHO SQ	LONDON W1	ENGLAND
REDING, GERALD F	COMPOSER-CONDUCTOR	808 S CURSON AVE #2	LOS ANGELES, CA	90036
REDLIN, JOEL	ACTOR	1258 N FAIRFAX AVE #4	LOS ANGELES, CA	90046
REDLINE	ROCK & ROLL GROUP	KASTLE, 213 N MAIN ST	ANN ARBOR, MI	48104
REDMAN, TIM	BASEBALL	POST OFFICE BOX 36407	LOUISVILLE, KY	40233
REDMOND, MARGE	ACTRESS	101 CENTRAL PARK W	NEW YORK, NY	10023
REDRIDER BAND, THE	C & W GROUP	TESSIER, 505 CANTON PASS	MADISON, TN	37115
REDUCERS, THE	ROCK & ROLL GROUP	RAVE ON/CAROLINE RECORDS		
		5 CROSBY ST	NEW YORK, NY	10013
REDUS, GARY	BASEBALL	POST OFFICE BOX 7000	PITTSBURGH, PA	15212
REED, ALEXANDER	ACTOR	6 W 87TH ST	NEW YORK, NY	10024
REED, ANDRE	FOOTBALL	BILLS, 1 BILLS DR	ORCHARD PARK, NJ	14127
REED, ANDRE L	COMPOSER	624 N HOWARD AVE #127	MONTEBELLO, CA	90640
REED, ANN	SINGER-GUITARIST	788 FULLER AVE	SAINT PAUL, MN	55104
REED, BOBBY	BASEBALL	POST OFFICE BOX 4448	TULSA, OK	74159
REED, BUTCH "THE NATURAL"	WRESTLER	POST OFFICE BOX 105366	ATLANTA, GA	31348
REED, DARREN	BASEBALL	TWINS, 501 CHICAGO AVE S	MINNEAPOLIS, MN	55415
REED, DENNIS	BASEBALL	POST OFFICE BOX 824	BURLINGTON, IA	52601
REED, EVERETT L	COMPOSER	11729 RIVERSIDE DR #5	NORTH HOLLYWOOD, CA	91607
REED, HADEN	SINGER	REEDSOUND RECORDS, 120 MIKEL DR	SUMMERVILLE, SC	29483
REED, JAKE	FOOTBALL	VIKINGS, 9520 VIKING DR	EDEN PRAIRIE, MN	55344
REED, JAMIE	BASEBALL TRAINER	ORIOLE PARK, 333 W CAMDEN ST	BALTIMORE, MD	21201
REED, JEFF	BASEBALL	RURAL ROUTE 7, BOX 3570	ELIZABETHTON, TN	37643
REED, JENNIFER	TV PRODUCER	1235 N KINGS RD #206	WEST HOLLYWOOD, CA	90069
REED, JERRY	SINGER-ACTOR	MOTTE, 369 GLYNN DR	BIRMINGHAM, AL	35215
REED, JERRY M	BASEBALL	21 GRANDVIEW RD	ASHEVILLE, NC	28806
REED, JODY	BASEBALL	FENWAY PARK, 4 YAWKEY WY	BOSTON, MA	02215
REED, JOHN F	U S CONGRESSMAN	355 CENTERVILLE RD #3	WARWICK, RI	02886
REED, LOU	SINGER-SONGWRITER	38 E 68TH ST	NEW YORK, NY	10021
REED, OLIVER	ACTOR	PINEHURST FARM, OAKWOOD HILLS	DORKING, SURREY	ENGLAND
REED, PAMELA	ACTRESS	1875 CENTURY PARK E #1300	LOS ANGELES, CA	90067
REED, PETER	FILM EXECUTIVE	2 W END CT, PRIORY RD	LONDON NW6	ENGLAND
REED, PHILIP	ACTOR	969 BEL AIR RD	LOS ANGELES, CA	90077
REED, REX	FILM CRITIC	1 W 72ND ST #86	NEW YORK, NY	10023
REED, RICK	BASEBALL	POST OFFICE BOX 3665	OMAHA, NE	68103
REED, RICK	BASEBALL UMPIRE	6190 BLUEHILL	DETROIT, MI	48224
REED, ROBERT	ACTOR	980 STONERIDGE DR	PASADENA, CA	91105
REED, SHANNA	ACTRESS	1649 S STERNS DR	LOS ANGELES, CA	90035
REED, STEVE	BASEBALL	POST OFFICE BOX 3448	SHREVEPORT, LA	71133
REED, TRACY	ACTRESS	10000 SANTA MONICA BLVD #305	LOS ANGELES, CA	90067
REED, WARREN H	TV WRITER	POST OFFICE BOX 7	SAYVILLE, NY	11782
REED, WILLIS	BASKETBALL-COACH	N J NETS, MEADOWLANDS ARENA	EAST RUTHERFORD, NJ	07073
REED HALL, ALAINA	ACTRESS	215 S LA CIENEGA BLVD #203	BEVERLY HILLS, CA	90211
REEDER, CARLOS A	DIRECTOR	9025 WILSHIRE BLVD #301	BEVERLY HILLS, CA	90212
REEDER, GORDON H	COMPOSER	11315 PLAYA ST	CULVER CITY, CA	90230
REEKIE, JOE	HOCKEY	NASSAU VETS MEMORIAL COLISEUM	UNIONDALE, NY	11553
REELEY, RON	SINGER	FIELDS, 3753 VINEYARD CT	MARIETTA, GA	30062
REEMS, HARRY	ACTOR-REALTOR	2528 GERONIMO CT	PARK CITY, UT	84060
REES, CARLYLE W	DIRECTOR	2927 CROOKS RD	ROYAL OAK, MI	48073
REES, DAVID	ACT-WRI-PROD	THAMES COTTAGE, THAMES ST	SUN-ON-THAMES TW16 6AG	ENGLAND
REES, ROB	BASEBALL	525 NW PEACOCK BLVD	PORT SAINT LUCIE, FL	34986
REES, ROGER	ACTOR	HEATH, PARAMOUNT HOUSE		
		162-170 WARDOUR ST	LONDON W1V 3AT	ENGLAND
REES, SEAN	BASEBALL	POST OFFICE BOX 9194	HAMPTON, VA	23670
REESE, CALVIN	BASEBALL	POST OFFICE BOX 4669	CHARLESTON, WV	25304
REESE, CHARLEY	COMMENTATOR	KING FEATURES, 216 E 45TH ST	NEW YORK, NY	10017
REESE, DELLA	SINGER-ACTRESS	1910 BEL AIR RD	LOS ANGELES, CA	90077
REESE, JIMMIE	BASEBALL-COACH	POST OFFICE BOX 2000	ANAHEIM, CA	92803
REESE, PEE WEE	BASEBALL	POST OFFICE BOX 35700		
		MAIN OFFICE STATION	LOUISVILLE, KY	40232
REESER, JEFF	BASEBALL EXECUTIVE	POST OFFICE BOX 7845	COLUMBIA, SC	29202
REEVE, CHRISTOPHER	ACTOR	POST OFFICE BOX 461	NEW YORK, NY	10024
REEVE, GEOFFREY JAMES	DIRECTOR-PRODUCER	THE PRODUCERS ASSOCIATION		
		162 WARDOUR ST	LONDON W1V 4AB	ENGLAND
REEVES, ALAN DAVID	COMPOSER	9000 SUNSET BLVD #1115	LOS ANGELES, CA	90069
REEVES, DAN	FOOTBALL COACH	BRONCOS, 13655 BRONCOS PKWY	ENGLEWOOD, CO	80112
REEVES, DEL	SINGER	991 HIGHWAY #100	CENTERVILLE, TN	37033
REEVES, DIANNE	SINGER	10100 SANTA MONICA BLVD #1600	LOS ANGELES, CA	90067
REEVES, JIM	BASEBALL SCOUT	METS, 126TH ST & ROOSEVELT AVE	FLUSHING, NY	11368

REEVES, KARI	SINGER	POST OFFICE BOX 242	HORSESHOE BEND, AR 72512
REEVES, KEANU	ACTOR	7920 SUNSET BLVD #250	LOS ANGELES, CA 90046
REEVES, MARTHA	SINGER	MARS, 168 ORCHID DR	PEARL RIVER, NY 10965
REEVES, MELISSA	ACTRESS	NBC-TV, "DAYS OF OUR LIVES"	
		3000 W ALAMEDA AVE	BURBANK, CA 91523
REEVES, RICHARD	COLUMNIST-REPORTER	UPS, 4900 MAIN ST, 9TH FLOOR	KANSAS CITY, MO 64112
REEVES, SCOTT	ACTOR	CBS-TV, "YOUNG & THE RESTLESS"	
		7800 BEVERLY BLVD #3305	LOS ANGELES, CA 90036
REEVES, STEVE	ACTOR-BODYBUILDER	POST OFFICE BOX 807	VALLEY CENTER, CA 92082
REEVES, WALTER	FOOTBALL	POST OFFICE BOX 888	PHOENIX, AZ 85001
REFUGEE	ROCK & ROLL GROUP	FALCON PRODUCTIONS	
		3080 LENWORTH DR	MISSISS, ONT L4X 2G1 CANADA
REGA, WILLIAM J	WRITER	8306 SKYLINE DR	LOS ANGELES, CA 90046
REGALBUTO, JOE	ACTOR	724 24TH ST	SANTA MONICA, CA 90402
REGAN, DENNIS	MUSICIAN-WRITER	23427 FRIAR ST	WOODLAND HILLS, CA 91367
REGAN, DONALD T	POLITICIAN	11 CANAL CENTER PLAZA #301	ALEXANDRIA, VA 22314
REGAN, EDWARD V	COMPTROLLER	STATE CAPITOL BUILDING	ALBANY, NY 12224
REGAN, KEN	PHOTOGRAPHER	6 W 20TH ST	NEW YORK, NY 10011
REGAN, PATRICK	WRITER-PRODUCER	3680 WILL ROGERS ST	SANTA MONICA, CA 90403
REGAN, PHIL	ACTOR	1123 S ORANGE GROVE BLVD	PASADENA, CA 91105
REGAN, RIFF	ACTRESS	SAVAGE, 6212 BANNER AVE	LOS ANGELES, CA 90038
REGARD, SUZANNE	ACTRESS-MODEL	THE ATHLETES REGISTRY	
		2221 S BARRY AVE	LOS ANGELES, CA 90064
REGAS, JACK	DIRECTOR	20518 SAN JOSE ST	CHATSWORTH, CA 91311
REGATTA	ROCK & ROLL GROUP	41 BRITAIN ST #200	TORONTO, ONT M5A 1R7 CANADA
REGEHR, DUNCAN	ACTOR	2401 MAIN ST	SANTA MONICA, CA 90405
REGENTS, THE	ROCK & ROLL GROUP	MARS, 168 ORCHID DR	PEARL RIVER, NY 10965
REGINA	SINGER	BELKIN, 28001 CHARGIN BLVD	CINCINNATI, OH 44122
REGINA, PAUL	ACTOR	9200 SUNSET BLVD #710	LOS ANGELES, CA 90069
REGINALD, REX	ACTOR	2051 HERCULES DR	LOS ANGELES, CA 90046
REGION, DANIEL	ACTOR	CBS-TV, 524 W 57TH ST	NEW YORK, NY 10019
REGISTER, BILL	BODYBUILDER	4530 NE 74TH ST	PORTLAND, OR 97218
REGISTER, LARRY	NEWS CORRESPONDENT	1050 TECHWOOD DR, NW	ATLANTA, GA 30318
REGULA, RALPH	U S CONGRESSMAN	4150 BELDEN VILLAGE ST, NW	CANTON, OH 44718
REGULAR GUYS, THE	ROCK & ROLL GROUP	POST OFFICE BOX 3278	LONG BEACH, CA 90803
REGULI, CHRISTINA	ACTRESS	TIFFANY, 23125 PARK CONTESSA	CALABASAS PARK, CA 91302
REHBEIN, DICK	FOOTBALL COACH	VIKINGS, 9520 VIKING DR	EDEN PRAIRIE, MN 55344
REHNQUIST, WILLIAM	CHIEF JUSTICE	111 2ND ST, NE	WASHINGTON, DC 20002
REHR, DARRYL	TV DIRECTOR	2227 PARNELL AVE	LOS ANGELES, CA 90064
REICH, FRANK	FOOTBALL	BILLS, 1 BILLS DR	ORCHARD PARK, NJ 14127
REICH, JOE	CASTING DIRECTOR	MCA/UNIVERSAL STUDIOS, INC	
		100 UNIVERSAL CITY PLAZA	
		BUILDING #463-104	UNIVERSAL CITY, CA 91608
REICH, STEVE	COMPOSER	LYNN GARON, 1199 PARK AVE	NEW YORK, NY 10028
REICHEL, ROBERT	HOCKEY	POST OFFICE BOX 1540, STA "M"	CALGARY, ALTA T2P 3BP CANADA
REICHENBACH, ERIC	BASEBALL	POST OFFICE BOX 7845	COLUMBIA, SC 29202
REICHENBACH, MIKE	FOOTBALL	DOLPHINS, 2269 NW 199TH ST	MIAMI, FL 33056
REICHENBACH, WILLIAM F	COMPOSER	14181 CLARETTA ST	PACOIMA, CA 91331
REICHLER, JOSEPH	AUTHOR	1212 6TH AVE	NEW YORK, NY 10036
REICHOW, JERRY	FOOTBALL EXECUTIVE	VIKINGS, 9520 VIKING DR	EDEN PRAIRIE, MN 55344
REID, ALASTAIR	FILM DIRECTOR	THE OLD STORES, CURLOAD	
		STOKE, NEAR TAUNTON	SOMERSET ENGLAND
REID, BERYL	ACTOR-COMEDIAN	HONEYPOT COTTAGE	
		WRAYSBURG, NEAR STAINES	MIDDLESEX ENGLAND
REID, BRENDA	TV PRODUCER	ANGLIA FILMS, 48 LEICESTER SQ	LONDON WC2 ENGLAND
REID, DAPHNE MAXWELL	ACTRESS	16030 VENTURA BLVD #380	ENCINO, CA 91436
REID, DAVE	HOCKEY	MAPLE LEAFS, 60 CARLTON ST	TORONTO, ONT M5B 1L1 CANADA
REID, DAVID	SCREENWRITER	2 SOUTH CLOSE, HIGHGATE	LONDON N6 5UQ ENGLAND
REID, DEREK	BASEBALL	POST OFFICE BOX 3448	SHREVEPORT, LA 71133
REID, DONALD	COMPOSER	POST OFFICE BOX 2703	STAUNTON, VA 24401
REID, ELLIOTT	ACTOR-WRITER	6310 SAN VICENTE BLVD #407	LOS ANGELES, CA 90048
REID, FRANCES	ACTRESS	9165 SUNSET BLVD #202	LOS ANGELES, CA 90069
REID, GREG	BASEBALL	POST OFFICE BOX 882	MADISON, WI 53701
REID, GREGORY D	DIRECTOR	DGA, 110 W 57TH ST	NEW YORK, NY 10019
REID, HAROLD	SINGER	POST OFFICE BOX 2703	STAUNTON, VA 24401
REID, HARRY	U S SENATOR	500 S RANCHO RD #7	LAS VEGAS, NV 89106
REID, J R	BASKETBALL	310 N KINGS DR	CHARLOTTE, NC 28204
REID, JESSIE	BASEBALL	3614 CEDAR AVE	LYNWOOD, CA 90262
REID, JOHN	BASEBALL	POST OFFICE BOX 64939	FAYETTEVILLE, NC 28306
REID, MAX	FILM WRITER-DIRECTOR	2512 4TH ST	SANTA MONICA, CA 90405
REID, MICHAEL	FOOTBALL	FALCONS, SUWANEE RD AT I-85	SUWANEE, GA 30174
REID, MIKE	ACTOR-COMEDIAN	EASTENDERS, BBC STUDIOS	BOREHAMWOOD, HERTS ENGLAND
REID, MIKE	GOLFER	POST OFFICE BOX 109601	PALM BCH GARDENS, FL 33418
REID, MIKE	SINGER-SONGWRITER	MORESS, 1209 16TH AVE S	NASHVILLE, TN 37212
REID, SCOTT	BASEBALL-SCOUT	1060 W ADDISON ST	CHICAGO, IL 60613
REID, SHEILA	ACTRESS	29 RYLETT RD	LONDON W12 ENGLAND
REID, TIM	ACTOR-PRODUCER	16030 VENTURA BLVD #380	ENCINO, CA 91436
REID, WILLIAM J	WRITER-PRODUCER	500 S BUENA VISTA ST	BURBANK, CA 91521
REIG, JUNE	TV WRITER-DIRECTOR	454 W 46TH ST	NEW YORK, NY 10036
REIK, WILLIAM, JR	BASEBALL EXECUTIVE	REDS, 100 RIVERFRONT STADIUM	CINCINNATI, OH 45202
REIKER, DON	PRODUCER	MGM, 10202 W WASHINGTON BLVD	CULVER CITY, CA 90230
REIKER, DONALD	TV WRITER	3695 SHANNON RD	LOS ANGELES, CA 90027
REIKES, ANDREW	TV DIRECTOR	287 HARVARD ST #23	CAMBRIDGE, MA 02139
REILLY, CHARLES NELSON	ACTOR	2341 GLOAMING WY	BEVERLY HILLS, CA 90210
REILLY, DEIRDRE	DIRECTOR	RIVER RD	LUMBERVILLE, PA 18933

REILLY, JACK	FOOTBALL COACH	POST OFFICE BOX 609609	SAN DIEGO, CA	92160
REILLY, JACK	TV PRODUCER	ENTERTAINMENT TONIGHT		
		PARAMOUNT TELEVISION		
		5555 MELROSE AVE	LOS ANGELES, CA	90038
REILLY, JOHN	ACTOR	ABC-TV, "GENERAL HOSPITAL"		
		4151 PROSPECT AVE	BURBANK, CA	91523
REILLY, JOHN M	TV DIRECTOR	322 W 57TH ST	NEW YORK, NY	10019
REILLY, MIKE	BASEBALL UMPIRE	44 LAKESIDE DR	BATTLE CREEK, MI	49015
REILLY, TOM	ACTOR	9000 SUNSET BLVD #1112	LOS ANGELES, CA	90069
REILLY, WALTER N	WRITER	5928 LINDENHURST AVE	LOS ANGELES, CA	90036
REIMER, KEVIN	BASEBALL	POST OFFICE BOX 90111	ARLINGTON, TX	76004
REIMERS, BRUCE	FOOTBALL	BENGALS, 200 RIVERFRONT STADIUM	CINCINNATI, OH	45202
REIMERS, NADINE	COSTUME DESIGNER	288 AMALFI DR	SANTA MONICA, CA	90402
REIMINK, BOB	BASEBALL	TIGERS, 89 WHARNCLIFFE RD N	LONDON, ONT N6H 2A7	CANADA
REIMUELLER, ROSS	CONDUCTOR	1647 ANGELUS AVE	LOS ANGELES, CA	90026
REIN, HAL	DIRECTOR	33 5TH AVE	NEW YORK, NY	10003
REINEBOLD, JIM	BASEBALL COACH	POST OFFICE BOX 4218	SOUTH BEND, IN	46634
REINER, ANDRES	BASEBALL SCOUT	POST OFFICE BOX 288	HOUSTON, TX	77001
REINER, CARL	ACTOR-DIRECTOR	714 N RODEO DR	BEVERLY HILLS, CA	90210
REINER, ESTELLE	SINGER	714 N RODEO DR	BEVERLY HILLS, CA	90210
REINER, ROB	ACT-WRI-DIR-PROD	255 CHADBOURNE AVE	LOS ANGELES, CA	90049
REINER, TRACY	ACTRESS	9161 HAZEN DR	BEVERLY HILLS, CA	90210
REINHARDT, SANDI	ACTRESS	NBC-TV, "ANOTHER WORLD"		
		1268 E 14TH ST	BROOKLYN, NY	11230
REINHART, RICHARD	TV WRITER	16000 VALERIO ST	VAN NUYS, CA	91406
REINHOLD, GADY	TV DIRECTOR	70 RIVERSIDE DR	NEW YORK, NY	10024
REINHOLD, JUDGE	ACTOR-PRODUCER	3855 LANKERSHIM BLVD #818	NORTH HOLLYWOOD, CA	91601
REININGER, GUSTAVE V	TV WRITER-PRODUCER	W S BLACK, 1350 6TH AVE	NEW YORK, NY	10017
REINKING, ANN	ACTRESS	CAA, 9830 WILSHIRE BLVD	BEVERLY HILLS, CA	90212
REINSDORF, JERRY	BB-BKBB EXECUTIVE	333 W 35TH ST	CHICAGO, IL	60616
REISBERG, RICHARD S	TV EXECUTIVE	15915 WOODVALE RD	ENCINO, CA	91436
REISER, ALOIS	COMPOSER-CONDUCTOR	1542 COURTNEY AVE	LOS ANGELES, CA	90046
REISER, HAROLD L	DIRECTOR	9256 SWINTON AVE	SEPULVEDA, CA	91343
REISER, PAUL	ACTOR-COMEDIAN	1134 ALTA LOMA RD #303	LOS ANGELES, CA	90069
REISHER, PAUL	COMEDIAN	CAA, 9830 WILSHIRE BLVD	BEVERLY HILLS, CA	90212
REISMAN, DAVID	DIRECTOR	70 E 10TH ST	NEW YORK, NY	10003
REISMAN, JOE	COMPOSER-CONDUCTOR	4337 CLYBOURNE AVE	NORTH HOLLYWOOD, CA	91602
REISMAN, MARK A	SCREENWRITER	8955 BEVERLY BLVD	WEST HOLLYWOOD, CA	90048
REISNER, ALLEN	DIRECTOR	9165 CORDELL DR	LOS ANGELES, CA	90069
REISS, JEFFREY C	TV EXECUTIVE	140 E 45TH ST, 40TH FLOOR	NEW YORK, NY	10017
REISS, MICHAEL	TV PRODUCER	UTA, 9560 WILSHIRE BL, 5TH FL	BEVERLY HILLS, CA	90212
REISTER, FREDRICK	DIRECTOR	6426 WOODARD BAY RD, NE	OLYMPIA, WA	98506
REISZ, KAREL	FILM DIRECTOR	11 CHALCOTT GARDENS, HAMPSTEAD	LONDON NW3	ENGLAND
REITEL, ENN	ACTOR	CAREY, 64 THORNTON AVE	LONDON W4 1QQ	ENGLAND
REITER, ANDREA	DIRECTOR	400 E 85TH ST #15-L	NEW YORK, NY	10028
REITH, BOB	GOLFER	PGA SENIORS, 112 T P C BLVD	PONTE VEDRA BEACH, FL	32082
REITMAN, IVAN	DIRECTOR-PRODUCER	1426 STONE CANYON RD	LOS ANGELES, CA	90077
RELAFORD, DESI	BASEBALL	POST OFFICE BOX 9194	HAMPTON, VA	23670
RELAY	MUSICAL GROUP	POST OFFICE BOX 6568	CINCINNATI, OH	45206
RELIFORD, CHARLES	BASEBALL UMPIRE	POST OFFICE BOX 608	GROVE CITY, OH	43123
RELIS, ROCHELLE	ACTRESS-SINGER	484 W 43RD ST #18-A	NEW YORK, NY	10036
RELPH, MICHAEL	WRITER-PRODUCER	PRIMOSE HILL STUDIOS		
		THE LODGES	LONDON NW1	ENGLAND
RELPH, SIMON	FILM PRODUCER	338 LIVERPOOL RD	LONDON N7	ENGLAND
RELYEA, ROBERT	DIRECTOR	12950 BLAIRWOOD DR	STUDIO CITY, CA	91604
REMAR, JAMES	ACTOR	151 S EL CAMINO DR	BEVERLY HILLS, CA	90212
REMBERT, JOHNNY	FOOTBALL	PATRIOTS, FOXBORO STADIUM, RT #1	FOXBORO, MA	02035
REMBERT, REGGIE	FOOTBALL	BENGALS, 200 RIVERFRONT STADIUM	CINCINNATI, OH	45202
REMLINGER, MIKE	BASEBALL	POST OFFICE BOX 3690, STA "B"	CALGARY, ALB T2B 4M4	CANADA
REMSEN, BERT	ACTOR	5722 MAMMOTH AVE	VAN NUYS, CA	91401
REMSEN, KERRY	ACTRESS	STONE MANNERS, 9113 SUNSET BL	LOS ANGELES, CA	90069
REMY, JERRY	BASEBALL-ANNOUNCER	NESN, 70 BROOKLINE AVE	BOSTON, MA	02215
RENAISSANCE	ROCK & ROLL GROUP	POST OFFICE BOX 1333	MONTCLAIR, NJ	07042
RENALDO AND THE LOAF	ROCK & ROLL GROUP	109 MINNA ST #391	SAN FRANCISCO, CA	94105
RENASCENCE TRIO	C & W GROUP	PROCESS, 439 WILEY AVE	FRANKLIN, PA	16323
RENAUD, LINE	ACTRESS	1417 N SPAULDING AVE	LOS ANGELES, CA	90046
RENAUD, TONY	BASKETBALL EXECUTIVE	310 N KINGS DR	CHARLOTTE, NC	28204
RENAY, LIZ	BURLESQUE	3708 SAN ANGELO AVE	LAS VEGAS, NV	89102
RENBOURN, JOHN	SINGER-GUITARIST	FOLKLORE, 1671 APPIAN WY	SANTA MONICA, CA	90401
RENDE, SAL	BASEBALL MANAGER	POST OFFICE BOX 3665	OMAHA, NE	68103
RENDELY, RICHARD	DIRECTOR	POST OFFICE BOX 231	GREENWICH, CT	06830
RENDINA, MIKE	BASEBALL	POST OFFICE BOX 2785	LAKELAND, FL	33806
RENDINA, VICTOR	ACTOR	141 N KENWOOD ST	GLENDALE, CA	91206
RENE, HENRI	CONDUCTOR	1081 LIGHTHOUSE AVE #214	PACIFIC GROVE, CA	93950
RENE, JOSEPH	COMPOSER	220 GREGORY PL	WEST PALM BEACH, FL	33405
RENEGADE	ROCK & ROLL GROUP	10020 PIONEER BLVD #104	SANTA FE SPRINGS, CA	90670
RENEGADES, THE	ROCK & ROLL GROUP	POST OFFICE BOX 57291	DALLAS, TX	75207
RENFROE, LADDIE	BASEBALL	CUBS, 2ND & RIVERSIDE DR	DES MOINES, IA	50309
RENFROW, EDWARD	AUDITOR	STATE CAPITOL BUILDING	RALEIGH, NC	27603
RENICK, JEANE	TV EXECUTIVE	CBS-TV, 51 W 52ND ST	NEW YORK, NY	10019
RENICK, RICK	BASEBALL-MANAGER	CANADIANS, 4601 ONTARIO ST	VANCOUVER, BC V5V 3H4	CANADA
RENKO, STEVE	BASEBALL	POST OFFICE BOX 3566	WEST PALM BEACH, FL	33402
RENNARD, DEBORAH	ACTRESS	9255 SUNSET BLVD #515	LOS ANGELES, CA	90069
RENNE, CINDY	SINGER	DON HALL, 1305 MILAM WY	CARROLLTON, TX	75006
RENNERT, DUTCH	BASEBALL UMPIRE	306 N LARK ST	OSHKOSH, WI	54901

RENO, JACK	SINGER	POST OFFICE BOX 1001	FLORENCE, KY	41042
RENO, RONNIE	SINGER-GUITARIST	135 CHIROC RD	HENDERSONVILLE, TN	37075
RENOIR, JEAN	FILM DIRECTOR	1273 LEONA DR	BEVERLY HILLS, CA	90210
RENSHAW, JEANNINE	ACTRESS	BDP, 10637 BURBANK BLVD	NORTH HOLLYWOOD, CA	91601
RENSLOW, RICK	WRESTLER	POST OFFICE BOX 3859	STAMFORD, CT	06905
RENTERIA, RICH	BASEBALL	POST OFFICE BOX 8053	SUN CITY, CA	92380
RENTON, NICHOLAS	TV DIRECTOR	23 CRESCENT LN	LONDON SW4 9PT	ENGLAND
RENZI, MAGGIE	FILM PRODUCER	RED DOG FILMS, 306 W 38TH ST	NEW YORK, NY	10018
REO, DON	TV WRITER-PRODUCER	8042 WOODROW WILSON DR	LOS ANGELES, CA	90046
REO SPEEDWAGON	ROCK & ROLL GROUP	8436 W 3RD ST #730	LOS ANGELES, CA	90048
REPARATA & THE DELRONS	ROCK & ROLL GROUP	MARS, 168 ORCHID DR	PEARL RIVER, NY	10965
REPCZYNSKI, JOHN	DIRECTOR	13458 FRIAR ST	VAN NUYS, CA	91401
RESCHER, DEE DEE	ACTRESS	1930 CENTURY PARK W #403	LOS ANGELES, CA	90067
RESCHER, GAYNE	CINEMATOGRAPHER	939 N WETHERLY DR	LOS ANGELES, CA	90069
RESETAR, ROBERT J	COMPOSER	2135 N BEACHWOOD DR #4	LOS ANGELES, CA	90068
RESIDENTS, THE	ROCK & ROLL GROUP	109 MINNA ST #391	SAN FRANCISCO, CA	94105
RESING, GEORGE	TV EXECUTIVE	GROUP W PRODUCTIONS		
		100 UNIVERSAL CITY PLAZA	UNIVERSAL CITY, CA	91608
RESNAIS, ALAIN	DIRECTOR	70 RUE DES PLANTES	F-75014 PARIS	FRANCE
RESNER, LAWRENCE	WRITER	11618 KIOWA AVE #115	LOS ANGELES, CA	90049
RESNICK, NOEL	TV EXECUTIVE	ABC-TV, 2040 AVE OF THE STARS	LOS ANGELES, CA	90067
RESNICK, PATRICIA	SCREENWRITER	8955 BEVERLY BLVD	WEST HOLLYWOOD, CA	90048
RESNICOFF, ETHEL	WRITER	14002 PALAWAN WY #3111	MARINA DEL REY, CA	90292
RESNIKOFF, ROBERT D	WRITER	861 CHATTANOOGA AVE	PACIFIC PALISADES, CA	90272
RESPONDEK, MARK	BASEBALL	POLECATS, 608 N SLAPPEY BLVD	ALBANY, GA	31701
RESTIVO, PETER	WRI-DIR-PROD	POST OFFICE BOX 31243	HATFORD, CT	06103
RESTLESS HEART	C & W GROUP	7250 BEVERLY BLVD #102	LOS ANGELES, CA	90036
RESTON, DANA	ACTRESS	8831 SUNSET BLVD #402	LOS ANGELES, CA	90069
RESTON, JAMES	AUTHOR	1804 KALLORAMA SQ, NW	WASHINGTON, DC	20008
RETTENMUND, MERV	BASEBALL-COACH	POST OFFICE BOX 2000	SAN DIEGO, CA	92112
RETTIG, RICHARD	TV EXECUTIVE	NBC-TV, 3000 W ALAMEDA AVE	BURBANK, CA	91523
RETTIG, TOMMY	ACTOR	13802 NW PASSAGE #302	MARINA DEL REY, CA	90291
RETTON, MARY LOU	GYMNAST	1637 BEVERLY BRD	FAIRMONT, WV	26554
REUBENS, PAUL	ACTOR-COMEDIAN	SEE - HERMAN, PEE WEE		
REUSCHEL, RICK	BASEBALL	1403 PICADILLY CIR	MOUNT PROSPECT, IL	60056
REUTEMAN, R C	BASEBALL EXECUTIVE	POST OFFICE BOX 1211	NORFOLK, VA	23502
REUTHER, STEPHEN D	FILM EXECUTIVE	9808 WILSHIRE BLVD #201	BEVERLY HILLS, CA	90212
REV, THE	ROCK & ROLL GROUP	25 HUNTINGTON AVE #420	BOSTON, MA	02116
REVEIZ, FUAD	FOOTBALL	VIKINGS, 9520 VIKING DR	EDEN PRAIRIE, MN	55344
REVELL, GRAEME	COMPOSER	6525 SUNSET BLVD #402	HOLLYWOOD, CA	90028
REVENIG, TODD	BASEBALL	POST OFFICE BOX 2769	HUNTSVILLE, AL	35804
REVERE, ANNE	ACTRESS	9 FOX LN	LOCUST VALLEY, NY	11560
REVERE, PAUL & THE RAIDERS	ROCK & ROLL GROUP	9044 MELROSE AVE #200	LOS ANGELES, CA	90069
REVILL, CLIVE	ACTOR	15029 ENCANTO DR	SHERMAN OAKS, CA	91403
REX, JEFF	SINGER-GUITARIST	734 TURF RD	NORTH WOODMERE, NY	11581
REY, ANDRE	ARTIST	1300 W 78TH ST	CLEVELAND, OH	44102
REY, FERNANDO	ACTOR	ORENSE 62	MADRID 20	SPAIN
REYES, ALBERTO	BASEBALL	POLECATS, 608 N SLAPPEY BLVD	ALBANY, GA	31701
REYES, CARLOS	BASEBALL	POST OFFICE BOX 4525	MACON, GA	31208
REYES, ERNIE, JR	ACTOR	1800 N VINE ST #120	LOS ANGELES, CA	90028
REYES, GILBERTO	BASEBALL	EXPOS, 4545 DE COUBERTIN AVE	MONTREAL, QUE H1V 3P2	CANADA
REYES, KERRY LEE	BODYBUILDER	WORLD OF FITNESS, 2110 WHITSON	SELMA, CA	93662
REYES, LUIS	WRITER-PRODUCER	4540 LAUREL CANYON BLVD	NORTH HOLLYWOOD, CA	91607
REYES, PIA	ACTRESS-MODEL	MARX, 11130 HUSTON ST #6	NORTH HOLLYWOOD, CA	91601
REYNOLDS, ALLIE	BASEBALL	2709 CASHION PL	OKLAHOMA CITY, OK	73112
REYNOLDS, BILL	FOOTBALL REFEREE	NFL, 410 PARK AVE	NEW YORK, NY	10022
REYNOLDS, BILLY RAY	SINGER-GUITARIST	ROUTE #1, BOX 176	PRIMM SPRINGS, TN	38476
REYNOLDS, BURT	ACT-DIR-PROD	1001 INDIANTOWN RD	JUPITER, FL	33458
REYNOLDS, CLARKE E	WRITER-PRODUCER	4139 VIA MARINA #1106-8	MARINA DEL REY, CA	90292
REYNOLDS, CRAIG	BASEBALL	5906 PARADISE VALLEY CT	HOUSTON, TX	77069
REYNOLDS, DALE	ACTOR	1538 N DETROIT ST #6	LOS ANGELES, CA	90046
REYNOLDS, DAVID	TV DIRECTOR	PENCOB HOUSE, SCOTTON		
		KNARESBOROUG	NORTH YORKS	ENGLAND
REYNOLDS, DEBBIE	ACTRESS	11595 LA MAIDA ST	NORTH HOLLYWOOD, CA	91602
REYNOLDS, DON	BASEBALL-COACH	POST OFFICE BOX 4209	JACKSON, MS	39296
REYNOLDS, GENE	ACTOR-DIRECTOR	2034 CASTILIAN DR	LOS ANGELES, CA	90068
REYNOLDS, HAROLD	BASEBALL	POST OFFICE BOX 4100	SEATTLE, WA	98104
REYNOLDS, JAMES V	ACTOR	1925 HAMSCOM DR	SOUTH PASADENA, CA	91030
REYNOLDS, JERRY	BASKETBALL	POST OFFICE BOX 76	ORLANDO, FL	32802
REYNOLDS, JOHN J	NEWS CORRESPONDENT	NBC NEWS, 4001 NEBRASKA AV, SW	WASHINGTON, DC	20016
REYNOLDS, JOSEPH J	TV DIRECTOR	POST OFFICE BOX 904	MARY ESTHER, FL	32569
REYNOLDS, LEE	DIRECTOR	2980 WILSON AVE	OAKTON, VA	22124
REYNOLDS, LEE	SINGER	POST OFFICE BOX 21322	SAN ANTONIO, TX	78221
REYNOLDS, LEE	TV PRODUCER	300 E 57TH ST	NEW YORK, NY	10022
REYNOLDS, LEE ALLEN	SINGER-GUITARIST	POST OFFICE BOX 120657	NASHVILLE, TN	37212
REYNOLDS, LEE D	SCREENWRITER	8955 BEVERLY BLVD	WEST HOLLYWOOD, CA	90048
REYNOLDS, MARIE	ACTRESS-MODEL	10 E 44TH ST #700	NEW YORK, NY	10017
REYNOLDS, RICHARD E	CONDUCTOR	4332 AGNES AVE	STUDIO CITY, CA	91604
REYNOLDS, RICKY	FOOTBALL	BUCCANEERS, 1 BUCCANEER PL	TAMPA, FL	33607
REYNOLDS, SCOTT	ARTIST	308 W 30TH ST #9-B	NEW YORK, NY	10001
REYNOLDS, SHANE	BASEBALL	POST OFFICE BOX 27045	TUCSON, AZ	85726
REYNOLDS, STERLING TOM	DIRECTOR	7141 N 16TH ST	PHOENIX, AZ	85020
REYNOLDS, TOMMIE	BASEBALL COACH	ATHLETICS'S, OAKLAND COLISEUM	OAKLAND, CA	94621
REYNOLDS HAFFEN, MARJORIE	ACTRESS	3 CATALINA CT	MANHATTAN BEACH, CA	90266
REYNOSO, ARMANDO	BASEBALL	POST OFFICE BOX 6667	RICHMOND, VA	23230

RHAPSODY	MUSICAL GROUP	5625 "O" STREET BLDG #7	LINCOLN, NE	68510
RHEDIN, JUDITH	ACTRESS	12 E 86TH ST #737	NEW YORK, NY	10028
RHEIN, JOE	FOOTBALL EXECUTIVE	POST OFFICE BOX 888	PHOENIX, AZ	85001
RHEINSTEIN, FREDERIC	DIRECTOR	6335 HOMEWOOD AVE	LOS ANGELES, CA	90028
RHETT, ALICIA	ACTRESS	50 TRADD ST	CHARLESTON, SC	29401
RHEY, ASHLIE	ACTRESS	PACIFIC, 515 N LA CIENEGA BLVD	LOS ANGELES, CA	90048
RHINE, LARRY	TV WRITER	567 CRESTLINE DR	LOS ANGELES, CA	90049
RHOADES, BARBARA	ACTRESS	12366 RIDGE CIR	LOS ANGELES, CA	90049
RHODEN, RICK	BASEBALL	POST OFFICE BOX 546	CRESCENT CITY, FL	33118
RHODES, ARTHUR	BASEBALL	500 NORTON ST	ROCHESTER, NY	14621
RHODES, BETTY JANE	ACTRESS	BROWN, 10693 CHALON RD	LOS ANGELES, CA	90024
RHODES, CYNTHIA	ACTRESS-DANCER	15250 VENTURA BLVD #900	SHERMAN OAKS, CA	91403
RHODES, DAVID	COMPOSER-CONDUCTOR	4848 COLLETT AVE	ENCINO, CA	91436
RHODES, DONNELLY	ACTOR	9744 WILSHIRE BLVD #308	BEVERLY HILLS, CA	90212
RHODES, DUSTIN	WRESTLER	POST OFFICE BOX 105366	ATLANTA, GA	31348
RHODES, DUSTY	BASEBALL COACH	POST OFFICE BOX 4606	HELENA, MT	59604
RHODES, DUSTY	WRESTLER	POST OFFICE BOX 105366	ATLANTA, GA	31348
RHODES, EMITT	SINGER-SONGWRITER	4636 W 132ND ST	HAWTHORNE, CA	90250
RHODES, ERIK	ACTOR	405 E 54TH ST	NEW YORK, NY	10022
RHODES, HARI	ACTOR	7826 TOPANGA CANYON #317	CANOGA PARK, CA	91309
RHODES, JAMES "DUSTY"	BASEBALL (GIANTS)	8577-A BOCA GLADES BLVD W	BOCA RATON, FL	33434
RHODES, JENNIFER	ACTRESS	2029 CENTURY PARK E #600	LOS ANGELES, CA	90067
RHODES, JOHN J	U S CONGRESSMAN	2345 S ALMA SCHOOL RD	MESA, AZ	85210
RHODES, JULIE	ACTRESS	11684 VENTURA BLVD #476	STUDIO CITY, CA	91604
RHODES, KARL "DUSTY"	BASEBALL	234 FOREST AVE	CINCINNATI, OH	45229
RHODES, LISA	SINGER-GUITARIST	SPINDLETOP RECORDS 1 CAMP ST	CAMBRIDGE, MA	02140
RHODES, MICHAEL	WRITER-PRODUCER	2672 HUTTON DR	BEVERLY HILLS, CA	90210
RHODES, MICHAEL R	DIRECTOR	17564 CASTELLAMMARE DR	PACIFIC PALISADES, CA	90272
RHODES, RAY	FOOTBALL COACH	S F 49ERS, 4949 CENTENNIAL BL	SANTA CLARA, CA	95054
RHODES, RICKY	BASEBALL	5301 NW 12TH AVE	FORT LAUDERDALE, FL	33309
RHODES, STEVE, BAND	ROCK & ROLL GROUP	GOOD, 2500 NW 39TH ST	OKLAHOMA CITY, OK	73112
RHOME, JERRY	FOOTBALL-COACH	POST OFFICE BOX 888	PHOENIX, AZ	85001
RHUE, MADLYN	ACTRESS	148 S MAPLE DR #D	BEVERLY HILLS, CA	90212
RHYAN, RICHARD	GOLFER	PGA SENIORS, 112 T P C BLVD	PONTE VEDRA BEACH, FL	32082
RHYS-DAVIS, JOHN	ACTOR	10100 SANTA MONICA BLVD #1600	LOS ANGELES, CA	90067
RHYS-JONES, GRIFF	ACT-WRI-DIR	TALKBACK, 33 PERCY ST	LONDON W1	ENGLAND
RHYTHM & NOISE	ROCK & ROLL GROUP	109 MINNA ST #391	SAN FRANCISCO, CA	94105
RHYTHM CORPS, THE	ROCK & ROLL GROUP	POST OFFICE BOX 37044	DETROIT, MI	48237
RHYTHM PALS, THE	C & W GROUP	4680 ELK LAKE DR #304	VICTORIA, BC V8Z 5M1	CANADA
RHYTHM PIGS, THE	ROCK & ROLL GROUP	POST OFFICE BOX 988	SAN FRANCISCO, CA	94101
RIBICOFF, ABRAMAM	U S SENATOR	425 PARK AVE	NEW YORK, NY	10022
RIBMAN, RONALD	PLAYWRIGHT	DRAMA GUILD, 234 W 44TH ST	NEW YORK, NY	10036
RICARDO, DON	CONDUCTOR	964 HILLSIDE TERR	PASADENA, CA	91105
RICARDO, KATHERINE	ACTRESS	10 APPLETON RD	BLOOMFIELD, NJ	07003
RICARDO, MICHAEL	ACTOR	10 APPLETON RD	BLOOMFIELD, NJ	07003
RICCI, CHUCK	BASEBALL	POST OFFICE BOX 3169	FREDERICK, MD	21701
RICCI, MIKE	HOCKEY	FLYERS, SPECTRUM, PATTISON PL	PHILADELPHIA, PA	19148
RICCIARDI, J P	BASEBALL SCOUT	ATHLETICS'S, OAKLAND COLISEUM	OAKLAND, CA	94621
RICCIARINI, PAUL	BASEBALL SCOUT	METS, 126TH ST & ROOSEVELT AVE	FLUSHING, NY	11368
RICE, ALLAN LEONARD	TV EXECUTIVE	10201 W PICO BLVD	LOS ANGELES, CA	90064
RICE, ALLEN	FOOTBALL	PACKERS, 1265 LOMBARDI AVE	GREEN BAY, WI	54307
RICE, AMANDA "RAVEN"	DANCER	CRAZY GIRLS, 1433 N LA BREA AVE	LOS ANGELES, CA	90028
RICE, ANNEKA	ACTRESS	RUN RIOT LTD, CROMWELL LODGE 8 THE TERRACE, BARNES	LONDON SW3 ONP	ENGLAND
RICE, BOBBY	SINGER	124 NATHAN FORREST DR	HENDERSONVILLE, TN	37075
RICE, DONNA	ACTRESS-MODEL	1204 INA LN	MC LEAN, VA	22102
RICE, GLEN	BASKETBALL	MIAMI HEAT, THE MIAMI ARENA	MIAMI, FL	33136
RICE, JAMES GOODWIN	ACTOR	280 RIVERSIDE DR #12-E	NEW YORK, NY	10025
RICE, JERRY	FOOTBALL	S F 49ERS, 4949 CENTENNIAL BL	SANTA CLARA, CA	95054
RICE, JIM	BASEBALL	96 CASTLEMERE PL	NORTH ANDOVER, MA	01845
RICE, LANCE	BASEBALL	POST OFFICE BOX 28268	SAN ANTONIO, TX	78228
RICE, NORMAN	ACTOR	24236 WELBY WY	CANOGA PARK, CA	91307
RICE, PAT	BASEBALL	POST OFFICE BOX 3690, STA "B"	CALGARY, ALB T2B 4M4	CANADA
RICE, STORMY	SINGER	POST OFFICE BOX 138	BLACK EARTH, WI	53515
RICE, SYLVESTER	MUSICIAN	4023 W 28TH ST	LOS ANGELES, CA	90018
RICE, TIM	LYRICIST	DAVID LAND, 118 WARDOUR ST NEAR CHICHESTER	SUSSEX	ENGLAND
RICE-TAYLOR, ALLYSON	ACTRESS	CBS-TV, "AS THE WORLD TURNS" 524 W 57TH ST #5330	NEW YORK, NY	10019
RICH, ADAM	ACTOR	21848 VANTAGE	CHATSWORTH, CA	91311
RICH, ALLAN	ACTOR	225 E 57TH ST	NEW YORK, NY	10022
RICH, BARBARA	ACTRESS	429 N OGDEN DR #3	LOS ANGELES, CA	90036
RICH, BOB, JR	BASEBALL EXECUTIVE	POST OFFICE BOX 1420	WICHITA, KS	67201
RICH, BOB, JR	BASEBALL EXECUTIVE	1201 HYDE PARK BLVD	NIAGARA FALLS, NY	14301
RICH, CHRISTOPHER	ACTOR	15760 VENTURA BLVD #1730	ENCINO, CA	91436
RICH, DAVID LOWELL	FILM-TV DIRECTOR	465 LORING AVE	LOS ANGELES, CA	90024
RICH, ELAINE	TV PRODUCER	9300 HAZEN DR	BEVERLY HILLS, CA	90210
RICH, FRANK	DRAMA CRITIC-WRITER	N Y TIMES, 229 W 43RD ST	NEW YORK, NY	10036
RICH, JUDY	TALENT AGENT	2029 CENTURY PARK E #600	LOS ANGELES, CA	90067
RICH, KATIE	ACTRESS	10100 SANTA MONICA BLVD #700	LOS ANGELES, CA	90067
RICH, LEE	TV PRODUCER	703 N BEVERLY DR	BEVERLY HILLS, CA	90212
RICH, MARTIN	CINEMATOGRAPHER	XCC PRODS, 301 W 53RD ST	NEW YORK, NY	10019
RICH, MELINDA	BASEBALL EXECUTIVE	POST OFFICE BOX 450	BUFFALO, NY	14205
RICH, MERT	ACTOR-WRITER	429 N OGDEN DR #3	LOS ANGELES, CA	90026

RICH, MICKEY	TV WRITER-DIRECTOR	DGA, 7920 SUNSET BLVD, 6TH FL	LOS ANGELES, CA	90046
RICH, PETER D L	TV DIRECTOR	21515 MARCHENA ST	WOODLAND HILLS, CA	91364
RICH, RICHARD	FILM WRITER-DIRECTOR	500 S BUENA VISTA ST	BURBANK, CA	91521
RICH, ROBERT E, SR	BASEBALL EXECUTIVE	POST OFFICE BOX 450	BUFFALO, NY	14205
RICH, ROBERT E, JR	BASEBALL EXECUTIVE	POST OFFICE BOX 450	BUFFALO, NY	14205
RICH, THEODORE M	TV EXECUTIVE	LORIMAR, 10202 W WASHINGTON BL	CULVER CITY, CA	90232
RICHARD, CLIFF	SINGER-ACTOR	POST OFFICE BOX 46-C, ESHER	SURREY KT10 9AA	ENGLAND
RICHARD, DICK	PRODUCER	RICHARDS, 4000 WARNER BLVD	BURBANK, CA	91522
RICHARD, EMILY	ACTRESS	MARMONT MANAGEMENT, LTD		
		LANGHAM HOUSE, 308 REGENT ST	LONDON W1R 5AL	ENGLAND
RICHARD, LOUIS	FOOTBALL REFEREE	NFL, 410 PARK AVE	NEW YORK, NY	10022
RICHARD, MAURICE	HOCKEY	10950 PELOQUIN	MONTREAL, PQ H2C 2KB	CANADA
RICHARD, MICHAEL	COMPOSER	841 1/2 N FORMOSA AVE	LOS ANGELES, CA	90046
RICHARD, STANLEY	FOOTBALL	POST OFFICE BOX 609609	SAN DIEGO, CA	92160
RICHARD, WENDY	ACTRESS	WHITE, 2 ORMOND RD, RICHMOND	SURREY TW10 6TH	ENGLAND
RICHARDS, ALUN	NOVELIST-PLAYWRIGHT	LEMON, 24 POTTERY, HOLLAND PK	LONDON W11 4LZ	ENGLAND
RICHARDS, ANN W	GOVERNOR	POST OFFICE BOX 12428	AUSTIN, TX	78711
RICHARDS, BEAH	ACTRESS	1308 S NEW HAMPSHIRE	LOS ANGELES, CA	90019
RICHARDS, CAROL R	WRITER-EDITOR	POST OFFICE BOX 500	WASHINGTON, DC	20044
RICHARDS, CURVIN	FOOTBALL	COWBOYS, 1 COWBOYS PARKWAY	IRVING, TX	75063
RICHARDS, DAVID	FOOTBALL	POST OFFICE BOX 609609	SAN DIEGO, CA	92160
RICHARDS, DAVID T	RECORD EXECUTIVE	POST OFFICE BOX 411	MAYWOOD, CA	90270
RICHARDS, DEKE	COMPOSER	9911 W PICO BLVD #610	LOS ANGELES, CA	90035
RICHARDS, DICK	ACTOR	5712 RIVERTON AVE	NORTH HOLLYWOOD, CA	91601
RICHARDS, DICK	FILM DIRECTOR	DGA, 7920 SUNSET BLVD, 6TH FL	LOS ANGELES, CA	90046
RICHARDS, ELISE	ACTRESS	8484 WILSHIRE BLVD #530	BEVERLY HILLS, CA	90211
RICHARDS, EVAN	ACTOR	10351 SANTA MONICA BLVD #211	LOS ANGELES, CA	90025
RICHARDS, GENE	BASEBALL-COACH	POST OFFICE BOX 1742	PALM SPRINGS, CA	92263
RICHARDS, JOHN	SINGER	POST OFFICE BOX 29543	ATLANTA, GA	30359
RICHARDS, JON F	ACTOR	257 W 99TH ST	NEW YORK, NY	10025
RICHARDS, KEITH	SINGER-SONGWRITER	REDLANDS, WEST WITTERING		
		NEAR CHICHESTER	SUSSEX	ENGLAND
RICHARDS, KEN H	ACTOR	444 E 82ND ST	NEW YORK, NY	10028
RICHARDS, KENNETH N	DIRECTOR	DGA, 110 W 57TH ST	NEW YORK, NY	10019
RICHARDS, KIM	ACTRESS	POST OFFICE BOX 5617	BEVERLY HILLS, CA	90213
RICHARDS, LLOYD	TV DIRECTOR	90 YORK SQ	NEW HAVEN, CT	06511
RICHARDS, LOU	ACTOR	2467 BRIGHTON DR #2-B	VALENCIA, CA	91355
RICHARDS, MARC	TV WRITER	17910 ACRE ST	NORTHRIDGE, CA	91325
RICHARDS, MARTIN	PRODUCER	PRODUCERS CIRCLE COMPANY		
		1350 AVE OF THE AMERICAS	NEW YORK, NY	10019
RICHARDS, MICHAEL	SINGER	ICM, 8899 BEVERLY BLVD	LOS ANGELES, CA	90048
RICHARDS, MICHAEL	TV WRITER	8955 BEVERLY BLVD	WEST HOLLYWOOD, CA	90048
RICHARDS, MIKE	WRESTLER	POST OFFICE BOX 3859	STAMFORD, CT	06905
RICHARDS, R M "DICK"	DIRECTOR	151 S EL CAMINO DR	BEVERLY HILLS, CA	90212
RICHARDS, RON	WRITER-PRODUCER	15151 ENADIA WY	VAN NUYS, CA	91405
RICHARDS, RUSTY	BASEBALL	POST OFFICE BOX 5645	ORLANDO, FL	32855
RICHARDS, SUE	SINGER	2501 12TH AVE S	NASHVILLE, TN	37204
RICHARDS, TED	ACTOR	29051 1/2 PACIFIC COAST HWY	MALIBU, CA	90265
RICHARDS, VIKKI	ACTRESS	RICHARDS, 59 KNIGHTBRIDGE	LONDON SW1X 7RA	ENGLAND
RICHARDSON, AIDA	ACTRESS	157 W 57TH ST #902	NEW YORK, NY	10019
RICHARDSON, BILL	U S CONGRESSMAN	548 AGUA FRIA	SANTE FE, NM	87501
RICHARDSON, CHERYL	ACTRESS	ABC-TV, "GENERAL HOSPITAL"		
		4151 PROSPECT AVE	BURBANK, CA	91523
RICHARDSON, CINDY	SINGER	HEARTLAND, 660 DOUGLAS AVE	ALTAMONTE SPRINGS, FL	32714
RICHARDSON, CLIVE	COMPOSER	398 WIMBLEDON PARK RD	LONDON SW19 6PN	ENGLAND
RICHARDSON, DAVE	BASEBALL	POST OFFICE BOX 4370	SALINAS, CA	93912
RICHARDSON, DON	TV DIRECTOR	14352 MIRANDA ST	VAN NUYS, CA	91401
RICHARDSON, ELLIOT	POLITICIAN	1100 CREST LN	MC LEAN, VA	22101
RICHARDSON, HAROLD	FOOTBALL COACH	BRONCOS, 13655 BRONCOS PKWY	ENGLEWOOD, CO	80112
RICHARDSON, HENRY	FILM EDITOR	178 ALBURY DR, PINNER	MIDDLESEX HA5 3RQ	ENGLAND
RICHARDSON, HUEY	FOOTBALL	STEELERS, 300 STADIUM CIR	PITTSBURGH, PA	15212
RICHARDSON, IAN	ACTOR	131 LAVENDER SWEEP	LONDON SW 11	ENGLAND
RICHARDSON, JEFF	BASEBALL	POST OFFICE BOX 450	BUFFALO, NY	14205
RICHARDSON, JIM	BASEBALL SCOUT	INDIANS, CLEVELAND STADIUM	CLEVELAND, OH	44114
RICHARDSON, JOELY	ACTRESS	HEATH, PARAMOUNT HOUSE		
		162-170 WARDOUR ST	LONDON W1V 3AT	ENGLAND
RICHARDSON, LEE	ACTOR	244 REDDING RD	WESTON, CT	06883
RICHARDSON, LINDA	WRITER-PRODUCER	ELKAR, 11 SANDUSKY RD	NEW YORK, NY	10956
RICHARDSON, LUKE	HOCKEY	MAPLE LEAFS, 60 CARLTON ST	TORONTO, ONT M5B 1L1	CANADA
RICHARDSON, MIRANDA	ACTRESS	GARDNER, 15 KENSINGTON HIGH ST	LONDON W8 5NP	ENGLAND
RICHARDSON, NATASHA	ACTRESS	180 W 59TH ST	NEW YORK, NY	10019
RICHARDSON, PATRICIA	ACTRESS	10100 SANTA MONICA BLVD #1600	LOS ANGELES, CA	90067
RICHARDSON, PETER	DIRECTOR	4510 BLACKFRIAR RD	WOODLAND HILLS, CA	91364
RICHARDSON, POOH	BASKETBALL	TIMBERWOLVES, 600 1ST AVE N	MINNEAPOLIS, MN	55403
RICHARDSON, SUSAN	ACTRESS	1680 N VINE ST #726	HOLLYWOOD, CA	90028
RICHARDSON, TRACY	BASEBALL EXECUTIVE	POST OFFICE BOX 802	WATERTOWN, NY	13601
RICHE, ROBERT	TV-COMEDY WRITER	POST OFFICE BOX 259	RIDGEFIELD, CT	06877
RICHE, WENDY	WRITER-PRODUCER	215 N FOOTHILL RD	BEVERLY HILLS, CA	90210
RICHER, STEPHANE	HOCKEY	CANADIENS, 2313 ST CATHERINE ST	MONTREAL, QUE H3H 1N2	CANADA
RICHERT, PETE	BASEBALL-COACH	POST OFFICE BOX 2437	MODESTO, CA	95351
RICHIE, LIONEL, JR	SINGER-SONGWRITER	5750 WILSHIRE BLVD #590	LOS ANGELES, CA	90036
RICHLAND, DANIEL A	TALENT AGENT	9220 SUNSET BLVD #311	LOS ANGELES, CA	90069
RICHLAND, JOSEPH	TALENT AGENT	9220 SUNSET BLVD #311	LOS ANGELES, CA	90069
RICHLAND, VERNA LYNN	ACTRESS	17 IRONSIDES ST	MARINA DEL REY, CA	90292
RICHMAN, ARTHUR	BASEBALL EXECUTIVE	N Y YANKEES, YANKEE STADIUM	BRONX, NY	10451

RICHMAN, CARYN	ACTRESS	LIGHT, 901 BRINGHAM AVE	LOS ANGELES, CA 90049
RICHMAN, DARYCE	ACTRESS	7715 SUNSET BLVD #214	LOS ANGELES, CA 90046
RICHMAN, DON C	WRITER	8707 SAINT IVES DR	LOS ANGELES, CA 90069
RICHMAN, JOAN	TV EXECUTIVE	CBS-TV, 524 W 57TH ST	NEW YORK, NY 10019
RICHMAN, JONATHAN & THE MODERN	ROCK & ROLL GROUP	EPSTEIN, 644 N DOHENY DR	LOS ANGELES, CA 90069
RICHMAN, PETER MARK	ACTOR	5114 DEL MORENO DR	WOODLAND HILLS, CA 91364
RICHMAN, PHYLLIS C	COLUMNIST	THE WASHINGTON POST	
		WRITERS GROUP	
		1150 15TH ST, NW	WASHINGTON, DC 20071
RICHMAN, ROGER	ACTOR	8574 APPIAN WY	LOS ANGELES, CA 90046
RICHMAN, STELLA	TV PRODUCER	GARDEN FLAT, 5 HILL RD	LONDON NW8 9QE ENGLAND
RICHMOND, ANTHONY B	DIRECTOR	DGA, 7920 SUNSET BLVD, 6TH FL	LOS ANGELES, CA 90046
RICHMOND, BILL	TV WRITER-PRODUCER	11812 MOORPARK ST #A	STUDIO CITY, CA 91604
RICHMOND, BOB	BASEBALL EXECUTIVE	POST OFFICE BOX 12	MIDLAND, TX 79702
RICHMOND, BOBBY	SINGER	OME, 233 W WOODLAND AVE	OTTUMWA, IA 52501
RICHMOND, KIM	COMPOSER	12800 MARTHA ST	NORTH HOLLYWOOD, CA 91607
RICHMOND, MITCH	BASKETBALL	GOLDEN STATE WARRIORS	
		OAKLAND COLISEUM ARENA	
		NIMITZ FWY & HEGENBERGER RD	OAKLAND, CA 94621
RICHMOND, TED	FILM PRODUCER	400 S BEVERLY DR #211	BEVERLY HILLS, CA 90212
RICHMOND, TONY	CINEMATOGRAPHER	GERARD, 2918 ALTA VISTA DR	NEWPORT BEACH, CA 92660
RICHTER, DEBORAH	ACTRESS	LIGHT, 901 BRINGHAM AVE	LOS ANGELES, CA 90049
RICHTER, EILEEN	SINGER	EAI, 2211 INDUSTRIAL BLVD	SARASOTA, FL 33580
RICHTER, RICHARD	TV PRODUCER	ABC NEWS, 7 W 66TH ST	NEW YORK, NY 10023
RICHTER, ROBERT	WRITER-PRODUCER	330 W 42ND ST	NEW YORK, NY 10036
RICHTER, ROMONA	ACTRESS	SEE - TOPPING, LYNNE	
RICHTER, WALTER D	SCREENWRITER	2049 CENTURY PARK E #1320	LOS ANGELES, CA 90067
RICHWINE, MARIA	ACTRESS	10913 FRUITLAND DR #217	STUDIO CITY, CA 91604
RICKARD, THOMAS O	TV DIRECTOR	1826 OVERLOOK LN	SANTA BARBARA, CA 93103
RICKARDS, JOCELYN	COSTUME DESIGNER	6 MEDINA PL	LONDON NW8 ENGLAND
RICKEL, KYLE	ACTOR	1155 PARK AVE	NEW YORK, NY 10128
RICKENBACHER, KARL ANTON	CONDUCTOR	111 W 57TH ST #1203	NEW YORK, NY 10019
RICKER, TROY	BASEBALL	POST OFFICE BOX 48	VISALIA, CA 93279
RICKETTS, TOM	FOOTBALL	STEELERS, 300 STADIUM CIR	PITTSBURGH, PA 15212
RICKEY, CARRIE	FILM CRITIC	NEW WOMAN, 215 LEXINGTON AVE	NEW YORK, NY 10016
RICKEY, CHARLES ED	TV DIRECTOR	518 N KENWOOD ST #206	GLENDALE, CA 91206
RICKLES, DON	COMEDIAN-ACTOR	925 N ALPINE DR	BEVERLY HILLS, CA 90210
RICKMAN, ALAN	ACTOR	9200 SUNSET BLVD #PH-25	LOS ANGELES, CA 90069
RICKMAN, THOMAS	FILM WRITER-DIRECTOR	CAA, 9830 WILSHIRE BLVD	BEVERLY HILLS, CA 90212
RIDDELL, SANDY	BODYBUILDER	9600 N 96TH ST #267	SCOTTSDALE, AZ 85258
RIDDINGTON, KEN	TV PRODUCER	BBC-TV, 56 WOOD LN	LONDON W12 7RJ ENGLAND
RIDDLE, GEORGE	SINGER-GUITARIST	POST OFFICE BOX 8288	NASHVILLE, TN 37207
RIDDLE, SAMUEL	TV PRODUCER	2536 ANGELO DR	LOS ANGELES, CA 90077
RIDDOCH, GREG	BASEBALL MANAGER	POST OFFICE BOX 2000	SAN DIEGO, CA 92112
RIDE, DR SALLY	ASTRONAUT-PHYSICIST	UCSD, ROOM #MS-0221	
		DEPARTMENT OF PHYSICS	
		9500 GILLMAN DR & LA JOLLA DR	LA JOLLA, CA 92093
RIDENOUR, DANA	BASEBALL	1501 W 16TH ST	INDIANAPOLIS, IN 46202
RIDERS IN THE SKY	C & W GROUP	SKEPNER & BUCKSKIN CO	
		7 MUSIC CIRCLE N	NASHVILLE, TN 37203
RIDGE, CLYDE H	COMPOSER	1400 E RENO AVE #45	LAS VEGAS, NV 89119
RIDGE, JOHN DAVID	COSTUME DESIGNER	13949 VENTURA BLVD #309	SHERMAN OAKS, CA 91423
RIDGE, THOMAS	U S CONGRESSMAN	108 FEDERAL OFFICE BUILDING	ERIE, PA 16501
RIDGELEY, ANDREW	SINGER-COMPOSER	8800 SUNSET BLVD #401	LOS ANGELES, CA 90069
RIDGEWAY, FRANK	CARTOONIST	KING FEATURES, 216 E 45TH ST	NEW YORK, NY 10017
RIDGWAY, GENE & BLACK KETTLE CO	C & W GROUP	POST OFFICE BOX 4234	PANORAMA CITY, CA 91412
RIDGWAY, MATTHEW	U S GENERAL	918 WALDHEIM RD	PITTSBURGH, PA 15215
RIDLEY, MIKE	HOCKEY	JETS, 15-1430 MAROONS RD	WINNIPEG, MAN R3G 0L5 CANADA
RIEFENSTAHL, LENI	FILM DIRECTOR	TENGSTRASSE 20	8000 MUNICH 40 GERMANY
RIEGEL, CINDY	ACTRESS	9229 SUNSET BLVD #311	LOS ANGELES, CA 90069
RIEGLE, DONALD W, JR	U S SENATOR	352 S SAGINAW ST	FLINT, MI 48502
RIEKER, RICH	BASEBALL UMPIRE	POST OFFICE BOX 608	GROVE CITY, OH 43123
RIEMAN-BAUZA, LETICIA	TV PRODUCER	153 E 57TH ST	NEW YORK, NY 10022
RIENSTRA, JOHN	FOOTBALL	BROWNS, 80 1ST ST	BEREA, OH 44017
RIERSON, CLAIR	BASEBALL SCOUT	TWINS, 501 CHICAGO AVE S	MINNEAPOLIS, MN 55415
RIESENBERG, DOUG	FOOTBALL	N Y GIANTS, GIANTS STADIUM	EAST RUTHERFORD, NJ 07073
RIFKIN, ARNOLD	TALENT AGENT	10100 SANTA MONICA BLVD #1600	LOS ANGELES, CA 90067
RIFKIN, IVA	ACTRESS	5604 HOLLY OAK DR	LOS ANGELES, CA 90068
RIFKIN, LEO	WRITER	815 S LORRAINE BLVD	LOS ANGELES, CA 90005
RIFKIN, RON	ACTOR	5604 HOLLY OAK DR	LOS ANGELES, CA 90068
RIFKINSON, JAN S	DIRECTOR	DGA, 110 W 57TH ST	NEW YORK, NY 10019
RIGACCI, BRUNO	CONDUCTOR	225 W 34TH ST #1012	NEW YORK, NY 10001
RIGAMONTI, ROBERT A	DIRECTOR	400 W 43RD ST #45-F	NEW YORK, NY 10036
RIGAZZO, RICK	BASEBALL SCOUT	S F GIANTS, CANDLESTICK PARK	SAN FRANICSCO, CA 94124
RIGBY, PAUL	CARTOONIST	531 MAIN ST #621	NEW YORK, NY 10044
RIGBY, TERENCE	ACTOR	CHARLESWORTH, 60 OLD BROMPTON	LONDON SW7 3LQ ENGLAND
RIGBY-MC COY, CATHY	TV PERSONALITY	110 E WILSHIRE #200	FULLERTON, CA 92632
RIGER, ELEANOR	WRITER-PRODUCER	DGA, 110 W 57TH ST	NEW YORK, NY 10019
RIGER, ROBERT	WRITER-PRODUCER	2 CHARLTON ST	NEW YORK, NY 10014
RIGG, DIANA	ACTRESS	LONDON MGT, 235-241 REGENT ST	LONDON W1R 4PH ENGLAND
RIGGINS, MARK	BASEBALL COACH	POST OFFICE BOX 36407	LOUISVILLE, KY 40233
RIGGINS, ROSE	TV DIRECTOR	392 CENTRAL PARK W #15-E	NEW YORK, NY 10025
RIGGLEMAN, JIM	BASEBALL MANAGER	STARS, 850 LAS VEGAS BLVD N	LAS VEGAS, NV 89101
RIGGS, BOBBY	TENNIS	508 EAST AVE	CORONADO, CA 92118
RIGGS, DENNIS	FOOTBALL REFEREE	NFL, 410 PARK AVE	NEW YORK, NY 10022

RIGGS, FRANK	U S CONGRESSMAN	708 4TH ST	EUREKA, CA	95501
RIGGS, JIM	FOOTBALL	BENGALS, 200 RIVERFRONT STADIUM	CINCINNATI, OH	45202
RIGGS, KEVIN	BASEBALL	POST OFFICE BOX 2001	CEDAR RAPIDS, IA	52406
RIGGS, RITA	COSTUME DESIGNER	THE LOFT, 5917 W 3RD ST	LOS ANGELES, CA	90036
RIGGS, TERRY ANN	DIRECTOR	917 N BEVERLY GLEN BLVD	LOS ANGELES, CA	90077
RIGGS-HALL, CARLA	SINGER-SONGWRITER	POST OFFICE BOX 473	RADCLIFFE, KY	40160
RIGHETTI, DAVE	BASEBALL	S F GIANTS, CANDLESTICK PARK	SAN FRANICSCO, CA	94124
RIGHT, ROBIN	SINGER	PENNY, 30 GUINAN ST	WALTHAM, MA	02154
RIGHT TIME	ROCK & ROLL GROUP	29 COMMONWEALTH AVE #705	BOSTON, MA	02116
RIGHTEOUS BROTHERS, THE	VOCAL DUO	10100 SANTA MONICA BLVD #1600	LOS ANGELES, CA	90067
RIGLEY, GARY	BASEBALL EXECUTIVE	POST OFFICE BOX 957	DUNEDIN, FL	34697
RIGNAC, JEAN	ASTROLOGER	175 5TH AVE #2500	NEW YORK, NY	10010
RIGNEY, BILL	BASEBALL-EXECUTIVE	ATHLETICS'S, OAKLAND COLISEUM	OAKLAND, CA	94621
RIGOLI, JOE	BASEBALL SCOUT	250 STADIUM PLAZA	ST LOUIS, MO	63102
RIGSBY, GORDON	TV DIRECTOR	117 S SWEETZER AVE	HOLLYWOOD, CA	90048
RIISNA, ENE	TV DIRECTOR-PRODUCER	14 W 10TH ST	NEW YORK, NY	10011
RIJO, JOSE	BASEBALL	REDS, 100 RIVERFRONT STADIUM	CINCINNATI, OH	45202
RIJO, RAFAEL	BASEBALL	POST OFFICE BOX 6748	ROCKFORD, IL	61125
RIKER-HASLEY, ROBIN	ACTRESS	10351 SANTA MONICA BLVD #211	LOS ANGELES, CA	90025
RIKLIS, MESHULAM	PRODUCER	23720 MALIBU COLONY RD	MALIBU, CA	90265
RIKLIS, PIA ZADORA	ACTRESS-SINGER	SEE - ZADORA, PIA		
RILES, ERNIE	BASEBALL	RURAL ROUTE 1, BOX 38	WHIGHAM, GA	31797
RILEY, BOB	SINGER	PENNY, 30 GUINAN ST	WALTHAM, MA	02154
RILEY, CHRIS	TV DIRECTOR-PRODUCER	TVS, NORTHAM RD	SOUTHAMPTON	ENGLAND
RILEY, DAN	FOOTBALL COACH	POST OFFICE BOX 17247 (DULLES)	WASHINGTON, DC	20041
RILEY, ED	BASEBALL	POST OFFICE BOX 1718	NEW BRITAIN, CT	06050
RILEY, EUGENE	FOOTBALL	LIONS, 1200 FEATHERSTONE RD	PONTIAC, MI	48432
RILEY, JACK	ACTOR-WRITER	1440 QUEENS RD	LOS ANGELES, CA	90069
RILEY, JEANNIE C	SINGER	POST OFFICE BOX 454	BRENTWOOD, TN	37027
RILEY, JEANNINE	ACTRESS	POST OFFICE BOX 11789	MARINA DEL REY, CA	90295
RILEY, JOHN	TV WRITER	9255 SUNSET BLVD #1122	LOS ANGELES, CA	90069
RILEY, LARRY	ACTOR	335 N MAPLE DR #360	BEVERLY HILLS, CA	90210
RILEY, PAT	BASKETBALL	KNICKS, 4 PENNYLVANIA PLAZA	NEW YORK, NY	10019
RILLING, HELMUTH	CONDUCTOR	STUTTGARRER MUSIKFREUND		
		EV D-7000	HASENBERGSTEIGE 3	GERMANY
RIMAN, CARLA	ACTRESS-SINGER	NATHANSON, 2200 WALTON AVE #6-E	BRONX, NY	10453
RIMMER, GERALD	TV DIRECTOR	14131 ARTESIAN ST	DETROIT, MI	48223
RIMMER, SHANE	ACTOR	HOWES, 66 BERKELEY HO, HAY HILL	LONDON W1X 7LH	ENGLAND
RINALDI, JOY	ACTRESS	WEBB, 7500 DEVISTA DR	LOS ANGELES, CA	90046
RINALDO, MATTHEW J	U S CONGRESSMAN	1961 MORRIS AVE	UNION, NJ	07083
RINEHART, ELAINE	ACTRESS	400 W 43RD ST #42-L	NEW YORK, NY	10036
RING, THERESA	ACTRESS	8484 WILSHIRE BLVD #530	BEVERLY HILLS, CA	90211
RINGEL, ELEANOR	FILM CRITIC	POST OFFICE BOX 4689	ATLANTA, GA	30302
RINGHAM, NANCY	ACTRESS	9255 SUNSET BLVD #515	LOS ANGELES, CA	90069
RINGKAMP, MARK	BASEBALL	14100 SIX MILE CYPRESS PKWY	FORT MYERS, FL	33912
RINGO, MARILYN	TV DIRECTOR-PRODUCER	TBS, 1050 TECHWOOD DR, NW	ATLANTA, GA	30318
RINGO, SHARON	ACTRESS	ATKINS, 303 S CRESCENT HEIGHTS	LOS ANGELES, CA	90048
RINGOLD, STEPHEN	JUGGLER	SPOTFIELD, 84 ELM ST	WESTFIELD, NJ	07090
RINGWALD, KIMMER	TV WRITER	900 SUNSET BLVD #611	LOS ANGELES, CA	90069
RINGWALD, MOLLY	ACTRESS	7680 MULHOLLAND DR	LOS ANGELES, CA	90046
RINKER, LARRY	GOLFER	POST OFFICE BOX 109601	PALM BCH GARDENS, FL	33418
RINKER, LAURIE	GOLFER	2750 VOLUSA AVE #B	DAYTON BEACH, FL	32114
RINNA, LISA	ACTRESS-MODEL	9200 SUNSET BLVD #625	LOS ANGELES, CA	90069
RINSLER, DENNIS	WRITER	7320 LENNOX AVE #I-15	VAN NUYS, CA	91405
RINTELS, DAVID W	TV WRITER-PRODUCER	2002 OLD RANCH RD	LOS ANGELES, CA	90049
RINTELS, JONATHAN B, JR	TV WRITER	330 S BARRINGTON AVE #306	LOS ANGELES, CA	90049
RINTOUL, DAVID	ACTOR	MC REDDIE, 91 REGENT ST	LONDON W1R 7TB	ENGLAND
RIO	C & W GROUP	5625 "O" STREET BLDG #7	LINCOLN, NE	68510
RIO	ROCK & ROLL GROUP	41 BRITAIN ST #200	TORONTO, ONT M5A 1R7	CANADA
RIOLO, VALENTE	TV DIRECTOR	1250 N KINGS RD #414	LOS ANGELES, CA	90069
RIPA, KELLY	ACTRESS	ABC-TV, "ALL MY CHILDREN"		
		320 W 66TH ST	NEW YORK, NY	10023
RIPANI, RICHARD JAY	MUSIC ARRANGER	204 THEODORE RD	NASHVILLE, TN	37214
RIPKEN, BILLY	BASEBALL	ORIOLE PARK, 333 W CAMDEN ST	BALTIMORE, MD	21201
RIPKEN, CAL, JR	BASEBALL	ORIOLE PARK, 333 W CAMDEN ST	BALTIMORE, MD	21201
RIPKEN, CAL, SR	BASEBALL-COACH	ORIOLE PARK, 333 W CAMDEN ST	BALTIMORE, MD	21201
RIPPEY, RODNEY ALLEN	ACTOR	5807 TOPANGA CANYON #J-305	WOODLAND HILLS, CA	91367
RIPPLEMEYER, BRAD	BASEBALL	POST OFFICE BOX 507	DURHAM, NC	27702
RIPPLEMEYER, RAY	BASEBALL-COACH	REDS, 100 RIVERFRONT STADIUM	CINCINNATI, OH	45202
RIPPLEY, STEVE	BASEBALL UMPIRE	11505 7TH WY N #2308	SAINT PETERSBURG, FL	33702
RIPPON, ANGELA	TV HOST	IMG, 23 EYOT GARDENS	LONDON W6 9TN	ENGLAND
RIPPS, LEONARD ALLEN	TV WRITER	3380 CAMINO DE LA CUMBRE	SHERMAN OAKS, CA	91423
RIPROCK, DASH & THE DRAGONS	ROCK & ROLL GROUP	NBA, 2605 NORTHRIDGE DR	GARLAND, TX	75043
RIPS, MARTIN	TV WRITER-PRODUCER	12196 LAUREL TERRACE DR	STUDIO CITY, CA	91604
RISKIN, RALPH	TV DIRECTOR	1344 N WETHERLY DR	LOS ANGELES, CA	90069
RISLEY, BILL	BASEBALL	1501 W 16TH ST	INDIANAPOLIS, IN	46202
RISO, ADRIAN A	DIRECTOR	47 BARLOW LN	RYE, NY	10580
RISON, ANDRE	FOOTBALL	FALCONS, SUWANEE RD AT I-85	SUWANEE, GA	30174
RISSIEN, EDWARD L	FILM PRODUCER	760 N LA CIENEGA BLVD	LOS ANGELES, CA	90069
RIST, ROBBIE	ACTOR	POST OFFICE BOX 867	WOODLAND HILLS, CA	91365
RITCHER, JIM	FOOTBALL	BILLS, 1 BILLS DR	ORCHARD PARK, NJ	14127
RITCHIE, CLINT	ACTOR	ABC-TV, "ONE LIFE TO LIVE"		
		56 W 66TH ST	NEW YORK, NY	10023
RITCHIE, DANIEL	TV EXECUTIVE	GROUP W, WESTINGHOUSE		
		COMPANY, 90 PARK AVE	NEW YORK, NY	10016

R&R
ENTERPRISES

We Will Pay You $500
for a Babe Ruth Signature

RITCHIE, GREGG	BASEBALL	5999 E VAN BUREN ST	PHOENIX, AZ	85008
RITCHIE, JEAN	SINGER	BENSON EAST #B-10	JENKINTOWN, PA	19046
RITCHIE, MICHAEL	DIRECTOR-PRODUCER	1801 AVE OF THE STARS #911	LOS ANGELES, CA	90067
RITCHIE, TODD	BASEBALL	POST OFFICE BOX 48	VISALIA, CA	93279
RITCHIE, WALLY	BASEBALL	POST OFFICE BOX 7575	PHILADELPHIA, PA	19101
RITELIS, VIKTORS	TV-FILM DIRECTOR	38 NITON RD, RICHMOND	SURREY TW9 4LH	ENGLAND
RITENOUR, LEE	GUITARIST-COMPOSER	POST OFFICE BOX 6774	MALIBU, CA	90265
RITMANIS, LOLITA	COMPOSER	13033 LANDALE ST	STUDIO CITY, CA	91604
RITTER, DARREN	BASEBALL	POST OFFICE BOX 507	DURHAM, NC	27702
RITTER, DON	U S CONGRESSMAN	2 BETHLEHEM PLAZA #300	BETHLEHEM, PA	18018
RITTER, HOWARD	TV DIRECTOR	4633 VENTURA CANYON AVE	SHERMAN OAKS, CA	91423
RITTER, JAMES	WRITER	1713 EWING ST	LOS ANGELES, CA	90026
RITTER, JOHN	ACTOR	236 TIGERTAIL RD	LOS ANGELES, CA	90049
RITZ, BEVERLY M	COMPOSER	19 COPRA LN	PACIFIC PALISADES, CA	90272
RITZ, JAMES J	SCREENWRITER	8955 BEVERLY BLVD	WEST HOLLYWOOD, CA	90048
RITZ, KEVIN	BASEBALL	TIGERS, TIGER STADIUM	DETROIT, MI	48216
RITZMAN, ALICE	GOLFER	2750 VOLUSA AVE #B	DAYTON BEACH, FL	32114
RIVAS, RAMON J	DIRECTOR	1001 POINSETTIA PL	HOLLYWOOD, CA	90024
RIVE, KENNETH	FILM PRODUCER	26 DANBURY ST	LONDON N1 8JU	ENGLAND
RIVEL, DEBORAH	TV EXECUTIVE	342 MADISON AVE #832	NEW YORK, NY	10173
RIVER STREET BAND	ROCK & ROLL GROUP	41 BRITAIN ST #200	TORONTO, ONT M5A 1R7	CANADA
RIVERA, BEN	BASEBALL	POST OFFICE BOX 4064	ATLANTA, GA	30302
RIVERA, CHITA	SINGER-ACTRESS	OSCARD, 24 W 40TH ST, 17TH FL	NEW YORK, NY	10011
RIVERA, DAVID	BASEBALL	POST OFFICE BOX 48	VISALIA, CA	93279
RIVERA, GERALDO	NEWS JOURNALIST	CBS-TV, 524 W 57TH ST	NEW YORK, NY	10019
RIVERA, JORGE	BASEBALL-SCOUT	SKYDOME, 300 BREMMER BL #3200	TORONTO, ONT M5V 3B3	CANADA
RIVERA, JOSE LUIS	WRESTLER	POST OFFICE BOX 3859	STAMFORD, CT	06905
RIVERA, LINO	BASEBALL	POST OFFICE BOX 5599	LITTLE ROCK, AR	72215
RIVERA, LUIS	BASEBALL	FENWAY PARK, 4 YAWKEY WY	BOSTON, MA	02215
RIVERA, RAFAEL	BASEBALL	POST OFFICE BOX 4370	SALINAS, CA	93912
RIVERA, ROBERTO	BASEBALL	POST OFFICE BOX 3452	KINSTON, NC	28502
RIVERA, RON	FOOTBALL	BEARS, 250 N WASHINGTON RD	LAKE FOREST, IL	60045
RIVERO, JORGE	ACTOR	SALVADOR NOVO 71	COYOACAN 21 DF	MEXICO
RIVERS, GLENN	BASKETBALL	1 CNN CENTER #405, SOUTH TOWER	ATLANTA, GA	30303
RIVERS, JOAN	COMED-DIR-TV HOST	"THE JOAN RIVERS SHOW"		
		524 W 57TH ST	NEW YORK, NY	10019
RIVERS, JOHNNY	SINGER-SONGWRITER	3141 COLDWATER CANYON LN	BEVERLY HILLS, CA	90210
RIVERS, MICKEY	BASEBALL (MAJORS)	350 NW 48TH ST	MIAMI, FL	33127
RIVERS, REGGIE	FOOTBALL	BRONCOS, 13655 BRONCOS PKWY	ENGLEWOOD, CO	80112
RIVERS, SANFORD	FOOTBALL REFEREE	NFL, 410 PARK AVE	NEW YORK, NY	10022
RIVETT-RIVER, JACKIE	WRITER-PRODUCER	LIFE STYLE PRODUCTIONS		
		2500 N LAKEVIEW AVE	CHICAGO, IL	60614
RIVETTI, JAMES J	COMPOSER	15159 HAMLIN ST	VAN NUYS, CA	91401
RIVKIN, ART	BASEBALL EXECUTIVE	POST OFFICE BOX 2000	SAN DIEGO, CA	92112
RIZO, MARCO	COMPOSER-CONDUCTOR	310 LEXINGTON AVE	NEW YORK, NY	10016
RIZZI, RON	BASEBALL SCOUT	BREWERS, 201 S 46TH ST	MILWAUKEE, WI	53214
RIZZO, JEFFREY J	COMPOSER-CONDUCTOR	144 N VALLEY ST	BURBANK, CA	91505
RIZZO, MIKE	BASEBALL SCOUT	333 W 35TH ST	CHICAGO, IL	60616
RIZZO, TONY	SINGER	5625 "O" STREET BLDG #7	LINCOLN, NE	68510
RIZZS, RICK	SPORTSCASTER	POST OFFICE BOX 4100	SEATTLE, WA	98104
RIZZUTO, PHIL	BASEBALL	912 WESTMINISTER AVE	HILLSIDE, NJ	07205
RJ'S LATEST ARRIVAL	ROCK & ROLL GROUP	DOUGLASS, 2600 BOOK BUILDING	DETROIT, MI	48226
ROA, HECTOR	BASEBALL	POST OFFICE BOX 507	DURHAM, NC	27702
ROA, JOSEPH	BASEBALL	525 NW PEACOCK BLVD	PORT SAINT LUCIE, FL	34986
ROACH, DARYL	ACTOR	11300 W OLYMPIC BLVD #870	LOS ANGELES, CA	90064
ROACH, DICK	FOOTBALL COACH	BILLS, 1 BILLS DR	ORCHARD PARK, NJ	14127
ROACH, HAL, SR	PRODUCER	1231 LAGO VISTA DR	BEVERLY HILLS, CA	90210
ROACH, JANET	WRITER-PRODUCER	511 E 80TH ST	NEW YORK, NY	10021
ROACH, MAX	DRUMMER-COMPOSER	415 CENTRAL PARK W	NEW YORK, NY	10025
ROACH, PAT	ACTOR	CHARLESWORTH, 60 OLD BROMPTON	LONDON SW7 3LQ	ENGLAND
ROAD, MIKE	ACTOR	11180 VALLEY SPRING PL	NORTH HOLLYWOOD, CA	91602
ROAD WARRIORS, THE	WRESTLING TAG TEAM	SEE - LEGION OF DOOM		
ROADCAP, STEVE	BASEBALL MANAGER	1524 W NEBRASKA AVE	PEORIA, IL	61604
ROADHOUSE RIDERS, THE	C & W GROUP	LST, 2138 FLAGMARSH RD	MOUNT AIRY, MD	21771
ROADMASTER	ROCK & ROLL GROUP	6325 GUILFORD AVE #4	INDIANAPOLIS, IN	46220
ROAR	ROCK & ROLL GROUP	SEE - R O A R		
ROARING, THE	ROCK & ROLL GROUP	POST OFFICE BOX 4307	HOLLYWOOD, CA	90078
ROARKE, ADAM	ACTOR	4520 AIDA PL	WOODLAND HILLS, CA	91364
ROARKE, JOHN	COMEDIAN	6310 SAN VICENTE BLVD #407	LOS ANGELES, CA	90048
ROARKE, MIKE	BASEBALL-COACH	POST OFFICE BOX 2000	SAN DIEGO, CA	92112
ROAT, RICHARD	ACTOR	329 N WETHERLY DR #101	BEVERLY HILLS, CA	90211
ROB, MEL	BASEBALL COACH	POST OFFICE BOX 7575	PHILADELPHIA, PA	19101
ROB BASE & E-Z ROCK	RAP DUO-RAPWRITERS	SEE - BASE, ROB & E-Z ROCK		
ROBAK, EDWARD	WRITER	1263 N FLORES ST	LOS ANGELES, CA	90069
ROBARDS, GLENN	ACTOR	11249 VICTORY BLVD	NORTH HOLLYWOOD, CA	91606
ROBARDS, JASON	ACTOR	WM MORRIS, 1350 AVE OF AMERICAS	NEW YORK, NY	10019
ROBARDS, JASON, III	ACTOR	8489 W 3RD ST #1105	LOS ANGELES, CA	90048
ROBARDS, SAM	ACTOR	2530 RIVERBEND DR	CRESTED BUTTE, CO	81224
ROBB, CHARLES S	U S SENATOR	1000 E BROAD ST	RICHMONDMC LEAN, VA	23219
ROBB, DAVID	ACTOR	WM MORRIS, 31-32 SOHO SQ	LONDON W1V 5DG	ENGLAND
ROBB, DAVID	COLUMNIST	5700 WILSHIRE BLVD #120	LOS ANGELES, CA	90036
ROBB, LARRY	ACTOR	4137 1/2 WARNER BLVD	BURBANK, CA	91505
ROBB, LYNDA JOHNSON	CELEBRITY	3050 CHAIN BRIDGE RD	MC LEAN, VA	22101
ROBB, SANDY	SINGER	POST OFFICE BOX 29262	INDIANAPOLIS, IN	46229
ROBBIE, DANIEL T	FOOTBALL EXECUTIVE	DOLPHINS, 2269 NW 199TH ST	MIAMI, FL	33056

ROBBIE, JANET	FOOTBALL EXECUTIVE	DOLPHINS, 2269 NW 199TH ST	MIAMI, FL	33056
ROBBIE, SEYMOUR	TV DIRECTOR	9980 LIEBE DR	BEVERLY HILLS, CA	90210
ROBBIE, SUE	TV HOST	ARLINGTON, 1-3 CHARLOTTE ST	LONDON W1P 1HD	ENGLAND
ROBBIE, TIMOTHY	FOOTBALL EXECUTIVE	DOLPHINS, 2269 NW 199TH ST	MIAMI, FL	33056
ROBBIN, IRVING	DIRECTOR	GIBSON HILL RD	CHESTER, NY	10918
ROBBIN, PETER	ACTOR	CAPRI, 8227 FOUNTAIN AVE #2	LOS ANGELES, CA	90046
ROBBINS, BRIAN	ACTOR	7743 WOODROW WILSON DR	LOS ANGELES, CA	90046
ROBBINS, DEANNA	ACTRESS	1830 HILTON DR	BURBANK, CA	91504
ROBBINS, DENNIS	SINGER	PORTER & ROUSSELL MGMT		
		9 MUSIC SQUARE W	NASHVILLE, TN	37203
ROBBINS, DOUG	BASEBALL	500 NORTON ST	ROCHESTER, NY	14621
ROBBINS, HARGUS	PIANIST	1206 HABER DR	BRENTWOOD, TN	37027
ROBBINS, HAROLD	NOVELIST	990 N PATENCIO	PALM SPRINGS, CA	92262
ROBBINS, JEROME	CHOREOGRAPHER	117 E 81ST ST	NEW YORK, NY	10028
ROBBINS, JIM	COLUMNIST	VARIETY, 475 PARK AVE S	NEW YORK, NY	10016
ROBBINS, KATE	SINGER-ACTRESS	GAY, 24 DENMARK ST	LONDON WC2H 8HJ	ENGLAND
ROBBINS, MATTHEW	WRITER-PRODUCER	DGA, 7920 SUNSET BLVD, 6TH FL	LOS ANGELES, CA	90046
ROBBINS, MICHAEL	ACTOR	KAL LTD, 42 PRIORY AVE	LONDON W4 1TY	ENGLAND
ROBBINS, RANDY	FOOTBALL	BRONCOS, 13655 BRONCOS PKWY	ENGLEWOOD, CO	80112
ROBBINS, RICHARD P	SCREENWRITER	3202 LONGRIDGE AVE	SHERMAN OAKS, CA	91423
ROBBINS, ROCKIE	SINGER	WM MORRIS, 1350 AVE OF AMERICAS	NEW YORK, NY	10019
ROBBINS, RONNY	SINGER	407 RAINTREE PL	HERMITAGE, TN	37076
ROBBINS, TIM	ACTOR	25 E 9TH ST	NEW YORK, NY	10003
ROBBINS, TOOTIE	FOOTBALL	POST OFFICE BOX 888	PHOENIX, AZ	85001
ROBELLO, TONY	BASEBALL-SCOUT	REDS, 100 RIVERFRONT STADIUM	CINCINNATI, OH	45202
ROBERSON, BOBBIE	SINGER-GUITARIST	POST OFFICE BOX 98	FOREST HILLS, NY	11375
ROBERSON, KEVIN	BASEBALL	CUBS, 2ND & RIVERSIDE DR	DES MOINES, IA	50309
ROBERTS, AL	FOOTBALL COACH	EAGLES, BROAD ST & PATTISON AVE	PHILADELPHIA, PA	19148
ROBERTS, ALFREDO	FOOTBALL	COWBOYS, 1 COWBOYS PARKWAY	IRVING, TX	75063
ROBERTS, ARTHUR	ACTOR	4139 VIA MARINA #906	MARINA DEL REY, CA	90292
ROBERTS, BARBARA	GOVERNOR	STATE CAPITOL BUILDING	SALEM, OR	97310
ROBERTS, BEVERLY	ACTRESS	30912 ARIANA LN	LAGUNA NIGUEL, CA	92677
ROBERTS, BIP	BASEBALL	3500 REDSTONE DR	OAKLAND, CA	94605
ROBERTS, BRIAN	BASEBALL	POST OFFICE BOX 186	BUTTE, MT	59703
ROBERTS, BRIAN KENDALL	DIRECTOR	DGA, 7920 SUNSET BLVD, 6TH FL	LOS ANGELES, CA	90046
ROBERTS, DANNY	SINGER	45 TUDOR CITY PL #911	NEW YORK, NY	10017
ROBERTS, DICK	BODYBUILDER	POST OFFICE BOX 110	NEWALLA, OK	74857
ROBERTS, DORIS	ACTRESS-DIRECTOR	6225 QUEBEC DR	LOS ANGELES, CA	90068
ROBERTS, DOUG	TREASURER	STATE CAPITOL BUILDING	LANSING, MI	48953
ROBERTS, ELLIOT	TALENT AGENT	LOOKOUT, 506 SANTA MONICA BLVD	SANTA MONICA, CA	90401
ROBERTS, ERIC	ACTOR	UTA, 9560 WILSHIRE BL, 5TH FL	BEVERLY HILLS, CA	90212
ROBERTS, FRANCESCA P	ACTRESS	2037 S SHERBOURNE DR	LOS ANGELES, CA	90034
ROBERTS, FRED	BASKETBALL	BRADLEY CENTER, 1001 N 4TH ST	MILWAUKEE, WI	53203
ROBERTS, GARY	HOCKEY	POST OFFICE BOX 1540, STA "M"	CALGARY, ALTA T2P 3BP	CANADA
ROBERTS, GEORGE E	ACTOR	13575 BORDEN AVE	SYLMAR, CA	91342
ROBERTS, GORDIE	HOCKEY	PENGUINS, CIVIC ARENA, CENTRE AV	PITTSBURGH, PA	15219
ROBERTS, JAKE "THE SNAKE"	WRESTLER	POST OFFICE BOX 105366	ATLANTA, GA	31348
ROBERTS, JIM	BASEBALL EXECUTIVE	POST OFFICE BOX 1110	MYRTLE BEACH, SC	29578
ROBERTS, JOAN	ACTRESS	2029 CENTURY PARK E #600	LOS ANGELES, CA	90067
ROBERTS, JOANNE	TV DIRECTOR-PRODUCER	230 E 79TH ST	NEW YORK, NY	10021
ROBERTS, JOHN	BASEBALL	POST OFFICE BOX 20849	CHARLESTON, SC	29413
ROBERTS, JOHN "SKY PILOT"	FIGHTER PILOT	2801 MEADOW LARK DR	SAN DIEGO, CA	92123
ROBERTS, JONATHAN	SCREENWRITER	8955 BEVERLY BLVD	WEST HOLLYWOOD, CA	90048
ROBERTS, JUDY	SINGER	845 VIA DE LA PAZ #365	PACIFIC PALISADES, CA	90272
ROBERTS, JULIA	ACTRESS	ICM, 8899 BEVERLY BLVD	LOS ANGELES, CA	90048
ROBERTS, KENNY	SINGER	KEARNEY, 16 FARM LN	WASHINGTONVILLE, NY	10992
ROBERTS, LARRY	FOOTBALL	S F 49ERS, 4949 CENTENNIAL BL	SANTA CLARA, CA	95054
ROBERTS, LES	WRITER	5761 OSTIN AVE	WOODLAND HILLS, CA	91367
ROBERTS, LOREN	GOLFER	POST OFFICE BOX 109601	PALM BCH GARDENS, FL	33418
ROBERTS, LOUIE E	SINGER-GUITARIST	POST OFFICE BOX 180	GREENBRIER, TN	37073
ROBERTS, LOUISE	ACTRESS	CBS-TV, "AS THE WORLD TURNS"		
		524 W 57TH ST #5330	NEW YORK, NY	10019
ROBERTS, MARY	BODYBUILDER	POST OFFICE BOX 10493	SANTA ANA, CA	92711
ROBERTS, MEL	BASEBALL MANAGER	POST OFFICE BOX 1721	SPARTANBURG, SC	29304
ROBERTS, MICHAEL D	ACTOR	10825 CAMARILLO ST	NORTH HOLLYWOOD, CA	91602
ROBERTS, MIKE	BASEBALL SCOUT	250 STADIUM PLAZA	ST LOUIS, MO	63102
ROBERTS, ORAL	EVANGELIST	7777 LEWIS ST	TULSA, OK	74130
ROBERTS, PAT	U S CONGRESSMAN	POST OFFICE BOX 550	DODGE CITY, KS	67801
ROBERTS, PAULA	ACTRESS	307 MARINE ST #B	SANTA MONICA, CA	90405
ROBERTS, PENNANT	TV DIRECTOR	67 BURLINGTON RD, ISLEWORTH	MIDDLESEX	ENGLAND
ROBERTS, PERNELL	ACTOR	POST OFFICE BOX 5617	BEVERLY HILLS, CA	90213
ROBERTS, RAY	SINGER	POST OFFICE BOX 25371	CHARLOTTE, NC	28212
ROBERTS, ROBIN	BASEBALL	504 TERRACE HILL DR	TEMPLE TERRACE, FL	33617
ROBERTS, ROY	TV PRODUCER	GRANADA, 36 GOLDEN SQ	LONDON W1	ENGLAND
ROBERTS, RUTH	COMPOSER-MUSIC EXEC	70 WINDING WOOD RD	PORT CHESTER, NY	10572
ROBERTS, STEPHEN	ACTOR	16701 MORRISON ST	ENCINO, CA	91436
ROBERTS, STEPHEN	DIRECTOR	4328 VALLEY MEADOW RD	ENCINO, CA	91436
ROBERTS, STEVE	FILM WRITER-DIRECTOR	MARTIN, 6-A DANBURY ST	LONDON N1 8JU	ENGLAND
ROBERTS, SUSAN	BODYBUILDER	ROBERTS HEALTH CLUB		
		930-B CARPENTER RD	MODESTO, CA	95351
ROBERTS, TANYA	ACTRESS	10090 CIELO DR	BEVERLY HILLS, CA	90210
ROBERTS, TEAL	ACTRESS-MODEL	POST OFFICE BOX 15745	NORTH HOLLYWOOD, CA	91615
ROBERTS, TONY	ACTOR	970 PARK AVE #8-N	NEW YORK, NY	10028
ROBERTS, TRACY	ACTRESS-DIRECTOR	141 S ROBERTSON BLVD	LOS ANGELES, CA	90046
ROBERTS, WILLIAM	FOOTBALL	N Y GIANTS, GIANTS STADIUM	EAST RUTHERFORD, NJ	07073

ROBERTSON, ALLEN B	TV DIRECTOR	59 W 69TH ST	NEW YORK, NY	10023
ROBERTSON, ALVIN	BASKETBALL	BRADLEY CENTER, 1001 N 4TH ST	MILWAUKEE, WI	53203
ROBERTSON, ANDRE	BASEBALL	2229 CROSS LANE ST	ORANGE, TX	77360
ROBERTSON, BAXTER, BAND	ROCK & ROLL GROUP	CAA, 9830 WILSHIRE BLVD	BEVERLY HILLS, CA	90212
ROBERTSON, BOB	BASEBALL COACH	POST OFFICE BOX 1556	ASHEVILLE, NC	28802
ROBERTSON, CLIFF	ACT-WRI-DIR	325 DUNEMERE DR	LA JOLLA, CA	92037
ROBERTSON, CLIFFORD E	CONDUCTOR	6701 YOLANDA DR	RESEDA, CA	91335
ROBERTSON, DALE	ACTOR	13263 VENTURA BLVD #4	STUDIO CITY, CA	91604
ROBERTSON, DENNIS	ACTOR	4704 1015 GAYLEY AVE #300 AVE	LOS ANGELES, CA	90024
ROBERTSON, DON I	COMPOSER	POST OFFICE BOX 4122	THOUSAND OAKS, CA	91359
ROBERTSON, FAYE	BASEBALL EXECUTIVE	POST OFFICE BOX 5646	PRINCETON, WV	24740
ROBERTSON, FRASER	TV PRODUCER	1445 W GEORGIA, 4TH FLOOR	VANCOUVER V69 2T3	CANADA
ROBERTSON, HARRY	FILM PRODUCER	PINEWOOD STUDIOS, IVER HEATH	BUCKINGHAMSHIRE	ENGLAND
ROBERTSON, JASON	BASEBALL	POST OFFICE BOX 2148	WOODBRIDGE, VA	22193
ROBERTSON, JAX	BASEBALL SCOUT	TIGERS, TIGER STADIUM	DETROIT, MI	48216
ROBERTSON, JAY	BASEBALL SCOUT	INDIANS, CLEVELAND STADIUM	CLEVELAND, OH	44114
ROBERTSON, JENNY	ACTRESS	888 7TH AVE #1602	NEW YORK, NY	10019
ROBERTSON, KATHY	SINGER	3125 19TH ST #217	BAKERSFIELD, CA	93301
ROBERTSON, MARCUS	FOOTBALL	OILERS, 6910 FANNIN ST	HOUSTON, TX	77070
ROBERTSON, MIKE	BASEBALL	1090 N EUCLID AVE	SARASOTA, FL	34237
ROBERTSON, NIC	SATELLITE ENGINEER	1050 TECHWOOD DR, NW	ATLANTA, GA	30318
ROBERTSON, PAT	EVANGELIST	CBN NETWORK CENTRE	VIRGINIA BEACH, VA	23463
ROBERTSON, RICH	BASEBALL	POST OFFICE BOX 842	SALEM, VA	24153
ROBERTSON, ROBBIE	SINGER-SONGWRITER	323 14TH ST	SANTA MONICA, CA	90402
ROBERTSON, ROD	BASEBALL	TIGERS, 89 WHARNCLIFFE RD N	LONDON, ONT N6H 2A7	CANADA
ROBERTSON, SHAWN	BASEBALL	POST OFFICE BOX 611	WATERLOO, IA	50704
ROBERTSON, STAN	BASEBALL	POLECATS, 608 N SLAPPEY BLVD	ALBANY, GA	31701
ROBERTSON, STANLEY GERALD	PRODUCER	11398 THURSTON CIR	LOS ANGELES, CA	90049
ROBERTSON, TOM G	TV DIRECTOR-PRODUCER	MULTIMEDIA ENTERTAINMENT 75 ROCKEFELLER PLAZA, 22TH FL	NEW YORK, NY	10019
ROBERTSON, TOMMY	BASEBALL	POST OFFICE BOX 30160	SAN BERNARDINO, CA	92413
ROBEY	ACTRESS	8721 SANTA MONICA BLVD #21	WEST HOLLYWOOD, CA	90069
ROBIDOUX, BILLY JOE	BASEBALL	RURAL ROUTE, BOX 148	WARE, MA	01082
ROBIN, ANDREW	TV WRITER	WM MORRIS, 1350 AVE OF AMERICAS	NEW YORK, NY	10019
ROBIN, CARYN	SINGER	SEE - RAVE		
ROBIN, DIANE	ACTRESS	1330 N CRESCENT HGTS BLVD	LOS ANGELES, CA	90046
ROBINS, BRIAN	FILM DIRECTOR	55 ELM PARK GARDENS, FLAT ONE	LONDON SW10 9PA	ENGLAND
ROBINS, CHRIS & THE COUNTRYMEN	C & W GROUP	POST OFFICE BOX 208	GOODLETTSVILLE, TN	37072
ROBINS, ISOBEL	THEATER PRODUCER	248 E 68TH ST	NEW YORK, NY	10021
ROBINS, JOHN M	TV DIRECTOR	18203 COASTLINE DR #4	MALIBU, CA	90265
ROBINS, LAWRENCE LEE	DIRECTOR	DGA, 7920 SUNSET BLVD, 6TH FL	LOS ANGELES, CA	90046
ROBINS, LISA	ACTRESS	4176 ARCH DR #314	STUDIO CITY, CA	91604
ROBINS, SYLVIA	TV PRODUCER	ALL ABOUT TV, 44 W 56TH ST	NEW YORK, NY	10019
ROBINSON, ALEXIA	ACTRESS	ABC-TV, "GENERAL HOSPITAL" 4151 PROSPECT AVE	BURBANK, CA	91523
ROBINSON, ANDREW	ACTOR	9301 WILSHIRE BLVD #312	BEVERLY HILLS, CA	90210
ROBINSON, ANN	ACTRESS	1800 N VINE ST #120	LOS ANGELES, CA	90028
ROBINSON, ANNE	TV JOURNALIST	IMG, 23 EYOT GARDENS	LONDON W6 9TN	ENGLAND
ROBINSON, BILL	BASEBALL MANAGER	POST OFFICE BOX 3448	SHREVEPORT, LA	71133
ROBINSON, BOB	BASEBALL	POST OFFICE BOX 48	VISALIA, CA	93279
ROBINSON, BROOKS	BASEBALL	1506 SHERBROOK RD	LUTHERVILLE, MD	21093
ROBINSON, BRUCE	FILM WRITER-DIRECTOR	DGA, 7920 SUNSET BLVD, 6TH FL	LOS ANGELES, CA	90046
ROBINSON, BUDD	SCREENWRITER	6815 SHOUP AVE	CANOGA PARK, CA	91309
ROBINSON, CARDEW	ACTOR-COMEDIAN	14 THE GROVE, SAINT MARGARET'S	TWICKENHAM	ENGLAND
ROBINSON, CHARLES	ACTOR	10000 SANTA MONICA BLVD #305	LOS ANGELES, CA	90067
ROBINSON, CHARLES KNOX	ACTOR	BDP, 10637 BURBANK BLVD	NORTH HOLLYWOOD, CA	91601
ROBINSON, CHRIS	ACTOR-DIRECTOR	9300 WILSHIRE BLVD #410	BEVERLY HILLS, CA	90212
ROBINSON, CHRIS	BASEBALL	POST OFFICE BOX 1742	PALM SPRINGS, CA	92263
ROBINSON, CLIFF	BASKETBALL	700 NE MULTNOMAH ST #600	PORTLAND, OR	97232
ROBINSON, CLIFFORD H	COMPOSER	14251 JUDD ST	PACOIMA, CA	91331
ROBINSON, DARRYL	BASEBALL	800 HOME RUN LN	MEMPHIS, TN	38104
ROBINSON, DAVID	BASKETBALL	600 E MARKET ST #102	SAN ANTONIO, TX	78205
ROBINSON, DEWEY	BASEBALL-INSTRUCTOR	1733 W ARTHUR AVE	CHICAGO, IL	60626
ROBINSON, DOLORES	TALENT AGENT	335 N MAPLE DR #250	BEVERLY HILLS, CA	90210
ROBINSON, DON	BASEBALL (MAJORS)	POST OFFICE BOX 2000	ANAHEIM, CA	92803
ROBINSON, DON	BASEBALL (MINORS)	POST OFFICE BOX 4525	MACON, GA	31208
ROBINSON, DWIGHT	BASEBALL	POST OFFICE BOX 7845	COLUMBIA, SC	29202
ROBINSON, EUGENE	FOOTBALL	SEAHAWKS, 11220 NE 53RD ST	KIRKLAND, WA	98033
ROBINSON, FENTON	SINGER	THE ROOSTER BLUES 2615 N WILTON AVE	CHICAGO, IL	60614
ROBINSON, FRANK	BASEBALL-MANAGER	15557 AQUA VERDE DR	LOS ANGELES, CA	90024
ROBINSON, GERALD	FOOTBALL	RAMS, 2327 W LINCOLN BLVD	ANAHEIM, CA	92801
ROBINSON, GREG	FOOTBALL COACH	N Y JETS, 1000 FULTON AVE	HEMPSTEAD, NY	11550
ROBINSON, HOLLY	ACTRESS	7743 WOODROW WILSON DR	LOS ANGELES, CA	90046
ROBINSON, J PETER	COMPOSER	4146 LANKERSHIM BLVD #300	NORTH HOLLYWOOD, CA	91602
ROBINSON, JAMES G	FILM PRODUCER	1875 CENTURY PARK E #200	LOS ANGELES, CA	90067
ROBINSON, JAMIE	PHOTOGRAPHER	222 W 23RD ST #105	NEW YORK, NY	10011
ROBINSON, JAY	ACTOR	13757 MILBANK AVE	SHERMAN OAKS, CA	91403
ROBINSON, JEFF	BASEBALL (MINORS)	CUBS, 2ND & RIVERSIDE DR	DES MOINES, IA	50309
ROBINSON, JEFF	BASEBALL (RANGERS)	POST OFFICE BOX 90111	ARLINGTON, TX	76004
ROBINSON, JERRY	FOOTBALL	RAIDERS, 332 CENTER ST	EL SEGUNDO, CA	90245
ROBINSON, JIMMY	BASEBALL	POST OFFICE DRAWER 1207	ZEBULON, NC	27597
ROBINSON, JIMMY	FOOTBALL COACH	FALCONS, SUWANEE RD AT I-85	SUWANEE, GA	30174
ROBINSON, JOE	BASEBALL SCOUT	TIGERS, TIGER STADIUM	DETROIT, MI	48216
ROBINSON, JOHN	FOOTBALL COACH	RAMS, 2327 W LINCOLN BLVD	ANAHEIM, CA	92801

ROBINSON, LARRY	BASKETBALL	BULLETS, 1 HARRY S TRUMAN DR	LANDOVER, MD	20785
ROBINSON, LARRY	HOCKEY	POST OFFICE BOX 17013	INGLEWOOD, CA	90308
ROBINSON, LEON	ACTOR	8230 SUNSET BLVD #23	LOS ANGELES, CA	90048
ROBINSON, MARY	POLITICIAN	OFFICE OF THE PRESIDENT		
		REPUBLIC OF IRELAND		
		PHOENIX PARK	DUBLIN	IRELAND
ROBINSON, MATTHEW	TV DIRECTOR	29 MOORE PARK RD	LONDON SW6 2HU	ENGLAND
ROBINSON, MAX W	CONDUCTOR	2821 ROSETTE ST	SIMI VALLEY, CA	93065
ROBINSON, NAPOLEON	BASEBALL	POST OFFICE BOX 6667	RICHMOND, VA	23230
ROBINSON, PAUL	BASEBALL SCOUT	POST OFFICE BOX 2000	ANAHEIM, CA	92803
ROBINSON, PHIL ALDEN	FILM WRITER-DIRECTOR	3000 W OLYMPIC BLVD #138	SANTA MONICA, CA	90404
ROBINSON, RICHARD R	SCREENWRITER	FLA IFC, 100 W SOUTH ST	ORLANDO, FL	32801
ROBINSON, RICKY & THE BAYOU BOY	C & W GROUP	PENNY, 30 GUINAN ST	WALTHAM, MA	02154
ROBINSON, ROBERT	TV PERSONALITY	BBC-TV, 56 WOOD LN	LONDON W12 7RJ	ENGLAND
ROBINSON, RON	BASEBALL	2850 W 20TH AVE	DENVER, CO	80211
ROBINSON, RUMEAL	BASKETBALL	1 CNN CENTER #405, SOUTH TOWER	ATLANTA, GA	30303
ROBINSON, SCOTT	BASEBALL	POST OFFICE BOX 4669	CHARLESTON, WV	25304
ROBINSON, SMOKEY	SINGER-SONGWRITER	17085 RANCHO ST	ENCINO, CA	91316
ROBINSON, SPENCER "HERK"	BASEBALL EXECUTIVE	POST OFFICE BOX 419969	KANSAS CITY, MO	64141
ROBINSON, STU	TALENT AGENT	R/W/G, 8428 MELROSE PL #C	LOS ANGELES, CA	90069
ROBINSON, STUART K	ACTOR	2000 N BEACHWOOD DR	LOS ANGELES, CA	90068
ROBINSON, SYLVIA	SINGER-RECORD EXEC	SUGARHILL RECORDS		
		96 WEST ST	ENGLEWOOD, NJ	07631
ROBINSON, TED	SPORTSCASTER	TWINS, 501 CHICAGO AVE S	MINNEAPOLIS, MN	55415
ROBINSON, TERRY JEAN	SINGER-DANCER	22200 CRAGGYVIEW ST	CHATSWORTH, CA	91311
ROBINSON, TONY	ACTOR-WRITER	43-A PRINCESS RD, REGENTS PK	LONDON NW1 8JS	ENGLAND
ROBINSON, VICKI SUE	SINGER	1650 BROADWAY #508	NEW YORK, NY	10019
ROBINSON, WAYNE E	COMPOSER-CONDUCTOR	20147 GRESHAM ST	CANOGA PARK, CA	91306
ROBINSON'S, TOM, SECTOR 27	MUSICAL GROUP	250 W 57TH ST #603	NEW YORK, NY	10107
ROBISKIE, TERRY	FOOTBALL COACH	RAIDERS, 332 CENTER ST	EL SEGUNDO, CA	90245
ROBISON, JOE	BASEBALL SCOUT	N Y YANKEES, YANKEE STADIUM	BRONX, NY	10451
ROBISON, JOHN	FOOTBALL REFEREE	NFL, 410 PARK AVE	NEW YORK, NY	10022
ROBITAILLE, LUC	HOCKEY	POST OFFICE BOX 17013	INGLEWOOD, CA	90308
ROBLEDO, NILSON	BASEBALL	1090 N EUCLID AVE	SARASOTA, FL	34237
ROBMAN, STEVEN	TV DIRECTOR	201 W 85TH ST	NEW YORK, NY	10024
ROBOTHAM, GEORGE	DIRECTOR	9840 WANDA PARK DR	BEVERLY HILLS, CA	90210
ROBSON, TOM	BASEBALL COACH	POST OFFICE BOX 90111	ARLINGTON, TX	76004
ROBUSTELLI, ANDY	FOOTBALL	74 WEDGEMERE RD	STAMFORD, CT	06901
ROBY, LAVELLE	ACTRESS	806 N SYCAMORE AVE #1	LOS ANGELES, CA	90038
ROBY, REGGIE	FOOTBALL	DOLPHINS, 2269 NW 199TH ST	MIAMI, FL	33056
ROCCO, ALEX	ACTOR	1755 OCEAN OAKS RD	CARPINTERIA, CA	93013
ROCCO, JOHN	BASEBALL EXECUTIVE	POST OFFICE BOX 2769	HUNTSVILLE, AL	35804
ROCCO, MARY	ACTRESS	5 RIVERSIDE DR	NEW YORK, NY	10023
ROCHA, VICTORIA	ACTRESS	1710 LAUREL CANYON BLVD #4	LOS ANGELES, CA	90046
ROCHE, CLAUDETTE	ACTRESS	1801 AVE OF THE STARS #1250	LOS ANGELES, CA	90067
ROCHE, EUGENE	ACTOR	451 1/2 KELTON AVE	LOS ANGELES, CA	90024
ROCHEFORT, JEAN	ACTRESS	LE CHENE ROGNEAUX	GROSVRE F078125	FRANCE
ROCHEFORT, NORMAND	HOCKEY	POST OFFICE BOX 90111	ARLINGTON, TX	76004
ROCHELLE, CARL	NEWS CORRESPONDENT	1050 TECHWOOD DR, NW	ATLANTA, GA	30318
ROCHELLE, LEA	ACTRESS	GRAFTON, 9 ORME CT	LONDON W2 4RL	ENGLAND
ROCHELLE, ROLLAN	SINGER	44-15 47TH AVE	WOODSIDE, NY	11377
ROCHES, THE	ROCK & ROLL GROUP	POST OFFICE BOX 1333	MONTCLAIR, NJ	07042
ROCHFORD, MIKE	BASEBALL	9 YANDOW DR	SOUTH BURLINGTON, VT	05401
ROCHON, LELA	ACTRESS	6310 SAN VICENTE BLVD #407	LOS ANGELES, CA	90048
ROCK, FELIPPA	ACTRESS	MICHAEL PATE, 21 BUKDARRA RD	BELLVUE HILL 2023	AUSTRALIA
ROCK, MONTI, III	SINGER-ACTOR	MOSMAN, 395 NE 21ST ST	MIAMI, FL	33137
ROCK, PHILLIP M	DIRECTOR	626 ACORN DR	SAINT LOUIS, MO	63126
ROCK GODDESS	ROCK & ROLL TRIO	JOHN TURNER MANAGEMENT		
		118 WANDSWORTH HIGH ST	LONDON SW18	ENGLAND
ROCKAS, ANGELIQUE	ACTRESS-DIRECTOR	97-F SAINT GEORGE'S SQ	LONDON SW1	ENGLAND
ROCKEFELLER, JOHN D, IV	U S SENATOR	813 QUARRIER ST	CHARLESTON, WV	25301
ROCKEFELLER, KEN	DIRECTOR	104 NORTHAMPTON DR	WHITE PLAINS, NY	10603
ROCKEFELLER, NELSON "HAPPY"	CELEBRITY	812 5TH AVE	NEW YORK, NY	10024
ROCKER, DAVID	FOOTBALL	OILERS, 6910 FANNIN ST	HOUSTON, TX	77070
ROCKETS, THE	ROCK & ROLL GROUP	LAZAR, 3222 BELINDA DR	STERLING HEIGHTS, MI	48077
ROCKEY, DAWN E	TREASURER	STATE CAPITOL BUILDING	LINCOLN, NE	68509
ROCKMASTER SCOTT & DYNAMIC III	RAP GROUP-RAPWRITERS	FAA, 1700 BROADWAY, 5TH FLOOR	NEW YORK, NY	10019
ROCKPILE	ROCK & ROLL GROUP	ICM, 40 W 57TH ST	NEW YORK, NY	10019
ROCKWELL	SINGER-SONGWRITER	GORDY, 801 SARBONNE RD	LOS ANGELES, CA	90077
ROCKWELL, ROBERT	ACTOR	650 TOYOPA DR	PACIFIC PALISADES, CA	90272
RODBY, JOHN L	CONDUCTOR	5351 PENFIELD AVE	WOODLAND HILLS, CA	91364
RODD, MARCIA	ACTRESS	11738 MOORPARK SR #C	STUDIO CITY, CA	91604
RODDAM, FRANC	FILM DIRECTOR	HEATH, PARAMOUNT HOUSE		
		162-170 WARDOUR ST	LONDON W1V 3AT	ENGLAND
RODENHAUSER, MARK	FOOTBALL	POST OFFICE BOX 609609	SAN DIEGO, CA	92160
RODER, RICHARD	BASEBALL UMPIRE	POST OFFICE BOX 25010	LITTLE ROCK, AZ	72221
RODGER, STRUAN	ACTOR	MARTIN, 6-A DANBURY ST	LONDON N1 8JU	ENGLAND
RODGERS, AGGIE GUERARD	COSTUME DESIGNER	4405 24TH ST	SAN FRANCISCO, CA	94114
RODGERS, ANNE	TV EXECUTIVE	125 E 93RD ST #6-C	NEW YORK, NY	10128
RODGERS, ANTON	ACTOR	THE WHITE HOUSE, LOWER BASILDON	BERSHIRE	ENGLAND
RODGERS, BEVERLY D	TV DIRECTOR	KGO-TV, 277 GOLDEN GATE AVE	SAN FRANCISCO, CA	94102
RODGERS, BUCK	BASEBALL-MNAGER	POST OFFICE BOX 2000	ANAHEIM, CA	92803
RODGERS, HARRY H	COMPOSER-CONDUCTOR	11 WILLOWBROOK LN #204	DELRAY BEACH, FL	33446
RODGERS, JIM	BASEBALL EXECUTIVE	POST OFFICE BOX 464	APPLETON, WI	54912
RODGERS, JIMMIE	SINGER-SONGWRITER	14155 MAGNOLIA BLVD #312	SHERMAN OAKS, CA	91423

RODGERS, JONATHAN	TV PRODUCER	CBS-TV, 524 W 57TH ST	NEW YORK, NY	10019
RODGERS, MARY	SCREENWRITER	8955 BEVERLY BLVD	WEST HOLLYWOOD, CA	90048
RODGERS, MIKE	WRESTLING REPORTER	RING AROUND THE NORTHWEST		
		2740 SE LEWELLYN	TROUTDALE, OR	97060
RODGERS, PAMELA	ACTRESS	DON SCHWARTZ, 8749 SUNSET BLVD	LOS ANGELES, CA	90069
RODGERS, PHIL	GOLFER	PGA SENIORS, 112 T P C BLVD	PONTE VEDRA BEACH, FL	32082
RODGERS, WILLARD	WRITER	POST OFFICE BOX 69799	LOS ANGELES, CA	90069
RODIS-JAMERO, NILO	COSTUME DESIGNER	13949 VENTURA BLVD #309	SHERMAN OAKS, CA	91423
RODMAN, DENNIS	BASKETBALL	THE PALACE OF AUBURN HILLS		
		2 CHAMPIONSHIP DR	AUBURN HILLS, MI	48326
RODMAN, ELLEN	TV EXECUTIVE	50 RIVERSIDE DR #3-B	NEW YORK, NY	10024
RODMAN, JOHN	MUSICIAN	1106 HOLLY HILL DR	FRANKLIN, TN	37064
RODMAN, JUDY	SINGER	POST OFFICE BOX 3654	WOFFORD HEIGHTS, CA	93285
RODNEY O & JOE COOLEY	RAP DUO-RAPWRITERS	FAA, 1700 BROADWAY, 5TH FLOOR	NEW YORK, NY	10019
RODRIGUES, STEVE	TV DIRECTOR	10707 CAMARILLO ST #111	NORTH HOLLYWOOD, CA	91602
RODRIGUEZ, AHMED	BASEBALL	POST OFFICE BOX 3004	SPRINGFIELD, IL	62708
RODRIGUEZ, AL	BASEBALL	POST OFFICE BOX 1295	CLINTON, IA	52733
RODRIGUEZ, ANDRES	BASEBALL	POST OFFICE BOX 2148	WOODBRIDGE, VA	22193
RODRIGUEZ, BOI	BASEBALL	POST OFFICE BOX 6667	RICHMOND, VA	23230
RODRIGUEZ, CARLOS	BASEBALL	ALBANY YANKEES, HERITAGE PARK	ALBANY, NY	12211
RODRIGUEZ, CARLOS	BODYBUILDER	703 E BROADWAY	TUCSON, AZ	85745
RODRIGUEZ, CHI CHI	GOLFER	PGA SENIORS, 112 T P C BLVD	PONTE VEDRA BEACH, FL	32082
RODRIGUEZ, EDDIE	BASEBALL-SCOUT	POST OFFICE BOX 2000	ANAHEIM, CA	92803
RODRIGUEZ, EDDY	BASEBALL	POST OFFICE BOX 2785	LAKELAND, FL	33806
RODRIGUEZ, EDWIN	BASEBALL SCOUT	TWINS, 501 CHICAGO AVE S	MINNEAPOLIS, MN	55415
RODRIGUEZ, ERNESTO	BASEBALL	POST OFFICE BOX 957	DUNEDIN, FL	34697
RODRIGUEZ, FRANK	BASEBALL	POST OFFICE BOX 10213	LYNCHBURG, VA	24506
RODRIGUEZ, HENRY	BASEBALL	POST OFFICE BOX 26267	ALBUQUERQUE, NM	87125
RODRIGUEZ, IVAN	BASEBALL	POST OFFICE BOX 90111	ARLINGTON, TX	76004
RODRIGUEZ, JAIME	BASEBALL EXECUTIVE	ORIOLE PARK, 333 W CAMDEN ST	BALTIMORE, MD	21201
RODRIGUEZ, JOHNNY	SINGER-SONGWRITER	POST OFFICE BOX 120725	NASHVILLE, TN	37212
RODRIGUEZ, JOSE LUIS	SINGER	151 S EL CAMINO DR	BEVERLY HILLS, CA	90212
RODRIGUEZ, LUIS	BASEBALL	POST OFFICE BOX 10213	LYNCHBURG, VA	24506
RODRIGUEZ, PAUL	COMEDIAN-ACTOR	2036 HANSCOM DR	SOUTH PASADENA, CA	91030
RODRIGUEZ, PETE	FOOTBALL COACH	POST OFFICE BOX 888	PHOENIX, AZ	85001
RODRIGUEZ, REUBEN	BASEBALL SCOUT	BREWERS, 201 S 46TH ST	MILWAUKEE, WI	53214
RODRIGUEZ, RICH	BASEBALL	POST OFFICE BOX 2000	SAN DIEGO, CA	92112
RODRIGUEZ, ROMAN	BASEBALL	POST OFFICE DRAWER 1218	ZEBULON, NC	27597
RODRIGUEZ, ROSARIO	BASEBALL	POST OFFICE BOX 450	BUFFALO, NY	14205
RODRIGUEZ, SAMMY	BASEBALL UMPIRE	POST OFFICE BOX 716	PLAINVILLE, CT	06062
RODRIGUEZ, VICTOR	BASEBALL	POST OFFICE BOX 1659	PORTLAND, OR	97207
RODRIQUES, CHARLIE	CARTOONIST	TRIBUNE, 64 E CONCORD ST	ORLANDO, FL	32801
RODRIQUEZ, IVAN	BASEBALL	POST OFFICE BOX 90111	ARLINGTON, TX	76004
RODRIQUEZ, ROBERT	ARTIST	1548 18TH ST #106	SANTA MONICA, CA	90404
RODS, THE	ROCK & ROLL GROUP	605 3RD ST #1501	NEW YORK, NY	10016
RODWAY, NORMAN	ACTOR	MARTIN, 6-A DANBURY ST	LONDON N1 8JU	ENGLAND
ROE, HOWARD	FOOTBALL REFEREE	NFL, 410 PARK AVE	NEW YORK, NY	10022
ROE, JOHN "ROCKY"	BASEBALL UMPIRE	2846 TAMWOOD CT	MILFORD, MI	48042
ROE, ROBERT A	U S CONGRESSMAN	POST OFFICE BOX 407	WAYNE, NJ	07470
ROE, TOMMY	SINGER-SONGWRITER	POST OFFICE BOX 26037	MINNEAPOLIS, MN	55426
ROEBUCK, DANIEL	ACTOR	POST OFFICE BOX 10194	GLENDALE, CA	91209
ROEBUCK, ED	BASEBALL-SCOUT	POST OFFICE BOX 7000	PITTSBURGH, PA	15212
ROEBUCK, JOE	BASEBALL	POST OFFICE BOX 3609	PORT CHARLOTTE, FL	33949
ROECA, SAMUEL F	TV WRITER	5461 ENCINO AVE	ENCINO, CA	91316
ROEG, NICOLAS	FILM DIRECTOR	BAKER, 17 GROVE HILL RD	LONDON SE5 8DF	ENGLAND
ROEHM, CAROLYNE	FASHION DESIGNER	834 5TH AVE	NEW YORK, NY	10021
ROEMER, BUDDY	GOVERNOR	POST OFFICE BOX 94004	BATON ROUGE, LA	70804
ROEMER, LARRY	TV DIRECTOR-PRODUCER	EMPIRE STUDIOS, 18 W 45TH ST	NEW YORK, NY	10036
ROEMER, TIM	U S CONGRESSMAN	217 N MAIN ST	SOUTH BEND, IN	46601
ROENICK, JEREMY	HOCKEY	BLACKHAWKS, 1800 W MADISON ST	CHICAGO, IL	60612
ROENICKE, GARY	BASEBALL	10800 MILL SPRINGS DR	NEVADA CITY, NV	95959
ROENICKE, RON	BASEBALL-COACH	829 MANCHESTER CT	CLAREMONT, CA	91711
ROERICK, WILLIAM	ACTOR	CBS-TV, "THE GUIDING LIGHT"		
		222 E 44TH ST	NEW YORK, NY	10017
ROESLER, MIKE	BASEBALL	POST OFFICE BOX 450	BUFFALO, NY	14205
ROESSIER, PAT	BASEBALL COACH	POST OFFICE BOX 360007	BIRMINGHAM, AL	35236
ROESSLER, PAT	BASEBALL COACH	POST OFFICE BOX 360007	BIRMINGHAM, AL	35236
ROETTER, RANDY	BASEBALL TRAINER	POST OFFICE BOX 3690, STA "B"	CALGARY, ALB T2B 4M4	CANADA
ROEVES, MAURICE	ACTOR-WRITER-DIRECTOR	HEATH, PARAMOUNT HOUSE		
		162-170 WARDOUR ST	LONDON W1V 3AT	ENGLAND
ROFFIS, JANE D	WRITER	311 MONTANA AVE #202	SANTA MONICA, CA	90403
ROFFMAN, RICHARD	TV HOST	687 W END AVE #6-A	NEW YORK, NY	10021
ROGAN, JOSH	SCREENWRITER	8955 BEVERLY BLVD	WEST HOLLYWOOD, CA	90048
ROGELL, ALBERT S	FILM DIRECTOR	10120 EMPYREAN WY	LOS ANGELES, CA	90067
ROGER	SINGER	TROUTMAN, 2010 SALEM AVE	DAYTON, OH	45406
ROGER & ROGER	COMEDY DUO	BRB, 666 N ROBERTSON BLVD	LOS ANGELES, CA	90060
ROGERS, ALLEN	TV DIRECTOR-PRODUCER	315 E 72ND ST #15-K	NEW YORK, NY	10021
ROGERS, BRUCE A	COMPOSER	13037 MOORPARK ST	STUDIO CITY, CA	91604
ROGERS, CHARLES "BUDDY"	ACTOR	1147 PICKFAIR WY	BEVERLY HILLS, CA	90210
ROGERS, CHARLIE	BASEBALL	POST OFFICE BOX 8550	STOCKTON, CA	95208
ROGERS, COLIN	TV PRODUCER	DESO FILMS, JACKSONS FARM		
		FAWLEY BOTTOM, HENLEY-ON-THAMES	OXON RG9 6JJ	ENGLAND
ROGERS, D J	SINGER	GOLDEN, 788 MONTECITO ST	LOS ANGELES, CA	90031
ROGERS, DARRELL	BASEBALL COACH	POST OFFICE BOX 4669	CHARLESTON, WV	25304
ROGERS, DAVID	SINGER	ACE, 3407 GREEN RIDGE DR	NASHVILLE, TN	37204

ROGERS, DOUG	DIRECTOR	5514 PACIFIC AVE	MARINA DEL REY, CA	90292
ROGERS, EDMUND H, JR	DIRECTOR	928 CHANTILLY RD	LOS ANGELES, CA	90077
ROGERS, EVAN	SINGER-GUITARIST	16130 VENTURA BLVD #640	ENCINO, CA	91436
ROGERS, FRED	TV HOST	4802 5TH AVE	PITTSBURGH, PA	15213
ROGERS, GAMBLE	SINGER	POST OFFICE BOX 1556	GAINESVILLE, FL	32602
ROGERS, GERALD T	WRITER-PRODUCER	5225 OLD ORCHARD RD	SKOKIE, IL	60077
ROGERS, GINGER	ACTRESS-DANCER	ROGERS ROGUE RIVER RANCH		
		18745 CRATER LAKE HWY	EAGLE POINT, OR	97524
ROGERS, GLENN	FOOTBALL	BUCCANEERS, 1 BUCCANEER PL	TAMPA, FL	33607
ROGERS, HARLAN DALE	COMPOSER	3301 S BEAR RD #51-A	SANTA ANA, CA	92704
ROGERS, HAROLD	U S CONGRESSMAN	203 E MOUNT VERNON ST	SOMEREST, KY	42501
ROGERS, JACK	COMPOSER	POST OFFICE BOX 404	HILLSBORO, OH	45133
ROGERS, JAMIE JUAN	DIRECTOR	6514 LANKERSHIM BLVD	NORTH HOLLYWOOD, CA	91606
ROGERS, JANE	ACTRESS	CBS-TV, "THE BOLD & BEAUTIFUL"		
		7800 BEVERLY BLVD #3371	LOS ANGELES, CA	90036
ROGERS, JANE A	ACTRESS	3500 W OLIVE AVE #1400	BURBANK, CA	91505
ROGERS, JIM	TV WRITER	16633 VENTURA BLVD #1421	ENCINO, CA	91436
ROGERS, JIM R	DIRECTOR	4348 BECK AVE	STUDIO CITY, CA	91604
ROGERS, JIMMY	BASEBALL	633 JESSAMINE ST	KNOXVILLE, TN	37917
ROGERS, JULIE	ACTRESS	1001 N VISTA ST	LOS ANGELES, CA	90046
ROGERS, KASEY	ACTRESS	6255 SUNSET BLVD #627	LOS ANGELES, CA	90028
ROGERS, KENNY	BASEBALL	POST OFFICE BOX 90111	ARLINGTON, TX	76004
ROGERS, KENNY	SINGER-SONGWRITER	BOX 100, ROUTE #1	COLBERT, GA	30628
ROGERS, KEVIN	BASEBALL	POST OFFICE BOX 3448	SHREVEPORT, LA	71133
ROGERS, LAMAR	FOOTBALL	BENGALS, 200 RIVERFRONT STADIUM	CINCINNATI, OH	45202
ROGERS, LYNNE	ACTRESS	411 E 53RD ST #19-A	NEW YORK, NY	10022
ROGERS, MAGGIE	ACTRESS	36 JOHN ALDEN RD	NEW ROCHELLE, NY	10801
ROGERS, MELODY	ACTRESS-TV HOST	2051 NICHOLS CANYON	LOS ANGELES, CA	90046
ROGERS, MICHAEL	SCREENWRITER	8955 BEVERLY BLVD	WEST HOLLYWOOD, CA	90048
ROGERS, MIMI	ACTRESS	15226 1/2 DICKENS ST	SHERMAN OAKS, CA	91403
ROGERS, MR	TV PERSONALITY	4802 5TH AVE	PITTSBURGH, PA	15213
ROGERS, NEIL PATTON	SINGER-GUITARIST	ROUTE #1, BOX 464		
		SHACKLE ISLAND RD	HENDERSONVILLE, TN	37075
ROGERS, PAUL	ACTOR	9 HILLSIDE GARDENS	LONDON N6 5SU	ENGLAND
ROGERS, PAUL	ARTIST	1616 N GARDNER ST	LOS ANGELES, CA	90046
ROGERS, PAULINE B	WRITER	920 N KINGS RD #229	LOS ANGELES, CA	90069
ROGERS, PETER	FILM WRITER-PRODUCER	DRUMMERS YARD, AMERSHAM RD		
		BEACONSFIELD	BUCKS	ENGLAND
ROGERS, REGGIE	FOOTBALL	BILLS, 1 BILLS DR	ORCHARD PARK, NJ	14127
ROGERS, RITA	DIRECTOR	4337 RHODES AVE	STUDIO CITY, CA	91604
ROGERS, RONNIE	SINGER-GUITARIST	ROUTE #6	FRANKLIN, TN	37064
ROGERS, ROY	ACTOR-SINGER	15650 SENECA RD	VICTORVILLE, CA	92392
ROGERS, ROY "DUSTY," JR	SINGER-GUITARIST	POST OFFICE BOX 1507	APPLE VALLEY, CA	92307
ROGERS, STEVE	BASEBALL	2718 S UTICA	TULSA, OK	74114
ROGERS, SUZANNE	ACTRESS	11266 CANTON DR	STUDIO CITY, CA	91604
ROGERS, TED	ACTOR	2121 VALDERAS DR #46	GLENDALE, CA	91208
ROGERS, TIMMIE	COMEDIAN	1911 GARTH AVE	LOS ANGELES, CA	90034
ROGERS, TRACY	FOOTBALL	CHIEFS, 1 ARROWHEAD DR	KANSAS CITY, MO	64129
ROGERS, WAYNE	ACT-WRI-DIR	11828 LA GRANGE AVE	LOS ANGELES, CA	90025
ROGERS, WILL, JR	ACTOR	SANTOS RANCH	TUBAC, AZ	85640
ROGERSON, KATE	GOLFER	2750 VOLUSA AVE #B	DAYTON BEACH, FL	32114
ROGGENBURK, GARY	BASEBALL-COACH	FENWAY PARK, 4 YAWKEY WY	BOSTON, MA	02215
ROGLER, HELEN	ACTRESS	7015 LANEWOOD AVE #A-2	LOS ANGELES, CA	90028
ROGOFF, LYNN	WRITER	WM MORRIS, 1350 AVE OF AMERICAS	NEW YORK, NY	10019
ROGOSIN, JOEL	WRITER-PRODUCER	6034 PENFIELD AVE	WOODLAND HILLS, CA	91367
ROGOSIN, ROY M	TV WRITER-CONDUCTOR	11488 HUSTON ST	NORTH HOLLYWOOD, CA	91601
ROGOWSKI, LEONARD J	COMPOSER	6532 KELVIN AVE	CANOGA PARK, CA	91306
ROGOWSKI, PHYLLIS LEE	WRITER	5700 CANNONSIDE RD	LA CRESCENTA, CA	91214
ROGOZENSKI, KARL	BASEBALL EXECUTIVE	300 STADIUM WY	DAVENPORT, FL	33837
ROGUCKI, BOB	FOOTBALL COACH	POST OFFICE BOX 888	PHOENIX, AZ	85001
ROHAUER, RAYMOND	TV PRODUCER	44 W 62ND ST #16-B	NEW YORK, NY	10023
ROHDE, BARRY C	WRITER	13637 CREWE ST	VAN NUYS, CA	91405
ROHDE, DAVE	BASEBALL	1707 PORT BARMOUTH	NEWPORT BEACH, CA	92660
ROHMER, ERIC	DIRECTOR	26 AVE PIERRE-LER-DE-SERBIE	F-75116 PARIS	FRANCE
ROHMER, PATRICE	ACTRESS	POST OFFICE BOX 49335	LOS ANGELES, CA	90049
ROHN, DAN	BASEBALL MANAGER	14100 SIX MILE CYPRESS PKWY	FORT MYERS, FL	33912
ROHNER, CLAYTON	ACTOR	POST OFFICE BOX 5617	BEVERLY HILLS, CA	90213
ROHRABACHER, DANA	U S CONGRESSWOMAN	4332 CERRITOS AVE #100	LOS ALAMITOS, CA	90720
ROHRMEIER, DAN	BASEBALL	800 HOME RUN LN	MEMPHIS, TN	38104
ROIG, TONY	BASEBALL-SCOUT	POST OFFICE BOX 7575	PHILADELPHIA, PA	19101
ROIZMAN, OWEN	CINEMATOGRAPHER	17533 MAGNOLIA BLVD	ENCINO, CA	91436
ROJAS, COOKIE	BASEBALL-SCOUT	10317 SW 118TH ST	MIAMI, FL	33176
ROJAS, LARRY	BASEBALL SCOUT	POST OFFICE BOX 7575	PHILADELPHIA, PA	19101
ROJAS, MEL	BASEBALL	KM 12 #41 PROL INDEPENDCIA	SANTO DOMINGO	DOM REP
ROJAS, RICKY	BASEBALL	TIGERS, 89 WHARNCLIFFE RD N	LONDON, ONT N6H 2A7	CANADA
ROKER, ROXIE	ACTRESS	4061 CLOVERDALE AVE	LOS ANGELES, CA	90008
ROLAND, FRITZ	DIRECTOR	2419 N RANDOLPH ST	ARLINGTON, VA	22207
ROLAND, GILBERT	ACTOR	518 N ROXBURY DR	BEVERLY HILLS, CA	90210
ROLAND, JOHNNY	FOOTBALL COACH	BEARS, 250 N WASHINGTON RD	LAKE FOREST, IL	60045
ROLAND, KATHLEEN	ACTRESS	320 W 75TH ST	NEW YORK, NY	10023
ROLAND, SANDRA W	SCREENWRITER	8955 BEVERLY BLVD	WEST HOLLYWOOD, CA	90048
ROLEN, STEVE	BASEBALL	POST OFFICE BOX 21727	SAN FRANCISCO, CA	95151
ROLEY, SUTTON	TV WRITER-DIRECTOR	777 ARDEN RD	PASADENA, CA	91106
ROLF, TOM	FILM EDITOR	ACE, 1041 N FORMOSA AVE	WEST HOLLYWOOD, CA	90046
ROLFE, DAVID	FILM DIRECTOR	SCREENPRO LTD, 5 MEARD ST	LONDON W1	ENGLAND

Name	Occupation	Address	City
ROLFE, MICHAEL	TV DIRECTOR	PANTECHNICON FILMS, LTD	
		45 BROOK END DR	
		HENLEY-ON-ARDEN	WARWICKSHIRE B95 5JD ..... ENGLAND
ROLFE, SAM H	TV WRITER	400 N CARMELINA AVE	LOS ANGELES, CA 90049
ROLLE, BUTCH	FOOTBALL	BILLS, 1 BILLS DR	ORCHARD PARK, NJ 14127
ROLLE, ESTHER	ACTRESS	POST OFFICE BOX 8986	LOS ANGELES, CA 90008
ROLLE, GREG	SINGER-KEYBOARDIST	POST OFFICE BOX 5952	SAN FRANCISCO, CA 94101
ROLLING, HENRY	FOOTBALL	POST OFFICE BOX 609609	SAN DIEGO, CA 92160
ROLLING STONES, THE	ROCK & ROLL GROUP	1776 BROADWAY #4419	NEW YORK, NY 10165
ROLLINS, BERNARD	TV WRITER	5443 OVERDALE DR	LOS ANGELES, CA 90043
ROLLINS, BETTY	NEWS CORRESPONDENT	ABC NEWS, 1717 DE SALES ST, NW	WASHINGTON, DC 20036
ROLLINS, BONNIE S	NEWS CORRESPONDENT	NBC NEWS, 4001 NEBRASKA AV, SW	WASHINGTON, DC 20016
ROLLINS, HOWARD E	ACTOR	1501 BROADWAY #1510	NEW YORK, NY 10036
ROLLINS, JACK	FILM-TV PRODUCER	ROLLINS/JOFFE, 130 W 57TH ST	NEW YORK, NY 10019
ROLLINS, SONNY	SAXOPHONIST	KURLAND, 173 BRIGHTON AVE	BOSTON, MA 02134
ROLLINS, SUSAN	TV PRODUCER	255 W 95TH ST	NEW YORK, NY 10025
ROLLINS, TREE	BASKETBALL	THE PALACE OF AUBURN HILLS	
		2 CHAMPIONSHIP DR	AUBURN HILLS, MI 48326
ROLLS, DAVID	BASEBALL	POST OFFICE BOX 3609	PORT CHARLOTTE, FL 33949
ROMA, PAUL	WRESTLER	POST OFFICE BOX 3859	STAMFORD, CT 06905
ROMAGNOLA, RICHARD	DIRECTOR	210 HIGHLAND RD	SOUTH ORANGE, NJ 07079
ROMAN, FREDDIE	COMEDIAN	JONAS, 101 W 57TH ST	NEW YORK, NY 10019
ROMAN, JOSE	BASEBALL	VISTA ALEGRE #10 SANCHES	LUPERON, PUERTO PLATA .... DOM REP
ROMAN, JUNIOR	BASEBALL SCOUT	METS, 126TH ST & ROOSEVELT AVE	FLUSHING, NY 11368
ROMAN, LAWRENCE	SCREENWRITER	4097 SAPPHIRE DR	ENCINO, CA 91436
ROMAN, LULU	ACTRESS	POST OFFICE BOX 140400	NASHVILLE, TN 37214
ROMAN, RUTH	ACTRESS	1220 CLIFF DR	LAGUNA BEACH, CA 92651
ROMAN, VINCE	BASEBALL	POST OFFICE BOX 422229	KISSIMMEE, FL 34742
ROMAN, VINCENT N	TV DIRECTOR	KGO-TV, 277 GOLDEN GATE AVE	SAN FRANCISCO, CA 94102
ROMAN HOLLIDAY	ROCK & ROLL GROUP	POST OFFICE BOX 475	LONDON ..... ENGLAND
ROMANO, ANDY	ACTOR	KOHNER, 9169 SUNSET BLVD	LOS ANGELES, CA 90069
ROMANO, SCOTT	BASEBALL	5301 NW 12TH AVE	FORT LAUDERDALE, FL 33309
ROMANOLI, PAUL	BASEBALL	POST OFFICE BOX 3004	SPRINGFIELD, IL 62708
ROMANOUSKY & PHILLIPS	VOCAL DUO	2269 MARKET ST #301	SAN FRANCISCO, CA 94114
ROMANOWSKI, BILL	FOOTBALL	S F 49ERS, 4949 CENTENNIAL BL	SANTA CLARA, CA 95054
ROMANTICS, THE	VOCAL GROUP	POST OFFICE BOX 133-LV	LATHROP VILLAGE, MI 48076
ROMANUS, RICHARD	ACTOR	1840 CAMINO PALMERO ST	LOS ANGELES, CA 90046
ROMANUS, ROBERT	ACTOR	1840 CAMINO PALMERO ST	LOS ANGELES, CA 90046
ROMAY, LINA	ACTRESS	1303 LYNDON ST #6	SOUTH PASADENA, CA 91030
ROMBERG, CAROLYN	ACTRESS	76 DUANE ST	NEW YORK, NY 10007
ROME, SYDNE	ACTRESS	VIA DI PORTA, PINCIANA 14	I-00100 ROME ..... ITALY
ROMEO, INA	ACTRESS	6605 HOLLYWOOD BLVD #220	HOLLYWOOD, CA 90028
ROMEO VOID	ROCK & ROLL GROUP	ICM, 40 W 57TH ST	NEW YORK, NY 10019
ROMER, ROY	GOVERNOR	STATE CAPITOL BUILDING	DENVER, CO 80203
ROMERO, BRIAN	BASEBALL	POST OFFICE BOX 4448	TULSA, OK 74159
ROMERO, CESAR	ACTOR	12115 SAN VICENTE BLVD #302	LOS ANGELES, CA 90049
ROMERO, GEORGE A	DIRECTOR-PRODUCER	3364 LAKE RD N	SANIBEL, FL 33957
ROMERO, KATE	ACTRESS	2029 CENTURY PARK E #600	LOS ANGELES, CA 90067
ROMERO, KAYLAN	ACTOR	3500 W OLIVE AVE #1400	BURBANK, CA 91505
ROMERO, MANDY	BASEBALL	POST OFFICE DRAWER 1218	ZEBULON, NC 27597
ROMERO, NED	ACTOR	19438 LASSEN ST	NORTHRIDGE, CA 91324
ROMINE, KEVIN	BASEBALL	FENWAY PARK, 4 YAWKEY WY	BOSTON, MA 02215
ROMMEL, MANFRED	MAYOR	POST OFFICE BOX 106034	D-W 7000 STUTTGART 10 .... GERMANY
ROMNEY, GEORGE	GOVERNOR	1840 E VALLEY RD	BLOOMFIELD HILLS, MI 48013
ROMSEY, LORD	FILM PRODUCER	BROADLANDS	ROMSEY SO5 9ZD ..... ENGLAND
RONAN, KERNAN	BASEBALL COACH	POST OFFICE BOX 12	MIDLAND, TX 79702
RONAN, MARC	BASEBALL	POST OFFICE BOX 3004	SPRINGFIELD, IL 62708
RONDEAU, CHARLES	FILM DIRECTOR	4251 FULTON AVE	SHERMAN OAKS, CA 91423
RONDELL, RIC	DIRECTOR	4062 WITZEL DR	SHERMAN OAKS, CA 91423
RONDELL, RONALD A	DIRECTOR	DGA, 7920 SUNSET BLVD, 6TH FL	LOS ANGELES, CA 90046
RONDON, ALBERTO	BASEBALL SCOUT	333 W 35TH ST	CHICAGO, IL 60616
RONKA, ILMARI	COMPOSER-CONDUCTOR	6217 ELMER AVE	NORTH HOLLYWOOD, CA 91606
RONNING, CLIFF	HOCKEY	CANUCKS, 100 N RENFREW ST	VANCOUVER, BC V5K 3N7 ..... CANADA
RONNY & THE DAYTONAS	VOCAL GROUP	ROBERT J MC KENZIE MGMT	
		114 PRINCE GEORGE DR	HAMPTON, VA 23669
RONSTADT, LINDA	SINGER	ASHER, 644 N DOHENY DR	LOS ANGELES, CA 90069
ROOD, NELSON	BASEBALL COACH	POST OFFICE BOX 1295	CLINTON, IA 52733
ROOD, RICHARD	WRESTLER	SEE - RUDE, RAVISHING RICK	
ROOD, RICHARD W	INSTRUMENTALIST	308 W 104TH ST #3-A	NEW YORK, NY 10025
ROOF, GENE	BASEBALL-COACH	TIGERS, TIGER STADIUM	DETROIT, MI 48216
ROOF, PHIL	BASEBALL-MANAGER	POST OFFICE BOX 5645	ORLANDO, FL 32855
ROOK, THOMAS	DIRECTOR	302 S MANSFIELD AVE	LOS ANGELES, CA 90036
ROOKE, RON	BASEBALL EXECUTIVE	POST OFFICE BOX 3690, STA "B"	CALGARY, ALB T2B 4M4 ..... CANADA
ROOKER, JIM	BASEBALL-ANNOUNCER	POST OFFICE BOX 7000	PITTSBURGH, PA 15212
ROOM OF FOOLS	ROCK & ROLL GROUP	41 BRITAIN ST #200	TORONTO, ONT M5A 1R7 ..... CANADA
ROOMEY, DANIEL M	FOOTBALL EXECUTIVE	STEELERS, 300 STADIUM CIR	PITTSBURGH, PA 15212
ROONEY, ANDY	ACTOR-WRITER-DIRECTOR	254 ROWAYTON AVE	ROWAYTON, CT 06853
ROONEY, ARTHUR J, JR	FOOTBALL EXECUTIVE	STEELERS, 300 STADIUM CIR	PITTSBURGH, PA 15212
ROONEY, JAN CHAMBERLIN	ACTRESS	7500 DEVISTA DR	LOS ANGELES, CA 90046
ROONEY, JOHN	SPORTSCASTER	333 W 35TH ST	CHICAGO, IL 60616
ROONEY, MICKEY	ACTOR	4165 THOUSAND OAKS BLVD #300	WESTLAKE VILLAGE, CA 91362
ROONEY, SHERRY	ACTRESS	8730 SUNSET BLVD #220-W	LOS ANGELES, CA 90069
ROOS, DONALD P	TV WRITER	3815 W OLIVE AVE #202	BURBANK, CA 91505
ROOS, FREDERICK	FILM PRODUCER	10020 WESTWANDA DR	BEVERLY HILLS, CA 90210
ROOSEVELT, PHIL	COLUMNIST	POST OFFICE BOX 500	WASHINGTON, DC 20044

ROOT, BARRY	ARTIST	300 FORT WASHINGTON AVE #21	NEW YORK, NY	10032
ROOT, WELLS	WRITER	701 HAMPDEN PL	PACIFIC PALISADES, CA	90272
ROOY, ROBERT	FILM DIRECTOR	819 SUPERBA AVE	VENICE, CA	90291
ROPER, BOB	RECORD EXECUTIVE	WEA MUSIC, 1810 BIRCHMONT RD	SCARBOROUGH, ONT M1P 2	CANADA
ROPER, CAROL	TV WRITER	2370 GLENDON AVE	LOS ANGELES, CA	90064
ROPER, JAY M	DIRECTOR	18340 KINZIE ST	NORTHRIDGE, CA	91325
ROPER, JOE	SINGER	214 OLD HICKORY BLVD #194	NASHVILLE, TN	37221
ROPER, JOHN	BASEBALL	POST OFFICE BOX 11002	CHATTANOOGA, TN	37401
ROPER, JOHN	FOOTBALL	BEARS, 250 N WASHINGTON RD	LAKE FOREST, IL	60045
ROPIAK, DEREK	RECORD EXECUTIVE	APEXTON, 44-27 PURVES ST	LONG ISLAND CITY, NY	11101
ROREM, NED	COMPOSER	BOOSEY & HAWKES, 30 W 57TH ST	NEW YORK, NY	10019
ROS-LEHTINEN, ILEANA	U S CONGRESSWOMAN	5757 BLUE LAGOON DR #240	MIAMI, FL	33126
ROSA, LUIS	BASEBALL SCOUT	1060 W ADDISON ST	CHICAGO, IL	60613
ROSADO, ED	BASEBALL	POST OFFICE BOX 15050	READING, PA	19612
ROSANO, VICTOR	BASEBALL	POST OFFICE BOX 6667	RICHMOND, VA	23230
ROSARIO, DAVE	BASEBALL	1155 W MOUND ST	COLUMBUS, OH	43223
ROSARIO, GABRIEL	BASEBALL	POST OFFICE BOX 1110	MYRTLE BEACH, SC	29578
ROSARIO, VICTOR	BASEBALL	AVE CIRCUM VALACION #36	SAN PEDRO DE MACORIS	DOM REP
ROSBURG, ROBERT	DIRECTOR	DGA, 110 W 57TH ST	NEW YORK, NY	10019
ROSCIUS, AFRICANUS	ACTOR	12021 WILSHIRE BLVD #230	LOS ANGELES, CA	90025
ROSCOE, GREG	BASEBALL	4385 TUTT BLVD	COLORADO SPRINGS, CO	80922
ROSE, ADELE	TV WRITER	FOSTER, 3 LONSDALE RD	LONDON SW13 9ED	ENGLAND
ROSE, ALEXANDRIA	FILM PRODUCER	6507 W 5TH ST	LOS ANGELES, CA	90048
ROSE, AXL	SINGER-SONGWRITER	2738 HOLLYRIDGE	LOS ANGELES, CA	90046
ROSE, BOB	BASEBALL	POST OFFICE BOX 2000	ANAHEIM, CA	92803
ROSE, CHARLIE	U S CONGRESSMAN	218 FEDERAL BUILDING	FAYETTEVILLE, NC	28301
ROSE, CLIFF	DIRECTOR	1423 S ROSEWOOD ST	SANTA ANA, CA	92707
ROSE, CLIFFORD	ACTOR	ICM, 388-396 OXFORD ST	LONDON W1	ENGLAND
ROSE, EARL	ARRANGER-COMPOSER	ARMADEUS MUSIC COMPANY		
		950 3RD AVE, 7TH FLOOR	NEW YORK, NY	10022
ROSE, HEATH	BASEBALL	POST OFFICE BOX 824	BURLINGTON, IA	52601
ROSE, JACK	SCREENWRITER	8955 BEVERLY BLVD	WEST HOLLYWOOD, CA	90048
ROSE, JAMIE	ACTRESS	13268 MULHOLLAND DR	BEVERLY HILLS, CA	90210
ROSE, JEFFREY	TALENT AGENT	MTA, 9320 WILSHIRE BL, 3RD FL	BEVERLY HILLS, CA	90212
ROSE, JIM	DIRECTOR	435 N OAKHURST DR	BEVERLY HILLS, CA	90210
ROSE, KEN	FOOTBALL	EAGLES, BROAD ST & PATTISON AVE	PHILADELPHIA, PA	19148
ROSE, LES	FILM DIRECTOR	17 MAPLE AVE	TORONTO, ONT	CANADA
ROSE, MARGOT	ACTRESS	606 N LARCHMONT BLVD #309	LOS ANGELES, CA	90004
ROSE, MARK	BASEBALL COACH	POST OFFICE BOX 22093	GREENSBORO, NC	27420
ROSE, MARY	COSTUME DESIGNER	13949 VENTURA BLVD #309	SHERMAN OAKS, CA	91423
ROSE, MICHAEL PAUL	COMPOSER-CONDUCTOR	1226 1/4 N OGDEN DR	LOS ANGELES, CA	90046
ROSE, PAULA	FILM CRITIC	VARIETY, 154 W 46TH ST	NEW YORK, NY	10036
ROSE, PETE, SR	BASEBALL (MAJORS)	10415 STONEBRIDGE BLVD	BOCA RATON, FL	33498
ROSE, PHILIP	THEATER PRODUCER	157 W 57TH ST	NEW YORK, NY	10019
ROSE, PLAYBOY BUDDY	WRESTLER	8725 N CHAUTAUQUA BLVD	PORTLAND, OR	97217
ROSE, RALPH	CONDUCTOR	1105 W OLIVE AVE #14	SUNNYVALE, CA	94086
ROSE, REGINALD	SCREENWRITER	20 WEDGEWOOD RD	WESTPORT, CT	06880
ROSE, ROBIN PEARSON	ACTRESS	6910 WOODROW WILSON DR	LOS ANGELES, CA	90068
ROSE, SCOTT	BASEBALL	POST OFFICE BOX 2437	MODESTO, CA	95351
ROSE, SIMON	TV WRITER	12350 VIEWCREST RD	NORTH HOLLYWOOD, CA	91604
ROSE, WILLIAM, SR	BASEBALL EXECUTIVE	N Y YANKEES, YANKEE STADIUM	BRONX, NY	10451
ROSE BROTHERS, THE	SOUL GROUP	SHIRLEY A MORGAN MGMT		
		127 S KENTER AVE	LOS ANGELES, CA	90049
ROSE MARIE	ACTRESS	6918 CHISOLM AVE	VAN NUYS, CA	91406
ROSE PRICE, TIM	TV WRITER	LONDON MGT, 235-241 REGENT ST	LONDON W1R 4PH	ENGLAND
ROSE ROYCE	VOCAL GROUP	7751 ALABAMA AVE #13	CANOGA PARK, CA	91304
ROSE-MARIE	SINGER	PROCESS, 439 WILEY AVE	FRANKLIN, PA	16323
ROSEBORO, JOHN	BASEBALL-INSTRUCTOR	1703 VIRGINIA RD	LOS ANGELES, CA	90019
ROSEBROOK, JEB J	SCREENWRITER	12301 COLLINS ST	NORTH HOLLYWOOD, CA	91607
ROSEFELD, MIKE	TV PRODUCER	CAA, 9830 WILSHIRE BLVD	BEVERLY HILLS, CA	90212
ROSELIN, PHILIP	TV DIRECTOR-PRODUCER	CLINE, DAVIS, MANN		
		767 3RD AVE, 28TH FLOOR	NEW YORK, NY	10017
ROSEMAN, DONNA	TV PRODUCER	IMERO FIORENTINO ASSOCIATES		
		44 W 63RD ST	NEW YORK, NY	10023
ROSEMAN, RALPH	THEATER PRODUCER	THEATRE NOW, 1515 BROADWAY	NEW YORK, NY	10036
ROSEMOND, PERRY	DIRECTOR	11928 KIOWA AVE #103	LOS ANGELES, CA	90049
ROSEMONT, DAVID	FILM PRDOUCER	PINEWOOD STUDIOS, IVER HEATH	IVER, BUCKS SLO ONH	ENGLAND
ROSEMONT, NORMAN	TV-FILM PRODUCER	ROSEMONT PRODUCTIONS, INC		
		PINEWOOD STUDIOS, IVER HEATH	IVER, BUCKS SLO ONH	ENGLAND
ROSEN, AL	BASEBALL-EXECUTIVE	611 WASHINGTON ST	SAN FRANCISCO, CA	94111
ROSEN, ALAN	TV WRITER-DIRECTOR	14964 GREENLEAF ST	SHERMAN OAKS, CA	91403
ROSEN, BARRY M	SCREENWRITER	8955 BEVERLY BLVD	WEST HOLLYWOOD, CA	90048
ROSEN, ERWIN	TV DIRECTOR	3675 DIXIE CANYON AVE	SHERMAN OAKS, CA	91423
ROSEN, ILENE	NEWS WRITER	WABC-TV, 7 LINCOLN SQ	NEW YORK, NY	10023
ROSEN, J & THE K-PROS	ROCK & ROLL GROUP	LCS, 1627 16TH AVE S	NASHVILLE, TN	37212
ROSEN, JACK	TV DIRECTOR	56 EBERLING DR	NEW YORK, NY	10956
ROSEN, LAWRENCE R	TV WRITER-PRODUCER	17025 COTTER PL	ENCINO, CA	91436
ROSEN, MILTON S	COMPOSER	12030 IREDELL ST	STUDIO CITY, CA	91604
ROSEN, NORMAN I	COMPOSER	8501 S SEPULVEDA BLVD #305-A	LOS ANGELES, CA	90045
ROSEN, PETER	DIRECTOR	9 E 78TH ST #5-A	NEW YORK, NY	10021
ROSEN, ROBERT L	DIRECTOR-PRODUCER	12424 WILSHIRE BLVD #1000	LOS ANGELES, CA	90025
ROSEN, STEVEN M	DIRECTOR	DGA, 110 W 57TH ST	NEW YORK, NY	10019
ROSEN, STUART	TV PRODUCER	7631 LEXINGTON AVE	LOS ANGELES, CA	90046
ROSEN, SY	TV WRITER	1650 WESTWOOD BLVD #201	LOS ANGELES, CA	90024
ROSENBALM, MARC	BASEBALL	POST OFFICE BOX 30160	SAN BERNARDINO, CA	92413

ROSENBAUM, DAVID	WRESTLING WRITER	POST OFFICE BOX 48	ROCKVILLE CENTRE, NY	11571
ROSENBAUM, HENRY	SCREENWRITER	8955 BEVERLY BLVD	WEST HOLLYWOOD, CA	90048
ROSENBAUM, JOEL H	COMPOSER	6049 VAN NOORD AVE	VAN NUYS, CA	91401
ROSENBAUM, RUSSELL ROBERT	DIRECTOR	11169 OPHIR DR	LOS ANGELES, CA	90024
ROSENBERG, ANDREW L	TV DIRECTOR	30 BIG OAK CIR	STAMFORD, CT	06903
ROSENBERG, BENJY	TV DIRECTOR	7172 HAWTHORN AVE #310	HOLLYWOOD, CA	90046
ROSENBERG, FRANK	FILM WRITER-PRODUCER	154 S SALTAIR AVE	LOS ANGELES, CA	90049
ROSENBERG, GRANT	TV EXECUTIVE	5451 MARATHON ST	HOLLYWOOD, CA	90038
ROSENBERG, HOWARD	TV CRITIC-WRITER	5859 LARBOARD LN	AGOURA HILLS, CA	91301
ROSENBERG, JEANNE	SCREENWRITER	119 MUERDAGO RD	TOPANGA CANYON, CA	90290
ROSENBERG, LEE	TALENT AGENT	10100 SANTA MONICA BLVD #1600	LOS ANGELES, CA	90067
ROSENBERG, LISA	SCREENWRITER	CARLSON, 249 DIMMICK AVE	VENICE, CA	90291
ROSENBERG, META	WRI-DIR-PROD	1126 SAN YSIDRO DR	BEVERLY HILLS, CA	90210
ROSENBERG, RICHARD	TALENT AGENT	10100 SANTA MONICA BLVD #1600	LOS ANGELES, CA	90067
ROSENBERG, STEVE	BASEBALL	STARS, 850 LAS VEGAS BLVD N	LAS VEGAS, NV	89101
ROSENBERG, STUART	WRITER-PRODUCER	1984 COLDWATER CANYON DR	BEVERLY HILLS, CA	90210
ROSENBERGER, JAMES	TV DIRECTOR	7907 CROYDON AVE	LOS ANGELES, CA	90045
ROSENBLATT, DENNIS	DIRECTOR	DGA, 7920 SUNSET BLVD, 6TH FL	LOS ANGELES, CA	90046
ROSENBLOOM, DAVID L	DIRECTOR	3237 BENDA ST	LOS ANGELES, CA	90068
ROSENBLOOM, RICHARD M	TV EXECUTIVE	1875 CENTURY PARK E #300	LOS ANGELES, CA	90067
ROSENBLUM, ARTHUR	DIRECTOR	DGA, 7920 SUNSET BLVD, 6TH FL	LOS ANGELES, CA	90046
ROSENBLUM, NINA	TV DIRECTOR-PRODUCER	DAEDALUS PRODS, 15 W 70TH ST	NEW YORK, NY	10023
ROSENBLUM, RALPH B	TV DIRECTOR	344 W 84TH ST	NEW YORK, NY	10024
ROSENFELD, JEROME E	DIRECTOR	1349 LEXINGTON AVE	NEW YORK, NY	10028
ROSENFELT, FRANK	FILM EXECUTIVE	MGM, 10202 W WASHINGTON BLVD	CULVER CITY, CA	90239
ROSENFIELD, DAVE	BASEBALL EXECUTIVE	POST OFFICE BOX 1211	NORFOLK, VA	23502
ROSENMAN, HOWARD	FILM-TV PRODUCER	PARAMOUNT PICTURES CORP		
		5555 MELROSE AVE	LOS ANGELES, CA	90038
ROSENMAN, LEONARD	COMPOSER-ARRANGER	23704 LONG VALLEY RD	HIDDEN HILLS, CA	91302
ROSENSCHEIN, WARNER	DIRECTOR	DGA, 110 W 57TH ST	NEW YORK, NY	10019
ROSENSTEIN, DONNA	CASTING DIRECTOR	PARAMOUNT PICTURES CORP		
		DIRECTOR'S BUILDING #401		
		5555 MELROSE AVE	LOS ANGELES, CA	90038
ROSENSTEIN, GERTRUDE	DIRECTOR	650 PARK AVE	NEW YORK, NY	10021
ROSENSTOCK, RICH	PRODUCER	MTM, 4024 RADFORD AVE	STUDIO CITY, CA	91604
ROSENTHAL, A M "ABE"	COLUMNIST	N Y TIMES, 229 W 43RD ST	NEW YORK, NY	10036
ROSENTHAL, ALAN	DIRECTOR	DGA, 110 W 57TH ST	NEW YORK, NY	10019
ROSENTHAL, ARNIE	TV PRODUCER	TELEFRANCE USA, LTD		
		1966 BROADWAY	NEW YORK, NY	10023
ROSENTHAL, ARNOLD H	DIRECTOR	DGA, 110 W 57TH ST	NEW YORK, NY	10019
ROSENTHAL, EDWARD	BASEBALL EXECUTIVE	N Y YANKEES, YANKEE STADIUM	BRONX, NY	10451
ROSENTHAL, GAY	TV PRODUCER	NBC NEWS, 30 ROCKEFELLER PLAZA	NEW YORK, NY	10020
ROSENTHAL, JACK	TV WRITER	RAMSAY, 14-A GOODWINS CT		
		SAINT MARTINS LN	LONDON WC2N 4LL	ENGLAND
ROSENTHAL, JANE	TV EXECUTIVE	CBS-TV, 6121 SUNSET BLVD	LOS ANGELES, CA	90028
ROSENTHAL, LAURENCE	COMPOSER	3815 W OLIVE AVE #202	BURBANK, CA	91505
ROSENTHAL, MARK DAVID	TV WRITER-FILM PROD	CAA, 9830 WILSHIRE BLVD	BEVERLY HILLS, CA	90212
ROSENTHAL, PHIL	TV CRITIC	POST OFFICE BOX 51400	LOS ANGELES, CA	90051
ROSENTHAL, RICHARD L, JR	TV WRITER	8904 WONDERLAND AVE	LOS ANGELES, CA	90046
ROSENTHAL, RICK	FILM DIRECTOR	7471 MELROSE AVE #17	LOS ANGELES, CA	90046
ROSENTHAL, ROBERT J	FILM WRITER-PRODUCER	116 N ROBERTSON BLVD #402	LOS ANGELES, CA	90048
ROSENTHAL, WAYNE	BASEBALL	POST OFFICE BOX 90111	ARLINGTON, TX	76004
ROSENWALD, RICHARD S	TALENT AGENT	1600 BROADWAY #1003-B	NEW YORK, NY	10019
ROSENWINK, KATHERINE	SCREENWRITER	8955 BEVERLY BLVD	WEST HOLLYWOOD, CA	90048
ROSENZWEIG, AARON B	CONDUCTOR	637 S BRADSHAWE	MONTEREY PARK, CA	91754
ROSENZWEIG, BARNEY	TV WRITER-PRODUCER	308 N SYCAMORE AVE #502	LOS ANGELES, CA	90036
ROSESON, SUSAN	TV DIRECTOR-PRODUCER	31636 BROAD BEACH RD	MALIBU, CA	90265
ROSEWALL, KEN	TENNIS	111 PENTACOST AVE	TURRAMURRA NSW 2074	AUSTRALIA
ROSIN, CHARLES	TV WRITER-PRODUCER	6131 BARROWS DR	LOS ANGELES, CA	90048
ROSLOFF, WENDY SUE	ACTRESS	248 N IRVING BLVD	LOS ANGELES, CA	90004
ROSNER, GEORGE	COMPOSER	1541 W PALMAIRE AVE	PHOENIX, AZ	85021
ROSNER, RICK	TV PRODUCER	NBC-TV, 3000 W ALAMEDA AVE	BURBANK, CA	91523
ROSO, JIMMY	BASEBALL	POST OFFICE BOX 3169	FREDERICK, MD	21701
ROSOFF, GILBERT	TV WRITER-PRODUCER	76 HIGHLAND RD	NEW YORK, NY	11542
ROSS, ALAN	ACTOR	400 W 43RD ST #38-O	NEW YORK, NY	10036
ROSS, ARNOLD	COMPOSER	1720 PACIFIC AVE #322	MARINA DEL REY, CA	90292
ROSS, BOB	FILM CRITIC	POST OFFICE BOX 191	TAMPA, FL	33601
ROSS, CHARLOTTE	ACTRESS	8715 BURTON WY #1	LOS ANGELES, CA	90265
ROSS, DAN	BASEBALL EXECUTIVE	TIGERS, 89 WHARNCLIFFE RD N	LONDON, ONT N6H 2A7	CANADA
ROSS, DANNY J	TV DIRECTOR	7942 S COLFAX AVE	CHICAGO, IL	60617
ROSS, DAVID	TV WRITER	151 S EL CAMINO DR	BEVERLY HILLS, CA	90212
ROSS, DEBBIE A	DIRECTOR	251 W 30TH ST #14-E	NEW YORK, NY	10001
ROSS, DEBORAH A	TV PRODUCER	251 W 30TH ST #14-E	NEW YORK, NY	10001
ROSS, DIANA	SINGER-ACTRESS	22028 PACIFIC COAST HWY	MALIBU, CA	90265
ROSS, DICK	DIRECTOR	4230 STANSBURY AVE	SHERMAN OAKS, CA	91403
ROSS, DON	ACTOR	1810 N BRONSON AVE #301	HOLLYWOOD, CA	90028
ROSS, DON	BODYBUILDER	POST OFFICE BOX 981	VENICE, CA	90294
ROSS, DONALD H	TV WRITER	151 S EL CAMINO DR	BEVERLY HILLS, CA	90212
ROSS, GARY A	SCREENWRITER	CAA, 9830 WILSHIRE BLVD	BEVERLY HILLS, CA	90212
ROSS, GEORGE, III	DIRECTOR	55 W 11TH ST	NEW YORK, NY	10011
ROSS, HERBERT	DIRECTOR-PRODUCER	9255 SUNSET BLVD #901	LOS ANGELES, CA	90069
ROSS, HOWARD	TV DIRECTOR-PRODUCER	118 WILLOUGHBY HOUSE, BARBICAN	LONDON EC2Y 8BL	ENGLAND
ROSS, IRVING	DIRECTOR	9611 ARBY DR	BEVERLY HILLS, CA	90210
ROSS, JERRY	TV WRITER	141 S EL CAMINO DR #205	BEVERLY HILLS, CA	90212
ROSS, JIM	WRESTLING ANNOUNCER	POST OFFICE BOX 105366	ATLANTA, GA	31348

ROSS, JONATHAN	TV HOST	CHANNEL 4, 60 CHARLOTTE ST	LONDON W1	ENGLAND
ROSS, JUDITH	SCREENWRITER	8955 BEVERLY BLVD	WEST HOLLYWOOD, CA	90048
ROSS, KATHARINE	ACTRESS	33050 PACIFIC COAST HWY	MALIBU, CA	90265
ROSS, KEN	CARTOONIST	UPS, 4900 MAIN ST, 9TH FLOOR	KANSAS CITY, MO	64112
ROSS, KENNETH	SCREENWRITER	1610 N CRESCENT HGTS BLVD	LOS ANGELES, CA	90069
ROSS, KEVIN	FOOTBALL	CHIEFS, 1 ARROWHEAD DR	KANSAS CITY, MO	64129
ROSS, KIMBERLY	ACTRESS	SELECTED, 3575 W CAHUENGA BLVD	LOS ANGELES, CA	90068
ROSS, MARION	ACTRESS	14159 RIVERSIDE DR #101	SHERMAN OAKS, CA	91423
ROSS, MARK	BASEBALL-COACH	POST OFFICE BOX 16683	GREENVILLE, SC	29606
ROSS, MARK	DIRECTOR	338 E 30TH ST	NEW YORK, NY	10016
ROSS, MERRIE LYNN	ACTRESS	3814 GLENRIDGE DR	SHERMAN OAKS, CA	91423
ROSS, MICHAEL	DIRECTOR	9350 WILSHIRE BLVD #400	BEVERLY HILLS, CA	90049
ROSS, MICHAEL	WRITER-PRODUCER	WAX MGMT, 9255 SUNSET BLVD	LOS ANGELES	90069
ROSS, MIKE	BASEBALL (TRAVELERS)	POST OFFICE BOX 5599	LITTLE ROCK, AR	72215
ROSS. MIKE	RECORD EXECUTIVE	DELICIOUS VINYL RECORDS		
		7471 MELROSE AVE	WEST HOLLYWOOD, CA	90046
ROSS, NATALIE	ACTRESS	ABC-TV, "ALL MY CHILDREN"		
		320 W 66TH ST	NEW YORK, NY	10023
ROSS, NICK	TV DIRECTOR-PRODUCER	BBC-TV, 56 WOOD LN	LONDON W12 7RJ	ENGLAND
ROSS, NORMAN	DIRECTOR	DGA, 110 W 57TH ST	NEW YORK, NY	10019
ROSS, RICCO	ACTOR	MANSON, 288 MUNSTER RD	LONDON SW6 6BQ	ENGLAND
ROSS, SEAN	BASEBALL	POST OFFICE BOX 6667	RICHMOND, VA	23230
ROSS, STAN	ACTOR	1410 N GARDNER ST	LOS ANGELES, CA	90046
ROSS, STANLEY RALPH	SCREENWRITER	451 BEVERWIL DR	BEVERLY HILLS, CA	90212
ROSS, STEVE	FILM EXECUTIVE	WARNER BROS, 4000 WARNER BLVD	BURBANK, CA	91522
ROSS, WILLIAM KING	COMPOSER-CONDUCTOR	24053 BESSEMER ST	WOODLAND HILLS, CA	91367
ROSS-LEMING, EUGENIE	ACTOR-WRITER-PRODUCER	5041 AMBROSE AVE	LOS ANGELES, CA	90027
ROSSEAU, ERNIE	BASEBALL-INSTRUCTOR	METS, 126TH ST & ROOSEVELT AVE	FLUSHING, NY	11368
ROSSELLI, JOE	BASEBALL	POST OFFICE BOX 21727	SAN FRANCISCO, CA	95151
ROSSELLINI, ISABELLA	ACTRESS	260 W BROADWAY #5-B	NEW YORK, NY	10013
ROSSEN, CAROL	ACTRESS	1119 23RD ST #8	SANTA MONICA, CA	90403
ROSSEN, ELLEN	TV PRODUCER	ABC-TV, 7 W 66TH ST	NEW YORK, NY	10023
ROSSEN, STEPHEN	WRITER	2010 GLENDON AVE	LOS ANGELES, CA	90025
ROSSER, JACKIE	SINGER	STM, 1311 CANDLELIGHT AVE	DALLAS, TX	75206
ROSSETTI, DOMINICK J	DIRECTOR	171 E 62ND ST	NEW YORK, NY	10021
ROSSI, AL	ACTOR	3050 W 7TH ST #101	LOS ANGELES, CA	90005
ROSSI, BOB	BASEBALL SCOUT	METS, 126TH ST & ROOSEVELT AVE	FLUSHING, NY	11368
ROSSI, PHIL	BASEBALL SCOUT	FENWAY PARK, 4 YAWKEY WY	BOSTON, MA	02215
ROSSINGTON, NORMAN	ACTOR	27 PARLIAMENT HILL	LONDON NW3	ENGLAND
ROSSINI, BIANCA	ACTRESS	BDP, 10637 BURBANK BLVD	NORTH HOLLYWOOD, CA	91601
ROSSITER, MIKE	BASEBALL	POST OFFICE BOX 882	MADISON, WI	53701
ROSSLEY, TOM	FOOTBALL COACH	FALCONS, SUWANEE RD AT I-85	SUWANEE, GA	30174
ROSSNER, DICK	ACTOR-WRITER	8645 LANGDON AVE	SEPULVEDA, CA	91343
ROSSOV, NANCI	WRITER-DIRECTOR	7224 HILLSIDE AVE #34	LOS ANGELES, CA	90046
ROSSOVICH, RICK	ACTOR	1539 SAWTELLE BLVD #10	LOS ANGELES, CA	90025
ROSSY, RICO	BASEBALL	POST OFFICE BOX 3665	OMAHA, NE	68103
ROSTEN, IRWIN	WRITER-PRODUCER	2217 CHELAN DR	LOS ANGELES, CA	90068
ROSTENKOWSKI, DAN	U S CONGRESSMAN	1372 W EVERGREEN ST	CHICAGO, IL	60622
ROSTON, RONALD	DIRECTOR	129 AMITY ST	BROOKLYN, NY	11201
ROSU, FRANCES L	CONDUCTOR	9722 3RD AVE	INGLEWOOD, CA	90305
ROSWELL, MAGGIE	ACTRESS	245 S VAN NESS AVE	LOS ANGELES, CA	90004
ROSZA, MIKLOS	COMPOSER	2936 MONTCALM DR	LOS ANGELES, CA	90046
ROTBERG, ALBERT	COMPOSER	17084 ESCALON DR	ENCINO, CA	91436
ROTCOP, J KENNETH	WRITER	616 VETERAN AVE #112	LOS ANGELES, CA	90024
ROTE, KYLE	FOOTBALL	1175 YORK AVE	NEW YORK, NY	10021
ROTE, TOBIN	FOOTBALL	1644 LEADBURY DR	BLOOMFIELD HILLS, MI	48013
ROTELLA, JOHNNY	COMPOSER	6654 ALLOTT AVE	VAN NUYS, CA	91401
ROTFELD, BERL	TV PRODUCER	SPORTS LEGENDS, 27 CITY LINE AVE	BALA CYNWYD, PA	19004
ROTH, ANN	COSTUME DESIGNER	ROAD 3, BOX 3124	BANGOR, PA	18013
ROTH, BOBBY	WRITER-PRODUCER	7957 FAREHOLM DR	LOS ANGELES, CA	90068
ROTH, DAVID G	DIRECTOR	134 GLENWOOD AVE	LEONIA, NJ	07605
ROTH, DAVID LEE	SINGER-SONGWRITER	3960 LAUREL CANYON BLVD #430	STUDIO CITY, CA	91604
ROTH, ENID	DIRECTOR	165 W END AVE	NEW YORK, NY	10023
ROTH, GREG	BASEBALL (BIRMINGHAM)	POST OFFICE BOX 360007	BIRMINGHAM, AL	35236
ROTH, JOE	FILM EXECUTIVE	10201 W PICO BLVD	LOS ANGELES, CA	90035
ROTH, JOYCE	ACTRESS	5917 CHULA VISTA WY #5	LOS ANGELES, CA	90068
ROTH, KATRINA	SINGER	150 E OLIVE AVE #111	BURBANK, CA	91502
ROTH, LAWRENCE	BASEBALL EXECUTIVE	POST OFFICE BOX 802	BATAVIA, NY	14021
ROTH, LYNN	WRITER-PRODUCER	448 N PALM DR #B	BEVERLY HILLS, CA	90210
ROTH, PAULA A	TV WRITER	3848 VANTAGE AVE	STUDIO CITY, CA	91604
ROTH, PETER A	TV EXECUTIVE	CANNELL, 7083 HOLLYWOOD BLVD	HOLLYWOOD, CA	90028
ROTH, PHIL	ACTOR	1252 N HAVENHURST DR #16	LOS ANGELES, CA	90046
ROTH, RICHARD	FILM PRODUCER	1741 COLDWATER CANYON DR	BEVERLY HILLS, CA	90210
ROTH, RICHARD	NEWS CORRESPONDENT	1050 TECHWOOD DR, NW	ATLANTA, GA	30318
ROTH, STEVE	FILM PRODUCER	ICM, 8899 BEVERLY BLVD	LOS ANGELES, CA	90048
ROTH, TIM	ACTOR	MARKHAM AND FROGGATT, LTD		
		JULIAN HOUSE, 4 WINDMILL ST	LONDON W1P 1HF	ENGLAND
ROTH, TOBY	U S CONGRESSMAN	126 N ONEIDA ST	APPLETON, WI	54911
ROTH, ULI	SINGER	ICM, 40 W 57TH ST	NEW YORK, NY	10019
ROTH, WILLIAM V, JR	U S SENATOR	3021 FEDERAL BLDG, 844 KING ST	WILMINGTON, DE	19801
ROTHBERG, HAL	WRITER-PRODUCER	22450 DOMINGO RD	WOODLAND HILLS, CA	91364
ROTHBERG, HOWARD	TALENT AGENT	1706 N DOHENY DR	LOS ANGELES, CA	90069
ROTHBERG, LEE	DIRECTOR	985 5TH AVE	NEW YORK, NY	10021
ROTHENBERG, MARVIN	DIRECTOR	405 E 54TH ST	NEW YORK, NY	10022
ROTHLEIN, LEWIS	COLUMNIST	CHRONICLE FEATURES		

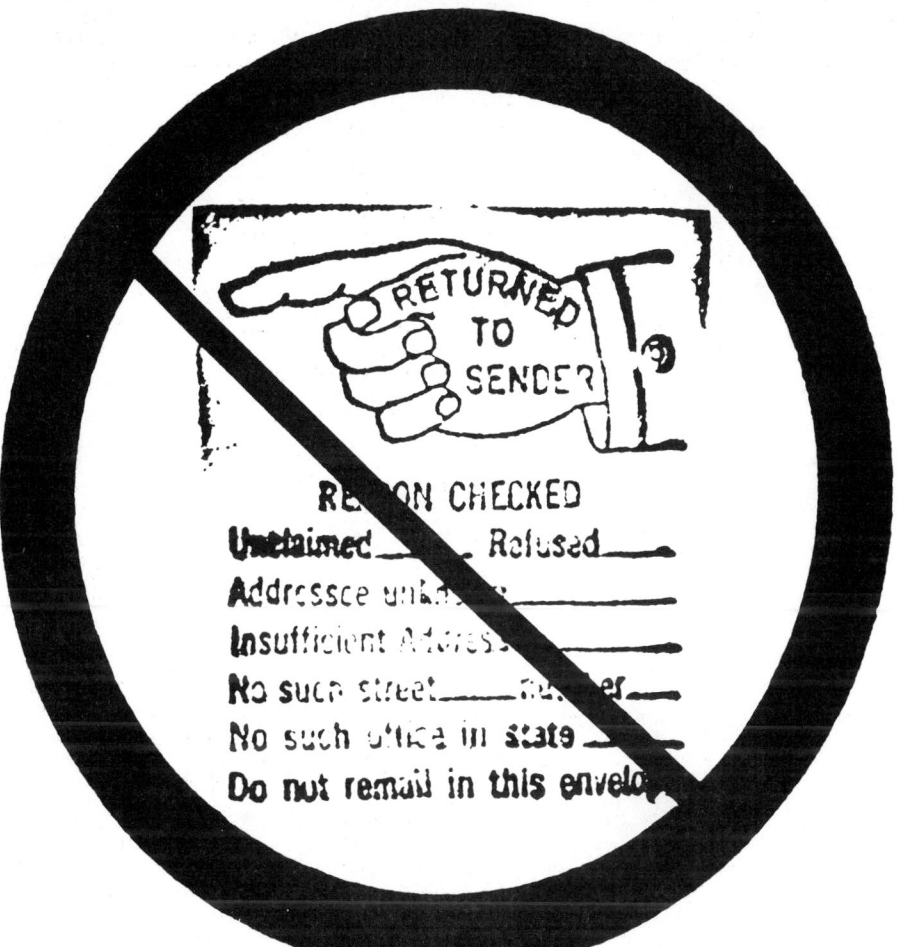

		870 MARKET ST	SAN FRANCISCO, CA	94102
ROTHMAN, JOSEPH	DIRECTOR	530 E 72ND ST	NEW YORK, NY	10021
ROTHMAN, KEITH	FILM EXECUTIVE	11 WATERLOO PL	LONDON SW1Y 4AU	ENGLAND
ROTHMAN, MARK	WRITER-PRODUCER	9930 LANCASTER-CIRCLEVILLE RD	AMANDA, OH	43102
ROTHMAN, MOSES	FILM EXECUTIVE	11 WATERLOO PL	LONDON SW1Y 4AU	ENGLAND
ROTHMAN, STEPHANIE	WRITER-PRODUCER	11925 MAYFIELD AVE #4	LOS ANGELES, CA	90049
ROTHSCHILD, LARRY	BASEBALL COACH	REDS, 100 RIVERFRONT STADIUM	CINCINNATI, OH	45202
ROTHSCHILD, LARRY	BASEBALL COACH	REDS, 100 RIVERFRONT STADIUM	CINCINNATI, OH	45202
ROTHSCHILD, RICHARD	FILM DIRECTOR	2021 WHITLEY TERR STEPS	LOS ANGELES, CA	90068
ROTHSTEIN, NORMAN	THEATER PRODUCER	1515 BROADWAY	NEW YORK, NY	10036
ROTHSTEIN, RICHARD	SCREENWRITER	201 S WINDSOR BLVD	LOS ANGELES, CA	90004
ROTHSTEIN, RON	BASKETBALL COACH	MIAMI HEAT, THE MIAMI ARENA	MIAMI, FL	33136
ROTONDI, EDWARD J	DIRECTOR	DGA, 110 W 57TH ST	NEW YORK, NY	10019
ROTONDI, JOE P, SR	COMPOSER	2260 BRONSON HILL DR	LOS ANGELES, CA	90068
ROTTEN, JOHNNY	SINGER-SONGWRITER	SEE - PUBLIC IMAGE, LTD		
ROTUNDA, MARJORIE N	TV DIRECTOR	3778 BALBOA TERR #A	SAN DIEGO, CA	92117
ROTUNDO, MIKE	WRESTLER	SEE - I R S		
ROTUNNO, GIUSEPPE	CINEMATOGRAPHER	POST OFFICE BOX 2230	HOLLYWOOD, CA	90078
ROUGEAU, JACQUES	WRESTLER	SEE - MOUNTIE, THE		
ROUGEAU, RAYMOND	WRESTLER	POST OFFICE BOX 3859	STAMFORD, CT	06905
ROUGH, MATT	TV CRITIC	POST OFFICE BOX 500	WASHINGTON, DC	20044
ROUGH CUTT	ROCK & ROLL GROUP	18653 VENTURA BLVD #307	TARZANA, CA	91356
ROUKEMA, MARGE	U S CONGRESSWOMAN	555 ROUTE 17 SOUTH	RIDGEWOOD, NJ	07450
ROULETTES, THE	VOCAL GROUP	9100 SUNSET BLVD #220	HOLLYWOOD, CA	90069
ROUMANIS, GEORGE Z	COMPOSER-CONDUCTOR	2332 CENTURY HILL	LOS ANGELES, CA	90067
ROUNDTREE, RICHARD	ACTOR	8721 SUNSET BLVD #202	LOS ANGELES, CA	90069
ROURKE, MICKEY	ACTOR	8439 SUNSET BLVD #107	LOS ANGELES, CA	90068
ROUSE, BOB	HOCKEY	MAPLE LEAFS, 60 CARLTON ST	TORONTO, ONT M5B 1L1	CANADA
ROUSE, JAMES	FOOTBALL	BEARS, 250 N WASHINGTON RD	LAKE FOREST, IL	60045
ROUSE, RUSSELL	DIRECTOR-PRODUCER	16632 OLDHAM ST	ENCINO, CA	91436
ROUSELLOT, JOHN	U S REPRESENTATIVE	7 N 5TH AVE	ARCADIA, CA	91006
ROUSON, LEE	FOOTBALL	BROWNS, 80 1ST ST	BEREA, OH	44017
ROUSSEL, ELVERA	ACTRESS	CASSELL, 843 N SYCAMORE AVE	LOS ANGELES, CA	90038
ROUSSEL, PAMELA	ACTRESS	9056 SANTA MONICA BLVD #201	LOS ANGELES, CA	90069
ROUSTABOUTS, THE	BLUEGRASS GROUP	POST OFFICE BOX 25371	CHARLOTTE, NC	28212
ROUTH, MAY	COSTUME DESIGNER	POST OFFICE BOX 5617	BEVERLY HILLS, CA	90213
ROUTLEDGE, PATRICIA	ACTRESS	MARMONT MANAGEMENT, LTD		
		LANGHAM HOUSE, 308 REGENT ST	LONDON W1R 5AL	ENGLAND
ROVERS, THE	VOCAL GROUP	UNICORN, 547 HOMER ST	VANCOUVER, BC V6B 2V7	CANADA
ROWAN, DAN	COMEDIAN	792 N MANASOTA KEY	ENGLEWOOD, FL	33533
ROWAN, RIP	BASEBALL EXECUTIVE	ALBANY YANKEES, HERITAGE PARK	ALBANY, NY	12211
ROWAND, NADA	ACTRESS	DOUGLAS-GORMAN, 1650 BROADWAY	NEW YORK, NY	10019
ROWE, ALAN	ACTOR	8 SHERWOOD CLOSE	LONDON SW13	ENGLAND
ROWE, ARTHUR	TV WRITER	325 S CANON DR	BEVERLY HILLS, CA	90212
ROWE, DEAN	TV DIRECTOR	6201 EDGEWOOD RD	CRYSTAL LAKE, IL	60014
ROWE, DON	BASEBALL COACH	BREWERS, 201 S 46TH ST	MILWAUKEE, WI	53214
ROWE, GORDON A	TV DIRECTOR	12415 RIVERSIDE DR #1	NORTH HOLLYWOOD, CA	91607
ROWE, KEN	BASEBALL-COACH	2501 ALLEN AVE, SE	CANTON, OH	44707
ROWE, MISTY	ACTRESS	880 GREENLEAF CANYON	TOPANGA, CA	90290
ROWE, PETE	BASEBALL-COACH	POST OFFICE BOX 957	DUNEDIN, FL	34697
ROWE, S ROBERT	WRITER-PRODUCER	2680 TIMBERCREEK CIR	BOCA RATON, FL	33431
ROWE, TOM	SCREENWRITER	8955 BEVERLY BLVD	WEST HOLLYWOOD, CA	90048
ROWELL, VICTORIA	ACTRESS	CBS-TV, "YOUNG & THE RESTLESS"		
		7800 BEVERLY BLVD #3305	LOS ANGELES, CA	90036
ROWEN, KEITH	FOOTBALL COACH	FALCONS, SUWANEE RD AT I-85	SUWANEE, GA	30174
ROWLAND, BETTY	BURLESQUE	MR B'S, 217 BROADWAY	SANTA MONICA, CA	90405
ROWLAND, DAVE	SINGER	POST OFFICE BOX 120021	NASHVILLE, TN	37212
ROWLAND, DON	BASEBALL SCOUT	TIGERS, TIGER STADIUM	DETROIT, MI	48216
ROWLAND, GEOFFREY	FILM EDITOR	2630 LACY ST	LOS ANGELES, CA	90031
ROWLAND, J ROY	U S CONGRESSMAN	POST OFFICE BOX 2047	DUBLIN, GA	31040
ROWLAND, RICH	BASEBALL	POST OFFICE BOX 6212	TOLEDO, OH	43614
ROWLAND, ROBERT	TV PRODUCER	MICHAEL BARRATT, LTD		
		5-7 FORLEASE RD, MAIDENHEAD	BERKS SL6 1RP	ENGLAND
ROWLAND, ROY	FILM DIRECTOR	DGA, 7920 SUNSET BLVD, 6TH FL	LOS ANGELES, CA	90046
ROWLANDS, DAVID	ACTOR	7917 WOODROW WILSON DR	LOS ANGELES, CA	90046
ROWLANDS, GENA	ACTRESS	7917 WOODROW WILSON DR	LOS ANGELES, CA	90046
ROWLANDS, PATSY	ACTRESS	SARABAND, 265 LIVERPOOL RD	LONDON N1 1LX	ENGLAND
ROWLES, JIMMY	COMPOSER	520 N BEL AIRE DR	BURBANK, CA	91501
ROWLES, KENNETH F	TV DIRECTOR-PRODUCER	RWH FILMS, 86 WARDOUR ST	LONDON W1V 3LF	ENGLAND
ROWLES, POLLY	ACTRESS	29 W 10TH ST	NEW YORK, NY	10011
ROWLEY, BILL	ACTOR	527 MADISON AVE #820	NEW YORK, NY	10022
ROWLEY, JIM	DIRECTOR	4430 WILDWOOD RD	DALLAS, TX	75209
ROWLEY, STEVE	BASEBALL	POST OFFICE BOX 4448	TULSA, OK	74159
ROXTON, STEVE	ACTOR	6 THORNTON RD, LEYTONSTONE	LONDON E11	ENGLAND
ROY, HAZEL	COSTUME DESIGNER	13949 VENTURA BLVD #309	SHERMAN OAKS, CA	91423
ROY, JACK	COMEDIAN-ACTOR	SEE - DANGERFIELD, RODNEY		
ROY, MICHAEL	FILM EXECUTIVE	3619 MOTOR AVE #300	LOS ANGELES, CA	90034
ROY, RICHARD FRANCIS	DIRECTOR	15 RAMSAY RD	MONTCLAIR, NJ	07042
ROYAL, BILLY JOE	SINGER-SONGWRITER	MC FADEN, 48 MUSIC SQUARE E	NASHVILLE, TN	37203
ROYAL, DANIEL C	DIRECTOR	1283 FRANKLIN CIR, NE	ATLANTA, GA	30324
ROYALS, MARK	FOOTBALL	BUCCANEERS, 1 BUCCANEER PL	TAMPA, FL	33607
ROYBAL, EDWARD R	U S CONGRESSMAN	300 N LOS ANGELES ST #7106	LOS ANGELES, CA	90012
ROYCE, KENNETH	AUTHOR	3 ABBOTTS CLOSE		
		ABBOTTS ANN, ANDOVER	HANTS SP11 7NP	ENGLAND
ROYER, CHRIS	BASEBALL SCOUT	POST OFFICE BOX 2000	ANAHEIM, CA	92803

ROYER, STAN	BASEBALL	POST OFFICE BOX 36407	LOUISVILLE, KY	40233
ROYKO, MIKE	COLUMNIST	THE CHICAGO TRIBUNE		
		TRIBUNE TOWER		
		435 N MICHIGAN AVE	CHICAGO, IL	60611
ROYLANCE, PAMELA	ACTRESS	7411 OSTROM AVE	VAN NUYS, CA	91406
ROYLE, CAROL	ACTRESS	HUTTON, 200 FULHAM RD	LONDON SW14 7AH	ENGLAND
ROYLE, DAVID B L	WRI-DIR-PROD	330 W 42ND ST #2420	NEW YORK, NY	10036
ROYSTER, JERRY	BASEBALL-MANAGER	POST OFFICE BOX 28268	SAN ANTONIO, TX	78228
ROZARIO, ROBERT V	COMPOSER-CONDUCTOR	5850 EL CANON AVE	WOODLAND HILLS, CA	91367
ROZELLE, PETE	FOOTBALL COMMISIONER	410 PARK AVE	NEW YORK, NY	10022
ROZENBERG, BERNARD	TV DIRECTOR	3671 HUDSON MANOR TERR	RIVERDALE, NY	10463
ROZENZWEIG, BARNEY	TV PRODUCER	615 S ROSSMORE AVE	LOS ANGELES, CA	90005
RROCKK	ROCK & ROLL GROUP	POST OFFICE BOX 18368	DENVER, CO	80218
RUBANOFF, JAYE	CONDUCTOR	13200 HARTSOOK ST	SHERMAN OAKS, CA	91423
RUBARGE, DENNIS	BASEBALL EXECUTIVE	POST OFFICE BOX 842	SALEM, VA	24153
RUBAUM, IRENE	ACTRESS	1225 CORSICA DR	PACIFIC PALISADES, CA	90272
RUBBER, VIOLA	THEATER PRODUCER	400 W 43RD ST	NEW YORK, NY	10036
RUBBER RODEO	ROCK & ROLL GROUP	FAT ARTISTS AGENCY		
		400 ESSEX ST	SALEM, MA	01970
RUBEL, MARC REID	SCREENWRITER	1670 MICHAEL LN	PACIFIC PALISADES, CA	90272
RUBEN, AARON	WRITER-PRODUCER	576 CHALETTE DR	BEVERLY HILLS, CA	90210
RUBEN, JOSEPH P	WRITER-PRODUCER	2680 WOODSTOCK RD	LOS ANGELES, CA	90046
RUBENS, WILLIAM S	TV EXECUTIVE	NBC-TV, 30 ROCKEFELLER PLAZA	NEW YORK, NY	10112
RUBENSTEIN, DAVID PAUL	ACTOR	210 W 89TH ST #31	NEW YORK, NY	10024
RUBENSTEIN, NEAL	TV DIRECTOR-PRODUCER	NSR PRODS, 366 N BROADWAY	JERICHO, NY	11753
RUBENSTEIN, SCOTT IAN	TV WRITER	10940 WESTWOOD BLVD	CULVER CITY, CA	90230
RUBIN, ANDREW	ACTOR	24001 HIGHWAY 140	EAGLE POINT, OR	97524
RUBIN, BERNARD	DIRECTOR	2295 S OCEAN BLVD	PALM BEACH, FL	33480
RUBIN, BOB	TV DIRECTOR	999 N DOHENY DR #1210	LOS ANGELES, CA	90069
RUBIN, BRUCE	SCREENWRITER	8955 BEVERLY BLVD	WEST HOLLYWOOD, CA	90048
RUBIN, CYMA	THEATER PRODUCER	170 E 77TH ST	NEW YORK, NY	10021
RUBIN, DOROTHY	AUTHOR-TV HOST	TRENTON STATE COLLEGE		
		HILLWOOD LAKES	TRENTON, NJ	08625
RUBIN, FRED	TV WRITER-PRODUCER	1900 N VINE ST #209	LOS ANGELES, CA	90068
RUBIN, KATT	ACTRESS	SEE - SHEA RUBIN, KATT		
RUBIN, LANCE M	COMPOSER	416 SAN VICENTE BLVD #112	SANTA MONICA, CA	90402
RUBIN, MANN	SCREENWRITER	11975 FOXBORO DR	LOS ANGELES, CA	90049
RUBIN, MAURY R	TV DIRECTOR	424 E 85TH ST	NEW YORK, NY	10028
RUBIN, PHILLIP S	TV DIRECTOR	290 UNDERWOOD ST	HOLLISTON, MA	01746
RUBIN, ROBERT H	TV EXECUTIVE	CBS-TV, 524 W 57TH ST	NEW YORK, NY	10019
RUBIN, RONALD	ORCHESTRA LEADER	1207 EL MEDIO AVE	PACIFIC PALISADES, CA	90272
RUBIN, SELMA	TALENT AGENT	104-60 QUEENS BLVD #10-C	FOREST HILLS, NY	11375
RUBIN, STANLEY	WRITER-PRODUCER	8818 RISING GLEN PL	LOS ANGELES, CA	90069
RUBIN-LA BOE, JENNIFER	ACTRESS	UTA, 9560 WILSHIRE BL, 5TH FL	BEVERLY HILLS, CA	90212
RUBINFIER, JAMES J	TV WRITER	1155 HACIENDA PL #205	LOS ANGELES, CA	90069
RUBINI, JAN	CONDUCTOR	8 RUE VILLARS	NEWPORT BEACH, CA	92660
RUBINI, MICHEL	COMPOSER	1646 S LA CIENEGA BLVD	LOS ANGELES, CA	90035
RUBINOOS, THE	ROCK & ROLL GROUP	POST OFFICE BOX 134	EL CERRITO, CA	94530
RUBINOWITZ, BARRY	TV WRITER	627 WESTMOUNT DR	LOS ANGELES, CA	90069
RUBINSTEIN, JOHN	ACTOR	STE, 888 7TH AVE, 18TH FLOOR	NEW YORK, NY	10106
RUBINSTEIN, JOHN A	COMPOSER-CONDUCTOR	1900 AVE OF THE STARS #1630	LOS ANGELES, CA	90067
RUBINSTEIN, RICHARD P	FILM EXECUTIVE	LAUREL, 928 BROADWAY	NEW YORK, NY	10010
RUBINSTEIN, SHOLOM	TV DIRECTOR	ABC-TV, 31 E 28TH ST	NEW YORK, NY	10016
RUBINSTEIN, ZELDA	ACTRESS	8730 SUNSET BLVD #220-W	LOS ANGELES, CA	90069
RUBY, GARY	BASEBALL COACH	10233 96TH AVE	EDMONTON, ALB TK5 0A5	CANADA
RUBY, JOSEPH C	WRITER-PRODUCER	9147 ENCINO AVE	NORTHRIDGE, CA	91325
RUCK, ALAN	ACTOR	4602 LOS FELIZ BLVD #204	LOS ANGELES, CA	90027
RUCKER, ALLEN	PRODUCER	MCA/UNIVERSAL STUDIOS, INC		
		100 UNIVERSAL CITY PLAZA #473	UNIVERSAL CITY, CA	91608
RUCKER, DAVE	BASEBALL	POST OFFICE BOX 559	PINION HILLS, CA	92372
RUCKER, DICK	CINEMATOGRAPHER	641 N WILCOX AVE #3-F	LOS ANGELES, CA	90004
RUDD, DELANEY	BASKETBALL	5 TRIAD CENTER #500	SALT LAKE CITY, UT	84180
RUDD, PAUL K	ACTOR	145 W 55TH ST	NEW YORK, NY	10019
RUDDY, ALBERT S	FILM WRITER-PRODUCER	1601 CLEARVIEW DR	BEVERLY HILLS, CA	90210
RUDE, RAVISHING RICK	WRESTLER	POST OFFICE BOX 105366	ATLANTA, GA	31348
RUDELSON, ROBERT	SCREENWRITER	15459 WYANDOTTE ST	VAN NUYS, CA	91406
RUDESILL, MIKE	SINGER	POST OFFICE DRAWER 20146	SAINT PETERSBURG, FL	33742
RUDIE, EVELYN	ACTRESS	7514 HOLLYWOOD BLVD	LOS ANGELES, CA	90046
RUDLEY, HERBERT	ACTOR	13056 MAXELLA AVE #1	MARINA DEL REY, CA	90292
RUDMAN, WARREN B	U S SENATOR	157 MAIN ST	BERLIN, NH	03570
RUDNAK, THEO	ARTIST	GRUBBS-BATE & ASSOCIATES		
		1151 W PEACHTREE ST	ATLANTA, GA	30309
RUDNER, RITA	COMEDIENNE	2447 BENEDICT CANYON	BEVERLY HILLS, CA	90210
RUDOLPH, ALAN	FILM WRITER-DIRECTOR	1020 S CARMELINA AVE	LOS ANGELES, CA	90049
RUDOLPH, LOUIS	PRODUCER	2001 WILSHIRE BLVD #301	SANTA MONICA, CA	90403
RUDOLPH, MASON	BASEBALL	525 NW PEACOCK BLVD	PORT SAINT LUCIE, FL	34986
RUDOLPH, WILMA	TRACK & FILED	3500 CENTENNIAL BLVD	NASHVILLE, TN	37203
RUEBEL, MATT	BASEBALL	POST OFFICE BOX 3746, HILL STA	AUGUSTA, GA	30904
RUEHL, MERCEDES	ACTRESS	306 W 100TH ST	NEW YORK, NY	10025
RUETER, KIRK	BASEBALL	POST OFFICE BOX 6748	ROCKFORD, IL	61125
RUETHER, MIKE	FOOTBALL	FALCONS, SUWANEE RD AT I-85	SUWANEE, GA	30174
RUETTGERS, KEN	FOOTBALL	PACKERS, 1265 LOMBARDI AVE	GREEN BAY, WI	54307
RUFF, DAN	BASEBALL	POST OFFICE BOX 2785	LAKELAND, FL	33806
RUFFALO, JOSEPH F	TALENT AGENT	11340 W OLYMPIC BLVD #357	LOS ANGELES, CA	90064
RUFFIANS, THE	ROCK & ROLL GROUP	2560 BANCROFT WY #33	BERKELEY, CA	94704

RUFFIN, BOBBY	SINGER	5300 POWERLINE RD #202	FORT LAUDERDALE, FL	33309
RUFFIN, BRUCE	BASEBALL	BREWERS, 201 S 46TH ST	MILWAUKEE, WI	53214
RUFFIN, JIMMY	SINGER-SONGWRITER	RSO RECORDS, 1775 BROADWAY	NEW YORK, NY	10019
RUFFIN, JOHNNY	BASEBALL	POST OFFICE BOX 360007	BIRMINGHAM, AL	35236
RUFFINS, REYNOLD	ARTIST	38 E 21ST ST	NEW YORK, NY	10010
RUFFNER, MARK	BASEBALL TRAINER	POST OFFICE BOX 15050	READING, PA	19612
RUFUS	SOUL GROUP	7250 BEVERLY BLVD #102	LOS ANGELES, CA	90036
RUGA, ELLIOT	TV DIRECTOR	SAND SPRING RD	MORRISTOWN, NJ	07960
RUGGEDY ANNES, THE	ROCK & ROLL GROUP	TABB RECORDS COMPANY		
		6201 SANTA MONICA BLVD	HOLLYWOOD, CA	90038
RUGGERO, ALFONSE, JR	TV PRODUCER	CAA, 9830 WILSHIRE BLVD	BEVERLY HILLS, CA	90212
RUGGIERI, PATRICIA	TV DIRECTOR-PRODUCER	117 DE HAVEN DR	YONKERS, NY	10703
RUGGLES, DERYA	ACTRESS	1801 AVE OF THE STARS #1250	LOS ANGELES, CA	90067
RUHM, JANE	COSTUME DESIGNER	13949 VENTURA BLVD #309	SHERMAN OAKS, CA	91423
RUIZ, JOSE LUIS	WRITER-PRODUCER	POST OFFICE BOX 27788	LOS ANGELES, CA	90027
RUKEYSER, LOUIS	TV HOST-JOURNALIST	306 TACONIC RD	GREENWICH, CT	06830
RUKEYSER, M S, JR	TV EXECUTIVE	NBC-TV, 30 ROCKEFELLER PLAZA	NEW YORK, NY	10112
RULE, JANICE	ACTRESS	3681 EMPIRE DR	LOS ANGELES, CA	90034
RUMANES, GEORGE N	WRITER	143 N HAMEL DR	BEVERLY HILLS, CA	90211
RUMBAUGH, DON	TV DIRECTOR	27522 RONDELL ST	AGOURA, CA	91301
RUMER, TIM	BASEBALL	POST OFFICE BOX 2148	WOODBRIDGE, VA	22193
RUMMAGE, J REID	DIRECTOR	DGA, 7920 SUNSET BLVD, 6TH FL	LOS ANGELES, CA	90046
RUMMELLS, DAVE	GOLFER	POST OFFICE BOX 109601	PALM BCH GARDENS, FL	33418
RUMOUR, THE	ROCK & ROLL GROUP	157 W 57TH ST PH #A	NEW YORK, NY	10019
RUMSEY, DAN	BASEBALL	POST OFFICE BOX 1742	PALM SPRINGS, CA	92263
RUMSEY, DERRELL	BASEBALL	14100 SIX MILE CYPRESS PKWY	FORT MYERS, FL	33912
RUMSHINSKY, MURRAY	COMPOSER-CONDUCTOR	1200 RIVERSIDE DR #233	BURBANK, CA	91506
RUN DMC	RAP GROUP	1133 BROADWAY #907	NEW YORK, NY	10010
RUNAWAYS, THE	ROCK & ROLL GROUP	FOWLEY, 6000 SUNSET BLVD	LOS ANGELES, CA	90028
RUNDGREN, TODD & UTOPIA	ROCK & ROLL GROUP	PANACEA ENTERTAINMENT		
		2705 GLENDOWER RD	LOS ANGELES, CA	90027
RUNDLE-LOFGREN, CIS	ACTRESS	151 S EL CAMINO DR	BEVERLY HILLS, CA	90212
RUNFOLO, PETER A	TV DIRECTOR-PRODUCER	641 W 59TH ST	NEW YORK, NY	10019
RUNGE, PAUL	BASEBALL (PLAYER)	646 DELAWARE AVE	LINGSTON, NY	12401
RUNGE, PAUL	BASEBALL (UMPIRE)	649 CALLE DE LA SIERRA	EL CAJON, CA	92021
RUNNELLS, TOM	BASEBALL-MANAGER	1942 29TH AVE	GREELEY, CO	80631
RUNNER	ROCK & ROLL GROUP	PROLOGUE RECORDS, 1674 BROADWAY	NEW YORK, NY	10019
RUNYEON, FRANK	ACTOR	11846 VENTURA BLVD #100	STUDIO CITY, CA	91604
RUNYON, ARTHUR L	TV DIRECTOR	3839 WEDDELL ST	DEARBORN, MI	48124
RUNYON, JENNIFER	ACTRESS	CED, 261 S ROBERTSON BLVD	BEVERLY HILLS, CA	90211
RUNYON, KEN R	COMPOSER	CMS, 26690 SAND CYN RD	CANYON COUNTRY, CA	91351
RUPLINGER, DALE	BODYBUILDER	4611 WASHINGTON ST	DAVENPORT, IA	52806
RUPPENTHAL, CHRIS	TV PRODUCER	CAA, 9830 WILSHIRE BLVD	BEVERLY HILLS, CA	90212
RUPRECHT, DAVID	ACTOR	8228 SUNSET BLVD #212	LOS ANGELES, CA	90046
RUSCHA, EDWARD	ACTOR	13775 VALLEY VISTA BLVD	SHERMAN OAKS, CA	91423
RUSH	ROCK & ROLL GROUP	41 BRITAIN ST #200	TORONTO, ONT M5A 1R7	CANADA
RUSH, ALVIN	TV EXECUTIVE	MCA-TV, 445 PARK AVE	NEW YORK, NY	10022
RUSH, ANDY	BASEBALL	POST OFFICE BOX 10213	LYNCHBURG, VA	24506
RUSH, BARBARA	ACTRESS	1708 TROPICAL AVE	BEVERLY HILLS, CA	90210
RUSH, BEVERLY	SINGER	POST OFFICE BOX 16	HILLSBORO, NH	03244
RUSH, CHRIS	SINGER	61-45 98TH ST #12-B	REGO PARK, NY	11374
RUSH, DEBORAH	ACTRESS	ICM, 8899 BEVERLY BLVD	LOS ANGELES, CA	90048
RUSH, HERMAN	TV EXECUTIVE	1984 STRADELLA RD	LOS ANGELES, CA	90077
RUSH, JAMES J	DIRECTOR	35-17 162ND ST	FLUSHING, NY	11358
RUSH, JENNIFER	SINGER	CBS SONGS COMPANY		
		BLEICHSTRASSE 64-66A	6000 FRANKFURT-MAIN	GERMANY
RUSH, JOHN	ARTIST	123 KEDZIE ST	EVANSTON, IL	60202
RUSH, MERRILLE	SINGER-SONGWRITER	SELECT ARTISTS ASSOCIATES		
		7300 E CAMELBACK RD	SCOTTSDALE, AZ	85251
RUSH, RICHARD	WRITER-PRODUCER	821 STRADELLA RD	LOS ANGELES, CA	90077
RUSH, SARAH	ACTRESS	1132 N VISTA ST #2	LOS ANGELES, CA	90046
RUSH, TOM	SINGER-SONGWRITER	POST OFFICE BOX 16	HILLSBORO, NH	03244
RUSHDIE, SALMAN	NOVELIST	ROGERS LTD, 49 BLENHEIM CRES	LONDON W11	ENGLAND
RUSHEN, PATRICE	SINGER	POST OFFICE BOX 6278	ALTADENA, CA	91001
RUSHMORE, KAREN	ACTRESS	8228 SUNSET BLVD #212	LOS ANGELES, CA	90046
RUSHNELL, ELAINE E	TV WRITER	46 ACADEMY ST	SKANEATELES, NY	13152
RUSHTON, DONALD A	DIRECTOR	520 N MICHIGAN AVE #1026	CHICAGO, IL	60611
RUSHTON, MATTHEW	TV-FILM PRODUCER	3500 W OLIVE AVE #500	BURBANK, CA	91505
RUSHTON, SHARON	ACTRESS	11618 GORHAM AVE #4	LOS ANGELES, CA	90049
RUSK, DEAN	POLITICIAN	1 LAYFAYETTE SQ, 620 HILL ST	ATHENS, GA	30601
RUSK, TROY	BASEBALL	POST OFFICE BOX 1721	SPARTANBURG, SC	29304
RUSKIN, COBY	TV DIRECTOR	10035 HILLGROVE DR	BEVERLY HILLS, CA	90210
RUSKIN, JOSEPH	ACTOR	13840 KITTRIDGE ST	VAN NUYS, CA	91405
RUSKIN, PHIL	DIRECTOR	4418 PRATT	LINCOLNWOOD, IL	60646
RUSKIN, SCOTT	BASEBALL	REDS, 100 RIVERFRONT STADIUM	CINCINNATI, OH	45202
RUSLER, ROBERT	ACTOR	335 N MAPLE DR #250	BEVERLY HILLS, CA	90210
RUSOFF, CATHERINE	ACTRESS	1539 SAWTELLE BLVD #10	LOS ANGELES, CA	90025
RUSOFF, GARRY	SCREENWRITER	620 MILWOOD AVE	VENICE, CA	90291
RUSS, KAREL	FILM PRODUCER	ROSEMAN, 8 POLAND ST	LONDON W1	ENGLAND
RUSS TAFF	GOSPEL GROUP	CAA, 9830 WILSHIRE BLVD	BEVERLY HILLS, CA	90212
RUSSELL, AARON	SINGER	TESSIER, 505 CANTON PASS	MADISON, TN	37115
RUSSELL, ALAN	TV DIRECTOR-PRODUCER	109 THE AVE	LONDON W13	ENGLAND
RUSSELL, ANNA	MUSICIAN	SHAFMAN, 723 7TH AVE, 7TH FL	NEW YORK, NY	10019
RUSSELL, ARLAND	ACTOR	244 RIVERSIDE DR #4-H	NEW YORK, NY	10025
RUSSELL, BILL	BASEBALL-MANAGER	11430 S FULTON AVE	TULSA, OK	74137

RUSSELL, BILL	BASKETBALL-COACH	POST OFFICE BOX 58	MERCER ISLAND, WA 98040
RUSSELL, BRENDA	SINGER	6640 SUNSET BLVD #200	HOLLYWOOD, CA 90028
RUSSELL, BRUCE ALAN	ACTOR	3814 LORADO WY	LOS ANGELES, CA 90043
RUSSELL, DEREK	FOOTBALL	BRONCOS, 13655 BRONCOS PKWY	ENGLEWOOD, CO 80112
RUSSELL, DEREK	FOOTBALL	BRONCOS, 13655 BRONCOS PKWY	ENGLEWOOD, CO 80112
RUSSELL, GEORGE H	COMPOSER	31423 COAST HWY #36	LAGUNA NIGUEL, CA 92677
RUSSELL, HAROLD	ACTOR	THE PRESIDENT'S COMMITTEE ON	
		EMPLOYMENT OF HANDICAPPED	
		DEPARTMENT OF LABOR	
		1111 20TH ST, NW	WASHINGTON, DC 20036
RUSSELL, JANE	ACTRESS	2934 LORITA RD	SANTA BARBARA, CA 93108
RUSSELL, JEFF	BASEBALL	ATHLETICS'S, OAKLAND COLISEUM	OAKLAND, CA 94621
RUSSELL, JOHN	BASEBALL	412 FOREMAN AVE	NORMAN, OK 73069
RUSSELL, JOHNNY	SINGER-SONGWRITER	POST OFFICE DRAWER 37	HENDERSONVILLE, TN 37075
RUSSELL, KAREN	ACTRESS	11846 VENTURA BLVD #100	STUDIO CITY, CA 91604
RUSSELL, KEN	FILM DIRECTOR	7 BELLMOUNT WOOD LN	WATFORD, HERTS ENGLAND
RUSSELL, KURT	ACTOR	1900 AVE OF THE STARS #1240	LOS ANGELES, CA 90067
RUSSELL, LE GRANDE	BASEBALL	POST OFFICE BOX 9194	HAMPTON, VA 23670
RUSSELL, LEON	SINGER-SONGWRITER	POST OFFICE BOX 1006	HENDERSONVILLE, TN 37077
RUSSELL, LEONARD	FOOTBALL	PATRIOTS, FOXBORO STADIUM, RT #1	FOXBORO, MA 02035
RUSSELL, MARK	SATIRIST-COMEDIAN	2828 WISCONSIN AVE, NW	WASHINGTON, DC 20007
RUSSELL, MIKE	BASEBALL-SCOUT	S F GIANTS, CANDLESTICK PARK	SAN FRANICSCO, CA 94124
RUSSELL, NIPSEY	COMED-WRI-DIR	353 W 57TH ST	NEW YORK, NY 10021
RUSSELL, PADDY	TV DIRECTOR	36 BACK LEEMING, OXENHOPE	WEST YORKS ENGLAND
RUSSELL, RANDEE	SCREENWRITER	8955 BEVERLY BLVD	WEST HOLLYWOOD, CA 90048
RUSSELL, ROY	TV WRITER	LEMON, 24 POTTERY, HOLLAND PK	LONDON W11 4LZ ENGLAND
RUSSELL, THERESA	ACTRESS	2 E OXFORD & CAMBRIDGE	
		OLD MAYBONE RD	LONDON NW1 ENGLAND
RUSSELL, TOM	SINGER-SONGWRITER	GOLDMINE, 700 E STATE ST	IOLA, WI 54990
RUSSIA	ROCK & ROLL GROUP	3 E 54TH ST #1400	NEW YORK, NY 10022
RUSSNOW, MICHAEL A	TV WRITER	12952 RIVERSIDE DR	SHERMAN OAKS, CA 91423
RUSSO, AARON	FILM PRODUCER	1145 GAYLEY AVE #301	LOS ANGELES, CA 90024
RUSSO, ANTHONY	ARTIST	373 BENEFIT ST	PROVIDENCE, RI 02903
RUSSO, BRYAN	TV DIRECTOR	43 CANTERBURY RD	WHITE PLAINS, NY 10607
RUSSO, GARY	TV DIRECTOR	288 NOME AVE	STATEN ISLAND, NY 10314
RUSSO, GIANNI	ACTOR	400 S BEVERLY DR #216	BEVERLY HILLS, CA 90212
RUSSO, HOWARD	TV DIRECTOR	327 10TH ST	SANTA MONICA, CA 90402
RUSSO, LILLIAN	TV DIRECTOR	9 TULIP LN	PORT WASHINGTON, NY 11050
RUSSO, MARTY	U S CONGRESSMAN	10634 S CICERO	OAK LAWN, IL 60453
RUSSO, PAT	BASEBALL	POST OFFICE BOX 5645	ORLANDO, FL 32855
RUSSO, RENE	ACTRESS	8046 FAREHOLM DR	LOS ANGELES, CA 90046
RUSSOM, LEON	ACTOR	247 S BEVERLY DR #102	BEVERLY HILLS, CA 90210
RUST, RON	FOOTBALL COACH	PATRIOTS, FOXBORO STADIUM, RT #1	FOXBORO, MA 02035
RUTAN, DICK	AVAITOR	614 SANDYDALE RD	NIPOMO, CA 93444
RUTENSCHROER, WIL	BASEBALL SCOUT	POST OFFICE BOX 419969	KANSAS CITY, MO 64141
RUTH, MIKE	BASEBALL SCOUT	TWINS, 501 CHICAGO AVE S	MINNEAPOLIS, MN 55415
RUTH, PAT	BASEBALL	POST OFFICE BOX 1721	SPARTANBURG, SC 29304
RUTH, PETER "MADCAT"	SINGER-GUITARIST	POST OFFICE BOX 8125	ANN ARBOR, MI 48107
RUTH ANN	SINGER-GUITARIST	IN TUNE MANAGEMENT	
		376 WOOLWICH ST	GUELPH, ONT N1H 3W7 CANADA
RUTHERFORD, ANN	ACTRESS	826 GREENWAY DR	BEVERLY HILLS, CA 90210
RUTHERFORD, JOHNNY	AUTO RACER	4919 BLACK OAK LN	FORT WORTH, TX 76114
RUTHSTEIN, ROY	TV EXECUTIVE	ABC-TV, 7 W 66TH ST	NEW YORK, NY 10023
RUTLAND, REGGIE	FOOTBALL	VIKINGS, 9520 VIKING DR	EDEN PRAIRIE, MN 55344
RUTLEDGE, JEFF	FOOTBALL	POST OFFICE BOX 17247 (DULLES)	WASHINGTON, DC 20041
RUTTAN, SUSAN	ACTRESS	2677 LA CUESTA DR	LOS ANGELES, CA 90046
RUTTER, SAM	BASEBALL	POST OFFICE BOX 855	BELOIT, WI 53511
RUUTTU, CHRISTIAN	HOCKEY	SABRES, MEMORIAL AUDITORIUM	BUFFALO, NY 14202
RUVAL, YULIIS	ACTRESS-MODEL	SEE - MULLER, LILLIAN	
RUXIN, JAMES	WRITER-PRODUCER	221 N BUNDY DR	LOS ANGELES, CA 90049
RUZEK, ROGER	FOOTBALL	EAGLES, BROAD ST & PATTISON AVE	PHILADELPHIA, PA 19148
RUZICKA, VLADIMIR	HOCKEY	BRUINS, 150 CAUSEWAY ST	BOSTON, MA 02114
RYACK, RITA	COSTUME DESIGNER	13949 VENTURA BLVD #309	SHERMAN OAKS, CA 91423
RYAN, BOB	SPORTS WRITER	BOSTON GLOBE, 135 MORRISSEY RD	BOSTON, MA 02107
RYAN, BUDDY	FOOTBALL COACH	EAGLES, BROAD ST & PATTISON AVE	PHILADELPHIA, PA 19148
RYAN, CHARLES	TALENT AGENT	6671 SUNSET BLVD #1574	LOS ANGELES, CA 90028
RYAN, DAN	TALENT AGENT	7250 BEVERLY BLVD #102	LOS ANGELES, CA 90036
RYAN, DESMOND	FILM CRITIC	PHILADELPHIA INQUIRER	
		400 N BROAD ST	PHILADELPHIA, PA 19101
RYAN, FRANKLIN P, JR	DIRECTOR	392 CENTRAL PARK W	NEW YORK, NY 10025
RYAN, GEORGE H	SECRETARY OF STATE	STATE HOUSE BUILDING	SPRINGFIELD, IL 62706
RYAN, KEN	BASEBALL	POST OFFICE BOX 1718	NEW BRITAIN, CT 06050
RYAN, KEVIN	BASEBALL	POST OFFICE BOX 3169	FREDERICK, MD 21701
RYAN, LISA DEAN	ACTRESS	1717 N HIGHLAND AVE #701	LOS ANGELES, CA 90028
RYAN, MADGE	ACTRESS	54 BLENHEIM TERR	LONDON NW8 OEG ENGLAND
RYAN, MARTY	TV PRODUCER	NBC-TV, 3000 W ALAMEDA AVE	BURBANK, CA 91523
RYAN, MEG	ACTRESS	8033 SUNSET BLVD #4048	LOS ANGELES, CA 90046
RYAN, MICHAEL M	ACTOR	48 E 3RD ST	NEW YORK, NY 10003
RYAN, MIKE	BASEBALL	POST OFFICE BOX 7575	PHILADELPHIA, PA 19101
RYAN, MITCHELL	ACTOR	30355 MULHOLLAND DR	CORNELL, CA 91301
RYAN, NOLAN	BASEBALL-RANCHER	POST OFFICE BOX 90111	ARLINGTON, TX 76004
RYAN, PEGGY	ACTRESS	1821 E OAKEY BLVD	LAS VEGAS, NV 89104
RYAN, SANDRA	ACTRESS	345 S ELM DR #402	BEVERLY HILLS, CA 90212
RYAN, SEAN	BASEBALL	POST OFFICE BOX 15050	READING, PA 19612
RYAN, TERRY	BASEBALL SCOUT	TWINS, 501 CHICAGO AVE S	MINNEAPOLIS, MN 55415

RYAN, TIM	FOOTBALL (BEARS)	BEARS, 250 N WASHINGTON RD	LAKE FOREST, IL 60045
RYAN, TIM	FOOTBALL (TAMPA BAY)	BUCCANEERS, 1 BUCCANEER PL	TAMPA, FL 33607
RYAN, TIM R	ACTOR	335 N MAPLE DR #360	BEVERLY HILLS, CA 90210
RYCHEL, KEVIN	BASEBALL	POST OFFICE BOX 3746, HILL STA	AUGUSTA, GA 30904
RYDBECK, WHITNEY	ACTOR	9780 VIA ZIBELLO	BURBANK, CA 91504
RYDELL, BOBBY	SINGER	917 BRYN MAWR AVE	NARBERTH, PA 19072
RYDELL, CHRISTOPHER	ACTOR	1 TOPSAIL	MARINA DEL REY, CA 90292
RYDELL, MARK	ACTOR-FILM DIRECTOR	1 TOPSAIL	MARINA DEL REY, CA 90292
RYDER, EDDIE	ACTOR	151 S EL CAMINO DR	BEVERLY HILLS, CA 90212
RYDER, MITCH	SINGER-SONGWRITER	WCSX-FM, 1 RADIO PLAZA	DETROIT, MI 48220
RYDER, RICHARD	ACTOR	17010 KNAPP ST	NORTHRIDGE, CA 91325
RYDER, SCOTT	BASEBALL	POST OFFICE BOX 507	DURHAM, NC 27702
RYDER, THOMAS A	DIRECTOR	DGA, 110 W 57TH ST	NEW YORK, NY 10019
RYDER, WINONA	ACTRESS	CAA, 9830 WILSHIRE BLVD	BEVERLY HILLS, CA 90210
RYE, RENNY	TV DIRECTOR	14 GLYNSWOOD, CHALFONT ST PETER	BUCKS ENGLAND
RYECART, PATRICK	ACTOR-PRODUCER	HEATH, PARAMOUNT HOUSE	
		162-170 WARDOUR ST	LONDON W1V 3AT ENGLAND
RYERSON, ANN	ACTRESS	144 S BEVERLY DR #405	BEVERLY HILLS, CA 90212
RYERSON, GEORGE S	MUSIC ARRANGER	4615 MARIA ST	CHATTANOOGA, TN 37411
RYLAND, DENECE	ACTRESS	SEM & M, 156 5TH AVE	NEW YORK, NY 10010
RYLES, JOHN WESLEY	SINGER	POST OFFICE BOX 1470	HENDERONVILLE, TN 37075
RYPIEN, MARK	FOOTBALL	POST OFFICE BOX 17247 (DULLES)	WASHINGTON, DC 20041
RYSK	ROCK & ROLL GROUP	POST OFFICE BOX 1578	SIOUX FALLS, SD 57101
RYUN, JIM	RUNNER	ROUTE #3, BOX 62-B	LAWRENCE, KS 66044
RZEWNICKI, JANET C	TREASURER	LEGISLATIVE HALL	DOVER, DE 19901

SAATZER, COBBY	BASEBALL SCOUT	TWINS, 501 CHICAGO AVE S	MINNEAPOLIS, MN 55415
SABAROFF, ROBERT	WRITER	11847 KIOWA AVE #8	LOS ANGELES, CA 90049
SABATINI, GABRIELA	TENNIS	2665 S BAYSHORE DR	MIAMI, FL 31333
SABATINO, CHUCK	FILM DIRECTOR	85 145 S FAIRFAX AVE #310 MANOR	LOS ANGELES, CA 90036
SABATINO, MICHAEL	ACTOR	9720 REGENT ST #8	LOS ANGELES, CA 90034
SABATO, ANTONIO	ACTOR	28035 DOROTHY DR #210-A	AGOURA, CA 91301
SABEAN, BRIAN	BASEBALL EXECUTIVE	N Y YANKEES, YANKEE STADIUM	BRONX, NY 10451
SABELLA, ERNIE	ACTOR	1145 GAYLEY AVE #309	LOS ANGELES, CA 90024
SABERHAGEN, BRETT	BASEBALL	METS, 126TH ST & ROOSEVELT AVE	FLUSHING, NY 11368
SABINSON, ALLEN C	TV EXECUTIVE	NBC-TV, 3000 W ALAMEDA AVE	BURBANK, CA 91523
SABLE, KENNETH S	DIRECTOR	CBS-TV, 524 W 57TH ST	NEW YORK, NY 10019
SABLE, LUKE	BASEBALL	POST OFFICE BOX 4448	TULSA, OK 74159
SABO, CHRIS	BASEBALL	141 BEWING DR	FAIRFIELD, OH 45014
SABO, MARTIN	U S CONGRESSMAN	462 FEDERAL COUNT BUILDING	
		110 S 4TH ST	MINNEAPOLIS, MN 55401
SABOURIN, KEN	HOCKEY	JETS, 15-1430 MAROONS RD	WINNIPEG, MAN R3G OL5 CANADA
SABULIS, TOM	FILM CRITIC	DALLAS TIMES HERALD	
		1101 PACIFIC AVE	DALLAS, TX 75202
SACCHARINE TRUST	ROCK & ROLL GROUP	POST OFFICE BOX 1	LAWNDALE, CA 90260
SACCHI, ROBERT	ACTOR	232 S WINDSOR BLVD	LOS ANGELES, CA 90004
SACHS, ADRIANNE	ACTRESS	8484 WILSHIRE BLVD #530	BEVERLY HILLS, CA 90211
SACHS, ANDREW	ACTOR	STONE, 25 WHITEHALL	LONDON SW1A 2BS ENGLAND
SACHS, GLORIA	DESIGNER	117 E 57TH ST	NEW YORK, NY 10022
SACHS, JERRY	BASKETBALL EXECUTIVE	BULLETS, 1 HARRY S TRUMAN DR	LANDOVER, MD 20785
SACHS, LLOYD	FILM CRITIC	THE CHICAGO SUN-TIMES	
		401 N WABASH AVE	CHICAGO, IL 60611
SACHS, ROBIN	ACTOR	SARABAND, 265 LIVERPOOL RD	LONDON N1 1LX ENGLAND
SACHS, WILLIAM	FILM WRITER-DIRECTOR	8955 BEVERLY BLVD	WEST HOLLYWOOD, CA 90048
SACHSE, SALLI	ACTRESS	233 ASHLAND AVE #G	SANTA MONICA, CA 90405
SACK, JOHN	ACTOR-TV WRITER	2005 LA BREA TERR	LOS ANGELES, CA 90046
SACK, STEVE	CARTOONIST	MINNEAPOLIS STAR & TRIBUNE	
		425 PORTLAND AVE	MINNEAPOLIS, MN 55488
SACK, VICTOR	TV DIRECTOR-PRODUCER	449 W 50TH ST	NEW YORK, NY 10019
SACKHEIM, JERRY	WRITER	3901 ETHEL AVE	NORTH HOLLYWOOD, CA 91604
SACKHEIM, WILLIAM	TV-FILM WRI-PROD	1118 TOWER RD	BEVERLY HILLS, CA 90210
SACKS, ALAN	WRITER-PRODUCER	20655 SHERMAN WY #51	CANOGA PARK, CA 91306
SACKS, DR OLIVER	AUTHOR-PSYCHIATRIST	ALBERT EINSTEIN COLLEGE	
		OF MEDICINE, DEPT OF PSYCHIATRY	
		1300 MORRIS PARK AVE	BRONX, NY 10461
SACKS, EZRA M	SCREENWRITER	8955 BEVERLY BLVD	WEST HOLLYWOOD, CA 90048
SACKS, STEVEN R "STORMY"	COMPOSER-CONDUCTOR	100 S DOHENY DR #1100	LOS ANGELES, CA 90048
SACRED RITE	ROCK & ROLL GROUP	GREENWALD, 20445 GRAMERCY PL	TORRANCE, CA 90501
SAD CAFE	ROCK & ROLL GROUP	3 E 54TH ST #1400	NEW YORK, NY 10022
SADAKA, NEIL	SINGER-SONGWRITER	10 COLUMBUS CIR	NEW YORK, NY 10019
SADANE, MARC	SINGER	1697 BROADWAY #600	NEW YORK, NY 10019
SADDLER, ROD	FOOTBALL	POST OFFICE BOX 888	PHOENIX, AZ 85001
SADE	SINGER-SONGWRITER	MORAGNS HOTEL, 237 MADISON AVE	NEW YORK, NY 10016
SADECKI, RAY	BASEBALL-COACH	1524 W NEBRASKA AVE	PEORIA, IL 61604
SADECKI, STEVE	BASEBALL	POST OFFICE BOX 309	GASTONA, NC 28053
SADER, LUKE	TV DIRECTOR	ENTERTAINMENT TONIGHT	
		PARAMOUNT TELEVISION	

Name	Occupation	Address	City	Zip/Country
		5555 MELROSE AVE	LOS ANGELES, CA	90038
SADLER, WILLIAM	ACTOR	1114 GRANT AVE	VENICE, CA	90291
SADOWSKI, TROY	FOOTBALL	CHIEFS, 1 ARROWHEAD DR	KANSAS CITY, MO	64129
SADWITH, JAMES S	WRITER	2752 HALSEY RD	TOPANGA CANYON, CA	90290
SAENZ, ORLANDO	BASEBALL	POST OFFICE BOX 4218	SOUTH BEND, IN	46634
SAETA, EDDIE	FILM DIRECTOR	DGA, 7920 SUNSET BLVD, 6TH FL	LOS ANGELES, CA	90046
SAETA, STEVEN	TV DIRECTOR	6628 E BUTTONWOOD AVE	AGOURA, CA	91301
SAETRE, DARON	BASEBALL	POST OFFICE BOX 9194	HAMPTON, VA	23670
SAFDIE, LIL	ACTRESS	9744 WILSHIRE BLVD #312	BEVERLY HILLS, CA	90212
SAFER, MORLEY	NEWS JOURNALIST	CBS-TV, 524 W 57TH ST	NEW YORK, NY	10019
SAFFELL, TOM	BASEBALL EXECUTIVE	1503 CLOWER CREEK DR #H-262	SARASOTA, FL	34231
SAFIR, LAWRENCE	FILM EXECUTIVE	22 SOHO SQ	LONDON W1V 5FJ	ENGLAND
SAFIR, SIDNEY	FILM EXECUTIVE	22 SOHO SQ	LONDON W1V 5FJ	ENGLAND
SAFIRE, WILLIAM	COLUMNIST-NEWS CORRES	6200 ELMWOOD RD	CHEVY CHASE, MD	20815
SAFLY, JOEL	BASEBALL TRAINER	POST OFFICE BOX 48	VISALIA, CA	93279
SAFRAN, DON	SCREENWRITER	8955 BEVERLY BLVD	WEST HOLLYWOOD, CA	90048
SAGA	ROCK & ROLL GROUP	41 BRITAIN ST #200	TORONTO, ONT M5A 1R7	CANADA
SAGAL, BORIS	DIRECTOR	POST OFFICE BOX 889		
		PROSPECT HILLS STATION	STOCKBRIDGE, MA	01262
SAGAL, ELIZABETH	ACTRESS	MTA, 9320 WILSHIRE BL, 3RD FL	BEVERLY HILLS, CA	90212
SAGAL, JEAN	ACTRESS	10351 SANTA MONICA BLVD #211	LOS ANGELES, CA	90025
SAGAL, JOEY	ACTOR	17250 SUNSET BLVD #202	PACIFIC PALISADES, CA	90272
SAGAL, KATEY	ACTRESS-SINGER	3498 TROY DR	LOS ANGELES, CA	90068
SAGAN, CARL	ASTRONOMER-WRITER	CORNELL UNIVERSITY		
		15 E 26TH ST	NEW YORK, NY	10010
SAGANSKY, JEFF	TV EXECUTIVE	145 OCEAN AVE	SANTA MONICA, CA	90402
SAGAPOLUTELE, PIO	FOOTBALL	BROWNS, 80 1ST ST	BEREA, OH	44017
SAGE, DE WITT L, JR	WRITER-PRODUCER	271 CENTRAL PARK W	NEW YORK, NY	10024
SAGE, GREG	SINGER	POST OFFICE BOX 2896	TORRANCE, CA	90509
SAGE, LIZ	TV WRITER-PRODUCER	WITT, 846 N CAHUENGA BLVD	LOS ANGELES, CA	90038
SAGE, ROBERT	DIRECTOR	41523 MAY CREEK RD	SULTAN, WA	98294
SAGEBRUSH	VOCAL GROUP	POST OFFICE BOX O	EXCELSIOR, MN	55331
SAGENDORF, BUD	CARTOONIST	KING FEATURES, 216 E 45TH ST	NEW YORK, NY	10017
SAGER, A J	BASEBALL	STARS, 850 LAS VEGAS BLVD N	LAS VEGAS, NV	89101
SAGER, CAROLE BAYER	SINGER-SONGWRITER	658 NIMES RD	LOS ANGELES, CA	90077
SAGER, CRAIG	SPORTSCASTER	3064 SPRING HILL RD	SMYRNA, GA	30080
SAGER, SUSAN	ACTRESS	9034 SUNSET BLVD #100	LOS ANGELES, CA	90069
SAGET, BOB	ACTOR	POST OFFICE BOX 4333	HOLLYWOOD, CA	90078
SAGLE, CHARLES H	MUSIC ARRANGER	POST OFFICE BOX 41012	NASHVILLE, TN	37204
SAHA, MARK	WRITER	2129 OCEAN AVE #5	SANTA MONICA, CA	90405
SAHL, MORT	COMEDIAN-WRITER	2325 SAN YSIDRO DR	BEVERLY HILLS, CA	90210
SAHM, DOUG	SINGER-SONGWRITER	ANTONE'S, 2928 GUADALUPE ST	AUSTIN, TX	78705
SAIDENBERG, DANIEL	CELLIST	980 5TH AVE	NEW YORK, NY	10021
SAIGER, SUSAN	ACTRESS	291 S LA CIENEGA BLVD	BEVERLY HILLS, CA	90211
SAILER	VOCAL GROUP	GOOD, 2500 NW 39TH ST	OKLAHOMA CITY, OK	73112
SAILOR, CHARLES	AUTHOR	1474 QUEENS RD	LOS ANGELES, CA	90069
SAINT, EVA MARIE	ACTRESS	8271 MELROSE AVE #110	LOS ANGELES, CA	90046
SAINT ANNE, JACQUELINE	COSTUME DESIGNER	1930 CENTURY PARK W #403	LOS ANGELES, CA	90067
SAINT CLAIR, BARRIE	FILM PRODUCER	TURKEY FILM SERVICES		
		POST OFFICE BOX 357	LONE HILL 2062	SO AFRICA
SAINT JAMES, SUSAN	ACTRESS	CAA, 9830 WILSHIRE BLVD	BEVERLY HILLS, CA	90212
SAINT TROPEZ	ROCK & ROLL GROUP	PERLE, 4475 VINELAND AVE	STUDIO CITY, CA	91602
SAINT VITUS	ROCK & ROLL GROUP	POST OFFICE BOX 1	LAWNDALE, CA	90260
SAINTE-MARIE, BUFFY	SINGER-SONGWRITER	RURAL ROUTE #1, BOX 368	KAPAA, KAUAI, HI	96746
SAINTS, THE	RHYTHM & BLUES GROUP	TAYLOR, 2501 TALBOT AVE	LOUISVILLE, KY	40205
SAIRE, REBECCA	ACTRESS	LONDON MGT, 235-241 REGENT ST	LONDON W1R 4PH	ENGLAND
SAITZ, ROBBIE	BASEBALL	POST OFFICE BOX 1742	PALM SPRINGS, CA	92263
SAJAK, PAT	TV HOST	3400 RIVERSIDE DR	BURBANK, CA	91505
SAKAMOTO, RYUICHI	COMPOSER	CAA, 9830 WILSHIRE BLVD	BEVERLY HILLS, CA	90212
SAKATA, LENN	BASEBALL-COACH	10233 96TH AVE	EDMONTON, ALB TK5 0A5	CANADA
SAKIC, JOE	HOCKEY	NORDIQUES, 2205 AVE DU COLISEE	QUEBEC, QUE G1L 4W7	CANADA
SAKS, GENE	DIRECTOR-ACTOR	DGA, 110 W 57TH ST	NEW YORK, NY	10019
SAKS, SOL	WRITER	145 S FAIRFAX AVE #310	LOS ANGELES, CA	90036
SALAFF, FRED	TV DIRECTOR-PRODUCER	DOKUMENTA PRODS, 322 W 57TH ST	NEW YORK, NY	10019
SALAMON, JULIE	FILM CRITIC	THE WALL STREET JOURNAL		
		200 LIBERTY ST	NEW YORK, NY	10281
SALAND, RONALD	DIRECTOR	500 E 77TH ST #516	NEW YORK, NY	10162
SALANT, RICHARD	TV EXECUTUVE	NBC-TV, 30 ROCKEFELLER PLAZA	NEW YORK, NY	10112
SALAS, MARK	BASEBALL	330 BARCA AVE	LA PUENTE, CA	91744
SALAZAR, ANGEL	BASEBALL	RODRIGUEZ DOMINGUES MANAZA G#7	VARINA	VENEZUELA
SALAZAR, CARLOS	BASEBALL	POST OFFICE BOX 2437	MODESTO, CA	95351
SALAZAR, JULIAN	BASEBALL	POST OFFICE BOX 855	BELOIT, WI	53511
SALAZAR, LUIS	BASEBALL	1060 W ADDISON ST	CHICAGO, IL	60613
SALAZAR, RITA	COSTUME DESIGNER	13949 VENTURA BLVD #309	SHERMAN OAKS, CA	91423
SALCEDO, EDWIN	BASEBALL	POST OFFICE BOX 2148	WOODBRIDGE, VA	22193
SALCIDO, MONIQUE	ACTRESS	LIGHT, 901 BRINGHAM AVE	LOS ANGELES, CA	90049
SALDANA, THERESA	ACTRESS	BDP, 10637 BURBANK BLVD	NORTH HOLLYWOOD, CA	91601
SALE, RICHARD	WRITER-PRODUCER	822 S ROBERTSON BLVD #200	LOS ANGELES, CA	90035
SALE, VIRGINIA	ACTRESS	23388 MULHOLLAND HIGHWAY	WOODLAND HILLS, CA	91364
SALEAUMUA, DAN	FOOTBALL	CHIEFS, 1 ARROWHEAD DR	KANSAS CITY, MO	64129
SALEM, JESSICA	ACTRESS	SHAPIRO, 2147 N BEACHWOOD DR #2	LOS ANGELES, CA	90068
SALEM, MURRAY	ACTOR	733 N KINGS RD #147	LOS ANGELES, CA	90069
SALEM, PAMELA	ACTRESS	CREATIVE TALENT, BRITANNIA HOUSE		
		1-11 GLENTHORNE RD	LONDON W6 OLF	ENGLAND
SALEM, RICHARD	ACTOR	14343 ADDISON ST #219	SHERMAN OAKS, CA	91423

SALENGER, MEREDITH	ACTRESS	151 S EL CAMINO DR	BEVERLY HILLS, CA	90212
SALERNO, ANTHONY	TV PRODUCER	IMERO FIORENTINO ASSOCIATES		
		44 W 63RD ST	NEW YORK, NY	10023
SALES, SOUPY	ACT-COMED-WRI	245 E 35TH ST	NEW YORK, NY	10016
SALESKI, STAN	BASEBALL SCOUT	N Y YANKEES, YANKEE STADIUM	BRONX, NY	10451
SALINAS, CARLOS	PRESIDENT	PRESIDENCIA PALACIO NACIONAL	MEXICO CITY DF 06220	MEXICO
SALINGER, DIANE	ACTRESS	11726 SAN VICENTE BLVD #300	LOS ANGELES, CA	90049
SALINGER, MATT	ACTOR	15760 VENTURA BLVD #1730	ENCINO, CA	91436
SALINGER, PIERRE	NEWS CORRES-AUTHOR	7 CARBURTON ST	LONDON W1P 7DT	ENGLAND
SALISBURY, FRANK P	TV WRITER	3631 DIXIE CANYON PL	SHERMAN OAKS, CA	91423
SALISBURY, SEAN	FOOTBALL	VIKINGS, 9520 VIKING DR	EDEN PRAIRIE, MN	55344
SALK, DR JONAS	SCIENTIST	2444 ELLENTOWN RD	LA JOLLA, CA	92037
SALKELD, ROGER	BASEBALL	POST OFFICE BOX 3690, STA "B"	CALGARY, ALB T2B 4M4	CANADA
SALKIN, JAMES	TV DIRECTOR	209 E 25TH ST #4-C	NEW YORK, NY	10010
SALKIN, LEO	WRITER	3584 MULTIVIEW DR	LOS ANGELES, CA	90068
SALKIND, ALEXANDER	FILM PRODUCER	PINEWOOD STUDIOS, IVER HEATH	IVER, BUCKS SLO ONH	ENGLAND
SALKIND, ILYA	FILM PRODUCER	PINEWOOD STUDIOS, IVER HEATH	IVER, BUCKS SLO ONH	ENGLAND
SALKOW, SIDNEY	WRITER-PRODUCER	12336 ADDISON ST	NORTH HOLLYWOOD, CA	91607
SALKOWITZ, JOEL	DIRECTOR	DGA, 110 W 57TH ST	NEW YORK, NY	10019
SALKOWITZ, SY	WRITER-PRODUCER	21632 PACIFIC COAST HWY	MALIBU, CA	90265
SALLAN, BRUCE	TV PRODUCER	ABC-TV, 4151 PROSPECT AVE	LOS ANGELES, CA	90027
SALLE, DAVID	PAINTER	MARY BOONE GALLERY		
		417 W BROADWAY	NEW YORK, NY	10012
SALLES, JOHN	BASEBALL	CUBS, 2ND & RIVERSIDE DR	DES MOINES, IA	50309
SALLET, EMMANUELLE	ACTRESS-MODEL	BLANCHARD, 957 N COLE AVE	LOS ANGELES, CA	90038
SALLEY, JOHN	BASKETBALL	THE PALACE OF AUBURN HILLS		
		2 CHAMPIONSHIP DR	AUBURN HILLS, MI	48326
SALLEY, RONALD	ACTOR	510 PACIFIC AVE #4	VENICE, CA	90291
SALLIN, ROBERT	DIRECTOR	1345 N WETHERLY DR	LOS ANGELES, CA	90069
SALLING, NORMAN	COSTUME DESIGNER	13949 VENTURA BLVD #309	SHERMAN OAKS, CA	91423
SALLIS, PETER	ACTOR	HEATH, PARAMOUNT HOUSE		
		162-170 WARDOUR ST	LONDON W1V 3AT	ENGLAND
SALLY & THE SOPHISTICATZ	ROCK & ROLL GROUP	25 HUNTINGTON AVE #420	BOSTON, MA	02116
SALMON, TIM	BASEBALL	10233 96TH AVE	EDMONTON, ALB TK5 0A5	CANADA
SALMONS, JANE LEE	ACTRESS-MODEL	9057 NEMO ST #A	WEST HOLLYWOOD, CA	90069
SALMORE, CHARLES	WRITER	828 7TH ST #A	SANTA MONICA, CA	90403
SALOB, LORIN	TV DIRECTOR	3819 MANDEVILLE CANYON RD	LOS ANGELES, CA	90049
SALOMON, MIKAEL	CINEMATOGRAPHER	POST OFFICE BOX 2230	HOLLYWOOD, CA	90078
SALOMON, RODRIGO	DIRECTOR	119 NORFOLK ST	NEW YORK, NY	10002
SALONEN, ESA-PEKKA	CONDUCTOR	ICM, 40 W 57TH ST	NEW YORK, NY	10019
SALT CREEK	VOCAL GROUP	POST OFFICE BOX O	EXCELSIOR, MN	55331
SALTER, HANS J	COMPOSER-CONDUCTOR	3658 WOODHILL CANYON RD	STUDIO CITY, CA	91604
SALTER, IVOR	ACTOR	PATRICK FREEMAN MANAGEMENT		
		4 CROMWELL GROVE, HAMMERSMITH	LONDON W6 7RG	ENGLAND
SALTER, JAMES	SCREENWRITER	8955 BEVERLY BLVD	WEST HOLLYWOOD, CA	90048
SALTER, JOYCE K	SCREENWRITER	8955 BEVERLY BLVD	WEST HOLLYWOOD, CA	90048
SALTZGABER, BRIAN	BASEBALL	POST OFFICE BOX 2785	LAKELAND, FL	33806
SALTZMAN, ERIC F	DIRECTOR	155 RIVERSIDE DR	NEW YORK, NY	10024
SALTZMAN, JOSEPH	TV WRITER-PRODUCER	2116 VIA ESTUDILLO	PALOS VERDES, CA	90274
SALTZMAN, PHILIP	TV WRITER-PRODUCER	10530 GARWOOD PL	LOS ANGELES, CA	90024
SALUGA, BILL	ACTOR	7014 TREASURE TR	LOS ANGELES, CA	90068
SALUGHTER, WEBSTER	FOOTBALL	BROWNS, 80 1ST ST	BEREA, OH	44017
SALVESEN, ARTHUR H	TV DIRECTOR	254 PARK AVE S #7-R	NEW YORK, NY	10010
SALVI, DELIA	ACTRESS	1132 N VISTA ST	LOS ANGELES, CA	90046
SALVIOR, TROY	BASEBALL	POST OFFICE BOX 12557	ST PETERSBURG, FL	33733
SALZER, ALBERT J	DIRECTOR	DGA, 7920 SUNSET BLVD, 6TH FL	LOS ANGELES, CA	90046
SALZMAN, BERTRAM	WRITER-PRODUCER	RUE DES PETITS PAS	PONTLEVOY 41400	FRANCE
SAM & DAVE	VOCAL DUO	J D BROWN, 300 W 55TH ST	NEW YORK, NY	10019
SAM THE SHAM	SINGER-SONGWRITER	SEE - SAMUDIO, SAM "THE SHAM"		
SAMBUL, NATHAN J	TV WRITER-PRODUCER	NJ SAMBUL, 5 E 16TH ST	NEW YORK, NY	10003
SAMET, NORMAN	TV DIRECTOR	60 145 S FAIRFAX AVE #310 PL S #7	LOS ANGELES, CA	90036
SAMETH, JACK R	TV DIRECTOR-PRODUCER	220 E 73RD ST #1-C	NEW YORK, NY	10021
SAMMETH, BARBARA	ACTRESS	1508 GREENFIELD AVE	LOS ANGELES, CA	90025
SAMMETH, BILL	TV PRODUCER	KTTV-TV, 5746 SUNSET BLVD	HOLLYWOOD, CA	90028
SAMMONS, LEE	BASEBALL	POST OFFICE BOX 4209	JACKSON, MS	39296
SAMMS, EMMA	ACTRESS-PHOTOGRAPGER	10401 WYTON DR	LOS ANGELES, CA	90024
SAMONDS, SHEREEN	BASEBALL EXECUTIVE	POST OFFICE BOX 5645	ORLANDO, FL	32855
SAMOYEDNY, JOHN	TV-COMEDY WRITER	JAKES HAIR STUDIO, 79 MAIN ST	DOBBS FERRY, NY	10522
SAMPEN, BILL	BASEBALL	EXPOS, 4545 DE COUBERTIN AVE	MONTREAL, QUE H1V 3P2	CANADA
SAMPLE, JOE	PIANIST-COMPOSER	9034 SUNSET BLVD #250	LOS ANGELES, CA	90069
SAMPLER, PHILECE	ACTRESS	BLAISDELL, 641 N NAOMI ST	BURBANK, CA	91505
SAMPLES, CANDY	ACTRESS-MODEL	POST OFFICE BOX 9786	MARINA DEL REY, CA	90295
SAMPLES, TODD	BASEBALL	POST OFFICE BOX 6748	ROCKFORD, IL	61125
SAMPSON, DON	SINGER	POST OFFICE BOX 84088	LOS ANGELES, CA	90073
SAMPSON, R J "PADDY"	DIRECTOR	33 WOOD ST #1005	TORONTO, ONT	CANADA
SAMPSON, RALPH	BASKETBALL	KINGS, 1 SPORTS PARKWAY	SACRAMENTO, CA	95834
SAMPSON-PARR, MARY ANN	ACTRESS	3138 GRIFFITH PARK BLVD	LOS ANGELES, CA	90027
SAMROCK, VICTOR	THEATER PRODUCER	745 5TH AVE	NEW YORK, NY	10022
SAMU, CHARLES	TV EXECUTIVE	HBO, 1100 6TH AVE	NEW YORK, NY	10036
SAMUDIO, DOMINGO	SINGER-SONGWRITER	SEE - SAMUDIO, SAM "THE SHAM"		
SAMUDIO, SAM "THE SHAM"	SINGER-SONGWRITER	3667 TETWILER AVE	MEMPHIS, TN	38122
SAMUEL, JUAN	BASEBALL	1000 ELYSIAN PARK DR	LOS ANGELES, CA	90012
SAMUELS, GEOFF	BASEBALL	POST OFFICE BOX 4370	SALINAS, CA	93912
SAMUELS, ROGER	BASEBALL	4865 TAMPICO WY	SAN JOSE, CA	95118
SAMUELS, SHERYL	ACTRESS	HANSEN, 2783 LA CASTANA DR	LOS ANGELES, CA	90046

SAMUELS, STU	TV EXECUTIVE	ABC-TV, 4151 PROSPECT AVE	LOS ANGELES, CA 90027
SAMUELSON, BETTY JEAN	ACTRESS	GILLY, 8721 SUNSET BLVD #103	LOS ANGELES, CA 90069
SAMUELSON, DAVID	FILM DIRECTOR	7 MONTAGUE MEWS WEST	LONDON W1H 1TF ENGLAND
SAMUELSON, MARC	DIRECTOR-PRODUCER	NEW ERA PRODUCTIONS, 1ST FLOOR	
		113 WARDOUR ST	LONDON W1V 3TD ENGLAND
SAMUELSON, MICHAEL	FILM EXECUTIVE	PINEWOOD STUDIOS, IVER HEATH	IVER, BUCKS SLO ONH ENGLAND
SAMUELSON, PETER	FILM PRODUCER	10401 WYTON DR	LOS ANGELES, CA 90024
SAMUELSON, SYDNEY W	FILM EXECUTIVE	UNIT 27, TAUNTON RD, GREENFIELD	MIDDLESEX UB6 8UQ ENGLAND
SAMUELSSON, KJELL	HOCKEY	FLYERS, SPECTRUM, PATTISON PL	PHILADELPHIA, PA 19148
SAMUELSSON, ULF	HOCKEY	PENGUINS, CIVIC ARENA, CENTRE AV	PITTSBURGH, PA 15219
SAMUL, JOSEPH	DIRECTOR	824 15TH ST #4	SANTA MONICA, CA 90403
SAN ANDRES, LUIS	WRITER-PRODUCER	28 CADMAN PLAZA W	BROOKLYN, NY 11201
SAN GIACOMO, LAURA	ACTRESS	8262 GOULD AVE	LOS ANGELES, CA 90046
SAN JUAN, OLGA	ACTRESS	4845 WILLOWCREST AVE	STUDIO CITY, CA 91604
SANBORN, DAVID	SAXOPHONIST	9034 SUNSET BLVD #250	LOS ANGELES, CA 90069
SANCHEZ, ADRIAN	BASEBALL	1524 W NEBRASKA AVE	PEORIA, IL 61604
SANCHEZ, ALEX	BASEBALL	POST OFFICE BOX 3665	OMAHA, NE 68103
SANCHEZ, CLARK	BODYBUILDER	PRO GYM FITNESS CENTER	
		322 MURIEL ST, NE	ALBUQUERQUE, NM 87123
SANCHEZ, ISRAEL	BASEBALL	500 NORTON ST	ROCHESTER, NY 14621
SANCHEZ, OZZIE	BASEBALL	POST OFFICE BOX 507	DURHAM, NC 27702
SANCHEZ, PATTY JOHNSON	BODYBUILDER	SEE - JOHNSON, PATTY-SANCHEZ	
SANCHEZ, PAUL	ACTOR	1015 GAYLEY AVE #300	LOS ANGELES, CA 90024
SANCHEZ, REY	BASEBALL	CUBS, 2ND & RIVERSIDE DR	DES MOINES, IA 50309
SANCHEZ, VICKI	COSTUME DESIGNER	13949 VENTURA BLVD #309	SHERMAN OAKS, CA 91423
SAND, FROMA	WRITER	1263 N HAYWORTH AVE #11	LOS ANGELES, CA 90046
SAND, H BARRY	TV WRITER-PRODUCER	1145 LONGWOOD AVE	LOS ANGELES, CA 90019
SAND, LAUREN JOY	TV WRITER	12000 SALTAIR PL	LOS ANGELES, CA 90049
SAND, PAUL	ACTOR-COMEDIAN	9301 WILSHIRE BLVD #312	BEVERLY HILLS, CA 90210
SAND, ROBERT L	TV WRITER	2236 OVERLAND AVE #7	LOS ANGELES, CA 90064
SANDA, DOMINIQUE	ACTRESS	3 QUIA MALAQUAIS	F-75006, FRANCE
SANDBANK, HENRY	DIRECTOR	24 NUTMEG DR	GREENWICH, CT 06830
SANDBERG, RYNE	BASEBALL	1060 W ADDISON ST	CHICAGO, IL 60613
SANDCASTLE	MUSICAL GROUP	POST OFFICE BOX 11283	RICHMOND, VA 23230
SANDEEN, DARRELL	ACTOR	12345 HUSTON ST	NORTH HOLLYWOOD, CA 91607
SANDEFUR, B W	TV WRITER	11166 VALLEY SPRING LN	NORTH HOLLYWOOD, CA 91602
SANDEFUR, DONALD DAVID	WRITER	11166 VALLEY SPRING LN	NORTH HOLLYWOOD, CA 91602
SANDER, BILL	GOLFER	POST OFFICE BOX 109601	PALM BCH GARDENS, FL 33418
SANDERLING, THOMAS	CONDUCTOR	ICM, 40 W 57TH ST	NEW YORK, NY 10019
SANDERS, AL	BASEBALL	POST OFFICE BOX 1718	NEW BRITAIN, CT 06050
SANDERS, BARBARA	ACTRESS	9040 HARRATT ST #5	LOS ANGELES, CA 90069
SANDERS, BARRY	FOOTBALL	LIONS, 1200 FEATHERSTONE RD	PONTIAC, MI 48432
SANDERS, BERNARD	U S CONGRESSMAN	191 BANK ST	BURLINGTON, VT 05401
SANDERS, BILL	CARTOONIST	POST OFFICE BOX 661	MILWAUKEE, WI 53201
SANDERS, CHARLES	BASEBALL EXECUTIVE	POST OFFICE BOX 16683	GREENVILLE, SC 29606
SANDERS, CHARLIE	FOOTBALL COACH	LIONS, 1200 FEATHERSTONE RD	PONTIAC, MI 48432
SANDERS, DEION	BASEBALL-FOOTBALL	POST OFFICE BOX 4064	ATLANTA, GA 30302
SANDERS, DOUG	GOLFER	8828 SANDRINGHAM DR	HOUSTON, TX 77024
SANDERS, DOUG	GOLFER	PGA SENIORS, 112 T P C BLVD	PONTE VEDRA BEACH, FL 32082
SANDERS, EARL	BASEBALL	POST OFFICE BOX 4209	JACKSON, MS 39296
SANDERS, ELIZABETH	ACTRESS	8721 SANTA MONICA BLVD #21	WEST HOLLYWOOD, CA 90069
SANDERS, ERIC	FOOTBALL	LIONS, 1200 FEATHERSTONE RD	PONTIAC, MI 48432
SANDERS, GERALD	BASEBALL SCOUT	POST OFFICE BOX 7575	PHILADELPHIA, PA 19101
SANDERS, GLENELL	FOOTBALL	RAMS, 2327 W LINCOLN BLVD	ANAHEIM, CA 92801
SANDERS, HENRY G	ACTOR	CBS-TV, "YOUNG & THE RESTLESS"	
		7800 BEVERLY BLVD #3305	LOS ANGELES, CA 90036
SANDERS, JACQUELINE	ACTRESS	20 RESIDENCES DE LA COTE	MORGES 1110
SANDERS, JAY O	ACTOR	2121 AVE OF THE STARS #950	LOS ANGELES, CA 90067
SANDERS, KELLY	ACTRESS	2151 GUTHRIE DR	LOS ANGELES, CA 90034
SANDERS, MARLENE	TV WRITER-DIRECTOR	175 RIVERSIDE DR	NEW YORK, NY 10024
SANDERS, MATT	BASEBALL	POST OFFICE BOX 418	SAINT CHARLES, IL 60174
SANDERS, MIKE	BASKETBALL	PACERS, 300 E MARKET ST	INDIANAPOLIS, IN 46204
SANDERS, PHAROAH	SAXOPHONIST	KURLAND, 173 BRIGHTON AVE	BOSTON, MA 02134
SANDERS, REGGIE	BASEBALL	REDS, 100 RIVERFRONT STADIUM	CINCINNATI, OH 45202
SANDERS, RICHARD	ACTOR-WRITER	2245 MAURICE AVE	LA CRESCENTA, CA 91214
SANDERS, RICKY	FOOTBALL	POST OFFICE BOX 17247 (DULLES)	WASHINGTON, DC 20041
SANDERS, SCOTT	BASEBALL	POST OFFICE BOX 1420	WICHITA, KS 67201
SANDERS, SUSAN	GOLFER	2750 VOLUSA AVE #B	DAYTON BEACH, FL 32114
SANDERS, SUZANNE	ACTRESS	7461 BEVERLY BLVD #400	LOS ANGELES, CA 90036
SANDERS, TERRY B	FILM WRITER-DIRECTOR	339 ADELAIDE DR	SANTA MONICA, CA 90402
SANDERS, THOMAS	FOOTBALL	EAGLES, BROAD ST & PATTISON AVE	PHILADELPHIA, PA 19148
SANDERS, TRACY	BASEBALL	2501 ALLEN AVE, SE	CANTON, OH 44707
SANDERSON, JIM	COLUMNIST	7720 EL CAMINO REAL #2-C	RANCHO LA COSTA, CA 92008
SANDERSON, SCOTT	BASEBALL	N Y YANKEES, YANKEE STADIUM	BRONX, NY 10451
SANDERSON, WILLIAM	ACTOR	469 N CROFT	LOS ANGELES, CA 90069
SANDESON, WILLIAM	CARTOONIST	119 W SHERWOOD TERR	FORT WAYNE, IN 46807
SANDIN, CARL H	DIRECTOR	5857 N KENMORE AVE	CHICAGO, IL 60660
SANDLAK, JIM	HOCKEY	CANUCKS, 100 N RENFREW ST	VANCOUVER, BC V5K 3N7 CANADA
SANDLER, BARRY	SCREENWRITER	515 N HUNTLEY DR	LOS ANGELES, CA 90048
SANDLER, MALLORY	ACTRESS	1440 23RD ST #317	SANTA MONICA, CA 90404
SANDLUND, DEBRA	ACTRESS	1999 AVE OF THE STARS #2850	LOS ANGELES, CA 90067
SANDOR, STEVE	ACTOR	1930 CENTURY PARK W #403	LOS ANGELES, CA 90067
SANDORA, SAM P	WRITER	7061 WHITSETT AVE #205	NORTH HOLLYWOOD, CA 91605
SANDOZ, DOLORES	ACTRESS	402 N PALM DR	BEVERLY HILLS, CA 90210
SANDRICH, JAY	ACTOR-DIRECTOR	1 NORTHSTAR ST #205	MARINA DEL REY, CA 90292

Name	Occupation	Address	City / Zip
SANDS, CHRISTOPHER	TV PRODUCER	962 N LA CIENEGA BLVD	LOS ANGELES, CA 90069
SANDS, HALLI	ACTRESS	12926 RIVERSIDE DR #C	SHERMAN OAKS, CA 91423
SANDS, JOHNNY	ACTOR	2333 KAPIOLANI BLVD	HONOLULU, HI 96814
SANDS, JULIAN	ACTOR	1287 OZETA TERR	LOS ANGELES, CA 90069
SANDS, TOMMY	ACTOR-SINGER	1047 21ST AVE	HONOLULU, HI 96816
SANDS, TRACY B, JR	COMPOSER	1201 N LADERA VISTA DR	FULLERTON, CA 92631
SANDS, WILLA	TV HOSTESS-PRODUCER	153 E 57TH ST #9-A	NEW YORK, NY 10022
SANDSTROM, TOMAS	HOCKEY	POST OFFICE BOX 17013	INGLEWOOD, CA 90308
SANDT, TOMMY	BASEBALL-COACH	POST OFFICE BOX 7000	PITTSBURGH, PA 15212
SANDUSKY, JOHN	FOOTBALL COACH	DOLPHINS, 2269 NW 199TH ST	MIAMI, FL 33056
SANDY, GARY	ACTOR	9229 SUNSET BLVD #311	LOS ANGELES, CA 90069
SANDY, JERRY L	TV DIRECTOR	644 DARTMOUTH AVE	SAN CARLOS, CA 94070
SANDY, TIM	BASEBALL	525 NW PEACOCK BLVD	PORT SAINT LUCIE, FL 34986
SANFORD, ALAN H	TV DIRECTOR	524 HALSEY AVE	FOREST HILLS, PA 15221
SANFORD, ARLENE	TV WRITER-DIRECTOR	1425 STANFORD ST #9	SANTA MONICA, CA 90404
SANFORD, BILLY	GUITARIST	2616 PENNINGTON BEND RD	NASHVILLE, TN 37214
SANFORD, CHARLES	FILM DIRECTOR	232 N WINDSOR BLVD	LOS ANGELES, CA 90004
SANFORD, DONALD S	TV WRITER	11515 AMANDA DR	NORTH HOLLYWOOD, CA 91604
SANFORD, GERALD	TV WRITER	9300 WILSHIRE BLVD #410	BEVERLY HILLS, CA 90212
SANFORD, ISABEL	ACTRESS	5657 WILSHIRE BLVD #290	LOS ANGELES, CA 90036
SANFORD, MARK	CINEMATOGRAPHER	7715 SUNSET BLVD #150	LOS ANGELES, CA 90046
SANFORD, MO	BASEBALL	POST OFFICE BOX 23290	NASHVILLE, TN 37202
SANFORD, TERRY	U S CONGRESSMAN	2418 BLUE RIDGE RD #204	RALEIGH, NC 27607
SANGER, ELEANOR	WRI-DIR-PROD	ABC SPORTS, 47 W 66TH ST	NEW YORK, NY 10023
SANGMEISTER, GEORGE E	U S CONGRESSMAN	101 N JOLIET ST	JOLIET, IL 60431
SANGSTER, JIMMY	WRITER-PRODUCER	1590 LINDACREST DR	BEVERLY HILLS, CA 90210
SANN, LAUREN	TV PRODUCER	JIM JOHNSTON FILMS, INC	
		140 E 39TH ST	NEW YORK, NY 10016
SANO, KAZUHIKO	ARTIST	105 STADIUM AVE	MILL VALLEY, CA 94941
SANOFF, JOEL R	WRITER	13429 MOORPARK ST #L	SHERMAN OAKS, CA 91423
SANSOM, ART	CARTOONIST	1050 EIRE CLIFF DR	CLEVELAND, OH 44107
SANTA ESMERALDA	ROCK & ROLL GROUP	AMUSEX, 970 O'BRIEN DR	MENLO PARK, CA 94025
SANTA MARIA, MONGO	CONGO DRUMMER	HOOKE, 78-08 223RD ST	BAYSIDE, NY 11364
SANTA MARIA, SILVERIO	BASEBALL	RED SOX, CHAIN O'LAKES PARK	WINTER HAVEN, FL 33880
SANTANA	ROCK & ROLL GROUP	201 11TH ST	SAN FRANCISCO, CA 94103
SANTANA, ANDRES	BASEBALL	S F GIANTS, CANDLESTICK PARK	SAN FRANICSCO, CA 94124
SANTANA, RAFAEL	BASEBALL COACH	300 STADIUM WY	DAVENPORT, FL 33837
SANTANA, RAUL	BASEBALL	POST OFFICE BOX 6748	ROCKFORD, IL 61125
SANTANA, RUBEN	BASEBALL	POST OFFICE BOX 9194	HAMPTON, VA 23670
SANTANA, TITO	WRESTLER	POST OFFICE BOX 3859	STAMFORD, CT 06905
SANTANGELO, F P	BASEBALL	1501 W 16TH ST	INDIANAPOLIS, IN 46202
SANTEE, CLARK K	DIRECTOR-PRODUCER	774 VILLAGE RD W	LAWRENCEVILLE, NJ 08648
SANTERS, THE	ROCK & ROLL GROUP	41 BRITAIN ST #200	TORONTO, ONT M5A 1R7 CANADA
SANTIAGO, BENITO	BASEBALL	POST OFFICE BOX 2000	SAN DIEGO, CA 92112
SANTIAGO, EDDIE	BASEBALL SCOUT	POST OFFICE BOX 4100	SEATTLE, WA 98104
SANTIAGO, ERNIE	BODYBUILDER	67-658 KUHE PL	WAIALUA, HI 96791
SANTIAGO, SAUNDRA	ACTRESS	10000 SANTA MONICA BLVD #305	LOS ANGELES, CA 90067
SANTILLAN, ANTONIO	DIRECTOR-PRODUCER	425 N ALFRED ST	LOS ANGELES, CA 90048
SANTIN, RUDY	BASEBALL SCOUT	N Y YANKEES, YANKEE STADIUM	BRONX, NY 10451
SANTING, MATHILDE	SINGER-PIANIST	GRAMAVISION, 121 W 27TH ST	NEW YORK, NY 10011
SANTO, MARK	WRITER	5750 WILSHIRE BLVD #512	LOS ANGELES, CA 90036
SANTO, RON	BASEBALL-ANNOUNCER	1060 W ADDISON ST	CHICAGO, IL 60613
SANTON, PENNY	ACTRESS	1918 N EDGEMONT ST	LOS ANGELES, CA 90027
SANTONI, RENI	ACTOR	4246 FARMDALE AVE	STUDIO CITY, CA 91604
SANTORUM, RICHARD JOHN	U S CONGRESSMAN	200 FLEET ST #4000	PITTSBURGH, PA 15220
SANTOS, GERRY	BASEBALL	POST OFFICE BOX 3004	SPRINGFIELD, IL 62708
SANTOS, JOE	ACTOR	10100 SANTA MONICA BLVD #700	LOS ANGELES, CA 90067
SANTOS, MISHAY	BODYBUILDER	GOLD'S GYM, 360 HAMPTON DR	VENICE, CA 90291
SANTOS, MOACIR	COMPOSER	1946 LAYTON ST	PASADENA, CA 91104
SANTOS, STEVEN J	DIRECTOR	900 HIGHLAND AVE #7	MANHATTAN BEACH, CA 90266
SANTOVENIA, NELSON	BASEBALL	CANADIANS, 4601 ONTARIO ST	VANCOUVER, BC V5V 3H4 CANADA
SANUCCI, FRANK	COMPOSER	226 N NAOMI ST	BURBANK, CA 91505
SAPERSTEIN, DAVID A	DIRECTOR	16 CALTON LN	NEW ROCHELLE, NY 10804
SAPERSTEIN, HENRY	FILM-TV PRODUCER	545 ARKELL DR	BEVERLY HILLS, CA 90210
SAPHIER, PETER	FILM PRODUCER	1800 CENTURY PARK E #1100	LOS ANGELES, CA 90067
SAPINSLEY, ALVIN	TV WRITER	15029 GREENLEAF ST	SHERMAN OAKS, CA 91403
SAPOLU, JESSE	FOOTBALL	S F 49ERS, 4949 CENTENNIAL BL	SANTA CLARA, CA 95054
SAPP, ROSS	BASEBALL SCOUT	POST OFFICE BOX 288	HOUSTON, TX 77001
SAPPHO, FRED	SCREENWRITER	8955 BEVERLY BLVD	WEST HOLLYWOOD, CA 90048
SARA, MIA	ACTRESS	POST OFFICE BOX 5617	BEVERLY HILLS, CA 90213
SARACENI, JOE	TV DIRECTOR-PRODUCER	NBC-TV, 30 ROCKEFELLER PLAZA	NEW YORK, NY 10112
SARACENO, CAROL	TV WRITER	1900 AVE OF THE STARS #2535	LOS ANGELES, CA 90067
SARAFIAN, RICHARD C	ACTOR	10000 SANTA MONICA BLVD #305	LOS ANGELES, CA 90067
SARAFIAN, RICHARD C	DIRECTOR	11901 SUNSET BLVD #203	LOS ANGELES, CA 90049
SARAH, DUCHESS OF YORK	DUCHESS	SUNNINGHILL PARK	WINDSOR ENGLAND
SARANDON, CHRIS	ACTOR	SMITH, 121 N SAN VICENTE BLVD	BEVERLY HILLS, CA 90211
SARANDON, SUSAN	ACTRESS	ICM, 40 W 57TH ST	NEW YORK, NY 10019
SARASOHN, CAROL	TV WRITER	30603 RAYO DEL SOL DR	MALIBU, CA 90265
SARASOHN, LANE	TV WRITER	30603 RAYO DEL SOL DR	MALIBU, CA 90265
SARAZAN, GENE	GOLFER	EMERALD BEACH, BOX 677	MARCO, FL 33937
SARBANES, PAUL S	U S SENATOR	309 HART SENATE OFFICE BLDG	WASHINGTON, DC 20510
SARBAUGH, MIKE	BASEBALL	2501 ALLEN AVE, SE	CANTON, OH 44707
SARD, SKIP	ACTOR	POST OFFICE BOX 755	BEVERLY HILLS, CA 90213
SARE, CHRIS	BODYBUILDER	WEIDER, 21100 ERWIN ST	WOODLAND HILLS, CA 91367
SARGENT, ALVIN	SCREENWRITER	267 MABERY RD	SANTA MONICA, CA 90402

Name	Occupation	Address	City	Zip
SARGENT, ANTHONY H	NEWS CORRESPONDENT	ABC NEWS, 1717 DE SALES ST, NW	WASHINGTON, DC	20036
SARGENT, BEN	CARTOONIST	UPS, 4900 MAIN ST, 9TH FLOOR	KANSAS CITY, MO	64112
SARGENT, BILL	THEATER PRODUCER	SPECIAL EVENTS ENTS		
		502 PARK AVE	NEW YORK, NY	10022
SARGENT, DICK	ACTOR	7422 PALO VISTA DR	LOS ANGELES, CA	90046
SARGENT, HERBERT	TV WRITER	LAZAROW & CO, 119 W 57TH ST	NEW YORK, NY	10019
SARGENT, JOSEPH	DIRECTOR-PRODUCER	33740 PACIFIC COAST HWY	MALIBU, CA	90265
SARIEGO, RALPH	DIRECTOR-PRODUCER	25682 MONTE NIDO DR	CALABASAS, CA	91302
SARKADY, CATHY	ACTRESS	305 E 40TH ST #12-E	NEW YORK, NY	10016
SARNE, MICHAEL	ACT-WRI-DIR	61 CAMPDEN HILL TOWERS	LONDON W11	ENGLAND
SARNO, ROBERT A	SCREENWRITER	8955 BEVERLY BLVD	WEST HOLLYWOOD, CA	90048
SARNOFF, JANE	TV WRITER	30 E END AVE	NEW YORK, NY	10028
SAROIAN, SUSAN	ACTRESS	22439 DARDENNE ST	WOODLAND HILLS, CA	91364
SAROYA, PRINCESS	PRINCESS	AVENUE MONTAIGNE	F-75008 PARIS	FRANCE
SAROYAN, HANK D	DIRECTOR	DGA, 7920 SUNSET BLVD, 6TH FL	LOS ANGELES, CA	90046
SARPALIUS, BILL	U S CONGRESSMAN	817 S POLK	AMARILLO, TX	79101
SARRER, JACK	BASEBALL EXECUTIVE	N Y YANKEES, YANKEE STADIUM	BRONX, NY	10451
SARRIS, ANDREW	FILM CRITIC	19 E 88TH ST	NEW YORK, NY	10028
SARSON, CHRISTOPHER	WRITER-PRODUCER	147 SYLVAN AVE	LEONIA, NJ	07605
SARTAIN, DAVID	BASEBALL	POST OFFICE BOX 661	KENOSHA, WI	53141
SARTAIN, GAILARD	ACTOR-WRITER	10000 SANTA MONICA BLVD #305	LOS ANGELES, CA	90067
SASDY, PETER	FILM-TV DIRECTOR	LONDON MGT, 235-241 REGENT ST	LONDON W1R 4PH	ENGLAND
SASSER, JIM	U S SENATOR	363 RUSSELL SENATE OFFICE BLDG	WASHINGTON, DC	20510
SASSER, MACKEY	BASEBALL	METS, 126TH ST & ROOSEVELT AVE	FLUSHING, NY	11368
SASSON, MICHAEL	CONDUCTOR	305 DEAN RD	BROOKLINE, MA	02146
SASSOON, BEVERLY ADAMS	ACTRESS-MODEL	1520 S BEVERLY GLEN #202	LOS ANGELES, CA	90024
SASSOON, CATYA	ACTRESS	738 N HOLMBY AVE	LOS ANGELES, CA	90024
SASSOON, VIDAL	HAIR STYLIST	2132 CENTURY PARK LN #108	LOS ANGELES, CA	90067
SATLOFF, RONALD	TV DIRECTOR-PRODUCER	15301 VENTURA BLVD #345	SHERMAN OAKS, CA	91403
SATTERFIELD, PAUL	ACTOR	ABC-TV, "GENERAL HOSPITAL"		
		4151 PROSPECT AVE	BURBANK, CA	91523
SATURDAY NIGHT BAND, THE	VOCAL GROUP	GOOD, 2500 NW 39TH ST	OKLAHOMA CITY, OK	73112
SAUER, DORIT	ACTRESS	10351 SANTA MONICA BLVD #211	LOS ANGELES, CA	90025
SAUER, ERNEST G	DIRECTOR	POST OFFICE BOX 20620		
		PARK WEST STATION	NEW YORK, NY	10025
SAUER, HANK	BASEBALL-SCOUT	S F GIANTS, CANDLESTICK PARK	SAN FRANICSCO, CA	94124
SAUER, LEO	ACTOR	2832 WAVERLY DR	LOS ANGELES, CA	90039
SAUER, MARK	BASEBALL EXECUTIVE	250 STADIUM PLAZA	ST LOUIS, MO	63102
SAUER, RICHARD C	SCREENWRITER	8955 BEVERLY BLVD	WEST HOLLYWOOD, CA	90048
SAUERS, GENE	GOLFER	POST OFFICE BOX 109601	PALM BCH GARDENS, FL	33418
SAUL, IRA	BASEBALL EXECUTIVE	POST OFFICE BOX 2148	WOODBRIDGE, VA	22193
SAUL, OSCAR	SCREENWRITER	448 HILGARD AVE	LOS ANGELES, CA	90024
SAULTER, KEVIN	BASEBALL	POST OFFICE BOX 4525	MACON, GA	31208
SAUNDERS, AL	FOOTBALL COACH	CHIEFS, 1 ARROWHEAD DR	KANSAS CITY, MO	64129
SAUNDERS, CARL R	COMPOSER	6506 BEN AVE	NORTH HOLLYWOOD, CA	91606
SAUNDERS, DOUG	BASEBALL	POST OFFICE BOX 598	BINGHAMTON, NY	13902
SAUNDERS, HERMAN S	TV PRODUCER	3551 VISTA HAVEN RD	SHERMAN OAKS, CA	91403
SAUNDERS, JEREMY	FILM EXECUTIVE	PRODUCTION CENTRE		
		40-44 CLIPSTONE ST	LONDON W1P 7EA	ENGLAND
SAUNDERS, JUDITH	DIRECTOR	DGA, 7920 SUNSET BLVD, 6TH FL	LOS ANGELES, CA	90046
SAUTTER, CARL G	TV WRITER	2151 N BEACHWOOD DR	LOS ANGELES, CA	90068
SAUVEUR, RICH	BASEBALL	POST OFFICE BOX 3665	OMAHA, NE	68103
SAVADOVE, LAURENCE	WRITER-PRODUCER	7420 FRANKLIN AVE	LOS ANGELES, CA	90046
SAVAGE, CHARLES	BASEBALL EXECUTIVE	POST OFFICE BOX 651	AUBURN, NY	13021
SAVAGE, ELIZABETH	ACTRESS	9000 SUNSET BLVD #1200	LOS ANGELES, CA	90069
SAVAGE, ELIZABETH	WRESTLING MANAGER	SEE - MISS ELIZABETH		
SAVAGE, FRED	ACTOR	ABC-TV, 4151 PROSPECT AVE	HOLLYWOOD, CA	90027
SAVAGE, GAIL, BAND	ROCK & ROLL GROUP	POST OFFICE BOX 1600	HAVERHILL, MA	01831
SAVAGE, GUS	U S CONGRESSMAN	11434 S HALSTED	CHICAGO, IL	60628
SAVAGE, JOHN	ACTOR	ICM, 8899 BEVERLY BLVD	LOS ANGELES, CA	90048
SAVAGE, JUDITH	AGENT	6212 BANNER AVE	LOS ANGELES, CA	90038
SAVAGE, LISA	ACTRESS	3575 W CAHUENGA BLVD #252	LOS ANGELES, CA	90068
SAVAGE, PETER	WRITER-PRODUCER	2803 WEEKS AVE	OCEANSIDE, NY	11572
SAVAGE, RANDY "MACHO MAN"	WRESTLER	POST OFFICE BOX 3859	STAMFORD, CT	06905
SAVAGE, TRACIE	ACTRESS	6212 BANNER AVE	LOS ANGELES, CA	90038
SAVAGE GRACE	ROCK & ROLL GROUP	232 S REEVES DR #101	BEVERLY HILLS, CA	90212
SAVAL, DANY	ACTRESS	131 RUE DE L'UNIVERSITE	F-75007 PARIS	FRANCE
SAVALAS, TELLY	ACT-WRI-DIR	101 WILSHIRE BLVD #309	SANTA MONICA, CA	90401
SAVARD, DENIS	HOCKEY	CANADIENS, 2313 ST CATHERINE ST	MONTREAL, QUE H3H 1N2	CANADA
SAVATAGE	ROCK & ROLL GROUP	ROBERT ZEMSKY, AMI PRODUCTIONS		
		1776 BROADWAY, 10TH FLOOR	NEW YORK, NY	10019
SAVEGAR, BRIAN	ART DIRECTOR	POST OFFICE BOX 5617	BEVERLY HILLS, CA	90213
SAVEL, DAVA	TV WRITER	8955 BEVERLY BLVD	WEST HOLLYWOOD, CA	90048
SAVENICK, PHILLIP ADAM	TV WRITER	8064 WILLOW GLEN RD	LOS ANGELES, CA	90046
SAVIANO, PAT	DIRECTOR	7901 W BLOOMINGDALE	ELMWOOD PARK, IL	60635
SAVIDGE, JENNIFER	ACTRESS	2705 GLENDOWER AVE	LOS ANGELES, CA	90027
SAVILE, DAVID	ACTOR	28 COLOMB ST	LONDON SE10 9EW	ENGLAND
SAVILLE, PHILIP	TV WRITER-DIRECTOR	RAE, CHARING CROSS RD	LONDON WC2H ODB	ENGLAND
SAVINON, ODALIS	BASEBALL	POST OFFICE BOX 12557	ST PETERSBURG, FL	33733
SAVITZ, CHARLOTTE	PRODUCER	7800 BEVERLY BLVD #3371	LOS ANGELES, CA	90036
SAVOY BROWN	ROCK & ROLL GROUP	FAA, 1700 BROADWAY, 5TH FLOOR	NEW YORK, NY	10019
SAWATSKI, CARL	BASEBALL-EXECUTIVE	POST OFFICE BOX 25010	LITTLE ROCK, AZ	72221
SAWKIW, WARREN	BASEBALL	POST OFFICE BOX 2785	LAKELAND, FL	33806

SAWMILL CREEK	VOCAL GROUP	LST, 2138 FLAG MARSH RD	MOUNT AIRY, MD	21771
SAWYER, BART	WRESTLER	8725 N CHAUTAUQUA BLVD	PORTLAND, OR	97217
SAWYER, BEVERLY M	FILM EDITOR	1523 CRENSHAW BLVD	LOS ANGELES, CA	90019
SAWYER, DEL	MUSIC ARRANGER	4400 BELMONT PARK TERR #204	NASHVILLE, TN	37215
SAWYER, DIANE	BROADCAST JOURNALIST	CBS NEWS, 524 W 57TH ST	NEW YORK, NY	10019
SAWYER, FORREST	TV HOST	CBS MORNING NEWS		
		51 W 52ND ST	NEW YORK, NY	10019
SAWYER, JOHN	FOOTBALL EXECUTIVE	BENGALS, 200 RIVERFRONT STADIUM	CINCINNATI, OH	45202
SAWYER, THOMAS	U S CONGRESSMAN	FEDERAL BUILDING		
		2 S MAIN ST	AKRON, OH	44308
SAWYER, THOMAS B	WRITER-PRODUCER	25301 MALIBU RD	MALIBU, CA	90265
SAWYER, TONI	ACTRESS	8228 SUNSET BLVD #212	LOS ANGELES, CA	90046
SAWYER BROWN	C & W GROUP	STARBOUND, 1516 16TH AVE S	NASHVILLE, TN	37212
SAX, DAVE	BASEBALL	1155 W MOUND ST	COLUMBUS, OH	43223
SAX, MICHAEL	COMEDY WRITER	3327 BROOKSIDE DR	MALIBU, CA	90265
SAX, STEVE	BASEBALL	333 W 35TH ST	CHICAGO, IL	60616
SAXON	ROCK & ROLL GROUP	POST OFFICE BOX 69	WOLVERHAMPTON WV6 9AQ	ENGLAND
SAXON, ERIC	SINGER	1209 BAYLOR ST	AUSTIN, TX	78703
SAXON, JAMES	FOOTBALL	CHIEFS, 1 ARROWHEAD DR	KANSAS CITY, MO	64129
SAXON, JOHN	ACTOR-WRITER	2432 BANYAN DR	LOS ANGELES, CA	90049
SAXON, MIKE	FOOTBALL	COWBOYS, 1 COWBOYS PARKWAY	IRVING, TX	75063
SAXON, SKY "SUNLIGHT"	SINGER-GUITARIST	POST OFFICE BOX 1984	KAILUA, HI	96734
SAXTON, JIM	U S CONGRESSMAN	1 MAINE AVE	CHERRY HILL, NJ	08002
SAXTON, JOHN C	SCREENWRITER	8955 BEVERLY BLVD	WEST HOLLYWOOD, CA	90048
SAYEGH, JAMES N	DIRECTOR	563 5TH ST	BROOKLYN, NY	11215
SAYER, LEO	SINGER-SONGWRITER	151 S EL CAMINO DR	BEVERLY HILLS, CA	90212
SAYERS, GALE	FOOTBALL	624 BUCH RD	NORTHBROOK, IL	60062
SAYERS, PETER	GUITARIST	ROSEWOOD HOUSE, WOODITTON RD		
		NEWMARKET	SUFFOLK CB8 9BQ	ENGLAND
SAYLE, ALEXEI	ACT-WRI-COMED	MAYER MGMT, GRAFTON HOUSE #44		
		2-3 GOLDEN SQ	LONDON W1R 3AD	ENGLAND
SAYLES, STEVE	BASEBALL TRAINER	POST OFFICE BOX 1420	WICHITA, KS	67201
SBARDELLATI, JIM	PRODUCER	2246 EDENDALE PL	LOS ANGELES, CA	90039
SBARGE, RAPHAEL	ACTOR	3151 W CAHUENGA BLVD #310	LOS ANGELES, CA	90068
SCAASI, ARNOLD	COSTUME DESIGNER	681 5TH AVE	NEW YORK, NY	10022
SCACCHI, GRETA	ACTRESS	HEATH, PARAMOUNT HOUSE		
		162-170 WARDOUR ST	LONDON W1V 3AT	ENGLAND
SCADUTO, AL	CARTOONIST	KING FEATURES, 216 E 45TH ST	NEW YORK, NY	10017
SCAGGS, BOZ	SINGER-SONGWRITER	345 N MAPLE DR #235	BEVERLY HILLS, CA	90210
SCALA, TINA	ACTRESS	915 ARIZONA AVE #7	SANTA MONICA, CA	90401
SCALES, GREG	FOOTBALL	SAINTS, 1500 POYDRAS ST	NEW ORLEANS, LA	90112
SCALES, HARVEY	SINGER	8467 BEVERLY BLVD #112	LOS ANGELES, CA	90048
SCALES, PRUNELLA	ACTRESS	CONWAY, 18-21 JERMYN ST	LONDON SW1	ENGLAND
SCALES, TOM	TV CRITIC	THE WASHINGTON POST		
		1150 15TH ST, NW	WASHINGTON, DC	20071
SCALIA, ANTONIN	SUPREME COURT JUDGE	1 1ST ST, NE	WASHINGTON, DC	20543
SCALICI, JACK	ACTOR	7215 HILLSIDE AVE #27	HOLLYWOOD, CA	90046
SCANCARELLI, JIM	CARTOONIST	TRIBUNE, 64 E CONCORD ST	ORLANDO, FL	32801
SCANLAN, BOB	BASEBALL	1060 W ADDISON ST	CHICAGO, IL	60613
SCANLAN, JOSEPH L	DIRECTOR	14004 PALAWAN WY #314	MARINA DEL REY, CA	90292
SCANLON, JAMES	ACTOR	1521 N SIERRA BONITA AVE	LOS ANGELES, CA	90046
SCANNELL, KEVIN	ACTOR	11726 SAN VICENTE BLVD #300	LOS ANGELES, CA	90049
SCANNELL, SUSAN	ACTRESS	247 S BEVERLY DR #102	BEVERLY HILLS, CA	90210
SCANNELLA, JOE	FOOTBALL COACH	RAIDERS, 332 CENTER ST	EL SEGUNDO, CA	90245
SCARABELLI, MICHELE	ACTRESS	4720 VINELAND AVE #216	NORTH HOLLYWOOD, CA	91602
SCARBER, SAM	ACTOR	12209 CREWE ST	NORTH HOLLYWOOD, CA	91605
SCARBOROUGH, JOHN	FILM EXECUTIVE	169 QUEENSGATE #8-A	LONDON SW7 5EH	ENGLAND
SCARBURY, JOEY	SINGER-SONGWRITER	LAVENDER, 444 2ND AVE	SEASIDE, OR	97138
SCARNECCHIA, DANTE	FOOTBALL COACH	POST OFFICE BOX 535000	INDIANPOLIS, IN	46253
SCARPACI, PHIL	ACTOR	6909 LASAINE AVE	VAN NUYS, CA	91406
SCARPELLI, GLENN	ACTOR	3480 BARHAM BLVD #320	LOS ANGELES, CA	90068
SCARSONE, STEVE	BASEBALL	POST OFFICE BOX 3449	SCRANTON, PA	18505
SCARWID, DIANA	ACTRESS	POST OFFICE BOX 3614	SAVANNAH, GA	31404
SCARZA, VINCENT J	DIRECTOR-PRODUCER	FADO, 145 E 15TH ST	NEW YORK, NY	10003
SCATES, JOE	RECORD EXECUTIVE	POST OFFICE BOX 12353	SAN ANTONIO, TX	78212
SCATTERDAY, PAUL	ACTOR	6040 CARLOS AVE #5	LOS ANGELES, CA	90028
SCATTINI, BEN	ACTOR	6461 KESTER AVE #11	VAN NUYS, CA	91411
SCAVULLO, FRANCESCO	PHOTOGRAPHER	212 E 63RD ST	NEW YORK, NY	10021
SCDMIDT, BILL	BASEBALL SCOUT	N Y YANKEES, YANKEE STADIUM	BRONX, NY	10451
SCERBO, FRANCES	ACTOR	347 W 57TH ST #16-F	NEW YORK, NY	10019
SCHAADT, JAMES G	DIRECTOR	POST OFFICE BOX 173	COTUIT, MA	02635
SCHAAL, RICHARD	ACT-WRI-DIR	5657 WILSHIRE BLVD #290	LOS ANGELES, CA	90036
SCHAAL, WENDY	ACTRESS	3701 LONGVIEW VALLEY RD	SHERMAN OAKS, CA	91403
SCHAD, MIKE	FOOTBALL	EAGLES, BROAD ST & PATTISON AVE	PHILADELPHIA, PA	19148
SCHAEFER, BOB	BASEBALL COACH	POST OFFICE BOX 419969	KANSAS CITY, MO	64141
SCHAEFER, CHRIS	BASEBALL	POST OFFICE BOX 3665	OMAHA, NE	68103
SCHAEFER, DAN	U S CONGRESSMAN	3615 S HURON ST #101	ENGLEWOOD, CO	80110
SCHAEFER, GEORGE	TV DIRECTOR-PRODUCER	1040 WOODLAND DR	BEVERLY HILLS, CA	90210
SCHAEFER, HAL	COMPOSER-CONDUCTOR	11 DERBY RD	PORT WASHINGTON, NY	11050
SCHAEFER, JEFF	BASEBALL	POST OFFICE BOX 4100	SEATTLE, WA	98104
SCHAEFER, LAURA	ACTRESS	6310 SAN VICENTE BLVD #407	LOS ANGELES, CA	90048
SCHAEFER, WILLIAM DONALD	GOVERNOR	STATE HOUSE BUILDING	ANNAPOLIS, MD	21401
SCHAEFER, WILLIS H	COMPOSER-CONDUCTOR	10850 RIVERSIDE DR #505	NORTH HOLLYWOOD, CA	91602
SCHAEFFER, IRENE	ART DIRECTOR	1340 BOXWOOD DR E	HEWLETT, NY	11557
SCHAEFFER, RICHARD M	WRITER	STAR INC, 4 WORLD TRADE CENTER	NEW YORK, NY	10048

Name	Occupation	Address	City/State	Zip
SCHAEFFER, S	FILM CRITIC	BOSTON HERALD, 1 HERALD SQ	BOSTON, MA	02106
SCHAETZLE, BUD	DIRECTOR	3855 LANKERSHIM BLVD #122	NORTH HOLLYWOOD, CA	91604
SCHAFER, JEFFREY	BASEBALL	20 BRIGHTWOOD ST	PATCHOGUE, NY	11772
SCHAFER, REUBEN	ACTOR	175 W 87TH ST #25-F	NEW YORK, NY	10024
SCHAFER, RUBE	SINGER	PROCESS, 439 WILEY AVE	FRANKLIN, PA	16323
SCHAFFEL, BETH	ACTRESS	17211 OROZCO ST	GRANADA HILLS, CA	91344
SCHAFFEL, LEWIS	BASKETBALL EXECUTIVE	MIAMI HEAT, THE MIAMI ARENA	MIAMI, FL	33136
SCHAFFNER, FRANKLIN	DIRECTOR	2158 LA MESA DR	SANTA MONICA, CA	90402
SCHAIN, DONALD	WRITER-PRODUCER	1865 N FULLER AVE #203	LOS ANGELES, CA	90046
SCHALL, GENE	BASEBALL	POST OFFICE BOX 1721	SPARTANBURG, SC	29304
SCHALLERT, WILLIAM	ACTOR	14920 RAMOS PL	PACIFIC PALISADES, CA	90272
SCHALOW, JACK	BASKETBALL COACH	700 NE MULTNOMAH ST #600	PORTLAND, OR	97232
SCHALY, JIM	BASEBALL UMPIRE	POST OFFICE BOX 716	PLAINVILLE, CT	06062
SCHANZ, SCOTT	BASEBALL	POST OFFICE BOX 30160	SAN BERNARDINO, CA	92413
SCHARF, WALTER	COMPOSER-CONDUCTOR	814 AMHERST AVE #102	LOS ANGELES, CA	90049
SCHARFF, TONY	BASEBALL	POST OFFICE BOX 882	MADISON, WI	53701
SCHARFMAN, MORT	TV WRITER	1616 PANDORA AVE	LOS ANGELES, CA	90024
SCHARHAG, KYLE	BASEBALL EXECUTIVE	POST OFFICE BOX 814	PULASKI, VA	24301
SCHARLACH, ED	TV WRITER	3570 VISTA HAVEN RD	SHERMAN OAKS, CA	91403
SCHATZBERG, JERRY	FILM WRITER-DIRECTOR	BARD & KASS, 551 5TH AVE	NEW YORK, NY	10176
SCHATZEDER, DAN	BASEBALL	33 E MADISON ST	VILLA PARK, IL	60181
SCHAYES, DAN	BASKETBALL	BRADLEY CENTER, 1001 N 4TH ST	MILWAUKEE, WI	53203
SCHEAR, MICHAEL A	DIRECTOR	98 EMWOOD DR	EMERSON, NJ	07630
SCHECTER, LES	THEATER PRODUCER	1501 BROADWAY	NEW YORK, NY	10036
SCHEER, CARL	BASKETBALL EXECUTIVE	POST OFFICE BOX 4658	DENVER, CO	80204
SCHEERER, ROBERT	WRITER-PRODUCER	4951 CARPENTER AVE	NORTH HOLLYWOOD, CA	91607
SCHEFF, MICHAEL	TV WRITER	10400 SUMMER HOLLY CIR	LOS ANGELES, CA	90077
SCHEFFER, RON	DIRECTOR	88 LEXINGTON AVE	NEW YORK, NY	10016
SCHEFFER, STEPHEN J	TV EXECUTIVE	HBO, 1100 6TH AVE	NEW YORK, NY	10036
SCHEFFLER, JOHN C	ART DIRECTOR	252 CARLTON AVE	BROOKLYN, NY	11205
SCHEFFLER, STEVE	BASKETBALL	310 N KINGS DR	CHARLOTTE, NC	28204
SCHEID, RICH	BASEBALL	CANADIANS, 4601 ONTARIO ST	VANCOUVER, BC V5V 3H4	CANADA
SCHEIDER, ROY	ACTOR	6220 DEL VALLE DR	LOS ANGELES, CA	90048
SCHEIMER, LOUIS	TV PRODUCER	18918 LA MONTANA PL	TARZANA, CA	91356
SCHEINMAN, ANDREW	FILM PRODUCER	CAA, 9830 WILSHIRE BLVD	BEVERLY HILLS, CA	90212
SCHELL, CATHERINE	ACTRESS	CCA, 4 COURT LODGE		
		48 SLOANE SQ	LONDON SW1W 8AT	ENGLAND
SCHELL, MARIA	ACTRESS	NORDSTR 5	D-(W) 8090 REITMEHRING	GERMANY
SCHELL, MAURICE	SOUND EDITOR	610 W 110TH ST #7-A	NEW YORK, NY	10025
SCHELL, MICHAEL	BASEBALL EXECUTIVE	POST OFFICE BOX 802	WATERTOWN, NY	13601
SCHELL, RONNIE	COMEDIAN-ACTOR	4024 SAPPHIRE DR	ENCINO, CA	91316
SCHELLA, MICHAEL	TV WRITER	8736 OAKDALE AVE	NORTHRIDGE, CA	91324
SCHELYER, JOHN	FOOTBALL REFEREE	NFL, 410 PARK AVE	NEW YORK, NY	10022
SCHEMBECHLER, BO	BASEBALL EXECUTIVE	TIGERS, TIGER STADIUM	DETROIT, MI	48216
SCHEMBECHLER, BO	FOOTBALL COACH	870 ARLINGTON BLVD	ANN ARBOR, MI	48106
SCHENCK, GEORGE	WRITER-PRODUCER	17949 KAREN DR	ENCINO, CA	91316
SCHENKEL, RICHARD	DIRECTOR	162 PEACEABLE ST	RIDGEFIELD, CT	06877
SCHENKEL, STEPHEN D	TV WRITER-PRODUCER	65 CENTRAL PARK W #11-E	NEW YORK, NY	10023
SCHEPISI, FREDERIC	FILM WRITER-DIRECTOR	10401 VENICE BLVD #230	LOS ANGELES, CA	90034
SCHEPPS, SHAWN	STORY EDITOR	MTA, 9320 WILSHIRE BL, 3RD FL	BEVERLY HILLS, CA	90212
SCHERER, PRISCILLA	FILM PRODUCER	COLOSSAL, 2800 3RD ST	SAN FRANCISCO, CA	94107
SCHERICK, EDGAR J	FILM PRODUCER	4000 W ALAMEDA AVE	BURBANK, CA	91505
SCHERMAN-STEIN, RONI	DIRECTOR	93 COUNTRY RIDGE DR		
		RYE BROOK	NEW YORK, NY	10573
SCHERRER, BILL	BASEBALL	7166 CASCADE ST	SPRING HILL, FL	33526
SCHERZER, LINDA	NEW CORRESPONDENT	1050 TECHWOOD DR, NW	ATLANTA, GA	30318
SCHEUER, CHRIS	BASEBALL EXECUTIVE	POST OFFICE BOX 3746, HILL STA	AUGUSTA, GA	30904
SCHEUER, JAMES	U S CONGRESSMAN	137-08 NORTHERN BLVD	FLUSHING, NY	11354
SCHIAVELLI, VINCENT	ACTOR	9200 SUNSET BLVD #710	LOS ANGELES, CA	90069
SCHIBI, MARGARET J	TV WRITER	2030 OAKSTONE WY	LOS ANGELES, CA	90046
SCHICK, ELLIOT	DIRECTOR-PRODUCER	2175 CASTILIAN DR	LOS ANGELES, CA	90068
SCHICK, STEPHANIE	ACTRESS-DANCER	9229 SUNSET BLVD #208	LOS ANGELES, CA	90069
SCHICKEL, RICHARD	FILM WRITER-PRODUCER	8955 BEVERLY BLVD	WEST HOLLYWOOD, CA	90048
SCHIEFFER, BOB	BROADCAST JOURNALIST	CBS NEWS, 524 W 57TH ST	NEW YORK, NY	10019
SCHIEFFER, J THOMAS	BASEBALL EXECUTIVE	POST OFFICE BOX 90111	ARLINGTON, TX	76004
SCHIFF, DAVID	TALENT AGENT	ICM, 8899 BEVERLY BLVD	LOS ANGELES, CA	90048
SCHIFF, MARK	COMEDIAN	12456 VENTURA BLVD #1	STUDIO CITY, CA	91604
SCHIFF, STEPHEN	FILM CRITIC	VANITY FAIR, 350 MADISON AVE	NEW YORK, NY	10017
SCHIFF, STEVEN	U S CONGRESSMAN	625 SILVER AVE #140, SW	ALBUQUERQUE, NM	87102
SCHIFFER, CLAUDIA	MODEL	AUSSENWALL 94	D-(W) 4134 RHEINBERG	GERMANY
SCHIFFER, MICHAEL	SCREENWRITER	8955 BEVERLY BLVD	WEST HOLLYWOOD, CA	90048
SCHIFFMAN, GLENN	SCREENWRITER	10328 LEOLANG AVE	SUNLAND, CA	91040
SCHIFRIN, LALO	COMPOSER-CONDUCTOR	710 N HILLCREST RD	BEVERLY HILLS, CA	90210
SCHILD, GREG	BASEBALL EXECUTIVE	POST OFFICE BOX 7893	EVERETT, WA	98201
SCHILLER, CRAIG	TV DIRECTOR-PRODUCER	4522 WOODMAN AVE #C-210	SHERMAN OAKS, CA	91423
SCHILLER, LAWRENCE J	DIRECTOR-PRODUCER	POST OFFICE BOX 5784	SHERMAN OAKS, CA	91413
SCHILLER, RHODA K	TV DIRECTOR	1741 "T" ST #303, NW	WASHINGTON, DC	20009
SCHILLER, ROBERT A	WRITER-PRODUCER	1661 CASALE RD	PACIFIC PALISADES, CA	90272
SCHILLER, THOMAS	WRITER-PRODUCER	DGA, 110 W 57TH ST	NEW YORK, NY	10019
SCHILLING, CURT	BASEBALL	POST OFFICE BOX 7575	PHILADELPHIA, PA	19101
SCHILLING, PETER	SINGER	ABANDA MUSIKUNTERNEHEM		
		39 ZENETTI ST	8000 MUNICH 2	GERMANY
SCHILLING, WILLIAM	ACTOR	626 N VALLEY ST	BURBANK, CA	91505
SCHILLIO, EMILE J	COMPOSER	106 S KINGS RD	LOS ANGELES, CA	90048
SCHILZ, TED G, JR	DIRECTOR	4714 ARCOLA AVE	NORTH HOLLYWOOD, CA	91602

SCHINDEL, HUGH	BASEBALL EXECUTIVE	POST OFFICE BOX 3169	FREDERICK, MD	21701
SCHINDLER, MAX A	DIRECTOR-NEWS CORRES	904 S BELGRADE RD	SILVER SPRING, MD	20902
SCHINDLER, MERRILL	FILM CRITIC	1888 CENTURY PARK E #920	LOS ANGELES, CA	90067
SCHINTZIUS, DWAYNE	BASKETBALL	600 E MARKET ST #102	SAN ANTONIO, TX	78205
SCHIOWITZ, JOSH	TALENT AGENT	8228 SUNSET BLVD #212	LOS ANGELES, CA	90046
SCHIPPER, HENRY	COLUMNIST	5700 WILSHIRE BLVD #120	LOS ANGELES, CA	90036
SCHIRALDI, CALVIN	BASEBALL	2102 SAN JUAN	AUSTIN, TX	78746
SCHIRALDI, FRANK	CINEMATOGRAPHER	185 APPLEGATE LN	EAST BRUNSWICK, NJ	08816
SCHIRRA, WALTER M, JR	ASTRONAUT	16834 VIA DE SANTA FE	RANCHO SANTA FE, CA	92067
SCHISGAL, MURRAY	SCREENWRITER	555 W 57TH ST #1230	NEW YORK, NY	10019
SCHLAFLY, PHYLLIS	NEWS CORRESPONDENT	68 FAIRMONT	ALTON, IL	62002
SCHLAMME, THOMAS D	TV DIRECTOR	123 W 88TH ST	NEW YORK, NY	10024
SCHLATTER, CHARLIE	ACTOR	9200 SUNSET BLVD #428	LOS ANGELES, CA	90069
SCHLATTER, GEORGE	WRITER-PRODUCER	8320 BEVERLY BLVD	LOS ANGELES, CA	90048
SCHLECHT, RICHARD	ARTIST	2724 S JUNE ST	ARLINGTON, VA	22202
SCHLENKER, DAVID	BASEBALL SCOUT	POST OFFICE BOX 2000	ANAHEIM, CA	92803
SCHLENKER, MARVIN	DIRECTOR	23 KRISTIN PL	OLD TAPPAN, NJ	07675
SCHLENKER, RICH	BASEBALL SCOUT	POST OFFICE BOX 2000	ANAHEIM, CA	92803
SCHLERETH, MARK	FOOTBALL	POST OFFICE BOX 17247 (DULLES)	WASHINGTON, DC	20041
SCHLESINGER, JOHN R	DIRECTOR	1896 RISING GLEN	LOS ANGELES, CA	90069
SCHLEUSSNER, CATHY	TALENT AGENT	4146 LANKERSHIM BLVD #300	NORTH HOLLYWOOD, CA	91602
SCHLISSEL, JACK	THEATER PRODUCER	234 W 44TH ST	NEW YORK, NY	10036
SCHLOSS, HANK	C$NEMATOGRAPHER	149 S MAPLE DR	BEVERLY HILLS, CA	90212
SCHMERER, JAMES	TV WRITER	15321 KINGSWOOD LN	SHERMAN OAKS, CA	91403
SCHMERTZ, HERB	COLUMNIST	HERITAGE FEATURES SYNDICATE		
		214 MASSACHUSETTS AVE, NE	WASHINGTON, DC	20002
SCHMIDT, BILL	BASEBALL SCOUT	POST OFFICE BOX 90111	ARLINGTON, TX	76004
SCHMIDT, CHUCK	FOOTBALL EXECUTIVE	LIONS, 1200 FEATHERSTONE RD	PONTIAC, MI	48432
SCHMIDT, DAVE J	BASEBALL	5144 E WAGNER WY	AGOURA, CA	91301
SCHMIDT, DAVID	BASEBALL	RED SOX, CHAIN O'LAKES PARK	WINTER HAVEN, FL	33880
SCHMIDT, JASON	BASEBALL	POST OFFICE BOX 4525	MACON, GA	31208
SCHMIDT, JOE	CARTOONIST	POST OFFICE BOX 1207	CHULA VISTA, CA	92011
SCHMIDT, KEITH	BASEBALL	POST OFFICE BOX 418	SAINT CHARLES, IL	60174
SCHMIDT, MIKE	BASEBALL	24 LAKEWOOD DR	MEDIA, PA	19063
SCHMIDT, TIM	BASEBALL SCOUT	N Y YANKEES, YANKEE STADIUM	BRONX, NY	10451
SCHMIETH, MARY T	CARTOONIST	TRIBUNE, 64 E CONCORD ST	ORLANDO, FL	32801
SCHMIT, TIMOTHY B	SINGER-GUITARIST	2416 CARMAN CREST DR	LOS ANGELES, CA	90068
SCHMITT, ANNE MARIE	TV PRODUCER	1717 N HIGHLAND AVE #807	HOLLYWOOD, CA	90028
SCHMITT, HARRISON	U S SENATOR	POST OFFICE BOX 14338	ALBUQUERQUE, NM	87191
SCHMITTOU, LARRY	BASEBALL EXECUTIVE	POST OFFICE BOX 23290	NASHVILLE, TN	37202
SCHMITZ, BILL	FOOTBALL REFEREE	NFL, 410 PARK AVE	NEW YORK, NY	10022
SCHMOELLER, DAVID	FILM WRITER-DIRECTOR	2244 STANLEY HILLS DR	LOS ANGELES, CA	90046
SCHNACKE, KEN	BASEBALL EXECUTIVE	1155 W MOUND ST	COLUMBUS, OH	43223
SCHNAPPER, BONNIE	TV PRODUCER	77 FULTON ST	NEW YORK, NY	10038
SCHNARRE, MONIKA	MODEL	FORD MODELS, 344 E 59TH ST	NEW YORK, NY	10022
SCHNECK, STEPHEN	SCREENWRITER	1628 N GARDNER ST	LOS ANGELES, CA	90046
SCHNEER, CHARLES H	FILM PRODUCER	ANDOR, 8 ILCHESTER PL	LONDON W14 8AA	ENGLAND
SCHNEIDER, ANDREW	TV WRITER-PRODUCER	3148 WAVERLY DR	LOS ANGELES, CA	90027
SCHNEIDER, ANDY	TV PRODUCER	LARSON, 10201 W PICO BLVD	LOS ANGELES, CA	90035
SCHNEIDER, DANIEL	ACTOR	12840 MOORPARK ST #308	STUDIO CITY, CA	91604
SCHNEIDER, HELEN	ACTRESS	LANTZ, 888 7TH AVE, 25TH FLOOR	NEW YORK, NY	10106
SCHNEIDER, HERM	BASEBALL TRAINER	333 W 35TH ST	CHICAGO, IL	60616
SCHNEIDER, JOHN	ACT-WRI-SING	12031 VENTURA BLVD #1	STUDIO CITY, CA	91604
SCHNEIDER, MARK D	DIRECTOR	258 BROADWAY #7-F	NEW YORK, NY	10007
SCHNEIDER, MARNI	TV DIRECTOR-PRODUCER	KCET-TV, 4401 SUNSET BLVD	LOS ANGELES, CA	90027
SCHNEIDER, MATHIEU	HOCKEY	CANADIENS, 2313 ST CATHERINE ST	MONTREAL, QUE H3H 1N2	CANADA
SCHNEIDER, RICHARD	DIRECTOR	139 E 35TH ST	NEW YORK, NY	10016
SCHNEIDER, SASCHA	TV PRODUCER	8480 BEVERLY BLVD #117	LOS ANGELES, CA	90048
SCHNEIDER, STANLEY	BASEBALL EXECUTIVE	POST OFFICE BOX 2000	ANAHEIM, CA	92803
SCHNEIDER, TOM	COLUMNIST	CHRONICLE FEATURES		
		870 MARKET ST	SAN FRANCISCO, CA	94102
SCHNELKER, BOB	FOOTBALL COACH	VIKINGS, 9520 VIKING DR	EDEN PRAIRIE, MN	55344
SCHNETZER, STEPHEN	ACTOR	NBC-TV, "ANOTHER WORLD"		
		1268 E 14TH ST	BROOKLYN, NY	11230
SCHNITZER, GERALD	WRITER-PRODUCER	1155 N LA CIENEGA BLVD #1203	LOS ANGELES, CA	90069
SCHNORF, ROBERT	TV DIRECTOR	KMOX-TV, 1 MEMORIAL DR	ST LOUIS, MO	63102
SCHNUR, JEROME	TV DIRECTOR-PRODUCER	135 CENTRAL PARK W	NEW YORK, NY	10023
SCHOELEN, JILL	ACTRESS	1999 AVE OF THE STARS #2850	LOS ANGELES, CA	90067
SCHOEN, BOB	ACTOR	2 SUNNYSIDE DR	YONKERS, NY	10705
SCHOEN, VIC	COMPOSER-CONDUCTOR	13324 70TH PL, NE	KIRKLAND, WA	98034
SCHOENBRUN, JOSEF	COMPOSER-CONDUCTOR	316 SAN VICENTE BLVD #104	SANTA MONICA, CA	90402
SCHOENBURG, STUART	PRODUCER	RANDOM, 5437 LAUREL CYN BLVD	NORTH HOLLYWOOD, CA	91607
SCHOENDIENST, RED	BASEBALL-COACH	331 LADUE WOODS CT	CREVE COEUR, MO	63141
SCHOENFELD, GERALD	THEATER PRODUCER	225 W 44TH ST	NEW YORK, NY	10036
SCHOENVOGEL, CHAD	BASEBALL	RED SOX, CHAIN O'LAKES PARK	WINTER HAVEN, FL	33880
SCHOETTLER, GAIL	TREASURER	STATE CAPITOL BUILDING	DENVER, CO	80203
SCHOFFMAN, STUART	WRITER	2899 RAMBLA PACIFICO	MALIBU, CA	90265
SCHOFIELD, ANNABEL	ACTRESS	10351 SANTA MONICA BLVD #211	LOS ANGELES, CA	90025
SCHOFIELD, DICK, JR	BASEBALL (ANGELS)	POST OFFICE BOX 2000	ANAHEIM, CA	92803
SCHOFIELD, DICK, SR	BASEBALL (PIRATES)	138 CIRCLE DR	SPRINGFIELD, IL	62703
SCHOFIELD, PHILLIP	TV HOST	BBC-TV, 56 WOOD LN	LONDON W12 7RJ	ENGLAND
SCHOLEFIELD, CINDY	GOLFER	2750 VOLUSA AVE #B	DAYTON BEACH, FL	32114
SCHOLL, ARTHUR	DIRECTOR	1041 MOFFATT ST	RIALTO, CA	92376
SCHONFELD, MAURICE W	TV EXECUTIVE	CTP INC, 1 W 67TH ST	NEW YORK, NY	10023
SCHONFELD, VICTOR	FILM-TV DIR-PROD	SPI 80, BCM SUMMER	LONDON WC1N 3XX	ENGLAND

Name	Occupation	Address	City	Zip
SCHONWANDT, MICHAEL	CONDUCTOR	ICM, 40 W 57TH ST	NEW YORK, NY	10019
SCHOOLER, MIKE	BASEBALL	POST OFFICE BOX 4100	SEATTLE, WA	98104
SCHOOLLY D	RAPPER-RAPWRITER	FAA, 1700 BROADWAY, 5TH FLOOR	NEW YORK, NY	10019
SCHOONMAKER, CHARLES L	COSTUME DESIGNER	NBC-TV, 1268 E 14TH ST	BROOKLYN, NY	11230
SCHOONMAKER, THELMA	FILM EDITOR	ACE, 1041 N FORMOSA AVE	WEST HOLLYWOOD, CA	90046
SCHOOR, BARRY J	TV PRODUCER	GLASS/SCHOOR, 42 W 38TH ST	NEW YORK, NY	10018
SCHOPPA, KELLY & THE AMARILLO B	VOCAL GROUP	POST OFFICE BOX 1373	LEWISVILLE, TX	75067
SCHOPPE, JAMES	ART DIRECTOR	POST OFFICE BOX 1166	PACIFIC PALISADES, CA	90272
SCHOR, LOUIS	WRITER-PRODUCER	5003 MAMMOTH AVE	VAN NUYS, CA	91423
SCHORR, BILL	CARTOONIST	POST OFFICE BOX 2416		
		TERMINAL ANNEX	LOS ANGELES, CA	90051
SCHORR, BRAD	BASEBALL	POST OFFICE BOX 7845	COLUMBIA, SC	29202
SCHORR, DANIEL	BROADCAST JOURNALIST	3113 WOODLEY RD	WASHINGTON, DC	20008
SCHOTT, DOROTHY	ACTRESS	60 W 57TH ST #PH-A	NEW YORK, NY	10019
SCHOTT, MARGE	BASEBALL EXECUTIVE	REDS, 100 RIVERFRONT STADIUM	CINCINNATI, OH	45202
SCHOTT, STEPHEN	BASEBALL EXECUTIVE	REDS, 100 RIVERFRONT STADIUM	CINCINNATI, OH	45202
SCHOTTENFELD, MATTHEW A	COMPOSER	2005 BEACHWOOD CYN RD	LOS ANGELES, CA	90068
SCHOTTENHEIMER, KURT	FOOTBALL COACH	CHIEFS, 1 ARROWHEAD DR	KANSAS CITY, MO	64129
SCHOTTENHEIMER, MARTY	FOOTBALL COACH	CHIEFS, 1 ARROWHEAD DR	KANSAS CITY, MO	64129
SCHOTZ, ERIC R	TV DIRECTOR	105 1/2 S CLARK DR	LOS ANGELES, CA	90048
SCHOUREK, PETE	BASEBALL	METS, 126TH ST & ROOSEVELT AVE	FLUSHING, NY	11368
SCHRADER, PAUL	WRITER-PRODUCER	DGA, 7920 SUNSET BLVD, 6TH FL	LOS ANGELES, CA	90046
SCHRAMM, CARL	BASEBALL	1524 W NEBRASKA AVE	PEORIA, IL	61604
SCHREDER, CAROL	TV WRITER-PRODUCER	21021 WAVEVIEW DR	TOPANGA CANYON, CA	90290
SCHREIBER, ADAM	FOOTBALL	VIKINGS, 9520 VIKING DR	EDEN PRAIRIE, MN	55344
SCHREIBER, AVERY	ACTOR-COMEDIAN	6612 RANCHITO	VAN NUYS, CA	91405
SCHREIBER, BRUCE	BASEBALL	POST OFFICE BOX 842	SALEM, VA	24153
SCHREIBMAN, MYRL	DIRECTOR	15913 ENADIA WY	VAN NUYS, CA	91406
SCHREIER, RICHARD LEE	DIRECTOR	DGA, 7920 SUNSET BLVD, 6TH FL	LOS ANGELES, CA	90046
SCHREINER, ELISSA	COMPOSER	MILLER-SCHREINER, 316 W 79TH ST	NEW YORK, NY	10024
SCHREMPF, DETLEF	BASKETBALL	PACERS, 300 E MARKET ST	INDIANAPOLIS, IN	46204
SCHRENK, STEVE	BASEBALL	1090 N EUCLID AVE	SARASOTA, FL	34237
SCHRIENER, DENISE LYNN	DIRECTOR	DGA, 110 W 57TH ST	NEW YORK, NY	10019
SCHRODER, RICK	ACTOR	921 N ROXBURY DR	BEVERLY HILLS, CA	90210
SCHRODER, SUSAN	ACTRESS	POST OFFICE BOX 491340	LOS ANGELES, CA	90049
SCHROEDER, BARBET	FILM DIRECTOR	MEISEL, 3264 ELLENDA AVE	LOS ANGELES, CA	90034
SCHROEDER, JAY	FOOTBALL	RAIDERS, 332 CENTER ST	EL SEGUNDO, CA	90245
SCHROEDER, MICHAEL	DIRECTOR-PRODUCER	30825 WHIM DR	WESTLAKE VILLAGE, CA	91362
SCHROEDER, PATRICIA	U S CONGRESSWOMAN	1600 EMERSON ST	DENVER, CO	80218
SCHROEDER, RICK	BASEBALL SCOUT	POST OFFICE BOX 90111	ARLINGTON, TX	76004
SCHROEDER, TODD	BASEBALL	POST OFFICE BOX 842	SALEM, VA	24153
SCHROEDER, WALTER K	DIRECTOR	2318 MOTOR PARKWAY	RONKONKOMA, NY	11779
SCHROER, RICHARD	DIRECTOR	14539 VALLEY VISTA BLVD	SHERMAN OAKS, CA	91403
SCHROM, KEN	BASEBALL-EXECUTIVE	POST OFFICE DRAWER 4797	EL PASO, TX	79914
SCHROM, MICHAEL STUART	DIRECTOR	DGA, 110 W 57TH ST	NEW YORK, NY	10019
SCHU, RICK	BASEBALL	POST OFFICE BOX 3449	SCRANTON, PA	18505
SCHUBB, MARK	ACTOR	9744 WILSHIRE BLVD #308	BEVERLY HILLS, CA	90212
SCHUBERT, BERNARD	WRITER	1036 N LAUREL AVE	LOS ANGELES, CA	90046
SCHUCK, JOHN	ACTOR	3543 WOODCLIFF RD	SHERMAN OAKS, CA	91403
SCHUELER, RON	BASEBALL EXECUTIVE	333 W 35TH ST	CHICAGO, IL	60616
SCHUERMAN, ART	BASEBALL SCOUT	BREWERS, 201 S 46TH ST	MILWAUKEE, WI	53214
SCHUERMANN, LANCE	BASEBALL	14100 SIX MILE CYPRESS PKWY	FORT MYERS, FL	33912
SCHUGEL, JEFF	BASEBALL SCOUT	TWINS, 501 CHICAGO AVE S	MINNEAPOLIS, MN	55415
SCHULBERG, BUDD	TV WRITER	BROOKSIDE, BOX 707	WESTHAMPTON BEACH, NY	11978
SCHULER, ANNIE CAROLINE	SCREENWRITER	8721 SUNSET BLVD #103	WEST HOLLYWOOD, CA	90069
SCHULER, DAVE	BASEBALL COACH	POST OFFICE BOX 2148	WOODBRIDGE, VA	22193
SCHULER, LAUREN	FILM PRODUCER	500 S BUENA VISTA ST	BURBANK, CA	91521
SCHULER, MARK	ARTIST	420 LEXINGTON AVE	NEW YORK, NY	10170
SCHULER, MIKE	BASKETBALL COACH	CLIPPERS, 3939 S FIGUEROA ST	LOS ANGELES, CA	90037
SCHULLER, REV ROBERT H, SR	EVANGELIST	464 S ESPLANADE ST	ORANGE, CA	92669
SCHULLER, REV ROBERT A, JR	EVANGELIST	464 S ESPLANADA ST	ORANGE, CA	92669
SCHULLSTROM, ERIK	BASEBALL	POST OFFICE BOX 230	HAGERSTOWN, MD	21740
SCHULMAN, ARNOLD	WRITER-PRODUCER	8755 SHOREHAM DR #402	LOS ANGELES, CA	90069
SCHULMAN, HEIDI	TV WRITER	470 SHERMAN CANAL #4	VENICE, CA	90291
SCHULMAN, ROBERT	ARTIST	12715 SADDLEBROOK PL	SILVER SPRING, MD	20906
SCHULMAN, TOM	SCREENWRITER	CAA, 9830 WILSHIRE BLVD	BEVERLY HILLS, CA	90212
SCHULTE, JOHN	BASEBALL	POST OFFICE BOX 3746, HILL STA	AUGUSTA, GA	30904
SCHULTE, RICH	BASEBALL	POST OFFICE BOX 824	BURLINGTON, IA	52601
SCHULTZ, DWIGHT	ACTOR	2824 NICHOLS CANYON DR	LOS ANGLES, CA	90046
SCHULTZ, EVELYN	TALENT AGENT	CED, 261 S ROBERTSON BLVD	BEVERLY HILLS, CA	90211
SCHULTZ, JEFF	BASEBALL	POST OFFICE BOX 23290	NASHVILLE, TN	37202
SCHULTZ, MICHAEL	FILM DIRECTOR	POST OFFICE BOX 8659	SAN MARINO, CA	91108
SCHULTZ, PHIL	DIRECTOR	2 PETER COOPER RD	NEW YORK, NY	10010
SCHULTZ, ROBERT	DIRECTOR-PRODUCER	4711 BIZET PL	WOODLAND HILLS, CA	91364
SCHULTZ, WILLIAM	FOOTBALL	POST OFFICE BOX 535000	INDIANPOLIS, IN	46253
SCHULZ, CHARLES	CARTOONIST	1 SNOOPY PL	SANTA ROSA, CA	95401
SCHULZ, JEFF	BASEBALL	1167 S STOCKWELL RD	EVANSVILLE, IN	47715
SCHULZ, JILL	ACTRESS	BDP, 10637 BURBANK BLVD	NORTH HOLLYWOOD, CA	91601
SCHULZ, TED	GOLFER	POST OFFICE BOX 109601	PALM BCH GARDENS, FL	33418
SCHULZE, DON	BASEBALL	313 E PINE	ROSELLE, IL	60172
SCHULZE, RICHARD T	U S CONGRESSMAN	10 S LEOPARD #204	PAOLI, PA	19301
SCHUMACHER, JOEL	COSTUME DESIGNER	13949 VENTURA BLVD #309	SHERMAN OAKS, CA	91423
SCHUMACHER, JOEL	WRITER-PRODUCER	10051 CIELO DR	BEVERLY HILLS, CA	90210
SCHUMACHER, JOSEPH S, JR	DIRECTOR	1262 BRIARWOOD LN	LIBERTYVILLE, IL	60048
SCHUMACHER, MAX	BASEBALL EXECUTIVE	1501 W 16TH ST	INDIANAPOLIS, IN	46202

MOVIE WORLD
★ MOVIE POSTERS
★ LOBBY CARDS
★ NEW BOOKS
★ AUTOGRAPHS
★ 8 x 10 PHOTOS
★ MOVIE MAGAZINES
★ PAPERBACK MOVIE TIE-INS
Come Visit Us in Beautiful Downtown Burbank.
We are Located in the Heart of the Movie-Entertainment Industry, Minutes from Warner, Columbia, Disney, and Universal!
"ANOTHER SATISFIED CUSTOMER"
SCREEN STORIES
OPEN 7 DAYS
11a.m.-6p.m.
MOVIE WORLD
212 N. San Fernando Blvd.
Burbank, CA 91502
(818) 846-0459

Name	Occupation	Address	City	Zip
SCHUMAN, TOM	KEYBOARDIST-COMPOSER	POST OFFICE BOX 239	TALLMAN, NY	10982
SCHUMAN, WILLIAM	COMPOSER	RICHMOND HILL RD	GREENWICH, CT	06830
SCHUMER, CHARLES	U S CONGRESSMAN	1628 KING'S HIGHWAY	BROOKLYN, NY	11229
SCHUNK, JERRY	BASEBALL	CHIEFS, MAC ARTHUR STADIUM	SYRACUSE, NY	13208
SCHUR, JOEL	BASEBALL EXECUTIVE	POST OFFICE BOX 12557	ST PETERSBURG, FL	33733
SCHURMAN, KARL NELSON	TV DIRECTOR	POST OFFICE BOX 14	GERTON, NC	28735
SCHURR, DIANE	SINGER	9000 SUNSET BLVD #1200	LOS ANGELES, CA	90069
SCHURTZ, CARL F	COMPOSER	401 E 82ND ST	NEW YORK, NY	10028
SCHUSTER, HAROLD	DIRECTOR	31620 BROAD BEACH RD	MALIBU, CA	90265
SCHUSTER, MARK	BASEBALL EXECUTIVE	POST OFFICE BOX 1143	BURLINGTON, NC	27216
SCHWAB, AARON	TV PRODUCER	MMA, 8484 WILSHIRE BLVD	BEVERLY HILLS, CA	90212
SCHWAB, DON	DIRECTOR	10333 ASHTON AVE	LOS ANGELES, CA	90024
SCHWAB, FAYE	TV PRODUCER	MMA, 8484 WILSHIRE BLVD	BEVERLY HILLS, CA	90212
SCHWAB, MICHAEL	ARTIST	118 KING ST	SAN FRANCISCO, CA	94107
SCHWABE, MIKE	BASEBALL	POST OFFICE BOX 1659	PORTLAND, OR	97207
SCHWADEL, RICHARD ALAN	DIRECTOR	2456 BEVERLY AVE #B	SANTA MONICA, CA	90405
SCHWARBER, TOM	BASEBALL	POST OFFICE BOX 64939	FAYETTEVILLE, NC	28306
SCHWARTZ, AL	TV PRODUCER	CLARK PRODS, 3003 W OLIVE AVE	BURBANK, CA	91510
SCHWARTZ, ALLEN	TV DIRECTOR	9707 ARBY DR	BEVERLY HILLS, CA	90210
SCHWARTZ, BERNIE	PRODUCER	MCA/UNIVERSAL STUDIOS, INC		
		100 UNIVERSAL CITY PLAZA		
		BUILDING #507-3-G	UNIVERSAL CITY, CA	91608
SCHWARTZ, BOB	DIRECTOR	501 E 79TH ST	NEW YORK, NY	10028
SCHWARTZ, CHARLES L	TV DIRECTOR-PRODUCER	223 E 61ST ST	NEW YORK, NY	10021
SCHWARTZ, DANIEL	ARTIST	48 E 13TH ST	NEW YORK, NY	10003
SCHWARTZ, DOUGLAS N	FILM WRITER-PRODUCER	8955 BEVERLY BLVD	WEST HOLLYWOOD, CA	90048
SCHWARTZ, ELROY	TV WRITER	471 E TAHQUITZ #20	PALM SPRINGS, CA	92262
SCHWARTZ, GERHARD	ACTOR-WRITER	2000 HAMBURG 60	POSTFACH 60-24-51	GERMANY
SCHWARTZ, JOHN D	DIRECTOR-PRODUCER	10488 EASTBOURNE AVE	LOS ANGELES, CA	90024
SCHWARTZ, JONATHAN M	DIRECTOR	36 RIVERSIDE DR	NEW YORK, NY	10023
SCHWARTZ, LILLIAN F	TV DIRECTOR-PRODUCER	524 RIDGE RD	WATCHUNG, NJ	07060
SCHWARTZ, LLOYD	WRITER-PRODUCER	12800 MILBANK ST	STUDIO CITY, CA	91604
SCHWARTZ, MARTIN N	DIRECTOR	DGA, 7920 SUNSET BLVD, 6TH FL	LOS ANGELES, CA	90046
SCHWARTZ, MORTON I	FILM EDITOR	POWER POST PROD, 25 W 43RD ST	NEW YORK, NY	10036
SCHWARTZ, MURRAY	FILM DIRECTOR	4015 PATRICK HENRY PL	AGOURA, CA	91301
SCHWARTZ, MURRAY	TV EXECUTIVE	1541 N VINE ST	HOLLYWOOD, CA	90028
SCHWARTZ, NAN L	COMPOSER	4410 SAINT CLAIR AVE	STUDIO CITY, CA	91604
SCHWARTZ, ROBERT	TV PRODUCER	EYE-VIEW FILMS, 420 E 81ST ST	NEW YORK, NY	10028
SCHWARTZ, SCOTT	TALENT AGENT	ICM, 8899 BEVERLY BLVD	LOS ANGELES, CA	90048
SCHWARTZ, SHERWOOD	TV WRITER-PRODUCER	1865 CARLA RIDGE	BEVERLY HILLS, CA	90210
SCHWARTZ, STEPHEN	COMPOSER-LYRICIST	PARAMOUSE ASSOCIATES		
		1414 AVE OF THE AMERICAS	NEW YORK, NY	10019
SCHWARTZ, STEPHEN	DIRECTOR	DGA, 110 W 57TH ST	NEW YORK, NY	10019
SCHWARTZ, STEPHEN	TV WRITER	8955 BEVERLY BLVD	WEST HOLLYWOOD, CA	90048
SCHWARTZ, SUSAN	TV PRODUCER	CHILDREN'S TV WORKSHOP		
		1 LINCOLN PLAZA	NEW YORK, NY	10023
SCHWARTZ, TONY	DIRECTOR	455 W 56TH ST	NEW YORK, NY	10019
SCHWARTZ, WILLIAM J	DIRECTOR-PRODUCER	212 S BEMISTON AVE	SAINT LOUIS, MO	63105
SCHWARY, RONALD L	FILM PRODUCER	19950 GREENBRIAR DR	TARZANA, CA	91356
SCHWARZ, HANK	BASEBALL UMPIRE	2101 E BROADWAY #35	TEMPE, AZ	85282
SCHWARZ, JEFF	BASEBALL	POST OFFICE BOX 360007	BIRMINGHAM, AL	35236
SCHWARZ, MILTON MICKEY	DIRECTOR	14-A WEAVERS HILL	GREENWICH, CT	06830
SCHWARZENEGGER, ARNOLD	ACTOR-BODYBUILDER	3110 MAIN ST #300	SANTA MONICA, CA	90405
SCHWARZWALD, H ARNOLD	COMPOSER	5636 COSTELLO AVE	VAN NUYS, CA	91401
SCHWECHHEIMER, LOU	BASEBALL EXECUTIVE	POST OFFICE BOX 2365	PAWTUCKET, RI	02861
SCHWED, PAULA	TV CRITIC	POST OFFICE BOX 2416	LOS ANGELES, CA	90051
SCHWEI, BARBARA	THEATER PRODUCER	1501 BROADWAY	NEW YORK, NY	10036
SCHWEITZER, GEORGE F	TV EXECUTIVE	CBS-TV, 51 W 52ND ST	NEW YORK, NY	10019
SCHWERIN, JULES VICTOR	DIRECTOR	317 W 83RD ST	NEW YORK, NY	10024
SCHWINGLE, KATHRYN	BASEBALL EXECUTIVE	POST OFFICE BOX 2183	IDAHO FALLS, ID	83402
SCIACCA, TOM	ARTIST	133-35 85TH ST	OZONE PARK, NY	11417
SCIALFA, PATTI	SINGER	9922 TOWER LN	BEVERLY HILLS, CA	90210
SCINTO, ROBERT L	TV DIRECTOR	POST OFFICE BOX 343	RINGWOOD, NJ	07456
SCIOSCIA, MIKE	BASEBALL	1000 ELYSIAN PARK DR	LOS ANGELES, CA	90012
SCIVNER, JOE	BASEBALL EXECUTIVE	POST OFFICE BOX 360007	BIRMINGHAM, AL	35236
SCOFFIELD, JON	TV DIRECTOR-PRODUCER	CENTRAL INDEPENDENT TV		
		LENTON LN	NOTTINGHAM NG7 2NA	ENGLAND
SCOFIELD, PAUL	ACTOR	THE GABLES, BALCOMBE	SUSSEX	ENGLAND
SCOGGINS, TRACY	ACTRESS-MODEL	POST OFFICE BOX 2262	MALIBU, CA	90265
SCOLARI, PETER	ACTOR	930 HILGARD AVE	LOS ANGELES, CA	90024
SCORE, HERB	BASEBALL-ANNOUNCER	INDIANS, CLEVELAND STADIUM	CLEVELAND, OH	44114
SCORER, IAN	FILM-TV EXECUTIVE	12 BOLINGBROKE GROVE	LONDON SW11 6ER	ENGLAND
SCORER, MISCHA	DIRECTOR-PRODUCER	ANTELOPE WEST, LTD		
		13 SYDENHAM HILL, COTHAM	BRISTOL BS6 5SL	ENGLAND
SCORPIO	ROCK & ROLL GROUP	BORSA PRODS, 112 4TH AVE	NORWOOD, MA	02062
SCORPIONS, THE	ROCK & ROLL GROUP	POST OFFICE BOX 5220	3000 HANNOVER 1	GERMANY
SCORSESE, MARTIN	FILM WRITER-DIRECTOR	146 W 57TH ST #75-B	NEW YORK, NY	10019
SCORTIA, THOMAS N	WRITER	7177 BRYDON RD	LA VERNE, CA	91750
SCORZA, PHILIP A	WRITER	14133 ARCHWOOD ST	VAN NUYS, CA	91405
SCOT, JOHN ANTONY	CONDUCTOR	POST OFFICE BOX 4638	LONG BEACH, CA	90804
SCOT, MARGARET W	DIRECTOR	4424 MOORPARK WY	NORTH HOLLYWOOD, CA	91602
SCOTELLARO, KEVIN	BASEBALL EXECUTIVE	POST OFFICE BOX 3452	KINSTON, NC	28502
SCOTFORD, SYBIL	ACTRESS	4155 CAMELLIA AVE	STUDIO CITY, CA	91604
SCOTT, ALEX	BASEBALL SCOUT	FENWAY PARK, 4 YAWKEY WY	BOSTON, MA	02215
SCOTT, ALLAN	TV WRITER-PRODUCER	RAFFORD FILMS, 1 HEREFORD SQ	LONDON SW7 4TT	ENGLAND

Name	Occupation	Address	City	ZIP
SCOTT, ALLAN G	SCREENWRITER	1441 S BEVERLY GLEN BLVD	LOS ANGELES, CA	90024
SCOTT, BILLY	SINGER	POST OFFICE BOX 25371	CHARLOTTE, NC	28212
SCOTT, BYRON	BASKETBALL	POST OFFICE BOX 10	INGLEWOOD, CA	90306
SCOTT, CAROL E	TV DIRECTOR	DGA, 7920 SUNSET BLVD, 6TH FL	LOS ANGELES, CA	90046
SCOTT, CHARLES	BASEBALL	POST OFFICE BOX 1659	PORTLAND, OR	97207
SCOTT, CLIFTON	AUDITOR	STATE CAPITOL BUILDING	OKLAHOMA CITY, OK	73105
SCOTT, DALE	BASEBALL UMPIRE	25 SW CANBY ST	PORTLAND, OR	97219
SCOTT, DARRYL	BASEBALL	POST OFFICE BOX 12	MIDLAND, TX	79702
SCOTT, DEAN	SINGER	4615 SOUTHWEST FREEWAY #475	HOUSTON, TX	77027
SCOTT, DEBORAH L	COSTUME DESIGNER	POST OFFICE BOX 5617	BEVERLY HILLS, CA	90213
SCOTT, DEBRALEE	ACTRESS	OSCARD, 24 W 40TH ST, 17TH FL	NEW YORK, NY	10011
SCOTT, DENNIS	BASKETBALL	POST OFFICE BOX 76	ORLANDO, FL	32802
SCOTT, DICK	BASEBALL MANAGER	POST OFFICE BOX 882	MADISON, WI	53701
SCOTT, DICK	TALENT AGENT	159 W 53RD ST	NEW YORK, NY	10019
SCOTT, DONNIE	BASEBALL	POST OFFICE BOX 23290	NASHVILLE, TN	37202
SCOTT, DR GENE	TV HOST-TEACHER	POST OFFICE BOX 1	LOS ANGELES, CA	90053
SCOTT, DUNCAN M	DIRECTOR-PRODUCER	90-50 UNION TURNPIKE	GLENDALE, NY	11385
SCOTT, ED	BASEBALL SCOUT	FENWAY PARK, 4 YAWKEY WY	BOSTON, MA	02215
SCOTT, EDWARD	TV PRODUCER	CBS-TV, "YOUNG & THE RESTLESS"		
		7800 BEVERLY BLVD #3305	LOS ANGELES, CA	90036
SCOTT, EDWARD J	DIRECTOR	13220 INGRES AVE	GRANADA HILLS, CA	91344
SCOTT, F M, III	COMPOSER	POST OFFICE BOX 2107	RANCHO SANTE FE, CA	92067
SCOTT, FRED	ACTOR	1765 E RAMON RD #42	PALM SPRINGS, CA	92264
SCOTT, FRED DANIEL	ACTOR	2028 N BEACHWOOD DR #304	LOS ANGELES, CA	90068
SCOTT, GARY	BASEBALL	1060 W ADDISON ST	CHICAGO, IL	60613
SCOTT, GARY (2)	COMPOSER	5128 GAVIOTA AVE	ENCINO, CA	91436
SCOTT, GENE	TV HOST-TEACHER	SEE - SCOTT, DR GENE		
SCOTT, GEOFFREY	ACTOR	3464 PRIMERA AVE	LOS ANGELES, CA	90068
SCOTT, GEORGE C	ACTOR-DIRECTOR	3211 RETREAT CT	MALIBU, CA	90265
SCOTT, HERBERT J	TV DIRECTOR	WCAU TELEVISION STATION		
		CITY LINE & MONUMENT RDS	PHILADEPHIA, PA	19131
SCOTT, IVAN	COMPOSER-CONDUCTOR	1420 QUUENS RD	LOS ANGELES, CA	90069
SCOTT, JACK	SINGER-SONGWRITER	POST OFFICE BOX 2342	THOUSAND OAKS, CA	91359
SCOTT, JACK ALBERT	TV DIRECTOR	4411 LOS FELIZ BLVD #901	LOS ANGELES, CA	90027
SCOTT, JACQUELINE	ACTRESS	12456 VENTURA BLVD #1	STUDIO CITY, CA	91604
SCOTT, JAMES	FILM DIRECTOR	FLAMINGO, 47 LONSDALE SQ	LONDON N1 1EW	ENGLAND
SCOTT, JANE	ROCK CRITIC	CLEVELAND PLAIN DEALER		
		1801 SUPERIOR AVE, NE	CLEVELAND, OH	44114
SCOTT, JEAN BRUCE	ACTRESS	8271 MELROSE AVE #110	LOS ANGELES, CA	90046
SCOTT, JEF	SINGER-GUITARIST	POST OFFICE BOX 2601	HOLLYWOOD, CA	90078
SCOTT, JEFFREY	WRITER-PRODUCER	CANNELL, 7083 HOLLYWOOD BLVD	LOS ANGELES, CA	90028
SCOTT, JOAN	TALENT AGENT	11726 SAN VICENTE BLVD #300	LOS ANGELES, CA	90049
SCOTT, JUDSON	ACTOR	10000 SANTA MONICA BLVD #305	LOS ANGELES, CA	90067
SCOTT, KAREN	TV PRODUCER	WNBC-TV, 30 ROCKEFELLER PLZ	NEW YORK, NY	10020
SCOTT, KAREN LYNN	ACTRESS	3800 BARHAM BLVD #303	LOS ANGELES, CA	90068
SCOTT, KATHRYN LEIGH	ACTRESS	12161 VALLEYHEART DR	STUDIO CITY, CA	91604
SCOTT, KEVIN	BASEBALL	POST OFFICE BOX 422229	KISSIMMEE, FL	34742
SCOTT, KEVIN	FOOTBALL	LIONS, 1200 FEATHERSTONE RD	PONTIAC, MI	48432
SCOTT, LARRY	BODYBUILDER	POST OFFICE BOX 162	NORTH SALT LAKE CITY,	84054
SCOTT, LIZABETH	ACTRESS	POST OFFICE BOX 5522	BEVERLY HILLS, CA	90213
SCOTT, LORNA	ACTRESS	KJAR, 10653 RIVERSIDE DR	TOLUCA LAKE, CA	91602
SCOTT, MARILYN	SINGER	VISION, 2112 N CAHUENGA BLVD	LOS ANGELES, CA	90068
SCOTT, MARTHA	ACTRESS	14054 CHANDLER BLVD	VAN NUYS, CA	91401
SCOTT, MARTY	BASEBALL EXECUTIVE	POST OFFICE BOX 90111	ARLINGTON, TX	76004
SCOTT, MARVIN	NEWSCASTER	WPIX-TV, 220 E 42ND ST	NEW YORK, NY	10017
SCOTT, MICHAEL	TV DIRECTOR	13261 1/2 BLOOMFIELD ST	SHERMAN OAKS, CA	91423
SCOTT, MICHAEL JAMES FOLEY	DIRECTOR-PRODUCER	84 QUEENSTON ST	WINNIPEG, MB	CANADA
SCOTT, MICHAEL T	COMPOSER	4401 KRAFT AVE #8	NORTH HOLLYWOOD, CA	91602
SCOTT, MICKEY	MAKE-UP ARTIST	15 EVERGREEN DR	CLIFTON, NJ	10017
SCOTT, NATHAN G	COMPOSER	14222 WEDDINGTON ST	VAN NUYS, CA	91401
SCOTT, OZ	TV DIRECTOR	6645 ALLOTT AVE	VAN NUYS, CA	91401
SCOTT, PETER GRAHAM	TV DIRECTOR-PRODUCER	HIGH PINES, WINDLESHAM	SURREY	ENGLAND
SCOTT, PETER RISDALE	DIRECTOR-PRODUCER	BAFTA, 195 PICCADILLY	LONDON W1V 9LG	ENGLAND
SCOTT, RENA	SINGER	BUDDAH RECORDS CO		
		810 7TH AVE	NEW YORK, NY	10019
SCOTT, RICHARD	BASEBALL	56 PINE ST	ELLSWORTH, ME	04605
SCOTT, RIDLEY	FILM DIRECTOR	PETERS, FRASER & DUNLOP, LTD		
		5TH FLOOR, THE CHAMBERS		
		CHELSEA HARBOUR, LOT RD	LONDON SW10 OXF	ENGLAND
SCOTT, RITA	DIRECTOR	12244 EMELITA ST	NORTH HOLLYWOOD, CA	91607
SCOTT, ROBERT	ACTOR	SEE - ROBERTS, MARK		
SCOTT, SELINA	TV HOST	KNIGHT AYTON, 70-A BERWICK ST	LONDON W1	ENGLAND
SCOTT, SHAWN	BASEBALL	633 JESSAMINE ST	KNOXVILLE, TN	37917
SCOTT, SHERI LEE	ACTRESS	244 MADISON AVE #10-D	NEW YORK, NY	10016
SCOTT, TERRY	ACTOR	GREENACRE, GASDEN COPSE, WILEY	SURREY	ENGLAND
SCOTT, THOMAS W	COMPOSER-CONDUCTOR	JESS MORGAN COMPANY		
		6420 WILSHIRE BLVD, 19TH FLOOR	LOS ANGELES, CA	90048
SCOTT, TIM	BASEBALL	STARS, 850 LAS VEGAS BLVD N	LAS VEGAS, NV	89101
SCOTT, TODD	FOOTBALL	VIKINGS, 9520 VIKING DR	EDEN PRAIRIE, MN	55344
SCOTT, TOM	SINGER	11 BAILEY AVE	RIDGEFIELD, CT	06877
SCOTT, TOMMY "DOC" & REAL MEDIC	C & W GROUP	POST OFFICE BOX 100	TOCCOA, GA	30577
SCOTT, TONY	BASEBALL COACH	POST OFFICE BOX 1721	SPARTANBURG, SC	29304
SCOTT, TONY	FILM DIRECTOR	151 S EL CAMINO DR	BEVERLY HILLS, CA	90212
SCOTT, TYRONE	BASEBALL	POST OFFICE BOX 824	BURLINGTON, IA	52601
SCOTT, WALTER	COLUMNIST	PARADE, 750 3RD AVE	NEW YORK, NY	10017

Name	Occupation	Address	City/State	Zip
SCOTT, WALTER E	DIRECTOR	14543 BLEDSOE ST	SYLMAR, CA	91342
SCOTT, WILLARD	WEATHERPERSON	30 ROCKEFELLER PLAZA #304	NEW YORK, NY	10112
SCOTT-HERON, GIL	SINGER-PIANIST	POST OFFICE BOX 1417-838	ALEXANDRIA, VA	22313
SCOTTI, VITO	ACTOR	5456 VANALDEN AVE	TARZANA, CA	91356
SCOTTY, JERRY	CARTOONIST	KING FEATURES, 216 E 45TH ST	NEW YORK, NY	10017
SCOWCROFT, GEN BRENT	U S GENERAL	THE WHITE HOUSE		
		1600 PENNSYLVANIA AVE	WASHINGTON, DC	20500
SCRANTON, NANCY	GOLFER	2750 VOLUSA AVE #B	DAYTON BEACH, FL	32114
SCRAWS	CARTOONIST	KING FEATURES, 216 E 45TH ST	NEW YORK, NY	10017
SCREAMING BLUE MESSIAHS, THE	ROCK & ROLL GROUP	JOHN DUMMER, 17 CRESCENT WY	LONDON SE4 1QL	ENGLAND
SCRIBNER, JO ANNE	ARTIST	3314 N LEE ST	SPOKANE, WA	99207
SCRIMA, VINCENT P	COMPOSER	4232 TORREON DR	WOODLAND HILLS, CA	91364
SCRIPPS, BILL	BASEBALL EXECUTIVE	POST OFFICE BOX 3746, HILL STA	AUGUSTA, GA	30904
SCRUFFY THE CAT	ROCK & ROLL GROUP	78 HILLSIDE ST #3	ROXBURY, MA	02120
SCRUGGS, EARL	BANJOIST-SONGWRITER	POST OFFICE BOX 66	MADISON, TN	37116
SCRUGGS, GARY	GUITARIST	774 ELYSIAN FIELDS RD	NASHVILLE, TN	37204
SCRUGGS, NOEL	FIDDLER	ROUTE 1, BOX 200	HARTSVILLE, TN	37074
SCRUGGS, RANDY	GUITARIST-BANJOIST	2821 BRANSFORD AVE	NASHVILLE, TN	37204
SCRUGGS, SHARON	ACTRESS	95 CHRISTOPHER ST #13-D	NEW YORK, NY	10014
SCUDDAY, MARY R	WRITER	1636 N VERDUGO RD #208	GLENDALE, CA	91208
SCUDDER, SCOTT	BASEBALL	POST OFFICE BOX 6	BLOSSOM, TX	75416
SCULLY, VIN	SPORTSCASTER	1555 CAPRI DR	PACIFIC PALISADES, CA	90272
SCZESNY, MATT	BASEBALL SCOUT	FENWAY PARK, 4 YAWKEY WY	BOSTON, MA	02215
SEA LEVEL	ROCK & ROLL GROUP	119 W 57TH ST #901	NEW YORK, NY	10019
SEABOLD, ELIZABETH	WRITER	11580 BLIX ST	NORTH HOLLYWOOD, CA	91602
SEABORG, GLENN T	SCIENTIST	1 CYCLOTRON RD	BERKELEY, CA	94720
SEABRIDGE, JUDY A	TV DIRECTOR	68 PARK AVE	ALBANY, NY	12202
SEADER, RICHARD	THEATER PRODUCER	344 W 72ND ST	NEW YORK, NY	10023
SEAGAL, STEVEN	ACTOR-MARTIAL ARTS	POST OFFICE BOX 727	LOS OLIVAS, CA	93441
SEAGO, DAVID A	TV DIRECTOR	23970 23 MILE RD	MOUNT CLEMENS, MI	48043
SEAGRAVE, JOCELYN	ACTRESS	CBS-TV, "THE GUIDING LIGHT"		
		222 E 44TH ST	NEW YORK, NY	10017
SEAGRAVE, MALCOLM R	COMPOSER	915 DOUGLAS ST	LOS ANGELES, CA	90026
SEAGROVE, JENNY	ACTRESS	10-A HIGHBURY, NEW PARK		
		GARDEN FLAT	LONDON N5 2DB	ENGLAND
SEAGULL, BARBARA	ACTRESS	SEE - HERSHEY, BARBARA		
SEALE, BOB	TREASURER	STATE CAPITOL BUILDING	CARSON CITY, NV	89710
SEALE, EUGENE	FOOTBALL	OILERS, 6910 FANNIN ST	HOUSTON, TX	77070
SEALE, JOHN	CINEMATOGRAPHER	POST OFFICE BOX 1166	PACIFIC PALISADES, CA	90272
SEALE, SAM	FOOTBALL	POST OFFICE BOX 609609	SAN DIEGO, CA	92160
SEALE, STANLEY M	COMPOSER	POST OFFICE BOX 951	POINT ANGELES, WA	98362
SEALES, FRANKLYN	ACTOR	10100 SANTA MONICA BLVD #1600	LOS ANGELES, CA	90067
SEALS, DAN	SINGER-SONGWRITER	POST OFFICE BOX 1770	HENDERSONVILLE, TN	37077
SEALS, LEON	FOOTBALL	BILLS, 1 BILLS DR	ORCHARD PARK, NJ	14127
SEALS, RAY	FOOTBALL	BUCCANEERS, 1 BUCCANEER PL	TAMPA, FL	33607
SEAMAN, PETER S	SCREENWRITER	8955 BEVERLY BLVD	WEST HOLLYWOOD, CA	90048
SEAMANS, WILLIAM	TV WRITER-PRODUCER	10 COLUMBUS CIR #2310	NEW YORK, NY	10019
SEANEZ, RUDY	BASEBALL	1000 ELYSIAN PARK DR	LOS ANGELES, CA	90012
SEARAGE, RAY	BASEBALL	10233 96TH AVE	EDMONTON, ALB TK5 0A5	CANADA
SEARCHERS, THE	VOCAL GROUP	1650 BROADWAY #508	NEW YORK, NY	10019
SEARCHINGER, GENE	FILM DIRECTOR	200 W 72ND ST #46	NEW YORK, NY	10023
SEARCY, STEVE	BASEBALL	4113 FULTON DR	KNOXVILLE, TN	37918
SEARLE, ROLAND	ARTIST	JOHN LOCKE, 15 E 76TH ST	NEW YORK, NY	10021
SEARS, DAVID R	COMPOSER-CONDUCTOR	5846 4TH AVE	LOS ANGELES, CA	90043
SEARS, MARY FRANCES	TV PRODUCER	FRAN SEARS PRODS, 630 9TH AVE	NEW YORK, NY	10036
SEARS, PETE & FRIENDS	ROCK & ROLL GROUP	REDWOOD RECORDS, 6400 HOLLIS ST	EMERYVILLE, CA	94608
SEARS, SALLY	THEATER PRODUCER	PRIM PRODS, 387 1/2 BLEEKER ST	NEW YORK, NY	10014
SEARY, LAWRENCE A	CINEMATOGRAPHER	WNBC NEWS, 30 ROCKEFELLER PLZ	NEW YORK, NY	10112
SEATON, EULA	SCREENWRITER	8955 BEVERLY BLVD	WEST HOLLYWOOD, CA	90048
SEAU, JUNIOR	FOOTBALL	POST OFFICE BOX 609609	SAN DIEGO, CA	92160
SEAVER, JEFF	ARTIST	130 W 24TH ST	NEW YORK, NY	10011
SEAVER, TOM	BASEBALL-ANNOUNCER	LARKSPUR LN	GREENWICH, CT	06830
SEAVERNS, CHARLES	ACTOR	8927 SAINT IVES DR	LOS ANGELES, CA	90069
SEAVERS, VICKY LYNNE	ACTRESS	3700 BAGLEY AVE #213	LOS ANGELES, CA	90034
SEAVEY, DAVID	CARTOONIST	POST OFFICE BOX 500	WASHINGTON, DC	20044
SEBACH, KYLE	BASEBALL	POST OFFICE BOX 3496	DAVENPORT, IA	52808
SEBASTIAN, JOHN	SINGER-SONGWRITER	BENDETT, 2431 BRIARCREST RD	BEVERLY HILLS, CA	90210
SEBASTIAN, SHARON	ACTRESS	7060 HOLLYWOOD BLVD #1216	HOLLYWOOD, CA	90028
SEBRA, BOB	BASEBALL	POST OFFICE BOX 75089	OKLAHOMA CITY, OK	73147
SEBRING, CAMI	ACTRESS	BLANCHARD, 957 N COLE AVE	LOS ANGELES, CA	90038
SECOMBE, ANDREW	ACTOR	LONDON MGT, 235-241 REGENT ST	LONDON W1R 4PH	ENGLAND
SECOMBE, SIR HARRY	ACTOR-SINGER	46 SAINT JAMES'S ST	LONDON SW1	ENGLAND
SECONDARI, HELEN JEAN	DIRECTOR	1148 5TH AVE	NEW YORK, NY	10028
SECORD, RICHARD	U S GENERAL	1 PENNSYLVANIA PLAZA #2400	NEW YORK, NY	10119
SECRET LIVES	ROCK & ROLL GROUP	41 BRITAIN ST #200	TORONTO, ONT M5A 1R7	CANADA
SECULES, SCOTT	FOOTBALL	DOLPHINS, 2269 NW 199TH ST	MIAMI, FL	33056
SEDAKA, NEIL	SINGER-SONGWRITER	THE SHOREHAM TOWERS		
		8787 SHOREHAM DR	LOS ANGELES, CA	90069
SEDAN	ROCK & ROLL GROUP	SANTINO PRODUCTIONS		
		10097 GRANDVIEW	WOODLAWN, OH	45215
SEDAWIE, NORMAN W	WRITER-PRODUCER	5352 TOPEKA DR	TARZANA, CA	91356
SEDELMAIER, JOHN JOSEF	DIRECTOR	520 N MICHIGAN AVE #1026	CHICAGO, IL	60611
SEDGWICK, KYRA	ACTRESS	800 W END AVE #7-A	NEW YORK, NY	10025
SEDWICK, CAROL	TV DIRECTOR	317 W 54TH ST #3-A	NEW YORK, NY	10019
SEDWICK, JOHN W	DIRECTOR	56 WILLOW ST	BROOKLYN, NY	11201

SEE, CHARLES E	COMPOSER	2464 W 1ST AVE #102	VANCOUVER, BC V6K 1G6	CANADA
SEED, PAUL	TV DIRECTOR	132 KYVERDALE RD	LONDON N16 6PU	ENGLAND
SEEFRIED, TATE	BASEBALL	POST OFFICE BOX 22093	GREENSBORO, NC	27420
SEEGER, ALAN	TV WRITER	817 W END AVE	NEW YORK, NY	10025
SEEGER, PETE	SINGER-SONGWRITER	BOX 431, DUCHESS JUNCTION	BEACON, NY	12508
SEEGER, SANFORD	ACTOR	545 W 126TH ST	NEW YORK, NY	10027
SEELBACH, CHRIS	BASEBALL	POST OFFICE BOX 4525	MACON, GA	31208
SEELEY, TOM	TV PRODUCER	8383 WILSHIRE BLVD #923	BEVERLY HILLS, CA	90211
SEELY, BRAD	FOOTBALL COACH	POST OFFICE BOX 535000	INDIANPOLIS, IN	46253
SEELY, JEANNIE	SINGER	38 MUSIC SQUARE E #300	NASHVILLE, TN	37203
SEELY, SCOTT B	COMPOSER	39 BELMONT AVE	RANCHO MIRAGE, CA	92270
SEEMAN, JERRY	FOOTBALL REFEREE	NFL, 410 PARK AVE	NEW YORK, NY	10022
SEFCIK, GEORGE	FOOTBALL COACH	BROWNS, 80 1ST ST	BEREA, OH	44017
SEGAL, A DAVID	DIRECTOR	DGA, 110 W 57TH ST	NEW YORK, NY	10019
SEGAL, ALLAN	TV DIRECTOR-PRODUCER	ICARUS ENDEAVOR, 300 W 21ST ST	NEW YORK, NY	10011
SEGAL, DANIEL	WRITER	19433 PACIFIC COAST HWY	MALIBU, CA	90265
SEGAL, ELLEN	DIRECTOR-PRODUCER	210 E 73RD ST	NEW YORK, NY	10021
SEGAL, ERICH	AUTHOR	53 THE PRYORS, EAST HEATH RD	LONDON NW3 1BP	ENGLAND
SEGAL, GEORGE	ACTOR	ICM, 8899 BEVERLY BLVD	LOS ANGELES, CA	90048
SEGAL, JEFFREY	ACTOR	MC LEAN, 23-B DEODAR RD	LONDON SW15 2NP	ENGLAND
SEGAL, JERRY	SCREENWRITER	8955 BEVERLY BLVD	WEST HOLLYWOOD, CA	90048
SEGAL, JOEL B	FILM DIRECTOR	2757 BENTLEY PL	MARIETTA, GA	30067
SEGAL, JONATHAN	ACTOR	600 RADCLIFFE AVE	PACIFIC PALISADES, CA	90272
SEGAL, JONATHAN L	PIANIST-COMPOSER	27 W 96TH ST #4-D	NEW YORK, NY	10025
SEGAL, MICHAEL	ACTOR	27 CYPRUS AVE, FINCHLEY	LONDON N3 1SS	ENGLAND
SEGAL, STEPHANIE	ACTRESS	WHITAKER, 12725 VENTURA BLVD	STUDIO CITY, CA	91604
SEGAL, VIVIENNE	SINGER-ACTRESS	152 N LE DOUX RD	BEVERLY HILLS, CA	90211
SEGALL, DONALD	TV WRITER-PRODUCER	156 S ALMONT DR	BEVERLY HILLS, CA	90211
SEGALL, STUART	TV PRODUCER	CANNELL, 7083 HOLLYWOOD BLVD	LOS ANGELES, CA	90028
SEGAN, NOAH	ACTOR	ABC-TV, "LOVING"		
		320 W 66TH ST, STUDIO 23	NEW YORK, NY	10023
SEGEL, RUSSELL	DIRECTOR	10311 RIVERSIDE DR #302	TOLUCA LAKE, CA	91602
SEGELIN, BERNARD	FILM EXECUTIVE	523 CASHMERE TERR	LOS ANGELES, CA	90049
SEGELSTEIN, IRWIN B	TV EXECUTIVE	NBC-TV, 30 ROCKEFELLER PLAZA	NEW YORK, NY	10112
SEGER, BOB & SILVER BULLET BAND	ROCK & ROLL GROUP	PUNCH ENTS, 567 PURDY ST	BIRMINGHAM, MI	48009
SEGERS, FRANK	COLUMNIST	VARIETY, 400 N MICHIGAN AVE	CHICAGO, IL	60611
SEGUI, DAVID	BASEBALL	ORIOLE PARK, 333 W CAMDEN ST	BALTIMORE, MD	21201
SEGURA, JOSE	BASEBALL	POST OFFICE BOX 23290	NASHVILLE, TN	37202
SEGURA, PANCHO	TENNIS	RANCHO LA COSTA HOTEL & SPA		
		COSTA DEL MAR RD	CARLSBAD, CA	92009
SEGURSON, HOWARD J	COMPOSER	6648 BOBBYBOYAR AVE	CAONGA PARK, CA	91307
SEIBERT, L H	COMPOSER	1102 E VINE AVE	WEST COVINA, CA	91790
SEIDELMAN, ARTHUR ALLAN	FILM-TV DIRECTOR	1015 GAYLEY AVE #1149	LOS ANGELES, CA	90024
SEIDELMAN, SUSAN	FILM DIRECTOR	DGA, 110 W 57TH ST	NEW YORK, NY	10019
SEIDLER, DAVID	TV WRITER	10351 SANTA MONICA BLVD #211	LOS ANGELES, CA	90025
SEIDLER, MRS ROLAND	BASEBALL EXECUTIVE	1000 ELYSIAN PARK DR	LOS ANGELES, CA	90012
SEIDLER, NED M	ARTIST	3 HAMPTON HARBOR LN	HAMPTON BAYS, NY	11946
SEIDLER, ROLAND	BASEBALL EXECUTIVE	1000 ELYSIAN PARK DR	LOS ANGELES, CA	90012
SEIDLER, ROSALIE	ARTIST	3 HAMPTON HARBOR LN	HAMPTON BAYS, NY	11946
SEIDMON, STEVEN	TV EXECUTIVE	MTV NETWORKS, 1775 BROADWAY	NEW YORK, NY	10019
SEIFERT, GEORGE	FOOTBALL COACH	S F 49ERS, 4949 CENTENNIAL BL	SANTA CLARA, CA	95054
SEIFERT, LINDA	TALENT AGENT	SEIFERT, 18 LADBROKE TERR	LONDON W11 3PG	ENGLAND
SEIFERT, LYNN	SCREENWRITER	CAA, 9830 WILSHIRE BLVD	BEVERLY HILLS, CA	90212
SEIGEL, DONALD L	TV WRITER-DIRECTOR	UTA, 9560 WILSHIRE BL, 5TH FL	BEVERLY HILLS, CA	90212
SEIKALY, RONY	BASKETBALL	MIAMI HEAT, THE MIAMI ARENA	MIAMI, FL	33136
SEINFELD, JERRY	COMEDIAN	1222 N KINGS RD #9	LOS ANGELES, CA	90069
SEIPLE, LARRY	FOOTBALL COACH	DOLPHINS, 2269 NW 199TH ST	MIAMI, FL	33056
SEIPT, VIRGINIA GAIL	TV DIRECTOR	30 ROCKEFELLER PLAZA #1455	NEW YORK, NY	10112
SEITER, CHRISTOPHER	TV DIRECTOR-PRODUCER	645 S EUCLID AVE	PASADENA, CA	91106
SEITZ, GEORGE B, JR	WRITER-PRODUCER	10375 WILSHIRE BLVD #5-F	LOS ANGELES, CA	90024
SEITZER, BRAD	BASEBALL	POST OFFICE BOX 3169	FREDERICK, MD	21701
SEITZER, KEVIN	BASEBALL	BREWERS, 201 S 46TH ST	MILWAUKEE, WI	53214
SEKACZ, ILONA	COMPOSER	HEATH, PARAMOUNT HOUSE		
		162-170 WARDOUR ST	LONDON W1V 3AT	ENGLAND
SEKANOVICH, DAN	FOOTBALL COACH	DOLPHINS, 2269 NW 199TH ST	MIAMI, FL	33056
SELBY, BETTY	ACTRESS	229 E 81ST #T	NEW YORK, NY	10028
SELBY, DAVID	ACTOR	15152 ENCANTO DR	SHERMAN OAKS, CA	91403
SELBY, ROB	FOOTBALL	EAGLES, BROAD ST & PATTISON AVE	PHILADELPHIA, PA	19148
SELBY, TONY	ACTOR	AIM, 5 DENMARK ST	LONDON WC2H 8LP	ENGLAND
SELBY-WRIGHT, SONYA	DIRECTOR	DGA, 110 W 57TH ST	NEW YORK, NY	10019
SELCER, DICK	FOOTBALL COACH	BENGALS, 200 RIVERFRONT STADIUM	CINCINNATI, OH	45202
SELDEN, ALBERT W	THEATER PRODUCER	246 W 44TH ST	NEW YORK, NY	10036
SELDON, JOIE	ACTRESS	810 N DOHENY DR	LOS ANGELES, CA	90069
SELE, AARON	BASEBALL	POST OFFICE BOX 10213	LYNCHBURG, VA	24506
SELF, WILLIAM	DIRECTOR	975 SOMERA RD	LOS ANGELES, CA	90077
SELFE, RAY	ACT-WRI-PROD	PROFILE, 73 NEW BOND ST	LONDON W1Y 9DD	ENGLAND
SELIG, ALLAN "BUD"	BASEBALL EXECUTIVE	BREWERS, 201 S 46TH ST	MILWAUKEE, WI	53214
SELIK, LILA	ACTRESS-CASTING DIR	4117 MC LAUGHLIN AVE #9	LOS ANGELES, CA	90066
SELIN, MARGO	BODYBUILDER	POST OFFICE BOX 9560		
		FRIENDSHIP STATION	WASHINGTON, DC	20016
SELIP, MARIAINE	TV PRODUCER	30 ROCKEFELLER PLAZA #827	NEW YORK, NY	10112
SELL, DAVID F	OPERA DIRECTOR	MET OPERA, 1 LINCOLN PLAZA	NEW YORK, NY	10023
SELLARS, BILL	TV PRODUCER	BBC-TV, 56 WOOD LN	LONDON W12 7RJ	ENGLAND
SELLARS, JOSEPH	ARTIST	2423 W 22ND ST	MINNEAPOLIS, MN	55405
SELLECA, CONNIE	ACTRESS	14755 VENTURA BLVD #1-916	SHERMAN OAKS, CA	91403

Name	Occupation	Address	City/State	Zip/Country
SELLECK, JACQUELYN RAY	ACTRESS-MODEL	11385 HOMEDALE ST	LOS ANGELES, CA	90049
SELLECK, TOM	ACTOR-PRODUCER	9021 MELROSE AVE #207	LOS ANGELES, CA	90069
SELLER, KEITH	BASEBALL	POST OFFICE BOX 2148	WOODBRIDGE, VA	22193
SELLERS, ARLENE	FILM PRODUCER	9720 WILSHIRE BLVD #706	BEVERLY HILLS, CA	90212
SELLERS, ARTHUR D	SCREENWRITER	6144 GLEN OAK ST	LOS ANGELES, CA	90068
SELLERS, JEFF	BASEBALL	5823 CLARK AVE	LAKEWOOD, CA	90712
SELLERS, RICK	BASEBALL	TIGERS, 89 WHARNCLIFFE RD N	LONDON, ONT N6H 2A7	CANADA
SELLICK, JOHN	BASEBALL	POST OFFICE BOX 5599	LITTLE ROCK, AR	72215
SELLINGER, DENNIS J	TALENT AGENT	ICM, 388-396 OXFORD ST	LONDON W1	ENGLAND
SELLS, GEORGE	BASEBALL	POST OFFICE BOX 5599	LITTLE ROCK, AR	72215
SELOVER, JAMES R	CONDUCTOR	2283 TERMINO AVE	LONG BEACH, CA	90815
SELTZER, LEO	WRITER-PRODUCER	368 E 69TH ST	NEW YORK, NY	10021
SELZER, MILTON	ACTOR	575 SAN JUAN ST	SANTA PAULA, CA	93060
SEMBELLO, MICHAEL	SINGER-COMPOSER	3575 W CAHUENGA BLVD #PH	LOS ANGELES, CA	90068
SEMENCHUK, K ANATOLE	DIRECTOR	10660 W GLENNON DR	LAKEWOOD, CO	80226
SEMENOV, ANATOLI	HOCKEY	OILERS, NORTHLANDS COLISEUM	EDMONTON, ALTA T5B 4M9	CANADA
SEMENOVICH, DENISE MARY	INSTRUMENTALIST	308 W 104TH ST #3-A	NEW YORK, NY	10025
SEMINARA, FRANK	BASEBALL	POST OFFICE BOX 2000	SAN DIEGO, CA	92112
SEMKOFF, OLEG NICHOLAS	TV DIRECTOR	4620 N PARK AVE #PH 2-E	CHEVY CHASE, MD	20815
SEMKOW, JERZY	CONDUCTOR	ICM, 40 W 57TH ST	NEW YORK, NY	10019
SEMLER, DEAN	CINEMATOGRAPHER	4260 ARCOLA AVE	TOLUCA LAKE, CA	91602
SEMON, SID	FOOTBALL REFEREE	NFL, 410 PARK AVE	NEW YORK, NY	10022
SEMPLE, LORENZO, JR	SCREENWRITER	8955 BEVERLY BLVD	WEST HOLLYWOOD, CA	90048
SEN, BACHOO	DIRECTOR-PRODUCER	6 WOODLAND WY, PETTS WOOD	KENT BR5 1ND	ENGLAND
SENDER, DAVID	TV EXECUTIVE	ARTS & ENTERTAINMENT NETWORK		
		250 HARBOR PLAZA DR	STAMFORD, CT	06904
SENDREY, ALBERT R	COMPOSER	1377 MILLER PL	LOS ANGELES, CA	90069
SENESKY, RALPH	DIRECTOR	1714 SUNSET PLAZA DR	LOS ANGELES, CA	90069
SENIA, PAUL A	COMPOSER-CONDUCTOR	2207 WEST AVE #N-8	PALMDALE, CA	93550
SENNA, LORRAINE	DIRECTOR	DGA, 7920 SUNSET BLVD, 6TH FL	LOS ANGELES, CA	90046
SENSENBRENNER, F JAMES, JR	U S CONGRESSMAN	120 BISHOPS WY #154	BROOKFIELD, WI	53005
SENTINEL BEAST	ROCK & ROLL GROUP	POST OFFICE BOX 2428	EL SEGUNDO, CA	90245
SENTRY, FRANK	WRITER-PRODUCER	7471 MELROSE AVE	HOLLYWOOD, CA	90046
SEOANE, MITCH	BASEBALL MANAGER	POST OFFICE BOX 3496	DAVENPORT, IA	52808
SERENDIPITY SINGERS, THE	VOCAL GROUP	POST OFFICE BOX 399	LISLE, IL	60532
SERESIN, MICHAEL S	DIRECTOR	BFCS, 218 E 50TH ST	NEW YORK, NY	10022
SERETAN, STEPHAN H	COMPOSER-CONDUCTOR	1317 12TH ST #9	SANTA MONICA, CA	90401
SERETEAN, M B "BUD"	BASKETBALL EXECUTIVE	1 CNN CENTER #405, SOUTH TOWER	ATLANTA, GA	30303
SERIOUS, YAHOO	ACTOR	GREG PEAD, 12/33 E CRESCENT ST	MC MAHONS PT NSW 2060	AUSTRALIA
SERLE, CHRIS	TV JOURNALIST	BROWN, 162-168 REGENT ST	LONDON W1R 5TB	ENGLAND
SERNA, GIL	ACTOR	CARROLL, 120 S VICTORY BL #104	BURBANK, CA	91502
SERNA, PEPE	ACTOR	2321 HILL DR	LOS ANGELES, CA	90041
SEROTOFF, NAOMI	ACTRESS	10727 MC CUNE AVE #3	LOS ANGELES, CA	90034
SERRA, RAYMOND	ACTOR	BUENA SERRA PRODS, 675 BAY ST	STATEN ISLAND, NY	10304
SERRANO, JOSE E	U S CONGRESSMAN	890 GRAND CONCOURSE	BRONX, NY	10451
SERRY, JOHN	SINGER	YAHM, 2593 BEACHWOOD DR	LOS ANGELES, CA	90068
SERTNER, ROBERT M	TV PRODUCER	1827 NICHOLS CANYON RD	LOS ANGELES, CA	90046
SERVAIS, MARK	BASEBALL SCOUT	6850 LAWRENCE RD	LANTANA, FL	33462
SERVAIS, SCOTT	BASEBALL	POST OFFICE BOX 288	HOUSTON, TX	77001
SERVELLO, DAN	BASEBALL	POST OFFICE BOX 464	APPLETON, WI	54912
SERVICE, SCOTT	BASEBALL	1501 W 16TH ST	INDIANAPOLIS, IN	46202
SERVICE, THE	ROCK & ROLL GROUP	POST OFFICE BOX 268043	CHICAGO, IL	60626
SESNO, FRANK	BROADCAST JOURNALIST	1050 TECHWOOD DR, NW	ATLANTA, GA	30318
SESSIONS, JOHN	ACTOR	43 CROMFORD RD, FLAT 2	LONDON SW15 1PA	ENGLAND
SESSIONS, RONNIE	SINGER-SONGWRITER	POST OFFICE BOX 4966	LITTLE ROCK, AK	72214
SESTO, CAMILO	SINGER	151 S EL CAMINO DR	BEVERLY HILLS, CA	90212
SETH, ROSHAN	ACTOR	169 QUEENSGATE #8-A	LONDON SW7 5EH	ENGLAND
SETTLE, MIKE	SINGER	RNJ PRODS, 11514 CALVERT ST	NORTH HOLLYWOOD, CA	91606
SETZER, BRIAN	SINGER-SONGWRITER	4161 FULTON AVE	SHERMAN OAKS, CA	91423
SEVAREID, ERIC	NEWS JOURNALIST	CBS NEWS, 2020 "M" ST, NW	WASHINGTON, DC	20036
SEVERANCE, JOAN	ACTRESS	POST OFFICE BOX 67492	LOS ANGELES, CA	90067
SEVEREID, SUSANNE	ACTRESS-MODEL	22 PASEO MARGARITA	CAMARILLO, CA	93012
SEVERINSEN, DOC	TRUMPETER	2807 NICHOLS CANYON	LOS ANGELES, CA	90046
SEVERTSON, TOM	BASEBALL SCOUT	REDS, 100 RIVERFRONT STADIUM	CINCINNATI, OH	45202
SEVIER, WAYNE	FOOTBALL COACH	POST OFFICE BOX 17247 (DULLES)	WASHINGTON, DC	20041
SEWELL, JOE	BASEBALL (MINORS)	POST OFFICE BOX 824	BURLINGTON, IA	52601
SEWELL, STEVE	FOOTBALL	BRONCOS, 13655 BRONCOS PKWY	ENGLEWOOD, CO	80112
SEXTON, DANIEL	ACTOR	330 N MAPLE ST #P	BURBANK, CA	91505
SEXTON, GARY	ACTOR	909 N GARDNER ST	LOS ANGELES, CA	90046
SEYMORE, DENNIS	SINGER	ACE, 3407 GREEN RIDGE DR	NASHVILLE, TN	37214
SEYMOUR, CAROLYN	ACTRESS	3500 W OLIVE AVE #1400	BURBANK, CA	91505
SEYMOUR, DAN	ACTOR	1839 HILLSBORO AVE	LOS ANGELES, CA	90035
SEYMOUR, JANE	ACTRESS-MODEL	SAINT CATHERINE'S CT	BATHEASTON, BATH, AVON	ENGLAND
SEYMOUR, JEFF	FILM DIRECTOR	LUNER-MAXFIELD MANAGEMENT		
		222 1/2 S REEVES DR	BEVERLY HILLS, CA	90212
SEYMOUR, JOHN	U S SENATOR	2400 E KATELLA AVE #1068	ANAHEIM, AL	92806
SGARRO, NICHOLAS	DIRECTOR	174 S ORANGE DR	LOS ANGELES, CA	90036
SGOBBA, MIKE	BASEBALL SCOUT	333 W 35TH ST	CHICAGO, IL	60616
SHA NA NA	ROCK & ROLL GROUP	9255 SUNSET BLVD #411	LOS ANGELES, CA	90069
SHAAD, STEVE	BASEBALL EXECUTIVE	POST OFFICE BOX 1420	WICHITA, KS	67201
SHABER, DAVID	SCREENWRITER	555 W 57TH ST #1230	NEW YORK, NY	10019
SHACHTMAN, TOM	WRITER	WM MORRIS, 1350 AVE OF AMERICAS	NEW YORK, NY	10019
SHACKELFORD, TED	ACTOR	12305 VALLEY HEART DR	STUDIO CITY, CA	91604
SHACKLE, RICK	BASEBALL	POST OFFICE BOX 5599	LITTLE ROCK, AR	72215
SHAFER, HAL	ACTOR	3349 W CAHUENGA BLVD #2-B	LOS ANGELES, CA	90068

Name	Occupation	Address	City	Zip
SHAFER, JOHN	BASEBALL SCOUT	S F GIANTS, CANDLESTICK PARK	SAN FRANICSCO, CA	94124
SHAFER, STEVE	FOOTBALL COACH	RAMS, 2327 W LINCOLN BLVD	ANAHEIM, CA	92801
SHAFFER, ANTHONY	SCREENWRITER	8955 BEVERLY BLVD	WEST HOLLYWOOD, CA	90048
SHAFFER, DUANE	BASEBALL SCOUT	333 W 35TH ST	CHICAGO, IL	60616
SHAFFER, GAIL	SECRETARY OF STATE	STATE CAPITOL BUILDING	ALBANY, NY	12224
SHAFFER, LLOYD	COMPOSER-CONDUCTOR	16295 AVENIDA NOBLEZA	SAN DIEGO, CA	92128
SHAGAN, STEVE	WRITER-PRODUCER	10000 SANTA MONICA BLVD #305	LOS ANGELES, CA	90067
SHAH, KRISHNA	WRITER-PRODUCER	POST OFFICE BOX 64515	LOS ANGELES, CA	90064
SHAHEED, DARAKA	BASEBALL SCOUT	METS, 126TH ST & ROOSEVELT AVE	FLUSHING, NY	11368
SHAHIDI, STELLA	ARTIST	336 CENTRAL PARK W	NEW YORK, NY	10025
SHAIMAN, MARC	COMPOSER	6525 SUNSET BLVD #402	HOLLYWOOD, CA	90028
SHAKER, TED	TV EXECUTIVE	CBS SPORTS, 51 W 52ND ST	NEW YORK, NY	10019
SHAKTMAN, BEN	TV WRITER-DIRECTOR	140 W 55TH ST	NEW YORK, NY	10019
SHALAMAR	SOUL GROUP	9229 SUNSET BLVD #319	LOS ANGELES, CA	90069
SHALIT, GENE	FILM CRITIC	225 W 79TH ST	NEW YORK, NY	10021
SHALLCROSS, ALAN	TV PRODUCER	PETERS, FRASER & DUNLOP, LTD		
		5TH FLOOR, THE CHAMBERS		
		CHELSEA HARBOUR, LOT RD	LONDON SW10 OXF	ENGLAND
SHALLECK, ALAN	DIRECTOR-PRODUCER	84 MORNINGSIDE DR	OSSINING, NY	10562
SHALLON, DAVID	CONDUCTOR	ICM, 40 W 57TH ST	NEW YORK, NY	10019
SHAMBERG, MICHAEL	FILM WRITER-PRODUCER	3328 MANDEVILLE CANYON RD	LOS ANGELES, CA	90049
SHAMBURG, KEN	BASEBALL	500 NORTON ST	ROCHESTER, NY	14621
SHAN, MC	RAPPER-RAPWRITER	SEE - MC SHAN		
SHANAHAN, BRENDAN	HOCKEY	POST OFFICE BOX 504	EAST RUTHERFORD, NJ	07073
SHANAHAN, CHRIS	BASEBALL	525 NW PEACOCK BLVD	PORT SAINT LUCIE, FL	34986
SHANAHAN, COLLEEN	ACTRESS	290 N CENTRAL AVE	HARTSDALE, NY	10530
SHANAHAN, JEANNE	TV PRODUCER	CHILDREN'S TV WORKSHOP		
		1 LINCOLN PLAZA, 3RD FLOOR	NEW YORK, NY	10023
SHANAHAN, MIKE	FOOTBALL COACH	BRONCOS, 13655 BRONCOS PKWY	ENGLEWOOD, CO	80112
SHANAHAN, RICHARD M	TV DIRECTOR-PRODUCER	744 FLORENCE DR	PARK RIDGE, IL	60068
SHAND, FRIEDA	ACTRESS	VINCENT SHAW, 20 JAY MEWS		
		KENSINGTON GORE	LONDON SW7 2EP	ENGLAND
SHAND, IAN	ACT-WRI-DIR	ROSEHILL HOUSE, ROSE HILL		
		BURNHAM	BUCKS	ENGLAND
SHANDEL, PAMELA	ACTRESS	937 1/2 N HARPER AVE	LOS ANGELES, CA	90046
SHANDLING, GARRY	COMED-ACT-WRI	9200 SUNSET BLVD #428	LOS ANGELES, CA	90069
SHANE, SAMANTHA	ACTRESS	POST OFFICE BOX 6685	NEW YORK, NY	10128
SHANER, JOHN HERMAN	SCREENWRITER	151 S EL CAMINO DR	BEVERLY HILLS, CA	90212
SHANGHAI DOG	ROCK & ROLL GROUP	550 W 6TH AVE	VANCOUVER, BC	CANADA
SHANK	ROCK & ROLL GROUP	SPINDLETOP RECORDS		
		1500 SUMMIT ST	AUSTIN, TX	78741
SHANK, WINIFRED	CASTING DIRECTOR	136 E 55TH ST #4-R	NEW YORK, NY	10022
SHANKAR, RAVI	SITARIST	17 WARDEN CT, GOWALIA TANK RD	BOMBAY 36	INDIA
SHANKMAN, GARY	AUTHOR-BODYBUILDER	POST OFFICE BOX 1491	WOODSTOCK, GA	30188
SHANKS, ANN	DIRECTOR-PRODUCER	2237 N NEW HAMPSHIRE AVE	LOS ANGELES, CA	90027
SHANKS, BOB	TV WRITER	ICM, 8899 BEVERLY BLVD	LOS ANGELES, CA	90048
SHANKS, JERRY	DIRECTOR	4 QUARTERDECK ST #102	MARINA DEL REY, CA	90292
SHANNON	SINGER-SONGWRITER	POST OFFICE BOX 395	MERRICK, NY	11566
SHANNON, DARRIN	HOCKEY	SABRES, MEMORIAL AUDITORIUM	BUFFALO, NY	14202
SHANNON, DAVID	ARTIST	410 E 13TH ST #33	NEW YORK, NY	10009
SHANNON, DONALD, III	DIRECTOR	WFLD-TV, 300 N STATE ST	CHICAGO, IL	60610
SHANNON, GEORGE EDWARD	TV EXECUTIVE	CBS-TV, 51 W 52ND ST	NEW YORK, NY	10019
SHANNON, MIKE	BASEBALL-ANNOUNCER	250 STADIUM PLAZA	ST LOUIS, MO	63102
SHANNON, RAY D	NEWS CORRESPONDENT	ABC NEWS, 1717 DE SALES ST, NW	WASHINGTON, DC	20036
SHANNON, SCOTT	BASEBALL TRAINER	POST OFFICE BOX 1088	ST CATH, ONT L2R 3BO	CANADA
SHANNON, WALTER	BASEBALL EXECUTIVE	BREWERS, 201 S 46TH ST	MILWAUKEE, WI	53214
SHANTE, ROXANNE	RAPPER-RAPWRITER	FAA, 1700 BROADWAY, 5TH FLOOR	NEW YORK, NY	10019
SHAPER, HAL	LYRICIST	41-A ONSLOW SQ	LONDON SW7	ENGLAND
SHAPIRO, ALBERT	FILM DIRECTOR	14623 ROUND VALLEY DR	SHERMAN OAKS, CA	91403
SHAPIRO, ALLAN M	TV DIRECTOR	DGA, 110 W 57TH ST	NEW YORK, NY	10019
SHAPIRO, ARNOLD J	PRODUCER-EXECUTIVE	839 MALCOLM AVE	LOS ANGELES, CA	90024
SHAPIRO, BERT	WRITER-PRODUCER	196 E 75TH ST	NEW YORK, NY	10021
SHAPIRO, CONSTANTINE	COMPOSER-CONDUCTOR	3231 LOWRY RD	LOS ANGELES, CA	90027
SHAPIRO, DAVID J	COMPOSER-CONDUCTOR	1135 ONTARIO ST	BURBANK, CA	91505
SHAPIRO, ERIC	TV DIRECTOR	19 ROCKFORD DR	W NYACK, NY	10994
SHAPIRO, ESTHER	TV WRITER-PRODUCER	617 N ALTA DR	BEVERLY HILLS, CA	90210
SHAPIRO, HOWARD S	TV DIRECTOR	9211 WASHINGTON	MORTON GROVE, IL	60053
SHAPIRO, JOSHUA J	FILM DIRECTOR	110 W END AVE	NEW YORK, NY	10023
SHAPIRO, KENNETH R	FILM DIRECTOR	2044 STANLEY HILLS DR	LOS ANGELES, CA	90036
SHAPIRO, KENNETH S	TV WRITER-PRODUCER	13035 MAGNOLIA BLVD	SHERMAN OAKS, CA	91423
SHAPIRO, LEONARD	FILM PRODUCER	3884 FREDONIA DR #B-14	LOS ANGELES, CA	90068
SHAPIRO, MARTY	TALENT AGENT	SHAPIRO, 8827 BEVERLY BLVD	LOS ANGELES, CA	90048
SHAPIRO, RICHARD ALLEN	TV WRITER-PRODUCER	617 N ALTA DR	BEVERLY HILLS, CA	90210
SHAPIRO, ROBERT W	FILM EXECUTIVE	607 N OAKHURST DR	BEVERLY HILLS, CA	90210
SHAPIRO, RUBIN	DIRECTOR	500 2ND AVE	NEW YORK, NY	10016
SHAPIRO, SAMUEL	TREASURER	STATE HOUSE BUILDING	AUGUSTA, GA	04333
SHAPIRO, STANLEY	WRITER-PRODUCER	9938 ROBBINS DR	BEVERLY HILLS, CA	90212
SHAPS, CYRIL	ACTOR	LONDON MGT, 235-241 REGENT ST	LONDON W1R 4PH	ENGLAND
SHARAFF, IRENE	COSTUME DESIGNER	116 E 66TH ST	NEW YORK, NY	10021
SHARGO, BECKY	COMPOSER	3815 W OLIVE AVE #202	BURBANK, CA	91505
SHARIF, OMAR	ACTOR	WM MORRIS, 31-32 SOHO SQ	LONDON W1V 5DG	ENGLAND
SHARKEY, JACK	BOXER	BOX 242, PLEASANT ST	EPPING, NH	03042
SHARKEY, RAY	ACTOR	12424 WILSHIRE BLVD #840	LOS ANGELES, CA	90025
SHARKO, GARY	BASEBALL	5999 E VAN BUREN ST	PHOENIX, AZ	85008
SHARKS, THE	ROCK & ROLL GROUP	2109 W RIDGE AVE	LANCASTER, PA	17603

Name	Occupation	Address	City	Zip/Country
SHARLAND, MIKE	PLAYWRIGHT-AGENT	THE SHARLAND ORGANISATION		
		9 MARLBOROUGH CRESCENT		
		BEDFORD PARK, CHISWICK	LONDON W4 1HF	ENGLAND
SHARMA, BARBARA	ACTRESS	9000 SUNSET BLVD #801	LOS ANGELES, CA	90069
SHARMA, MADHAV	ACTOR-DIRECTOR	MC REDDIE, 91 REGENT ST	LONDON W1R 7TB	ENGLAND
SHARMAN, BILL	BASKETBALL	229 3RD AVE	VENICE, CA	90291
SHARMAN, BRUCE	TV PRODUCER	41 PARK RD, TEDDINGTON	MIDDLESEX TW11 OAV	ENGLAND
SHARNIK, JOHN S	TV WRITER-DIRECTOR	125 HICKS ST	BROOKLYN, NY	11201
SHARON, RALPH	CONDUCTOR	4858 FULTON AVE	SHERMAN OAKS, CA	91423
SHARON, STEPHEN F	SCREENWRITER	8955 BEVERLY BLVD	WEST HOLLYWOOD, CA	90048
SHARP, CHRIS	FILM DIRECTOR-ARTIST	1 BURNABY WOODS, GREYSTONES	CO WICKLOW	IRELAND
SHARP, DON	TV WRITER-DIRECTOR	80 CASTELNAU, BARNES	LONDON SW13 9EX	ENGLAND
SHARP, IAN	FILM DIRECTOR	22 WESTBERE RD	LONDON NW2	ENGLAND
SHARP, JOHN	COMPTROLLER	POST OFFICE BOX 12428	AUSTIN, TX	78711
SHARP, JON	TV DIRECTOR	6197 TEMPLE HILL DR	LOS ANGELES, CA	90068
SHARP, MIKE	BASEBALL	POST OFFICE BOX 10031	BAKERSFIELD, CA	93389
SHARP, PHILIP	U S CONGRESSMAN	2900 W JACKSON #101	MUNCIE, IN	47304
SHARP, TODD	SINGER-GUITARIST	POST OFFICE BOX 2413	HOLLYWOOD, CA	90078
SHARPE, IRON MIKE	WRESTLER	POST OFFICE BOX 3859	STAMFORD, CT	06905
SHARPE, JIM	ARTIST	5 SIDE HILL RD	WESTPORT, CT	06880
SHARPE, LARRY "PRETTY BOY"	WRESTLER	MONSTER FACTORY WRESTLING SCHOOL		
		655 DELAWARE	PAULSBORO, NJ	08066
SHARPE, LUIS	FOOTBALL	POST OFFICE BOX 888	PHOENIX, AZ	85001
SHARPE, ROBERT K	WRITER-PRODUCER	765 N BROADWAY, DUPLEX #15-E	HASTING-ON-HUDSON, NY	10706
SHARPE, SHANNON	FOOTBALL	BRONCOS, 13655 BRONCOS PKWY	ENGLEWOOD, CO	80112
SHARPE, STERLING	FOOTBALL	PACKERS, 1265 LOMBARDI AVE	GREEN BAY, WI	54307
SHARPERSON, MIKE	BASEBALL	1000 ELYSIAN PARK DR	LOS ANGELES, CA	90012
SHARPLES, DICK	TV WRITER	28 MAKEPEACE AVE, HIGHGATE	LONDON N6	ENGLAND
SHARPTON, REV AL	CLERYMAN	BLACK ENTERTAINMENT TV		
		156 W 56TH ST	NEW YORK, NY	10019
SHARRAD, JOHN S	FILM DIRECTOR	THE PRODUCTION COMPANY		
		35 LITTLE RUSSELL ST	LONDON WC1	ENGLAND
SHASKY, JIM	DIRECTOR	DGA, 110 W 57TH ST	NEW YORK, NY	10019
SHASKY, JOHN	BASKETBALL	REUNION ARENA, 777 SPORTS ST	DALLAS, TX	75207
SHATNER, MELANIE	ACTRESS	8730 WILSHIRE BLVD #470	LOS ANGELES, CA	90069
SHATNER, WILLIAM	ACTOR-DIRECTOR	3674 BERRY AVE	STUDIO CITY, CA	91604
SHATTUCK, SHARI	ACTRESS	8721 SANTA MONICA BLVD #21	WEST HOLLYWOOD, CA	90069
SHAUGHNESSY, ALFRED	TV WRITER-PLAYWRIGHT	GLASS, 28 BERKELEY SQ	LONDON W1X 6HD	ENGLAND
SHAUGHNESSY, CHARLES	ACTOR	1817 ASHLAND AVE	SANTA MONICA, CA	90405
SHAUGHNESSY, ED & ENERGY FORCE	JAZZ GROUP	CASSIDY, 417 MARAWOOD DR	WOODSTOCK, IL	60098
SHAVE, JON	BASEBALL	POST OFFICE BOX 4448	TULSA, OK	74159
SHAVEL, GLORIA	ART DIRECTOR	225 5TH AVE	NEW YORK, NY	10010
SHAVELSON, MELVILLE	WRITER-PRODUCER	11947 SUNSHINE TERR	NORTH HOLLYWOOD, CA	91604
SHAVER, HELEN	ACTRESS	10390 SANTA MONICA BLVD #300	LOS ANGELES, CA	90025
SHAVER, JEFF	BASEBALL	25016 MOLOKAI DR	TEGA CAY, SC	29815
SHAW, ADRIANA	ACTRESS	7047 FRANKLIN AVE #221	LOS ANGELES, CA	90028
SHAW, ANTHONY	TV DIRECTOR	225 20TH ST	SANTA MONICA, CA	90402
SHAW, ARTIE	ORCHESTRA LEADER	2127 W PALOS CT	NEWBURY PARK, CA	91320
SHAW, BERNARD	NEWS CORRESPONDENT	1050 TECHWOOD DR, NW	ATLANTA, GA	30318
SHAW, BRAD	HOCKEY	WHALERS, 1 CIVIC CENTER PLAZA	HARTFORD, CT	06103
SHAW, BRIAN	BASKETBALL	151 MERRIMAC ST	BOSTON, MA	02114
SHAW, CEDRIC	BASEBALL	POST OFFICE BOX 4448	TULSA, OK	74159
SHAW, CURTIS	BASEBALL	POST OFFICE BOX 2437	MODESTO, CA	95351
SHAW, DAVID	HOCKEY	POST OFFICE BOX 90111	ARLINGTON, TX	76004
SHAW, JEFF	BASEBALL	419 EASTERN AVE	WASHINGTON CT HOUSE, O	43160
SHAW, JENNIFER	ACTRESS	8075 W 3RD ST #303	LOS ANGELES, CA	90048
SHAW, JEROME	WRITER-PRODUCER	16 ESTRELLA	RANCHO MIRAGE, CA	92276
SHAW, JOHN	FOOTBALL EXECUTIVE	RAMS, 2327 W LINCOLN BLVD	ANAHEIM, CA	92801
SHAW, KEVIN	BASEBALL	300 STADIUM WY	DAVENPORT, FL	33837
SHAW, LOU	PRODUCER	10201 W PICO BLVD	LOS ANGELES, CA	90035
SHAW, LOUIS	TV WRITER	12170 IREDELL ST	STUDIO CITY, CA	91604
SHAW, MARLENA	SINGER	POST OFFICE BOX 82	GREAT NECK, NY	11021
SHAW, MARTIN	ACTOR	204 BELSWINS LN, HEMEL	HEMPSTEAD, HERTS	ENGLAND
SHAW, PAMELA	COSTUME DESIGNER	13949 VENTURA BLVD #309	SHERMAN OAKS, CA	91423
SHAW, PETER	TV PRODUCER	UBAL, 73 SAINT JAMES'S ST	LONDON SW1	ENGLAND
SHAW, REBECCA	ACTRESS	2017 N HOOVER ST #2	LOS ANGELES, CA	90027
SHAW, RICHARD "RICK"	COMEDY WRITER	8955 BEVERLY BLVD	WEST HOLLYWOOD, CA	90048
SHAW, ROBERT J	TV WRITER	1515 N DOHENY DR	LOS ANGELES, CA	90069
SHAW, ROSE TOBIAS	CASTING DIRECTOR	219 LIVERPOOL RD	LONDON N1	ENGLAND
SHAW, SHELBY	BASEBALL	POST OFFICE BOX 3609	PORT CHARLOTTE, FL	33949
SHAW, STAN	ACTOR	1999 AVE OF THE STARS #2850	LOS ANGELES, CA	90067
SHAW, SUSAN	TV DIRECTOR	10 STRAND ST	SANTA MONICA, CA	90405
SHAW, TOM	GOLFER	PGA SENIORS, 112 T P C BLVD	PONTE VEDRA BEACH, FL	32082
SHAW, TOMMY	SINGER-SONGWRITER	E S "BUD" PRAGER MANAGEMENT		
		1790 BROADWAY, PENTHOUSE	NEW YORK, NY	10019
SHAW-STRAMONDO, JAN RENE	TV DIRECTOR	1503 REPUBLIC ST	SAN DIEGO, CA	92114
SHAWLEE, JOAN	ACTRESS-WRITER	STONE MANNERS, 9113 SUNSET BL	LOS ANGELES, CA	90069
SHAWYER, DAVID	ACTOR	16 RYLETT RD	LONDON W12	ENGLAND
SHAWYER, PENNY DELAMAR	MAKE-UP ARTIST	THE MAKE-UP ARTIST		
		26 BUTE ST	LONDON SW7	ENGLAND
SHAY, ROBERT E	TV EXECUTIVE	PRIMETIME ENTERTAINMENT		
		444 MADISON AVE, 32ND FLOOR	NEW YORK, NY	10022
SHAYE, LIN	ACTRESS	280 S BEVERLY DR #400	BEVERLY HILLS, CA	90212
SHAYE, ROBERT	FILM EXECUTIVE	NEW LINE CINEMA, 575 8TH AVE	NEW YORK, NY	10018
SHAYNE, LINDA	ACTRESS	2460 BEVERLY AVE	SANTA MONICA, CA	90405

SHAYNE, ROBERT	ACTOR	555 LAURIE LN #J-7	THOUSAND OAKS, CA	91360
SHAYNE, SHARRON	ACTRESS	9165 SUNSET BLVD #202	LOS ANGELES, CA	90069
SHAYS, CHRISTOPHER	U S CONGRESSMAN	888 WASHINGTON BLVD, 2ND FL	STAMFORD, CT	06901
SHEA, GEORGE BEVERLY	SINGER	1300 HARMON PL	MINNEAPOLIS, MN	55403
SHEA, JOHN	ACTOR	955 S CARRILLO DR #300	LOS ANGELES, CA	90048
SHEA, JOHN	BASEBALL	CHIEFS, MAC ARTHUR STADIUM	SYRACUSE, NY	13208
SHEA, JOHN P "JACK"	WRITER-PRODUCER	1128 16TH ST #B	SANTA MONICA, CA	90403
SHEA, MIKE & RAZORTALK	ROCK & ROLL GROUP	POST OFFICE BOX 4429	AUSTIN, TX	78765
SHEA, PATT	TV WRITER	R/W/G, 8428 MELROSE PL #C	LOS ANGELES, CA	90069
SHEA, RICK	EDUCATOR-PROFESSOR	2801 MEADOW LARK DR	SAN DIEGO, CA	92123
SHEA, ROGER M	TV DIRECTOR-PRODUCER	1930 W GATE AVE	LARGO, FL	33540
SHEA, WILLIAM A	FOOTBALL	POST OFFICE BOX 17247 (DULLES)	WASHINGTON, DC	20041
SHEAFFER, DANNY	BASEBALL	POST OFFICE BOX 1659	PORTLAND, OR	97207
SHEAR, JULES	SINGER-SONGWRITER	POST OFFICE BOX 7451	NEW YORK, NY	10022
SHEAR, RHONDA	ACTRESS-MODEL-COMED	KJAR, 10653 RIVERSIDE DR	TOLUCA LAKE, CA	91602
SHEARD, MICHAEL	ACTOR	EDWARDS, 275 KENNINGTON RD	LONDON SE1 6BY	ENGLAND
SHEARE, THADDEUS	CARTOONIST	ROUTE #1, BOX 21, TATUMUCK RD	POUND RIDGE, NY	10576
SHEARER, HARRY	ACTOR-COMEDIAN	1999 AVE OF THE STARS #2850	LOS ANGELES, CA	90067
SHEARING, GEORGE	PIANIST	605 MARKET ST #1350	SAN FRANCISCO, CA	94105
SHEASBY, JOHN S	DIRECTOR	1640 RIDGEWOOD E	GLENVIEW, IL	60025
SHEAVER, TED	CARTOONIST	KING FEATURES, 216 E 45TH ST	NEW YORK, NY	10017
SHEBIB, DONALD	FILM DIRECTOR	EUDON, 312 WRIGHT AVE	TORONTO, ONT W6R 1L9	CANADA
SHEDD, BEN A	FILM DIRECTOR	2009 N BRONSON AVE	LOS ANGELES, CA	90068
SHEDDAN, MARYLIN	ASTROLOGER	UPS, 4900 MAIN ST, 9TH FLOOR	KANSAS CITY, MO	64112
SHEEDY, ALLY	ACTRESS-POET	POST OFFICE BOX 6327	MAILBU, CA	90265
SHEEHAN, ANTHONY	TV WRITER-DIRECTOR	2000 NICHOLS CANYON RD	LOS ANGELES, CA	90046
SHEEHAN, DAVID	FILM CRITIC	7310 MULHOLLAND DR	HOLLYWOOD, CA	90046
SHEEHAN, DOUG	ACTOR	4019 GOLDFINCH ST #137	SAN DIEGO, CA	92103
SHEEHY, MARK	BASEBALL SCOUT	1000 ELYSIAN PARK DR	LOS ANGELES, CA	90012
SHEEN, ANDREA V C	TV PRODUCER	SHEEN & ASSOC, 88 BLEECKER ST	NEW YORK, NY	10012
SHEEN, CHARLIE	ACTOR	11770 PACIFIC COAST HWY	MALIBU, CA	90265
SHEEN, MARTIN	ACTOR-DIRECTOR	6916 DUME DR	MALIBU, CA	90265
SHEEN, RAMON	ACTOR	SEE - ESTEVEZ, RAMON		
SHEETS, LARRY	BASEBALL	1413 LYLE AVE	STAUNTON, VA	24401
SHEFFER, JONATHAN	COMPOSER	6525 SUNSET BLVD #402	HOLLYWOOD, CA	90028
SHEFFIELD, GARY	BASEBALL	POST OFFICE BOX 2000	SAN DIEGO, CA	92112
SHEFFIELD, JOHNNY	ACTOR	834 1ST AVE	CHULA VISTA, CA	92011
SHEFLIN, DAN	ACTOR	269 N FLORENCE ST	BURBANK, CA	91505
SHEFTER, BERT A	COMPOSER-CONDUCTOR	1737 BEL AIR RD	LOS ANGELES, CA	90077
SHEILA E	SINGER-PERCUSSIONIST	CAA, 9830 WILSHIRE BLVD	BEVERLY HILLS, CA	90212
SHEINER, DAVID S	ACTOR	351 S FULLER AVE #12-F	LOS ANGELES, CA	90036
SHELBY, JOHN	BASEBALL	711 HEADLEY AVE	LEXINGTON, KY	40508
SHELBY, RICHARD	U S SENATOR	POST OFFICE BOX 2570	TUSCALOOSA, AL	35403
SHELDON, DAVID	WRITER-PRODUCER	1437 RISING GLEN RD	LOS ANGELES, CA	90069
SHELDON, JAMES	TV DIRECTOR	9428 LLOYDCREST DR	BEVERLY HILLS, CA	90210
SHELDON, JIMMY	COMPOSER-CONDUCTOR	BLUE ECHOES BY THE SEA	HARMONY, CA	93435
SHELDON, KENNY	CONDUCTOR	1420 N FULLER AVE #304	LOS ANGELES, CA	90046
SHELDON, LEE	TV WRITER-PRODUCER	CANNELL, 7083 HOLLYWOOD BLVD	LOS ANGELES, CA	90028
SHELDON, RALPH	FILM EDITOR	8 PLOUGH FARM CLOSE	RUISLIP HA4 7GH	ENGLAND
SHELDON, RON	CINEMATOGRAPHER	7715 SUNSET BLVD #150	LOS ANGELES, CA	90046
SHELDON, RONALD D	DIRECTOR	6518 HERON DR	AUSTIN, TX	78759
SHELDON, SCOTT	BASEBALL	POST OFFICE BOX 882	MADISON, WI	53701
SHELDON, SIDNEY	WRITER	10250 SUNSET BLVD	LOS ANGELES, CA	90077
SHELL, ART	FOOTBALL COACH	RAIDERS, 332 CENTER ST	EL SEGUNDO, CA	90245
SHELL, TED	COSTUME DESIGNER	5708 GENTRY AVE	NORTH HOLLYWOOD, CA	91607
SHELLENBACK, JIM	BASEBALL COACH	POST OFFICE BOX 5645	ORLANDO, FL	32855
SHELLEY, CAROLE	ACTRESS	333 W 56TH ST	NEW YORK, NY	10019
SHELLEY, ELBERT	FOOTBALL	FALCONS, SUWANEE RD AT I-85	SUWANEE, GA	30174
SHELLEY, JOSHUA	DIRECTOR	1919 N BEVERLY GLEN BLVD	LOS ANGELES, CA	90077
SHELLEY, KATHLEEN A	TV WRITER	8425 MELROSE PL #C	LOS ANGELES, CA	90069
SHELLY, BRUCE	TV WRITER	SCHALLERT, 9350 WILSHIRE BLVD	BEVERLY HILLS, CA	90212
SHELMERDINE, MARK	FILM PRODUCER	LONDON FILMS, 44-A FLORAL ST	LONDON WC2E 9DA	ENGLAND
SHELTON, ABIGAIL	ACTRESS	1680 N VINE ST #726	HOLLYWOOD, CA	90028
SHELTON, ANTHONY	FOOTBALL	POST OFFICE BOX 609609	SAN DIEGO, CA	92160
SHELTON, BEN	BASEBALL	POST OFFICE DRAWER 1218	ZEBULON, NC	27597
SHELTON, DEBORAH	ACTRESS	1690 COLDWATER CANYON DR	BEVERLY HILLS, CA	90210
SHELTON, LESLEY	ACTRESS	953 DEXTER ST	LOS ANGELES, CA	90042
SHELTON, MIKE	CARTOONIST	POST OFFICE BOX 11626	SANTA ANA, CA	92711
SHELTON, REID	ACTOR	1524 LABAIG AVE	LOS ANGELES, CA	90028
SHELTON, RICHARD	FOOTBALL	STEELERS, 300 STADIUM CIR	PITTSBURGH, PA	15212
SHELTON, RONALD W	WRI-DIR-PROD	1861 S BUNDY DR	LOS ANGELES, CA	90025
SHENKAROW, JUSTIN	ACTOR	NBC-TV, 3000 W ALAMEDA AVE	BURBANK, CA	91523
SHENSON, WALTER	FILM PRODUCER	419 SAINT CLOUD RD	LOS ANGELES, CA	90077
SHEPARD, ADM ALAN B	ASTRONAUT	3435 WESTHEIMER RD #1005	HOUSTON, TX	77027
SHEPARD, DODIE	COSTUME DESIGNER	1018 N KENWOOD ST	BURBANK, CA	91505
SHEPARD, GERALD	FILM EDITOR	11628 CHENAULT ST #6	LOS ANGELES, CA	90049
SHEPARD, JACK	TV DIRECTOR-PRODUCER	500 S SUNSET CANYON DR	BURBANK, CA	91501
SHEPARD, JEAN	SINGER	TESSIER, 505 CANTON PASS	MADISON, TN	37115
SHEPARD, JEWEL	ACTRESS-MODEL	POST OFFICE BOX 480265	LOS ANGELES, CA	90048
SHEPARD, KEN	BASEBALL EXECUTIVE	POST OFFICE BOX 2148	WOODBRIDGE, VA	22193
SHEPARD, SAM	ACTOR-DIRECTOR	LOIS BERMAN, 240 W 44TH ST	NEW YORK, NY	10036
SHEPARD, VONDA	SINGER-SONGWRITER	9034 SUNSET BLVD #250	LOS ANGELES, CA	90069
SHEPHERD, BOB	WRI-DIR-PROD	SCREEN PLAY, COLONEY HATCH LN		
		MUSWELL HILL	LONDON N10 1EA	ENGLAND
SHEPHERD, CYBILL	ACTRESS-MODEL	POST OFFICE BOX 904	SAN JACINTO, CA	92383

Name	Occupation	Address	City	Zip/Country
SHEPHERD, ELIZABETH	TALENT AGENT	29 EVERSLEY CRESCENT	LONDON N21 1EL	ENGLAND
SHEPHERD, JACK	ACTOR-WRITER	MARKHAM AND FROGGATT, LTD		
		JULIAN HOUSE, 4 WINDMILL ST	LONDON W1P 1HF	ENGLAND
SHEPHERD, KEITH	BASEBALL	POST OFFICE BOX 360007	BIRMINGHAM, AL	35236
SHEPHERD, RON	BASEBALL	RURAL ROUTE 2, BOX 53-X	KILGORE, TX	75662
SHEPHERD, SHERRIE	CARTOONIST	UNITED FEATURE, 200 PARK AVE	NEW YORK, NY	10166
SHEPPARD, BOBBY	SINGER	PENNY, 30 GUINAN ST	WALTHAM, MA	02154
SHEPPARD, CAROLE S	DIRECTOR	DGA, 110 W 57TH ST	NEW YORK, NY	10019
SHEPPARD, COLLEEN	SINGER	GOOD, 2500 NW 39TH ST	OKLAHOMA CITY, OK	73112
SHEPPARD, DON	BASEBALL	POST OFFICE BOX 4370	SALINAS, CA	93912
SHEPPARD, GORDON	WRITER-PRODUCER	3449 PEEL ST	MONTREAL, QUE	CANADA
SHEPPARD, JILL	TV DIRECTOR	28 MURRAY MEWS	LONDON NW1 9RJ	ENGLAND
SHEPPARD, RAY	HOCKEY	POST OFFICE BOX 90111	ARLINGTON, TX	76004
SHEPPARD, T G	SINGER	SCOTTI BROS, 2128 PICO BLVD	SANTA MONICA, CA	90405
SHEPPERD, DAVID A E	FILM EXECUTIVE	GOLDEN COMMUNICATIONS, LTD		
		47 GREEK ST	LONDON W1V 5LQ	ENGLAND
SHEPPHIRD, CARROLL	FILM DIRECTOR	3008 CLUBHOUSE CIR	COSTA MESA, CA	92626
SHER, ANTONY	ACTOR	HOPE, 108 LEONARD ST	LONDON EC2A 4RH	ENGLAND
SHER, JACK	WRITER-PRODUCER	9520 DALEGROVE DR	BEVERLY HILLS, CA	90210
SHERA, MARK	ACTOR	9229 SUNSET BLVD #311	LOS ANGELES, CA	90069
SHERDEMAN, TED	WRITER	23388 MULHOLLAND HIGHWAY	WOODLAND HILLS, CA	91364
SHERER, MEL	TV WRITER	9209 WHITWORTH DR	BEVERLY HILLS, CA	90212
SHERER, WERNER G	HAIR STYLIST	125 CHRISTOPHER ST #5-D	NEW YORK, NY	10014
SHERIDAN, ARDELL	ACTRESS-AUTHORESS	CASTELLANO, 592 PENN AVE	TEANECK, NJ	07666
SHERIDAN, JAY	TV DIRECTOR	155 N HARBOR DR #5402	CHICAGO, IL	60601
SHERIDAN, JIM	FILM DIRECTOR	CAA, 9830 WILSHIRE BLVD	BEVERLY HILLS, CA	90212
SHERIDAN, NICOLETTE	ACTRESS	POST OFFICE BOX 25578	LOS ANGELES, CA	90025
SHERIDAN, PAT	BASEBALL	N Y YANKEES, YANKEE STADIUM	BRONX, NY	10451
SHERIDAN, RONDELL	COMEDIAN	1539 SAWTELLE BLVD #10	LOS ANGELES, CA	90025
SHERIFF	ROCK & ROLL GROUP	ICM, 40 W 57TH ST	NEW YORK, NY	10019
SHERIFF, JAIME	SINGER	JAY LANDERS, 9255 SUNSET BLVD	LOS ANGELES, CA	90069
SHERIN, EDWIN	FILM DIRECTOR	ROAD #2, GORDON RD	CARMEL, NY	10512
SHERLOCK, GLENN	BASEBALL MANAGER	5301 NW 12TH AVE	FORT LAUDERDALE, FL	33309
SHERLOCK, JOHN	CARTOONIST	POST OFFICE BOX 500	WASHINGTON, DC	20044
SHERMAN, ARLENE	TV PRODUCER	CHILDREN'S TV WORKSHOP		
		1 LINCOLN PLAZA	NEW YORK, NY	10023
SHERMAN, BOB	PRODUCER	LAYTON PRODUCTIONS		
		4000 WARNER BLVD	BURBANK, CA	91522
SHERMAN, BOBBY	SINGER-ACTOR	1870 SUNSET PLAZA DR	LOS ANGELES, CA	90069
SHERMAN, COURTNEY	ACTOR	CBS-TV, "AS THE WORLD TURNS"		
		524 W 57TH ST #5330	NEW YORK, NY	10019
SHERMAN, DARRELL	BASEBALL	POST OFFICE BOX 1420	WICHITA, KS	67201
SHERMAN, GARY ARON	WRITER-PRODUCER	4501 CEDROS AVE #328	SHERMAN OAKS, CA	91403
SHERMAN, GEOFFREY	DIRECTOR	10 E 44TH ST #700	NEW YORK, NY	10017
SHERMAN, HEATH	FOOTBALL	EAGLES, BROAD ST & PATTISON AVE	PHILADELPHIA, PA	19148
SHERMAN, JAMES P	ART DIRECTOR	34 W 65TH ST	NEW YORK, NY	10023
SHERMAN, JENNY LEE	ACTRESS-MODEL	POST OFFICE BOX 73	LOS ANGELES, CA	90078
SHERMAN, LLOYD R	TV EXECUTIVE	CYGNUS ENTS, 881 7TH AVE	NEW YORK, NY	10019
SHERMAN, P	FILM CRITIC	BOSTON HERALD, 1 HERALD SQ	BOSTON, MA	02106
SHERMAN, RALPH	COMEDIAN	ATTRACTIONS TALENT AGENCY		
		6525 N FRANCISCO AVE	CHICAGO, IL	60645
SHERMAN, RAY	FOOTBALL COACH	FALCONS, SUWANEE RD AT I-85	SUWANEE, GA	30174
SHERMAN, RICHARD	COMPOSER-LYRICIST	808 N CRESCENT DR	BEVERLY HILLS, CA	90210
SHERMAN, ROBERT	DIRECTOR	999 N DOHENY DR #403	LOS ANGELES, CA	90069
SHERMAN, ROBERT B	SONGWRITER	808 N CRESCENT DR	BEVERLY HILLS, CA	90210
SHERMAN, SAMUEL	DIRECTOR	DGA, 7920 SUNSET BLVD, 6TH FL	LOS ANGELES, CA	90046
SHERMAN, STANFORD L	SCREENWRITER	36 SUNSET AVE	VENICE, CA	90291
SHERMAN, SYLVAN ROBERT	ACTOR	170 W END AVE	NEW YORK, NY	10023
SHERMAN, VINCENT	FILM DIRECTOR	6355 SYCAMORE MEADOWS DR	MALIBU, CA	90265
SHEROHMAN, THOMAS K	SCREENWRITER	3534 DAHLIA AVE	LOS ANGELES, CA	90026
SHERRARD, MIKE	FOOTBALL	S F 49ERS, 4949 CENTENNIAL BL	SANTA CLARA, CA	95054
SHERRILL, BILLY	PIANIST-ARRANGER	3631 WOODLAWN DR	NASHVILLE, TN	37215
SHERRILL, TIM	BASEBALL	POST OFFICE BOX 36407	LOUISVILLE, KY	40233
SHERRILL, WILLIAM D	PIANIST	1708 GRAND AVE	NASHVILLE, TN	37212
SHERRIN, NED	WRITER-PRODUCER	4 CORNWALL MANSIONS		
		ASHBURNHAM RD	LONDON SW3	ENGLAND
SHERRY, NORM	BASEBALL-COACH	4383 NOBEL DR #89	SAN DIEGO, CA	92122
SHERTZER, JIM	FILM CRITIC	POST OFFICE BOX 3159	WINSTON-SALEM, NC	27102
SHERWIN, DAVID N	SCREENWRITER	8955 BEVERLY BLVD	WEST HOLLYWOOD, CA	90048
SHERWOOD, JAMES SHAMUS	ACTOR	10605 MOORPARK ST #2	NORTH HOLLYWOOD, CA	91602
SHERWOOD, MADELEINE	ACTRESS	32 LEROY ST	NEW YORK, NY	10014
SHERWOOD, ROBIN	ACTRESS	6565 SUNSET BLVD #310	HOLLYWOOD, CA	90068
SHIELDS, BROOKE	ACTRESS-MODEL	POST OFFICE BOX B	HAYWORTH, NJ	07641
SHIELDS, DOUG	BASEBALL	300 STADIUM WY	DAVENPORT, FL	33837
SHIELDS, KITTY	TALENT AGENT	19 W 44TH ST #1000	NEW YORK, NY	10036
SHIELDS, LORAINE	ACTRESS	159 N CLARK DR #4	BEVERLY HILLS, CA	90211
SHIELDS, MIKE	BASEBALL EXECUTIVE	POST OFFICE BOX 2437	MODESTO, CA	95351
SHIELDS, PAT R	DIRECTOR	2575 GARDNER PL #A-41	GLENDALE, CA	91206
SHIELDS, ROBERT	MIME-WRITER	7615 W NORTON AVE #1	LOS ANGELES, CA	90046
SHIELDS, STEVE	BASEBALL	LYNDA AVE, RURAL ROUTE 11	GASDEN, AL	35903
SHIELDS, TOMMY	BASEBALL	500 NORTON ST	ROCHESTER, NY	14621
SHIFFLET, MARK	BASEBALL COACH	5301 NW 12TH AVE	FORT LAUDERDALE, FL	33309
SHIFFLETT, STEVE	BASEBALL	POST OFFICE BOX 3665	OMAHA, NE	68103
SHIGETA, JAMES	ACTOR	8917 CYNTHIA ST #1	LOS ANGELES, CA	90069
SHIKLES, LARRY	BASEBALL	POST OFFICE BOX 2365	PAWTUCKET, RI	02861

Name	Occupation	Address	City	Zip
SHILS, JUDI A	DIRECTOR	DGA, 110 W 57TH ST	NEW YORK, NY	10019
SHILTON, GILBERT	TV DIRECTOR	5011 WESTPARK DR	NORTH HOLLYWOOD, CA	91601
SHILTS, RANDY	AUTHOR-CORRESPONDENT	S F CHRONICLE, 901 MISSION ST	SAN FRANCISCO, CA	94119
SHIMADA, YOKO	ACTRESS	7245 HILLSDALE AVE #415	LOS ANGELES, CA	90046
SHIMER, PORTER	COLUMNIST	UPS, 4900 MAIN ST, 9TH FLOOR	KANSAS CITY, MO	64112
SHIMKUS, JOANNA	ACTRESS	1007 COVE WY	BEVERLY HILLS, CA	90210
SHIMOKAWA, GARY K	DIRECTOR	2029 CENTURY PARK E #1300	LOS ANGELES, CA	90067
SHIMONO, SAB	ACTOR	3332 DESCANSO DR	LOS ANGELES, CA	90026
SHINALL, ZAK	BASEBALL	POST OFFICE BOX 26267	ALBUQUERQUE, NM	87125
SHINDLER, COLIN	TV PRODUCER	HEATH, PARAMOUNT HOUSE		
		162-170 WARDOUR ST	LONDON W1V 3AT	ENGLAND
SHINDO, TAK	COMPOSER	1322 W CAMINO DEL SUR	SAN DIMAS, CA	91773
SHINE, THOMAS A	NEWS CORRES-WRITER	ABC NEWS, 1717 DE SALES ST, NW	WASHINGTON, DC	20036
SHINES, JOHNNY	SINGER	CHICKLES, 15 MANSFIELD ST	BOSTON, MA	02134
SHINES, RAZOR	BASEBALL	1501 W 16TH ST	INDIANAPOLIS, IN	46202
SHINKAI, BILL	TV WRITER	18408 COLTMAN AVE	CARSON, CA	90746
SHINN, GEORGE	BASKETBALL EXECUTIVE	310 N KINGS DR	CHARLOTTE, NC	28204
SHIPLEY, CRAIG	BASEBALL	POST OFFICE BOX 2000	SAN DIEGO, CA	92112
SHIPLEY, DON	SINGER	POST OFFICE BOX 42466	TUCSON, AZ	85733
SHIPLEY, ELLEN	SINGER	3 E 54TH ST #1400	NEW YORK, NY	10022
SHIPMAN, KIM	GOLFER	2750 VOLUSA AVE #B	DAYTON BEACH, FL	32114
SHIPMAN, PETER	BASEBALL EXECUTIVE	POST OFFICE BOX 4488	WINSTON-SALEM, NC	27115
SHIPP, JOHN WESLEY	ACTOR	BLOOM, 233 PARK AVE S, 10TH FL	NEW YORK, NY	10017
SHIPPY, KENNETH ROBERT	ACTOR	1925 FOX HILLS DR	LOS ANGELES, CA	90025
SHIPSTON, B G	ACTRESS	406 E RANDOLPH ST	GLENDALE, CA	91207
SHIRE, DAVID	COMPOSER	14820 VALLEY VISTA BLVD	SHERMAN OAKS, CA	91403
SHIRE, NOEL	ACTOR	17730 POSETANO RD	PACIFIC PALISADES, CA	90272
SHIRE, SANFORD	CONDUCTOR	1550 N LAUREL AVE #305	LOS ANGELES, CA	90046
SHIRE, TALIA	ACTRESS	16633 VENTURA BLVD	ENCINO, CA	91436
SHIRELLES, THE	VOCAL GROUP	GALLUP, 93-40 QUEENS BLVD	REGO PARK, NY	11374
SHIREMAN, JEFF	BASEBALL	POST OFFICE BOX 36407	LOUISVILLE, KY	40233
SHIRLEY, ANNE	ACTRESS	LEDERER, 7416 ROSEWOOD AVE	LOS ANGELES, CA	90036
SHIRLEY, BOB	BASEBALL-COACH	CHIEFS, MAC ARTHUR STADIUM	SYRACUSE, NY	13208
SHIRLEY, DONALD L, JR	COSTUME DESIGNER	IMERO FIORENTINO ASSOCIATES		
		44 W 63RD ST	NEW YORK, NY	10023
SHIRLEY, MIKE	BASEBALL	14100 SIX MILE CYPRESS PKWY	FORT MYERS, FL	33912
SHIRLEY, RICHARD MARVIN	DIRECTOR	610 N FAIRBANKS CT	CHICAGO, IL	60611
SHIRRIFF, CATHERINE	ACTRESS-MODEL	12456 VENTURA BLVD #1	STUDIO CITY, CA	91604
SHIRTS, THE	ROCK & ROLL GROUP	SPHINX MANAGEMENT AGENCY		
		2 UNITY PL, WESTGATE		
		ROTHERHAM	SOUTH YORKS S60 1AR	ENGLAND
SHITTONS, THE	VOCAL GROUP	POST OFFICE BOX 4585	PORTSMOUTH, NH	03801
SHIVAS, MARK	TV DIRECTOR-PRODUCER	BBC-TV, 56 WOOD LN	LONDON W12 7RJ	ENGLAND
SHIVELY, DOUG	FOOTBALL COACH	FALCONS, SUWANEE RD AT I-85	SUWANEE, GA	30174
SHOBERG, RICHARD	ACTOR	ABC-TV, "ALL MY CHILDREN"		
		320 W 66TH ST	NEW YORK, NY	10023
SHOCK	ROCK & ROLL GROUP	DOUBLE TEE, 712 SW SALMON ST	PORTLAND, OR	97214
SHOCKEY, SCOTT	BASEBALL	POST OFFICE BOX 11087	TACOMA, WA	98411
SHOE, BOB & CAROLINA MOUNTAIN	C & W GROUP	POST OFFICE BOX 25371	CHARLOTTE, NC	28212
SHOEMAKER, CHARLES	CINEMATOGRAPHER	POST OFFICE BOX 108, GRACIE STA	NEW YORK, NY	10028
SHOEMAKER, CRAIG	COMEDIAN	9000 SUNSET BLVD #1112	LOS ANGELES, CA	90069
SHOEMAKER, JOHN	BASEBALL MANAGER	POST OFFICE BOX 28268	SAN ANTONIO, TX	78228
SHOEMAKER, STEVE	BASEBALL	POST OFFICE BOX 882	MADISON, WI	53701
SHOEMAKER, VAUGHN	CARTOONIST	POST OFFICE DRAWER V	CARMEL, CA	93921
SHOEMAKER, WILLIE	JOCKEY	2553 FAIRFIELD PL	SAN MARINO, CA	91108
SHOENMAN, ELLIOT	WRITER-PRODUCER	10530 TENNESSEE AVE	LOS ANGELES, CA	90064
SHOFNER, JIM	FOOTBALL COACH	BROWNS, 80 1ST ST	BEREA, OH	44017
SHOLEM, LEE	DIRECTOR	2346 ASTRAL DR	LOS ANGELES, CA	90046
SHOOB, MICHAEL	SCREENWRITER	908 14TH ST #1	SANTA MONICA, CA	90403
SHOOP, PAMELA SUSAN	ACTRESS	454 N PALM DR #A	BEVERLY HILLS, CA	90210
SHOOTING STAR	ROCK & ROLL GROUP	POST OFFICE BOX 32431	KANSAS CITY, MO	64111
SHOPE, ROGER H	DIRECTOR	51 RICHARDS RD	PT WASHINGTON, LI, NY	11050
SHOPPE	C & W GROUP	POST OFFICE BOX 973	BEDFORD, TX	76021
SHOR PATROL	ROCK & ROLL GROUP	ICM, 40 W 57TH ST	NEW YORK, NY	10019
SHORE, DINAH	SINGER-TV HOST	916 OXFORD WY	BEVERLY HILLS, CA	90210
SHORE, FREDRIC R	FILM WRITER-PRODUCER	ICM, 8899 BEVERLY BLVD	LOS ANGELES, CA	90048
SHORE, JEROME	DIRECTOR	330 E 33RD ST	NEW YORK, NY	10016
SHORE, PAULY	COMEDIAN	1375 N DOHENY DR	LOS ANGELES, CA	90069
SHORE, RAY	BASEBALL-SCOUT	POST OFFICE BOX 7575	PHILADELPHIA, PA	19101
SHORE, RICHARD	TV DIRECTOR	711 W END AVE	NEW YORK, NY	10025
SHORE, SAMMY	COMEDIAN	151 S EL CAMINO DR	BEVERLY HILLS, CA	90212
SHORE, SAMUEL R	TV DIRECTOR-PRODUCER	1939 VIRGINIA ST	BERKELEY, CA	94709
SHORES, BRAD	BASEBALL TRAINER	POST OFFICE BOX 464	APPLETON, WI	54912
SHORES, RICHARD W	COMPOSER-CONDUCTOR	16644 CHAPLIN AVE	ENCINO, CA	91316
SHORR, LONNIE	COMEDIAN	141 S EL CAMINO DR #205	BEVERLY HILLS, CA	90212
SHORR, RICHARD	WRITER-PRODUCER	8463 UTICA DR	LOS ANGELES, CA	90046
SHORT, BENJAMIN	BASEBALL	POST OFFICE BOX 22093	GREENSBORO, NC	27420
SHORT, BOBBY	ACTOR-SINGER	444 E 57TH ST #9-E	NEW YORK, NY	10022
SHORT, MARTIN	ACTOR	15907 ALCAMA AVE	PACIFIC PALISADES, CA	90272
SHORT STUFF	MUSICAL GROUP	MAC MGMT, 2222 N FARWELL AVE	MILWAUKEE, WI	53202
SHORTER, FRANK	RUNNER	787 LINCOLN PL	BOULDER, CO	80302
SHORTRIDGE, STEPHEN	ACTOR	1707 CLEARVIEW DR	BEVERLY HILLS, CA	90210
SHOTEL, BARBARA	WRITER	2812 MONTANA AVE #A	SANTA MONICA, CA	90403
SHOUP, DAVID W	CONDUCTOR	2204 OAKDALE RD	CLEVELAND HGTS, OH	44118
SHOUSE, BRIAN	BASEBALL	POST OFFICE DRAWER 1218	ZEBULON, NC	27597

Name	Occupation	Address	City	Zip
SHOVER, BRAD	BASEBALL EXECUTIVE	POST OFFICE BOX 1721	SPARTANBURG, SC	29304
SHOW, ERIC	BASEBALL	ATHLETICS'S, OAKLAND COLISEUM	OAKLAND, CA	94621
SHOW, GRANT	ACTOR	CAA, 9830 WILSHIRE BLVD	BEVERLY HILLS, CA	90212
SHOWALTER, BUCK	BASEBALL MANAGER	N Y YANKEES, YANKEE STADIUM	BRONX, NY	10451
SHOWALTER, MAX	ACTOR	5 GILBERT HILL RD	CHESTER, CT	06412
SHOWDOWN	C & W GROUP	POST OFFICE BOX 156	ROSELLE, NJ	07203
SHOWS, CHARLES	WRITER-PRODUCER	8955 BEVERLY BLVD	WEST HOLLYWOOD, CA	90048
SHRAPNEL, JOHN	ACTOR	64 RICHMOND AVE	LONDON N1	ENGLAND
SHREEVE, CRAIG	ACTOR	5743 RADFORD AVE	NORTH HOLLYWOOD, CA	91607
SHREEVE, LAURIE	ACTRESS	5743 RADFORD AVE	NORTH HOLLYWOOD, CA	91607
SHREVE, LESLIE	ACTRESS	PETER BEILIN, 230 PARK AVE	NEW YORK, NY	10169
SHREWSBURY, ALAINE	ACTRESS	6940 PACIFIC VIEW DR	HOLLYWOOD, CA	90068
SHREWSBURY, ROBERT	ACTOR	380 RIVERSIDE DR #5-C	NEW YORK, NY	10025
SHRICKBACK	ROCK & ROLL GROUP	WORD SERVICE AGENCY		
		235 UPPER RICHMOND RD	LONDON SW15 6SN	ENGLAND
SHRIMPTON COX, JEAN	ACTRESS	ABBEY HOTEL, PENZANCE	CORNWALL	ENGLAND
SHRINER, CATHY	ACTRESS	14833 VALLEY VISTA BLVD	SHERMAN OAKS, CA	91403
SHRINER, INDY	ACTRESS	LAYNE SIPOLE, 29604 TROTWOOD AVE	SAN PEDRO, CA	90732
SHRINER, KIN	ACTOR	4664 S WILLIS AVE	SHERMAN OAKS, CA	91403
SHRINER, WIL	ACT-WRI-COMED	14833 VALLEY VISTA BLVD	SHERMAN OAKS, CA	91403
SHRIVER, MARIA	TV HOST	3110 MAIN ST #300	SANTA MONICA, CA	90405
SHRIVER, R SARGENT	POLITICIAN	1350 NEW YORK AVE, NW	WASHINGTON, DC	20005
SHROG, MAURICE	ACTOR	473 F D ROOSEVELT DR	NEW YORK, NY	10009
SHROPSHIRE, ANNE	ACTRESS	31 MORTON ST	NEW YORK, NY	10014
SHROYER, SONNY	ACTOR	8322 BEVERLY BLVD #202	LOS ANGELES, CA	90048
SHRYACK, DENNIS R	SCREENWRITER	12192 LAUREL TERR DR	STUDIO CITY, CA	91604
SHTRUM, HAIM	COMPOSER	1434 COMSTOCK AVE	LOS ANGELES, CA	90024
SHUBIK, IRENE	TV WRITER-PRODUCER	RAE, CHARING CROSS RD	LONDON WC2H ODB	ENGLAND
SHUCK, JIM	ACTOR	305 CORONADO AVE #1	LONG BEACH, CA	90814
SHUE, ELISABETH	ACTRESS	217 TURELL AVE	SOUTH ORANGE, NJ	07079
SHUE, GENE	BASKETBALL EXEC	POST OFFICE BOX 25040	PHILADELPHIA, PA	19147
SHUFORD, ANDY	ACTOR	POST OFFICE BOX 119	EAGLEVILLE, TN	37060
SHULA, DAVE	FOOTBALL COACH	COWBOYS, 1 COWBOYS PARKWAY	IRVING, TX	75063
SHULA, DON	FOOTBALL COACH	16220 W PRESTWICK PL	MIAMI LAKES, CA	33014
SHULA, MIKE	FOOTBALL COACH	BUCCANEERS, 1 BUCCANEER PL	TAMPA, FL	33607
SHULER, LAUREN D	TV PRODUCER	400 S BEVERLY DR #211	BEVERLY HILLS, CA	90212
SHULER, MICKEY	FOOTBALL	EAGLES, BROAD ST & PATTISON AVE	PHILADELPHIA, PA	19148
SHULKIN, JOE	TV WRITER	CAA, 9830 WILSHIRE BLVD	BEVERLY HILLS, CA	90212
SHULL, RICHARD B	ACTOR	16 GRAMERCY PARK	NEW YORK, NY	10003
SHULMAN, LAWRENCE G	TV DIRECTOR	905 S WOOSTER ST	LOS ANGELES, CA	90035
SHULMAN, ROGER	TV PRODUCER	COLUMBIA PICTURES TV		
		THE BURBANK STUDIOS		
		4000 WARNER BLVD #8-101	BURBANK, CA	91505
SHULOCK, JOHN	BASEBALL UMPIRE	445 38TH SQUARE SW	VERO BEACH, FL	32962
SHUMLIN, DIANA	THEATER PRODUCER	150 E 77TH ST	NEW YORK, NY	10021
SHUMPERT, TERRY	BASEBALL	POST OFFICE BOX 419969	KANSAS CITY, MO	64141
SHURE, CAR	TV PRODUCER	690 GREENWICH ST	NEW YORK, NY	10014
SHURLEY, BRUCE L	DIRECTOR	DGA, 7920 SUNSET BLVD, 6TH FL	LOS ANGELES, CA	90046
SHURMUR, FRITZ	FOOTBALL COACH	RAMS, 2327 W LINCOLN BLVD	ANAHEIM, CA	92801
SHUSETT, RONALD	SCREENWRITER	8955 BEVERLY BLVD	WEST HOLLYWOOD, CA	90048
SHUSMAN, BERNARD	TV DIRECTOR-PRODUCER	200 W 57TH ST #1110	NEW YORK, NY	10019
SHUST, WILLIAM	ACTOR-MIME	SHAFMAN, 723 7TH AVE, 7TH FL	NEW YORK, NY	10019
SHUSTER, BUD	U S CONGRESSMAN	179 E QUEEN ST	CHAMBERSBURG, PA	17201
SHUSTER, RACHEL	SPORTS WRITER	POST OFFICE BOX 500	WASHINGTON, DC	20044
SHUTAN, JAN	ACTRESS	3115 DEEP CANYON DR	BEVERLY HILLS, CA	90210
SHWAM, DAN	BASEBALL COACH	1325 S MAIN #229	SALT LAKE CITY, UT	84115
SHWERY, DON	BASEBALL SCOUT	POST OFFICE BOX 90111	ARLINGTON, TX	76004
SHY D, MC	RAPPER-RAPWRITERS	SEE - MC SHY D		
SHY TALK	ROCK & ROLL GROUP	NEMPEROR ARTISTS, LTD		
		870 7TH AVE, 30TH FLOOR	NEW YORK, NY	10019
SHYER, CHARLES R	FILM WRITER-DIRECTOR	4040 STANSBURY AVE	SHERMAN OAKS, CA	91423
SHYLO	VOCAL GROUP	SHOWTIME, 50 MUSIC SQUARE W	NASHVILLE, TN	37203
SHYMAN, JIM	ACTOR	4622 GLENCOE AVE #5	MARINA DEL REY, CA	90292
SHYRE, PAUL	TV WRITER	KROLL, 390 W END AVE	NEW YORK, NY	10024
SIBBETT, JANE	ACTRESS	570 N ROSSMORE AVE #303	LOS ANGELES, CA	90004
SIBERRY, JANE	SINGER-GUITARIST	POST OFFICE BOX 9388	STANFORD, CA	94305
SICARI, JOSEPH R	ACTOR	2177 N ARGYLE AVE	LOS ANGELES, CA	90068
SIDARIS, ANDY	WRITER-PRODUCER	1891 CARLA RIDGE	BEVERLY HILLS, CA	90210
SIDARIS, ARLENE TERRY	WRITER-PRODUCER	1891 CARLA RIDGE	BEVERLY HILLS, CA	90210
SIDDALL, JOE	BASEBALL	POST OFFICE BOX 15757	HARRISBURG, PA	17105
SIDDALL, TEDDI	ACTRESS	636 1/2 N ORANGE DR	LOS ANGELES, CA	90036
SIDE EFFECT	VOCAL GROUP	HAMILTON, 9022 HAMILTON PL	LOS ANGELES, CA	90069
SIDELL, BOB	MAKE-UP ARTIST	CALIFORNIA COSMETICS		
		8025 DEERING AVE	CANOGA PARK, CA	91304
SIDEN, AUDREE	TV PRODUCER	311 E 72ND ST	NEW YORK, NY	10021
SIDES, PATRICIA A	TV WRITER-PRODUCER	55 E 67TH ST	NEW YORK, NY	10021
SIDEY, HUGH	PUBLISHER	888 16TH AVE, NW	WASHINGTON, DC	20006
SIDNEY, GEORGE	DIRECTOR-PRODUCER	910 N REXFORD DR	BEVERLY HILLS, CA	90210
SIDNEY, HUGH	WRITER-EDITOR	TIME/TIME & LIFE BLDG		
		ROCKEFELLER CENTER	NEW YORK, NY	10020
SIDNEY, P JAY	ACTOR	19 MAPLE ST	BROOKLYN, NY	11225
SIDNEY, ROBERT	DIRECTOR-CHOREO	1129 CORY AVE	LOS ANGELES, CA	90069
SIDNEY, SYLVIA	ACTRESS	9744 WILSHIRE BLVD #308	BEVERLY HILLS, CA	90212
SIDWELL, STEVE	FOOTBALL COACH	SAINTS, 1500 POYDRAS ST	NEW ORLEANS, LA	90112
SIEBELS, DAVID J	CONDUCTOR	7105 OWENS ST	TUJUNGA, CA	91042

SIEBERT, CHARLES	ACTOR-DIRECTOR	227 TOYOPA DR	PACIFIC PALISADES, CA	90272
SIEBERT, SONNY	BASEBALL-COACH	POST OFFICE BOX 1420	WICHITA, KS	67201
SIECKMANN, TOM	GOLFER	POST OFFICE BOX 109601	PALM BCH GARDENS, FL	33418
SIEFERT, CHRISTIAN	ACTOR	CBS-TV, "AS THE WORLD TURNS"		
		524 W 57TH ST #5330	NEW YORK, NY	10019
SIEG, CHARLES W	DIRECTOR	NBC-TV, 30 ROCKEFELLER PLAZA	NEW YORK, NY	10112
SIEGEL, BARRY MARTIN	SCREENWRITER	1045 OCEAN AVE #6	SANTA MONICA, CA	90403
SIEGEL, DANIEL C	COMPOSER-KEYBOARDIST	54 SHOOTING STAR	IRVINE, CA	92714
SIEGEL, ED	TV CRITIC	BOSTON GLOBE, 135 MORRISSEY BLVD	BOSTON, MA	02107
SIEGEL, ELWOOD "WOODY"	DIRECTOR	317 W 89TH ST	NEW YORK, NY	10024
SIEGEL, ERIC B	TV DIRECTOR	127 W 81ST ST	NEW YORK, NY	10024
SIEGEL, HENRY	TV EXECUTIVE	LBS COMMUNICATIONS, 875 3RD AVE	NEW YORK, NY	10022
SIEGEL, HERBERT J	TV EXECUTIVE	CHRIS-CRAFT, 600 MADISON AVE	NEW YORK, NY	10022
SIEGEL, JEROME M	DIRECTOR	619 N CRESCENT DR	BEVERLY HILLS, CA	90210
SIEGEL, JOEL	FILM CRITIC-WRITER	WNYW-TV, 205 E 67TH ST	NEW YORK, NY	10021
SIEGEL, LAUREN	TV DIRECTOR	311 E 75TH ST	NEW YORK, NY	10021
SIEGEL, LAWRENCE H	WRITER	11724 CHENAULT ST	LOS ANGELES, CA	90049
SIEGEL, LIONEL E	WRITER-PRODUCER	30 DORVAL RD	TORONTO, ONT M6P 2B4	CANADA
SIEGEL, MARC	WRITER-PRODUCER	75 CENTRAL PARK W	NEW YORK, NY	10023
SIEGEL, MORT	TV DIRECTOR	WABC-TV, 7 LINCOLN SQ	NEW YORK, NY	10023
SIEGEL, PETER	BODYBUILDER	444 LINCOLN BLVD #308	VENICE, CA	90291
SIEGEL, ROBERT J	DIRECTOR	DGA, 110 W 57TH ST	NEW YORK, NY	10019
SIEGEL, SANDRA KAY	TV WRITER	5003 TILDEN AVE #202	SHERMAN OAKS, CA	91423
SIEGEL, SCOTT W	WRITER	320 E 58TH ST #42	NEW YORK, NY	10022
SIEGFRIED & ROY	CIRCUS ACT	1639 N VALLEY DR	LAS VEGAS, NV	89108
SIEGLE, TONY	BASEBALL EXECUTIVE	S F GIANTS, CANDLESTICK PARK	SAN FRANICSCO, CA	94124
SIEGLER, ROBERT	DIRECTOR	DGA, 110 W 57TH ST	NEW YORK, NY	10019
SIEGLER, SCOTT	TV WRITER-EXECUTIVE	135 PALISADES AVE	SANTA MONICA, CA	90402
SIEMASZKO, CASEY	ACTOR	CAA, 9830 WILSHIRE BLVD	BEVERLY HILLS, CA	90212
SIERRA	VOCAL GROUP	38 MUSIC SQUARE E #217	NASHVILLE, TN	37203
SIERRA, CANDY	BASEBALL	BO TORRECILLA, BAJA BUZON 108	LOIZA, PR	00672
SIERRA, GREGORY	ACTOR	9200 SUNSET BLVD #PH-20	LOS ANGELES, CA	90069
SIERRA, JOHNNY	BASEBALL SCOUT	TWINS, 501 CHICAGO AVE S	MINNEAPOLIS, MN	55415
SIERRA, RUBEN	BASEBALL	ATHLETICS'S, OAKLAND COLISEUM	OAKLAND, CA	94621
SIEVERS, LEE	ARTIST	5516 QUEEN AVE S	MINNEAPOLIS, MN	55410
SIFF, HELEN J	ACTRESS	10650 DESPLAIN PL	CHATSWORTH, CA	91311
SIFFERMAN, TOM	FOOTBALL REFEREE	NFL, 410 PARK AVE	NEW YORK, NY	10022
SIFFORD, CHARLES	GOLFER	PGA SENIORS, 112 T P C BLVD	PONTE VEDRA BEACH, FL	32082
SIGGINS, JERRY	ACTOR	859 N JUNE ST	LOS ANGELES, CA	90038
SIGLER, BUNNY	SINGER-MUSICIAN	1515 MARKET ST #700	PHILADELPHIA, PA	19102
SIGMAN, LEE	BASEBALL SCOUT	BREWERS, 201 S 46TH ST	MILWAUKEE, WI	53214
SIGNORELLI, JAMES	DIRECTOR	DGA, 110 W 57TH ST	NEW YORK, NY	10019
SIKAHEMA, VAI	FOOTBALL	PACKERS, 1265 LOMBARDI AVE	GREEN BAY, WI	54307
SIKES, CYNTHIA	ACTRESS	250 N DELFERN DR	LOS ANGELES, CA	90077
SIKICH, DAVE	BASEBALL TRAINER	1325 S MAIN #229	SALT LAKE CITY, UT	84115
SIKKING, JAMES B	ACTOR	258 S CARMELINA AVE	LOS ANGELES, CA	90049
SIKMA, JACK	BASKETBALL	BRADLEY CENTER, 1001 N 4TH ST	MILWAUKEE, WI	53203
SIKORSKI, GERRY	U S CONGRESSMAN	277 COON RAPIDS BLVD #414, NW	COON RAPIDS, MN	55433
SIKORSKY, BOB	COLUMNIST-AUTHOR	N Y TIMES SYN, 130 5TH AVE	NEW YORK, NY	10011
SILAGYI, CHRIS	ACTOR	6342 IVARENE AVE	LOS ANGELES, CA	90068
SILANO, GEORGE	DIRECTOR	1641 3RD AVE	NEW YORK, NY	10028
SILAS, PAUL	BASKETBALL-COACH	KNICKS, 4 PENNYLVANIA PLAZA	NEW YORK, NY	10019
SILBAR, ADAM	ACTOR	1865 N FULLER AVE #310	HOLLYWOOD, CA	90046
SILBER, ART	BASEBALL EXECUTIVE	POST OFFICE BOX 2148	WOODBRIDGE, VA	22193
SILBER, BARBARA D	TV DIRECTOR	ABC-TV, 1926 BROADWAY	NEW YORK, NY	10023
SILBERG, ROBERT A	WRITER	6419 DEMPSEY AVE	VAN NUYS, CA	91406
SILBERSHER, MARVIN	TV WRITER-DIRECTOR	797 AVE OF THE AMERICAS	NEW YORK, NY	10001
SILBERSTANG, EDWIN	WRITER	12836 BLOOMFIELD ST	STUDIO CITY, CA	91604
SILCOX, RUSTY	BASEBALL	12000 STADIUM RD	ADELANTO, CA	92301
SILENT MOVIES	ROCK & ROLL GROUP	BRINSLEY, TALENT BANK MGMT		
		194 KENSINGTON PARK RD	LONDON W11 2ES	ENGLAND
SILENT RUNNING	ROCK & ROLL GROUP	3 E 54TH ST #1400	NEW YORK, NY	10022
SILK, THE	ROCK & ROLL GROUP	POST OFFICE BOX 8125	ANN ARBOR, MI	48107
SILKE, JAMES R	SCREENWRITER	18200 GRESHAM ST	NORTHRIDGE, CA	91325
SILKOSKY, RONALD	WRITER	1345 N ORANGE DR #14	LOS ANGELES, CA	90028
SILLER, RAYMOND D	TV WRITER	1373 MONUMENT ST	PACIFIC PALISADES, CA	90272
SILLIPHANT, STIRLING	FILM WRITER-PRODUCER	POST OFFICE BOX 351119	LOS ANGELES, CA	90035
SILLS, BEVERLY	SOPRANO	RURAL FARM DELIVERY		
		OFF LAMBERT'S COVE RD	VINEGARD HAVEN, MA	02568
SILLS, GREGORY	DIRECTOR	DGA, 7920 SUNSET BLVD, 6TH FL	LOS ANGELES, CA	90046
SILLS, PAUL	DIRECTOR	1356 LUCILE AVE	LOS ANGELES, CA	90026
SILLS, THEODORE B	WRITER	8911 CYNTHIA ST #12	LOS ANGELES, CA	90069
SILMAN, JAMES, JR	DIRECTOR	7700 HEMLOCK ST	BETHESDA, MD	20817
SILOS, THE	ROCK & ROLL GROUP	POST OFFICE BOX 20895 (TQS)	NEW YORK, NY	10019
SILVA, GENO	ACTOR	8325 RIDPATH DR	LOS ANGELES, CA	90046
SILVA, HENRY	ACTOR	8747 CLIFTON WY #305	BEVERLY HILLS, CA	90210
SILVA, STELLA	MEZZO SOPRANO	225 W 34TH ST #1012	NEW YORK, NY	10001
SILVA, TRINIDAD, JR	ACTOR	7250 BEVERLY BLVD #208	LOS ANGELES, CA	90036
SILVEIRA, LARRY	GOLFER	POST OFFICE BOX 109601	PALM BCH GARDENS, FL	33418
SILVEIRA, RICARDO	GUITARIST-SONGWRITER	WIGMAN, 120 N HARPER AVE	LOS ANGELES, CA	90048
SILVEIRA, RUTH	ACTRESS	149 N GRAMERCY PL	LOS ANGELES, CA	90004
SILVER, ARTHUR	FILM WRITER-DIRECTOR	ICM, 8899 BEVERLY BLVD	LOS ANGELES, CA	90048
SILVER, BARRY E	TV WRITER	5740 ETIWANDA AVE #3	TARZANA, CA	91356
SILVER, BORAH	ACTOR	1832 EL CERRITO PL #1	LOS ANGELES, CA	90068
SILVER, DIANE	WRITER-PRODUCER	1239 N SWEETZER AVE	LOS ANGELES, CA	90069

SILVER, FRANELLE	WRITER	1650 WESTWOOD BLVD #201	LOS ANGELES, CA	90024
SILVER, HORACE, QUINTET	JAZZ GROUP	BRIDGE, 106 FORT GREENE PL	BROOKLYN, NY	11217
SILVER, HOWARD	TV WRI-DIR-ED	171 W 79TH ST	NEW YORK, NY	10024
SILVER, JOAN MICKLIN	FILM WRITER-DIRECTOR	MIDWEST FILM PRODUCTIONS		
		600 MADISON AVE, 18TH FLOOR	NEW YORK, NY	10022
SILVER, JOE	SINGER	POST OFFICE BOX 211	EAST PRAIRIE, MO	63845
SILVER, JOEL	FILM PRODUCER	4000 WARNER BLVD, BLDG #90	BURBANK, CA	91522
SILVER, KEN	BASEBALL EXECUTIVE	POST OFFICE BOX 2437	MODESTO, CA	95351
SILVER, KENNETH	BASEBALL EXECUTIVE	POST OFFICE BOX 3783	SAVANNAH, GA	31414
SILVER, LEO	TV DIRECTOR	5727 W OLYMPIC BLVD	LOS ANGELES, CA	90036
SILVER, RAPHAEL D	TV WRITER-DIRECTOR	MIDWEST FILM PRODUCTIONS		
		600 MADISON AVE, 10TH FLOOR	NEW YORK, NY	10022
SILVER, RON	ACTOR	6116 TYNDALL AVE	RIVERSIDE, NY	10471
SILVER, SPIKE	STUNTMAN	3518 W CAHUENGA BLVD #300	LOS ANGELES, CA	90068
SILVER, STEPHANIE	ACTRESS	5643 RHODES AVE	NORTH HOLLYWOOD, CA	91607
SILVER, STUART BRANDT	TV DIRECTOR	106 PERRY ST	NEW YORK, NY	10014
SILVER, TONY	DIRECTOR	325 W END AVE #3-B	NEW YORK, NY	10023
SILVER, TRACY	ACTRESS	9000 SUNSET BLVD #801	LOS ANGELES, CA	90069
SILVER CONNECTION	VOCAL GROUP	FAA, 1700 BROADWAY, 5TH FLOOR	NEW YORK, NY	10019
SILVER CREEK	ROCK & ROLL GROUP	POST OFFICE BOX 448	RADFORD, VA	24141
SILVER STREET	MUSICAL GROUP	POST OFFICE BOX 1808	ASHEVILLE, NC	28802
SILVERA, CHARLIE	BASEBALL-COACH-SCOUT	BREWERS, 201 S 46TH ST	MILWAUKEE, WI	53214
SILVERADO	ROCK & ROLL GROUP	MAHLER, 29 LEXINGTON AVE	WATERBURY, CT	06710
SILVERBERG, SUSAN	DIRECTOR	2918 1/2 GRAND CANAL	VENICE, CA	90291
SILVERIO, LUIS	BASEBALL SCOUT	POST OFFICE BOX 419969	KANSAS CITY, MO	64141
SILVERIO, VICTOR	BASEBALL	POST OFFICE BOX 1742	PALM SPRINGS, CA	92263
SILVERMAN, BURT	ARTIST	324 W 71ST ST	NEW YORK, NY	10023
SILVERMAN, EDWIN ELLIS	DIRECTOR	DGA, 110 W 57TH ST	NEW YORK, NY	10019
SILVERMAN, EVE	TV EXECUTIVE	SUNBOW PRODS, 130 5TH AVE	NEW YORK, NY	10011
SILVERMAN, FRED	TV PRODUCER-EXECUTIVE	12400 WILSHIRE BLVD #920	LOS ANGELES, CA	90024
SILVERMAN, JONATHAN	ACTOR	854 BIRCHWOOD DR	LOS ANGELES, CA	90024
SILVERMAN, PETER	TV WRITER	11726 SAN VICENTE BLVD #300	LOS ANGELES, CA	90049
SILVERMAN, PETER H	DIRECTOR	80 WARREN ST #15	NEW YORK, NY	10007
SILVERMAN, STUART	TV WRITER	2049 CENTURY PARK E #1320	LOS ANGELES, CA	90067
SILVERS, CATHY	ACTRESS	1999 AVE OF THE STARS #2850	LOS ANGELES, CA	90067
SILVERS, HERB	CONDUCTOR	3839 ROYAL WOODS DR	SHERMAN OAKS, CA	91403
SILVERSTEIN, ELLIOT	FILM DIRECTOR	DGA, 7920 SUNSET BLVD, 6TH FL	LOS ANGELES, CA	90046
SILVERSTEIN, MORTON	WRI-DIR-PROD	WQED-TV, 509 MADISON AVE	NEW YORK, NY	10022
SILVERTON, DORIS	TV WRITER	MTA, 9320 WILSHIRE BL, 3RD FL	BEVERLY HILLS, CA	90212
SILVESTRE, EDDIE	BODYBUILDER	POST OFFICE BOX 176	SAN YSIDRO, CA	92073
SILVESTRI, DAVE	BASEBALL	1155 W MOUND ST	COLUMBUS, OH	43223
SILVESTRI, KEN	BASEBALL COACH	POST OFFICE BOX 802	WATERTOWN, NY	13601
SILWA, LISA	MODEL	ELITE MODELS, 111 E 22ND ST	NEW YORK, NY	10010
SIM, GERALD	ACTOR	REDWAY (AIM), 5 DENMARK ST	LONDON WC2H 8LP	ENGLAND
SIMIAN, TRACY	FOOTBALL	CHIEFS, 1 ARROWHEAD DR	KANSAS CITY, MO	64129
SIMMONDS, STANLEY	ACTOR	888 8TH AVE	NEW YORK, NY	10019
SIMMONS, ANN	SINGER	902 PINECONE TRAIL	ANDERSON, SC	29621
SIMMONS, ANTHONY	WRITER-PRODUCER	HATTON, 29 ROEHAMPTON GATE	LONDON SW15 5JR	ENGLAND
SIMMONS, CAROL L	WRITER	1411 MC COLLUM ST	LOS ANGELES, CA	90026
SIMMONS, CLYDE	FOOTBALL	EAGLES, BROAD ST & PATTISON AVE	PHILADELPHIA, PA	19148
SIMMONS, CRAIG	ACTOR	14350 ADDISON ST #214	SHERMAN OAKS, CA	91423
SIMMONS, DAVID	SINGER	WMOT MGMT, 1228 SPRUCE ST	PHILADELPHIA, PA	19107
SIMMONS, ED	FOOTBALL	POST OFFICE BOX 17247 (DULLES)	WASHINGTON, DC	20041
SIMMONS, EDWARD L	WRITER-PRODUCER	133 STONECREST RD	RIDGEFIELD, CT	06877
SIMMONS, ENOCH	BASEBALL	POST OFFICE BOX 11363	RENO, NV	89510
SIMMONS, GARNER	SCREENWRITER	10010 SANTA MONICA BLVD #1600	LOS ANGELES, CA	90067
SIMMONS, GENE	SING-ACT-COMP	6363 SUNSET BLVD #417	LOS ANGELES, CA	90028
SIMMONS, JEAN	ACTRESS	636 ADELAIDE WY	SANTA MONICA, CA	90402
SIMMONS, JERRY	FOOTBALL COACH	PATRIOTS, FOXBORO STADIUM, RT #1	FOXBORO, MA	02035
SIMMONS, JOAN	CASTING DIRECTOR	5224 TOPEKA DR	TARZANA, CA	91356
SIMMONS, JOHN	WRITER-PRODUCER	66 FRITH ST	LONDON W1V 5TA	ENGLAND
SIMMONS, LIONEL	BASKETBALL	KINGS, 1 SPORTS PARKWAY	SACRAMENTO, CA	95834
SIMMONS, LON	SPORTSCASTER	ATHLETICS'S, OAKLAND COLISEUM	OAKLAND, CA	94621
SIMMONS, MATTY	FILM WRITER-PRODUCER	715 N CANON DR	BEVERLY HILLS, CA	90210
SIMMONS, NELSON	BASEBALL	POST OFFICE BOX 11087	TACOMA, WA	98411
SIMMONS, PATRICK	SINGER-SONGWRITER	POST OFFICE BOX 7308	CARMEL, CA	93923
SIMMONS, PAUL	SINGER	POST OFFICE BOX 11321 (FLAGLER)	MIAMI, FL	33101
SIMMONS, RICHARD	EXERCISE INSTRUCTOR	1350 BELFAST DR	LOS ANGELES, CA	90069
SIMMONS, RICHARD ALAN	SCREENWRITER	514 N BEVERLY DR	BEVERLY HILLS, CA	90210
SIMMONS, RICHARD D	PUBLISH EXECUTIVE	NEWSWEEK, 444 MADISON AVE	NEW YORK, NY	10022
SIMMONS, ROBIN	TV PRODUCER	1438 N GOWER ST #31	LOS ANGELES, CA	90038
SIMMONS, ROGER	SINGER	902 PINECONE TRAIL	ANDERSON, SC	29621
SIMMONS, RON	WRESTLER	POST OFFICE BOX 105366	ATLANTA, GA	31348
SIMMONS, RUSSELL	COMEDIAN	HBO, 1100 6TH AVE	NEW YORK, NY	10036
SIMMONS, SARAH	ACTRESS	4647 WILLIS AVE	SHERMAN OAKS, CA	91403
SIMMONS, SCOTT	BASEBALL	POST OFFICE BOX 3004	SPRINGFIELD, IL	62708
SIMMONS, STACEY	FOOTBALL	PATRIOTS, FOXBORO STADIUM, RT #1	FOXBORO, MA	02035
SIMMONS, TED	BASEBALL-EXECUTIVE	250 STADIUM PLAZA	ST LOUIS, MO	63102
SIMMONS, TOM	BASEBALL EXECUTIVE	POST OFFICE BOX 2887	VERO BEACH, FL	32961
SIMMONS, WARREN	FOOTBALL COACH	POST OFFICE BOX 17247 (DULLES)	WASHINGTON, DC	20041
SIMMS, EARL EDWARD, JR	WRITER	4226 TOLUCA LAKE LN	BURBANK, CA	91505
SIMMS, GINNY	ACTRESS	1578 MURRAY CANYON DR	PALM SPRINGS, CA	92262
SIMMS, KIMBERLY	ACTRESS	CBS-TV, "THE GUIDING LIGHT"		
		222 E 44TH ST	NEW YORK, NY	10017
SIMMS, LARRY	ACTOR	POST OFFICE BOX 55	GRAYS RIVER, WA	98621

Name	Occupation	Address	City/State	Zip
SIMMS, MIKE	BASEBALL	POST OFFICE BOX 27045	TUCSON, AZ	85726
SIMMS, OLGA PALSSON	WRITER	4226 TOLUCA LAKE LN	BURBANK, CA	91505
SIMMS, PAUL	TV WRITER	CAA, 9830 WILSHIRE BLVD	BEVERLY HILLS, CA	90212
SIMMS, PHIL	FOOTBALL	N Y GIANTS, GIANTS STADIUM	EAST RUTHERFORD, NJ	07073
SIMON, BARRY E	TV DIRECTOR	3775 ROBERTA ST	LOS ANGELES, CA	90031
SIMON, CARLY	SINGER-SONGWRITER	135 CENTRAL PARK W	NEW YORK, NY	10023
SIMON, COURTNEY S	TV WRITER	88 POUND RIDGE RD	BEDFORD, NY	10506
SIMON, DANIEL	WRITER-PRODUCER	15233 MAGNOLIA BLVD #302	SHERMAN OAKS, CA	91403
SIMON, DERAY	GOLFER	PGA SENIORS, 112 T P C BLVD	PONTE VEDRA BEACH, FL	32082
SIMON, DYANNE ASIMOW	WRITER	8071 WILLOW GLEN RD	LOS ANGELES, CA	90046
SIMON, HERBERT	BASKETBALL EXECUTIVE	PACERS, 300 E MARKET ST	INDIANAPOLIS, IN	46204
SIMON, JACK	DIRECTOR	MADISON SQUARE GARDEN NETWORK		
		4 PENNSYLVANUA PLAZA	NEW YORK, NY	10001
SIMON, JEFF	FILM CRITIC	POST OFFICE BOX 100	BUFFALO, NY	14240
SIMON, JEFF	TV DIRECTOR	162 CROSS RD	OAKLAND, CA	94618
SIMON, JOE	SINGER	POST OFFICE BOX 82	GREAT NECK, NY	11021
SIMON, JOEL	ACTOR	168 W 86TH ST	NEW YORK, NY	10024
SIMON, LAUREN	ACTRESS	5904 CARLTON WY	LOS ANGELES, CA	90028
SIMON, LISA	TV PRODUCER	CHILDREN'S TV WORKSHOP		
		1 LINCOLN PLAZA	NEW YORK, NY	10023
SIMON, LISA D	DIRECTOR	20 E 9TH ST	NEW YORK, NY	10003
SIMON, MAYO	WRITER	574 CHAPALA DR	PACIFIC PALISADES, CA	90272
SIMON, MELVIN	BASKETBALL EXECUTIVE	PACERS, 300 E MARKET ST	INDIANAPOLIS, IN	46204
SIMON, NEIL	PLAYWRIGHT	10100 SANTA MONICA BLVD #400	LOS ANGELES, CA	90067
SIMON, PAUL	SCREENWRITER	555 W 57TH ST #1230	NEW YORK, NY	10019
SIMON, PAUL	SINGER-SONGWRI-ACTOR	1619 BROADWAY #500	NEW YORK, NY	10019
SIMON, PAUL	U S SENATOR	462 SD SENATE OFFICE BUILDING	WASHINGTON, DC	20510
SIMON, PETER	ACTOR	CBS-TV, "THE GUIDING LIGHT"		
		222 E 44TH ST	NEW YORK, NY	10017
SIMON, RICHIE	BASEBALL	POST OFFICE BOX 4209	JACKSON, MS	39296
SIMON, ROBERT D	FILM DIRECTOR	536 E 79TH ST #3-N	NEW YORK, NY	10021
SIMON, ROGER	COLUMNIST	POST OFFICE BOX 1377	BALTIMORE, MD	21278
SIMON, ROGER L	SCREENWRITER	21458 RAMBLA VISTA	MALIBU, CA	90265
SIMON, SAM	TV WRITER-PRODUCER	131 S RODEO DR #300	BEVERLY HILLS, CA	90212
SIMON, SIMONE	ACTRESS	5 RUE DE TILSITT	F-75008 PARIS	FRANCE
SIMON, SUSAN ORLIKOFF	TV WRITER-DIRECTOR	15239 RAYNETA DR	SHERMAN OAKS, CA	91403
SIMON, TODD H	TV DIRECTOR	11744 1/8 MAYFIELD AVE	LOS ANGELES, CA	90049
SIMON, TOM M	TV DIRECTOR-PRODUCER	114 W 16TH ST #3-G	NEW YORK, NY	10011
SIMON, WILLIAM	POLITICIAN	330 SOUTH ST	MORRISTOWN, NJ	07960
SIMONE, ANTHONY "TEX"	BASEBALL EXECUTIVE	CHIEFS, MAC ARTHUR STADIUM	SYRACUSE, NY	13208
SIMONE, JOHN	BASEBALL EXECUTIVE	CHIEFS, MAC ARTHUR STADIUM	SYRACUSE, NY	13208
SIMONE, JULIE	MODEL	9200 SUNSET BLVD #PH-20	LOS ANGELES, CA	90069
SIMONE, NINA	SINGER-PIANIST	1995 BROADWAY #501	NEW YORK, NY	10023
SIMONIDES, SCOTT	BASEBALL UMPIRE	POST OFFICE BOX 716	PLAINVILLE, CT	06062
SIMONS, DAVID A	ACTOR	6252 LUBAO AVE	WOODLAND HILLS, CA	91367
SIMONS, DOUG	BASEBALL	EXPOS, 4545 DE COUBERTIN AVE	MONTREAL, QUE H1V 3P2	CANADA
SIMONS, MITCH	BASEBALL	POLECATS, 608 N SLAPPEY BLVD	ALBANY, GA	31701
SIMONSEN, RENEE	MODEL	FORD MODELS, 344 E 59TH ST	NEW YORK, NY	10022
SIMPLE MINDS	ROCK & ROLL GROUP	SCHOOLHOUSE MGMT		
		63 FREDERICK ST	EDINBURGH EH2 1LH	SCOTLAND
SIMPLY RED	ROCK & ROLL GROUP	36 ATWOOD RD, DIDSBURY	MANCHESTER 20	ENGLAND
SIMPSON, ALAN	ACTOR-WRITER	LE BARS, 18 QUEEN ANNE ST	LONDON W1M 9LB	ENGLAND
SIMPSON, ALAN K	U S SENATOR	1737 E SHERIDAN #1	CODY, WY	82414
SIMPSON, CRAIG	HOCKEY	OILERS, NORTHLANDS COLISEUM	EDMONTON, ALTA T5B 4M9	CANADA
SIMPSON, DAVID	BASEBALL EXECUTIVE	POST OFFICE BOX 611	WATERLOO, IA	50704
SIMPSON, DON	FILM PROD-EXEC	9472 CHEROKEE LN	BEVERLY HILLS, CA	90210
SIMPSON, FRANCIS R	DIRECTOR	84-09 35TH AVE	JACKSON HEIGHTS, NY	11372
SIMPSON, FRANK	FILM DIRECTOR	POST OFFICE BOX 852	STOCKBRIDGE, MA	01262
SIMPSON, GARRY	TV DIRECTOR	RURAL DELIVERY #3, KELLOGG RD	VERGENNES, VT	05491
SIMPSON, JOE	BASEBALL-ANNOUNCER	POST OFFICE BOX 4100	SEATTLE, WA	98104
SIMPSON, O J	ACTOR-FOOTBALL	360 N ROCKINGHAM AVE	LOS ANGELES, CA	90049
SIMPSON, RED	SINGER	POST OFFICE BOX 4234	PANORAMA CITY, CA	91412
SIMPSON, SCOTT	GOLFER	POST OFFICE BOX 109601	PALM BCH GARDENS, FL	33418
SIMPSON, TIM	GOLFER	POST OFFICE BOX 109601	PALM BCH GARDENS, FL	33418
SIMS, DAVID	ARTIST	422 N BAYLEN ST	PENSACOLA, FL	32501
SIMS, JERRY	DIRECTOR	3765 W CAHUENGA BLVD	STUDIO CITY, CA	91604
SIMS, JOAN	ACTRESS	17 ESMOND CT, THACKERY ST	LONDON W8	ENGLAND
SIMS, KEITH	FOOTBALL	DOLPHINS, 2269 NW 199TH ST	MIAMI, FL	33056
SIMS, MARK	BASEBALL	POST OFFICE BOX 3449	SCRANTON, PA	18505
SIMS, SYLVIA	ACTRESS	135 E 63RD ST	NEW YORK, NY	10021
SIMS, TOM	FOOTBALL	CHIEFS, 1 ARROWHEAD DR	KANSAS CITY, MO	64129
SIMSON, BREN	TV DIRECTOR	HEATH, PARAMOUNT HOUSE		
		162-170 WARDOUR ST	LONDON W1V 3AT	ENGLAND
SINACORI, CHRIS	BASEBALL	POST OFFICE BOX 2887	VERO BEACH, FL	32961
SINATRA, FRANK	SINGER-ACTOR	70-588 FRANK SINATRA BLVD	RANCHO MIRAGE, CA	92270
SINATRA, FRANK, JR	SINGER	2211 FLORIAN PL	BEVERLY HILLS, CA	90210
SINATRA, NANCY, JR	SINGER-ACTOR	POST OFFICE BOX 69453	LOS ANGELES, CA	90069
SINATRA, RAY	COMPOSER-CONDUCTOR	1234 S 8TH PL	LAS VEGAS, NV	89104
SINATRO, MATT	BASEBALL	POST OFFICE BOX 4100	SEATTLE, WA	98104
SINBAD	COMEDIAN-ACTOR	20061 MERRIDAY ST	CHATSWORTH, CA	91311
SINCEROS	ROCK & ROLL GROUP	LIVE MGMT, 25 BULIVER ST		
		SHEPHERDS BUSH	LONDON W12 8AR	ENGLAND
SINCLAIR, BETTY	ACTRESS	871 1ST AVE	NEW YORK, NY	10017
SINCLAIR, ERIC	ACTOR	7735 ATLANTIC AVE #13	CUDAHY, CA	90201
SINCLAIR, GABRIELLE	ACTRESS	326 E 74TH ST #15	NEW YORK, NY	10021

Name	Occupation	Address	City/State	Zip/Country
SINCLAIR, MADGE	ACTRESS	POST OFFICE BOX 5617	BEVERLY HILLS, CA	90213
SINCLAIR, NANCY	ACTRESS	ATKINS, 303 S CRESCENT HEIGHTS	LOS ANGELES, CA	90048
SINDALL, PHILIP	CINEMATOGRAPHER	33 EGERTON GARDENSM EALING	LONDON W13 8HG	ENGLAND
SINDELAR, JOEY	GOLFER	POST OFFICE BOX 109601	PALM BCH GARDENS, FL	33418
SINDELL, JANE	TALENT AGENT	ICM, 8899 BEVERLY BLVD	LOS ANGELES, CA	90048
SINDEN, DONALD	ACTOR	60 TEMPLE FORTUNE LN	LONDON NW11	ENGLAND
SINDEN, JEREMY	ACTOR	ICM, 388-396 OXFORD ST	LONDON W1	ENGLAND
SINDEN, MARC	ACTOR	CCA, 4 COURT LODGE		
		48 SLOANE SQ	LONDON SW1W 8AT	ENGLAND
SINE, WAYNE	ACTOR	1059 ELLEN CIR	OREM, UT	84057
SINGEL, MARK	LT GOVERNOR	STATE CAPITOL BUILDING	HARRISBURG, PA	17120
SINGER, ABBY	TV PRODUCER	MTM, 4024 RADFORD AVE	STUDIO CITY, CA	91604
SINGER, ALEXANDER	TV DIRECTOR	989 BLUEGRASS LN	LOS ANGELES, CA	90049
SINGER, CARLA	TV PRODUCER	WARNER BROTHERS PICTURES		
		4000 WARNER BLVD	BURBANK, CA	91522
SINGER, DULCY	TV PRODUCER	CTW, 1 LINCOLN PLAZA	NEW YORK, NY	10023
SINGER, JACK	TV EXECUTIVE	49 W 87TH ST	NEW YORK, NY	10024
SINGER, JUDITH	TV WRITER	989 BLUEGRASS LN	LOS ANGELES, CA	90049
SINGER, LORI	ACTRESS	CAA, 9830 WILSHIRE BLVD	BEVERLY HILLS, CA	90212
SINGER, MARC	ACTOR	11218 CANTON DR	STUDIO CITY, CA	91604
SINGER, RAYMOND B	ACTOR	121 N SYCAMORE AVE	LOS ANGELES, CA	90036
SINGER, RAYMOND E	ACTOR-PRODUCER	1711 COLDWATER CANYON DR	BEVERLY HILLS, CA	90210
SINGER, ROBERT	FILM PRODUCER	4000 WARNER BLVD #32-28	BURBANK, CA	91522
SINGER, ROBERT S	DIRECTOR	DGA, 7920 SUNSET BLVD, 6TH FL	LOS ANGELES, CA	90046
SINGER, STEPHEN	ACTOR	66 E 7TH ST #7	NEW YORK, NY	10003
SINGER, STEVEN H	TV WRITER-PRODUCER	ABC NEWS, 7 W 66TH ST	NEW YORK, NY	10023
SINGER, SUSAN	ACTRESS	8721 SANTA MONICA BLVD #21	WEST HOLLYWOOD, CA	90069
SINGER, TOM	BASEBALL	POST OFFICE BOX 957	DUNEDIN, FL	34697
SINGER-GANS, LAURA	PRODUCER	8919 HARRAT ST	LOS ANGELES, CA	90069
SINGLETARY, MICHAEL	TV DIRECTOR	375 HAWTHORNE TERR	MOUNT VERNON, NY	10552
SINGLETARY, MIKE	FOOTBALL	BEARS, 250 N WASHINGTON RD	LAKE FOREST, IL	60045
SINGLETARY, TONY	TV DIRECTOR-PRODUCER	1218 S SYCAMORE AVE	LOS ANGELES, CA	90019
SINGLETON, CHARLIE	SINGER-GUITARIST	FAA, 1700 BROADWAY, 5TH FLOOR	NEW YORK, NY	10019
SINGLETON, CHRIS	FOOTBALL	PATRIOTS, FOXBORO STADIUM, RT #1	FOXBORO, MA	02035
SINGLETON, DORIS	ACTRESS	151 S EL CAMINO DR	BEVERLY HILLS, CA	90212
SINGLETON, DUANE	BASEBALL	POST OFFICE BOX 8550	STOCKTON, CA	95208
SINGLETON, JOHN	BASEBALL EXECUTIVE	POST OFFICE BOX 2000	ANAHEIM, CA	92803
SINGLETON, JOHN	WRITER-DIRECTOR	CAA, 9830 WILSHIRE BLVD	BEVERLY HILLS, CA	90212
SINGLETON, KEN	BASEBALL-ANNOUNCER	EXPOS, 4545 DE COUBERTIN AVE	MONTREAL, QUE H1V 3P2	CANADA
SINGLETON, MARJORIE	SINGER-GUITARIST	POST OFFICE BOX 567	HENDERSONVILLE, TN	37075
SINGLETON, PENNY	ACTRESS	13419 RIVERSIDE DR #C	SHERMAN OAKS, CA	91423
SINGLETON, VALERIE	ACTRESS	ARLINGTON, 1-3 CHARLOTTE ST	LONDON W1P 1HD	ENGLAND
SINISALO, IIKKA	HOCKEY	POST OFFICE BOX 17013	INGLEWOOD, CA	90308
SINISE, GARY	ACTOR	18227 CLARK ST	TARZANA, CA	91356
SINKYS, ALBERT	ACTOR	465 W END AVE	NEW YORK, NY	10024
SINN, PEARL	GOLFER	2750 VOLUSA AVE #B	DAYTON BEACH, FL	32114
SINNER, GEORGE A	GOVERNOR	STATE CAPITOL, 600 E BOULEVARD	BISMARCK, ND	58505
SINNOTT, PATRICIA	ACTRESS	4 PARK AVE	NEW YORK, NY	10016
SIODMAK, CURT	WRITER-PRODUCER	43422 S FORK DR	THREE RIVERS, CA	93271
SIOUXSIE & THE BANSHEES	ROCK & ROLL GROUP	127 ALDERGATE ST	LONDON EC1	ENGLAND
SIPORIN, RALPH	DIRECTOR	21880 GLENMORRA ST	SOUTHFIELD, MI	48076
SIR MIX-A-LOT	RAPPER-RAPWRITER	3500 W OLIVE AVE #630	BURBANK, CA	91505
SIRAGUSA, TONY	FOOTBALL	POST OFFICE BOX 535000	INDIANPOLIS, IN	46253
SIRAK, KENNY	BASEBALL	POST OFFICE BOX 10336	CLEARWATER, FL	34617
SIRIANNE, MARY FRANCES	TV DIRECTOR	WETA-TV, 3620 S 27TH ST	ARLINGTON, VA	22206
SIRIANNI, NANCY	ACTRESS	POST OFFICE BOX 62	EAST NORWICH, NY	11732
SIRIGNANO, JOHN	BASEBALL EXECUTIVE	POST OFFICE BOX 7000	PITTSBURGH, PA	15212
SIRINSKY, MARC	WRITER-PRODUCER	1483 N OCCIDENTAL BLVD	LOS ANGELES, CA	90026
SIRTIS, MARINA	ACTRESS	2436 CRESTON WY	LOS ANGELES, CA	90068
SIRULNICK, LEON	DIRECTOR	18 WHITTIER DR	ENGLISHTOWN, NJ	07726
SISISKY, NORMAN	U S CONGRESSMAN	309 COUNTRY ST	PORTSMOUTH], VA	23704
SISK, DOUG	BASEBALL	1408 BEACH DR NE	TACOMA, WA	98422
SISK, GENE	MUSIC ARRANGER	721 DUE WEST AVE #F-302	MADISON, TN	37115
SISK, LAURA	ACTRESS	ABC-TV, "LOVING"		
		320 W 66TH ST, STUDIO 23	NEW YORK, NY	10023
SISKEL, GENE	FILM CRITIC	THE CHICAGO TRIBUNE		
		TRIBUNE TOWER		
		435 N MICHIGAN AVE	CHICAGO, IL	60611
SISLER, RIC	BASEBALL EXECUTIVE	POST OFFICE BOX 3783	SAVANNAH, GA	31414
SISSON, DOUG	BASEBALL COACH	POST OFFICE BOX 3609	PORT CHARLOTTE, FL	33949
SISSON, ROSEMARY ANNE	TV WRITER	167 NEW KINGS RD	LONDON SW6	ENGLAND
SISSONS, KIMBER	ACTRESS	STONE MANNERS, 9113 SUNSET BL	LOS ANGELES, CA	90069
SISTER SLEDGE	VOCAL GROUP	10100 SANTA MONICA BLVD #1600	LOS ANGELES, CA	90067
SISTER SOULJAH	RAPPER-RAPWRITER	POST OFFICE BOX 4455	NEW YORK, NY	10101
SISTERS OF MERCY, THE	ROCK & ROLL GROUP	MERCIFUL RELEASE		
		19 ALL SAINTS RD	LONDON W11	ENGLAND
SITOWITZ, HAL	WRITER-PRODUCER	207 N ELM DR	BEVERLY HILLS, CA	90210
SITTENFIELD, JOAN	CASTING DIRECTOR	MCA/UNIVERSAL STUDIOS, INC		
		100 UNIVERSAL CITY PLAZA		
		BUILDING #426-1	UNIVERSAL CITY, CA	91608
SIVAD, DARRYL	COMEDIAN-ACTOR	6310 SAN VICENTE BLVD #407	LOS ANGELES, CA	90048
SIWA, JOE	BASEBALL	POST OFFICE BOX 5645	ORLANDO, FL	32855
SIX, JIM & CITY LIMITS	MUSICAL GROUP	POST OFFICE BOX 592	KING OF PRUSSIA, PA	19406
SIXX, NIKKI	DRUMMER	936 VISTA RIDGE LN	WESTLAKE VILLAGE, CA	91362
SIZE, DENNIS	CINEMATOGRAPHER	139 W 28TH ST #3-E	NEW YORK, NY	10001

SJOMAN, VILGOT	FILM DIRECTOR	POST OFFICE BOX 27126	S-10252 STOCKHOLM	SWEDEN
SKAALEN, JIM	BASEBALL EXECUTIVE	POST OFFICE BOX 4100	SEATTLE, WA	98104
SKADAN, SCOTT	BASEBALL EXECUTIVE	POST OFFICE BOX 2960	SUMTER, SC	29151
SKAFISH	ROCK & ROLL GROUP	CAMERON, 822 HILLGROVE AVE	WESTERN SPRINGS, IL	60558
SKAGGS, DAVID	U S CONGRESSMAN	9101 HARLAN ST #130	WESTMINISTER, CO	80030
SKAGGS, RICKY	SINGER-GUITARIST	380 FOREST RETREAT	HENDERSONVILLE, TN	37075
SKAGGS, SHARON WHITE	SINGER-GUITARIST	380 FOREST RETREAT	HENDERSONVILLE, TN	37075
SKALA, LILIA	ACTRESS	42-02 LAYTON ST	ELMHURST, NY	11373
SKALAK, WILLIAM	COMPOSER	6017 FAWN AVE	LAS VEGAS, NV	89107
SKALSKI, JOE	BASEBALL	14348 BENSLEY AVE	BURNHAM, IL	60633
SKANSI, PAUL	FOOTBALL	SEAHAWKS, 11220 NE 53RD ST	KIRKLAND, WA	98033
SKATT BROTHERS, THE	SOUL GROUP	AUCION MGMT, 645 MADISON AVE	NEW YORK, NY	10022
SKATULA, KATHRYN	ACTRESS	9856 1/2 VIDOR DR	LOS ANGELES, CA	90035
SKEELS, JERRY	COSTUME DESIGNER	8411 MELROSE PL	LOS ANGELES, CA	90069
SKEEN, JOE	U S CONGRESSMAN	FEDERAL BUILDING, ROOM 257	ROSWELL, NM	88201
SKELTON, BOBBY	FOOTBALL REFEREE	NFL, 410 PARK AVE	NEW YORK, NY	10022
SKELTON, IKE	U S CONGRESSMAN	1616 INDUSTRIAL DR	JEFFERSON CITY, MO	65101
SKELTON, RED	ACTOR-COMEDIAN	37801 THOMSON RD	RANCHO MIRAGE, CA	92270
SKERRITT, TOM	ACTOR	10100 SANTA MONICA BLVD #1600	LOS ANGELES, CA	90067
SKID ROW	ROCK & ROLL GROUP	240 CENTRAL PARK S #2-C	NEW YORK, NY	10019
SKID ROW JOE	SINGER	POST OFFICE BOX 211	EAST PRAIRIE, MO	63845
SKILES, KENNETH	TV DIRECTOR	4511 COLBATH AVE #8	SHERMAN OAKS, CA	91423
SKILES, SCOTT	BASKETBALL	POST OFFICE BOX 76	ORLANDO, FL	32802
SKILES & HENDERSON	COMEDIANS	32500 CONCORD DR #252	MADISON HEIGHTS, MI	48071
SKINNELL, ROBERT G	COMPOSER-CONDUCTOR	4004 ORANGEDALE AVE	MONTROSE, CA	91020
SKINNER, ANN	PRODUCER	SKREBA, 5-A NOEL ST	LONDON W1V 3RB	ENGLAND
SKINNER, BOB	BASEBALL-MANAGER	POST OFFICE BOX 27045	TUCSON, AZ	85726
SKINNER, JOEL	BASEBALL	INDIANS, CLEVELAND STADIUM	CLEVELAND, OH	44114
SKINNY BOYS, THE	RAP GROUP-RAPWRITERS	FAA, 1700 BROADWAY, 5TH FLOOR	NEW YORK, NY	10019
SKIP & LINDA	VOCAL DUO	38 MUSIC SQUARE E #217	NASHVILLE, TN	37203
SKIPPER, BUDDY	MUSIC ARRANGER	324 WILLOW BOUGH LN	OLD HICKORY, TN	37138
SKIPPER, JIM	FOOTBALL COACH	SAINTS, 1500 POYDRAS ST	NEW ORLEANS, LA	90112
SKIPWORTH & TURNER	RHYTHM & BLUES GROUP	FAA, 1700 BROADWAY, 5TH FLOOR	NEW YORK, NY	10019
SKLUT, MERYL	ARTIST	3 HAMILTON	PINE BROOK, NJ	07058
SKOG, ALAN	DIRECTOR	140 W 79TH ST #3-C	NEW YORK, NY	10024
SKOGLUND, CLIFF	MODEL	WILHELMINA, 300 PARK AVE	NEW YORK, NY	10010
SKOGLUND, JOHN	FOOTBALL EXECUTIVE	VIKINGS, 9520 VIKING DR	EDEN PRAIRIE, MN	55344
SKOLIMOWSKI, JERZY	FILM DIRECTOR	FILM POLASKI, U1 MAZOWIECKA 618	990947 WARSAW	POLAND
SKOLNEK, MORLEY	DIRECTOR-PRODUCER	10610 ROCHESTER AVE	LOS ANGELES, CA	90024
SKOPP, HARRY	CONDUCTOR	18930 CITRONIA ST	NORTHRIDGE, CA	91324
SKOURAS, SPYROS	TALENT AGENT	1015 GAYLEY AVE #300	LOS ANGELES, CA	90024
SKOVALD, FLORENCE	COMPOSER	138 N 2ND ST, BOX 621	BAYFIELD, WI	54814
SKOWRON, BILL "MOOSE"	BASEBALL	1118 BEACHCOMBER DR	SCHAUMBURG, IL	60193
SKREBNESKI, VICTOR	DIRECTOR	1350 N LA SALLE ST	CHICAGO, IL	60610
SKRENTNY, JAN E	TV DIRECTOR	7029 TROLLEY WY	PLAYA DEL REY, CA	90291
SKRIKO, PETRI	HOCKEY	BRUINS, 150 CAUSEWAY ST	BOSTON, MA	02114
SKROWACZEWSKI, STANISLAW	CONDUCTOR	ICM, 40 W 57TH ST	NEW YORK, NY	10019
SKRUDLAND, BRIAN	HOCKEY	CANADIENS, 2313 ST CATHERINE ST	MONTREAL, QUE H3H 1N2	CANADA
SKUTCH, IRA, JR	DIRECTOR-PRODUCER	3656 GLENRIDGE DR	SHERMAN OAKS, CA	91423
SKY KING	ROCK & ROLL GROUP	POST OFFICE BOX 18368	DENVER, CO	80218
SKYBOYS, THE	VOCAL GROUP	FAR WEST, 110 BOYLSTON AVE E	SEATTLE, WA	98102
SKYE, IONE	ACTRESS	3120 HOLLYRIDGE DR	LOS ANGELES, CA	90068
SKYLINERS, THE	VOCAL GROUP	MARS, 168 ORCHID DR	PEARL RIVER, NY	10965
SKYY	RHYTHM & BLUES GROUP	POST OFFICE BOX 846	NEW YORK, NY	10101
SLACK, BILL	BASEBALL COACH	POST OFFICE BOX 16683	GREENVILLE, SC	29606
SLADE	ROCK & ROLL GROUP	ICM, 40 W 57TH ST	NEW YORK, NY	10019
SLADE, BERNARD	SCREENWRITER	345 N SALTAIR AVE	LOS ANGELES, CA	90049
SLADE, MARK	ACTOR-PRODUCER	2247 LINDA FLORA DR	LOS ANGELES, CA	90077
SLADE, MELINDA	WRITER-PRODUCER	2247 LINDA FLORA DR	LOS ANGELES, CA	90077
SLADE, PAULA	WRITER-PRODUCER	205 S BEVERLY DR #210	BEVERLY HILLS, CA	90212
SLAGLE, LEE	BASEBALL TRAINER	POST OFFICE BOX 338	JAMESTOWN, NY	14702
SLASH, THE	ROCK & ROLL GROUP	SEE- NASH THE SLASH		
SLATE, HENRY	ACTOR	6310 SAN VICENTE BLVD #407	LOS ANGELES, CA	90048
SLATE, LANE	WRITER-PRODUCER	1169 AMALFI DR	PACIFIC PALISADES, CA	90272
SLATER, CHRISTIAN	ACTOR	5871 ALLOTT AVE	VAN NUYS, CA	91401
SLATER, DERRICK	ACTOR-WRITER	71 CHURCHFIELD RD, POOLE	DORSET BH15 2QW	ENGLAND
SLATER, GUY	TV WRITER-DIRECTOR	26 ORLEANS RD, TWICKENHAM	MIDDLESEX	ENGLAND
SLATER, HELEN	ACTRESS	151 S EL CAMINO DR	BEVERLY HILLS, CA	90212
SLATER, JACKIE	FOOTBALL	RAMS, 2327 W LINCOLN BLVD	ANAHEIM, CA	92801
SLATER, MILTON R	CASTING DIRECTOR	251 FARRINGTON AVE	NORTH TARRYTOWN, NY	10591
SLATER, SUZANNE M	ACTRESS-MODEL	MARX, 11130 HUSTON ST #6	NORTH HOLLYWOOD, CA	91601
SLATER, VAN RICHARD	WRESTLER	SEE - SLATER, DICK "THE REBEL"		
SLATER-WILSON, MARY JO	CASTING DIRECTOR	370 LEXINGTON AVE #707	NEW YORK, NY	10017
SLATKIN, LEONARD	CONDUCTOR	ICM, 40 W 57TH ST	NEW YORK, NY	10019
SLATON, JIM	BASEBALL-COACH	POST OFFICE BOX 11363	RENO, NV	89510
SLATTERY, JIM	U S CONGRESSMAN	400 SW 8TH ST, FIRST FLOOR	TOPEKA, KS	66603
SLATTERY, RICHARD X	ACTOR	POST OFFICE BOX 2410	AVALON, CA	90704
SLATTERY, TONY	ACTOR-COMEDIAN	HEATH, PARAMOUNT HOUSE		
		162-170 WARDOUR ST	LONDON W1V 3AT	ENGLAND
SLATZER, ROBERT	WRITER-PRODUCER	3033 HOLLYCREST DR #2	LOS ANGELES, CA	90068
SLAUGHT, DON	BASEBALL	POST OFFICE BOX 7000	PITTSBURGH, PA	15212
SLAUGHTER, D FRENCH, JR	U S CONGRESSMAN	POST OFFICE BOX 1075	CULPEPER, VA	22701
SLAUGHTER, ENOS	BASEBALL	RURAL ROUTE #2, BOX 159	ROXBORO, NC	27573
SLAUGHTER, LOUISE	U S CONGRESSWOMAN	216 E MAIN ST	BATAVIA, NY	14020
SLAUGHTER, SGT	WRESTLER	POST OFFICE BOX 3859	STAMFORD, CT	06905

Name	Occupation	Address	City/State	Zip
SLAVIN, HOWARD	FOOTBALL REFEREE	NFL, 410 PARK AVE	NEW YORK, NY	10022
SLAVIN, MILLIE	ACTRESS	KOHNER, 9169 SUNSET BLVD	LOS ANGELES, CA	90069
SLAYER	ROCK & ROLL GROUP	GEFFEN RECORDS COMPANY		
		9130 SUNSET BLVD	LOS ANGELES, CA	90069
SLAYTON, BOBBY	COMEDIAN	9200 SUNSET BLVD #915	LOS ANGELES, CA	90069
SLAYTON, DONALD "DEKE"	ASTRONAUT	7015 GULF FREEWAY #140	HOUSTON, TX	77087
SLEDGE, PERCY	SINGER	9850 SANDALFOOT BLVD #458	BOCA RATON, FL	33428
SLEEP, WAYNE	DANCER	PINEAPPLE DANCE CENTRE		
		7 LANGLEY ST	LONDON WC2	ENGLAND
SLEET, JACKSON	ACTOR	6533 HOLLYWOOD BLVD #201	HOLLYWOOD, CA	90028
SLESAR, HENRY	TV WRITER-COMPOSER	125 E 72ND ST	NEW YORK, NY	10021
SLESIN, AVIVA	DIRECTOR	DGA, 110 W 57TH ST	NEW YORK, NY	10019
SLEZAK, ERIKA	ACTRESS	ABC-TV, "ONE LIFE TO LIVE"		
		56 W 66TH ST	NEW YORK, NY	10023
SLICK, EARL	SINGER	3 E 54TH ST #1400	NEW YORK, NY	10022
SLICK, GRACE	SINGER-SONGWRITER	18 ESCALON DR	MILL VALLEY, CA	94941
SLICKEE BOYS, THE	ROCK & ROLL GROUP	POST OFFICE BOX 5073	FALMOUTH, VA	22403
SLIDER, RAC	BASEBALL-COACH	FENWAY PARK, 4 YAWKEY WY	BOSTON, MA	02215
SLINGLAND, FRANK D	DIRECTOR	DGA, 110 W 57TH ST	NEW YORK, NY	10019
SLINGSHOT	ROCK & ROLL GROUP	POST OFFICE BOX 448	RADFORD, VA	24141
SLINIGER, DENNIS	BASEBALL	POST OFFICE BOX 3004	SPRINGFIELD, IL	62708
SLIWA, CURTIS	GUARDIAN ANGEL-MODEL	983 E 89TH ST	BROOKLYN, NY	11236
SLOAN, JERRY	BASKETBALL-COACH	5 TRIAD CENTER #500	SALT LAKE CITY, UT	84180
SLOAN, MICHAEL	TV WRITER-PRODUCER	20722 PACIFIC COAST HWY #227	MALIBU, CA	90265
SLOAN, NANCY	ACTRESS	10000 RIVERSIDE DR #6	TOLUCA LAKE, CA	91602
SLOAN, RANDEL	PRODUCER	MARVIN PRODS, 658 OZONE ST	SANTA MONICA, CA	90405
SLOAN, TINA	ACTRESS	CBS-TV, "THE GUIDING LIGHT"		
		222 E 44TH ST	NEW YORK, NY	10017
SLOBODIEN, DOUGLAS A	PHOTOGRAPHER	130 MOUNT HARMONY RD	BERNARDSVILLE, NJ	07924
SLOCOMBE, DOUGLAS	CINEMATOGRAPHER	24 HEREFORD SQ	LONDON SW7	ENGLAND
SLOCUMB, HEATHCLIFF	BASEBALL	1060 W ADDISON ST	CHICAGO, IL	60613
SLOMAN, ANTHONY B	WRI-DIR-ED	FLAT 4, 29-A BROOK ST	LONDON W1	ENGLAND
SLOMAN, ROGER	ACTOR	10 KINGS COURT MANSIONS		
		FULHAM RD	LONDON SW6	ENGLAND
SLOSSER, R JOHN	DIRECTOR	1116 S ALVIRA ST	LOS ANGELES, CA	90035
SLOSSON, BILL	BASEBALL TRAINER	POST OFFICE BOX 2960	SUMTER, SC	29151
SLOTE, RICHARD	WRI-DIR-PROD	SIGNET PRODS, 200 W 58TH ST	NEW YORK, NY	10019
SLOVACEK, ALOIS, JR	CONDUCTOR	961 N CYPRESS	LA HABRA, CA	90631
SLOVENLY	ROCK & ROLL GROUP	POST OFFICE BOX 21	SAN PEDRO, CA	90733
SLOWIK, TAD	BASEBALL SCOUT	POST OFFICE BOX 288	HOUSTON, TX	77001
SLOYAN, JAMES	ACTOR	4442 VISTA DEL MONTE #1	SHERMAN OAKS, CA	91403
SLUGGERS, THE	ROCK & ROLL GROUP	POST OFFICE BOX 120235	NASHVILLE, TN	37204
SLUHAN, ELLIOTT D	DIRECTOR	4285 DEEPWOOD LN	TOLEDO, OH	43614
SLUMAN, JEFF	GOLFER	POST OFFICE BOX 109601	PALM BCH GARDENS, FL	33418
SLUSARSKI, JOE	BASEBALL	ATHLETICS'S, OAKLAND COLISEUM	OAKLAND, CA	94621
SLY DOG	ROCK & ROLL GROUP	POST OFFICE BOX 18368	DENVER, CO	80218
SLYTER BROTHERS, THE	C & W GROUP	PENNY, 30 GUINAN ST	WALTHAM, MA	02154
SMACK	ROCK & ROLL GROUP	POST OFFICE BOX 2428	EL SEGUNDO, CA	90245
SMAIL, DOUG	HOCKEY	NORTH STARS, 7901 CEDAR AVE S	BLOOMINGTON, MN	55425
SMAJSTRLA, CRAIG	BASEBALL	POST OFFICE BOX 32	PEARLAND, TX	77581
SMALDONE, ED	BASEBALL EXECUTIVE	POST OFFICE BOX 402	GENEVA, NY	14456
SMALL, AARON	BASEBALL	633 JESSAMINE ST	KNOXVILLE, TN	37917
SMALL, ADAM	TV WRITER	UTA, 9560 WILSHIRE BL, 5TH FL	BEVERLY HILLS, CA	90212
SMALL, JEFF	BASEBALL	POST OFFICE BOX 23290	NASHVILLE, TN	37202
SMALL, JESSIE	FOOTBALL	EAGLES, BROAD ST & PATTISON AVE	PHILADELPHIA, PA	19148
SMALL, MARK	BASEBALL	POST OFFICE BOX 422229	KISSIMMEE, FL	34742
SMALL, MERRYA	ACTRESS	5657 WILSHIRE BLVD #290	LOS ANGELES, CA	90036
SMALL, NORMA	SINGER	POST OFFICE BOX 171132	NASHVILLE, TN	37217
SMALL, WYLIE	ACTRESS	8228 SUNSET BLVD #311	LOS ANGELES, CA	90046
SMALLEY, JACK	COMPOSER	3762 ALTA MESA DR	STUDIO CITY, CA	91604
SMALLEY, STEVEN SCOTT	COMPOSER	4385 ALLOTT AVE	SHERMAN OAKS, CA	91423
SMALLWOOD, BILL	SINGER	POST OFFICE BOX 228	FREDERICKSBURG, TX	78624
SMALLWOOD, RICHARD, SINGERS	GOSPEL GROUP	TRIAD, 1114 17TH AVE S	NASHVILLE, TN	37212
SMALLWOOD, STEPHEB	TV PRODUCER	208 WESTBORUNE PARK RD	LONDON W11	ENGLAND
SMART, DOUGLAS	TV DIRECTOR	4183 FAIR AVE	NORTH HOLLYWOOD, CA	91602
SMART, PATSY	ACTRESS	46-A PRIMROSE MANSIONS		
		PRINCE OF WALES DR	LONDON SW11	ENGLAND
SMART,]JEAN	ACTRESS	4545 NOELINE AVE	ENCINO, CA	91316
SMARTIES, THE	ROCK & ROLL GROUP	JENS GALLMEYER, ROSEGGERSTR 5	3000 HANOVER 1	GERMANY
SMATHERS, BEN & THE STONEY MOUN	C & W GROUP	38 MUSIC SQUARE E #300	NASHVILLE, TN	37203
SMEDLEY-ASTON, BRIAN DAVID	FILM EDITOR	15 CEBTRAL PARK LODGE		
		BOLSOVER ST	LONDON W1P 7HL	ENGLAND
SMEENGE, JOEL	FOOTBALL	SAINTS, 1500 POYDRAS ST	NEW ORLEANS, LA	90112
SMERLAS, FRED	FOOTBALL	PATRIOTS, FOXBORO STADIUM, RT #1	FOXBORO, MA	02035
SMET, JONATHAN B	TV WRITER	2101 N BEACHWOOD DR	HOLLYWOOD, CA	90068
SMIETAN, BOB	COMPOSER	3412 LANTANA LN	COSTA MESA, CA	92626
SMIGEL, ROBERT	TV WRITER	CAA, 9830 WILSHIRE BLVD	BEVERLY HILLS, CA	90212
SMIGHT, JACK	DIRECTOR	255 TIGERTAIL RD	LOS ANGELES, CA	90049
SMILE	ROCK & ROLL GROUP	POST OFFICE BOX 69210	LOS ANGELES, CA	90069
SMILER, ALAN	FILM-SOUND EDITOR	136 W 75TH ST	NEW YORK, NY	10023
SMILEY, JOHN	BASEBALL	TWINS, 501 CHICAGO AVE S	MINNEAPOLIS, MN	55415
SMILEY, REUBEN	BASEBALL	POST OFFICE BOX 3448	SHREVEPORT, LA	71133
SMILOW, DAVID H	SCREENWRITER	22 19TH AVE #1	VENICE, CA	90291
SMIRNOFF, BRUCE	COMEDIAN	7400 FOUNTAIN AVE	LOS ANGELES, CA	90046
SMIRNOFF, YAKOV	COMEDIAN-ACTOR	1123 NAPOLI	PACIFIC PALISADES, CA	90272

SMITH, AL	FOOTBALL	OILERS, 6910 FANNIN ST	HOUSTON, TX	77070
SMITH, ALAN	MUSIC EXECUTIVE	BROADCAST MUSIC, 320 W 57TH ST	NEW YORK, NY	10019
SMITH, ALEXIS	ACTRESS	25 CENTRAL PARK W	NEW YORK, NY	10023
SMITH, ALLISON	ACTRESS	ICM, 8899 BEVERLY BLVD	LOS ANGELES, CA	90048
SMITH, ANTHONY	FOOTBALL	RAIDERS, 332 CENTER ST	EL SEGUNDO, CA	90245
SMITH, ANTHONY E	ACTOR	POST OFFICE BOX 1381 (MHS)	NEW YORK, NY	10156
SMITH, APRIL	TV WRITER	427 7TH ST	SANTA MONICA, CA	90402
SMITH, ARLANDO	TV DIRECTOR	9176 ONEIDA AVE	SUN VALLEY, CA	91352
SMITH, ARLENE & THE CHANTELLS	VOCAL GROUP	TRUMBALL PRODUCTIONS		
		60 SEAMAN AVE	BROOKLYN, NY	11222
SMITH, BARBARA E	SCREENWRITER	8955 BEVERLY BLVD	WEST HOLLYWOOD, CA	90048
SMITH, BEN	FOOTBALL	EAGLES, BROAD ST & PATTISON AVE	PHILADELPHIA, PA	19148
SMITH, BEN	GOLFER	PGA SENIORS, 112 T P C BLVD	PONTE VEDRA BEACH, FL	32082
SMITH, BERNARD	TV WRITER-DIRECTOR	30512 ABINGTON CT	LAGUNA NIGUEL, CA	92677
SMITH, BILL	BASEBALL EXECUTIVE	TWINS, 501 CHICAGO AVE S	MINNEAPOLIS, MN	55415
SMITH, BILL	BODYBUILDER	POST OFFICE BOX 11883	FRESNO, CA	93775
SMITH, BILLY RAY	DIRECTOR	STAR ROUTE #3, BOX 6-CC	TEHACHAPI, CA	93561
SMITH, BILLY RAY	FOOTBALL	POST OFFICE BOX 609609	SAN DIEGO, CA	92160
SMITH, BOBBY	HOCKEY	NORTH STARS, 7901 CEDAR AVE S	BLOOMINGTON, MN	55425
SMITH, BRUCE	FOOTBALL	BILLS, 1 BILLS DR	ORCHARD PARK, NJ	14127
SMITH, BRYN	BASEBALL	250 STADIUM PLAZA	ST LOUIS, MO	63102
SMITH, BUBBA	ACTOR-FOOTBALL	5178 SUNLIGHT PL	LOS ANGELES, CA	90016
SMITH, BUBBA	BASEBALL	POST OFFICE BOX 9194	HAMPTON, VA	23670
SMITH, BUFFALO BOB	ACTOR	BIG LAKE	PRINCETON, ME	04619
SMITH, BUFFY	SINGER	4822 ALBEMARLE RD	CHARLOTTE, NC	28205
SMITH, C A R	ACTOR	215 W 105TH ST #5-E	NEW YORK, NY	10025
SMITH, C M	SCREENWRITER	8955 BEVERLY BLVD	WEST HOLLYWOOD, CA	90048
SMITH, CAL	SINGER	POST OFFICE BOX 121089	NASHVILLE, TN	37212
SMITH, CARL	FOOTBALL COACH	SAINTS, 1500 POYDRAS ST	NEW ORLEANS, LA	90112
SMITH, CARL	SINGER	2510 FRANKLIN RD	NASHVILLE, TN	37204
SMITH, CARL M	GUITARIST	ROUTE #7, BERRY CHAPEL RD	FRANKLIN, TN	37064
SMITH, CARY	MODEL	2400 ASPEN DR	HOLLYWOOD, CA	90068
SMITH, CECIL	DRAMA CRITIC	LA TIMES, TIMES MIRROR SQ	LOS ANGELES, CA	90053
SMITH, CHARLES	BASKETBALL (CELTICS)	151 MERRIMAC ST	BOSTON, MA	02114
SMITH, CHARLES	BASKETBALL (CLIPPERS)	CLIPPERS, 3939 S FIGUEROA ST	LOS ANGELES, CA	90037
SMITH, CHARLES L	DIRECTOR	43 W ELFIN GREEN	PORT HUENEME, CA	93041
SMITH, CHARLES MARTIN	ACTOR	4328 CHAUMONT RD	WOODLAND HILLS, CA	91364
SMITH, CHRISTOPHER H	U S CONGRESSMAN	427 HIGH ST #1	BURLINGTON, NJ	08016
SMITH, CHUCK	BASEBALL	POST OFFICE BOX 1556	ASHEVILLE, NC	28802
SMITH, CONNIE	SINGER	TAYLOR, 2401 12TH AVE S	NASHVILLE, TN	37204
SMITH, COTTER	ACTOR	14755 VENTURA BLVD #1-904	SHERMAN OAKS, CA	91403
SMITH, D L	BASEBALL	4385 TUTT BLVD	COLORADO SPRINGS, CO	80922
SMITH, DAN	BASEBALL	POST OFFICE BOX 4448	TULSA, OK	74159
SMITH, DAN FREDERICK	TV DIRECTOR	CAPTAIN'S FARM, 7 CEMETERY RD	UNION, CT	06076
SMITH, DARDEN	SINGER-SONGWRITER	POST OFFICE BOX 2454	AUSTIN, TX	78768
SMITH, DARWOOD KAYE	ACTOR	9318 SCOTMONT DR	TUJUNGA, CA	91042
SMITH, DARYL	BASEBALL	POST OFFICE BOX 3665	OMAHA, NE	68103
SMITH, DAVE	BASEBALL	1060 W ADDISON ST	CHICAGO, IL	60613
SMITH, DAVEY BOY	WRESTLER	POST OFFICE BOX 3859	STAMFORD, CT	06905
SMITH, DAVID MARK	TV DIRECTOR	715 PACIFIC ST #B	SANTA MONICA, CA	90405
SMITH, DEBRA ZIMMER	TV DIRECTOR	380 VALLEJO ST	SAN FRANCISCO, CA	94133
SMITH, DENNIS	FOOTBALL	BRONCOS, 13655 BRONCOS PKWY	ENGLEWOOD, CO	80112
SMITH, DENNIS	SINGER	POST OFFICE BOX 25083	NASHVILLE, TN	37202
SMITH, DEREK	ACTOR	63 ELSTREE RD, BUSHEY HEATH	HERTS WD2 3QX	ENGLAND
SMITH, DERRICK	HOCKEY	FLYERS, SPECTRUM, PATTISON PL	PHILADELPHIA, PA	19148
SMITH, DOUG	FOOTBALL (OILERS)	OILERS, 6910 FANNIN ST	HOUSTON, TX	77070
SMITH, DOUG	FOOTBALL (RAMS)	RAMS, 2327 W LINCOLN BLVD	ANAHEIM, CA	92801
SMITH, DOUG	SPORTS WRITER	POST OFFICE BOX 500	WASHINGTON, DC	20044
SMITH, DOUGLAS	ARTIST	405 WASHINGTON ST #2	BROOKLINE, MA	02146
SMITH, DUNCAN R	SCREENWRITER	8955 BEVERLY BLVD	WEST HOLLYWOOD, CA	90048
SMITH, DWIGHT	BASEBALL	1060 W ADDISON ST	CHICAGO, IL	60613
SMITH, EARL	BASEBALL EXECUTIVE	POST OFFICE BOX 419969	KANSAS CITY, MO	64141
SMITH, ED	BASEBALL	POST OFFICE BOX 8550	STOCKTON, CA	95208
SMITH, ELWOOD H	ARTIST	2 LOCUST GROVE RD	RHINEBECK, NY	12572
SMITH, EMMITT	FOOTBALL	COWBOYS, 1 COWBOYS PARKWAY	IRVING, TX	75063
SMITH, EVERETT	BASEBALL EXECUTIVE	BREWERS, 201 S 46TH ST	MILWAUKEE, WI	53214
SMITH, G WARREN	TV DIRECTOR	4219 W OLIVE AVE #136	BURBANK, CA	91505
SMITH, GARY	SINGER	4615 SW FREEWAY #475	HOUSTON, TX	77027
SMITH, GEOFF	HOCKEY	OILERS, NORTHLANDS COLISEUM	EDMONTON, ALTA T5B 4M9	CANADA
SMITH, GEORGE T	TV DIRECTOR-PRODUCER	POST OFFICE BOX 1000	MOUNT FREEDOM, NJ	07970
SMITH, GORDON M	TV EXECUTIVE	TRANS WORLD INTERNATIONAL		
		22 E 71ST ST, 3RD FLOOR	NEW YORK, NY	10021
SMITH, GRAYSMITH	CARTOONIST	901 MISSION ST	SAN FRANCISCO, CA	94103
SMITH, GREG	BASEBALL	POST OFFICE BOX 6212	TOLEDO, OH	43614
SMITH, GREG	BASEBALL SCOUT	POST OFFICE BOX 2000	SAN DIEGO, CA	92112
SMITH, GREG	TV PRODUCER	ELSTREE PRODUCTION COMPANY		
		EMI STUDIOS, BOREHAMWOOD	HERTS	ENGLAND
SMITH, GREGORY P	DIRECTOR	8922 RANGELY AVE	LOS ANGELES, CA	90048
SMITH, HAL	BASEBALL SCOUT	250 STADIUM PLAZA	ST LOUIS, MO	63102
SMITH, HARRY	BASEBALL SCOUT	BREWERS, 201 S 46TH ST	MILWAUKEE, WI	53214
SMITH, HENRY C	DIRECTOR	201 FRONT ST	BROOKLYN, NY	11201
SMITH, HERBE	SINGER	1582 W DOROTHY LN #A	DAYTON, OH	45409
SMITH, HOLLY	ACTRESS	9332 W OLYMPIC BLVD	BEVERLY HILLS, CA	90212
SMITH, HOWARD	DIRECTOR	VILLAGE VOICE, 842 BROADWAY	NEW YORK, NY	10003
SMITH, HOWARD	SINGER	9200 SUNSET BLVD #PH-15	LOS ANGELES, CA	90069

Name	Occupation	Address	City/State	Zip/Country
SMITH, HUBERT W	SCREENWRITER	8955 BEVERLY BLVD	WEST HOLLYWOOD, CA	90048
SMITH, HY	FILM EXECUTIVE	UIP HOUSE, 45 BEADON RD		
		HAMMERSMITH	LONDON W6 0EG	ENGLAND
SMITH, IAIN	FILM PRODUCER	LIGHTHOUSE, 662 N ROBERTSON BLVD	LOS ANGELES, CA	90069
SMITH, IRA	BASEBALL	POST OFFICE BOX 10031	BAKERSFIELD, CA	93389
SMITH, JACK	BASEBALL	POST OFFICE BOX 5645	ORLANDO, FL	32855
SMITH, JACK P	NEWS CORRESPONDENT	ABC NEWS, 1717 DE SALES ST, NW	WASHINGTON, DC	20036
SMITH, JACLYN	ACTRESS-MODEL	773 STRADELLA RD	LOS ANGELES, CA	90024
SMITH, JAMES H	TV DIRECTOR	8527 WALNUT DR	LOS ANGELES, CA	90046
SMITH, JEFF	BASEBALL	POST OFFICE BOX 464	APPLETON, WI	54912
SMITH, JEFFERY	ARTIST	255 E PROSPECT AVE	MOUNT VERNON, NY	10550
SMITH, JEREMY	ACTOR	20718 PACIFIC COAST HWY #2	MALIBU, CA	90265
SMITH, JIM	SECRETARY OF STATE	STATE CAPITOL BUILDING	TALLAHASSEE, FL	32399
SMITH, JO JO	BASEBALL	POST OFFICE BOX 10031	BAKERSFIELD, CA	93389
SMITH, JOE	RECORD EXECUTIVE	962 N LA CIENEGA BLVD	LOS ANGELES, CA	90069
SMITH, JOHN J	DIRECTOR	16519 CALAHAN ST	SEPULVEDA, CA	91343
SMITH, JOHN V, JR	TV DIRECTOR	1009 COLLINGS AVE	WEST COLLINGSWOOD, NJ	08107
SMITH, JONATHAN	CINEMATOGRAPHER	708 JERSEY AVE #3-A	JERSEY CITY, NJ	07302
SMITH, JOSEPH KINGSBURY	COMMENTATOR	KING FEATURES, 216 E 45TH ST	NEW YORK, NY	10017
SMITH, JOSEPH L	TV DIRECTOR	1032 BRUSSELS ST	SAN FRANCISCO, CA	94134
SMITH, JULIA	DIRECTOR-PRODUCER	PETERS, FRASER & DUNLOP, LTD		
		5TH FLOOR, THE CHAMBERS		
		CHELSEA HARBOUR, LOT RD	LONDON SW10 0XF	ENGLAND
SMITH, KATHY	AEROBICS INSTRUCTOR	117 S LAXTON DR	LOS ANGELES, CA	90049
SMITH, KEITH	ACTOR	ELLISON COMBE ASSOCIATES		
		16 EVELYN GARDENS, RICHMOND	SURREY TW9 2PL	ENGLAND
SMITH, KELLY	BASEBALL SCOUT	ATHLETICS'S, OAKLAND COLISEUM	OAKLAND, CA	94621
SMITH, KENNY	BASKETBALL	POST OFFICE BOX 272349	HOUSTON, TX	77277
SMITH, KEVIN	FOOTBALL	STEELERS, 300 STADIUM CIR	PITTSBURGH, PA	15212
SMITH, KURTWOOD	ACTOR	400 S BEVERLY DR #216	BEVERLY HILLS, CA	90212
SMITH, L DAVID	SET DECORATOR	127 W 85TH ST #3-B	NEW YORK, NY	10024
SMITH, LAMAR	U S CONGRESSMAN	10010 SAN PEDRO AVE #530	SAN ANTONIO, TX	78216
SMITH, LANCE	BASEBALL	POST OFFICE BOX 824	BURLINGTON, IA	52601
SMITH, LANCE	FOOTBALL	POST OFFICE BOX 888	PHOENIX, AZ	85001
SMITH, LANE	ACTOR	MTA, 9320 WILSHIRE BL, 3RD FL	BEVERLY HILLS, CA	90212
SMITH, LARRY	BASKETBALL	POST OFFICE BOX 272349	HOUSTON, TX	77277
SMITH, LAURA	ARTIST	12 E 14TH ST	NEW YORK, NY	10003
SMITH, LAWRENCE J	U S CONGRESSMAN	4000 HOLLYWOOD BLVD #360-N	HOLLYWOOD, FL	33021
SMITH, LAWRENCE LEIGHTON	CONDUCTOR	ICM, 40 W 57TH ST	NEW YORK, NY	10019
SMITH, LEE	BASEBALL	250 STADIUM PLAZA	ST LOUIS, MO	63102
SMITH, LEE-------	COSTUME DESIGNER	6861 IRIS CIR	LOS ANGELES, CA	90068
SMITH, LEO	COMPOSER	39 DORCHESTER RD	BUFFALO, NY	14222
SMITH, LEONARD	FOOTBALL	BILLS, 1 BILLS DR	ORCHARD PARK, NJ	14127
SMITH, LESLIE	SINGER	4121 WILSHIRE BLVD #215	LOS ANGELES, CA	90010
SMITH, LEWIS	ACTOR	8271 MELROSE AVE #110	LOS ANGELES, CA	90046
SMITH, LITTLEFIELD & SMITH	C & W GROUP	POST OFFICE BOX 121542	NASHVILLE, TN	37212
SMITH, LIZ	ACTRESS	5 KING HENRY'S RD	LONDON NW3 3QP	ENGLAND
SMITH, LIZ	FILM CRITIC	N Y DAILY NEWS, 220 E 42ND ST	NEW YORK, NY	10017
SMITH, LOIS	ACTRESS	19 W 44TH ST #1000	NEW YORK, NY	10036
SMITH, LONNIE	BASEBALL	POST OFFICE BOX 4064	ATLANTA, GA	30302
SMITH, LYNNETTE H	COMPOSER	4291 COUNTRY CLUB DR	LONG BEACH, CA	90807
SMITH, MADOLYN	ACTRESS	SEE - SMITH OSBORNE, MADOLYN		
SMITH, MAGGIE	ACTRESS	ICM, 388-396 OXFORD ST	LONDON W1	ENGLAND
SMITH, MARGARET CHASE	U S SENATOR	NORRIDGEWOCK AVE	SHOWHEGAN, ME	04976
SMITH, MARGO	SINGER	38 MUSIC SQUARE E #300	NASHVILLE, TN	37203
SMITH, MARK	BASEBALL (OUTFIELD)	POST OFFICE BOX 230	HAGERSTOWN, MD	21740
SMITH, MARK	BASEBALL (PITCHER)	POST OFFICE BOX 3004	SPRINGFIELD, IL	62708
SMITH, MARTHA	ACTRESS-MODEL	POST OFFICE BOX 2241	BEVERLY HILLS, CA	90213
SMITH, MARTIN	TV WRITER-DIRECTOR	242 LAFAYETTE ST	NEW YORK, NY	10012
SMITH, MARTIN "BUD"	FILM DIRECTOR	234 N CORDOVA ST	BURBANK, CA	91505
SMITH, MARTIN C	SCREENWRITER	555 W 57TH ST #1230	NEW YORK, NY	10019
SMITH, MARTIN J	SCREENWRITER	8955 BEVERLY BLVD	WEST HOLLYWOOD, CA	90048
SMITH, MEL	ACTOR-DIRECTOR	TALKBACK, 33 PERCY ST	LONDON W1	ENGLAND
SMITH, MICHAEL	BASKETBALL	151 MERRIMAC ST	BOSTON, MA	02114
SMITH, MICHAEL "TEXAS"	BASEBALL	7605 ANTIQUE OAK	SAN ANTONIO, TX	78233
SMITH, MICHAEL W	SINGER-SONGWRITER	POST OFFICE BOX 25330	NASHVILLE, TN	37202
SMITH, MIKE	DIRECTOR-ANIMATOR	COLOSSAL, 2800 3RD ST	SAN FRANCISCO, CA	94107
SMITH, MIKE	GOLFER	POST OFFICE BOX 109601	PALM BCH GARDENS, FL	33418
SMITH, MIKE	TV-RADIO PERSONALITY	HEATH, PARAMOUNT HOUSE		
		162-170 WARDOUR ST	LONDON W1V 3AT	ENGLAND
SMITH, MONTE	FOOTBALL	BRONCOS, 13655 BRONCOS PKWY	ENGLEWOOD, CO	80112
SMITH, MR & MRS GEORGE	CARTOONISTS	UPS, 4900 MAIN ST, 9TH FLOOR	KANSAS CITY, MO	64112
SMITH, MURRAY	SCREENWRITER	BOURNE WOOD, HURSTBOURNE PRIORS	HAMPSHIRE RG28 7SD	ENGLAND
SMITH, NEAL	U S CONGRESSMAN	544 INSURANCE EXCHANGE BLVD	DES MOINES, IA	50309
SMITH, NEIL	FOOTBALL	CHIEFS, 1 ARROWHEAD DR	KANSAS CITY, MO	64129
SMITH, NEIL B	TV DIRECTOR	38 VERANDAH PL	BROOKLYN, NY	11201
SMITH, O C	SINGER	1650 BROADWAY #508	NEW YORK, NY	10019
SMITH, OTIS	BASEBALL	POST OFFICE BOX 7845	COLUMBIA, SC	29202
SMITH, OTIS	BASKETBALL	POST OFFICE BOX 76	ORLANDO, FL	32802
SMITH, OTIS	FOOTBALL	EAGLES, BROAD ST & PATTISON AVE	PHILADELPHIA, PA	19148
SMITH, OZZIE	BASEBALL	250 STADIUM PLAZA	ST LOUIS, MO	63102
SMITH, PATTI, GROUP	ROCK & ROLL GROUP	3 E 54TH ST #1400	NEW YORK, NY	10022
SMITH, PAUL	TV DIRECTOR-PRODUCER	CELADOR PRODS, 39 LONG ACRE	LONDON WC2	ENGLAND
SMITH, PAUL L	ACTOR	ICM, 8899 BEVERLY BLVD	LOS ANGELES, CA	90048
SMITH, PAUL S	TV DIRECTOR	23250 GILMORE ST	CANOGA PARK, CA	91307

LIGHTS!
CAMERA!
ACTION!

GEORGIA TERRY AUTOGRAPHS

We work actively from your WANT lists.

840 N.E. COCHRAN AVENUE
GRESHAM, OREGON 97030

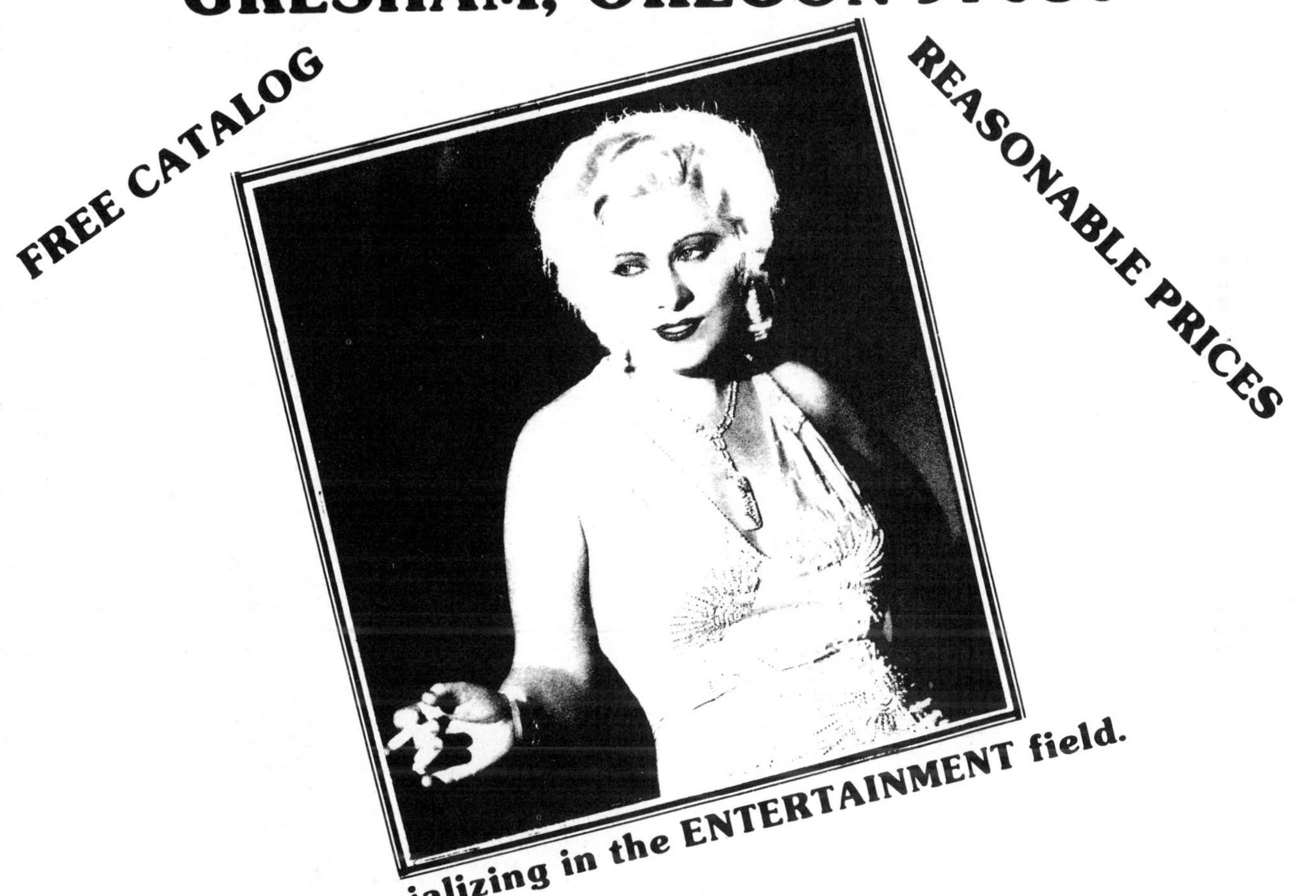

FAST, FRIENDLY SERVICE

Member U.A.C.C.

Collector since 1952
Dealer since 1978

LIGHTS!
CAMERA!
ACTION!

(503) 667-0950

LIGHTS!
CAMERA!
ACTION!

SMITH, PERRY N	TV DIRECTOR-PRODUCER	136 NYAC AVE	PELHAM, NY	10803
SMITH, PETE	BASEBALL	POST OFFICE BOX 6667	RICHMOND, VA	23230
SMITH, PETER	TV DIRECTOR	86 CANFIELD GARDENS	LONDON NW6 3EE	ENGLAND
SMITH, PETER K	DIRECTOR-CHOREO	POST OFFICE BOX 208	ARMONK, NY	10504
SMITH, PETER R E	FILM PRODUCER	PINEWOOD STUDIOS, IVER HEATH	IVER, BUCKS SLO ONH	ENGLAND
SMITH, R HARLAN	SINGER	POST OFFICE BOX 8768		
		STATION L	EDMONDTON, ALTA T6E	CANADA
SMITH, RALPH	CARTOONIST	KING FEATURES, 216 E 45TH ST	NEW YORK, NY	10017
SMITH, RANDY	BASEBALL COACH	POST OFFICE BOX 2183	IDAHO FALLS, ID	83402
SMITH, RANDY------YYYYY	BASEBALL SCOUT	POST OFFICE BOX 2000	SAN DIEGO, CA	92112
SMITH, RANKIN M, SR	FOOTBALL EXECUTIVE	FALCONS, SUWANEE RD AT I-85	SUWANEE, GA	30174
SMITH. RAY	ACTOR	DE WOLFE, MANFIELD HOUSE		
		376-378 THE STRAND	LONDON WC2R	ENGLAND
SMITH, RAY	BASEBALL MANAGER	136 S SYCAMORE	ELIZABETHTON, TN	37643
SMITH, REGGIE	BASEBALL-COACH	1000 ELYSIAN PARK DR	LOS ANGELES, CA	90012
SMITH, REID	ACTOR	8485 MELROSE PL #E	LOS ANGELES, CA	90069
SMITH, REX	ACTOR-SINGER	16 COURT ST #2400	BROOKLYN, NY	11241
SMITH, RICHARD	BASEBALL EXECUTIVE	1155 W MOUND ST	COLUMBUS, OH	43223
SMITH, RICHARD	FOOTBALL COACH	OILERS, 6910 FANNIN ST	HOUSTON, TX	77070
SMITH, RICHARD M	PUBLISHING EXECUTIVE	NEWSWEEK, 444 MADISON AVE	NEW YORK, NY	10022
SMITH, RICK	BASEBALL EXECUTIVE	POST OFFICE BOX 10031	BAKERSFIELD, CA	93389
SMITH, RICK	BASEBALL TRAINER	POST OFFICE BOX 2000	ANAHEIM, CA	92803
SMITH, RICKY & VINCE	C & W DUO	POST OFFICE BOX 1221	POTTSVILLE, PA	17901
SMITH, ROBBIE	BASEBALL	POST OFFICE BOX 1886	COLUMBUS, GA	31902
SMITH, ROBERT	SPECIAL EFFECTS	EAA, 84 WARDOUR ST, 1ST FLOOR	LONDON W1V 3LF	ENGLAND
SMITH, ROBERT	TV WRITER	BLAKE, 37-41 GOWER ST	LONDON WC1E 6HH	ENGLAND
SMITH, ROBERT C	U S SENATOR	136 PLEASANT ST	BERLIN, NH	03570
SMITH, ROBERT F "BOB"	U S CONGRESSMAN	771 PONDEROSA VILLAGE	BURNS, OR	97720
SMITH, ROBERT M	TV EXECUTIVE	DU ART VIDEO, 245 W 55TH ST	NEW YORK, NY	10019
SMITH, ROGER	ACTOR-WRITER	2707 BENEDICT CANYON DR	BEVERLY HILLS, CA	90210
SMITH, ROGER	BASEBALL SCOUT	250 STADIUM PLAZA	ST LOUIS, MO	63102
SMITH, ROLLAND G	NEWSCASTER	CBS-TV, 524 W 57TH ST	NEW YORK, NY	10019
SMITH, RON	ACTOR	7060 HOLLYWOOD BLVD #1215	LOS ANGELES, CA	90028
SMITH, ROY	BASEBALL	472 GRAMATON AVE	MOUNT VERNON, NY	10552
SMITH, RUSSELL	SINGER	MSS, 1000 ALABAMA AVE	SHEFFIELD, AL	35660
SMITH, SAMMI	SINGER	TAYLOR, 2401 12TH AVE S	NASHVILLE, TN	37204
SMITH, SAVANNAH	ACTRESS	SEE - BOUCHER, SAVANNAH SMITH		
SMITH, SEAN	BASEBALL	POST OFFICE BOX 22093	GREENSBORO, NC	27420
SMITH, SEAN	FOOTBALL	PATRIOTS, FOXBORO STADIUM, RT #1	FOXBORO, MA	02035
SMITH, SHAD	BASEBALL	POST OFFICE BOX 2148	WOODBRIDGE, VA	22193
SMITH, SHAWNEE	ACTRESS	6834 HOLLYWOOD BLVD #303	LOS ANGELES, CA	90028
SMITH, SHEAMUS	TV PROD-EXEC	22 ORWELL WOODS, RATHGAR	DUBLIN 6	IRELAND
SMITH, SHELDON	COMPOSER	1395 UNION ST #1	SAN FRANCISCO, CA	94109
SMITH, SHELLEY	ACTRESS-MODEL	10000 SANTA MONICA BLVD #305	LOS ANGELES, CA	90067
SMITH, SIDNEY F R	DIRECTOR-PRODUCER	240 CENTRAL PARK S	NEW YORK, NY	10019
SMITH, STAN	TREASURER	STATE CAPITOL BUILDING	CHEYENNE, WY	82002
SMITH, STEPHEN	PUBLISHING EXECUTIVE	NEWSWEEK, 444 MADISON AVE	NEW YORK, NY	10022
SMITH, STEVE	BASEBALL EXECUTIVE	POST OFFICE BOX 30160	SAN BERNARDINO, CA	92413
SMITH, STEVE	BASEBALL-MANAGER	POST OFFICE BOX 9194	HAMPTON, VA	23670
SMITH, STEVE	FOOTBALL	RAIDERS, 332 CENTER ST	EL SEGUNDO, CA	90245
SMITH, STEVE	HOCKEY	OILERS, NORTHLANDS COLISEUM	EDMONTON, ALTA T5B 4M9	CANADA
SMITH, STEVEN PHILLIP	SCREENWRITER	C LAKE, 1103 GLENDON AVE	LOS ANGELES, CA	90024
SMITH, SUSAN	TALENT AGENT	SMITH, 121 N SAN VICENTE BLVD	BEVERLY HILLS, CA	90211
SMITH, SYLVIA L	DIRECTOR	HOBBS RD	WAYLAND, MA	01778
SMITH, TARAN	ACTOR	ABC-TV, 2040 AVE OF THE STARS	LOS ANGELES, CA	90067
SMITH, TAYLOR	FOOTBALL EXECUTIVE	FALCONS, SUWANEE RD AT I-85	SUWANEE, GA	30174
SMITH, TERI A	MUSIC PROD-DIR	400 E 77TH ST	NEW YORK, NY	10021
SMITH, TERRY	BASEBALL TRAINER	TIGERS, 89 WHARNCLIFFE RD N	LONDON, ONT N6H 2A7	CANADA
SMITH, TERRY	SINGER-SONGWRITER	1404 HUFFINE ST	NASHVILLE, TN	37216
SMITH, TIM	BASEBALL (LYNCHBURG)	POST OFFICE BOX 1718	NEW BRITAIN, CT	06050
SMITH, TIM	MUSIC ARRANGER	340 CANE RIDGE RD #302	ANTIOCH, TN	37013
SMITH, TODD	BASEBALL	POST OFFICE BOX 2769	HUNTSVILLE, AL	35804
SMITH, TODD	SINGER	POST OFFICE BOX 70	BUCKLEY, WA	98321
SMITH, TOM	BASEBALL	300 STADIUM WY	DAVENPORT, FL	33837
SMITH, TONY	BASKETBALL	POST OFFICE BOX 10	INGLEWOOD, CA	90306
SMITH, TRACY N	ACTRESS	145 S FAIRFAX AVE #310	LOS ANGELES, CA	90036
SMITH, VAN	BASEBALL SCOUT	POST OFFICE BOX 2000	SAN DIEGO, CA	92112
SMITH, VARLEY R	SCREENWRITER	8955 BEVERLY BLVD	WEST HOLLYWOOD, CA	90048
SMITH, VERNICE	FOOTBALL	POST OFFICE BOX 888	PHOENIX, AZ	85001
SMITH, VINCE	SINGER-SONGWRITER	POST OFFICE BOX 1221	POTTSVILLE, PA	17901
SMITH, VINSON	FOOTBALL	COWBOYS, 1 COWBOYS PARKWAY	IRVING, TX	75063
SMITH, WENDY	ACTRESS	2925 TUNA CANYON RD	TOPANGA, CA	90290
SMITH, WILL	SINGER-ACTOR	298 ELIZABETH ST #1	NEW YORK, NY	10012
SMITH, WILLI	FASHION DESIGNER	209 W 38TH ST	NEW YORK, NY	10018
SMITH, WILLIAM	ACTOR	2552 LAUREL CANYON	LOS ANGELES, CA	90046
SMITH, WILLIE	BASEBALL	2501 ALLEN AVE, SE	CANTON, OH	44707
SMITH, YEARDLEY	ACTRESS	15760 VENTURA BLVD #1730	ENCINO, CA	91436
SMITH, ZANE	BASEBALL	POST OFFICE BOX 7000	PITTSBURGH, PA	15212
SMITH OSBORNE, MADOLYN	ACTRESS	6131 1/2 GLEN OAK	LOS ANGELES, CA	90069
SMITHEREENS, THE	ROCK & ROLL GROUP	POST OFFICE BOX 1665	NEW YORK, NY	10009
SMITHERS, JAN	ACTRESS	2401 COLORADO AVE #160	SANTA MONICA, CA	90404
SMITHERS, WILLIAM	ACTOR	11664 LAURELCREST DR	STUDIO CITY, CA	91604
SMITHS, THE	ROCK & ROLL GROUP	FBI, 1776 BORADWAY, 6TH FLOOR	NEW YORK, NY	10019
SMITHSON, MIKE	BASEBALL	POST OFFICE BOX 204	CENTERVILLE, TN	37033
SMITMAN, SUSAN E	DIRECTOR	1 BANK ST	NEW YORK, NY	10014

SMITROVICH, BILL	ACTOR	5052 RUBIO AVE	ENCINO, CA	91436
SMITS, JIMMY	ACTOR	110 S WESTGATE AVE	LOS ANGELES, CA	90049
SMITS, RIK	BASKETBALL	PACERS, 300 E MARKET ST	INDIANAPOLIS, IN	46204
SMOCK, GREG	BASEBALL	POST OFFICE BOX 882	MADISON, WI	53701
SMOLANOFF, MICHAEL	COMPOSER	20-A BROUN PL	BRONX, NY	10475
SMOLL, CLYDE	BASEBALL EXECUTIVE	POST OFFICE BOX 238	ELMIRA, NY	14902
SMOLLETT, MOLLY	TV DIRECTOR	41-23 HAMPTON ST	ELMHURST, NY	11373
SMOLLIN, MARK	ARTIST	4836 VIA COLINA	LOS ANGELES, CA	90042
SMOLLIN, MICHAEL J	ANIMATOR	15 REICHERT CIR	WESTPORT, CT	06880
SMOLTZ, JOHN	BASEBALL	POST OFFICE BOX 4064	ATLANTA, GA	30302
SMOTHERMAN, MICHAEL	SINGER	8467 BEVERLY BLVD #100	LOS ANGELES, CA	90048
SMOTHERS, DICK	COMEDIAN-ACTOR	8489 W 3RD ST #1020	LOS ANGELES, CA	90048
SMOTHERS, TOM	COMED-ACT-DIR	8489 W 3RD ST #1020	LOS ANGELES, CA	90048
SMOTHERS BROTHERS, THE	COMEDY-MUSICAL DUO	8489 W 3RD ST #1020	LOS ANGELES, CA	90069
SMOYER, MONTANA	ACTRESS	16079 YARNELL ST #1-B	SYLMAR, CA	91342
SMREK, MIKE	BASKETBALL	GOLDEN STATE WARRIORS		
		OAKLAND COLISEUM ARENA		
		NIMITZ FWY & HEGENBERGER RD	OAKLAND, CA	94621
SMUIN, MICHAEL	DANCER-CHOREOGRAPHER	SAN FRANCISCO BALLET		
		378 18TH AVE	SAN FRANCISCO, CA	94121
SMULCZENSKI, SCOTT	BASEBALL EXECUTIVE	250 STADIUM PLAZA	ST LOUIS, MO	63102
SMULLEN, JEFF	BODYBUILDER	GOLD'S GYM, 2085 SAN ELIJO AVE	CARDIFF, CA	92007
SMULYAN, JEFF	BASEBALL EXECUTIVE	POST OFFICE BOX 4100	SEATTLE, WA	98104
SMYL, STAN	HOCKEY	CANUCKS, 100 N RENFREW ST	VANCOUVER, BC V5K 3N7	CANADA
SMYTHE, MARCUS	ACTOR	24 W 83RD ST	NEW YORK, NY	10024
SMYTHE, REGGIE	CARTOONIST	WHITEGLASS CALEDONIAN RD		
		HARTLEP	CLEVELAND	ENGLAND
SNAILS, THE	ROCK & ROLL GROUP	RED RUN RECORDS CO		
		8861 ZENCARD AVE	SAN DIEGO, CA	92123
SNAKE OUT	ROCK & ROLL GROUP	GARAGELAND STUDIOS		
		19620 WAHRMAN	NEW BOSTON, MI	48164
SNAZELLE, E E GREGG	DIRECTOR	7 STRAWBERRY LANDING		
		413 E STRAWBERRY DR	MILL VALLEY, CA	94941
SNEAD, BILL	PHOTOGRAPHER	THE WASHINGTON POST		
		1150 15TH ST, NW	WASHINGTON, DC	20071
SNEAD, J C	GOLFER	POST OFFICE BOX 1152	PONTE VERDE BEACH, FL	32082
SNEAD, SAM	GOLFER	POST OFFICE BOX 777	HOT SPRINGS, VA	24445
SNEAKER	SINGER	POST OFFICE BOX 7308	CARMEL, CA	93921
SNEDDON, STEVE	SPORTS WRITER	POST OFFICE BOX 500	WASHINGTON, DC	20044
SNEDEKER, SEAN	BASEBALL	POST OFFICE BOX 28268	SAN ANTONIO, TX	78228
SNEED, MICHAEL	COLUMNIST	TRIBUNE, 64 E CONCORD ST	ORLANDO, FL	32801
SNELL, DAVID	COMPOSER-CONDUCTOR	29 EVERSLEY CRESCENT	LONDON N21 1EL	ENGLAND
SNELL, GEORGE	TV DIRECTOR	366 NEW PROVIDENCE RD	MOUNTAINSIDE, NJ	07092
SNELLING, RICHARD A	GOVERNOR	PAVILION OFF BLDG, 109 STATE ST	MONTPELIER, VT	05602
SNEPSTS, HAROLD	HOCKEY	BLUES, 5700 OAKLAND AVE	SAINT LOUIS, MO	63110
SNIDER, DEE	SINGER-SONGWRITER	POST OFFICE BOX 360	MERRICK, NY	11561
SNIDER, DUKE	BASEBALL	3037 LAKEMONT DR	FALLBROOK, CA	92028
SNIDER, KEITH	BASEBALL SCOUT	6850 LAWRENCE RD	LANTANA, FL	33462
SNIDER, MIKE	BANJOIST	POST OFFICE BOX 140710	NASHVILLE, TN	37214
SNIDER, MIKE & CROSS COUNTRY	BLUEGRASS GROUP	BEACHAM, 1012 16TH AVE S	NASHVILLE, TN	37212
SNIDER, VAN	BASEBALL	POST OFFICE BOX 2365	PAWTUCKET, RI	02861
SNIFF'N THE TEARS	ROCK & ROLL GROUP	E S "BUD" PRAGER MANAGEMENT		
		1790 BROADWAY, PENTHOUSE	NEW YORK, NY	10019
SNIPES, WESLEY	ACTOR	POST OFFICE BOX 5617	BEVERLY HILLS, CA	90213
SNIPP, LOU	BASEBALL SCOUT	TIGERS, TIGER STADIUM	DETROIT, MI	48216
SNIPP, MARK	BASEBALL SCOUT	SKYDOME, 300 BREMMER BL #3200	TORONTO, ONT M5V 3B3	CANADA
SNITKER, BRIAN	BASEBALL MANAGER	POST OFFICE BOX 4525	MACON, GA	31208
SNOAD, HAROLD	TV DIRECTOR-PRODUCER	FIR TREE COTTAGE, HAWKEWOOD RD		
		SUNBURY-ON-THAMES	MIDDLESEX	ENGLAND
SNODGRASS, QUINCY	SINGER	POST OFFICE BOX 4234	PANORAMA CITY, CA	91412
SNODGRASS, WILLIAM	COMPTROLLER	STATE CAPITOL BUILDING	NASHVILLE, TN	37243
SNODGRESS, CARRIE	ACTRESS	3025 SURRY ST	LOS ANGELES, CA	90027
SNORTLAND, ELLEN	ACTRESS	669 S BURLINGTON AVE	LOS ANGELES, CA	90057
SNOW, HANK	SINGER-SONGWRITER	POST OFFICE BOX 1084	NASHVILLE, TN	37202
SNOW, J T	BASEBALL	1155 W MOUND ST	COLUMBUS, OH	43223
SNOW, JIMMIE ROGERS	GUITARIST	POST OFFICE BOX 245	MADISON, TN	37115
SNOW, MARK	ARTIST	145 PIERPONT AVE	SALT LAKE CITY, UT	84101
SNOW, MARK	COMPOSER	4146 LANKERSHIM BLVD #300	NORTH HOLLYWOOD, CA	91602
SNOWDAY, JANE MORIN	TV WRITER	POST OFFICE BOX 458	TIVOLI, NY	12583
SNOWNE, OLYMPIA J	U S CONGRESSWOMAN	2 GREAT FALLS PLAZA	AUBURN, ME	04210
SNUFF	C & W GROUP	1180 INDIAN AVE	VIRGINIA BEACH, VA	23451
SNUGGERUD, DAVE	HOCKEY	SABRES, MEMORIAL AUDITORIUM	BUFFALO, NY	14202
SNUKA, JIMMY "SUPERFLY"	WRESTLER	POST OFFICE BOX 3859	STAMFORD, CT	06905
SNYDER, CLIFF	MUSICIAN-EXECUTIVE	SEE - STONE, CLIFFIE		
SNYDER, CORY	BASEBALL	S F GIANTS, CANDLESTICK PARK	SAN FRANICSCO, CA	94124
SNYDER, DARREL	TV DIRECTOR	25 ENTERPRISE DR	CORTE MADERA, CA	94925
SNYDER, DREW	ACTOR	10351 SANTA MONICA BLVD #211	LOS ANGELES, CA	90025
SNYDER, JIM	BASEBALL-COACH	POST OFFICE BOX 2000	SAN DIEGO, CA	92112
SNYDER, JIM	SINGER	POST OFFICE BOX 25371	CHARLOTTE, NC	28212
SNYDER, JIMMY "THE GREEK"	ODDSMAKER	870 7TH AVE #2049	NEW YORK, NY	10019
SNYDER, JOHN	CARTOONIST	LA TIMES, TIMES MIRROR SQ	LOS ANGELES, CA	90053
SNYDER, PETER B	TV DIRECTOR	310 W 56TH ST	NEW YORK, NY	10019
SNYDER, ROBERT	FILM DIRECTOR	1431 OCEAN AVE #1400	SANTA MONICA, CA	90401
SNYDER, RONALD	ARTIST	551 WEIR RD	ASTON, PA	19014
SNYDER, SUSAN MARIE	ACTRESS	CBS-TV, "AS THE WORLD TURNS"		

		524 W 57TH ST #5330	NEW YORK, NY	10019
SNYDER, SUZANNE	ACTRESS	151 S EL CAMINO DR	BEVERLY HILLS, CA	90212
SNYDER, TOM	DIRECTOR	730 AMOROSO PL	VENICE, CA	90291
SNYDER, TOM	TV HOST	2801 HUTTON DR	BEVERLY HILLS, CA	90210
SNYDER, WILLIAM L	FILM PRODUCER	400 S BEVERLY DR #211	BEVERLY HILLS, CA	90212
SOAMES, RICHARD M	FILM EXEC-PROD	FILM FINANCES, LTD		
		1-11 HAY HILL, BERKELEY SQ	LONDON W1X 7LF	ENGLAND
SOBECK, JERRY	BASEBALL SCOUT	SKYDOME, 300 BREMMER BL #3200	TORONTO, ONT M5V 3B3	CANADA
SOBEL, BARRY	COMEDIAN	9000 SUNSET BLVD #1200	LOS ANGELES, CA	90069
SOBEL, CURT E	COMPOSER	14001 PALAWAN WY PH #14	MARINA DEL REY, CA	90292
SOBEL, MARK S	TV DIRECTOR	190 S CANON DR #201	BEVERLY HILLS, CA	90210
SOBIESKI, CAROL	SCREENWRITER	541 LATIMER RD	SANTA MONICA, CA	90402
SOBOLOFF, ARNOLD	ACTOR	145 W 55TH ST	NEW YORK, NY	10019
SOCIAL DISTORTION	ROCK & ROLL GROUP	POST OFFICE BOX 6246	FULLERTON, CA	92634
SOCOL, GARY	ACTOR	939 N ALFRED ST #4	LOS ANGELES, CA	90069
SODDERS, MIKE	BASEBALL	POST OFFICE DRAWER 1207	ZEBULON, NC	27597
SODERBERGH, STEVEN	FILM WRITER-DIRECTOR	UTA, 9560 WILSHIRE BL, 5TH FL	BEVERLY HILLS, CA	90212
SOFF, RAY	BASEBALL	10233 96TH AVE	EDMONTON, ALB TK5 0A5	CANADA
SOFFER, SHELDON	IMPRESSARIO	130 W 56TH ST	NEW YORK, NY	10019
SOFT CELL	ROCK & ROCK DUO	BIZARRE, 17 SAINT ANNE'S CT	LONDON W1	ENGLAND
SOGARD, PHILLIP	TV DIRECTOR	32370 LAKE PLEASANT DR	WESTLAKE VILLAGE, CA	91361
SOHL, CHRIS	TV PRODUCER	1888 CENTURY PARK E #1100	LOS ANGELES, CA	90067
SOHMER, STEVE	TV DIRECTOR	2625 LARMAR RD	LOS ANGELES, CA	90068
SOILEAU, HODGES	ARTIST	350 FLAX HILL RD	NORWALK, CT	06854
SOJO, LUIS	BASEBALL	10233 96TH AVE	EDMONTON, ALB TK5 0A5	CANADA
SOKOLSKY, MELVIN	TV DIRECTOR	SUNLIGHT, 322 E 39TH ST	NEW YORK, NY	10018
SOLARS, STEPHEN J	U S CONGRESSMAN	241 DOVER ST	BROOKLYN, NY	11235
SOLARZ, STEPHEN J	U S CONGRESSMAN	343 SMITH ST	BROOKLYN, NY	11231
SOLBERG, STEVEN	ACTOR	SHERMAN, 1516 S BEVERLY DR #304	LOS ANGELES, CA	90035
SOLDO, CHRIS	FILM DIRECTOR	5121 WESTPARK DR	NORTH HOLLYWOOD, CA	91601
SOLE, ALFRED	FILM WRITER-DIRECTOR	1641 N KINGS RD	LOS ANGELES, CA	90069
SOLEATHER, JON	SINGER	130 W 42ND ST #1106	NEW YORK, NY	10036
SOLES, P J	ACTRESS	POST OFFICE BOX 2351	CAREFREE, AZ	85377
SOLL, JOSEPH M	ACTOR	CAT SYSTEMS, 401 E 74TH ST	NEW YORK, NY	10021
SOLMS, KENNY	ACTOR-WRITER	8484 HAROLD WY	LOS ANGELES, CA	90049
SOLO, ROBERT H	FILM PRODUCER	1121 OLIVE DR #113	LOS ANGELES, CA	90069
SOLOMON, ANTHONY J	TREASURER	STATE CAPITOL, 320 S MAIN ST	PROVIDENCE, RI	02903
SOLOMON, AUBREY	TV WRITER	8833 SUNSET BLVD #202	LOS ANGELES, CA	90069
SOLOMON, BURT	TV WRITER	31 CRESCENT TERR	BEDFORD HILLS, NY	10507
SOLOMON, DAVID	DIRECTOR	DGA, 110 W 57TH ST	NEW YORK, NY	10019
SOLOMON, GEORGE	ACTOR	1335 N DETROIT ST #207	LOS ANGELES, CA	90046
SOLOMON, GERALD B H	U S CONGRESSMAN	329 FAIRVIEW AVE	HUDSON, NY	12534
SOLOMON, JEAN THORNTON	DIRECTOR	6255 SUNSET BLVD #1005	LOS ANGELES, CA	90028
SOLOMON, JESSE	FOOTBALL	COWBOYS, 1 COWBOYS PARKWAY	IRVING, TX	75063
SOLOMON, LAURENCE D	CINEMATOGRAPHER	2805 GERKEN PL	OCEANSIDE, NY	11572
SOLOV, ZACHARY	CHOREOGRAPHER	200 W 58TH ST	NEW YORK, NY	10019
SOLOW, HERBERT F	WRITER-PRODUCER	29060 CLIFFSIDE DR	MALIBU, CA	90265
SOLOWAY, LEONARD	THEATER PRODUCER	230 CENTRAL PARK S	NEW YORK, NY	10019
SOLT, ANDREW W	WRITER-PRODUCER	1252 SHADYBROOK DR	BEVERLY HILLS, CA	90210
SOLT, RON	FOOTBALL	EAGLES, BROAD ST & PATTISON AVE	PHILADELPHIA, PA	19148
SOLTERO, SAUL	BASEBALL	POST OFFICE BOX 20849	CHARLESTON, SC	29413
SOLTI, SIR GEORG	CONDUCTOR	CHALET HAUT PRE, 1884	VILLARS-SUR-OLLON	SWITZERLAND
SOMAN, SHIRLEY C	WRITER	40 W 77TH ST #15-B	NEW YORK, NY	10024
SOMERS, BRETT	ACTRESS	315 W 57TH ST #4-H	NEW YORK, NY	10019
SOMERS, GWEN	ACTRESS	1539 SAWTELLE BLVD #10	LOS ANGELES, CA	90025
SOMERS, KRISTI	ACTRESS	9255 SUNSET BLVD #401	WEST HOLLYWOOD, CA	90069
SOMERS, SUZANNE	ACTRESS-SINGER	190 S CANON DR #201	BEVERLY HILLS, CA	90210
SOMERVILLE, WARREN	DIRECTOR	DGA, 110 W 57TH ST	NEW YORK, NY	10019
SOMLYO, ROY A	TV PRODUCER	234 W 44TH ST	NEW YORK, NY	10036
SOMMARS, JULIE	ACTRESS	7272 OUTPOST COVE DR	LOS ANGELES, CA	90068
SOMMER, ELKE	ACTRESS	540 N BEVERLY GLEN BLVD	LOS ANGELES, CA	90024
SOMMER, HANS	COMPOSER-CONDUCTOR	569 MOUNT HOLYOKE AVE	PACIFIC PALISADES, CA	90272
SOMMERS, DENNY	BASEBALL-SCOUT	210 W BATH	HORTONVILLE, WI	54944
SOMMERS RABE, TISH	TV PRODUCER	CHILDREN'S TV WORKSHOP		
		1 LINCOLN PLAZA	NEW YORK, NY	10023
SOMMERSCHIELD, BENGT	DIRECTOR	333 E 30TH ST	NEW YORK, NY	10016
SOMOROFF, BENJAMIN	CINEMATOGRAPHER	MILL RIVER RD	SOUTH SALEM, NY	10590
SONDHEIM, STEPHEN	COMPOSER-LYRICIST	246 E 49TH ST	NEW YORK, NY	10017
SONDRINI, JOE	BASEBALL	POST OFFICE BOX 842	SALEM, VA	24153
SONGE, CYNTHIA	ACTRESS	3575 W CAHUENGA BLVD #252	LOS ANGELES, CA	90068
SONJU, NORM	BASKETBALL EXECUTIVE	REUNION ARENA, 777 SPORTS ST	DALLAS, TX	75207
SONNEBORN, DANIEL A	COMPOSER	7870 CAMINO GLORITA	SAN DIEGO, CA	92122
SONNENFELD, NATHAN J	CINEMATOGRAPHER	LIGHT AMERICA, 23 E 22ND ST	NEW YORK, NY	10010
SONNETT, SHERRY	SCREENWRITER	3413 1/2 ADINA DR	LOS ANGELES, CA	90068
SONNIER, JO-EL	SINGER-SONGWRITER	1114 17TH AVE S #101	NASHVILLE, TN	37212
SONSKY, STEVE	TV CRITIC	THE MIAMI HERALD		
		1 HERALD PLAZA	MIAMI, FL	33101
SONTAG, ALAN	BASEBALL	POST OFFICE BOX 4370	SALINAS, CA	93912
SONTAG, SUSAN	AUTHOR-DIRECTOR	FARRAR, STRAUSS & GIROUX		
		19 UNION SQUARE W	NEW YORK, NY	10003
SOPANEN, JERI	DIRECTOR	110 RIVERSIDE DR	NEW YORK, NY	10024
SOPER, MIKE	BASEBALL	2501 ALLEN AVE, SE	CANTON, OH	44707
SOPHER, SHARON I	TV PRODUCER	315 W 57TH ST #7-D	NEW YORK, NY	10019
SOPKO, ANDREW S	COMPOSER-CONDUCTOR	POST OFFICE BOX 218473	HOUSTON, TX	77218
SORANNO, ALEX	TV DIRECTOR	6278 QUARTZ PL	NEWARK, CA	94560

Name	Occupation	Address	City	Zip/Country
SORCSEK, JEROME P	COMPOSER	9585 RESEDA BLVD #214	NORTHRIDGE, CA	91324
SOREL, EDWARD	ARTIST	156 FRANKLIN ST	NEW YORK, NY	10013
SOREL, JEAN	ACTRESS	3 QUAI MALAQUAIS	F-75006 PARIS	FRANCE
SOREL, LOUISE	ACTRESS	9255 SUNSET BLVD #515	LOS ANGELES, CA	90069
SORENSEN, DICKSON P	DIRECTOR	DGA, 110 W 57TH ST	NEW YORK, NY	10019
SORIANO, CARMEN	SINGER	POST OFFICE BOX 63	ORINDA, CA	94563
SORKIN, ARLA	WRITER-PRODUCER	1557 COURTNEY AVE	LOS ANGELES, CA	90046
SORKIN, ARLEEN	ACTRESS	100 S DOHENY DR #605	LOS ANGELES, CA	90048
SOROCA, KAREN	ACTRESS	3208 DOS PALOS DR	HOLLYWOOD, CA	90068
SORRENTO, PAUL	BASEBALL	7 JOSEPH AVE	PEABODY, MA	01960
SORVINO, PAUL	ACTOR	4 BOULDER RD	TENAFLY, NJ	07630
SOS BAND	ROCK BAND	119 W 57TH ST #901	NEW YORK, NY	10019
SOSA, JOSE	BASEBALL	POST OFFICE BOX 3746, HILL STA	AUGUSTA, GA	30904
SOSA, SAMMY	BASEBALL	1060 W ADDISON ST	CHICAGO, IL	60613
SOSNIK, HARRY	COMPOSER-CONDUCTOR	215 E 68TH ST	NEW YORK, NY	10023
SOTHERN, ANN	ACTRESS	POST OFFICE BOX 2285	KETCHUM, ID	83340
SOTIRAKIS, DIMITRI	DIRECTOR	DGA, 7920 SUNSET BLVD, 6TH FL	LOS ANGELES, CA	90046
SOTKIN, MARC	TV WRITER	25 FLEET ST	MARINA DEL REY, CA	90292
SOTO, LUIS	DIRECTOR	54 W 57TH ST	NEW YORK, NY	10019
SOTO, MARIO	BASEBALL	JOACHS LACHAUSTEGUI #42 SUR	BANI	DOM REP
SOTO, RAFAEL	BASEBALL	POST OFFICE BOX 4488	WINSTON-SALEM, NC	27115
SOTO, TALISA	ACTRESS	9057 NEMO ST #A	WEST HOLLYWOOD, CA	90069
SOTOMAYOR, JOHN	PHOTOGRAPHER	31 CENTRAL AVE	EAST BRUNSWICK, NJ	08816
SOUCHOCK, STEVE	BASEBALL SCOUT	TIGERS, TIGER STADIUM	DETROIT, MI	48216
SOUL, DAVID	ACT-SING-DIR	2232 MORENO DR	LOS ANGELES, CA	90039
SOUL ASYLUM	ROCK & ROLL GROUP	611 BROADWAY #526	NEW YORK, NY	10012
SOUL II SOUL	ROCK & ROLL GROUP	162 CAMDEN HIGH ST	LONDON	ENGLAND
SOUL QUEEN OF NEW ORLEANS	SINGER	SEE - THOMAS, IRMA		
SOUL SONIC FORCE	RHYTHM & BLUES GROUP	FAA, 1700 BROADWAY, 5TH FLOOR	NEW YORK, NY	10019
SOULS, THE	ROCK & ROLL GROUP	25 HUNTINGTON AVE #420	BOSTON, MA	02116
SOUND BARRIER	ROCK & ROLL GROUP	POST OFFICE BOX 35897	LOS ANGELES, CA	90035
SOUTER, DAVID	SUPREME COURT JUDGE	1 1ST ST, NE	WASHINGTON, DC	20543
SOUTHER, J D	SINGER	8263 HOLLYWOOD BLVD	LOS ANGELES, CA	90069
SOUTHERLAND, CRAIG	SINGER	POST OFFICE BOX 17272	MEMPHIS, TN	38187
SOUTHERN, COL HAL	SINGER	POST OFFICE BOX 4234	PANORAMA CITY, CA	91412
SOUTHERN, MIKE	CINEMATOGRAPHER	8 SAINT LEONARD'S ROAD	LONDON W13 8PW	ENGLAND
SOUTHERN, SHEILA	ACTRESS-SINGER	BOULTON, 76 CARLISLE MANSIONS CARLISLE PL	LONDON SW1P 1HZ	ENGLAND
SOUTHERN, TERRY	TV WRITER	RFD	EAST CANAAN, CT	06020
SOUTHERN BREEZE	C & W GROUP	POST OFFICE BOX 9393	PENSACOLA, FL	32513
SOUTHERN HIGH	C & W GROUP	POST OFFICE BOX 25371	CHARLOTTE, NC	28212
SOUTHSIDE JOHNNY & THE JUKES	ROCK & ROLL GROUP	POST OFFICE BOX 405	BOGOTA, NJ	07603
SOUTHWICK, SHAWN	ACTRESS-TV HOST	12700 VENTURA BLVD #350	STUDIO CITY, CA	91604
SOUZA, BRIAN	BASEBALL	POST OFFICE BOX 855	BELOIT, WI	53511
SOWARDS, JACK B	TV WRITER-PRODUCER	4428 CARPENTER AVE	NORTH HOLLYWOOD, CA	91607
SOYKA, ED	ARTIST	231 LAFAYETTE AVE	PEEKSKILL, NY	10566
SPAAK, CATHERINE	ACTRESS	PRO 2, VIALE PARIOLI 59	I-00197 ROME	ITALY
SPACEK, SISSY	ACTRESS	CAA, 9830 WILSHIRE BLVD	BEVERLY HILLS, CA	90212
SPADER, JAMES	ACTOR	ICM, 8899 BEVERLY BLVD	LOS ANGELES, CA	90048
SPAETH, NICHOLAS	ATTORNEY GENERAL	STATE CAPITOL, 600 E BOULEVARD	BISMARCK, ND	58505
SPAHN, WARREN	BASEBALL	RURAL ROUTE #2	HARTSHORNE, OK	74547
SPAIN, THOMAS	WRITER-PRODUCER	12021 WILSHIRE BLVD #230	LOS ANGELES, CA	90025
SPALDING, HARRY	SCREENWRITER	3936 GLENRIDGE DR	SHERMAN OAKS, CA	91423
SPALENKA, GREG	ARTIST	165 PERRY ST #1-B	NEW YORK, NY	10014
SPANARKEL, JIM	BASKETBALL	N J NETS, MEADOWLANDS ARENA	EAST RUTHERFORD, NJ	07073
SPANDAU BALLET	ROCK & ROLL GROUP	REFORMATION MANAGEMENT 89 GREAT PORTLAND	LONDON W1	ENGLAND
SPANFELLER, JIM	ARTIST	MUSTATO RD	KATONAH, NY	10536
SPANG, LAURETTE	ACTRESS	MC COOK, 4154 COLBATH AVE	SHERMAN OAKS, CA	91413
SPANGLER, LARRY G	FILM PRODUCER	1289 N CRESCENT HGTS BLVD	LOS ANGELES, CA	90046
SPANKY & OUR GANG	ROCK & ROLL GROUP	208 E MARCY ST #7	SANTE FE, NM	87501
SPANN, TOOKIE	BASEBALL	12000 STADIUM RD	ADELANTO, CA	92301
SPANO, JOE	ACTOR	POST OFFICE BOX 5617	BEVERLY HILLS, CA	90213
SPANO, VINCENT	ACTOR	ICM, 8899 BEVERLY BLVD	LOS ANGELES, CA	90048
SPANOS, ALEX G	FOOTBALL EXECUTIVE	POST OFFICE BOX 609609	SAN DIEGO, CA	92160
SPANOS, DEAN A	FOOTBALL EXECUTIVE	POST OFFICE BOX 609609	SAN DIEGO, CA	92160
SPARKS, DANA	ACTRESS	10000 SANTA MONICA BLVD #305	LOS ANGELES, CA	90067
SPARKS, DON	BASEBALL	ALBANY YANKEES, HERITAGE PARK	ALBANY, NY	12211
SPARKS, GREG	BASEBALL	TIGERS, 89 WHARNCLIFFE RD N	LONDON, ONT N6H 2A7	CANADA
SPARKS, JOE	BASEBALL-MANAGER	POST OFFICE BOX 6212	TOLEDO, OH	43614
SPARKS, RANDY & THE PATCH FAMIL	VOCAL GROUP	2701 COTTAGE WY #21	SACRAMENTO, CA	95825
SPARKS, RICHARD	ARTIST	2 W ROCKS RD	NORWALK, CT	06851
SPARKS, SHANE	BASEBALL	POST OFFICE BOX 3746, HILL STA	AUGUSTA, GA	30904
SPARKS, STEVE	BASEBALL	POST OFFICE DRAWER 4797	EL PASO, TX	79914
SPARKS, THE	ROCK & ROLL GROUP	10100 SANTA MONICA BLVD #1600	LOS ANGELES, CA	90067
SPARMA, BLASE	BASEBALL	POST OFFICE BOX 4525	MACON, GA	31208
SPARROW, RORY	BASKETBALL	KINGS, 1 SPORTS PARKWAY	SACRAMENTO, CA	95834
SPARV, CAMILLA	ACTRESS	1520 CIRCLE DR	SAN MARINO, CA	91108
SPEAKMAN, WILLIE	BASEBALL	POST OFFICE BOX 9194	HAMPTON, VA	23670
SPEARMAN, VERNON	BASEBALL	POST OFFICE BOX 2887	VERO BEACH, FL	32961
SPEARMANS, THE	GOSPEL GROUP	DYER ROUTE	COWEN, WV	26206
SPEARS, BILLIE JO	SINGER	TAYLOR, 2401 12TH AVE S	NASHVILLE, TN	37204
SPECHT, DON	COMPOSER-CONDUCTOR	11740 EL CERRO LN	STUDIO CITY, CA	91604
SPECIAL FORCES	ROCK & ROLL GROUP	8306 WILSHIRE BLVD #1531	BEVERLY HILLS, CA	90211
SPECK, B ALAN	NEWS CORRESPONDENT	ABC NEWS, 1717 DE SALES ST, NW	WASHINGTON, DC	20036

Name	Occupation	Address	City	Zip/Country
SPECK, JOSEPH M	CONDUCTOR	5454 ZELZAH AVE	ENCINO, CA	91316
SPECKTOR, FRED	TALENT AGENT	CAA, 9830 WILSHIRE BLVD	BEVERLY HILLS, CA	90212
SPECTER, ARLEN	U S SENATOR	600 ARCH ST #9400	PHILADELPHIA, PA	19106
SPECTER, BENJAMIN	DOCTOR	3417 WARDEN DR	PHILADELPHIA, PA	19129
SPECTOR, MAUDE	CASTING DIRECTOR	16 UPPER BROOK ST	LONDON W1Y 1PD	ENGLAND
SPECTOR, PHIL	RECORD PRODUCER	1210 S ARROYO BLVD	PASADENA, CA	91101
SPECTOR, RONNIE	SINGER	7 MAPLECREST DR	DANBURY, CT	06810
SPEDDING, CHRIS	SINGER-GUITARIST	225 CENTRAL PARK W	NEW YORK, NY	10024
SPEEK, FRANK	BASEBALL	POST OFFICE BOX 3004	SPRINGFIELD, IL	62708
SPEER, TERRY	ARTIST	181 FOREST ST	OBERLIN, OH	44074
SPEHR, TIM	BASEBALL	POST OFFICE BOX 3665	OMAHA, NE	68103
SPEIER, CHRIS	BASEBALL	6114 E MONTECITO	SCOTTSDALE, AZ	85251
SPEIGHT, JOHNNY	TV WRITER	LONDON MGT, 235-241 REGENT ST	LONDON W1R 4PH	ENGLAND
SPEIR, DONA	ACTRESS-MODEL	9229 SUNSET BLVD #208	LOS ANGELES, CA	90069
SPEIRS, JACK	WRITER-PRODUCER	7 OAKS, 56 LOWER LAKE RD	THOUSAND OAKS, CA	91360
SPELIUS, GEORGE	BASEBALL EXECUTIVE	POST OFFICE BOX 936	BELOIT, WI	53511
SPELL, WINSTON	ACTOR	809 5TH AVE	LOS ANGELES, CA	90005
SPELLER, ROBERT, JR	ACTOR	343 W 14TH ST	NEW YORK, NY	10014
SPELLING, AARON	TV WRITER-PRODUCER	594 MAPLETON DR	LOS ANGELES, CA	90077
SPELLING, TORI	ACTRESS	5700 WILSHIRE BLVD #575	LOS ANGELES, CA	90036
SPELMAN, SHARON	ACTRESS	11592 SUNSHINE TERR	STUDIO CITY, CA	91604
SPELVIN, GEORGINA	ACTRESS-WRITER	1418 N HIGHLAND AVE #102	LOS ANGELES, CA	90028
SPENCE, FLOYD	U S CONGRESSMAN	1681 CHESTNUT ST, NE	ORANGEBURG, SC	29116
SPENCE, LEW	COMPOSER	215 E 68TH ST #17-K	NEW YORK, NY	10021
SPENCE, SAMUEL L	COMPOSER	MENZINGERSTR 118	8 MUNICH 50	GERMANY
SPENCER, BUD	ACTOR	VIA CORTINA D'AMPEZZO 156	I-00191 ROME	ITALY
SPENCER, CHRISTINE	ACTRESS-SINGER	OMNI PARK CENTRAL, 850 7TH AVE	NEW YORK, NY	10019
SPENCER, DARYL	BASEBALL	2740 LARKIN DR	WICHITA, KS	67216
SPENCER, DIANE	ACTRESS	12211 WIXOM ST	NORTH HOLLYWOOD, CA	91605
SPENCER, FELTON	BASKETBALL	TIMBERWOLVES, 600 1ST AVE N	MINNEAPOLIS, MN	55403
SPENCER, LISA	TV PRODUCER	225 E 95TH ST #25-M	NEW YORK, NY	10128
SPENCER, RODERICK	ACTOR	602 BAY SR	SANTA MONICA, CA	90405
SPENCER, SCOTT	SCREENWRITER	555 W 57TH ST #1230	NEW YORK, NY	10019
SPENCER, SHANE	BASEBALL	POST OFFICE BOX 22093	GREENSBORO, NC	27420
SPENCER, STAN	BASEBALL	POST OFFICE BOX 15757	HARRISBURG, PA	17105
SPENCER, TOM	BASEBALL-COACH	POST OFFICE BOX 288	HOUSTON, TX	77001
SPENCER, WILLIAM M	CINEMATOGRAPHER	POST OFFICE BOX 2230	HOLLYWOOD, CA	90078
SPENGLER, PIERRE	FILM PRODUCER	PINEWOOD STUDIOS, IVER HEATH	IVER, BUCKS SLO ONH	ENGLAND
SPERBER, WENDIE JO	ACTRESS	4110 WITSETT DR	SHERMAN OAKS, CA	91423
SPERY, JOSEPH C	DIRECTOR-PRODUCER	47 GARFIELD ST	OAK PARK, IL	60304
SPHEERIS, PENELOPE	FILM DIRECTOR	8301 KIRKWOOD DR	LOS ANGELES, CA	90046
SPICER, MARIANNA CHASE	DIRECTOR	8947 TAMAR DR #301	COLUMBIA, MD	21045
SPICUZZA, PAUL	BASEBALL TRAINER	INDIANS, CLEVELAND STADIUM	CLEVELAND, OH	44114
SPIEGEL, DENNIS	ACTOR-WRITER	6923 PASEO DEL SERRA	LOS ANGELES, CA	90068
SPIEGEL, EDWARD	WRITER-PRODUCER	2739 NICHOLS CANYON RD	LOS ANGELES, CA	90046
SPIEGEL, LARRY J	WRITER-PRODUCER	2029 CENTURY PARK E #1850	LOS ANGELES, CA	90067
SPIEGEL, PENINA	TV WRITER	180 W END AVE	NEW YORK, NY	10023
SPIEGL, STEVE H	COMPOSER	2816 SHADY GLEN LN	ORANGE, CA	92667
SPIELBERG, ANNE	FILM WRITER-PRODUCER	CAA, 9830 WILSHIRE BLVD	BEVERLY HILLS, CA	90212
SPIELBERG, DAVID	ACTOR	3531 BENTLEY AVE	LOS ANGELES, CA	90034
SPIELBERG, STEVEN	DIRECTOR-PRODUCER	POST OFFICE BOX 6190	MALIBU, CA	90265
SPIELMAN, CHRIS	FOOTBALL	LIONS, 1200 FEATHERSTONE RD	PONTIAC, MI	48432
SPIELMAN, FRED	COMPOSER	710 WEST END AVE #16-B	NEW YORK, NY	10025
SPIER, DONA	ACTRESS-MODEL	9229 SUNSET BLVD #208	LOS ANGELES, CA	90069
SPIERS, BILL	BASEBALL	BREWERS, 201 S 46TH ST	MILWAUKEE, WI	53214
SPIERS, JUDI	TV HOST	ARLINGTON, 1-3 CHARLOTTE ST	LONDON W1P 1HD	ENGLAND
SPIES, ADRIAN	TV WRITER	11937 SUNSET BLVD	LOS ANGELES, CA	90049
SPIKES, THE	ROCK & ROLL GROUP	JANET MILLS, 83 MORIAH ST	CLAYTON 3168, VICTORIA..	AUSTRALIA
SPIKINGS, BARRY	FILM EXECUTIVE	56 MALIBU COLONY DR	MALIBU, CA	90265
SPIKOL, ALLEN	DIRECTOR	11 W 17TH ST #11	NEW YORK, NY	10011
SPILKER, SUSAN	ACTRESS	12365 LAUREL TERRACE DR	STUDIO CITY, CA	91604
SPILLANE, MICKEY	WRITER	GENERAL DELIVERY	MARRELLS INLET, SC	22117
SPILLER, DERRON	BASEBALL	POST OFFICE BOX 3783	SAVANNAH, GA	31414
SPILLMAN, SANDY	ACTOR	1353 ALVARADO TERR	LOS ANGELES, CA	90017
SPILLMAN, SANFORD	DIRECTOR	DGA, 7920 SUNSET BLVD, 6TH FL	LOS ANGELES, CA	90046
SPILMAN, CAROL	ACTRESS	1531 CABRILLO AVE #2	VENICE, CA	90291
SPILMAN, HARRY	BASEBALL-INSTRUCTOR	RURAL ROUTE 4, BOX 36	DAWSON, GA	31742
SPINA, HAROLD	COMPOSER-CONDUCTOR	2232 VISTA DEL MAR PL	LOS ANGELES, CA	90068
SPINDLER, MARK	FOOTBALL	LIONS, 1200 FEATHERSTONE RD	PONTIAC, MI	48432
SPINELLI, MARTIN J	DIRECTOR	12 E 86TH ST	NEW YORK, NY	10028
SPINER, BRENT	ACTOR	6922 1/2 PASEO DEL SERRA	LOS ANGELES, CA	90068
SPINETTI, VICTOR	ACTOR	15 DEVONSHIRE PL, BRIGHTON	SUSSEX	ENGLAND
SPINKS, MICHAEL	BOXER-ACTOR	20284 ARCHDALE ST	DETROIT, MI	48235
SPINKS, SCIPIO	BASEBALL-SCOUT	POST OFFICE BOX 2000	SAN DIEGO, CA	92112
SPINNER, ANTHONY	WRITER-PRODUCER	1223 MANNING AVE	LOS ANGELES, CA	90024
SPINNERS, THE	VOCAL GROUP	65 W 55TH ST #6-C	NEW YORK, NY	10019
SPINOSA, JOHN	BASEBALL TRAINER	1501 W 16TH ST	INDIANAPOLIS, IN	46202
SPIRO, STANLEY JEROME	DIRECTOR	44 WOOD LN	WOODSBURGH, NY	11598
SPISAK, NEIL	COSTUME DESIGNER	261 W 22ND ST	NEW YORK, NY	10011
SPITLER, RON	FOOTBALL REFEREE	NFL, 410 PARK AVE	NEW YORK, NY	10022
SPITZ, KATHRYN	ACTRESS	1930 CENTURY PARK W #403	LOS ANGELES, CA	90067
SPITZ, MARK	SWIMMER	383 DALEHURST AVE	LOS ANGELES, CA	90077
SPIVEY, DANIEL "GOLDEN BOY"	WRESTLER	POST OFFICE BOX 105366	ATLANTA, GA	31348
SPLITTGERBER, DOUG	BODYBUILDER	NAUTILUS FITNESS CENTER		
		150 NICOLET DR	APPLETON, WI	54914

SPLITTGERBER, JEANNE	BODYBUILDER	NAUTILUS FITNESS CENTER	
		150 NICOLET DR	APPLETON, WI 54914
SPLITTORFF, PAUL	BASEBALL-ANNOUNCER	POST OFFICE BOX 419969	KANSAS CITY, MO 64141
SPOCK, DR BENJAMIN	DOCTOR	POST OFFICE BOX 1890	SAINT THOMAS, VI 00803
SPOILER, THE	WRESTLER	POST OFFICE BOX 3859	STAMFORD, CT 06905
SPOLJARIC, PAUL	BASEBALL	POST OFFICE BOX 1110	MYRTLE BEACH, SC 29578
SPONSELLER, GAIL W	CONDUCTOR	POST OFFICE BOX 2235	ORANGE, CA 92669
SPOONER, BILL	SINGER-GUITARIST	109 MINNA ST #391	SAN FRANCISCO, CA 94105
SPOONIE GEE	RAPPER-RAPWRITER	FAA, 1700 BROADWAY, 5TH FLOOR	NEW YORK, NY 10019
SPOONS	ROCK & ROLL GROUP	41 BRITAIN ST #200	TORONTO, ONT M5A 1R7 CANADA
SPOTTISWOODE, ROGER	FILM DIRECTOR	2451 HOLLY DR	LOS ANGELES, CA 90068
SPOTTS, ROGER HAMILTON	COMPOSER	1362 LONGWOOD AVE #6	LOS ANGELES, CA 90019
SPOUND, MICHAEL	ACTOR	4304 FARMDALE AVE	STUDIO CITY, CA 91604
SPRADLIN, G D	ACTOR-DIRECTOR	POST OFFICE BOX 5617	BEVERLY HILLS, CA 90213
SPRAGUE, ED	BASEBALL (3RD BASE)	CHIEFS, MAC ARTHUR STADIUM	SYRACUSE, NY 13208
SPRAGUE, ED	BASEBALL (SCOUT)	ORIOLE PARK, 333 W CAMDEN ST	BALTIMORE, MD 21201
SPRATLEY, TOM	ACTOR	POST OFFICE BOX 1105	PACIFIC PALISADES, CA 90272
SPRATT, GREG	BASEBALL TRAINER	POST OFFICE BOX 22093	GREENSBORO, NC 27420
SPRATT, JOHN M, JR	U S CONGRESSMAN	POST OFFICE BOX 350	ROCK HILL, SC 29731
SPRECHER, SUSAN	TV PRODUCER	30 ROCKEFELLER PLAZA #827	NEW YORK, NY 10112
SPRINGER, ASHTON	THEATER PRODUCER	240 W 44TH ST	NEW YORK, NY 10036
SPRINGER, DENNIS	BASEBALL	POST OFFICE BOX 28268	SAN ANTONIO, TX 78228
SPRINGER, LAURA	TALENT AGENT	65 CENTRAL PARK W	NEW YORK, NY 10023
SPRINGER, MIKE	GOLFER	POST OFFICE BOX 109601	PALM BCH GARDENS, FL 33418
SPRINGER, PHILIP	COMPOSER-CONDUCTOR	POST OFFICE BOX 1174	PACIFIC PALISADES, CA 90272
SPRINGER, REED	DIRECTOR-PRODUCER	23 ACACIA AVE	BELVEDERE, CA 94920
SPRINGER, RUSS	BASEBALL	1155 W MOUND ST	COLUMBUS, OH 43223
SPRINGER, STEVE	BASEBALL	POST OFFICE BOX 1211	NORFOLK, VA 23502
SPRINGER, STEVEN	TV PRODUCER	POST OFFICE BOX 105366	ATLANTA, GA 30348
SPRINGFIELD, DUSTY	SINGER	130 W 57TH ST #8-B	NEW YORK, NY 10019
SPRINGFIELD, RICK	SINGER-SONGWRITER	9200 SUNSET BLVD #PH-15	LOS ANGELES, CA 90069
SPRINGSTEAD, MARTY	BASEBALL UMPIRE	5 BRUCE CT	SUFFERN, NY 10901
SPRINGSTEEN, BRUCE	SINGER-SONGWRITER	9922 TOWER LN	BEVERLY HILLS, CA 90210
SPRINGSTEEN, PAMELA	ACTRESS	165 W 46TH ST #1109	NEW YORK, NY 10036
SPRINGSTEEN, R G	DIRECTOR	401 "C" AVE	CORONADO, CA 92118
SPROSTY, PAUL J	COMPOSER	2126 MANNING AVE	LOS ANGELES, CA 90025
SPROUL, ROBIN	NEWS CORRESPONDENT	ABC NEWS, 1717 DE SALES ST, NW	WASHINGTON, DC 20036
SPROULS, KEVIN	ARTIST	THE WALL STREET JOURNAL	
		22 CORTLANDT ST, 6TH FLOOR	NEW YORK, NY 10007
SPRY, ROBIN	FILM DIRECTOR	5330 DUROCHER	MONTREAL, QUE H2V 3Y1 CANADA
SPUZICH, SANDRA	GOLFER	2750 VOLUSA AVE #B	DAYTON BEACH, FL 32114
SQUALLS, THE	ROCK & ROLL GROUP	POST OFFICE BOX 1742	ATHENS, GA 30603
SQUARE, JEFFREY L	TV DIRECTOR	4750 BEDFORD AVE	BROOKLYN, NY 11235
SQUEEZE	ROCK & ROLL GROUP	SQUEEZE 85 MANAGEMENT	
		40 GREENWICH MARKET	LONDON SE10 ENGLAND
SQUIER, BILLY	SINGER-GUITARIST	DELOTE MGMT, PETER LUBIN	
		850 7TH AVE	NEW YORK, NY 10019
SQUIER, ROBERT	TV DIRECTOR	THE COMMUNICATIONS COMPANY	
		514 SEWARD SQ, SE	WASHINGTON, DC 20003
SQUIRE, ANTHONY	WRITER-PRODUCER	MLR, 200 FULHAM RD	LONDON SW10 9PN ENGLAND
SQUIRE, JANIE	ACTRESS	2929 COLORADO AVE #18	SANTA MONICA, CA 90404
SQUIRE, SYDNE	ACTRESS	8730 SUNSET BLVD #480	LOS ANGELES, CA 90069
SQUIRES, EMILY H	TV DIRECTOR	250 W 94TH ST	NEW YORK, NY 10025
SQUIRES, MIKE	BASEBALL-COACH	333 W 35TH ST	CHICAGO, IL 60616
SREBNICK, ALAN	BASKETBALL	BULLETS, 1 HARRY S TRUMAN DR	LANDOVER, MD 20785
ST CALBRE, JEANNE	TALENT AGENT	11726 SAN VICENTE BLVD #300	LOS ANGELES, CA 90049
ST CLAIRE, RANDY	BASEBALL	POST OFFICE BOX 6667	RICHMOND, VA 23230
ST CLEMENT, PAM	ACTRESS	SARABAND, 265 LIVERPOOL RD	LONDON N1 1LX ENGLAND
ST CYR, LILI	BURLESQUE	630 1/4 N PLYMOUTH BLVD	LOS ANGELES, CA 90004
ST ELWOOD, JON	ACTOR	3500 W OLIVE AVE #1400	BURBANK, CA 91505
ST GEORGE, DAVID	SINGER	MALACO RECORDS COMPANY	
		3023 W NORTHSIDE DR	JACKSON, MS 39213
ST JAMES, LARRY	ACTOR	10841 WHIPPLE ST #217	NORTH HOLLYWOOD, CA 91602
ST JAMES, PHYLLIS	ACTRESS	7001 NAGLE AVE	NORTH HOLLYWOOD, CA 91605
ST JEAN, GARRY	BASKETBALL COACH	GOLDEN STATE WARRIORS	
		OAKLAND COLISEUM ARENA	
		NIMITZ FWY & HEGENBERGER RD	OAKLAND, CA 94621
ST JOHN, ANN	DIRECTOR	DGA, 7920 SUNSET BLVD, 6TH FL	LOS ANGELES, CA 90046
ST JOHN, JILL	ACTRESS	8271 MELROSE AVE #110	LOS ANGELES, CA 90046
ST JOHN, KRISTOFF	ACTOR	CBS-TV, "YOUNG & THE RESTLESS"	
		7800 BEVERLY BLVD #3305	LOS ANGELES, CA 90036
ST JOHNS, ADELA ROGERS	WRITER	32504 PACIFIC COAST HWY	MALIBU, CA 90265
ST JOHNS, RICHARD	FILM-TV EXECUTIVE	9091 ALTO CEDRO DR	BEVERLY HILLS, CA 90210
ST LAURENT, JIM	BASEBALL SCOUT	POST OFFICE BOX 90111	ARLINGTON, TX 76004
ST MARIE, SUSAN	SINGER	POST OFFICE BOX 418	BRENTWOOD, TN 37027
ST PIERRE, MONIQUE	ACTRESS-MODEL	GARAY, 13200 CHELTENHAM DR	SHERMAN OAKS, CA 91413
STAAB, REBECCA	ACTRESS	FLICK EAST-WEST TALENT	
		CARNEGIE HALL STUDIO 110	
		881 7TH AVE	NEW YORK, NY 10019
STAAHL, JIM	ACTOR-WRITER	7611 W NORTON AVE	LOS ANGELES, CA 90046
STAATS, DE WAYNE	SPORTSCASTER	N Y YANKEES, YANKEE STADIUM	BRONX, NY 10451
STABILE, TONI	WRITER	444 E 52ND ST	NEW YORK, NY 10022
STABILIZERS, THE	ROCK & ROLL GROUP	MGMT III, 4570 ENCINO AVE	ENCINO, CA 91316
STABLER, BENJAMIN G	CONDUCTOR	3201 NEW MEXICO AVE, NW	WASHINGTON, DC 20016
STACEY, ERIC, JR	WRITER-PRODUCER	2022 1/2 N ARGYLE AVE	LOS ANGELES, CA 90068

STACK, ROBERT	ACTOR-TV HOST	321 SAINT PIERRE RD	LOS ANGELES, CA	90077
STACK, ROSEMARIE	ACTRESS	321 SAINT PIERRE RD	LOS ANGELES, CA	90077
STACY, CHERYL	GOLFER	2750 VOLUSA AVE #B	DAYTON BEACH, FL	32114
STACY, JAMES	ACTOR	478 SEVERN AVE	TAMPA, FL	33606
STACY, MICHELLE	ACTRESS	11846 VENTURA BLVD #100	STUDIO CITY, CA	91604
STACY, NEIL	ACTOR	WHITEHALL, 125 GLOUCESTER RD	LONDON SW7 4TE	ENGLAND
STADD, ARLENE	WRITER	1541 1/2 N SIERRA BONITA AVE	LOS ANGELES, CA	90046
STADER, PAUL B	FILM DIRECTOR	25266 MALIBU RD	MALIBU, CA	90265
STADLER, CRAIG	GOLFER	POST OFFICE BOX 109601	PALM BCH GARDENS, FL	33418
STADNER, SUZAN	ACTRESS-TV HOST	9300 WILSHIRE BLVD #410	BEVERLY HILLS, CA	90212
STAFF, KATHY	ACTRESS	17 MAPLE MEWS	LONDON NW6	ENGLAND
STAFFORD, DAVID HUNT	ACTOR	7266 FOUNTAIN AVE	HOLLYWOOD, CA	90046
STAFFORD, GRACE	ACTRESS	LANTZ, 1715 CARLA RIDGE	BEVERLY HILLS, CA	90212
STAFFORD, JIM	SINGER-SONGWRITER	POST OFFICE BOX 6366	BRANSON, MO	65616
STAFFORD, JO	SINGER	2339 CENTURY HILL	LOS ANGELES, CA	90067
STAFFORD, JON	ACTOR	ASHER, 644 N DOHENY DR	LOS ANGELES, CA	90069
STAFFORD, MICHELLE	ACTRESS	5750 WILSHIRE BLVD #580	LOS ANGELES, CA	90037
STAFFORD, MIKE	BASEBALL SCOUT	ATHLETICS'S, OAKLAND COLISEUM	OAKLAND, CA	94621
STAFFORD, NANCY	ACTRESS	1999 AVE OF THE STARS #2850	LOS ANGELES, CA	90067
STAFFORD, STEVE	DIRECTOR	1901 AVE OF THE STARS #1040	LOS ANGELES, CA	90067
STAFFORD, SUSAN	ACTRESS	1250 S BEVERLY GLEN BLVD #104	LOS ANGELES, CA	90067
STAFFORD, WILLIAM L	COMPOSER	4561 REEVES AVE	RIDGECREST, CA	93555
STAFFORD-CLARK, NIGEL	TV PRODUCER	ZENITH, 43-45 DORSET ST	LONDON W1	ENGLAND
STAGGERS, HARLEY	U S CONGRESSMAN	101 N COURT ST	LEWISBURG, WV	24901
STAHL, LESLEY	JOURNALIST	CBS-TV, NEWS DEPARTMENT 40TH & BRANDYWINE STS, NW	WASHINGTON, DC	20016
STAHL, STANLEY	THEATER PRODUCER	277 PARK AVE	NEW YORK, NY	10017
STAHLER, ELLIOT	TALENT AGENT	8383 WILSHIRE BLVD #923	BEVERLY HILLS, CA	90211
STAHOVIAK, SCOTT	BASEBALL	POST OFFICE BOX 48	VISALIA, CA	93279
STAIMER, MARCIA	ARTIST-ILLUSTRATOR	POST OFFICE BOX 500	WASHINGTON, DC	20044
STAIN, STEVE	SINGER-GUITARIST	1800 BAILEY DR	TORRANCE, CA	90504
STAINS, THE	ROCK & ROLL GROUP	POST OFFICE BOX 448	RADFORD, VA	24141
STAIRCASE	ROCK & ROLL GROUP	POST OFFICE BOX 11283	RICHMOND, VA	23230
STAIRS, MATT	BASEBALL	1501 W 16TH ST	INDIANAPOLIS, IN	46202
STAIRWELL	ROCK & ROLL GROUP	POST OFFICE BOX 448	RADFORD, VA	24141
STALEY, CHUCK	TV DIRECTOR	2027 N CURSON AVE	LOS ANGELES, CA	90046
STALEY, CRAIG	FILM EXECUTIVE	SOVEREIGN, 11845 W OLYMPIC BLVD	LOS ANGELES, CA	90064
STALEY, JOAN	ACTRESS	24516-B WINDSOR DR	VALENCIA, CA	91355
STALEY, JOHN	ACTOR	9229 SUNSET BLVD #311	LOS ANGELES, CA	90069
STALEY, LORA	ACTRESS	1930 CENTURY PARK W #403	LOS ANGELES, CA	90067
STALLINGS, LYNWOOD	BASEBALL SCOUT	POST OFFICE BOX 288	HOUSTON, TX	77001
STALLINGS, RICHARD	U S CONGRESSMAN	304 N 8TH ST #444	BOISE, ID	83702
STALLION	C & W GROUP	POST OFFICE BOX 1373	LEWISVILLE, TX	75067
STALLONE, FRANK	ACTOR	10668 EASTBORUNE AVE #206	LOS ANGELES, CA	90025
STALLONE, JACKIE	WRESTLING MANAGER	323 SAN VICENTE BLVD #8	SANTA MONICA, CA	90402
STALLONE, SAGE	ACTOR	9750 WANDA PARK DR	BEVERLY HILLS, CA	90210
STALLONE, SASHA	PERSONALITY	9 BEVERLY PARK	BEVERLY HILLS, CA	90210
STALLONE, SYLVESTER	ACT-WRI-DIR	9750 WANDA PARK DR	BEVERLY HILLS, CA	90210
STALMASTER, LYNN	CASTING DIRECTOR	12100 WILSHIRE BLVD #200	LOS ANGELES, CA	90025
STALVEY, DORRANCE	COMPOSER-CONDUCTOR	2145 MANNING AVE	LOS ANGELES, CA	90025
STAMELMAN, PETER	TALENT AGENT	MTA, 9320 WILSHIRE BL, 3RD FL	BEVERLY HILLS, CA	90212
STAMM, BARBARA	ACTRESS	7080 HOLLYWOOD BLVD #704	HOLLYWOOD, CA	90028
STAMOS, JOHN	ACTOR	ABC-TV, 2040 AVE OF THE STARS	LOS ANGELES, CA	90067
STAMOS, NICHOLAS PETER	DIRECTOR	1756 N VAN NESS AVE	HOLLYWOOD, CA	90028
STAMP, TERENCE	ACTOR	THE ALBANY, PICCADILLY	LONDON W1	ENGLAND
STAMPLEY, JOE	SINGER	ENCORE, 2137 ZERCHER RD	SAN ANTONIO, TX	78209
STAMPS QUARTET, THE	VOCAL GROUP	POST OFFICE BOX 17272	MEMPHIS, TN	38187
STAMS, FRANK	FOOTBALL	RAMS, 2327 W LINCOLN BLVD	ANAHEIM, CA	92801
STANDER, LIONEL	ACTOR	13176 BOCA DE CANON LN	LOS ANGELES, CA	90049
STANDING, JOHN	ACTOR	28 BROOMHOUSE RD	LONDON SW6	ENGLAND
STANDRIDGE, RICHARD	DIRECTOR	125 TRUMAN PL	CENTERPORT, NY	11721
STANFEL, DICK	FOOTBALL COACH	BEARS, 250 N WASHINGTON RD	LAKE FOREST, IL	60045
STANFILL, JAMES "POLY"	SINGER	851 OLD HICKORY BLVD #D	JACKSON, TN	38301
STANFORD, DON	BASEBALL	1155 W MOUND ST	COLUMBUS, OH	43223
STANFORD, LARRY	BASEBALL	1155 W MOUND ST	COLUMBUS, OH	43223
STANG, ARNOLD	ACTOR	POST OFFICE BOX 786	NEW CANAAN, CT	06840
STANGE, LEE	BASEBALL-COACH	FENWAY PARK, 4 YAWKEY WY	BOSTON, MA	02215
STANICEK, PETE	BASEBALL	118 CHESTNUT	PARK FOREST, IL	60466
STANICEK, STEVE	BASEBALL	118 CHESTNUT	PARK FOREST, IL	60466
STANISLAVSKY, MICHAEL	DIRECTOR	8977 SAINT IVES DR	LOS ANGELES, CA	90069
STANKIEWICZ, ANDY	BASEBALL	1155 W MOUND ST	COLUMBUS, OH	43223
STANKUS, TOM "T-BONE"	SINGER	POST OFFICE BOX 93	BROAD BROOK, CT	06016
STANKY, EDDIE	BASEBALL	2100 SPRING HILL RD	MOBILE, AL	36607
STANLEY, ALLAN	DIRECTOR	DOLPHIN, 140 E 80TH ST	NEW YORK, NY	10021
STANLEY, BILL	FOOTBALL REFEREE	NFL, 410 PARK AVE	NEW YORK, NY	10022
STANLEY, BOB	BASEBALL	WILLIAM FAIRFIELD DR	WENHAM, MA	01984
STANLEY, FLORENCE	ACTRESS	POST OFFICE BOX 48876	LOS ANGELES, CA	90048
STANLEY, FRANK	CINEMATOGRAPHER	POST OFFICE BOX 2230	HOLLYWOOD, CA	90078
STANLEY, FRED	BASEBALL-COACH	BREWERS, 201 S 46TH ST	MILWAUKEE, WI	53214
STANLEY, HARRY	VAUDEVILLIAN	THE ACTOR'S FUND HOME 155 W HUDSON AVE	ENGLEWOOD, NJ	07631
STANLEY, JAMES LEE	SINGER	POST OFFICE BOX 1556	GAINESVILLE, FL	32602
STANLEY, JIM	FOOTBALL COACH	OILERS, 6910 FANNIN ST	HOUSTON, TX	77070
STANLEY, KIM	ACTRESS	1914 HILLCREST RD	LOS ANGELES, CA	90068
STANLEY, MIKE	BASEBALL	N Y YANKEES, YANKEE STADIUM	BRONX, NY	10451

STANLEY, PAMELA	SINGER	15775 N HILLCREST RD #508	DALLAS, TX	75248
STANLEY, PAUL	DIRECTOR	15301 VENTURA BLVD #345	SHERMAN OAKS, CA	91403
STANLEY, RALPH & THE CLINCH	C & W GROUP	380 LEXINGTON AVE #1119	NEW YORK, NY	10017
STANLEY, REBECCA	ACTRESS	10413 BLOOMFIELD ST	NORTH HOLLYWOOD, CA	91602
STANOE, LEE	BASEBALL COACH	RED SOX, CHAIN O'LAKES PARK	WINTER HAVEN, FL	33880
STANS, MAURICE	POLITICIAN	211 S ORANGE GROVE BLVD	PASADENA, CA	91105
STANSFIELD, LISA	SINGER	43 HILLCREST RD	ROCKDALE	ENGLAND
STANTON, HARRY DEAN	ACTOR	14527 MULHOLLAND DR	LOS ANGELES, CA	90077
STANTON, JACK	FOOTBALL COACH	RAIDERS, 332 CENTER ST	EL SEGUNDO, CA	90245
STANTON, LEROY	BASEBALL-COACH	POST OFFICE BOX 1110	MYRTLE BEACH, SC	29578
STANTON, MIKE	BASEBALL	POST OFFICE BOX 4064	ATLANTA, GA	30302
STANTON, MOOK	SINGER	POST OFFICE BOX 1385	MERCHANTVILLE, NJ	08109
STANTON, PAUL	HOCKEY	PENGUINS, CIVIC ARENA, CENTRE AV	PITTSBURGH, PA	15219
STAPLER, ROBIN	ACTRESS	8019 1/2 MELROSE AVE #3	LOS ANGELES, CA	90046
STAPLETON, DAVE E	BASEBALL	POST OFFICE BOX 702	CLAYPOOL, AZ	85532
STAPLETON, JEAN	ACTRESS	635 PERUGIA WY	LOS ANGELES, CA	90077
STAPLETON, MAUREEN	ACTRESS	1 BOLTON DR	LENOX, MA	01240
STAPLETON, WILLIAM J	COMPOSER	POST OFFICE BOX 1168-S-5105	STUDIO CITY, CA	91604
STARBECKER, GENE	WRITER-PRODUCER	SLIGO CREEK PARKWAY	SILVER SPRING, MD	20901
STARECKI, WITOLD	FILM DIRECTOR	38 GLOUCESTER RD	LONDON W3 8PD	ENGLAND
STARETSKI, JOSEPH	TV WRITER-PRODUCER	146 FRASER AVE	SANTA MONICA, CA	90405
STARGAR, MARTIN	TV WRITER-PRODUCER	10201 W PICO BLVD #215	LOS ANGELES, CA	90036
STARGELL, TONY	FOOTBALL	N Y JETS, 1000 FULTON AVE	HEMPSTEAD, NY	11550
STARGELL, WILLIE	BASEBALL	113 ASHLEY PL	STONE MOUNTAIN, GA	30083
STARGER, MARTIN	FILM PRODUCER	21404 PACIFIC COAST HWY	MALIBU, CA	90265
STARK, BARBARA	TALENT AGENT	3500 W OLIVE AVE #1400	BURBANK, CA	91505
STARK, CHARLES M	DIRECTOR	1212-D WESTLAKE BLVD	WESTLAKE VILLAGE, CA	91361
STARK, DOUGLAS	ACTOR	FELBER, 2126 N CAHUENGA BLVD	LOS ANGELES, CA	90068
STARK, GRAHAM	ACTOR-DIRECTOR	ICM, 388-396 OXFORD ST	LONDON W1	ENGLAND
STARK, KOO	ACTRESS-MODEL	52 SHAFTESBURY AVE	LONDON W1	ENGLAND
STARK, MATT	BASEBALL	CANADIANS, 4601 ONTARIO ST	VANCOUVER, BC V5V 3H4	CANADA
STARK, NED	TV DIRECTOR	SNEDENS LANDING	PALISADES, NY	10964
STARK, PETE	U S CONGRESSMAN	22320 FOOTHILL BLVD #500	HAYWARD, CA	94541
STARK, RAY	FILM PRODUCER	232 S MAPLETON DR	LOS ANGELES, CA	90077
STARK, ROHN	FOOTBALL	POST OFFICE BOX 535000	INDIANPOLIS, IN	46253
STARK, RONALD	DIRECTOR-PRODUCER	357 N SPRUCEWOOD AVE	AGOURA, CA	91301
STARK, SHELDON	WRITER	16401 AKRON ST	PACIFIC PALISADES, CA	90272
STARK, SUSAN	FILM CRITIC	THE DETROIT NEWS		
		615 LAFAYETTE BLVD	DETROIT, MI	48231
STARK, WILBUR	DIRECTOR-PRODUCER	3712 BARHAM BLVD #C-203	LOS ANGELES, CA	90068
STARKES, JAISON	SCREENWRITER	4077 S CLOVERDALE AVE	LOS ANGELES, CA	90008
STARKEY, LEE	FASHION SHOP OWNER	PLANET ALICE, 7223 MELROSE AVE	LOS ANGELES, CA	90046
STARKIE, SHERI	ACTRESS	9165 SUNSET BLVD #202	LOS ANGELES, CA	90069
STARKS, JOHN	BASKETBALL	KNICKS, 4 PENNYLVANIA PLAZA	NEW YORK, NY	10019
STARLITE RAMBLERS	C & W GROUP	8119 WCR 48 1/2	JOHNSTOWN, CO	80534
STARNES, GALE	BASEBALL EXECUTIVE	2908 ASHLEY ST	KINGSPORT, TN	37664
STARPOINT	SOUL GROUP	POST OFFICE BOX 224	CROWNSVILLE, MD	21032
STARR, BART	FOOTBALL	7501 E MC CORMICK PKWY #220-N	SCOTTSDALE, AZ	85258
STARR, BEAU	ACTOR	301 N CANON DR #305	BEVERLY HILLS, CA	90210
STARR, BEN	TV WRITER	1506 S BENTLEY AVE	LOS ANGELES, CA	90025
STARR, BLAZE	BURLESQUE	CARROLLTOWN MALL	ELDERSBURG, MD	21784
STARR, BOB	SPORTSCASTER	WRKO-AM, 3 FENWAY PLAZA	BOSTON, MA	02215
STARR, BRENDA K	SINGER	65 W 55TH ST #6-C	NEW YORK, NY	10019
STARR, EDWIN	SINGER	1680 N VINE ST #214	HOLLYWOOD, CA	90028
STARR, ELVIS	SINGER	POST OFFICE BOX 11276	ROCHESTER, NY	14611
STARR, ERROLL	SINGER	41 BRITAIN ST #200	TORONTO, ONT M5A 1R7	CANADA
STARR, FREDDIE	ACTOR-COMEDIAN	CLIFFORD, 109 NEW BOND ST	LONDON W1	ENGLAND
STARR, GARY	WRESTLER	POST OFFICE BOX 3859	STAMFORD, CT	06905
STARR, JACK & BURNING STARR	ROCK & ROLL GROUP	POST OFFICE BOX 251	HUNTINGTON STA, NY	11761
STARR, KAY	SINGER	417 MARAWOOF DR	WOODSTOCK, IL	60098
STARR, KENNY	SINGER	POST OFFICE BOX 23470	NASHVILLE, TN	37202
STARR, LEONARD	CARTOONIST	TRIBUNE, 64 E CONCORD ST	ORLANDO, FL	32801
STARR, MANYA	TV WRITER	15 W 26TH ST	NEW YORK, NY	10010
STARR, MAURICE	SINGER	POST OFFICE BOX 82	GREAT NECK, NY	11021
STARR, NADYA	ACTRESS	1015 BELLA VISTA AVE	PASADENA, CA	91107
STARR, RINGO	ACTOR-DRUMMER	24 AVE PRINCESS GRACE	MONTE CARLO	MONACO
STARR, TONY	SINGER	POST OFFICE BOX 11276	ROCHESTER, NY	14611
STARRETT, JACK	ACT-WRI-DIR	STONE MANNERS, 9113 SUNSET BL	LOS ANGELES, CA	90069
STARRETTE, HERM	BASEBALL COACH	POST OFFICE BOX 6748	ROCKFORD, IL	61125
STARSHIP, THE	ROCK & ROLL GROUP	2400 FULTON ST	SAN FRANCISCO, CA	94118
START	ROCK & ROLL GROUP	GO NOW INC, 4108 BURBANK BLVD	BURBANK, CA	91505
STARTZ, JANE	TV PRODUCER	SCHOLASTIC PRODS, 730 BROADWAY	NEW YORK, NY	10003
STASSEN, HAROLD E	GOVERNOR	310 SALEM CHURCH RD	SUNFISH LAKE, MN	55118
STASTNY, PETER	HOCKEY	POST OFFICE BOX 504	EAST RUTHERFORD, NJ	07073
STATE LINE BAND	C & W GROUP	POST OFFICE BOX 25371	CHARLOTTE, NC	28212
STATES, THE	ROCK & ROLL GROUP	POST OFFICE BOX 6231	NORFOLK, VA	23508
STATHAKIS, JONATHAN	TV PRODUCER	ROUTE #1, BOX 354	HIGH FALLS, NY	12440
STATHIS, JIMMY	ACTOR	ATKINS, 303 S CRESCENT HEIGHTS	LOS ANGELES, CA	90048
STATLER, MARC T	DIRECTOR	9 CEDAR LANE TERR	OSSINING, NY	10562
STATLER BROTHERS, THE	VOCAL GROUP	POST OFFICE BOX 2703	STAUNTON, VA	24401
STATON, CANDI	SINGER	6 TERRACE CIR #2-A	GREAT NECK, NY	11021
STATON, DAVE	BASEBALL	STARS, 850 LAS VEGAS BLVD N	LAS VEGAS, NV	89101
STATUS QUO	ROCK & ROLL GROUP	HYDON GRANGE, HAMBLEDONE	SURREY	ENGLAND
STAUB, RUSTY	BASEBALL-ANNOUNCER	1271 3RD AVE	NEW YORK, NY	10021
STAUBACH, ROGER	FOOTBALL	6750 L B JOHNSON FREEWAY #1100	DALLAS, TX	75240

STAUDIGL, HENRY	WRITER-PRODUCER	12909 HANOVER ST	LOS ANGELES, CA	90049
STAUFFER, ANDREW K	TV WRITER-PRODUCER	170 BROADWAY #201	NEW YORK, NY	10038
STAUFFER, JACK	ACTOR	4063 WOODCLIFF RD	SHERMAN OAKS, CA	91403
STAUFFER, KEN	BASEBALL SCOUT	N Y YANKEES, YANKEE STADIUM	BRONX, NY	10451
STAUROVSKY, JASON	FOOTBALL	PATRIOTS, FOXBORO STADIUM, RT #1	FOXBORO, MA	02035
STAVEACRE, TONY	TV DIRECTOR-PRODUCER	CHANNEL VIEW BLAGDON	AVON	ENGLAND
STAVIN, MARY	ACTRESS	KOHNER, 9169 SUNSET BLVD	LOS ANGELES, CA	90069
STAVRENOS, HARRY	BASEBALL EXECUTIVE	POST OFFICE BOX 21727	SAN FRANCISCO, CA	95151
STAXX	ROCK & ROLL GROUP	POST OFFICE BOX 448	RADFORD, VA	24141
STAYDOHAR, DAVID	BASEBALL	POST OFFICE BOX 3496	DAVENPORT, IA	52808
STAYSKAL, WAYNE	CARTOONIST	POST OFFICE BOX 191	TAMPA, FL	33601
STEAD, ARTHUR W	COMPOSER	69 S HAMILTON ST	POUGHKEEPSIE, NY	12601
STEADMAN, ALISON	ACTRESS	COULSON, 37 BERWICK ST	LONDON W1V 3RF	ENGLAND
STEADMAN, JACK	FOOTBALL EXECUTIVE	CHIEFS, 1 ARROWHEAD DR	KANSAS CITY, MO	64129
STEADY B	RAPPER-RAPWRITER	POST OFFICE BOX 15591	PHILADELPHIA, PA	19131
STEAFEL, SHEILA	ACTRESS	CROUCH, 59 FRITH ST	LONDON W1	ENGLAND
STEAGALL, RED	SINGER	WILLIAMS ARTISTS MANAGEMENT		
		816 N LA CIENEGA BLVD	LOS ANGELES, CA	90069
STEAMBOAT, RICKY "THE DRAGON"	WRESTLER	STEAMBOAT'S MID-ATLANTIC GYM		
		6838 NEWELL HICKORY RD	CHARLOTTE, NC	28205
STEARNS, CLIFFORD	U S CONGRESSMAN	501 SE 26TH CT #125	OCALA, FL	32671
STEARNS, JOHN	BASEBALL-MANAGER	633 JESSAMINE ST	KNOXVILLE, TN	37917
STEARNS, MICHAEL O	DIRECTOR	5871 CHABOT RD	OAKLAND, CA	94618
STEBER, ELEANOR	SOPRANO	POST OFFICE BOX 342	PORT JEFFERSON, NY	11777
STECKEL, NED	DIRECTOR	OGLEBAY PARK	WHEELING, WV	26003
STECKLER, DOUGLAS	ACTOR-WRITER	832 S NORTON AVE	LOS ANGELES, CA	90005
STECKLER, LEN	DIRECTOR	9530 HEATHER RD	BEVERLY HILLS, CA	90210
STECKLER, RALPH	DIRECTOR-PRODUCER	14159 DICKENS ST #308	SHERMAN OAKS, CA	91423
STEED, MAGGIE	ACTRESS	MARTIN, 6-A DANBURY ST	LONDON N1 8JU	ENGLAND
STEED, RICK	BASEBALL	POST OFFICE BOX 957	DUNEDIN, FL	34697
STEEG, BRUCE	CONDUCTOR	6000 34TH AVE	HYATTSVILLE, MD	20782
STEEL, AMY	ACTRESS-FASH DESIGN	POST OFFICE BOX 5617	BEVERLY HILLS, CA	90213
STEEL, DAWN	FILM EXECUTIVE	COLUMBIA PICTURES		
		COLUMBIA PLAZA	BURBANK, CA	91505
STEEL, MARK	ARTIST	551 TREMONT ST #301	BOSTON, MA	02116
STEEL, ROBERT	DIRECTOR	DGA, 110 W 57TH ST	NEW YORK, NY	10019
STEEL, TERRY	TV DIRECTOR	142 WARDOUR ST, 5TH FLOOR	LONDON W1V 3AU	ENGLAND
STEEL BREEZE	ROCK & ROLL GROUP	151 S EL CAMINO DR	BEVERLY HILLS, CA	90212
STEELE, BARBARA	ACTRESS	442 S BEDFORD DR	BEVERLY HILLS, CA	90212
STEELE, BILL	ACTOR	79 HORATIO ST	NEW YORK, NY	10014
STEELE, CYNTHIA	ACTRESS	1539 SAWTELLE BLVD #10	LOS ANGELES, CA	90025
STEELE, DON	RADIO PERSONALITY	SEE - STEELE, REAL DON		
STEELE, GEORGE "THE ANIMAL"	WRESTLER	POST OFFICE BOX 3859	STAMFORD, CT	06905
STEELE, JACK	FOOTBALL EXECUTIVE	VIKINGS, 9520 VIKING DR	EDEN PRAIRIE, MN	55344
STEELE, JON	COMPOSER	19481 ROSITA ST	TARZANA, CA	91356
STEELE, KITTY	ACTRESS	319 AVE "C"	NEW YORK, NY	10009
STEELE, MARTY	BASEBALL EXECUTIVE	POST OFFICE BOX 22093	GREENSBORO, NC	27420
STEELE, REAL DON	RADIO PERSONALITY	KODJ-FM, 6121 SUNSET BLVD	LOS ANGELES, CA	90028
STEELE, RICHARD S	BOXING REFEREE	5009 LONG VIEW DR	LAS VEGAS, NV	89120
STEELE, ROBERT GANTT	ARTIST	14 WILMONT ST	SAN FRANCISCO, CA	94115
STEELE, SAUNDRA	SINGER	PICALIC, 1204 16TH AVE S	NASHVILLE, TN	37212
STEELE, TERRY	SINGER	10100 SANTA MONICA BLVD #1600	LOS ANGELES, CA	90067
STEELEYE SPAN	ROCK & ROLL GROUP	ALLIED AGENCY & MANAGEMENT		
		76 TOTTENHAM COURT RD	LONDON W10 9PA	ENGLAND
STEELS, JAMES	BASEBALL	1268 ESTES DR	SANTA MARIA, CA	93454
STEELSMITH, MARY	ACTRESS	5122 W 9TH ST	LOS ANGELES, CA	90036
STEEN, NANCY	ACTRESS-WRITER	5127 GREENBUSH AVE	SHERMAN OAKS, CA	91423
STEEN, THOMAS	HOCKEY	JETS, 15-1430 MAROONS RD	WINNIPEG, MAN R3G 0L5	CANADA
STEENBURGEN, MARY	ACTRESS	ICM, 8899 BEVERLY BLVD	LOS ANGELES, CA	90048
STEENERSON, ROBERT	DIRECTOR	6025 W 86TH PL	LOS ANGELES, CA	90045
STEENSLAND, MELANIE	DIRECTOR	3952 BORA BORA WY	MARINA DEL REY, CA	90292
STEERE, CLIFTON	ACTOR	305 W 45TH ST	NEW YORK, NY	10036
STEFANO, JOHN	ACTOR	135 N KENWOOD ST	BURBANK, CA	91505
STEFANO, JOHN	SCREENWRITER	1801 AVE OF THE STARS #1250	LOS ANGELES, CA	90067
STEFANO, JOSEPH	WRITER-PRODUCER	10216 CIELO DR	BEVERLY HILLS, CA	90210
STEFANSKI, MIKE	BASEBALL	POST OFFICE BOX 855	BELOIT, WI	53511
STEFFE, EDWIN	ACTOR	145 W 55TH ST	NEW YORK, NY	10019
STEFFENS, MARK	BASEBALL	POST OFFICE BOX 1721	SPARTANBURG, SC	29304
STEHNEY, MICHAEL	DIRECTOR	25051 COSTEAU	LAGUNA HILLS, CA	92653
STEIBEL, WARREN	DIRECTOR-PRODUCER	150 E 35TH ST	NEW YORK, NY	10022
STEIG, SUSANNA	ARTIST	149 FORSHAY AVE	PLEASANTVILLE, NY	10570
STEIGER, JOEL	TV WRITER-PROUCER	ICM, 8899 BEVERLY BLVD	LOS ANGELES, CA	90048
STEIGER, PAULA ELLIS	ACTRESS	6324 ZUMIREZ DR	MALIBU, CA	90265
STEIGER, ROD	ACTOR	6324 ZUMIREZ DR	MALIBU, CA	90265
STEIN, ABBEY	COMEDIENNE	EAI, 2211 INDUSTRIAL BLVD	SARASOTA, FL	33580
STEIN, BENJAMIN	WRITER	7251 PACIFIC VIEW DR	LOS ANGELES, CA	90068
STEIN, BILL	BASEBALL	POST OFFICE BOX 1295	CLINTON, IA	52733
STEIN, CRAIG	BASEBALL EXECUTIVE	POST OFFICE BOX 15050	READING, PA	19612
STEIN, HERB	BASEBALL SCOUT	TWINS, 501 CHICAGO AVE S	MINNEAPOLIS, MN	55415
STEIN, HERBERT D	TV DIRECTOR	4233 GLENALBYN DR	LOS ANGELES, CA	90065
STEIN, HERMAN	COMPOSER	3787 AMESBURY RD	LOS ANGELES, CA	90027
STEIN, JAMES RONALD	WRITER-PRODUCER	2765 BOTTLEBRUSH DR	LOS ANGELES, CA	90024
STEIN, JEFFREY A	FILM WRITER-PRODUCER	2870 BENEDICT CANYON DR	BEVERLY HILLS, CA	90210
STEIN, JEFFREY L	SCREENWRITER	8955 BEVERLY BLVD	WEST HOLLYWOOD, CA	90048
STEIN, JOHN	BASEBALL EXECUTIVE	1325 S MAIN #229	SALT LAKE CITY, UT	84115

STEIN, JOSEPH	PLAYWRIGHT	1130 PARK AVE	NEW YORK, NY 10028
STEIN, LEONARD D	COMPOSER	2635 CARMEN CREST DR	LOS ANGELES, CA 90068
STEIN, MAX	TV DIRECTOR	5307 WILKINSON AVE #6	NORTH HOLLYWOOD, CA 91607
STEIN, NICHOLAS A	TV DIRECTOR-PRODUCER	2426 HOLLYRIDGE DR	HOLLYWOOD, CA 90068
STEIN, ROBERT A	BASKETBALL EXECUTIVE	TIMBERWOLVES, 600 1ST AVE N	MINNEAPOLIS, MN 55403
STEIN, RON	FILM DIRECTOR	3518 W CAHUENGA BLVD	HOLLYWOOD, CA 90068
STEIN, RONALD	COMPOSER-CONDUCTOR	POST OFFICE BOX 2037	EVERGREEN, CO 80439
STEIN, SEYMOUR	RECORD EXECUTIVE	SIRE RECORDS COMPANY	
		75 ROCKEFELLER PLAZA	NEW YORK, NY 10019
STEINBACH, TERRY	BASEBALL	ATHLETICS'S, OAKLAND COLISEUM	OAKLAND, CA 94621
STEINBERG, ALBERT	CONDUCTOR	11918 KIOWA AVE #301	LOS ANGELES, CA 90049
STEINBERG, ANNE "HONEY"	SINGER	POST OFFICE BOX 11321 (FLAGLER)	MIAMI, FL 33101
STEINBERG, BARRY	FILM DIRECTOR	3819 SEAHORN DR	MALIBU, CA 90265
STEINBERG, BERNICE	TV EXECUTIVE	ANI-LIVE FILM SERVICE	
		45 W 45TH ST	NEW YORK, NY 10036
STEINBERG, DAVID	COMED-ACT-WRI-DIR	WM MORRIS, 1350 AVE OF AMERICAS	NEW YORK, NY 10019
STEINBERG, DICK	FOOTBALL EXECUTIVE	N Y JETS, 1000 FULTON AVE	HEMPSTEAD, NY 11550
STEINBERG, GAIL	TV PRODUCER	"DONAHUE", 30 ROCKEFELLER PLZ	NEW YORK, NY 10112
STEINBERG, HARRIET	SCREENWRITER	WORDS, PHRASES, ETC	
		4 WASHINGTON SQUARE VILLAGE	NEW YORK, NY 10012
STEINBERG, JAMES	ARTIST	17 TUDOR ST	CAMBRIDGE, MA 02139
STEINBERG, JEFFREY E	MUSIC ARRANGER	POST OFFICE BOX 121464	NASHVILLE, TN 37212
STEINBERG, MELVIN A	LT GOVERNOR	STATE HOUSE BUILDING	ANNAPOLIS, MD 21401
STEINBERG, NORMAN	WRITER-PRODUCER	2800 SEATTLE DR	LOS ANGELES, CA 90046
STEINBERG, SARI	TV DIRECTOR	2517 MAPLE AVE	MANHATTAN BEACH, CA 90266
STEINBERG, STEVEN J	WRITER-PRODUCER	POST OFFICE BOX 373	NEW YORK, NY 11374
STEINBERG, ZIGGY	TV WRITER	2038 BENEDICT CANYON DR	BEVERLY HILLS, CA 90210
STEINBERGER, BERT	TV EXECUTIVE	5460 WHITE OAK AVE #E-132	ENCINO, CA 91316
STEINBRENNER, GEORGE	BASEBALL	N Y YANKEES, YANKEE STADIUM	BRONX, NY 10451
STEINBRENNER, JOAN Z	BASEBALL EXECUTIVE	N Y YANKEES, YANKEE STADIUM	BRONX, NY 10451
STEINEM, GLORIA	AUTHORESS	118 W 73RD ST	NEW YORK, NY 10021
STEINER, FRANK A	ARTIST	1355 N HIGHWAY DR	SAINT LOUIS, MO 63026
STEINER, FREDERICK	COMPOSER-CONDUCTOR	4455 GABLE DR	ENCINO, CA 91316
STEINER, GITTA	COMPOSER-PIANIST	71-81 244TH ST	DOUGLASTON, NY 11362
STEINER, JOAN	ARTIST	PLATTEKILL RD	GREENVILLE, NY 12083
STEINFELD, JAKE	ACTOR-BODYBUILDER	2112 ROSCOMARE RD	LOS ANGELES, CA 90077
STEINHAUER, STERRI	GOLFER	2750 VOLUSA AVE #B	DAYTON BEACH, FL 32114
STEINHAUSER, BERT	DIRECTOR	126 E 36TH ST	NEW YORK, NY 10016
STEINKE, DR GREG	COMPOSER-CONDUCTOR	UNIVERSITY OF IDAHO	
		SCHOOL OF MUSIC	MOSCOW, ID 83843
STEINKUHLER, DEAN	FOOTBALL	OILERS, 6910 FANNIN ST	HOUSTON, TX 77070
STEINMETZ, DENNIS	TV DIRECTOR	10546 DEERING AVE	CHATSWORTH, CA 91311
STEINMETZ, EARL	BASEBALL	POST OFFICE BOX 507	DURHAM, NC 27702
STEINMETZ, JOHN	DIRECTOR	315 W 70TH ST	NEW YORK, NY 10023
STEIS, BILL	ACTOR	2943 ESCONDIDO DR	MALIBU, CA 90265
STELA, JOSE	BASEBALL	POST OFFICE BOX 3496	DAVENPORT, IA 52808
STELFOX, SHIRLEY	ACTRESS	AIM, 5 DENMARK ST	LONDON WC2H 8LP ENGLAND
STELLAR UNIT	VOCAL GROUP	POST OFFICE BOX 39	LAS VEGAS, NV 89101
STELLMACK, KATHRYN	TV PRODUCER	440 E 88TH ST	NEW YORK, NY 10128
STELMASZEK, RICK	BASEBALL COACH	TWINS, 501 CHICAGO AVE S	MINNEAPOLIS, MN 55415
STENBERG, DON	ATTORNEY GENERAL	STATE CAPITOL BUILDING	LINCOLN, NE 68509
STENGEL, RICHARD	WRITER-EDITOR	TIME/TIME & LIFE BLDG	
		ROCKEFELLER CENTER	NEW YORK, NY 10020
STENGER, FRED	FILM DIRECTOR	651-A QUEEN ST	TORONTO ONT M5V 1V3 CANADA
STENHOLM, CHARLES	U S CONGRESSMAN	POST OFFICE BOX 1237	STAMFORD, TX 79553
STEPH, RODNEY	BASEBALL	POST OFFICE BOX 2001	CEDAR RAPIDS, IA 52406
STEPHAN, ROBERT T	ATTORNEY GENERAL	STATE CAPITOL BUILDING	TOPEKA, KS 66617
STEPHAN, TODD	BASEBALL	500 NORTON ST	ROCHESTER, NY 14621
STEPHEN, BEVERLY	COLUMNIST	N Y DAILY NEWS, 220 E 42ND ST	NEW YORK, NY 10017
STEPHEN, SCOTT	FOOTBALL	PACKERS, 1265 LOMBARDI AVE	GREEN BAY, WI 54307
STEPHENS, CARL	BASEBALL	RURAL ROUTE 1, BOX 134	CHARLESTON, TN 37310
STEPHENS, GARN	ACTRESS	4538 WORSTER AVE	STUDIO CITY, CA 91604
STEPHENS, JAMES	ACTOR-DIRECTOR	822 S ROBERTSON BLVD #200	LOS ANGELES, CA 90035
STEPHENS, JAMES ANTHONY	ACTOR	10000 RIVERSIDE DR #6	TOLUCA LAKE, CA 91602
STEPHENS, JAMES, III	COMEDIAN	151 S EL CAMINO DR	BEVERLY HILLS, CA 90212
STEPHENS, JERRY	BASEBALL SCOUT	POST OFFICE BOX 419969	KANSAS CITY, MO 64141
STEPHENS, JOHN	FOOTBALL	PATRIOTS, FOXBORO STADIUM, RT #1	FOXBORO, MA 02035
STEPHENS, JOHN	PRODUCER	MCA/UNIVERSAL STUDIOS, INC	
		100 UNIVERSAL CITY PLAZA #473	UNIVERSAL CITY, CA 91608
STEPHENS, JOHN D	COMPOSER	11782 GAGER ST	SYLMAR, CA 91342
STEPHENS, JOHN G	DIRECTOR	9300 WILSHIRE BLVD #410	BEVERLY HILLS, CA 90212
STEPHENS, JOHN M	DIRECTOR	10950 VENTURA BLVD	STUDIO CITY, CA 91604
STEPHENS, JOHN M	TV DIRECTOR	6744 HILLPARK DR	LOS ANGELES, CA 90068
STEPHENS, LARAINE	ACTRESS	1900 AVE OF THE STARS #2270	LOS ANGELES, CA 90067
STEPHENS, RAY	BASEBALL	POST OFFICE BOX 3449	SCRANTON, PA 18505
STEPHENS, ROBERT	ACTOR	FILM RIGHTS, 483 SOUTHBANK HOUSE	
		BLACK PRINCE RD	
		ALBERT EMBANKMENT	LONDON SE1 7SJ ENGLAND
STEPHENS, ROD	FOOTBALL	SEAHAWKS, 11220 NE 53RD ST	KIRKLAND, WA 98033
STEPHENS, RON	BASEBALL	CANADIANS, 4601 ONTARIO ST	VANCOUVER, BC V5V 3H4 CANADA
STEPHENS, RONNIE	ACTOR	DAWSON, 47 COURTFIELD RD #9	LONDON SW7 4DB ENGLAND
STEPHENS, STAN	GOVERNOR	STATE CAPITOL BUILDING	HELENA, MT 59620
STEPHENSON, JAN	GOLFER	6300 RIDGLEA #1118	FORT WORTH, TX 76116
STEPHENSON, JOE	BASEBALL SCOUT	FENWAY PARK, 4 YAWKEY WY	BOSTON, MA 02215
STEPHENSON, KENT	FOOTBALL COACH	SEAHAWKS, 11220 NE 53RD ST	KIRKLAND, WA 98033

STEPHENSON, PAMELA	ACTRESS	REID, 32 GALENA RD	LONDON W6 OLT ENGLAND
STEPHENSON, PHIL	BASEBALL	604 N BROAD	GUTHRIE, OK 73044
STEPHENSON, RON	CASTING DIRECTOR	MCA/UNIVERSAL STUDIOS, INC	
		100 UNIVERSAL CITY PLAZA	
		BUILDING #463-106	UNIVERSAL CITY, CA 91608
STEPHENSON, SKIP	COMEDIAN-ACTOR	3920 SUNNY OAK RD	SHERMAN OAKS, CA 91403
STEPIEN, CHRISTOPHER L	TV DIRECTOR-PRODUCER	6540 JONATHON ST	DEARBORN, MI 48126
STEPNOSKI, MARK	FOOTBALL	COWBOYS, 1 COWBOYS PARKWAY	IRVING, TX 75063
STEPPE BROTHERS, THE	C & W GROUP	BURCHAN, 129 TOBLER LN	KNOXVILLE, TN 37919
STERLING, AVA	TV WRITER-PRODUCER	185 W HOUSTON ST #2-E	NEW YORK, NY 10014
STERLING, DAVID-MICHAEL	ACTOR	4966 FRANKLIN AVE #1	LOS ANGELES, CA 90027
STERLING, DONALD T	BASKETBALL EXECUTIVE	CLIPPERS, 3939 S FIGUEROA ST	LOS ANGELES, CA 90037
STERLING, JOHN	SPORTSCASTER	N Y YANKEES, YANKEE STADIUM	BRONX, NY 10451
STERLING, PHILIP	ACTOR	4114 BENEDICT CANYON DR	SHERMAN OAKS, CA 91423
STERLING, ROBERT	ACTOR	121 S BENTLEY AVE	LOS ANGELES, CA 90049
STERLING, RONNIE	COMEDIAN	CLOUSHER, 193 KONHAUS RD	MECHANICSBURG, PA 17055
STERLING, TISHA	ACTRESS	BDP, 10637 BURBANK BLVD	NORTH HOLLYWOOD, CA 91601
STERN, BARRY	DIRECTOR-PRODUCER	8744 SKYLINE DR	LOS ANGELES, CA 90046
STERN, DANIEL	ACTOR	5657 WILSHIRE BLVD #290	LOS ANGELES, CA 90036
STERN, DAVID	DIRECTOR	ASSOCIATES & TOBACK	
		6532 SUNSET BLVD	HOLLYWOOD, CA 90028
STERN, DAVID B	TV DIRECTOR-PRODUCER	225 W 34TH ST #1905	NEW YORK, NY 10122
STERN, DAVID J	BASKETBALL EXECUTIVE	NBA, OLYMPIC TOWER, 645 5TH AVE	NEW YORK, NY 10022
STERN, DAVID M	TV WRITER	ICM, 8899 BEVERLY BLVD	LOS ANGELES, CA 90048
STERN, DONALD H	DIRECTOR	11582 LONGACRE RD	GRANADA HILLS, CA 91344
STERN, ELLIOT	TV WRITER	3021 1/2 LAUREL CANYON BLVD	STUDIO CITY, CA 91604
STERN, HOWARD	TV-RADIO PERSONALITY	WXRK, 600 MADISON AVE, 4TH FL	NEW YORK, NY 10022
STERN, ISAAC	VIOLINIST	211 CENTRAL PARK W	NEW YORK, NY 10024
STERN, LEONARD	WRITER-PRODUCER	1709 ANGELO DR	BEVERLY HILLS, CA 90210
STERN, PETER R	DIRECTOR	DGA, 110 W 57TH ST	NEW YORK, NY 10019
STERN, RICHARD A	DIRECTOR	DGA, 7920 SUNSET BLVD, 6TH FL	LOS ANGELES, CA 90046
STERN, RONNIE	HOCKEY	POST OFFICE BOX 1540, STA "M"	CALGARY, ALTA T2P 3BP CANADA
STERN, RUTH	ACTRESS-SINGER	1 LINCOLN PLAZA	NEW YORK, NY 10023
STERN, SANDOR	WRITER-PRODUCER	474 PECK DR	BEVERLY HILLS, CA 90212
STERN, STEVEN HILLIARD	WRITER-PRODUCER	4321 CLEAR VALLEY DR	ENCINO, CA 91436
STERNBERG, SCOTT	TV WRITER-PRODUCER	15030 MARBLE DR	SHERMAN OAKS, CA 91403
STERNHAGEN, FRANCES	ACTRESS	152 SUTTON MANOR RD	NEW ROCHELLE, NY 10805
STERNIN, ROBERT	TV WRITER	6538 COSTELLO AVE	VAN NUYS, CA 91401
STERRETT, JANE	ARTIST	160 5TH AVE	NEW YORK, NY 10010
STERRITT, DORREESE	ACTRESS	10850 RIVERSIDE DR #505	NORTH HOLLYWOOD, CA 91602
STETSASONIC	RAP GROUP-RAPWRITERS	FAA, 1700 BROADWAY, 5TH FLOOR	NEW YORK, NY 10019
STETTIN, MONTE DAVID	TV WRITER	1231 9TH ST #4	SANTA MONICA, CA 90401
STEVENS, ANDREW	ACTOR-WRITER-PROD	9612 ARBY DR	BEVERLY HILLS, CA 90210
STEVENS, APRIL	SINGER	19530 SUPERIOR ST	NORTHRIDGE, CA 91324
STEVENS, ART	DIRECTOR	500 S BUENA VISTA ST	BURBANK, CA 91521
STEVENS, BEVERLY	MODEL	10430 WILSHIRE BLVD #2006	LOS ANGELES, CA 90024
STEVENS, BRINKE	ACTRESS-MODEL	8033 SUNSET BLVD #557	HOLLYWOOD, CA 90046
STEVENS, CAT	SINGER-SONGWRITER	SEE - ISLAM, YUSUF	
STEVENS, CLARK	ACTOR	DON SCHWARTZ, 8749 SUNSET BLVD	LOS ANGELES, CA 90069
STEVENS, CONNIE	ACTRESS-SINGER	9551 CHEROKEE LN	BEVERLY HILLS, CA 90210
STEVENS, CRAIG	ACTOR	25 CENTRAL PARK W	NEW YORK, NY 10023
STEVENS, DANIEL R	WRITER	O'CONNOR, 4654 BECK AVE	STUDIO CITY, CA 91602
STEVENS, DAVE	ARTIST	DARK HORSE, 10956 SE MAIN	MILWAUKIE, OR 97222
STEVENS, DAVE	BASEBALL	POST OFFICE DRAWER 1207	ZEBULON, NC 27597
STEVENS, DORIT	MODEL-ACTRESS	STEVENS, 11524 AMANDA DR	STUDIO CITY, CA 91604
STEVENS, EDMOND MICHAEL	SCREENWRITER	6924 OAKWOOD AVE	LOS ANGELES, CA 90036
STEVENS, EVEN	GUITARIST	POST OFFICE BOX 140110	NASHVILLE, TN 37214
STEVENS, FRAN	ACTRESS	209 W 80TH ST	NEW YORK, NY 10024
STEVENS, GARY	FOOTBALL COACH	DOLPHINS, 2269 NW 199TH ST	MIAMI, FL 33056
STEVENS, GEORGE, JR	DIRECTOR-PRODUCER	THE AMERICAN FILM INSTITUTE	
		JOHN F KENNEDY CENTER	WASHINGTON, DC 20566
STEVENS, HERB	ACTOR	10845 LINDBROOK DR #3	LOS ANGELES, CA 90024
STEVENS, JEAN	SINGER-ACTRESS	8467 BEVERLY BLVD #100	LOS ANGELES, CA 90048
STEVENS, JEREMY	SCREENWRITER	613 EL MEDIO AVE	PACIFIC PALISADES, CA 90272
STEVENS, JOEL	TALENT AGENT	STEVENS, 11524 AMANDA DR	STUDIO CITY, CA 91604
STEVENS, JOHN PAUL	SUPREME COURT JUDGE	1 1ST ST, NE	WASHINGTON, DC 20543
STEVENS, JOSEPH	BASEBALL EXECUTIVE	FENWAY PARK, 4 YAWKEY WY	BOSTON, MA 02215
STEVENS, K G "KATHY"	HANDWRITING EXPERT	4375 W DESERT INN #D-122	LAS VEGAS, NV 89102
STEVENS, K T	ACTRESS	147 GRETNA GREEN WY	LOS ANGELES, CA 90069
STEVENS, KAYE	ACTRESS	WEBB, 7500 DEVISTA DR	LOS ANGELES, CA 90046
STEVENS, KEVIN	HOCKEY	PENGUINS, CIVIC ARENA, CENTRE AV	PITTSBURGH, PA 15219
STEVENS, LEE	BASEBALL	POST OFFICE BOX 2000	ANAHEIM, CA 92803
STEVENS, LESLIE	WRI-DIR-PROD	POST OFFICE BOX 4220	CULVER CITY, CA 90231
STEVENS, MARK	ACTOR	13348 ROBLAR PL	SHERMAN OAKS, CA 91403
STEVENS, MATT	BASEBALL	POST OFFICE BOX 15050	READING, PA 19612
STEVENS, MORTON	COMPOSER-CONDUCTOR	16883 SEVERO PL	ENCINO, CA 91436
STEVENS, RAY	SINGER-SONGWRITER	1708 GRAND AVE	NASHVILLE, TN 37212
STEVENS, RAY "THE CRIPPLER"	WRESTLER	2965 SNELLING AVE N	ROSEVILLE, MN 55113
STEVENS, RISE	MEZZO SOPRANO	930 5TH AVE	NEW YORK, NY 10021
STEVENS, ROBERT	DIRECTOR	DGA, 110 W 57TH ST	NEW YORK, NY 10019
STEVENS, ROGER L	THEATER PRODUCER	1501 BROADWAY	NEW YORK, NY 10036
STEVENS, RON	ACTOR-COMEDIAN	9665 WILSHIRE BLVD #400	BEVERLY HILLS, CA 90212
STEVENS, SCOTT	BASEBALL	300 STADIUM WY	DAVENPORT, FL 33837
STEVENS, SCOTT	HOCKEY	BLUES, 5700 OAKLAND AVE	SAINT LOUIS, MO 63110
STEVENS, SHADOE	RADIO-TV PERSONALITY	10430 WILSHIRE BLVD #2006	LOS ANGELES, CA 90024

STEVENS, SHAKIN'	SINGER	822 S ROBERTSON BLVD #200	LOS ANGELES, CA	90035
STEVENS, SHAWN	ACTOR	10055 RIVERSIDE DR	TOLUCA LAKE, CA	91602
STEVENS, STELLA	ACTRESS-DIRECTOR	2180 COLDWATER CANYON DR	BEVERLY HILLS, CA	90210
STEVENS, TED	U S SENATOR	109 MAIN ST	KETCHIKAN, AK	99901
STEVENS, TONY	CHOREOGRAPHER	370 LEXINGTON AVE #707	NEW YORK, NY	10017
STEVENS, WARREN	ACTOR	14155 MAGNOLIA BLVD #44	SHERMAN OAKS, CA	91403
STEVENS, WESLEY	ACTRESS	5967 W 3RD ST #205	LOS ANGELES, CA	90036
STEVENS & GRDNIC	COMEDY DUO	2029 CENTURY PARK E #1670	LOS ANGELES, CA	90067
STEVENSON, ADLAI, III	U S SENATOR	231 S LA SALLE ST	CHICAGO, IL	60604
STEVENSON, B W	SINGER	NBA, 8517 SHAGROCK LN	DALLAS, TX	75238
STEVENSON, BOBBI	ACTRESS	10845 LINDBROOK DR #3	LOS ANGELES, CA	90024
STEVENSON, JOY	TALENT AGENT	3500 W OLIVE AVE #1400	BURBANK, CA	91505
STEVENSON, MC LEAN	ACTOR-WRITER	151 S EL CAMINO DR	BEVERLY HILLS, CA	90212
STEVENSON, MICHAEL A	FILM EDITOR	ACE, 1041 N FORMOSA AVE	WEST HOLLYWOOD, CA	90046
STEVENSON, PARKER	ACTOR	4875 LOUISE AVE	ENCINO, CA	91316
STEWART, ALANA	ACTRESS	12824 EVANSTON ST	LOS ANGELES, CA	90049
STEWART, ANDY	BASEBALL	300 STADIUM WY	DAVENPORT, FL	33837
STEWART, ART	BASEBALL SCOUT	POST OFFICE BOX 419969	KANSAS CITY, MO	64141
STEWART, BOB	TV PRODUCER	1717 N HIGHLAND AVE #807	HOLLYWOOD, CA	90028
STEWART, BRADY	BASEBALL	300 STADIUM WY	DAVENPORT, FL	33837
STEWART, BRUCE	TV WRITER	LEMON, 24 POTTERY, HOLLAND PK	LONDON W11 4LZ	ENGLAND
STEWART, CARL	BASEBALL	POST OFFICE BOX 4669	CHARLESTON, WV	25304
STEWART, CATHERINE MARY	ACTRESS	500 BELOIT AVE	LOS ANGELES, CA	90049
STEWART, CHARLOTTE	ACTRESS	KJAR, 10653 RIVERSIDE DR	TOLUCA LAKE, CA	91602
STEWART, CHUCK	SINGER	HOT, 306 W CHURCH ST	HORSESHOE BEND, AR	72512
STEWART, DALE	DIRECTOR	DCA PRODS, 285 MADISON AVE	NEW YORK, NY	10017
STEWART, DAVE	BASEBALL	ATHLETICS'S, OAKLAND COLISEUM	OAKLAND, CA	94621
STEWART, DAVID	TALENT AGENT	1888 CENTURY PARK E #622	LOS ANGELES, CA	90067
STEWART, DEREK	DIRECTOR-PRODUCER	15 BEACONSFIELD RD	LONDON NW10 2LE	ENGLAND
STEWART, DONALD E	DIRECTOR	151 S EL CAMINO DR	BEVERLY HILLS, CA	90212
STEWART, DONALD L	SCREENWRITER	2500 4TH ST #5	SANTA MONICA, CA	90405
STEWART, DOUGLAS DAY	SCREENWRITER	8955 BEVERLY BLVD	WEST HOLLYWOOD, CA	90048
STEWART, DOUGLAS S	DIRECTOR	14150 HARTSOOK ST	SHERMAN OAKS, CA	91423
STEWART, DOUGLASS M, JR	TV DIRECTOR	2522 NELSON AVE #B	REDONDO BEACH, CA	90278
STEWART, FRED MUSTARD	SCREENWRITER	POST OFFICE BOX 7	CORNWALL BRIDGE, CT	06754
STEWART, GARY	SINGER	POST OFFICE BOX 25371	CHARLOTTE, NC	28212
STEWART, GEORGE	FOOTBALL COACH	STEELERS, 300 STADIUM CIR	PITTSBURGH, PA	15212
STEWART, JACKIE	AUTO RACER	24 ROUTE DE DIVONNE	1260 NYON	SWITZERLAND
STEWART, JAMES	ACTOR-DIRECTOR	918 N ROXBURY DR	BEVERLY HILLS, CA	90210
STEWART, JAMES O	CONDUCTOR	1953 REDESDALE AVE	LOS ANGELES, CA	90039
STEWART, JEFF	SINGER	213 N MAIN ST	ANN ARBOR, MI	48104
STEWART, JERMAINE	SINGER-SONGWRITER	4-A LAUCESTON PL, KENSINGTON	LONDON W8 5RL	ENGLAND
STEWART, JIM	BASEBALL SCOUT	REDS, 100 RIVERFRONT STADIUM	CINCINNATI, OH	45202
STEWART, JOHN	SINGER-SONGWRITER	7247 BIRDVIEW AVE	MALIBU, CA	90265
STEWART, LARRY	DIRECTOR	9300 WILSHIRE BLVD #410	BEVERLY HILLS, CA	90212
STEWART, LIZA	COSTUME DESIGNER	13949 VENTURA BLVD #309	SHERMAN OAKS, CA	91423
STEWART, MARLENE	COSTUME DESIGNER	13949 VENTURA BLVD #309	SHERMAN OAKS, CA	91423
STEWART, MICHAEL	FOOTBALL	RAMS, 2327 W LINCOLN BLVD	ANAHEIM, CA	92801
STEWART, PATRICK	ACTOR	ICM, 8899 BEVERLY BLVD	LOS ANGELES, CA	90048
STEWART, PAULA	ACTRESS	6310 SAN VICENTE BLVD #407	LOS ANGELES, CA	90048
STEWART, PAYNE	GOLFER	POST OFFICE BOX 109601	PALM BCH GARDENS, FL	33418
STEWART, PEGGY	ACTRESS	11139 HORTENSE ST	NORTH HOLLYWOOD, CA	91602
STEWART, REDD	SINGER	TESSIER, 505 CANTON PASS	MADISON, TN	37115
STEWART, RICHARD J	TV WRITER	11726 SAN VICENTE BLVD #300	LOS ANGELES, CA	90049
STEWART, ROBERT BANKS	TV PRODUCER	BBC-TV, 56 WOOD LN	LONDON W12 7RJ	ENGLAND
STEWART, ROD	SINGER-SONGWRITER	391 N CAROLWOOD DR	LOS ANGELES, CA	90077
STEWART, SAMMY	BASEBALL	107 SCENIC VIEW DR	SWANNANOA, NC	28778
STEWART, SUSAN MISTY	TV WRITER	2049 CENTURY PARK E #1320	LOS ANGELES, CA	90067
STEWART, SYLVESTER	SINGER-SONGWRITER	SEE - STONE, SLY		
STEWART, WILLIAM GLADSTONE	TV DIRECTOR-PRODUCER	REGENT PRODUCTIONS, THE MEWS		
		6 PUTNEY COMMON	LONDON SW15 1HL	ENGLAND
STEWART, WILMOT I	ACTRESS	942 N GARDNER ST #206	LOS ANGELES, CA	90046
STEWART & STEWART	VOCAL DUO	5625 "O" STREET BLDG #7	LINCOLN, NE	68510
STEWER, DANIEL J	COMPOSER-CONDUCTOR	17401 SE 39TH ST #89	CAMAS, WA	98607
STICKNEY, DOROTHY	ACTRESS	13 E 94TH ST	NEW YORK, NY	10028
STICKNEY, HENRY	BASEBALL EXECUTIVE	POST OFFICE BOX 30160	SAN BERNARDINO, CA	92413
STICKNEY, PHYLLIS	ACTRESS	15301 VENTURA BLVD #345	SHERMAN OAKS, CA	91403
STIDHAM, PHIL	BASEBALL	POST OFFICE BOX 2785	LAKELAND, FL	33806
STIEB, DAVE	BASEBALL	SKYDOME, 300 BREMMER BL #3200	TORONTO, ONT M5V 3B3	CANADA
STIEGLER, JACK	ACT-SING-WRI	7010 BIRDVIEW AVE	MALIBU, CA	90265
STIENER, SALLY	CASTING DIRECTOR	1438 N GOWER ST	LOS ANGELES, CA	90028
STIERS, DAVID OGDEN	ACTOR-DIRECTOR	SMITH, 121 N SAN VICENTE BLVD	BEVERLY HILLS, CA	90211
STIERWALT, WILLIAM L	DIRECTOR	22227 CAPULIN CT	WOODLAND HILLS, CA	91364
STIGWOOD, ROBERT	FILM-RECORD PROD	1775 BROADWAY	NEW YORK, NY	10023
STILES, LYNN	FOOTBALL COACH	S F 49ERS, 4949 CENTENNIAL BL	SANTA CLARA, CA	95054
STILL, KEN	GOLFER	PGA SENIORS, 112 T P C BLVD	PONTE VEDRA BEACH, FL	32082
STILLE, ROBIN	ACTRESS	3627 VALLEY MEADOW RD	SHERMAN OAKS, CA	91403
STILLER, JERRY	COMED-ACT-WRI	118 RIVERSIDE DR #5-A	NEW YORK, NY	10024
STILLMAN, WHIT	DIRECTOR	WM MORRIS, 1350 AVE OF AMERICAS	NEW YORK, NY	10019
STILLMAN, WINSLOW	SINGER-GUITARIST	2824 AZALEA PL	NASHVILLE, TN	37204
STILLS, STEPHEN	SINGER-SONGWRITER	CAA, 9830 WILSHIRE BLVD	BEVERLY HILLS, CA	90212
STILLWELL, KURT	BASEBALL	POST OFFICE BOX 2000	SAN DIEGO, CA	92112
STILWELL, DIANE	ACTRESS	9620 HIGHLAND GORGE RD	BEVERLY HILLS, CA	90210
STIMPSON, VIOLA KATES	ACTRESS	522 N ROSSMORE AVE #303	LOS ANGELES, CA	90004
STIMSON, KEN	ACTOR	10249 TUJUNGA CYN BLVD #16	TUJUNGA, CA	91042

Name	Occupation	Address	City/State	Zip/Country
STING	ACT-SING-COMP	2 THE GROVE, HIGHGATE VILLAGE	LONDON N16	ENGLAND
STING	WRESTLER	POST OFFICE BOX 105366	ATLANTA, GA	31348
STINGERS, THE	ROCK & ROLL GROUP	9514-9 RESEDA BLVD #429	NORTHRIDGE, CA	91324
STINGLEY, DARRYL	FOOTBALL-EXECUTIVE	PATRIOTS, FOXBORO STADIUM, RT #1	FOXBORO, MA	02035
STINNETT, KELLY	BASEBALL	2501 ALLEN AVE, SE	CANTON, OH	44707
STINSON, JOSEPH C	SCREENWRITER	11726 SAN VICENTE BLVD #300	LOS ANGELES, CA	90049
STINSON, LEMUEL	FOOTBALL	BEARS, 250 N WASHINGTON RD	LAKE FOREST, IL	60045
STIPANICH, MICHAEL	TALENT AGENT	11726 SAN VICENTE BLVD #300	LOS ANGELES, CA	90049
STIPO, JERRY	BASEBALL EXECUTIVE	POST OFFICE BOX 10031	BAKERSFIELD, CA	93389
STIRDIVANT, MARC	WRITER-PRODUCER	8532 DA COSTA ST	DOWNEY, CA	90240
STIRLING, LINDA	ACTRESS	1800 N HIGHLAND AVE #405	LOS ANGELES, CA	90028
STIRLING, SCOTTY	BASKETBALL	KINGS, 1 SPORTS PARKWAY	SACRAMENTO, CA	95834
STIRNWEIS, SHANNON	ARTIST	31 FAWN PL	WILTON, CT	06897
STITT, MILAN	TV WRITER	460 W 24TH ST #14-B	NEW YORK, NY	10011
STITZEL, ROBERT DEAN	FILM WRITER-DIRECTOR	4167 KLUMP AVE	NORTH HOLLYWOOD, CA	91602
STIVENDER, EDWARD	CONDUCTOR	170 W 81ST ST #3-A	NEW YORK, NY	10024
STIVERS, BARBARA	TV WRITER	1883 RISING GLEN RD	LOS ANGELES, CA	90069
STOCK, BARBARA	ACTRESS-SINGER	13421 CHELTENHAM DR	SHERMAN OAKS, CA	91423
STOCK, MIKE	FOOTBALL COACH	BENGALS, 200 RIVERFRONT STADIUM	CINCINNATI, OH	45202
STOCK, WES	BASEBALL-COACH	ATHLETICS'S, OAKLAND COLISEUM	OAKLAND, CA	94621
STOCKDALE, GARY W	COMPOSER	450 SAN VICENTE BLVD #104	SANTA MONICA, CA	90402
STOCKER, KEVIN	BASEBALL	POST OFFICE BOX 10336	CLEARWATER, FL	34617
STOCKHAUSEN, KARLHEINZ	COMPOSER	STOCKHAUSEN-VERLAG	5067 KURTEN	GERMANY
STOCKSTILL, JOHN	BASEBALL SCOUT	1060 W ADDISON ST	CHICAGO, IL	60613
STOCKTON, DAVE	GOLFER	POST OFFICE BOX 38	KEYSTONE, CO	80435
STOCKTON, JOHN	BASKETBALL	5 TRIAD CENTER #500	SALT LAKE CITY, UT	84180
STOCKWELL, DEAN	ACTOR	535 CONCHA LOMA DR	CARPINTERIA, CA	93013
STOCKWELL, GUY	ACTOR	4924 CAHUENGA BLVD	NORTH HOLLYWOOD, CA	91601
STOCKWELL, JEREMY L	ACTOR	307 W 82ND ST	NEW YORK, NY	10024
STOCKWELL, JOHN	ACTOR	1524 N ORANGE GROVE AVE	LOS ANGELES, CA	90046
STODDARD, BARRY	TV DIRECTOR	10447 MELVIN AVE	NORTHRIDGE, CA	91326
STODDARD, BOB	BASEBALL	15760 SUNNYSIDE AVE	MORGAN HILL, CA	95037
STODDARD, BRANDON	FILM-TV EXECUTIVE	240 N GLENROY AVE	LOS ANGELES, CA	90049
STODDARD, TIM	BASEBALL	3928 E BUTTERNUT ST	EAST CHICAGO, IN	46312
STOECKEL, JIM	BASEBALL SCOUT	1000 ELYSIAN PARK DR	LOS ANGELES, CA	90012
STOFFEL, RONALD A	CONDUCTOR	1109 PEDEN ST #A	HOUSTON, TX	77006
STOKES, FRED	FOOTBALL	POST OFFICE BOX 17247 (DULLES)	WASHINGTON, DC	20041
STOKES, LOUIS	U S CONGRESSMAN	2140 LEE RD #211	CLEVELAND HEIGHTS, OH	44118
STOKES, RODNEY	FOOTBALL COACH	BUCCANEERS, 1 BUCCANEER PL	TAMPA, FL	33607
STOKEY, MICHAEL	ACTOR-PRODUCER	11924 RIVERSIDE DR #107	NORTH HOLLYWOOD, CA	91607
STOKOE, JOHN	BASEBALL SCOUT	ORIOLE PARK, 333 W CAMDEN ST	BALTIMORE, MD	21201
STOLLER, BRENDA	TV-NEWS WRITER	155 W 85TH ST #5-B	NEW YORK, NY	10024
STOLLMACK, FRED	TV DIRECTOR	53 STONEBRIDGE RD	MONTCLAIR, NJ	07042
STOLOFF, VICTOR	TV WRITER-DIRECTOR	400 W 43RD ST #45-S	NEW YORK, NY	10036
STOLPER, DARRYL	ACTOR	950 KAGAWA ST	PACIFIC PALISADES, CA	90272
STOLTZ, ERIC	ACTOR	2320 VISTA MADERA	SANTA BARBARA, CA	93101
STOLTZMAN, RICHARD	CLARINETIST	201 W 54TH ST #4-C	NEW YORK, NY	10019
STOMPERS, THE	ROCK & ROLL GROUP	25 HUNTINGTON AVE #420	BOSTON, MA	02116
STONE, ALLEN	TV WRITER	9000 SUNSET BLVD #1200	LOS ANGELES, CA	90069
STONE, ANDREW	DIRECTOR-PRODUCER	10478 WYTON DR	LOS ANGELES, CA	90024
STONE, CHARLES M, JR	TV DIRECTOR	2720 CLARKE'S LANDING DR	OAKTON, VA	22124
STONE, CHRISTOPHER	ACTOR-WRITER	23035 CUMORAH CREST DR	WOODLAND HILLS, CA	91364
STONE, CORDELIA	DIRECTOR	2006 N HOBART BLVD	LOS ANGELES, CA	90027
STONE, DICK	DIRECTOR	381 PARK AVE S #612	NEW YORK, NY	10016
STONE, DOUG	SINGER-SONGWRITER	HALLMARK, 15 MUSIC SQUARE W	NASHVILLE, TN	37203
STONE, DWIGHT	FOOTBALL	STEELERS, 300 STADIUM CIR	PITTSBURGH, PA	15212
STONE, ERIC	BASEBALL	POST OFFICE BOX 3452	KINSTON, NC	28502
STONE, EZRA	ACTOR-DIRECTOR	STONE MEADOWS FARM		
		BOX 1-D, BUCKS COUNTY	NEWTOWN, PA	18940
STONE, FRED	DIRECTOR	5325 NEWCASTLE AVE #229	ENCINO, CA	91316
STONE, HAROLD F, JR	DIRECTOR	306 E GREENTREE LN	LAKE MARY, FL	32746
STONE, IRVING	SCREENWRITER	1360 SUMMITRIDGE PL	BEVERLY HILLS, CA	90210
STONE, JERICHO	SCREENWRITER	8955 BEVERLY BLVD	WEST HOLLYWOOD, CA	90048
STONE, JON	WRITER-PRODUCER	1 SHERMAN SQ #PH-A	NEW YORK, NY	10023
STONE, MARIANNE	ACTRESS	46 ABBEY RD	LONDON NW8	ENGLAND
STONE, MARSHALL	BASEBALL EXECUTIVE	POST OFFICE BOX 1742	PALM SPRINGS, CA	92263
STONE, MARSHALL A	CINEMATOGRAPHER	STEPPINGSTONE FARM	SHERMAN, CT	06784
STONE, MARTIN	BASEBALL EXECUTIVE	5999 E VAN BUREN ST	PHOENIX, AZ	85008
STONE, NOREEN	TV WRITER	12309 9TH HELENA DR	LOS ANGELES, CA	90049
STONE, OLIVER	FILM WRITER-DIRECTOR	321 HAMPTON DR #105	VENICE, CA	90291
STONE, PERRY	RADIO PERSONALITY	KSJO-FM, 1420 KNOLL CIR	SAN JOSE, CA	95112
STONE, PETER	TV WRITER	ICM, 8899 BEVERLY BLVD	LOS ANGELES, CA	90048
STONE, PETER H	PLAYWRIGHT	160 E 71ST ST	NEW YORK, NY	10021
STONE, PHILIP	ACTOR	LONDON MGT, 235-241 REGENT ST	LONDON W1R 4PH	ENGLAND
STONE, RAE	TV PRODUCER	500 E 77TH ST	NEW YORK, NY	10021
STONE, RICHARD	COMPOSER	20720 SCHOENBORN	CANOGA PARK, CA	91306
STONE, SLY	SINGER-SONGWRITER	6255 SUNSET BLVD #200	HOLLYWOOD, CA	90028
STONE, TIM	TALENT AGENT	STONE MANNERS, 9113 SUNSET BL	LOS ANGELES, CA	90069
STONE, TRUDE	ACTRESS	372 CENTRAL PARK W	NEW YORK, NY	10025
STONE, VIRGINIA	DIRECTOR-PRODUCER	4248 VIA MARINA #83	MARINA DEL REY, CA	90292
STONE OAK	C & W GROUP	OBA, 5601 ODANA RD	MADISON, WI	53719
STONEBOLT	VOCAL GROUP	1 ALEXANDER ST #400	VANCOUVER, BC V6A 1B2	CANADA
STONEBREAKER, MIKE	FOOTBALL	BEARS, 250 N WASHINGTON RD	LAKE FOREST, IL	60045
STONECIPHER, ERIC	BASEBALL	POST OFFICE BOX 1295	CLINTON, IA	52733

STONEMAN, BILL	BASEBALL EXECUTIVE	EXPOS, 4545 DE COUBERTIN AVE	MONTREAL, QUE H1V 3P2 ..... CANADA
STONEMAN, RONI	SINGER	TAYLOR, 2401 12TH AVE S	NASHVILLE, TN 37204
STONEMAN FAMILY, THE	VOCAL GROUP	48 MUSIC SQUARE E	NASHVILLE, TN 37203
STONEMANS, THE	C & W GROUP	ACE, 3407 GREEN RIDGE DR	NASHVILLE, TN 37214
STONER, SHERRI	ACTRESS	9229 SUNSET BLVD #311	LOS ANGELES, CA 90069
STOOKEY, NOEL PAUL	SINGER-SONGWRITER	NEWORLD, ROUTE #175	SOUTH BLUE HILL, ME 04615
STOPAK, CHARLES	TV DIRECTOR	715 HORTON DR	SILVER SPRING, MD 20902
STOPPARD, TOM	DIRECTOR-WRITER	PETERS, FRASER & DUNLOP, LTD	
		5TH FLOOR, THE CHAMBERS	
		CHELSEA HARBOUR, LOT RD	LONDON SW10 OXF ..... ENGLAND
STORCH, ARTHUR	DIRECTOR	JEFFERSON TOWERS	SYRACUSE, NY 13203
STORCH, LARRY	ACTOR	336 W END AVE #17-F	NEW YORK, NY 10023
STOREY, BARRON	ARTIST	852 UNION ST	SAN FRANCISCO, CA 94133
STORM, GALE	ACTRESS-SINGER	308 N SYCAMORE AVE #104	LOS ANGELES, CA 90036
STORM, HOWARD	ACT-WRI-DIR	6224 WARNER DR	LOS ANGELES, CA 90048
STORM, JIM	ACTOR-SINGER	CBS-TV, "THE BOLD & BEAUTIFUL"	
		7800 BEVERLY BLVD #3371	LOS ANGELES, CA 90036
STORM, MICHAEL	ACTOR	108 BELLAIR DR	DOBBS FERRY, NY 10522
STORM, WARREN	SINGER	MEAUX, 566 BROCK ST	HOUSTON, TX 77023
STORY, LIZ	SINGER	POST OFFICE BOX 9532	MADISON, WI 53715
STORY, MARK	DIRECTOR	DGA, 110 W 57TH ST	NEW YORK, NY 10019
STOSSEL, JOHN	BROADCAST JOURNALIST	211 CENTRAL PARK W #15-K	NEW YORK, NY 10024
STOTTLEMYRE, MEL, JR	BASEBALL	SKYDOME, 300 BREMMER BL #3200	TORONTO, ONT M5V 3B3 ..... CANADA
STOTTLEMYRE, MEL, SR	BASEBALL-COACH	METS, 126TH ST & ROOSEVELT AVE	FLUSHING, NY 11368
STOTTLEMYRE, TODD	BASEBALL	1187 CLAYS TRAIL	OLDSMAR, FL 34677
STOUDEMIERE, DAVID	WRESTLER	POST OFFICE BOX 3859	STAMFORD, CT 06905
STOUDT, CLIFF	FOOTBALL	COWBOYS, 1 COWBOYS PARKWAY	IRVING, TX 75063
STOUFFER, MARK	WRI-DIR-PROD	POST OFFICE BOX 2638	SANTA BARBARA, CA 93120
STOUT, DAVID G	COMPOSER	7522 JAMIESON AVE	RESEDA, CA 91335
STOVALL, COUNT	ACTOR	330 W 42ND ST #104	NEW YORK, NY 10036
STOVALL, DAROND	BASEBALL	POST OFFICE BOX 3783	SAVANNAH, GA 31414
STOVER, MATT	FOOTBALL	BROWNS, 80 1ST ST	BEREA, OH 44017
STOWE, TYRONNE	FOOTBALL	POST OFFICE BOX 888	PHOENIX, AZ 85001
STOWELL, BRAD	BASEBALL	POST OFFICE BOX 882	MADISON, WI 53701
STOYANOV, MICHAEL	ACTOR	NBC-TV, 3000 W ALAMEDA AVE	BURBANK, CA 91523
STRACHAN, ALAN	FILM EDITOR	14 CLIFFORD GROVE, ASHFORD	MIDDLESEX ..... ENGLAND
STRACHAN, BRUCE	ARTIST	224 E 11TH ST #24	NEW YORK, NY 10003
STRADLING, HARRY, JR	CINEMATOGRAPHER	7715 SUNSET BLVD #150	LOS ANGELES, CA 90046
STRAIGHT, BEATRICE	ACTRESS	30 NORFOLK RD	SOUTHFIELD, MA 01259
STRAIGHT A'S	ROCK & ROLL GROUP	POST OFFICE BOX 448	RADFORD, VA 24141
STRAIN, JOE	BASEBALL SCOUT	S F GIANTS, CANDLESTICK PARK	SAN FRANICSCO, CA 94124
STRAIT, GEORGE	SINGER-SONGWRITER	ERV WOOLSEY MANAGEMENT	
		1000 18TH AVE S	NASHVILLE, TN 37212
STRALKA, BILL	ACTOR	5600 ROCK CREEK RD	AGOURA HILLS, CA 91301
STRAM, HANK	FOOTBALL	194 BELLE TERRE BLVD	COVINGTON, LA 70483
STRAND, MANNY	CONDUCTOR	11045 CALIFA ST	NORTH HOLLYWOOD, CA 91601
STRAND, PETER	DIRECTOR	520 N MICHIGAN AVE #1026	CHICAGO, IL 60611
STRAND, ROBIN	ACTOR	4118 ELMER	NORTH HOLLYWOOD, CA 91607
STRANG, JOHN P	DIRECTOR	35 145 S FAIRFAX AVE #310 PL	LOS ANGELES, CA 10036
STRANGE, CURTIS	GOLFER	POST OFFICE BOX 109601	PALM BCH GARDENS, FL 33418
STRANGE, DON	BASEBALL	POST OFFICE BOX 16683	GREENVILLE, SC 29606
STRANGE, DOUG	BASEBALL	CUBS, 2ND & RIVERSIDE DR	DES MOINES, IA 50309
STRANGE, KEITH	BASEBALL	1090 N EUCLID AVE	SARASOTA, FL 34237
STRANGE ADVANCE	ROCK & ROLL GROUP	41 BRITAIN ST #200	TORONTO, ONT M5A 1R7 ..... CANADA
STRANGER	ROCK & ROLL GROUP	POST OFFICE BOX 7877 (CPS)	ORLANDO, FL 32854
STRANGIS, GREGORY	TV WRITER-PRODUCER	14057 MARGATE ST	VAN NUYS, CA 91401
STRANGIS, SAM J	TV DIRECTOR-PRODUCER	232 S BENTLEY AVE	LOS ANGELES, CA 90049
STRANGLERS, THE	VOCAL GROUP	FAST FORWARD, 110 W 57TH ST	NEW YORK, NY 10019
STRASBERG, ANDY	BASEBALL EXECUTIVE	POST OFFICE BOX 2000	SAN DIEGO, CA 92112
STRASBERG, SUSAN	ACTRESS	135 CENTRAL PARK W	NEW YORK, NY 10023
STRASFOGEL, IAN	OPERA-STAGE DIRECTOR	915 W END AVE	NEW YORK, NY 10025
STRASSBURG, ROBERT	CONDUCTOR	5157 FRANKLIN AVE	LOS ANGELES, CA 90027
STRASSER, ROBIN	ACTRESS	9301 WILSHIRE BLVD #312	BEVERLY HILLS, CA 90210
STRASSMAN, DAVID	VENTRILOQUIST	LIGHT, 901 BRINGHAM AVE	LOS ANGELES, CA 90049
STRASSMAN, MARCIA	ACTRESS	1111 LAS PULGAS PL	PACIFIC PALISADES, CA 90272
STRASSNER, NORMAN H	TV DIRECTOR	1950 N NORMANDIE AVE	LOS ANGELES, CA 90027
STRATAS, TERESA	SOPRANO	MET OPERA, 186 S BROADWAY	NEW YORK, NY 10023
STRATTON, GIL	SPORTSCASTER	4227 COLFAX AVE #B	STUDIO CITY, CA 91604
STRATTON, WILLIAM R	TV WRITER	9000 SUNSET BLVD #1200	LOS ANGELES, CA 90069
STRAUBING, HAROLD	WRITER	10722 BELMAR AVE	NORTHRIDGE, CA 91326
STRAULI, CHRISTOPHER	ACTOR	4 MONTROSE AVE, CRAIGHALL PARK	JOHANNESBURG 2196 ..... SO AFRICA
STRAUS, BARNARD	THEATER PRODUCER	LFR & CO, 666 5TH AVE	NEW YORK, NY 10019
STRAUSS, BOB	FILM CRITIC	POST OFFICE BOX 51400	LOS ANGELES, CA 90051
STRAUSS, HERBERT H	DIRECTOR	30 PARK AVE	NEW YORK, NY 10016
STRAUSS, JOHN L	CONDUCTOR	1134 N OGDEN DR #5	LOS ANGELES, CA 90046
STRAUSS, JOSEPH	TV DIRECTOR	5545 OSTIN AVE	WOODLAND HILLS, CA 91367
STRAUSS, JULIO	BASEBALL	POST OFFICE DRAWER 1207	ZEBULON, NC 27597
STRAUSS, PAUL	CONDUCTOR	36 RUS DU TRONE, BTE 45	1050 BRUSSELS ..... BELGIUM
STRAUSS, PETER	ACTOR	1900 AVE OF THE STARS #1425	LOS ANGELES, CA 90067
STRAUSS, ROBERT	U S AMBASADOR	AMERICAN EMBASSY MOSCOW	APO AE, NY 09721
STRAUTHERS, THOMAS	FOOTBALL	VIKINGS, 9520 VIKING DR	EDEN PRAIRIE, MN 55344
STRAW DOGS, THE	ROCK & ROLL GROUP	118 RIVERWAY ST #7	BOSTON, MA 02215
STRAWBERRY, DARRYL	BASEBALL	1000 ELYSIAN PARK DR	LOS ANGELES, CA 90012
STRAWBERRY ALARM CLOCK	ROCK & ROLL GROUP	SPCA, 205 MC CLELLAN	CARSON CITY, CA 89704
STRAWN, C J	PRODUCTION DESIGNER	GERARD, 2918 ALTA VISTA DR	NEWPORT BEACH, CA 92660

STRAWTHER, LARRY	TV WRITER	8180 MANITOBA ST #215	PLAYA DEL REY, CA	90293
STRAY CATS, THE	ROCK & ROLL TRIO	POST OFFICE BOX 38246	HOLLYWOOD, CA	90038
STREBECK, RICK	BASEBALL	POST OFFICE BOX 2769	HUNTSVILLE, AL	35804
STREEP, MERYL	ACTRESS	CAA, 9830 WILSHIRE BLVD	BEVERLY HILLS, CA	90212
STREET, GREG	BASEBALL UMPIRE	POST OFFICE BOX 716	PLAINVILLE, CT	06062
STREET, REBECCA	ACTRESS	291 AMALFI DR	SANTA MONICA, CA	90402
STREET-PORTER, JANET	TV PRODUCER	BBC-TV, 56 WOOD LN	LONDON W12 7RJ	ENGLAND
STREETLIFE	ROCK & ROLL GROUP	NBA, 2605 NORTHRIDGE DR	GARLAND, TX	75043
STREETS, THE	ROCK & ROLL GROUP	ICM, 8899 BEVERLY BLVD	LOS ANGELES, CA	90048
STREICH, FRANK	TV DIRECTOR-PRODUCER	25 CENTRAL PARK W #6-J	NEW YORK, NY	10023
STREICH, NINA R	TV PRODUCER-EDITOR	23 E 10TH ST #4-E	NEW YORK, NY	10003
STREISAND, BARBRA	SING-ACT-DIR	301 N CAROLWOOD DR	LOS ANGELES, CA	90077
STRELITZ, LEN	BASEBALL SCOUT	POST OFFICE BOX 90111	ARLINGTON, TX	76004
STRICK	C & W GROUP	POST OFFICE BOX 25371	CHARLOTTE, NC	28212
STRICK, JOSEPH	FILM DIRECTOR	266 RIVER RD	GRANDVIEW, NY	10960
STRICK, WESLEY E	SCREENWRITER	555 W 57TH ST #1230	NEW YORK, NY	10019
STRICKLAND, AMZIE	ACTRESS	1329 N OGDEN DR	LOS ANGELES, CA	90046
STRICKLAND, CHAD	BASEBALL	POST OFFICE BOX 464	APPLETON, WI	54912
STRICKLAND, FRED	FOOTBALL	RAMS, 2327 W LINCOLN BLVD	ANAHEIM, CA	92801
STRICKLAND, GAIL	ACTRESS	7280 CAVERNA DR	LOS ANGELES, CA	90068
STRICKLAND, RICK	BASEBALL	ALBANY YANKEES, HERITAGE PARK	ALBANY, NY	12211
STRICKLAND, ROD	BASKETBALL	600 E MARKET ST #102	SAN ANTONIO, TX	78205
STRICKLER, JERRY	ACTOR	496-A HUDSON ST #E-17	NEW YORK, NY	10014
STRICKLIN, DEBRA	ACTRESS	606 N LARCHMONT BLVD #309	LOS ANGELES, CA	90004
STRICKLYN, RAY	ACTOR	852 N GENESEE AVE	LOS ANGELES, CA	90046
STRIDE, JOHN	ACTOR	HATTON, 29 ROEHAMPTON GATE	LONDON SW15 5JR	ENGLAND
STRIGLOS, BILL	ACTOR	3642 FREDONIA DR	HOLLYWOOD, CA	90068
STRIKE, GEORGE	BASEBALL EXECUTIVE	REDS, 100 RIVERFRONT STADIUM	CINCINNATI, OH	45202
STRINGER, HOWARD	WRI-DIR-PROD	186 RIVERSIDE DR	NEW YORK, NY	10024
STRINGER, MICHAEL	PRODUCTION DESIGNER	20 SOUTH ST, E HOATHLY, LEWES	EAST SUSSEX BN8 6DS	ENGLAND
STRINGER, NICK	ACTOR	33 PARK RD	KENILWORTH CV8 2GF	ENGLAND
STRINGER, ROBERT W	DIRECTOR	SOUTH MOUNTAIN PASS	GARRISON, NY	10524
STRINGFIELD, SHERRY	ACTRESS	CBS-TV, "THE GUIDING LIGHT"		
		222 E 44TH ST	NEW YORK, NY	10017
STRIS, MARVIN A	ACTOR	4614 MALEZA PL	TARZANA, CA	91356
STRITCH, ELAINE	ACTRESS	822 S ROBERTSON BLVD #200	LOS ANGELES, CA	90035
STROBEL, CRAIG	BASEBALL TRAINER	POST OFFICE BOX 10336	CLEARWATER, FL	34617
STROCK, HERBERT	WRITER-PRODUCER	1630 HILTS AVE #205	LOS ANGELES, CA	90024
STRODE, LESTER	BASEBALL COACH	POST OFFICE BOX 4488	WINSTON-SALEM, NC	27115
STRODE, WOODY	ACTOR	POST OFFICE BOX 501	GLENDORA, CA	91740
STROHMEYER, DONNA J	WRITER	14854 TAMARIX DR	HACIENDA HEIGHTS, CA	91745
STROLLER, LOU	PRODUCER	MCA/UNIVERSAL STUDIOS, INC		
		100 UNIVERSAL CITY PLAZA #507	UNIVERSAL CITY, CA	91608
STROM, BRENT	BASEBALL-COACH	POST OFFICE BOX 27045	TUCSON, AZ	85726
STROMBERG, GARY	FILM PRODUCER	4461 BABCOCK AVE	STUDIO CITY, CA	91604
STROME, EDWIN F	ACTOR	POST OFFICE BOX 623	NEW YORK, NY	10001
STROMQUIST, ROBERT W, JR	COMPOSER	7036 AURA AVE	RESEDA, CA	91335
STROMSOE, FRED	DIRECTOR	430 TUMBLE CREEK LN	FALLBROOK, CA	92028
STRONG, BRENDA	ACTRESS	5750 WILSHIRE BLVD #512	LOS ANGELES, CA	90036
STRONG, GLEN	BASEBALL EXECUTIVE	2501 ALLEN AVE, SE	CANTON, OH	44707
STRONG, JOHN C, III	WRITER-PRODUCER	8278 SUNSET BLVD #401	LOS ANGELES, CA	90046
STRONG, PATRICK	ACT-WRI-DIR	722 HILL ST #A	SANTA MONICA, CA	90405
STROOCK, GLORIA	ACTRESS	STERN, 4 LIGHTHOUSE ST #14	MARINA DEL REY, CA	90292
STROUD, DON	ACTOR	15301 VENTURA BLVD #345	SHERMAN OAKS, CA	91403
STROUD, MARIE L	TV WRITER-TALENT AGT	119 W 57TH ST	NEW YORK, NY	10019
STROUD, RICHARD	TV DIRECTOR	DAISH, 83 EASTBOURNE MEWS	LONDON W2 6LQ	ENGLAND
STROUD, STEVE	ARTIST	1031 HOWE AVE	SHELTON, CT	06468
STROUSE, CHARLES	COMPOSER	171 W 57TH ST	NEW YORK, NY	10019
STRUBLE, EDGAR M	MUSIC ARRANGER	333 INDIAN LAKE RD	HENDERSONVILLE, TN	37075
STRUCK, ARTHUR	DIRECTOR	70 BELDEN HILL RD	WILTON, CT	06897
STRUNK, JUD	SINGER-MUSICIAN	38 MUSIC SQUARE E #300	NASHVILLE, TN	37203
STRUTHERS, SALLY	ACTRESS	9229 SUNSET BLVD #520	LOS ANGELES, CA	90069
STRYDOM, GARY	BODYBUILDER	POST OFFICE BOX 2612	PEARLAND, TX	77588
STRYKER, ED	BASEBALL	POST OFFICE BOX 2887	VERO BEACH, FL	32961
STRYPER	ROCK & ROLL GROUP	225 W 57TH ST #300	NEW YORK, NY	10019
STRYZINSKI, DAN	FOOTBALL	STEELERS, 300 STADIUM CIR	PITTSBURGH, PA	15212
STRZELCZYK, JUSTIN	FOOTBALL	STEELERS, 300 STADIUM CIR	PITTSBURGH, PA	15212
STUART, ANNA	ACTRESS	NBC-TV, "ANOTHER WORLD"		
		1268 E 14TH ST	BROOKLYN, NY	11230
STUART, BARBARA	ACTRESS	12747 ADDISON ST	NORTH HOLLYWOOD, CA	91607
STUART, CASSIE	ACTRESS	MARTIN, 6-A DANBURY ST	LONDON N1 8JU	ENGLAND
STUART, DOUGLAS	BASEBALL SCOUT	REDS, 100 RIVERFRONT STADIUM	CINCINNATI, OH	45202
STUART, GLORIA	ACTRESS	884 S BUNDY DR	LOS ANGELES, CA	90049
STUART, JASON	ACTOR-COMEDIAN	8228 SUNSET BLVD #212	LOS ANGELES, CA	90046
STUART, JOHN T, SR	ACTOR	18224 SUGARMAN ST	TARZANA, CA	91356
STUART, JOSEPH	TV DIRECTOR-PRODUCER	360 CONCORD DR	MAYWOOD, NJ	07607
STUART, LEN	EXEC-TV PRODUCER	10100 SANTA MONICA BLVD #348	LOS ANGELES, CA	90067
STUART, LYNNE	TV EXECUTIVE	1 ASTOR PLZ, 1515 BROADWAY #3802	NEW YORK, NY	10036
STUART, MARIE	ACTRESS	65 W 90TH ST	NEW YORK, NY	10024
STUART, MARTY	SINGER-SONGWRITER	38 MUSIC SQ E #218	NASHVILLE, TN	37203
STUART, MARY ELLEN	ACTRESS	CBS-TV, "AS THE WORLD TURNS"		
		524 W 57TH ST #5330	NEW YORK, NY	10019
STUART, MAXINE	ACTRESS	9744 WILSHIRE BLVD #308	BEVERLY HILLS, CA	90212
STUART, MEL	WRI-DIR-PROD	11508 THURSTON CIR	LOS ANGELES, CA	90049
STUART, PATRICK	ACTOR	ABC-TV, "ALL MY CHILDREN"		

		320 W 66TH ST	NEW YORK, NY	10023
STUART, PETER Z	DIRECTOR	DGA, 7920 SUNSET BLVD, 6TH FL	LOS ANGELES, CA	90046
STUART, REX	FOOTBALL REFEREE	NFL, 410 PARK AVE	NEW YORK, NY	10022
STUART, ROY	ACTOR	4948 RADFORD AVE	NORTH HOLLYWOOD, CA	91607
STUART, WALKER	FILM DIRECTOR	TOWN LN	AMAGANSETT, NY	11930
STUART, WAYNE G	TV WRITER-PRODUCER	57 PARK BLVD	MALVERNE, NY	11565
STUART, WILLIAM L	WRITER	11692 CHENAULT ST	LOS ANGELES, CA	90049
STUARTI, ENZO	SINGER	2 BALFOUR LN	SCOTCH PLAINS, NJ	07076
STUBBS, DANIEL	FOOTBALL	COWBOYS, 1 COWBOYS PARKWAY	IRVING, TX	75063
STUBBS, FRANKLIN	BASEBALL	BREWERS, 201 S 46TH ST	MILWAUKEE, WI	53214
STUBBS, IMOGEN	ACTRESS	HEATH, PARAMOUNT HOUSE		
		162-170 WARDOUR ST	LONDON W1V 3AT	ENGLAND
STUCKER, LANNY	TV DIRECTOR	68-17 DOUGLASTON PARKWAY	DOUGLASTON, NY	11362
STUCKEY, AMY	ACTRESS	6310 SAN VICENTE BLVD #407	LOS ANGELES, CA	90048
STUCKMANN, EUGENE	ACTOR	159 E 55TH ST	NEW YORK, NY	10022
STUDDS, GERRY	U S CONGRESSMAN	146 MAIN ST	HYANNIS, MA	02601
STUDER, HAL	ACTOR	6 W 77TH ST	NEW YORK, NY	10024
STUDLEY, CHUCK	FOOTBALL COACH	BENGALS, 200 RIVERFRONT STADIUM	CINCINNATI, OH	45202
STUDSTILL, PAT	ACTOR	301 N CANON DR #305	BEVERLY HILLS, CA	90210
STUDY, LOMAX	ACTOR	440 DENSLOW AVE	LOS ANGELES, CA	90049
STUFF	ROCK & ROLL GROUP	YANDOLINO, 1775 BROADWAY	NEW YORK, NY	10019
STUMP, BOB	U S CONGRESSMAN	211 CANNON HOUSE OFFICE BLDG	WASHINGTON, DC	20515
STUPER, JOHN	BASEBALL COACH	POST OFFICE BOX 12557	ST PETERSBURG, FL	33733
STURGES, JEFFREY A	CONDUCTOR	22270 DEL VALLE ST	WOODLAND HILLS, CA	91364
STURGES, JOHN	FILM WRITER-DIRECTOR	DGA, 7920 SUNSET BLVD, 6TH FL	LOS ANGELES, CA	90046
STURGES, LEATHA	ACTRESS-SINGER	762 10TH AVE #4-N	NEW YORK, NY	10019
STURGES, SHANNON	ACTRESS	NBC-TV, "DAYS OF OUR LIVES"		
		3000 W ALAMEDA AVE	BURBANK, CA	91523
STURGIS, WILLIAM	ACTOR	1558 E 19TH ST	BROOKLYN, NY	11230
STURHAHN, LAWRENCE C	TV DIRECTOR-PRODUCER	ODYSSEUS PRODS, 52 LOCUST AVE	MILL VALLEY, CA	94941
STURR, JIMMY & HIS BAND	POLKA BAND	POST OFFICE BOX 1	FLORIDA, NY	10921
STURRIDGE, CHARLES	TV DIRECTOR	PETERS, FRASER & DUNLOP, LTD		
		5TH FLOOR, THE CHAMBERS		
		CHELSEA HARBOUR, LOT RD	LONDON SW10 OXF	ENGLAND
STURTZE, TANYON	BASEBALL	POST OFFICE BOX 2437	MODESTO, CA	95351
STUTZKE, CHERYL A	TV DIRECTOR	3033 W LOGAN BLVD	CHICAGO, IL	60647
STYLE COUNCIL, THE	ROCK & ROLL GROUP	THE TORCH SOCIETY		
		45-53 SINCLAIR RD	LONDON W14	ENGLAND
STYLER, ADELE	TV WRITER	12653 MILBANK ST	NORTH HOLLYWOOD, CA	91604
STYLER, BURT	TV WRITER	12653 MILBANK ST	NORTH HOLLYWOOD, CA	91604
STYLES, BEVERLY	COMPOSER	POST OFFICE BOX 615	JOSHUA TREE, CA	92252
STYLES, BOB & THE COUNTRY SWING	C & W GROUP	POST OFFICE BOX O	EXCELSIOR, MN	55331
STYLISTICS, THE	VOCAL GROUP	POST OFFICE BOX 82	GREAT NECK, NY	11021
STYNE, JULE	SONGWRITER-ROCK PROD	237 W 51ST ST	NEW YORK, NY	10019
STYNES, CHRIS	BASEBALL	POST OFFICE BOX 1110	MYRTLE BEACH, SC	29578
STYX	ROCK & ROLL GROUP	BOB GARCIA, A & M RECORDS		
		1416 N LA BREA AVE	HOLLYWOOD, CA	90028
SUAREZ, PHILIP	DIRECTOR	DGA, 110 W 57TH ST	NEW YORK, NY	10019
SUAREZ, SANTIAGO F	DIRECTOR	DGA, 110 W 57TH ST	NEW YORK, NY	10019
SUBIS, NICK	FOOTBALL	BRONCOS, 13655 BRONCOS PKWY	ENGLEWOOD, CO	80112
SUBURBAN NIGHTMARE	ROCK & ROLL GROUP	SEE - DWARVES, THE		
SUBURBS, THE	ROCK & ROLL GROUP	LEVY MANAGEMENT AGENCY		
		526 NICOLLET MALL, 2ND FLOOR	MINNEAPOLIS, MN	55402
SUCH, DICK	BASEBALL-COACH	TWINS, 501 CHICAGO AVE S	MINNEAPOLIS, MN	55415
SUCHER, HENRY	WRITER	6654 ETHEL AVE	NORTH HOLLYWOOD, CA	91606
SUCHET, DAVID	ACTOR	169 QUEENSGATE #8-A	LONDON SW7 5EH	ENGLAND
SUCHIN, MILTON B	TALENT AGENT	201 N ROBERTSON BLVD #A	BEVERLY HILLS, CA	90211
SUDAKIS, BILL	BASEBALL	16641 ALGONQUIN	HUNTINGTON BEACH, CA	92649
SUDAVICIUS, DALIA	ARTIST	5619 BURDETTE ST	OMAHA, NE	68104
SUDBURY, CRAIG	BASEBALL	POST OFFICE BOX 2437	MODESTO, CA	95351
SUDDETH, JAMES ALLEN	CHOREOGRAPHER	131 LINDEN AVE	GLEN RIDGE, NJ	07028
SUDROW, PENELOPE	ACTRESS	1999 AVE OF THE STARS #2850	LOS ANGELES, CA	90067
SUED, NICK	BASEBALL	POST OFFICE BOX 1886	COLUMBUS, GA	31902
SUERO, WILLIAM	BASEBALL	BREWERS, 201 S 46TH ST	MILWAUKEE, WI	53214
SUES, ALAN	ACTOR	1492 2ND AVE	NEW YORK, NY	10021
SUFFIN, JORDAN	ACTOR	7733 OAKWOOD AVE	LOS ANGELES, CA	90036
SUGAR HOLLOW	ROCK & ROLL GROUP	POST OFFICE BOX 448	RADFORD, VA	24141
SUGARHILL GANG	RAP GROUP	FAA, 1700 BROADWAY, 5TH FLOOR	NEW YORK, NY	10019
SUGARMAN, BURT	ROCK PRODUCER	400 TROUSDALE PL	BEVERLY HILLS, CA	90210
SUGARMAN, PETER B	DIRECTOR	301 W 53RD ST #5-B	NEW YORK, NY	10019
SUGHRUE, JOHN J, JR	DIRECTOR	56 TENNIS PL	FOREST HILLS, NY	11375
SUHOSKY, ROBERT A	FILM WRITER-PRODUCER	4544 COLBATH AVE #5	SHERMAN OAKS, CA	91423
SUHR, BRENDAN	BASKETBALL COACH	THE PALACE OF AUBURN HILLS		
		2 CHAMPIONSHIP DR	AUBURN HILLS, MI	48326
SUKONICK, ARNOLD	COMPOSER	1308 N POINSETTIA PL	LOS ANGELES, CA	90046
SULLIVAN, BARRY	ACTOR	14687 ROUND VALLEY DR	SHERMAN OAKS, CA	91403
SULLIVAN, BETH	TV WRITER	8150 BEVERLY BLVD #201	LOS ANGELES, CA	90048
SULLIVAN, BRENDON V, JR	ATTORNEY	839 17TH ST, NW	WASHINGTON, DC	20006
SULLIVAN, CHARLES H	WRITER	14722 HUSTON ST	SHERMAN OAKS, CA	91403
SULLIVAN, CHRIS	ACTOR	WADE, 54 HARLEY ST	LONDON W1N 1AD	ENGLAND
SULLIVAN, DAN	FILM-THEATER CRITIC	LA TIMES, TIMES MIRROR SQ	LOS ANGELES, CA	90053
SULLIVAN, DANNY	AUTO RACER	201 N ROCKINGHAM AVE	LOS ANGELES, CA	90049
SULLIVAN, GENE J	COMPOSER	300 E COAST HWY #262	NEWPORT BEACH, CA	92660
SULLIVAN, GLENN	BASEBALL	CUBS, 2ND & RIVERSIDE DR	DES MOINES, IA	50309
SULLIVAN, GRANT	BASEBALL	POST OFFICE BOX 22093	GREENSBORO, NC	27420

Name	Occupation	Address	City
SULLIVAN, HAYWOOD	BASEBALL-EXECUTIVE	FENWAY PARK, 4 YAWKEY WY	BOSTON, MA 02215
SULLIVAN, JAMES A	DIRECTOR	1207 BEACON HILL	IRVING, TX 75061
SULLIVAN, JASON "SULLY"	ACTOR-COACH	2801 MEADOW LARK DR	SAN DIEGO, CA 92123
SULLIVAN, JENNY	ACTRESS	5750 WILSHIRE BLVD #512	LOS ANGELES, CA 90036
SULLIVAN, JOHN	BASEBALL COACH	SKYDOME, 300 BREMMER BL #3200	TORONTO, ONT M5V 3B3 CANADA
SULLIVAN, JOHN	TV WRITER	7 WOODBURY DR, SUTTON	SURREY ENGLAND
SULLIVAN, JOHN W	TV DIRECTOR	61 CLINTON RD	GLEN RIDGE, NJ 07028
SULLIVAN, JOSEPH H	TV DIRECTOR	1323 EUTAW PL	BALTIMORE, MD 21217
SULLIVAN, JOSEPH M	DIRECTOR	14 PARK ST CT	MEDFORD, MA 02155
SULLIVAN, K	DANCER	AMERICAN BALLET THEATRE	
		890 BROADWAY	NEW YORK, NY 10003
SULLIVAN, KATHIE	SINGER	6750 W 75TH ST, BLDG #2-A	OVERLAND PARK, KS 66204
SULLIVAN, KATHLEEN	BROADCAST JOURNALIST	CBS NEWS, 524 W 57TH ST	NEW YORK, NY 10019
SULLIVAN, KENT	FOOTBALL	OILERS, 6910 FANNIN ST	HOUSTON, TX 77070
SULLIVAN, KERRY	TV WRITER-DIRECTOR	4409 STERN AVE	SHERMAN OAKS, CA 91423
SULLIVAN, MAUREEN	ACTRESS	7200 HOLLYWOOD BLVD #110	LOS ANGELES, CA 90046
SULLIVAN, MAXINE	SINGER	THE HOUSE THAT JAZZ BUILT	
		1312 STEBBINS AVE	BRONX, NY 10459
SULLIVAN, MICHAEL J "MIKE"	GOVERNOR	STATE CAPITOL BUILDING	CHEYENNE, WY 82002
SULLIVAN, MIKE	BASEBALL	POST OFFICE BOX 10336	CLEARWATER, FL 34617
SULLIVAN, MIKE	GOLFER	POST OFFICE BOX 109601	PALM BCH GARDENS, FL 33418
SULLIVAN, NIKI	SINGER-GUITARIST	517 LEE DR	BLUE SPRINGS, MO 64015
SULLIVAN, PAT	BASEBALL SCOUT	ATHLETICS'S, OAKLAND COLISEUM	OAKLAND, CA 94621
SULLIVAN, PATRICIA M	TV DIRECTOR	832 O'DONNELL AVE	SCOTCH PLAINS, NJ 07076
SULLIVAN, SUSAN	ACTRESS	8642 ALLENWOOD RD	LOS ANGELES, CA 90046
SULLIVAN, TIM	SINGER	GOOD, 2500 NW 39TH ST	OKLAHOMA CITY, OK 73112
SULLIVAN, TOM	SINGER-SONGWRI-ACTOR	1504 VIA CASTILLA	PALOS VERDES ESTATES, 90274
SULLIVAN, WILLIAM H, JR	FOOTBALL EXECUTIVE	PATRIOTS, FOXBORO STADIUM, RT #1	FOXBORO, MA 02035
SULLIVAN-STORPER, BETH	SCREENWRITER	8955 BEVERLY BLVD	WEST HOLLYWOOD, CA 90048
SULLIVANS, THE	C & W GROUP	GOOD, 2500 NW 39TH ST	OKLAHOMA CITY, OK 73112
SULTAN OF BRUNEI, THE	SULTAN	BANDAR SERI	BEGAWAN BRUNEI
SULTAN OF OMAN	SULTAN	HM QUABOOS BIN SAID, THE PALACE	MUSLAT OMAN
SUMICHRAST, JOZEF	ARTIST	860 N NORTHWOODS	DEERFIELD, IL 60015
SUMMER, CREE	ACTRESS	421 N SYCAMORE AVE #1	LOS ANGELES, CA 90036
SUMMER, DONNA	SINGER-ACTRESS	714 W POTRERO RD	THOUSAND OAKS, CA 91361
SUMMER, JULIE	ACTRESS	7471 MELROSE AVE #14	LOS ANGELES, CA 90046
SUMMERALL, PAT	FOOTBALL-SPORTSCASTER	12536 MARSH CREEK DR	PONTE VEDRA, FL 32082
SUMMERFIELD, ELEANOR	ACTRESS	10 KILDARE TERR	LONDON W2 ENGLAND
SUMMERS, ANDY	SINGER-SONGWRITER	BUGLE HOUSE, 21-A NOEL ST	LONDON W1V 3PD ENGLAND
SUMMERS, BILL & SUMMERS HEAT	ROCK & ROLL GROUP	199 CALIFORNIA ST #208	MILLBRAE, CA 94030
SUMMERS, BOB R	COMPOSER	2407 GRAND AVE	COVINA, CA 91723
SUMMERS, DANA	CARTOONIST	POST OFFICE BOX 2833	ORLANDO, FL 32802
SUMMERS, GENE	SINGER-SONGWRITER	3006 W NORTHWEST HWY	DALLAS, TX 75220
SUMMERS, JARON	TV WRITER	9000 SUNSET BLVD #611	LOS ANGELES, CA 90069
SUMMERS, JEREMY	TV WRITER-DIRECTOR	L'EPINE SMITH, 10 WYNDHAM PL	LONDON W1H 1AS ENGLAND
SUMMERS, NEIL	BASEBALL SCOUT	SKYDOME, 300 BREMMER BL #3200	TORONTO, ONT M5V 3B3 CANADA
SUMMERS, RAY	COSTUME DESIGNER	20832 PACIFIC COAST HIGHWAY	MALIBU, CA 90265
SUMMERS, RENEE	ACTRESS-MODEL	POST OFFICE BOX 9786	MARINA DEL REY, CA 90265
SUMMERS, STAN	COMPOSER	1729 JENNER ST	LANCASTER, CA 93534
SUMMERS, YALE	ACTOR	9490 CHEROKEE LN	BEVERLY HILLS, CA 90210
SUMMERVILLE CREEK	C & W GROUP	POST OFFICE BOX O	EXCELSIOR, MN 55331
SUMNER, CHARLIE	FOOTBALL COACH	PATRIOTS, FOXBORO STADIUM, RT #1	FOXBORO, MA 02035
SUMNER, J D	SINGER-GUITARIST	POST OFFICE BOX 150592	NASHVILLE, TN 37215
SUMNER, J D & THE STAMPS	C & W GROUP	POST OFFICE BOX 17272	MEMPHIS, TN 38117
SUMROY, JACK R	TV DIRECTOR	125 HUNTERS DR, MUTTONTOWN	SYOSSET PO, NY 11791
SUN, IRENE YAH-LING	ACTRESS	17420 VENTURA BLVD #4	ENCINO, CA 91316
SUND, RICK	BASKETBALL EXECUTIVE	REUNION ARENA, 777 SPORTS ST	DALLAS, TX 75207
SUNDANCER	ROCK & ROLL GROUP	POST OFFICE BOX 942	RAPID CITY, SD 57709
SUNDBERG, CLINTON	ACTOR	827 21ST ST	SANTA MONICA, CA 90403
SUNDBERG, JIM	BASEBALL-ANNOUNCER	POST OFFICE BOX 90111	ARLINGTON, TX 76004
SUNDIN, MATS	HOCKEY	NORDIQUES, 2205 AVE DU COLISEE	QUEBEC, QUE G1L 4W7 CANADA
SUNDLUN, BRUCE	GOVERNOR	STATE CAPITOL, 320 S MAIN ST	PROVIDENCE, RI 02903
SUNDQUIST, DON	U S CONGRESSMAN	5909 SHELBY OAKS DR #213	MEMPHIS, TN 38134
SUNDQUIST, GERRY	ACTOR	MARKHAM AND FROGGATT, LTD	
		JULIAN HOUSE, 4 WINDMILL ST	LONDON W1P 1HF ENGLAND
SUNDRUD, JACK	SINGER-GUITARIST	4700 HUMBER DR #G-10	NASHVILLE, TN 37211
SUNDSTROM, PATRIK	HOCKEY	POST OFFICE BOX 504	EAST RUTHERFORD, NJ 07073
SUNDVOID, JON	BASKETBALL	MIAMI HEAT, THE MIAMI ARENA	MIAMI, FL 33136
SUNGA, GEORGE	PRODUCER	NRW COMPANY, 5746 SUNSET BLVD	LOS ANGELES, CA 90028
SUNLEY, ED	COSTUME DESIGNER	4719 TYRONE AVE	SHERMAN OAKS, CA 91423
SUNNY COWBOYS, THE	C & W GROUP	OFF THE TRAIL PRODUCTIONS	
		72 PARK AVE	WAKEFIELD, MA 01880
SUNOK, JERI LYNN	BODYBUILDER	5118 VINELAND AVE #103	NORTH HOLLYWOOD, CA 91601
SUNSHINE, MADELINE	TV WRITER-PRODUCER	11582 OTSEGO ST	NORTH HOLLYWOOD, CA 91601
SUNSHINE, STEVEN	TV WRITER-PRODUCER	11582 OTSEGO ST	NORTH HOLLYWOOD, CA 91601
SUNSHINE BOYS, THE	C & W GROUP	POST OFFICE BOX 973	BEDFORD, TX 76021
SUNSHINE COMPANY	ROCK & ROLL GROUP	POST OFFICE BOX 133	MANHATTAN, KS 66502
SUNWALL, PAT	BASEBALL EXECUTIVE	POST OFFICE BOX 10213	LYNCHBURG, VA 24506
SUPER, BEATRICE	ACTRESS	7 ROBIN HILL RD	GREAT NECK, NY 11024
SUPER, GLENN	COMEDIAN	21229 PACIFIC COAST HWY #1042	MALIBU, CA 90265
SUPER GRIT COWBOY BAND	C & W GROUP	POST OFFICE BOX 1204	GREENVILLE, NC 27835
SUPERIOR MOVEMENT	ROCK & ROLL GROUP	POST OFFICE BOX 14524	CHICAGO, IL 60614
SUPERTRAMP	ROCK & ROLL GROUP	16530 VENTURA BLVD #201	ENCINO, CA 91436
SUPLIZIO, SAM	BASEBALL SCOUT	BREWERS, 201 S 46TH ST	MILWAUKEE, WI 53214
SURE!, AL B	SINGER-SONGWRITER	636 WARREN ST	BROOKLYN, NY 11217

SURECK, DAVID	TV PRODUCER	140 E 45TH ST, 36TH FLOOR	NEW YORK, NY	10022
SURFARIES, THE	ROCK & ROLL GROUP	MONARCH PRODUCTIONS		
		9227 NICHOLS ST	BELLFLOWER, CA	90706
SURGAL, JON	WRITER-PRODUCER	838 NW KNOLL DR	HOLLYWOOD, CA	90069
SURGENT, PENELOPE	ACTRESS	POST OFFICE BOX 2124	CLIFTON, NJ	07015
SURHOFF, B J	BASEBALL	9926 W BROOKSIDE DR	HALES CORNER, WI	53130
SUROVY, NICOLAS	ACTOR	ICM, 8899 BEVERLY BLVD	LOS ANGELES, CA	90048
SURTEES, BRUCE	CINEMATOGRAPHER	25535 HACIENDA PL	CARMEL, CA	93923
SURVIVOR	ROCK & ROLL GROUP	10100 SANTA MONICA BLVD #2460	LOS ANGELES, CA	90067
SUSCA, VITO	COMPOSER	1025 OLIVE LN	LA CANADA, CA	91011
SUSCHITZKY, WOLFGANG	CINEMATOGRAPHER	6 MAIDA AVE #11	LONDON W2	ENGLAND
SUSMAN, TODD	ACTOR	10340 KEOKUK AVE	CHATSWORTH, CA	91311
SUSSMAN, GERALD	SCREENWRITER	555 W 57TH ST #1230	NEW YORK, NY	10019
SUSSMAN, SALLY	TV WRITER	UTA, 9560 WILSHIRE BL, 5TH FL	BEVERLY HILLS, CA	90212
SUSSMAN, STANLEY B	CONDUCTOR	2109 BROADWAY #3157	NEW YORK, NY	10023
SUSSMAN, SUE	AUTHORESS-NOVELIST	927 NOYES ST	EVANSTON, IL	60201
SUSTARSIC, STEPHEN, II	TV WRITER	18645 HATTERAS ST #299	TARZANA, CA	91356
SUTCH, RAY	BASEBALL	POST OFFICE BOX 882	MADISON, WI	53701
SUTCLIFFE, RICK	BASEBALL	ORIOLE PARK, 333 W CAMDEN ST	BALTIMORE, MD	21201
SUTER, GARY	HOCKEY	POST OFFICE BOX 1540, STA "M"	CALGARY, ALTA T2P 3BP	CANADA
SUTER, WILLIAM A	COMPOSER	2535 LA MESA DR	SANTA MONICA, CA	90402
SUTHERLAND, ALEX	BASEBALL	POST OFFICE BOX 30160	SAN BERNARDINO, CA	92413
SUTHERLAND, DALE	BASEBALL SCOUT	POST OFFICE BOX 2000	SAN DIEGO, CA	92112
SUTHERLAND, DONALD	ACTOR	760 N LA CIENEGA BLVD #300	LOS ANGELES, CA	90069
SUTHERLAND, KATHERINE LEIGH	TV DIRECTOR	3039 "Q" ST #42, NW	WASHINGTON, DC	20007
SUTHERLAND, KIEFER	ACTOR	1033 GAYLEY AVE #208	LOS ANGELES, CA	90024
SUTHERLAND, KRISTINE	ACTRESS	145 W 45TH ST #1204	NEW YORK, NY	10036
SUTHERLAND, NANCY ELLEN	ACTRESS	470 W 24TH ST	NEW YORK, NY	10011
SUTHERLAND, TAYLOR	SCREENWRITER	8955 BEVERLY BLVD	WEST HOLLYWOOD, CA	90048
SUTKO, GLENN	BASEBALL	POST OFFICE BOX 46	CUMMING, GA	30130
SUTORIUS, JAMES	ACTOR	10100 SANTA MONICA BLVD #700	LOS ANGELES, CA	90067
SUTT, JO	SINGER	POST OFFICE BOX 171132	NASHVILLE, TN	37217
SUTTER, BRENT	HOCKEY	NASSAU VETS MEMORIAL COLISEUM	UNIONDALE, NY	11553
SUTTER, BRUCE	BASEBALL	1368 HAMILTON RD	KENNESAW, GA	30144
SUTTER, DANIEL	DIRECTOR	DGA, 110 W 57TH ST	NEW YORK, NY	10019
SUTTER, RICH	HOCKEY	BLUES, 5700 OAKLAND AVE	SAINT LOUIS, MO	63110
SUTTER, RON	HOCKEY	FLYERS, SPECTRUM, PATTISON PL	PHILADELPHIA, PA	19148
SUTTERFIELD, ALAN	TV WRITER	2049 CENTURY PARK E #1320	LOS ANGELES, CA	90067
SUTTON, ALBERT H	COMPOSER	POST OFFICE BOX 11	ZEPHYR COVE, NV	89448
		FINSBURY PARK	LONDON N4 2AT	ENGLAND
SUTTON, CHRISTOPHER	FILM PRODUCER	17-A ADOLPHUS RD		
SUTTON, DON	BASEBALL	3390 VANDIVER DR	MARIETTA, GA	30066
SUTTON, DUDLEY	ACTOR	12 CARLYLE HOUSE		
		OLD CHURCH ST	LONDON SW3	ENGLAND
SUTTON, GRADY	ACTOR	1207 N ORANGE DR	LOS ANGELES, CA	90038
SUTTON, HAL	GOLFER	POST OFFICE BOX 109601	PALM BCH GARDENS, FL	33418
SUTTON, HENRY	ACTOR	1550 N HAYWORTH AVE #3	LOS ANGELES, CA	90046
SUTTON, KEN	HOCKEY	SABRES, MEMORIAL AUDITORIUM	BUFFALO, NY	14202
SUTTON, MARK	ACTOR	759 HEMPSTEAD AVE	WEST HEMPSTEAD, NY	11552
SUTTON, PHOEF	PLAYWRIGHT	BERMAN, 240 W 44TH ST	NEW YORK, NY	10036
SUVALLE, RUTHIE	COMPOSER	15541 NORDHOFF ST #48	SEPULVEDA, CA	91343
SUZMAN, JANET	ACTRESS	FAIRCROFT, 11 KEATS GROVE		
		HAMPSTEAD	LONDON NW3	ENGLAND
SVANOE, BILL	SCREENWRITER	9200 SUNSET BLVD #1009	LOS ANGELES, CA	90069
SVENSON, BO	ACTOR	10100 SANTA MONICA BLVD #700	LOS ANGELES, CA	90067
SVEUM, DALE	BASEBALL	POST OFFICE BOX 7575	PHILADELPHIA, PA	19101
SVOBODA, PETR	HOCKEY	CANADIENS, 2313 ST CATHERINE ST	MONTREAL, QUE H3H 1N2	CANADA
SWACKHAMER, E W	WRITER-PRODUCER	16671 OAK VIEW DR	ENCINO, CA	91436
SWACKHAMER, ELIZABETH	ACTRESS	9000 SUNSET BLVD #1200	LOS ANGELES, CA	90069
SWADOS, ELIZABETH	COMPOSER-LYRICIST	360 CENTRAL PARK W #16-G	NEW YORK, NY	10025
SWAGGERT, JIMMY	EVANGELIST-SINGER	POST OFFICE BOX 2550	BATON ROUGE, LA	70821
SWAIL, STEVE	BASEBALL	POST OFFICE BOX 4525	MACON, GA	31208
SWAIN, JACK	CINEMATOGRAPHER	POST OFFICE BOX 2230	HOLLYWOOD, CA	90078
SWAIN, ROB	BASEBALL COACH	POST OFFICE BOX 3452	KINSTON, NC	28502
SWAIN, VIRGINIA	ACTRESS	300 E 40TH ST	NEW YORK, NY	10016
SWAINE, MICHAEL	ARTIST	6735 N 10TH PL	PHOENIX, AZ	85014
SWALE, THOMAS BENJAMIN	WRITER-PRODUCER	7353 PACIFIC VIEW DR	LOS ANGELES, CA	90068
SWALLOW, NORMAN	TV WRITER-PRODUCER	36 CROOMS HILL	LONDON SE10	ENGLAND
SWAN, BILLY	SINGER	151 S EL CAMINO DR	BEVERLY HILLS, CA	90212
SWAN, MICHAEL	ACTOR	CBS-TV, "AS THE WORLD TURNS"		
		524 W 57TH ST #5330	NEW YORK, NY	10019
SWAN, RUSS	BASEBALL	POST OFFICE BOX 4100	SEATTLE, WA	98104
SWAN, WILLIAM	ACTOR	81 PROSPECT PL	BROOKLYN, NY	11217
SWANN, ELAINE	ACTRESS	304 BLEECKER ST	NEW YORK, NY	10014
SWANN, ERIC	FOOTBALL	POST OFFICE BOX 888	PHOENIX, AZ	85001
SWANN, LYNN	FOOTBALL	5750 WILSHIRE BLVD #475-W	LOS ANGELES, CA	90036
SWANSON, GARY	ACTOR	888 7TH AVE #1602	NEW YORK, NY	10019
SWANSON, GLEN OWEN	TV DIRECTOR	9800 VANALDEN ST	NORTHRIDGE, CA	91324
SWANSON, GLENWOOD J	DIRECTOR	DGA, 7920 SUNSET BLVD, 6TH FL	LOS ANGELES, CA	90046
SWANSON, JACKIE	ACTRESS	11726 SAN VICENTE BLVD #300	LOS ANGELES, CA	90049
SWANSON, KATHY	ACTRESS	9255 SUNSET BLVD #401	WEST HOLLYWOOD, CA	90069
SWANSON, KRISTY	ACTRESS	9000 SUNSET BLVD #1200	LOS ANGELES, CA	90069
SWANSON, ROBERT E	TV WRITER	ICM, 8899 BEVERLY BLVD	LOS ANGELES, CA	90048
SWANTON, SCOTT JAMES	TV WRITER	2715 6TH ST	SANTA MONICA, CA	90405
SWARD, ANNE	ACTRESS	CBS-TV, "AS THE WORLD TURNS"		

		524 W 57TH ST #5330	NEW YORK, NY	10019
SWARTHOUT, MILES H	WRITER	29257 1/2 HEATHERCLIFF RD	MALIBU, CA	90265
SWARTZ, NICK	BASEBALL TRAINER	POST OFFICE BOX 419969	KANSAS CITY, MO	64141
SWARTZBAUGH, DAVE	BASEBALL	POST OFFICE DRAWER 1207	ZEBULON, NC	27597
SWAYBILL, ROGER	SCREENWRITER	9200 SUNSET BLVD #808	LOS ANGELES, CA	90069
SWAYNE, HARRY	FOOTBALL	POST OFFICE BOX 609609	SAN DIEGO, CA	92160
SWAYZE, PATRICK	ACTOR-SINGER	1033 GAYLEY AVE #208	LOS ANGELES, CA	90024
SWEAT, KEITH	SINGER-SONGWRITER	POST OFFICE BOX 1002	BRONX, NY	10466
SWEAT, LYNN	ARTIST	POST OFFICE BOX 1124	WESTON, CT	06883
SWEATMAN, MIKE	FOOTBALL COACH	N Y GIANTS, GIANTS STADIUM	EAST RUTHERFORD, NJ	07073
SWEENEY, BOB	DIRECTOR-PRODUCER	5757 OWENSMITH AVE #5	WOODLAND HILLS, CA	91364
SWEENEY, BOB	HOCKEY	BRUINS, 150 CAUSEWAY ST	BOSTON, MA	02114
SWEENEY, DON	HOCKEY	BRUINS, 150 CAUSEWAY ST	BOSTON, MA	02114
SWEENEY, DONALD P	CONDUCTOR	5000 WOODMAN AVE #9	SHERMAN OAKS, CA	91423
SWEENEY, JIM	FOOTBALL	N Y JETS, 1000 FULTON AVE	HEMPSTEAD, NY	11550
SWEENEY, JOHN	NEWS CORRESPONDENT	1050 TECHWOOD DR, NW	ATLANTA, GA	30318
SWEENEY, JULIA	ACTRESS	WESSLER, 2552 DEARBORN DR	LOS ANGELES, CA	90068
SWEENEY, LARRY	MUSIC EXECUTIVE	BROADCAST MUSIC, 320 W 57TH ST	NEW YORK, NY	10019
SWEENEY, MARK	BASEBALL (COLUMBUS)	POST OFFICE BOX 1886	COLUMBUS, GA	31902
SWEENEY, MARK	BASEBALL (QUAD CITY)	POST OFFICE BOX 3496	DAVENPORT, IA	52808
SWEENEY, MAXWELL	COLUMNIST	5700 WILSHIRE BLVD #120	LOS ANGELES, CA	90036
SWEENEY, ROB	BASEBALL	POST OFFICE BOX 10031	BAKERSFIELD, CA	93389
SWEENEY, ROBERT E	TV DIRECTOR	135 CARL ST	SAN FRANCISCO, CA	94117
SWEET	ROCK & ROLL GROUP	9229 SUNSET BLVD #625	LOS ANGELES, CA	90069
SWEET, MATTHEW	SINGER	1680 N VINE ST #1101	HOLLYWOOD, CA	90028
SWEET, RACHEL	SINGER	11726 SAN VICENTE BLVD #300	LOS ANGELES, CA	90049
SWEET, RICK	BASEBALL-MANAGER	POST OFFICE BOX 4209	JACKSON, MS	39296
SWEET G	RHYTHM & BLUES GROUP	POST OFFICE BOX 82	GREAT NECK, NY	11022
SWEET INSPIRATIONS, THE	VOCAL GROUP	SCHILLING, 6534 SUNSET BLVD	HOLLYWOOD, CA	90028
SWEETHEARTS OF THE RODEO	C & W GROUP	POST OFFICE BOX 121885	NASHVILLE, TN	37212
SWEETIN, JODIE	ACTRESS	ABC-TV, 2040 AVE OF THE STARS	LOS ANGELES, CA	90067
SWEETWATER	C & W GROUP	POST OFFICE BOX 475	MADISONVILLE, TN	37354
SWEETWATER EXPRESS	C & W GROUP	POST OFFICE BOX 4	LAKE LURE, NC	28746
SWENARTON, GORDON	ARTIST	40 DRUID HILL RD	SUMMIT, NJ	07901
SWENSON, INGA	ACTRESS	3475 CABRILLO BLVD	LOS ANGELES, CA	90066
SWENSON, LINDA L	ACTRESS	205 W 95TH ST	NEW YORK, NY	10025
SWENSON, SWEN	ACTOR	16 MINETTA LN	NEW YORK, NY	10012
SWERDLOFF, ARTHUR	WRITER-DIRECTOR	4224 ELLENITA AVE	TARZANA, CA	91356
SWERDLOW, EZRA N	DIRECTOR	5400 FIELDSTON RD	RIVERDALE, NY	10471
SWERLING, JO, JR	WRITER-PRODUCER	25745 VISTA VERDE DR	CALABASAS, CA	91302
SWERTLOW, FRANK	COLUMNIST	UPS, 4900 MAIN ST, 9TH FLOOR	KANSAS CITY, MO	64112
SWETT, DICK	U S CONGRESSMAN	5 COLISEUM AVE	NASHUA, NH	03063
SWICK, LUCILLE	ACTRESS	651 ELDER AVE	PHILLIPSBURG, NJ	08865
SWICKARD, RALPH	COMPOSER	169 LITTLE PARK LN	LOS ANGELES, CA	90049
SWICORD, ROBIN	SCREENWRITER	3014 3RD ST	SANTA MONICA, CA	90405
SWIDLER, HOWARD	TV DIRECTOR	413 WINSTON DR	DEERFIELD, IL	60601
SWIFT, AL	U S CONGRESSMAN	FEDERAL BUILDING, ROOM 308		
		104 W MAGNOLIA	BELLINGHAM, WA	98225
SWIFT, BILL	BASEBALL	S F GIANTS, CANDLESTICK PARK	SAN FRANICSCO, CA	94124
SWIFT, CLIVE	ACTOR	PTA, BUGLE HOUSE, 21-A NOEL ST	LONDON W1V 3PD	ENGLAND
SWIFT, DAVID	WRITER-DIRECTOR	12831 HANOVER ST	LOS ANGELES, CA	90069
SWIFT, JAMES A	CONDUCTOR	8741 WHITE OAK AVE	NORTHRIDGE, CA	91324
SWIFT, LELA	TV DIRECTOR	27 W 86TH ST	NEW YORK, NY	10024
SWIFT, MIKE	ARTIST	1351 OCEAN PARK WALK #106	SANTA MONICA, CA	90405
SWIFT, WENDON	TALENT AGENT	725 S BARRINGTON ST #202	LOS ANGELES, CA	90049
SWILLING, PAT	FOOTBALL	SAINTS, 1500 POYDRAS ST	NEW ORLEANS, LA	90112
SWINBURNE, NORA	ACTRESS	52 CRAMMER CT, WHITEHEAD'S GROVE	LONDON SW3	ENGLAND
SWINDELL, GREG	BASEBALL	7706 TWIN HILLS	HOUSTON, TX	77071
SWING, MARLIN GRAM	TV DIRECTOR	245 E 35TH ST	NEW YORK, NY	10016
SWING OUT SISTER	ROCK & ROLL DUO	STIRLING ARTISTES MANAGEMENT		
		132 LIVERPOOL RD	LONDON N1 ILA	ENGLAND
SWINGLE, PAUL	BASEBALL	POST OFFICE BOX 12	MIDLAND, TX	79702
SWINTON, JERMAINE	BASEBALL	POST OFFICE BOX 824	BURLINGTON, IA	52601
SWIRNOFF, BRADLEY R	WRITER-PRODUCER	10564 CUSHDON AVE	LOS ANGELES, CA	90064
SWIRNOFF, MARY A	WRITER	10564 CUSHDON AVE	LOS ANGELES, CA	90064
SWISHER, STEVE	BASEBALL-MANAGER	POST OFFICE BOX 598	BINGHAMTON, NY	13902
SWIT, LORETTA	ACTRESS	151 S EL CAMINO DR	BEVERLY HILLS, CA	90212
SWITZER, MICHAEL	TV DIRECTOR	130 MONTREAL ST	PLAYA DEL REY, CA	90291
SWOPE, MARK	BASEBALL	POST OFFICE BOX 5645	ORLANDO, FL	32855
SWOPE, MEL	TV DIRECTOR-PRODUCER	MTA, 9320 WILSHIRE BL, 3RD FL	BEVERLY HILLS, CA	90212
SWOPE, TOPO	ACTRESS	2255 BENEDICT CANYON DR	BEVERLY HILLS, CA	90210
SWOPE, TRACY BROOKS	ACTRESS	14455 DICKENS ST	SHERMAN OAKS, CA	90210
SYBERBERG, HANS-JURGEN	FILM DIRECTOR	BUNDESVERBAND DEUTSCHER		
		FILM PRODUZENTEN		
		LANGENBECK STR #9	6200 WIESBADEN	GERMANY
SYDDALL, CLIVE	TV PRODUCER	17 ASHCHURCH TERR	LONDON W12 9SL	ENGLAND
SYDNEY, HARRY	FOOTBALL	S F 49ERS, 4949 CENTENNIAL BL	SANTA CLARA, CA	95054
SYDNOR, EARL	ACTOR	413 GRAND ST #F-1603	NEW YORK, NY	10002
SYKES, ERIC	ACT-WRI-DIR-PROD	9 ORME CT	LONDON W2	ENGLAND
SYKES, PETER	WRITER-PRODUCER	ICM, 388-396 OXFORD ST	LONDON W1	ENGLAND
SYKES, PHIL	HOCKEY	JETS, 15-1430 MAROONS RD	WINNIPEG, MAN R3G OL5	CANADA
SYKES, TOM	SINGER	POST OFFICE BOX 29543	ATLANTA, GA	30359
SYLBERT, ANTHEA	COSTUME DESIGNER	13949 VENTURA BLVD #309	SHERMAN OAKS, CA	91423
SYLBERT, PAUL	FILM WRITER-DIRECTOR	52 E 64TH ST #3	NEW YORK, NY	10021
SYLVEST, DONOVAN L	COMPOSER-LYRICIST	309 W 43RD ST #3-D	NEW YORK, NY	10036

SYLVESTER, DAVID S	COMPOSER	807 DEERFLATS DR	SAN DIMAS, CA	91773
SYLVESTER, HAROLD	ACTOR	12343 CALVERT ST	NORTH HOLLYWOOD, CA	91606
SYLVESTER, TERRY	SINGER	GOOD, 2500 NW 39TH ST	OKLAHOMA CITY, OK	73112
SYLVIA	SINGER	MORESS, 1209 16TH AVE S	NASHVILLE, TN	37212
SYMINGTON, FIFE	GOVERNOR	STATE CAPITOL, 1700 W WASHINGTON	PHOENIX, AZ	85007
SYMMS, STEVE	U S SENATOR	POST OFFICE BOX 1190	BOISE, ID	83701
SYMON, JAMES G	DIRECTOR	351 ELM RD	BRIARCLIFF, NY	10510
SYMONDS, ROBERT	BASEBALL SCOUT	REDS, 100 RIVERFRONT STADIUM	CINCINNATI, OH	45202
SYMS, SYLVIA	ACTRESS	135 E 63RD ST	NEW YORK, NY	10021
SYNAR, MIKE	U S CONGRESSMAN	2-B-22 FEDERAL BUILDING		
		125 S MAIN	MUSKOGEE, OK	74401
SYNES, ROBERT	TV WRITER	3325 BONNIE HILL DR	LOS ANGELES, CA	90068
SZABO, ISTVAN	FILM DIRECTOR	KOHNER, 9169 SUNSET BLVD	LOS ANGELES, CA	90069
SZATHMARY, IRVING	COMPOSER-CONDUCTOR	DAVID LICHT, 9171 WILSHIRE BLVD	BEVERLY HILLS, CA	90210
SZCZEPANSKI, JOE	BASEBALL	POST OFFICE BOX 4488	WINSTON-SALEM, NC	27115
SZEGO, LESLIE	COMPOSER	1530 DOGWOOD PL	LOS ANGELES, CA	90042
SZEKELY, JOE	BASEBALL	POST OFFICE BOX 6667	RICHMOND, VA	23230
SZIGMOND, VILMOS	CINEMATOGRAPHER	POST OFFICE BOX 2230	HOLLYWOOD, CA	90078
SZOLLOSI, THOMAS E	TV WRITER	5127 STERN AVE	SHERMAN OAKS, CA	91423
SZOTT, DAVID	FOOTBALL	CHIEFS, 1 ARROWHEAD DR	KANSAS CITY, MO	64129
SZWARC, JEANNOT	FILM DIRECTOR	16633 VENTURA BLVD #1100	ENCINO, CA	91436
SZYMKOWSKI, BOB	BASEBALL SCOUT	REDS, 100 RIVERFRONT STADIUM	CINCINNATI, OH	45202

T

T, ICE	RAPPER-RAPWRITER	SEE - ICE-T		
T, MR	ACTOR	395 GREEN BAY RD	LAKE FOREST, IL	60045
T S O L	ROCK & ROLL GROUP	6253 HOLLYWOOD BLVD #800	HOLLYWOOD, CA	90028
T T QUICK	ROCK & ROLL GROUP	POST OFFICE BOX 327	LEONIA, NJ	07605
T-CONNECTION	SOUL GROUP	9400 S DADELAND BLVD #220	MIAMI, FL	33156
T-LA-ROCK	RAPPER-RAPWRITER	FAA, 1700 BROADWAY, 5TH FLOOR	NEW YORK, NY	10019
TABACK, SIMMS	ARTIST	38 E 21ST ST	NEW YORK, NY	10010
TABAKA, JEFF	BASEBALL	POST OFFICE DRAWER 4797	EL PASO, TX	79914
TABET, SYLVIO	FILM DIRECTOR	845 SUNSET BLVD	LOS ANGELES, CA	90077
TABLER, PAT	BASEBALL	SKYDOME, 300 BREMMER BL #3200	TORONTO, ONT M5V 3B3	CANADA
TABORI, KRISTOFFER	ACTOR-DIRECTOR	172 E 95TH ST	NEW YORK, NY	10028
TACHOIR, JERRY	MUSIC ARRANGER	145 TOWNSHIP DR	HENDERSONVILLE, TN	37075
TACHOIR, MARLENE	MUSIC ARRANGER	145 TOWNSHIP DR	HENDERSONVILLE, TN	37075
TACKETT, FREDDIE	GUITARIST	1229 ALPINE TRAIL	TOPANGA CANYON, CA	90290
TACKETT, JEFF	BASEBALL	ORIOLE PARK, 333 W CAMDEN ST	BALTIMORE, MD	21201
TACO	SINGER-SONGWRITER	8124 W 3RD ST #204	LOS ANGELES, CA	90048
TADMAN, AUBREY	TV WRITER	20111 MAYALL ST	CHATSWORTH, CA	91311
TAEGER, RALPH	ACTOR	5619 MOTHER LODE	PLACERVILLE, CA	95667
TAFFET, SAUL S	WRI-DIR-PROD	POST OFFICE BOX 176, PRINCE STA	NEW YORK, NY	10012
TAFOYA, DENNIS	BASEBALL	POST OFFICE DRAWER 1218	ZEBULON, NC	27597
TAFT, GENE	PRODUCER	185 N REXFORD DR	BEVERLY HILLS, CA	90210
TAFT, ROBERT	SECRETARY OF STATE	STATE CAPITOL BUILDING	COLUMBUS, OH	43266
TAFT, STEVEN GENE	WRITER-PRODUCER	DGA, 7920 SUNSET BLVD, 6TH FL	LOS ANGELES, CA	90046
TAG-YR-IT	ROCK & ROLL GROUP	AFTERHOURS RECORDS		
		300 PROSPECT AVE	CLEVELAND, OH	44115
TAGGART, JOSEPH	ACTOR	11247 LA MAIDA ST #205	NORTH HOLLYWOOD, CA	91601
TAGGART, RITA	ACTRESS	201 OCEAN AVE #1110	SANTA MONICA, CA	90402
TAGGERT, BRIAN W	TV WRITER	4342 BELLINGHAM AVE	STUDIO CITY, CA	91604
TAGLE, HANK	BASEBALL	POST OFFICE BOX 4218	SOUTH BEND, IN	46634
TAGLIAFERRO, JOHN A	TV EXECUTIVE	HUGHES TV, 260 MADISON AVE	NEW YORK, NY	10016
TAGLIANETTI, PETER	HOCKEY	PENGUINS, CIVIC ARENA, CENTRE AV	PITTSBURGH, PA	15219
TAGLIARINO, SALVATORE	ART DIRECTOR	172 W 79T HST #19-F	NEW YORK, NY	10024
TAHAN, KEVIN	BASEBALL	POST OFFICE BOX 3004	SPRINGFIELD, IL	62708
TAHSE, MARTIN	TV PRODUCER	11727 BARRINGTON CT	LOS ANGELES, CA	90049
TAILGATORS, THE	ROCK & ROLL GROUP	101 W 12TH ST #8-T	NEW YORK, NY	10011
TAIT, DONALD S	TV WRITER	7085 BIRDVIEW AVE	MALIBU, CA	90265
TAJ MAHAL	SINGER-SONGWRITER	FOLKLORE, 1671 APPIAN WY	SANTA MONICA, CA	90401
TAKA, MIIKO	ACTRESS	14560 ROUND VALLEY RD	SHERMAN OAKS, CA	91403
TAKA BOOM	SINGER	SEE - BOOM, TAKA		
TAKARAGAWA, DOUG	BASEBALL SCOUT	INDIANS, CLEVELAND STADIUM	CLEVELAND, OH	44114
TAKE SIX	GOSPEL GROUP	4404 SUMATRA DR	NASHVILLE, TN	37218
TAKEI, GEORGE	ACTOR	3800 BARHAM BLVD #303	LOS ANGELES, CA	90068
TAKIFF, SANFORD	BASKETBALL EXECUTIVE	980 N MICHIGAN AVE #1600	CHICAGO, IL	60611
TALANOA, SCOTT	BASEBALL	POST OFFICE BOX 855	BELOIT, WI	53511
TALAS	ROCK & ROLL GROUP	STARSTRUCK PRODUCTIONS		
		2650 DELAWARE AVE	BUFFALO, NY	14216
TALAVERA, TRACEE	GYMNAST	106 MANDALA CT	WALNUT CREEK, CA	94598
TALBERT, DOUGLAS F	COMPOSER-CONDUCTOR	7250 FRANKLIN AVE #1108	LOS ANGELES, CA	90046
TALBERT, THOMAS	COMPOSER	1268 GLENNEYRE ST	LAGUNA BEACH, CA	92651
TALBOT, LYLE	ACTOR	149 FAIRMOUNT ST	SAN FRANISCO, CA	94131
TALBOT, NITA	ACTRESS	3420 MERRIMAC RD	LOS ANGELES, CA	90049
TALESE, GAY	WRITER	154 E ATLANTIC BLVD	OCEAN CITY, NJ	08226
TALK TALK	ROCK & ROLL GROUP	ASPDEN, 121-A REVELSTONE N		
		WIMBLETON PL	LONDON W15	ENGLAND

TALKING HEADS, THE	ROCK & ROLL GROUP	GARY KURFIRST, OVERLAND PRODS		
		1775 BROADWAY, 7TH FLOOR	NEW YORK, NY	10019
TALL, TOM	SINGER	DOWN HOME MUSIC COMPANY		
		10341 SAN PABLO AVE	EL CERRITO, CA	94530
TALLCHIEF, MARIA	BALLERINA	2739 ELSTON AVE	CHICAGO, IL	60747
TALLEY, DARRYL	FOOTBALL	BILLS, 1 BILLS DR	ORCHARD PARK, NJ	14127
TALLEY, DEBORAH ANN	TV DIRECTOR	4545 CONNECTICUT AVE, NW	WASHINGTON, DC	20008
TALLICHET, MARGARET	ACTRESS	1121 SUMMIT DR	BEVERLY HILLS, CA	90210
TALLMAN, TROY	BASEBALL	POST OFFICE BOX 418	SAINT CHARLES, IL	60174
TALLMER, JERRY	FILM CRITIC	N Y POST, 210 SOUTH ST	NEW YORK, NY	10002
TALLON, ROBIN	U S CONGRESSMAN	POST OFFICE BOX 6286	FLORENCE, SC	29501
TALLY, TED	COMPOSER	ICM, 8899 BEVERLY BLVD	LOS ANGELES, CA	90048
TALSKY, RON	COSTUME DESIGNER	100 N KILKEA DR	LOS ANGELES, CA	90048
TAMADA, TSUTOMU	BASEBALL	POST OFFICE BOX 4370	SALINAS, CA	93912
TAMAREZ, ADAME	BASEBALL	POST OFFICE BOX 1295	CLINTON, IA	52733
TAMARGO, JOHN	BASEBALL MANAGER	525 NW PEACOCK BLVD	PORT SAINT LUCIE, FL	34986
TAMARKIN, JEFF	ROCK & ROLL HISTORIAN	POST OFFICE BOX 497	HOBOKEN, NJ	07030
TAMBLING, RICHARD F	WRI-DIR-PROD	1 WESTBURY CT, 23 THE AVENUE	BECKENHAM BR3 2DN	ENGLAND
TAMBLYN, RUSS	ACTOR	2310 6TH ST #2	SANTA MONICA, CA	90405
TAMBOR, JEFFREY	ACTOR	5526 CALHOUN AVE	VAN NUYS, CA	91401
TAMBURRELLI, KARLA	ACTRESS	9000 SUNSET BLVD #801	LOS ANGELES, CA	90069
TAMBURRO, CHARLES	DIRECTOR	DGA, 7920 SUNSET BLVD, 6TH FL	LOS ANGELES, CA	90046
TAMBURRO, MICHAEL	BASEBALL EXECUTIVE	POST OFFICE BOX 2365	PAWTUCKET, RI	02861
TAMKUS, DAMOE	SCREENWRITER	555 W 57TH ST #1230	NEW YORK, NY	10019
TAMM, MARY	ACTRESS	BARRY LANGFORD, GARDEN STUDIOS		
		BETTERTON ST	LONDON WC2H 9PB	ENGLAND
TAMM, RALPH	FOOTBALL	BROWNS, 80 1ST ST	BEREA, OH	44017
TAMPOSI, SAMUEL	BASEBALL EXECUTIVE	FENWAY PARK, 4 YAWKEY WY	BOSTON, MA	02215
TAMS, THE	ROCK & ROLL GROUP	CAROLINA ATTRACTIONS		
		203 CULVER AVE	CHARLESTON, SC	29407
TANANA, FRANK	BASEBALL	TIGERS, TIGER STADIUM	DETROIT, MI	48216
TANASESCU, GINO	DIRECTOR	DGA, 7920 SUNSET BLVD, 6TH FL	LOS ANGELES, CA	90046
TANDY, JESSICA	ACTRESS	63-23 CARLTON ST	REGO PARK, NY	11374
TANDY & MORGAN	ROCK & ROLL GROUP	POST OFFICE BOX 2924	LAGUNA HILLS, CA	92654
TANEN, NED	FILM PROD-EXEC	659 E CHANNEL RD	SANTA MONICA, CA	90402
TANENBAUM, MICHELLE	ACTRESS	145 S FAIRFAX AVE #310	LOS ANGELES, CA	90036
TANGERINE DREAM	ROCK & ROLL GROUP	POST OFFICE BOX 303340	1000 BERLIN 30	GERMANY
TANKER, JAMES E	TV DIRECTOR	4650 FORMAN AVE	TOLUCA LAKE, CA	91602
TANNEN, PETER S	TV WRITER	BTA, 540 MADISON AVE	NEW YORK, NY	10022
TANNEN, STEVE	ACTOR	743 N SPARKS ST	BURBANK, CA	91506
TANNEN, WILLIAM P	DIRECTOR	129 FRASER AVE	SANTA MONICA, CA	90405
TANNENBAUM, THOMAS D	TV PRODUCER	VIACOM, 10900 WILSHIRE BLVD	LOS ANGELES, CA	90024
TANNER, BRUCE	BASEBALL-COACH	12000 STADIUM RD	ADELANTO, CA	92301
TANNER, CHUCK	BASEBALL-MANAGER	34 MAITLAND LN E	NEW CASTLE, PA	16101
TANNER, JOHN S	U S CONGRESSMAN	POST OFFICE BOX 629	UNION CITY, TN	38261
TANNER, PETER	FILM EDITOR	LONDON MGT, 235-241 REGENT ST	LONDON W1R 4PH	ENGLAND
TANNER, ROBERT C	DIRECTOR	925 MICHIGAN AVE	EVANSTON, IL	60202
TANNER, ROY	BASEBALL SCOUT	POST OFFICE BOX 7575	PHILADELPHIA, PA	19101
TANTI, TONY	HOCKEY	SABRES, MEMORIAL AUDITORIUM	BUFFALO, NY	14202
TANTRUM, THE	ROCK & ROLL GROUP	RUFFIAN MANAGEMENT		
		6914 W NORTH AVE	CHICAGO, IL	60635
TAPANI, KEVIN	BASEBALL	TWINS, 501 CHICAGO AVE S	MINNEAPOLIS, MN	55415
TAPER, MARK	ACTOR	816 ALPINE DR	BEVERLY HILLS, CA	90210
TAPESTRY	MUSICAL GROUP	MARS, 168 ORCHID DR	PEARL RIVER, NY	10965
TAPP, GORDIE	SINGER-SONGWRITER	GASTONI, 3815 BEAUMONT	BROSSARD, PQ JJ4Z 2NB	CANADA
TAPPER, DAVID A	TV WRITER-PRODUCER	133 W 17TH ST #PH-B	NEW YORK, NY	10011
TAPPIS, JOEL	TV WRITER	5663 RUTHWOOD DR	CALABASAS, CA	91302
TAPSCOTT, MARK	ACTOR	8303 SKYLINE DR	LOS ANGELES, CA	90046
TARADASH, DANIEL	WRITER-PRODUCER	9140 HAZEN DR	BEVERLY HILLS, CA	90210
TARAN, CAROLE	SINGER	ADAM, 2501 S OCEAN DR	HOLLYWOOD, FL	33019
TARASCO, TONY	BASEBALL	POST OFFICE BOX 16683	GREENVILLE, SC	29606
TARBUCK, BARBARA	ACTRESS	3468 ASHWOOD AVE	LOS ANGELES, CA	90066
TARBUCK, JIMMY	COMEDIAN	PRICHARD, 118 BEAUFORT ST	LONDON SW3 6BU	ENGLAND
TARDITS, RICHARD	FOOTBALL	PATRIOTS, FOXBORO STADIUM, RT #1	FOXBORO, MA	02035
TARGETS, THE	ROCK & ROLL GROUP	POST OFFICE BOX 34553	LOS ANGELES, CA	90034
TARGOSZ, CYNTHIA	ACTRESS	FELBER, 2126 N CAHUENGA BLVD	LOS ANGELES, CA	90068
TARGOWNIK, THOMAS T	ART DIRECTOR	203 W 102ND ST #5-R	NEW YORK, NY	10025
TARKINGTON, FRAN	FOOTBALL	3340 PEACHTREE RD, NE	ATLANTA, GA	30326
TARLAU, ROBERT S	WRITER	11749 SEMINOLE CIR	NORTHRIDGE, CA	91326
TARLOFF, ERIK	TV WRITER	9596 SHIRLEY LN	BEVERLY HILLS, CA	90210
TARLOFF, FRANK	SCREENWRITER	9596 SHIRLEY LN	BEVERLY HILLS, CA	90210
TARPEY, TOM	ACTOR	1907 SELBY AVE #5	LOS ANGELES, CA	90025
TARPLEY, ROY	BASKETBALL	REUNION ARENA, 777 SPORTS ST	DALLAS, TX	75207
TARRANT, ALAN	TV PRODUCER	19 GROVE RD, CHERTSEY	SURREY KT16 9DN	ENGLAND
TARRANT, CHRIS	TV-RADIO PERS	PVA, ALPHA TOWER, PARADISE CIRCUS	BIRMINGHAM B11 1TT,	ENGLAND
TARSES, JAY	SCREENWRITER	17708 TRAMONTO DR	PACIFIC PALISADES, CA	90272
TARTABULL, DANNY	BASEBALL	N Y YANKEES, YANKEE STADIUM	BRONX, NY	10451
TARTAGLIA, JOHN ANDREW	COMPOSER-CONDUCTOR	11300 W OLYMPIC BLVD #610	LOS ANGELES, CA	90064
TARTAN, JAMES	ACTOR- TV DIRECTOR	1155 N BRONSON AVE	LOS ANGELES, CA	90038
TARTER, FRED C	TV PRODUCER	RAINBOW GROUP, 210 E 39TH ST	NEW YORK, NY	10016
TARTIKOFF, BRANDON	TV EXECUTIVE	1479 LINDACREST DR	BEVERLY HILLS, CA	90210
TASCO, RAI	ACTOR-DIRECTOR	12838 KLING ST	STUDIO CITY, CA	91604
TASEFF, CARL	FOOTBALL COACH	DOLPHINS, 2269 NW 199TH ST	MIAMI, FL	33056
TASH, MAX D	TV WRITER	1819 N SIERRA BONITA AVE	LOS ANGELES, CA	90046
TASKER, STEVE	FOOTBALL	BILLS, 1 BILLS DR	ORCHARD PARK, NJ	14127

Name	Occupation	Address	City/Country
TASKER, WILLIAM D, JR	COMPOSER-CONDUCTOR	WILHELMSHOHER STR 26	BERLIN 4, 1000 GERMANY
TASTE OF HONEY, A	VOCAL GROUP	DENIS VAUGHAN MGMT	
		HEATHCOAT HOUSE	
		19-20 SAVILLE ROW	LONDON W1 ENGLAND
TATA, TERRY	BASEBALL UMPIRE	300 VILLAGE DR	CHESHIRE, CT 06410
TATANKA	WRESTLER	POST OFFICE BOX 3859	STAMFORD, CT 06905
TATAR, KEVIN	BASEBALL	POST OFFICE BOX 11002	CHATTANOOGA, TN 37401
TATARIAN, DEAN	BASEBALL	300 STADIUM WY	DAVENPORT, FL 33837
TATARINOV, PETER	HOCKEY	JETS, 15-1430 MAROONS RD	WINNIPEG, MAN R3G 0L5 CANADA
TATE, DAVID	FOOTBALL	BEARS, 250 N WASHINGTON RD	LAKE FOREST, IL 60045
TATE, LAURA MAE	ACTRESS	8831 SUNSET BLVD #304	LOS ANGELES, CA 90069
TATOIAN, MIKE	BASEBALL EXECUTIVE	POST OFFICE BOX 3496	DAVENPORT, IA 52808
TATOR, JOEL	DIRECTOR	DGA, 7920 SUNSET BLVD, 6TH FL	LOS ANGELES, CA 90046
TATRO, DUANE	COMPOSER-CONDUCTOR	15705 SUPERIOR ST	SEPULVEDA, CA 91343
TATTA, JOHN	TV EXECUTIVE	CABLEVISION SYSTEMS CORP	
		1 MEDIA CROSSWAYS	WOODBURY, NY 11797
TATTERSON, GARY	BASEBALL	POST OFFICE BOX 3452	KINSTON, NC 28502
TATUM, BILL	ACTOR	CBS-TV, "AS THE WORLD TURNS"	
		524 W 57TH ST #5330	NEW YORK, NY 10019
TATUM, JIM	BASEBALL	2850 W 20TH AVE	DENVER, CO 80211
TATUM, MARK	SINGER	6750 W 75TH ST, BLDG #2-A	OVERLAND PARK, KS 66204
TATUM, TANI	GOLFER	2750 VOLUSA AVE #B	DAYTON BEACH, FL 32114
TATUM, WILLIE	BASEBALL	POST OFFICE BOX 1718	NEW BRITAIN, CT 06050
TATUPU, MOSI	FOOTBALL	RAMS, 2327 W LINCOLN BLVD	ANAHEIM, CA 92801
TAUB, HENRY	BASKETBALL EXECUTIVE	N J NETS, MEADOWLANDS ARENA	EAST RUTHERFORD, NJ 07073
TAUB, WILLIAM STEVEN	TV WRITER	1844 WESTHOLME AVE	LOS ANGELES, CA 90025
TAUBENSEE, EDDIE	BASEBALL	POST OFFICE BOX 288	HOUSTON, TX 77001
TAUBIN, AMY	FILM CRITIC	THE VILLAGE VOICE	
		80 UNIVERSITY PL	NEW YORK, NY 10003
TAUBIN, WILLIAM	DIRECTOR	60 HICKORY DR	EAST HILLS, LI, NY 11576
TAUPIN, BERNIE	LYRICIST	1422 DEVLIN DR	LOS ANGELES, CA 90069
TAUSS, HERBERT	ARTIST	42 BOND ST #4	NEW YORK, NY 10012
TAUZIN, W J "BILLY"	U S CONGRESSMAN	210 E MAIN ST	NEW IBERIA, LA 70560
TAVAREZ, HECTOR	BASEBALL	POST OFFICE BOX 957	DUNEDIN, FL 34697
TAVAREZ, JESUS	BASEBALL	POST OFFICE BOX 4756	JACKSONVILLE, FL 32201
TAVERNIER, BERTRAND	FILM DIRECTOR	LITTLE BEAR PRODUCTIONS	
		66 BLVD, MALESHERDES	PARIS 75008 FRANCE
TAVIS, WARREN J	COMPOSER	1820 N GRACE AVE #6	LOS ANGELES, CA 90028
TAWEEL, GEORGE	WRITER-PRODUCER	5609 COLFAX AVE #250	NORTH HOLLYWOOD, CA 91601
TAXIER, ARTHUR	ACTOR	9200 SUNSET BLVD #625	LOS ANGELES, CA 90069
TAXXI	ROCK & ROLL GROUP	POST OFFICE BOX 7308	CARMEL, CA 93923
TAYLFORTH, GILLIAN	ACTRESS	SARABAND, 265 LIVERPOOL RD	LONDON N1 1LX ENGLAND
TAYLOR, AARON	BASEBALL	POST OFFICE BOX 4488	WINSTON-SALEM, NC 27115
TAYLOR, ANNE F	SCREENWRITER	8955 BEVERLY BLVD	WEST HOLLYWOOD, CA 90048
TAYLOR, BAZ	TV DIRECTOR-PRODUCER	17 ALEXANDER ST	LONDON W2 5NT ENGLAND
TAYLOR, BENEDICT	ACTOR	HAMPER, 4 GREAT QUEEN ST	LONDON WC2B 5DG ENGLAND
TAYLOR, BILL	BASEBALL	POST OFFICE BOX 16683	GREENVILLE, SC 29606
TAYLOR, BILLY	BASEBALL	POST OFFICE BOX 6667	RICHMOND, VA 23230
TAYLOR, BILLY E	MUSICIAN	555 KAPPOCK ST	RIVERDALE, NY 10463
TAYLOR, BILLY, TRIO	JAZZ TRIO	CASSIDY, 417 MARAWOOD DR	WOODSTOCK, IL 60098
TAYLOR, BOB	CARTOONIST	DALLAS TIMES-HERALD	
		1101 PACIFIC AVE	DALLAS, TX 75202
TAYLOR, BRIAN	FOOTBALL	BILLS, 1 BILLS DR	ORCHARD PARK, NJ 14127
TAYLOR, BRIEN	BASEBALL	5301 NW 12TH AVE	FORT LAUDERDALE, FL 33309
TAYLOR, BUCK	ACTOR	2899 AGOURA RD #275	WESTLAKE VILLAGE, CA 91361
TAYLOR, CHARLES	ACTOR	SAVAGE, 6212 BANNER AVE	LOS ANGELES, CA 90038
TAYLOR, CHARLES	BASEBALL SCOUT	POST OFFICE BOX 90111	ARLINGTON, TX 76004
TAYLOR, CHARLES H	U S CONGRESSMAN	22 S PACK SQ #330	ASHEVILLE, NC 28801
TAYLOR, CHARLEY	FOOTBALL COACH	POST OFFICE BOX 17247 (DULLES)	WASHINGTON, DC 20041
TAYLOR, CHARLIE	BASEBALL COACH	POST OFFICE BOX 4209	JACKSON, MS 39296
TAYLOR, CHARLIE	FOOTBALL EXECUTIVE	FALCONS, SUWANEE RD AT I-85	SUWANEE, GA 30174
TAYLOR, CLARICE	ACTRESS	35 HAMITON TERR	NEW YORK, NY 10031
TAYLOR, CRAIG	FOOTBALL	BENGALS, 200 RIVERFRONT STADIUM	CINCINNATI, OH 45202
TAYLOR, CURTIS L	ACTOR	5411 RUSSELL AVE #12	LOS ANGELES, CA 90027
TAYLOR, DAHL	ARTIST	508 GRAND ST	TROY, NY 12180
TAYLOR, DAVE	HOCKEY	POST OFFICE BOX 17013	INGLEWOOD, CA 90308
TAYLOR, DAVID C	SCREENWRITER	131 S RODEO DR #300	BEVERLY HILLS, CA 90212
TAYLOR, DELBERT	CONDUCTOR	1266 MEADOWBROOK AVE	LOS ANGELES, CA 90019
TAYLOR, DON	FILM DIRECTOR	1111 SAN VICENTE BLVD	SANTA MONICA, CA 90402
TAYLOR, DUB	ACTOR	21417 GAONA ST	WOODLAND HILLS, CA 91364
TAYLOR, DWIGHT	BASEBALL	POST OFFICE BOX 11002	CHATTANOOGA, TN 37401
TAYLOR, ELIZABETH	ACTRESS	700 NIMES RD	LOS ANGELES, CA 90077
TAYLOR, ERNEST J W	COMPOSER	11167 KLING ST	NORTH HOLLYWOOD, CA 91607
TAYLOR, ERNEST-FRANK	ACTOR	3857 TRACY ST	LOS ANGELES, CA 90027
TAYLOR, EVE	ACTRESS	10 AVENUE COURT, RIVERDALE PK	
		RANMOOR	SHEFFIELD S10 3DR ENGLAND
TAYLOR, FRANK	TV DIRECTOR	4201 ARCH DR	STUDIO CITY, CA 91604
TAYLOR, GENE	U S CONGRESSMAN	1225 JACKSON AVE	PASCAGOULA, MS 39569
TAYLOR, GLENHALL	WRITER	1603 GLENDON AVE #6	LOS ANGELES, CA 90024
TAYLOR, GREG	SCREENWRITER	8955 BEVERLY BLVD	WEST HOLLYWOOD, CA 90048
TAYLOR, GREG "FINGERS"	HARMONICIST	RED LIGHTNIN, THE WHITE HOUSE	
		THE SAINT, NORTH LOPHAM, DISS	NORFOLK IP22 2LU ENGLAND
TAYLOR, HOLLAND	ACTRESS	POST OFFICE BOX 5617	BEVERLY HILLS, CA 90213
TAYLOR, JACKIE LYNN	ACTRESS	115 THORN ST	SAN DIEGO, CA 92103
TAYLOR, JAMES	SINGER-SONGWRITER	ASHER, 644 N DOHENY DR	LOS ANGELES, CA 90069

Name	Occupation	Address	City/State	Zip/Country
TAYLOR, JAY	FOOTBALL	POST OFFICE BOX 888	PHOENIX, AZ	85001
TAYLOR, JEFF	BASEBALL SCOUT	N Y YANKEES, YANKEE STADIUM	BRONX, NY	10451
TAYLOR, JEFFREY	FILM PRODUCER	118 CLEVELAND ST	LONDON W1P 5DN	ENGLAND
TAYLOR, JERI	TV WRITER-DIRECTOR	3861 KINGSWOOD RD	SHERMAN OAKS, CA	91403
TAYLOR, JOHN	FOOTBALL	S F 49ERS, 4949 CENTENNIAL BL	SANTA CLARA, CA	95054
TAYLOR, JOHNNIE	SINGER	POST OFFICE BOX 82	GREAT NECK, NY	11021
TAYLOR, JOSH	ACTOR	422 S CALIFORNIA ST	BURBANK, CA	91505
TAYLOR, JUD	DIRECTOR	1438 RISING GLEN RD	LOS ANGELES, CA	90069
TAYLOR, KATE	SINGER	POST OFFICE BOX 36	CHILMARK, MA	02535
TAYLOR, KEITH	FOOTBALL	POST OFFICE BOX 535000	INDIANPOLIS, IN	46253
TAYLOR, KEN	TV WRITER	17 CREIGHTON AVE	LONDON N10 INX	ENGLAND
TAYLOR, KERRY	BASEBALL	POST OFFICE BOX 661	KENOSHA, WI	53141
TAYLOR, KITRICK	FOOTBALL	POST OFFICE BOX 609609	SAN DIEGO, CA	92160
TAYLOR, KOKO	SINGER	161 W 54TH ST #1203	NEW YORK, NY	10019
TAYLOR, KURT B	COMEDY WRITER	572 E LOMA ALTA DR	ALTADENA, CA	91001
TAYLOR, LARRY	ACTOR	4 MONTROSE AVE, CRAIGHALL PARK	JOHANNESBURG 2196	SO AFRICA
TAYLOR, LAUREN-MARIE	ACTRESS	ABC-TV, "LOVING"		
		320 W 66TH ST, STUDIO 23	NEW YORK, NY	10023
TAYLOR, LAWRENCE	FOOTBALL	N Y GIANTS, GIANTS STADIUM	EAST RUTHERFORD, NJ	07073
TAYLOR, LES	COMPOSER	17000 LISETTE ST	GRANADA HILLS, CA	91344
TAYLOR, LILI	ACTRESS	CAA, 9830 WILSHIRE BLVD	BEVERLY HILLS, CA	90212
TAYLOR, LIONEL	FOOTBALL COACH	BROWNS, 80 1ST ST	BEREA, OH	44017
TAYLOR, LIVINGSTON	SINGER-SONGWRITER	POST OFFICE BOX 16	HILLSBORO, NH	03244
TAYLOR, MALCOLM	TV DIRECTOR	TOPAZ PRODS, 46 WORMHOLT RD	LONDON W12	ENGLAND
TAYLOR, MESHACH	ACTOR	969 MOUNT CURCE AVE	ALTADENA, CA	91001
TAYLOR, MICK	SINGER-SONGWRITER	FOLSOM PRODS, 43 MC KEE DR	MAHWAH, NJ	07430
TAYLOR, MIKE	BASEBALL (KNOXVILLE)	633 JESSAMINE ST	KNOXVILLE, TN	37917
TAYLOR, MIKE	BASEBALL (MYRTLE BCH)	POST OFFICE BOX 1110	MYRTLE BEACH, SC	29578
TAYLOR, MIKE	BASEBALL SCOUT	333 W 35TH ST	CHICAGO, IL	60616
TAYLOR, NOEL	COSTUME DESIGNER	444 WESTBOURNE DR	LOS ANGELES, CA	90048
TAYLOR, PAUL	CHOREOGRAPHER	YESSELMAN, 550 BROADWAY	NEW YORK, NY	10012
TAYLOR, PAUL K	TV WRITER	999 N DOHENY DR #403	LOS ANGELES, CA	90069
TAYLOR, PHILIP JOHN	TV WRITER	9200 SUNSET BLVD #431	LOS ANGELES, CA	90069
TAYLOR, PRISCILLA	ACTRESS	1033 LAS PULGAS RD	PACIFIC PALISADES, CA	90272
TAYLOR, RACHEL	ACTRESS	77 W 85TH ST	NEW YORK, NY	10024
TAYLOR, RANDY	BASEBALL SCOUT	POST OFFICE BOX 90111	ARLINGTON, TX	76004
TAYLOR, RENEE	ACTRESS-WRITER	613 N ARDEN DR	BEVERLY HILLS, CA	90210
TAYLOR, RICH	BASEBALL EXECUTIVE	POST OFFICE BOX 186	BUTTE, MT	59703
TAYLOR, RICHARD	FILM WRITER-PRODUCER	5-65 CANFIELD GARDENS	LONDON NW6	ENGLAND
TAYLOR, RICHARD	TV PRODUCER	65-66 DEAN ST, SOHO	LONDON W1	ENGLAND
TAYLOR, RICKY	BASEBALL SCOUT	TWINS, 501 CHICAGO AVE S	MINNEAPOLIS, MN	55415
TAYLOR, RIP	ACTOR-COMEDIAN	1950 SAWTELLE BLVD	LOS ANGELES, CA	90025
TAYLOR, ROB	BASEBALL	POST OFFICE BOX 3448	SHREVEPORT, LA	71133
TAYLOR, ROB	FOOTBALL	BUCCANEERS, 1 BUCCANEER PL	TAMPA, FL	33607
TAYLOR, ROD	ACTOR	2375 BOWMONT DR	BEVERLY HILLS, CA	90210
TAYLOR, RODERICK	SCREENWRITER	13233 STONERIDGE PL	SHERMAN OAKS, CA	91423
TAYLOR, RONNIE	CINEMATOGRAPHER	37 MOUNT AVE	LONDON W5 1PU	ENGLAND
TAYLOR, SAM	BASEBALL	POST OFFICE BOX 15050	READING, PA	19612
TAYLOR, SCOTT	BASEBALL (GREENVILLE)	POST OFFICE BOX 16683	GREENVILLE, SC	29606
TAYLOR, SCOTT	BASEBALL (PAWTUCKET)	POST OFFICE BOX 2365	PAWTUCKET, RI	02861
TAYLOR, TAMMY	ACTRESS	KELMAN, 7813 SUNSET BLVD	LOS ANGELES, CA	90046
TAYLOR, TERRANCE "TERRY"	WRESTLER	POST OFFICE BOX 105366	ATLANTA, GA	31348
TAYLOR, TERRY	BASEBALL (MAJORS)	9255 S MC CLELLAND ST	CRESTVIEW, FL	32536
TAYLOR, TERRY	BASEBALL (MINORS)	POST OFFICE BOX 12	MIDLAND, TX	79702
TAYLOR, TOMMY	BASEBALL	POST OFFICE BOX 3169	FREDERICK, MD	21701
TAYLOR, TONY	BASEBALL-COACH	5999 E VAN BUREN ST	PHOENIX, AZ	85008
TAYLOR, TROY	FOOTBALL	N Y JETS, 1000 FULTON AVE	HEMPSTEAD, NY	11550
TAYLOR, WADE	BASEBALL	1155 W MOUND ST	COLUMBUS, OH	43223
TAYLOR, WALLY	ACTOR	10100 SANTA MONICA BLVD #700	LOS ANGELES, CA	90067
TAYLOR, WILL	BASEBALL	STARS, 850 LAS VEGAS BLVD N	LAS VEGAS, NV	89101
TAYLOR, WILLIAM A, JR	DIRECTOR	34 ESSEX LN	DEERFIELD, IL	60015
TAYLOR, WILLIAM B	ACTOR	10845 LINDBROOK DR #3	LOS ANGELES, CA	90024
TAYLOR-GOOD, KAREN	SINGER	ESSEX MANAGEMENT		
		1111 16TH AVE S	NASHVILLE, TN	37212
TAYLOR-MEAD, ELIZABETH	TV PRODUCER	METROPOLIS, 147 CROUCH HILL	LONDON N8 9QH	ENGLAND
TAYLOR-YOUNG, LEIGH	ACTRESS	1279 BEVERLY ESTATE DR	BEVERLY HILLS, CA	90210
TEAGAN	BODYBUILDER	POST OFFICE BOX 621	VENICE, CA	90294
TEAGLE, TERRY	BASKETBALL	POST OFFICE BOX 10	INGLEWOOD, CA	90306
TEAGUE, LEWIS	FILM DIRECTOR	2190 N BEVERLY GLEN BLVD	LOS ANGELES, CA	90077
TEAGUE, MARSHALL	ACTOR	8271 MELROSE AVE #110	LOS ANGELES, CA	90046
TEARS, THE	ROCK & ROLL GROUP	618 1/4 N DOHENY DR	LOS ANGELES, CA	90069
TEARS FOR FEARS	ROCK & ROCK DUO	POST OFFICE BOX 4ZN	LONDON W1A 4ZN	ENGLAND
TEBBETTS, BIRDIE	BASEBALL-SCOUT	ORIOLE PARK, 333 W CAMDEN ST	BALTIMORE, MD	21201
TECHMAN, MARC	BASEBALL EXECUTIVE	POST OFFICE BOX 651	AUBURN, NY	13021
TEDESCO, LOU	TV DIRECTOR	11666 MAYFIELD AVE	LOS ANGELES, CA	90049
TEDICK, FEODORE	ACTOR	POST OFFICE BOX 397	CLIFTON, NJ	07011
TEE, KING & MIX MASTER SPADE	RAP DUO-RAPWRITERS	SEE - KING TEE & MIX MASTER SPADE		
TEED, DICK	BASEBALL-SCOUT	1000 ELYSIAN PARK DR	LOS ANGELES, CA	90012
TEEFY, MAUREEN	ACTRESS	LIGHT, 901 BRINGHAM AVE	LOS ANGELES, CA	90049
TEEL, ROSS	TV WRITER	132 S LASKY DR #B	BEVERLY HILLS, CA	90212
TEEMS, DAVID & BLUE EAGLE	ROCK & ROLL GROUP	POST OFFICE BOX 723591	ATLANTA, GA	30339
TEENA MARIE	SINGER	151 S EL CAMINO DR	BEVERLY HILLS, CA	90212
TEENAGE HEAD	ROCK & ROLL GROUP	41 BRITAIN ST #200	TORONTO, ONT M5A 1R7	CANADA
TEENAGERS, THE	VOCAL GROUP	JOEL WARSHAW MANAGEMENT		
		11 MIDDLE NECK RD	GREAT NECK, NY	11021

Name	Occupation	Address	City/State	Zip
TEERLINCK, JOHN	FOOTBALL COACH	BROWNS, 80 1ST ST	BEREA, OH	44017
TEESDALE, CAROL	ACTRESS	2141 S BENTLEY AVE #201	LOS ANGELES, CA	90025
TEEZE	ROCK & ROLL GROUP	POST OFFICE BOX 308	LANSDALE, PA	19446
TEGMAN, SUSANNE	ACTRESS	ATKINS, 303 S CRESCENT HEIGHTS	LOS ANGELES, CA	90048
TEICH, MICHAEL	BASEBALL	POST OFFICE BOX 3746, HILL STA	AUGUSTA, GA	30904
TEICHER, ROY	TV WRITER-PRODUCER	4415 PLACIDIA AVE	NORTH HOLLYWOOD, CA	91602
TEITELBAUM, IRVING	TV PRODUCER	23 HAMILTON GARDENS	LONDON WC2	ENGLAND
TEITLER, WILLIAM	DIRECTOR	434 GREENWICH ST	NEW YORK, NY	10013
TEJADA, FRANCISCO	BASEBALL	POST OFFICE BOX 1721	SPARTANBURG, SC	29304
TEJERO, FAUSTO	BASEBALL	10233 96TH AVE	EDMONTON, ALB TK5 0A5	CANADA
TEKULVE, KENT	BASEBALL	1531 SEQUOIA	PITTSBURGH, PA	15241
TELETUNES, THE	ROCK & ROLL GROUP	POST OFFICE BOX 427	BROOMFIELD, CO	80020
TELFORD, ANTHONY	BASEBALL	500 NORTON ST	ROCHESTER, NY	14621
TELFORD, ROBERT S	ACTOR-DIRECTOR	3925 E 14TH ST	LONG BEACH, CA	90804
TELGENHOF, PAM	ACTRESS	20652 LASSEN ST #70	CHATSWORTH, CA	91311
TELGENHOF, TAM	ACTRESS	20652 LASSEN ST #70	CHATSWORTH, CA	91311
TELGHEDER, DAVE	BASEBALL	POST OFFICE BOX 1211	NORFOLK, VA	23502
TELL, ARTHUR	ACTOR	360 E 72ND ST	NEW YORK, NY	10021
TELLER, DR EDWARD	SCIENTIST	RADIATION LABORATORY, BOX 80	LIVERMORE, CA	94550
TELLERS, DAVE	BASEBALL	POST OFFICE BOX 842	SALEM, VA	24153
TELLES, RICK	ACTOR	LIGHT, 901 BRINGHAM AVE	LOS ANGELES, CA	90049
TELLGREN, PHILLIP	BASEBALL EXECUTIVE	1100 ALAMEDA	POCATELLO, ID	83201
TEMIANKA, HENRI	VIOLINIST	2915 PATRICIA AVE	LOS ANGELES, CA	90064
TEMPCHIN, JACK	SINGER-SONGWRITER	103 N HWY 101 #1013	ENCINITAS, CA	92008
TEMPE	C & W GROUP	POST OFFICE BOX 256577	CHICAGO, IL	60625
TEMPERLY, KEVIN	BASEBALL EXECUTIVE	POST OFFICE BOX 1295	CLINTON, IA	52733
TEMPLE, JULIEN	FILM DIRECTOR	DIRECTORS, 125 TOTTENHAM CT RD	LONDON W1P 9HN	ENGLAND
TEMPLE, LEW	BASEBALL EXECUTIVE	POST OFFICE BOX 288	HOUSTON, TX	77001
TEMPLE BLACK, SHIRLEY	ACTRESS-AMBASADOR	AMER EMB PRAGUE, UNIT 25302	APO AE, NY	09213
TEMPLETON, BEN	CARTOONIST	TRIBUNE, 64 E CONCORD ST	ORLANDO, FL	32801
TEMPLETON, CHRISTOPHER	ACTRESS-SINGER	5309 LEMP AVE	NORTH HOLLYWOOD, CA	91601
TEMPLETON, GARRY	BASEBALL	13552 DEL POMONTE RD	POWAY, CA	92064
TEMPO, NINO	SINGER	19530 SUPERIOR ST	NORTHRIDGE, CA	91324
TEMPTATIONS, THE	VOCAL GROUP	STAR DIRECTION MGMT		
		605 N OAKHURST DR	BEVERLY HILLS, CA	90210
TEN BROECK, LANCE	GOLFER	POST OFFICE BOX 109601	PALM BCH GARDENS, FL	33418
TEN TEN	ROCK & ROLL GROUP	POST OFFICE BOX 27983	RICHMOND, VA	23261
TENA, PAULINO	BASEBALL	14100 SIX MILE CYPRESS PKWY	FORT MYERS, FL	33912
TENACE, GENE	BASEBALL-COACH	15368 MARKER RD	POWAY, CA	92064
TENAN, JODY LYNN	ACTRESS	11339 1/2 HOMEDALE ST	LOS ANGELES, CA	90049
TENENBAUM, JERRY	VIDEO EDITOR	ENTERTAINMENT TONIGHT		
		PARAMOUNT TELEVISION		
		5555 MELROSE AVE	LOS ANGELES, CA	90038
TENNANT, ANDY	ACTOR-WRITER	10807 ASHTON AVE	LOS ANGELES, CA	90024
TENNANT, CRAIG	ARTIST	51 ORCHARD LN	HILLSDALE, NJ	07642
TENNANT, VICTORIA	ACTRESS	POST OFFICE BOX 929	BEVERLY HILLS, CA	90213
TENNESSEANS, THE	C & W GROUP	POST OFFICE BOX 17272	MEMPHIS, TN	38187
TENNESTEDT, KLAUS	CONDUCTOR	ROESELL 13, 2305 HEIKENDORF	HAMBURG	GERMANY
TENNILLE, TONI	SINGER	POST OFFICE BOX 262	GLENBROOK, NV	89143
TENNISON, JAMES E	ARTIST	117 IRONWORKS RD	CLINTON, CT	06413
TENNYSON, BRIAN	GOLFER	POST OFFICE BOX 109601	PALM BCH GARDENS, FL	33418
TENOWICH, THOMAS F	TV WRITER	4936 GLORIA AVE	ENCINO, CA	91436
TENSER, MARILYN	FILM PRODUCER	CROWN INTERNATIONAL, INC		
		8701 WILSHIRE BLVD	BEVERLY HILLS, CA	90211
TENTER, MICHAEL	FOOTBALL	EAGLES, BROAD ST & PATTISON AVE	PHILADELPHIA, PA	19148
TENUTA, JUDY	COMEDIENNE	332 E EUCLID AVE	OAK PARK, IL	60302
TEPPER, CRAIG	TV WRITER	9200 SUNSET BLVD #402	LOS ANGELES, CA	90069
TEPPER, MARVIN	BASEBALL EXECUTIVE	METS, 126TH ST & ROOSEVELT AVE	FLUSHING, NY	11368
TEPPER, ROBERT	SINGER-GUITARIST	SCOTTI BROS, 2128 PICO BLVD	SANTA MONICA, CA	90405
TEPPER, WILLIAM	ACTOR-WRITER	STONE MANNERS, 9113 SUNSET BL	LOS ANGELES, CA	90069
TEQUILA SUNRISE	C & W GROUP	BENNETT, 4630 DEEPDALE DR	CORPUS CHRISTI, TX	78413
TERDOSLAVICH, DANIEL	WRI-DIR-PROD	630 1ST AVE #18-D	NEW YORK, NY	10016
TEREFENKO, THOMAS P	TV WRITER	199 E 76TH ST	NEW YORK, NY	10021
TERESA, MOTHER	HUMANITARIAN	MISSION OF CHARITY		
		54-A LOWER CIRCULAR RD	CALCUTTA 7000016	INDIA
TERESE, EMMA	ACTRESS	BLOOM, 233 PARK AVE S, 10TH FL	NEW YORK, NY	10017
TERILLI, JOEY	BASEBALL	1524 W NEBRASKA AVE	PEORIA, IL	61604
TERILLI, JOHN	BODYBUILDER	POST OFFICE BOX M47	HOBOKEN, NJ	07030
TERLECKY, BILL	BASEBALL EXECUTIVE	POST OFFICE BOX 3449	SCRANTON, PA	18505
TERPLAK, HELEN E	TV EXECUTIVE	VIACOM INTERNATIONAL, INC		
		1211 AVE OF THE AMERICAS	NEW YORK, NY	10036
TERRASAS, RUDY	BASEBALL SCOUT	POST OFFICE BOX 90111	ARLINGTON, TX	76004
TERREL, WALT	BASEBALL	TIGERS, TIGER STADIUM	DETROIT, MI	48216
TERRELL, JAMES	BASEBALL	POST OFFICE BOX 9194	HAMPTON, VA	23670
TERRELL, JERRY	BASEBALL-SCOUT	TWINS, 501 CHICAGO AVE S	MINNEAPOLIS, MN	55415
TERRELL, PAT	FOOTBALL	RAMS, 2327 W LINCOLN BLVD	ANAHEIM, CA	92801
TERRELL, WALT	BASEBALL	2188 RICE PIKE	UNION, KY	41091
TERRENCE, PHILIP	TV DIRECTOR-PRODUCER	12214 IREDELL ST	STUDIO CITY, CA	91604
TERRILL, HOWARD	FILM EDITOR	ACE, 1041 N FORMOSA AVE	WEST HOLLYWOOD, CA	90046
TERRIO, DENEY	DANCER-TV HOST	8535 W KNOLL DR #311	LOS ANGELES, CA	90069
TERRIS, MALCOLM	ACTOR	14 ENGLAND'S LN	LONDON NW3	ENGLAND
TERRIS, NORMA	SINGER-ACTRESS	SEA RANCH CLUB		
		5100 N OCEAN BLVD #711	FORT LAUDERDALE, FL	33308
TERRY, BLOSSOM	ACTOR	SOUTH PARK TOWERS		
		124 W 60TH ST #29-K	NEW YORK, NY	10023

		660 MADISON AVE	NEW YORK, NY	10021
TERRY, JOSEPH C	DIRECTOR	DGA, 110 W 57TH ST	NEW YORK, NY	10019
TERRY, KEN	COLUMNIST	5700 WILSHIRE BLVD #120	LOS ANGELES, CA	90036
TERRY, MARY SUE	ATTORNEY GENERAL	STATE CAPITOL BUILDING	RICHMOND, VA	23219
TERRY, MEGAN	PLAYWRIGHT	2309 HANSCOM BLVD	OMAHA, NE	68105
TERRY, NIGEL	ACTOR	43-A PRINCESS RD, REGENTS PK	LONDON NW1 8JS	ENGLAND
TERRY, SCOTT	BASEBALL	250 STADIUM PLAZA	ST LOUIS, MO	63102
TERRY & THE PIRATES	ROCK & ROLL GROUP	POST OFFICE BOX 4355	ARLINGTON, VA	22204
TERRY-COSTIN, KIM	ACTRESS-MODEL	1801 AVE OF THE STARS #1250	LOS ANGELES, CA	90067
TERWILLIGER, TOM	BODYBUILDER	BETTER BODIES MODEL & SPORTS		
		12 W 21ST ST	NEW YORK, NY	10010
TERWILLIGER, WAYNE	BASEBALL-COACH	TWINS, 501 CHICAGO AVE S	MINNEAPOLIS, MN	55415
TESH, JOHN	TV HOST-COMPOSER	ENTERTAINMENT TONIGHT		
		PARAMOUNT TELEVISION		
		5555 MELROSE AVE	LOS ANGELES, CA	90038
TESH, JULIE	ACTRESS	GEDDES, 8457 MELROSE PL #200	LOS ANGELES, CA	90069
TESICH, STEVE	SCREENWRITER	ICM, 40 W 57TH ST	NEW YORK, NY	10019
TESLER, BRIAN	TV EXECUTIVE	LWT, SOUTH BANK, TV CENTRE	LONDON SE1 9LT	ENGLAND
TESREAU, KRISTA	ACTRESS	315 W 57TH ST #4-H	NEW YORK, NY	10019
TESSIER, ALBERT D	COMPOSER-CONDUCTOR	3926 ARLINGTON AVE	LOS ANGELES, CA	90008
TESTA, ANN L	COMPOSER	1811 N PEPPER ST	BURBANK, CA	91505
TESTAVERDE, VINNY	FOOTBALL	BUCCANEERS, 1 BUCCANEER PL	TAMPA, FL	33607
TESTO, RUSS	BODYBUILDER	3 OXFORD RD	TROY, NY	12180
TESTREAU-MIONE, KRISTA	ACTRESS	247 S BEVERLY DR #102	BEVERLY HILLS, CA	90210
TETENBAUM, LAWRENCE	TV DIRECTOR	555 W 57TH ST #1323	NEW YORK, NY	10019
TETER, JIM	COMEDIAN	ROHRBACH, 1525 CEDAR CLIFF DR	CAMP HILL, PA	17011
TETREAULT, MARY	ACTRESS	860 5TH AVE	NEW YORK, NY	10021
TETRICK, MICHAEL C	TV DIRECTOR	622 PRAIRIE	WILMETTE, IL	60091
TETTLETON, MICKEY	BASEBALL	TIGERS, TIGER STADIUM	DETROIT, MI	48216
TETZLAFF, TED	FILM DIRECTOR	DGA, 7920 SUNSET BLVD, 6TH FL	LOS ANGELES, CA	90046
TEUBER, JERRY	COMPOSER	POST OFFICE BOX 1193	DESERT HOT SPGS, CA	92240
TEUFEL, RON	BODYBUILDER	THE UNIVERSE GYM		
		18763 W 107TH AVE	MIAMI, FL	33157
TEUFEL, TIM	BASEBALL	POST OFFICE BOX 2000	SAN DIEGO, CA	92112
TEWELL, DOUG	GOLFER	POST OFFICE BOX 109601	PALM BCH GARDENS, FL	33418
TEWELL, TERRY	BASEBALL	POST OFFICE BOX 10336	CLEARWATER, FL	34617
TEWES, LAUREN	ACTRESS	8271 MELROSE AVE #110	LOS ANGELES, CA	90046
TEWKESBURY, JOAN	FILM WRITER-DIRECTOR	201 OCEAN AVE #1702-B	SANTA MONICA, CA	90402
TEWKSBURY, BOB	BASEBALL	250 STADIUM PLAZA	ST LOUIS, MO	63102
TEWSON, JOSEPHINE	ACTRESS	INTERNATIONAL ARTISTES LTD		
		MEZZANINE FL, 235 REGENT ST	LONDON W1R 8AX	ENGLAND
TEX AND THE HORSEHEADS	ROCK & ROLL GROUP	POST OFFICE BOX 2428	EL SEGUNDO, CA	90245
TEXAS RENEGADE	C & W GROUP	POST OFFICE BOX 57291	DALLAS, TX	75207
TEXAS THUNDER BAND	C & W GROUP	POST OFFICE BOX 171132	NASHVILLE, TN	37217
TEXAS TRADITION	C & W GROUP	POST OFFICE BOX 57291	DALLAS, TX	75207
TEXAS VOCAL CO	C & W GROUP	3198 ROYAL LN #204	DALLAS, TX	75229
TEXAS WATER	C & W GROUP	1311 CANDLELIGHT AVE	DALLAS, TX	75216
TEXEIRA, MARK	ARTIST	2908 HEATH AVE	BRONX, NY	10463
TEXIDOR, JOSE	BASEBALL	POST OFFICE BOX 309	GASTONA, NC	28053
TEXTONES, THE	ROCK & ROLL GROUP	151 S EL CAMINO DR	BEVERLY HILLS, CA	90212
THACKERY, FRANK	CINEMATOGRAPHER	4530 CARPENTER AVE	NORTH HOLLYWOOD, CA	91423
THALBERG, DEBORAH	ACTRESS	8271 MELROSE AVE #110	LOS ANGELES, CA	90046
THALER, ALVIN	TV DIRECTOR-PRODUCER	8 E 83RD ST	NEW YORK, NY	10028
THALER, FRED R	COMPOSER-CONDUCTOR	16169 SUNSET BLVD #306	PACIFIC PALISADES, CA	90272
THALER, ROBERT	ACTOR	200 N ROBERTSON BLVD #219	BEVERLY HILLS, CA	90211
THATCHER, GERALD T	CONDUCTOR	1134 E COLLINS AVE	ORANGE, CA	92667
THATCHER, JAMES W	COMPOSER	13521 TERRACE PL	WHITTIER, CA	90601
THATCHER, MARGARET	PRIME MINISTER	11 DULWICH GATE	LONDON SE21	ENGLAND
THAU, LINDA E	TV WRITER-PRODUCER	828 14TH ST #5	SANTA MONICA, CA	90403
THAW, JOHN	ACTOR	REDWAY (AIM), 5 DENMARK ST	LONDON WC2H 8LP	ENGLAND
THAW, MORT	WRITER	1263 N FLORES ST	LOS ANGELES, CA	90069
THAXTER, PHYLLIS	ACTRESS	716 RIOMAR DR	VERO BEACH, FL	32960
THAXTON, GARLAND	FOOTBALL	POST OFFICE BOX 609609	SAN DIEGO, CA	92160
THAYER, BRYNN	ACTRESS	9301 WILSHIRE BLVD #312	BEVERLY HILLS, CA	90210
THAYER, LORNA	ACTRESS	4055 TUJUNGA AVE #210	STUDIO CITY, CA	91604
THAYER, NANCI	ACTRESS	1541 E 18TH ST	BROOKLYN, NY	11230
THAYER, TOM	FOOTBALL	BEARS, 250 N WASHINGTON RD	LAKE FOREST, IL	60045
THEBERGE, TINA	ACTRESS	POST OFFICE BOX 69590	LOS ANGELES, CA	90069
THEIDOR, MARLON	SINGER-GUITARIST	1335 LOUREL AVE	TOLEDO, OH	43614
THEISMANN, JOE	FOOTBALL	150 BRANCH RD, SE	VIENNA, VA	22180
THEISS, WILLIAM WARE	COSTUME DESIGNER	POST OFFICE BOX 1166	PACIFIC PALISADES, CA	90272
THELEN, JEFF	BASEBALL	POST OFFICE BOX 48	VISALIA, CA	93279
THEMMEN, HAROLD B	CONDUCTOR	10734 VALLEY SPRING LN	NORTH HOLLYWOOD, CA	91602
THEODORE, DONNA	SINGER	20121 VENTURA BLVD #343	WOODLAND HILLS, CA	91364
THEODORE, NICK A	LT GOVERNOR	POST OFFICE BOX 11369	COLUMBIA, SC	29211
THEODORE, SONDRA	ACT-SING-MOD	8306 WILSHIRE BLVD #7018	BEVERLY HILLS, CA	90211
THERESA	SINGER	POST OFFICE BOX 4	LAKE LURE, NC	28746
THEUS, REGGIE	BASKETBALL	N J NETS, MEADOWLANDS ARENA	EAST RUTHERFORD, NJ	07073
THIBAULT, RYAN	BASEBALL	12000 STADIUM RD	ADELANTO, CA	92301
THIBEAU, JACK	ACTOR	280 S BEVERLY DR #400	BEVERLY HILLS, CA	90212
THIBERT, JOHN	BASEBALL	POST OFFICE BOX 22093	GREENSBORO, NC	27420
THIBODEAU, JEFF	BASEBALL UMPIRE	POST OFFICE BOX 608	GROVE CITY, OH	43123
THIBODEAU, TOM	BASKETBALL COACH	TIMBERWOLVES, 600 1ST AVE N	MINNEAPOLIS, MN	55403
THICKE, ALAN	TV HOST-SINGER	10505 SARAH ST	NORTH HOLLYWOOD, CA	91602
THIELE, CHRISTOPHER W	TV DIRECTOR-EDITOR	3156 COOLIDGE AVE	LOS ANGELES, CA	90066

Name	Occupation	Address	City	Zip/Country
THIELE, JOHN C	WRITER-PRODUCER	6255 LE SAGE AVE	WOODLAND HILLS, CA	91367
THIELEN, D J	BASEBALL	POST OFFICE BOX 1295	CLINTON, IA	52733
THIESS, URSULA	ACTRESS	1940 BEL AIR RD	LOS ANGELES, CA	90077
THIGPEN, BOBBY	BASEBALL	333 W 35TH ST	CHICAGO, IL	60616
THIGPEN, KEVIN	ACTOR	CBS-TV, "AS THE WORLD TURNS"		
		524 W 57TH ST #5330	NEW YORK, NY	10019
THIGPEN, LYNNE	ACTRESS	35 W 20TH ST	NEW YORK, NY	10011
THINGS, THE	ROCK & ROLL GROUP	POST OFFICE BOX 7112	BURBANK, CA	91510
THINNES, ROY	ACTOR	8016 WILLOW GLEN RD	LOS ANGELES, CA	90046
THIRD FINGER UP	ROCK & ROLL GROUP	POST OFFICE BOX 48597	NILES, IL	60648
THOMA, STEVE	COMPOSER-CONDUCTOR	548 1/2 W CALIFORNIA ST	GLENDALE, CA	91203
THOMAS, ANDRES	BASEBALL	5999 E VAN BUREN ST	PHOENIX, AZ	85008
THOMAS, ANNA	PRODUCER	NAVA, 10541 BLYTHE AVE	LOS ANGELES, CA	90064
THOMAS, ANNA	SCREENWRITER	ICM, 8899 BEVERLY BLVD	LOS ANGELES, CA	90048
THOMAS, ANTHONY	WRI-DIR-PROD	HEATH, PARAMOUNT HOUSE		
		162-170 WARDOUR ST	LONDON W1V 3AT	ENGLAND
THOMAS, B J	SINGER-SONGWRITER	POST OFFICE BOX 120003	ARLINGTON, TX	76012
THOMAS, BARB	GOLFER	2750 VOLUSA AVE #B	DAYTON BEACH, FL	32114
THOMAS, BETTY	ACTRESS-DIRECTOR	3585 WOODHILL CANYON	STUDIO CITY, CA	91604
THOMAS, BILL	COSTUME DESIGNER	13949 VENTURA BLVD #309	SHERMAN OAKS, CA	91423
THOMAS, BLAIR	FOOTBALL	N Y JETS, 1000 FULTON AVE	HEMPSTEAD, NY	11550
THOMAS, BRODERICK	FOOTBALL	BUCCANEERS, 1 BUCCANEER PL	TAMPA, FL	33607
THOMAS, CAL	COLUMNIST	LA TIMES, TIMES MIRROR SQ	LOS ANGELES, CA	90053
THOMAS, CHARLIE	BASKETBALL EXECUTIVE	POST OFFICE BOX 272349	HOUSTON, TX	77277
THOMAS, CHRISTOPHER	ACTOR	POST OFFICE BOX 69590	LOS ANGELES, CA	90069
THOMAS, CLARENCE	COMPOSER	3908 DEGNAN BLVD	LOS ANGELES, CA	90008
THOMAS, CLARENCE	SUPREME COURT JUDGE	1 1ST ST, NE	WASHINGTON, DC	20543
THOMAS, COREY	BASEBALL	POST OFFICE BOX 10336	CLEARWATER, FL	34617
THOMAS, CRAIG	U S CONGRESSMAN	FEDERAL BUILDING, ROOM 4003	CASPER, WY	82601
THOMAS, DAMIEN	ACTOR	31 KINGS RD	LONDON SW3 4RD	ENGLAND
THOMAS, DARRELL, BAND	C & W GROUP	POST OFFICE BOX B	CARLISLE, IA	50047
THOMAS, DAVID	SINGER	TWIN TONE RECORDS		
		2541 NICOLLET AVE	MINNEAPOLIS, MN	55404
THOMAS, DAVID L	TV DIRECTOR-PRODUCER	295 N MAPLE AVE #2336-G2	BASKING, NY	07920
THOMAS, DEBI	SKATER	22 E 71ST ST	NEW YORK, NY	10021
THOMAS, DERREL	BASEBALL-COACH	POST OFFICE BOX 11363	RENO, NV	89510
THOMAS, DERRICK	FOOTBALL	CHIEFS, 1 ARROWHEAD DR	KANSAS CITY, MO	64129
THOMAS, DOUG	FOOTBALL	SEAHAWKS, 11220 NE 53RD ST	KIRKLAND, WA	98033
THOMAS, ED	FOOTBALL	BUCCANEERS, 1 BUCCANEER PL	TAMPA, FL	33607
THOMAS, ELVIN B	SINGER-GUITARIST	ROUTE #1	CASTALIAN SPRINGS, TN	37031
THOMAS, EMMITT	FOOTBALL COACH	POST OFFICE BOX 17247 (DULLES)	WASHINGTON, DC	20041
THOMAS, ERIC	FOOTBALL	BENGALS, 200 RIVERFRONT STADIUM	CINCINNATI, OH	45202
THOMAS, FRANK	BASEBALL	333 W 35TH ST	CHICAGO, IL	60616
THOMAS, FRANK M	ACTOR	4140 WARNER BLVD #210	BURBANK, CA	91505
THOMAS, GAVIN OWEN	DIRECTOR	DGA, 110 W 57TH ST	NEW YORK, NY	10019
THOMAS, GEORGE	FOOTBALL	FALCONS, SUWANEE RD AT I-85	SUWANEE, GA	30174
THOMAS, GEORGIE A	TREASURER	STATE HOUSE BUILDING	CONCORD, NH	03301
THOMAS, GERALD	FILM DIRECTOR	PINEWOOD STUDIOS, IVER HEATH	IVER, BUCKS SLO ONH	ENGLAND
THOMAS, GORMAN	BASEBALL	POST OFFICE BOX 718	ELK GROVE, WI	53122
THOMAS, GUY	SCREENWRITER	8955 BEVERLY BLVD	WEST HOLLYWOOD, CA	90048
THOMAS, HEATHER	ACTRESS-MODEL	1433 SAN VICENTE BLVD	SANTA MONICA, CA	90402
THOMAS, HELEN	NEWS CORRESPONDENT	2501 CALVERT ST, NW	WASHINGTON, DC	20008
THOMAS, HENRY	ACTOR	9200 SUNSET BLVD #710	LOS ANGELES, CA	90069
THOMAS, HENRY	FOOTBALL	VIKINGS, 9520 VIKING DR	EDEN PRAIRIE, MN	55344
THOMAS, IAN	SINGER-SONGWRITER	41 BRITAIN ST #200	TORONTO, ONT M5A 1R7	CANADA
THOMAS, IRMA	SINGER	ROUNDER RECORDS, 1 CAMP ST	CAMBRIDGE, MA	02140
THOMAS, IRVING	BASKETBALL	POST OFFICE BOX 10	INGLEWOOD, CA	90306
THOMAS, ISIAH	BASKETBALL	THE PALACE OF AUBURN HILLS		
		2 CHAMPIONSHIP DR	AUBURN HILLS, MI	48326
THOMAS, JAY	SINGER-SONGWRITER	POST OFFICE BOX 110423	NASHVILLE, TN	37211
THOMAS, JEREMY	FILM PRODUCER	RECORDED PICTURE COMPANY		
		8-12 BROADWICK ST	LONDON W1	ENGLAND
THOMAS, JIM	BASKETBALL	TIMBERWOLVES, 600 1ST AVE N	MINNEAPOLIS, MN	55403
THOMAS, JOEL	ACTOR	16 STUYVESANT OVAL	NEW YORK, NY	10009
THOMAS, JOHN	DIRECTOR	91 W GAINSBOROUGH RD	THOUSAND OAKS, CA	91360
THOMAS, JONATHAN TAYLOR	ACTOR	ABC-TV, 2040 AVE OF THE STARS	LOS ANGELES, CA	90067
THOMAS, KEITH	BASEBALL	POST OFFICE BOX 842	SALEM, VA	24153
THOMAS, KEN	BASEBALL SCOUT	250 STADIUM PLAZA	ST LOUIS, MO	63102
THOMAS, KEVIN	FILM CRITIC	LA TIMES, TIMES MIRROR SQ	LOS ANGELES, CA	90053
THOMAS, KURT	ACTOR-ATHLETIC	8431 N 75TH ST	SCOTTSDALE, AZ	85258
THOMAS, LARRY	BASEBALL (PITCHER)	1090 N EUCLID AVE	SARASOTA, FL	34237
THOMAS, LARRY	BASEBALL (SCOUT)	FENWAY PARK, 4 YAWKEY WY	BOSTON, MA	02215
THOMAS, LEE	BASEBALL-EXECUTIVE	POST OFFICE BOX 7575	PHILADELPHIA, PA	19101
THOMAS, LILLO	SINGER	HUSH PRODS, 231 W 58TH ST	NEW YORK, NY	10019
THOMAS, MARK	COLUMNIST	5700 WILSHIRE BLVD #120	LOS ANGELES, CA	90036
THOMAS, MARLO	ACTRESS-WRITER	420 E 54TH ST #22-F	NEW YORK, NY	10022
THOMAS, MIKE	BASEBALL (ROCKFORD)	POST OFFICE BOX 2960	SUMTER, SC	29151
THOMAS, PAMELA JEAN	TV DIRECTOR-PRODUCER	MTV NETWORKS, 1775 BROADWAY	NEW YORK, NY	10019
THOMAS, PAT	FOOTBALL COACH	OILERS, 6910 FANNIN ST	HOUSTON, TX	77070
THOMAS, PEG	SINGER	RNJ, 11514 CALVERT ST	NORTH HOLLYWOOD, CA	91606
THOMAS, PHILIP MICHAEL	ACTOR	12156 W DIXIE HIGHWAY	NORTH MIAMI, FL	33161
THOMAS, RALPH	FILM DIRECTOR	PINEWOOD STUDIOS, IVER HEATH	IVER, BUCKS SLO ONH	ENGLAND
THOMAS, RALPH L	FILM DIRECTOR	365 MARKHAM ST	TORONTO, ONT M6G 2K8	CANADA
THOMAS, RAY	COMEDIAN	TUNSTALL, 16654 WYANDOTTE ST	VAN NUYS, CA	91406
THOMAS, RICHARD	ACTOR-DIRECTOR	4834 BONVUE AVE	LOS ANGELES, CA	90027

THOMAS, RICHARD	SINGER	611 BROADWAY #415	NEW YORK, NY	10012
THOMAS, ROBB	FOOTBALL	CHIEFS, 1 ARROWHEAD DR	KANSAS CITY, MO	64129
THOMAS, ROBERT B	COMPOSER	22923 INGOMAR ST	CANOGA PARK, CA	91304
THOMAS, ROBERT G	TV PRODUCER	POST OFFICE BOX 1787	WAYNE, NJ	07470
THOMAS, ROBERT L	U S CONGRESSMAN	POST OFFICE BOX 33	STATESBORO, GA	30458
THOMAS, RODNEY	FOOTBALL	RAMS, 2327 W LINCOLN BLVD	ANAHEIM, CA	92801
THOMAS, ROGER	TV DIRECTOR-PRODUCER	29 COURTNELL ST	LONDON W2	ENGLAND
THOMAS, ROY	SCREENWRITER	11726 SAN VICENTE BLVD #300	LOS ANGELES, CA	90049
THOMAS, ROYAL	BASEBALL	POST OFFICE BOX 1420	WICHITA, KS	67201
THOMAS, RUFUS	SINGER	KINGSNAKES, 205 LAKE BLVD	SANFORD, FL	32771
THOMAS, RUSS	SINGER	POST OFFICE BOX 655	HUDSON, OH	44236
THOMAS, SHAWNA	ACTRESS	8831 SUNSET BLVD #304	LOS ANGELES, CA	90069
THOMAS, SKEETS	BASEBALL	POST OFFICE BOX 5599	LITTLE ROCK, AR	72215
THOMAS, STAN	FOOTBALL	BEARS, 250 N WASHINGTON RD	LAKE FOREST, IL	60045
THOMAS, STEVE	BASEBALL	POST OFFICE BOX 7845	COLUMBIA, SC	29202
THOMAS, STEVE	HOCKEY	BLACKHAWKS, 1800 W MADISON ST	CHICAGO, IL	60612
THOMAS, THOM	TV WRITER	151 S EL CAMINO DR	BEVERLY HILLS, CA	90212
THOMAS, THOMAS D	DIRECTOR	16460 AKRON ST	PACIFIC PALISADES, CA	90272
THOMAS, THURMAN	FOOTBALL	BILLS, 1 BILLS DR	ORCHARD PARK, NJ	14127
THOMAS, TIMMY	SINGER-SONGWRITER	FAA, 1700 BROADWAY, 5TH FLOOR	NEW YORK, NY	10019
THOMAS, TODD	BASEBALL SCOUT	S F GIANTS, CANDLESTICK PARK	SAN FRANICSCO, CA	94124
THOMAS, TONY	FILM-TV PRODUCER	846 N CAHUENGA BLVD	LOS ANGELES, CA	90038
THOMAS, WALTER L, JR	TV DIRECTOR	2600 PINE LAKE RD	WEST BLOOMFIELD, MI	48033
THOMAS, WILLIAM	FOOTBALL	EAGLES, BROAD ST & PATTISON AVE	PHILADELPHIA, PA	19148
THOMAS, WILLIAM M	U S CONGRESSMAN	4100 TRUXTUN AVE #220	BAKERSFIELD, CA	93301
THOMAS-SCOTT, MELODY	ACTRESS	CBS-TV, "YOUNG & THE RESTLESS" 7800 BEVERLY BLVD #3305	LOS ANGELES, CA	90036
THOMASON, HARRY	TV PRODUCER	9220 SUNSET BLVD #311	LOS ANGELES, CA	90069
THOMASSON, DAVID	DIRECTOR-PRODUCER	45 FERN AVE, JESMOND	NEWS UPON TYNE NE2 2QU	ENGLAND
THOME, CHRIS	FOOTBALL	BROWNS, 80 1ST ST	BEREA, OH	44017
THOME, JIM	BASEBALL	INDIANS, CLEVELAND STADIUM	CLEVELAND, OH	44114
THOMERSON, TIM	ACTOR-COMEDIAN	2440 LONE JACK RD	ENCINITAS, CA	92024
THOMI, PATRICK P	COMPOSER	12814 PACIFIC AVE #3	LOS ANGELES, CA	90066
THOMOPOULOS, TONY	FILM EXECUTIVE	1280 STONE CANYON RD	LOS ANGELES, CA	90077
THOMPSON, ANDREA	ACTRESS	POST OFFICE BOX 5617	BEVERLY HILLS, CA	90213
THOMPSON, ANTHONY	FOOTBALL	POST OFFICE BOX 888	PHOENIX, AZ	85001
THOMPSON, BENNIE	FOOTBALL	SAINTS, 1500 POYDRAS ST	NEW ORLEANS, LA	90112
THOMPSON, BILLY	BASKETBALL	MIAMI HEAT, THE MIAMI ARENA	MIAMI, FL	33136
THOMPSON, BRIAN	ACTOR	5750 WILSHIRE BLVD #512	LOS ANGELES, CA	90036
THOMPSON, BRODERICK	FOOTBALL	POST OFFICE BOX 609609	SAN DIEGO, CA	92160
THOMPSON, BRUCE	TV DIRECTOR-PRODUCER	BBC-TV, 56 WOOD LN	LONDON W12 7RJ	ENGLAND
THOMPSON, BUDDY	MUSIC ARRANGER	6807 PENNYWELL DR	NASHVILLE, TN	37205
THOMPSON, CAROLINE	SCREENWRITER	151 S EL CAMINO DR	BEVERLY HILLS, CA	90212
THOMPSON, CHARLES	WRI-DIR-PROD	IFPA, 87 DEAN ST	LONDON W1V 5AA	ENGLAND
THOMPSON, CHARLES P	COMPOSER	6513 LANKERSHIM BLVD, BOX 126	NORTH HOLLYWOOD, CA	91606
THOMPSON, CHRISTIE	SINGER	POST OFFICE BOX 171132	NASHVILLE, TN	37217
THOMPSON, CHRISTOPHER N	WRITER-PRODUCER	3855 BERRY DR	STUDIO CITY, CA	91604
THOMPSON, CHUCK	SPORTSCASTER	WBAL RADIO, 3800 HOOPER AVE	BALTIMORE, MD	21211
THOMPSON, CYNTHIA L	TV WRITER	CAA, 9830 WILSHIRE BLVD	BEVERLY HILLS, CA	90212
THOMPSON, DALEY	TRACK & FIELD	1 CHURCH ROW, WANDSWORTH PLAIN	LONDON SW18	ENGLAND
THOMPSON, DARRELL	FOOTBALL	PACKERS, 1265 LOMBARDI AVE	GREEN BAY, WI	54307
THOMPSON, DONALD B	COMPOSER	12671 CHASE ST	GARDEN GROVE, CA	92641
THOMPSON, DONALD G	SCREENWRITER	8955 BEVERLY BLVD	WEST HOLLYWOOD, CA	90048
THOMPSON, DONNELL	FOOTBALL	POST OFFICE BOX 535000	INDIANPOLIS, IN	46253
THOMPSON, E FRANCIS	DIRECTOR	310 E 51ST ST	NEW YORK, NY	10022
THOMPSON, ELLEN	ARTIST	97 PINE GROVE AVE	SOMERSET, NJ	08873
THOMPSON, EMMA	ACTRESS	GAY, 24 DENMARK ST	LONDON WC2H 8HJ	ENGLAND
THOMPSON, ERNEST	SCREENWRITER	8955 BEVERLY BLVD	WEST HOLLYWOOD, CA	90048
THOMPSON, EVELYN	COSTUME DESIGNER	13949 VENTURA BLVD #309	SHERMAN OAKS, CA	91423
THOMPSON, FAY	BASEBALL SCOUT	FENWAY PARK, 4 YAWKEY WY	BOSTON, MA	02215
THOMPSON, FLETCHER	BASEBALL	POST OFFICE BOX 824	BURLINGTON, IA	52601
THOMPSON, FRANKLIN	SCREENWRITER	8955 BEVERLY BLVD	WEST HOLLYWOOD, CA	90048
THOMPSON, GENE	BASEBALL SCOUT	S F GIANTS, CANDLESTICK PARK	SAN FRANICSCO, CA	94124
THOMPSON, GEORGE	TV DIRECTOR	6701 COLGATE AVE	LOS ANGELES, CA	90048
THOMPSON, GREG	SINGER	JIMAK, 600 NEVAN RD	VIRGINIA BEACH, VA	23451
THOMPSON, HANK	SINGER-SONGWRITER	BRAY, 5 RUSHING CREEK CT	ROANOKE, TX	76272
THOMPSON, HILARIE	ACTRESS	3800 BARHAM BLVD #303	LOS ANGELES, CA	90068
THOMPSON, HUNTER	AUTHOR	POST OFFICE BOX 220	WOODY CREEK, CO	81656
THOMPSON, IAN	ACTOR	MARSHALL, 44 PERRYN RD	LONDON W3 7NA	ENGLAND
THOMPSON, J LEE	FILM DIRECTOR	9595 LIME ORCHARD RD	BEVERLY HILLS, CA	90210
THOMPSON, J W	SINGER	POST OFFICE BOX 9104	SHREVEPORT, LA	71139
THOMPSON, JAMES	BASEBALL EXECUTIVE	POST OFFICE BOX 5646	PRINCETON, WV	24740
THOMPSON, JAMES E	DIRECTOR	4826 PATRAE ST	LOS ANGELES, CA	90066
THOMPSON, JOHN G	SCREENWRITER	8955 BEVERLY BLVD	WEST HOLLYWOOD, CA	90048
THOMPSON, JOHN M	ARTIST	64 GANUNG DR	OSSINING, NY	10562
THOMPSON, JUSTIN	BASEBALL	POST OFFICE BOX 64939	FAYETTEVILLE, NC	28306
THOMPSON, LA SALLE	BASKETBALL	PACERS, 300 E MARKET ST	INDIANAPOLIS, IN	46204
THOMPSON, LARRY	FILM PRODUCER	1888 CENTURY PARK E, 6TH FLOOR	LOS ANGELES, CA	90067
THOMPSON, LEA	ACTRESS	7966 WOODROW WILSON DR	LOS ANGELES, CA	90046
THOMPSON, LEROY	FOOTBALL	STEELERS, 300 STADIUM CIR	PITTSBURGH, PA	15212
THOMPSON, LINDA	ACTRESS	1930 CENTURY PARK W #403	LOS ANGELES, CA	90067
THOMPSON, LINDA (2)	SINGER	WM MORRIS, 31-32 SOHO SQ	LONDON W1V 5DG	ENGLAND
THOMPSON, MARK F	SINGER-GUITARIST	1420 OTTER CREEK RD	NASHVILLE, TN	37215
THOMPSON, MILT	BASEBALL	250 STADIUM PLAZA	ST LOUIS, MO	63102
THOMPSON, MYCHAL	BASKETBALL	POST OFFICE BOX 10	INGLEWOOD, CA	90306

THOMPSON, NEIL H	ACTOR-WRITER	5101 LEDGE AVE	NORTH HOLLYWOOD, CA 91601
THOMPSON, RAYMOND W	ACTOR-WRITER	MLR, 200 FULHAM RD	LONDON SW10 9PN .... ENGLAND
THOMPSON, REYNA	FOOTBALL	N Y GIANTS, GIANTS STADIUM	EAST RUTHERFORD, NJ 07073
THOMPSON, RICH	BASEBALL	7 CHAMBERS CT	HUNTINGTON STATION, NY...... 11746
THOMPSON, RICHARD	SINGER-GUITARIST	POST OFFICE BOX 7095	NEW YORK, NY 10116
THOMPSON, ROBBY	BASEBALL	S F GIANTS, CANDLESTICK PARK	SAN FRANICSCO, CA 94124
THOMPSON, ROBERT C	DIRECTOR-PRODUCER ...	4536 MARY ELLEN AVE	SHERMAN OAKS, CA 91423
THOMPSON, ROCKY	GOLFER	PGA SENIORS, 112 T P C BLVD	PONTE VEDRA BEACH, FL 32082
THOMPSON, RON & THE RESISTORS .	C & W GROUP	POST OFFICE BOX 1909	MILL VALLEY, CA 94942
THOMPSON, RYAN	BASEBALL	CHIEFS, MAC ARTHUR STADIUM	SYRACUSE, NY 13208
THOMPSON, SADA	ACTRESS	POST OFFICE BOX 490	SOUTHBURY, CT 06488
THOMPSON, SCOTT "THE SCATMAN" .	GOLFER-STUD	POST OFFICE BOX 23596	SAN DIEGO, CA 92193
THOMPSON, STEVE	BASKETBALL	POST OFFICE BOX 4658	DENVER, CO 80204
THOMPSON, TIM	BASEBALL SCOUT	250 STADIUM PLAZA	ST LOUIS, MO 63102
THOMPSON, TOMMY	BASEBALL SCOUT	BREWERS, 201 S 46TH ST	MILWAUKEE, WI 53214
THOMPSON, TOMMY	TV PRODUCER	9220 SUNSET BLVD #311	LOS ANGELES, CA 90069
THOMPSON, TOMMY . (OKLA CITY) .	BASEBALL MANAGER	POST OFFICE BOX 75089	OKLAHOMA CITY, OK 73147
THOMPSON, TOMMY . (SOUTH BEND)	BASEBALL MANAGER	POST OFFICE BOX 4218	SOUTH BEND, IN 46634
THOMPSON, TOMMY G	GOVERNOR	STATE CAPITOL BUILDING	MADISON, WI 53702
THOMPSON, VIRGIL	COMPOSER	222 W 23RD ST	NEW YORK, NY 10011
THOMPSON, WES	DIRECTOR	15619 W SOLEDAD CANYON RD	CANYON COUNTRY, CA 91351
THOMPSON BAKER, SCOTT	ACTOR	ABC-TV, "ALL MY CHILDREN"	....
	....	320 W 66TH ST	NEW YORK, NY 10023
THOMPSON TWINS, THE	ROCK & ROLL TRIO	TEEFAX, 9 ECCLESTON ST	LONDON SW1 .... ENGLAND
THOMPSON-GROCH, SHARON	ARTIST	215 MARTIN AVE	PITTSBURGH, PA 15216
THOMSON, ALEX	CINEMATOGRAPHER	64 MINCING LN, CHOBHAM	SURREY GU24 8RT .... ENGLAND
THOMSON, BOBBY	BASEBALL	122 SUNLIT DR	WATCHUNG, NJ 07060
THOMSON, BRENDA	ACTRESS	4704 CAHUENGA BLVD	NORTH HOLLYWOOD, CA 91602
THOMSON, KIM	ACTRESS	LONDON MGT, 235-241 REGENT ST ...	LONDON W1R 4PH .... ENGLAND
THOMSON, ROB	BASEBALL COACH	ALBANY YANKEES, HERITAGE PARK ...	ALBANY, NY 12211
THON, DICKIE	BASEBALL	POST OFFICE BOX 90111	ARLINGTON, TX 76004
THON, FRANKIE	BASEBALL SCOUT	POST OFFICE BOX 288	HOUSTON, TX 77001
THORNBER, THOMAS A	TV DIRECTOR	GENERAL DELIVERY	LITCHFIELD, CT 06759
THORNBURG, LACY H	ATTORNEY GENERAL	STATE CAPITOL BUILDING	RALEIGH, NC 27603
THORNDIKE, CHUCK	CARTOONIST	11660 CANAL DR	NORTH MIAMI, FL 33161
THORNE, ANGELA	ACTRESS	WHITEHALL, 125 GLOUCESTER RD	LONDON SW7 4TE .... ENGLAND
THORNE, DONALD K	TV DIRECTOR	9255 DOHENY RD	LOS ANGELES, CA 90069
THORNE, DYANNE	ACTRESS	8360 MELROSE AVE #203	LOS ANGELES, CA 90069
THORNE, FRANCIS	COMPOSER	116 E 66TH ST	NEW YORK, NY 10021
THORNE, FRED	DIRECTOR	4453 GENTRY AVE	NORTH HOLLYWOOD, CA 91604
THORNE, KENNETH R	COMPOSER	8040 BOBBY BOYAR AVE	CANOGA PARK, CA 91304
THORNE, WORLEY	TV WRITER	SHAPIRO, 8827 BEVERLY BLVD	LOS ANGELES, CA 90048
THORNE-SMITH, COURTNEY	ACTRESS	9301 WILSHIRE BLVD #312	BEVERLY HILLS, CA 90210
THORNLEY, STEVEN	SCREENWRITER	8955 BEVERLY BLVD	WEST HOLLYWOOD, CA 90048
THORNTON, ANDRE	BASEBALL	POST OFFICE BOX 395	CHAGRIN FALLS, OH 44022
THORNTON, BOB	BASKETBALL	POST OFFICE BOX 25040	PHILADELPHIA, PA 19147
THORNTON, GEORGE	FOOTBALL	POST OFFICE BOX 609609	SAN DIEGO, CA 92160
THORNTON, JAMES	FOOTBALL	BEARS, 250 N WASHINGTON RD	LAKE FOREST, IL 60045
THORNTON, LES	WRESTLER	POST OFFICE BOX 3859	STAMFORD, CT 06905
THORNTON, LOU	BASEBALL	115 MC LEAN RD	HOPE HULL, AL 36043
THORNTON, PHILIP J	DIRECTOR	703 BELLEVUE AVE E #F-31	SEATTLE, WA 98102
THORNTON, RAY	U S CONGRESSMAN	1705 LONGWORTH HOUSE OFF BLDG ...	WASHINGTON, DC 20515
THORNTON, REGGIE	FOOTBALL	POST OFFICE BOX 535000	INDIANPOLIS, IN 46253
THORNTON, WILLIAM J, JR	COMPOSER	347 SHARON DR	SAN ANTONIO, TX 78216
THOROGOOD, GEORGE & THE DESTROY	ROCK & ROLL GROUP ...	POST OFFICE BOX 170429	SAN FRANCISCO, CA 94117
THORP, MAUREEN	TV DIRECTOR	54 W 74TH ST	NEW YORK, NY 10023
THORPE, BILLY	SINGER-GUITARIST	PASHA, 5615 MELROSE AVE	HOLLYWOOD, CA 90038
THORPE, JERRY	DIRECTOR	865 S BUNDY DR	LOS ANGELES, CA 90049
THORPE, OTIS	BASKETBALL	POST OFFICE BOX 272349	HOUSTON, TX 77277
THORSON, BRIAN	BASEBALL TRAINER	POST OFFICE BOX 2769	HUNTSVILLE, AL 35804
THORSON, LINDA	ACTRESS	145 W 45TH ST #1204	NEW YORK, NY 10036
THOUGHT	ROCK & ROLL GROUP ...	POST OFFICE BOX 2896	TORRANCE, CA 90509
THOUTSIS, PAUL	BASEBALL	POST OFFICE BOX 1718	NEW BRITAIN, CT 06050
THRASHER BROTHERS, THE	C & W GROUP	POST OFFICE BOX 22707	NASHVILLE, TN 37203
THREATT, SEDALE	BASKETBALL	POST OFFICE BOX C-900911	SEATTLE, WA 98109
THREE DEGREES, THE	VOCAL GROUP	19 THE WILLOWS, MAIDENHEAD RD ...	WINDSOR, BERKSHIRE .... ENGLAND
THREE JOHNS, THE	ROCK & ROLL GROUP ...	ABSTRACT RECORDS COMPANY	....
	....	10 TIVERTON RD	LONDON NW10 .... ENGLAND
THREE O'CLOCK, THE	ROCK & ROLL GROUP ...	POST OFFICE BOX 1018	SUN VALLEY, CA 91333
THRELFALL, DAVID	ACTOR	SHARKEY, 15 GOLDEN SQ #315	LONDON W1R 3AG .... ENGLAND
THRIFT, JIM	BASEBALL MANAGER	POST OFFICE BOX 328	PITTSFIELD, MA 01202
THROWER, JOEY	ACTOR	ABC-TV, "ONE LIFE TO LIVE"	....
	....	56 W 66TH ST	NEW YORK, NY 10023
THULIN, INGRID	ACTRESS	KEVINGESTRAND 7-B	DANDERYD .... SWEDEN
THUNDER ROAD	C & W GROUP	JIMKA, 600 NEVAN RD	VIRGINIA BEACH, VA 23451
THUNDER ROAD	ROCK & ROLL GROUP ...	POST OFFICE BOX 448	RADFORD, VA 24141
THUNDERBIRDS, THE FABULOUS	ROCK & ROLL GROUP ...	SEE - FABULOUS THUNDERBIRDS, THE	....
THUNDERKLOUD, BILLY & THE CHIEF	C & W GROUP	1300 DIVISION ST #200	NASHVILLE, TN 37203
THURMAN, GARY	BASEBALL	POST OFFICE BOX 419969	KANSAS CITY, MO 64141
THURMAN, UMA	ACTRESS	9057 NEMO ST #A	WEST HOLLYWOOD, CA 90069
THURMOND, J STROM	U S SENATOR	POST OFFICE BOX 981	AIKEN, SC 29801
THURMOND, MARK	BASEBALL	5999 E VAN BUREN ST	PHOENIX, AZ 85008
THURMOND, NATE	BASKETBALL-EXECUTIVE	GOLDEN STATE WARRIORS	....
	....	OAKLAND COLISEUM ARENA	....
	....	NIMITZ FWY & HEGENBERGER RD	OAKLAND, CA 94621

Name	Occupation	Address	City/State	Zip
THURMOND, STROM	U S SENATOR	FEDERAL BUILDING		
		211 YORK ST, NE	AIKEN, SC	29801
THURSTON, JERREY	BASEBALL	POST OFFICE BOX 611	WATERLOO, IA	50704
THURSTON, MICHAEL R	COMPOSER	13910 SHERMAN OAKS #309	VAN NUYS, CA	91406
TIANT, LUIS	BASEBALL	150 INDIAN LN	CANTON, MA	02021
TIBBETS, PAUL	PILOT	5574 KNOLLWOOD DR	COLUMBUS, OH	44327
TIBBLES, CHRISTINE	TV WRITER	2160 CENTURY PARK E #711	LOS ANGELES, CA	90067
TIBBS, JAY	BASEBALL	216 REDSTONE WY	BIRMINGHAM, AL	35215
TIBBS, T BOOMER	ACTOR	15 ORCHARD FARM RD	PORT WASHINGTON, NY	11050
TICE, JOHN	FOOTBALL	SAINTS, 1500 POYDRAS ST	NEW ORLEANS, LA	90112
TICE, MIKE	FOOTBALL	SEAHAWKS, 11220 NE 53RD ST	KIRKLAND, WA	98033
TICHO, CHARLES J	TV DIRECTOR-PRODUCER	PERFORMANCE DESIGNS		
		100 5TH AVE	NEW YORK, NY	10011
TICOTIN, RACHEL	ACTRESS	14231 MARGATE ST	VAN NUYS, CA	91404
TIDROW, DICK	BASEBALL-SCOUT	N Y YANKEES, YANKEE STADIUM	BRONX, NY	10451
TIDWELL, MIKE	BASEBALL	1524 W NEBRASKA AVE	PEORIA, IL	61604
TIDWELL, RICHARD WILLIAM	DIRECTOR	1262 LEAFWOOD HGTS	NOVATO, CA	94947
TIDYMAN, CHRIS-CLARK	SCREENWRITER	8955 BEVERLY BLVD	WEST HOLLYWOOD, CA	90048
TIEGS, CHERYL	MODEL-SPORTSWEAR DES	9219 FLICKER WY	LOS ANGELES, CA	90069
TIERNEY, LAWRENCE	ACTOR	840 N LARRABEE #2-218	LOS ANGELES, CA	90069
TIERNEY, THOMAS	COMPOSER-LYRICIST	315 RIVERSIDE DR #16-A	NEW YORK, NY	10025
TIFFANY	SINGER-SONGWRITER	13659 VICTORY BLVD #550	VAN NUYS, CA	91041
TIFFANY, PATTY	ACTRESS	8831 SUNSET BLVD #304	LOS ANGELES, CA	90069
TIFFANY & CO	C & W GROUP	POST OFFICE BOX 2642	KALAMAZOO, MI	49003
TIFFIN, PAMELA	ACTRESS-MODEL	15 W 67TH ST	NEW YORK, NY	10023
TIFFIN, PETER	TV PRODUCER	19 OBSERVATORY RD	LONDON SW14 7QB	ENGLAND
TIGAR, KENNETH	ACTOR	225 WINDWARD AVE	VENICE, CA	90291
TIGERT, SUZANNE	BODYBUILDER	POST OFFICE BOX 881	REDONDO BEACH, CA	90277
TIGGLE, CALVIN	FOOTBALL	BUCCANEERS, 1 BUCCANEER PL	TAMPA, FL	33607
TIGHE, KEVIN	ACTOR	250 LAKEWOOD RD	WALNUT CREEK, CA	94598
TIJERINA, ANTHONY	BASEBALL	525 NW PEACOCK BLVD	PORT SAINT LUCIE, FL	34986
TIKARAM, TANITA	SINGER	ASGARD MGMT, 125 PARKWAY	LONDON NW1 7PS	ENGLAND
TIKKANEN, ESA	HOCKEY	OILERS, NORTHLANDS COLISEUM	EDMONTON, ALTA T5B 4M9	CANADA
TIL TUESDAY	ROCK & ROLL GROUP	SYMMETRY, 48 W 75TH ST	NEW YORK, NY	10023
TILL, ERIC	FILM DIRECTOR	62 CHAPLIN CRESCENT	TORONTO, ONT M5P 1A3	CANADA
TILL, LEROY P	TV DIRECTOR	3540 CARRIAGE HILL CIR #T-3	RANDALLSTOWN, MD	21133
TILLEN, JODIE	COSTUME DESIGNER	13949 VENTURA BLVD #309	SHERMAN OAKS, CA	91423
TILLERY, LINDA "TUI"	SINGER	POST OFFICE BOX 3336	BERKELEY, CA	94703
TILLES, JACK H	DIRECTOR	4 DURHAM CT	LINCOLNSHIRE, IL	60045
TILLEY, TOM	HOCKEY	BLUES, 5700 OAKLAND AVE	SAINT LOUIS, MO	63110
TILLIS, MEL	SINGER-SONGWRITER	MC FADEN, 48 MUSIC SQUARE E	NASHVILLE, TN	37203
TILLIS, PAM	SINGER-SONGWRITER	POST OFFICE BOX 2977	HENDERSONVILLE, TN	37077
TILLMAN, DARREN	BASEBALL	1524 W NEBRASKA AVE	PEORIA, IL	61604
TILLMAN, FLOYD	SINGER	4 MUSIC SQUARE E	NASHVILLE, TN	37203
TILLMAN, LEWIS	FOOTBALL	N Y GIANTS, GIANTS STADIUM	EAST RUTHERFORD, NJ	07073
TILLMAN, RUSTY	FOOTBALL COACH	SEAHAWKS, 11220 NE 53RD ST	KIRKLAND, WA	98033
TILLMAN, SPENCER	FOOTBALL	S F 49ERS, 4949 CENTENNIAL BL	SANTA CLARA, CA	95054
TILLY, JENNIFER	ACTRESS	MTA, 9320 WILSHIRE BL, 3RD FL	BEVERLY HILLS, CA	90212
TILTON, CHARLENE	ACTRESS	10351 SANTA MONICA BLVD #211	LOS ANGELES, CA	90025
TILTON, MARTHA	SINGER-ACTRESS	760 LAUSANNE RD	LOS ANGELES, CA	90077
TILTON, ROBERT	EVANGELIST	POST OFFICE BOX 819000	DALLAS, TX	75381
TILVERN, ALAN	ACTOR	12 GROSVENOR RD	LONDON N3	ENGLAND
TIM, TINY	SINGER-SONGWRITER	HOTEL OLCOTT, 27 W 72ND ST	NEW YORK, NY	10023
TIM & THE TURBOS	ROCK & ROLL GROUP	41 BRITAIN ST #200	TORONTO, ONT M5A 1R7	CANADA
TIMBERLAKE, JOHN	BASEBALL EXECUTIVE	POST OFFICE BOX 10336	CLEARWATER, FL	34617
TIME	VOCAL GROUP	POST OFFICE BOX 10119	MINNEAPOLIS, MN	55401
TIMEX SOCIAL CLUB	ROCK & ROLL GROUP	1442-A WALNUT ST	BERKELEY, CA	94709
TIMLIN, MIKE	BASEBALL	SKYDOME, 300 BREMMER BL #3200	TORONTO, ONT M5V 3B3	CANADA
TIMMINS, CALI	ACTRESS	10351 SANTA MONICA BLVD #211	LOS ANGELES, CA	90025
TIMMONS, KIRBY	TV WRITER	4605 LANKERSHIM BLVD #213	NORTH HOLLYWOOD, CA	91602
TIMMONS, OZZIE	BASEBALL	POST OFFICE BOX 4488	WINSTON-SALEM, NC	27115
TIMOC, SUZANA	COSTUME DESIGNER	742 GALAXY HEIGHTS	LA CANADA, CA	91011
		JULIAN HOUSE, 4 WINDMILL ST	LONDON W1P 1HF	ENGLAND
TIMOTHY, CHRISTOPHER	ACTOR	MARKHAM AND FROGGATT, LTD		
TIMOTHY, RAYMOND J	TV EXECUTIVE	NBC-TV, 30 ROCKEFELLER PLAZA	NEW YORK, NY	10112
TIMPSON, MICHAEL	FOOTBALL	PATRIOTS, FOXBORO STADIUM, RT #1	FOXBORO, MA	02035
TINDALL, HILARY	ACTRESS	BURNETT, 42-43 GRAFTON HOUSE		
		2-3 GOLDEN SQ	LONDON W1R 3AD	ENGLAND
TINERINO, DENNIS	BODYBUILDER	POST OFFICE BOX 299	NORTHRIDGE, CA	91328
TINGLEY, RON	BASEBALL	POST OFFICE BOX 2000	ANAHEIM, CA	92803
TINKER, GRANT	TV EXECUTIVE	531 BARNABY RD	LOS ANGELES, CA	90077
TINKER, MARK C	WRITER-PRODUCER	12335 OTSEGO ST	NORTH HOLLYWOOD, CA	91607
TINNELL, PAUL	BASEBALL SCOUT	POST OFFICE BOX 7000	PITTSBURGH, PA	15212
TINORDI, MARK	HOCKEY	NORTH STARS, 7901 CEDAR AVE S	BLOOMINGTON, MN	55425
TINSLEY, LEE	BASEBALL	4385 TUTT BLVD	COLORADO SPRINGS, CO	80922
TIPPETT, ANDRE	FOOTBALL	PATRIOTS, FOXBORO STADIUM, RT #1	FOXBORO, MA	02035
TIPPETT, DAVE	HOCKEY	JETS, 15-1430 MAROONS RD	WINNIPEG, MAN R3G 0L5	CANADA
TIPPETT, HOWARD	FOOTBALL COACH	PACKERS, 1265 LOMBARDI AVE	GREEN BAY, WI	54307
TIPPETT, SIR MICHAEL	COMPOSER-CONDUCTOR	48 GREAT MARLBOROUGH ST	LONDON W1V 2BN	ENGLAND
TIPPIN, AARON	SINGER-SONGWRITER	POST OFFICE BOX 121996	NASHVILLE, TN	37212
TIPPINS, KEN	FOOTBALL	FALCONS, SUWANEE RD AT I-85	SUWANEE, GA	30174
TIPPIT, G WAYNE	ACTOR	203 HEIGHTS RD	RIDGEWOOD, NJ	07450
TIPPIT, JACK	CARTOONIST	KING FEATURES, 216 E 45TH ST	NEW YORK, NY	10017
TIPPITT, BRADLEY	BASEBALL	POST OFFICE BOX 3169	FREDERICK, MD	21701
TIPTON, GORDON	BASEBALL	POST OFFICE BOX 10031	BAKERSFIELD, CA	93389

TIRCE, LEE	DIRECTOR	4147 DAVANA RD	SHERMAN OAKS, CA	91423
TISCH, LAWRENCE	TV EXECUTIVE	CBS-TV, 51 W 52ND ST	NEW YORK, NY	10019
TISCH, STEVE	TV-FILM PRODUCER	14454 SUNSET BLVD	PACIFIC PALISADES, CA	90272
TISCHLER, GAYE	TV DIRECTOR	WDIV-TV, 550 LAFAYETTE BLVD	DETROIT, MI	48231
TISDALE, JIM	TV WRITER	9300 WILSHIRE BLVD #410	BEVERLY HILLS, CA	90212
TISDALE, TOM	BASEBALL TRAINER	POST OFFICE BOX 309	GASTONA, NC	28053
TISDALE, WAYMAN	BASKETBALL	KINGS, 1 SPORTS PARKWAY	SACRAMENTO, CA	95834
TITCHMARSH, ALAN	TV HOST	ARLINGTON, 1-3 CHARLOTTE ST	LONDON W1P 1HD	ENGLAND
TITTLE, Y A	FOOTBALL	310 S LAFAYETTE ST	MARSHALL, TX	75670
TIVERS, CYNTHIA	TV WRITER	1454 EDRIS DR	LOS ANGELES, CA	90035
TKACH, JOHN R	SPORTS WRITER	POST OFFICE BOX 500	WASHINGTON, DC	20044
TLC	RAP TRIO	LA FACE RECORDS, 6 W 57TH ST	NEW YORK, NY	10019
TNT	ROCK & ROLL GROUP	FREEFAL PRESENTATIONS		
		40 UNDERHILL BLVD	SYOSSET, NY	11791
TO, TONY	TV PRODUCER	ASCATO, 6650 SANTA MONICA BLVD	HOLLYWOOD, CA	90038
TOALE, JOHN	BASEBALL	ALBANY YANKEES, HERITAGE PARK	ALBANY, NY	12211
TOBACK, JAMES	FILM WRITER-DIRECTOR	11 E 87TH ST	NEW YORK, NY	10028
TOBACK, NORMAN	DIRECTOR-PRODUCER	3234 OAKDELL RD	STUDIO CITY, CA	91604
TOBER, BARBARA D	WRITER-EDITOR	BRIDE'S MAGAZINE, 350 MADISON AVE	NEW YORK, NY	10017
TOBIAS, MARICE	FILM DIRECTOR	386 S BURNSIDE	LOS ANGELES, CA	90036
TOBIAS, OLIVER	ACTOR	GERANIENSTR 3	D-(W) 8022 GRUNWALD	GERMANY
TOBIN, BILL	FOOTBALL EXECUTIVE	BEARS, 250 N WASHINGTON RD	LAKE FOREST, IL	60045
TOBIN, DAN	ACTOR	919 RIVAS CYN RD	PACIFIC PALISADES, CA	90272
TOBIN, JOHN H	DIRECTOR	3212 ANNRAE ST	SAN DIEGO, CA	92123
TOBIN, VINCE	FOOTBALL COACH	BEARS, 250 N WASHINGTON RD	LAKE FOREST, IL	60045
TOCCHET, RICK	HOCKEY	FLYERS, SPECTRUM, PATTISON PL	PHILADELPHIA, PA	19148
TODD, BEVERLY	ACTRESS	4888 VALLEY RIDGE AVE	LOS ANGELES, CA	90043
TODD, BOB	ACTOR	INTERNATIONAL ARTISTES LTD		
		MEZZANINE FL, 235 REGENT ST	LONDON W1R 8AX	ENGLAND
TODD, HALLIE	ACTRESS	10100 SANTA MONICA BLVD #700	LOS ANGELES, CA	90067
TODD, JACKSON	BASEBALL-COACH	POST OFFICE BOX 4448	TULSA, OK	74159
TODD, JOY	CASTING DIRECTOR	1 W 32ND ST	NEW YORK, NY	10001
TODD, LISA MARIE	ACTRESS-DANCER	1717 N HIGHLAND AVE #414	LOS ANGELES, CA	90028
TODD, PALMER LEE	ACTRESS	4444 WOODMAN AVE #28	SHERMAN OAKS, CA	91423
TODD, RACHEL	ACTRESS	8228 SUNSET BLVD #212	LOS ANGELES, CA	90046
TODD, RICHARD	ACTOR	CHINHAM FARM, FARINGDON	OXFORDSHIRE	ENGLAND
TODD, RUSSELL	ACTOR	NBC-TV, "ANOTHER WORLD"		
		1268 E 14TH ST	BROOKLYN, NY	11230
TODDS, WALTER	TV PRODUCER	17 PRINCE OF WALES TERR	LONDON W8	ENGLAND
TOIBIN, NIALL	ACTOR	15 WESTFIELD RD	DUBLIN 6	IRELAND
TOKATYAN, LEON	TV WRITER	13958 STROUD ST	VAN NUYS, CA	91402
TOKHELM, DAVID	BASEBALL	POST OFFICE BOX 10336	CLEARWATER, FL	34617
TOKOFSKY, JERRY	FILM PRODUCER	11755 MONTANA AVE #302	LOS ANGELES, CA	90049
TOKYO ROSE	RADIO PERSONALITY	IVA TOGURI, 851 W BELMONT AVE	CHICAGO, IL	60657
TOLAN, MICHAEL	ACTOR	1130 PARK AVE	NEW YORK, NY	10128
TOLAND, DAVE	SINGER	POST OFFICE BOX O	EXCELSIOR, MN	55331
TOLAND, JOHN	AUTHOR	1 LONG RIDGE RD	DANBURY, CT	06810
TOLAND, MICHAEL	ACTOR	10351 SANTA MONICA BLVD #211	LOS ANGELES, CA	90025
TOLAR, KEVIN	BASEBALL	POST OFFICE BOX 4370	SALINAS, CA	93912
TOLBERT, BERLINDA	ACTRESS	8271 MELROSE AVE #110	LOS ANGELES, CA	90046
TOLBERT, TOM	BASKETBALL	GOLDEN STATE WARRIORS		
		OAKLAND COLISEUM ARENA		
		NIMITZ FWY & HEGENBERGER RD	OAKLAND, CA	94621
TOLBERT, TONY	FOOTBALL	COWBOYS, 1 COWBOYS PARKWAY	IRVING, TX	75063
TOLEDO, EDDY	BASEBALL SCOUT	METS, 126TH ST & ROOSEVELT AVE	FLUSHING, NY	11368
TOLENTINO, JOSE	BASEBALL	POST OFFICE BOX 450	BUFFALO, NY	14205
TOLES, TOM	CARTOONIST	BUFFALO NEWS, 1 NEWS PLAZA	BUFFALO, NY	14240
TOLIVER, FREDDIE	BASEBALL	1601 BARTON RD #1005	REDLANDS, CA	92373
TOLKIN, MEL	TV WRITER-PRODUCER	2187 SUMMITRIDGE DR	BEVERLY HILLS, CA	90210
TOLL, THEODORE	DIRECTOR	1074 CALLE CASTANO	THOUSAND OAKS, CA	91360
TOLLESON, WAYNE	BASEBALL	352 LANHAM CIR	SPARTANBURG, SC	29302
TOLLISON, DAVID	BASEBALL	633 JESSAMINE ST	KNOXVILLE, TN	37917
TOLLIVER, BILLY JOE	FOOTBALL	FALCONS, SUWANEE RD AT I-85	SUWANEE, GA	30174
TOLLIVER, JEROME	BASEBALL	POST OFFICE BOX 7845	COLUMBIA, SC	29202
TOLLNER, TED	FOOTBALL COACH	POST OFFICE BOX 609609	SAN DIEGO, CA	92160
TOLMAN, TIM	BASEBALL-MANAGER	8601 E FAIRMONT PL	TUCSON, AZ	85715
TOLMAN, TOM	BASEBALL-MANAGER	POST OFFICE BOX 824	BURLINGTON, IA	52601
TOM, HEATHER	ACTRESS	CBS-TV, "YOUNG & THE RESTLESS"		
		7800 BEVERLY BLVD #3305	LOS ANGELES, CA	90036
TOM TOM CLUB	ROCK & ROLL GROUP	GARY KURFIRST, OVERLAND PRODS		
		1775 BROADWAY, 7TH FLOOR	NEW YORK, NY	10019
TOMAN, BONNIE	ACTRESS	6863 SUMMY COVE	HOLLYWOOD, CA	90068
TOMARKEN, PETER	ACT-WRI-DIR	337 S ALMONT DR	BEVERLY HILLS, CA	90211
TOMAS, DONNA	COSTUME DESIGNER	13949 VENTURA BLVD #309	SHERMAN OAKS, CA	91423
TOMASSI, MALGOSIA	ACTRESS	KEACH, 27522 WINDING WY	MALIBU, CA	90265
TOMBERLIN, ANDY	BASEBALL	POST OFFICE BOX 6667	RICHMOND, VA	23230
TOMCZAK, MIKE	FOOTBALL	PACKERS, 1265 LOMBARDI AVE	GREEN BAY, WI	54307
TOMEI, CONCETTA	ACTRESS	9200 SUNSET BLVD #710	LOS ANGELES, CA	90069
TOMEI, MARISA	ACTRESS	BYMEL, 723 WESTMOUNT DR	WEST HOLLYWOOD, CA	90069
TOMITA, TAMLYN	ACTRESS	1930 CENTURY PARK W #403	LOS ANGELES, CA	90067
TOMIZAWA, THOMAS M	DIRECTOR	DGA, 110 W 57TH ST	NEW YORK, NY	10019
TOMJANOVICH, RUDY	BASKETBALL COACH	POST OFFICE BOX 272349	HOUSTON, TX	77277
TOMLAK, MIKE	HOCKEY	WHALERS, 1 CIVIC CENTER PLAZA	HARTFORD, CT	06103
TOMLIN, GARY D	TV WRITER-DIRECTOR	60 E 42ND ST #1158	NEW YORK, NY	10165
TOMLIN, JANICE E	TV PRODUCER	ABC NEWS, "20/20"		

Name	Occupation	Address	City	Zip/Country
		157 COLUMBUS AVE	NEW YORK, NY	10023
TOMLIN, RANDY	BASEBALL	POST OFFICE BOX 7000	PITTSBURGH, PA	15212
TOMLIN, RICK	BASEBALL COACH	136 S SYCAMORE	ELIZABETHTON, TN	37643
TOMLINSON, DAVID	ACTOR	BROOK COTTAGE	MURSLEY BUCKS	ENGLAND
TOMPKINS, ANGEL	ACTRESS	8019 1/2 MELROSE AVE #3	LOS ANGELES, CA	90046
TOMPKINS, BEN	FOOTBALL REFEREE	NFL, 410 PARK AVE	NEW YORK, NY	10022
TOMPKINS, JOE I	COSTUME DESIGNER	10100 SANTA MONICA BLVD #1600	LOS ANGELES, CA	90067
TOMPKINS, STEVE	TV WRITER	131 S RODEO DR #300	BEVERLY HILLS, CA	90212
TOMPKINS, TOBY	ACTOR	210 W 107TH ST #5-I	NEW YORK, NY	10025
TOMPSON, SALLY	TREASURER	STATE CAPITOL BUILDING	TOPEKA, KS	66617
TOMS, DONALD	TV PRODUCER	63 SEELEYS RD, BEACONSFIELD	BUCKS	ENGLAND
TONE-LOC	RAPPER-ACTOR	7932 HILLSIDE AVE	LOS ANGELES, CA	90046
TONELLI, JOHN	HOCKEY	POST OFFICE BOX 17013	INGLEWOOD, CA	90308
TONI, JOLENE	SINGER	MEAUX, 566 BROCK ST	HOUSTON, TX	77023
TONY! TONI! TONE!	RAPPERS-RAWRITERS	LEFT BANK, 6255 SUNSET BLVD	HOLLYWOOD, CA	90028
TOO $HORT	RAPPER	ZOMBA RECORD COMPANY		
		137-139 W 25TH ST	NEW YORK, NY	10001
TOOD, SWEENEY	ROCK GROUP	SEE - SWEENEY TODD		
TOOK, BARRY	TV-RADIO WRITER	17 HANOVER HOUSE		
		SAINT JOHN'S WOOD, HIGH ST	LONDON NW8	ENGLAND
TOOLE, DOUG	FOOTBALL REFEREE	NFL, 410 PARK AVE	NEW YORK, NY	10022
TOOLEY, SIR JOHN	OPERA DIRECTOR	2 MART ST	LONDON WC2	ENGLAND
TOOLSON, ANDY	BASKETBALL	5 TRIAD CENTER #500	SALT LAKE CITY, UT	84180
TOOMEY, MIKE	BASEBALL SCOUT	S F GIANTS, CANDLESTICK PARK	SAN FRANICSCO, CA	94124
TOON, AL	FOOTBALL	N Y JETS, 1000 FULTON AVE	HEMPSTEAD, NY	11550
TOPAZ	ROCK & ROLL GROUP	POST OFFICE BOX 448	RADFORD, VA	24141
TOPOL, CHAIM	ACTOR-DIRECTOR	22 VALE CT, MAIDVILLE	LONDON W9	ENGLAND
TOPOR, TOM	SCREENWRITER	555 W 57TH ST #1230	NEW YORK, NY	10019
TOPOROFF, RALPH M	DIRECTOR	219 W 81ST ST	NEW YORK, NY	10024
TOPOU IV, HRM	KING OF TONGA	PALACE OFFICIALE	NUKU'ALOFA	TONGA
TOPPER, BURT	WRITER-PRODUCER	999 N DOHENY DR #403	LOS ANGELES, CA	90069
TOPPING, LYNNE	ACTRESS	1680 N VINE ST #1003	HOLLYWOOD, CA	90028
TORBORG, JEFF	BASEBALL-MANAGER	METS, 126TH ST & ROOSEVELT AVE	FLUSHING, NY	11368
TORCHIA, TONY	BASEBALL-COACH	STARS, 850 LAS VEGAS BLVD N	LAS VEGAS, NV	89101
TORGESON, LA VERN	FOOTBALL COACH	POST OFFICE BOX 17247 (DULLES)	WASHINGTON, DC	20041
TORK, PETER	SINGER-ACTOR	SEE - MONKEES, THE		
TORMOHLEN, GENE	BASKETBALL	POST OFFICE BOX 10	INGLEWOOD, CA	90306
TORN, RIP	ACTOR-DIRECTOR	130 W 42ND ST #2400	NEW YORK, NY	10036
TORNOW, TED	BASEBALL EXECUTIVE	800 HOME RUN LN	MEMPHIS, TN	38104
TOROKVEI, PETER J	SCREENWRITER	11342 DONA LISA DR	STUDIO CITY, CA	91406
TORP, JONATHAN	SCREENWRITER	2049 CENTURY PARK E #1320	LOS ANGELES, CA	90067
TORPEY, ERIN	ACTRESS	ABC-TV, "ONE LIFE TO LIVE"		
		56 W 66TH ST	NEW YORK, NY	10023
TORRE, JOE	BASEBALL-MANAGER	250 STADIUM PLAZA	ST LOUIS, MO	63102
TORRE, MARIE	TV WRITER-PRODUCER	842 QUINTON RD	SALEM, NJ	08079
TORRENCE, DEAN	SINGER-SONGWRITER	6310 RODGERTON DR	LOS ANGELES, CA	90068
TORRES, ANGELO	CARTOONIST	MAD MAGAZINE, 485 MADISON AVE	NEW YORK, NY	10022
TORRES, CESAR A	DIRECTOR	DGA, 110 W 57TH ST	NEW YORK, NY	10019
TORRES, ESTEBAN E	U S CONGRESSMAN	8819 WHITTIER BLVD #101	PICO RIVERA, CA	90660
TORRES, HECTOR	BASEBALL-COACH	SKYDOME, 300 BREMMER BL #3200	TORONTO, ONT M5V 3B3	CANADA
TORRES, JESSIE	BASEBALL	POST OFFICE DRAWER 1218	ZEBULON, NC	27597
TORRES, JOAN E	SCREENWRITER	2649 34TH ST #C	SANTA MONICA, CA	90405
TORRES, LEO	BASEBALL	TIGERS, 89 WHARNCLIFFE RD N	LONDON, ONT N6H 2A7	CANADA
TORRES, LIZ	SINGER-ACTRESS	1711 N AVENUE "53"	LOS ANGELES, CA	90042
TORRES, PAUL	BASEBALL	POST OFFICE BOX 4488	WINSTON-SALEM, NC	27115
TORRES, SALOMON	BASEBALL	POST OFFICE BOX 3448	SHREVEPORT, LA	71133
TORREY, RICH	CARTOONIST	KING FEATURES, 216 E 45TH ST	NEW YORK, NY	10017
TORRICELLI, ROBERT	U S CONGRESSMAN	COURT PLAZA, 25 MAIN ST	HACKENSACK, NJ	07601
TORTELIER, YAN PASCAL	CONDUCTOR	ICM, 40 W 57TH ST	NEW YORK, NY	10019
TORTORIELLO, DONALD	DIRECTOR	417 E 84TH ST	NEW YORK, NY	10028
TORVE, KELVIN	BASEBALL	2608 LAWNDALE	RAPID CITY, SD	57701
TOSCA, CARLOS	BASEBALL MANAGER	300 STADIUM WY	DAVENPORT, FL	33837
TOSI, MARIO	CINEMATOGRAPHER	1512 MARLAY DR	LOS ANGELES, CA	90069
TOSTADO, E M	COMPOSER	360 AVENIDA OLANCHA	PALM SPRINGS, CA	92262
TOSTENSON, RON	BASEBALL SCOUT	SKYDOME, 300 BREMMER BL #3200	TORONTO, ONT M5V 3B3	CANADA
TOTALLY INSANE	RAP DUO-RAPWRITERS	IN-A-MINUTE RECORDS		
		1025 W WASHINGTON BLVD	OAKLAND, CA	94608
TOTH, DAVID	BASEBALL	POST OFFICE BOX 4525	MACON, GA	31208
TOTH, ROBERT	BASEBALL	POST OFFICE BOX 464	APPLETON, WI	54912
TOTO	ROCK & ROLL GROUP	7250 BEVERLY BLVD #102	LOS ANGELES, CA	90036
TOTTEN, ROBERT	ACT-WRI-DIR	13819 RIVERSIDE DR	SHERMAN OAKS, CA	91423
TOTTER, AUDREY	ACTRESS	1945 GLENDON AVE #301	LOS ANGELES, CA	90025
TOUBER, SELWYN	DIRECTOR	3546 LAURELVALE DR	STUDIO CITY, CA	91604
TOUCHSTONE, TOM	BODYBUILDER	POST OFFICE BOX 663	LAMONT, CA	93241
TOUFEXIS, ANASTASIA	WRITER-EDITOR	TIME/TIME & LIFE BLDG		
		ROCKEFELLER CENTER	NEW YORK, NY	10020
TOUSSAINT, BETH	ACTRESS	10351 SANTA MONICA BLVD #211	LOS ANGELES, CA	90025
TOUZET, RENE	COMPOSER	7680 NW 4TH ST	MIAMI, FL	33126
TOVATT, PATRICK	ACTOR	CBS-TV, "AS THE WORLD TURNS"		
		524 W 57TH ST #5330	NEW YORK, NY	10019
TOWB, HARRY	ACTOR	17 BRIARDALE GARDENS	LONDON NW3 7PN	ENGLAND
TOWBIN, FREDI	TV WRITER	10550 LAURISTON AVE	LOS ANGELES, CA	90064
TOWER OF POWER	ROCK & ROLL GROUP	151 S EL CAMINO DR	BEVERLY HILLS, CA	90212
TOWER SUITE	ROCK & ROLL GROUP	POST OFFICE BOX 397	MOUNT JULIET, TN	37122
TOWERS, CONSTANCE	ACTRESS	2415 CENTURY HILL	LOS ANGELES, CA	90067

Name	Occupation	Address	City
TOWERS, HARRY ALAN	FILM WRITER-PRODUCER	59 DEVONSHIRE ST #9	LONDON W1 ENGLAND
TOWERS, KEVIN	BASEBALL SCOUT	POST OFFICE BOX 2000	SAN DIEGO, CA 92112
TOWNE, ROBERT	FILM WRITER-DIRECTOR	1417 SAN REMO DR	PACIFIC PALISADES, CA 90272
TOWNE, ROGER	SCREENWRITER	8955 BEVERLY BLVD	WEST HOLLYWOOD, CA 90048
TOWNES, HARRY	ACTOR	100 TEMPO CIRCLE HWY #53	HARVEST, AL 35719
TOWNES, JAZZY JEFF	RAPPER-RAPWRITER	SEE - DJ JAZZY JEFF/FRESH PRINCE	
TOWNLEY, JASON	BASEBALL	633 JESSAMINE ST	KNOXVILLE, TN 37917
TOWNLEY, RICHARD	TV HOST-PRODUCER	220 E 23RD ST #601	NEW YORK, NY 10010
TOWNS, EDOLPHUS	U S CONGRESSMAN	545 BROADWAY, 2ND FLOOR	BROOKLYN, NY 11206
TOWNSEND, BARBARA	ACTRESS	1930 CENTURY PARK W #403	LOS ANGELES, CA 90067
TOWNSEND, BUD	FILM DIRECTOR	5917 BLAIRSTONE DR	CULVER CITY, CA 90230
TOWNSEND, GREG	FOOTBALL	RAIDERS, 332 CENTER ST	EL SEGUNDO, CA 90245
TOWNSEND, JULIAN C	DIRECTOR	65 ABERDEEN DR	TROY, MI 48098
TOWNSEND, LEO	SCREENWRITER	25403 PINE CREEK LN	WILMINGTON, CA 90744
TOWNSEND, MILTON	ARTIST	HUNGRY DOG STUDIO	
		1911 FOUNTAINVIEW #16	HOUSTON, TX 77057
TOWNSEND, ROBERT	COMED-ACT-WRI-PROD	3000 DURAND DR	LOS ANGELES, CA 90068
TOWNSEND-EVANS, COLLEEN	ACTRESS	503 SEWARD ST, NE	WASHINGTON, DC 20003
TOWNSHEND, PETER	SINGER-SONGWRITER	THE BOATHOUSE, RANELAGH DR	TWICKENHAM TW1 1Q2 ENGLAND
TOWNSHEND, SIMON	SINGER	TRINFOLD, 112 WARDOUR ST	LONDON W1 ENGLAND
TOWNSHEND-ZELLNER, JOSH	ACTOR	10845 LINDBROOK DR #3	LOS ANGELES, CA 90024
TOWNSON, RON	SINGER	ICM, 8899 BEVERLY BLVD	LOS ANGELES, CA 90048
TOYNTON, IAN	TV DIRECTOR	PETERS, FRASER & DUNLOP, LTD	
		5TH FLOOR, THE CHAMBERS	
		CHELSEA HARBOUR, LOT RD	LONDON SW10 OXF ENGLAND
TOZER, GEOFF	SINGER-COMPOSER	10557 TROON AVE	LOS ANGELES, CA 90064
TRABER, JIM	BASEBALL	11674 LITTLE PATUXENT #203	COLUMBIA, MD 21044
TRACEWSKI, DICK	BASEBALL-COACH	TIGERS, TIGER STADIUM	DETROIT, MI 48216
TRACHSEL, STEVE	BASEBALL	POST OFFICE DRAWER 1207	ZEBULON, NC 27597
TRACHTA, JEFF	ACTOR	1040 N MAPLE	BURBANK, CA 91505
TRACHTE, DON	CARTOONIST	KING FEATURES, 216 E 45TH ST	NEW YORK, NY 10017
TRACHTENBERG, LEO	DIRECTOR-PRODUCER	98 RIVERSIDE DR	NEW YORK, NY 10024
TRACI, DONNA	SINGER	POST OFFICE BOX 171132	NASHVILLE, TN 37217
TRACY, ARTHUR	ACTOR	350 W 57TH ST	NEW YORK, NY 10019
TRACY, JAMES	BASEBALL	4785 CELADON AVE	FAIRFIELD, OH 45014
TRACY, JEANIE	SINGER	BORZOI, 222 DUNIC ST	SAN FRANCISCO, CA 94131
TRACY, JIM	BASEBALL	POST OFFICE BOX 450	BUFFALO, NY 14205
TRACY, JIM	BASEBALL MANAGER	POST OFFICE BOX 11002	CHATTANOOGA, TN 37401
TRACY, JOHN	TV DIRECTOR	3510 RIDGEFORD DR	WESTLAKE VILLAGE, CA 91361
TRACZ, MARK	BASEBALL EXECUTIVE	POST OFFICE BOX 2148	WOODBRIDGE, VA 22193
TRAFICANT, JAMES A, JR	U S CONGRESSMAN	391 MAHONING AVE	WARREN, OH 44483
TRAFTON, TODD	BASEBALL	POST OFFICE BOX 23290	NASHVILLE, TN 37202
TRAIL	ROCK & ROLL GROUP	HOT RECORDS & ROUGH TRADE	
		326 6TH ST	SAN FRANCISCO, CA 94103
TRAIN, WIRE	ROCK & ROLL GROUP	SEE - WIRE TRAIN	
TRAINER, DAVID	TV WRITER-PRODUCER	WM MORRIS, 1350 AVE OF AMERICAS	NEW YORK, NY 10019
TRAINER, SUSAN	ARTIST	321 UNION ST	SLATINGTON, PA 18080
TRAINOR, MARY ELLEN	ACTRESS	ROSENBERG, 8428 MELROSE PL #C	LOS ANGELES, CA 90069
TRAMER, BENNETT	TV WRITER	418 9TH ST	SANTA MONICA, CA 90402
TRAMMELL, ALAN	BASEBALL	TIGERS, TIGER STADIUM	DETROIT, MI 48216
TRAMMPS, THE	SOUL GROUP	BROTHERS, 141 DUNBAR AVE	FORDS, NJ 08863
TRAMONT, JEAN-CLAUDE	WRITER-DIRECTOR	ICM, 40 W 57TH ST	NEW YORK, NY 10019
TRAMPS, THE	R & B GROUP	BROTHERS, 141 DUNBAR AVE	FORDS, NJ 08863
TRANBARGER, MARK	BASEBALL	POST OFFICE BOX 3004	SPRINGFIELD, IL 62708
TRANELLI, DEBORAH	ACTRESS	280 S BEVERLY DR #400	BEVERLY HILLS, CA 90212
TRAPNELL, COLES	WRITER-PRODUCER	10577 ROCHESTER AVE	LOS ANGELES, CA 90024
TRAPNELL, JANE	COSTUME DESIGNER	1697 BROADWAY #307	NEW YORK, NY 10016
TRAPNELL, JANE R	COSTUME DESIGNER	13949 VENTURA BLVD #309	SHERMAN OAKS, CA 91423
TRASK, DIANA	SINGER	10889 WILSHIRE BLVD #1146	LOS ANGELES, CA 90024
TRAUM, ARTIE & PAT ALGER	VOCAL GROUP	49 W 96TH ST #5-C	NEW YORK, NY 10025
TRAUTWEIN, DAVE	BASEBALL	POST OFFICE BOX 4370	SALINAS, CA 93912
TRAUTWEIN, JOHN	BASEBALL	452 W OAKWOOD DR	BARRINGTON, IL 60010
TRAVANTI, DANIEL J	ACTOR	14205 SUNSET BLVD	PACIFIC PALISADES, CA 90272
TRAVELIN' BAND, THE	C & W GROUP	TM, 1019 17TH AVE S	NASHVILLE, TN 37212
TRAVERS, BILL	ACT-WRI-DIR-PROD	BELFRAGE, 68 SAINT JAMES'S ST	LONDON SW1A 1LE ENGLAND
TRAVERS, PAT, BAND	ROCK & ROLL GROUP	POST OFFICE BOX 7877	
		COLLEGE PARK STATION	ORLANDO, FL 32854
TRAVERS, PETER	FILM CRITIC	PEOPLE/TIME & LIFE BLDG	
		ROCKEFELLER CENTER	NEW YORK, NY 10020
TRAVERS, SY	ACTOR	357 W 43RD ST	NEW YORK, NY 10036
TRAVILLA, WILLIAM	COSTUME DESIGNER	122 E 7TH ST	LOS ANGELES, CA 90014
TRAVIS, JIM	SINGER-GUITARIST	113 SCOTCH ST	HENDERSONVILLE, TN 37075
TRAVIS, MERLE	SINGER-GUITARIST	ROUTE #1, BOX 128	PARK HILL, OK 74451
TRAVIS, MICHAEL	COSTUME DESIGNER	2203 BOWMONT DR	BEVERLY HILLS, CA 90210
TRAVIS, NANCY	ACTRESS	131 S RODEO DR #300	BEVERLY HILLS, CA 90212
TRAVIS, NEIL	FILM EDITOR	ACE, 1041 N FORMOSA AVE	WEST HOLLYWOOD, CA 90046
TRAVIS, RANDY	SINGER-SONGWRITER	POST OFFICE BOX 121137	NASHVILLE, TN 37212
TRAVIS, STACEY	ACTRESS	9000 SUNSET BLVD #1200	LOS ANGELES, CA 90069
TRAVOLTA, ELLEN	ACTRESS	5832 NAGLE AVE	VAN NUYS, CA 91401
TRAVOLTA, JOEY	ACTOR	4975 CHIMINEAS AVE	TARZANA, CA 91356
TRAVOLTA, JOHN	ACTOR-SINGER	1504 LIVE OAK LN	SANTA BARBARA, CA 93105
TRAVOLTA, SAM	ACTOR	9300 WILSHIRE BLVD #410	BEVERLY HILLS, CA 90212
TRAXLER, BOB	U S CONGRESSMAN	323 FEDERAL BUILDING	BAY CITY, MI 48708
TRAXLER, BRIAN	BASEBALL	POST OFFICE BOX 26267	ALBUQUERQUE, NM 87125
TRAYLOR, KEITH	FOOTBALL	BRONCOS, 13655 BRONCOS PKWY	ENGLEWOOD, CO 80112

Name	Occupation	Address	City	Zip/Country
TRAYLOR, WILLIAM	ACTOR	11610 BELLAGIO RD	LOS ANGELES, CA	90049
TRAYNOR, PETER	DIRECTOR	20940 WAVE VIEW DR	TOPANGA CANYON, CA	90290
TRBOVICH, THOMAS	TV DIRECTOR	1369 EL HITO CIR	PACIFIC PALISADES, CA	90272
TRCKA, SCOTT	BASEBALL SCOUT	POST OFFICE BOX 7575	PHILADELPHIA, PA	19101
TREACHER, BILL	ACTOR	BBC, ELSTREE TV CENTRE	BOREHAMWOOD, HERTS	ENGLAND
TREADWAY, JEFF	BASEBALL	POST OFFICE BOX 4064	ATLANTA, GA	30302
TREADWELL, DAVID	FOOTBALL	BRONCOS, 13655 BRONCOS PKWY	ENGLEWOOD, CO	80112
TREADWELL, JODY	BASEBALL	POST OFFICE BOX 28268	SAN ANTONIO, TX	78228
TREANOR, DEAN	BASEBALL COACH	POST OFFICE BOX 11363	RENO, NV	89510
TREAS, TERRI	ACTRESS	9000 SUNSET BLVD #1200	LOS ANGELES, CA	90069
TREASE, DENNY	SPORTSCASTER	POST OFFICE BOX 419969	KANSAS CITY, MO	64141
TREBEK, ALEX	TV HOST	7966 MULHOLLAND DR	LOS ANGELES, CA	90046
TREBELHORN, TOM	BASEBALL-COACH	1060 W ADDISON ST	CHICAGO, IL	60613
TREDANARI, LEE J	DIRECTOR	307 W 103RD ST	NEW YORK, NY	10025
TREE, MICHAEL	VIOLINIST	45 E 89TH ST	NEW YORK, NY	10028
TREECE, TOM	BASEBALL EXECUTIVE	POST OFFICE BOX 7000	PITTSBURGH, PA	15212
TREEN, MARY	ACTRESS	SHERRELL, 1354 LAS ROBLES DR	PALM SPRINGS, CA	92262
TREIMER, WINIFRED	STORY EDITOR	2300 VASANTA WY	LOS ANGELES, CA	90068
TRELA, MARK ANTHONY	WRITER	3011 MANHATTAN AVE	LA CRESCENTA, CA	91214
TREMAYNE, LES	ACTOR	901 S BARRINGTON AVE	LOS ANGELES, CA	90049
TREMBLAY, LUCIE BLUE	SINGER-GUITARIST	OLIVIA RECORDS COMPANY		
		4400 MARKET ST	OAKLAND, CA	94608
TREMBLEY, DAVE	BASEBALL MANAGER	POST OFFICE BOX 20849	CHARLESTON, SC	29413
TRENCHARD-SMITH, BRIAN	WRITER-PRODUCER	26 MARANKA ST	HORNSBY NSW	ENGLAND
TRENNER, BARON "MICKEY"	DIRECTOR	DGA, 110 W 57TH ST	NEW YORK, NY	10019
TRENNER, DONN R	COMPOSER-CONDUCTOR	21418 SALAMANCA AVE	WOODLAND HILLS, CA	91364
TRENT, BUCK	SINGER-MUSICIAN	742-B LINDEN GREEN DR	HERMITAGE, TN	37076
TRENT, JOHN	FILM DIRECTOR	50 DALE AVE	TORONTO, ONT	CANADA
TRES HOMBRES	ROCK & ROLL GROUP	41 BRITAIN ST #200	TORONTO, ONT M5A 1R7	CANADA
TRESS, DAVID	ACTOR	3456 WADE ST	LOS ANGELES, CA	90066
TRESTMAN, MARC	FOOTBALL COACH	VIKINGS, 9520 VIKING DR	EDEN PRAIRIE, MN	55344
TRETIAK, PAUL	BASEBALL SCOUT	BREWERS, 201 S 46TH ST	MILWAUKEE, WI	53214
TRETTIN, HENRY	DIRECTOR	868 BROOKTREE RD	PACIFIC PALISADES, CA	90272
TREUBER, ROBERT	TV PRODUCER	KALAMAR PRODS, 928 BROADWAY	NEW YORK, NY	10010
TREUEL, RALPH	BASEBALL COACH	POST OFFICE BOX 6212	TOLEDO, OH	43614
TREUTELAAR, BARBARA	ACTRESS	1801 AVE OF THE STARS #1250	LOS ANGELES, CA	90067
TREVES, FREDERICK	ACTOR-WRITER	YOUNG, 31 KING'S RD	LONDON SW3 4RP	ENGLAND
TREVINO, ALEX	BASEBALL	POST OFFICE BOX 36407	LOUISVILLE, KY	40233
TREVINO, JESUS SALVADOR	WRITER-PRODUCER	2358 YORKSHIRE DR	LOS ANGELES, CA	90065
TREVINO, LEE	GOLFER	1221 ABRAMS RD #327	RICHARDSON, TX	75081
TREVINO, TONY	BASEBALL	POST OFFICE BOX 10336	CLEARWATER, FL	34617
TREVOR, CLAIRE	ACTRESS	THE PIERCE HOTEL		
		2 E 61ST ST & 5TH AVE	NEW YORK, NY	10021
TREVOR, DON M	DIRECTOR	1-3 POND BROOK RD	NEWTOWN, CT	06470
TREVOR, JOHN	CARTOONIST	POST OFFICE BOX J	ALBUQUERQUE, NM	87103
TREXLER, PAT	COLUMNIST	UPS, 4900 MAIN ST, 9TH FLOOR	KANSAS CITY, MO	64112
TREYZ, RUSSELL L	TV DIRECTOR	107 BEDFORD ST	NEW YORK, NY	10014
TRIBE CALLED QUEST, A	RAP GROUP	231 W 29TH ST #705	NEW YORK, NY	10001
TRICE, WALLY	BASEBALL	2501 ALLEN AVE, SE	CANTON, OH	44707
TRICKER, GEORGE J	TV WRITER	22100 VICTORY BLVD	WOODLAND HILLS, CA	91367
TRICKSTER	ROCK & ROLL GROUP	2049 CENTURY PARK E #414	LOS ANGELES, CA	90067
TRIESAULT, JON	DIRECTOR	8562 CRESCENT DR	HOLLYWOOD, CA	90046
TRIFFIDS, THE	ROCK & ROLL GROUP	HOT RECORDS & ROUGH TRADE		
		326 6TH ST	SAN FRANCISCO, CA	94103
TRIKILIS, MICHAEL	DIRECTOR-PRODUCER	493 LORING AVE	LOS ANGELES, CA	90024
TRIKONIS, GUS	TV DIRECTOR	1015 GAYLEY AVE #300	LOS ANGELES, CA	90024
TRILLIN, CALVIN	AUTHOR-REPORTER	KING FEATURES, 216 E 45TH ST	NEW YORK, NY	10017
TRILLION	ROCK & ROLL GROUP	TWOGETHER, 2137 LINDEN LN	PALATINE, IL	60067
TRILLO, MANNY	BASEBALL	CENTRO RES HUMBOLDT #1B	PRADOS DEL ESTE CARACA..	VENEZUELA
TRIMBLE, LESTER	COMPOSER	98 RIVERSIDE DR	NEW YORK, NY	10023
TRIMIS, EDWARD A	COMPOSER	4629 LA CRESENTA AVE	LA CRESCENTA, CA	91214
TRINGHAM, DAVID	FILM DIRECTOR	40 LANGTHORNE ST	LONDON SW6 6JY	ENGLAND
TRINIDAD, HECTOR	BASEBALL	1524 W NEBRASKA AVE	PEORIA, IL	61604
TRIO	ROCK & ROLL GROUP	REGENSTESTR 10-A	2907 GROBENKNETEN 2	GERMANY
TRIOLA, MICHELLE	PERSONALITY	23215 MARIPOSA DE ORO	MALIBU, CA	90265
TRIPLETS, THE	ROCK & ROLL GROUP	MC DERMOTT, MEGA MANAGEMENT		
		71 W 23RD ST	NEW YORK, NY	10010
TRIPLETT, KIRK	GOLFER	POST OFFICE BOX 109601	PALM BCH GARDENS, FL	33418
TRIPP, ALLEN	SINGER	111 OLD HICKORY BLVD #W-299	NASHVILLE, TN	37221
TRIPP, TERRY	BASEBALL SCOUT	METS, 126TH ST & ROOSEVELT AVE	FLUSHING, NY	11368
TRIPPEL, RICHARD C "BUCK"	DIRECTOR	DGA, 7920 SUNSET BLVD, 6TH FL	LOS ANGELES, CA	90046
TRIPUCKA, KELLY	BASKETBALL	310 N KINGS DR	CHARLOTTE, NC	28204
TRISKA, JAN	ACTOR	ROSENBERG, 8428 MELROSE PL #C	LOS ANGELES, CA	90069
TRISTAN	C & W GROUP	POST OFFICE BOX 29543	ATLANTA, GA	30359
TRITT, TRAVIS	SINGER-SONGWRITER	POST OFFICE BOX 440099	KENNESAW, GA	30144
TRIUMPH	ROCK & ROLL GROUP	3611 MAVIS RD #5	MISSISSAUGA, ONT L5C 1..	CANADA
TRIVETTE, BUTCH	SINGER	POST OFFICE BOX 13584	ATLANTA, GA	30324
TRIVOLA, MICHELLE	PERSONALITY	23215 MARIPOSA DE ORO	MALIBU, CA	90265
TRLICEK, RICK	BASEBALL	SKYDOME, 300 BREMMER BL #3200	TORONTO, ONT M5V 3B3	CANADA
TROCCOLI'S DOG, TOM	ROCK & ROLL GROUP	POST OFFICE BOX 1	LAWNDALE, CA	90260
TRODD, KENITH	TV PRODUCER	188 GLOUCESTER TERR	LONDON W2	ENGLAND
TROMBLEY, MIKE	BASEBALL	POST OFFICE BOX 1659	PORTLAND, OR	97207
TRONCOSO, DANILO	BASEBALL SCOUT	POST OFFICE BOX 90111	ARLINGTON, TX	76004
TRONSON, ROBERT	FILM DIRECTOR	HEATH, PARAMOUNT HOUSE		
		162-170 WARDOUR ST	LONDON W1V 3AT	ENGLAND

TROOBNICK, EUGENE	ACTOR	CBS-TV, "THE GUIDING LIGHT"	
		222 E 44TH ST	NEW YORK, NY 10017
TROOP	RAP GROUP	9200 SUNSET BLVD #1220	LOS ANGELES, CA 90069
TROOPER	ROCK & ROLL GROUP	41 BRITAIN ST #200	TORONTO, ONT M5A 1R7 CANADA
TROTTIER, BRYAN	HOCKEY	PENGUINS, CIVIC ARENA, CENTRE AV	PITTSBURGH, PA 15219
TROUP, BOBBY	ACT-COMP-SING	16074 ROYAL OAK ST	ENCINO, CA 91316
TROUT, STEVE	BASEBALL	919 RIVERVIEW DR	SOUTH HOLLAND, IL 60473
TROWER, ROBIN	SINGER-GUITARIST	STARDUST, 2650 GLENDOWER AVE	LOS ANGELES, CA 90027
TROY, BENNY & COMPANY	ROCK & ROLL GROUP	BROTHERS, 141 DUNBAR AVE	FORDS, NJ 08863
TRUCHAN, JUDY	COSTUME DESIGNER	1270 GRANVILLE AVE	LOS ANGELES, CA 90025
TRUCKS, BUTCH	SINGER	POST OFFICE BOX 1566	MONTCLAIR, NJ 07042
TRUDEAU, JACK	FOOTBALL	POST OFFICE BOX 535000	INDIANPOLIS, IN 46253
TRUDEAU, PIERRE ELLIOT	POLITICIAN	24 SUSSEX DR	OTTAWA, ONT CANADA
TRUE MATHEMATICS	RAP GROUP-RAPWRITERS	FAA, 1700 BROADWAY, 5TH FLOOR	NEW YORK, NY 10019
TRUE WEST	ROCK & ROLL GROUP	JEM RECORDS, 3619 KENNEDY RD	SOUTH PLAINFIELD, NJ 07080
TRUEBLOOD, GUERDON	WRITER-PRODUCER	DGA, 7920 SUNSET BLVD, 6TH FL	LOS ANGELES, CA 90046
TRUEMAN, ANDREW	TALENT AGENT	24514 CALBERT ST #210	WOODLAND HILLS, CA 91367
TRUJILLO, MIKE	BASEBALL	2636 S STUART WY	DENVER, CO 80219
TRULL, TERESA	SINGER	OLIVIA RECORDS COMPANY	
		4400 MARKET ST	OAKLAND, CA 94608
TRUMAN, EDWARD	COMPOSER-CONDUCTOR	1826 JEWETT DR	LOS ANGELES, CA 90046
TRUMAN, MARGARET	AUTHORESS	SEE - DANIEL, MARGARET TRUMAN	
TRUMBO, MARION	BASEBALL SCOUT	REDS, 100 RIVERFRONT STADIUM	CINCINNATI, OH 45202
TRUMBULL, DOUGLAS	WRITER-PRODUCER	1133 GEORGINA AVE	SANTA MONICA, CA 90402
TRUMP, DONALD	SPORTS EXECUTIVE	721 5TH AVE	NEW YORK, NY 10022
TRUMP, IVANA	CELEBRITY	1100 PALM BEACH BLVD	PALM BEACH, FL 33480
TRUMPER, JOHN	FILM EDITOR	WAYSIDE, VINE RD	LONDON SW13 ONE ENGLAND
TRUNDY, NATALIE	ACTRESS	6140 LINDENHURST AVE	LOS ANGELES, CA 90048
TRUSCOTT, JOHN	COSTUME DESIGNER	13949 VENTURA BLVD #309	SHERMAN OAKS, CA 91423
TRUSEL, LISA	ACTRESS	9200 SUNSET BLVD #625	LOS ANGELES, CA 90069
TRUSSELL, CHRISTOPHER M	COMPOSER-CONDUCTOR	1175 W BASELINE RD	CLAREMONT, CA 91711
TRUSSELL, ROBERT	FILM CRITIC	THE KANSAS CITY STAR	
		1729 GRAND AVE	KANSAS CITY, MO 64108
TRUTH	MUSICAL GROUP	POST OFFICE BOX 8554	MOBILE, AL 36608
TRUTH, THE	ROCK & ROLL GROUP	194 KENSINGSTON PARK RD	LONDON W11 2ES ENGLAND
TRYBITS, PAUL	TV PRODUCER	WICKED FILMS & TV, LTD	
		3-6 WINNETT ST	LONDON W1N 7HS ENGLAND
TRYFLES, THE	ROCK & ROLL GROUP	POST OFFICE BOX 390	
		OLD CHELSEA STATION	NEW YORK, NY 10113
TSAMIS, CHARLES R, JR	DIRECTOR	10820 PEACHGROVE ST	NORTH HOLLYWOOD, CA 91601
TSAMIS, GEORGE	BASEBALL	POST OFFICE BOX 1659	PORTLAND, OR 97207
TSCHETTER, KRIS	GOLFER	2750 VOLUSA AVE #B	DAYTON BEACH, FL 32114
TSCHIDA, TIM	BASEBALL UMPIRE	2296 BENSON AVE	SAINT PAUL, MN 55116
TSCHUDIN, RICHARD	DIRECTOR	POST OFFICE BOX 281	LAKE ARROWHEAD, CA 92352
TSOL	ROCK & ROLL GROUP	SEE - T S O L	
TSOUKALAS, JOHN	BASEBALL	POST OFFICE BOX 1110	MYRTLE BEACH, SC 29578
TSU, IRENE	ACTRESS	3349 W CAHUENGA BLVD #2-B	LOS ANGELES, CA 90068
TSUKAMOTH, KEIICHI	BASEBALL EXECUTIVE	POST OFFICE BOX 48	VISALIA, CA 93279
TUAOLO, ESERA	FOOTBALL	PACKERS, 1265 LOMBARDI AVE	GREEN BAY, WI 54307
TUATAGALOA, NATU	FOOTBALL	BENGALS, 200 RIVERFRONT STADIUM	CINCINNATI, OH 45202
TUBB, BARRY	ACTOR	662 N VAN NESS AVE #305	LOS ANGELES, CA 90004
TUBB, ERNEST, JR	SINGER-GUITARIST	513 JANICE DR	ANTIOCH, TN 37013
TUBB, JUSTIN	SINGER-GUITARIST	POST OFFICE BOX 500	NASHVILLE, TN 37202
TUBBS, GREG	BASEBALL	POST OFFICE BOX 450	BUFFALO, NY 14205
TUBES, THE	ROCK & ROLL GROUP	POST OFFICE BOX 6894	SAN FRANCISCO, CA 94101
TUCCI, MICHAEL	ACTOR	8075 W 3RD ST #303	LOS ANGELES, CA 90048
TUCH, CHARLENE	COSTUME DESIGNER	13949 VENTURA BLVD #309	SHERMAN OAKS, CA 91423
TUCHNER, MICHAEL	FILM DIRECTOR	4 KENT RD, EAST MOLESEY	SURREY ENGLAND
TUCK, GARY	BASEBALL MANAGER	POST OFFICE BOX 802	WATERTOWN, NY 13601
TUCKER, ARLIN	SINGER	POST OFFICE BOX 25371	CHARLOTTE, NC 28212
TUCKER, BILL	BASEBALL EXECUTIVE	1316 KING ST	BELLINGHAM, WA 98226
TUCKER, COLIN	TV PRODUCER	PETERS, FRASER & DUNLOP, LTD	
		5TH FLOOR, THE CHAMBERS	
		CHELSEA HARBOUR, LOT RD	LONDON SW10 OXF ENGLAND
TUCKER, DAVID	TV DIRECTOR	PETERS, FRASER & DUNLOP, LTD	
		5TH FLOOR, THE CHAMBERS	
		CHELSEA HARBOUR, LOT RD	LONDON SW10 OXF ENGLAND
TUCKER, JIM GUY	LT GOVERNOR	STATE CAPITOL BUILDING	LITTLE ROCK, AR 72201
TUCKER, JOHN	HOCKEY	NASSAU VETS MEMORIAL COLISEUM	UNIONDALE, NY 11553
TUCKER, KEN	TV CRITIC	PHILADELPHIA INQUIRER	
		400 N BROAD ST	PHILADELPHIA, PA 19101
TUCKER, LA COSTA	SINGER	50 MUSIC SQUARE W #907	NASHVILLE, TN 37212
TUCKER, LARRY	FILM WRITER-PRODUCER	CAA, 9830 WILSHIRE BLVD	BEVERLY HILLS, CA 90212
TUCKER, MARSHALL, BAND	ROCK & ROLL GROUP	SUGAR PINE, 300 E HENRY ST	SPARTANBURG, SC 69302
TUCKER, MAUREEN	SINGER-GUITARIST	POST OFFICE BOX 22012	PHOENIX, AZ 85028
TUCKER, MELODY	BASEBALL EXECUTIVE	POST OFFICE BOX 7893	EVERETT, WA 98201
TUCKER, MELVILLE	FILM PRODUCER	2115 MANDEVILLE CANYON RD	LOS ANGELES, CA 90049
TUCKER, MICHAEL	ACTOR	2183 MANDEVILLE CANYON	LOS ANGELES, CA 90049
TUCKER, ORIN	CONDUCTOR	POST OFFICE BOX 013	LOS ANGELES, CA 90042
TUCKER, PATRICK	TV DIRECTOR	52 BARROWGATE RD	LONDON W4 4QY ENGLAND
TUCKER, PAULA MC KINNEY	WRITER-PRODUCER	26126 MEADOWCREST	HUNTINGTON WOODS, MI 48070
TUCKER, ROGER	TV DIRECTOR	SEIFERT, 18 LADBROKE TERR	LONDON W11 3PG ENGLAND
TUCKER, SCOOTER	BASEBALL	POST OFFICE BOX 27045	TUCSON, AZ 85726
TUCKER, TANYA	SINGER	POST OFFICE BOX 15245	NASHVILLE, TN 37215
TUCKER, TRENT	BASKETBALL	KNICKS, 4 PENNYLVANIA PLAZA	NEW YORK, NY 10019

TUCKER, TUCK	BASEBALL EXECUTIVE	POST OFFICE BOX 3452	KINSTON, NC 28502
TUDOR, CHRISTINE	ACTRESS	SEE - NEMWNA, CHRISTINE TUDOR	
TUDOR, THOMAS	COMPOSER	10960 HESBY ST	NORTH HOLLYWOOD, CA 91601
TUFANO, DENNIS	ACTOR-SINGER	5455 WILSHIRE BLVD #1406	LOS ANGELES, CA 90036
TUFELD, LYNN	ACTRESS	167 S SYCAMORE AVE	LOS ANGELES, CA 90036
TUGEND, HARRY	WRITER-PRODUCER	838 N DOHENY DR #100	LOS ANGELES, CA 90069
TUGGLE, JESSIE	FOOTBALL	FALCONS, SUWANEE RD AT I-85	SUWANEE, GA 30174
TUGGLE, RICHARD ALLAN	WRITER-PRODUCER	840 21ST ST #C	SANTA MONICA, CA 90403
TUINEI, MARK	FOOTBALL	COWBOYS, 1 COWBOYS PARKWAY	IRVING, TX 75063
TUKE, SIMON	COSTUME DESIGNER	143 S HARPER AVE	LOS ANGELES, CA 90048
TULCHIN, HAROLD M	DIRECTOR-PRODUCER	240 E 45TH ST	NEW YORK, NY 10017
TULL, JETHRO	ROCK & ROLL GROUP	SEE - JETHRO TULL	
TULL, JOHN	BASEBALL EXECUTIVE	POST OFFICE BOX 4218	SOUTH BEND, IN 46634
TULLIER, MIKE	BASEBALL SCOUT	ORIOLE PARK, 333 W CAMDEN ST	BALTIMORE, MD 21201
TUMAS, DAVE	BASEBALL TRAINER	POST OFFICE BOX 7000	PITTSBURGH, PA 15212
TUNE, TOMMY	DAN-DIR-CHOR	50 E 89TH ST	NEW YORK, NY 10128
TUNIE, TAMARA	ACTRESS	CBS-TV, "AS THE WORLD TURNS"	
		524 W 57TH ST #5330	NEW YORK, NY 10019
TUNISON, RICH	BASEBALL	800 HOME RUN LN	MEMPHIS, TN 38104
TUNNEY, JIM	FOOTBALL REFEREE	NFL, 410 PARK AVE	NEW YORK, NY 10022
TUNNEY, JOHN	U S SENATOR	15000 CORONA DEL MAR	PACIFIC PALISADES, CA 90272
TUPA, TOM	FOOTBALL	POST OFFICE BOX 888	PHOENIX, AZ 85001
TUPELO CHAIN SEX	ROCK & ROLL GROUP	SELMA RECORD CO, 6657 YUCCA ST	HOLLYWOOD, CA 90028
TURAN, KENNETH	FILM CRITIC	GENTLEMEN'S QUARTERLY	
		350 MADISON AVE	NEW YORK, NY 10017
TURANG, BRIAN	BASEBALL	POST OFFICE BOX 4756	JACKSONVILLE, FL 32201
TURBINES, THE	ROCK & ROLL GROUP	33 MUSIC SQUARE W #100	NASHVILLE, TN 37203
TURBOS, THE	ROCK & ROLL GROUP	SEE - TIM & THE TURBOS	
TURCO, FRANK	BASEBALL	POST OFFICE BOX 3609	PORT CHARLOTTE, FL 33949
TURCO, PAUL	BASEBALL SCOUT	N Y YANKEES, YANKEE STADIUM	BRONX, NY 10451
TURCO, STEVE	BASEBALL COACH	80 OTTAWA ST N	HAMILTON, ONT L8H 3Z1 CANADA
TURCOTTE, DARREN	HOCKEY	POST OFFICE BOX 90111	ARLINGTON, TX 76004
TUREK, JOE	BASEBALL	2501 ALLEN AVE, SE	CANTON, OH 44707
TURETSKY, ELI	DIRECTOR	49 BROOKLAWN TERR	FAIRFIELD, CT 06430
TURGEON, PIERRE	HOCKEY	SABRES, MEMORIAL AUDITORIUM	BUFFALO, NY 14202
TURGEON, SYLVAIN	HOCKEY	CANADIENS, 2313 ST CATHERINE ST	MONTREAL, QUE H3H 1N2 CANADA
TURIEL, DANIEL E	COMPOSER-CONDUCTOR	441 8TH AVE S	NAPLES, FL 33940
TURK, CARL W	TV DIRECTOR	9100 MC VICKER	MORTON GROVE, IL 60053
TURK, DAN	FOOTBALL	RAIDERS, 332 CENTER ST	EL SEGUNDO, CA 90245
TURKUS, ANN	ACTRESS	B J GOTTESMAN COMPANY, INC	
		9 W 57TH ST	NEW YORK, NY 10019
TURLEY, JACK BRADFORD	TV WRITER	10072 WESTWANDA DR	BEVERLY HILLS, CA 90210
TURLEY, PATRICK	CINEMATOGRAPHER	68 CHARTFIELD AVE	LONDON SW15 6HQ ENGLAND
TURMAN, GLYNN	ACTOR	9000 SUNSET BLVD #1200	LOS ANGELES, CA 90069
TURMAN, LAWRENCE	FILM PRODUCER	21336 PACIFIC COAST HWY	MALIBU, CA 90265
TURNBULL, NICK	TV PRODUCER	ARCHERY HOUSE, NORTH RD, HALE	CHESHIRE ENGLAND
TURNBULL, RENALDO	FOOTBALL	SAINTS, 1500 POYDRAS ST	NEW ORLEANS, LA 90112
TURNER, BILL	TV DIRECTOR-PRODUCER	7 GREEN ST	LONDON W1Y 3RF ENGLAND
TURNER, BONNIE	TV WRITER	UTA, 9560 WILSHIRE BL, 5TH FL	BEVERLY HILLS, CA 90212
TURNER, BRIAN	BASEBALL	5301 NW 12TH AVE	FORT LAUDERDALE, FL 33309
TURNER, CHARLES L	DIRECTOR	33 N SOUND BEACH AVE	RIVERSIDE, CT 06878
TURNER, CHRIS	BASEBALL	POST OFFICE BOX 3496	DAVENPORT, IA 52808
TURNER, CLIFFORD	TV PRODUCER	49-B CHRISTCHURCH ST, CHELSEA	LONDON SW3 4AS ENGLAND
TURNER, DEASA	ACTRESS	6255 SUNSET BLVD #627	LOS ANGELES, CA 90028
TURNER, ED	TV EXECUTIVE	1050 TECHWOOD DR, NW	ATLANTA, GA 30318
TURNER, FLOYD	FOOTBALL	SAINTS, 1500 POYDRAS ST	NEW ORLEANS, LA 90112
TURNER, GRANT	SINGER	POST OFFICE BOX 414	BRENTWOOD, TN 37027
TURNER, JANINE	ACTRESS	315 W 57TH ST #4-H	NEW YORK, NY 10019
TURNER, JEFF	BASKETBALL	POST OFFICE BOX 76	ORLANDO, FL 32802
TURNER, KATHLEEN	ACTRESS	130 W 42ND ST	NEW YORK, NY 10036
TURNER, LANA	ACTRESS	10100 SANTA MONICA BLVD #700	LOS ANGELES, CA 90067
TURNER, LEE	MUSIC ARRANGER	4263 SAN JOSE BLVD	JACKSONVILLE, FL 32207
TURNER, MARCUS	FOOTBALL	POST OFFICE BOX 888	PHOENIX, AZ 85001
TURNER, MARY LOU	SINGER	TESSIER, 505 CANTON PASS	MADISON, TN 37204
TURNER, MATT	BASEBALL	POST OFFICE BOX 27045	TUCSON, AZ 85726
TURNER, NORVAL	FOOTBALL COACH	RAMS, 2327 W LINCOLN BLVD	ANAHEIM, CA 92801
TURNER, ODESSA	FOOTBALL	N Y GIANTS, GIANTS STADIUM	EAST RUTHERFORD, NJ 07073
TURNER, RET	COSTUME DESIGNER	13949 VENTURA BLVD #309	SHERMAN OAKS, CA 91423
TURNER, RONALD G	COMPOSER	938 E FAIRVIEW BLVD	INGLEWOOD, CA 90302
TURNER, RUSSELL	FILM-TV PRODUCER	RANK, 127 WARDOUR ST	LONDON W1V 4AD ENGLAND
TURNER, RYAN	BASEBALL	POST OFFICE BOX 48	VISALIA, CA 93279
TURNER, SHANE	BASEBALL	POST OFFICE BOX 3690, STA "B"	CALGARY, ALB T2B 4M4 CANADA
TURNER, SPYDER	SINGER	POST OFFICE BOX 1235	NEW ROCHELLE, NY 10802
TURNER, T J	FOOTBALL	DOLPHINS, 2269 NW 199TH ST	MIAMI, FL 33056
TURNER, TED	BROADCAST EXECUTIVE	1050 TECHWOOD DR, NW	ATLANTA, GA 30318
TURNER, TERRY	TV WRITER	UTA, 9560 WILSHIRE BL, 5TH FL	BEVERLY HILLS, CA 90212
TURNER, TINA	SINGER-ACTRESS	14755 VENTURA BLVD #1-710	SHERMAN OAKS, CA 91403
TURNER, VENRON	FOOTBALL	RAMS, 2327 W LINCOLN BLVD	ANAHEIM, CA 92801
TUROVSKY, YULI	CONDUCTOR	WENTWORTH, 5 LOCKWOOD RD	SCARSDALE, NY 10583
TURPIN, GEORGE	TV DIRECTOR-PRODUCER	2131 OAK KNOLL AVE	SAN MARINO, CA 91108
TURRE, MICHAEL J	COMPOSER	1548 CABRILLO AVE	VENICE, CA 90291
TURRENTINE, RICHARD	BASEBALL	POST OFFICE BOX 22093	GREENSBORO, NC 27420
TURRENTINE, ROGERS	TV WRITER	PLESHETTE, 2700 N BEACHWOOD DR	HOLLYWOOD, CA 90028
TURTELTAUB, SAUL	WRITER-PRODUCER	1126 COLDWATER CANYON DR	BEVERLY HILLS, CA 90210
TURTLES, THE	ROCK & ROLL GROUP	POST OFFICE BOX 26037	MINNEAPOLIS, MN 55416

Name	Occupation	Address	City
TURTURICE, ROBERT	COSTUME DESIGNER	13949 VENTURA BLVD #309	SHERMAN OAKS, CA 91423
TURTURRO, JOHN	ACTOR	POST OFFICE BOX 5617	BEVERLY HILLS, CA 90213
TURVEY, JOE	BASEBALL	POST OFFICE BOX 3783	SAVANNAH, GA 31414
TUSHER, WILL	COLUMNIST	5700 WILSHIRE BLVD #120	LOS ANGELES, CA 90036
TUSHINGHAM, RITA	ACTRESS	LONDON MGT, 235-241 REGENT ST ...	LONDON W1R 4PH .... ENGLAND
TUSS, JEFF	BASEBALL	POST OFFICE BOX 3566	WEST PALM BEACH, FL 33402
TUTEN, ALLEN	MUSIC ARRANGER	3008 HILLSIDE RD #B	NASHVILLE, TN 37207
TUTEN, RICK	FOOTBALL	PACKERS, 1265 LOMBARDI AVE	GREEN BAY, WI 54307
TUTIN, DOROTHY	ACTRESS	13 SAINT MARTINS RD	LONDON SW9 .... ENGLAND
TUTONE, TOMMY	SINGER-DANCER	FAA, 1700 BROADWAY, 5TH FLOOR ...	NEW YORK, NY 10019
TUTOR, RIP	BASEBALL SCOUT	BREWERS, 201 S 46TH ST	MILWAUKEE, WI 53214
TUTTLE, DAVID	BASEBALL	POST OFFICE BOX 4669	CHARLESTON, WV 25304
TUTTLE, MARK	TV WRITER	10646 ART ST	SUNLAND, CA 91040
TUTTLE, STEVE	HOCKEY	BLUES, 5700 OAKLAND AVE	SAINT LOUIS, MO 63110
TUTTMAN, PETER M	WRITER-PRODUCER	311 E 72ND ST	NEW YORK, NY 10021
TUTU, ARCH BISHOP DESMOND	ARCH BISHOP	POST OFFICE BOX 31190	....
	....	BRAAMFONTEIN	JOHNANNESBURG .... SO AFRICA
TUXEDOMOON	ROCK & ROLL GROUP ...	POST OFFICE BOX 2428	EL SEGUNDO, CA 90245
TWARDOSKI, MIKE	BASEBALL	POST OFFICE BOX 2365	PAWTUCKET, RI 02861
TWARDZIK, DAVE	BASKETBALL	310 N KINGS DR	CHARLOTTE, NC 28204
TWAY, BOB	GOLFER	POST OFFICE BOX 109601	PALM BCH GARDENS, FL 33418
TWEED, SHANNON	ACTRESS-MODEL	9300 WILSHIRE BLVD #410	BEVERLY HILLS, CA 90212
TWEEDY, DONALD W	MUSIC ARRANGER	504 DORAL COUNTRY DR	NASHVILLE, TN 37221
TWEEDY, LLOYD F	DIRECTOR	498 MANOR LN	PELHAM, NY 10802
TWENTY CENTURY REBELS	ROCK & ROLL GROUP ...	41 BRITAIN ST #200	TORONTO, ONT M5A 1R7 ...... CANADA
TWIGGE, JENNY	ACTRESS	ALVAREZ MGT, 86 MUSWELL RD	....
	....	MUSWELL HILL	LONDON N10 2BF .... ENGLAND
TWIGGY	MODEL-ACTRESS-DANCER	SEE - LAWSON, TWIGGY	....
TWILIGHT	RHYTHM & BLUES GROUP	KINGSLAND, 108 SHARON DR	WEST MONROE, LA 71291
TWILLEY, DWIGHT	SINGER-SONGWRITER ...	8306 WILSHIRE BLVD #196	BEVERLY HILLS, CA 90211
TWIST, TONY	HOCKEY	NORDIQUES, 2205 AVE DU COLISEE ..	QUEBEC, QUE G1L 4W7 .... CANADA
TWISTED SISTER	ROCK & ROLL GROUP ...	ARNOLD FREEDMAN MANAGEMENT	....
	....	1200 PROVIDENCE HWY	SHARON, MA 02067
TWITTY, CONWAY	SINGER-SONGWRITER ...	1 MUSIC VILLAGE BLVD	HENDERSONVILLE, TN 37075
TWITTY, HOWARD	GOLFER	POST OFFICE BOX 109601	PALM BCH GARDENS, FL 33418
TWITTY, MICHAEL	SINGER	POST OFFICE BOX 23470	NASHVILLE, TN 37202
TWITTY, SEAN	BASEBALL	POST OFFICE BOX 9194	HAMPTON, VA 23670
TWO LIVE CREW	RAP GROUP	LUKE RECORDS, 8400 NE 2ND AVE ...	MIAMI, FL 33138
TWO MINDS CRACK	ROCK & ROLL GROUP ...	HOWFREE MGMT, 31 NORFOLK PL	LONDON W2 1QH .... ENGLAND
TWOHIE, JAMES J, III	COMEDY WRITER	SHOWTIME/THE MOVIE CHANNEL	....
	....	1633 BROADWAY, 37TH FLOOR	NEW YORK, NY 10019
TYCOON	ROCK & ROLL GROUP ...	330 W 58TH ST #7-J	NEW YORK, NY 10019
TYLER, BEVERLY	ACTRESS	JORDAN, 14585 GERONEMO TRAIL	RENO, NV 89511
TYLER, BONNIE	SINGER-SONGWRITER ...	THE STATION AGENCY	....
	....	132 LIVERPOOL RD	LONDON N1 1LA .... ENGLAND
TYLER, BRAD	BASEBALL	POST OFFICE BOX 3169	FREDERICK, MD 21701
TYLER, CHARLES, JR	TV DIRECTOR	ABC NEWS, 1717 DE SALES ST, NW ..	WASHINGTON, DC 20036
TYLER, ROBERT	ACTOR	ABC-TV, "LOVING"	....
	....	320 W 66TH ST, STUDIO 23	NEW YORK, NY 10023
TYLER, ROBIN	SINGER-COMPOSER	13514 HART ST	VAN NUYS, CA 91405
TYLER, STEVEN K	CONDUCTOR	19638 HARTLAND ST	RESEDA, CA 91335
TYLO, HUNTER	ACTRESS	CBS-TV, "THE BOLD & BEAUTIFUL" ..	....
	....	7800 BEVERLY BLVD #3371	LOS ANGELES, CA 90036
TYLO, MICHAEL	ACTOR	CBS-TV, "YOUNG & THE RESTLESS" ..	....
	....	7800 BEVERLY BLVD #3305	LOS ANGELES, CA 90036
TYMCHYSHYN, MARK	ACTOR	CBS-TV, "AS THE WORLD TURNS"	....
	....	524 W 57TH ST #5330	NEW YORK, NY 10019
TYNAN, TRACY	COSTUME DESIGNER	13949 VENTURA BLVD #309	SHERMAN OAKS, CA 91423
TYNE, GEORGE	ACTOR-DIRECTOR	1449 BENEDICT CANYON DR	BEVERLY HILLS, CA 90210
TYRANT	ROCK & ROLL GROUP ...	POST OFFICE BOX 2428	EL SEGUNDO, CA 90245
TYREE, DAVID	COMEDIAN	9145 SUNSET BLVD #228	LOS ANGELES, CA 90069
TYRRELL, ELLIOTT L	DIRECTOR	12 CLARK ST	BROOKLYN, NY 11201
TYRRELL, LOU	TV DIRECTOR	300 E 34TH ST	NEW YORK, NY 10016
TYRRELL, R EMMETT	COMMENTATOR	KING FEATURES, 216 E 45TH ST	NEW YORK, NY 10017
TYRRELL, ROBERT	WRITER-DIRECTOR	51 GLENHOUSE RD	LONDON SE9 1JH .... ENGLAND
TYRRELL, SUSAN	ACTRESS	826 AMOROSO PL	VENICE, CA 90291
TYSON, KATHY	ACTRESS	PETERS, FRASER & DUNLOP, LTD	....
	....	5TH FLOOR, THE CHAMBERS	....
	....	CHELSEA HARBOUR, LOT RD	LONDON SW10 OXF .... ENGLAND
TYSON, MIKE	BOXER	INDIANA YOUTH CENTER	....
	....	727 MOON RD (#922335)	PLAINFIELD, NJ 46168
TYSON, RICHARD	ACTOR	11500 W OLYMPIC BLVD #400	LOS ANGELES, CA 90064
TYTLA, PETER THOMAS	DIRECTOR-EDITOR	1138 1/2 POINSETTIA PL	HOLLYWOOD, CA 90046
TYTLE, HARRY	DIRECTOR-PRODUCER ...	1515 IRVING AVE	GLENDALE, CA 91201
TYZACK, MARGARET	ACTRESS	EDWARDS, 275 KENNINGTON RD	LONDON SE1 6BY .... ENGLAND

Name	Occupation	Address	City
U F O	ROCK & ROLL GROUP ...	PERFORMING ART NETWORK	....

		10 SUTHERLAND	LONDON W9 24Q ENGLAND
U K	ROCK & ROLL GROUP	E G RECORDS, 246 E 62ND ST	NEW YORK, NY 10021
U S E	ROCK & ROLL GROUP	SEE - UNITED STATES OF EXISTENCE	
U-2	ROCK & ROLL GROUP	PRINCIPLE MANAGEMENT AGENCY	
		4 WINDMILL LN, DUBLIN 2	EIRE IRELAND
UBELL, JANE	TV PRODUCER	ENTERTAINMENT TONIGHT	
		PARAMOUNT TELEVISION	
		5555 MELROSE AVE	LOS ANGELES, CA 90038
UCHINOKURA, TOKASHI	BASEBALL	POST OFFICE BOX 4370	SALINAS, CA 93912
UDALL, MORRIS K	U S CONGRESSMAN	142 S CALLE CHAPARITA	TUCSON, AZ 85716
UDALL, STEWART	POLITICIAN	1900 "M" ST, NW	WASHINGTON, DC 20036
UDALL, TOM	ATTORNEY GENERAL	SATE CAPITOL BUILDING	SANTE FE, NM 87503
UDENIO, FABIANA	ACTRESS	8730 SUNSET BLVD #220-W	LOS ANGELES, CA 90069
UDOFF, YALE MAURICE	SCREENWRITER	3383 N KNOLL DR	LOS ANGELES, CA 90068
UDY, HELENE	ACTRESS	9255 SUNSET BLVD #515	LOS ANGELES, CA 90069
UEBERROTH, PETER	BASEBALL EXECUTIVE	184 EMERALD BAY	LAGUNA BEACH, CA 92651
UECKER, BOB	BASEBALL-ACTOR	NORTH 60 WEST 15734 HAWTHORNE DR	MENOMONEE FALLS, WI 53051
UECKER, KEITH	FOOTBALL	PACKERS, 1265 LOMBARDI AVE	GREEN BAY, WI 54307
UFFNER, BETH	TALENT AGENT	9242 BEVERLY DR #200	BEVERLY HILLS, CA 90210
UFLAND, HARRY	FILM PRODUCER	7055 FERNHILL DR	MALIBU, CA 90265
UFLAND, LEN	DIRECTOR	4400 HILLCREST DR #901	HOLLYWOOD, FL 33021
UFO	ROCK & ROLL GROUP	SEE - U F O	
UGER, ALAN	TV WRITER-PRODUCER	4803 CROMWELL AVE	LOS ANGELES, CA 90027
UGGAMS, LESLIE	SINGER-ACTRESS	151 S EL CAMINO DR	BEVERLY HILLS, CA 90212
UGUETO, JESUS	BASEBALL	POST OFFICE BOX 3783	SAVANNAH, GA 31414
UHEY, JACK	BASEBALL SCOUT	S F GIANTS, CANDLESTICK PARK	SAN FRANICSCO, CA 94124
UHLAENDER, TED	BASEBALL-COACH	1155 W MOUND ST	COLUMBUS, OH 43223
UHLMAN, FRED, JR	BASEBALL SCOUT	ORIOLE PARK, 333 W CAMDEN ST	BALTIMORE, MD 21201
UHLMAN, FRED, SR	BASEBALL-EXECUTIVE	ORIOLE PARK, 333 W CAMDEN ST	BALTIMORE, MD 21201
UHRHAN, KEVIN	BASEBALL	POST OFFICE BOX 1718	NEW BRITAIN, CT 06050
ULENE, DR ART	TV DOCTOR	10810 VIA VERONA	LOS ANGELES, CA 90077
ULICK, MICHAEL	FILM DIRECTOR	55 GREENE ST	NEW YORK, NY 10013
ULLGER, SCOTT	BASEBALL MANAGER	POST OFFICE BOX 1659	PORTLAND, OR 97207
ULLMAN, LIV	ACTRESS	15 W 81ST ST	NEW YORK, NY 10024
ULLMAN, TRACEY	ACTRESS-SINGER	13555 D'ESTE DR	PACIFIC PALISADES, CA 90272
ULLMAN, VALLIE	ACTRESS	7036 MIDDLESBURY RIDGE CIR	CANOGA PARK, CA 91307
ULMER, DANIEL	BASEBALL EXECUTIVE	POST OFFICE BOX 36407	LOUISVILLE, KY 40233
ULRICH, GEORGE	BASEBALL UMPIRE	POST OFFICE BOX 25010	LITTLE ROCK, AZ 72221
ULRICH, KIM JOHNSTON	ACTRESS	9744 WILSHIRE BLVD #308	BEVERLY HILLS, CA 90212
ULRICH, MARK	ARTIST	41 E 22ND ST	NEW YORK, NY 10010
ULRICH, RICHARD	COMPOSER	3009 ALLENTON AVE	HACIENDA HGTS, CA 91745
ULSTAD, RON	ACTOR	4051 RADFORD AVE #A	STUDIO CITY, CA 91604
ULTIMATE WARRIOR, THE	WRESTLER	POST OFFICE BOX 3859	STAMFORD, CT 06905
ULTRAVOX	ROCK & ROLL GROUP	O'DONNELL MANAGEMENT	
		9 DISRAELI RD	LONDON SW15 ENGLAND
UMLAS, JUDITH W	TV EXECUTIVE	20 E 46TH ST #301	NEW YORK, NY 10017
UMPHRED, NEAL	ROCK COLUMNIST	POST OFFICE BOX 40116	BELLEVUE, WA 98004
UNDERTAKER, THE	WRESTLER	POST OFFICE BOX 3859	STAMFORD, CT 06905
UNDERWOOD, BETTY	ACTRESS	DEUTSCH, 715 N PALM DR	BEVERLY HILLS, CA 90210
UNDERWOOD, BLAIR	ACTOR	7148 WOODROW WILSON DR	LOS ANGELES, CA 90046
UNDERWOOD, CURTIS	BASEBALL	POST OFFICE BOX 3783	SAVANNAH, GA 31414
UNDERWOOD, HANK	ACTOR	MURPHY, 6014 GREENBUSH AVE	VAN NUYS, CA 91401
UNDERWOOD, JAY	ACTOR	9000 SUNSET BLVD #1200	LOS ANGELES, CA 90069
UNDERWOOD, PATRICK	TV DIRECTOR-PRODUCER	WXYZ-TV, 20777 W 10 MILE RD	SOUTHFIELD, MI 48037
UNDERWOOD, RAY	ACTOR	9007 NORMA PL	LOS ANGELES, CA 90069
UNDERWOOD, RON	FILM DIRECTOR	ROBERTS CO, 427 N CANON DR	BEVERLY HILLS, CA 90210
UNDORF, BOB	BASEBALL	POST OFFICE BOX 2785	LAKELAND, FL 33806
UNGER, ANTHONY B	FILM PRODUCER	1272 S BEVERLY GLEN BLVD	LOS ANGELES, CA 90024
UNGER, ARTHUR	TV CRITIC	220 E 42ND ST #3006	NEW YORK, NY 10017
UNGER, DANIEL	FILM EXECUTIVE	6 BASIL MANSIONS, BASIL ST	LONDON SW3 ENGLAND
UNGER, DONALD J	BASKETBALL EXECUTIVE	N J NETS, MEADOWLANDS ARENA	EAST RUTHERFORD, NJ 07073
UNGER, JIM	CARTOONIST	UPS, 4900 MAIN ST, 9TH FLOOR	KANSAS CITY, MO 64112
UNGER, LEANNE	SCREENWRITER	555 W 57TH ST #1230	NEW YORK, NY 10019
UNGER, MAURICE	DIRECTOR	6 NORTHSTAR ST #203	MARINA DEL REY, CA 90292
UNGER, STEPHEN A	FILM EXECUTIVE	11774 MOORPARK ST #G	STUDIO CITY, CA 91604
UNIDOS	RHYTHM & BLUES GROUP	POST OFFICE BOX 634	LAWRENCE, KS 66044
UNITED STATES OF EXISTENCE, THE	ROCK & ROLL GROUP	BAM CARUSO RECORDS COMPANY	
		9 RIDGEMONT RD, SAINT ALBANS	HERTSHIRE ENGLAND
UNRUH, JACK	ARTIST	2706 FAIRMONT ST	DALLAS, TX 75201
UNSELD, WES	BASKETBALL COACH	BULLETS, 1 HARRY S TRUMAN DR	LANDOVER, MD 20785
UNSER, BOBBY	AUTO RACER	7700 CENTRAL AVE, SW	ALBUQUERQUE, NM 87105
UNSER, DEL	BASEBALL-EXECUTIVE	POST OFFICE BOX 7575	PHILADELPHIA, PA 19101
UNSOELD, JOLENE	U S CONGRESSWOMAN	207 FEDERAL BUILDING	OLYMPIA, WA 98501
UNTOLD FABLES, THE	ROCK & ROLL GROUP	POST OFFICE BOX 1975	BURBANK, CA 91507
UPCHURCH, PHIL	SINGER	WIRTZ, 86 S SIERRA MADRE BLVD	PASADENA, CA 91107
UPDIKE, JOHN	NOVELIST	675 HALE ST	BEVERLY, MS 01915
UPSHAW, WILLIE	BASEBALL	POST OFFICE BOX 395	BLANCO, TX 78606
UPSTILL, CARIN E	TV WRITER-PRODUCER	REEVES CORPORATE SERVICES	
		708 3RD AVE, 11TH FLOOR	NEW YORK, NY 10019
UPTON, DALE	SINGER	POST OFFICE BOX 25371	CHARLOTTE, NC 28212
UPTON, FREDERICK	U S CONGRESSMAN	421 MAIN ST	SAINT JOSEPH, MI 49085
UPTOWN	RAP GROUP	POST OFFICE BOX 1126	CORONA, NY 11373
URAM, LAUREN	ARTIST	251 WASHINGTON AVE #2-F	BROOKLYN, NY 11205
URBAN, STUART	WRITER-PRODUCER	SEIFERT, 18 LADBROKE TERR	LONDON W11 3PG ENGLAND
URBAND, JEFF	ARRANGER-COMPOSER	8506 NORRIS AVE	SUN VALLEY, CA 91352

URBANI, TOM	BASEBALL	POST OFFICE BOX 5599	LITTLE ROCK, AR 72215
URBANIK, BILL	FOOTBALL COACH	RAIDERS, 332 CENTER ST	EL SEGUNDO, CA 90245
URBATIONS, THE	ROCK & ROLL GROUP	MSA, 442 E LAFAYETTE BLVD	DETROIT, MI 48226
URBINA, UGUETH	BASEBALL	POLECATS, 608 N SLAPPEY BLVD	ALBANY, GA 31701
URBISCI, ROCCO N	TV WRITER	10519 WILKINS AVE	LOS ANGELES, CA 90049
URBON, JOE	BASEBALL	POST OFFICE BOX 10336	CLEARWATER, FL 34617
URBONT, JACK	COMPOSER-CONDUCTOR	330 W 72ND ST	NEW YORK, NY 10023
URCIOLI, JOHN	BASEBALL	14100 SIX MILE CYPRESS PKWY	FORT MYERS, FL 33912
URIAH HEEP	ROCK & ROLL GROUP	HARRY MALONEY MANAGEMENT	
		18-19 WARWICK ST, 3RD FLOOR	LONDON W1R 5RB ENGLAND
URIBE, JOSE	BASEBALL	S F GIANTS, CANDLESTICK PARK	SAN FRANICSCO, CA 94124
URICCHIO, MARYLYNNE	FILM CRITIC	PITTSBURGH POST-GAZETTE	
		34 BLVD OF ALLIES	PITTSBURGH, PA 15230
URICH, HEATHER MENZIES	ACTRESS	475 WESTERN AVE	BOSTON, MA 02135
URICH, ROBERT	ACTOR-WRITER	15930 WOODVALE RD	ENCINO, CA 91436
URIE, JOHN	WRITER-PRODUCER	1415 INNES PL	VENICE, CA 90291
URIOSTE, FRANK J	FILM EDITOR	1610 HIGHLAND AVE	GLENDALE, CA 91202
URIS, LEON	AUTHOR	POST OFFICE BOX 1559	ASPEN, CO 81611
URMSON, KATHERINE ANN	ART DIRECTOR	252 CARLTON AVE	BROOKLYN, NY 11205
URQUHART, ROBERT	ACTOR	FRENCH'S, 52 HOLLAND PARK MEWS	LONDON W11 ENGLAND
URRIBARRI, GEORGE	BASEBALL SCOUT	POST OFFICE BOX 90111	ARLINGTON, TX 76004
URSO, SALVY	BASEBALL	POST OFFICE BOX 30160	SAN BERNARDINO, CA 92413
USTINOV, PETER	ACTOR-WRITER-DIRECTOR	11 RUE DE SILLY	F-92100 BOULOGNE FRANCE
UTAL, MATTHEW	COMPOSER	POST OFFICE BOX 9864	GLENDALE, CA 91206
UTH, TONY	CARTOONIST	PHILADELPHIA INQUIRER	
		400 N BROAD ST	PHILADELPHIA, PA 19101
UTLEY, C GARRICK	NEWS CORRESPONDENT	12 HANOVER TERR	LONDON NW1 ENGLAND
UTLEY, JERRY	SINGER	YENOWINE, 10630 ST RENE	JEFFERSTOWN, KY 40299
UTLEY, MIKE	FOOTBALL	LIONS, 1200 FEATHERSTONE RD	PONTIAC, MI 48432
UTLEY, STAN	GOLFER	POST OFFICE BOX 109601	PALM BCH GARDENS, FL 33418
UTOPIA	ROCK & ROLL GROUP	PANACEA, 132 NASSAU ST	NEW YORK, NY 10038
UTT, KENNETH	TV PRODUCER	180 RIVERSIDE DR	NEW YORK, NY 10024

V, JOHNNY	WRESTLER-MANAGER	POST OFFICE BOX 3859	STAMFORD, CT 06905
VACCARINO, MAURICE	TV DIRECTOR	3593 BERRY DR	STUDIO CITY, CA 91604
VACCARO, BRENDA	ACTRESS	14423 DICKENS ST #3	SHERMAN OAKS, CA 91403
VACZY, RICHARD A	TV WRITER	2128 ASHLAND AVE	SANTA MONICA, CA 90405
VADENBONCOEUR, JOAN E	FILM CRITIC	POST OFFICE BOX 4915	SYRACUSE, NY 13221
VADIM, ROGER	FILM DIRECTOR	2429 BEVERLY AVE	SANTA MONICA, CA 90406
VADIM, VANESSA	ACTRESS	316 ALTA AVE	SANTA MONICA, CA 90402
VAINES, COLIN	WRITER	15 QUEEN'S GATE PLACE MEWS	LONDON SW7 5BG ENGLAND
VAINISI, JEROME R	FOOTBALL EXECUTIVE	LIONS, 1200 FEATHERSTONE RD	PONTIAC, MI 48432
VAIVE, RICK	HOCKEY	SABRES, MEMORIAL AUDITORIUM	BUFFALO, NY 14202
VAJNA, ANDREW	FILM PRODUCER	8810 MELROSE AVE #201	LOS ANGELES, CA 90069
VAL, STEVE	SINGER-GUITARIST	POST OFFICE BOX 44024	SYLMAR, CA 91342
VALADEZ, JORGE	COMPOSER	2813 MERRITT AVE	LAS VEGAS, NV 89102
VALAND, THEODORE L	TV EXECUTIVE	BASYS INC, 1995 BROADWAY	NEW YORK, NY 10023
VALDES, DAVID	FILM PRODUCER	4000 WARNER BLVD #16	BURBANK, CA 91522
VALDEZ, EFRAIN	BASEBALL	2850 W 20TH AVE	DENVER, CO 80211
VALDEZ, JOE	BODYBUILDER	POST OFFICE BOX 5175	WHITTIER, CA 90607
VALDEZ, JULIO	BASEBALL-INSTRUCTOR	1060 W ADDISON ST	CHICAGO, IL 60613
VALDEZ, LUIS M	WRITER-PRODUCER	DGA, 7920 SUNSET BLVD, 6TH FL	LOS ANGELES, CA 90046
VALDEZ, PATTI	ARTIST	THE ARIZONA REPUBLIC	
		120 E VAN BUREN ST	PHOENIX, AZ 85004
VALDEZ, PEDRO	BASEBALL	1524 W NEBRASKA AVE	PEORIA, IL 61604
VALDEZ, RAFAEL	BASEBALL	STARS, 850 LAS VEGAS BLVD N	LAS VEGAS, NV 89101
VALDEZ, SERGIO	BASEBALL	1501 W 16TH ST	INDIANAPOLIS, IN 46202
VALDY	MUSICAL GROUP	4680 ELK LAKE DR #304	VICTORIA, BC CANADA
VALDY, SIOUTH	SINGER	4680 ELK LAKE DR #304	VICTORIA, BC V8Z 5M1 CANADA
VALE, JERRY	SINGER	621 N PALM DR	BEVERLY HILLS, CA 90210
VALE, SHANNON	TALENT AGENT	POST OFFICE BOX 2454	AUSTIN, TX 78768
VALEN, NANCY	ACTRESS	10000 SANTA MONICA BLVD #305	LOS ANGELES, CA 90067
VALENTA, LEONARD	TV DIRECTOR	134 CAMPUS RD	STATEN ISLAND, NY 10301
VALENTE, RENEE	FILM PRODUCER	PRODUCERS GUILD OF AMERICA	
		400 S BEVERLY DR	BEVERLY HILLS, CA 90212
VALENTE, RICK	BODYBUILDER	POST OFFICE BOX 11117	MARINA DEL REY, CA 90295
VALENTI, JACK	FILM EXECUTIVE	1600 "I" ST, NW	WASHINGTON, DC 20006
VALENTI, JOSEPH A	COMPOSER-CONDUCTOR	4417 LUCERA CIR	PALOS VERDES EST, CA 90274
VALENTIN, DAVE	SINGER	3RD WAVE MGMT, 155 W 72ND ST	NEW YORK, NY 10023
VALENTIN, JOHN	BASEBALL	POST OFFICE BOX 2365	PAWTUCKET, RI 02861
VALENTIN, JOSE	BASEBALL	2850 W 20TH AVE	DENVER, CO 80211
VALENTINE, ANTHONY	ACTOR	LONDON MGT, 235-241 REGENT ST	LONDON W1R 4PH ENGLAND
VALENTINE, BILL	BASEBALL EXECUTIVE	POST OFFICE BOX 5599	LITTLE ROCK, AR 72215
VALENTINE, BOBBY	BASEBALL-MANAGER	POST OFFICE BOX 90111	ARLINGTON, TX 76004
VALENTINE, GREG "THE HAMMER"	WRESTLER	POST OFFICE BOX 105366	ATLANTA, GA 31348
VALENTINE, KAREN	ACTRESS	145 W 67TH ST #42-H	NEW YORK, NY 10023
VALENTINE, PAUL	ACTOR	POST OFFICE BOX 36-D-71	LOS ANGELES, CA 90036

VALENTINE, SCOTT	ACTOR	433 N BOWLING GREEN WY	LOS ANGELES, CA	90049
VALENTINE, TIM	U S CONGRESSMAN	522 S DUKE ST	DURHAM, NC	27707
VALENTINO	SINGER	2 E 70TH ST	NEW YORK, NY	10021
VALENTINO, PATRICK M	COMPOSER-CONDUCTOR	91223 INDEX ST #4	NORTHRIDGE, CA	91326
VALENTINO & THE SHAHAN EXPRESS	C & W GROUP	POST OFFICE BOX 528	BRACKETTVILLE, TX	78832
VALENZA, TASIA	ACTRESS	8730 SUNSET BLVD #220-W	LOS ANGELES, CA	90069
VALENZUELA, FERNANDO	BASEBALL	3004 N BEACHWOOD DR	LOS ANGELES, CA	90068
VALERA, JULIO	BASEBALL	POST OFFICE BOX 1211	NORFOLK, VA	23502
VALERIANI, RICHARD	NEWS JOURNALIST	3025 ARIZONA AVE, NW	WASHINGTON, DC	20016
VALERIO, JOE	FOOTBALL	CHIEFS, 1 ARROWHEAD DR	KANSAS CITY, MO	64129
VALERY, ANNE	TV WRITER	5 ABBOT'S PL	LONDON NW6	ENGLAND
VALERY, DANA	ACTRESS	OSCARD, 24 W 40TH ST, 17TH FL	NEW YORK, NY	10011
VALESENTE, BOB	FOOTBALL COACH	STEELERS, 300 STADIUM CIR	PITTSBURGH, PA	15212
VALK, GARRY	HOCKEY	CANUCKS, 100 N RENFREW ST	VANCOUVER, BC V5K 3N7	CANADA
VALL, SEYMOUR	THEATER PRODUCER	35 W 81ST ST	NEW YORK, NY	10024
VALLA, EUGENE	BASEBALL EXECUTIVE	S F GIANTS, CANDLESTICK PARK	SAN FRANICSCO, CA	94124
VALLE, DAVE	BASEBALL	POST OFFICE BOX 4100	SEATTLE, WA	98104
VALLE, DAVID	BASEBALL	POST OFFICE BOX 4100	SEATTLE, WA	98104
VALLELY, JEAN	TV WRITER	10100 SANTA MONICA BLVD #1600	LOS ANGELES, CA	90067
VALLELY, TANNIS	ACTRESS	142 S CLARK DR #103	LOS ANGELES, CA	90048
VALLEY, PAUL MICHAEL	ACTOR	NBC-TV, "ANOTHER WORLD"		
		1268 E 14TH ST	BROOKLYN, NY	11230
VALLI, ALIDA	ACTRESS	VIALE LIEGI 42	I-00100 ROME	ITALY
VALLI, FRANKIE	SINGER	26 OAK TRAIL RD	ENGLEWOOD, NJ	07631
VALLI, JUNE	SINGER	MERCHANT, 1158 BRIAR WY	FORT LEE, NJ	07024
VALRIE, KERRY	BASEBALL	POST OFFICE BOX 4218	SOUTH BEND, IN	46634
VAN, GARWOOD	CONDUCTOR	341 DESERT INN RD	LAS VEGAS, NV	89109
VAN AMERONGEN, JERRY	CARTOONIST	KING FEATURES, 216 E 45TH ST	NEW YORK, NY	10017
VAN ARK, JOAN	ACTRESS	10950 ALTA VIEW DR	STUDIO CITY, CA	91604
VAN ARSDALE, DICK	BASKETBALL EXECUTIVE	SUNS, 2910 N CENTRAL AVE	PHOENIX, AZ	85012
VAN ATTA, DONALD	DIRECTOR-PRODUCER	4818 CORBIN AVE	TARZANA, CA	91356
VAN BUREN, ABIGAIL	COLUMNIST-LECTURER	9200 SUNSET BLVD #1003	LOS ANGELES, CA	90069
VAN BURKLEO, TY	BASEBALL	10233 96TH AVE	EDMONTON, ALB TK5 0A5	CANADA
VAN CITTERS, JOEL	DIRECTOR	391-A NORMANDY DR	NORWOOD, MA	02062
VAN DAM, R PAUL	ATTORNEY GENERAL	STATE CAPITOL BUILDING	SALT LAKE CITY, UT	84114
VAN DAMME, JEAN-CLAUDE	ACTOR-BODYBUILDER	POST OFFICE BOX 4149	CHATSWORTH, CA	91313
VAN DE VEN, MONIQUE	ACTRESS	ROSENBERG, 8428 MELROSE PL #C	LOS ANGELES, CA	90069
VAN DECKTER, GIGI	WRI-DIR-PROD	38 8TH AVE #2-C	NEW YORK, NY	10014
VAN DEN ECKER, BEAU	DIRECTOR	DGA, 7920 SUNSET BLVD, 6TH FL	LOS ANGELES, CA	90046
VAN DEN HERICK, YOLANDA	ACTRESS	L A TALENT, 8335 SUNSET BLVD	LOS ANGELES, CA	90069
VAN DER FEER, TOM	DIRECTOR	160 W 46TH ST	NEW YORK, NY	10036
VAN DER VELDE, NADINE	ACTRESS	145 S FAIRFAX AVE #310	LOS ANGELES, CA	90036
VAN DEVERE, TRISH	ACTRESS	3211 RETREAT CT	MALIBU, CA	90265
VAN DOREN, MAMIE	ACTRESS-SINGER-AUTHOR	EICHLER, 1524 LA BAIG AVE	LOS ANGELES, CA	90028
VAN DUSEN, GRANVILLE	ACTOR	144 S BEVERLY DR #405	BEVERLY HILLS, CA	90212
VAN DUZER, DONNA	BASEBALL TRAINER	POST OFFICE BOX 3609	PORT CHARLOTTE, FL	33949
VAN DYKE, DICK	ACTOR-WRITER	23215 MARIPOSA DE ORO	MALIBU, CA	90265
VAN DYKE, JERRY	ACTOR-COMEDIAN	1717 N HIGHLAND AVE #414	LOS ANGELES, CA	90028
VAN DYKE, LEROY	SINGER-SONGWRITER	ROUTE #1, BOX 271	SMITHTON, MO	65350
VAN DYKE, RICHARD W	DIRECTOR	4335 MARINA CITY DR	MARINA DEL REY, CA	90292
VAN DYKE, ROD	BASEBALL	POST OFFICE BOX 1742	PALM SPRINGS, CA	92263
VAN DYKE, WILLARD	FILM DIRECTOR	505 W END ST	NEW YORK, NY	10024
VAN EGMOND, TIM	BASEBALL	POST OFFICE BOX 10213	LYNCHBURG, VA	24506
VAN EMAN, CHARLES	ACTOR	8730 SUNSET BLVD #220-W	LOS ANGELES, CA	90069
VAN ENGER, DICK, JR	FILM EDITOR	ACE, 1041 N FORMOSA AVE	WEST HOLLYWOOD, CA	90046
VAN EPS, ROBERT	COMPOSER	1618 EL RITO AVE	GLENDALE, CA	91208
VAN EYKEN, RAYMOND	COMPOSER	15455 VANOWEN ST #4	VAN NUYS, CA	91406
VAN FLEET, JAMES A	GENERAL	5210 VAN FLEET RD	POLK CITY, FL	33868
VAN FLEET, JOHN	ARTIST	380 2ND ST #2-R	BROOKLYN, NY	11215
VAN FLEET, RICHARD	ACTOR	ABC-TV, "ALL MY CHILDREN"		
		320 W 66TH ST	NEW YORK, NY	10023
VAN GUNDY, JEFF	BASKETBALL COACH	KNICKS, 4 PENNYLVANIA PLAZA	NEW YORK, NY	10019
VAN HALEN	ROCK & ROLL GROUP	10100 SANTA MONICA BLVD #2460	LOS ANGELES, CA	90067
VAN HEUSEN, JAMES	COMPOSER-PIANIST	POST OFFICE BOX 44	BRANT LAKE, NY	12815
VAN HORN, BUDDY	FILM DIRECTOR	4409 PONCA AVE	TOLUCA LAKE, CA	91602
VAN HORNE, DAVE	SPORTSCASTER	EXPOS, 4545 DE COUBERTIN AVE	MONTREAL, QUE H1V 3P2	CANADA
VAN HORNE, KEITH	FOOTBALL	BEARS, 250 N WASHINGTON RD	LAKE FOREST, IL	60045
VAN LIEROP, TOY RUSSELL	MAKE-UP ARTIST	1120 AVE OF THE AMERICAS #4147	NEW YORK, NY	10036
VAN MAELE, ARTHUR, JR	TV DIRECTOR	21724 LA SALLE	WARREN, MI	48089
VAN NORDEN, PETER	ACTOR	14133 COHASSET ST	VAN NUYS, CA	91405
VAN NOTE, JACK A	TV WRITER-STORY ED	JAV INC, 60 MITCHELL AVE	TOTOWA, NJ	07512
VAN ORNUM, JOHN	BASEBALL-SCOUT	S F GIANTS, CANDLESTICK PARK	SAN FRANICSCO, CA	94124
VAN OST, VALERIE	ACTRESS-CASTING DIR	57 OAKWOOD CT, KENSINGTON	LONDON W14 8JY	ENGLAND
VAN PATTEN, DICK	ACTOR	13920 MAGNOLIA BLVD	SHERMAN OAKS, CA	91423
VAN PATTEN, JAMES	ACTOR	14411 RIVERSIDE DR #15	SHERMAN OAKS, CA	91423
VAN PATTEN, JOYCE	ACTRESS	1321 N HAYWORTH AVE #C	LOS ANGELES, CA	90046
VAN PATTEN, NELS	ACTOR	14411 RIVERSIDE DR #18	SHERMAN OAKS, CA	91423
VAN PATTEN, PATRICIA	ACTRESS	13920 MAGNOLIA BLVD	SHERMAN OAKS, CA	91423
VAN PATTEN, TIM	ACTOR	7461 BEVERLY BLVD #400	LOS ANGELES, CA	90036
VAN PATTEN, VINCENT	ACTOR	13926 MAGNOLIA BLVD	SHERMAN OAKS, CA	91423
VAN PEEBLES, MARIO	ACTOR	ICM, 40 W 57TH ST	NEW YORK, NY	10019
VAN PEEBLES, MEGAN	ACTOR	353 W 56TH ST #10-F	NEW YORK, NY	10019
VAN PEEBLES, MELVIN	ACT-WRI-DIR	353 W 56TH ST #10-F	NEW YORK, NY	10019
VAN POPPEL, TODD	BASEBALL	POST OFFICE BOX 11087	TACOMA, WA	98411
VAN PRAAG, WILLIAM	TV DIRECTOR-PRODUCER	135 E 55TH ST	NEW YORK, NY	10022

VAN PROYEN, GLEN	BASEBALL SCOUT	1000 ELYSIAN PARK DR	LOS ANGELES, CA 90012
VAN REES, JOOST	TV DIRECTOR	210 RIVERSIDE DR	NEW YORK, NY 10025
VAN RELLIM, TIM	FILM PRODUCER	22 WINDSOR CT, MOSCOW RD	LONDON W2 ENGLAND
VAN RONK, DAVE	SINGER-GUITARIST	FOLKLORE, 1671 APPIAN WY	SANTA MONICA, CA 90401
VAN RUNKLE, THEADORA	COSTUME DESIGNER	8805 LOOKOUT MOUNTAIN RD	LOS ANGELES, CA 90046
VAN SCHAACK, TOM	BASEBALL EXECUTIVE	POST OFFICE BOX 802	WATERTOWN, NY 13601
VAN SCOYK, ROBERT E	TV WRITER	1740 WESTRIDGE RD	LOS ANGELES, CA 90069
VAN SCOYOC, JIM	BASEBALL COACH	1201 HYDE PARK BLVD	NIAGARA FALLS, NY 14301
VAN SHELDON, RICKY	SINGER-SONGWRITER	818 19TH ST S	NASHVILLE, TN 37203
VAN SLYKE, ANDY	BASEBALL	POST OFFICE BOX 7000	PITTSBURGH, PA 15212
VAN THIEU, NGUYEN	GENERAL	COOMBE PARK, KINGSTON-ON-THAMES	SURREY ENGLAND
VAN VALKENBURGH, DEBORAH	ACTRESS	2025 STANLEY HILLS DR	LOS ANGELES, CA 90046
VAN VOGT, A E	WRITER	2850 BELDEN DR	LOS ANGELES, CA 90068
VAN VOOREN, MONIQUE	ACTRESS-SINGER	165 E 66TH ST	NEW YORK, NY 10021
VAN WINKLE, JOSEPH	SCREENWRITER	4836 STROHM AVE	NORTH HOLLYWOOD, CA 91601
VAN ZANDT, STEVE	SINGER-SONGWRITER	322 W 57TH ST	NEW YORK, NY 10019
VAN ZANT, JOHNNY, BAND	ROCK & ROLL GROUP	POST OFFICE BOX 4804	MACON, GA 31201
VAN-DELLS, THE	VOCAL GROUP	POST OFFICE BOX 40686	NASHVILLE, TN 37204
VANACORE, VICTOR A	CONDUCTOR	9712 SALOMA AVE	SEPULVEDA, CA 91343
VANCE, CYRUS	POLITICIAN	425 LEXINGTON AVE	NEW YORK, NY 10017
VANCE, LEIGH	WRITER-PRODUCER	1801 BEL AIR RD	LOS ANGELES, CA 90077
VANCE-STRAKER, MARILYN	COSTUME DESIGNER	13949 VENTURA BLVD #309	SHERMAN OAKS, CA 91423
VANDE BERG, ED	BASEBALL	POST OFFICE BOX 3690, STA "B"	CALGARY, ALB T2B 4M4 CANADA
VANDENBERG	ROCK & ROLL GROUP	ICM, 40 W 57TH ST	NEW YORK, NY 10019
VANDENBURG, WILLIAM	CONDUCTOR	25281 LA ESTRADA	LAGUNA NIGUEL, CA 92677
VANDER JAGT, GUY	U S CONGRESSMAN	900 E FRONT ST	TRAVERSE CITY, MI 49684
VANDER MEER, JOHNNY	BASEBALL	4005 LEONA AVE	TAMPA, FL 33606
VANDER POEL, MARK	FOOTBALL	POST OFFICE BOX 535000	INDIANPOLIS, IN 46253
VANDER WAL, JOHN	BASEBALL	EXPOS, 4545 DE COUBERTIN AVE	MONTREAL, QUE H1V 3P2 CANADA
VANDER WEELE, DOUG	BASEBALL	POST OFFICE BOX 1295	CLINTON, IA 52733
VANDERVALK, BRUCE	COMPOSER-CONDUCTOR	1563 DEVONSHIRE AVE	WESTLAKE VILLAGE, CA 91361
VANDERVORT, PHILIP	TV PRODUCER	RALPH EDWARDS PRODUCTIONS	
		"THE PEOPLE'S COURT"	
		1717 N HIGHLAND AVE, 10TH FL	HOLLYWOOD, CA 90028
VANDEWEGHE, KIKI	BASKETBALL	KNICKS, 4 PENNYLVANIA PLAZA	NEW YORK, NY 10019
VANDIS, TITOS	ACTOR	1551 MIDVALE AVE #1	LOS ANGELES, CA 90024
VANDROSS, LUTHER	SINGER	ALIVE, 8271 SUNSET BLVD, 2ND FL	LOS ANGELES, CA 90046
VANE, CHRISTOPHER L	TV WRITER	1844 THAYER AVE	LOS ANGELES, CA 90025
VANE, NORMAN THADDEUS	SCREENWRITER	1121 OLIVE DR #104	LOS ANGELES, CA 90069
VANEL, CHARLES	ACTOR	ARTMEDIA, 10 AVE GEORGE V	PARIS 75008 FRANCE
VANELLI, GINO	SINGER-SONGWRITER	31270 LA BAYA DR #110	WESTLAKE VILLAGE, CA 91362
VANGELIS	COMPOSER	YANUS ZOGRAPHON, NEMO STUDIOS	
		HAMPDEN GURNEY ST	LONDON ENGLAND
VANILLA ICE	RAPPER-RAPWRITER	1290 AVE OF THE AMERICAS #4200	NEW YORK, NY 10104
VANITY	SINGER-ACTRESS	151 S EL CAMINO DR	BEVERLY HILLS, CA 90212
VANLANDINGHAM, BILLY	BASEBALL	POST OFFICE BOX 21727	SAN FRANCISCO, CA 95151
VANN, BRANDY	BASEBALL	POST OFFICE DRAWER 4797	EL PASO, TX 79914
VANNER, SUE	ACTRESS	AIM, 5 DENMARK ST	LONDON WC2H 8LP ENGLAND
VANOCUR, SANDOR	NEWS CORRESPONDENT	ABC NEWS, 1717 DE SALES ST, NW	WASHINGTON, DC 20036
VANOVER, LARRY	BASEBALL UMPIRE	POST OFFICE BOX 608	GROVE CITY, OH 43123
VANRYN, BEN	BASEBALL	POST OFFICE BOX 2887	VERO BEACH, FL 32961
VANTIGER, TOM	BASEBALL	POST OFFICE BOX 3452	KINSTON, NC 28502
VANWARMER, RANDY	SINGER-SONGWRITER	65 MUSIC SQAUER W	NASVHILLE, TN 37203
VAPORS, THE	ROCK & ROLL GROUP	MAYBURY, 44 BALMORAL DR	WOKING, SURREY ENGLAND
VARDY, MIKE	TV DIRECTOR	RAE, CHARING CROSS RD	LONDON WC2H ODB ENGLAND
VARELA, DANTE	COMPOSER	7725 GREENBUSH	PANORAMA CITY, CA 91402
VARGAS, HECTOR	BASEBALL	ALBANY YANKEES, HERITAGE PARK	ALBANY, NY 12211
VARGAS, RAYMOND C	VIDEOGRAPHER-PRODUCER	441 48TH ST	BROOKLYN, NY 11220
VARHOL, MICHAEL C	DIRECTOR	920 S WOOSTER ST	LOS ANGELES, CA 90035
VARNEY, JIM	ACTOR	700 CRAIGHEAD #204	NASHVILLE, TN 37204
VARON, DARVIN	ACTOR	17 E 7TH ST	NEW YORK, NY 10003
VARON, EDITH	ACTRESS	8075 W 3RD ST #550	LOS ANGELES, CA 90048
VARON, RUDY	CONDUCTOR	940 MALTMAN AVE	LOS ANGELES, CA 90026
VARSHO, GARY	BASEBALL	POST OFFICE BOX 7000	PITTSBURGH, PA 15212
VARTAN, SYLVIE	SINGER-ACTRESS	706 N BEVERLY DR	BEVERLY HILLS, CA 90210
VASEY, JOHN C	WRITER	10941 STRATHMORE DR #44	LOS ANGELES, CA 90024
VASQUEZ, ANGEL	BASEBALL SCOUT	6850 LAWRENCE RD	LANTANA, FL 33462
VASQUEZ, CHRIS	BASEBALL	POST OFFICE BOX 2001	CEDAR RAPIDS, IA 52406
VASQUEZ, JULIAN	BASEBALL	POST OFFICE BOX 598	BINGHAMTON, NY 13902
VASQUEZ, ROBERTA	ACTRESS-MODEL	8033 SUNSET BLVD #801	LOS ANGELES, CA 90046
VASSAR, DAVID A	TV DIRECTOR	POST OFFICE BOX 43	VENICE, CA 90291
VASSER, RONALD T	TV DIRECTOR	929 MARGATE TERR	CHICAGO, IL 60657
VATCHER, JIM	BASEBALL	STARS, 850 LAS VEGAS BLVD N	LAS VEGAS, NV 89101
VAUGHAN, CLIFFORD	CONDUCTOR	12700 ELLIOTT AVE #455	EL MONTE, CA 91732
VAUGHAN, JACK	FOOTBALL REFEREE	NFL, 410 PARK AVE	NEW YORK, NY 10022
VAUGHAN, PARIS	ACTRESS	POST OFFICE BOX 5617	BEVERLY HILLS, CA 90213
VAUGHAN, PETER	ACTOR	ICM, 388-396 OXFORD ST	LONDON W1 ENGLAND
VAUGHN, COUNTESS	ACTRESS	606 N LARCHMONT BLVD #309	LOS ANGELES, CA 90004
VAUGHN, DE WAYNE	BASEBALL	1404 FORDSON	OKLAHOMA CITY, OK 73127
VAUGHN, DEREK	BASEBALL	POST OFFICE BOX 611	WATERLOO, IA 50704
VAUGHN, GREG	BASEBALL	BREWERS, 201 S 46TH ST	MILWAUKEE, WI 53214
VAUGHN, JON	FOOTBALL	PATRIOTS, FOXBORO STADIUM, RT #1	FOXBORO, MA 02035
VAUGHN, MO	BASEBALL	FENWAY PARK, 4 YAWKEY WY	BOSTON, MA 02215
VAUGHN, ROBERT	ACTOR-DIRECTOR	162 OLD W MOUNTAIN RD	RIDGEFIELD, CT 06877
VAUGHN, RON	BASEBALL SCOUT	ATHLETICS'S, OAKLAND COLISEUM	OAKLAND, CA 94621

VAUGHN, VINCENT RAY	MUSIC ARRANGER	608-A MC PHERSON CT S	NASHVILLE, TN	37221
VAUGHN BROTHERS, THE	ROCK & ROLL DUO	505 BARTON SPRINGS #1150	AUSTIN, TX	78704
VAUGHT, LOY	BASKETBALL	CLIPPERS, 3939 S FIGUEROA ST	LOS ANGELES, CA	90037
VAUS, STEVE	SINGER-SONGWRITER	STEVE VAUS PRODUCTIONS		
		9590 CHESAPEAKE DR	SAN DIEGO, CA	92123
VAVRA, JOE	BASEBALL MANAGER	POST OFFICE BOX 483	YAKIMA, WA	98907
VAZAK, P H	SCREENWRITER	ICM, 8899 BEVERLY BLVD	LOS ANGELES, CA	90048
VAZQUEZ, MARCOS	BASEBALL	POST OFFICE BOX 507	DURHAM, NC	27702
VEASEY, CRAIG	FOOTBALL	STEELERS, 300 STADIUM CIR	PITTSBURGH, PA	15212
VEASEY, PAM	TV WRITER	131 S RODEO DR #300	BEVERLY HILLS, CA	90212
VECCHIA, CHRISTOPHER R, JR	TV DIRECTOR	7 BULLFINCH PL	BOSTON, MA	02114
VECCHIO, ROSS	BASEBALL EXECUTIVE	525 NW PEACOCK BLVD	PORT SAINT LUCIE, FL	34986
VECHIARELLA, JIM	FOOTBALL COACH	BROWNS, 80 1ST ST	BEREA, OH	44017
VEE, BOBBY	SINGER-SONGWRITER	POST OFFICE BOX 41	SAUK RAPIDS, MN	56379
VEE BAND, THE	ROCK & ROLL GROUP	3717 W 50TH ST #L-2	MINNEAPOLIS, MN	55410
VEECK, MICHAEL	BASEBALL EXECUTIVE	POST OFFICE BOX 726	POMPANO BEACH, FL	33064
VEGA, SUZANNE	SINGER-SONGWRITER	1500 BROADWAY #1703	NEW YORK, NY	10036
VEHICLE	ROCK & ROLL GROUP	41 BRITAIN ST #200	TORONTO, ONT M5A 1R7	CANADA
VEITCH, JOHN	FILM PRODUCER	COLUMBIA PICTURES INDUSTRIES		
		COLUMBIA PLAZA	BURBANK, CA	91505
VEITH, SANDY	PRODUCER	MCA/UNIVERSAL STUDIOS, INC		
		100 UNIVERSAL CITY PLAZA #507	BURBANK, CA	91505
VEJAR, RUDOLPH L	DIRECTOR	640 PRISCILLA LN	BURBANK, CA	91505
VELA, ROSIE	MODEL-SINGER	FORD MODELS, 344 E 59TH ST	NEW YORK, NY	10022
VELARDE, RANDY	BASEBALL	N Y YANKEES, YANKEE STADIUM	BRONX, NY	10451
VELASQUEZ, GUILLERMO	BASEBALL	STARS, 850 LAS VEGAS BLVD N	LAS VEGAS, NV	89101
VELAZQUEZ, RACHEL	ACTRESS	1524 LELAND AVE	BRONX, NY	10460
VELEZ, EDDIE	ACTOR	10661 WHIPPLE ST	TOLUCA LAKE, CA	91602
VELEZ, JOSE	BASEBALL	POST OFFICE BOX 3783	SAVANNAH, GA	31414
VELEZ, KAREN	MODEL	23826 MALIBU RD	MALIBU, CA	90265
VELEZ, LISA	SINGER-SONGWRITER	SEE - LISA LISA		
VELGOS, ALICIA	ACTRESS	1636 N CAHUENGA BLVD #203	LOS ANGELES, CA	90028
VELISCHEK, RANDY	HOCKEY	NORDIQUES, 2205 AVE DU COLISEE	QUEBEC, QUE G1L 4W7	CANADA
VELJOHNSON, REGINALD	ACTOR	9229 SUNSET BLVD #311	LOS ANGELES, CA	90069
VELLINE, BOBBY	SINGER-SONGWRITER	SEE - VEE, BOBBY		
VELNGRAD, ALAN	FOOTBALL	COWBOYS, 1 COWBOYS PARKWAY	IRVING, TX	75063
VELONS, THE	VOCAL GROUP	POST OFFICE BOX 22372	SAN FRANCISCO, CA	94122
VELORE & DOUBLE O	RAP DUO-RAPWRITERS	FAA, 1700 BROADWAY, 5TH FLOOR	NEW YORK, NY	10019
VELOZ, YOLANDA	ACTRESS	19413 OLIVOS DR	TARZANA, CA	91356
VELTE, PAUL	BASEBALL EXECUTIVE	POST OFFICE BOX 402	GENEVA, NY	14456
VENABLE, EVELYN	ACTRESS	141 GRETNA GREEN WY	LOS ANGELES, CA	90049
VENABLE, MAX	BASEBALL	2528 LAS CASAS WY	RANCHO CORDOVA, CA	95670
VENER, VICTOR	CONDUCTOR	265 S SIERRA BONITA AVE	PASADENA, CA	91106
VENET, NICK	RECORD PRODUCER	POST OFFICE BOX 638	MALIBU, CA	90265
VENGENCE	ROCK & ROLL GROUP	POST OFFICE BOX 530	NL 3140 AM WAALWIJK	
VENGER, RICHARD R	COMPOSER	250 S OAK KNOLL #102	PASADENA, CA	91101
VENNARI, JIM	BASEBALL SCOUT	REDS, 100 RIVERFRONT STADIUM	CINCINNATI, OH	45202
VENNEMA, JOHN C	ACTOR	BRET ADAMS, 448 W 44TH ST	NEW YORK, NY	10036
VENOM	ROCK & ROLL GROUP	IRD, 149-03 GUY R BREWER BLVD	JAMAICA, NY	11434
VENTHAM, WANDA	ACTOR	SARABAND, 265 LIVERPOOL RD	LONDON N1 1LX	ENGLAND
VENTO, BRUCE	U S CONGRESSMAN	175 E 5TH ST #727	SAINT PAUL, MN	55101
VENTURA, JESSE "THE BODY"	WRESTLER-ACTOR-MAYOR	5800 85TH AVE N	BROOKLYN, MN	55443
VENTURA, JOSE	BASEBALL	POST OFFICE BOX 360007	BIRMINGHAM, AL	35236
VENTURA, ROBIN	BASEBALL	333 W 35TH ST	CHICAGO, IL	60616
VENTURA, SAMUEL	DIRECTOR	2128 N SEDGWICK ST #10	CHICAGO, IL	60614
VENTURES, THE	ROCK & ROLL GROUP	POST OFFICE BOX 1646	BURBANK, CA	91507
VENTURI, KEN	GOLFER	POST OFFICE BOX 12458	PALM BCH GARDENS, FL	33410
VENTURI, RICK	FOOTBALL COACH	POST OFFICE BOX 535000	INDIANPOLIS, IN	46253
VENUTA, BENAY	ACTRESS	50 E 79TH ST	NEW YORK, NY	10021
VER DORN, GERALD	ACTOR	18 ARCADIAN DR	SPRING VALLEY, NY	10977
VER DORN, JERRY	ACTOR	CBS-TV, "THE GUIDING LIGHT"		
		222 E 44TH ST	NEW YORK, NY	10017
VERA, BILLY	SINGER-ACTOR	9000 SUNSET BLVD #1200	LOS ANGELES, CA	90069
VERA, BILLY & THE BEATERS	ROCK & ROLL GROUP	9000 SUNSET BLVD #1200	LOS ANGELES, CA	90069
VERAS, QUILVIO	BASEBALL	POST OFFICE BOX 7845	COLUMBIA, SC	29202
VERBEEK, PAT	HOCKEY	WHALERS, 1 CIVIC CENTER PLAZA	HARTFORD, CT	06103
VERDI, ANTHONY C	TV DIRECTOR	9900 AUTUMNWOOD WY	POTOMAC, MD	20854
VERDI, MIKE	BASEBALL MANAGER	RED SOX, CHAIN O'LAKES PARK	WINTER HAVEN, FL	33880
VERDIN, CLARENCE	FOOTBALL	POST OFFICE BOX 535000	INDIANPOLIS, IN	46253
VERDIN, JULIA	FILM PRODUCER	JULES FILMS, 355 FULHAM RD	LONDON SW10 9TW	ENGLAND
VERDIN, OCTAVIA	ACTRESS	MANSON, 288 MUNSTER RD	LONDON SW6 6BQ	ENGLAND
VERDON, GWEN	ACT-DAN-CHOREO	91 CENTRAL PARK W	NEW YORK, NY	10023
VERDUGO, ELENA	ACTRESS	POST OFFICE BOX 2048	CHULA VISTA, CA	92012
VEREECKE, AIME	COMPOSER	1474 CLYBOURN AVE	BURBANK, CA	91505
VERES, DAVE	BASEBALL	POST OFFICE BOX 26267	ALBUQUERQUE, NM	87125
VERES, RANDY	BASEBALL	5999 E VAN BUREN ST	PHOENIX, AZ	85008
VERIS, GARIN	FOOTBALL	PATRIOTS, FOXBORO STADIUM, RT #1	FOXBORO, MA	02035
VERMETTE, MARK	HOCKEY	NORDIQUES, 2205 AVE DU COLISEE	QUEBEC, QUE G1L 4W7	CANADA
VERNA, CHRIS	BASEBALL TRAINER	POST OFFICE BOX 4756	JACKSONVILLE, FL	32201
VERNA, TONY	DIRECTOR	500 OCAMPO DR	PACIFIC PALISADES, CA	90272
VERNIERE, J	FILM CRITIC	BOSTON HERALD, 1 HERALD SQ	BOSTON, MA	02106
VERNO, HELEN	TV EXECUTIVE	HIGHGATE PICTURES COMPANY		
		130 E 59TH ST, 10TH FLOOR	NEW YORK, NY	10022
VERNON, GLEN	ACTOR	12016 MOORPARK ST	STUDIO CITY, CA	91604
VERNON, JOHN	ACTOR	15125 MULHOLLAND DR	LOS ANGELES, CA	90077

VERNON, KATE	ACTRESS	LIGHT, 901 BRINGHAM AVE	LOS ANGELES, CA 90049
VERNON, RICHARD	ACTOR	BELFRAGE, 68 SAINT JAMES'S ST	LONDON SW1A 1LE ENGLAND
VERONA, STEPHEN	WRITER-PRODUCER	1251 STONE CANYON RD	LOS ANGELES, CA 90024
VERRELL, CEC	ACTRESS	8730 SUNSET BLVD #220-W	LOS ANGELES, CA 90069
VERRET, CATHERINE	FILM EXECUTIVE	FRENCH FILM INTL, 745 5TH AVE	NEW YORK, NY 10151
VERSACE, DICK	BASKETBALL COACH	PACERS, 300 E MARKET ST	INDIANAPOLIS, IN 46204
VERTELNEY, REED P	COMPOSER	511 RAYMOND AVE #4	SANTA MONICA, CA 90405
VERTUE, BERYL	FILM-TV PRODUCER	HARTSWOOD FILMS, STARLINGS	
		NEW HOUSE LN, SALFORDS	SURREY RH1 5RE ENGLAND
VESAK, NORBERT	DIRECTOR-CHOREO	METROPOLITAN OPERA	
		LINCOLN CENTER	NEW YORK, NY 10023
VESLING, DON	BASEBALL	TIGERS, 89 WHARNCLIFFE RD N	LONDON, ONT N6H 2A7 CANADA
VESSEY, TIM	BASEBALL UMPIRE	POST OFFICE BOX 25010	LITTLE ROCK, AZ 72221
VEST, JAKE	CARTOONIST	TRIBUNE, 64 E CONCORD ST	ORLANDO, FL 32801
VETRI, VICTORIA	ACTRESS-MODEL	POST OFFICE BOX 69793	LOS ANGELES, CA 90069
VETTER, RICHARD H	FILM EXECUTIVE	17627 CAMINO YATASTO	PACIFIC PALISADES, CA 90272
VEVIUS, CRAIG J	SCREENWRITER	9000 SUNSET BLVD #1200	LOS ANGELES, CA 90069
VEX, THE	ROCK & ROLL GROUP	25 HUNTINGTON AVE #420	BOSTON, MA 02116
VHW	ROCK & ROLL GROUP	FAA, 1700 BROADWAY, 5TH FLOOR	NEW YORK, NY 10019
VIAHOS, JOHN	TV WRITER	18 CRAWFORD RD	WESTPORT, CT 06880
VIAL, DENNIS	HOCKEY	RED WINGS, 600 CIVIC CENTER DR	DETROIT, MI 48226
VIATOR, CASEY	BODYBUILDER	POST OFFICE BOX 31616	TUSCON, AZ 85751
VIBRATIONS, THE	VOCAL GROUP	POST OFFICE BOX 262	CARTERET, NJ 07008
VICAR, JAMES F	DIRECTOR	600 W 111TH ST	NEW YORK, NY 10025
VICAS, GEORGE A	WRITER-PRODUCER	4011 N 26TH ST	ARLINGTON, VA 22207
VICE, DARRYL	BASEBALL	POST OFFICE BOX 2769	HUNTSVILLE, AL 35804
VICKERS, DARRELL	TV WRITER	9255 SUNSET BLVD #1122	LOS ANGELES, CA 90069
VICKERS, MIKE	COMPOSER	THE FIRST COMPOSERS COMPANY	
		IRON BRIDGE HOUSE	
		3 BRIDGE APPROACH, CHALK FARM	LONDON NW1 8BD ENGLAND
VICKERS, YVETTE	ACTRESS	POST OFFICE BOX 664	PINON HILLS, CA 92372
VICKERY, MACK	SINGER	POST OFFICE BOX 6025	NEWPORT NEWS, VA 23606
VICTOR, DAVID	WRITER-PRODUCER	147 GROVERTON PL	LOS ANGELES, CA 90077
VICTOR, MARK A	SCREENWRITER	707 ALMA REAL DR	PACIFIC PALIADES, CA 90272
VICTOR, RICHARD	DIRECTOR	520 N MICHIGAN AVE #1026	CHICAGO, IL 60611
VIDAL, GORE	WRITER	2562 OUTPOST DR	LOS ANGELES, CA 90068
VIDAL, MARIA	SINGER	CATCH A RISING STAR, INC	
		157 W 57TH ST	NEW YORK, NY 10019
VIDEEO	ROCK & ROLL GROUP	HARVEY/LYNCH AGENCY	
		7600 W TIDWELL RD	HOUSTON, TX 77040
VIDMAR, DON	BASEBALL	10233 96TH AVE	EDMONTON, ALB TK5 0A5 CANADA
VIDOR, ZOLL	CINEMATOGRAPHER	124 S CANON DR	BEVERLY HILLS, CA 90212
VIEIRA, GEORGE D	DIRECTOR-PRODUCER	20032 PACIFIC COAST HWY	MALIBU, CA 90265
VIEIRA, PETER J	DIRECTOR	4331 TALOFA AVE	NORTH HOLLYWOOD, CA 91602
VIERA, JOHN	BASEBALL	ALBANY YANKEES, HERITAGE PARK	ALBANY, NY 12211
VIERRA, JOEY	BASEBALL	POST OFFICE BOX 23290	NASHVILLE, TN 37202
VIERRA, JOSE	BASEBALL	POST OFFICE BOX 4488	WINSTON-SALEM, NC 27115
VIERTEL, CHRISTIAN T	TV EXECUTIVE	GERMAN TV, 506 W 57TH ST	NEW YORK, NY 10019
VIERTEL, PETER	AUTHOR-SCREENWRITER	WYHERGUT, 7250 KLOSTERS	GRISONS SWIZTERLAND
VIETA, JONA	NEWS WRITER	301 E 66TH ST	NEW YORK, NY 10021
VIETRO, ROBERT A	DIRECTOR	20 WESTMERE AVE	ROWAYTON, CT 06853
VIG, TOMMY	COMPOSER	8530 WILSHIRE BLVD #500	BEVERLY HILLS, CA 90211
VIGIL, ROBERT E	AUDITOR	SATE CAPITOL BUILDING	SANTE FE, NM 87503
VIGIL, SHANNON	TALENT AGENT	725 S BARRINGTON #202	LOS ANGELES, CA 90049
VIGNOLES, TIMOTHY	TV EXECUTIVE	17 ONSLOW RD, RICHMOND	SURREY TW10 6QH ENGLAND
VIGODA, ABE	ACTOR	1215 BEVERLY VIEW DR	BEVERLY HILLS, CA 90210
VIGON, BARRY	TV WRITER	11812 SAN VICENTE BLVD #510	LOS ANGELES, CA 90049
VILANCH, BRUCE	ACTOR-WRITER	8730 SUNSET BLVD #600	LOS ANGELES, CA 90069
VILAS, GUILLERMO	TENNIS	AVENUE FOCH #86	PARIS FRANCE
VILLA, BORIS	BASEBALL SCOUT	POST OFFICE BOX 90111	ARLINGTON, TX 76004
VILLA, DANNY	FOOTBALL	PATRIOTS, FOXBORO STADIUM, RT #1	FOXBORO, MA 02035
VILLADESEN, M KURT	WRITER	20503 BIG ROCK DR	MALIBU, CA 90265
VILLAGE PEOPLE, THE	ROCK & ROLL GROUP	251 PARK AVE S	NEW YORK, NY 10010
VILLALOBOS, GARY	BASEBALL	RED SOX, CHAIN O'LAKES PARK	WINTER HAVEN, FL 33880
VILLANUEVA, HECTOR	BASEBALL	1060 W ADDISON ST	CHICAGO, IL 60613
VILLARD, TOM	ACTOR	1999 AVE OF THE STARS #2850	LOS ANGELES, CA 90067
VILLASENOR, VICTOR E	SCREENWRITER	UTA, 9560 WILSHIRE BL, 5TH FL	BEVERLY HILLS, CA 90212
VILLIERS, JAMES	ACTOR	HEATH, PARAMOUNT HOUSE	
		162-170 WARDOUR ST	LONDON W1V 3AT ENGLAND
VINA, FERNANDO	BASEBALL	525 NW PEACOCK BLVD	PORT SAINT LUCIE, FL 34986
VINAS, JULIO	BASEBALL	POST OFFICE BOX 4218	SOUTH BEND, IN 46634
VINCENT, DON	COMPOSER	3591 ALGOQUIN DR	LAS VEGAS, NV 89109
VINCENT, E DUKE	WRITER-PRODUCER	9526 DALEGROVE DR	BEVERLY HILLS, CA 90210
VINCENT, FAYE	BASEBALL COMMISSIONER	350 PARK AVE, 17TH FLOOR	NEW YORK, NY 10022
VINCENT, JAN-MICHAEL	ACTOR	POST OFFICE BOX 7000	REDONDO BEACH, CA 90277
VINCENT, LARRY	DIRECTOR	DGA, 7920 SUNSET BLVD, 6TH FL	LOS ANGELES, CA 90046
VINCENT, MAL	FILM CRITIC	POST OFFICE BOX 449	NORFOLK, VA 23501
VINCENT, PAUL	ACTOR	1650 BROADWAY #302	NEW YORK, NY 10019
VINCENT, RUSSEL	TV WRITER-DIRECTOR	7182 CHELAN WY	HOLLYWOOD, CA 90068
VINCENT, SAM	BASKETBALL	POST OFFICE BOX 76	ORLANDO, FL 32802
VINCENT, SHAWN	FOOTBALL	STEELERS, 300 STADIUM CIR	PITTSBURGH, PA 15212
VINCENT, VINNIE	SINGER-GUITARIST	ITG, 729 7TH AVE, 16TH FLOOR	NEW YORK, NY 10019
VINCENT, VIRGINIA	ACTRESS	1001 HAMMOND ST	LOS ANGELES, CA 90069
VINCZ, MELANIE	ACTRESS-MODEL	1151 3RD ST	MANHATTAN BEACH, CA 90266
VINCZE, ERNEST	CINEMATOGRAPHER	25 MARVILLE RD	LONDON SW6 ENGLAND

VINE, DOROTHY	WRITER	180 W 58TH ST	NEW YORK, NY 10019
VINE DYKES, LINDA L	TV PRODUCER	5 VALLEY PL	UPPER MONCLAIR, NJ 10019
VINER, JOHN	TV WRITER-PRODUCER	66 GAINSBOROUGH CT	
		WALTON-ON-THAMES	SURREY ENGLAND
VINER, MICHAEL	SCREENWRITER-AGENT	12711 VENTURA BLVD #250	STUDIO CITY, CA 91604
VINING, DANIEL	SCREENWRITER	8955 BEVERLY BLVD	WEST HOLLYWOOD, CA 90048
VINSON, HELEN	ACTRESS	2213 CAROL WOODS	CHAPEL HILL, NC 27514
VINSON, JAMES W	NEWS WRITER	4228 LOS FELIZ BLVD	LOS ANGELES, CA 90027
VINSON, LAURA & RED WYNG	C & W GROUP	POST OFFICE BOX 8768	
		STATION L	EDMONDTON, ALT CANADA
VINT, ALAN	ACTOR	POST OFFICE BOX 8589	UNIVERSAL CITY, CA 91608
VINT, ROBERT	TV DIRECTOR	649 E 14TH ST	NEW YORK, NY 10009
VINTAS, GUSTAV	ACTOR	12456 VENTURA BLVD #1	STUDIO CITY, CA 91604
VINTON, BOBBY	SINGER	1905 COLD CANYON RD	CALABASAS, CA 91302
VINTON, WILL	CLAY-ANIMATOR	2580 NW UPSHUR ST	PORTLAND, OR 97210
VIOLA, ALFRED M	FILM DIRECTOR	2049 CENTURY PARK E #1320	LOS ANGELES, CA 90067
VIOLA, FRANK	BASEBALL	FENWAY PARK, 4 YAWKEY WY	BOSTON, MA 02215
VIOLA, GAIL	COSTUME DESIGNER	13949 VENTURA BLVD #309	SHERMAN OAKS, CA 91423
VIOLA, JOSEPH	WRITER-PRODUCER	926 N HARPER AVE	LOS ANGELES, CA 90046
VIOLENT FEMMES, THE	ROCK & ROLL GROUP	POST OFFICE BOX 1304	BURBANK, CA 91507
VIOLETT, ELLEN M	TV WRITER	230 E 50TH ST	NEW YORK, NY 10022
VIOTTI, D E	COMPOSER	2205 BUTTERFIELD RD #262	YAKIMA, WA 98901
VIPERS, THE	ROCK & ROLL GROUP	348 E 9TH ST #10	NEW YORK, NY 10003
VIRDON, BILL	BASEBALL-MANAGER	1311 RIVER RD	SPRINGFIELD, MO 65804
VIRGIL, OSSIE, SR	BASEBALL-COACH	4316 W MESCAL ST	GLENDALE, AZ 85301
VIRGIL, OZZIE, JR	BASEBALL	4316 W MERCAL ST	GLENDALE, AZ 85301
VIRGILIO, GEORGE	BASEBALL	POST OFFICE BOX 4525	MACON, GA 31208
VIRGIN PRUNES, THE	ROCK & ROLL GROUP	POST OFFICE BOX 433	DEARBORN, MI 48121
VIRGINIA WOLF	ROCK & ROLL GROUP	PERFORMING ARTS NETWORK	
		10 SUTHERLAND AVE	LONDON W9 ENGLAND
VIRGO, TONY	TV WRITER-DIRECTOR	WM MORRIS, 31-32 SOHO SQ	LONDON W1V 5DG ENGLAND
VIRKLER, DENNIS	DIRECTOR	19730 VALLEY VIEW DR	TOPANGA CANYON, CA 90290
VIRSIS, PETER	DIRECTOR	DGA, 110 W 57TH ST	NEW YORK, NY 10019
VISA	ROCK & ROLL GROUP	BRAD SIMON, 122 E 57TH ST	NEW YORK, NY 10022
VISCA, DENNIS	ACTOR	909 6TH ST #10	SANTA MONICA, CA 90403
VISCLOSKY, PETER	U S CONGRESSMAN	215 W 35TH AVE	GARY, IN 46408
VISCOTT, DR DAVID	THERAPIST	POST OFFICE BOX 36817	LOS ANGELES, CA 90036
VISELLI, BRIAN	BASEBALL EXECUTIVE	POST OFFICE BOX 4758	SPOKANE, WA 99202
VISELTEAR, MICHAEL	WRITER	9741 1/2 HELEN AVE	SUNLAND, CA 91040
VISITOR, NANA	ACTRESS	10390 SANTA MONICA BLVD #300	LOS ANGELES, CA 90025
VISKOZKI, RON	BASEBALL EXECUTIVE	POST OFFICE BOX 3448	SHREVEPORT, LA 71133
VISKUPIC, GARY	CARTOONIST	NEWSDAY, 1500 BROADWAY	NEW YORK, NY 10036
VISONE, JUSTINE	ACTRESS	1605 N CAHUENGA BLVD #202	LOS ANGELES, CA 90028
VIT & SALUTATIONS	VOCAL GROUP	POST OFFICE BOX 82	GREAT NECK, NY 11022
VITAMIN Z	ROCK & ROLL GROUP	PETE SMITH MANAGEMENT	
		360 OXFORD ST	LONDON W1 ENGLAND
VITARELLI, ARTHUR J	DIRECTOR	200 1/2 EMERALD AVE	BALBOA ISLAND, CA 92662
VITARELLI, ROBERT E	TV DIRECTOR-PRODUCER	11104 GILCRIST CT	POTOMAC, MD 20854
VITELLO, DONALD	TV DIRECTOR	145 S FAIRFAX AVE #310	LOS ANGELES, CA 90036
VITIELLO, JOE	BASEBALL	300 STADIUM WY	DAVENPORT, FL 33837
VITKO, JOE	BASEBALL	POST OFFICE BOX 598	BINGHAMTON, NY 13902
VITT, JOE	FOOTBALL COACH	SEAHAWKS, 11220 NE 53RD ST	KIRKLAND, WA 98033
VITTES, MICHAEL	TV WRITER	2049 CENTURY PARK E #1320	LOS ANGELES, CA 90067
VITTI, MONICA	ACTRESS	VIA VICENZO TIBERIO 18	ROME ITALY
VITTORI, EMILY LOVE	ACTRESS	124 W OAK AVE	EL SEGUNDO, CA 90245
VIZCAINO, JOSE	BASEBALL	1060 W ADDISON ST	CHICAGO, IL 60613
VIZQUEL, OMAR	BASEBALL	POST OFFICE BOX 4100	SEATTLE, WA 98104
VLASIC, MARK	FOOTBALL	CHIEFS, 1 ARROWHEAD DR	KANSAS CITY, MO 64129
VLASIS, CHRIS	BASEBALL	POST OFFICE BOX 3004	SPRINGFIELD, IL 62708
VLECK, JAMES	BASEBALL	POST OFFICE BOX 3609	PORT CHARLOTTE, FL 33949
VOEGE, RAY	MAKE-UP ARTIST	POST OFFICE BOX 103	STAMFORD, NY 12167
VOGEL, CAROL	ACTRESS	8400 LOOKOUT MOUNTAIN AVE	LOS ANGELES, CA 90046
VOGEL, DARLENE	ACTRESS	8730 SUNSET BLVD #220-W	LOS ANGELES, CA 90069
VOGEL, HELEN	ACTRESS	8350 SANTA MONICA BLVD #102	LOS ANGELES, CA 90069
VOGEL, JULES	CONDUCTOR	17611 BASTANCHURY RD	YORBA LINDA, CA 92686
VOGEL, MIKE	BASEBALL	POST OFFICE BOX 4218	SOUTH BEND, IN 46634
VOGEL, TONY	ACTOR	ICM, 388-396 OXFORD ST	LONDON W1 ENGLAND
VOGEL, VIRGIL	FILM DIRECTOR	5550 COLBATH AVE	VAN NUYS, CA 91401
VOGELSANG, JUDITH AYERS	TV DIRECTOR	5659 BECK AVE	NORTH HOLLYWOOD, CA 91601
VOGT, MARY E	COSTUME DESIGNER	POST OFFICE BOX 5617	BEVERLY HILLS, CA 90213
VOGUES, THE	VOCAL GROUP	POST OFFICE BOX 399	LISLE, IL 60532
VOIGHT, JON	ACTOR	13340 GALEWOOD DR	SHERMAN OAKS, CA 91423
VOIGHTS, RICHARD	ACTOR	160 W END AVE	NEW YORK, NY 10023
VOIGT, JACK	BASEBALL	500 NORTON ST	ROCHESTER, NY 14621
VOINOVICH, GEORGE V	GOVERNOR	STATE CAPITOL BUILDING	COLUMBUS, OH 43266
VOISS, TOM	PRODUCER	THE BURBANK STUDIOS	
		4000 WARNER BLVD	BURBANK, CA 91522
VOKES, HOWARD	SINGER-GUITARIST	POST OFFICE BOX 12	NEW KENSINGTON, PA 15068
VOLDSTAD, JOHN	ATCTOR	6435 BELLAIRE	NORTH HOLLYWOOD, CA 91606
VOLEK, DAVID	HOCKEY	NASSAU VETS MEMORIAL COLISEUM	UNIONDALE, NY 11553
VOLKMER, HAROLD	U S CONGRESSMAN	FEDERAL BUILDING #370	HANNIBAL, MO 63401
VOLKOFF, NIKOLAI	WRESTLER	POST OFFICE BOX 3859	STAMFORD, CT 06905
VOLKOV, ALEXANDER	BASKETBALL	1 CNN CENTER #405, SOUTH TOWER	ATLANTA, GA 30303
VOLLEN, RENEE	SCREENWRITER	2950 NEILSON WY #504-A	SANTA MONICA, CA 90405
VOLLENWEIDER, ANDREAS	HARPIST-COMPOSER	1501 BROADWAY #1506	NEW YORK, NY 10036

VOLPICELLI, LOUIS	DIRECTOR-PRODUCER	38 PHILLIPS LN	DARIEN, CT 06820
VOLTAGE BROTHERS, THE	RHYTHM & BLUES GROUP	POST OFFICE BOX 11283	RICHMOND, VA 23230
VOLTAGGIO, VIC	BASEBALL UMPIRE	646 BRENTWOOD DR	VINELAND, NJ 08360
VOLZ, NEDRA	ACTRESS	615 TULARE WY	UPLAND, CA 91786
VON AROLDINGEN, KARIN	BALLERINA	NEW YORK CITY BALLET	
		LINCOLN CENTER PLAZA	NEW YORK, NY 10023
VON CRAMM, TINA	ACTRESS	3800 BARHAM BLVD #303	LOS ANGELES, CA 90068
VON DERLEITH, SCOTT	BASEBALL	POST OFFICE BOX 855	BELOIT, WI 53511
VON DOHLEN, LENNY	ACTOR	MTA, 9320 WILSHIRE BL, 3RD FL	BEVERLY HILLS, CA 90212
VON ERICH, KERRY	WRESTLER	POST OFFICE BOX 3859	STAMFORD, CT 06905
VON ERNST, RICHARD	COSTUME DESIGNER	100 BRIGHT ST	JERSEY CITY, NJ 07302
VON FREMD, MIKE	SINGER	POST OFFICE BOX 6025	NEWPORT NEWS, VA 23606
VON FURSTENBERG, DIANE	FASHION DESIGNER	745 5TH AVE	NEW YORK, NY 10151
VON HOELTKE, JERRY	ACTOR	8401 FOUNTAIN AVE	HOLLYWOOD, CA 90069
VON HOFFMAN, ALEXANDRA	ACTRESS	SEE - HOFFMAN, ALEXANDRA VON	
VON HOFFMAN, NICHOLAS	COMMENTATOR	KING FEATURES, 216 E 45TH ST	NEW YORK, NY 10017
VON KARAJAN, HERBERT	CONDUCTOR	FESTSPIELHAUS A-5010	SALZBURG AUSTRIA
VON LEER, HUNTER	ACTOR	RITCH, 1443 N HAYWORTH AVE	LOS ANGELES, CA 90046
VON LENNARTZ, PAULETTE	WRITER	821 3RD ST #105	SANTA MONICA, CA 90403
VON RHEIN, JOHN	MUSIC CRITIC	435 N MICHIGAN AVE	CHICAGO, IL 60611
VON SYDOW, MAX	ACTOR	AVD C-G RISBERG, STRANDVEGEN B	114-56 STOCKHOLM SWEDEN
VON ZERNECK, DANIELLE	ACTRESS	10390 SANTA MONICA BLVD #300	LOS ANGELES, CA 90025
VON ZERNECK, FRANK	FILM-TV PRODUCER	PORTRAIT OF A BOOKSTORE	
		10061 RIVERSIDE DR	TOLUCA LAKE, CA 91602
VOO, RHONDA	ARTIST	8800 VENICE BLVD	LOS ANGELES, CA 90034
VOODOO DOLLS	ROCK & ROLL GROUP	POST OFFICE BOX 139	447-00 VARGARDA SWEDEN
VOORHEES, JOE	DIRECTOR	7606 GOODLAND AVE	NORTH HOLLYWOOD, CA 91605
VORBECK, ERIC	BASEBALL	POST OFFICE BOX 10031	BAKERSFIELD, CA 93389
VORGAN, GIGI	ACTRESS	3676 STONE CANYON AVE	SHERMAN OAKS, CA 91403
VORKAPICH, SLAVOMIR	DIRECTOR	DGA, 110 W 57TH ST	NEW YORK, NY 10019
VORTEX	RHYTHM & BLUES GROUP	KINGSLAND, 108 SHARON DR	WEST MONROE, LA 71291
VOSBURGH, TILLY	ACTRESS	STONE, 9 NEWBURGH ST	LONDON W1V 1LH ENGLAND
VOSS, KENNETH JUDE	DIRECTOR	3 CIRCLE DR	HAWTHORNE WOODS, IL 60047
VOSS, ROBERT W	COMPOSER	68 BINNEY LN	OLD GREENWICH, CT 06870
VOUDOURIS, ROGER	SINGER	10100 SANTA MONICA BLVD #1600	LOS ANGELES, CA 90067
VOUTSAS, GEORGE	DIRECTOR	116 YANKEE POINT DR	CARMEL, CA 93923
VOW WOW	ROCK & ROLL GROUP	FAA, 1700 BROADWAY, 5TH FLOOR	NEW YORK, NY 10019
VOWELL, DAVID	TV WRITER	11427 SUNSHINE TERR	STUDIO CITY, CA 91604
VOYEUR	ROCK & ROLL GROUP	10100 SANTA MONICA BLVD #1600	LOS ANGELES, CA 90067
VOYTEK	TV DIRECTOR	12 THE VARONS #1	
		SAINT MARGARETS	
		TWICKENHAM	MIDDLESEX TW1 2AN ENGLAND
VRANKOVIC, STOJKO	BASKETBALL	151 MERRIMAC ST	BOSTON, MA 02114
VRBANCICH, E	CARTOONIST	4 PHYLLIS ST	DEE-WHY NSW 2099 AUSTRALIA
VUCANOVICH, BARBARA	U S CONGRESSWOMAN	300 BOOTH ST	RENO, NV 89509
VUCKOVICH, PETE	BASEBALL-ANNOUNCER	BREWERS, 201 S 46TH ST	MILWAUKEE, WI 53214
VUKOVICH, JOHN	BASEBALL-COACH	POST OFFICE BOX 7575	PHILADELPHIA, PA 19101
VUKSANOVICH, BILL	ARTIST	3224 N NORDICA AVE	CHICAGO, IL 60634
VYPER	ROCK & ROLL GROUP	15 W 10TH ST #900	KANSAS CITY, MO 64105

W A S P	ROCK & ROLL GROUP	ICM, 40 W 57TH ST	NEW YORK, NY 10019
WACHS, ROBERT D	TALENT AGENT	345 N MAPLE DR #179	BEVERLY HILLS, CA 90210
WACHTER, DEREK	BASEBALL	POST OFFICE BOX 855	BELOIT, WI 53511
WADDELL, TERRY	MUSIC ARRANGER	1615 18TH AVE S	NASHVILLE, TN 37212
WADDELL, TOM	FOOTBALL	BEARS, 250 N WASHINGTON RD	LAKE FOREST, IL 60045
WADE, ADAM	ACTOR-SINGER	118 E 25TH ST #600	NEW YORK, NY 10010
WADE, ED	BASEBALL EXECUTIVE	POST OFFICE BOX 7575	PHILADELPHIA, PA 19101
WADE, ELVIS	SINGER	POST OFFICE BOX 22707	NASHVILLE, TN 37202
WADE, HARKER	TV PRODUCER	LARSON, 10201 W PICO BLVD	LOS ANGELES, CA 90035
WADE, JUNIOR	FOOTBALL COACH	DOLPHINS, 2269 NW 199TH ST	MIAMI, FL 33056
WADE, KEVIN	SCREENWRITER	8955 BEVERLY BLVD	WEST HOLLYWOOD, CA 90048
WADE, SALLY	SCREENWRITER	8955 BEVERLY BLVD	WEST HOLLYWOOD, CA 90048
WADE, SCOTT	BASEBALL	CHIEFS, MAC ARTHUR STADIUM	SYRACUSE, NY 13208
WADE, WILLIS	SINGER-GUITARIST	POST OFFICE BOX 841	HENDERSONVILLE, TN 37075
WADER, DAVID	TV DIRECTOR	2153 N ROOSEVELT ST	ALTADENA, CA 91001
WADKINS, BOBBY	GOLFER	POST OFFICE BOX 109601	PALM BCH GARDENS, FL 33418
WADKINS, LANNY	GOLFER	POST OFFICE BOX 109601	PALM BCH GARDENS, FL 33418
WADLEIGH, MICHAEL	FILM WRITER-DIRECTOR	DGA, 7920 SUNSET BLVD, 6TH FL	LOS ANGELES, CA 90046
WADSWORTH	C & W GROUP	POST OFFICE BOX 25677	CHICAGO, IL 60625
WAEKER, DUHHAINE	WRITER-PRODUCER	5030 TUJUNGA AVE	NORTH HOLLYWOOD, CA 91601
WAFUL, DONALD	BASEBALL EXECUTIVE	CHIEFS, MAC ARTHUR STADIUM	SYRACUSE, NY 13208
WAGES, WILLIAM	CINEMATOGRAPHER	POST OFFICE BOX 1166	PACIFIC PALISADES, CA 90272
WAGGONER, AUBREY	BASEBALL	POST OFFICE BOX 16683	GREENVILLE, SC 29606
WAGGONER, JIM	BASEBALL	POST OFFICE BOX 11363	RENO, NV 89510
WAGHORN, KERRY	CARICATURIST	CHRONICLE FEATURES	
		870 MARKET ST	SAN FRANCISCO, CA 94102
WAGLIN, ED	TV DIRECTOR	330 CARIBBEAN RD	KEY BISCAYNE, FL 33149

WAGNER, ADAM	BASEBALL TRAINER	POST OFFICE BOX 2148	WOODBRIDGE, VA	22193
WAGNER, ALAN CYRIL	FILM PRODUCER	950 3RD AVE	NEW YORK, NY	10022
WAGNER, BEN	FOOTBALL REFEREE	NFL, 410 PARK AVE	NEW YORK, NY	10022
WAGNER, BRUCE	SCREENWRITER	8955 BEVERLY BLVD	WEST HOLLYWOOD, CA	90048
WAGNER, BRYAN	FOOTBALL	PATRIOTS, FOXBORO STADIUM, RT #1	FOXBORO, MA	02035
WAGNER, CHARLES	BASEBALL SCOUT	FENWAY PARK, 4 YAWKEY WY	BOSTON, MA	02215
WAGNER, DAVE	WRESTLER	POST OFFICE BOX 3859	STAMFORD, CT	06905
WAGNER, DICK	BASEBALL EXECUTIVE	AMERICAN LEAGUE, 350 PARK AVE	NEW YORK, NY	10022
WAGNER, FRED	CARTOONIST	TRIBUNE, 64 E CONCORD ST	ORLANDO, FL	32801
WAGNER, GEORGE	FILM DIRECTOR	POST OFFICE BOX 5777	SANTA MONICA, CA	90405
WAGNER, HECTOR	BASEBALL	POST OFFICE BOX 3665	OMAHA, NE	68103
WAGNER, HELEN	ACTRESS	CBS-TV, "AS THE WORLD TURNS"		
		524 W 57TH ST #5330	NEW YORK, NY	10019
WAGNER, JACK P	ACTOR-SINGER	1750 N BEVERLY DR	BEVERLY HILLS, CA	90210
WAGNER, JANE	WRITER-PRODUCER	POST OFFICE BOX 27700	LOS ANGELES, CA	90027
WAGNER, JOHN M	ARTIST	2008 W 48TH TERR	WESTWOOD HILLS, KS	66205
WAGNER, KATE	ACTRESS	1500 OLD OAK RD	LOS ANGELES, CA	90077
WAGNER, KEVIN	BASKETBALL	MIAMI HEAT, THE MIAMI ARENA	MIAMI, FL	33136
WAGNER, LINDSAY	ACTRESS	POST OFFICE BOX 188	PACIFIC PALISADES, CA	90272
WAGNER, LOU	ACTOR	8527 WONDERLAND AVE	LOS ANGELES, CA	90046
WAGNER, MADELINE D	TV WRITER	BLS & A, 800 S ROBERTSON BLVD	LOS ANGELES, CA	90025
WAGNER, MARIA	TV DIRECTOR	145 E 16TH ST	NEW YORK, NY	10003
WAGNER, MARK	BASEBALL COACH	POST OFFICE BOX 6212	TOLEDO, OH	43614
WAGNER, MICHAEL	SCREENWRITER	8955 BEVERLY BLVD	WEST HOLLYWOOD, CA	90048
WAGNER, PAUL	BASEBALL	POST OFFICE DRAWER 1218	ZEBULON, NC	27597
WAGNER, ROBERT	ACTOR	10100 SANTA MONICA BLVD #1600	LOS ANGELES, CA	90067
WAGNER, ROBERT F	MAYOR	425 PARK AVE	NEW YORK, NY	10022
WAGNER, ROGER	CONDUCTOR	5930 PENFIELD AVE	WOODLAND HILLS, CA	91367
WAGNER, ROY H	CINEMATOGRAPHER	21243 VENTURA BLVD #221	WOODLAND HILLS, CA	91364
WAGNER, SUE	LT GOVERNOR	STATE CAPITOL BUILDING	CARSON CITY, NV	89710
WAGON, CHUCK & THE WHEELS	C & W GROUP	CMP, 5353 E FORT LOWELL RD	TUCSON, AZ	85712
WAGONER, PORTER	SINGER-SONGWRITER	1830 AIR LANE DR	NASHVILLE, TN	37210
WAGONER, RALPH W, JR	TV DIRECTOR	CUTTING ROOM FLOOR PRODS		
		1216 S CRESCENT	PARK RIDGE, IL	60068
WAGONHURST, ROCK	ACTOR	5134 CALENDA DR	WOODLAND HILLS, CA	91367
WAGREICH, HERBERT	DIRECTOR	9 ICHABOD LN	OSSINING, NY	10562
WAHL, KEN	ACTOR	6622 PORTSHEAD DR	MALIBU, CA	90265
WAHLER, JIM	FOOTBALL	POST OFFICE BOX 888	PHOENIX, AZ	85001
WAHRMAN, WAYNE	FILM EDITOR	ACE, 1041 N FORMOSA AVE	WEST HOLLYWOOD, CA	90046
WAIHEE, JOHN D, III	GOVERNOR	STATE CAPITOL BUILDING	HONOLULU, HI	96813
WAIN, BEA	SINGER	9955 DURANT DR #305	BEVERLY HILLS, CA	90212
WAIN, JOHN	SINGER	BMP, 732 BRANDON AVE, SW	ROANOKE, VA	24015
WAINHOUSE, DAVID	BASEBALL	1501 W 16TH ST	INDIANAPOLIS, IN	46202
WAINWRIGHT, JAMES	ACTOR	SHERRELL, 1354 LAS ROBLES DR	PALM SPRINGS, CA	92262
WAINWRIGHT, SUSAN M	TV DIRECTOR	750 N DEARBORN ST #3303	CHICAGO, IL	60601
WAINWRIGHT, WALTER	ARTIST	40 GREEN OAKS RD	NEWPORT NEWS, VA	23607
WAISBREN, BRAD	ACTOR	3146 HUTTON DR	BEVERLY HILLS, CA	90210
WAISSMAN, KENNETH	THEATER PRODUCER	1501 BROADWAY	NEW YORK, NY	10036
WAITE, BARCIE	COSTUME DESIGNER	13949 VENTURA BLVD #309	SHERMAN OAKS, CA	91423
WAITE, RALPH	ACTOR-DIRECTOR	23 DUKE DR	RANCHO MIRAGE, CA	92270
WAITE, STEVE	BASEBALL	POST OFFICE BOX 64939	FAYETTEVILLE, NC	28306
WAITERS, VAN	FOOTBALL	BROWNS, 80 1ST ST	BEREA, OH	44017
WAITS, TOM	SINGER-SONGWRITER	POST OFFICE BOX 498	VALLEY FORD, CA	94972
WAJDA, ANDRZEJ	DIRECTOR	UL HAUKEGO 14	01-540 WARSAW	POLAND
WAKAMATSU, DON	BASEBALL	POST OFFICE BOX 26267	ALBUQUERQUE, NM	87125
WAKEFIELD, DAN	SCREENWRITER	939 N WETHERLY DR	LOS ANGELES, CA	90069
WAKEFIELD, FOSTER C	COMPOSER-CONDUCTOR	2828 ROWENA AVE	LOS ANGELES, CA	90039
WAKEFIELD, TIM	BASEBALL	POST OFFICE BOX 7000	PITTSBURGH, PA	15212
WAKEHAM, DEBORAH	ACTRESS	9229 SUNSET BLVD #311	LOS ANGELES, CA	90069
WAKEMAN, RICK	SINGER	SUN ARTISTS, 9 HILLGATE ST	LONDON W8	ENGLAND
WALBECK, MATT	BASEBALL	POST OFFICE DRAWER 1207	ZEBULON, NC	27597
WALBERG, PAUL L	COMPOSER-CONDUCTOR	POST OFFICE BOX 305	REDONDO BEACH, CA	90277
WALCOTT, GREGORY	ACTOR	22246 SATICOY ST	CANOGA PARK, CA	91306
WALCOTT, JERSEY JOE	BOXER	1500 BAIRD AVE	CAMDEN, NJ	08103
WALCUTT, JOHN	ACTOR	4265 COLFAX AVE #16	STUDIO CITY, CA	91604
WALD, CAROL	ARTIST	57 E 78TH ST	NEW YORK, NY	10021
WALD, JEFF	TALENT AGENT	2276 CENTURY HILL	LOS ANGELES, CA	90067
WALD, MALVIN	TV WRITER-PRODUCER	4525 GREENBUSH AVE	VAN NUYS, CA	91423
WALDEN, ALAN	BASEBALL	POST OFFICE BOX 1886	COLUMBUS, GA	31902
WALDEN, JEAN HOUSTON	TV DIRECTOR	322 W 57TH ST	NEW YORK, NY	10019
WALDEN, NARADA MICHAEL	SINGER	POST OFFICE BOX 690	SAN FRANCISCO, CA	94101
WALDEN, ROBERT	ACTOR	1450 ARROYO VIEW DR	PASADENA, CA	91103
WALDEN, STANLEY	COMPOSER-CLARINET	ROUTE #3, BOX 438	HOPEWELL, NY	12533
WALDEN, SUSAN	ACTRESS	9744 WILSHIRE BLVD #308	BEVERLY HILLS, CA	90212
WALDHEIM, KURT	PRESIDENT	HOFBURG, BALLHAUSPLATZ	1010 VIENNA	AUSTRIA
WALDHORN, GARY	ACTOR	HUTTON, 200 FULHAM RD	LONDON SW14 7AH	ENGLAND
WALDMAN, HONEY	ACTRESS	145 SPRING ST	NEW YORK, NY	10012
WALDMAN, JULES	DIRECTOR	74 5TH AVE #2-A	NEW YORK, NY	10011
WALDMAN, LESLIE D	TV DIRECTOR	4369 BECK AVE	STUDIO CITY, CA	91604
WALDMAN, RANDY B	CONDUCTOR	5634 CAMELLIA AVE	NORTH HOLLYWOOD, CA	91601
WALDO, CHARLES	COSTUME DESIGNER	2424 WILSHIRE BLVD #714	LOS ANGELES, CA	90057
WALDO, ELISABETH	COMPOSER	POST OFFICE BOX 101	NORTHRIDGE, CA	91324
WALDORF, DUFFY	GOLFER	POST OFFICE BOX 109601	PALM BCH GARDENS, FL	33418
WALDRON, CHARLES E	COMPOSER	SEE - WILD, CHUCK		
WALDRON, GYNETH M	DIRECTOR	1900 AVE OF THE STARS #2270	LOS ANGELES, CA	90067

Name	Occupation	Address	City	Code
WALDRON, JOE	BASEBALL	POST OFFICE BOX 611	WATERLOO, IA	50704
WALDROP, GIDEO	COMPOSER-CONDUCTOR	160 RIVERSIDE DR	NEW YORK, NY	10024
WALESA, LECH	PRESIDENT OF POLAND	UL PILOTOW 17/D3	GDANSK-ZASPA	POLAND
WALEWANDER, JIM	BASEBALL	1155 W MOUND ST	COLUMBUS, OH	43223
WALK, BOB	BASEBALL	POST OFFICE BOX 7000	PITTSBURGH, PA	15212
WALK THE WEST	ROCK & ROLL GROUP	POST OFFICE BOX 150973	NASHVILLE, TN	37215
WALKDEN, MIKE	BASEBALL	POST OFFICE BOX 10031	BAKERSFIELD, CA	93389
WALKEN, CHRISTOPHER	ACTOR	142 CEDAR RD	WILTON, CT	06897
WALKER, ALAN	CINEMATOGRAPHER	7715 SUNSET BLVD #150	LOS ANGELES, CA	90046
WALKER, ALLY	ACTRESS	KOHNER, 9169 SUNSET BLVD	LOS ANGELES, CA	90069
WALKER, ARNETIA	ACTRESS	SMITH, 121 N SAN VICENTE BLVD	BEVERLY HILLS, CA	90211
WALKER, BILLY	SINGER-GUITARIST	POST OFFICE BOX 618	HENDERSONVILLE, TN	37075
WALKER, BILLY JOE, JR	GUITARIST	SIRE RECORDS, 3300 WARNER BLVD	BURBANK, CA	91510
WALKER, CHARLES	ACTOR	301 N CANON DR #305	BEVERLY HILLS, CA	90210
WALKER, CHARLIE	SINGER	HOT, 306 W CHURCH ST	HORSHEHOE BEND, AR	72512
WALKER, CHICO	BASEBALL	1060 W ADDISON ST	CHICAGO, IL	60613
WALKER, CLINT	ACTOR	10113 JOERSCHKE DR #202	GRASS VALLEY, CA	95945
WALKER, DANE	BASEBALL	POST OFFICE BOX 882	MADISON, WI	53701
WALKER, DARRELL	BASKETBALL	BULLETS, 1 HARRY S TRUMAN DR	LANDOVER, MD	20785
WALKER, DAVE	BASEBALL EXECUTIVE	POST OFFICE BOX 824	BURLINGTON, IA	52601
WALKER, DENNIS	BASEBALL	1090 N EUCLID AVE	SARASOTA, FL	34237
WALKER, DERRICK	FOOTBALL	POST OFFICE BOX 609609	SAN DIEGO, CA	92160
WALKER, DOAK	FOOTBALL	POST OFFICE BOX TT	STEAMBOAT SPRINGS, CO	80477
WALKER, DUANE	BASEBALL	3108 GRANT ST	PASADENA, TX	77503
WALKER, EAMONN	ACTOR	JOSEPH, 2 TUNSTALL RD, STUDIO 1	LONDON SW9 8BN	ENGLAND
WALKER, FIONA	ACTRESS	13 DESPARD RD	LONDON N19	ENGLAND
WALKER, GREG	BASEBALL	FOREST CIRCLE DR	DOUGLAS, GA	31533
WALKER, HERSCHEL	FOOTBALL	VIKINGS, 9520 VIKING DR	EDEN PRAIRIE, MN	55344
WALKER, HUGH	BASEBALL	800 HOME RUN LN	MEMPHIS, TN	38104
WALKER, JERRY	BASEBALL EXECUTIVE	1316 KING ST	BELLINGHAM, WA	98226
WALKER, JERRY	BASEBALL-SCOUT	TIGERS, TIGER STADIUM	DETROIT, MI	48216
WALKER, JERRY JEFF	SINGER-SONGWRITER	POST OFFICE BOX 39	AUSTIN, TX	78767
WALKER, JIMMIE	ACTOR-COMEDIAN	8665 WILSHIRE BLVD #208	BEVERLY HILLS, CA	90211
WALKER, JOE LOUIS	SINGER-GUITARIST	FALK/MORROW, 143 S CEDROS AVE	SOLONA BEACH, CA	92075
WALKER, JUNIOR & THE ALL STARS	SOUL GROUP	UNIVERSAL, 218 W 57TH ST	NEW YORK, NY	10019
WALKER, KENNETH	DIRECTOR	23147 FRESCA DR	VALENCIA, CA	91355
WALKER, KENNY	BASKETBALL	KNICKS, 4 PENNYLVANIA PLAZA	NEW YORK, NY	10019
WALKER, KENNY	FOOTBALL	BRONCOS, 13655 BRONCOS PKWY	ENGLEWOOD, CO	80112
WALKER, KEVIN	FOOTBALL	BENGALS, 200 RIVERFRONT STADIUM	CINCINNATI, OH	45202
WALKER, LARRY	BASEBALL (MAJORS)	EXPOS, 4545 DE COUBERTIN AVE	MONTREAL, QUE H1V 3P2	CANADA
WALKER, LARRY	BASEBALL (MINORS)	5301 NW 12TH AVE	FORT LAUDERDALE, FL	33309
WALKER, MARCY	ACTRESS	15301 VENTURA BLVD #345	SHERMAN OAKS, CA	91403
WALKER, MIKE	BASEBALL	POST OFFICE BOX 4756	JACKSONVILLE, FL	32201
WALKER, MITCH	MUSIC ARRANGER	179 ROBINHOOD CIR	HENDERSONVILLE, TN	37075
WALKER, MORT	CARTOONIST	61 STUDIO CT	STAMFORD, CT	06903
WALKER, NICHOLAS	ACTOR	6925 TUNA CANYON RD	TOPANGA, CA	90290
WALKER, NORM	ARTIST	37 STONEHENGE RD	WESTON, CT	06883
WALKER, PETE	BASEBALL	POST OFFICE BOX 598	BINGHAMTON, NY	13902
WALKER, PETER L	WRI-DIR-PROD	TWITTER BARN, MONYASH	DERBYSHIRE	ENGLAND
WALKER, ROBERT W	U S CONGRESSMAN	POST OFFICE BOX 69	COCHRANVILLE, PA	19330
WALKER, ROBERT, JR	ACTOR	20828 PACIFIC COAST HWY	MALIBU, CA	90265
WALKER, RUBE	BASEBALL-SCOUT	250 STADIUM PLAZA	ST LOUIS, MO	63102
WALKER, RUDOLPH	ACTOR	MAYER MGMT, GRAFTON HOUSE #44 2-3 GOLDEN SQ	LONDON W1R 3AD	ENGLAND
WALKER, SHIRLEY A	COMPOSER-CONDUCTOR	8509 CAPISTRANO AVE	CANOGA PARK, CA	91304
WALKER, TONJA	ACTRESS	ABC-TV, "ONE LIFE TO LIVE" 56 W 66TH ST	NEW YORK, NY	10023
WALKER, TONY	FOOTBALL	POST OFFICE BOX 535000	INDIANPOLIS, IN	46253
WALKER, TRICIA	MUSIC ARRANGER	2101 BELMONT BLVD #D-3	NASHVILLE, TN	37212
WALKER, WILLIAM ALFRED	MUSIC ARRANGER	POST OFFICE BOX 22224	NASHVILLE, TN	37202
WALKER, WILLIAM F	ACTOR-WRITER	350 S FULLER AVE #6-D	LOS ANGELES, CA	90036
WALL, DON	TV WRITER-PRODUCER	ABC NEWS, 1106 N HWY 360 #110	GRAND PRAIRIE, TX	75050
WALL, DONNE	BASEBALL	POST OFFICE BOX 422229	KISSIMMEE, FL	34742
WALL, ERIC	DIRECTOR	4901 BEVERLY BLVD #24	LOS ANGELES, CA	90004
WALL, MICHAEL B	TV DIRECTOR	190 N STATE ST	CHICAGO, IL	60601
WALLACE, AARON	FOOTBALL	RAIDERS, 332 CENTER ST	EL SEGUNDO, CA	90245
WALLACE, CHRIS	BROADCAST JOURNALIST	ABC NEWS, 1717 DE SALES ST, NW	WASHINGTON, DC	20036
WALLACE, CRAIG	TALENT AGENT	8228 SUNSET BLVD #212	LOS ANGELES, CA	90046
WALLACE, DANIEL	ART DIRECTOR	295 W 11TH ST #6-F	NEW YORK, NY	10014
WALLACE, DAVE	BASEBALL EXECUTIVE	1000 ELYSIAN PARK DR	LOS ANGELES, CA	90012
WALLACE, DAVID	ACTOR	ABC-TV, "GENERAL HOSPITAL" 4151 PROSPECT AVE	BURBANK, CA	91523
WALLACE, DAVID	BASEBALL	POST OFFICE BOX 1556	ASHEVILLE, NC	28802
WALLACE, EARL W	SCREENWRITER	UTA, 9560 WILSHIRE BL, 5TH FL	BEVERLY HILLS, CA	90212
WALLACE, GEORGE	COMEDIAN	141 S EL CAMINO DR #205	BEVERLY HILLS, CA	90212
WALLACE, GEORGE	SINGER	9255 SUNSET BLVD #526	LOS ANGELES, CA	90069
WALLACE, GEORGE, III	TREASURER	ALA STATE HOUSE, 11 S UNION ST	MONTGOMERY, AL	36130
WALLACE, GEORGE, SR	GOVERNOR	POST OFFICE BOX 17222	MONTGOMERY, AL	36104
WALLACE, IRVIN	DIRECTOR	5629 BABBIT AVE	ENCINO, CA	91316
WALLACE, JEAN	ACTRESS	1003 WALLACE RIDGE	BEVERLY HILLS, CA	90210
WALLACE, JERRY	SINGER-COMPOSER	POST OFFICE BOX 17272	MEMPHIS, TN	38187
WALLACE, JULIE T	ACTRESS	STONE, 9 NEWBURGH ST	LONDON W1V 1LH	ENGLAND
WALLACE, MIKE	BASEBALL SCOUT	TIGERS, TIGER STADIUM	DETROIT, MI	48216
WALLACE, MIKE	BROADCAST JOURNALIST	CBS NEWS, 524 W 57TH ST	NEW YORK, NY	10019
WALLACE, RICK	TV DIRECTOR-PRODUCER	6041 GRACIOSA DR	LOS ANGELES, CA	90068

Name	Occupation	Address	City/State	Zip
WALLACE, ROGER A	CONDUCTOR	7934 VANALDEN AVE	RESEDA, CA	91335
WALLACE, ROYCE	ACTRESS	2442 W 18TH ST	LOS ANGELES, CA	90019
WALLACE, STEVE	FOOTBALL	S F 49ERS, 4949 CENTENNIAL BL	SANTA CLARA, CA	95054
WALLACE, TOMMY LEE	FILM WRITER-DIRECTOR	1999 AVE OF THE STARS #2850	LOS ANGELES, CA	90067
WALLACE-STONE, DEE	ACTRESS	12700 VENTURA BLVD #350	STUDIO CITY, CA	91604
WALLACH, ALLAN	DRAMA CRITIC	64 LONG ST	HUNTINGTON STATION, NY	11746
WALLACH, ELI	ACTOR	90 RIVERSIDE DR	NEW YORK, NY	10024
WALLACH, GEORGE	TV DIRECTOR-PRODUCER	14 LAWRENCE ST	NEW HYDE PARK, NY	11040
WALLACH, IRA	SCREENWRITER	345 W 58TH ST	NEW YORK, NY	10019
WALLACH, TIM	BASEBALL	EXPOS, 4545 DE COUBERTIN AVE	MONTREAL, QUE H1V 3P2	CANADA
WALLAS, WESLEY	FOOTBALL	S F 49ERS, 4949 CENTENNIAL BL	SANTA CLARA, CA	95054
WALLENBROCK, CRAIG	BASEBALL SCOUT	ATHLETICS'S, OAKLAND COLISEUM	OAKLAND, CA	94621
WALLENGREN, ERNIE	PRODUCER	CBS-MTM, 4024 RADFORD AVE	STUDIO CITY, CA	91604
WALLENSTEIN, JOSEPH B	WRITER-PRODUCER	13027 DELANO ST	VAN NUYS, CA	91401
WALLER, ALBERT C	WRITER-PRODUCER	300 E 74TH ST	NEW YORK, NY	10021
WALLER, CASEY	BASEBALL	POST OFFICE BOX 15050	READING, PA	19612
WALLER, DAVID	ACTOR	PETERS, FRASER & DUNLOP, LTD		
		5TH FLOOR, THE CHAMBERS		
		CHELSEA HARBOUR, LOT RD	LONDON SW10 0XF	ENGLAND
WALLER, KEN	BODYBUILDER	POST OFFICE BOX 212	SANTA MONICA, CA	90405
WALLER, KENNETH	ACTOR	HAMILTON, 21 GOODGE ST	LONDON W1P 1FD	ENGLAND
WALLER, TYE	BASEBALL-INSTRUCTOR	POST OFFICE BOX 2000	SAN DIEGO, CA	92112
WALLER FAMILY, THE	RHYTHM & BLUES GROUP	POST OFFICE BOX 25654	RICHMOND, CA	23260
WALLERSTEIN, ROWE	DIRECTOR	2049 CENTURY PARK E #1320	LOS ANGELES, CA	90067
WALLEY, DEBORAH	ACTRESS	31 1/2 24TH AVE	VENICE, CA	90291
WALLIN, LES	BASEBALL	RED SOX, CHAIN O'LAKES PARK	WINTER HAVEN, FL	33880
WALLING, DENNY	BASEBALL	POST OFFICE BOX 288	HOUSTON, TX	77001
WALLIS, ALAN	DIRECTOR-PRODUCER	2 CHAPEL TERR	BRIGHTON	ENGLAND
WALLIS, DARVIN	FOOTBALL COACH	CHIEFS, 1 ARROWHEAD DR	KANSAS CITY, MO	64129
WALLIS, MARTHA HYER	ACTRESS-WRITER	515 S MAPLETON DR	LOS ANGELES, CA	90024
WALLIS, SHANI	ACTRESS	ATKINS, 303 S CRESCENT HEIGHTS	LOS ANGELES, CA	90048
WALLOP, MALCOLM	U S SENATOR	2009 FEDERAL CENTER	CHEYENNE, WY	82001
WALLS, BYRON	SINGER	BIRDSONG, 2714 WESTWOOD DR	NASHVILLE, TN	37204
WALLS, EVERSON	FOOTBALL	N Y GIANTS, GIANTS STADIUM	EAST RUTHERFORD, NJ	07073
WALLS, GEORGE	DIRECTOR	POST OFFICE BOX 523	DESERT HOT SPRINGS, CA	92240
WALLWORK, DAVID	BASEBALL TRAINER	POST OFFICE BOX 360007	BIRMINGHAM, AL	35236
WALSH, ADDIE	TV WRITER	215 W 91ST ST #67	NEW YORK, NY	10024
WALSH, BOB	TV DIRECTOR-PRODUCER	1223 FILSON WY	PITTSBURGH, PA	15212
WALSH, DENNIS	BASEBALL	POST OFFICE BOX 64939	FAYETTEVILLE, NC	28306
WALSH, DONNIE	BASKETBALL EXECUTIVE	PACERS, 300 E MARKET ST	INDIANAPOLIS, IN	46204
WALSH, HERB	CONDUCTOR	1637 N VINE ST #1006	LOS ANGELES, CA	90028
WALSH, JAMES	DIRECTOR	HAVILAND HOLLOW RD	PATTERSON, NY	12563
WALSH, JAMES T	U S CONGRESSMAN	POST OFFICE BOX 7306	SYRACUSE, NY	13261
WALSH, JOE	SINGER-GUITARIST	9044 MELROSE AVE #306	LOS ANGELES, CA	90069
WALSH, JOHN	BASEBALL SCOUT	REDS, 100 RIVERFRONT STADIUM	CINCINNATI, OH	45202
WALSH, JOHN	TV HOST	"AMERICA'S MOST WANTED"		
		FOX TELEVISION, STUDIO 2		
		5151 WISCONSIN AVE, NW	WASHINGTON, DC	20016
WALSH, M EMMET	ACTOR	4173 MOTOR AVE	CULVER CITY, CA	90232
WALSH, PATRICK	DIRECTOR-PRODUCER	3919 W 8TH ST	LOS ANGELES, CA	90005
WALSH, RON	WRITER-PRODUCER	1211 HORN AVE #702	LOS ANGELES, CA	90069
WALSH, STEVE	FOOTBALL	SAINTS, 1500 POYDRAS ST	NEW ORLEANS, LA	90112
WALSH, SYDNEY	ACTRESS	1999 AVE OF THE STARS #2850	LOS ANGELES, CA	90067
WALSH, TOM	BASEBALL SCOUT	BREWERS, 201 S 46TH ST	MILWAUKEE, WI	53214
WALSH, TOM	FOOTBALL COACH	RAIDERS, 332 CENTER ST	EL SEGUNDO, CA	90245
WALSTON, RAY	ACTOR	423 REXFORD DR #205	BEVERLY HILLS, CA	90212
WALTER, DOUGLAS E	CONDUCTOR	8312 KITTYHAWK AVE	LOS ANGELES, CA	90045
WALTER, E V	COMPOSER	15243 S PURDUE AVE	GARDENA, CA	90249
WALTER, GENE	BASEBALL	CHIEFS, MAC ARTHUR STADIUM	SYRACUSE, NY	13208
WALTER, JESSICA	ACTRESS	10530 STRATHMORE DR	LOS ANGELES, CA	90024
WALTER, JOE	FOOTBALL	BENGALS, 200 RIVERFRONT STADIUM	CINCINNATI, OH	45202
WALTER, MIKE	FOOTBALL	S F 49ERS, 4949 CENTENNIAL BL	SANTA CLARA, CA	95054
WALTER, RICHARD F	WRITER	2127 VESTAL AVE	LOS ANGELES, CA	90026
WALTER, RYAN	HOCKEY	CANADIENS, 2313 ST CATHERINE ST	MONTREAL, QUE H3H 1N2	CANADA
WALTER, TRACEY	ACTOR	257 N REXFORD DR	BEVERLY HILLS, CA	90210
WALTERS, BARBARA	NEWS JOURNALIST	33 W 60TH ST	NEW YORK, NY	10023
WALTERS, CASEY	ACTOR	783 8TH AVE	NEW YORK, NY	10036
WALTERS, DAN	BASEBALL	POST OFFICE BOX 2000	SAN DIEGO, CA	92112
WALTERS, DAVID	BASEBALL	POST OFFICE BOX 2365	PAWTUCKET, RI	02861
WALTERS, DAVID	GOVERNOR	STATE CAPITOL BUILDING	OKLAHOMA CITY, OK	73105
WALTERS, GEORGE T	COMPOSER	419 N ORANGE AVE	MONTEREY PARK, CA	91754
WALTERS, HUGH	ACTOR	15 CHRISTCHURCH AVE	LONDON NW6 7QP	ENGLAND
WALTERS, JAMES M	FILM DIRECTOR	POST OFFICE BOX 8504	UNIVERSAL CITY, CA	91608
WALTERS, JULIE	ACTRESS	SARABAND, 265 LIVERPOOL RD	LONDON N1 1LX	ENGLAND
WALTERS, LAURIE	ACTRESS	4450 KENSINGTON RD #5	LOS ANGELES, CA	90065
WALTERS, NORBY	TALENT AGENT	WALTERS, 400 E 56TH ST	NEW YORK, NY	10022
WALTERS, RON	BASEBALL SCOUT	6850 LAWRENCE RD	LANTANA, FL	33462
WALTERS, STEVE	FOOTBALL COACH	SAINTS, 1500 POYDRAS ST	NEW ORLEANS, LA	90112
WALTERS, SUSAN	ACTRESS	888 7TH AVE #1602	NEW YORK, NY	10019
WALTERS, THORLEY	ACTOR	808 KEYES HOUSE, DOLPHIN SQ	LONDON SW1	ENGLAND
WALTERS, VINCENT C	DIRECTOR	DGA, 110 W 57TH ST	NEW YORK, NY	10019
WALTON, ALVIN	FOOTBALL	POST OFFICE BOX 17247 (DULLES)	WASHINGTON, DC	20041
WALTON, BENNIE	BASEBALL UMPIRE	235 MAIN ST #103	TRUSSVILLE, AL	35173
WALTON, BRUCE	BASEBALL	ATHLETICS'S, OAKLAND COLISEUM	OAKLAND, CA	94621
WALTON, FREDERICK	DIRECTOR	2420 DETOUR DR	LOS ANGELES, CA	90068

WALTON, GLADYS	ACTRESS	HERBEL, 225 MAIN ST	MORRO BAY, CA	93442
WALTON, JEROME	BASEBALL	1060 W ADDISON ST	CHICAGO, IL	60613
WALTON, JESS	ACTRESS	CBS-TV, "YOUNG & THE RESTLESS"		
		7800 BEVERLY BLVD #3305	LOS ANGELES, CA	90036
WALTON, JOE	FOOTBALL COACH	STEELERS, 300 STADIUM CIR	PITTSBURGH, PA	15212
WALTON, KIP	TV DIRECTOR	11019 WRIGHTWOOD LN	STUDIO CITY, CA	91604
WALTON, ROSELIE	CASTING DIRECTOR	19 E 71ST ST	NEW YORK, NY	10021
WALTON, SUNNI	ACTRESS	6612 CANTALOUPE AVE	VAN NUYS, CA	91405
WALTON, TONY	COSTUME DESIGNER	ICM, 40 W 57TH ST	NEW YORK, NY	10019
WALTON, TREVOR	TALENT AGENT	11726 SAN VICENTE BLVD #300	LOS ANGELES, CA	90049
WALTZ, LISA	ACTRESS	11726 SAN VICENTE BLVD #300	LOS ANGELES, CA	90049
WALWIN, KENT	DIRECTOR-PRODUCER	YELLOWBILL, 11 CROSS KEYS CLOSE	LONDON W1M 5FY	ENGLAND
WAMBAUGH, JOSEPH	NOVELIST	WM MORROW, 105 MADISON AVE	NEW YORK, NY	10016
WAMPFLER, JERRY	FOOTBALL COACH	LIONS, 1200 FEATHERSTONE RD	PONTIAC, MI	48432
WANAMAKER, SAM	ACTOR-DIRECTOR	354 N CROFT AVE	LOS ANGELES, CA	90048
WANAMAKER, ZOE	ACTRESS	CONWAY, 18-21 JERMYN ST	LONDON SW1	ENGLAND
WANDS, RANDOLPH H	TV DIRECTOR	64 KENSINGTON RD	BRONXVILLE, NY	10708
WANKE, CHUCK	BASEBALL	POST OFFICE BOX 1295	CLINTON, IA	52733
WANNBERG, KENNETH	MUSIC ED-COMP	10738 MOLONY RD	CULVER CITY, CA	90230
WANNSTEDT, DAVE	FOOTBALL COACH	COWBOYS, 1 COWBOYS PARKWAY	IRVING, TX	75063
WAPNER, JOSEPH A	JUDGE	RALPH EDWARDS PRODUCTIONS		
		1717 N HIGHLAND AVE, 10TH FL	HOLLYWOOD, CA	90028
		"THE PEOPLE'S COURT"		
WAPNICK, STEVE	BASEBALL	CANADIANS, 4601 ONTARIO ST	VANCOUVER, BC V5V 3H4	CANADA
WARBECK, DAVID	ACTOR	ICM, 388-396 OXFORD ST	LONDON W1	ENGLAND
WARD, AL C	TV WRITER-DIRECTOR	ALFA PRODUCTIONS, MGM STUDIOS		
		10202 W WADHINGTON BLVD	CULVER CITY, CA	90230
WARD, ANITA	SINGER	FAA, 1700 BROADWAY, 5TH FLOOR	NEW YORK, NY	10019
WARD, ANTHONY	BASEBALL	CHIEFS, MAC ARTHUR STADIUM	SYRACUSE, NY	13208
WARD, BRUCE A	WRITER	2324 OCEAN PARK BLVD #B	SANTA MONICA, CA	90405
WARD, BURT	ACTOR	1559 PACIFIC COAST HWY #815	HERMOSA BEACH, CA	90254
WARD, COLBY	BASEBALL	4385 TUTT BLVD	COLORADO SPRINGS, CO	80922
WARD, DAVID	FILM WRITER-DIRECTOR	246 21ST ST	SANTA MONICA, CA	90402
WARD, DAVID P	COMPOSER	5619 AUCKLAND AVE	NORTH HOLLYWOOD, CA	91601
WARD, DICKSON	TV DIRECTOR-PRODUCER	710 WESTMOUNT DR	LOS ANGELES, CA	90069
WARD, DOUGLAS	ACTOR-PLAYWRIGHT	AEA, 165 W 46TH ST	NEW YORK, NY	10036
WARD, DUANE	BASEBALL	SKYDOME, 300 BREMMER BL #3200	TORONTO, ONT M5V 3B3	CANADA
WARD, EDMUND	SCREENWRITER	HANCOCK, GREENER HOUSE		
		66-68 HAYMARKET	LONDON SW1Y 4AW	ENGLAND
WARD, FRED	ACTOR	9301 WILSHIRE BLVD #312	BEVERLY HILLS, CA	90210
WARD, IRENA FERRIS	ACTRESS	10100 SANTA MONICA BLVD #700	LOS ANGELES, CA	90067
WARD, JACKY	SINGER	1808 W END AVE #700	NASHVILLE, TN	37203
WARD, JANET	ACTRESS	43 W 73RD ST	NEW YORK, NY	10023
WARD, JAY	BASEBALL-COACH	EXPOS, 4545 DE COUBERTIN AVE	MONTREAL, QUE H1V 3P2	CANADA
WARD, JENNA	MODEL	WILHELMINA, 300 PARK AVE	NEW YORK, NY	10010
WARD, JOHN	TV DIRECTOR	6933 CAMROSE DR	HOLLYWOOD, CA	90068
WARD, JOHN D	DIRECTOR	DGA, 110 W 57TH ST	NEW YORK, NY	10019
WARD, JON PARKER	DIRECTOR	DGA, 7920 SUNSET BLVD, 6TH FL	LOS ANGELES, CA	90046
WARD, JONATHAN	WRITER-NEWS CORRES	CBS NEWS, 2020 "M" ST, NW	WASHINGTON, DC	20036
WARD, KELLY	ACTOR	19338 ARCHWOOD ST	RESEDA, CA	91335
WARD, KEVIN	BASEBALL	POST OFFICE BOX 2000	SAN DIEGO, CA	92112
WARD, LYMAN	ACTOR	9255 SUNSET BLVD #515	LOS ANGELES, CA	90069
WARD, MARGARET	GOLFER	2750 VOLUSA AVE #B	DAYTON BEACH, FL	32114
WARD, PHILIP SCOTT	TV DIRECTOR	2015 PHEASANT HILL RD	LANSDALE, PA	19446
WARD, PHYLLIS J	DIRECTOR	20 8TH ST, SE	WASHINGTON, DC	20003
WARD, RICKY	BASEBALL	POST OFFICE BOX 21727	SAN FRANCISCO, CA	95151
WARD, ROBERT	BASEBALL	1601 E HOBBLECREEK	SPRINGVILLE, UT	84663
WARD, ROBERT M	SCREENWRITER	555 W 57TH ST #1230	NEW YORK, NY	10019
WARD, SAM	ILLUSTRATOR	POST OFFICE BOX 500	WASHINGTON, DC	20044
WARD, SELA	ACTRESS	2101 CENTURY PARK KN #202	LOS ANGELES, CA	90067
WARD, SIMON	ACTOR	ICM, 388-396 OXFORD ST	LONDON W1	ENGLAND
WARD, SKIP	PRODUCER	POST OFFICE BOX 755	BEVERLY HILLS, CA	90213
WARD, SOPHIE	ACTRESS	CHATTO AND LINNIT, LTD		
		PRINCE OF WALES THEATRE		
		COVENTRY ST	LONDON W1V 7FE	ENGLAND
WARD, STUART	ACTOR	CBS-TV, "THE GUIDING LIGHT"		
		222 E 44TH ST	NEW YORK, NY	10017
WARD, TURNER	BASEBALL	232 AUTUMN DR	SARALAND, AL	36571
WARDELL, GARETH	DIRECTOR-PRODUCER	JAM JAR FILMS, BALERNO	EDINBURGH EH14 7DH	ENGLAND
WARDELL, JOHN	ACTOR	165 W 46TH ST #710	NEW YORK, NY	10036
WARDEN, JACK	ACTOR	23604 MALIBU COLONY DR	MALIBU, CA	90265
WARDEN, VERONICA FREDRICKS	ACTRESS	POST OFFICE BOX 68	SIERRA MADRE, CA	91024
WARE, ANDRE	FOOTBALL	LIONS, 1200 FEATHERSTONE RD	PONTIAC, MI	48432
WARE, CLYDE	WRITER-PRODUCER	1252 N LAUREL AVE #B	LOS ANGELES, CA	90046
WARE, HERTA	ACTRESS	POST OFFICE BOX 151	TOPANGA CANYON, CA	90290
WARE, JEFF	BASEBALL	POST OFFICE BOX 957	DUNEDIN, FL	34697
WARE, KOKO B	WRESTLER	POST OFFICE BOX 3859	STAMFORD, CT	06905
WARE, SUSAN	ACTRESS-WRITER	4375 CAMELLIA AVE	STUDIO CITY, CA	91604
WARE, TIMMIE	FOOTBALL	2801 MEADOW LARK DR	SAN DIEGO, CA	92123
WARFIELD, DR WILLIAM	ACTOR-SINGER	706 PHOENIX DR	CHAMPAIGN, IL	61820
WARFIELD, JIM	BASEBALL TRAINER	INDIANS, CLEVELAND STADIUM	CLEVELAND, OH	44114
WARFIELD, KENNETH J	COMPOSER	4627 W 18TH ST	LOS ANGELES, CA	90019
WARFIELD, MARSHA	COMEDIENNE	POST OFFICE BOX 691713	LOS ANGELES, CA	90069
WARFIELD, POLLY	FILM CRITIC	DRAMA-LOGUE, 1456 N GORDON ST	HOLLYWOOD, CA	90028
WARGA, WAYNE	TV WRITER	15320 KINGSWOOD LN	SHERMAN OAKS, CA	91403

Name	Occupation	Address	City
WARINER, STEVE	SINGER-SONGWRITER	POST OFFICE BOX 157	NOLENSVILLE, TN 37135
WARING, AMANDA	ACTRESS	8 CHESTER CLOSE, QUEEN'S RIDE	BARNES ENGLAND
WARING, DEREK	ACTOR	BURNETT, 42-43 GRAFTON HOUSE 2-3 GOLDEN SQ	LONDON W1R 3AD ENGLAND
WARING, JIM	BASEBALL	POST OFFICE BOX 824	BURLINGTON, IA 52601
WARING, RICHARD	TV WRITER	17 CHESTER CLOSE, BARNES	LONDON SW13 ENGLAND
WARING, TODD	ACTOR	10351 SANTA MONICA BLVD #211	LOS ANGELES, CA 90025
WARK, MARTIN	WRITER	4169 VIA MARINA #214	MARINA DEL REY, CA 90292
WARLOCK	ROCK & ROLL GROUP	POLYGRAM RECORDS, 810 7TH AVE	NEW YORK, NY 10019
WARLOCK, BILLY	ACTOR	6822 LASAINE AVE	VAN NUYS, CA 91406
WARLORD	ROCK & ROLL GROUP	POST OFFICE BOX 2896	TORRANCE, CA 90509
WARLORD, THE	WRESTLER	POST OFFICE BOX 3859	STAMFORD, CT 06905
WARNE, GARY R	WRITER	16633 VENTURA BLVD #1421	ENCINO, CA 91436
WARNER, CHERYL K	SINGER	NAOMI HATCHER MANAGEMENT 4601 BARKBRIDGE CT	CHESTERFIELD, VA 23832
WARNER, DARYL	TV WRITER	SHAPIRO, 8827 BEVERLY BLVD	LOS ANGELES, CA 90048
WARNER, DAVID	ACTOR	BELFRAGE, 68 SAINT JAMES'S ST	LONDON SW1A 1LE ENGLAND
WARNER, DON	SINGER-GUITARIST	DON LIGHT, 1100 17TH AVE S	NASHVILLE, TN 37212
WARNER, FREDERICK	SCREENWRITER	PINEWOOD STUDIOS, IVER HEATH	IVER, BUCKS SLO ONH ENGLAND
WARNER, GLENN ALLYN, JR	WRITER	3662 BARHAM BLVD #M-223	LOS ANGELES, CA 90068
WARNER, JAMES ALAN	TV EXECUTIVE	HBO, 1100 6TH AVE	NEW YORK, NY 10036
WARNER, JERRY	TV WRITER-DIRECTOR	DGA, 7920 SUNSET BLVD, 6TH FL	LOS ANGELES, CA 90046
WARNER, JOHN W	U S SENATOR	ATOKA FARMS	MIDDLEBURG, VA 22117
WARNER, LAVINIA	TV DIRECTOR-PRODUCER	WARNER SISTERS, 21 RUSSELL ST	LONDON WC2 5HP ENGLAND
WARNER, LESLIE O	DIRECTOR	POST OFFICE BOX 653	YUCCA VALLEY, CA 92284
WARNER, MALCOLM-JAMAL	ACTOR-DIRECTOR	1301 THE COLONY	HARTSDALE, NY 10530
WARNER, MARSHA	ACTRESS	5738 WILLIS AVE	VAN NUYS, CA 91411
WARNER, ROBERT	DIRECTOR	7 E 78TH ST	NEW YORK, NY 10021
WARNER, ROBERT E	TV DIRECTOR	7 MAIN ST	FLANDERS, NJ 07836
WARNER, RON	BASEBALL	POST OFFICE BOX 3783	SAVANNAH, GA 31414
WARNER, WYNN	CONDUCTOR	13131 MINDANAO WY #1	MARINA DEL REY, CA 90292
WARNES, JENNIFER	SINGER-SONGWRITER	10100 SANTA MONICA BLVD #1600	LOS ANGELES, CA 90067
WARNICK, ALLAN	ACTOR	2878 HUME RD	MALIBU, CA 90265
WARNICK, BOB	TV PRODUCER	237 E 54TH ST	NEW YORK, NY 10022
WARNIER, STEVE	SINGER-SONGWRITER	POST OFFICE BOX 120308	NASHVILLE, TN 37212
WARNKEN, RODNEY G	WRITER	8705 WONDERLAND PARK AVE	LOS ANGELES, CA 90046
WARREN, BRIAN	BASEBALL	TIGERS, 89 WHARNCLIFFE RD N	LONDON, ONT N6H 2A7 CANADA
WARREN, CHRIS	FOOTBALL	SEAHAWKS, 11220 NE 53RD ST	KIRKLAND, WA 98033
WARREN, CLIFF	BASEBALL EXECUTIVE	12000 STADIUM RD	ADELANTO, CA 92301
WARREN, FRANK	FOOTBALL	SAINTS, 1500 POYDRAS ST	NEW ORLEANS, LA 90112
WARREN, GENE	DIRECTOR-PRODUCER	9725 HENSAL RD	BEVERLY HILLS, CA 90210
WARREN, GERALD L	NEWSPAPER EDITOR	POST OFFICE BOX 191	SAN DIEGO, CA 92112
WARREN, GLORIA	SINGER	16872 BOSQUE DR	ENCINO, CA 91316
WARREN, JEFF	ACTOR	2266 1/2 COVE AVE	LOS ANGELES, CA 90069
WARREN, JENNIFER	ACTRESS	1675 OLD OAK RD	LOS ANGELES, CA 90049
WARREN, JOAN	ACTOR	200 E 66TH ST	NEW YORK, NY 10021
WARREN, L D	CARTOONIST	1815 WM H TAFT RD	CINCINNATI, OH 45206
WARREN, LESLEY ANN	ACTRESS	8730 SUNSET BLVD #PH-W	LOS ANGELES, CA 90069
WARREN, MADELINE	FILM EXECUTIVE	10313 CHEVIOT DR	LOS ANGELES, CA 90064
WARREN, MARC	TV WRITER	CAA, 9830 WILSHIRE BLVD	BEVERLY HILLS, CA 90212
WARREN, MARK	TV DIRECTOR	1830 OUTPOST DR	HOLLYWOOD, CA 90028
WARREN, MICHAEL	ACTOR	189 GREENFIELD AVE	LOS ANGELES, CA 90049
WARREN, MICHAEL	ARRANGER-CONDUCTOR	12233 LAUREL TERRACE DR	STUDIO CITY, CA 91604
WARREN, MICHAEL	PRODUCER	WARNER, 1041 N FORMOSA AVE	LOS ANGELES, CA 90046
WARREN, MICHAEL R	TV WRITER	ZIFFREN, 2121 AVE OF THE STARS	LOS ANGELES, CA 90067
WARREN, MIKE	BASEBALL	12281 DIANE ST	GARDEN GROVE, CA 92640
WARREN, NORMAN J	FILM-TV DIRECTOR	59 SHEPHERDS BUSH RD HAMMERSMITH	LONDON W6 ENGLAND
WARREN, PATRICIA	TV WRITER	23 BEREWEEKE RD, FELPHAM BOGNOR REGIS	WEST SUSSEX PO22 7EG ENGLAND
WARREN, PAUL & EXPLORER	ROCK & ROLL GROUP	COASTAL ARTISTS AGENCY 8744 WILSHIRE BLVD	BEVERLY HILLS, CA 90212
WARREN, ROBERT PENN	WRITER	2495 REDDING RD	FAIRCHILD, CT 06430
WARREN, SMOKEY	SINGER	116 PRINCETON RD	LINDEN, NJ 07036
WARRICK, RUTH	ACTRESS	903 PARK AVE	NEW YORK, NY 10021
WARRINGTON, DON	ACTOR	ICM, 388-396 OXFORD ST	LONDON W1 ENGLAND
WARRIOR, JAMES	ACTOR	NARROW, 21 POLAND ST	LONDON W1V 3DD ENGLAND
WARTHEN, DAN	BASEBALL-COACH	POST OFFICE BOX 4100	SEATTLE, WA 98104
WARWICK, DIONNE	SINGER	9200 SUNSET BLVD #420	LOS ANGELES, CA 90069
WARWICK, JAMES	ACTOR	BURNETT, 42-43 GRAFTON HOUSE 2-3 GOLDEN SQ	LONDON W1R 3AD ENGLAND
WARWICK, NORMAN	CINEMATOGRAPHER	BURWOOD, 36 OATLANDS CHASE WEYBRIDGE	SURREY ENGLAND
WARWICK, RICHARD	ACTOR	ICM, 388-396 OXFORD ST	LONDON W1 ENGLAND
WAS (NOT WAS)	ROCK & ROLL GROUP	10100 SANTA MONICA BLVD #1600	LOS ANGELES, CA 90067
WASHBROOK, JOHNNY	ACTOR	8356 CAPISTARNO AVE	CANOGA PARK, CA 91304
WASHBURN, CHARLES C	FILM WRITER-DIRECTOR	22034 TIARA ST	WOODLAND HILLS, CA 91367
WASHBURN, DERIC	SCREENWRITER	8955 BEVERLY BLVD	WEST HOLLYWOOD, CA 90048
WASHBURN, JAMES	DIRECTOR	6921 PASEO DEL SERRA	HOLLYWOOD, CA 90068
WASHBURN, MILTON	CONDUCTOR	9782 ROYAL PALM BLVD	GARDEN GROVE, CA 92641
WASHINGTON, ART	WRITER-PRODUCER	1870 PACIFIC AVE #601	SAN FRANCISCO, CA 94109
WASHINGTON, BRIAN	FOOTBALL	N Y JETS, 1000 FULTON AVE	HEMPSTEAD, NY 11550
WASHINGTON, CHARLES	FOOTBALL	CHIEFS, 1 ARROWHEAD DR	KANSAS CITY, MO 64129
WASHINGTON, CLAUDELL	BASEBALL	12 CHARLES HILL RD	ORINDA, CA 94563
WASHINGTON, CRAIG A	U S CONGRESSMAN	1919 SMITH #820	HOUSTON, TX 77002

WASHINGTON, DENZEL	ACTOR	4701 SANCOLA AVE	TOLUCA LAKE, CA 91602
WASHINGTON, DESIREE	BEAUTY CONTESTANT	DEVAL L PATRICK, ATTY AT LAW	
		1 INTERNATIONAL PL	BOSTON, MA 02110
WASHINGTON, DONNA	SINGER	DON DANIELS, 160 PARK AVE	BELMONT SHORES, CA 90803
WASHINGTON, ERWIN	TV WRITER	CONNELL, 4605 LANKERSHIM BLVD	NORTH HOLLYWOOD, CA 91602
WASHINGTON, GROVER, JR	SAXOPHONIST	ZANE MANAGEMENT AGENCY	
		700 THREE PENN CENTER PL	PHILADELPHIA, PA 19102
WASHINGTON, JAMES	FOOTBALL	COWBOYS, 1 COWBOYS PARKWAY	IRVING, TX 75063
WASHINGTON, JOHN	FOOTBALL	N Y GIANTS, GIANTS STADIUM	EAST RUTHERFORD, NJ 07073
WASHINGTON, KYLE	BASEBALL	2501 ALLEN AVE, SE	CANTON, OH 44707
WASHINGTON, LIONEL	FOOTBALL	RAIDERS, 332 CENTER ST	EL SEGUNDO, CA 90245
WASHINGTON, MARVIN	FOOTBALL	N Y JETS, 1000 FULTON AVE	HEMPSTEAD, NY 11550
WASHINGTON, MICKEY	FOOTBALL	PATRIOTS, FOXBORO STADIUM, RT #1	FOXBORO, MA 02035
WASHINGTON, RON	BASEBALL-COACH	POST OFFICE BOX 1211	NORFOLK, VA 23502
WASHINGTON, TED	FOOTBALL	S F 49ERS, 4949 CENTENNIAL BL	SANTA CLARA, CA 95054
WASHINGTON, TYRONE	BASEBALL	14100 SIX MILE CYPRESS PKWY	FORT MYERS, FL 33912
WASHINGTON, U L	BASEBALL-COACH	800 HOME RUN LN	MEMPHIS, TN 38104
WASHINGTON SQUARES, THE	ROCK & ROLL GROUP	ATI, 888 7TH AVE, 21ST FLOOR	NEW YORK, NY 10106
WASINGER, MARK	BASEBALL	10233 96TH AVE	EDMONTON, ALB TK5 0A5 CANADA
WASS, TED	ACTOR	7667 SEATTLE PL	LOS ANGELES, CA 90046
WASSEL, JOHN S	DIRECTOR	3961 SAPPHIRE DR	ENCINO, CA 91436
WASSENAAR, ROB	BASEBALL	POST OFFICE BOX 1659	PORTLAND, OR 97207
WASSERMAN, ALBERT	WRITER-PRODUCER	259 W 11TH ST	NEW YORK, NY 10014
WASSERMAN, CHARLES H	DIRECTOR	326 SAN VICENTE BLVD #C	SANTA MONICA, CA 90402
WASSERMAN, DALE	PLAYWRIGHT	1680 VALECROFT AVE	WESTLAKE VILLAGE, CA 91361
WASSERMAN, LEW	FILM EXECUTIVE	911 N FOOTHILL RD	BEVERLY HILLS, CA 90210
WASZGIS, ROBERT	BASEBALL	POST OFFICE BOX 418	SAINT CHARLES, IL 60174
WATANABE, GEDDE	ACTOR	3855 LANKERSHIM BLVD	STUDIO CITY, CA 91604
WATANABE, SADAO	SAXOPHONIST	WM MORRIS, 1350 AVE OF AMERICAS	NEW YORK, NY 10019
WATER, DENNIS	ACTOR	ICM, 388-396 OXFORD ST	LONDON W1 ENGLAND
WATERBOYS, THE	ROCK & ROLL GROUP	3 MONMOUTH PL, OFF MONMOUTH RD	LONDON W2 ENGLAND
WATERFRONT	SINGER	BROTHERS, 141 DUNBAR AVE	FORDS, NJ 08863
WATERHOUSE, ERIC	ACTOR	10600 HOLMAN AVE #1	LOS ANGELES, CA 90024
WATERHOUSE, KEITH	TV WRITER	LONDON MGT, 235-241 REGENT ST	LONDON W1R 4PH ENGLAND
WATERMAN, DENNIS	ACTOR	ICM, 388-396 OXFORD ST	LONDON W1 ENGLAND
WATERMAN, FELICITY	ACTRESS	3500 W OLIVE AVE #1400	BURBANK, CA 91505
WATERS, ANDRE	FOOTBALL	EAGLES, BROAD ST & PATTISON AVE	PHILADELPHIA, PA 19148
WATERS, CHARLIE	FOOTBALL COACH	BRONCOS, 13655 BRONCOS PKWY	ENGLEWOOD, CO 80112
WATERS, E S	TV WRITER	31537 VICTORIA POINT RD	MALIBU, CA 90265
WATERS, JOE & APPALACHIAN BAND	C & W GROUP	455 MASSIEVILLE RD #K	CHILICOTHE, OH 45601
WATERS, JOHN	FILM DIRECTOR	575 8TH AVE #1600	NEW YORK, NY 10018
WATERS, KIM	SAXOPHONIST	POST OFFICE BOX 213	HAVREDEGRACE, MD 21078
WATERS, MAXINE	U S CONGRESSWOMAN	4509 S BROADWAY	LOS ANGELES, CA 90037
WATERS, WILLIE ANTHONY	CONDUCTOR	225 W 34TH ST #1012	NEW YORK, NY 10001
WATERSTON, SAM	ACTRESS	9000 SUNSET BLVD #1200	LOS ANGELES, CA 90069
WATFORD, GWEN	ACTRESS	PETERS, FRASER & DUNLOP, LTD	
		5TH FLOOR, THE CHAMBERS	
		CHELSEA HARBOUR, LOT RD	LONDON SW10 0XF ENGLAND
WATHAN, JOHN	BASEBALL-MANAGER	POST OFFICE BOX 419969	KANSAS CITY, MO 64141
WATKIN, DAVID	CINEMATOGRAPHER	6 SUSSEX MEWS	BRIGHTON BN2 1GZ ENGLAND
WATKINS, GREG	ACTOR	CBS-TV, "AS THE WORLD TURNS"	
		524 W 57TH ST #5330	NEW YORK, NY 10019
WATKINS, MICHAEL	CINEMATOGRAPHER	POST OFFICE BOX 2230	HOLLYWOOD, CA 90078
WATKINS, MICHELLE	ACTRESS	9300 WILSHIRE BLVD #410	BEVERLY HILLS, CA 90212
WATKINS, MYLIN J	NEWS PRODUCER	ENTERTAINMENT TONIGHT	
		PARAMOUNT TELEVISION	
		5555 MELROSE AVE	LOS ANGELES, CA 90038
WATKINS, ROBIN RENEE	ACTRESS	POST OFFICE BOX 5617	BEVERLY HILLS, CA 90213
WATKINS, WILLIAM	DIRECTOR	7038 WHITAKER AVE	VAN NUYS, CA 91406
WATKINSON, BRENT	ARTIST	1100 COUNTY LINE RD	
		BUILDING #12-28	KANSAS CITY, KS 66103
WATSON, ALLEN	BASEBALL	POST OFFICE BOX 12557	ST PETERSBURG, FL 33733
WATSON, ANGELA	ACTRESS	ABC-TV, 2040 AVE OF THE STARS	LOS ANGELES, CA 90067
WATSON, ANGIE	ACTRESS	9171 WILSHIRE BLVD #300	BEVERLY HILLS, CA 90210
WATSON, ARTHUR A	TV EXECUTIVE	30 ROCKEFELLER PLAZA #1550	NEW YORK, NY 10020
WATSON, BOB	BASEBALL-EXECUTIVE	POST OFFICE BOX 288	HOUSTON, TX 77001
WATSON, DAVE	BASEBALL	POST OFFICE BOX 842	SALEM, VA 24153
WATSON, DOC	SINGER-GUITARIST	FOLKLORE, 1671 APPIAN WY	SANTA MONICA, CA 90401
WATSON, GENE	SINGER-SONGWRITER	POST OFFICE BOX 22419	NASHVILLE, TN 37202
WATSON, JACK	ACTOR	JOSEPH, 2 TUNSTALL RD, STUDIO 1	LONDON SW9 8BN ENGLAND
WATSON, JAMES A, JR	ACTOR-WRITER	5738 BURNET AVE	VAN NUYS, CA 91411
WATSON, JOHN	TV DIRECTOR	1915 COMSTOCK AVE	LOS ANGELES, CA 90025
WATSON, JOHNNY "GUITAR"	SINGER-GUITARIST	PDQ DIRECTIONS AGENCY	
		1474 N KINGS RD	LOS ANGELES, CA 90069
WATSON, LAKE	HAIR STYLIST	205 W 95TH ST #5-J	NEW YORK, NY 10025
WATSON, MERVYN	TV PRODUCER-WRITER	10 LEIGH RD, HALE, ALTRINCHAM	CHESHIRE ENGLAND
WATSON, MILLS	ACTOR	1930 CENTURY PARK W #403	LOS ANGELES, CA 90067
WATSON, MORAY	ACTOR	MC REDDIE, 91 REGENT ST	LONDON W1R 7TB ENGLAND
WATSON, PAUL	TV WRITER-DIRECTOR	103 GRANDISON RD	LONDON SW11 ENGLAND
WATSON, PETER	SPECIAL EFFECTS	24 MONTPELIER CT	
		MONTPELIER RD, EALING	LONDON W1 ENGLAND
WATSON, PRESTON	BASEBALL	POST OFFICE BOX 16683	GREENVILLE, SC 29606
WATSON, RON	BASEBALL	POST OFFICE BOX 3496	DAVENPORT, IA 52808
WATSON, TOM	GOLFER	911 MAIN ST #1313	KANSAS CITY, MO 64105
WATSTEIN, MIRIAM J	TV PRODUCER	91 LARCH RD	CAMBRIDGE, MA 02138

Name	Occupation	Address	City/State	Zip/Country
WATT, CHRISTOPHER	DIRECTOR	DGA, 7920 SUNSET BLVD, 6TH FL	LOS ANGELES, CA	90046
WATT, DENISE	ARTIST	2130 1/2 SOUTH BLVD	HOUSTON, TX	77098
WATT, JAMES	POLITICIAN	1800 N SPIRIT DANCE RD	JACKSON HOLE, WY	83001
WATTERS, MARK E	COMPOSER-CONDUCTOR	415 BEIRUT AVE	PACIFIC PALISADES, CA	90272
WATTERS, TIM	HOCKEY	POST OFFICE BOX 17013	INGLEWOOD, CA	90308
WATTERSON, BILL	CARTOONIST	UPS, 4900 MAIN ST, 9TH FLOOR	KANSAS CITY, MO	64112
WATTERSON, STEVE	FOOTBALL COACH	OILERS, 6910 FANNIN ST	HOUSTON, TX	77070
WATTS, ERNIE	SINGER	7250 BEVERLY BLVD #207	LOS ANGELES, CA	90036
WATTS, ROBERT	FILM PRODUCER	EVERYMAN FILMS, LTD		
		TWICKENHAM STUDIOS		
		ST MARGARET'S, TWICKENHAM	MIDDLESEX TW1 2AW	ENGLAND
WATTS, TONY	TV EXECUTIVE	POST OFFICE BOX 3819	AUCKLAND	
WAUGH, FRED	STUNTMAN	33231 CYN QUAIL TRAIL	SAUGUS, CA	91350
WAWRUCK, JIM	BASEBALL	POST OFFICE BOX 3169	FREDERICK, MD	21701
WAX, RUBY	ACTRESS-WRITER	PETERS, FRASER & DUNLOP, LTD		
		5TH FLOOR, THE CHAMBERS		
		CHELSEA HARBOUR, LOT RD	LONDON SW10 OXF	ENGLAND
WAXING POETICS	ROCK & ROLL GROUP	225 LAFAYETTE ST #709	NEW YORK, NY	10012
WAXMAN, AL	ACTOR	9200 SUNSET BLVD #428	LOS ANGELES, CA	90069
WAXMAN, HENRY	U S CONGRESSMAN	8425 W 3RD ST #400	LOS ANGELES, CA	90048
WAXMAN, MARK	DIRECTOR-PRODUCER	9725 CRESTA DR	LOS ANGELES, CA	90035
WAY, ANN	ACTRESS	53 CONSTANTINE RD	LONDON NW3 2LP	ENGLAND
WAYANS, DAMON	ACTOR-COMEDIAN	KTTV, 5746 SUNSET BLVD	HOLLYWOOD, CA	90028
WAYANS, KEENEN IVORY	ACT-DIR-PROD-COMED	KTTV, 5746 SUNSET BLVD	HOLLYWOOD, CA	90028
WAYANS, KIM	ACTRESS	KTTV, 5746 SUNSET BLVD	HOLLYWOOD, CA	90028
WAYMER, DAVE	FOOTBALL	S F 49ERS, 4949 CENTENNIAL BL	SANTA CLARA, CA	95054
WAYNE, BERNIE	COMPOSER	P SCHREIBMAN MANAGEMENT		
		1900 AVE OF THE STARS	LOS ANGELES, CA	90067
WAYNE, DAVID	ACTOR	868 NAPOLI DR	PACIFIC PALISADES, CA	90272
WAYNE, FREDD	ACTOR-WRITER	11846 VENTURA BLVD #100	STUDIO CITY, CA	91604
WAYNE, GARY	BASEBALL	TWINS, 501 CHICAGO AVE S	MINNEAPOLIS, MN	55415
WAYNE, HILARY	TALENT AGENT	11726 SAN VICENTE BLVD #300	LOS ANGELES, CA	90049
WAYNE, JOHN ETHAN	ACTOR	3800 BARHAM BLVD #303	LOS ANGELES, CA	90068
WAYNE, LINDA	COSTUME DESIGNER	13949 VENTURA BLVD #309	SHERMAN OAKS, CA	91423
WAYNE, MICHAEL	FILM EXECUTIVE	10425 KLING ST	NORTH HOLLYWOOD, CA	91602
WAYNE, PHILIP	TV PRODUCER	CBS-TV, "THE PRICE IS RIGHT"		
		7800 BEVERLY BLVD	LOS ANGELES, CA	90036
WAYNE, SUSAN	TV DIRECTOR-PRODUCER	420 E 55TH ST #7-N	NEW YORK, NY	10022
WAYSTED	ROCK & ROLL GROUP	ICM, 40 W 57TH ST	NEW YORK, NY	10019
WBEER, PAUL ANTHONY	ACTOR	9165 SUNSET BLVD #202	LOS ANGELES, CA	90069
WE THE PEOPLE	MUSICAL GROUP	POST OFFICE BOX 399	LISLE, IL	60532
WE'VE GOT A FUZZBOX & WE'RE	ROCK & ROLL GROUP	POST OFFICE BOX 235		
		BALSALL HEATH	BIRMINGHAM B1Z 9RZ	ENGLAND
WEARING, MELVIN	BASEBALL	POST OFFICE BOX 230	HAGERSTOWN, MD	21740
WEATHER REPORT	ROCK & ROLL GROUP	ICM, 8899 BEVERLY BLVD	LOS ANGELES, CA	90048
WEATHERLEY, PETER	FILM EDITOR	20 HALFORD RD, ICKENHAM	MIDDLESEX UB10 8PY	ENGLAND
WEATHERLY, JIM	SINGER-GUITARIST	10351 SANTA MONICA BLVD #300	LOS ANGELES, CA	90025
WEATHERLY, SHAWN	ACTRESS-MODEL	838 S BARRINGTON AVE #304	LOS ANGELES, CA	90049
WEATHERS, CARL	ACTOR	7083 HOLLYWOOD BLVD	LOS ANGELES, CA	90028
WEATHERS, CLARENCE	FOOTBALL	PACKERS, 1265 LOMBARDI AVE	GREEN BAY, WI	54307
WEATHERS, DAVE	BASEBALL	CHIEFS, MAC ARTHUR STADIUM	SYRACUSE, NY	13208
WEATHERS, JOHNNY & CROSS ROADS	C & W GROUP	POST OFFICE BOX 4	LAKE LURE, NC	28746
WEATHERSPOON, CHUCK	FOOTBALL	BUCCANEERS, 1 BUCCANEER PL	TAMPA, FL	33607
WEATHERWAX, BOB	ANIMAL TRAINER	16133 SOLEDAD CANYON RD	CANYON COUNTRY, CA	91351
WEATHERWAX, THOMAS P	DIRECTOR	2300 KIEL 14	LANGER REHM 7	GERMANY
WEAVER, DENNIS	ACTOR	POST OFFICE BOX 983	MALIBU, CA	90265
WEAVER, DEWITT	GOLFER	PGA SENIORS, 112 T P C BLVD	PONTE VEDRA BEACH, FL	32082
WEAVER, DOODLES	ACTOR	333 W CALIFORNIA #302	PASADENA, CA	91105
WEAVER, EARL	BASEBALL	19016 W LAKE DR	HIALEAH, FL	33015
WEAVER, GARY A	MUSIC ARRANGER	411 SENECA CT	NASHVILLE, TN	37214
WEAVER, HASCAL B	PHOTOGRAPHER	13303 CARTHAGE LN	DALLAS, TX	75243
WEAVER, JOHN V	TV PRODUCER	790 AMSTERDAM AVE #7-B	NEW YORK, NY	10025
WEAVER, PATTY	ACTRESS-SINGER	5009 HAYVENHURST DR	ENCINO], CA	91316
WEAVER, PAUL	BASEBALL SCOUT	POST OFFICE BOX 288	HOUSTON, TX	77001
WEAVER, RICK	PRODUCER	MCA/UNIVERSAL STUDIOS, INC		
		100 UNIVERSAL CITY PLAZA #105	UNIVERSAL CITY, CA	91608
WEAVER, ROBBY	ACTOR	1930 CENTURY PARK W #403	LOS ANGELES, CA	90067
WEAVER, ROBERT	ARTIST	42 E 12TH ST	NEW YORK, NY	10003
WEAVER, ROSE	ACTRESS	SCHWARTZ, 935 N CROFT AVE	LOS ANGELES, CA	90069
WEAVER, ROSIE CRUZ	DIRECTOR	520 N MICHIGAN AVE #1026	CHICAGO, IL	60611
WEAVER, S MASON, JR	TV DIRECTOR	32210 FARMERSVILLE ST	FARMINGTON HILLS, MI	48018
WEAVER, SIGOURNEY	ACTRESS	12 W 72ND ST	NEW YORK, NY	10023
WEBB, ALEXANDER	PHOTOGRAPHER	50 MANOR RD	STATEN ISLAND, NY	10310
WEBB, ALYCE E	ACTRESS-SINGER	875 COLUMBUS AVE	NEW YORK, NY	10025
WEBB, ANITA	ACTRESS	400 W 43RD ST #23-F	NEW YORK, NY	10036
WEBB, BEN	BASEBALL	POST OFFICE DRAWER 1218	ZEBULON, NC	27597
WEBB, CHLOE	ACTRESS	BYMEL, 723 WESTMOUNT DR	WEST HOLLYWOOD, CA	90069
WEBB, ELLIOT	TALENT AGENT	9242 BEVERLY DR #200	BEVERLY HILLS, CA	90210
WEBB, JIMMY	SINGER-COMPOSER	SIEGEL, 133 W 19TH ST, 8TH FL	NEW YORK, NY	10011
WEBB, KEVIN	BASEBALL	POST OFFICE BOX 1556	ASHEVILLE, NC	28802
WEBB, LONNIE	BASEBALL	POST OFFICE BOX 10031	BAKERSFIELD, CA	93389
WEBB, LUCY	ACTRESS-COMEDIENNE	1360 N CRESCENT HEIGHTS #38	LOS ANGELES, CA	90046
WEBB, RICHARD	ACTOR	13330 CHANDLER BLVD	VAN NUYS, CA	91401
WEBB, RICHMOND	FOOTBALL	DOLPHINS, 2269 NW 199TH ST	MIAMI, FL	33056
WEBB, ROBERT DELANEY	DIRECTOR	13063 VENTURA BLVD #201	STUDIO CITY, CA	91604

Name	Occupation	Address	City/State	Zip
WEBB, ROBERT H	CONDUCTOR	750 N KINGS RD #107	LOS ANGELES, CA	90069
WEBB, ROGER	COMPOSER-PIANIST	13 PALACE MEWS, FULHAM	LONDON SW6 7QT	ENGLAND
WEBB, RON	COMPOSER	1819 WOLLAM ST	LOS ANGELES, CA	90065
WEBB, RUTH	ACTRESS-AGENT	7500 DEVISTA DR	LOS ANGELES, CA	90046
WEBB, SPUD	BASKETBALL	1 CNN CENTER #405, SOUTH TOWER	ATLANTA, GA	30303
WEBB, SPYDER	BASEBALL TRAINER	1316 KING ST	BELLINGHAM, WA	98226
WEBB, WILLIAM H	DIRECTOR	164 BOONTON AVE	KINNELON, NJ	07405
WEBBER, ANDREW LLOYD	COMPOSER	725 5TH AVE	NEW YORK, NY	10022
WEBBER, JULIAN LLOYD	CELLIST-VIOLIST	IBBSP TILLETT, 450 EDGWARE	LONDON W2 1EG	ENGLAND
WEBBER, PEGGY	ACTRESS	6612 WHITLEY TERR	LOS ANGELES, CA	90068
WEBBER, SHARON	ACTRESS	5930 FRANKLIN AVE	LOS ANGELES, CA	90028
WEBER, BEN	BASEBALL	POST OFFICE BOX 1110	MYRTLE BEACH, SC	29578
WEBER, BOB, SR	CARTOONIST	KING FEATURES, 216 E 45TH ST	NEW YORK, NY	10017
WEBER, BRUCE	DIRECTOR	DGA, 110 W 57TH ST	NEW YORK, NY	10019
WEBER, EBERHARD	GUITARIST	KURLAND, 173 BRIGHTON AVE	BOSTON, MA	02134
WEBER, FRANK	SINGER	ED NEWMARK, 793 BINGHAM RD	RIDGEWOOD, NJ	07540
WEBER, JOHN ROY	COMPOSER-CONDUCTOR	203 CALLE DE ANZA	SAN CLEMENTE, CA	92672
WEBER, JOY	CASTING DIRECTOR	JOY WEBER INC, 250 W 57TH ST	NEW YORK, NY	10019
WEBER, LARRY	ACTOR	35 W 64 TH ST	NEW YORK, NY	10023
WEBER, NINA	WRI-DIR-PROD	12 E 86TH ST #524	NEW YORK, NY	10028
WEBER, PAUL	SINGER	NATA MANAGEMENT AGENCY		
		84 AMARANTH ST E		
		GRAND VALLEY	ONATRIO, ONT	CANADA
WEBER, PETE	BASEBALL	POST OFFICE BOX 3448	SHREVEPORT, LA	71133
WEBER, RON	BASEBALL	POST OFFICE BOX 12557	ST PETERSBURG, FL	33733
WEBER, SABINA	ACTRESS	POST OFFICE BOX 691736	LOS ANGELES, CA	90069
WEBER, VIN	U S CONGRESSMAN	919 S 1ST ST	WILLMAR, MN	56201
WEBER, WESTON	BASEBALL	POST OFFICE BOX 11087	TACOMA, WA	98411
WEBLEY, SCOTT	ACTOR	15029 WYANDOTTE ST	VAN NUYS, CA	91405
WEBSTER, ANTHONY C	WRITER	999 N DOHENY DR #1110	LOS ANGELES, CA	90069
WEBSTER, BYRON	ACTOR	4273 STERN AVE	SHERMAN OAKS, CA	91423
WEBSTER, CHARLES D	WRITER	21686 YUCATAN AVE	WOODLAND HILLS, CA	91364
WEBSTER, DIANA	ACTRESS	BREWIS, 12429 LAUREL TERRACE	STUDIO CITY, CA	91604
WEBSTER, GENE	DIRECTOR	DGA, 7920 SUNSET BLVD, 6TH FL	LOS ANGELES, CA	90046
WEBSTER, GENE	EDITORIALIST	12021 VALLEYHEART DR #206	STUDIO CITY, CA	91604
WEBSTER, JOHN	SINGER	GOOD, 2500 NW 39TH ST	OKLAHOMA CITY, OK	73112
WEBSTER, LENNY	BASEBALL	TWINS, 501 CHICAGO AVE S	MINNEAPOLIS, MN	55415
WEBSTER, MITCH	BASEBALL	1000 ELYSIAN PARK DR	LOS ANGELES, CA	90012
WEBSTER, NICHOLAS	WRITER-PRODUCER	4135 FULTON AVE	SHERMAN OAKS, CA	91423
WEBSTER, RAMON	BASEBALL-SCOUT	SKYDOME, 300 BREMMER BL #3200	TORONTO, ONT M5V 3B3	CANADA
WEBSTER, SONJA	FILM DIRECTOR	121 E 31ST ST	NEW YORK, NY	10016
WEBSTER, WILLIAM	ATTORNEY GENERAL	POST OFFICE BOX 720	JEFFERSON CITY, MO	65102
WECHSBERG, VON	BASEBALL	POST OFFICE BOX 20849	CHARLESTON, SC	29413
WECHTER, DAVID J	TV WRITER-DIRECTOR	4508 FARMDALE AVE	NORTH HOLLYWOOD, CA	91602
WEDDELL, MIMI	ACTRESS	1349 LEXINGTON AVE	NEW YORK, NY	10028
WEDDINGTON, ELAINE	BASEBALL EXECUTIVE	FENWAY PARK, 4 YAWKEY WY	BOSTON, MA	02215
WEDDLE, VERNON	ACTOR	18608 VINCENNES ST	NORTHRIDGE, CA	91324
WEDEL, RENEE	ACTRESS	4143 VIA MARINA #8-815	MARINA DEL REY, CA	90292
WEDGE, DON	FOOTBALL REFEREE	NFL, 410 PARK AVE	NEW YORK, NY	10022
WEDGE, ERIC	BASEBALL	POST OFFICE BOX 2365	PAWTUCKET, RI	02861
WEDGEWORTH, ANN	ACTRESS	822 S ROBERTSON BLVD #200	LOS ANGELES, CA	90035
WEDLOCK, HUGH, JR	TV WRITER	11825 MAGNOLIA BLVD #205	NORTH HOLLYWOOD, CA	91607
WEDNER, ALAN	ACTOR	3153 WELDON AVE	LOS ANGELES, CA	90065
WEED, GENE	WRITER-PRODUCER	10405 OKLAHOMA AVE	CHATSWORTH, CA	91311
WEED, MARLENE	WRITER	VIRGIRIA R WELLS		
		1540 WILSHIRE BLVD	LOS ANGELES, CA	90017
WEEGE, REINHOLD	TV WRITER	4131 LONGRIDGE AVE	SHERMAN OAKS, CA	91423
WEEKS, KIM	ACTRESS	1750 VENTURA BLVD #202	STUDIO CITY, CA	91604
WEEKS, STEPHEN	WRITER-PRODUCER	PENHOW CASTLE, NEAR NEWPORT	GWENT NP6 3AD	ENGLAND
WEGHER, BARBARA JEAN	TV WRITER	4329 BELLINGHAM AVE	STUDIO CITY, CA	91604
WEGMAN, BILL	BASEBALL	BREWERS, 201 S 46TH ST	MILWAUKEE, WI	53214
WEGMANN, TOM	BASEBALL	POST OFFICE BOX 598	BINGHAMTON, NY	13902
WEHMEIER, JIM	BASEBALL EXECUTIVE	POST OFFICE BOX 27045	TUCSON, AZ	85726
WEHNER, JOHN	BASEBALL	POST OFFICE BOX 450	BUFFALO, NY	14205
WEHRMAN, RICHARD	ARTIST	BOB WRIGHT CREATIVE GROUP		
		247 N GOODMAN ST	ROCHESTER, NY	14607
WEIBRING, D A	GOLFER	POST OFFICE BOX 109601	PALM BCH GARDENS, FL	33418
WEICKER, LOWELL P, JR	GOVERNOR	STATE CAPITOL BUILDING	HARTFORD, CT	06106
WEIDE, ROBERT B	TV PRODUCER	9110 SUNSET BLVD #120	LOS ANGELES, CA	90069
WEIDEMAIER, MARK	BASEBALL SCOUT	INDIANS, CLEVELAND STADIUM	CLEVELAND, OH	44114
WEIDLINGER, TOM	TV DIRECTOR	1572 S GLENVILLE DR	LOS ANGELES, CA	90035
WEIDNER, BERT	FOOTBALL	DOLPHINS, 2269 NW 199TH ST	MIAMI, FL	33056
WEIDNER, PAUL	FOOTBALL REFEREE	NFL, 410 PARK AVE	NEW YORK, NY	10022
WEIGEL, JIM	BASEBALL EXECUTIVE	POST OFFICE BOX 75089	OKLAHOMA CITY, OK	73147
WEIHE, N FREDERICK	TV DIRECTOR	RURAL DELIVERY 2		
WEIL, BUD	DIRECTOR	3671 HUDSON MANOR TERR	RIVERDALE, NY	10463
WEIMERSKIRCH, MIKE	BASEBALL	POST OFFICE BOX 3566	WEST PALM BEACH, FL	33402
WEINBACH, ROBERT D	WRITER-PRODUCER	12023 LORNE ST	NORTH HOLLYWOOD, CA	91605
WEINBERG, BARRY	BASEBALL TRAINER	ATHLETICS'S, OAKLAND COLISEUM	OAKLAND, CA	94621
WEINBERG, DICK	TV DIRECTOR	12959 VALLEYHEART DR	STUDIO CITY, CA	91604
WEINBERG, HOWARD L	TV WRITER-PRODUCER	104 E 37TH ST	NEW YORK, NY	10016
WEINBERG, JOE	FOOTBALL	POST OFFICE BOX 609609	SAN DIEGO, CA	92160
WEINBERG, ROBERT ADAM	DIRECTOR	3025 HEWITT AVE #472	SILVER SPRING, MD	20906
WEINBERGER, CASPAR	POLITICIAN	60 5TH AVE	NEW YORK, NY	10011
WEINBERGER, EDWIN	TV WRITER-PRODUCER	1625 SUNSET PLAZA DR	LOS ANGELES, CA	90069

Name	Occupation	Address	City, State	Zip
WEINBERGER, MICHAEL	TV WRITER	15319 DEL GADO DR	SHERMAN OAKS, CA	91403
WEINBERGER, SYBIL	MUSIC PROD-DIR	ABC-TV, 320 W 66TH ST	NEW YORK, NY	10023
WEINER, ARN	ACTOR	THE MANHATTAN PLAZA		
		400 W 43RD ST	NEW YORK, NY	10036
WEINER, DONALD J	DIRECTOR	DGA, 7920 SUNSET BLVD, 6TH FL	LOS ANGELES, CA	90046
WEINER, HYMAN	FILM DIRECTOR	245 E 19TH ST	NEW YORK, NY	10003
WEINER, JANE	TV DIRECTOR-PRODUCER	611 BROADWAY #826	NEW YORK, NY	10012
WEINER, JUDITH	CASTING DIRECTOR	1438 N GOWER ST, 4TH FLOOR	HOLLYWOOD, CA	90028
WEINER, ROBERTA	COSTUME DESIGNER	13949 VENTURA BLVD #309	SHERMAN OAKS, CA	91423
WEINER, RON	TV DIRECTOR	412 CAROL CT	HIGHLAND PARK, IL	60035
WEINGART, ROBERT J	MUSIC ARRANGER	113 LAUDERDALE RD #A	NASHVILLE, TN	37205
WEINGROD, HERSCHEL	SCREENWRITER	1200 N BEVERLY GLEN BLVD	LOS ANGELES, CA	90077
WEINKE, CHRIS	BASEBALL	POST OFFICE BOX 1110	MYRTLE BEACH, SC	29578
WEINMAN, RICHARD C	DIRECTOR	3333 HENRY HUDSON PARKWAY	RIVERDALE, NY	10463
WEINRICH, ERIC	HOCKEY	POST OFFICE BOX 504	EAST RUTHERFORD, NJ	07073
WEINSCHENKER, GREGORY J	DIRECTOR	BOX 176, TRAVIS RD	HYDE PARK, NY	12538
WEINSTEIN, BOBBY	MUSIC EXECUTIVE	BROADCAST MUSIC, 320 W 57TH ST	NEW YORK, NY	10019
WEINSTEIN, DANIEL J	COMPOSER	13015 1/2 VENICE BLVD	LOS ANGELES, CA	90066
WEINSTEIN, JUDITH	TV WRITER-STORY ED	75 E END AVE	NEW YORK, NY	10028
WEINSTEIN, PAULA	FILM EXECUTIVE	24016 MALIBU RD	MALIBU, CA	90265
WEINSTEIN, SOL	TV WRITER	5807 TOPANGA CANYON BLVD #M-105	WOODLAND HILLS, CA	91367
WEINSTEIN-MILLER, FRAN	WRI-DIR-PROD	664 FOREST AVE	LARCHMONT, NY	10538
WEINSTOCK, KEN	TV PRODUCER	9533 MOONRIDGE TERR	BEVERLY HILLS, CA	90210
WEINTRAUB, CARL	ACTOR	MTA, 9320 WILSHIRE BL, 3RD FL	BEVERLY HILLS, CA	90212
WEINTRAUB, FRED	FILM PRODUCER	11939 GORHAM AVE #305	LOS ANGELES, CA	90049
WEINTRAUB, JERRY	PRODUCER	11111 SANTA MONICA BLVD	LOS ANGELES, CA	90025
WEINTRAUB, SANDY	SINGER	6236 W 6TH ST	LOS ANGELES, CA	90048
WEINTRAUB ROLAND, SANDRA	SCREENWRITER	11939 GORHAM AVE #305	LOS ANGELES, CA	90049
WEINTRAUG, BERNIE	TALENT AGENT	R/W/G, 8428 MELROSE PL #C	LOS ANGELES, CA	90069
WEIR, CLYDE	BASEBALL SCOUT	TIGERS, TIGER STADIUM	DETROIT, MI	48216
WEIR, PETER	FILM DIRECTOR	ANTHONY WILLIAMS MANAGEMENT		
		55 VICTORIA ST, POTTS POINTS	SYDNEY NSW 2011	AUSTRALIA
WEIR, SANDRA L	DIRECTOR	ANCHOR PRODUCTIONS		
		2335 W BELDEN AVE	CHICAGO, IL	60647
WEIR, TOM	SPORTS WRITER	POST OFFICE BOX 500	WASHINGTON, DC	20044
WEIS, JACK	WRITER-PRODUCER	6771 MARSHALL FOCH ST	NEW ORLEANS, LA	70124
WEISBARTH, MICHAEL L	TV PRODUCER	ICM, 8899 BEVERLY BLVD	LOS ANGELES, CA	90048
WEISBERG, ROGER E	TV DIRECTOR-PRODUCER	POST OFFICE BOX 548	PALISADES, NY	10964
WEISENBORN, GORDON	TV WRITER-DIRECTOR	544 W WELLINGTON AVE	CHICAGO, IL	60657
WEISER-FINLEY, SUSAN	SCREENWRITER	151 S EL CAMINO DR	BEVERLY HILLS, CA	90212
WEISGALL, HUGO	COMPOSER-CONDUCTOR	81 MAPLE DR	GREAT NECK, NY	11021
WEISINGER, RALPH	TV DIRECTOR-PRODUCER	511 W 54TH ST	NEW YORK, NY	10019
WEISKOPF, KIM ROBERT	TV WRITER-DIRECTOR	4022 MADELIA AVE	SHERMAN OAKS, CA	91403
WEISKOPF, ROBERT	TV WRITER	21612 RAMBLA VISTA	MALIBU, CA	90265
WEISKOPF, TOM	GOLFER	5412 E MORRISON LN	PARADISE VALLEY, AZ	85253
WEISMAN, BENJAMIN	COMPOSER	4527 ALLA RD #3	MARINA DEL REY, CA	90292
WEISMAN, BRICE	TV DIRECTOR-PRODUCER	140 RIVERSIDE DR	NEW YORK, NY	10024
WEISMAN, JOEL M	DIRECTOR	939 MAYFIELD RD	WOODMERE, NY	11598
WEISMAN, SAM	TV DIRECTOR	10490 SELKIRK LN	LOS ANGELES, CA	90077
WEISS, ADRIAN	DIRECTOR	5155 TERRAMAR WY	OXNARD SHORES, CA	93030
WEISS, BARBARA	COSTUME DESIGNER	114 SULLIVAN ST #B-15	NEW YORK, NY	10025
WEISS, BOB	BASKETBALL COACH	1 CNN CENTER #405, SOUTH TOWER	ATLANTA, GA	30303
WEISS, CAROL	CONDUCTOR	1415 N FORMOSA AVE	LOS ANGELES, CA	90046
WEISS, HARRIETT	TV WRITER	18701 HATTERAS ST #16	TARZANA, CA	91356
WEISS, HENRY J	TV DIRECTOR	12724 BYRON AVE	GRANADA HILLS, CA	91344
WEISS, JOSEPH	COMPOSER	6142 MANTON AVE	WOODLAND HILLS, CA	91367
WEISS, JULIE	COSTUME DESIGNER	10100 SANTA MONICA BLVD #1600	LOS ANGELES, CA	90067
WEISS, LOUIS P	TALENT AGENT	WM MORRIS, 1350 AVE OF AMERICAS	NEW YORK, NY	10019
WEISS, MARTY	TV WRITER	UTA, 9560 WILSHIRE BL, 5TH FL	BEVERLY HILLS, CA	90212
WEISS, MICHAEL J	FILM PRODUCER	1735 NEW HAMPSHIRE AVE	WASHINGTON, DC	20009
WEISS, MICHAEL T	ACTOR	151 S EL CAMINO DR	BEVERLY HILLS, CA	90212
WEISS, NEIL A	TV DIRECTOR	15 SPINNING WHEEL RD #7-A	MASSAPEQUA, NY	11758
WEISS, PETER	ACTOR-WRITER	3262 TILDEN AVE	LOS ANGELES, CA	90034
WEISS, ROBERT K	FILM PRODUCER	MCA/UNIVERSAL STUDIOS, INC		
		100 UNIVERSAL CITY PLAZA #448	UNIVERSAL CITY, CA	91608
WEISS, SCOTT	BASEBALL	POST OFFICE BOX 4488	WINSTON-SALEM, NC	27115
WEISS, TED	U S CONGRESSMAN	252 7TH AVE	NEW YORK, NY	10001
WEISS, WALT	BASEBALL	ATHLETICS'S, OAKLAND COLISEUM	OAKLAND, CA	94621
WEISS, WILLIAM WARE	COSTUME DESIGNER	POST OFFICE BOX 1166	PACIFIC PALISADES, CA	90272
WEISS-ADLER, VICKY	TV PRODUCER	357 E 68TH ST #2-D	NEW YORK, NY	10021
WEISSBOURD, BURT	FILM PRODUCER	240 BENTLY CIR	LOS ANGELES, CA	90049
WEISSER, NORBERT	ACTOR	9301 WILSHIRE BLVD #312	BEVERLY HILLS, CA	90210
WEISSMAN, BEN	FILM PRODUCER	4216 BEEMAN AVE	STUDIO CITY, CA	91604
WEISSMAN, JERRY	WRITER-PRODUCER	DGA, 7920 SUNSET BLVD, 6TH FL	LOS ANGELES, CA	90046
WEISSMAN, KAREN	FILM EDITOR	4216 BEEMAN AVE	STUDIO CITY, CA	91604
WEISSMAN, NORMAN	WRITER-PRODUCER	188 WHITFIELD ST	GUILFORD, CT	06437
WEISSMAN, SEYMOUR J	WRITER-PRODUCER	562 W END AVE	NEW YORK, NY	10024
WEIST, DIANE	ACTRESS	320 CENTRAL PARK W	NEW YORK, NY	10025
WEITHORN, MICHAEL J	TV WRITER-PRODUCER	653 HANLEY AVE	LOS ANGELES, CA	90049
WEITMAN, ROBERT M	FILM EXECUTIVE	1880 CARLA RIDGE	BEVERLY HILLS, CA	90210
WEITZ, BARRY JON	FILM WRITER-PRODUCER	13642 SUNSET BLVD	PACIFIC PALISADES, CA	90272
WEITZ, BRUCE	ACTOR-DIRECTOR	3061 LAKE HOLLYWOOD DR	LOS ANGELES, CA	90068
WEITZ, JOHN	FASHION DESIGNER	600 MADISON AVE	NEW YORK, NY	10022
WEITZ, KRISTINE	ACTRESS	LENZ, 1456 E CHARLESTON BLVD	LAS VEGAS, NV	89104
WEITZEL, THOMAS A	DIRECTOR	308 PALMETTO AVE #24	PACIFICA, CA	94044

WEITZENHOFFER, A MAX	THEATER PRODUCER	70 E 77TH ST	NEW YORK, NY	10021
WEITZMAN, CAROLE	TV EXECUTIVE	SUNBOW PRODS, 130 5TH AVE	NEW YORK, NY	10011
WEITZNER, DAVID A	FILM EXECUTIVE	22601 FEDERALIST RD	WOODLAND HILLS, CA	91364
WEITZNER, LESTER E	STORY EDITOR	ELEUTHYRA FILMS, 555 W 57TH ST	NEW YORK, NY	10019
WELCH, BOB	BASEBALL	ATHLETICS'S, OAKLAND COLISEUM	OAKLAND, CA	94621
WELCH, CHARLES C	ACTOR	610 W END AVE	NEW YORK, NY	10024
WELCH, DOUG	BASEBALL	POST OFFICE DRAWER 1207	ZEBULON, NC	27597
WELCH, ELIZABETH	ACTRESS-SINGER	4-A CAPENTERS CLOSE	LONDON SW1	ENGLAND
WELCH, HERB	FOOTBALL	LIONS, 1200 FEATHERSTONE RD	PONTIAC, MI	48432
WELCH, KEN	COMPOSER-LYRICIST	9200 SUNSET BLVD #808	LOS ANGELES, CA	90069
WELCH, LENNY	SINGER	POST OFFICE BOX 82	GREAT NECK, NY	11021
WELCH, MARILYN	TV WRITER	11506 ORUM RD	LOS ANGELES, CA	90049
WELCH, MITZI	COMPOSER-LYRICIST	9200 SUNSET BLVD #808	LOS ANGELES, CA	90069
WELCH, PAT	COSTUME DESIGNER	3320 BONNIE HILL DR	HOLLYWOOD, CA	90068
WELCH, RAQUEL	ACT-SING-WRI	134 DUANE ST	NEW YORK, NY	10013
WELCH, ROBERT	WRITER-PRODUCER	43 FLETCHER RD	BELMONT, MA	02178
WELCH, TAHNEE	ACTRESS	134 DUANE ST	NEW YORK, NY	10013
WELCH, TINA	SINGER	PENNY, 30 GUINAN ST	WALTHAM, MA	02154
WELCH, VICENT	ACTOR	POST OFFICE BOX 8497, FDR STA	NEW YORK, NY	10150
WELD, WILLIAM F	GOVERNOR	STATE HOUSE BUILDING	BOSTON, MA	02133
WELDON, ANN	ACTRESS	11555 DON TERESA DR	STUDIO CITY, CA	91604
WELDON, CURT	U S CONGRESSMAN	1554 GARRETT RD	UPPER DARBY, PA	19082
WELK, LAWRENCE	MUSICAN	1221 OCEAN AVE #602	SANTA MONICA, CA	90401
WELK, TANYA	SINGER	10433 KLING ST	NORTH HOLLYWOOD, CA	91602
WELKE, DON	BASEBALL SCOUT	SKYDOME, 300 BREMMER BL #3200	TORONTO, ONT M5V 3B3	CANADA
WELKE, TIM	BASEBALL UMPIRE	5843 THUNDER BAY	KALAMAZOO, MI	49002
WELKER, MARYANN	DIRECTOR	DGA, 7920 SUNSET BLVD, 6TH FL	LOS ANGELES, CA	90046
WELL RED	ROCK & ROLL GROUP	FAA, 1700 BROADWAY, 5TH FLOOR	NEW YORK, NY	10019
WELLAND, COLIN	SCREENWRITER	CHARLESWORTH, 60 OLD BROMPTON	LONDON SW7 3LQ	ENGLAND
WELLER, DON	ARTIST	1398 AERIE DR	PARK CITY, UT	84060
WELLER, FREDDY	SINGER-SONGWRITER	TAYLOR, 2401 12TH AVE S	NASHVILLE, TN	37204
WELLER, MARY LOUISE	ACTRESS	9300 WILSHIRE BLVD #410	BEVERLY HILLS, CA	90212
WELLER, MICHAEL	SCREENWRITER	555 W 57TH ST #1230	NEW YORK, NY	10019
WELLER, PETER	ACTOR	853 7TH AVE #9-A	NEW YORK, NY	10019
WELLER, ROB	TV HOST	4249 BECK AVE	STUDIO CITY, CA	91604
WELLER, WALTER	CONDUCTOR	ICM, 40 W 57TH ST	NEW YORK, NY	10019
WELLES, STEVE	ACTOR	12229 VENTURA BLVD #201	STUDIO CITY, CA	91604
WELLESLEY, JANE	TV PRODUCER	WARNER SISTERS FILM & TV, LTD		
		21 RUSSELL ST	LONDON WC2B 5HP	ENGLAND
WELLINGS, BOB	TV HOST	40 KENT GARDENS, EALING	LONDON W13 8BW	ENGLAND
WELLMAN, BOB	BASEBALL-SCOUT	METS, 126TH ST & ROOSEVELT AVE	FLUSHING, NY	11368
WELLMAN, BRAD	BASEBALL	18081 JOSEPH DR	CASTRO VALLEY, CA	94546
WELLMAN, PHILLIP	BASEBALL COACH	POST OFFICE BOX 814	PULASKI, VA	24301
WELLMAN, WENDELL	SCREENWRITER	1122 9TH ST #2	SANTA MONICA, CA	90403
WELLS, AARIKA	ACTRESS	POST OFFICE BOX 69590	LOS ANGELES, CA	90069
WELLS, BRANDI	SINGER	1125 ATLANTIC AVE #413	ATLANTIC CITY, NJ	08401
WELLS, CLAUDETTE	ACTRESS	10401 WILSHIRE BLVD #415	LOS ANGELES, CA	90024
WELLS, CLYDE	CARTOONIST	POST OFFICE BOX 1928	AUGUSTA, GA	30913
WELLS, CORY	SINGER-SONGWRITER	POST OFFICE BOX 82	MALIBU, CA	90265
WELLS, DAVID	BASEBALL	SKYDOME, 300 BREMMER BL #3200	TORONTO, ONT M5V 3B3	CANADA
WELLS, DAWN	ACTRESS	11684 VENTURA BLVD #364	STUDIO CITY, CA	91604
WELLS, EDWARD	TV DIRECTOR	309 CENTURY PARK W	DESTIN, FL	32541
WELLS, GEORGE	WRESTLER	POST OFFICE BOX 3859	STAMFORD, CT	06905
WELLS, GORDON	FOOTBALL REFEREE	NFL, 410 PARK AVE	NEW YORK, NY	10022
WELLS, JOHN	ACTOR-WRITER	1-A SCARSDALE VILLAS	LONDON W8	ENGLAND
WELLS, JOHN	TV PRODUCER	CAA, 9830 WILSHIRE BLVD	BEVERLY HILLS, CA	90212
WELLS, JUNIOR	SINGER-HARPIST	SEE - BUDDY GUY & JUNIOR WELLS		
WELLS, KITTY	SINGER	264 OLD HICKORY BLVD	MADISON, TN	35117
WELLS, MARIAN	NOVELIST	BETHANY HOUSE PUBLISHING		
		6820 AUTO CLUB RD	MINNEAPOLIS, MN	55438
WELLS, RACHEL	ACTRESS	AIMEE, 13743 VICTORY BLVD	VAN NUYS, CA	91401
WELLS, RICHARD A	DIRECTOR	DGA, 7920 SUNSET BLVD, 6TH FL	LOS ANGELES, CA	90046
WELLS, RICHARD J	DIRECTOR	DGA, 7920 SUNSET BLVD, 6TH FL	LOS ANGELES, CA	90046
WELLS, TIM	BASEBALL	POST OFFICE BOX 309	GASTONA, NC	28053
WELLSTONE, PAUL D	U S SENATOR	105 2ND AVE S	VIRGINIA, MN	55792
WELSH, MICHAEL K	COMPOSER	8026 FOUNTAIN AVE #6	LOS ANGELES, CA	90046
WELTY, ELDORA	NOVELIST	1119 PINEHURST ST	JACKSON, MS	39202
WELZ, JOEY	SINGER-GUITARIST	JOANNE VEE, 201 N MILDRED ST	RANSON, WV	25438
WENDELL, TURK	BASEBALL	CUBS, 2ND & RIVERSIDE DR	DES MOINES, IA	50309
WENDELSTEDT, HARRY	BASEBALL UMPIRE	88 S SAINT ANDREWS	ORMOND BEACH, FL	32074
WENDERS, WIM	TV DIRECTOR	KOHNER, 9169 SUNSET BLVD	LOS ANGELES, CA	90069
WENDKOS, PAUL	FILM DIRECTOR	DGA, 7920 SUNSET BLVD, 6TH FL	LOS ANGELES, CA	90046
WENDLANDT, TERRY	BASEBALL EXECUTIVE	POST OFFICE BOX 3665	OMAHA, NE	68103
WENDLING, LIONEL R	GUITARIST	11 ALLEE DE LA ROBERTSAU	6700 STRASBOURG	FRANCE
WENDT, GEORGE	ACTOR	PARAMOUNT, 5555 MELROSE AVE	LOS ANGELES, CA	90038
WENDY & LISA	ROCK & ROLL DUO	GARY KURFIRST, OVERLAND PRODS		
		1775 BROADWAY, 7TH FLOOR	NEW YORK, NY	10019
WENGERT, BILL	BASEBALL	POST OFFICE BOX 2887	VERO BEACH, FL	32961
WENMAN, DIANA B	TV DIRECTOR	151 E 83RD ST	NEW YORK, NY	10028
WENNINGTON, BILL	BASKETBALL	KINGS, 1 SPORTS PARKWAY	SACRAMENTO, CA	95834
WENSLOW, MICHAEL F	COMPOSER	1172 N KINGSLEY DR #103	LOS ANGELES, CA	90029
WENTZ, BILL	SINGER	POST OFFICE BOX 25371	CHARLOTTE, NC	28212
WENTZ, LENNY	BASEBALL	POST OFFICE BOX 4669	CHARLESTON, WV	25304
WERK, SHELLEY	COMEDIENNE	151 S EL CAMINO DR	BEVERLY HILLS, CA	90212
WERLAND, HENRY	BASEBALL	POST OFFICE BOX 507	DURHAM, NC	27702

Name	Occupation	Address	City/State	Zip/Country
WERLE, BARBARA	ACTRESS	7204 ESTRELLA DEL MAR RD	LA COSTA, CA	92008
WERLE, BILL	BASEBALL-SCOUT	INDIANS, CLEVELAND STADIUM	CLEVELAND, OH	44114
WERNER, DAVID	SINGER	3 E 54TH ST #1400	NEW YORK, NY	10022
WERNER, DON	BASEBALL-MANAGER	POST OFFICE DRAWER 1218	ZEBULON, NC	27597
WERNER, JEFFREY L	DIRECTOR-PRODUCER	4212 TEESDALE AVE	STUDIO CITY, CA	91604
WERNER, MICHAEL H	WRITER	11011 1/2 STRATHMORE DR	LOS ANGELES, CA	90024
WERNER, PETER	DIRECTOR-PRODUCER	359 20TH ST	SANTA MONICA, CA	90402
WERNER, TOM	TV PROD-BB EXEC	1438 N GOWER ST #376	LOS ANGELES, CA	90028
WERNING, PAT	BASEBALL	STARS, 850 LAS VEGAS BLVD N	LAS VEGAS, NV	89101
WERRENRATH, REINALD, JR	DIRECTOR	2108 PARK LN	HIGHLAND PARK, IL	60035
WERTH, PAUL	THEATER PRODUCER	223 S BRIGHTON ST	BURBANK, CA	91506
WERTMULLER, LINA	FILM DIRECTOR	VIA PRINCIPESSA CLOTILDE 5	I-00196 ROME	ITALY
WERTZ, BILL	BASEBALL	2501 ALLEN AVE, SE	CANTON, OH	44707
WESLEY, GLEN	HOCKEY	BRUINS, 150 CAUSEWAY ST	BOSTON, MA	02114
WESSON, BERNARD C	DIRECTOR	465 W BROADWAY	NEW YORK, NY	10012
WESSON, DICK	ACTOR-WRITER	150 E OLIVE AVE #111	BURBANK, CA	91502
WESSON, EILEEN	ACTRESS	335 N MAPLE DR #360	BEVERLY HILLS, CA	90210
WEST, ADAM	ACTOR	POST OFFICE BOX 3446	KETCHUM, ID	83340
WEST, ALVY	COMPOSER-CONDUCTOR	39 ANDOVER RD	ROSLYN HEIGHTS, NY	11577
WEST, BERNIE	PRODUCER	NRW COMP, 5746 SUNSET BLVD	LOS ANGELES, CA	90028
WEST, BRIAN	CINEMATOGRAPHER	LONDON MGT, 235-241 REGENT ST	LONDON W1R 4PH	ENGLAND
WEST, BROOKS	ACTOR	9066 SAINT IVES DR	LOS ANGELES, CA	90069
WEST, CARYN	ACTRESS	1930 CENTURY PARK W #403	LOS ANGELES, CA	90067
WEST, DAN	SINGER	HOT, 306 W CHURCH ST	HORSESHOE BEND, AR	71512
WEST, DAVID	BASEBALL	POST OFFICE BOX 1659	PORTLAND, OR	97207
WEST, DOUG	BASKETBALL	TIMBERWOLVES, 600 1ST AVE N	MINNEAPOLIS, MN	55403
WEST, ED	FOOTBALL	PACKERS, 1265 LOMBARDI AVE	GREEN BAY, WI	54307
WEST, ELLIOT	NOVELIST	8955 BEVERLY BLVD	WEST HOLLYWOOD, CA	90048
WEST, JAMES D	WRITER	4112 SHADYGLADE AVE	STUDIO CITY, CA	91604
WEST, JERRY	BASKETBALL-EXECUTIVE	POST OFFICE BOX 10	INGLEWOOD, CA	90306
WEST, JOE	BASEBALL UMPIRE	114 N EASTERN ST	GREENVILLE, NC	27834
WEST, MARK	BASKETBALL	SUNS, 2910 N CENTRAL AVE	PHOENIX, AZ	85012
WEST, MARTIN	ACTOR	10035 KEOKUK AVE	CHATSWORTH, CA	91311
WEST, MATT	BASEBALL COACH	POST OFFICE BOX 4525	MACON, GA	31208
WEST, MORRIS L	NOVELIST	8955 BEVERLY BLVD	WEST HOLLYWOOD, CA	90048
WEST, NORMA	ACTRESS	EDWARDS, 275 KENNINGTON RD	LONDON SE1 6BY	ENGLAND
WEST, ORMAND J, JR	DIRECTOR	140 W END AVE	NEW YORK, NY	10023
WEST, RED	ACTOR-AUTHOR	BDP, 10637 BURBANK BLVD	NORTH HOLLYWOOD, CA	91601
WEST, ROY	SINGER	PROCESS, 439 WILEY AVE	FRANKLIN, PA	16323
WEST, SHELLY	SINGER	GOOD, 2500 NW 39TH ST	OKLAHOMA CITY, OK	73112
WEST, TIMOTHY	ACTOR	46 NORTH SIDE		
		WANDSWORTH COMMON	LONDON SW18	ENGLAND
WEST, TOMMY	SINGER	POST OFFICE BOX 29543	ATLANTA, GA	30359
WEST, TONY	TREASURER	STATE CAPITOL, 1700 W WASHINGTON	PHOENIX, AZ	85007
WEST, WALLY	ACTOR	12418 LAUREL TERR "D"	STUDIO CITY, CA	91604
WESTBERG, REBECCA	ACTRESS	4173 W 5TH AVE	LOS ANGELES, CA	90020
WESTBERRY, KENT	SINGER-GUITARIST	515 UTLEY DR	GOODLETTSVILLE, TN	37072
WESTBROOKS, LOGAN	RECORD EXECUTIVE	15223 RAYNETA DR	SHERMAN OAKS, CA	91403
WESTBURY, KENNETH	CINEMATOGRAPHER	32 NELSON RD, WHITTON		
		TWICKINGHAM	MIDDLESEX TW2 7AU	ENGLAND
WESTERGAARD, LOUISE	TV PRODUCER	955 PARK AVE	NEW YORK, NY	10028
WESTERMARK, VICTORIA	WRITER	1911 IDAHO AVE	SANTA MONICA, CA	90403
WESTHEAD, PAUL	BASKETBALL COACH	POST OFFICE BOX 4658	DENVER, CO	80204
WESTHEIMER, DAVID	TV WRITER	11722 DARLINGTON AVE	LOS ANGELES, CA	90049
WESTHEIMER, DR RUTH	SEX THERAPIST	900 W 190TH ST	NEW YORK, NY	10040
WESTHOFF, MIKE	FOOTBALL COACH	DOLPHINS, 2269 NW 199TH ST	MIAMI, FL	33056
WESTIN, AV	TV EXECUTIVE	115 CENTRAL PARK W	NEW YORK, NY	10023
WESTIN, AVRAM ROBERT	TV DIRECTOR	ABC-TV, 7 W 66TH ST	NEW YORK, NY	10023
WESTMAN, JAMES A	DIRECTOR	4849 CASTLE RD	LA CANADA, CA	91011
WESTMORELAND, DICK	FOOTBALL	POST OFFICE BOX 23596	SAN DIEGO, CA	92193
WESTMORELAND, GEN WILLIAM	U S GENERAL	107 1/2 TRADD ST, BOX 1059	CHARLESTON, SC	29401
WESTMORELAND, JAMES	ACTOR	8019 1/2 W NORTON AVE	LOS ANGELES, CA	90046
WESTON, CAROLYN	WRITER	505 OLYMPIC BLVD #49	SANTA MONICA, CA	90401
WESTON, DAVID	ACTOR	123-A GROSVENOR RD	LONDON SW 1	ENGLAND
WESTON, ELLEN	ACTRESS	10513 HOLMAN AVE	LOS ANGELES, CA	90024
WESTON, ERIC	DIRECTOR	DGA, 7920 SUNSET BLVD, 6TH FL	LOS ANGELES, CA	90046
WESTON, JACK	ACTOR	101 CENTRAL PARK W	NEW YORK, NY	10023
WESTON, JEFF	ACTOR	FOLGO, 1502 QUEENS DR	LOS ANGELES, CA	90069
WESTON, KIM	SINGER	614 CHRYSLER DR #304	DETROIT, MI	48207
WESTON, MICKEY	BASEBALL	3281 HORRELL CT	FENTON, MI	48430
WESTON, PAUL	MUSICIAN-COMPOSER	2339 CENTURY HILL	LOS ANGELES, CA	90067
WESTON, RICHARD	TALENT AGENT	MTA, 9320 WILSHIRE BL, 3RD FL	BEVERLY HILLS, CA	90212
WESTON, TIM	BASEBALL TRAINER	ALBANY YANKEES, HERITAGE PARK	ALBANY, NY	12211
WESTPHAL, PAUL	BASKETBALL-COACH	SUNS, 2910 N CENTRAL AVE	PHOENIX, AZ	85012
WESTWOOD, BARRY	ACTOR-PRODUCER	231 WEST ST, FAREHAM	HANTS	ENGLAND
WET BEHIND THE EARS	C & W GROUP	OBA, 5601 ODANA RD	MADISON, WI	53719
WET WILLIE	ROCK & ROLL GROUP	210 25TH AVE N #N-101	NASHVILLE, TN	37203
WETHERBEE, DAN	FILM EDITOR	6464 SUNSET BLVD #1150	HOLLYWOOD, CA	90028
WETHERBY, JEFF	BASEBALL	POST OFFICE BOX 3690, STA "B"	CALGARY, ALB T2B 4M4	CANADA
WETTELAND, JOHN	BASEBALL	EXPOS, 4545 DE COUBERTIN AVE	MONTREAL, QUE H1V 3P2	CANADA
WETTIG, PATRICIA	ACTRESS	11850 CHAPPARAL ST	LOS ANGELES, CA	90049
WETZEL, JOHN	BASKETBALL COACH	700 NE MULTNOMAH ST #600	PORTLAND, OR	97232
WETZEL, TERRY	BASEBALL SCOUT	POST OFFICE BOX 419969	KANSAS CITY, MO	64141
WEVER, NED	ACTOR	355 AVENIDA SEVILLA	LAGUNA HILLS, CA	92653
WEVERKA, ROBERT	WRITER	317 S HOLLISTON AVE	PASADENA, CA	91106

WEXELBERG, ROGER	BASEBALL EXECUTIVE	POST OFFICE BOX 726	POMPANO BEACH, FL	33064
WEXLER, CONSTANCE R	COSTUME DESIGNER	277 W END AVE	NEW YORK, NY	10023
WEXLER, HASKELL	CINEMATOGRAPHER	26701 LATIGO SHORE DR	MALIBU, CA	90265
WEXLER, NORMAN	SCREENWRITER	8955 BEVERLY BLVD	WEST HOLLYWOOD, CA	90048
WEXLER, ROBERT	ACTOR	5628 BELLINGHAM AVE	NORTH HOLLYWOOD, CA	91607
WEXLER, YALE	PRODUCER	9360 WILSHIRE BLVD	BEVERLY HILLS, CA	90212
WEYMAN, ANDREW D	DIRECTOR	DAVIS/WEYMAN, 68 E END AVE	NEW YORK, NY	10028
WHALEN, SEAN	ACTOR	1539 SAWTELLE BLVD #10	LOS ANGELES, CA	90025
WHALEN, SHAWN	BASEBALL	POST OFFICE BOX 611	WATERLOO, IA	50704
WHALEN, WILLIAM	TV DIRECTOR	1346 MIDLAND AVE	BRONXVILLE, NY	10708
WHALEY, PAT	WRITER-EDITOR	POST OFFICE BOX 500	WASHINGTON, DC	20044
WHALEY-KILMER, JOANNE	ACTRESS	POST OFFICE BOX 362	TESUQUE, NM	87574
WHALUM, KIRK	SAXOPHONIST	POST OFFICE BOX 61116	HOUSTON, TX	77208
WHARMBY, TONY	TV DIRECTOR	11530 SUNSET BLVD	LOS ANGELES, CA	90049
WHARTON, ANNIE	ACTRESS	434 N OAKHURST DR #11	BEVERLY HILLS, CA	90210
WHARTON, WALLY	ACTRESS-WRITER	7461 BEVERLY BLVD #400	LOS ANGELES, CA	90036
WHAT IS THIS	ROCK & ROLL GROUP	6520 SELMA AVE #211	HOLLYWOOD, CA	90028
WHATELY, KEVIN	ACTOR	CDA, 47 COURTFIELD #9	LONDON SW7	ENGLAND
WHATHAM, CLAUDE	TV DIRECTOR-PRODUCER	AIM, 5 DENMARK ST	LONDON WC2H 8LP	ENGLAND
WHEAT, ALAN	U S CONGRESSMAN	811 GRAND #935	KANSAS CITY, MO	64106
WHEAT, WARREN	FOOTBALL	SEAHAWKS, 11220 NE 53RD ST	KIRKLAND, WA	98033
WHEAT, WARREN	WRITER-EDITOR	POST OFFICE BOX 500	WASHINGTON, DC	20044
WHEATLEY, DARLENE	ACTRESS	272-60 GRAND CENTRAL PARKWAY	FLORAL PARK, NY	11105
WHEATON, JACK W	CONDUCTOR	4469 VENTURA CANYON AVE #E-110	SHERMAN OAKS, CA	91423
WHEATON, KEN	SINGER	POST OFFICE BOX 6025	NEWPORT NEWS, VA	23606
WHEATON, PAMELA	TV WRITER	ENTERTAINMENT TONIGHT		
		PARAMOUNT TELEVISION		
		5555 MELROSE AVE	LOS ANGELES, CA	90038
WHEATON, WIL	ACTOR	POST OFFICE BOX 12567	LA CRESCENTA, CA	91214
WHEDON, THOMAS	TV WRITER	1730 MICHAEL LN	PACIFIC PALISADES, CA	90272
WHEDON, TOM	TV PRODUCER	UTA, 9560 WILSHIRE BL, 5TH FL	BEVERLY HILLS, CA	90212
WHEELER, BILLY EDD	SINGER	POST OFFICE BOX 7	SWANNONOA, NC	28778
WHEELER, CHRIS	BASEBALL	POST OFFICE BOX 7575	PHILADELPHIA, PA	19101
WHEELER, DAVID F	DIRECTOR	DGA, 110 W 57TH ST	NEW YORK, NY	10019
WHEELER, DEBBIE	ACTRESS	17 RICHMOND HILL, RICHMOND	SURREY	ENGLAND
WHEELER, DONNA M	DIRECTOR	DGA, 7920 SUNSET BLVD, 6TH FL	LOS ANGELES, CA	90046
WHEELER, HUGH C	SCREENWRITER	8955 BEVERLY BLVD	WEST HOLLYWOOD, CA	90048
WHEELER, JOHN	FILM EDITOR	POST OFFICE BOX 5617	BEVERLY HILLS, CA	90213
WHEELER, KEN	BASEBALL	POST OFFICE BOX 422229	KISSIMMEE, FL	34742
WHEELER, MARGARET	ACTRESS	3546 MULTIVIEW DR	HOLLYWOOD, CA	90068
WHEELER, ROCKET	BASEBALL COACH	CHIEFS, MAC ARTHUR STADIUM	SYRACUSE, NY	13208
WHEELER, SUSAN	ACTRESS	8721 SANTA MONICA BLVD #21	WEST HOLLYWOOD, CA	90069
WHEELER, TOM	BASEBALL SCOUT	POST OFFICE BOX 288	HOUSTON, TX	77001
WHEELOCK, GARY	BASEBALL COACH	POST OFFICE BOX 30160	SAN BERNARDINO, CA	92413
WHELAN, JOHN W, JR	WRITER	UTA, 9560 WILSHIRE BL, 5TH FL	BEVERLY HILLS, CA	90212
WHELAN CAGNEY, ARLEEN	ACTRESS	POST OFFICE BOX 76	ORLANDO, FL	32802
WHELCHEL, LISA	ACTRESS	11906 SHOSHONE AVE	GRANADA HILLS, CA	91344
WHELEN, CHRISTOPHER	COMPOSER	55 CONRWALL GARDENS #12	LONDON SW7	ENGLAND
WHELPLEY, JOHN FRANCIS	TV WRITER	22561 CARBON MESA RD	MALIBU, CA	90265
WHETZELL, SUSAN	WRITER	1820 CANYON DR	LOS ANGELES, CA	90028
WHINNERY, BARBARA	ACTRESS	1823 11TH ST #4	SANTA MONICA, CA	90404
WHIPP, JOSEPH	ACTOR	1418 N HIGHLAND AVE #102	LOS ANGELES, CA	90028
WHIPPLE, TORY	TALENT AGENT	MTA, 9320 WILSHIRE BL, 3RD FL	BEVERLY HILLS, CA	90212
WHISENANT, MARK	BASEBALL	POST OFFICE BOX 1721	SPARTANBURG, SC	29304
WHISENHUNT, KEN	FOOTBALL	N Y JETS, 1000 FULTON AVE	HEMPSTEAD, NY	11550
WHISITT, BOB	BASKETBALL EXECUTIVE	POST OFFICE BOX C-900911	SEATTLE, WA	98109
WHISKEY HOLLOW	C & W GROUP	PT & M, 2464 BRASILIA CIR	MISSISSAUGA, ONT	CANADA
WHISKEY RIVER	C & W GROUP	LST, 2138 FLAG MARSH RD	MOUNT AIRY, MD	21771
WHISLER, RANDY	BASEBALL COACH	POST OFFICE BOX 4448	TULSA, OK	74159
WHISPERINGS, THE	VOCAL GROUP	5625 "O" STREET BLDG #7	LINCOLN, NE	68510
WHISPERS, THE	VOCAL GROUP	FAA, 1700 BROADWAY, 5TH FLOOR	NEW YORK, NY	10019
WHISTLE	RAP GROUP-RAPWRITERS	FAA, 1700 BROADWAY, 5TH FLOOR	NEW YORK, NY	10019
WHITAKER, ANITA	ACTRESS	KJAR, 10653 RIVERSIDE DR	TOLUCA LAKE, CA	91602
WHITAKER, DAVID	COMPOSER	NETHER BARN, NETHERCOTE RD		
		TACKLEY	OXON OX5 3AW	ENGLAND
WHITAKER, FOREST	ACTOR	131 S RODEO DR #300	BEVERLY HILLS, CA	90212
WHITAKER, JOHNNY	ACTOR	13263 VENTURA BLVD #4	STUDIO CITY, CA	91604
WHITAKER, LOU	BASEBALL	TIGERS, TIGER STADIUM	DETROIT, MI	48216
WHITAKER, STEVE	BASEBALL	POST OFFICE BOX 21727	SAN FRANCISCO, CA	95151
WHITBREAD, PETER	ACTOR-WRITER	39 THE STREET, HINDOLVESTON		
		DEREHAM	NORFOLK NR20 5AS	ENGLAND
WHITBY, JOY	WRITER-PRODUCER	50 PEEL ST	LONDON W8 7PD	ENGLAND
WHITCOMB, IAN	SING-ACT-PROD	POST OFFICE BOX 451	ALTADENA, CA	91001
WHITCOMB, KENNETH G	COMPOSER-CONDUCTOR	1423 W CHATEAU AVE	ANAHEIM, CA	92802
WHITE, ADRIAN	FOOTBALL	N Y GIANTS, GIANTS STADIUM	EAST RUTHERFORD, NJ	07073
WHITE, AL	ACTOR	1930 CENTURY PARK W #403	LOS ANGELES, CA	90067
WHITE, ANDY	TV WRITER	10100 SANTA MONICA BLVD #1600	LOS ANGELES, CA	90067
WHITE, BARRY	SINGER-SONGWRITER	10502 WHIPPLE ST	NORTH HOLLYWOOD, CA	91604
WHITE, BETTY	ACTRESS	POST OFFICE BOX 3713	GRANADA HILLS, CA	91344
WHITE, BILL	BASEBALL COMMISSIONER	NATIONAL LEAGUE, 350 PARK AVE	NEW YORK, NY	10022
WHITE, BOY	RAPPER	SEE - BOY WHITE		
WHITE, BUCK & DOWN HOME FOLKS	C & W GROUP	380 LEXINGTON AVE #1119	NEW YORK, NY	10017
WHITE, BYRON	SUPREME COURT JUDGE	1 1ST ST, NE	WASHINGTON, DC	20543
WHITE, CAROL	ACTRESS	8019 1/2 MELROSE AVE #3	LOS ANGELES, CA	90046
WHITE, CAROLE ITA	ACTRESS-WRITER	517 N REXFORD DR	BEVERLY HILLS, CA	90210

Name	Occupation	Address	City
WHITE, CHARLES	ACTOR	2 STUYVESANT OVAL	NEW YORK, NY 10009
WHITE, D BERGEN	GUITARIST	2907 TYNE BLVD	NASHVILLE, TN 37215
WHITE, DAVE	BASEBALL EXECUTIVE	1100 ALAMEDA	POCATELLO, ID 83201
WHITE, DAVID	DIRECTOR	DGA, 7920 SUNSET BLVD, 6TH FL	LOS ANGELES, CA 90046
WHITE, DEBORAH	ACTRESS	9255 SUNSET BLVD #515	LOS ANGELES, CA 90069
WHITE, DERRICK	BASEBALL	POST OFFICE BOX 15757	HARRISBURG, PA 17105
WHITE, DERWIN	SINGER-COMPOSER	2984 AMULET AVE	SAN DIEGO, CA 92123
WHITE, DEVON	BASEBALL	474 W 158TH ST #42	NEW YORK, NY 10032
WHITE, DIANE	COLUMNIST	BOSTON GLOBE, 135 MORRISSEY BLVD	BOSTON, MA 02107
WHITE, DUCK	SINGER-GUITARIST	POST OFFICE BOX 15871	NASHVILLE, TN 37215
WHITE, DWAYNE	FOOTBALL	N Y JETS, 1000 FULTON AVE	HEMPSTEAD, NY 11550
WHITE, DWIGHT L	COMPOSER-CONDUCTOR	1432 OLIVE ST	SAN BERNARDINO, CA 92410
WHITE, FRANK	BASEBALL	13950 SWITZER RD	SHAWNEE MISSION, KS 66221
WHITE, FRED	BASEBALL	POST OFFICE BOX 5645	ORLANDO, FL 32855
WHITE, FRED	SPORTSCASTER	POST OFFICE BOX 419969	KANSAS CITY, MO 64141
WHITE, GABE	BASEBALL	POST OFFICE BOX 6748	ROCKFORD, IL 61125
WHITE, GARRY MICHAEL	TV WRITER	7018 WOODROW WILSON DR	LOS ANGELES, CA 90068
WHITE, HENRY S	TV PRODUCER	45 TUDOR CITY PL #920	NEW YORK, NY 10017
WHITE, HUBERT BILL	DIRECTOR	5907 W PICO BLVD	LOS ANGELES, CA 90035
WHITE, JALEEL	ACTRESS	1450 BELFAST DR	LOS ANGELES, CA 90069
WHITE, JERRY	BASEBALL-INSTRUCTOR	TWINS, 501 CHICAGO AVE S	MINNEAPOLIS, MN 55415
WHITE, JESSE	ACTOR	1944 GLENDON AVE #304	LOS ANGELES, CA 90025
WHITE, JIMMY	BASEBALL	POST OFFICE BOX 824	BURLINGTON, IA 52601
WHITE, JOHN	PHOTOGRAPHER	CHICAGO SUN-TIMES	
		401 N WABASH AVE	CHICAGO, IL 60611
WHITE, JOHNNY	C & W GROUP	PENNY, 30 GUINAN ST	WALTHAM, MA 02154
WHITE, JOSEPH JOHN	DIRECTOR	DGA, 110 W 57TH ST	NEW YORK, NY 10019
WHITE, JOSH, JR	SINGER	DAY PRODS, 300 W 55TH ST	NEW YORK, NY 10019
WHITE, JOSHUA W	DIRECTOR	33 5TH AVE	NEW YORK, NY 10003
WHITE, KENNETH	ACTOR	132 S LASKY DR #B	BEVERLY HILLS, CA 90212
WHITE, KENNETH	MUSIC ARRANGER	POST OFFICE BOX 22564	NASHVILLE, TN 37202
WHITE, LARRY	BASEBALL UMPIRE	POST OFFICE BOX 25010	LITTLE ROCK, AZ 72221
WHITE, LARRY	PRODUCER	COLUMBIA PICTURES TV	
		COLUMBIA PLAZA	BURBANK, CA 91505
WHITE, LARRY B	COMPOSER-CONDUCTOR	1628 N FAIRFAX AVE	LOS ANGELES, CA 90046
WHITE, LEON	FOOTBALL	BENGALS, 200 RIVERFRONT STADIUM	CINCINNATI, OH 45202
WHITE, LEONARD	ACTOR-DIRECTOR	HIGHLANDS, 40 HILL CREST RD	
		NEWHAVEN	SUSSEX BN9 9EG ENGLAND
WHITE, LOGAN	BASEBALL SCOUT	ORIOLE PARK, 333 W CAMDEN ST	BALTIMORE, MD 21201
WHITE, MARCUS D F	TV DIRECTOR	1-A RADBOURNE AVE	LONDON W5 4XD ENGLAND
WHITE, MARVIN	BASEBALL COACH	POST OFFICE BOX 3609	PORT CHARLOTTE, FL 33949
WHITE, MAURICE	SINGER-COMPOSER	POST OFFICE BOX 5880	SHERMAN OAKS, CA 91413
WHITE, MICHAEL	FILM PRODUCER	13 DUKE ST, SAINT JAMES'S ST	LONDON SW1Y 6DB ENGLAND
WHITE, MICHELE	SINGER	TALENT MANAGEMENT	
		2460 SPRING LAKE DR	MARIETTA, GA 30062
WHITE, MICKEY	BASEBALL SCOUT	INDIANS, CLEVELAND STADIUM	CLEVELAND, OH 44114
WHITE, MIKE	BASEBALL	POST OFFICE BOX 598	BINGHAMTON, NY 13902
WHITE, MIKE	FOOTBALL COACH	RAIDERS, 332 CENTER ST	EL SEGUNDO, CA 90245
WHITE, NANCY	GOLFER	2750 VOLUSA AVE #B	DAYTON BEACH, FL 32114
WHITE, NAOMI	ACTRESS	22660 PACIFIC COAST HWY #5-A	MALIBU, CA 90265
WHITE, NATHANIAL	ACTOR	250 E 113TH ST	NEW YORK, NY 10029
WHITE, ONNA	CHOREOGRAPHER	SSD & C, 1501 BROADWAY	NEW YORK, NY 10036
WHITE, PAUL GREGORY	ACTOR	MAX AGENCY, 166 N CANON DR	BEVERLY HILLS, CA 90210
WHITE, PETER	ACTOR	LIGHT, 901 BRINGHAM AVE	LOS ANGELES, CA 90049
WHITE, PETER V	TV DIRECTOR-PRODUCER	12433 MOORPARK ST #216	STUDIO CITY, CA 91604
WHITE, RANDY	BASKETBALL	REUNION ARENA, 777 SPORTS ST	DALLAS, TX 75207
WHITE, REGGIE	FOOTBALL	EAGLES, BROAD ST & PATTISON AVE	PHILADELPHIA, PA 19148
WHITE, RENAULD	ACTOR	CBS-TV, "THE GUIDING LIGHT"	
		222 E 44TH ST	NEW YORK, NY 10017
WHITE, RICH	BASEBALL	RED SOX, CHAIN O'LAKES PARK	WINTER HAVEN, FL 33880
WHITE, RICK	BASEBALL	POST OFFICE BOX 842	SALEM, VA 24153
WHITE, ROBERT F	DIRECTOR	DGA, 7920 SUNSET BLVD, 6TH FL	LOS ANGELES, CA 90046
WHITE, RONDELL	BASEBALL	POST OFFICE BOX 3566	WEST PALM BEACH, FL 33402
WHITE, ROY E	CONDUCTOR	13733 PHILADELPHIA ST	WHITTIER, CA 90601
WHITE, RUTH S	COMPOSER	POST OFFICE BOX 34485	LOS ANGELES, CA 90034
WHITE, SAM	DIRECTOR-PRODUCER	18579 BRASILIA DR	NORTHRIDGE, CA 91326
WHITE, SHARON SKAGGS	SINGER-GUITARIST	SEE - SKAGGS, SHARON WHITE	
WHITE, SHELDON	FOOTBALL	LIONS, 1200 FEATHERSTONE RD	PONTIAC, MI 48432
WHITE, STEPHEN W	WRITER	4915 AGNES AVE	NORTH HOLLYWOOD, CA 91607
WHITE, TOM	FOOTBALL REFEREE	NFL, 410 PARK AVE	NEW YORK, NY 10022
WHITE, TONY JOE	SINGER-SONGWRITER	35 MUSIC SQUARE E	NASHVILLE, TN 37203
WHITE, VANNA	LETTER TURNER-MODEL	3400 RIVERSIDE DR	BURBANK, CA 91505
WHITE, WILLIAM	FOOTBALL	LIONS, 1200 FEATHERSTONE RD	PONTIAC, MI 48432
WHITE BUFFALO BAND	MUSICAL GROUP	SOUTHERN TALENT INTL	
		2925 FALLOWRIDGE CT	SNELLVILLE, GA 30278
WHITE CHINA	ROCK & ROLL GROUP	41 BRITAIN ST #200	TORONTO, ONT M5A 1R7 CANADA
WHITE LIGHTIN'	ROCK & ROLL GROUP	41 BRITAIN ST #200	TORONTO, ONT M5A 1R7 CANADA
WHITE NILLARD, THELMA	ACTRESS-COMEDIENNE	8431 LENNOX AVE	PANORAMA CITY, CA 91402
WHITE ZOMBIE	ROCK & ROLL GROUP	CAROLINE RECRODS, 114 W 26TH ST	NEW YORK, NY 10016
WHITED, ED	BASEBALL	22 YORKTOWN RD	BORDENTOWN, NJ 08505
WHITEFORD, STEVEN	ACTOR	1638 1/4 EDGECLIFFE DR	LOS ANGELES, CA 90026
WHITEHALL, MICHAEL	TAL AGT-PRODUCER	WHITEHALL, 125 GLOUCESTER RD	LONDON SW7 4TE ENGLAND
WHITEHALL, WAYNE	ACTOR	214 W 82ND ST	NEW YORK, NY 10024
WHITEHEAD, GEOFFREY	ACTOR	BRYAN DREW, MEZANNINE FLOOR	
		QUADRANT HOUSE, 80-82 REGENT ST	LONDON W1R 6AU ENGLAND

WHITEHEAD, ROBERT	THEATER PRODUCER	1501 BROADWAY	NEW YORK, NY 10036
WHITEHEAD, STEVE	BASEBALL	POST OFFICE BOX 6748	ROCKFORD, IL 61125
WHITEHILL, LOU	WRITER	1020 N DOHENY DR #3	LOS ANGELES, CA 90069
WHITEHOUSE, BRIAN	TV DIRECTOR-PRODUCER	BBC-TV, 56 WOOD LN	LONDON W12 7RJ ENGLAND
WHITEHOUSE, RONNIE	TV DIRECTOR	34-C NETERHALL GARDENS	LONDON NW3 5TP ENGLAND
WHITEHURST, DEREK	FILM DIRECTOR	171 HILLCREST, BAKER ST	WEYBRIDGE KT13 8AS ENGLAND
WHITEHURST, WALLY	BASEBALL	METS, 126TH ST & ROOSEVELT AVE	FLUSHING, NY 11368
WHITELACE	ROCK & ROLL GROUP	FAA, 1700 BROADWAY, 5TH FLOOR	NEW YORK, NY 10019
WHITELAW, ARTHUR	THEATER PRODUCER	132 E 38TH ST	NEW YORK, NY 10016
WHITELAW, BILLIE	ACTRESS	535 KINGS RD, 19 THE PLAZA #2	LODNON SW10 OSZ ENGLAND
WHITELEY, SANDY	TV DIRECTOR	2043 W FARWELL AVE #2-N	CHICAGO, IL 60645
WHITEMORE, HUGH	PLAYWRIGHT	DAISH, 83 EASTBOURNE MEWS	LONDON W2 6LQ ENGLAND
WHITEN, MARK	BASEBALL	1373 RULE ST	PENSACOLA, FL 32514
WHITES, THE	C & W GROUP	HALLMARK, 15 MUSIC SQUARE W	NASHVILLE, TN 37203
WHITESELL, JOHN P, II	DIRECTOR	265 RIVERSIDE DR	NEW YORK, NY 10025
WHITESIDE, MATT	BASEBALL	POST OFFICE BOX 4448	TULSA, OK 74159
WHITESIDES, KIM	ARTIST	252 MARSAC AVE	PARK CITY, UT 84060
WHITESNAKE	ROCK & ROLL GROUP	345 N MAPLE ST #235	BEVERLY HILLS, CA 90210
WHITFIELD, BARBARA & THE SAVAGE	ROCK & ROLL GROUP	25 HUNTINGTON AVE #420	BOSTON, MA 02116
WHITFIELD, JUNE	ACTRESS	YOUNG, 31 KING'S RD	LONDON SW3 4RP ENGLAND
WHITFIELD, LYNN	ACTRESS	SMITH, 121 N SAN VICENTE BLVD	BEVERLY HILLS, CA 90211
WHITFIELD, VANTILE E	TV DIRECTOR	1429 VARNUM ST, NW	WASHINGTON, DC 20011
WHITFORD, ERIC	BASEBALL	POST OFFICE BOX 8550	STOCKTON, CA 95208
WHITING, JOE	SINGER	POST OFFICE BOX 11276	ROCHESTER, NY 14611
WHITING, MARGARET	SINGER	41 W 58TH ST #5-A	NEW YORK, NY 10019
WHITING, RICHARD	TV WRITER	45 ROCKEFELLER PLAZA	NEW YORK, NY 10111
WHITING SMITH, BARBARA	ACTRESS	1085 WADDINGTON ST	BIRMINGHAM, MI 48009
WHITLEY, BRIAN	ACTOR-DIRECTOR	POST OFFICE BOX 18512	LOS ANGELES, CA 90018
WHITLEY, RICHARD FRANCIS	SCREENWRITER	172 N SYCAMORE AVE	LOS ANGELES, CA 90036
WHITLOW, JILL	ACTRESS	LIGHT, 901 BRINGHAM AVE	LOS ANGELES, CA 90049
WHITLOW, ZETTA	ACTRESS	11600 MONTANA AVE #210	LOS ANGELES, CA 90049
WHITMAN, JACK	TV DIRECTOR	14046 FENTON LN	SYLMAR, CA 91342
WHITMAN, KARI KENNELL	ACTRESS	9255 SUNSET BLVD #515	LOS ANGELES, CA 90069
WHITMAN, SLIM	SINGER	PURCELL, 210 E 51ST ST	NEW YORK, NY 10022
WHITMAN, STUART	ACTOR	749 SAN YSIDRO RD	SANTA BARBARA, CA 93108
WHITMER, DAN	BASEBALL COACH	TIGERS, TIGER STADIUM	DETROIT, MI 48216
WHITMORE, DARRELL	BASEBALL	POST OFFICE BOX 3452	KINSTON, NC 28502
WHITMORE, DAVID	FOOTBALL	S F 49ERS, 4949 CENTENNIAL BL	SANTA CLARA, CA 95054
WHITMORE, JAMES	ACTOR	4990 PUESTA DEL SOL	MALIBU, CA 90265
WHITMORE, JAMES, JR	ACTOR	1284 LA BREA DR	THOUSAND OAKS, CA 91362
WHITMORE, STANFORD	WRITER	4816 GLORIA AVE	ENCINO, CA 91436
WHITMORE, STEPHEN	ACTOR	1324 MYRTLE ST #D	GLENDALE, CA 91203
WHITNEY, CECE	ACTRESS	840 N ODGEN DR	LOS ANGELES, CA 90046
WHITNEY, JOHN	WRITER-PRODUCER	IBA, 70 BROMPTON RD	LONDON SW3 1EY ENGLAND
WHITNEY, PHYLLIS	ACTRESS	310 MADISON AVE #607	NEW YORK, NY 10017
WHITNEY, ROBERT	ACTOR	3792 HARRISON ST #36	OAKLAND, CA 94611
WHITNEY, RUTH	WRITER-EDITOR	GLAMOUR, 350 MADISON AVE	NEW YORK, NY 10017
WHITNEY, WHEELOCK	FOOTBALL EXECUTIVE	VIKINGS, 9520 VIKING DR	EDEN PRAIRIE, MN 55344
WHITROW, BENJAMIN	ACTOR	MC REDDIE, 91 REGENT ST	LONDON W1R 7TB ENGLAND
WHITSETT, EDWARD "RED"	BASEBALL SCOUT	BREWERS, 201 S 46TH ST	MILWAUKEE, WI 53214
WHITSITT, JAMES E	COMPOSER	6609 HILLGROVE DR	SAN DIEGO, CA 92120
WHITSON, ED	BASEBALL	POST OFFICE BOX 2000	SAN DIEGO, CA 92112
WHITT, ERNIE	BASEBALL	18330 13 MILE RD	ROSEVILLE, MI 48066
WHITTAKER, DONALD T	TV DIRECTOR	170 AMBERWOOD LN	WALNUT, CA 91789
WHITTAKER, GEORGE	COSTUME DESIGNER	13949 VENTURA BLVD #309	SHERMAN OAKS, CA 91423
WHITTAKER, RICHARD R	WRITER	POST OFFICE BOX 471	CORTE MADERA, CA 94925
WHITTAKER, ROGER	SINGER-SONGWRITER	IRENE COLLINS MANAGEMENT	
		50 REGENTS PARK RD	
		PRIMROSE HILL	LONDON NW1 7SX ENGLAND
WHITTEMORE, GLORIA	FILM EDITOR	19 W 85TH ST #4-B	NEW YORK, NY 10024
WHITTEMORE, JACK	TALENT AGENT	80 PARK AVE #2-G	NEW YORK, NY 10022
WHITTEN, BILL	COSTUME DESIGNER	3488 TROY DR	LOS ANGELES, CA 90068
WHITTEN, JAMIE L	U S CONGRESSMAN	POST OFFICE BOX 1482	TUPELO, MS 38802
WHITTINGHAM, FRED	FOOTBALL COACH	RAMS, 2327 W LINCOLN BLVD	ANAHEIM, CA 92801
WHITTINGHILL, DICK	RADIO PERSONALITY	11310 VALLEY SPRING LN	TOLUCA LAKE, CA 91602
WHITTINGTON, MIKE	SINGER	POST OFFICE BOX 25371	CHARLOTTE, NC 28212
WHITTON, MARGARET	ACTRESS	151 S EL CAMINO DR	BEVERLY HILLS, CA 90212
WHO, THE	ROCK & ROLL GROUP	48 HARLEY HOUSE, MARLEBONE RD	LONDON NW1 ENGLAND
WHODINI	RAP GROUP	RUSH ARTISTS, 298 ELIZABETH ST	NEW YORK, NY 10012
WHOLIGANS, THE	ROCK & ROLL GROUP	41 BRITAIN ST #200	TORONTO, ONT M5A 1R7 CANADA
WHORF, DAVID M	TV DIRECTOR	1326 GREENWICH ST	SAN FRANCISCO, CA 94109
WIARD, WILLIAM O	FILM DIRECTOR	1142 LAS PULGAS PL	PACIFIC PALISADES, CA 90272
WIATT, JIM	TALENT AGENT	ICM, 8899 BEVERLY BLVD	LOS ANGELES, CA 90048
WICKANDER, KEVIN	BASEBALL	4385 TUTT BLVD	COLORADO SPRINGS, CO 80922
WICKER, IREENE	WRITER-SINGER	781 5TH AVE	NEW YORK, NY 10022
WICKERSHEIM, THEODORE J	COMPOSER	3716 MAINE	BALDWIN PARK, CA 91706
WICKES, DAVID	WRITER-PRODUCER	REDWAY (AIM), 5 DENMARK ST	LONDON WC2H 8LP ENGLAND
WICKES, MARY	ACTRESS	2160 CENTURY PARK E #503	LOS ANGELES, CA 90067
WICKHAM, DAN	BASEBALL UMPIRE	2101 E BROADWAY #35	TEMPE, AZ 85282
WICKHAM, JEFFREY	ACTOR	MARKHAM AND FROGGATT, LTD	
		JULIAN HOUSE, 4 WINDMILL ST	LONDON W1P 1HF ENGLAND
WICKI, BERNHARD	DIRECTOR	RESTELBERGSTRASSE 60	8 ZURICH
WICKMAN, BOB	BASEBALL	ALBANY YANKEES, HERITAGE PARK	ALBANY, NY 12211
WIDDOES, KATHLEEN	ACTRESS	CBS-TV, "AS THE WORLD TURNS"	
		524 W 57TH ST #5330	NEW YORK, NY 10019

Name	Occupation	Address	City	Zip/Country
WIDDRINGTON, P N T	BASEBALL EXECUTIVE	SKYDOME, 300 BREMMER BL #3200	TORONTO, ONT M5V 3B3	CANADA
WIDEL, ROSS	ACTOR	22744 CLARENDON ST	WOODLAND HILLS, CA	91367
WIDELL, DAVE	FOOTBALL	BRONCOS, 13655 BRONCOS PKWY	ENGLEWOOD, CO	80112
WIDELL, DOUG	FOOTBALL	BRONCOS, 13655 BRONCOS PKWY	ENGLEWOOD, CO	80112
WIDEMAN, M G	ACTOR	POST OFFICE BOX 491373	LOS ANGELES, CA	90014
WIDENHOFER, WOODY	FOOTBALL COACH	LIONS, 1200 FEATHERSTONE RD	PONTIAC, MI	48432
WIDERBERG, BO	DIRECTOR	SVENSKA FILMINSTITUTET, KUNG	STOCKHOLM C	SWEDEN
WIDLAKE, BRIAN	ACTOR-WRITER	51 NASSAU RD, BARNES	LONDON SW13	ENGLAND
WIDMAR, AL	BASEBALL-EXECUTIVE	SKYDOME, 300 BREMMER BL #3200	TORONTO, ONT M5V 3B3	CANADA
WIDMARK, RICHARD	ACTOR	ICM, 8899 BEVERLY BLVD	LOS ANGELES, CA	90048
WIDOW	ROCK & ROLL GROUP	POST OFFICE BOX 66558	SEATTLE, WA	98166
WIEBERG, STEVE	SPORTS WRITER	POST OFFICE BOX 500	WASHINGTON, DC	20044
WIEDENBAUER, TOM	BASEBALL-INSTRUCTOR	POST OFFICE BOX 288	HOUSTON, TX	77001
WIEDERHORN, KEN	FILM DIRECTOR	9080 WONDERLAND PARK AVE	LOS ANGELES, CA	90046
WIEGANDT, SCOTT	BASEBALL	POST OFFICE BOX 15050	READING, PA	19612
WIEGERT, BOB	RECORD PRODUCER	POST OFFICE BOX 186	CEDARBURG, WI	53102
WIELAND, DICK	ACTOR	13760 OXNARD ST #201	VAN NUYS, CA	91401
WIEMER, JIM	HOCKEY	BRUINS, 150 CAUSEWAY ST	BOSTON, MA	02114
WIEMER, ROBERT E	TV DIRECTOR	332 N PALM DR	BEVERLY HILLS, CA	90210
WIEMERS, DAVID	WRITER	918 1/2 N VERDUGO RD	GLENDALE, CA	91206
WIEN, IRWIN I	COMPOSER	1235 N KINGS RD #410	LOS ANGELES, CA	90069
WIENCEK, DICK	BASEBALL SCOUT	TIGERS, TIGER STADIUM	DETROIT, MI	48216
WIENER, CHARLIE	SINGER	GREG, 1288 E 168TH ST	CLEVELAND, OH	44110
WIENER, JON	AUTHOR	UNIV OF CALIF AT IRVINE		
		DEPARTMENT OF HISTORY	IRVINE, CA	92717
WIENER, ROBERT	TV PRODUCER	1050 TECHWOOD DR, NW	ATLANTA, GA	30318
WIENER, WILLARD	WRITER	2600 CARMAN CREST DR	LOS ANGELES, CA	90068
WIER, RUSTY	SINGER	WATKINS, 3819 JEFFERSON ST	AUSTIN, TX	78703
WIERE, HARRY	COMEDIAN-ACTOR	14350 ADDISON ST	SHERMAN OAKS, CA	91423
WIERE, HERBERT	COMEDIAN-ACTOR	12360 MAGNOLIA BLVD	NORTH HOLLYWOOD, CA	91607
WIESEN, BERNARD	TV DIRECTOR-PRODUCER	2565 CRESTON DR	HOLLYWOOD, CA	90068
WIEST, DIANNE	ACTRESS	ICM, 8899 BEVERLY BLVD	LOS ANGELES, CA	90048
WIETELMANN, WHITEY	BASEBALL	7712 GOLFCREST DR	SAN DIEGO, CA	92119
WIGAN, GARETH	FILM PRODUCER	1902 COLDWATER CANYON DR	BEVERLY HILLS, CA	90210
WIGGIN, TOM	ACTOR	CBS-TV, "AS THE WORLD TURNS"		
		524 W 57TH ST #5330	NEW YORK, NY	10019
WIGGINS, GERALD F	COMPOSER	20142 CLARK ST	WOODLAND HILLS, CA	91367
WIGGINS, ROY	GUITARIST	309 BONNACROFT DR	HERMITAGE, TN	37076
WIGGS, HILDRED A	TV DIRECTOR	1 GLENWOOD AVE #5-M	YONKERS, NY	10701
WIGGS, JOHNNY	BASEBALL	POST OFFICE BOX 4756	JACKSONVILLE, FL	32201
WIGLE, SHARI LYNN	TV WRITER	1411 KITTRIDGE ST #223	VAN NUYS, CA	91405
WIKE, CHARLES B	COMPOSER	3150 WELDON AVE #3	LOS ANGELES, CA	90065
WILAND, HARRY A	DIRECTOR	639 HILL ST #B	SANTA MONICA, CA	90405
WILBER, CAREY	TV DIRECTOR	8955 BEVERLY BLVD	WEST HOLLYWOOD, CA	90048
WILBOURN, CLAUDIA	BODYBUILDER	POST OFFICE BOX 167	SANTA MONICA, CA	90406
WILBURN, LESLIE FLOYD	SINGER-GUITARIST	ROUTE #4, 225 DEVINS DR	BRENTWOOD, TN	37027
WILBURN, LESTER LLOYD	SINGER-GUITARIST	5042 MARCHANT DR	NASHVILLE, TN	37211
WILBURN, TEDDY	SINGER-GUITARIST	60 MUSIC SQUARE W	NASHVILLE, TN	37203
WILBURN BROTHERS, THE	C & W GROUP	POST OFFICE BOX 50	GOODLETTSVILLE, TN	37072
WILBY, JAMES	ACTOR	HEATH, PARAMOUNT HOUSE		
		162-170 WARDOUR ST	LONDON W1V 3AT	ENGLAND
WILCHER, MIKE	FOOTBALL	POST OFFICE BOX 609609	SAN DIEGO, CA	92160
WILCOTS, SOLOMON	FOOTBALL	VIKINGS, 9520 VIKING DR	EDEN PRAIRIE, MN	55344
WILCOX, DAN	TV PRODUCER	MTM, 4024 RADFORD AVE	STUDIO CITY, CA	91604
WILCOX, DANIEL HARRIS	TV WRITER	3610 LOWRY RD	LOS ANGELES, CA	90027
WILCOX, DAVE	SINGER	41 BRITAIN ST #200	TORONTO, ONT M5A 1R7	CANADA
WILCOX, DESMOND JOHN	WRITER-PRODUCER	WILCOX-BULMER PRODUCTIONS		
		12 CAMBRIDGE CT		
		210 SHEPHERD'S BUSH RD	LONDON W6 7NL	ENGLAND
WILCOX, DON	TV WRITER	1900 AVE OF THE STARS #1530	LOS ANGELES, CA	90067
WILCOX, JOHN	TV PRODUCER	314-C MEDITERRANEAN AVE	ASPEN, CO	81612
WILCOX, LARRY	ACTOR-DIRECTOR	13 APPALOSA LN, BELL CANYON	CANOGA PARK, CA	91305
WILCOX, LISA	ACTRESS	STONE MANNERS, 9113 SUNSET BL	LOS ANGELES, CA	90069
WILCOX, MARY	ACTRESS-MODEL	SEE - WILCOX, SHANNON		
WILCOX, PAULA	ACTRESS	BURNETT, 42-43 GRAFTON HOUSE		
		2-3 GOLDEN SQ	LONDON W1R 3AD	ENGLAND
WILCOX, SHANNON	ACTRESS	SMITH, 121 N SAN VICENTE BLVD	BEVERLY HILLS, CA	90211
WILD, CHUCK	COMPOSER	WALDRON, 6520 SELMA AVE #525	LOS ANGELES, CA	90028
WILD, JACK	ACTOR	47 THE GROVE, ILSWORTH	MIDDLESEX	ENGLAND
WILD, PETER D	TV DIRECTOR-PRODUCER	CREATIVE PROGRAMMING INC		
		30 E 60TH ST	NEW YORK, NY	10022
WILD CHERRY	ROCK & ROLL GROUP	28001 CHARGRIN BLVD #205	CLEVELAND, OH	44122
WILDE, CAROLYN	ACTRESS	ABC-TV, "ALL MY CHILDREN"		
		320 W 66TH ST	NEW YORK, NY	10023
WILDE, EUGENE	SINGER	POST OFFICE BOX 11981	PHILADELPHIA, PA	19145
WILDE, JOHN K	WRITER-PRODUCER	264 CONWAY AVE	LOS ANGELES, CA	90024
WILDE, KIM	SINGER-SONGWRITER	1 STEVENAGE RD	NEBWORTH, HERTS	ENGLAND
WILDE, TIMOTHY	TV DIRECTOR	119 KINGS ROW	ARLINGTON, TX	76010
WILDER, ALEC V	ACTOR	25 MINETA LN	NEW YORK, NY	10012
WILDER, BILLY	WRITER-PRODUCER	10375 WILSHIRE BLVD	LOS ANGELES, CA	90024
WILDER, DAVE	BASEBALL SCOUT	ATHLETICS'S, OAKLAND COLISEUM	OAKLAND, CA	94621
WILDER, GENE	ACT-WRI-DIR	9350 WILSHIRE BLVD #400	BEVERLY HILLS, CA	90212
WILDER, GLENN R	DIRECTOR	STUNTS UNLIMITED ASSOC		
		3518 W CAHUENGA BLVD	LOS ANGELES, CA	90068
WILDER, JOHN	BASEBALL	POST OFFICE BOX 4525	MACON, GA	31208

WILDER, JOHN	LT GOVERNOR	STATE CAPITOL BUILDING	NASHVILLE, TN	37243
WILDER, KELLY	ACTRESS	12926 RIVERSIDE DR #C	SHERMAN OAKS, CA	91423
WILDER, L DOUGLAS	GOVERNOR	STATE CAPITOL BUILDING	RICHMOND, VA	23219
WILDER, L DOUGLAS	GOVERNOR	STATE HOUSE	RICHMOND, VA	33219
WILDER, MATTHEW	SINGER	10100 SANTA MONICA BLVD #1600	LOS ANGELES, CA	90067
WILDER, MYLES H	TV WRITER-PRODUCER	280 HOMEWOOD RD	LOS ANGELES, CA	90049
WILDER, WILLIE	BASEBALL	POST OFFICE BOX 9194	HAMPTON, VA	23670
WILDER, YVONNE	ACTRESS	5450 TOPEKA DR	TARZANA, CA	91356
WILDFLOWERS, THE	ROCK & ROLL GROUP	41 BRITAIN ST #200	TORONTO, ONT M5A 1R7	CANADA
WILDING, MICHAEL, JR	ACTOR	8428 MELROSE #C	LOS ANGELES, CA	90069
WILDMAN, VALERIE	ACTRESS	STONE MANNERS, 9113 SUNSET BL	LOS ANGELES, CA	90069
WILDSMITH, DAWN	ACTRESS	6605 HOLLYWOOD BLVD #220	HOLLYWOOD, CA	90028
WILENSKY, STEWART	DIRECTOR	443 19TH ST	SANTA MONICA, CA	90402
WILES, GORDON	DIRECTOR	17123 ADLON RD	ENCINO, CA	91436
WILEY, CHUCK	BASEBALL	POST OFFICE BOX 9194	HAMPTON, VA	23670
WILEY, MARK	BASEBALL-COACH	INDIANS, CLEVELAND STADIUM	CLEVELAND, OH	44114
WILEY, MORLAN	BASKETBALL	POST OFFICE BOX 76	ORLANDO, FL	32802
WILEY, SKIP	BASEBALL	800 HOME RUN LN	MEMPHIS, TN	38104
WILF, HOWLIN' & THE VEE-JAYS	ROCK & ROLL GROUP	ACE, 48-50 STEELE RD	LONDON NW10 7AS	ENGLAND
WILF, RUTH ANN	ACTRESS	9 ROLLING RD	PHILADELPHIA, PA	19151
WILFONG, ROB	BASEBALL-SCOUT	TIGERS, TIGER STADIUM	DETROIT, MI	48216
WILHELM, ERIK	FOOTBALL	BENGALS, 200 RIVERFRONT STADIUM	CINCINNATI, OH	45202
WILHELM, HOYT	BASEBALL	3102 N HIMES AVE	TAMPA, FL	33607
WILHELM, JOSEPH FRANKLIN	TV WRITER	3606 WOODHILL CYN RD	STUDIO CITY, CA	91604
WILHOITE, KATHLEEN	ACTRESS	POST OFFICE BOX 5617	BEVERLY HILLS, CA	90213
WILK, ANDREW CARL	TV WRITER-DIRECTOR	30 LINCOLN PLAZA #4-W	NEW YORK, NY	10023
WILK, DAVID	BASEBALL UMPIRE	POST OFFICE BOX 716	PLAINVILLE, CT	06062
WILKEN, TIM	BASEBALL SCOUT	SKYDOME, 300 BREMMER BL #3200	TORONTO, ONT M5V 3B3	CANADA
WILKENS, LENNY	BASKETBALL COACH	POST OFFICE BOX 5000	RICHFIELD, OH	44286
WILKERSON, BRUCE	FOOTBALL	RAIDERS, 332 CENTER ST	EL SEGUNDO, CA	90245
WILKERSON, CURTIS	BASEBALL	POST OFFICE BOX 419969	KANSAS CITY, MO	64141
WILKES, BECKY	ACTRESS	2160 S BEVERLY GLEN BLVD #357	LOS ANGELES, CA	90025
WILKES, DONNA	ACTRESS	3802 N EARL AVE	ROSEMEAD, CA	91770
WILKES, JAMAAL	BASKETBALL	7846 W 81ST ST	PLAYA DEL REY, CA	90291
WILKINS, ANN MARIE	TALENT AGENT	POST OFFICE BOX 55398	WASHINGTON, DC	20040
WILKINS, DEAN	BASEBALL	POST OFFICE BOX 27045	TUCSON, AZ	85726
WILKINS, DOMINIQUE	BASKETBALL	1 CNN CENTER #405, SOUTH TOWER	ATLANTA, GA	30303
WILKINS, EDDIE LEE	BASKETBALL	KNICKS, 4 PENNYLVANIA PLAZA	NEW YORK, NY	10019
WILKINS, GERALD	BASKETBALL	KNICKS, 4 PENNYLVANIA PLAZA	NEW YORK, NY	10019
WILKINS, LITTLE DAVID	SINGER	ACE, 3407 GREEN RIDGE DR	NASHVILLE, TN	37204
WILKINS, RICH	BASEBALL	1060 W ADDISON ST	CHICAGO, IL	60613
WILKINS, RICK	BASEBALL	1060 W ADDISON ST	CHICAGO, IL	60613
WILKINS, WILLIAM H, JR	TV DIRECTOR	607 TEXAS ST	SAN FRANCISCO, CA	94107
WILKINSON, ANN E	ACTRESS	6255 SUNSET BLVD #627	LOS ANGELES, CA	90028
WILKINSON, BILL	BASEBALL	POST OFFICE BOX 2769	HUNTSVILLE, AL	35804
WILKINSON, CHRISTOPHER G	DIRECTOR	DGA, 7920 SUNSET BLVD, 6TH FL	LOS ANGELES, CA	90046
WILKINSON, CHUCK	ARTIST	17194 PLAINVIEW AVE	DETROIT, MI	48219
WILKINSON, DAVID	ACTOR-TV PRODUCER	BRITANNIA TELEVISION LIMITED		
		THE STUDIO, TOWN PLACE		
		SCAYNES HILL	WEST SUSSEX RH17 7NR	ENGLAND
WILKINSON, JUNE	ACTRESS	3653 FAIRESTA ST	LA CRESCENTA, CA	91214
WILKINSON, KRISTIN	MUSIC ARRANGER	905 CANTRELL AVE	NASHVILLE, TN	37215
WILKINSON, NEIL	HOCKEY	NORTH STARS, 7901 CEDAR AVE S	BLOOMINGTON, MN	55425
WILKINSON, TOM	ACTOR	COULSON, 37 BERWICK ST	LONDON W1V 3RF	ENGLAND
WILKINSON, WALLACE G	GOVERNOR	STATE CAPITOL BUILDING	FRANKFORT, KY	40601
WILKMAN, JON K	WRITER	6160 RODGERTON DR	HOLLYWOOD, CA	90068
WILKOSZ, JUSUP	BODYBUILDER	JUSUP'S GALAXY FITNESS		
		BRUCKSTRASSE	D-7012 FELLBACH	GERMANY
WILL, GEORGE F	WRITER-COLUMNIST	THE WASHINGTON POST		
		WRITERS GROUP		
		1150 15TH ST, NW	WASHINGTON, DC	20071
WILL, SANDRA	ACTRESS	2105 N BEVERLY GLEN BLVD	LOS ANGELES, CA	90077
WILL, STU	SINGER	POST OFFICE BOX 6025	NEWPORT NEWS, VA	23606
WILL TO POWER	ROCK & ROLL GROUP	FAA, 1700 BROADWAY, 5TH FLOOR	NEW YORK, NY	10019
WILLARD, FRED	ACTOR	5056 WOODLEY AVE	ENCINO, CA	91436
WILLARD, JERRY	BASEBALL	POST OFFICE BOX 4064	ATLANTA, GA	30302
WILLENS, MICHELE	TV WRITER	3870 RAMBLA ORIENTA	MALIBU, CA	90265
WILLENS, SHELDON MILES	TV WRITER	3140 CHANDELLE RD	LOS ANGELES, CA	90046
WILLENSON, SETH M	TV WRITER	285 RIVERSIDE DR	NEW YORK, NY	10025
WILLES, JEAN	ACTRESS	COWHIG, 14244 CALIFA ST	VAN NUYS, CA	91401
WILLEY, WALT	ACTOR	ABC-TV, "ALL MY CHILDREN"		
		320 W 66TH ST	NEW YORK, NY	10023
WILLIAMS, AENEAS	FOOTBALL	POST OFFICE BOX 888	PHOENIX, AZ	85001
WILLIAMS, ALFRED	FOOTBALL	BENGALS, 200 RIVERFRONT STADIUM	CINCINNATI, OH	45202
WILLIAMS, ALLEN	ACTOR	10100 SANTA MONICA BLVD #700	LOS ANGELES, CA	90067
WILLIAMS, ALLEN	TV WRITER-DIRECTOR	2049 CENTURY PARK E #1320	LOS ANGELES, CA	90067
WILLIAMS, ANDY	SINGER-ACTOR	10100 SANTA MONICA BLVD #1600	LOS ANGELES, CA	90067
WILLIAMS, ANN MARIE	ACTRESS	6621 W FALCON LEA DR	DAVIE, FL	33331
WILLIAMS, ANSON	ACT-SING-DIR	10100 SANTA MONICA BLVD #1600	LOS ANGELES, CA	90067
WILLIAMS, ANTHONY	FILM PRODUCER	ODEON WEST END, 40 LEICESTER SQ	LONDON WC2H 7LP	ENGLAND
WILLIAMS, ANTHONY V	DIRECTOR	1436 WINDSOR PARK LN	HAVERTOWN, PA	19083
WILLIAMS, BANKS	FOOTBALL REFEREE	NFL, 410 PARK AVE	NEW YORK, NY	10022
WILLIAMS, BARBARA	ACTRESS	15760 VENTURA BLVD #1730	ENCINO, CA	91436
WILLIAMS, BARRY	ACTOR	1930 CENTURY PARK W #403	LOS ANGELES, CA	90067
WILLIAMS, BART	ACTOR	10742 1/2 CAMARILLO ST	NORTH HOLLYWOOD, CA	91602

WILLIAMS, BENNETT "STRETCH"	BASEBALL SCOUT	ORIOLE PARK, 333 W CAMDEN ST	BALTIMORE, MD	21201
WILLIAMS, BERNARD T	FILM PRODUCER	4027 HAYVENHURST DR	ENCINO, CA	91436
WILLIAMS, BERNIE	BASEBALL	N Y YANKEES, YANKEE STADIUM	BRONX, NY	10451
WILLIAMS, BERT	ACTOR	4731 LAUREL CANYON BLVD #5	NORTH HOLLYWOOD, CA	91607
WILLIAMS, BILL	ACTOR	POST OFFICE BOX 1980	NORTH HOLLYWOOD, CA	91604
WILLIAMS, BILLIE JO	SINGER	POST OFFICE BOX 783	MADISON, TN	37115
WILLIAMS, BILLY	BASEBALL (CUBS)	586 PRINCE EDWARD RD	GLEN ELLYN, IL	60137
WILLIAMS, BILLY	BB-COACH (INDIANS)	INDIANS, CLEVELAND STADIUM	CLEVELAND, OH	44114
WILLIAMS, BILLY	CINEMATOGRAPHER	THE COACH HOUSE		
		HAWKSHILL PL, ESHER	SURREY KT10 9HY	ENGLAND
WILLIAMS, BILLY DEE	ACTOR	1240 LOMA VISTA DR	BEVERLY HILLS, CA	90210
WILLIAMS, BOB	COMPOSER	4513 MORSE AVE	STUDIO CITY, CA	91604
WILLIAMS, BRENT	FOOTBALL	PATRIOTS, FOXBORO STADIUM, RT #1	FOXBORO, MA	02035
WILLIAMS, BRIAN	BASEBALL	POST OFFICE BOX 27045	TUCSON, AZ	85726
WILLIAMS, BRIAN	FOOTBALL	N Y GIANTS, GIANTS STADIUM	EAST RUTHERFORD, NJ	07073
WILLIAMS, BUCK	BASKETBALL	700 NE MULTNOMAH ST #600	PORTLAND, OR	97232
WILLIAMS, CALVIN	FOOTBALL	EAGLES, BROAD ST & PATTISON AVE	PHILADELPHIA, PA	19148
WILLIAMS, CARA	ACTRESS	146 S PECK DR	BEVERLY HILLS, CA	90212
WILLIAMS, CAROLINE	ACTRESS	MTA, 9320 WILSHIRE BL, 3RD FL	BEVERLY HILLS, CA	90212
WILLIAMS, CARY	BASEBALL	POST OFFICE BOX 3449	SCRANTON, PA	18505
WILLIAMS, CHARLES	BASEBALL UMPIRE	5020 S LAKE DR #1715	CHICAGO, IL	60615
WILLIAMS, CHRIS	FOOTBALL	POST OFFICE BOX 888	PHOENIX, AZ	85001
WILLIAMS, CHUCK	BODYBUILDER	POST OFFICE BOX 8421	FOUNTAIN VALLEY, CA	92728
WILLIAMS, CINDY	ACTRESS	709 19TH ST	SANTA MONICA, CA	90402
WILLIAMS, CLARENCE, III	ACTOR	8019 1/2 MELROSE AVE #3	LOS ANGELES, CA	90046
WILLIAMS, CURT	ACTOR	305 CONVENT AVE	NEW YORK, NY	10031
WILLIAMS, DALE	FOOTBALL REFEREE	NFL, 410 PARK AVE	NEW YORK, NY	10022
WILLIAMS, DALLAS	BASEBALL-INSTRUCTOR	INDIANS, CLEVELAND STADIUM	CLEVELAND, OH	44114
WILLIAMS, DANA	BASEBALL	1404 OAKTREE CT	MOBILE, AL	36609
WILLIAMS, DANNY	BASEBALL COACH	POST OFFICE BOX 3452	KINSTON, NC	28502
WILLIAMS, DARNELL	ACTOR	400 MADISON AVE #2000	NEW YORK, NY	10017
WILLIAMS, DAVID	BASEBALL	POST OFFICE BOX 507	DURHAM, NC	27702
WILLIAMS, DAVID	FOOTBALL	OILERS, 6910 FANNIN ST	HOUSTON, TX	77070
WILLIAMS, DEBBIE	SINGER	888 8TH AVE #1-F	NEW YORK, NY	10019
WILLIAMS, DENIECE	SINGER	ALIVE, 8271 MELROSE AVE, 2ND FL	LOS ANGELES, CA	90046
WILLIAMS, DENNIS E	COMPOSER	1133 CAMPBELL ST #1	GLENDALE, CA	91207
WILLIAMS, DICK	BASEBALL SCOUT	POST OFFICE BOX 2000	SAN DIEGO, CA	92112
WILLIAMS, DICK	BASEBALL-MANAGER	POST OFFICE BOX 21068	SEATTLE, WA	98111
WILLIAMS, DICK ANTHONY	ACTOR	ICM, 8899 BEVERLY BLVD	LOS ANGELES, CA	90048
WILLIAMS, DON	SINGER-SONGWRITER	MORESS, 1209 16TH AVE S	NASHVILLE, TN	37212
WILLIAMS, DWIGHT J	FILM DIRECTOR	POST OFFICE BOX 746	NEW YORK, NY	10150
WILLIAMS, ED	ACTOR	CARROLL, 120 S VICTORY BL #104	BURBANK, CA	91502
WILLIAMS, EDDIE	BASEBALL (RICHMOND)	POST OFFICE BOX 6667	RICHMOND, VA	23230
WILLIAMS, EDDIE	BASEBALL (SAVANNAH)	POST OFFICE BOX 3783	SAVANNAH, GA	31414
WILLIAMS, EDY	ACTRESS-MODEL	1638 BLUE JAY WY	LOS ANGELES, CA	90069
WILLIAMS, ELMO	FILM EXECUTIVE	9255 SUNSET BLVD #800	LOS ANGELES, CA	90069
WILLIAMS, ERIC	FOOTBALL	POST OFFICE BOX 17247 (DULLES)	WASHINGTON, DC	20041
WILLIAMS, ERIK	FOOTBALL	COWBOYS, 1 COWBOYS PARKWAY	IRVING, TX	75063
WILLIAMS, ESTHER	ACTRESS-SWIMMER	9377 READCREST DR	BEVERLY HILLS, CA	90210
WILLIAMS, FLORENCE	ACTRESS	POST OFFICE BOX 307	ROCKPORT, ME	04856
WILLIAMS, FRANK	ACTOR	31 MANOR PARK CRESCENT	EDGEWARE	ENGLAND
WILLIAMS, GENE	FOOTBALL	DOLPHINS, 2269 NW 199TH ST	MIAMI, FL	33056
WILLIAMS, GEORGE	BASEBALL	POST OFFICE BOX 882	MADISON, WI	53701
WILLIAMS, GERALD	BASEBALL	1155 W MOUND ST	COLUMBUS, OH	43223
WILLIAMS, GERALD	FOOTBALL	STEELERS, 300 STADIUM CIR	PITTSBURGH, PA	15212
WILLIAMS, GILBERT	WRITER-PRODUCER	16 NORMAN PL	TENAFLY, NJ	07670
WILLIAMS, HAL	ACTOR	CASSELL, 843 N SYCAMORE AVE	LOS ANGELES, CA	90038
WILLIAMS, HANK, JR	SINGER-SONGWRITER	POST OFFICE BOX 850	PARIS, TN	38242
WILLIAMS, HARVEY	FOOTBALL	CHIEFS, 1 ARROWHEAD DR	KANSAS CITY, MO	64129
WILLIAMS, HERB	BASKETBALL	REUNION ARENA, 777 SPORTS ST	DALLAS, TX	75207
WILLIAMS, JACK	COLUMNIST	POST OFFICE BOX 500	WASHINGTON, DC	20044
WILLIAMS, JACKIEE LEE	SINGER	PENNY, 30 GUINAN ST	WALTHAM, MA	02154
WILLIAMS, JAMES	FOOTBALL (BEARS)	BEARS, 250 N WASHINGTON RD	LAKE FOREST, IL	60045
WILLIAMS, JAMES	FOOTBALL (BILLS)	BILLS, 1 BILLS DR	ORCHARD PARK, NJ	14127
WILLIAMS, JAMES	FOOTBALL (SAINTS)	SAINTS, 1500 POYDRAS ST	NEW ORLEANS, LA	90112
WILLIAMS, JAMES E	FILM EXEC-DIR	956 CORSICA DR	PACIFIC PALISADES, CA	90272
WILLIAMS, JAMIE	FOOTBALL	S F 49ERS, 4949 CENTENNIAL BL	SANTA CLARA, CA	95054
WILLIAMS, JAN WARREN	FILM PRODUCER	2264 LAUGHLIN ST	LA CANADA, CA	91011
WILLIAMS, JARVIS	FOOTBALL	DOLPHINS, 2269 NW 199TH ST	MIAMI, FL	33056
WILLIAMS, JASMIN H	TV WRITER-PRODUCER	55 PINEAPPLE ST #3-F	BROOKLYN, NY	11201
WILLIAMS, JAYSON	BASKETBALL	POST OFFICE BOX 25040	PHILADELPHIA, PA	19147
WILLIAMS, JEFF	BASEBALL	POST OFFICE BOX 230	HAGERSTOWN, MD	21740
WILLIAMS, JENNIFER	ACTRESS	135 EASTERN PARKWAY #2	BROOKLYN, NY	11238
WILLIAMS, JERROL	FOOTBALL	STEELERS, 300 STADIUM CIR	PITTSBURGH, PA	15212
WILLIAMS, JERRONE	BASEBALL	POST OFFICE DRAWER 1207	ZEBULON, NC	27597
WILLIAMS, JIMMY	BASEBALL (COACH)	POST OFFICE BOX 4064	ATLANTA, GA	30302
WILLIAMS, JIMMY	BASEBALL (PITCHER)	5999 E VAN BUREN ST	PHOENIX, AZ	85008
WILLIAMS, JIMMY	FOOTBALL	VIKINGS, 9520 VIKING DR	EDEN PRAIRIE, MN	55344
WILLIAMS, JO BETH	ACTRESS	3529 BEVERLY GLEN BLVD	SHERMAN OAKS, CA	91423
WILLIAMS, JOE	SINGER	3337 KNOLLWOOD CT	LAS VEGAS, NV	89121
WILLIAMS, JOHN	BASKETBALL (BULLETS)	BULLETS, 1 HARRY S TRUMAN DR	LANDOVER, MD	20785
WILLIAMS, JOHN	BASKETBALL (CAVS)	POST OFFICE BOX 5000	RICHFIELD, OH	44286
WILLIAMS, JOHN	GUITARIST	HOLT, 31 SINCLAIR RD	LONDON W14	ENGLAND
WILLIAMS, JOHN C	DIRECTOR	1008 PRINCE ST	ALEXANDRIA, VA	22314
WILLIAMS, JOHN L	FOOTBALL	SEAHAWKS, 11220 NE 53RD ST	KIRKLAND, WA	98033

Name	Occupation	Address	City	Code
WILLIAMS, JOHN T	COMPOSER-CONDUCTOR	301 MASSACHUSETTS AVE	BOSTON, MA	02115
WILLIAMS, JUAN	BASEBALL	POST OFFICE BOX 4525	MACON, GA	31208
WILLIAMS, KEITH	COMPOSER	POST OFFICE BOX 6	PACIFIC PALISADES, CA	90272
WILLIAMS, KEITH R	COMPOSER-CONDUCTOR	13349 WENTWORTH ST	PACOIMA, CA	91331
WILLIAMS, KELLIE	ACTRESS	ABC-TV, 2040 AVE OF THE STARS	LOS ANGELES, CA	90067
WILLIAMS, KEN	BASKETBALL	PACERS, 300 E MARKET ST	INDIANAPOLIS, IN	46204
WILLIAMS, KENNETH	ACTOR	ICM, 388-396 OXFORD ST	LONDON W1	ENGLAND
WILLIAMS, KENNY	ACTOR-DIRECTOR	18 ANTIGUA CT	CORONADO, CA	92118
WILLIAMS, KENNY	BASEBALL	CHIEFS, MAC ARTHUR STADIUM	SYRACUSE, NY	13208
WILLIAMS, KENT	ARTIST	320 7TH AVE #3	BROOKLYN, NY	11215
WILLIAMS, LANNY	BASEBALL	POST OFFICE BOX 309	GASTONA, NC	28053
WILLIAMS, LAWRENCE	SONGWRITER	306 N SAINT CRISPEN	BREA, CA	92621
WILLIAMS, LAWRENCE E, JR	DIRECTOR	RURAL DELIVERY #2, BOX 409		
		SCOTCHTOWN RD	MONTGOMERY, NY	12549
WILLIAMS, LEE	FOOTBALL	OILERS, 6910 FANNIN ST	HOUSTON, TX	77070
WILLIAMS, LENNY	SINGER	1326 N FLORES ST #26	LOS ANGELES, CA	90069
WILLIAMS, LLANDYS	COSTUME DESIGNER	13949 VENTURA BLVD #309	SHERMAN OAKS, CA	91423
WILLIAMS, MACK RAY, JR	DIRECTOR	1674 CHIMNEY HOUSE RD	RESTON, VA	22090
WILLIAMS, MARCELYN ANN	ACTRESS	6605 HOLLYWOOD BLVD #220	HOLLYWOOD, CA	90028
WILLIAMS, MARSHALL L	TV WRITER	157 HART AVE	SANTA MONICA, CA	90405
WILLIAMS, MASON	SINGER-SONGWRITER	POST OFFICE BOX 25	OAKBRIDGE, OR	97463
WILLIAMS, MATT	BASEBALL	S F GIANTS, CANDLESTICK PARK	SAN FRANICSCO, CA	94124
WILLIAMS, MATT	TV-COMEDY WRITER	ZEIDERMAN, 211 E 48TH ST	NEW YORK, NY	10017
WILLIAMS, MAURICE & THE ZODIACS	VOCAL GROUP	INSIGHT, 2300 E INDEPENDENCE BL	CHARLOTTE, NC	28205
WILLIAMS, MICHAEL	BASKETBALL	PACERS, 300 E MARKET ST	INDIANAPOLIS, IN	46204
WILLIAMS, MIKE	BASEBALL	POST OFFICE BOX 15050	READING, PA	19612
WILLIAMS, MITCH	BASEBALL	POST OFFICE BOX 7575	PHILADELPHIA, PA	19101
WILLIAMS, MONTEL	TV HOST	151 S EL CAMINO DR	BEVERLY HILLS, CA	90212
WILLIAMS, OSCAR	FILM WRITER-DIRECTOR	856 S SAINT ANDREWS PL	LOS ANGELES, CA	90005
WILLIAMS, PAGE	COMPOSER-CONDUCTOR	POST OFFICE BOX 325	ALHAMBRA, CA	91802
WILLIAMS, PAT	BASEBALL EXECUTIVE	POST OFFICE BOX 5645	ORLANDO, FL	32855
WILLIAMS, PAT	BASKETBALL EXECUTIVE	POST OFFICE BOX 76	ORLANDO, FL	32802
WILLIAMS, PAT	BODYBUILDER	POST OFFICE BOX 6100	ROSEMEAND, CA	91770
WILLIAMS, PAT	U S CONGRESSMAN	32 N LAST CHANCE GULCH	HELENA, MT	59601
WILLIAMS, PATRICK	COMPOSER	532 17TH ST	SANTA MONICA, CA	90402
WILLIAMS, PAUL	BASEBALL	POST OFFICE BOX 230	HAGERSTOWN, MD	21740
WILLIAMS, PAUL	SINGER-SONGWRITER	645 SAND POINT RD	CARPINTERIA, CA	93013
WILLIAMS, PAUL W	DIRECTOR	40101 PACIFIC COAST HWY	MALIBU, CA	90265
WILLIAMS, PERRY	FOOTBALL	N Y GIANTS, GIANTS STADIUM	EAST RUTHERFORD, NJ	07073
WILLIAMS, REGGIE	BASEBALL (MAJORS)	6669 PONDSIDE CIR	MEMPHIS, TN	38119
WILLIAMS, REGGIE	BASEBALL (MINORS)	10233 96TH AVE	EDMONTON, ALB TK5 0A5	CANADA
WILLIAMS, REGGIE	BASKETBALL	600 E MARKET ST #102	SAN ANTONIO, TX	78205
WILLIAMS, RICHARD	ARTIST	112 RUSKIN AVE	SYRACUSE, NY	13207
WILLIAMS, RICHARD E	TV DIRECTOR	3193 WADE ST	LOS ANGELES, CA	90066
WILLIAMS, RICK	BASEBALL-INSTRUCTOR	EXPOS, 4545 DE COUBERTIN AVE	MONTREAL, QUE H1V 3P2	CANADA
WILLIAMS, ROBERT	FOOTBALL	COWBOYS, 1 COWBOYS PARKWAY	IRVING, TX	75063
WILLIAMS, ROBERT F	SCREENWRITER	8955 BEVERLY BLVD	WEST HOLLYWOOD, CA	90048
WILLIAMS, ROBIN	COMED-ACT-WRI	CAA, 9830 WILSHIRE BLVD	BEVERLY HILLS, CA	90212
WILLIAMS, ROBIN & LINDA	VOCAL DUO	POST OFFICE BOX 8753	ALBANY, NY	12208
WILLIAMS, ROBIN M	DIRECTOR	POST OFFICE BOX 48516	LOS ANGELES, CA	90048
WILLIAMS, ROGER	PIANIST	VIRTUOSO, 5710 WALLIS LN	WOODLAND HILLS, CA	91364
WILLIAMS, RUGG	ACTOR	6255 SUNSET BLVD #627	LOS ANGELES, CA	90028
WILLIAMS, SAMM-ART	PLAYWRIGHT-WRITER	WM MORRIS, 1350 AVE OF AMERICAS	NEW YORK, NY	10019
WILLIAMS, SCOTT	BASKETBALL	980 N MICHIGAN AVE #1600	CHICAGO, IL	60611
WILLIAMS, SPICE	ACTRESS	8831 SUNSET BLVD #304	LOS ANGELES, CA	90069
WILLIAMS, SPIN	BASEBALL COACH	POST OFFICE BOX 450	BUFFALO, NY	14205
WILLIAMS, STAN	BASEBALL-COACH	4702 HAYTER AVE	LAKEWOOD, CA	90712
WILLIAMS, STEPHANIE E	ACTRESS	7471 MELROSE AVE #14	LOS ANGELES, CA	90046
WILLIAMS, STEVE	BASEBALL SCOUT	TWINS, 501 CHICAGO AVE S	MINNEAPOLIS, MN	55415
WILLIAMS, STEVE "DR DEATH"	WRESTLER	POST OFFICE BOX 105366	ATLANTA, GA	31348
WILLIAMS, STEVEN	ACTOR	GEDDES, 8457 MELROSE PL #200	LOS ANGELES, CA	90069
WILLIAMS, STEVEN H	DIRECTOR	1142 MANHATTAN AVE #232-CP	MANHATTAN BEACH, CA	90266
WILLIAMS, TED	BASEBALL (MAJORS)	POST OFFICE BOX 590	COPPERSTOWN, NY	13326
WILLIAMS, TED	BASEBALL (MINORS)	POST OFFICE BOX 3690, STA "B"	CALGARY, ALB T2B 4M4	CANADA
WILLIAMS, TERENCE PAUL	DIRECTOR-PRODUCER	L'EPINE SMITH, 10 WYNDHAM PL	LONDON W1H 1AS	ENGLAND
WILLIAMS, TODD	BASEBALL	POST OFFICE BOX 10031	BAKERSFIELD, CA	93389
WILLIAMS, TONYA LEE	ACTRESS	CBS-TV, "YOUNG & THE RESTLESS"		
		7800 BEVERLY BLVD #3305	LOS ANGELES, CA	90036
WILLIAMS, TREAT	ACTOR	215 W 78TH ST #10-A	NEW YORK, NY	10024
WILLIAMS, VAN	ACTOR	1630 OCEAN PARK BLVD	SANTA MONICA, CA	90405
WILLIAMS, VANESSA	ACT-SING-MOD	ROUTE #100	MILLWOOD, NY	10546
WILLIAMS, VICKI	COMMENTATOR	KING FEATURES, 216 E 45TH ST	NEW YORK, NY	10017
WILLIAMS, VINCE	ACTOR	CBS-TV, "THE GUIDING LIGHT"		
		222 E 44TH ST	NEW YORK, NY	10017
WILLIAMS, WALT	BASEBALL-COACH	POST OFFICE BOX 309	GASTONA, NC	28053
WILLIAMS, WALTER E	COLUMNIST	HERITAGE FEATURES SYNDICATE		
		214 MASSACHUSETTS AVE, NE	WASHINGTON, DC	20002
WILLIAMS, WARREN	FOOTBALL	STEELERS, 300 STADIUM CIR	PITTSBURGH, PA	15212
WILLIAMS, WENDY	ACTRESS	56 CLAREMONT RD, SURBITON	SURREY	ENGLAND
WILLIAMS, WILLIE	FOOTBALL	POST OFFICE BOX 888	PHOENIX, AZ	85001
WILLIAMS & REE	VOCAL DUO	POST OFFICE BOX 163	HENDERSONVILLE, TN	37077
WILLIAMS-JONES, MICHAEL	FILM EXECUTIVE	UIP HOUSE, 45 BEADON RD		
		HAMMERSMITH	LONDON W6 0EG	ENGLAND
WILLIAMSON, BRUCE	SINGER	POST OFFICE BOX 25371	CHARLOTTE, NC	28212
WILLIAMSON, CHRIS	SINGER	OLIVIA RECORDS CO		

Name	Occupation	Address	City	Zip/Country
		4400 MARKET ST	OAKLAND, CA	94608
WILLIAMSON, FRED	ACTOR-DIRECTOR	113 N SAN VICENTE BLVD #202	BEVERLY HILLS, CA	90211
WILLIAMSON, JACK	WRITER	POST OFFICE BOX 76	ORLANDO, FL	32802
WILLIAMSON, JAMES E	COMPOSER	8444 HILLROSE ST	SUNLAND, CA	91040
WILLIAMSON, MARK	BASEBALL	ORIOLE PARK, 333 W CAMDEN ST	BALTIMORE, MD	21201
WILLIAMSON, MYKEL T	ACTOR	LIGHT, 901 BRINGHAM AVE	LOS ANGELES, CA	90049
WILLIAMSON, NICOL	ACTOR	ICM, 388-396 OXFORD ST	LONDON W1	ENGLAND
WILLIAMSON, RICHARD	FOOTBALL COACH	BUCCANEERS, 1 BUCCANEER PL	TAMPA, FL	33607
WILLIAMSON, TONY	TV WRITER	MLR, 200 FULHAM RD	LONDON SW10 9PN	ENGLAND
WILLIG, ALLAN	TALENT AGENT	337 W 43RD ST #1-B	NEW YORK, NY	10036
WILLINGHAM, CALDER	PLAYWRIGHT	THE VANGUARD PRESS		
		424 MADISON AVE	NEW YORK, NY	10017
WILLINGHAM, NOBLE	ACTOR	9200 SUNSET BLVD #710	LOS ANGELES, CA	90069
WILLIS, BRUCE	ACTOR-SINGER	1122 S ROBERTSON BLVD #15	LOS ANGELES, CA	90035
WILLIS, CARL	BASEBALL	TWINS, 501 CHICAGO AVE S	MINNEAPOLIS, MN	55415
WILLIS, CHUCK	SINGER-GUITARIST	VELVET PRODS, 517 W 57TH ST	LOS ANGELES, CA	90037
WILLIS, GARRY	COLUMNIST	UPS, 4900 MAIN ST, 9TH FLOOR	KANSAS CITY, MO	64112
WILLIS, GORDON	CINEMATOGRAPHER	7715 SUNSET BLVD #150	LOS ANGELES, CA	90046
WILLIS, HENRY	TV DIRECTOR	7449 RUFFNER AVE	VAN NUYS, CA	91406
WILLIS, HERB	ACTOR-DIRECTOR	GERRITSEN, 8721 SUNSET BL #103	LOS ANGELES, CA	90069
WILLIS, JOEL	TV DIRECTOR	24 FERN VALLEY RD	WESTON, CT	06883
WILLIS, JOHN	TV DIRECTOR	CHANNEL 4, 60 CHARLOTTE ST	LONDON W1	ENGLAND
WILLIS, KEITH	FOOTBALL	STEELERS, 300 STADIUM CIR	PITTSBURGH, PA	15212
WILLIS, KEN	FOOTBALL	COWBOYS, 1 COWBOYS PARKWAY	IRVING, TX	75063
WILLIS, KEVIN	BASKETBALL	1 CNN CENTER #405, SOUTH TOWER	ATLANTA, GA	30303
WILLIS, LYNN	COMPOSER	24736 SEASHELL WY	DANA POINT, CA	92629
WILLIS, MARTY	BASEBALL	TIGERS, 89 WHARNCLIFFE RD N	LONDON, ONT N6H 2A7	CANADA
WILLIS, MARY PLESHETTE	WRITER	8955 BEVERLY BLVD	WEST HOLLYWOOD, CA	90048
WILLIS, PETER TOM	FOOTBALL	BEARS, 250 N WASHINGTON RD	LAKE FOREST, IL	60045
WILLIS, SCOTT	CARTOONIST	POST OFFICE BOX 5533	SAN JOSE, CA	95190
WILLIS, SUSAN C	ACTRESS	37 CHARLES ST	NEW YORK, NY	10014
WILLIS, TED	WRITER-PRODUCER	5 SHEPHERDS GREEN		
		CHISLEHURST	KENT	ENGLAND
WILLOUGHBY, LARRY	SINGER	POST OFFICE BOX 121542	NASHVILLE, TN	37212
WILLS, BUMP	BASEBALL-MANAGER	POST OFFICE BOX 3609	PORT CHARLOTTE, FL	33949
WILLS, FRANK	BASEBALL	733 GENERAL PERSHING ST	NEW ORLEANS, LA	70115
WILLS, MAURY	BASEBALL	30100 TOWN CENTER DR #0209	LAGUNA NIGUEL, CA	92677
WILLS, TOMMY	SINGER-SAXOPHONIST	THE TOWN & COUNTRY		
		10319 BARIBEAU LN	INDIANAPOLIS, IN	46229
WILMER, DOUGLAS	ACTOR	BELFRAGE, 68 SAINT JAMES'S ST	LONDON SW1A 1LE	ENGLAND
WILMET, PAUL	BASEBALL	226 N 6TH ST	DEPERE, WI	54115
WILMINGTON, MICHAEL	FILM CRITIC	LA TIMES, TIMES MIRROR SQ	LOS ANGELES, CA	90053
WILMOT, GARY	ACTOR	O'REILLY, 8 PARK PARADE	LONDON W3 9BD	ENGLAND
WILMOT, MICHAEL D	DIRECTOR	727 MIRAMONTES ST	HALF MOON BAY, CA	94019
WILPON, FRED	BASEBALL EXECUTIVE	METS, 126TH ST & ROOSEVELT AVE	FLUSHING, NY	11368
WILSON, AL	SINGER	POST OFFICE BOX 82	GREAT NECK, NY	11021
WILSON, ALBERT P	FILM EDITOR	ACE, 1041 N FORMOSA AVE	WEST HOLLYWOOD, CA	90046
WILSON, BOB	BASEBALL EXECUTIVE	POST OFFICE BOX 1553	BILLINGS, MT	59103
WILSON, BOBBY	FOOTBALL	POST OFFICE BOX 17247 (DULLES)	WASHINGTON, DC	20041
WILSON, BRANDON	BASEBALL	1090 N EUCLID AVE	SARASOTA, FL	34237
WILSON, BRUCE B	BASKETBALL EXECUTIVE	1 CNN CENTER #405, SOUTH TOWER	ATLANTA, GA	30303
WILSON, CAREY	HOCKEY	POST OFFICE BOX 1540, STA "M"	CALGARY, ALTA T2P 3BP	CANADA
WILSON, CARL	SINGER-SONGWRITER	8860 EVAN VIEW DR	LOS ANGELES, CA	90069
WILSON, CHARLES	FOOTBALL	PACKERS, 1265 LOMBARDI AVE	GREEN BAY, WI	54307
WILSON, CHARLES	U S CONGRESSMAN	701 N 1ST ST #201	LUFKIN, TX	75901
WILSON, CHUCK	SINGER	SODP, 29 HUDSON ST	WATERFORD, NY	12188
WILSON, CRAIG	BASEBALL (MAJORS)	250 STADIUM PLAZA	ST LOUIS, MO	63102
WILSON, CRAIG	BASEBALL (MINORS)	POST OFFICE BOX 4756	JACKSONVILLE, FL	32201
WILSON, DAN	BASEBALL	POST OFFICE BOX 23290	NASHVILLE, TN	37202
WILSON, DANIEL	TV PRODUCER	300 W 55TH ST	NEW YORK, NY	10019
WILSON, DAVE	TV DIRECTOR	15 MAPLEWOOD DR	PARSIPPANY, NJ	07054
WILSON, DAVID E	DIRECTOR	2207 LINDEN DR, SE	CEDAR RAPIDS, IA	52403
WILSON, DEMOND	ACTOR	CHURCH OF GOD IN CHRIST	FORT WASHINGTON, MD	20022
WILSON, DENNIS	PIANIST-COMPOSER	CARTHAGENA LODGE		
		SUTTON, SANDY	BEDS SG19 2NQ	ENGLAND
WILSON, DICK	BASEBALL SCOUT	TIGERS, TIGER STADIUM	DETROIT, MI	48216
WILSON, DON "THE DRAGON"	ACTOR-KICKBOXER	MGM/UA HOME VIDEO PRODUCTIONS		
		10000 WASHINGTON BLVD	CULVER CITY, CA	90232
WILSON, DONNICE	ACTRESS	ATKINS, 303 S CRESCENT HEIGHTS	LOS ANGELES, CA	90048
WILSON, DOROTHY	ACTRESS	330 W HWY 246, SPACE 129	BUELLTON, CA	93427
WILSON, DOUG	HOCKEY	BLACKHAWKS, 1800 W MADISON ST	CHICAGO, IL	60612
WILSON, DOUG	TV DIRECTOR	LEWIS RD	IRVING-ON-HUDSON, NY	10533
WILSON, ELIZABETH	ACTRESS	9301 WILSHIRE BLVD #312	BEVERLY HILLS, CA	90210
WILSON, ERICA	COLUMNIST	TRIBUNE, 64 E CONCORD ST	ORLANDO, FL	32801
WILSON, FLIP	COMED-ACT-WRI	21970 PACIFIC COAST HWY	MALIBU, CA	90265
WILSON, GARY	BASEBALL	POST OFFICE BOX 3449	SCRANTON, PA	18505
WILSON, HUGH	WRITER-PRODUCER	11940 CHAPARAL ST	LOS ANGELES, CA	90049
WILSON, HULEN	SINGER-SONGWRITER	POST OFFICE BOX 655	HUDSON, OH	44236
WILSON, IAN	CINEMATOGRAPHER	40 CHARLTON KINGS RD	LONDON NW5	ENGLAND
WILSON, JEANNIE	ACTRESS	9229 SUNSET BLVD #311	LOS ANGELES, CA	90069
WILSON, JIM	BASEBALL	5999 E VAN BUREN ST	PHOENIX, AZ	85008
WILSON, JIM	FILM PRODUCER	650 N BRONSON AVE #211	LOS ANGELES, CA	90004
WILSON, JOHN	BASEBALL SCOUT	TWINS, 501 CHICAGO AVE S	MINNEAPOLIS, MN	55415
WILSON, JOHN C	DIRECTOR	DGA, 110 W 57TH ST	NEW YORK, NY	10019
WILSON, JOHN G	WRITER-PRODUCER	16188 MEADOWCREST RD	SHERMAN OAKS, CA	91403

WILSON, JOHN RICHARD	COMPOSER	21056 LAS FLORES MESA DR	MALIBU, CA	90265
WILSON, JUSTIN	SINGER	POST OFFICE BOX 267	FORT SETTLEMENT, LA	70733
WILSON, KARL	FOOTBALL	RAMS, 2327 W LINCOLN BLVD	ANAHEIM, CA	92801
WILSON, KEN	BASEBALL EXECUTIVE	POST OFFICE BOX 7000	PITTSBURGH, PA	15212
WILSON, KEN	BASEBALL EXECUTIVE	HAWKS, 5600 N GLENWOOD	BOISE, ID	83714
WILSON, KEN	SPORTSCASTER	KTLA, 5800 SUNSET BLVD	HOLLYWOOD, CA	90028
WILSON, KENT	DIRECTOR	6961 SUNNYDELL TRAIL	HOLLYWOOD, CA	90068
WILSON, LANFORD	PLAYWRIGHT	DRAMATISTS GUILD, 110 W 57TH ST	NEW YORK, NY	10019
WILSON, LARRY	FOOTBALL EXECUTIVE	POST OFFICE BOX 888	PHOENIX, AZ	85001
WILSON, MARK	BASEBALL EXECUTIVE	POST OFFICE BOX 21727	SAN FRANCISCO, CA	95151
WILSON, MARY	SING-ACT-AUTHOR	1601 E FLAMINGO RD	LAS VEGAS, NV	89110
WILSON, MELANIE	ACTRESS	POST OFFICE BOX 93344	LOS ANGELES, CA	90093
WILSON, MIHCAEL G	FILM WRITER-PROD	EON PRODS, 2 S AUDLEY ST	LONDON W1Y 6AJ	ENGLAND
WILSON, MOOKIE	BASEBALL	SKYDOME, 300 BREMMER BL #3200	TORONTO, ONT M5V 3B3	CANADA
WILSON, NANCY	SINGER-ACTRESS	5455 WILSHIRE BLVD #1606	LOS ANGELES, CA	90036
WILSON, NIGEL	BASEBALL	633 JESSAMINE ST	KNOXVILLE, TN	37917
WILSON, PAUL E	WRITER-PRODUCER	9 OYSTER BAY DR	RUMSON, NJ	07760
WILSON, PETE	GOVERNOR	STATE CAPITOL BUILDING	SACRAMENTO, CA	95814
WILSON, PHIL	COMPOSER-MUSICIAN	8 HAMMOND RD	BELMONT, MA	02178
WILSON, RALPH C, JR	FOOTBALL	BILLS, 1 BILLS DR	ORCHARD PARK, NJ	14127
WILSON, RALPH GABY	SCREENWRITER	9022 SUNSET BLVD #531	LOS ANGELES, CA	90069
WILSON, RICHARD	ACTOR-DIRECTOR	CONWAY, 18-21 JERMYN ST	LONDON SW1	ENGLAND
WILSON, RICHARD L	CONDUCTOR	22623 MAPLE AVE	TORRANCE, CA	90505
WILSON, RITA	ACTRESS	151 S EL CAMINO DR	BEVERLY HILLS, CA	90212
WILSON, ROBERT	FOOTBALL	BUCCANEERS, 1 BUCCANEER PL	TAMPA, FL	33607
WILSON, RON	HOCKEY	BLUES, 5700 OAKLAND AVE	SAINT LOUIS, MO	63110
WILSON, RONALD	TV DIRECTOR-PRODUCER	CONWAY, 18-21 JERMYN ST	LONDON SW1	ENGLAND
WILSON, ROWLAND BRAGG	CARTOONIST	33871 CALLE ACORDARSE	SAN JUAN CAPISTRANO, C.	92675
WILSON, SCOTT	ACTOR	1999 AVE OF THE STARS #2850	LOS ANGELES, CA	90067
WILSON, SCOTT	BODYBUILDER	GOLD'S GYM, 35 NOTRE DAME AVE	SAN JOSE, CA	95113
WILSON, SCOTT	TRAINER	POST OFFICE BOX 21727	SAN FRANCISCO, CA	95151
WILSON, SHEREE J	ACTRESS	LIGHT, 901 BRINGHAM AVE	LOS ANGELES, CA	90049
WILSON, STEVE	BASEBALL	1000 ELYSIAN PARK DR	LOS ANGELES, CA	90012
WILSON, STUART	ACTOR	MARKHAM AND FROGGATT, LTD		
		JULIAN HOUSE, 4 WINDMILL ST	LONDON W1P 1HF	ENGLAND
WILSON, TEDDY	PIANIST	EDITH KIGGEN, 50 E 72ND ST	NEW YORK, NY	10021
WILSON, THOMAS S	BASKETBALL EXECUTIVE	THE PALACE OF AUBURN HILLS		
		2 CHAMPIONSHIP DR	AUBURN HILLS, MI	48326
WILSON, TOM	BASEBALL (CATCHER)	POST OFFICE BOX 22093	GREENSBORO, NC	27420
WILSON, TOM	BASEBALL (SCOUT)	REDS, 100 RIVERFRONT STADIUM	CINCINNATI, OH	45202
WILSON, TREVOR	BASEBALL	S F GIANTS, CANDLESTICK PARK	SAN FRANICSCO, CA	94124
WILSON, TREVOR	BASKETBALL	1 CNN CENTER #405, SOUTH TOWER	ATLANTA, GA	30303
WILSON, TY "THE RULER"	CARD COLLECTOR	2801 MEADOW LARK DR	SAN DIEGO, CA	92123
WILSON, WADE	FOOTBALL	VIKINGS, 9520 VIKING DR	EDEN PRAIRIE, MN	55344
WILSON, WARREN D "BILLY"	CONDUCTOR	602 2ND AVE N	COLUMBUS, MS	39701
WILSON, WILLIE	BASEBALL	ATHLETICS'S, OAKLAND COLISEUM	OAKLAND, CA	94621
WILSON PHILLIPS	VOCAL TRIO	1290 AVE OF THE AMERICAS #4200	NEW YORK, NY	10104
WILSTEAD, RANDY	BASEBALL	POST OFFICE BOX 3566	WEST PALM BEACH, FL	33402
WILTON, NICHOLAS	ARTIST	147 SULLIVAN ST #2-C	NEW YORK, NY	10012
WILTON, NICK	ACTOR-WRITER	STONE, 25 WHITEHALL	LONDON SW1A 2BS	ENGLAND
WILTON, PENELOPE	ACTRESS	BELFRAGE, 68 SAINT JAMES'S ST	LONDON SW1A 1LE	ENGLAND
WILTSE, KRIS	ARTIST	12530 SE 53RD ST	BELLEVUE, WA	98006
WIMBERLY, WILLIAM J	COMPOSER-CONDUCTOR	1552 LUCRETIA AVE	LOS ANGELES, CA	90026
WIMMER, BRIAN	ACTOR	641 SWARTHMORE AVE	PACIFIC PALISADES, CA	90272
WIMMER, CHUCK	ARTIST	7760 OAKHURST CIR	BRECKSVILLE, OH	44141
WIMMER, RICHARD S	TV WRITER	10100 SANTA MONICA BLVD #1600	LOS ANGELES, CA	90067
WINANS, MATT	BASEBALL UMPIRE	POST OFFICE BOX 716	PLAINVILLE, CT	06062
WINANS, THE	GOSPEL GROUP	10100 SANTA MONICA BLVD #1600	LOS ANGELES, CA	90067
WINANT, BRUCE	ACTOR	4864 1/2 TUJUNGA AVE	NORTH HOLLYWOOD, CA	91601
WINANT, SCOTT	TV DIRECTOR	CAA, 9830 WILSHIRE BLVD	BEVERLY HILLS, CA	90212
WINBURN, GEORGE R, JR	DIRECTOR	DGA, 7920 SUNSET BLVD, 6TH FL	LOS ANGELES, CA	90046
WINCELBERG, ANITA M	WRITER	301 S WETHERLY DR	BEVERLY HILLS, CA	90211
WINCELBERG, SIMON	WRITER	301 S WETHERLY DR	BEVERLY HILLS, CA	90211
WINCHELL, DEREK	BASEBALL TRAINER	POST OFFICE BOX 1742	PALM SPRINGS, CA	92263
WINCHELL, PAUL	ACTOR	32262 OAKSTONE DR	WESTLAKE VILLAGE, CA	91361
WINCHELL, PAUL	DIRECTOR-PRODUCER	2800 OLYMPIC BLVD	SANTA MONICA, CA	90404
WINCHESTER, JESSE	SINGER-SONGWRITER	POST OFFICE BOX 7308	CARMEL, CA	93921
WINCHESTER, KENNARD	BASKETBALL	POST OFFICE BOX 272349	HOUSTON, TX	77277
WINCHESTER, MAUD	ACTRESS	141 S EL CAMINO DR #205	BEVERLY HILLS, CA	90212
WINCOTT, JEFF	ACTOR	3880 FREDONIA DR #B	LOS ANGELES, CA	90068
WIND, THE	ROCK & ROLL GROUP	POST OFFICE BOX 390 (CHELSEA)	NEW YORK, NY	10113
WINDBREAKERS, THE	ROCK & ROLL GROUP	450 14TH ST #201	ATLANTA, GA	30318
WINDER, MICHAEL	SCREENWRITER	8955 BEVERLY BLVD	WEST HOLLYWOOD, CA	90048
WINDES, RODNEY	BASEBALL	POST OFFICE BOX 4209	JACKSON, MS	39296
WINDHAM, BARRY	WRESTLER	POST OFFICE BOX 105366	ATLANTA, GA	31348
WINDING, VICTOR	ACTOR	PENTWYN FARM COTTAGE		
		FOREST COAL PIT, ABERGAVENNY	GWENT NP7 7LY	ENGLAND
WINDSOR, BETH	ACTRESS	GOLAN, 651 N KILKEA DR	LOS ANGELES, CA	90048
WINDSOR, MARIE	ACTRESS	9501 CHEROKEE LN	BEVERLY HILLS, CA	90210
WINDSOR, ROMY	ACTRESS	132 S LASKY DR #B	BEVERLY HILLS, CA	90212
WINDUST, PENELOPE	ACTRESS	11726 SAN VICENTE BLVD #300	LOS ANGELES, CA	90049
WINE, NATHANIEL B	CONDUCTOR	12717 WEDDINGTON AVE	NORTH HOLLYWOOD, CA	91607
WINER, DEBORAH GRACE	TV-COMEDY WRITER	1199 PARK AVE	NEW YORK, NY	10128
WINER, HARRY S	TV DIRECTOR	1033 OCEAN AVE #204	SANTA MONICA, CA	90403
WINFIELD, DAVE	BASEBALL	367 W FOREST	TEANECK, NJ	07666

WINFIELD, PAUL	ACTOR	5693 HOLLY OAK DR	LOS ANGELES, CA	90068
WINFREY, LEE	TV CRITIC	PHIL INQ, 400 N BROAD ST	PHILADELPHIA, PA	19101
WINFREY, OPRAH	ACTRESS-TV HOST-PROD	POST OFFICE BOX 909715	CHICAGO, IL	60690
WING, LESLIE	ACTRESS	247 S BEVERLY DR #102	BEVERLY HILLS, CA	90210
WING MERRILL, TOBY	ACTRESS-DANCER	POST OFFICE BOX 1997	LAKE ELSINORE, CA	92330
WINGER, DEBRA	ACTRESS	POST OFFICE BOX 1368	PACIFIC PALISADES, CA	90272
WINGERT, DICK	CARTOONIST	KING FEATURES, 216 E 45TH ST	NEW YORK, NY	10017
WINGREEN, JASON	ACTOR	4224 TEESDALE AVE	NORTH HOLLYWOOD, CA	91604
WINIARSKI, CHIP	BASEBALL	POST OFFICE BOX 3452	KINSTON, NC	28502
WINITSKY, ALEX	FILM PRODUCER	9720 WILSHIRE BLVD #704	BEVERLY HILLS, CA	90212
WINK, DAVE	ARTIST	16 HONOUR AVE	ATLANTA, GA	30305
WINKELMAN, WALT	BASEBALL EXECUTIVE	POST OFFICE BOX 8550	STOCKTON, CA	95208
WINKLER, HENRY	ACT-DIR-PROD	POST OFFICE BOX 1764	STUDIO CITY, CA	91604
WINKLER, IRWIN	FILM PRODUCER	10125 W WASHINGTON BLVD	CULVER CITY, CA	90230
WINKLES, BOBBY	BASEBALL-COACH	EXPOS, 4545 DE COUBERTIN AVE	MONTREAL, QUE H1V 3P2	CANADA
WINKLESS, NELSON	DIRECTOR	11745 LANDALE ST	NORTH HOLLYWOOD, CA	91607
WINN, DAVID	ACTOR	8961 MEGAN AVE	CANOGA PARK, CA	91304
WINN, EARL	BASEBALL SCOUT	1060 W ADDISON ST	CHICAGO, IL	60613
WINN, KITTY	ACTRESS	10000 SANTA MONICA BLVD #305	LOS ANGELES, CA	90067
WINNER, CHARLEY	FOOTBALL EXECUTIVE	DOLPHINS, 2269 NW 199TH ST	MIAMI, FL	33056
WINNER, CHRISTOPHER P	COLUMNIST	POST OFFICE BOX 500	WASHINGTON, DC	20044
WINNER, MICHAEL	WRITER-PRODUCER	WRITERS GUILD, 430 EDGWARE RD	LONDON W2 1EH	ENGLAND
WINNER, MIKE	WRESTLER	8725 N CHAUTAUQUA BLVD	PORTLAND, OR	97217
WINNICK, JERRY	TV WRITER	9300 WILSHIRE BLVD #410	BEVERLY HILLS, CA	90212
WINNINGHAM, HERM	BASEBALL	FENWAY PARK, 4 YAWKEY WY	BOSTON, MA	02215
WINNINGHAM, MARE	ACTRESS	12256 LA MAIDA ST	NORTH HOLLYWOOD, CA	91607
WINOKUR, MARC	SINGER	POST OFFICE BOX 98	FOREST HILLS, NY	11375
WINSLOIW, STEPHANIE	SINGER	POST OFFICE BOX 1750	HOLLYWOOD, CA	90028
WINSLOW, BIRGIT	ACTRESS	1122 26TH ST	SANTA MONICA, CA	90403
WINSLOW, BRYANT	BASEBALL	POST OFFICE BOX 422229	KISSIMMEE, FL	34742
WINSLOW, KELLEN	FOOTBALL	4786 QUITO CT	SAN DIEGO, CA	92124
WINSLOW, MICHAEL	ACTOR-COMEDIAN	19321 PALOMAR PL	TARZANA, CA	91356
WINSTEN, ARCHER	FILM CRITIC	425 W BROADWAY	NEW YORK, NY	10012
WINSTON, DARRIN	BASEBALL	1501 W 16TH ST	INDIANAPOLIS, IN	46202
WINSTON, ELLEN M	JOURNALIST	10969 WELLWORTH AVE #311	LOS ANGELES, CA	90024
WINSTON, HATTIE	ACTRESS	13025 JARVIS AVE	LOS ANGELES, CA	90061
WINSTON, SUSAN	TV PRODUCER	LORIMAR-TELEPICTURES		
		3970 OVERLAND AVE	CULVER CITY, CA	90230
WINSTON, SUSAN B	DIRECTOR	310 W 72ND ST	NEW YORK, NY	10023
WINSTONE, RAY	ACTOR	HAMMOND, GOLDEN HOUSE		
		29 GREAT PULTENEY ST	LONDON W1R 3DD	ENGLAND
WINTER, ALEX	ACTOR	9350 WILSHIRE BLVD #324	BEVERLY HILLS, CA	90212
WINTER, CATHY	SINGER	POST OFFICE BOX 6380	ALBANY, NY	12206
WINTER, EDGAR	SINGER-GUITARIST	350 5TH AVE #5215	NEW YORK, NY	10018
WINTER, EDWARD	ACTOR	4359 HAYVENHURST AVE	ENCINO, CA	91436
WINTER, GARY	DIRECTOR	DGA, 7920 SUNSET BLVD, 6TH FL	LOS ANGELES, CA	90046
WINTER, JACK	WRITER-PRODUCER	470 W END AVE	NEW YORK, NY	10024
WINTER, JOHNNY	SINGER-GUITARIST	POST OFFICE BOX 60234	CHICAGO, IL	60660
WINTER, JOY	SINGER-SONGWRITER	322 W 57TH ST #44-G	NEW YORK, NY	10019
WINTER, MICHAEL	TV DIRECTOR	437 N OAKHURST DR	BEVERLY HILLS, CA	90210
WINTER, TEX	BASKETBALL COACH	980 N MICHIGAN AVE #1600	CHICAGO, IL	60611
WINTER HOURS	ROCK & ROLL GROUP	AAM, 277 CHURCH ST	NEW YORK, NY	10013
WINTERS, BRIAN	BASKETBALL COACH	POST OFFICE BOX 5000	RICHFIELD, OH	44286
WINTERS, DAVID	DIRECTOR	13850 MULHOLLAND DR	BEVERLY HILLS, CA	90210
WINTERS, FRANK	FOOTBALL	CHIEFS, 1 ARROWHEAD DR	KANSAS CITY, MO	64129
WINTERS, GLENN S	WRITER-PRODUCER	1855 FOOTHILL BLVD	LA CANADA, CA	91011
WINTERS, JERRY	DIRECTOR	11 PALM ISLAND	MIAMI BEACH, FL	33139
WINTERS, JONATHAN	COMEDIAN-ACTOR	4310 ARCOLA AVE	NORTH HOLLYWOOD, CA	91602
WINTERS, KAREN COLE	TV WRITER	1855 FOOTHILL BLVD	LA CANADA, CA	91011
WINTERS, MATT	BASEBALL	16 HUNTINGTON CT	WILLIAMSVILLE, NY	14221
WINTERS, MIKE	BASEBALL UMPIRE	NATIONAL LEAGUE, 350 PARK AVE	NEW YORK, NY	10022
WINTERS, RALPH E	FILM EDITOR	9242 BEVERLY DR #200	BEVERLY HILLS, CA	90210
WINTERS, TIME	ACTOR	136 E 57TH ST #2-C	NEW YORK, NY	10022
WINTERSOLE, WILLIAM	ACTOR	1177 N ARDMORE AVE #6	LOS ANGELES, CA	90029
WINTHER, JORN	TV DIRECTOR-PRODUCER	7 GREENWOOD LN	WESTPORT, CT	06880
WINWOOD, STEVE	SINGER-SONGWRITER	888 7TH AVE #1602	NEW YORK, NY	10019
WIPERS, THE	ROCK & ROLL GROUP	POST OFFICE BOX 2428	EL SEGUNDO, CA	90245
WIRE TRAIN	ROCK & ROLL GROUP	POST OFFICE BOX 14563	SAN FRANCISCO, CA	94114
WIRTH, BILLY	ACTOR	8730 SUNSET BLVD #220-W	LOS ANGELES, CA	90069
WIRTH, TIMOTHY	U S SENATOR	830 N TEJON ST #226	COLORADO SPRINGS, CO	81501
WISDOM, NORMAN	ACTOR	28 BERKELEY SQ	LONDON 6HD	ENGLAND
WISDOM, VICTORIA	TALENT AGENT	STONE MANNERS, 9113 SUNSET BL	LOS ANGELES, CA	90069
WISE, HERBERT	FILM-TV DIRECTOR	PETERS, FRASER & DUNLOP, LTD		
		5TH FLOOR, THE CHAMBERS		
		CHELSEA HARBOUR, LOT RD	LONDON SW10 OXF	ENGLAND
WISE, LEONARD	AUTHOR	2250 FOX HILLS DR	LOS ANGELES, CA	90064
WISE, PAUL A	DIRECTOR	5993 WESTERN RUN DR	BALTIMORE, MD	21209
WISE, RICK	BASEBALL-COACH	POST OFFICE BOX 1718	NEW BRITAIN, CT	06050
WISE, RICK	DIRECTOR	DGA, 7920 SUNSET BLVD, 6TH FL	LOS ANGELES, CA	90046
WISE, ROBERT	FILM DIR-PROD	315 S BEVERLY DR #214	BEVERLY HILLS, CA	90212
WISE, ROBERT E, JR	U S CONGRESSMAN	107 PENNSYLVANIA AVE	CHARLESTON, WV	25302
WISE, THOMAS	ARTIST	THE FLAT TULIP STUDIO		
		BOX 146, RD #1	MARIETTA, PA	17547
WISEMAN, BARRY	ACTOR	550 S BARRINGTON AVE #1119	LOS ANGELES, CA	90049
WISEMAN, DEBBIE	COMPOSER	1 BARONSCLERE CT, 23 AVENUE RD	LONDON N6 5YA	ENGLAND

WISEMAN, DENNY	BASEBALL	POST OFFICE BOX 5599	LITTLE ROCK, AR	72215
WISEMAN, MAC B	SINGER-GUITARIST	2732 MOSS DALE DR	NASHVILLE, TN	37217
WISER, BERNARD T	TV WRITER	11725 SUNSHINE TERR	STUDIO CITY, CA	91604
WISER, BUD	TV PRODUCER	EMBASSY TV, 1438 N GOWER ST	LOS ANGELES, CA	90028
WISH, JEROME W	WRITER	115 S SWALL DR #3	LOS ANGELES, CA	90068
WISHBONE ASH	ROCK & ROLL GROUP	JOHN SHERRY, 65 E 55TH ST	NEW YORK, NY	10022
WISHNER, SUZANNE	ACTRESS	612 N SYCAMORE AVE	LOS ANGELES, CA	90036
WISHNEVSKI, ROB	BASEBALL	POST OFFICE DRAWER 4797	EL PASO, TX	79914
WISLON, LOIS	ACTRESS	11579 HESBY ST	NORTH HOLLYWOOD, CA	91601
WISLON, RICHARD A	FILM WRITER-DIRECTOR	501 OCEAN FRONT WALK	SANTA MONICA, CA	90402
WISNIEWSKI, STEVE	FOOTBALL	RAIDERS, 332 CENTER ST	EL SEGUNDO, CA	90245
WISSLER, BILL	BASEBALL	POST OFFICE BOX 661	KENOSHA, WI	53141
WITANOWSKI, EDWARD S	DIRECTOR	116 WEEKS RD	EAST WILLISTON, NY	11596
WITHERS, BILL	SINGER-SONGWRITER	2600 BENEDICT CANYON DR	BEVERLY HILLS, CA	90210
WITHERS, JANE	ACTRESS	1801 N CURSON	LOS ANGELES, CA	90046
WITHERS, MARK	ACTOR	6426 BALCOM AVE	RESEDA, CA	91335
WITHERSPOON, JIMMY	SINGER-MUSICIAN	HOFFER, 233 1/2 E 48TH ST	NEW YORK, NY	10017
WITHROW, MARY ELLEN	TREASURER	STATE CAPITOL BUILDING	COLUMBUS, OH	43266
WITJAS, JEFF	TALENT AGENT	151 S EL CAMINO DR	BEVERLY HILLS, CA	90212
WITKIND, CHALOTTE	BASEBALL EXECUTIVE	N Y YANKEES, YANKEE STADIUM	BRONX, NY	10451
WITKIND, RICHARD	BASEBALL EXECUTIVE	N Y YANKEES, YANKEE STADIUM	BRONX, NY	10451
WITKOWSKI, MATT	BASEBALL	POST OFFICE BOX 1420	WICHITA, KS	67201
WITMEYER, RON	BASEBALL	POST OFFICE BOX 11087	TACOMA, WA	98411
WITNEY, WILLIAM N	DIRECTOR	DGA, 7920 SUNSET BLVD, 6TH FL	LOS ANGELES, CA	90046
WITT, BOBBY	BASEBALL	ATHLETICS'S, OAKLAND COLISEUM	OAKLAND, CA	94621
WITT, DAVID	TV PRODUCER	METROMEDIA, 5746 SUNSET BLVD	LOS ANGELES, CA	90028
WITT, HOWARD	ACTOR	1825 N GRAMERCY PL #309	LOS ANGELES, CA	90028
WITT, KATARINA	SKATER	REICHENHEIMER STR	(D-(O) 9023 CHEMNITZ	GERMANY
WITT, MIKE	BASEBALL	N Y YANKEES, YANKEE STADIUM	BRONX, NY	10451
WITT, PAUL F	COMPOSER-CONDUCTOR	3322 MENTONE AVE #3	LOS ANGELES, CA	90034
WITT, PAUL JUNGER	WRI-DIR-PROD	16032 VALLEY VISTA BLVD	ENCINO, CA	91436
WITTE, ORA LAAS	ACTOR	853 7TH AVE	NEW YORK, NY	10019
WITTEN, FREDERICK G	DIRECTOR	3654 BARHAM BLVD #Q-213	LOS ANGELES, CA	90068
WITTER, JERE D	WRITER	POST OFFICE BOX 1525	BIG BEAR LAKE, CA	92315
WITTER, KAREN	ACTRESS-MODEL	ABC-TV, "ONE LIFE TO LIVE"		
		56 W 66TH ST	NEW YORK, NY	10023
WITTLIFF, WILLIAM D	FILM WRITER-DIRECTOR	1301 KENT LN	AUSTIN, TX	78703
WITTMAN, ELLEN	TV WRITER-PRODUCER	2612 ELM AVE	MANHATTAN BEACH, CA	90266
WITTMAN, RANDY	BASKETBALL	PACERS, 300 E MARKET ST	INDIANAPOLIS, IN	46204
WITTY, RICHARD	DIRECTOR	327 CENTRAL PARK W	NEW YORK, NY	10025
WITUS, BARBARA	WRITER	1341 OCEAN AVE #323	SANTA MONICA, CA	90401
WITZER, TED	TALENT AGENT	WITZER, 6310 SAN VICENTE #407	LOS ANGELES, CA	90048
WIXEN, RANDALL	TALENT AGENT	POST OFFICE BOX 49217	LOS ANGELES, CA	90049
WIXTED, KEVIN	ACTOR	10100 SANTA MONICA BLVD #700	LOS ANGELES, CA	90067
WLCEK, JAMES	ACTOR	CBS-TV, "AS THE WORLD TURNS"		
		524 W 57TH ST #5330	NEW YORK, NY	10019
WLLIAMS, SHAD	BASEBALL	POST OFFICE BOX 3496	DAVENPORT, IA	52808
WOCKENFUSS, JOHN	BASEBALL MANAGER	POST OFFICE BOX 842	SALEM, VA	24153
WODWARD, DIANE	ACTRESS	4401 KLING ST #39	BURBANK, CA	91505
WOESSNER, FREDERICK T	COMPOSER-CONDUCTOR	952 N HUDSON AVE #2	LOS ANGELES, CA	90038
WOFF, WILLIAM	ACTOR	1251 N CRESCENT HGTS BLVD #B	LOS ANGELES, CA	90046
WOFFORD, HARRIS	U S SENATOR	277 RUSSELL SENATE OFFICE BLDG	WASHINGTON, DC	20510
WOGAN, TERRY	TV HOST	GURNETT, 2 NEW KINGS RD	LONDON SW6 4SA	ENGLAND
WOHL, ALFRED	COMPOSER	6122 GOODLAND AVE	NORTH HOLLYWOOD, CA	91606
WOHL, DAVE	BASKETBALL COACH	MIAMI HEAT, THE MIAMI ARENA	MIAMI, FL	33136
WOHL, WALLY	ACTOR-DIRECTOR	345 S EL CAMINO DR	BEVERLY HILLS, CA	90212
WOHLERS, MARK	BASEBALL	POST OFFICE BOX 6667	RICHMOND, VA	23230
WOICIK, MIKE	FOOTBALL COACH	COWBOYS, 1 COWBOYS PARKWAY	IRVING, TX	75063
WOJCIECHOWSKI, JOHN	FOOTBALL	BEARS, 250 N WASHINGTON RD	LAKE FOREST, IL	60045
WOJCIECHOWSKI, STEVE	BASEBALL	POST OFFICE BOX 2437	MODESTO, CA	95351
WOJNO, STAN, JR	ACTOR	8780 SHOREHAM DR #304	LOS ANGELES, CA	90069
WOLAK, JERRY	BASEBALL	1090 N EUCLID AVE	SARASOTA, FL	34237
WOLANIN, CRAIG	HOCKEY	NORDIQUES, 2205 AVE DU COLISEE	QUEBEC, QUE G1L 4W7	CANADA
WOLCOTT, BOB	GOLFER	POST OFFICE BOX 109601	PALM BCH GARDENS, FL	33418
WOLCOTT, CHARLES	COMPOSER	POST OFFICE BOX 155	HAIFA	ISRAEL
WOLEBEN, MIKE	BASEBALL EXECUTIVE	POST OFFICE BOX 418	SAINT CHARLES, IL	60174
WOLEVER, CHUCK	BASEBALL SCOUT	POST OFFICE BOX 2000	ANAHEIM, CA	92803
WOLEVER, MARTI	BASEBALL SCOUT	333 W 35TH ST	CHICAGO, IL	60616
WOLF, BONGO	MUSICIAN	521 N BEVERLY DR	BEVERLY HILLS, CA	90210
WOLF, DALE E	LT GOVERNOR	LEGISLATIVE HALL	DOVER, DE	19901
WOLF, DAVID M	SCREENWRITER	1162 N WETHERLY DR	LOS ANGELES, CA	90069
WOLF, FRANK R	U S CONGRESSMAN	1651 OLD MEADOW RD #115	MC LEAN, VA	22102
WOLF, GARIN	TV WRITER	84-37 123RD ST	KEW GARDENS, NY	11415
WOLF, GARY	SINGER-GUITARIST	POST OFFICE BOX 397	FRANKLIN, OH	45005
WOLF, GEORGE E	DIRECTOR	330 W 45TH ST #J	NEW YORK, NY	10036
WOLF, HARRY L	CINEMATOGRAPHER	502 N LA JOLLA AVE	LOS ANGELES, CA	90048
WOLF, JAMES H	TV DIRECTOR-PRODUCER	GEMINI COMM, 42 BLANCHARD RD	EASTON, CT	06612
WOLF, JEANNE	TV REPORTER	ENTERTAINMENT TONIGHT		
		PARAMOUNT TELEVISION		
		5555 MELROSE AVE	LOS ANGELES, CA	90038
WOLF, JOE	BASKETBALL	POST OFFICE BOX 4658	DENVER, CO	80204
WOLF, JOE	FOOTBALL	POST OFFICE BOX 888	PHOENIX, AZ	85001
WOLF, JOHN C, III	DIRECTOR	87 STATE ST	BROOKLYN, NY	11201
WOLF, KELLY	ACTRESS	151 S EL CAMINO DR	BEVERLY HILLS, CA	90212
WOLF, MARCIA	ACTRESS	POST OFFICE BOX 2422	NORTH HOLLYWOOD, CA	91602

Name	Occupation	Address	City	Zip/Country
WOLF, MICHAEL	ACTOR	41 LANSDOWNE RD	LONDON W11 2LQ	ENGLAND
WOLF, PETER	SINGER-SONGWRITER	LIPPMAN, 9669 OAK PASS RD	BEVERLY HILLS, CA	90210
WOLF, PETER F	COMPOSER	1506 DOROTHY AVE	SIMI VALLEY, CA	93063
WOLF, RICHARD A	WRITER-PRODUCER	2393 CASTILIAN DR	LOS ANGELES, CA	90068
WOLF, RITA	ACTRESS	1 KINGSWAY HOUSE, ALBION RD	LONDON N16 OTA	ENGLAND
WOLF, RON	FOOTBALL EXECUTIVE	RAIDERS, 332 CENTER ST	EL SEGUNDO, CA	90245
WOLF, STEVE	BASEBALL	TIGERS, 89 WHARNCLIFFE RD N	LONDON, ONT N6H 2A7	CANADA
WOLF, SUSAN G	ACTRESS	681 LATIMER RD	SANTA MONICA, CA	90402
WOLF, THOMAS H	WRITER	13430 QUERY MILL	GATHERSBURG, MD	20879
WOLF, WILLIAM	FILM CRITIC	POST OFFICE BOX 7858	WASHINGTON, DC	20044
WOLFBERG, DENNIS	COMEDIAN	9000 SUNSET BLVD #1200	LOS ANGELES, CA	90069
WOLFE, BOB	BASKETBALL EXECUTIVE	1 CNN CENTER #405, SOUTH TOWER	ATLANTA, GA	30303
WOLFE, BRUCE	ARTIST	206 EL CERRITO AVE	PIEDMONT, CA	94611
WOLFE, DIANA	ACTRESS	7461 BEVERLY BLVD #400	LOS ANGELES, CA	90036
WOLFE, DIGBY	TV WRITER-PRODUCER	1642 N BEVERLY DR	BEVERLY HILLS, CA	90210
WOLFE, DUSTY	WRESTLER	POST OFFICE BOX 3859	STAMFORD, CT	06905
WOLFE, HOWARD	U S CONGRESSMAN	106 ALLEGAN ST #206	LANSING, MI	48933
WOLFE, ISABEL	ACTRESS	1705 CARLA RIDGE	BEVERLY HILLS, CA	90210
WOLFE, JOEL	BASEBALL	POST OFFICE BOX 11363	RENO, NV	89510
WOLFE, JOEL R	ACTOR	325 W 86TH ST	NEW YORK, NY	10024
WOLFE, KEDRIC	ACTOR	POST OFFICE BOX 584	TOPANGA CANYON, CA	90290
WOLFE, PAKI	COSTUME DESIGNER	113 31ST ST	MANHATTAN BEACH, CA	90266
WOLFE, ROBERT L	FILM EDITOR	ACE, 1041 N FORMOSA AVE	WEST HOLLYWOOD, CA	90046
WOLFE, ROBERT T	DIRECTOR	175 E 74TH ST	NEW YORK, NY	10021
WOLFE, RONALD	WRITER-PRODUCER	1 GROSVENOR GARDENS	LONDON NW11 OHH	ENGLAND
WOLFE, SCOTT	BASEBALL EXECUTIVE	POST OFFICE BOX 2000	SAN DIEGO, CA	92112
WOLFE, STANLEY	COMPOSER	32 FERNDALE DR	HASTINGS-ON-HUDSON, NY	10706
WOLFE, TOM	AUTHOR-NOVELIST	FARRAR, STARUS & GIROUX, INC		
		19 UNION SQUARE W	NEW YORK, NY	10017
WOLFE, WENDY	ACTRESS	18 MARY ANN LN	HARRINGTON PARK, NJ	07640
WOLFENSON, MARV	BASKETBALL EXECUTIVE	TIMBERWOLVES, 600 1ST AVE N	MINNEAPOLIS, MN	55403
WOLFF, ART	DIRECTOR	120 E 74TH ST	NEW YORK, NY	10021
WOLFF, F ROGER	COMPOSER	340 N BEACHWOOD DR	LOS ANGELES, CA	90004
WOLFF, JIM	BASEBALL	1524 W NEBRASKA AVE	PEORIA, IL	61604
WOLFF, MILES .. (BUTTE)	BASEBALL EXECUTIVE	POST OFFICE BOX 186	BUTTE, MT	59703
WOLFF, MILES .. (BURLINGTON)	BASEBALL EXECUTIVE	POST OFFICE BOX 1143	BURLINGTON, NC	27216
WOLFF, RICK	BASEBALL CONSULTANT	INDIANS, CLEVELAND STADIUM	CLEVELAND, OH	44114
WOLFF, RUTH	WRITER	165 W 46TH ST #409	NEW YORK, NY	10036
WOLFF, WILLIAM J	WRITER	1631 19TH ST	MANHATTAN BEACH, CA	90266
WOLFINGTON, IGGIE	ACTOR	11216 AQUA VISTA ST	NORTH HOLLYWOOD, CA	91602
WOLFLEY, CRAIG	FOOTBALL	VIKINGS, 9520 VIKING DR	EDEN PRAIRIE, MN	55344
WOLFLEY, RON	FOOTBALL	POST OFFICE BOX 888	PHOENIX, AZ	85001
WOLFMAN JACK	RADIO-TV PERSONALITY	ROUTE #1, BOX56	BELVIDERE, NC	27919
WOLFORD, WILL	FOOTBALL	BILLS, 1 BILLS DR	ORCHARD PARK, NJ	14127
WOLFREY, EDITH	ACTRESS	1319 S RIMPAU BLVD	LOS ANGELES, CA	90019
WOLFSON, AARON W	COMPOSER	8456 ALLENWOOD RD	LOS ANGELES, CA	90046
WOLFSON, SHOSHANAH G	TV PRODUCER	303 W 66TH ST	NEW YORK, NY	10023
WOLGEMUTH, ROBERT	PUBLISHER	5110 MARYLAND WY	BRENTWOOD, TN	37027
WOLL, CYNTHIA	ACTRESS	2050 HIGH TOWER DR #2	HOLLYWOOD, CA	90068
WOLLERT, DAVE	TV DIRECTOR	6854 PACIFIC VIEW DR	HOLLYWOOD, CA	90068
WOLLET, MICHAEL	ACTOR	1329 N COLUMBUS AVE #D	GLENDALE, CA	91202
WOLLMAN, MARJORIE RECK	WRITER	8715 LOOKOUT MOUNTAIN AVE	LOS ANGELES, CA	90046
WOLMAN, DAN	FILM DIRECTOR	POST OFFICE BOX 229	JERUSALEM	ISRAEL
WOLODARSKY, WALLACE	TV PRODUCER	UTA, 9560 WILSHIRE BL, 5TH FL	BEVERLY HILLS, CA	90212
WOLPER, DAVID L	FILM-TV PRODUCER	10847 BELLAGIO DR	LOS ANGELES, CA	90077
WOLPERT, JAY	TV PRODUCER	6311 ROMAINE ST #7114	HOLLYWOOD, CA	90036
WOLPERT, ROLAND	TV WRITER	6444 HAYES DR	LOS ANGELES, CA	90048
WOLPERT, STUART	TV WRITER-PRODUCER	EMBASSY TV, 1438 N GOWER ST	LOS ANGELES, CA	90028
WOLSK, EUGENE	THEATER PRODUCER	165 W 46TH ST	NEW YORK, NY	10036
WOLSKY, ALBERT	COSTUME DESIGNER	11444 DECENTE CT	STUDIO CITY, CA	91604
WOLSTENHOLME, JOHN	WRITER-PRODUCER	UNITED HOUSE, 20 WELLS MEWS	LONDON W1P 3FJ	ENGLAND
WOLTER, SHERILYN	ACTRESS	20338 PACIFIC COAST HWY	MALIBU, CA	90265
WOLTERSTORFF, ROBERT A	TV WRITER	1267 MONUMENT ST	PACIFIC PALISADES, CA	90272
WOMACK, BOBBY	SINGER	TRUTH RECORDS COMPANY		
		2841 FIRENZE PL	LOS ANGELES, CA	90048
WOMACK, LEON	SINGER	3125 19TH ST #217	BAKERSFIELD, CA	93301
WOMACK, PAMELA	SEC OF COMMONWEALTH	STATE CAPITOL BUILDING	RICHMOND, VA	23219
WOMACK, STEVE A	TV DIRECTOR	1315 GLADE DR	FRANKLIN, TN	37064
WOMACK, TONY	BASEBALL	POST OFFICE BOX 3746, HILL STA	AUGUSTA, GA	30904
WOMACK & WOMACK	VOCAL DUO	1174 LONGWOOD AVE	LOS ANGELES, CA	90019
WON, KYUNG-SOO	CONDUCTOR	HIGHAM INTERNATIONAL ARTISTS		
		16 LAURISTON RD, WIMBLETON	LONDON SW19 4TQ	ENGLAND
WONDER, STEVIE	SINGER-SONGWRITER	2270 ASTRAL PL	LOS ANGELES, CA	90068
WONG, ALAN LEE	ACTOR	623 NECTARINE ST #A	INGLEWOOD, CA	90301
WONG, KEVIN	BASEBALL	POST OFFICE BOX 4370	SALINAS, CA	93912
WONG, LEONARD	DIRECTOR	DGA, 110 W 57TH ST	NEW YORK, NY	10019
WOOD, BILL	BASEBALL EXECUTIVE	POST OFFICE BOX 288	HOUSTON, TX	77001
WOOD, BRIAN	BASEBALL	POST OFFICE BOX 1420	WICHITA, KS	67201
WOOD, CHARLES	SCREENWRITER	WM MORRIS, 31-32 SOHO SQ	LONDON W1V 5DG	ENGLAND
WOOD, CHRISTOPHER	SCREENWRITER	VALENCE DE COLLONGES	MEYSSAS 19500	FRANCE
WOOD, DAVID	ACTOR-WRITER	BURNETT, 42-43 GRAFTON HOUSE		
		2-3 GOLDEN SQ	LONDON W1R 3AD	ENGLAND
WOOD, DAVID	BASKETBALL	POST OFFICE BOX 272349	HOUSTON, TX	77277
WOOD, DEL	SINGER	POST OFFICE BOX 82	GREENBRIER, TN	37073
WOOD, DIANA PAGE	DIRECTOR	DGA, 110 W 57TH ST	NEW YORK, NY	10019

Name	Occupation	Address	City
WOOD, DON	ARTIST	417 W LOS OLIVOS ST	SANTA BARBARA, CA 93105
WOOD, DON	COMPOSER-CONDUCTOR	1329 WOODRUFF AVE	LOS ANGELES, CA 90024
WOOD, DURINDA	COSTUME DESIGNER	6041 GRACIOSA DR	HOLLYWOOD, CA 90068
WOOD, FORREST	ACTOR	2056 RODNEY DR #4	LOS ANGELES, CA 90027
WOOD, GARY	ACTOR	BREWIS, 12429 LAUREL TERRACE	STUDIO CITY, CA 91604
WOOD, HELEN ATKINSON	ACTRESS	PETERS, FRASER & DUNLOP, LTD	
		5TH FLOOR, THE CHAMBERS	
		CHELSEA HARBOUR, LOT RD	LONDON SW10 OXF ENGLAND
WOOD, JACK K	TV WRITER-DIRECTOR	400 E 54TH ST #26-E	NEW YORK, NY 10022
WOOD, JANET	ACTRESS	1800 N VINE ST #120	LOS ANGELES, CA 90028
WOOD, JASON	BASEBALL	POST OFFICE BOX 1457	MEDFORD, OR 97501
WOOD, JEFF	BASEBALL TRAINER	500 NORTON ST	ROCHESTER, NY 14621
WOOD, JOAN	TV DIRECTOR	521 E 14TH ST #3-E	NEW YORK, NY 10009
WOOD, JOHN	ACTOR	ICM, 388-396 OXFORD ST	LONDON W1 ENGLAND
WOOD, JUDITH	ACTRESS	1300 1/4 N SYCAMORE AVE	HOLLYWOOD, CA 90028
WOOD, JUDY	COMPOSER	1237 N ORANGE GROVE	LOS ANGELES, CA 90046
WOOD, KIM	FOOTBALL COACH	BENGALS, 200 RIVERFRONT STADIUM	CINCINNATI, OH 45202
WOOD, LAUREN	SINGER	JACK DALEY, 825 LAS PALMAS RD	PASADENA, CA 91105
WOOD, LYNN	ACTRESS	9300 WILSHIRE BLVD #410	BEVERLY HILLS, CA 90212
WOOD, RANDY	HOCKEY	NASSAU VETS MEMORIAL COLISEUM	UNIONDALE, NY 11553
WOOD, RICHARD	FOOTBALL COACH	PATRIOTS, FOXBORO STADIUM, RT #1	FOXBORO, MA 02035
WOOD, ROBIN	SINGER	POST OFFICE BOX 171132	NASHVILLE, TN 37217
WOOD, TED	BASEBALL	5999 E VAN BUREN ST	PHOENIX, AZ 85008
WOOD, VICTORIA	COMEDIENNE-WRITER	STONE, 25 WHITEHALL	LONDON SW1A 2BS ENGLAND
WOOD, WALTER J	TV PRODUCER	19513 BOWERS DR	TOPANGA, CA 90290
WOOD, YVONNE	COSTUME DESIGNER	13949 VENTURA BLVD #309	SHERMAN OAKS, CA 91423
WOOD-BALTER, LANA	ACTRESS	12124 GOSHEN AVE #104	LOS ANGELES, CA 90049
WOODALL, ANN	TV WRITER	1755 N ALEXANDRIA AVE	LOS ANGELES, CA 90027
WOODALL, BRAD	BASEBALL	POST OFFICE BOX 507	DURHAM, NC 27702
WOODALL, ERIC	ACTOR	ABC-TV, "LOVING"	
		320 W 66TH ST, STUDIO 23	NEW YORK, NY 10023
WOODALL, KEVIN	BASEBALL	POST OFFICE BOX 309	GASTONA, NC 28053
WOODARD, ALFRE	WRITER	3630 MOUNTAIN VIEW	LOS ANGELES, CA 90066
WOODARD, CHARLAYNE	ACTRESS	777 W END AVE	NEW YORK, NY 10025
WOODBECK, VICTORIA	ACTRESS	3607 PACIFIC AVE #3	VENICE, CA 90291
WOODBURN, WILLIAM	DIRECTOR	5229 BALBOA BLVD #15	ENCINO, CA 91316
WOODCOCK, JOHN M	FILM EDITOR	ACE, 1041 N FORMOSA AVE	WEST HOLLYWOOD, CA 90046
WOODEN, JOHN	BASKETBALL	17711 MARGATE ST #102	ENCINO, CA 91316
WOODEN, TERRY	FOOTBALL	SEAHAWKS, 11220 NE 53RD ST	KIRKLAND, WA 98033
WOODEN NICKEL	ROCK & ROLL GROUP	5625 "O" STREET BLDG #7	LINCOLN, NE 68510
WOODFIELD, WILLIAM READ	TV WRITER-PRODUCER	1367 CASIANO RD	LOS ANGELES, CA 90049
WOODLOCK, JOAN	ACTRESS	POST OFFICE BOX 167	WOODLAND HILLS, CA 91364
WOODMAN, WILLIAM E	DIRECTOR	320 W END AVE #4-B	NEW YORK, NY 10023
WOODRUFF, FRANK	DIRECTOR-PRODUCER	170 N CRESCENT DR	BEVERLY HILLS, CA 90210
WOODRUFF, JUDY	BROADCAST JOURNALIST	POST OFFICE BOX 2626	WASHINGTON, DC 20013
WOODS, AUBREY	ACTOR	21 GERRARD RD	LONDON SW13 ENGLAND
WOODS, DANNY	ACTOR	18 FISKE PL	BROOKLYN, NY 11215
WOODS, DONALD	ACTOR	479 TAHQUITZ-MC CALLUM	PALM SPRINGS, CA 92262
WOODS, GARY	BASKETBALL EXECUTIVE	600 E MARKET ST #102	SAN ANTONIO, TX 78205
WOODS, GRANT	ATTORNEY GENERAL	STATE CAPITOL, 1700 W WASHINGTON	PHOENIX, AZ 85007
WOODS, H DONALD	COMPOSER-CONDUCTOR	POST OFFICE BOX 311	LOS ANGELES, CA 90078
WOODS, JAMES	ACT-DIR-PROD	1612 GILCREST DR	BEVERLY HILLS, CA 90210
WOODS, LESLEY	ACTRESS	115 S ROSE ST	BURBANK, CA 91505
WOODS, MARIAN	ACTRESS	165 W 46TH ST #409	NEW YORK, NY 10036
WOODS, MICHAEL	ACTOR	1999 AVE OF THE STARS #2850	LOS ANGELES, CA 90067
WOODS, PHIL	SAXOPHONIST-CLARINET	POST OFFICE BOX 278	DELAWARE WATER GAP, PA 18327
WOODS, PHIL, QUARTET	JAZZ QUARTET	HOFFER, 233 1/2 E 48TH ST	NEW YORK, NY 10017
WOODS, REN	SINGER	2372 W 29TH PL	LOS ANGELES, CA 90018
WOODS, RICHARD	SCREENWRITER	8955 BEVERLY BLVD	WEST HOLLYWOOD, CA 90048
WOODS, ROBERT S	ACTOR	ABC-TV, "ONE LIFE TO LIVE"	
		56 W 66TH ST	NEW YORK, NY 10023
WOODS, ROSEMARY	WATERGATE CELEBRITY	2500 VIRGINIA AVE, NW	WASHINGTON, DC 20037
WOODS, ROZALIN	SINGER	ED MARTINEZ, 1344 COLVER PL	COVINA, CA 91724
WOODS, STEVIE	SINGER-MUSICIAN	151 S EL CAMINO DR	BEVERLY HILLS, CA 90212
WOODS, TONY	FOOTBALL	SEAHAWKS, 11220 NE 53RD ST	KIRKLAND, WA 98033
WOODS, TYRONE	BASEBALL	POST OFFICE BOX 6748	ROCKFORD, IL 61125
WOODSIDE, KEITH	FOOTBALL	PACKERS, 1265 LOMBARDI AVE	GREEN BAY, WI 54307
WOODSMOKE	C & W GROUP	PROCESS, 439 WILEY AVE	FRANKLIN, PA 16323
WOODSON, KERRY	BASEBALL	POST OFFICE BOX 4756	JACKSONVILLE, FL 32201
WOODSON, MIKE	BASKETBALL	POST OFFICE BOX 272349	HOUSTON, TX 77277
WOODSON, ROD	FOOTBALL	STEELERS, 300 STADIUM CIR	PITTSBURGH, PA 15212
WOODSON, TRACY	BASEBALL	POST OFFICE BOX 36407	LOUISVILLE, KY 40233
WOODWARD, BOB	REPORTER-NOVELIST	1150 15TH ST, NW	WASHINGTON, DC 20005
WOODWARD, CHARLES	THEATER PRODUCER	226 W 47TH ST	NEW YORK, NY 10036
WOODWARD, EDWARD	ACTOR	10 E 40TH ST #2700	NEW YORK, NY 10016
WOODWARD, JIM	BASEBALL SCOUT	METS, 126TH ST & ROOSEVELT AVE	FLUSHING, NY 11368
WOODWARD, JOANNE	ACTRESS-DIRECTOR	1120 5TH AVE #1-C	NEW YORK, NY 10128
WOODWARD, MORGAN	ACTOR	2111 ROCKLEDGE RD	LOS ANGELES, CA 90068
WOODWARD, PETER	ACTOR	84 PARK RD, KINGSTON GATE	SURREY KT2 5JZ ENGLAND
WOODWARD, ROB	BASEBALL	500 NORTON ST	ROCHESTER, NY 14621
WOODWARD, STEVE	SPORTS WRITER	POST OFFICE BOX 500	WASHINGTON, DC 20044
WOODWARD, TIM	ACTOR	58 ASTBURY RD, PECKHAM	LONDON SE ENGLAND
WOODWARD, WOODY	BASEBALL EXECUTIVE	POST OFFICE BOX 4100	SEATTLE, WA 98104
WOODWORTH, JON	BASEBALL TRAINER	POST OFFICE BOX 957	DUNEDIN, FL 34697
WOODWORTH, MARJORIE	ACTRESS	807 N LA BREA DR	INGLEWOOD, CA 90301

Name	Occupation	Address	City/State	Zip/Country
WOODY, RUSS	TV WRITER-PRODUCER	9242 BEVERLY DR #200	BEVERLY HILLS, CA	90210
WOOLARD, GREG	MUSIC ARRANGER	300 BAKERTOWN RD #26-A	ANTIOCH, TN	37013
WOOLDRIDGE, SUSAN	ACTRESS	MARKHAM AND FROGGATT, LTD		
		JULIAN HOUSE, 4 WINDMILL ST	LONDON W1P 1HF	ENGLAND
WOOLERY, CHUCK	SINGER-TV HOST	1138 COLDWATER CANYON DR	BEVERLY HILLS, CA	90210
WOOLEY, SHEB	ACTOR-SINGER	RT #3, BOX 231, SUNSET ISL TRAIL	GALLATIN, TN	37066
WOOLF, SIR JOHN	FILM-TV PRODUCER	214 THE CHAMBERS, CHELSEA HARB	LONDON SW10 OXF	ENGLAND
WOOLFORD, DONNELL	FOOTBALL	BEARS, 250 N WASHINGTON RD	LAKE FOREST, IL	60045
WOOLLARD, TONY	ART DIRECTOR	23 PARSONS GREEN LN	LONDON SW6	ENGLAND
WOOLLEY, JAMES A	DIRECTOR	41-41 51ST ST	WOODSIDE, NY	11377
WOOLLEY, JANET	ARTIST	34 STANHOPE RD	LONDON N6	ENGLAND
WOOLLEY, JOE	FOOTBALL EXECUTIVE	EAGLES, BROAD ST & PATTISON AVE	PHILADELPHIA, PA	19148
WOOLLEY, ROBERT	BASEBALL EXECUTIVE	TWINS, 501 CHICAGO AVE S	MINNEAPOLIS, MN	55415
WOOLLEY, STEPHEN	PRODUCER	PALACE PICTURES, LTD		
		16-17 WARDOUR MEWS	LONDON W1V 3FF	ENGLAND
WOOLRIDGE, ORLANDO	BASKETBALL	POST OFFICE BOX 4658	DENVER, CO	80204
WOOLSTON-SMITH, PAUL	FILM DIRECTOR	FILM AUSTRALIA, LINDFIELD	SYDNEY NSW 2070	AUSTRALIA
WOOSNAM, IAN	GOLFER	POST OFFICE BOX 109601	PALM BCH GARDENS, FL	33418
WOOSTER, ARTHUR G	FILM-TV DIRECTOR	KINGHAMS MEADOWS		
		LITTLE GADDESDON		
		BERSHAMSTED	HERTS	ENGLAND
WOOTEN, JOHN	FOOTBALL EXECUTIVE	COWBOYS, 1 COWBOYS PARKWAY	IRVING, TX	75063
WOOTTEN, LAWRENCE	COMPOSER	9836 KALE ST	SOUTH EL MONTE, CA	91733
WORCHESTER, MARJORIE	TV DIRECTOR	8955 BEVERLY BLVD	WEST HOLLYWOOD, CA	90048
WORD, BARRY	FOOTBALL	CHIEFS, 1 ARROWHEAD DR	KANSAS CITY, MO	64129
WORKMAN, CARL	FILM WRITER-DIRECTOR	711 N OLD TOPANGA CANYON RD	TOPANGA CANYON, CA	90290
WORKMAN, CHUCK	GOLFER	PGA SENIORS, 112 T P C BLVD	PONTE VEDRA BEACH, FL	32082
WORKMAN, HAYWOODE	BASKETBALL	BULLETS, 1 HARRY S TRUMAN DR	LANDOVER, MD	20785
WORKMAN, VINCE	FOOTBALL	PACKERS, 1265 LOMBARDI AVE	GREEN BAY, WI	54307
WORLEY, JO ANNE	ACTRESS	4714 ARCOLA AVE	NORTH HOLLYWOOD, CA	91602
WORLEY, PAUL N	SINGER-GUITARIST	210 OLD HICKORY BLVD #178	NASHVILLE, TN	37221
WORLEY, TIM	FOOTBALL	STEELERS, 300 STADIUM CIR	PITTSBURGH, PA	15212
WORMSER, RICHARD L	WRI-DIR-PROD	VIDEO LINE, 800 RIVERSIDE DR	NEW YORK, NY	10032
WORONOV, MARY	ACTRESS	400 S BEVERLY DR #216	BEVERLY HILLS, CA	90212
WORRELL, BILL	SPORTSCASTER	POST OFFICE BOX 288	HOUSTON, TX	77001
WORRELL, TIM	BASEBALL	POST OFFICE BOX 1420	WICHITA, KS	67201
WORRELL, TODD	BASEBALL	306 HARVARD DR	ARCADIA, CA	91006
WORTH, FRANK J	COMPOSER-CONDUCTOR	20101 VILLAGE #20	CAMARILLO, CA	93010
WORTH, HOWARD	DIRECTOR	1393 ROSE ST	VENICE, CA	90291
WORTH, IRENE	ACTRESS	333 W 56TH ST	NEW YORK, NY	10019
WORTH, MARTIN	SCREENWRITER	MBA, 45 FITZROY ST	LONDON W1P 5HR,	ENGLAND
WORTH, MARVIN	FILM WRITER-PRODUCER	9784 DRAKE LN	BEVERLY HILLS, CA	90210
WORTH, MERLE	TV DIRECTOR-PRODUCER	390 RIVERSIDE DR	NEW YORK, NY	10025
WORTHINGTON, CRAIG	BASEBALL	72 CRANBROOK RD #172	COCKEYS-HUNT VLY, MD	21030
WORTHY, JAMES	BASKETBALL	POST OFFICE BOX 10	INGLEWOOD, CA	90306
WORTMAN, BOB	FOOTBALL REFEREE	NFL, 410 PARK AVE	NEW YORK, NY	10022
WOTRING, JAMES D	DIRECTOR	322 N KENMORE AVE	CHICAGO, IL	60657
WOTUS, RON	BASEBALL MANAGER	POST OFFICE BOX 21727	SAN FRANCISCO, CA	95151
WOUK, HERMAN	AUTHOR	3255 "N" ST, NW	WASHINGTON, DC	20007
WOUK, SUZANNE	ACTRESS	KOHNER, 9169 SUNSET BLVD	LOS ANGELES, CA	90069
WOULFE, MICHAEL	COSTUME DESIGNER	13949 VENTURA BLVD #309	SHERMAN OAKS, CA	91423
WOW II	MUSICAL GROUP	POST OFFICE BOX 1235	NEW ROCHELLE, NY	10802
WPHL, JACK	WRITER-PRODUCER	711 N ROXBURY DR	BEVERLY HILLS, CA	90210
WRANGLER, JACK	ACTOR	41 W 58TH ST #5-A	NEW YORK, NY	10019
WRATH	ROCK & ROLL GROUP	POST OFFICE BOX 466	WAUKEGAN, IL	60079
WRAY, FAY	ACTRESS	2160 CENTURY PARK E #1901	LOS ANGELES, CA	90067
WRAY, JAMES	BASEBALL	POST OFFICE BOX 2887	VERO BEACH, FL	32961
WRAY, JOHN	DIRECTOR	511 CIRCLE DR #C21-2	HUDSON, NC	28638
WRECKING CREW	ROCK & ROLL GROUP	ATI, 888 7TH AVE, 21ST FLOOR	NEW YORK, NY	10106
WRECKS N' EFFECTS	RAP GROUP-RAPWRITERS	FAA, 1700 BROADWAY, 5TH FLOOR	NEW YORK, NY	10019
WREEN, ROBERT	GOLFER	POST OFFICE BOX 109601	PALM BCH GARDENS, FL	33418
WREN, CLARE	ACTRESS	5750 WILSHIRE BLVD #512	LOS ANGELES, CA	90036
WREN, FRANK	BASEBALL SCOUT	6850 LAWRENCE RD	LANTANA, FL	33462
WREN, JEFF	BASEBALL SCOUT	6850 LAWRENCE RD	LANTANA, FL	33462
WRENN, LUKE	BASEBALL SCOUT	1335 COVEY CIR N	LAKELAND, FL	33809
WRIGHT, ALEXANDER	FOOTBALL	COWBOYS, 1 COWBOYS PARKWAY	IRVING, TX	75063
WRIGHT, ALVIN	FOOTBALL	RAMS, 2327 W LINCOLN BLVD	ANAHEIM, CA	92801
WRIGHT, AMY	ACTRESS	19 W 44TH ST #1000	NEW YORK, NY	10036
WRIGHT, BEN	ACTOR	7454 VISTA DEL MONTE	VAN NUYS, CA	91405
WRIGHT, BERNARD	SINGER	POST OFFICE BOX 38	SAINT ALBANS, NY	11412
WRIGHT, BETTY	SINGER	POST OFFICE BOX 4603	MACON, GA	31208
WRIGHT, CARTER	COMPOSER	1607 TALMADGE ST	LOS ANGELES, CA	90027
WRIGHT, CHRISTOPHER B	NEWS CORRESPONDENT	ABC NEWS, 1717 DE SALES ST, NW	WASHINGTON, DC	20036
WRIGHT, COBINA, JR	ACTRESS	1326 DOVE MEADOW RD	SOLVANG, CA	93463
WRIGHT, DON	CARTOONIST	THE MIAMI NEWS		
		1 HERALD PLAZA	MIAMI, FL	33101
WRIGHT, DR JAMES	BODYBUILDER	7863 GRASS HOLLOW	SAN ANTONIO, CA	78233
WRIGHT, EUGENIA	ACTRESS	8831 SUNSET BLVD #402	LOS ANGELES, CA	90069
WRIGHT, FELIX	FOOTBALL	VIKINGS, 9520 VIKING DR	EDEN PRAIRIE, MN	55344
WRIGHT, FRED	BASEBALL SCOUT	6850 LAWRENCE RD	LANTANA, FL	33462
WRIGHT, GARY	SINGER-SONGWRITER	3 E 54TH ST #1400	NEW YORK, NY	10022
WRIGHT, GEORGE	BASEBALL	3704 PELICAN CT	ARLINGTON, TX	76016
WRIGHT, GEORGE	CONDUCTOR	6565 SUNSET BLVD #315	LOS ANGELES, CA	90028
WRIGHT, HEATHER	ACTRESS	1 SUNNYSIDE, WIMBLEDON	LONDON SW19	ENGLAND
WRIGHT, HERBERT J	WRITER-PRODUCER	2069 WATSONIA TERR	LOS ANGELES, CA	90068

WRIGHT, HILARY	COSTUME DESIGNER	1999 AVE OF THE STARS #2850	LOS ANGELES, CA	90067
WRIGHT, HOWARD	BASKETBALL	1 CNN CENTER #405, SOUTH TOWER	ATLANTA, GA	30303
WRIGHT, JAMES R	DIRECTOR	DGA, 110 W 57TH ST	NEW YORK, NY	10019
WRIGHT, JEFF	FOOTBALL	BILLS, 1 BILLS DR	ORCHARD PARK, NJ	14127
WRIGHT, JENNY	ACTRESS	245 W 104TH ST	NEW YORK, NY	10025
WRIGHT, JIM	BASEBALL COACH	POST OFFICE BOX 3449	SCRANTON, PA	18505
WRIGHT, JIM	U S CONGRESSMAN	9A10 LANHAN FEDERAL BUILDING		
		819 TAYLOR ST	FORT WORTH, TX	76102
WRIGHT, JOHNNIE	SINGER-GUITARIST	1302 SAUNDERS AVE	MADISON, TN	37115
WRIGHT, LENORE A	SCREENWRITER	8955 BEVERLY BLVD	WEST HOLLYWOOD, CA	90048
WRIGHT, MARVIN	BASEBALL UMPIRE	235 MAIN ST #103	TRUSSVILLE, AL	35173
WRIGHT, MAURICE	DIRECTOR	1210 PARK NEWPORT #410	NEWPORT BEACH, CA	92660
WRIGHT, MAX	ACTOR	15760 VENTURA BLVD #1730	ENCINO, CA	91436
WRIGHT, NORMAN HALL	TV WRITER-DIRECTOR	16661 PARADISE MOUNTAIN RD	VALLEY CENTER, CA	92082
WRIGHT, NORTON W	TV DIRECTOR	3639 SHADY OAK RD	STUDIO CITY, CA	91604
WRIGHT, PAMELA	GOLFER	2750 VOLUSA AVE #B	DAYTON BEACH, FL	32114
WRIGHT, ROBERT VINCENT	WRITER	3462 STANDISH DR	ENCINO, CA	91436
WRIGHT, ROBIN	ACTRESS	POST OFFICE BOX 2630	MALIBU, CA	90265
WRIGHT, RUDY R	DIRECTOR	POST OFFICE BOX 19519	SAN DIEGO, CA	92119
WRIGHT, SEAN	TV WRITER	1541 N VINE ST	HOLLYWOOD, CA	90028
WRIGHT, STEVE	FOOTBALL	RAIDERS, 332 CENTER ST	EL SEGUNDO, CA	90245
WRIGHT, STEVE	SINGER	PROCESS, 439 WILEY AVE	FRANKLIN, PA	16323
WRIGHT, STEVEN	COMEDIAN	9000 SUNSET BLVD #1200	LOS ANGELES, CA	90069
WRIGHT, TERESA	ACTRESS	OSCARD, 24 W 40TH ST, 17TH FL	NEW YORK, NY	10011
WRIGHT, THOMAS	DIRECTOR	2143 SUNNYBANK DR	LA CANADA, CA	91011
WRIGHT, TOM	TV WRITER	LEMON, 24 POTTERY, HOLLAND PK	LONDON W11 4LZ	ENGLAND
WRIGHT BROTHERS, THE	C & W GROUP	214 OLD HICKORY BLVD #198	NASHVILLE, TN	37205
WRIGHT MILLER, JONATHAN	TV DIRECTOR	LONDON MGT, 235-241 REGENT ST	LONDON W1R 4PH	ENGLAND
WRIGLEY, BEN	COMEDIAN	DOWNING, 3038 E BURNSIDE ST	PORTLAND, OR	97214
WRIGLEY, WILLIAM	BASEBALL	410 N MICHIGAN AVE	CHICAGO, IL	60611
WRONA, DAVE	BASEBALL	POST OFFICE BOX 8550	STOCKTON, CA	95208
WRONA, RICK	BASEBALL	7514 E 17TH ST	TULSA, OK	74112
WRYE, DONALD	WRITER-PRODUCER	6101 CAVALLERI RD	MALIBU, CA	90265
WUGUTOW, DANIEL	TV PRODUCER	ICM, 8899 BEVERLY BLVD	LOS ANGELES, CA	90048
WUHL, ROBERT	COMED-ACT-WRI-DIR	10590 HOLMAN AVE	LOS ANGELES, CA	90024
WULFF, KAI	ACTOR	POST OFFICE BOX 69590	LOS ANGELES, CA	90069
WUNSCH, ROBERT J	TALENT AGENCT	9220 SUNSET BLVD #311	LOS ANGELES, CA	90069
WUNTCH, PHILIP	FILM CRITIC	POST OFFICE BOX 225237	DALLAS, TX	75265
WURTH, LEON	BASEBALL SCOUT	N Y YANKEES, YANKEE STADIUM	BRONX, NY	10451
WUSSLER, ROBERT J	BASKETBALL EXECUTIVE	POST OFFICE BOX 4658	DENVER, CO	80204
WYANT, FRED	FOOTBALL REFEREE	NFL, 410 PARK AVE	NEW YORK, NY	10022
WYATT, ALAN "WILL"	TV EXECUTIVE	38 ABINGER RD	LONDON W4	ENGLAND
WYATT, ALLAN	DIRECTOR	DGA, 7920 SUNSET BLVD, 6TH FL	LOS ANGELES, CA	90046
WYATT, IAN	TV DIRECTOR	4 SHEEN GATE GARDENS	LONDON SW14 7NY	ENGLAND
WYATT, JANE	ACTRESS	651 SIENA WY	LOS ANGELES, CA	90077
WYATT, MILTON	FILM EDITOR	WNBC-TV, 30 ROCKEFELLER PLZ	NEW YORK, NY	10020
WYATT, ROBERT	DRUMMER-SINGER	GRAMAVISION RECORDS		
		260 W BROADWAY	NEW YORK, NY	10013
WYATT, SHARON	ACTRESS	1801 AVE OF THE STARS #1250	LOS ANGELES, CA	90067
WYATT, TESSA	ACTRESS	MILLER, 82 BROOM PK, TEDDINGTON	MIDDLESEX TW11 9RR	ENGLAND
WYCHE, SAM	FOOTBALL COACH	BENGALS, 200 RIVERFRONT STADIUM	CINCINNATI, OH	45202
WYCKOFF, CRAIG	TALENT AGENT	280 S BEVERLY DR #400	BEVERLY HILLS, CA	90212
WYCOFF, MICHAEL	SINGER	151 S EL CAMINO DR	BEVERLY HILLS, CA	90212
WYDEN, RON	U S CONGRESSMAN	500 NE MULTNOMAH #250	PORTLAND, OR	97232
WYETH, ANDREW	ARTIST	POSTMASTER/GENERAL DELIVERY	CHADDS FORD, PA	19317
WYETH, SANDY BROWN	ACTRESS	SHERMAN, 1516 S BEVERLY DR #304	LOS ANGELES, CA	90035
WYLE, GEORGE	CONDUCTOR	4212 ELLENITA AVE	TARZANA, CA	91356
WYLER, GRETCHEN	ACTRESS	11515 LAURELCREST DR	STUDIO CITY, CA	91604
WYLES, DOUG	DIRECTOR	160 W 87TH ST	NEW YORK, NY	10024
WYLIE, BOB	FOOTBALL COACH	N Y JETS, 1000 FULTON AVE	HEMPSTEAD, NY	11550
WYLIE, CHALMERS P	U S CONGRESSMAN	200 N HIGH ST #500	COLUMBUS, OH	43215
WYMAN, DANIEL N	COMPOSER	17760 VISTA AVE	LOS GATOS, CA	95030
WYMAN, DAVID	FOOTBALL	SEAHAWKS, 11220 NE 53RD ST	KIRKLAND, WA	98033
WYMAN, DOUGLAS	TV WRITER	12358 CANTURA ST	STUDIO CITY, CA	91604
WYMAN, JANE	ACTRESS	POST OFFICE BOX 540148	ORLANDO, FL	32854
WYMAN, STEPHEN J	TV DIRECTOR	20 CONTINENTAL AVE #3-T	FOREST HILLS, CA	11375
WYMAN, THOMAS H	TV EXECUTIVE	CBS-TV, 51 W 52ND ST	NEW YORK, NY	10019
WYNANT, H M	ACTOR	1021 N BEVERLY GLEN BLVD	LOS ANGELES, CA	90077
WYND, NADYA	ACTRESS	MARX, 11130 HUSTON ST #6	NORTH HOLLYWOOD, CA	91601
WYNDHAM, VICTORIA	ACTRESS	OSCARD, 24 W 40TH ST, 17TH FL	NEW YORK, NY	10011
WYNDHAM-DAVIES, JUNE	TV DIRECTOR	HEATH, PARAMOUNT HOUSE		
		162-170 WARDOUR ST	LONDON W1V 3AT	ENGLAND
WYNEE, MARVEL	BASEBALL	8052 S CALUMET	CHICAGO, IL	60619
WYNEGAR, BUTCH	BASEBALL	POST OFFICE BOX 915811	LONGWOOD, FL	32791
WYNER, GEORGE	ACTOR	3450 LAURIE PL	STUDIO CITY, CA	91604
WYNER, YEHUDI	COMPOSER-PIANIST	THE SCHOOL OF MUSIC		
		NEW YORK STATE UNIVERSITY	PURCHASE, NY	10577
WYNETTE, TAMMY	SINGER-ACTRESS	POST OFFICE BOX 7532	RICHBORO, PA	18059
WYNN, BOB	GOLFER	PGA SENIORS, 112 T P C BLVD	PONTE VEDRA BEACH, FL	32082
WYNN, BOB	PRODUCER	SCHLATTER, 8321 BEVERLY BLVD	LOS ANGELES, CA	90048
WYNN, DAN	TV DIRECTOR	170 E 73 RD ST	NEW YORK, NY	10021
WYNN, EARLY	BASEBALL	POST OFFICE BOX 218	NOKOMIS, FL	33551
WYNN, NED K	ACTOR-WRITER	937 19TH ST #6	SANTA MONICA, CA	90403
WYNN, ROBERT	TV DIRECTOR-PRODUCER	3115 W OLIVE AVE	BURBANK, CA	91505
WYNNE, JIM	BASEBALL	POLECATS, 608 N SLAPPEY BLVD	ALBANY, GA	31701

WYSE, BILL R	DIRECTOR	12021 VALLEYHEART DR	STUDIO CITY, CA	91604
WYSONG, DUDLEY	GOLFER	PGA SENIORS, 112 T P C BLVD	PONTE VEDRA BEACH, FL	32082
WYSS, AMANDA	ACTRESS	9000 SUNSET BLVD #1200	LOS ANGELES, CA	90069

X	ROCK & ROLL GROUP	10100 SANTA MONICA BLVD #1600	LOS ANGELES, CA	90067
X, MR	WRESTLER	POST OFFICE BOX 3859	STAMFORD, CT	06905
X T C BAND	ROCK & ROLL GROUP	MID-ATLANTIC PRODUCTIONS 501 JARMAN ST	JACKSONVILLE, NC	28540
X Y Z	ROCK & ROLL GROUP	POST OFFICE BOX 448	RADFORD, VA	24141
XEREXS	ROCK & ROLL GROUP	POST OFFICE BOX 448	RADFORD, VA	24141
XIAOPING, DENG	POLITICIAN	OFFICE OF THE CHAIRMAN	CAC-BEIJING	PEO RE CHINA
XIFARAS, TEX	SINGER	6215 SHELTER CREEK #144	SAN BRUNO, CA	94066
XKE	ROCK & ROLL GROUP	4407 MEDICAL PARKWAY #2	AUSTIN, TX	78756
XL	ROCK & ROLL GROUP	PEGASUS PRODUCTIONS, INC 306 S WEBSTER AVE	INDIANPOLIS, IN	46219
XMAL	ROCK & ROLL GROUP	STATION AGENCY 132 LIVERPOOL RD	LONDON N1 1LA	ENGLAND
XTC	ROCK & ROLL GROUP	FBI, 1776 BORADWAY, 6TH FLOOR	NEW YORK, NY	10019
XYZ	ROCK & ROLL GROUP	POST OFFICE BOX 448	RADFORD, VA	24141

Y & T	ROCK & ROLL GROUP	845 VIA DE LA PAZ #365	PACIFIC PALISADES, CA	90272
YA YA	ROCK & ROLL GROUP	FAA, 1700 BROADWAY, 5TH FLOOR	NEW YORK, NY	10019
YABLANS, FRANK	FILM WRITER-PRODUCER	9712 HEATHER RD	BEVERLY HILLS, CA	90210
YABLANS, IRWIN	FILM PRODUCER	706 N PALM DR	BEVERLY HILLS, CA	90210
YABLONSKY, YABO	WRITER-PRODUCER	10960 WILSHIRE BLVD #922	LOS ANGELES, CA	90024
YACOPINO, ED	BASEBALL	500 NORTON ST	ROCHESTER, NY	14621
YAGEMANN, WILLIAM F	DIRECTOR	1818 POINT ABBEY PL	NEWPORT BEACH, CA	92660
YAGEMANN, WILLIAM SCOTT	DIRECTOR	3928 BLUE CANYON DR	STUDIO CITY, CA	91604
YAGHER, JEFF	ACTOR	10000 SANTA MONICA BLVD #305	LOS ANGELES, CA	90067
YALEM, RICHARD	TV WRITER	11168 ACAMA ST #4	NORTH HOLLYWOOD, CA	91602
YALOR, MICK	SINGER-SONGWRITER	150 5TH AVE #1103	NEW YORK, NY	10011
YALOWITZ, PAUL	ARTIST	598 FREEMAN AVE	BRENTWOOD, NY	11717
YAMAMOTO, PAUL	TALENT AGENT	11726 SAN VICENTE BLVD #300	LOS ANGELES, CA	90049
YAMANI, SHEIK AHMEND	SHEIK	CHERMIGNON, NEAR CRANS-MONTANA	VALAIS	FRANCE
YAN, JULIAN	BASEBALL	633 JESSAMINE ST	KNOXVILLE, TN	37917
YANCEY, BERT	GOLFER	PGA SENIORS, 112 T P C BLVD	PONTE VEDRA BEACH, FL	32082
YANCY, EMILY	ACTRESS	247 S BEVERLY DR #102	BEVERLY HILLS, CA	90210
YANE, JOHN, BAND	ROCK & ROLL GROUP	25 HUNTINGTON AVE #420	BOSTON, MA	02116
YANKEE, ALAN L	COMPOSER	12022 POUTOUS CT	SUNNYMEAD, CA	92388
YANKOVIC, WEIRD AL	SINGER-SONGWRITER	8842 HOLLYWOOD BLVD	LOS ANGELES, CA	90069
YANKS, THE	ROCK & ROLL GROUP	POST OFFICE BOX 22129	SAN FRANCISCO, CA	94122
YANNI	COMPOSER-KEYBOARDIST	PRIVATE MUSIC, 9014 MELROSE AVE	LOS ANGELES, CA	90069
YANOK, GEORGE	TV WRITER-PRODUCER	EL-DON PRODS, 5746 SUNSET BLVD	LOS ANGELES, CA	90028
YARALIAN, ZAVEN	FOOTBALL COACH	BEARS, 250 N WASHINGTON RD	LAKE FOREST, IL	60045
YARBOROUGH & PEOPLES	VOCAL DUO	FAA, 1700 BROADWAY, 5TH FLOOR	NEW YORK, NY	10019
YARBROUGH, BURL	BASEBALL EXECUTIVE	POST OFFICE BOX 28268	SAN ANTONIO, TX	78228
YARBROUGH, GLENN	SINGER	2835 WOODSTOCK RD	LOS ANGELES, CA	90046
YARDLEY, STEPHEN	ACTOR	PHYSICK, 78 TEMPLE SHEEN RD	LONDON SW14 7RR	ENGLAND
YARLETT, CLAIRE	ACTRESS	9300 WILSHIRE BLVD #410	BEVERLY HILLS, CA	90212
YARMAT, MEL	BASEBALL EXECUTIVE	12000 STADIUM RD	ADELANTO, CA	92301
YARNELL, CELESTE	ACTRESS	CED, 261 S ROBERTSON BLVD	BEVERLY HILLS, CA	90211
YARWOOD, MIKE	COMIC-IMPRESSIONIST	MARSH, 19 DENMARK ST	LONDON WC2H 8NA	ENGLAND
YARWOOD, TERRY	TV DIRECTOR-PRODUCER	8 WILTON CT, WILTON RD	SOUTHAMPTON SO1 5RU	ENGLAND
YASBECK, AMY	ACTRESS	2170 CENTURY PARK E #1111	LOS ANGELES, CA	90067
YASTRZEMSKI, CARL	BASEBALL	FENWAY PARK, 4 YAWKEY WY	BOSTON, MA	02215
YATES, BILL	CARTOONIST-COMICS ED	KING FEATURES, 216 E 45TH ST	NEW YORK, NY	10017
YATES, BROCK	SCREENWRITER	ICM, 8899 BEVERLY BLVD	LOS ANGELES, CA	90048
YATES, CASSIE	ACTRESS	10100 SANTA MONICA BLVD #700	LOS ANGELES, CA	90067
YATES, DAN	BASEBALL EXECUTIVE	POST OFFICE BOX 611	WATERLOO, IA	50704
YATES, HAROLD R	DIRECTOR	DGA, 110 W 57TH ST	NEW YORK, NY	10019
YATES, JOHN	ACTOR	9825 SHADOW ISLAND DR	SUNLAND, CA	91040
YATES, KEN	PRODUCER	1112 N SHERBOURNE DR	LOS ANGELES, CA	90069
YATES, PAULINE	ACTRESS	43-A PRINCESS RD, REGENTS PK	LONDON NW1 8JS	ENGLAND
YATES, PETER	FILM DIRECTOR	334 CAROLINE AVE	CULVER CITY, CA	90230
YATES, SIDNEY	U S CONGRESSMAN	230 S DEARBORN ST #3920	CHICAGO, IL	60604
YATRON, GUS	U S CONGRESSMAN	1940 N 13TH ST	READING, PA	19604
YATTER, RON	TALENT AGENT	WM MORRIS, 1350 AVE OF AMERICAS	NEW YORK, NY	10019
YAUGHN, KIP	BASEBALL	POST OFFICE BOX 230	HAGERSTOWN, MD	21740
YAVNEH, CYRUS	ACTOR-DIRECTOR	254 S ROBERTSON BLVD #204	BEVERLY HILLS, CA	90210

Name	Occupation	Address	City
YAWKEY, JEAN R	BASEBALL EXECUTIVE	FENWAY PARK, 4 YAWKEY WY	BOSTON, MA 02215
YAWN, OTTICE	SINGER	POST OFFICE BOX 344	NOLENSVILLE, TN 37135
YAWNEY, TRENT	HOCKEY	BLACKHAWKS, 1800 W MADISON ST	CHICAGO, IL 60612
YEAGER, GEN CHUCK	PILOT-TV PERSONALITY	POST OFFICE BOX 128	CEDAR RIDGE, CA 95924
YEAGER, JEANA	AVAITRIX	614 SHADYDALE RD	NIPOMO, CA 93444
YEAGER, STEVE	BASEBALL	11550 SUMAC LN	CAMARILLO, CA 93012
YEARWOOD, TRISHA	SINGER-SONGWRITER	1109 17TH AVE S	NASHVILLE, TN 37212
YELDHAM, PETER	TV WRITER	20 LAVONI ST, MOSMAN	SYDNEY 2088 AUSTRALIA
YELDING, ERIC	BASEBALL	POST OFFICE BOX 325	MONTROSE, AL 36559
YELLEN, LINDA	WRITER-PRODUCER	3 SHERIDAN SQ	NEW YORK, NY 10014
YELLEN, SHERMAN	TV WRITER	UTA, 9560 WILSHIRE BL, 5TH FL	BEVERLY HILLS, CA 90212
YELLON, ALVIN H	TV DIRECTOR	516 WEST BRIAR #2-D	CHICAGO, IL 60601
YELLOW MAGIC ORCHESTRA	ROCK & ROLL GROUP	151 S EL CAMINO DR	BEVERLY HILLS, CA 90212
YELLOWJACKETS, THE	JAZZ GROUP	9220 SUNSET BLVD #320	LOS ANGELES, CA 90069
YELTON, ROB	BASEBALL	POST OFFICE BOX 64939	FAYETTEVILLE, NC 28306
YELTON, ROY LEE	SINGER	POST OFFICE BOX 25371	CHARLOTTE, NC 28212
YELTSIN, BORIS	RUSSIAN PRESIDENT	ULIZA TWERSKAYA, JAMSKAYA 2	MOSCOW RUSSIA
YENTOB, ALAN	TV DIRECTOR-PRODUCER	99 BLENHEIM CRESCENT	LONDON W11 ENGLAND
YEOMAN, BRIAN	FILM EXECUTIVE	PARAMOUNT, 162-170 WARDOUR ST	LONDON W1V 3AT ENGLAND
YERED, JIMMY	ACTOR	5000 LANKERSHIM BLVD #7 & 9	NORTH HOLLYWOOD, CA 91601
YERETSKY, JAMES	BASEBALL EXECUTIVE	POST OFFICE BOX 3665	OMAHA, NE 68103
YERKOVICH, ANTHONY HENDEN	TV WRITER-PRODUCER	1802 ASHLAND AVE	SANTA MONICA, CA 90405
YES	ROCK & ROLL GROUP	SUN ARTISTS, 9 HILLGATE ST	LONDON W8 7SP ENGLAND
YETNIKOFF, WALTER	RECORD EXECUTIVE	CBS RECORDS COMPANY	
		1801 CENTURY PARK W	LOS ANGELES, CA 90067
YETT, RICH	BASEBALL	1140 N HIGLEY #109, BOX 161	MESA, AZ 85205
YINGLING, JOHN	DIRECTOR	975 WINSTON AVE	SAN MARINO, CA 91108
YIP, DAVID	ACTOR	SHARKEY, 15 GOLDEN SQ #315	LONDON W1R 3AG ENGLAND
YNOCENCIO, JO	COSTUME DESIGNER	302 E 88TH ST	NEW YORK, NY 10128
YO	ROCK & ROLL GROUP	POST OFFICE BOX 2428	EL SEGUNDO, CA 90245
YO LA TENGO	ROCK & ROLL GROUP	POST OFFICE BOX 112	
		UPTOWN STATION	HOBOKEN, NJ 07030
YOAKAM, DWIGHT	SINGER-GUITARIST	15840 VENTURA BLVD #465	ENCINO, CA 91436
YOAKUM, DAVE	BASEBALL SCOUT	SKYDOME, 300 BREMMER BL #3200	TORONTO, ONT M5V 3B3 CANADA
YOCHIM, LENNY	BASEBALL SCOUT	POST OFFICE BOX 7000	PITTSBURGH, PA 15212
YOCKEY, MARK	BASEBALL	POST OFFICE BOX 3448	SHREVEPORT, LA 71133
YODER, EDWIN M, JR	COLUMNIST	THE WASHINGTON POST	
		WRITERS GROUP	
		1150 15TH ST, NW	WASHINGTON, DC 20071
YOELS, NANCY	ACTRESS	210 E 36TH ST	NEW YORK, NY 10016
YOHE, JEFFREY E	MUSIC ARRANGER	371 WALLACE RD #H-55	NASHVILLE, TN 37211
YOHE, THOMAS G	DIRECTOR	WILD GOOSE LN	NORWALK, CT 06851
YOHN, ERICA	ACTRESS	10630 CHIQUITA ST	NORTH HOLLYWOOD, CA 91602
YOKLAVICH, JOSEPH	DIRECTOR	23451 SCHOOLCRAFT ST	CANOGA PARK, CA 91307
YOLL, YAEL R	DIRECTOR	PEA POND RD	BEDFORD VILLAGE, NY 10506
YOLLAND, PETER	TV DIRECTOR-PRODUCER	TRANSNETWORK, 1 LAMBOURN RD	LONDON SW4 OLX ENGLAND
YORDAN, PHILIP	SCREENWRITER	4895 MOUNT ELBRUS DR	SAN DIEGO, CA 92117
YORK, BETH	SINGER	POST OFFICE BOX 3142	DURHAM, NC 27705
YORK, BRIAN	BASEBALL SCOUT	POST OFFICE BOX 2000	ANAHEIM, CA 92803
YORK, ELODIA	ACTRESS	8484 WILSHIRE BLVD #530	BEVERLY HILLS, CA 90211
YORK, FRANCINE	ACTRESS	CARROLL, 120 S VICTORY BL #104	BURBANK, CA 91502
YORK, GARY	BASEBALL SCOUT	TIGERS, TIGER STADIUM	DETROIT, MI 48216
YORK, JOHN J	ACTOR	ABC-TV, "GENERAL HOSPITAL"	
		4151 PROSPECT AVE	BURBANK, CA 91523
YORK, MARK	ACTOR	29633 STRAWBERRY HILL DR	AGOURA HILLS, CA 91301
YORK, MICHAEL	ACTOR	9100 CORDELL DR	LOS ANGELES, CA 90069
YORK, MIKE	BASEBALL	STARS, 850 LAS VEGAS BLVD N	LAS VEGAS, NV 89101
YORK, SUSANNAH	ACTRESS	59 KNIGHTSBRIDGE	LONDON SW1 ENGLAND
YORKIN, ALAN "BUD"	WRITER-PRODUCER	124 DELFERN	LOS ANGELES, CA 90077
YORTY, SAM	MAYOR	12979 BLAIRWOOD DR	STUDIO CITY, CA 91604
YOSHIOKA, ADELE	ACTRESS-DANCER-MODEL	3754 ROSEWOOD AVE	LOS ANGELES, CA 90066
YOSHIOKA, EMMETT G	COMPOSER-CONDUCTOR	5223 APO DR	HONOLULU, HI 96821
YOST, NED	BASEBALL-COACH	POST OFFICE BOX 4064	ATLANTA, GA 30302
YOST, ROBERT A	COMPOSER	11478 E WINCHELL ST	WHITTIER, CA 90606
YOTHERS, TINA	ACTRESS	9000 SUNSET BLVD #1200	LOS ANGELES, CA 90069
YOUMANS, FLOYD	BASEBALL	3200 GIBRALTOR DR	RIVERSIDE, CA 92506
YOUNG, AIDA	FILM-TV PRODUCER	HEATH, PARAMOUNT HOUSE	
		162-170 WARDOUR ST	LONDON W1V 3AT ENGLAND
YOUNG, ALAN	ACTOR	33872 BARCELLONA PL	DANA POINT, CA 92629
YOUNG, ANDREW	MAYOR	1088 VELTRIE CIR SW	ATLANTA, GA 30311
YOUNG, ANGEL	SINGER	SOUNDS, 1210 PALM ST	ABILINE, TX 79602
YOUNG, ANTHONY	BASEBALL	METS, 126TH ST & ROOSEVELT AVE	FLUSHING, NY 11368
YOUNG, BARBARA	ACTRESS	59 BELSIZE AVE #1	LONDON NW3 4BN ENGLAND
YOUNG, BARBARA	ACTRESS	MC KENNA, 16 MONTAGU MEWS N	LONDON W1H 1AJ ENGLAND
YOUNG, BOB	FOOTBALL COACH	OILERS, 6910 FANNIN ST	HOUSTON, TX 77070
YOUNG, BRIAN	BASEBALL	RED SOX, CHAIN O'LAKES PARK	WINTER HAVEN, FL 33880
YOUNG, BRUCE	TALENT AGENT	POST OFFICE BOX 22129	SAN FRANCISCO, CA 94122
YOUNG, BURT	ACTOR-SCREENWRITER	5820 WILSHIRE BLVD #503	LOS ANGELES, CA 90036
YOUNG, C W "BILL"	U S CONGRESSMAN	144 1ST AVE S #627	SAINT PETERSBURG, FL 33701
YOUNG, CHARLES	ACTOR	CED, 261 S ROBERTSON BLVD	BEVERLY HILLS, CA 90211
YOUNG, CLIFF	BASEBALL	POST OFFICE BOX 75, GOLDEN ST	WILLIS, TX 77378
YOUNG, COLEMAN	MAYOR	2 WOODWARD AVE	DETROIT, MI 49226
YOUNG, COLIN	FILM DIRECTOR	BEACONSFIELD STUDIOS	
		STATION RD, BEACONSFIELD	BUCKS HP9 1LG ENGLAND
YOUNG, CURT	BASEBALL	13354 N 100TH PL	SCOTTSDALE, AZ 85260

YOUNG, DANNY	BASEBALL	POST OFFICE BOX 1556	ASHEVILLE, NC	28802
YOUNG, DAVE "THE WAVE"	FIREARMS EXPERT	2801 MEADOW LARK DR	SAN DIEGO, CA	92123
YOUNG, DAVID	BASEBALL SCOUT	BREWERS, 201 S 46TH ST	MILWAUKEE, WI	53214
YOUNG, DEAN	CARTOONIST	KING FEATURES, 216 E 45TH ST	NEW YORK, NY	10017
YOUNG, DEY	ACTRESS	822 S ROBERTSON BLVD #200	LOS ANGELES, CA	90035
YOUNG, DMITRI	BASEBALL	POST OFFICE BOX 3004	SPRINGFIELD, IL	62708
YOUNG, DON	U S CONGRESSMAN	109 MAIN ST	KETCHIKAN, AK	99902
YOUNG, ERIC	BASEBALL	POST OFFICE BOX 26267	ALBUQUERQUE, NM	87125
YOUNG, ERNIE	BASEBALL	POST OFFICE BOX 2437	MODESTO, CA	95351
YOUNG, FARON	SINGER-SONGWRITER	607 ELBA DR	GOODLETTSVILLE, TN	37072
YOUNG, FREDDY	CINEMATOGRAPHER	3 ROEHAMPTON CLOSE	LONDON SW15	ENGLAND
YOUNG, GARY	SINGER	5625 "O" STREET BLDG #7	LINCOLN, NE	68510
YOUNG, GARY A	DIRECTOR	35 E 20TH ST	NEW YORK, NY	10003
YOUNG, GEORGE	FOOTBALL EXECUTIVE	N Y GIANTS, GIANTS STADIUM	EAST RUTHERFORD, NJ	07073
YOUNG, GERALD	BASEBALL	POST OFFICE BOX 288	HOUSTON, TX	77001
YOUNG, JAMES P	DIRECTOR	POST OFFICE BOX 781	COUPEVILLE, WA	98239
YOUNG, JEFFREY	FILM DIRECTOR	DGA, 7920 SUNSET BLVD, 6TH FL	LOS ANGELES, CA	90046
YOUNG, JESSE COLIN	SINGER-SONGWRITER	POST OFFICE BOX 569	FRANKLIN, PA	16323
YOUNG, JO ANN G	TV PRODUCER	CAMERA THREE, 1 MADISON AVE	NEW YORK, NY	10010
YOUNG, JOHN	BASEBALL SCOUT	POST OFFICE BOX 90111	ARLINGTON, TX	76004
YOUNG, JOHN	BASEBALL TRAINER	POST OFFICE BOX 23290	NASHVILLE, TN	37202
YOUNG, JOHN SACRET	TV WRITER-PRODUCER	3456 WONDER VIEW DR	LOS ANGELES, CA	90068
YOUNG, KAC S	TV DIRECTOR	3474 LA SOMBRA DR	HOLLYWOOD, CA	90068
YOUNG, KAREN	ACTRESS	POST OFFICE BOX 5617	BEVERLY HILLS, CA	90213
YOUNG, KAREN	SINGER	SUNSHINE, 800 S 4TH ST	PHILADELPHIA, PA	19147
YOUNG, KEONE	ACTOR	9255 SUNSET BLVD #515	LOS ANGELES, CA	90069
YOUNG, KEVIN	BASEBALL	POST OFFICE BOX 450	BUFFALO, NY	14205
YOUNG, LARRY	BASEBALL UMPIRE	3538 SHADY BLUDD DR	LARGO, FL	33540
YOUNG, LINDA	SINGER	TC TALENT, 3725 HILLTOP LN	NASHVILLE, TN	37216
YOUNG, LONNIE	FOOTBALL	N Y JETS, 1000 FULTON AVE	HEMPSTEAD, NY	11550
YOUNG, LORETTA	ACTRESS	1705 AMBASSADOR AVE	BEVERLY HILLS, CA	90210
YOUNG, MARK D	WRITER-PRODUCER	11123 LANDALE ST	NORTH HOLLYWOOD, CA	91602
YOUNG, MARL	COMPOSER	3602 COUNTRY CLUB DR	LOS ANGELES, CA	90019
YOUNG, MATT	BASEBALL	FENWAY PARK, 4 YAWKEY WY	BOSTON, MA	02215
YOUNG, MELISSA	ACTRESS	FELBER, 2126 N CAHUENGA BLVD	LOS ANGELES, CA	90068
YOUNG, MICHAEL	ACTOR-TV HOST	2029 CENTURY PARK E #3250	LOS ANGELES, CA	90067
YOUNG, MICHAEL	FOOTBALL	BRONCOS, 13655 BRONCOS PKWY	ENGLEWOOD, CO	80112
YOUNG, MIGHTY JOE	SINGER-GUITARIST	CAMERON, 822 HILLGROVE AVE	WESTERN SPRINGS, IL	60558
YOUNG, MIKE	BASEBALL COACH	500 NORTON ST	ROCHESTER, NY	14621
YOUNG, NEIL	SINGER-SONGWRITER	LOOKOUT, 506 SANTA MONICA BLVD	SANTA MONICA, CA	90401
YOUNG, NELSON	SINGER-SONGWRITER	6870-A NEWELL HICKORY GROVE RD	CHARLOTTE, NC	28212
YOUNG, OTIS	ACTOR	540 S KENMORE AVE #6	LOS ANGELES, CA	90020
YOUNG, PAUL	SINGER-SONGWRITER	POST OFFICE BOX 40	LONDON WC2H 8FB	ENGLAND
YOUNG, PETE	BASEBALL	1501 W 16TH ST	INDIANAPOLIS, IN	46202
YOUNG, RAYMOND	ACTOR	HAMPTON COTTAGE, 7 CHURCH ST	LITTLEHAMPTON BN1Y 5EL	ENGLAND
YOUNG, RHONDA	CASTING DIRECTOR	PARAMOUNT PICTURES CORP		
		DIRECTORS BUILDING #401		
		5555 MELROSE AVE	LOS ANGELES, CA	90038
YOUNG, RICHARD	ACTOR	8380 MELROSE AVE #207	LOS ANGELES, CA	90069
YOUNG, ROBERT	FOOTBALL	RAMS, 2327 W LINCOLN BLVD	ANAHEIM, CA	92801
YOUNG, ROBERT M	WRITER-PRODUCER	125 W 76TH ST	NEW YORK, NY	10023
YOUNG, ROBERT WILLIAM	DIRECTOR-PRODUCER	HEATH, PARAMOUNT HOUSE		
		162-170 WARDOUR ST	LONDON W1V 3AT	ENGLAND
YOUNG, ROGER E	TV DIRECTOR	9242 BEVERLY DR #200	BEVERLY HILLS, CA	90210
YOUNG, RON	SINGER	POST OFFICE BOX 29543	ATLANTA, GA	30359
YOUNG, SCOTT	HOCKEY	PENGUINS, CIVIC ARENA, CENTRE AV	PITTSBURGH, PA	15219
YOUNG, SEAN	ACTRESS	300 MERCER ST #7-E	NEW YORK, NY	10003
YOUNG, STEVE	FOOTBALL	S F 49ERS, 4949 CENTENNIAL BL	SANTA CLARA, CA	95054
YOUNG, STEVE	SINGER	POST OFFICE BOX 121264	NASHVILLE, TN	37212
YOUNG, STEVEN	TV WRITER	WM MORRIS, 1350 AVE OF AMERICAS	NEW YORK, NY	10019
YOUNG, TERENCE	FILM WRITER-DIRECTOR	61 EATON SQ	LONDON SW1	ENGLAND
YOUNG, TONY	ACTOR	1221 N KINGS RD #PH-405	LOS ANGELES, CA	90069
YOUNG, WILLIAM A	DIRECTOR	4525 MORSE AVE	STUDIO CITY, CA	91604
YOUNG, WILLIAM ALLEN	ACTOR	1213 W 122ND ST	LOS ANGELES, CA	90044
YOUNG, WILLIAM L, JR	DIRECTOR	4819 WILLOW CREST AVE	NORTH HOLLYWOOD, CA	91601
YOUNG FRESH FELLOWS, THE	ROCK & ROLL GROUP	POST OFFICE BOX 95364	SEATTLE, WA	98145
YOUNG M C	RAPPER-RAPWRITER	9229 SUNSET BLVD #319	LOS ANGELES, CA	90069
YOUNGBLOOD, JACK	FOOTBALL EXECUTIVE	RAMS, 2327 W LINCOLN BLVD	ANAHEIM, CA	92801
YOUNGBLOOD, JOEL	BASEBALL-COACH	POST OFFICE BOX 418	SAINT CHARLES, IL	60174
YOUNGER, JAMES & MICHAEL	VOCAL DUO	POST OFFICE BOX 973	ALIEF, TX	77411
YOUNGER BROTHERS, THE	C & W GROUP	POST OFFICE BOX 973	ALIEF, TX	77411
YOUNGFELLOW, BARRIE	ACTRESS	10927 MISSOURI AVE	LOS ANGELES, CA	90025
YOUNGMAN, HENNY	COMEDIAN	77 W 55TH ST	NEW YORK, NY	10019
YOUNGMAN, PETER	BASEBALL TRAINER	POST OFFICE BOX 2365	PAWTUCKET, RI	02861
YOUNT, ROBIN	BASEBALL	BREWERS, 201 S 46TH ST	MILWAUKEE, WI	53214
YOUSE, WALTER	BASEBALL SCOUT	BREWERS, 201 S 46TH ST	MILWAUKEE, WI	53214
YOUTH IN ASIA	ROCK & ROLL GROUP	345 N MAPLE ST #235	BEVERLY HILLS, CA	90210
YRIGOYEN, JOSEPH	DIRECTOR	32171 SAILVIEW LN	WESTLAKE VILLAGE, CA	91361
YSEBAERT, PAUL	HOCKEY	RED WINGS, 600 CIVIC CENTER DR	DETROIT, MI	48226
YUDAIN, CAROLE G	WRITER	22 VALLEYWOOD RD	COS COB, CT	06807
YUILL, BILL	BASEBALL EXECUTIVE	POST OFFICE BOX 465	MED HAT, ALB T1A 7G2	CANADA
YUNG, ROBERT	DIRECTOR	DGA, 110 W 57TH ST	NEW YORK, NY	10019
YUNUS, TARIQ	ACTOR	FRAZER, 34 BRAMERTON ST	LONDON SW3 5LA	ENGLAND
YUST, LARRY	DIRECTOR	520 S ROSSMORE AVE	LOS ANGELES, CA	90020
YUSUF, JAVED	WRITER-PRODUCER	31 CREIGHTON AVE	LONDON N10 1NX	ENGLAND

Name	Profession	Address	City	Code
YZERMAN, STEVE	HOCKEY	RED WINGS, 600 CIVIC CENTER DR	DETROIT, MI	48226

Z

Name	Profession	Address	City	Code
ZABALA, GEORGE	BASEBALL SCOUT	BREWERS, 201 S 46TH ST	MILWAUKEE, WI	53214
ZABKA, STANLEY	COMPOSER-DIRECTOR	5723 STAR LN	WOODLAND HILLS, CA	91367
ZABKA, WILLIAM	ACTOR-SINGER	345 N MAPLE DR #183	BEVERLY HILLS, CA	90210
ZABRISKIE, GRACE	ACTRESS	1536 MURRAY DR	LOS ANGELES, CA	90026
ZABRISKIE, P JAY	DIRECTOR	2377 N DANVILLE ST	ARLINGTON, VA	22207
ZACCARO, JAMES	DIRECTOR	315 E 68TH ST	NEW YORK, NY	10021
ZACHA, WILLIAM T	ACTOR-WRITER	22954 COLLINS ST	WOODLAND HILLS, CA	91367
ZACHARIAS, HANK	BASEBALL SCOUT	POST OFFICE BOX 2000	SAN DIEGO, CA	92112
ZACHARIAS, STEFFEN	ACTOR-WRITER	6234 BAKMAN AVE	NORTH HOLLYWOOD, CA	91606
ZACHARIAS, STEVE	SCREENWRITER	165 N ANITA AVE	LOS ANGELES, CA	90049
ZACHAROW, M CHRISTOPHER	ARTIST	11 WAVERLY PL #52	NEW YORK, NY	10003
ZACHERY, TONY	FOOTBALL	PATRIOTS, FOXBORO STADIUM, RT #1	FOXBORO, MA	02035
ZACK, DOTTY	SINGER	234 POTTERS AVE	WARWICK, RI	02886
ZACK, EDDIE	SINGER	234 POTTERS AVE	WARWICK, RI	02886
ZACK, RICHIE	SINGER	234 POTTERS AVE	WARWICK, RI	02886
ZADAN, CRAIG	FILM PRODUCER	TRI-STAR PICTURES COMPANY		
		1875 CENTURY PARK E	LOS ANGELES, CA	90067
ZADORA, PIA	ACTRESS-SINGER	8 BEVERLY PARK	BEVERLY HILLS, CA	90210
ZAENTZ, SAUL	FILM-RECORD PRODUCER	FANTASY RECORDS COMPANY		
		10TH & PARKER STS	BERKELEY, CA	94710
ZAFFINO, PATRICIA ANN	TV PRODUCER	SYNTHESIS COMM, 15 W 72ND ST	NEW YORK, NY	10023
ZAGONE, ROBERT	DIRECTOR	2300 VINE ST	BERKELEY, CA	94708
ZAGOREN, MARC ALAN	TV-COMEDY WRITER	5 ROOSEVELT PL	MONTCLAIR, NJ	07042
ZAHL, EDA	ACTRESS	2124 N BEACHWOOD DR #16	LOS ANGELES, CA	90068
ZAHLER, ANDREAS	DIRECTOR	49 HORATIO ST	NEW YORK, NY	10014
ZAHREMA	ACTRESS	33-A ALDBURY HS, SUTTON ESTATE		
		CALE ST	LONDON SW3 3RY	ENGLAND
ZAID, BARRY	ARTIST	1515 10TH ST	BOULDER, CO	80302
ZAILLIAN, STEVEN	SCREENWRITER	8455 BEVERLY BLVD #309	LOS ANGELES, CA	90048
ZAK, JOHN	TV DIRECTOR	11846 VENTURA BLVD #100	STUDIO CITY, CA	91604
ZAK, JOHN C	ACTOR-DIRECTOR	4455 LOS FELIZ BLVD #401	HOLLYWOOD, CA	90027
ZAL, ROXANA	ACTRESS	10390 SANTA MONICA BLVD #300	LOS ANGELES, CA	90025
ZALA, NANCY	ACTRESS-WRITER	11939 GORHAM AVE #308	LOS ANGELES, CA	90049
ZALAPSKI, ZARLEY	HOCKEY	WHALERS, 1 CIVIC CENTER PLAZA	HARTFORD, CT	06103
ZAMBRANO, EDDIE	BASEBALL	POST OFFICE BOX 450	BUFFALO, NY	14205
ZAMIARA, ARLENE	COSTUME DESIGNER	13949 VENTURA BLVD #309	SHERMAN OAKS, CA	91423
ZAMMIT, EDDIE	ACTOR	329 N WETHERLY DR #101	BEVERLY HILLS, CA	90211
ZAMPESE, ERNIE	FOOTBALL COACH	RAMS, 2327 W LINCOLN BLVD	ANAHEIM, CA	92801
ZANCANARO, DAVE	BASEBALL	POST OFFICE BOX 11087	TACOMA, WA	98411
ZANDER, CHRISTINE	TV WRITER	WM MORRIS, 1350 AVE OF AMERICAS	NEW YORK, NY	10019
ZANE, BILLY	ACTOR	CAA, 9830 WILSHIRE BLVD	BEVERLY HILLS, CA	90212
ZANE, FRANK	BODYBUILDER	POST OFFICE BOX 2031	PALM SPRINGS, CA	92263
ZANE, LISA	ACTRESS	1722 N SERRANO #4	LOS ANGELES, CA	90027
ZANETOS, DEAN	TV DIRECTOR-PRODUCER	3170 HOLLYRIDGE DR	HOLLYWOOD, CA	90068
ZANN, LENORE	ACTRESS	10351 SANTA MONICA BLVD #211	LOS ANGELES, CA	90025
ZANY, BOB	COMEDIAN	8075 W 3RD ST #303	LOS ANGELES, CA	90048
ZAP, SAM	ACTOR	1355 1/4 N HAVENHURST DR	LOS ANGELES, CA	90046
ZAPATA, CARMEN	ACTRESS	6107 ETHEL AVE	VAN NUYS, CA	91401
ZAPATA, RAMON	BASEBALL	POST OFFICE BOX 3746, HILL STA	AUGUSTA, GA	30904
ZAPP	RHYTHM & BLUES GROUP	FAA, 1700 BROADWAY, 5TH FLOOR	NEW YORK, NY	10019
ZAPPA, DWEEZIL	ACTOR-SINGER	POST OFFICE BOX 5265	NORTH HOLLYWOOD, CA	91606
ZAPPA, FRANK	SINGER-MUSICAN	POST OFFICE BOX 5418	NORTH HOLLYWOOD, CA	91616
ZAPPA, MOON UNIT	SINGER	345 N MAPLE DR #183	BEVERLY HILLS, CA	90210
ZAPPACOSTA	ROCK & ROLL GROUP	41 BRITAIN ST #200	TORONTO, ONT M5A 1R7	CANADA
ZAPPELLI, MARK	BASEBALL	POST OFFICE BOX 12	MIDLAND, TX	79702
ZARCOFF, MORTON	WRITER	1616 WARNALL AVE	LOS ANGELES, CA	90024
ZARETSKY, ALAN	TV PRODUCER	PROGRAM PARTNETS CORPORATION		
		65 SPRUCE ST	ROSLYN HARBOR, NY	11576
ZARKONS, THE	ROCK & ROLL GROUP	6253 HOLLYWOOD BLVD #727	HOLLYWOOD, CA	90028
ZARRAS, BILL	RECORD EXECUTIVE	WEA MUSIC, 1810 BIRCHMONT RD	SCARBOROUGH, ONT	CANADA
ZASLOW, MICHAEL	ACTOR	CBS-TV, "THE GUIDING LIGHT"		
		222 E 44TH ST	NEW YORK, NY	10017
ZASTOUPIL, RICH	BASEBALL	POST OFFICE BOX 4669	CHARLESTON, WV	25304
ZASTUPNEVICH, PAUL	COSTUME DESIGNER	75-179 LA SIERRA DR	PALM DESERT, CA	92260
ZATESLO, GEORGE T	TV WRITER	11755 NEBRASKA AVE #9	LOS ANGELES, CA	90025
ZAUN, GREGG	BASEBALL	POST OFFICE BOX 3169	FREDERICK, MD	21701
ZAVADA, ERVIN	WRITER-PRODUCER	16763 LONDELIUS ST	SEPULVEDA, CA	91343
ZAVARAS, CLINT	BASEBALL	POST OFFICE BOX 3690, STA "B"	CALGARY, ALB T2B 4M4	CANADA
ZAWATSON, DAVE	FOOTBALL	DOLPHINS, 2269 NW 199TH ST	MIAMI, FL	33056
ZAY, BOB L	ACTOR	1121 N OLIVE DR #303	LOS ANGELES, CA	90069
ZBYSZKO, LARRY	WRESTLER	POST OFFICE BOX 105366	ATLANTA, GA	31348
ZDERKO, MICHAEL	ACTOR	CBS-TV, "AS THE WORLD TURNS"		
		524 W 57TH ST #5330	NEW YORK, NY	10019
ZDURIENCIK, JACK	BASEBALL SCOUT	POST OFFICE BOX 7000	PITTSBURGH, PA	15212

ZEA, KRISTI	COSTUME DESIGNER	13949 VENTURA BLVD #309	SHERMAN OAKS, CA	91423
ZEAROTT, MICHAEL F	COMPOSER-CONDUCTOR	701 OHIO AVE #3	LONG BEACH, CA	90804
ZEBRO, LISA	ACTRESS	4958 WOODMAN AVE #109	SHERMAN OAKS, CA	91423
ZEE, ELEANOR	ACTRESS	1322 N HAVENHURST DR #26	LOS ANGELES, CA	90046
ZEFFERELLI, FRANCO	FILM DIRECTOR	9247 SWALLOW DR	LOS ANGELES, CA	90069
ZEGLER, PAUL	ACTOR	1942 RODNEY DR #10	LOS ANGELES, CA	90027
ZEHMS, CRAIG	ACTOR	438 N SYCAMORE AVE #7	LOS ANGELES, CA	90036
ZEIDEN, JAY	ACTOR	4724 FARMDALE AVE	NORTH HOLLYWOOD, CA	91602
ZEIGLER, MARK	BASEBALL EXECUTIVE	POST OFFICE BOX 3169	FREDERICK, MD	21701
ZEIGLER, TED	ACTOR-WRITER	4040 SHADYGLADE AVE	STUDIO CITY, CA	91604
ZEIHEN, BOB	BASEBALL COACH	14100 SIX MILE CYPRESS PKWY	FORT MYERS, FL	33912
ZEILE, TODD	BASEBALL	250 STADIUM PLAZA	ST LOUIS, MO	63102
ZEITMAN, JERRY	TALENT AGENT	10351 SANTA MONICA BLVD #211	LOS ANGELES, CA	90025
ZELENKA, JERRY	ACTOR	4410 HENLEY CT	WESTLAKE, CA	91361
ZELIFF, BILL, JR	U S CONGRESSMAN	340 COMMERCIAL ST	MANCHESTER, NH	03101
ZELIG, EVA	TV WRITER-PRODUCER	408 W 57TH ST	NEW YORK, NY	10019
ZELLEN, MICHAEL	TV DIRECTOR-PRODUCER	PARINEU FILMS, 60 E 42ND ST	NEW YORK, NY	10165
ZELLER, ART	BODYBUILDER	POST OFFICE BOX 254	SANTA MONICA, CA	90406
ZELLIN, ROBERT F	COMPOSER	6643 LOCHE ALENE	PICO RIVERA, CA	90660
ZELLMAN, SHELLEY	TV WRITER	9869 EASTON DR	BEVERLY HILLS, CA	90210
ZELLO, MARK	BASEBALL TRAINER	POST OFFICE BOX 418	SAINT CHARLES, IL	60174
ZEMAN, BOB	FOOTBALL COACH	S F 49ERS, 4949 CENTENNIAL BL	SANTA CLARA, CA	95054
ZEMAN, JACKLYN	ACTRESS	STONE MANNERS, 9113 SUNSET BL	LOS ANGELES, CA	90069
ZEMANN, DON	RECORD EXECUTIVE	POST OFFICE BOX 3082	LONG ISLAND CITY, NY	11103
ZEMBRISKI, WALTER	GOLFER	PGA SENIORS, 112 T P C BLVD	PONTE VEDRA BEACH, FL	32082
ZEMECKIS, ROBERT	WRITER-DIRECTOR	9125 ALTO CEDRO DR	BEVERLY HILLS, CA	90210
ZENDAR, FRED V	DIRECTOR	134 CHAUTAUQUA BLVD	SANTA MONICA, CA	90402
ZENDEJAS, TONY	FOOTBALL	RAMS, 2327 W LINCOLN BLVD	ANAHEIM, CA	92801
ZENK, TOM "Z-MAN"	WRESTLER	POST OFFICE BOX 105366	ATLANTA, GA	31348
ZENK-PINTER, COLLEEN MARIE	ACTRESS	CBS-TV, "AS THE WORLD TURNS"		
		524 W 57TH ST #5330	NEW YORK, NY	10019
ZENOR, SUZANNE	ACTRESS	3158 OAKSHIRE DR	LOS ANGELES, CA	90068
ZENTALL, KATE	ACTRESS	2922 2ND ST #B	SANTA MONICA, CA	90405
ZENTNER, SIMON	COMPOSER-CONDUCTOR	4825 FAIRFAX AVE	LAS VEGAS, NV	89120
ZERBE, ANTHONY	ACTOR	SMITH, 121 N SAN VICENTE BLVD	BEVERLY HILLS, CA	90211
ZETTEL, PHILIP	ACTOR	7300 LANKERSHIM BLVD	NORTH HOLLYWOOD, CA	91605
ZETTELMEYER, MARK	BASEBALL EXECUTIVE	5301 NW 12TH AVE	FORT LAUDERDALE, FL	33309
ZETTERLING, MAI	ACT-WRI-DIR	RAE, CHARING CROSS RD	LONDON WC2H ODB	ENGLAND
ZETTLER, ROB	HOCKEY	NORTH STARS, 7901 CEDAR AVE S	BLOOMINGTON, MN	55425
ZEUSKE, CATHY S	TREASURER	STATE CAPITOL BUILDING	MADISON, WI	53702
ZEVNIK, NEIL	ACTOR	3349 W CAHUENGA BLVD #2-B	LOS ANGELES, CA	90068
ZEVON, WARREN	SINGER-SONGWRITER	1880 CENTURY PARK E #900	LOS ANGELES, CA	90067
ZEZEL, PETER	HOCKEY	MAPLE LEAFS, 60 CARLTON ST	TORONTO, ONT M5B 1L1	CANADA
ZHUKOV, BORIS	WRESTLER	POST OFFICE BOX 3859	STAMFORD, CT	06905
ZICK, BILL	BASEBALL TRAINER	POST OFFICE BOX 3746, HILL STA	AUGUSTA, GA	30904
ZICK, BRUCE	ARTIST	1351 OCEAN PARK WALK #106	SANTA MONICA, CA	90405
ZIEFF, HOWARD	FILM DIRECTOR	1243 SUNSET PLAZA DR	LOS ANGELES, CA	90069
ZIEGLER, JACK	CARTOONIST	N Y MAGAZINE, 25 W 43RD ST	NEW YORK, NY	10036
ZIEGLER, JAMES E	TV DIRECTOR	1640 REDESDALE AVE	LOS ANGELES, CA	90026
ZIEGLER, LARRY	GOLFER	PGA SENIORS, 112 T P C BLVD	PONTE VEDRA BEACH, FL	32082
ZIELINSKI, STAN	BASEBALL SCOUT	6850 LAWRENCE RD	LANTANA, FL	33462
ZIELKE, W D "OZ"	DIRECTOR	11948 RANCHO BERNARDO RD #D	SAN DEIGO, CA	92128
ZIEMIENSKI, DENNIS	ARTIST	55 CHEEVER PL	BROOKLYN, NY	11231
ZIERING, BOB	ARTIST	151 W 74TH ST	NEW YORK, NY	10023
ZIERING, IAN ANDREW	ACTOR	5700 WILSHIRE BLVD #575	LOS ANGELES, CA	90036
ZIGMAN, JOSEPH	DIRECTOR	473 S HOLT AVE	LOS ANGELES, CA	90048
ZIKER, RICHARD	FILM DIRECTOR	11268 SUNSHINE TRAIL	STUDIO CITY, CA	91604
ZILSKE, BRUCE	WRITER	2050 RODNEY DR #9	LOS ANGELES, CA	90027
ZIMBALIST, EFREM, JR	ACTOR	4750 ENCINO AVE	ENCINO, CA	91316
ZIMBALIST, STEPHANIE	ACTRESS	10100 SANTA MONICA BLVD #1600	LOS ANGELES, CA	90067
ZIMMER, DICK	U S CONGRESSMAN	1 MORRIS ST	MORRISTOWN, NJ	07960
ZIMMER, DON	BASEBALL-COACH	FENWAY PARK, 4 YAWKEY WY	BOSTON, MA	02215
ZIMMER, HANS	COMPOSER	4146 LANKERSHIM BLVD #300	NORTH HOLLYWOOD, CA	91602
ZIMMER, KIM	ACTRESS	BLOOM, 233 PARK AVE S, 10TH FL	NEW YORK, NY	10017
ZIMMER, LEE	ACTOR	51 5TH AVE	NEW YORK, NY	10003
ZIMMER, NORMA	SINGER	661 WOOD LAKE DR	BREA, CA	92621
ZIMMER, TOM	BASEBALL-SCOUT	S F GIANTS, CANDLESTICK PARK	SAN FRANICSCO, CA	94124
ZIMMER-SMITH, DEBRA	DIRECTOR	DGA, 7920 SUNSET BLVD, 6TH FL	LOS ANGELES, CA	90046
ZIMMERLY, ELYNID	ACTOR	321 W 105TH ST #1-A	NEW YORK, NY	10025
ZIMMERMAN, DICK	PHOTOGRAPHER	201 N ROBERTSON BLVD #A	BEVERLY HILLS, CA	90211
ZIMMERMAN, DON	FILM EDITOR	ACE, 1041 N FORMOSA AVE	WEST HOLLYWOOD, CA	90046
ZIMMERMAN, DONALD PAUL	DIRECTOR	DGA, 7920 SUNSET BLVD, 6TH FL	LOS ANGELES, CA	90046
ZIMMERMAN, GAIL ABBOTT	DIRECTOR	205 W END AVE #1-N	NEW YORK, NY	10023
ZIMMERMAN, GARY	FOOTBALL	VIKINGS, 9520 VIKING DR	EDEN PRAIRIE, MN	55344
ZIMMERMAN, GORDON	ACTOR	1766 WASHINGTON WY	VENICE, CA	90291
ZIMMERMAN, JEFF	BASEBALL SCOUT	REDS, 100 RIVERFRONT STADIUM	CINCINNATI, OH	45202
ZIMMERMAN, JERRY	BASEBALL SCOUT	ORIOLE PARK, 333 W CAMDEN ST	BALTIMORE, MD	21201
ZIMMERMAN, JONATHAN	ACTOR	6909 1/2 BONITA TERR	HOLLYWOOD, CA	90068
ZIMMERMAN, KEVIN	COLUMNIST	VARIETY, 475 PARK AVE S	NEW YORK, NY	10016
ZIMMERMAN, MARGARITA	SINGER	2171 CAMPO SAN ROLO	VINCENZIA	ITALY
ZIMMERMAN, MATT	ACTOR	562 EASTERN AVE, ILFORD	ESSEX 1G2 6PH	ENGLAND
ZIMMERMAN, MIKE	BASEBALL	POST OFFICE DRAWER 1218	ZEBULON, NC	27597
ZIMMERMAN, PAUL	COMEDIAN	LIGHT, 901 BRINGHAM AVE	LOS ANGELES, CA	90049
ZIMMERMAN, VERNON	WRITER-DIRECTOR	POST OFFICE BOX 900	BEVERLY HILLS, CA	90213
ZINBERG, MICHAEL	WRITER-PRODUCER	1539 SAN YSIDRO DR	BEVERLY HILLS, CA	90210

ZINDEL, PAUL	PLAYWRIGHT	HARPER & ROW, 10 E 53RD ST	NEW YORK, NY	10022
ZINER, PETER	FILM EDITOR	334 ARNO WY	PACIFIC PALISADES, CA	90272
ZINGALE, MICHAEL C	DIRECTOR	11750 CLONLEE AVE	GRANADA HILLS, CA	91344
ZINNEMANN, FRED	FILM DIRECTOR	37 BLOOMFIELD RD	LONDON W9	ENGLAND
ZINTER, ED	BASEBALL	12000 STADIUM RD	ADELANTO, CA	92301
ZIPAY, ALAN	SCREENWRITER	907 19TH AVE E	SEATTLE, WA	98112
ZIPPER	ROCK & ROLL GROUP	POST OFFICE BOX 448	RADFORD, VA	24141
ZIPPER, HERBERT	CONDUCTOR	1091 PALISAIR PL	PACIFIC PALISADES, CA	90272
ZIPRODT, PATRICIA	COSTUME DESIGNER	HARVEY STUART, 635 MADISON AVE	NEW YORK, NY	10022
ZIRATO, BRUNO, JR	DIRECTOR	6330 N 3RD ST	PHOENIX, AZ	85012
ZISK, RICHIE	BASEBALL-INSTRUCTOR	1060 W ADDISON ST	CHICAGO, IL	60613
ZISKIE, DAN	ACTOR	CBS-TV, "AS THE WORLD TURNS"		
		524 W 57TH ST #5330	NEW YORK, NY	10019
ZISKIN, LAURA E	WRITER	6473 RODGERTON DR	LOS ANGELES, CA	90068
ZITELLA, JAMES	ACTOR	5922 TAMPA AVE	TARZANA, CA	91356
ZLOTNICK, VICKI LYN	WRITER	2323 S BEVERLY BLVD #6	LOS ANGELES, CA	90064
ZLOTOFF, LEE D	TV WRITER	458 19TH ST	SANTA MONICA, CA	90402
ZMED, ADRIAN	ACTOR	23500 DAISY TRAIL	CALABASAS, CA	91302
ZNOWHITE	ROCK & ROLL GROUP	5342 N WINTHROP AVE #2-E	CHICAGO, IL	60640
ZOELLER, FUZZY	GOLFER	12 BELLEWOOD CT	NEW ALBANY, IN	47150.
ZOFFER, PAT	SCENIC DESIGNER	8 E 83RD ST	NEW YORK, NY	10028
ZOHAR, RITA	ACTRESS	11726 SAN VICENTE BLVD #300	LOS ANGELES, CA	90049
ZOLA, MARION	WRITER	999 N DOHENY DR #604	LOS ANGELES, CA	90069
ZOLLO, FREDERICK	FILM PRODUCER	CAA, 9830 WILSHIRE BLVD	BEVERLY HILLS, CA	90212
ZOLLO, RON	BASEBALL EXECUTIVE	POST OFFICE BOX 11087	TACOMA, WA	98411
ZOLO, VICTOR	CONDUCTOR	7060 FRANKLIN AVE #4	LOS ANGELES, CA	90028
ZOMBO, RICK	HOCKEY	RED WINGS, 600 CIVIC CENTER DR	DETROIT, MI	48226
ZORDICH, MICHAEL	FOOTBALL	POST OFFICE BOX 888	PHOENIX, AZ	85001
ZOREK, MICHAEL	ACTOR	11927 MAGNOLIA BLVD #9	NORTH HOLLYWOOD, CA	91607
ZORICH, CHRIS	FOOTBALL	BEARS, 250 N WASHINGTON RD	LAKE FOREST, IL	60045
ZORICH, LOUS	ACTOR	192 LEXINGTON AVE #1204	NEW YORK, NY	10016
ZORINA, VERA	ACTRESS	10 GRACIE SQ	NEW YORK, NY	10009
ZOSKY, EDDIE	BASEBALL	CHIEFS, MAC ARTHUR STADIUM	SYRACUSE, NY	13208
ZSIGMOND, VILMOS	CINEMATOGRAPHER	9229 SUNSET BLVD #700	LOS ANGELES, CA	90069
ZUBA, BOB	ARTIST	105 W SAYLOR AVE	PLAINS, PA	18705
ZUCKER, DAVID	WRITER-PRODUCER	1849 SAWTELLE BLVD #500	LOS ANGELES, CA	90025
ZUCKER, JERRY	FILM WRI-DIR-PROD	481 DENSLOW AVE	LOS ANGELES, CA	90049
ZUCKERMAN, FAYE	COLUMNIST	N Y TIMES SYN, 130 5TH AVE	NEW YORK, NY	10011
ZUCKERMAN, HOWARD	DIRECTOR	5361 BLANCO AVE	WOODLAND HILLS, CA	91367
ZUCKERMAN, STEVE	COMPOSER-CONDUCTOR	5311 HAZELTINE AVE	VAN NUYS, CA	91401
ZUDECK, DARRYL	ARTIST	35 W 92ND ST	NEW YORK, NY	10025
ZUFFELATO, BOB	BASKETBALL COACH	REUNION ARENA, 777 SPORTS ST	DALLAS, TX	75207
ZUGSMITH, ALBERT	WRITER-PRODUCER	1210 N WETHERLY DR	LOS ANGELES, CA	90069
ZUK, MURRAY	BASEBALL SCOUT	REDS, 100 RIVERFRONT STADIUM	CINCINNATI, OH	45202
ZUKERMAN, EUGENIA	FLUTIST	BROOKLYN COLLEGE		
		MUSIC DEPARTMENT		
		BEDFORD AVE & AVE "H"	BROOKLYN, NY	11210
ZUKERMAN, JAY	ACTOR	15942 TOBIN WY	SHERMAN OAKS, CA	91403
ZUKOR, EUGENE	FILM EXECUTIVE	1161 SHADOW HILL WY	BEVERLY HILLS, CA	90210
ZUKOW, CHARLES	ACTOR	13004 VALLEYHEART DR #10	STUDIO CITY, CA	91604
ZULUS	ROCK & ROLL GROUP	11 TREMLETT ST	DORCHESTER, MA	02124
ZUMMOS, THE	ROCK & ROCK DUO	POST OFFICE BOX 118	HOLLYWOOD, CA	90078
ZUMWALT, ELMO	ADMIRAL	1500 WILSON BLVD	ARLINGTON, VA	22209
ZUNIGA, DAPHNE	ACTRESS	POST OFFICE BOX 1249	WHITE RIVER JUNCT, VT	05001
ZUNIGA, FRANK	FILM DIRECTOR	12050 VALLEYHEART DR #102	STUDIO CITY, CA	91604
ZUNINO, GREG	BASEBALL SCOUT	6850 LAWRENCE RD	LANTANA, FL	33462
ZUPANCIC, TOM	FOOTBALL COACH	POST OFFICE BOX 535000	INDIANPOLIS, IN	46253
ZUPCIC, BOB	BASEBALL	POST OFFICE BOX 2365	PAWTUCKET, RI	02861
ZURAWIEC, RICHARD W	TV DIRECTOR	418 MACKINAW AVE	CALUMET CITY, IL	60409
ZURLA, LESLIE	DIRECTOR-PRODUCER	5746 RADFORD AVE	NORTH HOLLYWOOD, CA	91607
ZURN, RICK	BASEBALL	POST OFFICE BOX 855	BELOIT, WI	53511
ZUVELLA, PAUL	BASEBALL	1396 LASSEN AVE	MILPITAS, CA	95305
ZUVICH, DENNIS M	CONDUCTOR	3916 VINELAND AVE	STUDIO CITY, CA	91604
ZWANG, LARRAINE	TV DIRECTOR	88 LEXINGTON AVE	NEW YORK, NY	10016
ZWEBEN, JERRY	DIRECTOR	12 HEBRON DR	EAST WINDSOR, NJ	08520
ZWEIBACK, A MARTIN	WRITER-DIRECTOR	1117 S BEDFORD ST	LOS ANGELES, CA	90035
ZWEIBEL, ALAN	TV-COMEDY WRI-PROD	AMZ PRODS, 1619 BROADWAY	NEW YORK, NY	10019
ZWEIG, FREDERIC	CONDUCTOR	637 N SWEETZER AVE	LOS ANGELES, CA	90048
ZWERIN, CHARLOTTE M	DIRECTOR-PRODUCER	43 MORTON ST	NEW YORK, NY	10014
ZWERMAN, SUSAN	FILM DIRECTOR	10711 BLUFFSIDE DR #5	STUDIO CITY, CA	91604
ZWICK, EDWARD M	TV WRI-DIR-PROD	309 SUMAC LN	SANTA MONICA, CA	90402
ZWICK, JOEL	DIRECTOR	18588 LINNET ST	TARZANA, CA	91356
ZWIRN, ROBERT S	COMPOSER-CONDUCTOR	1028 HI POINT ST	LOS ANGELES, CA	90035
ZWOLENSKY, MITCH	BASEBALL COACH	POST OFFICE BOX 8550	STOCKTON, CA	95208
ZYDECO, BUCKWHEAT	CAJUN BAND	227 E 25TH ST #A	NEW YORK, NY	10010
ZZ TOP	ROCK & ROLL TRIO	POST OFFICE BOX 19744	HOUSTON, TX	77024

MOVIE & TELEVISION STARS

Portrait/P • Movie Stills/S • Pin-ups/PU
& Super Pin-ups/SPU - $1.00 Each

BEVERLY AADLAND - P
WILLIE AAMES - P/S
F MURRAY ABRAHAM - P
JOSS ACKLAND - P
BURMA ACQUANETTA - P
BROOKE ADAMS - P/S
CATLIN ADAMS - P
DON ADAMS - P
EDIE ADAMS - P
JULIE ADAMS - P
MASON ADAMS - P
MAUD ADAMS - P
NEILE ADAMS - P
WESLEY ADDY - P
ISABELLE ADJANI - P
JOHN AGAR - P
JENNY AGUTTER - P
DANNY AIELLO - P
ANOUK AIMEE - P
ANNA MARIA ALBERGHETTI - P
EDDIE ALBERT - P
EDWARD ALBERT - P
LOLA ALBRIGHT - P
ALAN ALDA - P
KAY ALDRIDGE - P
JANE ALEXANDER - P
KIM ALEXIS - P
KRISTIAN ALFONSO - P
REX ALLEN, SR - P
DEBBIE ALLEN - P
NANCY ALLEN - P/PU
STEVE ALLEN - P
WOODY ALLEN - P/S
KIRSTIE ALLEY -P
JUNE ALLYSON - P
MARIA CONCHITA ALONZO - P
KIRK ALYN - P
DON AMECHE - P/S
ED AMES - P
LEON AMES - P
MADCHEN AMICK - P
BIBI ANDERSON - P
HARRY ANDERSON - P
LONI ANDERSON - P/PU
LOUIE ANDERSON - P
MELISSA SUE ANDERSON - P
MELODY ANDERSON - P
RICHARD ANDERSON - P
RICHARD DEAN ANDERSON (MC GYVER)
URSULA ANDRESS - P/S
JULIE ANDREWS - P/S/POPPINS
TIGE ANDREWS - P
HEATHER ANGEL - P
ANN-MARGRET - P/S
MICHAEL ANSARA - P
SUSAN ANSPACH - P
LYSETTE ANTHONY - P
LAURA ANTONELLI - P
SUSAN ANTON - P/S
CHRISTINA APPLEGATE - P
APPOLONIA - PU/SPU
ALAN ARBUS - P
ANNE ARCHER - P/S
EVE ARDEN - P
ALAN ARKIN - P
ALICE ARMAND - P
BESS ARMSTRONG - P
DESI ARNAZ, JR - P
LUCY ARNAZ - P
JAMES ARNESS - P/MATT DILLON
ROSANNA ARQUETTE - P
BEA ARTHUR - P
ELIZABETH ASHLEY - P/S
EDWARD ASNER - P
CHUCK ASPEGREN - P
ARMAND ASSANTE - P/S
JOHN ASTIN - P
CHRISTOPHER ATKINS - P
RICHARD ATTENBOROUGH - P/S
CLAUDINE AUGER - P/S
JEAN-PIERRE AUMONT - P
GENE AUTRY - P
NINA AXELROD - P
DAN AYKROYD - P
LEW AYRES - P

BARBARA BABCOCK - PU
LAUREEN BACALL - P
BARBARA BACH - P/S
CATHERINE BACH - P
KEVIN BACON - P
BUDDY BAER - P
BARBARA BAIN - P
SCOTT BAIO - P/S
CARROLL BAKER - P/PU
JOE DON BAKER - P/S
WILLIAM BAKEWELL - P
SCOTT BAKULA - P
BELINDA BALASKI - P
ALEC BALDWIN - P
MARTIN BALSAM - P/S
ANNE BANCROFT - P
JIM BANNON - P
ADRIENNE BARBEAU -P/S
BRIGITTE BARDOT - P/PU/SPU
LYNN BARI - P
ELLEN BARKIN - P
PRISCILLA BARNES - P/S
SONNY BARNES - S
DOUG BARR - P
ROSEANNE BARR ARNOLD - P
MARIE BARRAULT - S
RONA BARRETT - P
MONA BARRIE - P
CHUCK BARRIS - P
GENE BARRY - P
DREW BARRYMORE - P
BILLY BARTY - P
KIM BASINGER - P/BATMAN
LINA BASQUETTE - P
JASON BATEMAN - P
JUSTIN BATEMAN - P
ALAN BATES - P
JAIME LYN BAUER - P
STEVEN BAUER - P
LINDSAY BAXTER - P/S
MEREDITH BAXTER - P
JOHN BEAL - P
JENNIFER BEALS - P
ORSON BEAN - P
NED BEATTY - P/S
WARREN BEATTY - P/TRACY/CLYDE
BONNIE BEDELIA - P
GREGG BEEMAN - P
BARBARA BEL GEDDES - P
SHARI BELAFONTE - P
MADGE BELLAMY - P
KATHLEEN BELLER - P/S
JEAN PAUL BELMONDO - P/S
JAMES BELUSHI - P
DIRK BENEDICT - P
RICHARD BENJAMIN - P/S
JOAN BENNETT - P
ROBBIE BENSON - P/S
BARBIE BENTON - P
TOM BERENGER - P
MERISSA BERENSON - P
CANDICE BERGEN - P/PU
POLLY BERGEN - P
SENTA BERGER - P/PU
GARY BERGHOFF - P
HERBERT BERGHOF - P
SANDAHL BERGMAN - P
MILTON BERLE - P
WARREN BERLINGER - P
CORBIN BERNSEN - P
ELIZABETH BERRIDGE - S
NOAH BERRY, JR - P
VALERIE BERTINELLI - P/PU
BIBI BESCH - S
MARTINE BESWICK - PU/SPU
JACK BEUTEL - P
TURHAN BEY - P
MICHAEL BIEHN - P
BING BINGHAM - S
DAVID BIRNEY - P/S
JULIE BISHOP - P
JACQUELINE BISSET - P/PU/SPU/T-SHIRT
BILL BIXBY - P/HULK
KAREN BLACK - P/PU/S
HONOR BLACKMAN - P
VIVIAN BLAINE - P
JANET BLAIR - P
LINDA BLAIR - P/S.
RONNEE BLAKELY - P
SUSAN BLAKELY - P
ROBERT BLAKE - P/S/HOFFA
CLAIRE BLOOM - P/S
LISA BLOUNT - P
BLUES BROTHERS - S
THE BLUES BROTHERS - S
ANN BLYTH - P
HART BOCHNER - P
DIRK BOGARDE - P/S
HEIDI BOHAY - P
PETER BONERZ - P
LISA BONET - P
FRANK BONNER - P
SHIRLEY BOOTH - P
VICTOR BORGE - P
ERNEST BORGNINE - P/S
JOE BOTTOMS - P
SAM BOTTOMS - P

JULIE ADAMS

JAMES ARNESS

GENE AUTRY

ANN-MARGRET

ELIZABETH ASHLEY

BARBARA BACH

JULIE ANDREWS

JOHN ASTIN

CATHARINE BACH

TIMOTHY BOTTOMS - P
BARBARA BOUCHET - P
CAROLE BOUQUET - P
JUDI BOWKER - S
BRUCE BOXLEITNER - P
JIMMY BOYD - P
PETER BOYLE - P/S
EDDIE BRACKEN - P
SONIA BRAGGA - P/PU/SPU
KENNETH BRANAGH - P
JOCELYN BRANDO - P/S
MARLON BRANDO - P/S
MICHAEL BRANDON - P/S
TRACY BREGMAN - P
MICHAEL BREHN - P
EILEEN BRENNAN - P
DAVID BRENNER - P
BEAU BRIDGES - P/S
JEFF BRIDGES - P/S
LLOYD BRIDGES - P/S
WILFORD BRIMLEY - P/S
CHRISTIE BRINKLEY - P/PU
MORGAN BRITTANY - P
MAY BRITT - P/PU
BARBARA BRITTON - P
MATTHEW BRODERICK - P
JAMES BROLIN - P
CHARLES BRONSON - P/S
FOSTER BROOKS - P
MEL BROOKS - P/S
RAND BROOKS - P
RANDI BROOKS - P
PIERCE BROSNAN - P
CANDI BROUGH - P
RANDI BROUGH - P
BLAIR BROWN - P
JAMES BROWN - S
JIM BROWN - P/S
TOM BROWN - P
HORST BUCHOLTZ - P
SUSAN BUCKNER - P
GENEVIEVE BUJOLD - P/S
BROOKE BUNDY - P
GARY BURGHOFF - P
DELTA BURKE - P
TOM BURLINSON - P
CAROL BURNETT - P/S
GEORGE BURNS - P/S
RAYMOND BURR - P
ELLEN BURSTYN - P/S
LEVAR BURTON - P
GARY BUSEY - P/S
RED BUTTONS - P
PAT BUTTRAM (AS MR HANEY)
JEFFREY BYRON - P

MICHAEL CAINE - P/S
RORY CALHOUN - P/S
CORINNE CALVET - P/PU
KIRK CAMERON - P
COLLEEN CAMP - P
JOSEPH CAMPANELLA - P
JOHN CANDY - P
DYAN CANNON - P/S
DIANA CANOVA - P
CANTINFLAS - P
KATE CAPSHAW - P
IRENE CARA - P
CLAUDIA CARDINALE - P/PU
MC DONALD CAREY - P
MICHELLE CAREY - P
KITTY CARLISLE - P
MARY CARLISLE - P/PU
ART CARNEY - P/S
LESLIE CARON - P/S/PU
DAVID CARRADINE - P/S
KEITH CARRADINE - P/S
ROBERT CARRADINE - P
BARBARA CARRERA - P
SUNSET CARSON - P
DIXIE CARTER - P
JANIS CARTER - P/PU
LYNDA CARTER - P/WOMAN WOMAN
VERONICA CARTWRIGHT - P/S
PEGGY CASS - P
DAVID CASSIDY - P
JOANNA CASSIDY - P/S
SHAWN CASSIDY - P
NICK CASTLE - P
PHOEBE CATES - P
ANNE CAUDRY - S
JOAN CAULFIELD - P
MAXWELL CAULFIELD - P
CHRISTOPHER CAZENONE - P
GEORGE CHAKIRIS - P
MARILYN CHAMBERS - P/PU/SPU
RICHARD CHAMBERLAIN - P
CAROL CHANNING - P/S
STOCKARD CHANNING - P/S
ROSALIND CHAO - S
GERALDINE CHAPLIN - P
JUDITH CHAPMAN - P
MARGUERITE CHAPMAN - P
CYD CHARISSE - P
CHEVY CHASE - P/S
CHEECH & CHONG - S
JOAN CHEN, JR - P
CHER - P/S/AWARD POSE
CHEWBACCA (STAR WARS)
GEORGE CHIKIRIS - P
LOIS CHILES - P
RAE DAWN CHONG - P
JULIE CHRISTIE - PU/SPU
LINDA CHRISTIAN - P
WILLIAM CHRISTOPHER (MASH)
CANDY CLARK - P
DANE CLARK - P
SUSAN CLARK - P
JILL CLAYBURGH - P/S
JOHN CLEESE - P
PAUL CLEMENS - S
DEBRA CLINGER - P
GLENN CLOSE - P
JAMES COBURN - P/S
IMOGENE COCA - P
IRON EYES CODY - P
CLAUDETTE COLBERT - P/S
DABNEY COLEMAN - P
GARY COLEMAN - P
JOHN COLICOS - P/S
GARY COLLINS - P
JACKIE COLLINS - P
JOAN COLLINS - P/S/PU/SPU
PAULINE COLLINS - P
ANJANETTE COMER - S
JENNIFER CONNELLY - P
SEAN CONNERY - P/S
CARROLL CONNORS - P/ARCHIE
CHUCK CONNORS - P
MIKE CONNORS - P
ROBERT CONRAD - P/S/BOYINGTON
WILLIAM CONRAD - P
TOM CONTI - P
TIM CONWAY - P
ELISHA COOK - P/S
JACKIE COOPER - P
(ADULT & CHILD)
JEFF COOPER - S
JOAN COPELAND - P
TERI COPLEY - P
GRETCHEN CORBETT - S
ALEX CORD - P
ANN CORIO - P
DON CORNELIUS - P
LYDIA CORNELL - P/PU
JOSEPH CORTESE - P
BILL COSBY - P/S
KEVIN COSTNER - P
JOSEPH COTTEN - P/S
COURTNEY COX - P
RICHARD COX - P
RONNIE COX - P
YVONNE CRAIG - P
JEANNE CRAIN - P
NORMA CRANE - S
GEMMA CRAVEN - P
CINDY CRAWFORD - P/PU/SPU
JOHNNY CRAWFORD - P
RICHARD CRENNA - P/S
LINDA CRISTAL - P/S
HUME CRONYN - P
CATHY LEE CROSBY - P
KATHRYN CROSBY - P
MARY CROSBY - P
LINDSAY CROUSE - P
PAT CROWLEY - P
TOM CRUISE - P
BILLY CRYSTAL - P/S
ROBERT CULP - P/S
PEGGY CUMMINS - P
JANE CURTIN - P
VALERIE CURTIN - P/S
BILLY CURTIS - S
JAMIE LEE CURTIS - P/S
KEN CURTIS - P
TONY CURTIS - P/S
JOHN CUSACK - P
PETER CUSHING - P/S

BEVERLY D'ANGELO - P/S
PATTI D'ARBANVILLE - P
WILLIAM DAFOE - P/JESUS
DAGMAR - P
ARLENE DAHL - P/PU
ABBY DALTON - P
TIMOTHY DALTON (AS 007)
BILL DALY - P
TYNE DALY - P
BILL DANA - P
RODNEY DANGERFIELD - P
BLYTHE DANNER - P
SYBIL DANNING - P
ROYAL DANO - P
TED DANSON - P
TONY DANZA - P/S
KIM DARBY - P
SEVERIN DARDEN - P
JAMES DARREN - P
ROBERT DAVI - P
LOLITA DAVIDOVICH - PU/S
GAIL DAVIES - P
SAMMY DAVIS, JR - P
ANNE E DAVIS
BRAD DAVIS - P
GEENA DAVIS - P
NANCY DAVIS - P
BRUCE DAVISON - P
OZZIE DAVIS - P
PHYLLIS DAVIS - P
PAM DAWBER - P
DORIS DAY - P/PU/SPU/MERMAID
LARRAINE DAY - P/S/PU/SPU
ROSEMARY DE CAMP - P
YVONNE DE CARLO - P/PU
DON DE FORE - P
GLORIA DE HAVEN - P

PIERCE BROSNAN

KEN CURTIS

ALICE FAYE

IMOGENE COCA

BILLY CRYSTAL

DALE EVANS

CLAUDETTE COLBERT

DABNEY COLEMAN

DANNY DE VITO

OLIVIA DE HAVILLAND - P/MELANIE
DOM DE LUISE - P/S
KATHARINE DE MILLE - P
REBECCA DE MORNAY - P
ROBERT DE NIRO - P/S/NY, NY
JOE DE RITA - P
JOYCE DE WITT - P
PRISCILLA DEAN - P
FRANCIS DEE - P
RUBY DEE - P
SANDRA DEE - P/S/PU/SPU
DON DEFOE - P
DANA DELANEY (CHINA BEACH)
GABRIEL DELL - P
MYRNA DELL - P
GABRIEL DELL
ALAIN DELON - P/S
SUSAN DENBERG - SPU
CATHERINE DENEUVE - P/S
RICHARD DENNING - P/S
BOB DENVER - P/S/GILLIGAN
JOHNNY DEPP - P
BO DEREK - P/S/PU/SPU
JOHN DEREK - P
BRUCE DERN - P
LAURA DERN - P
WILLIAM DEVANE - P
COLLEEN DEWHURST - P
SUSAN DEY - P
ANGIE DICKINSON - P
URSULA "USCHI" DIGARD - P
PHYLLIS DILLER - P
BRADFORD DILLMAN - P
KEVIN DILLON - P
MATT DILLON - P
ANN DITCHBURN - P
DONNA DIXON - P
KEVIN DOBSON - P
SHANNON DOHERTY - P
FAITH DOMERGUE - P
AMANDA DONAHUE - P
ELEANOR DONAHUE - P/PU
TROY DONAHUE - P
PETER DONAT - P
ALLISON DOODY - P
JAMES DOOHAN - P
ANN DORAN - P
DONNA DOUGLAS - P/PU
KIRK DOUGLAS - P/S
MICHAEL DOUGLAS - P/S
SARAH DOUGLAS - P
BRAD DOURIF - S
BILLIE DOVE - P
TONY DOW - P
DORIS DOWLING - P
LESLIE-ANNE DOWN - P/S/PU
ROBERT DOWNEY, JR - P
BETSY DRAKE - P
ELLEN DREW - P/S
RICHARD DREYFUSS - P/S
JOANNE DRU - P
JAMES DRURY - P
FRED DRYER - P
HOWARD DUFF - P/S
PATRICK DUFFY - P
OLYMPIA DUKAKIS (ACAD AWARD)
PATTY DUKE - P
KEIR DULLEA - P
FAYE DUNAWAY - P/S/BONNIE & CLYDE
SANDY DUNCAN - P/S
IRENE DUNNE - P
DEANNA DURBIN - P/IN CONCERT
CHARLES DURNING - P/S
ANN DUSENBERRY - P
ROBERT DUVALL - P/S
SHELLY DUVALL - P/S

Movie & TV Stars $1.00 each

JEFF EAST - S
CLINT EASTWOOD - P/S/HORSE
BUDDY EBSEN - P/S/AS JED
BARBARA EDEN - P/AS JEANNIE
PENNY EDWARDS - P
VINCE EDWARDS - P
SAMANTHA EGGAR - P/S/PU
LISA EICHORN - P/S
JILL EIKENBERRY - P/S
BRITT EKLAND - P
JACK ELAM - P
ERIKA ELENICK - SPU
TAINA ELG - P
SAM ELLIOTT - P
STEPHEN ELLIOTT - P
EMMY AWARD
GEORGIA ENGEL - P
MARIA ENGLISH - P
ERIK ESTRADA - P
DALE EVANS - P
LINDA EVANS - P
CHAD EVERETT - P/S
GREG EVIGAN - P
TOM EWELL - P

SHELLEY FABARES - P/PU
NANETTE FABRAY - P
DOUGLAS FAIRBANKS, JR - P
MORGAN FAIRCHILD - P/SPU
PETER FALK - P/S/COLUMBO
JAMES FARENTINO - P
ANTONIO FARGAS - P/S
RICHARD FARNSWORTH - P
FELICIA FARR - P
JAMIE FARR - P/IN DRAG
MIKE FARRELL - P
MIA FARROW - P/S
FARRAH FAWCETT - P/S/PU
ALICE FAYE - P/PU
COREY FELDMAN - P
BARBARA FELDON - P
TOVAH FELDSHUH - P/S
NORMAN FELL - P
SHERALYN FENN - PU (TWIN PEAKS)
CRISTINA FERRARE - P
LOU FERRIGNO - P/AS HULK
SALLY FIELD - P/S/FLYING NUN
KIM FIELDS - P
ALBERT FINNEY - P/S
CARRIE FISHER - P/S/LEIA
GAIL FISHER - S
GERALDINE FITZGERALD - P
FANNIE FLAGG - P
ED FLANDERS - P
RHONDA FLEMING - P/PU
LOUISE FLETCHER - P/S
NINA FOCH - P
BRIGET FONDA - PU
JANE FONDA - P/S/PU
PETER FONDA - P/S
JOAN FONTAINE - P/PU
BRENDA FORBES - P
FAITH FORD (MURPHY BROWN)
GLENN FORD - P/S
HARRISON FORD - P/S
STEPHEN FORD - P
FREDERIC FORREST - P
STEVE FORREST - P/S
JOHN FORSYTHE - P
JODIE FOSTER - P/S/PU
MEG FOSTER - P/S
MICHAEL J FOX - P
SAMANTHA FOX - P
FANNIE FOXE - P
ROBERT FOXWORTH - S
ANNE FRANCIS - P/S
ARLENE FRANCIS - P
GENIE FRANCIS - P
GARY FRANK - P
BONNIE FRANKLIN - P
ARTHUR FRANZ - S
JANE FRAZEE - P
LYNN FREDERICK - P
MONA FREEMAN - P
MORGAN FREEMAN - P
SOLIEL MOON FRYE - P
ANNETTE FUNICELLO - P/S
ALLEN FUNT - P

EVA GABOR - P
ZSA ZSA GABOR - P/PU
PETER GALLAGHER - P/S
RITA GAM - P
ANDY GARCIA - P
VINCENT GARDENIA - P
BEVERLY GARLAND - P
JAMES GARNER - P/S
TERI GARR - P/S
GREER GARSON - P/PU/SPU
JENNIE GARTH - P
VITTORIO GASSMAN - P/S
JOHN GAVIN - P
MITZI GAYNOR - P
BEN GAZZARA - P
MICHAEL GAZZO - S
TONY GEARY - P
LINDA DAY GEORGE - P
PHYLLIS GEORGE - P
GIL GERARD - P/S
RICHARD GERE - P
ESTELLE GETTY - P
GIANCARLO GIANNINI - P/S
CINDY GIBB - P
MARLA GIBBS - P
HENRY GIBSON - P/S
MEL GIBSON - P/S
JOHN GIELGUD - P/S
ELAINE GIFTOS - PU
MELISSA GILBERT - P
JACK GILFORD - S
LILLIAN GISH (AGES 20/30/60)
ROBIN GIVENS - P
MICHAEL GLASER - P/S
SCOTT GLENN - P
SHARON GLESS - P/S
DANNY GLOVER - P
MARK GODDARD - P
TRACY GOLD - P
WHOOPI GOLDBERG - P/S
JEFF GOLDBLUM - BEEFCAKE
BOBCAT GOLDWAITHT - P
JOHN GOODMAN - P
GALE GORDON - P
FRANK GORSHIN - P
LOU GOSSETT - P
FARLEY GRANGER - P
STEWART GRANGER - P
LEE GRANT - P/S
RODNEY GRANT - P

C. THOMAS HOWELL

STACY KEACH

SUSAN LUCCI

DON JOHNSON

AUDREY LANDERS

NANCY MC KEON

LYNN-HOLLY JOHNSON

ROB LOWE

EDDIE MURPHY

PETER GRAVES - P
ERIN GRAY - P/PU
LINDA GRAY - P
KATHRYN GRAYSON - P
SHECKY GREENE - P
JANE GREER - P
ROSE GREGARIO - P
ANDRE GREGORY - P/S
JENNIFER GREY - P
JOEL GREY - P/CABARET
RICHARD GRIECO - PU
PAM GRIER - P/S
ROSEY GRIER - P
ANDY GRIFFITH - P/S
MELANIE GRIFFITH - P
TAMMY GRIMES - P
GEORGE GRIZZARD - P/S
CHARLES GRODIN - P/S
MICHAEL GROSS - P
HARRY GUARDINO - P
CORNELIA GUEST - P
ROBERT GUILLAUME - P
ALEC GUINESS - P/STARWARS
MOSES GUNN - P
STEVE GUTTENBURG - P
JASMINE GUY - P
FRED GWYNNE - P

SHELLY HACK - P
BUDDY HACKETT - P/S
GENE HACKMAN - P/S/LUTHER
JULIE HAGERTY - P
DAN HAGGERTY - P
LARRY HAGMAN - P
COREY HAIM - P
BARBARA HALE - P/PU
MONTE HALE - P
JACKIE EARL HALEY - P
HUNTZ HALL - P
JERRI HALL - P
LUKE HALPIN - P/S
VERONICA HAMEL - P
MARK HAMILL - P/S/SKYWALKER
ANTHONY HAMILTON - P
GEORGE HAMILTON - P/S
LEIGH HAMILTON - P/S
CARRIE HAMILTON - P
HARRY HAMLIN - P/S
SUSAN HAMPSHIRE - P/S
DARRYL HANNAH - P/S
JESSICA HARPER - P
TESS HARPER - P
VALERIE HARPER - P
PAT HARRINGTON - P
BARBARA HARRIS - P
GREG HARRISON - P
JENILEE HARRISON - P
JULIE HARRIS - P/S
LINDA HARRISON - PU/SPU
NEIL PATRICK HARRIS (DOOGIE)
PHIL HARRIS - P
RICHARD HARRIS - P
KATHERINE HARROLD - P
JOHN HART - P
SUSAN HART - P
VERONICA HART - P/PU
MARIETTE HARTLEY - P
DAVID HARTMAN - P
LISA HARTMAN - P/PU
DAVID HASSELHOFF - P
MARILYN HASSETT - P/S
SIGNE HASSO - P

RICHARD HATCH - P
RUTGER HAUER - P
WINGS HAUSER - P
JUNE HAVER - P
JUNE HAVOC - P
GOLDIE HAWN - P/S/PU
ALEXANDRA HAY - P
HELEN HAYES - P
ROBERT HAYS - P
SHARI HEADLEY - P
MARY HEALY - P
MYRON HEALY - P
JOHN HEARD - P/S
JOEY HEATHERTON - P
EILEEN HECKART - P
TIPPI HEDREN - P/THE BIRDS
SUSAN HELFOND - P/S
MARGE HELGENBERGER - P
MARGOUX HEMINGWAY - S
MARIEL HEMINGWAY - P/S
DAVID HEMMINGS - P
SHERMAN HEMSLEY - P
FLORENCE HENDERSON - P
GLORIA HENDRY - P
MARY LOU HENNER - P
BUCK HENRY - P
GREG HENRY - P/S
MIKE HENRY (TARAZAN)
PAM HENSLEY - P
AUDREY HEPBURN - P
KATHARINE HEPBURN - P
EDWARD HERMANN - P
PEE WEE HERMAN - P
BARBARA HERSHEY - P/S
IRENE HERVEY - P
HOWARD HESSMAN - P
CHARLTON HESTON - P/S/BEN HUR/MOSES
ROBERT HEYGES - P
ANNE HEYWOOD - P/S
ARTHUR HILL - P/S
DANA HILL - S
TERRENCE HILL - P/S
HARRIET HILLARD - P
JOHN HILLERMAN - P
WENDY HILLER - P
GREGORY HINES - P
PAT HINGLE - P
JUDD HIRSCH - P
EDDIE HODGES - P/S
DUSTIN HOFFMAN - P/TOOTSIE
HAL HOLBROOK - P/S/LINCOLN
SARAH HOLCOMB - P/S
REBECCA HOLDEN - P
JEFFREY HOLDER - P
VALERIE HOLIND - P
EARL HOLLIMAN - P
STERLING HOLLOWAY - P
CELESTE HOLM - P
JENNIFER HOLT - P
BOB HOPE - P/S
ANTHONY HOPKINS - P
BO HOPKINS - P/S
DENNIS HOPPER - P/S
LENA HORNE (THE WIZ)
LEE HORSLEY - P
BOB HOSKINS - P
KEN HOWARD - P
RON HOWARD - P/(AS OPIE)
SUSAN HOWARD - P
TREVOR HOWARD - P
C THOMAS HOWELL - P
MARK HOWELL - P/S
SALLY ANN HOWES - P
SEASON HUBLEY - P
MARY BETH HUGHES - P
DIANE HULL - P
GAYLE HUNNICUT - P
MARSHA HUNT - P

KHAKI HUNTER - S
KIM HUNTER - P
RACHEL HUNTER - P/PU
TAB HUNTER - P
PAM HUNTINGTON - S
ISABELLE HUPPERT - P/S
MARY BETH HURT - P/S
WILLIAM HURT - P/S
OLIVIA HUSSEY - P
RUTH HUSSEY - P
ANGELICA HUSTON - P
BETTY HUTTON - P
LAUREN HUTTON - P
TIM HUTTON - P/S

IMAN - P/S
JILL IRELAND - P/S
JOHN IRELAND - P
JEREMY IRONS - P/S
AMY IRVING - P/S

ANNE JACKSON - P/S
GLENDA JACKSON - P/S
KATE JACKSON - P
MICHAEL JACKSON (THE WIZ)
SHERRY JACKSON - P/S/PU
VICTORIA JACKSON - P
RICHARD JAECKEL - P
JOHN JAMES - P
CONRAD JANIS - P
GLORIA JEAN - P
ANN JEFFRIES - P
FRAN JEFFRIES - P
RITA JENRETTE - P
KAREN JENSEN - P/PU
MAREN JENSEN - P/S
ADELE JERGENS - P/PU
ANN JILLIAN - P
ZITA JOHANN - P
I S JOHAR - P
GLYNIS JOHNS - P
ARTE JOHNSON - P
BEN JOHNSON - P/S
DOROTHY JOHNSON - P
LYNN-HOLLY JOHNSON - P
MICHELLE JOHNSON - P
VAN JOHNSON - P/S
DEAN JONES - P/S
GRACE JONES - P
JAMES EARL JONES - P
JENNIFER JONES - P
L Q JONES - P
SAM J JONES - P
SHIRLEY JONES - P/PU
TOMMY LEE JONES - P
LOUIS JOURDAN - P
BRENDA JOYCE - P
RAUL JULIA - P
CALVIN JUNG - P

Pin-Ups or Portraits Only $1.00!

MADELINE KAHN - P/S
STEVE KANALY - P
CAROL KANE - P
GABE KAPLAN - P/S
VALERIE KAPRISKY - P
ALEX KARRAS - P
JEAN KASEM - P
ANNA KASHFI - P
WILLIAM KATT - P
CHRISTINE KAUFMAN - P/S
STACY KEACH - P/S
DIANE KEATON - P/S
MICHAEL KEATON - P/S
RUBY KEELER - P
HARVEY KEITEL - P
BRIAN KEITH - P/S
DAVID KEITH - P
SALLY KELLERMAN - P/S/PU/MASH
DE FORREST KELLY - P
GENE KELLY - P
GENE KELLY (SING IN RAIN)
NANCY KELLY - P
PAULA KELLY - P
SUZY KENDALL - P
ARTHUR KENNEDY - P/S
GEORGE KENNEDY - P/S
ISAAC KENNEDY - P
JAYNE KENNEDY - P
KERMIT THE FROG
DEBORAH KERR - P/S
LANCE KERWIN - P
EVELYN KEYES - P/S
PERSIS KHAMBATTA - P
MARGOT KIDDER - P
RICHARD KIEL - P/S
RICHARD KILEY - P
VAL KILMER - P
MABEL KING (THE WIZ)
ALAN KING - P
ANDREA KING - P
JOHN KING - P
PERRY KING - P
BEN KINGSLEY - P/GHANDI
KLAUS KINSKI - P
NASTASSIA KINSKI - P/PU
BRUNO KIRBY - P
GEORGE KIRBY - P
PHYLLIS KIRK - P
SALLY KIRKLAND - P
TAWNY KITAEN - P
EARTHA KITT - P
WERNER KLEMPERER - P
KEVIN KLINE - P
JACK KLUGMAN - P
HILDEGARDE KNEF - P
EVELYN KNIGHT - P
JUNE KNIGHT - P
SHIRLEY KNIGHT - P
DON KNOTTS - P/ASTRONAUT
ELSIE KNOX - P
SUSAN KOHNER - P
JON KORKES - P
HARVEY KORMAN - P
APOLLONIA KOTERO - P
YAPHET KOTTO - P/S
LINDA KOZLOWSKI - P
STEPHANIE KRAMER - P/PU
CONNIE KRESKI - P
ALICE KRIGE - P
SYLVIA KRISTEL - P
KRIS KRISTOFFERSON - P/S
SWOOZIE KURTZ - P
NANCY KWAN - P/S/PU

LAURA LA PLANTE - P
LASH LA RUE - P
CHERYL LADD - P
DIANE LADD - P
CHRISTINE LAHTI - P
HEDY LAMARR - P/PU/SPU
LORENZO LAMAS - P
DOROTHY LAMOUR - P
BURT LANCASTER - P/S
PAUL LAND - P/S
MARTIN LANDAU - P
AUDREY LANDERS - P/PU
JUDY LANDERS - P/PU
LORRAINE LANDON - P
DIANE LANE - P
PRISCILLA LANE - P
ROCKY LANE - P
SUE ANN LANGDON - P
HOPE LANGE - P/PU
JESSICA LANGE - P/S/KONG
KELLY LANGE - P
FRANK LANGELLA - P/S
MURRAY LANGSTON - P
LORRAINE LANON - P
ANGELA LANSBURY - P
ROBERT LANSING - P
SHERRY LANSING - P
JOHN LARROQUETTE - P
LOUISE LASSER - P
TOM LAUGHLIN - P
PIPER LAURIE - P/PU
DALIAH LAVI - P
LINDA LAVIN - P
VICKI LAWRENCE - P
GEORGE LAZENBY - P
KELLY LE BROCK - P
PAUL LE MAT - P
GLORIA LE ROY - P
HAL LE ROY - P
CLORIS LEACHMAN - P/S
AMANDA LEAR - SPU
MICHAEL LEARNED - P
FRANCIS LEDERER - P
CHRISTOPHER LEE - P/S
MICHELLE LEE - P
PINKY LEE - P
JANET LEIGH - P
JENNIFER JASON LEIGH - P
JACK LEMMON - P/S
KAY LENZ - P
JOAN LESLIE - P
JERRY LESTER - P
AL LEWIS - P
DANIEL DAY LEWIS - P
EMMANUEL LEWIS - P
JERRY LEWIS - P/S
RON LIEBMAN - P/S
HAL LINDEN - P
JENNIE LINDEN - P
VIVECA LINDFORS - P
PAUL LINKE - P
LARRY LINVILLE - P
PEGGY LIPTON - P
VERNA LISI - P/S
JOHN LITHGOW - P
LITTLE MERMAID (CARTOON)
CLEAVON LITTLE - P
RICH LITTLE - P
BOB LIVINGSTON - P
CHRISTOPHER LLOYD - P
EMILY LLOYD - P
KATHLEEN LLOYD - P/S
TONY LO BIANCO - P
SONDRA LOCKE - P
JUNE LOCKHART - P
HEATHER LOCKLEAR - P
JACQUELINE LOGAN - P
GINA LOLLOBRIGIDA - P/S/PU
HERBERT LOM - P/S
JULIE LONDON - P/S
PAM LONG - P
SHELLY LONG - P/PU
CLAUDINE LONGET - P
MICHEL LONSDALE - P/S
JACK LORD - P
SOPHIA LOREN - P/S/PU/SPU
DOROTHY LOUDON - P
TINA LOUISE - P/PU/SPU
LINDA LOVELACE - P
ROB LOWE - P
MYRNA LOY - P/S
SUSAN LUCCI - P
LORNA LUFT - P
KEYE LUKE - P
IDA LUPINO - P
JIMMY LYDON - P
CAROL LYNLEY - P
SUE LYON - P

JAMES MAC ARTHUR - P
ALI MAC GRAW - P/S
KYLE MAC LACHLIN - P
SHIRLEY MAC LAINE - P/S
PETER MAC LEAN - P/S
PATRICK MAC NEE - P
RALPH MACCHIO - P
BILL MACY - P
AMY MADIGAN - P
GUY MADISON - P
VIRGINIA MADSEN - P
GEORGE MAHARIS - P
LEE MAJORS - P
JOHN MALCOVICH - PU
KARL MALDEN - P/S
DOROTHY MALONE - P
NICK MANCUSO - P
RICK MANCUSO - P
ROBERT MANDAN - P
HOWIE MANDEL - P
SILVANO MANGANO - P
DAVID MANNERS
NANCY MARCHAND - P
JANET MARGOLIN - P
PHILIPPE MARLAND - P
JUNE MARLOWE - P
LUCY MARLOWE - P
E G MARSHALL - P/S
PENNY MARSHALL - P
PETER MARSHALL - P
MARION MARSH - P
ANNE MARIE MARTIN - P
DEAN MARTIN - P/S
ELSA MARTINELLI - P
MARY MARTIN - P
PAMELA SUE MARTIN - P
MICHELLE MARVIN - P
MARSHA MASON - P/S
MART STUART MASTERSON - P
MARY ELIZ MASTRANTOVIA - P
MARCELLO MASTROIANNI - P
JERRY MATHERS - P

TIM MATHESON - P
JOYCE MATHEWS - P
MARLEE MATLIN - P
WALTER MATTHAU - P/S
VICTOR MATURE - P
ELAINE MAY - P
VIRGINIA MAYO - P
PAUL MAZURSKY - P
RAY MC ANALY - P
ANDREA MC ARDLE - P
DIANE MC BAIN - P
DAVID MC CALLUM - P
IRISH MC CALLA - P
MERCEDES MC CAMBRIDGE - P
ANDREW MC CARTHY - P
KEVIN MC CARTHY - S
RUE MC CLANAHAN - P
LEIGH MC CLOSKY - P
DOUG MC CLURE - P
KENT MC CORD - P
MAUREEN MC CORMICK - P
PAT MC CORMICK - P
PATTY MC CORMICK - P
SIMON MC CORKINDALE - P
JULIE MC CULLOUGH - PU
MALCOLM MC DONALD - P
ANDIE MC DOWELL - P
RODDY MC DOWELL - P/S
SPANKY MC FARLAND - P
DARREN MC GAVIN - P
KELLY MC GILLIS - P
PATRICK MC GOOHAN - P
ELIZABETH MC GOVERN - P
MAUREEN MC GOVERN - P
DOROTHY MC GUIRE - P/S
JOHN MC INTYRE - P
GARDNER MC KAY - P
DOUG MC KEON - P
NANCY MC KEON - P
PHILIP MC KEON - P
LEO MC KERN - S
GAVIN MC LEOD - P
KEN MC MILLAN - P
STEPHEN MC NALLY - P/S
JIMMIE MC NICHOL - P
KRISTY MC NICHOL - P/S
PETER MC NICHOL - P
BUTTERFLY MC QUEEN - P/S
AUDREY MEADOWS - P
JAYNE MEADOWS - P
ANN MEARA - P/S
JAMES MEILLON - P
JOHN MEILLON - P
SID MELTON - P
HEATHER MENZIES - P
MELINA MERCOURI - S
BURGESS MEREDITH - P/S
LEE MEREDITH - P
LEE MERIWETHER - P
UNA MERKEL - P
DINA MERRILL - P
ANN-LAURE MEURY - P
TOSHIRO MIFUNE - P
ALYSSA MILANO - P
JOANNA MILES - P
SARAH MILES - P/S
SYLVIA MILES - P
VERA MILES - P
PENELOPE MILFORD - S
TOMAS MILIAN - P
ANN MILLER - P/PU
DENNIS MILLER (TARZAN)
PENELOPE ANN MILLER - P
DONNA MILLS - P
HAYLEY MILLS - P
JOHN MILLS - P
MARTIN MILNER - P
YVETTE MIMIEUX - P
LIZA MINELLI - P/S/3 YRS OLD

MISS PIGGY
CAMERON MITCHELL - P
JIM MITCHUM -P/S/BEEFCAKE
ROBERT MITCHUM - P/S
ZAKES MOKAE - P
JOE MONTAGNA - P
RICARDO MONTALBAN - P/S
YVES MONTAND - P
JOE MONTEGNA
ELIZABETH MONTGOMERY - P/PU
GEORGE MONTGOMERY - P/S
CLAYTON MOORE (LONE RANGER)
CLEO MOORE - P
COLLEEN MOORE - P
CONSTANCE MOORE - P
DEMI MOORE - P
DUDLEY MOORE - P/S
MARY TYLER MOORE - P/S
ROGER MOORE - P/S/007
TERRY MOORE - P
ERIN MORAN - P
RICK MORANIS - P
LOIS MORAN - P
RITA MORENO - P/S
HARRY MORGAN - P
CATHY MORIARTY - P
MICHAEL MORIARTY - P
PAT MORITA - P
LOUISA MORITZ - S
GREG MORRIS - P
HOWARD MORRIS - P
PATRICIA MORRISON - P
ROBERT MORSE - P/S
DONNY MOST - P/S
JEAN MUIR - P
DIANA MULDAUR - P
KATE MULGREW - P
EDWARD MULHARE - P
MARTIN MULL - P/S
CAROLYN MUNRO - P
EDDIE MURPHY - P
MARY MURPHY - P
MICHAEL MURPHY - P
BILL MURRAY - P
DON MURRAY - P/S
JAN MURRAY - P/S
TONY MUSANTE - P
ORNELLA MUTI - P/PU

JIM NABORS - P
GEORGE NADER - P/S
KITTEN NATIVIDAD - P
DAVID NAUGHTON - P
JAMES NAUGHTON - P
PATRICIA NEAL - P
TED NEELEY - P/AS JESUS
NOEL NEILL- P
BRIGET NEILSEN - P
KATE NELLIGAN - P/S
BARRY NELSON - P
JUDD NELSON - P
CORKY NEMEC (PARKER LEWIS)
FRANCO NERO - P
LOIS NETTLETON - P
BOB NEWHART - P
ANTHONY NEWLEY - P
BARRY NEWMAN - P/S/BEEFCAKE
LARRAINE NEWMAN - P
NANETTE NEWMAN - P
PAUL NEWMAN - P/S
JULIE NEWMAR - P/S
DR HAING G NGOR - P
JACK NICHOLSON - P/S/JOKER

KELLY NICHOLS - P
MICHELLE NICHOLS - P
BRIGETTE NIELSEN - P
LESLIE NIELSEN - P
LEONARD NIMOY - P/S
CHRIS NOEL - S
NICK NOLTE - P/S
CHRISTOPHER NORRIS - P
CHUCK NORRIS - P/S
JAY NORTH - P/S
SHEREE NORTH - P
RICHARD NORTON - S
KIM NOVAK - P/S
NURYEV - P/S
FRANCE NUYEN - P

HUGH O'BRIAN - P
ERIN O'BRIEN - PU
MARGARET O'BRIEN - S
CARROLL O'CONNOR - P
DONALD O'CONNOR - P/S
GLYNNIS O'CONNOR - P
NELL O'DAY - P
MARTHA O'DRISCOLL - P
JACK O'HALLORAN - P
MAUREEN O'HARA - P
CATLIN O'HEANNEY - S
MILES O'KEEFE - P
JENNIFER O'NEIL - P/S
PATRICK O'NEIL - P
RYAN O'NEIL - P/S
TATUM O'NEIL - P/S
MAUREEN O'SULLAVAN - P
PETER O'TOOLE - P
RANDI OAKES - P/PU
LENA OLIN - P
NANCY OLSON - P
MICHAEL ONTKEAN - P/S
BILLY ORTEGA - S
KEN OSMOND - P
CARRIE OTIS - P
CATHERINE OXENBURG - P

AL PACINO - P/S
JOANNE PACULA - P
ANITA PAGE - P
GENEVIEVE PAGE - P/S
DEBRA PAGET - P/S
JANIS PAIGE - P/S
JACK PALANCE - P/S
MICHAEL PALIN - P
BETSY PALMER - P
IRENE PAPPAS - P
ELEANOR PARKER - P
FESS PARKER - P/CROCKETT
JAMESON PARKER - P/S
BARBARA PARKINS - P
MICHAEL PARKS - S
LESLIE PARRISH - P/S
ESTELLE PARSONS - P
NANCY PARSONS - P
MANDY PATINKIN - P
BUTCH PATRICK - P
JASON PATRIC - P
LORNA PATTERSON - P
PAULINA - PU
PAT PAULSEN - P

CHRISTOPHER NORRIS

AL PACINO

JANE SEYMOUR

SHEREE NORTH

SUSAN SARANDON

TALIA SHIRE

CARROLL O'CONNOR

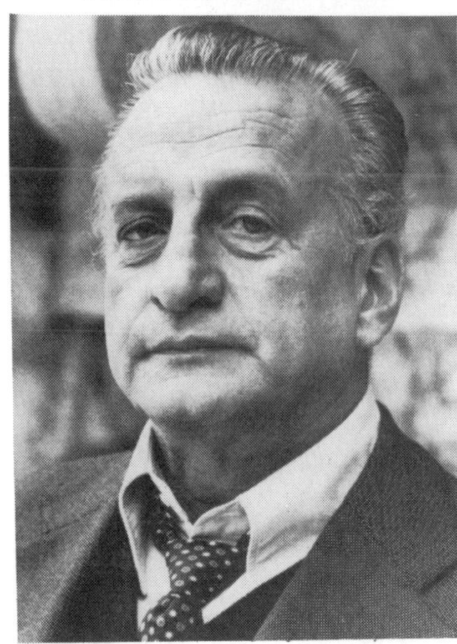
GEORGE C. SCOTT

MARY STEENBERGEN

GREGORY PECK - P/S/MAC ARTHUR
LISA PELIKAN - P
CHRISTOPHER PENN - P
SEAN PENN - P
ANN PENNINGTON - P
PEOPLE'S CHOICE AWARD
GEORGE PEPPARD - P
ANTHONY PERKINS - P/S
ELIZABETH PERKINS - P
MILLIE PERKINS - P/PU
RHEA PERLMAN - P
GIGI PERREAU - P
VALERIE PERRINE - P
LUKE PERRY - P
NEHEMIAH PERSOFF - P
DONNA PESCOW - P/S
JOE PESCOW - P/S
BERNADETTE PETERS - P
BROCK PETERS - P
JOANNA PETTIT - P
PENNY PEYSER - P
MICHELLE PFEIFFER - P
JOANNE PFLUG - P/PU
MARY PHILBIN - P
CHYNNA PHILLIPS - P
JULIANNE PHILLIPS - P
KAREN PHILLIPS - P
LOU DIAMOND PHILLIPS - P
MC KENZIE PHILLIPS - P
MICHELLE PHILLIPS - P
SIAN PHILLIPS - P
RIVER PHOENIX - P
CINDY PICKETT - P/S
MOLLY PICON - S
JOE PISCOPO - P
MARIE FRANCE PISIER - P/S
MARY KAY PLACE - P
DONALD PLEASANCE - P
SUZANNE PLESHETTE - P
JOAN PLOWRIGHT - P
CHRISTOPHER PLUMMER - P/S
SIDNEY POITIER - P/S
TRACY POLLAN - P
MICHAEL J POLLARD - S
DON PORTER - P
MARKIE POST - P
TOM POSTON - P
ANNIE POTTS - P/S
JANE POWELL - P
STEFANIE POWERS - P
PAULA PRENTISS - P/S/PU
PRISCILLA PRESLEY - P
HARVE PRESNELL - P
KELLY PRESTON - P
VINCENT PRICE - P
JASON PRIESTLY - P
VICTORIA PRINCIPAL - P/PU
EILEEN PRINGLE - P
DOROTHY PROVINE - S
JULIETTE PROWSE - P
RICHARD PRYOR - P/S
LEE PURCELL - P
SARAH PURCELL - P
LINDA PURL - P/S

DENNIS QUAID - P/S
RANDY QUAID - P
ANTHONY QUALE - P/S
EDDIE QUILLAN - P
KATHLEEN QUINLAN - P
AILEEN QUINN - P
ANTHONY QUINN - P/S

R2D2
PEGGY RAE - P
DEBORAH RAFFIN - P
STEVE RAILSBACK - P
LUISE RAINER - P
CHRISTINA RAINES - P
ELLA RAINES - P
JOHN RAITT - P
ESTHER RALSTON - P
VERA RALSTON - P
DACK RAMBO - P
HAROLD RAMOS - P
CHARLOTTE RAMPLING - P/S/PU
TONY RANDALL - P/S
PHYLICIA RASHAD - P
MARTHA RAYE - P
ROBERT REDFORD - P/S
LYNN REDGRAVE - P
VANESSA REDGRAVE - P
JERRY REED - P/S
OLIVER REED - P
PAMELA REED - P
SHANNON REED - PU/MAJOR DAD
SHARINA REED - PU
CHRISTOPHER REEVE - P
STEVE REEVES - P
TIM REID - P
CARL REINER - P/S
ROB REINER - P
JUDGE REINHOLD - P
ANN REINKING - P
KELLY RENO - P/S
TOMMY RETTIG - P
ANNE REVERE - P
DOROTHY REVERE - P
BURT REYNOLDS - P/S
DEBBIE REYNOLDS - P/S
MADELINE RHUE - P
DON RICKLES - P
ALAN RICKMAN - P
DIANA RIGG - P
COLLEEN RILEY - S
JEANNINE RILEY - P
JOHN RITTER - P/S
CHITA RIVERA - P
JOAN RIVERS - P/S
JASON ROBARDS - P/S
CLIFF ROBERTSON - P/S
DALE ROBERTSON - P
DORIS ROBERTS - P/S
ERIC ROBERTS - P/BEEFCAKE
JULIA ROBERTS - P
PERNELL ROBERTS - P
RACHEL ROBERTS - P
TANYA ROBERTS - P/S
ALEX ROCCO - P
EUGENE ROCHE - P
GINGER ROGERS - P/PU
ROY ROGERS - P
WAYNE ROGERS - P
GILBERT ROLAND - P
RUTH ROMAN - P/PU
CEASAR ROMERO - P
MICKEY ROONEY - P/S/TEEN
ISABELLA ROSALINI - P
ROSE MARIE - P
DIANA ROSS (AS DOROTHY)
TED ROSS (THE WIZ)
KATHARINE ROSS - P/S/PU
RICHARD ROUNDTREE - P
MICKEY ROURKE - P
MISTY ROWE - P
GINA ROWLANDS - P
JANICE RULE - P/PU
BARBARA RUSH - P
JANE RUSSELL - P/S/PU
KURT RUSSELL - P
MARK RUSSELL - P
NIPSEY RUSSELL (THE WIZ)
THERESA RUSSELL - P
MEG RYAN - P
PEGGY RYAN - P
MARK RYDELL - P
WINONA RYDER - P

EVA MARIE SAINT - P
SUSAN SAINT JAMES - P
SOUPY SALES - P/S
EMMA SAMMS - P
OLGA SAN JUAN - P
CHRIS SARANDON - S
SUSAN SARANDON - P
MICHAEL SARRAZIN - P
JOHN SAVAGE - P
TELLY SAVALES - P
JOHN SAXON - P
GRETA SCACCHI - P
DIANE SCARWID - P
NATALIE SCHAFER - P
ROY SCHEIDER - P/S
MAXIMILIAN SCHELL - P
CLAUDIA SCHIFFER - P
JOHN SCHNEIDER - P
MARIA SCHNEIDER - P/S
ROMY SCHNEIDER - P
BOB SCHOOT - S
MARIA SCHRIBER - P
RICKY SCHROEDER - P/S
JOHN SCHUCK - P
DWIGHT SCHULTZ - P
ARNOLD SCHWARZENEGGER - P/CONAN
PAUL SCOFIELD - P
TRACY SCOGGINS - P
ELIZABETH SCOTT - P
FRED SCOTT - P
GEORGE C SCOTT - P/S
MARTHA SCOTT - P
STEVEN SEAGAL - P
GEORGE SEGAL - P/S
SEKA - P
DAVID SELBY - P
CONNIE SELLECA - P
TOM SELLECK - P
MICHAEL SERRAULT - S
ANNE SEYMOUR - P
JANE SEYMOUR - P/PU
TED SHACKLEFORD - P
OMAR SHARIF - P/S
RAY SHARKEY - P/S
CORNELIA SHARPE - P
KAREN SHARPE - P
WILLIAM SHATNER - P
HELEN SHAVER - P
WALLACE SHAWN - S
ALLEY SHEEDY - P
CHARLIE SHEEN - P
MARTIN SHEEN - P/S
JOHNNY SHEFFIELD - P
CYBIL SHEPHERD - P
SAM SHEPHERD - P
BROOKE SHIELDS - P/S/PU
JOANNE SHIMKUS - P
JOHN SHIPP WESLEY (THE FLASH)
TALIA SHIRE - P/S
ANNE SHIRLEY - P

SYLVIA SIDNEY - P
GREGORY SIERRA - P
RON SILVER - P
JEAN SIMMONS - P/S
SIMONE SIMONE - P
O J SIMPSON - P
FRANK SINATRA - P/S/MAGEE
MADGE SINCLAIR - P
LORI SINGER - P
MARC SINGER - P
PENNY SINGLETON - P
RED SKELTON - P/S
TOM SKERRITT - P
CHRISTIAN SLATER - P
HELEN SLATER - P/SUPERGIRL
ALEXIS SMITH - P
BUBBA SMITH - P
BUFFALO BOB SMITH
JACQUELINE SMITH - P
MAGGIE SMITH - P/S
ROBERT SMITH - P
ROGER SMITH - P/S
SHELLY SMITH - P
JIMMY SMITS - P
CARRIE SNODGRASS - P/S
SUZANNE SOMERS - P/PU
ELKE SOMMER - P
JOANIE SOMMERS - P
PAUL SORVINO - P
ANN SOTHERN - P
TALISA SOTO - P
DAVID SOUL - P
CATHERINE SPAAK - P
SISSY SPACEK - P/S
CAMILLA SPARV - P
CLINTON SPILSBURY - P
G D SPRADLIN - P
LILI ST CYR - P
JILL ST JOHN - P
ROBERT STACK - P/NESS
ARMIH MUELLER STAHL - P
FRANK STALLONE - P
SYLVESTER STALLONE - P/S/ROCKY/RAMBO
JOHN STAMOS - P
TERENCE STAMP - P
LIONEL STANDER - P
ARNOLD STANG - P
EILEEN STANLEY - P
HARRY DEAN STANTON - P/S
JEAN STAPLETON - P
MAUREEN STAPLETON - P
CHARLES STARRETT - P
RINGO STARR - P/S
MARY STEENBERGEN - P/S
ROD STEIGER - P/S
DAVID STEINBERG - P
SOPHIE STEIN - P
LINDA`STERLING - P/PU
ROBERT STERLING - P
TISHA STERLING - P
DANIEL STERN - P
ANDREW STEVENS - P
CONNIE STEVENS - P
K T STEVENS - P
MC LEAN STEVENSON - P
PARKER STEVENSON - P
SHAWN STEVENS - S
STELLA STEVENS - P
JAMES STEWART - P/S/COWBOY/MILLER
PATRICK STEWART - P
PAULA STEWART - S
PEGGY STEWART - P
DAVID OGDEN STIERS - P
JERRY STILLER - P/S
DEAN STOCKWELL - P
GUY STOCKWELL - P/S
OLIVER STONE - P
SHARON STONE - P
GAIL STORM - P
TEMPEST STORM - P
BEATRICE STRAIGHT - P
SUSAN STRASBERG - P
ROBIN STRASSER - P
PETER STRAUSS - P
MERYL STREEP - P
BARBRA STREISAND - P/S/OSCAR
WOODY STRODE - P
DON STROUD - P/S
SALLY STRUTHERS - P
AMY STRYKER - S
BARRY SULLIVAN - P
DONALD SUTHERLAND - P/S
KEIFER SUTHERLAND -P/S
JANET SUZMAN - P
PAT SUZUKI - P
GABRIEL SWANN - P/S
PATRICK SWAYZE - P
INGA SWENSON - P
LORETTA SWIT - P
CYNTHIA SYKES - P
SYLVIA SYMS - S

T - U

MR T - P
KEN TAKAKURA - P
GEORGE TAKEI - P
JESSICA TANDY - P
ELIZABETH TAYLOR - P/S/PU/SPU
LEIGH TAYLOR-YOUNG - P
RIP TAYLOR - CAPT HOOK
ROD TAYLOR - P
VERA TEASDALE - P
SHIRLEY TEMPLE - P
ALICE TERRY - P
LAUREN TEWES - P
URSULA THIESS - P
LYNNE THIGPEN -P
ROY THINNES - P
KURT THOMAS - P
MARLO THOMAS - P
PHILIP MICHAEL THOMAS - P
RICHARD THOMAS - P
TIM THOMERSON - S
JACK THOMPSON - P
LEA THOMPSON - P
UMA THURMAN - P
GRETA THYSSEN - P
CHERYL TIEGS - P
GENE TIERNEY - P
PAMELA TIFFIN - P
MEG TILLY - P/PU
CHARLENE TILTON - P/PU
ANN TODD - P
BEVERLY TODD - P
UGO TOGNAZZI - P/S
LILY TOMLIN - P/S/ERNESTINE
ANGEL TOMPKINS - P
TONY AWARD
TOPOL - S
RIP TORN - P
RAQUEL TORRES - P
AUDREY TOTTER - P
CONSTANCE TOWERS - P
DANIEL TRAVANTI - P
JOHN TRAVOLTA - P/S
CLAIRE TREVOR - P
TUNDI - SPU
ANN TURKEL - P
KATHLEEN TURNER - P/S
LANA TURNER - P/S/PU/SPU
RITA TUSHINGHAM - P
SHANNON TWEED - P/SPU
TWIGGY - P
CICELY TYSON - P
BOB UECKER - P
LIV ULLMAN - P
TRACEY ULLMAN - P
ROBERT URICH - P

BRENDA VACCARO - P/S
KAREN VALENTINE - P
RAF VALLONE - P
JOAN VAN ARK - P
CLAUDE VAN DAMME - P
TRISH VAN DEVERE - P
MAMIE VAN DOREN - P/PU
JOHM VAN DREELEN - P
DICK VAN DYKE - P/S
JERRY VAN DYKE - P
JO VAN FLEET - P
DICK VAN PATTEN - P
JIMMY VAN PATTEN - P
JOYCE VAN PATTEN - P
VINCE VAN PATTEN - S
MARIO VAN PEEBLES - P
DEBRA VAN VOLKENBURGH - P
VANITY - PU
DIANE VARSI - P
SYLVIA VARTAN - P
ROBERT VAUGHN - P
LENO VENTURA - P
GWEN VERDON - P
BEN VEREEN - P
MARTHA VICKERS - P
ROBERT VIHARO - P
HERVE VILLECHAIZE - P
JAN-MICHAEL VINCENT - P/S
MITCH VOGEL - P
JON VOIGHT - P/S
BETTY VON FURSTENBERG - P
MAX VON SYDOW - P/S

LYLE WAGGONER - P
LINDSAY WAGNER - P
ROBERT WAGNER - P
KEN WAHL - P
ROBERT WALDREN - P
CHRISTOPHER WALKEN - P/S
CLINT WALKER - P
JIMMY WALKER - P
NANCY WALKER - P
DEE WALLACE STONE - P/S
ELI WALLACH - P/S
RAY WALSTON - P
JESSICA WALTER - P/PLAY MISTY
JULIE WALTERS - P
RACHEL WARD - P
JACK WARDEN - P/S
MALCOM JAMAL WARNER - P
JENNIFER WARREN - P
LESLIE ANN WARREN - P/S
DIANE WARWICK - P
DENZEL WASHINGTON - P
SAM WATERSTON - P
PAT WAYNE - P/S
CARL WEATHERS - P/S
DENNIS WEAVER - P

MARJORIE WEAVER - P
SIGOURNEY WEAVER - P
PEGGY WEBBER - P
ROBERT WEBBER - P
RAQUEL WELCH - P/S
TAWNE WELCH - P
TUESDAY WELD - P
PETER WELLER (ROBO COP)
DAWN WELLS - P
ADAM WEST - P
ARLENE WHELAN - P
LISA WHELCHEL - P
BETTY WHITE - P
VANNA WHITE - P
STUART WHITMAN - P/S
JAMES WHITMORE - P/WILL ROGERS
RICHARD WIDMARK - P/S
BRUNO WIEST - P
LARRY WILCOX - P
GENE WILDER - P/S
JUNE WILKINSON - P/PU
BRUNO WILLERS - P
ANDY WILLIAMS - P/S
BILLY DEE WILLIAMS - P/S
CINDY WILLIAMS - P
CLARENCE WILLIAMS, III - P
EDY WILLIAMS - P/PU
EMLYN WILLIAMS - P
ESTHER WILLIAMS - P/PU
FRED WILLIAMSON - P
HAL WILLIAMS - P
JO BETH WILLIAMS - P
NICOL WILLIAMSON - P
ROBIN WILLIAMS - P/S
TREAT WILLIAMS - P/S
BRUCE WILLIS - P
DEMOND WILSON - P
FLIP WILSON - P
LOIS WILSON - P
THOMAS F WILSON - P
MARIE WINDSOR - P/PU
PAUL WINFIELD - P
OPRAH WINFREY - P
DEBRA WINGER - P
HENRY WINKLER - P
JONATHAN WINTERS - P/S
ROLAND WINTERS - P
SHELLY WINTERS - P/S
JANE WITHERS - P
LANA WOOD - P/S/PU
JAMES WOODS - P/S
EDWARD WOODWARD - P/S
JOANNE WOODWARD - P/S
JO ANN WORLEY - P
IRENE WORTH - P/S
FAY WRAY - P/S
TERESA WRIGHT - P
JANE WYATT - P
GRETCHEN WYLER - P
JANE WYMAN - P/S/PU
PATRICE WYMORE - P
DANA WYNTER - P/PU

MICHAEL YORK - P/S
SUSANNAH YORK - P/S
TINA YOTHERS - P
BURT YOUNG - P
LORETTA YOUNG - P
ROBERT YOUNG - P
SEAN YOUNG - P

Z

PIA ZADORA - P
JACKLYN ZEMAN - P/PU/SPU
ANTHONY ZERBE - P
EFREM ZIMBALIST - P
STEPHANIE ZIMBALIST - P
ADRIAN ZMED - P
VERA ZORINA - P

Black & White Photos Only $1.00

HEATHER THOMAS

FLIP WILSON

SHELLY WINTERS

JOANNE WOODWARD

JANE WYMAN

COLOR PHOTOGRAPHS

Portrait/P • Movie Stills/S • Pin-ups/PU & Super Pin-ups/SPU - $2.50 Each

WILLIE AAMES - P
KAREEM ABDUL-JABBAR
PAULA ABDUL - P
MAUDE ADAMS - P/PU/SPU
ISABELLA ADJANI - P/PU
ROSANNA AEQUETTE - P
ALAN ALDA - P
KIM ALEXIS - P/PU
KRISTIAN ALFONSO - P
MUHAMMED ALI (BOXING)
WOODY ALLEN - P
KIRSTIE ALLEY - P
MARIA CONCHITA ALONZO - P
CAROL ALT - PU
AMERICAN GLADIATORS (GROUP)
MADCHEN AMISH (TWIN PEAKS)
LONI ANDERSON - P
MELODY ANDERSON (COSTUME)
RICHARD DEAN ANDERSON - P
URSULA ANDRESS - SPU
JULIE ANDREWS - P
ANGEL - P
ROBIN ANGERS - PU
ANN-MARGRET - P/PU
LAURA ANTONELLI - SPU
CHRISTINA APPLEGATE - P
ANNE ARCHER - P
R G ARMSTRONG (DICK TRACY)
ROSEANNE ARNOLD - P
CHRIS ATKINS & BROOKE SHIELDS
GENE AUTRY - P/WITH HORSE

LAUREN BACALL & ROBERT STACK
BARBARA BACH - SPU
CATHERINE BACH - P
CARROLL BAKER - P/S/PU
SCOTT BAKULA - P
LUCILLE BALL - P
ADRIENNE BARBEAU - P
BRIGITTE BARDOT - P/S/PU/SPU
BARISHNIKOV - P
ELLEN BARKAN - P
EMMANUELLE BART - P
KIM BASINGER - P/PU/SPU
JUSTINE BATEMAN - P
BATMAN, PENGUIN & JOKER
BATMAN, ROBIN & BATGIRL
BATMAN, BATGIRL & ROBIN
BATMAN, PENGUIN & JOKER
JENNIFER BEALS - P
WARREN BEATTY (DICK TRACY)
BEAUTY & THE BEAST
BONNIE BEDELIA - P
BEE GEES (GROUP PHOTO)
SHARI BELAFONTE - P
PAT BENETAR - P
ANNETTE BENING - P
BARBI BENTON - PU
SENTA BERGER - SPU
SANDAHL BERGMAN - P
CHUCK BERRY - P
BENAZIR BHUTO (PAKISTAN)
LARRY BIRD & KEVIN MC HALE
LARRY BIRD & MAGIC JOHNSON
LARRY BIRD & JAMES WORTHY
JANE BIRKIN - P
JULIE BISHOP - P
JACQUELINE BISSET - P/PU/SPU
BONNIE BLAIR (SKATER)
JANET BLAIR - P
LINDA BLAIR - PU/SPU
ANN BLYTHE - PU
HEIDI BOHAY - P
MICHAEL BOLTON
LISA BONET
LISA BONET - P
ALISON BOODY - P
CAROLE BOUQUET - P
DAVID BOWIE - P
CHRISTIE BRINKLEY - P/PU
MORGAN BRITTANY - P
CHARLES BRONSON - P
RANDI BROOKS - P
BLAIR BROWN - P
JAMES BROWN
DELTA BURKE - P

JOANNA CAMERON - PU
KIRK CAMERON - P
NAOMI CAMPBELL - PU
DYAN CANNON - P
JENNIFER CAPRIATTI (TENNIS)
KATE CAPSHAW - P/PU
ANGEL CARDERO (JOCKEY)
CLAUDIA CARDINALE - P
MARIAH CAREY
ART CARNEY (HARRY & TONTO)
BARBARA CARRERA - P/PU
LYNDA CARTER - P/PU
JOANNA CASSIDY - PU
PHOEBE CATES - P
KIM CATTRELL - P
JOAN CAULFIELD - P
MARILYN CHAMBERS - P/PU
RICHARD CHAMBERLAIN - P/COSTUME
GERALDINE CHAPLIN - P
CHARLIES ANGELS (W/ ROBERTS)
CYD CHARRISE - PU
JOAN CHEN
CHER - P/PU
RAE DAWN CHONG - P
JULIE CHRISTIE - P
DICK CLARK - P
JILL CLAYBURGH - P
CORRINE CLEARY - PU
CLAUDETTE COLBERT - P/CLEOPATRA
NATALIE COLE
COLLINS, EVANS & CARROLL
JOAN COLLINS - PU/SPU
JENNIFER CONNELLY - P
KIMBERLY CONRAD - PU
KIMBERLY CONRAD & HUGH HEFNER
GERRY COONEY (BOXING)
TERI COPLEY - PU
KEVIN COSTNER - P
COWBOYS
COURTNEY COX - P
CINDY CRAWFORD - PU
MICHAEL CRAWFORD (PHANTOM OF OPERA)
CATHY LEE CROSBY - P
DENISE CROSBY - PU
BILLY CRYSTAL & MEG RYAN
LINDA CRYSTAL - P
MACAULEY CULKIN - P
PEGGY CUMMINGS - P
JAMIE LEE CURTIS - P/PU/SPU
TONY CURTIS & JACK LEMMON (DRAG)
JOHN CUSAK - P

MYRIAM D'ABO - PU
BEVERLY D'ANGELO - P
PATTI D'ARBANVILLE
SALVADOR DALI
SYBIL DANNING - PU
LOLITA DAVIDOVICH - S
SAMMY DAVIS, JR
GEENA DAVIS - P
YVONNE DE CARLO & FRED GWYNNE
YVONNE DE CARLO (VAMPIRA)
OLIVIA DE HAVILAND - P
PETER DE LUISE - P
REBECCA DE MORNAY - P
ROBERT DE NIRO (BOXING)
DANA DELANEY (CHINA BEACH)
CATHERINE DENEUVE - P/PU/SPU
JOHNNY DEPP - P
BO DEREK - PU/SPU
LAURA DERN - P
COLEEN DEWHURST - P
SUSAN DEY - P
ANGIE DICKINSON - P
BO DIDDLEY - P
MATT DILLON - P
DONNA DIXON - P/PU/SPU
PLACIDO DOMINGO
FATS DOMINO - P
TROY DONAHUE - P
JAMES DOOHAN (STAR TREK)
KIRK DOUGLAS (COWBOY)
MICHAEL DOUGLAS - P
LESLIE-ANNE DOWN - P
FRED DRYER & STEPHANIE KRAMER
FRED DRYER - P
FAYE DUNAWAY (BONNIE)

SHEENA EASTON - P

CLINT EASTWOOD - P/COWBOY
BARBARA EDEN - PU
IKE EISENHOWER
MAMIE EISENHOWER
ROBIN EISENMAN - PU
ERICA ELENIAK - PU/SPU
KELLY EMBERG - P/PU
EMPTY NEST (CAST)
MARLA ENGLISH - PU
LINDA EVANS - P/PU
CHRIS EVERT & MARTINA NAVATOLOVA
GREG EVIGAN - P

MORGAN FAIRCHILD - PU
PETER FALK (AS COLUMBIO)
MIA FARROW - P
FARRAH FAWCETT - P/PU
SHERILYN FENN - P
FERGIE (ENGLAND)
SALLY FIELD - P
FLASH GORDON (SAM J JONES)
FLASH GORDON (KRISTINA WAYBORN)
FLASH GORDON (MELODY ANDERSON)
FLASH GORDON (ORNELLI MUTI)
FLASH GORDON (MAX VON SYDOW)
FLASH GORDON (CHAIM TOPAL)
PEGGY FLEMING
RHONDA FLEMING - PU
BRIDGET FONDA - P
JANE FONDA - P
JOAN FONTAINE - P
BETTY FORD - P
FAITH FORD - P
GERALD R FORD - P
LITA FORD - P
STEVEN FORD - P
FOREMAN & FRAZIER (BOXING)
STEVE FORREST - P
JODIE FOSTER - P/PU
MICHAEL J FOX - P
SAMANTHA FOX - PU/SPU
PETER FRAMPTON - P
ANNE FRANCIS - P
LYNN FREDERICK - P
ANNETTE FUNICELLO (MM CLUB)

EVA GABOR - P
ZSA ZSA GABOR
ANDY GARCIA
AVA GARDNER - P
JAMES GARNER (COWBOY)
TERRI GARR - PU
MITZI GAYNOR - P
RICHARD GERE (BEEFCAKE)
ANDY GIBB - P
CINDY GIBB - P
DEBBIE GIBSON - P
DEBBIE GIBSON
MELISSA GILBERT - P
ROBIN GIVINS - P
TRACI GOLD - P
WHOOPI GOLDBERG
GOLDEN GIRLS (CAST)
VALERIE GOLINA
JILL GOODACRE - PU
JOHN GOODMAN -P/AS RUTH
BILLY GRAHAM - P
PETER GRAVES - P
ERIN GRAY - PU
WAYNE GRETZKY - P
MELANIE GRIFFITH - PU
MELANIE GRIFFITH & TOM HANKS
CORNELIA GUEST
STEVE GUTTENBERG -P/BEEFCAKE

SHELLEY HACK - P
JULIE HAGERTY - P
JESSICA HAHN - P/PU
ARSENIO HALL - P
DIEDRE HALL - P
FAWN HALL - P
JERRI HALL - PU
LOIS HAMILTON - PU
HARRY HAMLIN - P
HAMMER
TOM HANKS - P
DARRYL HANNAH - P
MARK HARMON - P
JESSICA HARPER - P
VALERIE HARPER - P
JONATHAN HARRIS & BILL MUMY
JONATHAN HARRIS (LOST IN SPACE)
NEIL PAT HARRIS (DOOGIE HOWSER)
REX HARRISON - P/MY FAIR LADY
KATHRYN HARROLD - P
VERONICA HART - PU
MARIETTE HARTLEY - P
LISA HARTMAN - PU/SPU
GOLDIE HAWN & KURT RUSSELL
GOLDIE HAWN - P
ALEXANDRIA HAY - P
MAX HEADROOM - P
TIPPI HEDREN - P
MARGE HELGENBERGER - P/
CHINA BEACH
MARIEL HEMINGWAY - P/PU/SPU
AUDREY HEPBURN - P
BARBARA HERSHEY - P
CHARLETON HESTON (BEN HUR)
PAUL HOGAN - P
VALERIE HOLIND - P
LARRY HOLMES
HONEYMOONERS (CAST IN KITCHEN)
BOB HOPE - P
DENNIS HOPPER
LEE HORSLEY - P
BOB HOSKINS (ROGER RABBIT)
WHITNEY HOUSTON - P
LINDA HUNT - P
HOLLY HUNTER - P
RACHEL HUNTER - PU
WILLIAM HURT - P
LAUREN HUTTON - P/PU
IMAN - PU
KATHY IRELAND - PU
AMY IRVING -P

BO JACKSON (BASEBALL)
JANET JACKSON - P
LA TOYA JACKSON - P/PU
MICHAEL JACKSON - P
REV JESSE JACKSON - P
MICK JAGGER - P
ANNE JEFFRIES - PU
RITA JENRETTE - PU
ADELE JERGENS - PU
ANN JILLIAN - P
INGMAR JOHANSON (BOXER)
LYNN-HOLLY JOHNSON - P
MICHELLE JOHNSON - PU/SPU
JANET JONES - P/PU
SAM J JONES - P
MICHAEL JORDAN (ACTION)
LOUIS JOURDAN - P
JACKIE JOYNER-KERSIE
(OLYMPICS)

MADELINE KAHN - P
VALERIE KAPRISKY - PU
MICHAEL KEATON
SALLY KELLERMAN - P
KELLY & REYNOLDS (SING IN RAIN)
JOHN KENNEDY, JR - P
JOANNA KERNS - P
EVELYN KEYES
PERSIS KHAMBATTA (STAR TREK)
MARGOT KIDDER
NICOLE KIDMAN - P
JOANNE WHALLEY KILMER - PU
VAL KILMER - P
PERRY KING - P
NATASSIA KINSKI - PU
SALLY KIRKLAND - P
STEPHANIE KRAMER - P
FREDDY KRUGER (MAKE UP)

CHERYL LADD - P/PU
LADY DIANA
CHRISTINE LAHTI - P
BURT LANCASTER (GANTRY)
ELSA LANCESTER & BORIS KARLOF
KATHERINE KELLY LANG - P
JESSICA LANGE - P
ANGELA LANSBURY - P
TOMMY LASORDA
LASSIE (CAST PHOTO)
CYNDI LAUPER - PU
PIPER LAURIE - P
KELLY LE BROCK - PU/SPU
MICHAEL LEARNED
LEAVE IT TO BEAVER (CAST)
SPIKE LEE - P
JANET LEIGH - PU
JENNIFER JASON LEIGH - P
JACK LEMMON - P
JOAN LESLIE
DANIEL DAY LEWIS - P
HUEY LEWIS - P
JERRY LEWIS (AS CLOWN)
CHRISTOPHER LLOYD (FUTURE)
HEATHER LOCKLEAR - PU/SPU
GINA LOLABRIGIDA - PU
SHELLY LONG - P
NANCY LOPEZ (GOLF)
TRACI LORDS - PU
SOPHIA LOREN - P
ROB LOWE - P/BEEKCAKE
CAREY LOWELL - P
LUCY & DESI
KELLY LYNCH - P

M*A*S*H (CAST)
SHIRLEY MAC CLAINE - P/S/PU
ANDIE MAC DOWALL - P
ELLE MAC PHERSON - PU
MADONNA - P/PU
VIRGINIA MADSEN - P/PU
JOHN MALCOVICH - P
DOROTHY MALONE - P
RAY "BOOM BOOM" MANCINI
NICK MANCUSO - P
BARBARA MANDRELL - P
JAYNE MANSFIELD - SPU
MARRIED WITH CHILDREN (CAST)
ELSA MARTINELLI - P
MARY MARTIN - P
PAMELA SUE MARTIN - PU
MARY ELIZ MASTRANTONIO - P
DIANE MATLIN - P
DIANE MC BAIN - P
ANDREW MC CARTHY - P
JULIE MC CULLOUGH - P
KELLY MC GILLIS - P/PU
ELIZABETH MC GOVERN - P
PATTI MC GUIRE - SPU
JIM MC MAHON (FOOTBALL)
ELLE MC PHERSON - PU
GERALD MC RANDY & JAMESON PARKER
GEORGE MICHAEL - P
BETTE MIDLER - P
ALLYSA MILANO - P
VERA MILES - P
ANN MILLER - P
PENELOPE ANN MILLER - P
DONNA MILLS - P/PU
YVETTE MIMEAUX - P
LIZA MINNELI - P
MARILYN MONROE - P/PU
RICARDO MONTALBAN (AS KHAN)
ELIZABETH MONTGOMERY - P
DEMI MOORE - P
MARY TYLER MOORE - P
TERRY MOORE - PU
MUNSTERS (DE CARLO & GWYNNE)
ORNELLA MUTI - PU/COSTUME

BRIGIT NEILSEN - P/PU/SPU
LESLIE NEILSEN
JACK NEILSON - P
CORKY NEMEC (PARKER LEWIS)
ANTHONY NEWLEY - S
PAUL NEWMAN - P
JULIE NEWMAR - P/S/PU/CATWOMAN
OLIVIA NEWTON-JOHN - P
JACK NICHOLSON - P
STEVIE NICKS - P
LEONARD NIMOY (STAR TREK)
PATRICIA NIXON - P
DEBORAH NORVILLE - P
KIM NOVAK - P/S/PU

CARROLL O'CONNOR - P
DONALD O'CONNOR - P
SINEAD O'CONNOR - P
MAUREEN O'HARA - P
TATUM O'NEAL - P
JENNIFER O'NEIL - P
RANDI OAKES - P
LENA OLIN - P
OLYMPIC MEDALS (GOLD, SILVER
& BRONZE)
BOBBY ORR (HOCKEY)
CATHERINE OXENBERG - P

AL PACINO -GODFATHER/TRACY
JOANNE PACULA - P
JACK PALANCE - P
MARISA PARE (LACE)
MICHAEL PARE - P
ELEANOR PARKER - P
JAMESON PARKER - P
DOLLY PARTON - P
PAULINA - PU/SPU
GREGORY PECK - P
PELE (SOCCER)
PERFECT STRANGERS (CAST)
VALERIE PERRINE - PU/SPU
PERRY MASON (CAST)
BERNADETTE PETERS - P
MICHELLE PFEIFFER - P/PU
CHYNNA PHILLIPS - P
LOU DIAMOND PHILLIPS
RIVER PHOENIX - P
BRAD PITT - P
SUZANNE PLESHETTE - P
ROMAN POLANSKI (DIRECTOR)
TRACY POLLAN - P
MARKIE POST - P/LEOTARDS
JANE POWELL - PU
STEPHANIE POWERS - P
ELVIS PRESLEY - P
PRICILLA PRESLEY - /PU
KELLY PRESTON - P
VINCENT PRICE - EGGHEAD/HORROR
PRINCESS ANNE (ENGLAND)
VICTORIA PRINCIPAL - P
ROXANNE PULITZER - SPU
LINDA PURL - P
DENNIS QUAID - P

KATIE RABETT - PU
BONNIE RAITT - P
DACK RAMBO - P
CHARLOTTE RAMPLING - PU
ELIZABETH RAY - -PU
RONALD REAGAN (ON HORSE)
DONNA REED - P
SHANNON REED - P
CHRISTOPHER REEVE - P/SUPERMAN
DEBBIE REYNOLDS - P
CYNTHIA RHODES - P
DONNA RICE - PU
LIONEL RICHIE - P
MOLLY RINGWALD - P
CLIFF ROBERTSON - P
ERIC ROBERTS
JULIA ROBERTS - P
TANYA ROBERTS - PU
HOLLY ROBINSON
CHI CHI RODRIGUEZ (GOLF)
KENNY ROGERS - P
MIMI ROGERS - P
ROY ROGERS - P/ON HORSE
GILBERT ROLAND - P
CESAR ROMERO (JOKER)
LINDA RONSTADT - P
AXEL ROSE
ISABELLA ROSELLINI - P
DIANA ROSS - P
KATHERINE ROSS - P
MICKEY ROURKE - P
MISTY ROWE - PU
BETSY RUSSELL - SPU
JANE RUSSELL - P/-PU
KURT RUSSELL - P
ROSALIND RUSSELL - P
WINONA RYDER - P

EMMA SAMMS - P/PU
CANDY SAMPLES - P/PU
LORI SANDERS - P
GENE SARAZIN (GOLF)
FRED SAVAGE - P
MAXIMILLIAN SCHELL - P
ARNOLD SCHWARZENEGGER - P
TRACY SCOGGINS - PU/SPU
STEVEN SEAGAL - P
SEKA - PU
CONNIE SELLECA - P
TOM SELLECK - P
JOAN SEVERANCE - PU
JANE SEYMOUR - PU
STEPHANIE SEYMOUR - PU
MOIRA SHEARER (RED SHOES)
ALLY SHEEDY - P
CHARLIE SHEEN - P
MARTIN SHEEN - P
CYBIL SHEPHERD - P
BROOKE SHIELDS - PU/AGE 13
DINAH SHORE - P
KATHY SHOWER - PU
CARLY SIMON - P
O J SIMPSON
LORI SINGER - PU
CHRISTIAN SLATER
HELEN SLATER (SUPERGIRL)
ALEXIS SMITH - P
JACLYN SMITH - P/PU
SHELLEY SMITH - PU
WESLEY SNIPES
ELKE SOMER - P
SUZANNE SOMERS - P/PU
DONNA SOMMER - P
RICK SPRINGFIELD - BEEFCAKE
ROBERT STACK & LAUREN BACALL
BARBARA STANWYCK - P
STAR TREK (CAST)
STAR TREK (SHATNER, NIMOY
& KELLY)
STAR TREK (LEONARD NIMOY)
STAR TREK (MARK LEONARD)
STAR TREK (PERSIS KHAMBATA)
STAR TREK (DE FOREST KELLY)
STAR TREK (CAST II PHOTO)
STAR TREK (GEORGE TAKEI)
STAR TREK (JANE WYATT)

STAR TREK (JAMES DOOHAN)
STAR TREK (RICARDO MONTALBAN)
STAR WARS (CAST)
RINGO STARR - P
STELLA STEVENS - PU
JIMMY STEWART - P/ON BIKE
STING (BEEKCAKE)
ERIC STOLZ
OLIVER STONE (DIRECTOR)
SHARON STONE - P/PU
SUSAN STRASBERG - PU
MERYL STREEP - P
DANNY SULLIVAN (RACER)
KEIFER SUTHERLAND (COWBOY)
SWAYZE & GRAY (DIRTY DANCING)
PATRICK SWAYZE - P

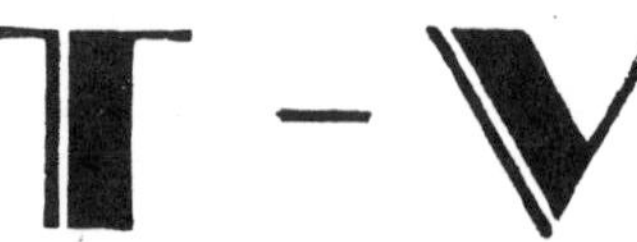

JESSICA TANDY - P
ELIZABETH TAYLOR - P
SHIRLEY TEMPLE - P
MARGARET THATCHER - P
REGGIE THEISS (BASKETBALL)
THIRTY (30) SOMETHING (CAST)
DEBBIE THOMAS - P/OLYMPICS
HEATHER THOMAS - P
MARLO THOMAS - P
LEA THOMPSON - P
CHERYL TIEGS - P/PU/SPU
GENE TIERNEY - P/PU
MEG TILLY
RANDY TRAVIS - P
DONALD TRUMP - P
IVANA TRUMP - P
KATHLEEN TURNER - P/PU
TINA TURNER - P/PU
SHANNON TWEED - SPU
TRACY ULLMAN - P
JOAN VAN ARK - P
JEAN CLAUDE VAN DAMME
MAMIE VAN DOREN - PU/SPU
MARIO VAN PEEBLES
VANITY - PU
SYLVIA VARTAN

RACHEL WARD - P/PU
JODY WATLEY - P
SIGORNEY WEAVER -P/PU/GORILLAS
RAQUEL WELCH - PU/SPU
TAWNEE WELCH - P
TUESDAY WELD - P
TERRI WELLES - PU
DAWN WELLS - P
BETTY WHITE - P
VANNA WHITE - P/PU
ESTHER WILLIAMS - PU
VANESSA WILLIAMS - P
BRUCE WILLIS - P
OPRAH WINFREY - P
K C WINKLER - P
LANA WOOD - PU
JANE WYATT - P
JANE WYMAN - P
ALAN YOUNG (MR ED)
SEAN YOUNG - P
STEVE YZERMAN (HOCKEY)
PIA ZADORA - PU
JACKIE ZEMAN - PU
KIM ZMESKAL (OLYMPICS)

UNITED STATES ORDERS

B&W PHOTOS ( ) X $1.00 = ______
COLOR PHOTOS ( ) X $2.50 = ______
POSTAGE AND HANDLING $3.00
TOTAL ENCLOSED: ______

SEND ORDER TO:
NAME ______
ADDRESS ______
CITY ______
STATE ______ ZIP ______

CANADIAN ORDERS

B&W PHOTOS ( ) X $1.25 = ______
COLOR PHOTOS ( ) X $2.75 = ______
POSTAGE AND HANDLING $5.00
TOTAL ENCLOSED: ______

SEND ORDER TO:
NAME ______
ADDRESS ______
CITY ______
PROVINCE ______ ZIP ______

FOREIGN ORDERS

B&W PHOTOS ( ) X $1.50 = ______
COLOR PHOTOS ( ) X $2.75 = ______
POSTAGE AND HANDLING $10.00
TOTAL ENCLOSED: ______

SEND ORDER TO:
NAME ______
ADDRESS ______
CITY ______
STATE ______ ZIP ______

ORDER FORM

SY SUSSMAN PORTRAITS • 2962 S. MANN ST. • LAS VEGAS, NV 89102

TELEVISION & MOVIE CAST PHOTOS

All Photographs $1.00 Each

A-TEAM
ABBOTT & COSTELLO
ADAM 12
ADDAMS FAMILY
AFTER MASH
AIN'T MISBEHAVING
AIRWOLF
ALICE
ALL'S FAIR
AMEN
AMOS 'N' ANDY
GENE AUTRY SHOW
AVENGERS

BACHELOR FATHER
BANACEK
BARETTA
BATMAN (BATMAN, ROBIN & VILLANS)
BATTLESTAR GALACTICA
BEAUTY & THE BEAST
NEW BEAVER FAMILY
BENSON
EDGAR BERGEN & CHARLIE MC SHOW
MILTON BERLE SHOW
BEVERLY HILLS 90210
BEVERLY HILLBILLIES
BEWITCHED
BIG VALLEY
BOLD ONES (DOCTORS)
BOLD ONES (LAWYERS)
BONANZA
DANIEL BOONE
VICTOR BORGE SHOW
BOSOM BUDDIES
BRADY BUNCH
BROKEN ARROW
BUFFALO BILL
CAROL BURNETT SHOW
BURNS & ALLEN

CAGNEY & LACEY
CANNON
CAPTAIN & TENNILE
JOHNNY CARSON (CAST)
JOHNNY CARSON - P
BEN CASEY
CHARLIE'S ANGELS (FARRAH FAWCETT)
CHARLIE'S ANGELS (TANYA ROBERTS)
CHARLIE'S ANGELS (CHERYL LADD)
CHEERS
CHEYENNE
CHIPS
CISCO KID
COLT 45
COLUMBO
COMBAT
THE COSBY SHOW
CRAZY LIKE A FOX
BOB CUMMINGS SHOW

DAGWOOD & BLONDIE
DALLAS
DEAD END KIDS
DENNIS THE MENACE
DESIGNING WOMAN
DIFFERENT STROKES
DONNY & MARIE SHOW
DRAGNET
NANCY DREW MYSTERIES
PATTY DUKE SHOW
DUKES OF HAZARD
DYNASTY

WYATT EARP
EIGHT IS ENOUGH
ELLERY QUEEN
EMERGENCY
EMPTY NEST
EQUALIZER

F B I
F TROOP
FACTS OF LIFE
FALCON CREST
FALL GUY
FAME
FAMILY
FANTASY ISLAND
FATHER KNOWS BEST
FAMILY FEUD (RICHARD DAWSON)
FLAMINGO ROAD
WAYLAND FLOWERS & MADAME
FLYING NUN
FORBIDDEN PLANET
FRANCIS THE TALKING MULE
FRANK'S PLACE

GET SMART
GHOST & MRS MUIR
GREAT GILDERSLEEVE
GILLIGAN'S ISLAND
DOBIE GILLIS SHOW
GIMMIE A BREAK
GEORGIE GOBEL SHOW
GOLDEN GIRLS
GOOD TIMES
LOU GRANT
GREATEST AMERICAN HERO
GREEN ACRES
ANDY GRIFFITH SHOW
GUNFIGHT AT OK CORRAL
PETER GUNN
GUNSMOKE (CAST)
GUNSMOKE (ARNESS & WEAVER)

BUDDY HACKETT SHOW
MIKE HAMMER
HAPPY DAYS
HARDCASTLE & MC CORMICK
HARDY BOYS
HART TO HART
HAVE GUN WILL TRAVEL
HAWAIIAN EYE
HAWAII 5-0
HAZEL
HEAD OF THE CLASS
HEE HAW
PEE WEE HERMAN
HIGHWAY TO HEAVEN
HILL STREET BLUES
HOHAN'S HEROS
SHERLOCK HOLMES
HONEYMOONERS (ALL DRINKING)
HONEYMOONERS (ALL SINGING)
HONEYMOONERS (RALPH DRIVING BUS)
HONEYMOONERS (NORTON IN SEWER)
HONEYMOONERS (AT RESTAURANT)
HONEYMOONERS (LOOKING AT MAGAZINE)
HONEYMOONERS (TRIXIE LOOKING)
HONEYMOONERS (ALL ON TRIP)
HONEYMOONERS (ALL ON STAGE)
HONEYMOONERS (ALL ON BUS)
HONEYMOONERS (ALL IN KITCHEN)
BOB HOPE, GEORGE BURNS & JOHNNY CARSON
HOTEL
MATT HOUSTON
HOWDY DOODY
HULK
HUNTER

I DREAM OF JEANNIE
I LOVE LUCY
I SPY

A-TEAM

THE AVENGERS

DUKES OF HAZZARD

ALICE

CHARLIE'S ANGELS

DYNASTY

ALL IN THE FAMILY

CHEERS

FACTS OF LIFE

I'VE GOT A SECRET
INCREDIBLE HULK
IRONSIDE
IT TAKES A THIEF
IT'S A LIVING

JEFFERSONS
JOANIE LOVES CHACHIE
BARNABY JONES
CAPTAIN KANGAROO
KATE & ALLIE
DR KILDARE
KING KONG (ARMSTRONG & WRAY)
KING KONG (W/ FAY WRAY)
KNOTS LANDING
KOJAK
ERNIE KOVACS
KUKLA, FRAN & OLLIE
KUNG FU

L A LAW
LARAMIE
LASSIE
LAUGH IN
LAVERNE & SHIRLEY
LEAVE IT TO BEAVER (ALL 5)
LEAVE IT TO BEAVER (DOW & MATHERS)
SHERI LEWIS & LAMBCHOP
LITTLE HOUSE ON THE PRAIRIE
LOGANS RUN (TV SERIES)

Cast Photos of Your Favorite T.V. and Movie Stars for just $1.00 Each

LONE RANGER (MOORE)
LONE RANGER (SPILLSBURY)
LONE RANGER (HART)
LOST IN SPACE
LOVE AT FIRST BITE
LOVE BOAT
LOVE, SIDNEY
LUCY SHOW
LUM & ABNER

M*A*S*H (ALAN ALDA)
M*A*S*H (ALAN ARBUS)
M*A*S*H (GARY BURHOFF)
M*A*S*H (JAMIE FARR)
M*A*S*H (MIKE FARRELL)
M*A*S*H (SALLY KELLERMAN)
M*A*S*H (HARRY MORGAN)
M*A*S*H (WAYNE ROGERS)
M*A*S*H (DAVID OGDEN STEIRS)
M*A*S*H (MC LAIN STEVENSON)
M*A*S*H (LORETTA SWIT)
M*A*S*H (CAST)
GUY MADISON (W B HICKOCK)
MAGNUM P I
MAKE ROOM FOR DADDY
MAKING A LIVING
MAMA'S PLACE
MAN FROM U.N.C.L.E.
MANNIX
MANY LOVES OF DOBIE GILLIS
MARRIED WITH .... CHILDREN
MARTIN & LEWIS SHOW
THE MARX BROTHERS
GROUCHO MARX SHOW
MARY TYLER MOORE SHOW
PERRY MASON
BAT MASTERSON
MAUDE
MAVERICK
MC CLOUD
FIBBER MC GEE & MOLLY
MC HALES NAVY
MEDICAL CENTER
MIAMI VICE
MICKEY MOUSE CLUB
CAPTAIN MIDNIGHT
BARNEY MILLER
THE MILLIONAIRE
MISSION IMPOSSIBLE
NEW MISSION IMPOSSIBLE
MISTER ED (ALAN YOUNG)
MOD SQUAD
MONTY PYTHON
MOONLIGHTING
MARY TYLER MOORE
MORK & MINDY
MORNING SHOW
MR ED (ALAN YOUNG)
MUNSTERS
MURDER SHE WROTE

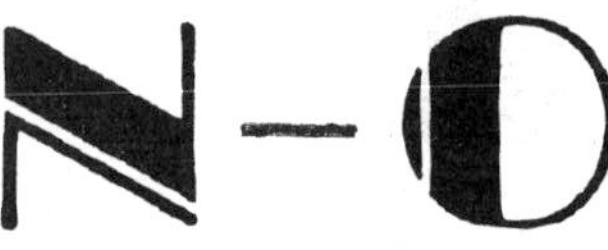

NAKED CITY
NBC FOLLIES
NBC SHOW
NEW ANGELS OF 1988
BOB NEWHART SHOW
NIGHT STALKER (W/ MC GAVIN)
NIGHT COURT
NIGHTINGALES
ODD COUPLE
ONE DAY AT A TIME
OZZIE & HARRIET SHOW

PARTNERS IN CRIME
THE PARTRIDGE FAMILY
PETTICOAT JUNCTION
PHOENIX (JUDSON SCOTT)
POLICE WOMAN
MARY POPPINS
PUNKY BREWSTER PUNKY BREWSTER
GOMER PYLE
QUINCY

RAT PACK (SINATRA, DAVIS & MARTIN)
RAWHIDE (W/ EASTWOOD)
THE REAL MC COYS
REMINGTON STEELE
RHODA
THE RIFLEMAN (CONNORS & CRAWFORD)
RIN-TIN-TIN
RIPTIDE
ROBIN HOOD
ROCKFORD FILES
BUCK ROGERS IN THE 21ST CENTURY
BUCK ROGERS
ROY ROGERS (W/ EVANS & TRIGGER)
ROY ROGERS (ALONE)
ROY ROGERS & DALE EVANS
ROOTS (W/ ASNER)
ROSEANNE
ROUTE 66

THE SAINT
SANFORD & SON
SATURDAY NIGHT LIVE (CONEHEADS)
SATURDAY NIGHT LIVE (ORIG CAST)
SCARECROW & MRS KING
SEA HUNT
SEVENTY-SEVEN (77) SUNSET STRIP
SGT BILKO
DINAH SHORE SHOW
SHOW OF SHOWS
SILVER SPOONS
PHIL SILVERS SHOW
SIMON & SIMON
SISTERS
SIX MILLION DOLLAR MAN
SIXTY MINUTES
ALIAS SMITH & JONES
THE SMOTHERS BROTHERS
SNOOPS
SOAP
SONNY & CHER
SPACE 1990
SPENSER FOR HIRE
ST ELSEWHERE
STAR TREK (NEXT GENERATION)
STAR TREK (ORGINAL CAST)

GUNSMOKE

LOVE BOAT

PARTNERS IN CRIME

HAPPY DAYS

BARNABY JONES

ROCKFORD FILES

LEAVE IT TO BEAVER

MIAMI VICE

THE UNTOUCHABLES

BATMAN

HAWAIIAN EYE

BIG VALLEY

THE HONEYMOONERS

DALLAS

I LOVE LUCY

THE F.B.I.

MARY TYLER MOORE SHOW

POLICEWOMAN

77 SUNSET STRIP

SPACE 1999

STARSKY & HUTCH

SUPERMAN

TOO CLOSE FOR COMFORT

TRAPPER JOHN, M.D.

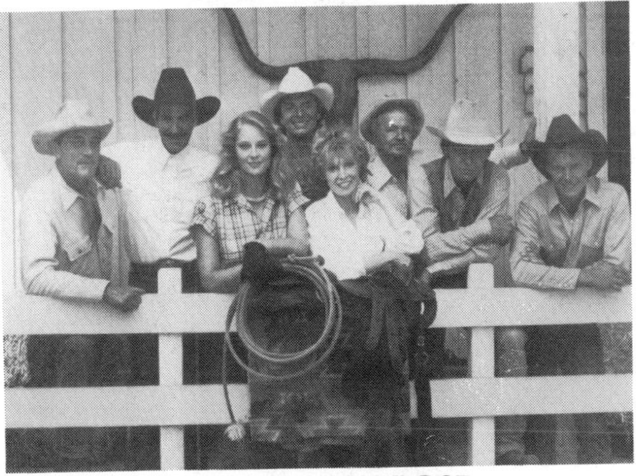

THE YELLOW ROSE

STAR WARS (C-3PO - ARTHUR DANIELS)
STAR WARS (CHEWBACCA)
STAR WARS (CARRIE FISHER)
STAR WARS (HARRISON FORD)
STAR WARS (ALEC GUINESS)
STAR WARS (GUINESS & LUCAS)
STAR WARS (MARK HAMMIL)
STAR WARS (CHRISTOPHER LEE)
STAR WARS (JAMES EARL JONES)
STAR WARS (R2-D2) (KENNY BAKER)
STAR WARS (BILLY DEE WILLIAMS)
STARSKY & HUTCH
REMINGTON STEELE
STEVE & EYDIE SHOW
STREETS OF SAN FRANCISCO
SUGARFOOT
SUPERMAN (CHRIS REEVE)
SUPERMAN (KIRK ALYN)
SWITCH

T - Z

T J HOOKER
TALES OF WELLS FARGO
TARZAN (JANE & BOY)
TAXI
TEMPERATURES RISING
TONI TENNILLE SHOW
TENSPEED & BROWNSHOE
THAT GIRL
THE BOLD ONES
THIS IS YOUR LIFE
DANNY THOMAS SHOW
THREE'S COMPANY (W/ SOMERS & ROBERTS)
THREE'S COMPANY (W/ SOMERS)
THE THREE STOOGES
TIME TUNNEL
TO CATCH A THIEF
THE TODAY SHOW
TOMA (W/ TONY MUSANTE)
TONIGHT SHOW
TOO CLOSE FOR COMFORT
TRAPPER JOHN, MD
TV BLOOPERS & PRACTICAL JOKES
TWENTY-ONE (21) JUMP STREET
TWILIGHT ZONE
UNTOUCHABLES
VALERIE
DICK VAN DYKE SHOW
VEGAS
THE VIRGINIANS
THE WALTONS
WANTED DEAD OR ALIVE
WEBSTER
MARCUS WELBY, MD
WELCOME BACK KOTTER
HONEY WEST
WHAT A COUNTRY!
WHAT'S HAPPENING
WHAT'S MY LINE
WHAT'S HAPPENING!!
WHO'S THE BOSS
WILD, WILD WEST
WISE GUY
WIZ
WIZARD OF OZ
WKRP IN CINCINNATI
WONDER WOMAN
WONDERFUL WORLD OF ANIMALS
YELLOW ROSE
THE YELLOW ROSE
YOU BET YOUR LIFE
YOUR SHOW OF SHOWS
ZORRO (W/ GUY WILLIAMS)

JAMES BOND PHOTOGRAPHS
Black & White $1.00 Ea./ Color $2.50 Ea.

Black & White

MAUDE ADAMS
URSULA ANDRESS
CLAUDINE AUGER - PU
BARBARA BACH (007 POSE)
JOE DON BAKER
PRICILLA BARNES
HONOR BLACKMAN
CAROLE BOUQUET
LOIS CHILES
SEAN CONNERY
SEAN CONNERY & MAUDE ADAMS
SEAN CONNERY & LOIS MAXWELL
SEAN CONNERY & HAROLD SAKATA
TIMOTHY DALTON - P/(AS 007)
TIMOTHY DALTON & CAREY LOWELL
JIMMY DEAN
BRITT EKLUND
GERT FROBE
GLORIA HENDRY - PU
JEFFREY HOLDER
LYNN-HOLLY JOHNSON
GRACE JONES
LOUIS JOURDAN
YAPHET KHOTO
RICHARD KIEL (JAWS)
GEORGE LAZENBY
GEORGE LAZENBY & DIANA RIGG
CHRISTOPHER LEE
LOTTE LENYA
MICHAEL LONSDALE - P/S
JACK LORD
LOIS MAXWELL (MONEYPENNY)
ROGER MOORE - P/007 POSE
ROGER MOORE (W/ SPORTSCAR)
ROGER MOORE (HOLDING RATTLER)
ROGER MOORE & BARBARA BACH
ROGER MOORE & LOIS CHILES
ROGER MOORE & CAROLE BOUQUET
ROGER MOORE & EMILY BOLTON
CAROLINE MUNRO - PU
BARRY NELSON
WAYNE NEWTON
DONALD PLEASANCE
DIANA RIGG
TANYA ROBERTS
JANE SEYMOUR
ROBERT SHAW
SKEAD
TALISA SOTO
JILL ST JOHN - PU
DON STROUD
TOPOL & CAROLE CARQUET
HERVE VILLACHAISE
CHRISTOPHER WALKEN
LANA WOOD - P/PU
ANTHONY ZERBE

Color

MAUDE ADAMS - PU/007 POSE
CLAUDINE AUGER - PU/007 POSE
BARBARA BACH - 007 POSE
MARTINE BESWICKE - P
DANIELA BIANCHI
HONOR BLACKMAN
CAROLE BOUQUET
CORRINE CLERY
SEAN CONNERY & LANA WOOD
MARYAM D'ABO - 007 POSE
TIMOTHY DALTON
KARIN DOR (IN 24K GOLD)
SHIRLEY EATON - P (IN GOLD)
BRITT EKLAND - 007 POSE
GEORGE LAZENBY - 007 POSE
CAREY LOWELL - 007 POSE
JOANNA LUMLEY
LOIS MAXWELL (MONEYPENNY)
CAROLINE MUNRO (007 POSE)
ONELLA MUTI - PU
MOLLY PETERS - SPU
PRICILLA PRESLEY
DIANE RIGG
TANYA ROBERTS
JANE SEYMOUR
TALISA SOTO
KRISTINA WAYBORN
LANA WOOD - SPU

BATMAN
B&W $1.00 Each

JOHN ASTIN (THE RIDDLER)
KIM BASINGER (BATWOMAN)
BATMAN & ROBIN (WITH 4 VILLANS)
BATMAN (WITH BATMOBILE)
BATMAN & JOKER (MOVIE)
BATMAN & ROBIN (BATMOBILE)
ANNE BAXTER (ZELDA)
MILTON BERLE (LOUIE THE LILA)
VICTOR BUONO (KING TUT)
ART CARNEY (THE ARCHER)
YVONNE CRAIG (BATGIRL)
YVONNE CRAIG (BATMOBILE)
FRANK GORSHIN (THE RIDDLER)
VAN JOHNSON (THE MINSTREL)
BOB KANE (BATMAN ARTIST)
MICHAEL KEATON (BATMAN)
EARTHA KITT (CATWOMAN)
ROBERT LOWERY (EARLY BATMAN)
RODDY MC DOWALL (BOOKWORM)
BURGESS MEREDITH (THE PENGUIN)
LEE MERIWETHER (CATWOMAN)
ALAN NAPIER (THE BUTLER)
JULIE NEWMAR (CATWOMAN)
JACK NICHOLSON (JOKER)
OTTO PREMINGER (MR FREEZE)
VINCENT PRICE (EGGHEAD)
STAFFORD RAPP (CHIEF O'HARA)
CLIFF ROBERTSON (SHANE)
CESAR ROMERO (THE JOKER)
GEORGE SANDERS (MR FREEZE)
TISHA STERLING (LEGS)
BURT WARD (ROBIN) - P/FULL LENGHTH
DAVID WAYNE (MAD HATTER)
ADAM WEST & BURT WARD (BATMAN & ROBIN)
ADAM WEST (BATMAN)
SHELLY WINTERS (MA PARKER)

JOHN ASTIN

FRANK GORSHIN

CESAR ROMERO

ART CARNEY

EARTHA KITT

BURGESS MEREDITH

YVONNE CRAIG

JULIE NEWMAR

WEST & WARD

FILM & TELEVISION DIRECTORS

All Portrait Photographs
Black & White $1.00 Each

LOU ADLER
ROBERT ALDRICH
ROBERT ALTMAN
JEAN-JACQUES ANNAUD
MICHAEL APTED
HAL ASHBY
RICHARD ATTENBOROUGH
JOHN G AVILSEN

JOHN BADHAM
GRAHAM BAKER
RALPH BAKSHI
CARROLL BALLARD
HAROLD BECKER
BRUCE BEREFORD
INGMAR BERGMAN
BERNARDO BERTOLUCCI
TONY BILL
MEL BLANC
PETER BOGDANOVICH
KENNETH BRANAGH
ALBERT BROOKS
TIM BURTON

JAMES CAAN
CHRISTOPHER CAIN
FRANK CAPRA
JOHN CARPENTER
ALLEN CARR
WILLIAM CASTLE
GILBERT CATES
MICHAEL CIMENO
WALTER COBLENZ
FRANCIS COPPOLA
JOHN CORNELL
WILLIAM COWAN
DAVID CRONENBURG
CAMERON CROWE
DAN CURTIS

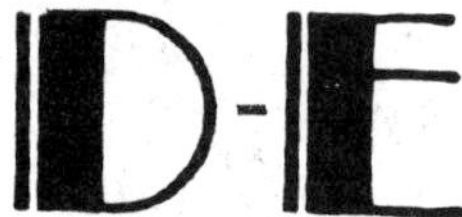

JOE DANTE
MARTIN DAVIDSON
DINO DE LAURENTIIS
BRIAN DE PALMA
JONATHAN DEMME
MICHAEL DEVILLE
CLIVE DONNER
RICHARD DONNER
BLAKE EDWARDS

FREDERICO FELLINI
RICHARD FLEISCHER
BRYAN FORBES
GEORGE FORMAN
JOHN FORMAN
MILOS FORMAN
BOB FOSSE
JOHN FRANKENHEIMER
RICHARD FRANKLIN

COSTA GARVAS
LEWIS GILBERT
JEAN-LUC GODARD
MENAHEM GOLAN
COSTA GRAVAS
ULA GROSBARD

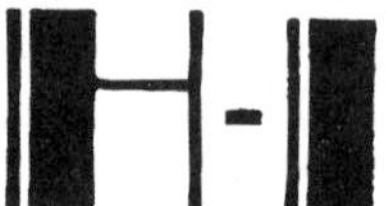

GUY HAMILTON
RAY HARRYHAUSEN
AMY HECKERLING
JIM HENSEN
WALTER HILL
AGNIESZKA HOLLAND
RON HOWARD
JOHN HUGHES
TIM HUNTER
JOHN IRVIN

J-K

JAMES JAMERSON
NORMAN JEWISON
LAMONT JOHNSON
NEIL JORDAN
JEREMY PAUL KAGAN
GARSON KANIN
STANLEY KUBRICK

JOHN LANDIS
JESSE LASKY
MERVYN LE ROY
DAVID LEAN
SPIKE LEE & DANNY DIEHL
SPIKE LEE
SERGIO LEONE
MARK LESTER
RICHARD LESTER
ART LINSON
GEORGE LUCAS
SIDNEY LUMET

LOUIS MALLE
DAVID MAMET
ROUBEN MAMOULIAN
ROBERT MARKOWITZ
PENNY MARSHALL
LEO MC CAREY
JOHN MC TIERNAN
RUSS MEYER
JOHN MILIUS
VINCENT MINNELLI
MICHAEL MOORE
BILL MURRAY

RONALD NEAME
HAL NEEDHAM
MIKE NICHOLS
B W L NORTON
NOEL NOSSECK
SVEN NYKVIST

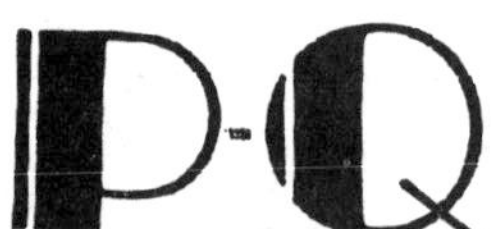

ALAN PAKULA
EUZHAN PALEY
ALAN PARKER
RICHARD PEARCE
LARRY PEERCE
DON PHILLIPS
ROMAN POLANSKI
SYDNEY POLLACK
OTTO PREMINGER

MICHAEL PRESSMAN
RICHARD QUINNE

MICHAEL RADFORD
KAREL RAISZ
ROBERT REDFORD
CARL REINER
ROB REINER
IVAN RETTMAN
KEVIN REYNOLDS
DICK RICHARDS
TONY RICHARDSON
MICHAEL RITCHIE
HAL ROACH
PHIL ROBINSON
GENE RODDENBERRY
HERBERT ROSS

FRANKLIN J SCHAFFNER
JOHN SCHLESSINGER
PAUL SCHRADER
MARTIN SCORESE
RIDLEY SCOTT
DAVID SELTZER
STEVE SHAGAN
STEVE SHAGAN
RON SHELTON
JERRY SKOLIMOWSKI
STEVEN SODERBERGH
STEVEN SPIELBERG
EZRA STONE
FRED C SULLIVAN

LEWIS TEAGUE
FRANCOIS TRUFFAUT
ROGER VADIM
KING VIDOR
JOSEPH WAMBAUGH
PETER WEIR
BILLY WILDER
SOL ZAENTZ
FRANCO ZEFFIRELLI
ROBERT ZEMEKIS
HOWARD ZIFF
FRED ZINNEMAN
EDWARD ZWICK

Black &White Photos Only $1.00

BERNARDO BERTOLUCCI

BOB FOSSE

STANLEY KUBRICK

ALAN PAKULA

SIDNEY POITIER

JOHN SCHLESSINGER

GROUP PHOTOGRAPHS
All Movie & Cast Scenes
$1.00 Each

BUD ABBOTT & LOU COSTELLO
MASON ADAMS, ASNER & MARCHAND
BROOKE ADAMS & DONALD SUTHERLAND
ISABELLE ADJANI & RYAN O'NEAL
DANNY AIELLO & OLYMPIA DUKAKIS
DANNY AIELLO & SPIKE LEE
EDDIE ALBERT & BURT REYNOLDS
EDWARD ALBERT & SUSAN GEORGE
EDWARD ALBERT, ANSPACH & NOAH BEERY, JR
ALAN ALDA & JANE FONDA
ALAN ALDA & LORETTA SWIT
WOODY ALLEN & MARIEL HEMINGWAY
WOODY ALLEN & ALBERT FINNEY
WOODY ALLEN & GEORGE BURNS
WOODY ALLEN & MARY STEENBURGEN
WOODY ALLEN & MIA FARROW
WOODY ALLEN & CARLO DI PALMA
WOODY ALLEN & SVEN NYKVIST
DON AMECHE & JOE MANTEGNA
DON AMECHE, WILFRORD BRIMLEY & HUME CRONYN
DON AMECHE & GWEN VERDON
MOREY AMSTERDAM, THOMAS & MARJ LORD
LONI ANDERSON & BURT REYNOLDS
JULIE ANDREWS & JAMES GARNER
JULIE ANDREWS, DUDLEY MOORE & BO DEREK
SUSAN ANTON & JAMES COBURN
ALAN ARKIN & MARIETTE HARTLEY
BESS ARMSTRONG & DENNIS QUAID
LUCIE ARNAZ & TONY ROBERTS
JIM ARNESS & DENNIS WEAVER
CHRIS ATKINS & BROOKE SHIELDS
CHRIS ATKINS & KRISTY MC NICHOL
CHRISTOPHER ATKINS & KRISTY MC NICHOL
FRANKIE AVALON & LINDA EVANS
LEW AYRES & LORRAINE DAY

BARBARA BACH & RINGO STARR
ALEC BALDWIN & SEAN CONNERY
LUCILLE BALL & AVA GABOR
LUCILLE BALL & BOB HOPE
ANNE BANCROFT & SHIRLEY MAC LAINE
BARISHNIKOV & GREGORY HINES
PRISCILLA BARNES & ROGER MOORE
ALAN BATES & BETTE MIDLER
ALAN BATES & MARY ELIZ MASTRANTONIO
BATMAN (KEATON) & JOKER (NICHOLSON)
NOAH BEERY & JAMES GARNER
DIRK BENEDICT & RICHARD HATCH
ANNETTE BENING & COLIN FIRTH
ANNETTE BENING, JOHN CUSAK & ANGELICA HUSTON
RICHARD BENJAMIN & GEORGE BURNS
ROBBY BENSON & KIM CATTRALL
ROBBY BENSON & LYNN-HOLLY JOHNSON
ROBBY BENSON & JACK LEMMON
LIZA BERENSON & LIZA MINNIELLI
CANDICE BERGEN & JACQUELINE BISSET
CANDICE BERGEN & BURT REYNOLDS
EDGAR BERGEN & CHARLIE MC CARTHY
SANDAHL BERGMAN & ARNOLD SCHWARZENEGGER
DAVID BIRNEY & MEREDITH BAXTER
DAVID BIRNEY, ARTHUR HILL & MORGAN BRITTANY
JACQUELINE BISSET & NICK NOLTE
KAREN BLACK & ROBERT DUVALL
LINDA BLAIR & LARRY HAGMAN
LINDA BLAIR & RICHARD BURTON
BLONDIE & DAGWOOD
BOB, CAROL, TED & ALICE
SONNY BONO, CHER & CHASTITY
DEBBIE BOONE & PAT BOONE
DAVID BOWIE & CATHERINE DENEUIVE
PETER BOYLE & BILL MURRAY
EDDIE BRACKEN & CHEVY CHASE
MARLON BRANDO & JACK NICHOLSON
BEAU BRIDGES & MARILYN HASSETT
BEAU BRIDGES & ANDY GRIFFITH
BEAU BRIDGES, JEFF BRIDGES & MICHELLE PFEIFFER
JEFF BRIDGES & AMY MADIGAN
JEFF BRIDGES & SALLY FIELD
JEFF BRIDGES & FARRAH FAWCETT
WILFORD BRIMLEY & MAUREEN STAPLETON
MATTHEW BRODERICK, SEAN CONNERY & DUSTIN HOFFMAN
MATTHEW BRODERICK & MAKO
MATTHEW BRODERICK & MARSHA MASON
CHARLES BRONSON & RANDY QUAID
CHARLES BRONSON & JILL IRELAND
CHARLES BRONSON, JACQUELINE BISSET & MAX SCHELL
HAYNES BROOKE, SPACEK, RANDALL, GOLDBERG
MEL BROOKS & SID CAESAR
RAND BROOKS & VIVIEN LEIGH (GWTW)
BRYAN BROWN & SIGORNEY WEAVER
NIGEL BRUCE & BASIL RATHBONE
YUL BRYNNER & DEBORAH KERR (KING & I)
GENEVIEVE BUJOLD & JEREMY IRONS
GENEVIEVE BUJOLD & RICHARD WIDMARK
GENEVIEVE BUJOLD & CHARLTON HESTON
BILLIE BURKE & JUDY GARLAND
TOM BURLINGAME & JENNIFER JASON LEIGH
CAROLE BURNETT & RITA MORENO
GEORGE BURNS, WALTER MATTHAU & DEBBIE REYNOLDS
GEORGE BURNS, WALTER MATTHAU & RICHARD BENJAMIN
GEORGE BURNS, BOB HOPE & JOHNNY CARSON
GEORGE BURNS & ART CARNEY
ELLEN BURSTYN & TOM SKERRITT
ELLEN BURSTYN, GENE HACKMAN & ALLY SHEEDY
LEVAR BURTON & CHUCK CONNORS
RICHARD BURTON & ELIZABETH TAYLOR
GEORGE BUSH & ORNITE YOUNG

JAMES CAAN & JANE FONDA
JAMES CAAN & MANDY PATINKIN
CAGNEY & LACEY (GROUP)
MICHAEL CAINE & MAX VON SYDOW
MICHAEL CAINE & MICKEY ROONEY
MICHAEL CAINE & JULIE WALTERS
MICHAEL CAINE & MICHELLE JOHNSON

ARNAZ & ROBERTS

CATRALL, LEMMON & BENSON

FLETCHER & FALK

BRONSON & IRELAND

CHER & SONNY

IRELAND & MC CALLUM

CAINE & ROONEY

DOW & MATHERS

JONES & INGELS

MICHAEL CAINE & SALLY FIELDS
DYAN CANNON, CLUP, WOOD & GOULD
FRANK CAPRA & GARY COOPER
KATE CAPSHAW & TIM MATHESON
DAVID CARRADINE & STOCKARD CHANNING
KEITH CARRADINE & SALLY KIRKLAND
DIAHANN CARROLL & BILLY DEE WILLIAMS
JOHNNY CASH & WAYLON JENNINGS
JOHN CASSAVETES, GENA ROWLANDS & MOLLY RINGWALD
SHAUN CASSIDY & PARKER STEVENSON
PHOEBE CATES & WILLIE AAMES
PHOEBE CATES & JUDGE REINHOLD
KIM CATRALL, JACK LEMMON & ROBBY BENSON
LON CHANEY, JR & MARY PHILBIN
GERALDINE CHAPLIN & PAUL NEWMAN
CYD CHARISSE & GENE KELLY
CYD CHARISSE & FRED ASTAIRE
CYD CHARRISE & GENE KELLY
CHEECH & CHONG
CHER, HOSKINS, RYDER & RICCI
LOIS CHILES & ROGER MOORE
LOIS CHILES & ROBERT REDFORD
JILL CLAYBURGH & ROBERT PRESTON
GLENN CLOSE, HURT, KLINE & WILLIAMS
COLEMAN & KATHARINE HEPBURN
DABNEY COLEMAN & KATHARINE HEPBURN
JOAN COLLINS & CHARLES GRODIN
JOAN COLLINS & JACKIE COLLINS
SEAN CONNERY, HARRISON FORD & STEVEN SPIELBERG
SEAN CONNERY & HARRISON FORD
CHUCK CONNORS & BEN VEREEN
CHUCK CONNORS & JOHNNY CRAWFORD
ROBERT CONRAD & HENRY MORGAN
TIM CONWAY, DON KNOTTS & HARVEY KORMAN
BILL COSBY & SAMMY DAVIS, JR
HOWARD COSELL, ALEX KARRAS & FRANK GIFFORD
SEAN COSTNER & SEAN YOUNG
COURTNEY COX & STEVE GUTTENBERG
JOAN CRAWFORD & CHRISTINE CRAWFORD
HUME CRONYN & JESSICA TANDY
TOM CRUISE & DUSTIN HOFFMAN
JON CRYER & DEMI MOORE
BILLY CRYSTAL & MEG RYAN
BILLY CRYSTAL, DANIEL STERN & BRUNO KIRBY
BOB CUMMINGS & BARBRA STREISAND
JAMIE LEE CURTIS & STACY KEACH, JR
JAMIE LEE CURTIS, PALIN, CLEESE & KLINE
KEN CURTIS, SAM ELLIOTT & CYBILL SHEPHERD
ROBERT CURTIS & ROBERT DE NIRO
TONY CURTIS & JACK LEMMON (IN DRAG)
TONY CURTIS & SAM ELLIOTT
JOHN CUSACK, JOHN MAHONEY & IONE SKYE

ABBY DALTON & JONATHAN WINTERS
TIMOTHY DALTON & JONATHAN WINTERS
TIMOTHY DALTON & CAREY LOWELL
MARGARET TRUMAN DANIEL & JAMES WHITMORE
TED DANSON & JACK LEMMON
TED DANSON, SCHUMACHER & ROSELLINI
BOBBY DARIN & ANNETTE FUNICELLO
LOLITA DAVIDOVITCH & PAUL NEWMAN
BETTE DAVIS, GISH, PRICE & ANN SOTHERN
SAMMY DAVIS, JR, FRANK SINATRA & DEAN MARTIN
BILLY DAVIS & MARILYN MC COO
GEENA DAVIS & SUSAN SARADAN
LORRAINE DAY & LANA TURNER
OLIVIA DE HAVILLAND, HOWARD & LEIGH
DOM DE LUISE & PETER FALK
MARIA DE MEDEROS, FRED WARD & UNA THURMAN
ROBERT DE NIRO & TONY CURTIS
ROBERT DE NIRO & BURGESS MEREDITH
ROBERT DE NIRO & SEAN PENN
ROBERT DE NIRO & CHARLES GRODIN
DANNY DE VITO & ARNOLD SCHWARZENEGGER
DEAD END KIDS
CATHERINE DENEUVE & DAVID BOWIE
BRIAN DENNEHY & GENE HACKMAN
GERARD DEPARDEAU & ANDIE MC DOWELL
BO DEREK & MILES O'KEEFE
ANDY DEVINE & GUY MADISON
MATT DILLON & MEG TILLY
KEVIN DOBSON & DIANE LADD
RICHARD DONNER & BILL MURRAY
JAMES DOOHAN & WILLIAM SHATNER
KIRK DOUGLAS & FARRAH FAWCETT
KIRK DOUGLAS & HAL HOLBROOK
KIRK DOUGLAS & BURT LANCASTER
MICHAEL DOUGLAS & KATHLEEN TURNER
MICHAEL DOUGLAS & AVA GARDNER
MICHAEL DOUGLAS & ELAINE MAY
MICHAEL DOUGLAS & ANDY GARCIA
TONY DOW & JERRY MATHERS
HUGH DOWNS & SENATOR EDWARD KENNEDY
RICHARD DREYFUSS, HOLLY HUNTER & BRAD JOHNSON
VICTORIA DUFFY & VICTORIA PRINCIPAL
ROBERT DUVALL & SISSY SPACEK
ROBERT DUVALL, KATHRYN HARROLD & TREAT WILLIAMS
SHELLEY DUVALL & ROBIN WILLIAMS
ROGER EBERT & GENE SISKEL
BUDDY EBSEN & SHIRLEY TEMPLE
NELSON EDDY & JEANETTE MC DONALD
BARBARA EDEN & LARRY HAGMAN
SAM ELLIOTT & KATHARINE ROSS
ET & DEE WALLACE STONE
DALE EVANS & ROY ROGERS

DOUGLAS FAIRBANKS, JR & PAMELA TIFFIN
MIA FARROW & ROBERT REDFORD
MIA FARROW, BARBARA HERSHEY & DIANNE WEST
FARRAH FAWCETT & JEFF BRIDGES
FARRAH FAWCETT & CHARLES GRODIN
COREY FELDMAN & COREY HAIM
SALLY FIELD, DOLLY PARTON & DARRYL HANNAH
SALLY FIELD & STEVE SUTTENBERG
SALLY FIELD & JULIA ROBERTS
SALLY FIELD & HENRY WINKLER
SALLY FIELD & TOM HANKS
SALLY FIELD & ARNOLD SCHWARZENEGGER
SALLY FIELD & PAUL NEWMAN
ALBERT FINNEY & KAREN ALLEN
PETER FIRTH & NASTASSIA KINSKI
LESTER FLATT & EARL SCRUGGS
LOUISE FLETCHER & PETER FALK
JANE FONDA & HENRY FONDA
JANE FONDA & VANESSA REDGRAVE
JODIE FOSTER & SALLY KELLERMAN
JODIE FOSTER & KELLY MC GILLIS
JODIE FOSTER, ROB LOWE & NATASSIA KINSKI
JODIE FOSTER, HAYES, FURNICAUX & PERKINS
MICHAEL J FOX & CHRISTOPHER LLOYD
MICHAEL J FOX, SEAN PENN & DON HARVEY
TONY FRANCIOSA & PAMELA TIFFIN
PAMELA FRANKLIN, LUKE HALPHIN & FLIPPER

CLARK GABLE & VIVIAN LEIGH
JUDY GARLAND & MICKEY ROONEY
JUDY GARLAND, LANA TURNER & HEDY LA MARR
JUDY GARLAND, RAY BOLGER & JACK HALEY
JAMES GARNER & SIDNEY pOITIER
TERI GARR & ROBERT WAGNER

GREER GARSON & CESAR ROMERO
JENNIE GARTH & JASON PRIESTLY
LOU GEHRIG & BABE RUTH
GIL GERARD & PAMELA HENSLEY
GIL GERARD, JAMIE FARR & SUZANNE
MEL GIBSON & DANNY GLOVER
MEL GIBSON, DANNY GLOVER & JOE PESCI
MEL GIBSON & GOLDIE HAWN
JACK GILFORD & ELAINE STRICH
JACKIE GLEASON & TERI GARR
WHOOPI GOLDBERG & PATRICK STEWART
WHOOPI GOLDBERG, LAXI & FAITH RANDALL
EYDIE GORME & STEVE LAWRENCE
CARY GRANT, SOPHIA LOREN & FRANK SINATRA
LEE GRANT & WILLIAM SHATNER
KATHERINE GRAYSON (DESERT SONG SCENE)
LORNE GREENE, MAREN JENSEN & RICHARD HATCH
MR GREENYEARS, MR ROGERS & CAPT KANGAROO
JAMES GREGORY & ANGELA LANSBURY
JENNIFER GREY & PATRICK SWAYZE
JENNIFER GREY & PAUL NEWMAN
ANDY GRIFFITH & DON KNOTTS
ANDY GRIFFITH, KNOTTS & JIM NABORS
ALEC GUINESS & GEORGE LUCAS
STEVE GUTTENBERG & TAWNEE WELCH

GENE HACKMAN & BARBRA STREISAND
GENE HACKMAN & BURT REYNOLDS
GENE HACKMAN, ALLY SHEEDY & ELLEN BURNSTYN
LARRY HAGMAN & BARBARA EDEN
H R HALDERMAN & MIKE WALLACE
ARSENIO HALL & EDDIE MURPHY
ARSENIO HALL, JOHN LANDIS & EDDIE MURPHY
LUKE HALPIN, PAMELA FRANKLIN & FLIPPER
GEORGE HAMILTON & SUZANNE PLESHETTE
GEORGE HAMILTON & SUSAN ST JAMES
SUSAN HAMILTON & SUSAN ST JAMES
HARRY HAMLIN & DEBORAH VAN VALKENBURGH
TOM HANKS & ROBERT LOGGIA
TOM HANKS & ELIZABETH PERKINS
RICHARD HATCH & DIRK BENEDICT
GOLDIE HAWN & KURT RUSSELL
HELEN HAYES & JODIE FOSTER
EILEEN HECKART & BURGESS MEREDITH
MARIEL HEMINGWAY & WOODY ALLEN
MARIEL HEMINGWAY & ERIC ROBERTS
PAM HENSLEY, DUKE BUTLER & HENRY SILVA
KATHARINE HEPBURN & SPENCER TRACY
CHARLETON HESTON & GREGORY PECK
MARTIN HEWITT & BROOKE SHIELDS
ARTHUR HILL, MORGAN BRITTANY & DAVID BIRNEY
GREGORY HINES & BARISHNIKOV
GREGORY HINES & MAURICE HONES
DUSTIN HOFFMAN & MERYL STREEP
DUSTIN HOFFMAN & KATHARINE ROSS
PAUL HOGAN & LINDA KOZLOWSKI
HAL HOLBROOK & MICHAEL DOUGLAS
LARRY HOLMES & KEN NORTON (FIGHT)
BOB HOPE & LUCILLE BALL
BOB HOPE & SOUPY SALES
BOB HOPE & DOROTHY LA MOUR
RON HOWARD & HENRY WINKLER
ENGELBERT HUMPERDINK & TOM JONES
GAYLE HUNNICUTT & MICHAEL SARAZIN
ISABELLE HUPPERT & KRIS KRISTOFFERSON
WILLIAM HURT & SIGORNEY WEAVER
WILLIAM HURT & KATHLEEN TURNER
ANGELICA HUSTON, OLIN, SILVER, S & M STEIN
MARTHA HYER & DONALD O'CONNOR
MARTHA HYER & FRANK SINATRA
MARTHA HYER & DONALD O'CONNOR
MARTY INGLES & SHIRLEY JONES
JILL IRELAND & DAVID MC CALLUM
JILL IRELAND & CHARLES BRONSON
JEREMY IRONS & MERYL STREEP
AMY IRVING, DUDLEY MOORE & ANN REINKING
AMY IRVING & DUDLEY MOORE
JAMES IVORY & PAUL NEWMAN

LYNN-HOLLY JOHNSON & TOM SKERRITT
BILLY JONES & ERNIE HARE
SHIRLEY JONES & MARTY INGLES
TOM JONES & CONNIE STEVENS
TOMMY JONES & SISSY SPACEK
MADELINE KAHN, BOB NEWHART & GILDA RADNER
CAROL KANE & BILL MURRAY
ALEX KARRAS, HOWARD COSELL & FRANK GIFFORD
STACEY KEACH & JAMIE LEE CURTIS
DIANE KEATON & HENRY WINKLER
MICHAEL KEATON & JACK NICHOLSON
MICHAEL KEATON & HENRY WINKLER
HOWARD KEEL & DONNA REED
BRIAN KEITH & JONATHAN WINTERS
SALLY KELLERMAN & JODY FOSTER
GENE KELLY & SHIRLEY MAC LAINE
GENE KELLY & OLIVIA NETWON-JOHN
GENE KELLY & FRED ASTAIRE
GENE KELLY & FRANK SINATRA
GENE KELLY & CYD CHARISSE
DEBORAH KERR & ROBERT MITCHUM
MARGOT KIDDER & CHRISTOPHER
R KIGER, PENNY PEYSER & JOHN RUBENSTEIN
BILLIE JEAN KING & BOBBY RIGGS
NASTASSIA KINSKI, ROB LOWE & JODIE FOSTER
KIRK & MC COY (STAR TREK)
ROBERT KLEMPERER & ROBERT CLARY
KEVIN KLINE & PETER MC NICHOL
KEVIN KLINE & MERYL STREEP
STEVE KLOVES & MICHELLE PFEIFFER
GLADYS KNIGHT & WILSON
SHIRLEY KNIGHT & BROOKE SHIELDS
DON KNOTTS & TIM CONWAY
WALTER KOENIG & GEORGE TAKEI
KRIS KRISTOFFERSON & TALIA SHIRE
KRIS KRISTOFFERSON & SARAH MILES

CHERYL LADD & KEN WAHL
BURT LANCASTER & DEBORAH KERR
MARTIN LANDAU & JERRY ORBACH
JESSICA LANGE & ARMIN-MUELLER STAHL
JESSICA LANGE & KING KONG
STEVE LAWRENCE & EYDIE GORME
GEORGE LAZENBY & DIANA RIGG
MICHELLE LEE & ROBERT MORSE
SPIKE LEE & DENZEL WASHINGTON
MICHELLE LEE, PRICE & PETERS
VIVIAN LEIGH & BUTTERFLY MC QUEEN
JACK LEMMON & SISSY SPACEK
JACK LEMMON & ROBBY BENSON
JACK LEMMON, ROBBY BENSON & KIM CATRALL
LEONARD & HEARNS (FIGHT)
DANIEL DAY LEWIS & RUTH CABE
JERRY LEWIS & DEAN MARTIN
JERRY LEE LEWIS & DENNIS QUAID
SHARI LEWIS & LAMCHOP
RON LIEBMAN & DOLLY PARTON
JOHN LINDSEY & PETER O'TOOLE
EMILY LLOYD & BRUCE WILLIS
GINA LOLABRIGIDA & ANTHONY QUINN
MYRNA LOY & WILLIAM POWELL

SHIRLEY MAC LAINE & GENE KELLY
SHIRLEY MAC LAINE & ANNE BANCROFT
SHIRLEY MAC LAINE & TOM SKERRITT
SHIRLEY MAC LAINE & FRANK SINATRA
RALPH MACCHIO & PAT MORITA
MADONNA & SEAN PENN
CHEECH MARIN & THOMAS CHONG
PENNY MARSHALL & CINDY WILLIAMS
DEAN MARTIN & JOE NAMATH
DEAN MARTIN & FRANK SINATRA
DEAN MARTIN & JERRY LEWIS
PAMELA SUE MARTIN & PARKER STEVENSON
LEE MARVIN & BURT REYNOLDS
LEE MARVIN & BURT LANCASTER
JACKIE MASON & ED SULLIVAN
MARSHA MASON & MATTHEW BRODERICK
MARSHA MASON & KRISTY MC NICHOL
MARSHA MASON & NEIL SIMON
MASTERS & JOHNSON
MARY ELIZABETH MASTRONTONIO & STEVEN BAUER
TIM MATHESON & KATE CAPSHAW
WALTER MATTHAU & ROBIN WILLIAMS
ELAINE MAY & MIKE DOUGLAS
MARILYN MC COO & BILLY DAVIS, JR
FIBBER MC GEE & MOLLY
ALI MC GRAW & MAXIMILLIAN SCHELL
GERALD MC RAINEY & JAMESON PARKER
BURGESS MEREDITH & EILEEN HECKART
BURGESS MEREDITH & SYLVESTER STALLONE
BURGESS MEREDITH & PRISCILLA PRESLEY
MICKEY MOUSE CLUB
HAYLEY MILLS & JANE WYMAN
LIZA MINNELLI & MARISSA BERENSON
ZAKES MOKAE & DONALD SUTHERLAND
DEMI MOORE, AMY IRVING & ANN REINKING
CLAYTON MOORE & JAY SILVERHEELS
DUDLEY MOORE & MARY TYLER MOORE
MELBA MOORE & BEN VEREEN
ROGER MOORE & SUZANNA YORK
RITA MORENO & CAROL BURNETT
NANCY MORGAN & PETER RIEGERT
EDDIE MURPHY & RICHARD PRYOR

JIM NABORS, DON KNOTTS & ANDY GRIFFITH
WILLIE NELSON & ISELA VEGA
PAUL NEWMAN & JOEL GREY
PAUL NEWMAN & GERALDINE CHAPLIN
PAUL NEWMAN & SALLY FIELD
PAUL NEWMAN & ROBERT REDFORD
OLIVIA NEWTON-JOHN & JOHN TRAVOLTA
OLIVIA NEWTON-JOHN & GENE KELLY
LESLIE NIELSEN, PRISCILLA PRESLEY & DIRECTORS
LESLIE NIELSEN & PRISCILLA PRESLEY
KIM NOVAK & JIMMY STEWART (VERTIGO)

MAUREEN O'HARA & DOUGLAS FAIRBANKS, JR
MILES O'KEEFE & BO DEREK
RYAN O'NEAL & BRUCE DERN
RYAN O'NEAL & JACK WARDEN
MAUREEN O'SULLIVAN & JOHNNY WEISMUELLER
PETER O'TOOLE & JOHN V LINDSAY
MICHAEL ONTKEAN & JO BETH WILLIAMS
OUR GANG

AL PACINO & TUESDAY WELD
DOLLY PARTON & SLYVESTER STALLONE
DOLLY PARTON & BURT REYNOLDS
DOLLY PARTON & SALLY FIELD
PEACHES & HERB
MINNIE PEARL & SISSY SPACEK
SEAN PENN & ALLY SHEEDY
SEAN PENN & MADONNA
ANTHONY PERKINS & YVONNE FURNEAUX
ANTHONY PERKINS & DIANA ROSS
SUZANNE PLESHETTE, GIL GERARD & JAMIE FARR
CHRISTOPHER PLUMMER & SIGORNEY WEAVER
SIDNEY POITIER & JAMES GARNER
ELEANOR POWELL & JIMMY STEWART
STEPHANIE POWERS & ROBERT WAGNER
ROBERT PRESTON & JILL CLAYBURGH
VINCENT PRICE, DAVIS, GISH & ANN SOTHERN
VINCENT PRICE, LEE, CUSHING & CARRIDINE
VICTORIA PRINCIPAL & PATRICK DUFFY
RICHARD PRYOR & EDDIE MURPHY
KATHLEEN QUINLAN & GENE WILDER

TONY RANDALL & JACK KLUGMAN
BASIL RATHBONE & NIGEL BRUCE
ROBERT REDFORD & MIA FARROW
ROBERT REDFORD & LOIS CHILES
ROBERT REDFORD & LEN OLIN
ROBERT REDFORD & BARBRA STREISAND
LYNN REDGRAVE & JANE FONDA
VANESSA REDGRAVE & JANE FONDA
DONNA REED & HOWARD KEEL
CHRISTOPHER REEVE & PATRICK STEWART
JUDGE REINHOLD & PHOEBE CATES
BURT REYNOLDS & LONI ANDERSON
BURT REYNOLDS & DOLLY PARTON
BURT REYNOLDS & GENE HACKMAN
BURT REYNOLDS & CANDICE BERGEN
BURT REYNOLDS & SALLY FIELD
CYNTHIA RHODES & JOHNNY TRAVOLTA
ERIC ROBERTS & SISSY SPACEK
TONY ROBERTS, FERRER, FARROW & JULIE HAGGARTY
ROGERS & HART
FRED (MR) ROGERS & CAPT KANGAROO
KENNY ROGERS & DOTTIE WEST
ROY ROGERS & DALE EVANS
CESAR ROMERO & GREER GARSON
MICKEY ROONEY & JUDY GARLAND
DIANA ROSS & ANTHONY PERKINS
KATHARINE ROSS & SAM ELLIOTT
JOHN RUSSELL, ROGERS, MAHONEY & LEE MAJORS
KURT RUSSELL & MERYL STREEP
RUTAN & YEAGER

PAT SAJAK & VANNA WHITE
SUSAN SARANDON & JAMES SPADER
MICHAEL SARRAZIN & CORNELIA SHARPE
GRETA SCACCHI & CHARLES DANISE

KARRAS, COSELL & GIFFORD

MACCHIO & MORITA

MEREDITH & HECKERT

MARTIN & LEWIS

MARTIN & STEVENSON

MC COO & DAVIS

LADD & WAHL

MARVIN & LANCASTER

PARTON & REYNOLDS

MAXIMILLIAN SCHELL & ALI MAC GRAW
ARNOLD SCHWARZENEGGER & SALLY FIELD
ARNOLD SCHWARZENEGGER & SANDAHL BERGMAN
JANE SEYMOUR & CHRISTOPHER REEVE
WILLIAM SHATNER & LEE GRANT
ALLY SHEEDY & SEAN PENN
BROOKE SHIELDS & SHIRLEY KNIGHT
BROOKE SHIELDS & CHRISTOPHER ATKINS
BROOKE SHIELDS & CHRISTOPHER REEVE
SIEGFRIED & ROY
FRANK SINATRA & GENE KELLY
FRANK SINATRA, SOPHIA LOREN & CARY GRANT
FRANK SINATRA & SHIRLEY MAC LAINE
FRANK SINATRA & MARTHA HYER
FRANK SINATRA, DEAN MARTIN & SAMMY DAVIS, JR
NANCY SINATRA & FRANK SINATRA, JR
TOM SKERRITT & LYNN-HOLLY JOHNSON
TOM SKERRITT & SHIRLEY MAC LAINE
MAGGIE SMITH & PETER USTINOV
SONNY & CHER
SONNY, CHER & CHASTITY
DAVID SOUL & FRIEND
DAVID SOUL & PAUL MICHAEL GLASER
SISSY SPACEK & ERIC ROBERTS
SISSY SPACEK, MINNIE PEARL & WAYLON JENNINGS
SISSY SPACEK & SHELLY DUVALL
SPOCK & KIRK (STAR TREK)
SYLVESTER STALLONE & DOLLY PARTON
SYLVESTER STALLONE & TALIA SHIRE
BARBARA STANWYCK & ROBERT CUMMINGS
STAR TREK CREW & PERSIS KHAMBATTA
STAR TREK (W/ KHAMBATTA)
MARY STEENBURGEN & WOODY ALLEN
PARKER STEVENSON & SHAUN CASSIDY
JIMMY STEWART & AUDIE MURPHY
MERYL STREEP & JEREMY IRONS
MERYL STREEP, WILLIE AAMES & PHOEBE CATES
BARBRA STREISAND & ROBERT REDFORD
BARBRA STREISAND & GENE HACKMAN
DONALD SUTHERLAND & BROOKE ADAMS
DONALD SUTHERLAND & SUZANNE SOMERS
DONALD SUTHERLAND & ZAKES MOKAE

GEORGE TAKAI & WALTER KOENIG
SHIRLEY TEMPLE & BUDDY EBSEN
PAMELA TIFFIN & ANTHONY FRANCIOSA
MEG TILLY & MATT DILLON
LILY TOMLIN & JOHN TRAVOLTA
JOHN TRAVOLTA & CYNTHIA RHODES
MARGARET TRUMAN & JAMES WHITEMORE
MICHAEL TUCKER & JILL EICHENBERRY
MYOSHI UMECKI & RED BUTTONS
PETER USTINOV & MAGGIE SMITH
VAN PATTEN FAMILY
MAX VAN SYDOW & SOPHIA LOREN
BEN VEREEN & JEFF GOLDBLUM
BEN VEREEN & MELBA MOORE

ROBERT WAGNER & STEFANIE POWERS
KEN WAHL & CHERYL LADD
JULIE WALTERS & MICHAEL CAINE
SIGORNEY WEAVER & CHRISTOPHER PLUMMER
WHALES OF AUGUST (CAST)
RICHARD WIDMARK & GENEVIEVE BUJOLD
GENE WILDER & KATHLEEN QUINLAN
KATHLEEN WILDER & KATHLEEN QUINLAN
BILLY DEE WILLIAMS & DIAHANN CARROLL
JO BETH WILLIAMS, KLINE, HURT & GLENN CLOSE
ROBIN WILLIAMS & SHELLY DUVALL
TREAT WILLIAMS, HARROLD & ROBERT DUVALL
FLIP WILSON & GLADYS KNIGHT
HENRY WINKLER & MICHAEL KEATON
HENRY WINKLER & SALLY FIELD
JONATHAN WINTERS & BRIAN KEITH
JONATHAN WINTERS & ABBY DALTON
WIZ OF OZ (BOLGER, GARLAND, LAHR, ETC)
JOANNE WOODWARD & PAUL NEWMAN

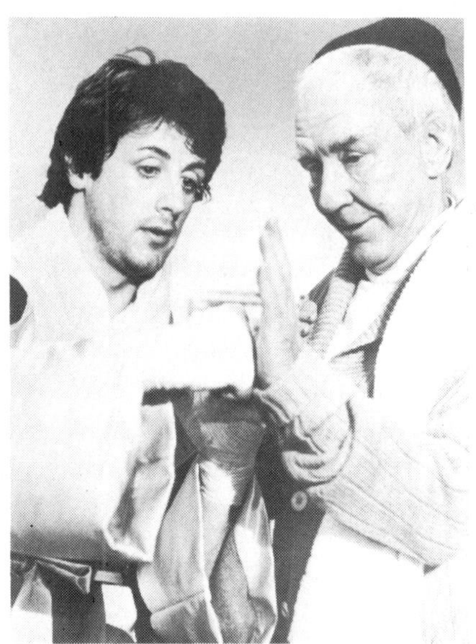

STALLONE & MEREDITH

WILLIAMS & DUVALL

COWBOYS & COWGIRLS

All Portrait Photographs
$1.00 Each

KAY ALDRIDGE
REX ALLEN
ROBERT ALLEN
GENE AUTRY

SMITH BALLEW
JIM BANNON
DON "RED" BARRY
RICHARD BASEHART
REX BELL
WILLIAM BENDIX
TOM BERENGER
LYLE BETTGER
DAN BLOCKER
RICHARD BOONE
ADRIAN BOOTH
BILL BOYD
SCOTT BRADY
LLOYD BRIDGES
CHARLES BRONSON
RAND BROOKS
JOHNNY MACK BROWN
YUL BRYNNER
SMILEY BURNETTE
PAT BUTTRAM

JAMES CAAN
RORY CALHOUN
ROD CAMERON
YAKIMA CANNUTT
HARRY CAREY, JR
HARRY CAREY, SR
LEO CARRILLO
SUNSET CARSON
HOPALONG CASSIDY
CHUCK CONNORS
BEN COOPER
RAY "CRASH" CORRIGAN
KEVIN COSTNER
BUSTER CRABBE
KEN CURTIS
TONY CURTIS

JIM DAVIS - P/S
EDDIE DEAN
MYRNA DELL
RICHARD DENNING
JOHN DEREK
ANDY DEVINE
JAMES DRURY
CLINT EASTWOOD
JACK ELAM
BILL ELLIOT
DALE EVANS

RICHARD FARNSWORTH
GLENN FORD
TONY FRANCIOSA
ROBERT FULLER
JAMES GARNER
KIRBY GRANT
ANDY GRIFFITH
MONTE HALE
JACK HOLT
JENNIFER HOLT

BEN JOHNSON

BUCK JONES
VICTOR JORY
JOHN "DUSTY" KING
FUZZY KNIGHT
LASH LA RUE
MICHAEL LANDON
ROCKY LANE
JANET LEIGH
BOB LIVINGSTON

JOHNNY MAC BROWN
GUY MADISON
GEORGE MAHARIS
LEE MAJORS
DEAN MARTIN
LEE MARVIN
KEN MAYNARD
TIM MC COY
TOM MIX
GEORGE MONTGOMERY
CLAYTON MOORE
AUDIE MURPHY
DON MURRAY

NOEL NEILL
WILLIE NELSON

JACK PALANCE
GEORGE PEPPARD
JACK PERRIN
BROCK PETERS
SLIM PICKENS
DENVER PYLE

RONALD REAGAN
BURT REYNOLDS
TEX RITTER
CLIFF ROBERTSON
DALE ROBERTSON
ROY ROGERS
ROY ROGERS & DALE EVANS
JOHN RUSSELL

WILL SAMPSON
CAL SCHRUM
FRED SCOTT
RANDOLPH SCOTT
CAL SHRUM
JAY SILVERHEELS
DAVID SOUL
CLINTON SPILSBURY (RANGER)
AL "FUZZY" ST JOHN
BARBARA STANWYCK
CHARLES STARRETT
LINDA STERLING
JIMMY STEWART
PEGGY STEWART
GEORGE STRAIT

TOM TYLER
LEE VAN CLEEF
WALLY VERNON
JIMMY WAKELY
CLINT WALKER
JOHN WAYNE
RAQUEL WELCH
WHIP WILSON
JOAN WOODBURY

JIM ARNESS

ROGERS & EVANS

MUSICAL PERFORMERS & GROUPS (LIVING)

All Portrait Photographs $1.00 Each

PAULA ABDUL
AEROSMITH
AIR SUPPLY
ALABAMA
HERB ALPERT & TIJUANA BRASS
BILL ANDERSON
JOHN ANDERSON
MARION ANDERSON
ANDREWS SISTERS
PAUL ANKA
ADAM ANT
TONI ARDEN
EDDY ARNOLD
CHET ATKINS
PATTI AUSTIN
FRANKIE AVALON - P/S
AVERAGE WHITE BAND
HOYT AXTON

BURT BACHARACH
JOAN BAEZ
ANITA BAKER
BANAMARAMA
THE BANGLES
BOBBY BARE
SHIRLEY BASSEY
BAY CITY ROLLERS
BEATLES
BEE GEES
HARRY BELAFONTE
PAT BENETAR
TONY BENNETT
CHUCK BERRY
DICKIE BETTS
BROTHER BLUE
BON JOVI (GROUP)
JOHN BON JOVI
TAKA BOOM
DEBBY BOONE
PAT BOONE
DAVID BOWIE
BOBBIE BREEN
TERESA BREWER
JACKSON BROWNE
JAMES BROWN
ED BRUCE
ANITA BRYANT
BEBE BUELL - PU
KATE BUSH

CAB CALLOWAY
GLEN CAMPBELL
KIM CANTRELL
LANA CANTRELL
CAPT & TENNILLE
IRENE CARA
KIM CARNES
DIAHANN CARROLL
VICKIE CARR
THE CARS
CARLENE CARTER
NELL CARTER
JOHNNY CASH
SHAWN CASSIDY
TOM CHAPIN
RAY CHARLES
CHARLIE
CHARO
CHUBBY CHECKER
JUNE CHRISTIE
ERIC CLAPTON
DICK CLARK
PETULA CLARK
ROY CLARK
ROSEMARY CLOONEY
JOE COCKER
NATALIE COLE
JUDY COLLINS
JESSI COLTER
BETTY COMDEN & ADOLPH GREEN
THE COMMODORES
PERRY COMO
EARL THOMAS CONLEY
RITA COOLIDGE
ALICE COOPER
DON CORNELIUS
HELEN CORNELIUS
ELVIS COSTELLO
CROSBY, STILLS & NASH
CHRISTOPHER CROSS

LACY J DALTON
ROGER DALTRY
VIC DAMONE
BILLY DANIELS
CHARLIE DANIELS
CHARLIE DANIELS BAND
JAMES DARREN
JOHN DAVIDSON
BILLY DAVIS, JR
MAC DAVIS
PATTI DAVIS
DENNIS DAY
DORIS DAY
JACKIE DE SHANNON
JIMMY DEAN
DEF LEPPARD
JOHN DENVER
JOHNNY DESMOND
NEIL DIAMOND
JIMMY DICKENS
DION
DIRE STRAITS
FATS DOMINO
THE DOORS
JESSICA DRAGONETTE
PETER DUCHIN
DURAN DURAN
BOB DYLAN

EARTH, WIND & FIRE
SHEENA EASTON
BILLY ECKSTINE
JOE EGAN
JOE EGAN
THE EVERLY BROTHERS

FABIAN
LOLA FALANA
DONNA FARGO
MARK FARNER
JOSE FELICIANO
FREDDY FENDER
MAYNARD FERGUSON
FERRANTE & TEICHER
FIFTH DIMENSION
EDDIE FISHER
ELLA FITZGERALD
FLATT & SCRUGGS
FLEETWOOD MAC
DAN FOGELBURG
PETE FOUNTAIN
THE FOUR FRESHMAN
THE FOUR LADS
ORIGINAL FOURS ACES
PETER FRAMPTON
CONNIE FRANCIS - P/PU
GARY FRANK
ARETHA FRANKLIN
JANEE FRICKE

JERRY GARCIA
ART GARFUNKEL
LARRY GATLIN
CRYSTAL GAYLE
BOB GELDOF
BOBBY GENTRY
BOY GEORGE
CINDY GIBB
GEORGIA GIBBS
DEBBIE GIBSON
DIZZY GILLESPIE
MICKEY GILLEY

ADAM ANT

JOHNNY CASH

EARL THOMAS CONLEY

PAUL ANKA

RAY CHARLES

BOB DYLAN

TONY BENNETT

NATALIE COLE

SHEENA EASTON

VINCE GILL
THE GO-GO'S
GEORGE GOBEL
BOBBY GOLDSBORO
EYDIE GORME
ROBERT GOULET
AMY GRANT
GOGI GRANT
TOM GRANT
GRATEFUL DEAD
BUDDY GRECO
LEE GREENWOOD
ARLO GUTHRIE

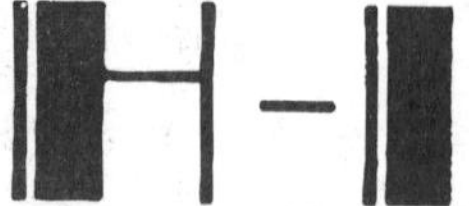

MERLE HAGGARD
CONNIE HAINES
HALL & OATES
TOM T HALL
MARVIN HAMLISH
HAMMER
HERBIE HANCOCK
GUS HARDIN
EMMY LOU HARRIS
GEORGE HARRISON
DEBBIE HARRY
ISAAC HAYES
HEART
JERRY HERMAN
AL HIRT
EDDIE HODGES
LENA HORNE
WHITNEY HOUSTON
BILL HUDSON
BRETT HUDSON
MARK HUDSON
THE HUDSON BROTHERS
BILLY HUFSEY
ENGELBERT HUMPERDINCK
FERLIN HUSKY
JULIO IGLESIAS
THE IMPERIALS
IRON MAIDEN
BURL IVES

JANET JACKSON
MICHAEL JACKSON
MICK JAGGER
JONI JAMES
RICK JAMES
AL JARREAU
FRAN JEFFRIES - PU
HERB JEFFRIES
WAYLON JENNINGS
JOAN JETT
BILLY JOEL
ELTON JOHN
GEORGE JONES
QUINCY JONES
THE JUDDS

CHAKA KAHN
KITTY KALLEN
LAINIE KAZAN
B B KING
PEE WEE KING
THE KINKS
PHYLLIS KIRK
KISS
EARTHA KITT
GLADYS KNIGHT
GLADYS KNIGHT & THE PIPS
KOOL & THE GANG
KRIS KRISTOFFERSON

PATTI LA BELLE
FRANKIE LAINE
ABBE LANE
FRANCIS LANGFORD
CYNDI LAUPER
CAROL LAWRENCE
STEVE LAWRENCE
LED ZEPPLIN
BRENDA LEE
JOHNNY LEE
PEGGY LEE
JULIAN LENNON
JEFF LEPPER
HUEY LEWIS & THE NEWS
HUEY LEWIS
JERRY LEE LEWIS
RAMSEY LEWIS TRIO
THE LIMELIGHTERS
LITTLE ANTHONY
LITTLE RICHARD
KENNY LOGGINS
JULIE LONDON
TRINI LOPEZ
LORETTA LYNN

MADONNA
MAMAS & THE PAPAS
MELISSA MANCHESTER
HENRY MANCINI
BARBARA MANDRELL
LOUISE MANDRELL
CHUCK MANGIONE
BARRY MANILOW
AL MARTINO
TONY MARTIN
JOHNNY MATHIS
KATHY MATTEA
PAUL MC CARTNEY
MARILYN MC COO
REBA MC INTYRE
GIZELLE MC KENZIE
BARBARA MC NAIR
MEATLOAF
JOHN COUGAR MELLENCAMP
MENUDO
GEORGE MICHAEL
BETTE MIDLER
MITCH MILLER
ROGER MILLER
STEVE MILLER
STEPHANIE MILLS
RONNIE MILSAP
LIZA MINNELLI
TONY MITCHELL
EDDIE MONEY
THE MOODY BLUES
MELBA MOORE
JAYE P MORGAN
GARY MORRIS
VAN MORRISON
ELLA MAE MORSE
MOTLEY CRUE
PATRICE MUNSEL
ANNE MURRAY

WILLIE NELSON
PETER NERO
NEW KIDS ON THE BLOCK
ANTHONY NEWLEY
JIMMIE C NEWMAN
RANDY NEWMAN
JUICE NEWTON
OLIVIA NEWTON-JOHN
WAYNE NEWTON
STEVIE NICKS
TED NUGENT

HELEN O'CONNELL
THE OAK RIDGE BOYS
ORIGINAL WEAVERS
TONY ORLANDO
DONNY OSMOND
MARIE OSMOND

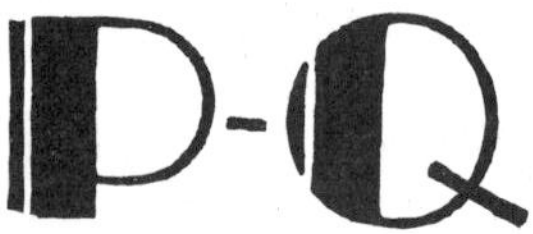

PATTI PAGE
ROY PARKER, JR
DOLLY PARTON
LUCIANO PAVORATTI
JOHNNY PAYCHECK
PEACHES & HERB
MINNIE PEARL
TEDDY PENDERGRASS
CARL PERKINS
PETER, PAUL & MARY
JANE PICKENS
WEBB PIERCE
PINK FLOYD PINK FLOYD
ROBERT PLANT
THE POINTER SISTERS
IGGY POP
ANDRE PREVIN
RAY PRICE
CHARLIE PRIDE
PRINCE
SUZI QUATRO

EDDIE RABBITT
BONNIE RAITT
JOHN RAITT

AMY GRANT

ELTON JOHN

MOODY BLUES

GEORGE HARRISON

GLADYS KNIGHT

POINTER SISTERS

AL JARREAU

MADONNA

PRINCE

EDDY RAVEN
LOU RAWLS
HELEN REDDY
JERRY REED
LOU REED
DELLA REESE
REO SPEEDWAGON
PAUL REVERE & THE RAIDERS
KEITH RICHARDS
CHARLIE RICH
LIONEL RICHIE
RIDERS IN THE SKY
THE RIGHTEOUS BROTHERS
JEANNIE C RILEY
JIMMIE RODGERS
KENNY ROGERS
KENNY ROGERS & DOTTIE WEST
LINDA RONSTADT
AXEL ROSE
DIANA ROSS
DAVID LEE ROTH
JOHNNY ROTTON
LEON RUSSELL
BOBBY RYDELL

SANDLER & YOUNG
TOMMY SANDS
BOZ SCAGGS
DAN SEALS
NEIL SEDAKA
THE SERENDIPITY SINGERS
JEAN SHEPPARD
BOBBY SHERMAN
ROBERTA SHERWOOD
DINAH SHORE
BEVERLY SILLS
CARLY SIMON
PAUL SIMON
FRANK SINATRA
NANCY SINATRA
RICKEY SKAGGS
GRACE SLICK
CARL SMITH
KEELY SMITH
SMOTHERS BROTHERS
P J SOLES
JOANIE SOMMERS
SONNY & CHER
DAVID SOUL
RONNIE SPECTOR
BRUCE SPRINGSTEEN
RICK SPRINGFIELD
JO STAFFORD
KAY STARR
RINGO STARR
TOMMY STEELE
CAT STEVENS
RAY STEVENS
ROD STEWART
STING STING
SLY STONE
DONNA SUMMER
THE SUPREMES
SYLVIA

THE TEMPTATIONS
TONI TENNILLE
THE THRASHER BROTHERS
TIFFANY
MEL TILLIS
MEL TORME
MERLE TRAVIS
RANDY TRAVIS
BOBBY TROUP
TANYA TUCKER
TOMMY TUNE
TINA TURNER
CONWAY TWITTY
BONNIE TYLER
LESLIE UGGAMS

JUNE VALI
EDDIE VAN HALEN
VANILLA ICE
SYLVIE VARTON
BENAY VENUTA
VILLAGE PEOPLE
BOBBY VINTON

LEN WADE
PORTER WAGGONER
FRAN WARREN
DIONNE WARWICK
KITTY WELLS
SHELLY WEST
THE WHITES
MARGARET WHITING
ANDY WILLIAMS
BILLY WILLIAMS
HANK WILLIAMS, JR
HANK WILLIAMS, JR & BAND
JOE WILLIAMS
PAUL WILLIAMS
MARY WILSON (SUPREMES)
NANCY WILSON
GARY WOLF
WOLFMAN JACK
STEVIE WONDER
THE WRIGHT BROTHERS
TAMMY WYNETTE
GLENN YARBOROUGH
FARON YOUNG
DWEEZIL ZAPPA
FRANK ZAPPA

Musical Legends Black &White Photos Only $1.00

LIONEL RICHIE

BRUCE SPRINGSTEEN

STEVIE WONDER

DECEASED MUSICAL PERFORMERS

All Portrait Photographs $1.00 Each

RAY ANTHONY
DESI ARNAZ, SR
GENE AUSTIN

COUNT BASIE
TEX BENEKE
IRVING BERLIN
LEONARD BERNSTEIN
OSCAR BRAND

HOAGY CARMICHAEL
ENRICO CARUSO
MAURICE CHEVALIER
JIMMY CLANTON
BUDDY CLARK
PATSY CLINE
GEORGE M COHAN
NAT "KING" COLE
BING CROSBY
SCATMAN CROTHERS

DOROTHY DANDRIDGE
BILLY DANIELS
BOBBY DARIN
SAMMY DAVIS, JR
MILES DAVIS
DENNIS DAY
JIMMY DORSEY
TOMMY DORSEY
NELSON EDDY
RUTH ETTING

ERNIE FORD
STEPHEN FOSTER
SERGIO FRANCHI

GEORGE GERSHWIN
STAN GETZ
ANDY GIBB
BENNY GOODMAN
JOSE GRECO
TEXAS GUINNAN
TITO GUIZAR

BILL HALEY
LIONEL HAMPTON
PHIL HARRIS
TED HEALY
JOSHUA HEIFITZ
JIMMY HENDRIX
WOODY HERMAN
BUDDY HOLLY & CRICKETS
VLADIMIR HOROWITZ
JOSE ITURBI

MAHALIA JACKSON
AL JOLSON
SPIKE JONES
JANIS JOPLIN

SAMMY KAYE
STAN KENTON
JEROME KERN
GENE KRUPA

MARIO LANZA

GERTRUDE LAWRENCE
JOHN LENNON
TED LEWIS
LIBERACE
GUY LOMBARDO

JEANETTE MC DONALD
LAWRENCE MELCHOIR
ETHEL MERMAN
GLENN MILLER
MILLS BROTHERS
CARMEN MIRANDA
GRACE MOORE
HELEN MORGAN

RICK NELSON
ROY ORBISON

LARRY PARKS
ENZIO PINZA
LILY PONS
COLE PORTER
ELVIS PRESLEY

JOHNNY RAY
BUDDY RICH
TEX RITTER
MARTY ROBBINS
PAUL ROBSON
ROGERS & HART
LANNY ROSS
ARTUR RUBERSTEIN

HAZEL SCOTT
ANDRE SEGOVIA
ARTIE SHAW
GEORGE SHEARING
KATE SMITH
JOHN PHILLIP SOUSA
IGOR STRAVINSKY

PETER TCHAIKOWSY
LAURENCE TIBBETT
ERNEST TUBB
SOPHIE TUCKER

RUDY VALLEE
SARAH VAUGHN

FRED WARING
DINAH WASHINGTON
ETHEL WATERS
DOTTIE WEST
KEITH WHITLEY
RAY WHITLEY
PAUL WHITMAN
HANK WILLIAMS, SR

Black & White Photos Only $1.00

PRESIDENTS & BOXERS

Photos $1.00 Each

Presidents

GEORGE BUSH
JIMMY CARTER
ROSALYN CARTER
CALVIN COOLIDGE
DWIGHT "IKE" EISENHOWER
MAMIE EISENHOWER
FORD, NIXON, CARTER & REAGAN
BETTY FORD
JERRY FORD
U S GRANT
HERBERT HOOVER
LYNDON B JOHNSON
JACQUELINE KENNEDY
JOHN KENNEDY
PATRICIA NIXON
RICHARD NIXON
NANCY REAGAN
RONALD REAGAN - P
RONALD REAGAN (COWBOY)
RONALD REAGAN (SHERRIFF)
RONALD REAGAN (BONZO)
ELEANOR ROOSEVELT
FRANKLIN D ROOSEVELT
THEODORE ROOSEVELT
HARRY TRUMAN
BETTY FORD
JERRY FORD
LADY BIRD JOHNSON
NANCY REAGAN
RONALD REAGAN (ON HORSE)

Boxers

MUHAMMED ALI - ACTION
MAX BAER, SR
PRIMO CARNERA
JERRY COONEY
JACK DEMPSEY
ROBERTO DURAN
FOREMAN & FRAZIER
GEORGE FORMAN
JOE FRAZIER
TONY GALENTE
ROCKY GRAZIANO
MARVIN HAGLER
HOLMES & HEARNS
LARRY HOLMES
INGEMAR JOHANSON
JAKE LA MOTTA
LEONARD & HEARNS
SONNY LISTON
RAY "BOOM BOOM" MANCINI
MARCIANO & EZZARD CHARLES
ROCKY MARCIANO
ARCHIE MOORE
KEN NORTON - S
SUGAR RAY ROBINSON
MAX SCHMELLING
LEON SPINKS
GENE TUNNEY
MIKE TYSON
JERSEY JOE WOLCOTT (COLOR)

FAMOUS CELEBRITIES
All Portrait Photographs
$1.00 Each

HANK AARON
KAREEM ABDUL-JABBAR
PRINCESS YASMIN AGA KHAN
ANDRE AGASI
EDWARD ALBEE
MUHAMMAD ALI - P/ACTION
MARTIN AMIS (AUTHOR)
JACK ANDERSON
YURI ANDROPOV
PRINCESS ANNE (ENGLAND)
CORIZON AQUINO
JACK ARMSTRONG
NEIL ARMSTRONG
ARTHUR ASHE
TRACY AUSTIN

BURT BACHARACH
ROGER BANNISTER
MIKHAIL BARISHNIKOV
CHRISTIAN BARNARD
RONA BARRETT
BORIS BECKER
CHARLES BECKWITH
MELVIN BELLI
IRVING BERLIN
LEONARD BERNSTEIN
BJORN BORG
JAMES BRADY
DR JOYCE BROTHERS
HELEN GURLEY BROWN
CMDR LLOYD BUCHNER
DON BUDGE
JACK BURNS
SIDNEY BIDDLE BURROWS
GEORGE BUSH

SAMMY CAHN
ROY CAMPANELLA
CAPUCINE
PRINCESS CAROLINE (MONACO)
JOHNNY CARSON
JIMMY CARTER
ROSALYN CARTER
BARBARA CARTLAND
SUZY CHAFFEE
WILT CHAMBERLAIN
MARGE CHAMPION -P/S
MICHAEL CHANG
CESAR CHAVEZ
CONNIE CHUNG
LADY SARAH CHURCHILL
IRON EYES CODY
JACKIE COLLINS
BETTY COMDEN & ADOLPH GREEN
NADIA COMENICI
JIMMIE CONNORS
DAVID COPPERFIELD
DOUGLAS CORRIGAN
HOWARD COSELL
JACQUES COUSTEAU
SCOTT CROSSFIELD
MARIO CUOMO

DR WILLIAM DE VRIES
JOE DI MAGGIO
PRINCESS DIANE (ENGLAND)
DIMAGGIO, MANTLE & GREENBERG
PHIL DONAHUE
KITTY DUKAKIS
CAMILLE DUVALL (OLYMPICS)

ABBA EBAN
RICHARD EBERHART
RALPH EDWARDS
JULIUS ERVING
CHRIS EVERETT-LLOYD

BOB FELLER
MARY JANE FERNANDEZ (TENNIS)
MEL FISHER (TREASURE)
PEGGY FLEMING
PEGGY FLEMING & BIG BIRD
BETTY FORD
JERRY FORD
GEORGE FOREMAN
FANNIE FOXXE
DAVID FROST

JOHN KENNETH GAILBRAITH
GALLAGHER
MIKAEL GARBACHEV
JOHN GLENN - P/NASA
ALEXANDER GODUNOV
STEFI GRAF
BILLY GRAHAM
MARTHA GRAHAM
ROCKY GRAZIANO
JOSE GRECO
DICK GREGORY
MERV GRIFFIN
MATT GROENING (SIMPSON'S)

WALTER HAGEN
MARVIN HAGLER
GENERAL ALEXANDER HAIG
ALEX HAILEY
ARTHUR HAILEY
ARSENEO HALL
DOROTHY HAMILL
MARY HART
PATTY HEARST
DOUG HENNING
HULK HOGAN
XAXIER HOLLANDER
ELEANOR HOLM
LARRY HOLMES (ACTION)
VLADIMER HOROWITZ
LEE IACCOCCA
ROBERT INDIANA

REGGIE JACKSON
REV JESSE JACKSON
BIANCA JAGGER
DR ROBERT JARVICK
BRUCE JENNER
JOCKEYS (LUCKEY DEBONAIR &
JOCKEYS (WHIRLAWAY & ARCARO)
SHOEMAKER)
JOCKEYS (COUNT FLEET & JOHN
LONGDON)
JOCKEYS (RIVA RIDGE & RON
TURCOTTE)
JOCKEYS (SWAPS & SHOEMAKER)
JOCKEYS (CITATION & ARCARO)
JASPER JOHN
FLO JO JOINER (OLYMPICS)
ERICA JONG

YOUSIF KARASH
BOB KEESHAN (CAPT KANGAROO)
EMMETT KELLY, JR
KITTY KELLY

MUHAMMAD ALI

JAKE LA MOTTA

JOHN MC ENROE

PEGGY FLEMING

MICKEY MANTLE

JOE NAMATH

BRUCE JENNER

WILLIE MAYS

MICKEY SPILLANE

EDWARD KENNEDY
TED KEY
MICHAEL KIDD
JEANNE KILPATRICK
BILLIE JEAN KING
DON KING
STEPHEN KING
HENRY KISSINGER
NANCY KISSINGER
EVIL KNIEVEL
WILLIAM C KNIGHT
MAYOR ED KOCH

JOHN LA CARCE (AUTHOR)
JAKE LA MOTTA
MURRAY LANGSTON
DON LARSON
TOMMY LASORDA
JOHN LE CARRE (AUTHOR)
MEADOWLARK LEMON
IVAN LENDL
JAY LENO
DAVID LETTERMAN
CARL LEWIS (OLYMPICS)
SHARI LEWIS (W/ PORKCHOP)
ART LINKLETTER
GREGG LOUGANIS
CLAIRE BOOTH LUCE
SID LUCKMAN
STEVE LUNDQUIST

NORMAN MAILER
RAY "BOOM BOOM" MANCINI
WILLIE MANDELLA
WINNIE MANDELLA
MICKEY MANTLE
MARLA MAPLES
MARCEL MARCEAU
FERDINAND & AMELIA MARCOS
MARTIN & JOHNSON
PETER MARTINS
MICHELLE MARVIN
BOB MATHIAS
WILLIE MAYS
JOHN MC ENROE
JIM MC INERNEY (AUTHOR)
ROD MC KUEN
ED MC MAHON
DON MEREDITH
BESS MEYERSON
JAMES MICHNER
CAPTAIN MIDNIGHT
DENNIS MILLER
PHOEBE MILLS (GYMNAST)
REV S M MOON
ARCHIE MOORE
GARY MOORE
EDWIN MOSES (OLYMPICS)
MOTHER TERESA
STAN MUSIAL

JOE NAMATH
MARTINA NATRAVLOVA
LEROY NEIMAN
LOUISE NEVELSON
PATRICIA NIXON
RICHARD NIXON
GEN MANUEL NORIEGA (PANAMA)
KEN NORTON - S
SANDRA DAY O'CONNOR
JACKIE ONASSIS
TINA ONASSIS-NIARCHOS

ROSA PARKS
JACK PARR
LINUS PAULING
PELE
ITZHAK PERLMAN
PALOMA PICASSO
PRESIDENTS
JAMES PURDY
DAN QUAYLE

I I RABI
LEE RADZIWELL
ELIZABETH RAY
MAUREEN REAGAN
NANCY REAGAN
RONALD REAGAN
RONALD REAGAN - (COWBOY)
RONALD REAGAN, JR
RONALD REAGAN & BONZO
MARY LOU RETTON
CATHY RIGBY
GERALDO RIVERA
HAROLD ROBBINS
ORAL ROBERTS
PAT ROBERTSON
FRED ROGER (MR ROGERS)
PHILIP ROTH (AUTHOR)
WILMA RUDOLPH
MARK RUSSELL

DR CARL SAGAN
MORT SAHL
PAT SAJAK
DR JONAS SALK
GENE SARAZIN & WALTER HAGEN
GUIDO SARDUCCI
MAX SCHMELLING
FRITZ SCHOLDER
GEORGE SCHULTZ
GARY SHANDLING
ARIEL SHARON
JILL SHIPSTEAD
A SHOSTEKOVICH
SIEGFRIED & ROY
RICHARD SIMMONS
NEIL SIMON
ISAAC B SINGER
BOB SMITH & HOWDY DOODY
KATHY SMITH
STEVEN SONDHEIM
MICKEY SPILLANE
LEON SPINKS
MARK SPITZ

GAY TALESE (AUTHOR)
DR EDWARD TELLER
MOTHER TERESA
ALAN THICKE
DEBBY THOMAS (SKATER)
JAMES THURBER (AUTHOR)
TOMMY TUNE
TED TURNER
REV DESMOND TUTU
MIKE TYSON
PETER UBERRUTH
JOHN UPDIKE
ABIGAIL VAN BUREN
GLORIA VANDERBILT
KURT VONNEGUT, JR

LECH WALESA
HERSCHEL WALKER
IRVING WALLACE
BARBARA WALTERS
ROBERT PENN WARREN
DR RUTH WESTHEIMIER
GEN WILLIAM WESTMORELAND
TED WILLIAMS
VANESSA WILLIAMS
MAURY WILLS
PAUL WINCHELL & JERRY MAHONEY
DUKE & DUCHESS WINDSOR
JERSEY JOE WOLCOTT
TOM WOLFE
ANDREW WYETH
WEIRD AL YANKOVIC
GENERAL CHUCK YEAGER
YEAGER & RUTAN
ANDREW YOUNG
KIM ZMESKAL (OLYMPICS)

GORE VIDAL

UNITED STATES ORDERS

B&W PHOTOS ( ) X $1.00 = ______

COLOR PHOTOS ( ) X $2.50 = ______

POSTAGE AND HANDLING $3.00

TOTAL ENCLOSED: ______

SEND ORDER TO:

NAME ______

ADDRESS ______

CITY ______

STATE ______ ZIP ______

CANADIAN ORDERS

B&W PHOTOS ( ) X $1.25 = ______

COLOR PHOTOS ( ) X $2.75 = ______

POSTAGE AND HANDLING $5.00

TOTAL ENCLOSED: ______

SEND ORDER TO:

NAME ______

ADDRESS ______

CITY ______

PROVINCE ______ ZIP ______

FOREIGN ORDERS

B&W PHOTOS ( ) X $1.50 = ______

COLOR PHOTOS ( ) X $2.75 = ______

POSTAGE AND HANDLING $10.00

TOTAL ENCLOSED: ______

SEND ORDER TO:

NAME ______

ADDRESS ______

CITY ______

STATE ______ ZIP ______

NOTE:

The minimum order for all countries outside the United States is ten (10) photos.
The minimum order within the USA is two (2) photos.

DECEASED TV & MOVIE STARS

All Portrait Photographs
$1.00 Each

ABBOTT & COSTELLO
WALTER ABEL
DAWN ADDAMS
LUTHER ADLER
IRIS ADRIAN
BRIAN AHERNE
JACK ALBERTSON
ROBERT ALDA
FERNANDO ALLENDE
FRED ALLEN
GRACIE ALLEN
PETER ALLEN
AMOS 'N" ANDY
JUDITH ANDERSON
DANA ANDREWS
PIER ANGELI
EVELYN ANKERS
FATTY ARBUCKLE
RICHARD ARLEN
GEORGE ARLISS
LOUIS ARMSTRONG
DESI ARNAZ, SR
EDWARD ARNOLD
JEAN ARTHUR
FRED ASTAIRE & GENE KELLY
FRED ASTAIRE & SHIRLEY MAC LAINE
FRED ASTAIRE & FRANK SINATRA
FRED ASTAIRE
FRED ASTAIRE & GINGER ROGERS
FRED ASTAIRE & CYD CHARISSE
NILES ASTER
MARY ASTOR
LIONEL ATWELL
MISHA AUER

JIM BACKUS
PEARL BAILEY - P/S
FAY BAINTER
SMITH BALLEW
LUCILLE BALL
GEORGE BANCROFT
TALLULAH BANKHEAD
VILMA BANKY
THEDA BARA
GEORGE BARBIER
LEX BARKER
BINNIE BARNES
DON "RED" BARRY
ETHEL BARRYMORE
JOHN BARRYMORE
LIONEL BARRYMORE
RICHARD BARTHELMESS
FREDDIE BARTHOLOMEW
RICHARD BASEHART
FRANCES BAVIER
ANNE BAXTER
WARNER BAXTER
JOHN BEAL
STYMIE BEARD
CECIL BEATON
NOAH BEERY, SR
WALLACE BEERY
RALPH BELLAMY
REX BELL
JOHN BELUSHI
WILLIAM BENDIX
CONSTANCE BENNETT
JACK BENNY
EDGAR BERGEN & CHARLIE MC CARTHY
INGRID BERGMAN
WARREN BERLINGER
HERSCHEL BERNARDI
JOE BESSER
LYLE BETTGER
AMANDA BLAKE
DAN BLOCKER
JOAN BLONDELL - P/S
ERIC BLORE
BEN BLUE
HUMPHREY BOGART
JOHN BOLES
RAY BOLGER (SCARECROW)
BEAULAH BONDI
WARD BOND
RICHARD BOONE
CLARA BOW
LEE BOWMAN
BILL BOYD
CHARLES BOYER
SCOTT BRADY
NEVILLE BRAND
EL BRENDEL
WALTER BRENNAN
GEORGE BRENT
MARY BRIAN
FANNY BRICE
HELEN BRODERICK
STEVE BRODIE
BETTY BRONSON
LOUISE BROOKS - PU
JOE E BROWN
JOHNNY MACK BROWN
NIGEL BRUCE
VIRGINIA BRUCE
VICTOR BRUNO - P/S
YUL BRYNNER
EDGAR BUCHANAN
VICTOR BUONO - S
BILLIE BURKE
SMILEY BURNETTE
BOB BURNS
RICHARD BURTON
MAX BUSCH
FRANCES X BUSHMAN

SEBASTIAN CABOT
JAMES CAGNEY - P/ GRAPEFRUIT
ROD CAMERON
JUDY CANOVA
EDDIE CANTOR
YAKIMA CANUTT
HARRY CAREY
HOAGY CARMICHAEL
JOHN CARRADINE
LEO CARRILLO
JOHN CARROLL
LEO G CARROLL
MADELINE CARROLL
NANCY CARROLL
JACK CARSON
JOHN CASSAVETES
PEGGY CASS
GOWER CHAMPION
JEFF CHANDLER
LON CHANEY, SR - P/S
LON CHANEY, JR
TOM CHAPIN
CHARLIE CHAPLIN
CHARLIE CHASE
ILKA CHASE
MAURICE CHEVALIER
MARGUERITE CHURCHILL
JIMMY CLANTON
BUDDY CLARK
MAE CLARKE (GRAPEFRUIT SCENE)
MONTGOMERY CLIFT
ANDY CLYDE
LEE J COBB
CHARLES COBURN
JAMES COCO - P/S
NAT "KING" COLE
JUNE COLLYER
RONALD COLMAN
BETTY COMPSON
HANS CONREID
JACKIE COOGAN
GARY COOPER
GLADYS COOPER
MELVILLE COOPER
RAY "CRASH" CORRIGAN
DOLORES COSTELLO
LOU COSTELLO
WALLY COX
BUSTER CRABBE
JAMES CRAIG
BOB CRANE
BRODERICK CRAWFORD - P/S
JOAN CRAWFORD
DONALD CRISP
BING CROSBY
SCATMAN CROTHERS
GEORGE CUKOR
ROBERT CUMMINGS

FRED ASTAIRE

JOHN BELUSHI

RICHARD BOONE

JOHN BARRYMORE

DAN BLOCKER

CHARLES BOYER

INGRID BERGMAN

RAY BOLGER

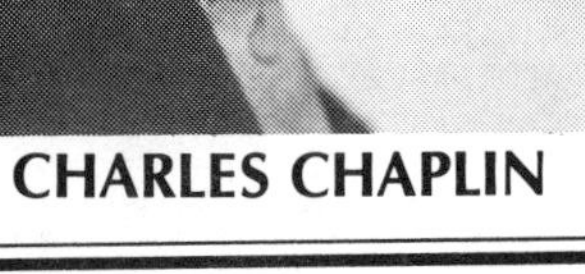

CHARLES CHAPLIN

FIFI D'ORSAY
BEBE DANIELS
ROYAL DANO
LINDA DARNELL
DANIELLE DARRIEUX
FRANKIE DARRO
JANE DARWELL
BETTE DAVIS - P/S/PU
JIM DAVIS - P/S
MARION DAVIS
RUFE DAVIS
CECIL B DE MILLE
VITTORIO DE SICA
BILLY DE WOLFE
JAMES DEAN
DOLORES DEL RIO
WILLIAM DEMEREST
CAROL DEMPSTER
SANDY DENNIS
REGINALD DENNY
ANDY DEVINE
MARLENE DIETRICH - P/PU
WALT DISNEY
RICHARD DIX
BRIAN DONLEVY
DIANA DORS
JIMMY DORSEY
TOMMY DORSEY
MELVIN DOUGLAS
PAUL DOUGLAS
CONSTANCE DOWLING
JESSICA DRAGONETTE
MARIE DRESSLER
ANDREW DUGGAN
JAMES DUNN
JIMMY DURANTE
DAN DUREYA
ANN DVORAK

JEANNE EAGLES
NELSON EDDY
SALLY EILERS
FAYE EMERSON
LEIF ERICKSON
LEON ERROL
STU ERWIN
MADGE EVANS

DOUGLAS FAIRBANKS, SR
JINX FALKENBERG
FARINA (AL HOSKINS)
FRANCES FARMER
CHARLES FARRELL
MARTY FELDMAN
JOSE FERRER - P/S
STEPHEN FETCHIT
GRACIE FIELDS
KIM FIELDS
W C FIELDS
LARRY FINE
BARRY FITZGERALD
BESS FLOWERS
WAYLAND FLOWERS & MADAME
ERROLL FLYNN
HENRY FONDA
DICK FORAN
PRESTON FOSTER
REDD FOXX - P/S
EDDIE FOY, JR
EDDIE FOY, SR
JAMES FRANCISCUS - P/S
TONY FRANCIOSA - P/S

CLARK GABLE
TONY GALENTE
GRETA GARBO
REGINALD GARDINER
AVA GARDNER
JOHN GARFIELD
JUDY GARLAND
PEGGY ANN GARNER
JANET GAYNOR
WILL GEER
CHIEF DAN GEORGE
GLADYS GEORGE
ALICE GHOSTLEY
HOOT GIBSON
WYNN GIBSON
BILLY GILBERT
HERMIONE GINGOLD
JACKIE GLEASON (RALPH CRAMDEN)
JAMES GLEASON
PAULETTE GODDARD
ARTHUR GODFREY
SAMUEL GOLDWYN
BENNY GOODMAN
RUTH GORDON
JETTA GOUDAL
BETTY GRABLE
GLORIA GRAHAME - S
MARTHA GRAHAM
CARY GRANT
KIRBY GRANT
BONITA GRANVILLE
LORNE GREENE
SYDNEY GREENSTREET
D W GRIFFITH
TEXAS GUINNAN
TITO GUIZAR
SIGRID GURIE

JOAN HACKETT
WILLIAM HAINES
ALAN HALE, JR
BILL HALEY
JACK HALEY - P/TIN MAN
JON HALL
MARGARET HAMILTON
NEIL HAMILTON
OLIVER HARDY
JEAN HARLOW
REX HARRISON - P/DR DOOLITTLE
WILLIAM S HART
RAYMOND HATTON
SESSUE HAYAKAWA
STERLING HAYDEN - P/S
GABBY HAYES
LOUIS HAYWARD
SUSAN HAYWARD - P/PU
RITA HAYWORTH
EDITH HEAD
TED HEALY
JIMI HENDRIX
WANDA HENDRIX - P/S/PU
SONJA HENIE
PAUL HENREID
JIM HENSON (MUPPETS)
HUGH HERBERT
JEAN HERSHOLT
JON ERIK HEXUM
BENNY HILL
PAT HINGLE
ALFRED HITCHCOCK
JOHN HODIAK
WILLIAM HOLDEN
STERLING HOLLOWAY
JACK HOLT
TIM HOLT
LOU HOLTZ
MIRIAM HOPKINS
EDWARD EVERETT HORTON
JOHN HOUSEMAN
LESLIE HOWARD
MOE HOWARD
WILLIE HOWARD
JACK HOXIE
ROCK HUDSON
HENRY HULL
JOHN HUSTON
WALTER HUSTON
JIM HUTTON
MARTHA HYER

EMIL JANNINGS
CLAUDIA JENNINGS
GEORGE JESSEL
SONNY JOHNSON
AL JOLSON
BUCK JONES
CAROLYN JONES - P/S
SPIKE JONES
JANIS JOPLIN
VICTOR JORY
LEATRICE JOY
ARLENE JUDGE
CURT JURGENS - P/S

HELEN KANE
BORIS KARLOFF (FRANKENSTEIN)
ROSCOE KARNS
JULIE KAVNER
DANNY KAYE - P/S
SAMMY KAYE
BUSTER KEATON
GRACE KELLY
PATSY KELLY
DORIS KENYON
FUZZY KNIGHT
MICHAEL KNIGHT
ERNIE KOVACS
OTTO KRUGER

FRANCES FARMER

CARY GRANT

JEAN HARLOW

DICK FORAN

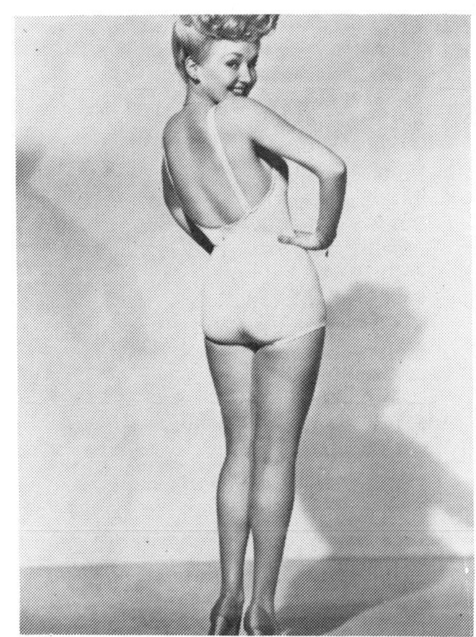
BETTY GRABLE

SUSAN HAYWARD

CLARK GABLE

JUDY GARLAND

DANNY KAYE

ROSEMARY LA PLANTE
JACK LA RUE
ALAN LADD
BERT LAHR -P/COWARDLY LION
VERONICA LAKE - P/PU
ARTHUR LAKE
FERNANDO LAMAS
ELSA LANCASTER (FRANKENSTEIN)
ELSA LANCHESTER
ELISSA LANDI
CAROL LANDIS - P/S
MICHAEL LANDON
ALLEN LANE
HARRY LANGDON, SR
JOI LANSING
MARIO LANZA
JACK LARUE
CHARLES LAUGHTON
LAUREL & HARDY
STAN LAUREL
PETER LAWFORD
GERTRUDE LAWRENCE
BRUCE LEE
ANDREA LEEDS
GYPSY ROSE LEE
VIVIAN LEIGH
OSCAR LEVANT
MONICA LEWIS
TED LEWIS
ART LINKLETTER
BEATRICE LITTLE
HAROLD LLOYD
JOHN LODER
CAROLE LOMBARD
PETER LORRE
ANITA LOUISE
BESSIE LOVE
FRANK LOVEJOY
MONTAGUE LOVE
EDMOND LOWE
PAUL LUCAS
BELA LUGOSI
LUM & ABNER - P/S
WILLIAM LUNDIGAN
JOHN LUND
PAUL LYNDE -P/S
DIANA LYNN
JEFFREY LYNN
BEN LYON
BERT LYTELL

MAE MAC AVOY
FRED MAC MURRAY - P/S
JOCK MAHONEY - P/S/TARZAN/COWBOY
MARJORIE MAIN
JAYNE MANSFIELD
HERBERT MARSHALL
DEAN PAUL MARTIN
MARY MARTIN - P/PETER PAN
STROTHER MARTIN
LEE MARVIN - P/S/CAT BALLOUW
MARX BROTHERS
CHICO MARX
GROUCHO MARX
HARPO MARX
JAMES MASON
IONA MASSEY
RAYMOND MASSEY
JOHN MATUSZAK - P/S
KEN MAYNARD
MIKE MAZURKI
TIM MC COY
JOEL MC CREA - P/S
HATTIE MC DANIEL
JEANETTE MC DONALD
FIBBER MC GEE & MOLLY
FRANK MC HUGH
VICTOR MC LAUGHLIN
STEVE MC QUEEN
KAY MEDFORD
DONALD MEEK
RALPH MEEKER
THOMAS MEIGAN
ADOLPH MENJOU
UNA MERKLE
RAY MILLAND - P/S/LOST WEEKEND
GLENN MILLER
MARILYN MILLER
PATSY RUTH MILLER
MARY MILES MINTER
THOMAS MITCHELL
TOM MIX
MARILYN MONROE - P/SC/SPU
MARIA MONTEZ
DOUGLAS MONTGOMERY
ROBERT MONTGOMERY
VICTOR MOORE
JEANNE MOREAU
DENNIS MORGAN
FRANK MORGAN
JEANNE MORGAN
ROBERT MORLEY
CHESTER MORRIS
WAYNE MORRIS
VIC MORROW
ZERO MOSTEL
ALAN MOWBRAY
JEAN MUIR
PAUL MUNI - P/SC/GOOD EARTH
ONA MUNSON
AUDIE MURPHY
GEORGE MURPHY
MARY MURPHY - P/S
CHARLES MURRAY
CLARENCE MUSE
CARMEL MYERS

ALAN NAPIER
J CARROL NASH
OLGA NAZIMOVA
ANNA NEAGLE
TOM NEAL
POLA NEGRI
ANNA Q NIELSEN
DAVID NIVEN - P/S
MARION NIXON
LLOYD NOLAN
MABEL NORMAND
RAYMOND NOVARRO
EDMOND O'BRIEN
GEORGE O'BRIEN
PAT O'BRIEN
JACK OAKIE
SIMON OAKLAND
MERLE OBERON
WARNER OLAND
EDNA MAE OLIVER
SUSAN OLIVER
SIR LAURENCE OLIVIER - P/S
OLSON & JOHNSON

GERALDINE PAGE
LILI PALMER
JEAN PARKER
PARKYAKARKUS
HELEN PARRISH
GAIL PATRICK
JOHN PAYNE
ANN PENNINGTON
JACK PERRIN
JANE PICKENS
SLIM PICKENS - P/S
WALTER PIDGEON
JAMES PIERCE
ZASU PITTS
SNUB POLLARD
DICK POWELL
WILLIAM POWELL
TYRONE POWER
ROBERT PRESTON
EDMUND PURDOM

GILDA RADNER
MARJORIE RAMBEAU
BASIL RATHBONE & NIGEL BRUCE
BASIL RATHBONE (HOLMES)
GREGORY RATHOFF
ALDO RAY - P/S
MICHAEL REDGRAVE
DONNA REED
GEORGE REEVES (SUPERMAN)
JIM REEVES
LEE REMICK - P/S/PU
HARRY RICHMAN
RITZ BROTHERS
PAUL ROBESON
BILL ROBINSON
EDWARD G ROBINSON
MAE ROBSON
JEAN ROGERS
WILL ROGERS, SR
LINA ROMAY
SHIRLEY ROSS
LILLIAN ROTH
CHARLES RUGGLES
GAIL RUSSELL
JOHN RUSSELL
LILLIAN RUSSELL
ROSALIND RUSSELL
ANN RUTHERFORD - P/PU

SABU
CHICK SALE
WILL SAMPSON
JOSEPH SCHILDKRAUT
CAL SCHRUM
RANDOLPH SCOTT
ZACHARY SCOTT
JEAN SEBERG
PETER SELLERS - P/S
MACK SENNETT

CAROLE LANDIS

PAT O'BRIEN

TYRONE POWER

CAROLE LOMBARD

GROUCHO MARX

ELVIS PRESLEY

BELA LUGOSI

CARMEN MIRANDA

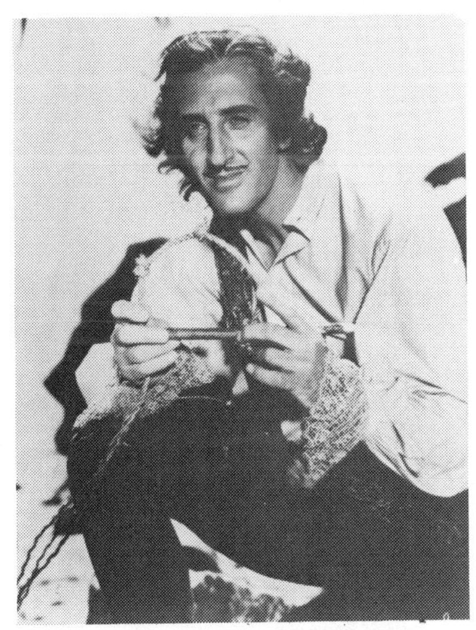

BASIL RATHBONE

ROD SERLING
DICK SHAWN - P/S
ROBERT SHAW
NORMA SHEARER
JACK SHELDON
ANN SHERIDAN
HERB SHRINER
MILTON SILLS
JAY SILVERHEELS
PHIL SILVERS - P/S
C AUBREY SMITH
LEIGH SNOWDEN
GALE SONDERGAARD
NED SPARKS
RAYMOND ST JACQUES
AL (FUZZY) ST JOHN
BARBARA STANWYCK
CHARLES STARRETT
BOB STEELE
HENRY STEPHENSON
JAN STERLING
INGER STEVENS
LEWIS STONE
LEE STRASBERG
DOROTHY STRATTON -P/PU
MARGARET SULLIVAN
GLORIA SWANSON
BLANCHE SWEET

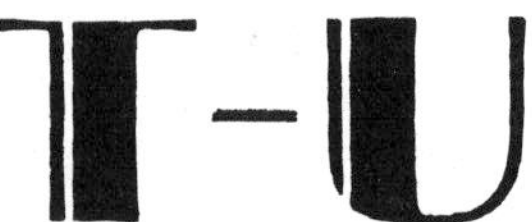

CONSTANCE TALMAGE
RICHARD TALMAGE
TAMARA
RUSS TAMBLYN
SHARON TATE
VIC TAYBACK
ROBERT TAYLOR - P/S
RUTH TAYLOR
CONWAY TEARLE
TERRY-THOMAS
DANNY THOMAS
THREE STOOGES
LAWRENCE TIBBETT
GEORGE TOBIAS
GENEVIEVE TOBIN
THELMA TODD
SIDNEY TOLER
FRANCHOT TONE
REGIS TOOMEY
LEE TRACY
SPENCER TRACY
ARTHUR TREACHER
ERNEST TRUEX
FORREST TUCKER
SONNY TUFTS
TOM TULLY - S
BEN TURPIN
HELEN TWELVETREES
TOM TYLER
PETER USTINOV - P/S/CHAN

VERA VAGUE
RUDOLPH VALENTINO
RUDY VALLEE
LEE VAN CLEEF - P/S
WALLY VERNON
MARTHA VICKERS
ERIC VON STROHEIM

JIMMY WAKELY
RAYMOND WALDBURN
JEAN WALLACE
H B WARNER
DINAH WASHINGTON
ETHEL WATERS
DAVID WAYNE - P/ELLERY QUEEN
JOHN WAYNE
MAJORIE WEAVER
CLIFTON WEBB - P/S
RICHARD WEBB - P/CAPT MIDNIGHT
JOHNNY WEISSMULLER
ORSON WELLES - P/S
OSKAR WERNER
MAE WEST
MICHAEL WHALEN
BERT WHEELER
ALICE WHITE
HENRY WILCOXON
CORNEL WILDE
MICHAEL WILDING
BIG BOY WILLIAMS
GUY WILLIAMS (ZORRO)
WARREN WILLIAMS
MARIE WILSON
WHIP WILSON
TOBY WING
ROLAND WINTERS
ANNA MAY WONG
NATALIE WOOD - P/PU
JOAN WOODBURY
GRETCHEN WYLER
KEENAN WYNN
DICK YORK
ROLAND YOUNG
JOE YULE
E Z ZAKALL

The Legends Live On Only $1.00

GEORGE REEVES

PETER SELLERS

INGER STEVENS

JOHNNY WEISSMULLER

UNITED STATES ORDERS

B&W PHOTOS ( ) X $1.00 = ______

COLOR PHOTOS ( ) X $2.50 = ______

POSTAGE AND HANDLING $3.00

TOTAL ENCLOSED: ______

SEND ORDER TO:

NAME ______

ADDRESS ______

CITY ______

STATE ______ ZIP ______

CANADIAN ORDERS

B&W PHOTOS ( ) X $1.25 = ______

COLOR PHOTOS ( ) X $2.75 = ______

POSTAGE AND HANDLING $5.00

TOTAL ENCLOSED: ______

SEND ORDER TO:

NAME ______

ADDRESS ______

CITY ______

PROVINCE ______ ZIP ______

FOREIGN ORDERS

B&W PHOTOS ( ) X $1.50 = ______

COLOR PHOTOS ( ) X $2.75 = ______

POSTAGE AND HANDLING $10.00

TOTAL ENCLOSED: ______

SEND ORDER TO:

NAME ______

ADDRESS ______

CITY ______

STATE ______ ZIP ______

NOTE:

The minimum order for all countries outside the United States is ten (10) photos.
The minimum order within the USA is two (2) photos.

DECEASED CELEBRITIES

All Portrait Phptographs
$1.00 Each

ANSEL ADAMS
JANE ADAMS
LOUISA MAE ALCOTT
AMOS 'N' ANDY
ROLAND AMUNDSEN
SUSAN B ANTHONY
GENE AUSTIN

MAX BAER, SR
PHINNEAS T BARNUM
CLARA BARTON
COUNT BASIE
CLYDE BEATTY
ALEXANDER GRAHAM BELL
REX BELL
ROBERT BENCHLEY
THOMAS HART BENTON
IRVING BERLIN
FRANK BONNER
MAJOR EDWARD BOWES
ROBERT BROWING
WILLIAM JENNINGS BRYAN
FRANK BUCK
PEARL BUCK
LUTHER BURBANK
BURNS & ALLEN
EDGAR RICE BURROUGHS
SIDNEY BIDDLE BURROWS
RICHARD E BYRD

TRUMAN CAPOTE
HOAGY CARMICHAEL
ANDREW CARNEGIE
PRIMO CARNERA
BARBARA CARTLAND
ENRICO CARUSO
GEORGE WASHINGTON CARVER
IRENE CASTLE
HARRY CHAPIN
CARRIE CHAPMAN COTT
WINSTON CHURCHILL
BUDDY CLARK
SAMUEL CLEMENS
TY COBB
GEORGE M COHAN
NAT "KING" COLE
CALVIN COOLIDGE
AARON COPELAND
MADAME CURRIE

CLARENCE DARROW
CHARLES DARWIN
SAMMY DAVIS, JR
JEFFERSON DAVIS
MOISHE DAYAN
DR LEE DE FORREST
CHARLES DE GAULEE
JACK DEMPSEY
JIMMY DORSEY
TOMMY DORSEY
JESSICA DRAGONETTE
W E B DU BOIS

AMELIA EARHART
GEORGE EASTMAN
THOMAS A EDISON
ALBERT EINSTEIN
GEN IKE EISENHOWER
MAMIE EISENHOWER
RALPH WALDO EMERSON

CLIFTON FAIDMAN
DAVID FARRAGUT
WILLIAM FAULKNER
EDNA FERBER
ENRICO FERMI
F SCOTT FITZGERALD
FLAG RAISING ON IWO JIMA
HENRY FORD, SR
STEPHEN FOSTER
ROBERT FROST

LOU GEHRIG
LOU GEHRIG & BABE RUTH
GEORGE GERSHWIN
SAMUEL GOLDWYN
SAMUEL GOMPERS
RED GRANGE
ULYSSES S GRANT
HORACE GREELEY
ZANE GREY
TITO GUIZAR

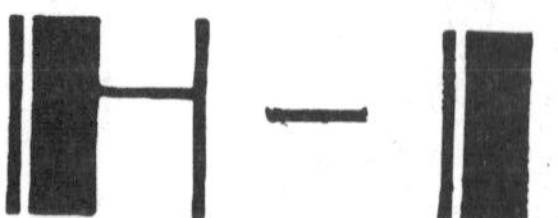

ALEX HALEY
BILL HALEY
SIR ARTHUR HARRIS
MOSS HART
NATHANIEL HAWTHORNE
EDITH HEAD
TED HEALY
BEN HECHT
JACHUA HEIFITZ
SONJA HEINIE
WILD BILL HITCHCOCK
ADOLPH HITLER
BUDDY HOLLY & CRICKETS
OLIVER WENDELL HOLMES
HARRY HOUDINI
SAM HOUSTON
ELIAS HOWE
HOWARD HUGHES
FRANKIE HURST
WASHINGTON IRVING
JOSE ITURBI

GREGORY JARVIS (CHALLENGER)
LYNDON B JOHNSON
BOBBY JONES
GEORGE S KAUFMAN
HELEN KELLER
EMMETT KELLY, SR
PRESIDENT JOHN F KENNEDY
ROBERT F KENNEDY
JEROME KERN
DR MARTIN LUTHER KING

GERTRUDE LAWRENCE
SOL LESSER
CHARLES A LINDBERGH, JR
WALTER LIPPMAN
SONNY LISTON
GUY LOMBARDO
HENRY W LONGFELLOW
ANITA LOOS

CHARLES MAC ARTHUR
DOUGLAS MAC ARTHUR
HORACE MANN

ROBERT BENCHLEY

NAT "KING" COLE

F. SCOTT FITZGERALD

FRANK BUCK

GEORGE EASTMAN

HENRY FORD, JR.

RICHARD E. BYRD

THOMAS A. EDISON

WILLIAM S. HART

GEORGE S. KAUFMAN

JOHN F. KENNEDY

HELEN MORGAN

HELEN KELLER

MARTIN LUTHER KING, JR.

ANNIE OAKLEY

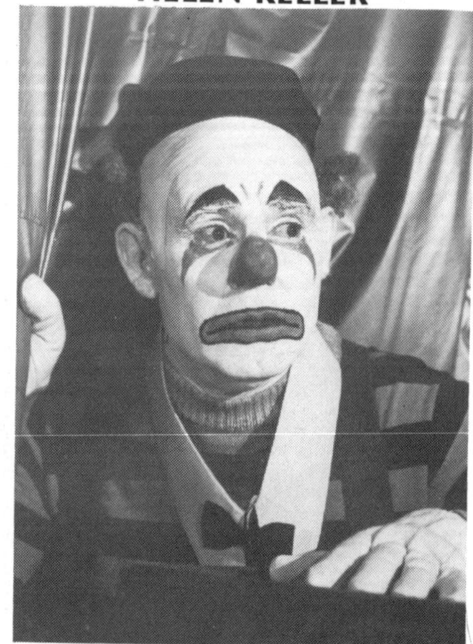

EMMETT KELLY, SR.

GENERAL MONTGOMERY

PABLO PICASSO

GUGLIELMO MARCONI
ROGER MARIS
BAT MASTERSON
HENRI MATISSE
W SOMERSET MAUGHAN
CHRISTA MC AULIFFE (CHALLENGER)
CYRUS MC CORMICK
GEORGE B MC LELLAN
RONALD E MC NAIR (CHALLENGER)
GEORGE MEADE
GOLDA MEIER
HERMAN MELVILLE
JAMES MICHENER
HO CHI MIHN
GENERAL MONTGOMERY (BRITISH)
HENRY MOORE
LORD LOUIS MOUNTBATTEN
GEORGE MURPHY

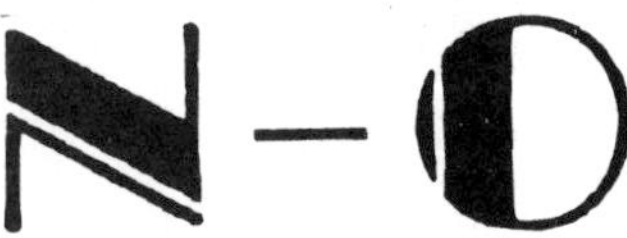

CARRIE NATION
ANNIE OAKLEY
ELLISON S ONIZUKA (CHALLENGER)
J ROBERT OPPENHEIMER
JESSE OWENS

BERT PARKS
GEN GEORGE S PATTON
DREW PEARSON
FRED PERRY
HAL "GILDERSLEEVE" PERRY
ROBERT E PERRY
PABLO PICASSO
EDGAR ALLEN POE
COLE PORTER
WILEY POST
ERNIE PYLE

SALLY RAND
JOHNNY RAY
HARRY REASONER
WALTER REED
JUDITH RESNICK (CHALLENGER)
JEROME ROBBINS
MARTY ROBBINS
SUGAR RAY ROBINSON
NORMAN ROCKWELL
GENE RODDENBERRY
RODGERS & HART RODGERS & HART
ELEANOR ROOSEVELT
FRANKLIN D ROOSEVELT
ARTUR RUBENSTEIN
BABE RUTH - P/TRIBUTE

ALBERT SCHWEITZER
DICK SCOBEE (CHALLENGER)
HAZEL SCOTT
ANDRES SEGOVIA
DAVID SELZNICK
ROD SERLING
WILLIAM H SEWARD
GEORGE BERNARD SHAW
WILLIAM T SHERMAN
KATE SMITH
MICHAEL J SMITH (CHALLENGER)
ELIZABETH CODY STANTON
CHARLES STEINMETZ
ADLAI STEVENSON
HARRIET BEECHER STOWE
IGOR STRAVINSKY
ED SULLIVAN

LOWELL THOMAS
HENRY THOREAU
BILL TILDEN
GENE TUNNEY
VIRGINIA WADE
JACK WARNER
EARL WARREN
BOOKER T WASHINGTON
GEORGE WASHINGTON CARVER
ETHEL WATERS
H G WELLS
OLIVER WENDELL HOLMES
GEORGE WHITE
WALT WHITMAN
WENDELL WILKEE
TENNESSEE WILLIAMS
WALTER WINCHELL
ALEXANDER WOLCOTT
FRANK LLOYD WRIGHT
WILBUR & ORVILLE WRIGHT
YALTA CONFERENCE
BRIGHAM YOUNG
DARRYL F ZANNUCK
FLORENCE ZIEGFIELD

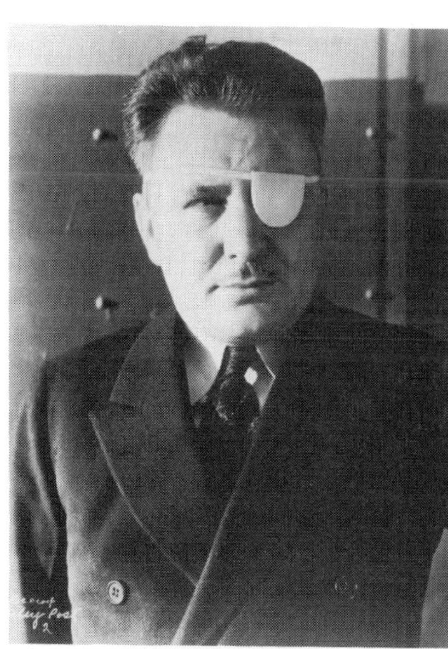

WILEY POST

ALBERT SCHWEITZER

ROD SERLING

DARRYL F. ZANUCK

ORDER FORM

SY SUSSMAN PORTRAITS • 2962 S. MANN ST. • LAS VEGAS, NV 89102

UNITED STATES ORDERS

B&W PHOTOS ( ) X $1.00 = ______
COLOR PHOTOS ( ) X $2.50 = ______
POSTAGE AND HANDLING $3.00
TOTAL ENCLOSED: ______

SEND ORDER TO:

NAME ______

ADDRESS ______

CITY ______

STATE ______ ZIP ______

CANADIAN ORDERS

B&W PHOTOS ( ) X $1.25 = ______
COLOR PHOTOS ( ) X $2.75 = ______
POSTAGE AND HANDLING $5.00
TOTAL ENCLOSED: ______

SEND ORDER TO:

NAME ______

ADDRESS ______

CITY ______

PROVINCE ______ ZIP ______

FOREIGN ORDERS

B&W PHOTOS ( ) X $1.50 = ______
COLOR PHOTOS ( ) X $2.75 = ______
POSTAGE AND HANDLING $10.00
TOTAL ENCLOSED: ______

SEND ORDER TO:

NAME ______

ADDRESS ______

CITY ______

STATE ______ ZIP ______

NOTE:

The minimum order for all countries outside the United States is ten (10) photos.
The minimum order within the USA is two (2) photos.

Notes